UNITS

Quantity	Name of unit	In terms of base units	common terms
Capacitance (C)	farad (F)	$kg^{-1} \cdot m^{-2} \cdot s^4 \cdot A^2$	C/V
Electric charge (q)	coulomb (C)	$s \cdot A$	
Electric field (**E**)		$kg \cdot m \cdot s^{-3} \cdot A^{-1}$	N/C or V/m
Electric potential (V) (also EMF [$\mathscr{E}$])	volt (V)	$kg \cdot m^2 \cdot s^{-3} \cdot A^{-1}$	J/C or W/A
Electric resistance (R)	ohm (Ω)	$kg \cdot m^2 \cdot s^{-3} \cdot A^{-2}$	V/A
Energy (E)	joule (J)	$kg \cdot m^2/s^2$	$N \cdot m$
Force (**F**)	newton (N)	$kg \cdot m/s^2$	
Frequency (ν)	hertz (Hz)	s^{-1}	
Inductance (L)	henry (H)	$kg \cdot m^2 \cdot s^{-2} \cdot A^{-2}$	Wb/A or $V \cdot s$/A
Magnetic field (**B**)	tesla (T)	$kg \cdot s^{-2} \cdot A^{-1}$	Wb/m^2
Magnetic flux (Φ_B)	weber (Wb)	$kg \cdot m^2 \cdot s^{-2} \cdot A^{-1}$	$V \cdot s$
Magnetic intensity (**H**)		A/m	
Power (P)	watt (W)	$kg \cdot m^2/s^3$	J/s
Pressure (ρ)	pascal (Pa)	$kg \cdot m^{-1}s^{-2}$	N/m^2 or J/m^3

PHYSICAL PROPERTIES

AIR (room temperature and atmospheric pressure)

Density	1.20 kg/m^3
Specific heat (c$_p$)	1.00×10^3 J kg^{-1} K^{-1}
Speed of sound	343 m/s
Index of refraction	1.000293 (visible light)

WATER (room temperature and atmospheric pressure)

Density	1.00×10^3 kg/m^3
Specific heat	4.18×10^3 J kg^{-1} K^{-1}
Speed of sound	1.26×10^3 m/s
Index of refraction	1.33 (visible light)

EARTH

Density	5.49×10^3 kg/m^3
Radius	6.38×10^6 m
Mass	5.97×10^{24} kg
Atmospheric pressure	1.01×10^5 Pa (surface)
Mean earth-moon distance	3.84×10^8 m

SOLAR SYSTEM (see Appendix A for more data)

Body	Mean radius of orbit (m)	Mean radius of body (m)	Mass (kg)
Sun		6.96×10^8	1.99×10^{30}
Mercury	5.79×10^{10}	2.42×10^6	3.35×10^{23}
Venus	1.08×10^{11}	6.10×10^6	4.89×10^{24}
Earth	1.50×10^{11}	6.38×10^6	5.97×10^{24}
Mars	2.28×10^{11}	3.38×10^6	6.46×10^{23}
Jupiter	7.78×10^{11}	7.13×10^7	1.90×10^{27}
Saturn	1.43×10^{12}	6.04×10^7	5.69×10^{26}
Moon	3.84×10^8	1.74×10^6	7.35×10^{22}

PI

CLASS

PHYSICS
CLASSICAL AND MODERN

W. Edward Gettys CLEMSON UNIVERSITY

Frederick J. Keller CLEMSON UNIVERSITY

Malcolm J. Skove CLEMSON UNIVERSITY

McGRAW-HILL BOOK COMPANY

NEW YORK   ST. LOUIS   SAN FRANCISCO   AUCKLAND   BOGOTÁ   CARACAS

COLORADO SPRINGS   HAMBURG   LISBON   LONDON   MADRID   MEXICO

MILAN   MONTREAL   NEW DELHI   OKLAHOMA CITY   PANAMA   PARIS

SAN JUAN   SÃO PAULO   SINGAPORE   SYDNEY   TOKYO   TORONTO

PHYSICS: CLASSICAL AND MODERN

1 2 3 4 5 6 7 8 9 0 V N H V N H 8 9 3 2 1 0 9 8

ISBN 0-07-033523-0

This book was set in Zapf Book Light by Progressive Typographers, Inc.
The editors were Randi B. Rossignol, John Zumerchik, and Steven Tenney;
the designer was Hermann Strohbach;
the production supervisor was Salvador Gonzales.
The drawings were done by J&R Services, Inc.
Cover illustration © 1988 by Tom Lulevitch.
Von Hoffmann Press, Inc. was printer and binder.

Library of Congress Cataloging-in Publication Data

Gettys, W. Edward.
    Physics, classical and modern.

    Includes index.
    1. Physics.   I. Keller, Frederick J., (date).
II. Skove, Malcolm J., (date).   III. Title.
QC23.G377   1989   530   88-13361
ISBN 0-07-033523-0

On the cover: These reknowned physicists appear against a backdrop of Newton's records of Halley's Comet sightings in September, 1682. (Courtesy of the Syndics of Cambridge University Library.)

| GALILEO | SIR ISAAC | JAMES CLERK | ALBERT | NIELS |
| GALILEI | NEWTON | MAXWELL | EINSTEIN | BOHR |

ABOUT THE AUTHORS

W. Edward Gettys was born in Gaffney, South Carolina on March 16, 1939. He graduated from Union High School and received his B. S. and M. S. degrees in Physics at Clemson University. He earned the Ph. D. in Physics at Ohio University, and joined the faculty at Clemson University in 1963, where he is Professor of Physics. In addition to research in condensed matter physics, he has been active in the Advanced Placement Physics program and has worked toward improving high school physics instruction.

Frederick J. Keller was born in Huntington, West Virginia on May 10, 1934. After graduating from St. Joseph's High School in 1952, he served in the United States Air Force for four years as an aircraft navigator. He took his B. S. from Marshall University in 1960, and his M. S. and Ph. D. from The University of Tennessee in 1962 and 1966. He joined the faculty of Clemson University in 1966 where he is now Professor of Physics. Dr. Keller has been deeply involved with the training of high school physics teachers for many years. He was the director of two summer institutes for high school teachers and the associate director of six others. He is married and has four children and two grandchildren.

Malcolm J. Skove was born in Cleveland, Ohio on March 3, 1931. He graduated from Cleveland Heights High School in 1949. He served as a midshipman in the United States Navy and a corporal in the United States Army. He attended The University of New Mexico, Pennsylvania State University, Jyochi Diagaku (Tokyo), and Clemson University, where he obtained a B. S. in Industrial Physics in 1956. He was awarded a Ph. D. in Physics from the University of Virginia in 1960. He has taught at the University of Virginia, Illinois State University, University of Puerto Rico, Clemson University, Haile Selassie University (Addis Ababa), and the Swiss Federal Institute of Technology. In 1988 he was program director for Solid State Physics at the National Science Foundation.

CONTENTS IN BRIEF

*For those instructors who wish to discuss waves earlier in the course, Chapter 32 is easily placed after Chapter 14, Oscillations.

CONTENTS

PREFACE

Physics is designed for a sequence of courses in physics for science and engineering majors. This sequence of courses usually incorporates two or three 3-semester-hour courses (or two or three 5-quarter-hour courses). The text is available in two versions: *Physics,* which contains 39 chapters and ends with the Bohr model of hydrogen; and *Physics: Classical and Modern,* which contains an additional four chapters on modern physics. We presume that students beginning in this physics sequence will either have completed or will be concurrently enrolled in a first course in calculus.

The premise we have used in writing this book is that physics can be enjoyable if it is first understandable. Since joy comes from discovery, our goal has been to satisfy the students' desire for knowledge. We have strived to make clarity the distinctive feature of this book.

To help accomplish this, any new concept or topic is introduced with a familiar example, whenever possible. With this specific-to-general approach, we draw on the students' experience and avoid launching into an unfamiliar subject with an abstract discussion. Typically, the discussion flow in a chapter is familiar example → general principle → further examples. Similarly, models are frequently used to explain physical phenomena. The technique of constructing and using a model to provide an approximate description of a real process is demonstrated whenever the opportunity arises.

ORGANIZATION

The chapter-by-chapter organization of material is largely traditional: mechanics (Chapters 2–15), thermodynamics (Chapters 16–19), electricity and magnetism (Chapters 20–31), waves (Chapters 32–34), optics (Chapters 35–37), and modern physics (Chapters 38–43).

Non-traditional aspects of the text's organization are the placement of Newton's Law of Universal Gravitation (Chapter 7) and Waves (Chapter 32). The rationale for an early introduction to gravitation is to have the gravitational force law available for the discussion of potential energy (Chapter 9) and to be able to apply a fundamental force law to Newton's Second Law as early as possible.

The rationale for the placement of waves after electricity and magnetism is to provide a cohesive treatment of mechanical, sound, and electromagnetic waves and a stronger demonstration and utilization of the unifying principles in physics. For those instructors who wish to treat waves earlier in the course, Chapter 32 is easily placed after Oscillations, Chapter 14.

The breadth of material in each chapter is intended to correspond to that presented in three or four one-hour class meetings. To satisfy the diverse needs of different curricula and different instructors, most chapters contain more information than can be discussed in this time. The *Instructor's Manual* offers suggestions for adapting various chapters to suit different instructors' requirements. Chapters 15, 30, 31, 33, 35, and 37 contain material that has little or no bearing on subsequent chapters, and a course sequence can be designed that omits one or more of them.

CHAPTER DESIGN

Each chapter begins with a short Introduction that is intended to orient and motivate the student toward the chapter's goals. Each chapter ends with a concise summary that includes specific applications of the material in each section. Most chapters include a Commentary which is designed to pique the student's interest. Some of the Commentaries are biographies about famous or especially interesting personalities in physics such as Isaac Newton or Count Rumford. Others are about important and rapidly developing technologies such as lasers or high-T_c superconductors. Still others are about interesting philosophical points such as determinism or the meaning of a physical law.

PROBLEM SOLVING

Since learning physics goes hand-in-hand with developing students' problem-solving skills, we have given careful attention to the placement and level of examples in each chapter and in end-of-chapter questions, exercises, and problems. Each chapter contains about 10 examples, 25 questions, 40 exercises, and 15 problems. Answers to the odd-numbered exercises and problems are listed in the back of the book. For the sake of accuracy, these answers have been checked by at least two persons working independently.

Examples. Examples appearing early in a chapter are usually simple, and are often used to illustrate the definition and units of a newly introduced physical quantity. Later, examples become more difficult, and demonstrate problem-solving techniques. A few examples are used to show how to make order-of-magnitude estimates, and to discuss simple models.

Questions. A question can usually be answered without the need of pencil, paper, or calculator. The difficulty level of the questions has a wide range; some can be answered with a simple application of a definition, while others may require an extension of an idea presented in the text. Indeed, in some cases a question should be regarded as a springboard for a classroom discussion of an advanced topic. For instance, Question 24-13 leads to the conclusion that the carrier drift velocity in some materials is not necessarily parallel to the electric field (that is, the electric conductivity is a tensor quantity), and a marble-and-pegboard model is used to visualize this phenomenon.

Exercises. Most of the exercises are not difficult; many involve a simple one-step calculation. We believe it is important to provide a mechanism whereby a reasonably industrious student can enjoy quick success. Since exercises are keyed to specific sections of the chapter, a student has a limited amount of material to grasp in order to attack an exercise.

Problems. Problems are usually more difficult than exercises, and involve more steps and a wider range of material. Some problems develop material beyond the level of that presented in the text. A few of the problems are very challenging.

Numerical exercises and problems. Some chapters include instruction on how to solve a problem numerically with the aid of computer, and there are a few numerical exercises and problems at the ends of these chapters.

ACKNOWLEDGMENTS

We gratefully acknowledge the dedicated work of Randi Rossignol, Steve Tenney and Randy Matusow at McGraw-Hill. Tom Richard at Clemson University and Danny Overcash at Lenoir-Rhyne College granted us their talents as photographers. Herb Shore of San Diego State University and Don Liebenberg of the National Science Foundation set us straight on the current state of superconductivity.

We are indebted to our reviewers for their patience and helpful suggestions: Albert Altman, University of Lowell; John P. Barach, Vanderbilt University; Richard G. Barnes, Iowa State University; John H. Broadhurst, University of Minnesota; Richard R. Bukrey, Loyola University of Chicago; Joseph S. Chalmers, University of Louisville; Colston Chandler, University of New Mexico; William R. Cochran, Youngstown State University; Peter R. Fontana, Oregon State University; Anthony P. French, Massachusetts Institute of Technology; J. David Gavenda, University of Texas, Austin; Vince Griffin, Tulsa Junior College; Robert B. Hallock, University of Massachusetts, Amherst; Paul Heckert, Western Carolina University; Virgil L. Highland, Temple University; Robert P. Hurst, SUNY at Buffalo; Mario Iona, University of Denver; Alvin W. Jenkins, Jr., North Carolina State University; Peter B. Kahn, SUNY–Stony Brook; Carl A. Kocher, Oregon State University; Donald Kydon, University of Waterloo; B. A. Logan, University of Ottawa; Oscar Lumpkin, University of California, San Diego; Joseph L. McCauley, University of Houston; Alvin Meckler, University of Maryland, Baltimore County; Ralph C. Minehart, University of Virginia; William J. Mullin, University of Massachusetts, Amherst; Jack H. Noon, University of Central Florida; Benedict Oh, Pennsylvania State University; Lawrence S. Pinsky, University of Houston; Stanley J. Shepherd, Pennsylvania State University; Wilbur C. Thoburn, Iowa State University; James Trefil, George Mason University; Somdev Tyagi, Drexel University; Gordon G. Wiseman, University of Kansas; Lowell Wood, University of Houston; Richard K. Yamamoto, Massachusetts Institute of Technology, and Jens Zorn, University of Michigan.

We especially acknowledge the contributions of Wendy Schaffer and Vineeta Ribeiro, who provided the students' perspective — the most important of all.

Finally, we acknowledge the support of our families. It was they who also endured the many long hours and the occasional short tempers that accompany such a project.

W. Edward Gettys
Frederick J. Keller
Malcolm J. Skove

The text is accompanied by a complete supporting package of instructional materials.

FOR THE INSTRUCTOR

Instructor's Manual/Test Bank by Gettys, Keller, and Skove. This complete package of instructional materials is available to instructors upon request.

Overhead transparencies. Over 130 2-color acetates of useful figures from the text as well as from other sources.

McGraw-Hill Testing System. This computerized version of the examination questions in the Instructor's Manual/Test Bank enables the instructor to select questions by section, topic, question type, difficulty level, and other criteria. Instructors may add their own criteria and edit their own questions.

FOR THE STUDENT

Study Guide by Marllin Simon of Auburn University. Each chapter of this student-oriented study aid includes a review and recall section, a practice problem-solving section, worked examples, and a self-test.

Student Solutions Manual by Stanley Shepherd of Pennsylvania State University and Tom Pickett of Clemson University. Contains the solutions to odd-numbered problems and selected odd-numbered exercises and questions.

Schaum's 3000 Solved Problems in Physics. A complete and expert source of problems with solutions. Also includes sections on problem solving tips, computer applications and lists of available software.

TK solver. This powerful tool builds and solves mathematical equations and models. It handles algebraic equations, matrix algebra, differentiation, integration, statistical analysis, and complex numbers. It plots, uses 3D graphics and charts, and has spreadsheet functions.

Schaum's Outline of Modern Physics by Ronald Gautreau and William Savin. Each chapter consists of a succinct presentation of a particular subject followed by a large number of completely solved problems that naturally develop the subject and illustrate the principles.

Instructors should contact their local McGraw-Hill sales representative to obtain the complete supplements package. Students can order their study aids through the college bookstore if the desired items are not in stock.

PHYSICS
CLASSICAL AND MODERN

CHAPTER 1
INTRODUCTION

1-1 INTRODUCTION

Until about 1850, there were texts and courses in what was called natural or experimental philosophy. The name recognized the contrast between subjects that were dependent on experiments and those, such as literature and religion, that were not. As the results and conclusions of experimental philosophy accumulated, it became difficult for a single person to work in the whole field, and subdivisions appeared. Long before 1850, chemistry, astronomy, geology, and other such studies split off into independent disciplines. As this happened, the core that was left came to be known as *physics.* Because of its central importance in the sciences, an understanding of physics is required in many other disciplines.

Physics, the core that was left, is a quantitative science that includes mechanics, thermal phenomena, electricity and magnetism, optics, and sound. These subjects are part of classical physics. If speeds near that of light or sizes near that of an atom are important in a physical problem, the topics of modern physics, the discoveries of the 1900s, must be discussed. These topics include relativity and quantum mechanics.

Physics studies particularly simple systems, such as single atoms. Scientific methods are often expressed more clearly in these simple systems of physics than in many other sciences. Because of this, physics is often regarded as a model for the "scientific method."

1-2 STANDARDS

In physics, we carefully define the quantities that are measured. Not only must the number which is measured be precise, but the measurement must be referred to a common standard, such as an inch or a meter. Often the measurements will contain more than one of these agreed-upon standards. Velocities, for example, are often measured in units of meters per second. The meters and the seconds must be traceable to a standard meter and a standard second.

In the first part of this course you will need only three standards, those for time, length, and mass. One more standard will be needed later when we discuss electricity. All other quantities that are used in this part of the course can be built from the standards for time, length, and mass. Since these three standard quantities are not defined in terms of any others, they are sometimes called *indefinable*. The standards for time, length, and mass are laid down in prescriptions which give a method for reproducing them and for comparing them with measured quantities. This is called an *operational definition*, because it specifies the operations that must be performed to reproduce the standards and to compare them with measured quantities. Thus although time, length, and mass are indefinable in terms of other quantities, they each have an operational definition.

Consider the desirable features of a standard:

1 It should be immutable, so that measurements made today can be compared with those made in the next century.
2 It should be easily available, so that as many laboratories as possible can duplicate it.
3 It should be precise, so that the standard is available to whatever precision is technologically possible.
4 It should be universally agreed upon, so that results obtained in different countries are comparable.

As an example, consider the definition of the standard of time. The second was originally defined in terms of the length of the day. Later it was found that the length of the day, as measured by clocks based on other phenomena, varied throughout the year, from year to year, and from century to century. If a second were defined to be 1/86,000 of a day, then such a variation in the

Time, length, and mass have operational definitions.

Sundial from the ancient city of Aquileia in Italy. The hole is for the "gnomon," a vertical rod which casts a shadow from the sun. The 11 straight lines are hour lines. When the shadow reached these lines, it was an even hour. Lines *A*, *B*, and *C* indicate the path of the sun on special days. Path *A* is followed on the summer solstice, the longest day of the year and the beginning of summer, path *B* on the equinoxes which mark the beginning of spring and fall, and path *C* on the winter solstice, the shortest day of the year. Such sundials were common in Roman cities, with more than 30 found in the town of Pompeii. *(Museo Archeologico, Italy)*

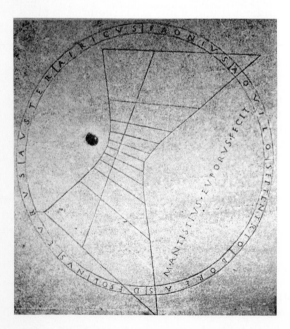

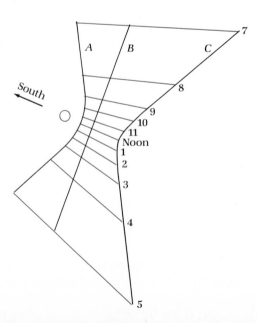

length of a day would be impossible by definition. But this definition would have consequences that would be disconcerting. We would find that the vibrational period of an atom or the speed of light depended on the date it was measured. Since we believe that the vibrations of atoms and the speed of light do not vary with time, a definition of time that is based on the properties of atoms or on what we believe to be constants of nature, such as the speed of light, is preferred.

An international organization, the Conférence Générale des Poids et Mesures, or CGPM (in English, the General Conference on Weights and Measures), is internationally recognized as the authority on the definition of units.

At present the CGPM definition of the standards for time, length, and mass are

Time. One *second* is 9,192,631,770 periods of a certain vibration of the atom Ce^{133}. You need not be concerned with the details of the atomic behavior or the insides of clocks that use these atoms, except that these clocks are the most reproducible timekeepers that are now known. Two of these clocks will agree with each other to a precision of one part in 10^{13}, or about one second in a million years. As far as being immutable, we believe that atomic properties are independent of time, but that is only one of the assumptions that go into this definition. You might consider what would happen if the properties of atoms did change over the age of the universe! The observed properties of the universe put severe restrictions on how much the properties of atoms can change in time.

These clocks are not cheap nor particularly easy to build, but they are being used in the standards laboratories of several nations, including the National Bureau of Standards near Washington, D.C.

Length. The *meter* is defined as the length of the path traveled by light in vacuum during a time interval of *1/299,792,458* of a second. Note that the definition of the meter depends on the definition of the second, and on a presumption of the constancy of the speed of light.

Mass. The *kilogram* is defined to be the mass of a particular platinum-iridium cylinder kept near Paris, France. This was agreed upon at the first meeting of the CGPM in 1889. The reason this standard is not yet based on atomic standards is that the measurement of atomic masses and their comparison with large-scale masses is not yet as precise as the measurements that can be made on large-scale objects such as the standard kilogram. The kilogram was defined so that the mass of 10^{-3} cubic meter of water is very nearly one kilogram near room temperature.

Secondary and tertiary standards that are compared with the primary standards are kept in standardization laboratories throughout the world. It is possible to trace the length of a common laboratory meter stick through these standards to a measurement of the path covered by light in 1/299,792,458 of a second, the second of a watch to the vibrations of a cesium atom, and the scale in a grocery store to the standard kilogram in France.

The standard kilogram at the Bureau of Standards in Washington, D.C. It is the cylinder on the right. It is being compared with a lower-level standard. *(U.S. Bureau of Standards)*

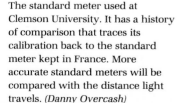

The standard meter used at Clemson University. It has a history of comparison that traces its calibration back to the standard meter kept in France. More accurate standard meters will be compared with the distance light travels. *(Danny Overcash)*

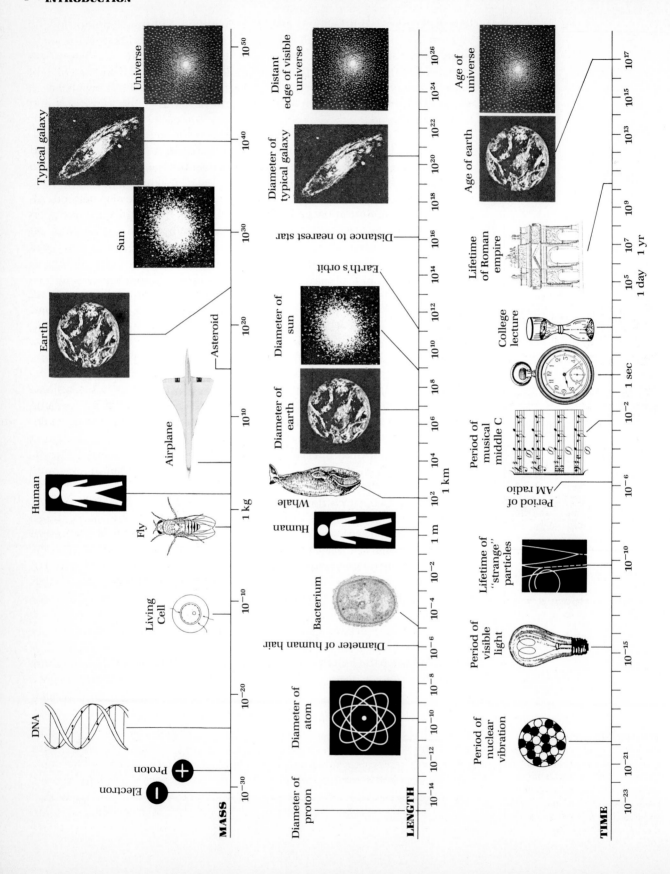

1-3 SYSTEMS OF UNITS

Besides the standards on which all measurements are based, we need a system of units. A system of units includes (i) the standards, (ii) a method of forming larger and smaller units, and (iii) definitions of derived quantities such as energy, power, and force. For example, much of the commerce in the United States uses the British system of units in which the unit of distance is the inch (defined to be 0.0254 of the standard meter) and the unit of mass is a pound-mass (defined to be 0.4359237 of the mass of the standard kilogram). Larger and smaller units, such as the foot (12 inches) and the ounce ($\frac{1}{16}$ of a pound), are also part of the British system of units. Derived units, such as that for the horse-power (550 feet squared pound-mass per second cubed) are also defined. Although still in common usage in the United States, these units are not often used elsewhere and are almost never used in scientific work. Engineers in the United States generally must be familiar with both the British system and the SI system, which we now describe.

The Système Internationale d'Unités, or SI system of units, was set up in 1960 by the CGPM. This is the system used by most of the world, essentially all science, and this book. It uses the kilogram (kg), the meter (m), and the second (s) as fundamental units and has a general method of forming larger and smaller units. The larger and smaller units are formed with prefixes that modify the fundamental and derived units by factors of various powers of a thousand. These prefixes and their abbreviations are listed in Table 1-1. Derived units, such as the unit for power, the watt (defined as a kg m² s⁻³, where s⁻³, means seconds to the −3), are modified in the same manner by the same prefixes. Thus one microwatt (1 μW) is one-millionth of a watt, and one kilowatt (1 kW) is 1000 watts.

The definition of a derived quantity will not always be in agreement with common English usage. When an advertisement refers to a detergent as being powerful or someone is described as having a lot of force or energy, the words "powerful," "force," and "energy" are being used to create an impression. These words in physics have a very exact meaning, one that allows assigning a number to them. This may lose some of the allusive beauty of the language, but it allows us to build an exact science with a beauty and proven utility all its own.

The range of measurements that are made in physics is illustrated in Fig. 1-1. The behavior of objects even over these ranges seems to have some order. Physics attempts to describe this order.

Table 1-1. Prefixes for SI units

Symbol	Name	Amount
E	exa	10^{18}
P	peta	10^{15}
T	tera	10^{12}
G	giga	10^9
M	mega	10^6
k	kilo	10^3
↓	↓	↓
m	milli	10^{-3}
μ	micro	10^{-6}
n	nano	10^{-9}
p	pico	10^{-12}
f	femto	10^{-15}
a	atto	10^{-18}
Accepted but not recommended:		
h	hecto	10^2
da	deka	10^1
d	deci	10^{-1}
c	centi	10^{-2}

Figure 1-1. An indication of the range over which physical measurements are made. Measurements of time and distance extend over a range of 10^{40}, and measurements of mass extend over a range of 10^{80}. *(Arthlyn Ferguson and Clifford Swartz/Physics Teacher)*

1-4 DIMENSIONS, UNITS, AND SIGNIFICANT FIGURES

Physics is a quantitative science. Most instructors believe that the goal of a course in physics is both an understanding of the concepts and an ability to apply that knowledge quantitatively. In order to achieve that ability, you must solve many problems as you work your way through this or any other text in a quantitative discipline. As much as possible, we will try to make the problems in this text refer to common experience so that as you gain the ability to solve quantitative problems, you will also see how physics applies to the real world.

There are several things which distinguish problem solving in physics from problem solving in mathematics. The differences arise because physics is more

The result of a measurement has dimensions, units, and precision.

closely related to the real world than mathematics is. Physics must be concerned with the grubby details of measurement. A measurement of a physical quantity, such as a length of 4.2 m, must carry with it dimensions, units, and precision. The "m" tells us that the dimension is length and that the units of length being used are meters. The "4.2" (rather than 4.21569) gives us an idea of the precision with which the measurement was made. Thus we must consider dimensions, units, and precision.

Dimensions. An equation such as $6 = 6$ is a mathematical tautology, but a similar equation in physics, 6 m = 6 inches, is wrong! And the equation 6 m = 6 kg makes no sense at all, since no measurement of length can be the same as a measurement of mass. *The dimension of a quantity is the physical property that it describes.* The equation $x = y$ makes no sense if x represents a distance while y represents a mass. Thus symbols connected by equality signs must represent quantities that have the same dimensions. Similarly, if $x + y = z$, then both x

All terms in an equation must have the same dimensions.

and y must have the same dimensions as z, since measurements of qualitatively different physical quantities cannot be combined. You cannot meaningfully add meters to kilograms, nor compare apples with oranges. Thus all terms in an equation connected by $+$ or $-$ signs must have the same dimensions. If the quantities are multiplied or divided, as in $x = vt$, where x represents length, v speed, and t time, then the dimensions of v multiplied by the dimensions of t must be the same as the dimensions of x. In this case the dimensions of v are length divided by time, the dimension of t is time, and the dimension of x is length. Here the dimensions are treated as if they multiply and divide just as numbers do. We represent the dimensional part of the equation above by putting the dimensions of each symbol in brackets:

$$x = vt$$

$$[\text{Length}] = [(\text{length})/(\text{time})][\text{time}]$$

$$[\text{Length}] = [\text{length}]$$

A somewhat more complicated example is the equation

$$x = vt + \frac{at^2}{2}$$

where the dimensions of x, v, and t are the same as above and the acceleration a has the dimensions of length divided by time squared. You can see that the dimensions of the equation check, provided that the divisor 2 in the last term is dimensionless. Thus the rules for dimensional analysis of an equation are (i) assign a dimension to each symbol in the equation according to the qualitative nature of the thing it measures, such as mass, length, or time; (ii) multiply or divide dimensions with the same algebra as used with numbers; and (iii) make sure that the resulting dimensions of each term in the equation are the same.

A further rule is that the arguments of transcendental functions such as the sine or the exponential function must be dimensionless — that is, they must be pure numbers. For example, sin (6 m) makes no sense, nor does e^{4s}. You can see that this must be true if you remember that sin x can be represented as the infinite sum $x + x^3/3! + x^5/5! + \cdots$. Only if x is dimensionless could this sum make sense. The expression "cos (t/T)" does make sense if t and T have the same dimensions, since their ratio will be dimensionless.

This sort of dimensional analysis cannot determine if pure numbers occur in an equation, nor the values of any such numbers. It can serve as a check on the validity of any equation you use. If the dimensions are not consistent, then the equation cannot be correct. If the dimensions are consistent, then the equation may be correct.

When examining an equation that you have just derived or that you suspect may be wrong, one of the first and easiest checks is that for dimensional consistency. If it is not dimensionally correct, then the equation cannot be correct.

EXAMPLE 1-1. Write the dimensions of each quantity in the equation

$$v^2 = 2a(x - x_1) + v_1^2$$

and determine if the equation is dimensionally correct. Use the abbreviations L for length and T for time, and assign the same dimensions to each symbol as used in the text above.

SOLUTION. In the equation

$$v^2 = 2a(x - x_1) + v_1^2$$

the dimensions are

$$[L/T]^2 = [L/T^2][L] + [L/T]^2$$

or

$$[L^2/T^2] = [L^2/T^2] + [L^2/T^2]$$

Therefore, the dimensions of each term are the same and the equation is at least dimensionally correct.

Units. Not only must each term in an equation have the same dimensions, but every quantity of the same dimension should have the same scale of measurement. *Units are the scale with which we measure dimensions.* The dimension of each term in an equation may be length, but if one term is given in inches and the other in meters, the numbers cannot be directly added. An answer of 3 m and 6 inches, while dimensionally correct, is hard to check with an ordinary measuring stick. Since an inch is defined to be 0.0254 m, 6 inches is the same as 0.1524 m. Thus 3.0000 m plus 6.000 inches is better written as 3.1524 m.

The units of all terms in an equation should be the same.

Occasionally you will know a quantity in one set of units and need it in another set of units. A convenient method of converting a quantity from one kind of unit to another (always with the same dimension) is to write an equality expressing the relative sizes of the units. For example,

$$0.0254 \text{ m} = 1 \text{ inch}$$

By dividing one side of the equation by the other, we may write this as either

$$1 = \frac{1 \text{ inch}}{0.0254 \text{ m}}$$

or

$$1 = \frac{0.0254 \text{ m}}{1 \text{ inch}}$$

The factor 0.0254 m/1 inch is the pure number 1. It is called a *conversion factor* and can always be used as a multiplicative factor in any equation. For example,

$$1 \text{ km} = (1 \text{ km}) \left(\frac{1000 \text{ m}}{1 \text{ km}}\right)\left(\frac{1 \text{ inch}}{0.0254 \text{ m}}\right)$$

$$= 39{,}370 \text{ inches}$$

Notice that the km and the m cancel out. The result, 1 km = 39,370 inches, has the same dimension (length) on both sides of the equation.

In the problems you work in this text, do not consider your answer correct unless it has the proper units. An answer of 32 ft for a problem whose solution is 32 m is incorrect.

Significant figures. Suppose that you were asked to estimate your height in SI units and knew it to be 68 inches in British units. You could convert by multiplying 68 inches by 0.0254 m/inch on your calculator to get 1.7272 m for your estimated height. But that seems to imply that you know your height to 0.1 mm, or about the thickness of a piece of paper. Few of us know our height to that kind of precision. In order not to claim too much precision for your estimate, you should give the SI estimate about the same precision as you gave to your height in British units, 1 part in 68. An answer of 1.7 m or 1.73 m implies about the same precision that the 68 inches did, and conveys about the same information. The same principle applies to any measurement. The precision with which a quantity is known should be reflected in the number that is used to represent it.

A *significant figure* is a digit in the number representing a quantity, other than a leading or trailing zero. Trailing zeros do count if they are after the decimal point. Thus 0.2547 has four significant figures, as does 345,600. Further examples are 3.14 (three significant figures), 0.003800 (four significant figures), pi (3.1415926 · · · known beyond a million significant figures), and 3.4560×10^5 (five significant figures). The meaningful digit in a number that is furthest to right is called the *least significant digit*. For example, the least significant digit in 3.456 is the 6 and in 0.003800 is the rightmost zero. The rules of significant figures that we use in this book are

1 When numbers are multiplied or divided, the result has the same number of significant figures as are in the least precise quantity given. For example, (0.456 s)(7.8 m)/9.0123 m = 0.39 s.

2 When adding or subtracting, find the input quantity whose least significant digit is farthest to the left with respect to the decimal point. The least significant figure of the answer is in the same position with respect to the decimal point. For example, 8.5675 kg − 8.556 kg is equal to 0.011 kg, so that input data with six and four significant figures may lead to a result with but two significant figures. On the other hand, 8.4 m + 3.2 m + 6.2 m − 1.1 m is equal to 16.7 m, and the answer has one more significant figure than the

The number of significant figures indicates the precision of the result.

Several realizations of 1 m with varying precision. *(Danny Overcash)*

input data. If we add 0.032 s to 11.6 s, the 0.032 s is smaller than the uncertainty in the 11.6 s and the answer is 11.6 s.

3 Transcendental functions such as the sine, arctangent, and exponential function have the same number of significant figures as their arguments. For example, sin 35.4° = 0.579, sin 35° = 0.58, ln 9.356 = 2.236, ln 9.3 = 2.2, $e^{4.11}$ = 60.9, and exp 4 = 50.

While the rules of significant figures introduced here do not have the full sophistication of statistics, it does give an indication of the precision to which an answer is known. If you blindly follow whatever your calculator shows on its readout, you will almost always be quoting nonsense!

EXAMPLE 1-2. Find the density of the metal sheet shown in Fig. 1-2. The *density* of an object is defined as the mass m divided by the volume.

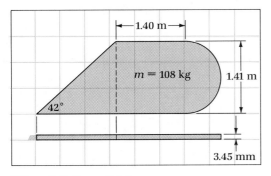

Figure 1-2. Example 1-2.

SOLUTION. The volume of the sheet is the area times the thickness. Thus

Area = semicircle + rectangle + triangle

$$= \frac{\pi(0.705 \text{ m})^2}{2} + (1.40 \text{ m})(1.41 \text{ m})$$

$$+ \tfrac{1}{2}(1.41 \text{ m})[(1.41 \text{ m})/(\tan 42°)]$$

$$= 0.781 \text{ m}^2 + 1.97 \text{ m}^2 + 1.1 \text{ m}^2$$

$$= 3.9 \text{ m}^2$$

Volume = (area)(thickness)

$$= (3.9 \text{ m}^2)(3.45 \times 10^{-3} \text{ m})$$

$$= 0.013 \text{ m}^3$$

$$\text{Density} = \frac{\text{mass}}{\text{volume}}$$

$$= \frac{108 \text{ kg}}{0.013 \text{ m}^3}$$

$$= 8.3 \times 10^3 \text{ kg/m}^3$$

We write the units here as "kg/m³." Occasionally we will write "kg m⁻³" if it avoids confusion later in a calculation.

Note that if you are using a calculator to get this result you should keep intermediate results to at least one more significant figure than given by these rules. That lessens the chance that round-off errors will affect the answer. Better still is to store the intermediate results in the calculator, where they are usually kept to about nine places. The calculator will not tell you the number of significant figures in the result, however. That must be obtained from the rules given above.

1-5 PROBLEM-SOLVING TECHNIQUES

In almost all courses in physics, your progress in learning is judged by how well you can solve problems. A standard approach to solving problems is useful. It can organize your thoughts and help you find where to begin. The procedures listed below are a distillation of techniques previous students have found to be useful. If you adopt them early, you may not have to unlearn less useful habits later.

- Draw a diagram. Use the diagram to make explicit the conditions of the problem. Use it as an extension of your memory; write the given information on the page. Identify the unknown(s) on the diagram if possible.

- Select an equation. It is usually best to use the most general equation that fits the problem. If there is more than one unknown, you may need more than one equation.
- Solve the equations. First solve the equations symbolically, so that the algebra is as simple as possible. Then plug in the numbers and check the units for consistency.
- Evaluate your answer. Compare the answer with your diagram. Check the answer against your intuition and common sense.

SUMMARY

Physics includes mechanics, thermal phenomena, electricity and magnetism, optics, and sound. The standards that are used to define the quantities used in physics were set up by the CGPM. They are the second (given as a certain number of vibrational periods of a cesium atom), the meter (given as the distance that light travels in a certain time), and the kilogram (given as the mass of a cylinder kept near Paris).

The SI system of units consists of three basic units—the second, meter, and kilogram; a method of naming larger and smaller units which differ by factors of a thousand; and a set of derived units, such as those for force and power.

Quantities in physics have dimensions as well as magnitude. When solving problems in physics, you must be sure that the dimensions of the quantities used are consistent, that they are expressed in the same units, and that the precision of the answer is correctly indicated. In this text, the precision is indicated by the number of significant figures.

It is wise to use a standard technique for solving problems in physics. When possible, you should draw a diagram, select an equation or equations, solve the equations, and evaluate your answer.

QUESTIONS

1-1   What are the dimensions of the volume of a cube? Of the volume of a sphere? Of the ratio of the volume of a sphere to the volume of a cube whose side is equal to the diameter of the sphere?

1-2   What are the dimensions of the unit "liter"?

1-3   What are the dimensions of 60 mi/h, 3 qt, and 2.5 kg/m³?

1-4   If you were told that everything in the universe had expanded to twice its former size while you slept last night, how would you check to see if it was true? What if all clocks suddenly ran at half speed? What if the mass of everything in the universe doubled? What if all of these things happened simultaneously?

1-5   Suppose we made contact with a civilization in another galaxy. Could we tell them the size of any of our standards? Of all of our standards?

1-6   There are really two parts to the standard of time, the size of the unit and the origin of time. How would you tell if your watch had the correct size for the second? How would you tell if it had the correct origin? Which is the answer to the question, "What time is it?"

1-7   Because civil time is based on the properties of the sun's apparent motion and physical time is based on atomic properties, occasionally "leap seconds" must

be inserted as a correction. Do you think the correction is put into physical time or into civil time? Why?

1-8   Because of relativistic effects, time scales based on atomic properties are different both in size and in synchronization for observers moving with respect to each other. What does this say about the existence of a universal time?

1-9   Why do we keep a standard kilogram but no standard meter or standard clock?

1-10 What is the difference between dimensions and units?

1-11 If an equation is consistent in one set of units, is it dimensionally consistent? Why or why not?

1-12 If we multiply several numbers with differing precision, which one determines the precision of the answer?

1-13 If we add a series of numbers with the same precision but differing magnitudes, which one determines the precision of the answer?

1-14 If I give my mass as 75.6234 kg, in what sense am I being misleading?

1-15 The speed of light is approximately 3×10^8 m/s. If we define a new unit of time as 1 blink = 30 μs, what is the speed of light in meters per blink? How far does light travel in one blink?

EXERCISES

In Exercises 1-1 through 1-6, x represents a length, t represents a time, v represents a velocity (with dimensions [length]/[time]), a represents an acceleration (with dimensions [length]/[time]^2), m represents mass, and k represents a dimensionless number.

1-1 Is the equation $x = vt + kat^2$ dimensionally correct?

1-2 (a) In the equation $v^n = ka^jx$, what numbers must n and j be to make the equation dimensionally correct? (b) What, if anything, can you learn about k from dimensional analysis?

1-3 We will later use the equation $W = (ma)x$. What are the dimensions of W?

1-4 Check the following equations for dimensional consistency:
(a) $v^2 + v^3 = 2ax$
(b) $x = v^2/a$
(c) $v = 3at + x/t$
(d) $x = at^2 \sin [(x/t^2)/a]$

1-5 Find the nonzero integers b, c, and d such that $a^bv^ct^d$ is dimensionless.

1-6 The frequency of vibration f of a mass hung from a spring has the dimension of reciprocal time, $1/[T]$. Experiments show that f depends on the amount of mass m and on the stiffness s of the spring. If s has units $[M]/[T]^2$, determine the exponents b and c in the relation $f = (\text{constant})m^bs^c$.

1-7 What is the conversion factor between km/h and m/s?

1-8 A furlong is defined in terms of the length of the furrow in a 10-acre square field and is 1/8 mi long. Convert 15 furlongs per fortnight into m/s.

1-9 An automobile has an acceleration of 10 mi/h/s. What is its acceleration in m/s^2?

1-10 A carat is a unit of mass equal to 200 mg. A pound-mass is equal to 0.454 kg. How many 1-carat diamonds does it take to make a pound?

1-11 What is the density of water in pound-mass/ft^3? (A pound-mass is equal to 0.454 kg.)

1-12 Find the product of 21.6 m and 5.3 m.

1-13 Find the sum of 84.626 s and 923.1 s.

1-14 Do the computation

$$(46.1 \text{ m})(0.231 \text{ s}) + \frac{492 \text{ s}}{13 \text{ m}^{-1}}$$

1-15 Do the computation

$$\frac{5.47 \times 10^4 \text{ m/s}^2}{(26.67 \times 10^{-8} \text{ s}^{-1})^2} - (3.63 \times 10^{11} \text{ m}) (\cos 56°)$$

1-16 Do the computation

$$\frac{8.0786 \times 10^5 \text{ kg}}{5.8832 \times 10^4 \text{ s}} + (1.070653 \text{ kg/s}) \cos \frac{1.3745 \text{ m}}{0.96782 \text{ m}}$$

where the argument of the cosine is in radians.

1-17 By what fraction does the sin 1° differ from the sin 1.01°? By what fraction does the sin 88° differ from the sin 89°? Comment on the number of significant figures in the transcendental function sin x for values of x near zero and for values of x near 90°.

CHAPTER 2
VECTORS

2-1 INTRODUCTION

In this course you will encounter many different kinds of quantities. Some of them, such as the speed of an automobile, are already part of your experience. Others involve concepts that are less familiar and therefore more difficult to understand. There are also differences in the mathematical complexity of the quantities used in this course. Fortunately, this complexity extends only to two levels. That is, each quantity that we use in this text falls into one of two categories—it is either a *scalar* or a *vector* quantity.

2-2 SCALARS AND VECTORS

Scalars combine according to the rules of algebra.

The simplest type of quantity is a *scalar*. A scalar quantity is specified by giving a single number, along with the proper unit. Here are some examples of scalar quantities:

A distance, or length: The distance around your waistline is 0.85 m.
A mass: Your mass is 58 kg.
A temperature: Your internal body temperature is 37°C.

The rules for combining scalars are the rules of ordinary algebra. Scalars can be added and subtracted, multiplied and divided, just as with ordinary numbers. For example, consider a rectangle of dimensions 3.0 by 4.0 m. The perimeter, or length around, is the sum of the lengths of the four sides, 3.0 m + 4.0 m + 3.0 m + 4.0 m = 14.0 m. The length of each side is a scalar, and the perimeter is also a scalar.

A vector has a direction.

A displacement is a vector from one point to another point.

A *vector* is more complicated than a scalar. A vector is specified by giving a direction as well as an amount or size, so that specifying a vector requires more than just a number. An example of a vector is a *displacement*. Suppose that you walk from a point P to a point Q. Your displacement can be represented by a directed line segment such as the one shown in Fig. 2-1a. The sense, or direc-

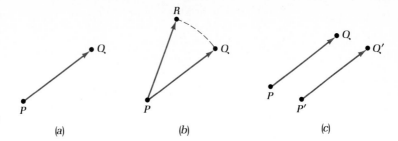

Figure 2-1. (*a*) A displacement locates point *Q* relative to point *P*. (*b*) Points *Q* and *R* are equidistant from point *P*, but the two displacements are different because they have different directions. (*c*) Two displacements are equal if they have the same length and the same direction.

tion, of the line segment is indicated by the arrowhead. This displacement is a vector that locates point *Q* relative to point *P*.

Notice that the displacement from point *P* to point *Q* involves more than just the distance between the two points. The orientation, or direction, of the line segment in the plane is also needed. Suppose that you walked from point *P* to a different point *R*, as shown in Fig. 2-1*b*. The distance between points *P* and *R* is the same as the distance between points *P* and *Q*, but the two displacements, the two vectors, are different because they have different directions. That is, a displacement is characterized by a distance and a direction.

Two displacements are equal if they have the same length and the same direction. Two equal displacements are shown in Fig. 2-1*c*. One displacement is from point *P* to point *Q*, and the other displacement is from point *P'* to point *Q'*. You can imagine picking up one of the displacements and moving it, without changing its length or its direction, until it coincides with the other displacement. We shall use this procedure, moving a displacement while preserving its length and direction, in the next section.

> Equal displacements have the same length and direction.

A displacement will be used in Chaps. 3 and 4 to discuss the motion of an object. As an object moves in space, a representative point on the object, say the center of a ball, traces out a path. Such a path is shown in Fig. 2-2. A given point *P* on the path is located relative to the origin *O* in the figure by a displacement. A displacement that locates a point relative to an origin is called a *position vector*. Notice that this displacement, or position vector, is independent of the details of the path of the particle; the position vector locates one point in the path relative to an origin.

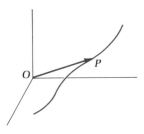

Figure 2-2. A position vector locates a point *P* on a path relative to an origin *O*.

Other vector quantities will be introduced in the following chapters. You will soon be dealing with force, velocity, and acceleration as vectors. Like displacement, other vector quantities are specified by a direction and a *magnitude*. The magnitude of a vector is a nonnegative number (with a unit) that indicates the size of the vector without regard to its direction. The magnitude of a displacement is just the distance between the two points. For example, the magnitude of the displacement of the upper-right-hand corner of this page relative to the lower-left-hand corner is about 0.3 m. What is the magnitude of the displacement of the upper-left-hand corner relative to the lower-right-hand corner? *Remember that the magnitude of a vector is independent of its direction and is never negative.*

> The magnitude of a vector is independent of its direction.

To distinguish the symbol for a vector from that for a scalar, we use a boldface type in the text to represent a vector quantity. Thus a displacement can be represented by a symbol such as **D**. Since boldface is difficult to produce when written by hand, a vector symbol is often denoted by an arrow placed over a letter. Thus both **A** and $\vec{A}$ represent a vector. The magnitude of a vector is often called its *absolute value*, indicated by $|\mathbf{A}| = A$. That is, the vector is repre-

> The vector **A** has magnitude *A*.

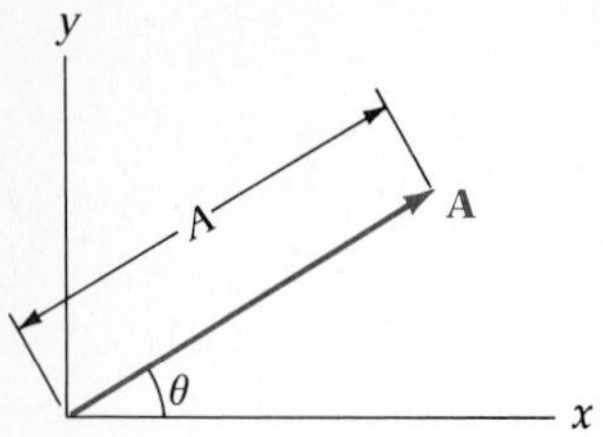

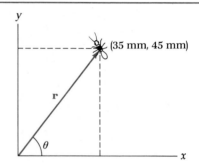

Figure 2-3. A vector **A** in a plane can be specified by its magnitude A and the angle θ.

sented by the boldface **A** (or by $\vec{A}$) and its magnitude by the lightface A. A scalar is also indicated by a lightface symbol. Indeed, the *magnitude* of a vector, being independent of the *direction* of the vector, is a scalar.

How many numbers are required to specify a vector? Consider the special case of a vector in a plane such as the vector **A** in Fig. 2-3. Giving the magnitude A of the vector requires one number. To distinguish the direction of this vector from other directions in the plane, we need an additional number. It is convenient to specify the angle θ between the direction of the vector and a reference direction. Often the reference direction is chosen as the positive x direction, as in the figure. If measured counterclockwise from this direction, the angle θ is taken as positive. Thus the vector **A** in the plane of Fig. 2-3 is specified by the two numbers, A and θ, that give the magnitude and direction of the vector. Two numbers are required to specify a vector in the two spatial dimensions of a plane. For the more general case of a vector in three spatial dimensions, three numbers are required. We shall consider such vectors in Sec. 2-4.

EXAMPLE 2-1. An ant crawls on a tabletop. A position vector **r** locates the ant at a point P with coordinates $x = 35$ mm, $y = 45$ mm relative to the origin of the coordinate system shown in Fig. 2-4. Determine the magnitude and the direction of this vector.

SOLUTION. The magnitude r of the position vector is the distance from the origin to point P. From the pythagorean theorem, this distance is $r = \sqrt{x^2 + y^2}$, or

$$r = \sqrt{(35\ \text{mm})^2 + (45\ \text{mm})^2} = 57\ \text{mm}$$

The direction of the vector is determined by the angle θ, where $\tan \theta = y/x = 45$ mm$/35$ mm. Then

$$\theta = \tan^{-1}(45/35) = 52°.$$

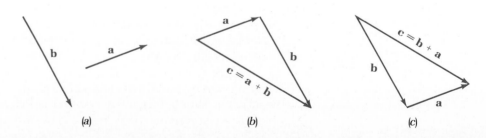

Figure 2-4. Example 2-1: A position vector **r** locates an ant at the point $x = 35$ mm, $y = 45$ mm.

2-3 GRAPHICAL ADDITION OF VECTORS

Since a vector has both magnitude and direction, vector addition does not obey the rules of ordinary algebra. We must define the procedure for adding vectors. The process is conveniently expressed in graphical terms: Consider two vectors **a** and **b** that lie in the plane of Fig. 2-5a. The lengths of the line segments representing these vectors are proportional to the magnitudes of the vectors. To form the sum **a** + **b**, place vector **b** so that its tail is at the head of vector **a**, as

Graphical addition of vectors by the head-to-tail method

Figure 2-5. Vectors **a** and **b** are added graphically with the head-to-tail method.

(a)   (b)   (c)

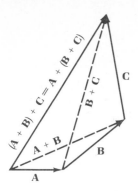

Figure 2-6. Vectors may be grouped and added in any order.

in Fig. 2-5*b*. Construct the directed line segment from the tail of **a** to the head of **b**. This represents a vector **c** = **a** + **b**, which is the sum, or *resultant*, of vectors **a** and **b**. Since the vectors to be added are arranged head to tail, this graphical method is called the *head-to-tail method*.

Suppose that vector **a** is a displacement from one corner of a room, where two walls meet the floor, to the next corner, and vector **b** is a displacement from that second corner to the third corner, all at floor level. The resultant **c** = **a** + **b** is a displacement from the first corner diagonally across the floor to the opposite corner.

Commutative law of vector addition

If the roles of the two vectors in Fig. 2-5*b* are interchanged so as to form the sum **b** + **a**, as in Fig. 2-5*c*, the same resultant **c** is obtained. Thus vector addition is commutative, and

$$\mathbf{a} + \mathbf{b} = \mathbf{b} + \mathbf{a} \tag{2-1}$$

This is in agreement with our experience with displacements. Walking 3 km north and then 2 km east takes us to the same point as walking 2 km east and then 3 km north.

Associative law of vector addition

The addition of vectors also obeys the associative law illustrated in Fig. 2-6. The result of adding vectors **A** and **B** first and then adding in vector **C** is the same as adding **B** and **C** together first and then adding in vector **A**, or

$$(\mathbf{A} + \mathbf{B}) + \mathbf{C} = \mathbf{A} + (\mathbf{B} + \mathbf{C}) \tag{2-2}$$

Because of the associative and commutative laws of vector addition, vectors may be grouped and added in any convenient order.

Product of a scalar and a vector

Suppose that a vector is added to itself. The vector sum **A** + **A** is illustrated in Fig. 2-7. The resultant is a vector with the same direction as **A** and with magnitude 2*A*. This vector is denoted 2**A**. More generally, consider the product of a scalar *s* and a vector **A**. We define the combination as a vector, **B** = *s***A**, such that if *s* is positive, then **B** is parallel to **A** and has magnitude *B* = *sA*. If the scalar *s* is negative, then **B** is opposite in direction to **A** and has magnitude $B = |s\mathbf{A}| = |s|A$. (Remember that the magnitude of a vector cannot be negative.) Two examples are shown in Fig. 2-8.

Consider now the vector −1**A** or, more simply, −**A**. The vector −**A** has a direction opposite the direction of **A** and a magnitude equal to *A*. We say that the vector −**A** is equal but opposite to the vector **A**. These two vectors are shown in Fig. 2-9. Notice that their sum, **A** + (−**A**), results in a vector of magnitude 0, the *null vector*. That is, **A** + (−**A**) = **A** − **A** = 0.

The null vector has magnitude zero.

By using the negative of a vector, we have tacitly introduced the idea of

Figure 2-7. Vector **A** added to itself gives the vector 2**A**.

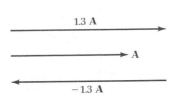

Figure 2-8. The vector 1.3**A** is parallel to **A**; the vector −1.3**A** is opposite to **A**.

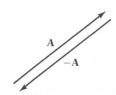

Figure 2-9. Vectors **A** and −**A** have equal magnitudes and opposite directions. Their sum is the null vector 0.

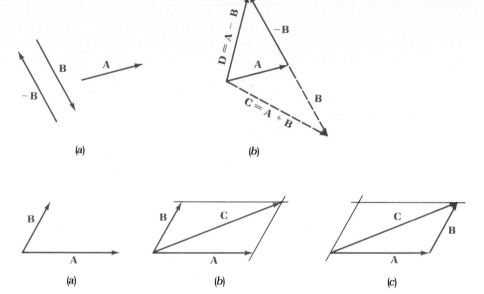

Figure 2-10. The vector **D** = **A** − **B** is obtained by adding **A** and −**B**. For comparison, the vector **C** = **A** + **B** is also shown.

Figure 2-11. (a) Two vectors have a common origin. (b) The resultant **C** = **A** + **B** is constructed using the parallelogram method. (c) The parallelogram method of vector addition is equivalent to the head-to-tail method.

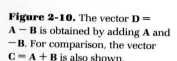

subtraction of vectors. In the general case of two vectors **A** and **B**, we define the difference **A** − **B** as the sum of the vectors **A** and −**B**,

Subtraction of vectors

$$\mathbf{A} - \mathbf{B} = \mathbf{A} + (-\mathbf{B}) \tag{2-3}$$

An example of subtracting two vectors is shown in Fig. 2-10. The vector −**B** is added to vector **A** to form **D** = **A** − **B**. The vector **C** = **A** + **B** is also shown for comparison.

It is often convenient to display two or more vectors with their tails at a common point, as in Fig. 2-11a. The graphical addition of two vectors can be performed, without placing them head to tail, by using the *parallelogram method:* Given two vectors placed with a common origin, as in Fig. 2-11a, complete the parallelogram by constructing sides parallel to the two vectors **A** and **B**, as shown in Fig. 2-11b. The resultant vector **C** is directed from the common origin along the diagonal of the parallelogram. Using Fig. 2-11c, you should be able to see the equivalence of the parallelogram method and the head-to-tail method for adding vectors.

Parallelogram method of vector addition

EXAMPLE 2-2. A helicopter leaves an airport and makes two stops. For each of the three cases in Fig. 2-12, the vectors **a** and **b** represent successive displacements of the helicopter. In each case determine the resultant displacement, **c** = **a** + **b**. Take the magnitudes in each part to be a = 3.0 km, b = 4.0 km.

SOLUTION. (a) Vectors **a** and **b** are arranged head to tail so that **c** = **a** + **b** is given by the line segment from the tail of **a** to the head of **b**. The vector **c** is shown just above the other two vectors so that all of them can be seen. Since both **a** and **b** are directed east, their sum **c** is also directed east and the magnitude of **c** is the sum of the magnitudes of **a** and **b**: c = 3.0 km + 4.0 km = 7.0 km. (b) Vectors **a** and **b** have op-

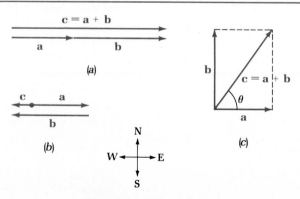

Figure 2-12. Example 2-2.

posite directions in this case, and **b** is shown just below **a** so that the vectors can be seen separately. The head-to-tail method has been used in the figure to obtain **c** = **a** + **b**. The direction of **c** is west, parallel to **b** and opposite to **a**. Since **a** and **b** have opposite directions, the magnitude of **c** is given by $c = |b - a| = 4.0$ km $- 3.0$ km $= 1.0$ km. (c) Vectors **a** and **b** are displayed in the figure with a common origin, and the parallelogram method has been used to add the two vectors. The magnitude of **c** can be determined by measuring the length of the line representing **c**. On a scale for which $a = 3.0$ km, we find that $c = 5.0$ km. The direction of **c** is determined by the angle θ, which is measured with a protractor

to be 53°. Thus the net displacement of the helicopter is 5.0 km in a direction 53° north of east. As a check, measurement also shows that **a** and **b** are at right angles, so that a, b, and c are the lengths of sides of a right triangle. Thus

$$c = \sqrt{a^2 + b^2} = \sqrt{(3.0 \text{ km})^2 + (4.0 \text{ km})^2} = 5.0 \text{ km}$$

Further,

$$\tan \theta = \frac{b}{a} = \frac{4.0 \text{ km}}{3.0 \text{ km}} = \frac{4.0}{3.0}$$

and $\theta = 53°$.

2-4 UNIT VECTORS AND THE RESOLUTION OF VECTORS

It is often convenient to use a vector to specify a direction in space. For example, a vector can be used to give a direction that is perpendicular to a surface, such as the plane of this page. Consider a vector **n** that is perpendicular to this page and directed out of the page toward you. Since we use the vector to specify a direction only, we can choose the magnitude of **n** to be 1: $|\mathbf{n}| = 1$, a dimensionless number with no physical units. The numeral 1 is associated with the word "unity," so that a dimensionless vector of magnitude 1 is called a *unit vector*. Thus the vector **n** introduced above is a unit vector directed perpendicularly out of the plane of the page.

Unit vectors directed along coordinate axes are particularly convenient. We shall use **i**, **j**, and **k** to represent unit vectors along the x, y, and z axes, respectively, of a cartesian coordinate system, as shown in Fig. 2-13. Since these are unit vectors, we have

$$|\mathbf{i}| = |\mathbf{j}| = |\mathbf{k}| = 1 \tag{2-4}$$

These three unit vectors are mutually perpendicular.

If we multiply a unit vector **n** by a scalar s, then from the last section the result is a vector, **s** = s**n**. If s is positive, then the vector **s** is parallel to the unit vector **n**. And since $|\mathbf{n}| = 1$, we have $|\mathbf{s}| = s|\mathbf{n}| = s$. That is, a vector **s** of magnitude s can be written in terms of a unit vector **n** that has the same direction as **s**, **s** = s**n**. See Prob. 2-5 in this connection.

The resolution of vectors. We have seen how two vectors can be added graphically to give a resultant vector. Now we consider an opposite kind of problem. Given a vector **C**, find vectors with directions along coordinate axes which, when added together, have **C** as the resultant. For simplicity we consider a vector in the plane of the page which we choose as the xy plane. Suppose that a vector **C** lies in the first quadrant, as shown in Fig. 2-14a, along with the unit vectors **i** and **j**. By constructing lines from the head of **C** perpendicular to the coordinate axes, as in Fig. 2-14b, we can obtain vectors **C**₁ and **C**₂ along the axes. Notice that $\mathbf{C}_1 + \mathbf{C}_2 = \mathbf{C}$ by the parallelogram method of vector addition.

We express the vectors **C**₁ and **C**₂ in terms of the unit vectors **i** and **j**. For the case illustrated in Fig. 2-14b, vector **C**₁ is parallel to **i** so that $\mathbf{C}_1 = C_x\mathbf{i}$. Similarly, $\mathbf{C}_2 = C_y\mathbf{j}$. The quantities C_x and C_y are called the x component and the y compo-

Unit vectors **i**, **j**, **k** along the x, y, z axes

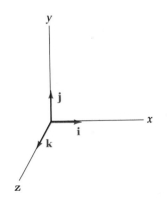

Figure 2-13. Unit vectors **i**, **j**, **k** lie along the x, y, z axes.

Components of a vector: C_x and C_y

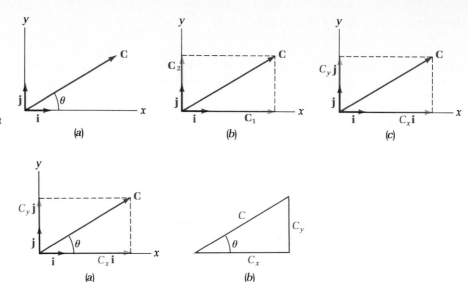

Figure 2-14. A vector **C** is resolved into its components so that $C = C_x\mathbf{i} + C_y\mathbf{j}$.

Figure 2-15. The components are given by $C_x = C \cos \theta$ and $C_y = C \sin \theta$.

nent of the vector **C**. Thus vector **C** can be expressed in terms of its components C_x and C_y as

$$\mathbf{C} = C_x\mathbf{i} + C_y\mathbf{j} \tag{2-5}$$

This expression is illustrated in Fig. 2-14c. It is important to distinguish between a component of a vector, such as C_x, and a vector. The component C_x is not itself a vector, but $C_x\mathbf{i}$ is a vector, as is $C_y\mathbf{j}$.

The process of determining the components of a vector is called *resolving a vector into its components.* The graphical method described above for this process projects the vector **C** onto the x and y axes, and the components C_x and C_y can be measured with a ruler relative to the scale chosen for the magnitude C of vector **C**.

Resolving a vector **C** into its components

Using simple trigonometry, we can develop an analytical method of resolving a vector into its components. Consider again the vector **C** specified by its magnitude C and its angle θ, as shown in Fig. 2-15a. The components C_x and C_y form the sides of a right triangle with hypotenuse C shown in Fig. 2-15b. Since $\cos \theta = C_x/C$ and $\sin \theta = C_y/C$, we have

$$C_x = C \cos \theta$$
$$C_y = C \sin \theta \tag{2-6}$$

These equations give the components of a vector in terms of its magnitude and direction. For example, if $C = 12$ mm and $\theta = 28°$, then $C_x = 12$ mm cos 28° = 11 mm, and $C_y = 12$ mm sin 28° = 5.6 mm. Although Eqs. (2-6) were obtained for the case of a vector lying in the first quadrant in Fig. 2-15a, the expressions are valid for any quadrant. (See Exercise 2-10.) A component of a vector may be positive, negative, or zero. For example, the vector **D** in Fig. 2-17 has D_x negative and D_y positive.

A vector can be specified by its magnitude and direction or by its components.

A vector **C** in a plane can be specified in either of two ways: It is specified by its magnitude C and direction θ or by its components C_x and C_y. If the magnitude and direction are given, then the components can be obtained from Eqs. (2-6). Alternatively, these equations can be solved for C and θ in terms of C_x and C_y. Squaring the equations and adding, we have, since $\sin^2 \theta + \cos^2 \theta = 1$, $C_x{}^2 + C_y{}^2 = C^2$. Dividing the second of Eqs. (2-6) by the first gives $C_y/C_x =$

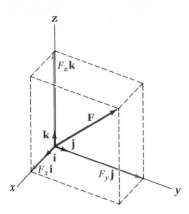

Figure 2-16. A vector **F** in three dimensions has components F_x, F_y, F_z.

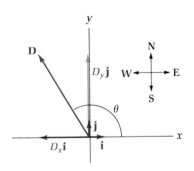

Figure 2-17. Example 2-3.

Position vector $\mathbf{r} = x\mathbf{i} + y\mathbf{j} + z\mathbf{k}$ locates the point (x, y, z).

Equal vectors have the same components.

$\sin \theta / \cos \theta = \tan \theta$. Thus

$$C = \sqrt{C_x^2 + C_y^2}$$

$$\tan \theta = \frac{C_y}{C_x}$$

(2-7)

For example, if $C_x = 8.1$ m and $C_y = 5.2$ m, then $C = \sqrt{(8.1 \text{ m})^2 + (5.2 \text{ m})^2}$ and $\theta = \tan^{-1}(5.2/8.1) = 33°$. The two sets of relations, Eqs. (2-6) and (2-7), allow us to move back and forth between these two alternative ways to specify a vector.

The second of Eqs. (2-7) gives the tangent of the angle θ. If θ is increased or decreased by $180°$ or π radians, the tangent has the same value, $\tan (\theta \pm 180°) = \tan \theta$. Thus there is an ambiguity in the value of θ obtained by using the arctangent function (arctan or $\tan^{-1}$). When $\theta = \tan^{-1}(C_y/C_x)$ is evaluated on most calculators, the result ranges between $-90°$ and $+90°$. That is, the angle returned by the calculator is in either the first or the fourth quadrant. If the vector actually lies in the second quadrant (C_x negative, C_y positive), then the calculator gives an angle in the fourth quadrant. You must add $180°$ to this angle to obtain the proper angle in the second quadrant. This procedure is illustrated in the example below. (What if the vector lies in the third quadrant?) Some calculators have a key that performs a conversion between a cartesian pair (C_x, C_y) and a polar pair (C, θ). Most of these calculators will give the angle in the proper quadrant if this routine is used. If you have a calculator with this feature, ask your instructor if you may use it on homework and tests.

Vectors in three spatial dimensions are usually specified in terms of three components. Thus vector **F**, shown in perspective in Fig. 2-16, can be written as

$$\mathbf{F} = F_x\mathbf{i} + F_y\mathbf{j} + F_z\mathbf{k}$$

The magnitude of the vector is given by

$$F = \sqrt{F_x^2 + F_y^2 + F_z^2}$$

The direction of the vector can be expressed in terms of angles relative to coordinate axes. However, it is usually more convenient in three dimensions to just give the three components F_x, F_y, F_z. As a special case, let **F** represent a position vector **r** that locates a point with coordinates (x, y, z) relative to the origin of a coordinate system. For a position vector, the coordinates are also the components: $\mathbf{r} = x\mathbf{i} + y\mathbf{j} + z\mathbf{k}$. For example, $\mathbf{r} = (3 \text{ m})\mathbf{i} + (4 \text{ m})\mathbf{j} + (-5 \text{ m})\mathbf{k}$ locates the point $(3 \text{ m}, 4 \text{ m}, -5 \text{ m})$.

Suppose that two vectors are equal, $\mathbf{A} = \mathbf{B}$. Since equal vectors have the same magnitude and direction, they must have the same components; that is, $A_x = B_x$, $A_y = B_y$, $A_z = B_z$. Conversely, if two vectors have the same components, then these two vectors are equal. What are the components of the null vector?

EXAMPLE 2-3. An airplane, taxiing on a runway, has a displacement with components $D_x = -1.78$ km and $D_y = 2.96$ km. The coordinate axes are oriented so that **i** points east and **j** points north, as shown in Fig. 2-17. Determine the magnitude and direction of this displacement.

SOLUTION. Using the first of Eqs. (2-7), we obtain

$$D = \sqrt{(-1.78 \text{ km})^2 + (2.96 \text{ km})^2} = 3.45 \text{ km}$$

The second equation determines the angle:

$$\theta = \tan^{-1} \frac{2.96 \text{ km}}{-1.78 \text{ km}} = \tan^{-1}(-1.66)$$

A calculator gives $-59.0°$ for the angle, which is in the fourth quadrant. However, since D_x is negative and D_y is positive, we add $180°$ to obtain an angle in the second quadrant. Thus $\theta = -59.0° + 180° = 121.0°$.

2-5 VECTOR ADDITION, ANALYTICAL METHOD

Although the graphical method of adding vectors aids in visualizing vectors and how they are added, it is not capable of much accuracy. We usually need to add and subtract vectors using an analytical or algebraic approach. Suppose that the components of two vectors are given: $\mathbf{A} = A_x\mathbf{i} + A_y\mathbf{j} + A_z\mathbf{k}$ and $\mathbf{B} = B_x\mathbf{i} + B_y\mathbf{j} + B_z\mathbf{k}$. Let $\mathbf{C}$ represent their sum: $\mathbf{C} = \mathbf{A} + \mathbf{B}$. Expressing $\mathbf{A}$ and $\mathbf{B}$ in terms of their components, we have

$$\mathbf{C} = (A_x\mathbf{i} + A_y\mathbf{j} + A_z\mathbf{k}) + (B_x\mathbf{i} + B_y\mathbf{j} + B_z\mathbf{k})$$

The commutative and associative laws allow us to rearrange the terms in the sum in any order. We collect together those terms that contain each unit vector, so that

$$\mathbf{C} = (A_x + B_x)\mathbf{i} + (A_y + B_y)\mathbf{j} + (A_z + B_z)\mathbf{k}$$

Adding vectors in component form

Since vector $\mathbf{C}$, expressed in terms of its components, is $\mathbf{C} = C_x\mathbf{i} + C_y\mathbf{j} + C_z\mathbf{k}$, a comparison with the above equation shows that

$$C_x = A_x + B_x \qquad C_y = A_y + B_y \qquad C_z = A_z + B_z \tag{2-8}$$

Thus each component of the resultant vector $\mathbf{C}$ is the sum of the corresponding components of $\mathbf{A}$ and $\mathbf{B}$.

This analytical method is easily extended to adding and subtracting any number of vectors. For example, if vectors $\mathbf{e}$, $\mathbf{f}$, and $\mathbf{g}$ are given in terms of their components, then the vector $\mathbf{h} = \mathbf{e} - \mathbf{f} + \mathbf{g}$ has components

$$h_x = e_x - f_x + g_x$$
$$h_y = e_y - f_y + g_y$$
$$h_z = e_z - f_z + g_z$$

In many of the following chapters, we shall encounter the problem of adding analytically several vectors that lie in the same plane. Each of these vectors will be specified by a magnitude and direction instead of by components. To add these vectors, we first determine their components. Then the components are added using equations of the type in Eqs. (2-8). Finally the magnitude and direction of the resultant vector are obtained from its components. This procedure is illustrated in the next example. After studying this example, you should practice the method, using the exercises at the end of the chapter.

Products of vectors are discussed in Chaps. 8 and 11.

Addition and subtraction of vectors were introduced in this chapter, along with the product of a scalar and a vector. It will be necessary in later chapters to consider products of two vectors. One type of vector multiplication is introduced in Chap. 8 and another type in Chap. 11. Since such products will not be used for a while, we postpone further discussion of them until they are needed.

EXAMPLE 2-4. A cruise ship leaves port and sails due east for a distance of 231 km. To avoid a storm, it turns and sails 42.1° south of east for 209 km, and then sails 54.8° north of east for 262 km. Determine the magnitude and direction of the resultant displacement $\mathbf{R}$. Neglect the curvature of the earth and assume that all displacements lie in the same plane.

SOLUTION. Calling the successive displacements $\mathbf{E}$, $\mathbf{F}$, and $\mathbf{G}$, we first determine their components relative to the coordinate axes shown in Fig. 2-18. Thus

$$E_x = 231 \text{ km} \cos 0 = 231 \text{ km}$$

$$F_x = 209 \text{ km} \cos (-42.1°) = 155 \text{ km}$$

$G_x = 262$ km cos $54.8° = 151$ km

$E_y = 231$ km sin $0 = 0$

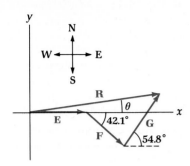

Figure 2-18. Example 2-4.

$F_y = 209$ km sin $(-42.1°) = -140$ km

$G_y = 262$ km sin $54.8° = 214$ km

Notice that $-42.1°$ was used for **F** since an angle is negative if measured clockwise from the positive x axis and positive if measured counterclockwise from that axis. The x and y components of the resultant **R** are given by

$$R_x = E_x + F_x + G_x = 537 \text{ km}$$

$$R_y = E_y + F_y + G_y = 74 \text{ km}$$

Using Eqs. (2-7), we obtain

$$R = \sqrt{(537 \text{ km})^2 + (74 \text{ km})^2} = 542 \text{ km}$$

$$\theta = \tan^{-1}(74/537) = 7.8°$$

EXAMPLE 2-5. *The law of cosines.* Consider two vectors **A** and **B** with an angle θ between their directions, as shown in Fig. 2-19. (a) Show that the magnitude of the resultant vector **C** is given by the *law of cosines,*

$$C = \sqrt{A^2 + B^2 + 2AB \cos \theta}$$

(b) Suppose you walk 350 m south on Broadway, turn $65°$ toward the east and continue for 280 m on 42nd Street. Use the law of cosines to determine the magnitude of the resultant displacement.

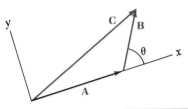

Figure 2-19. Example 2-5: $C = \sqrt{A^2 + B^2 + 2AB \cos \theta}$.

SOLUTION. (a) For simplicity, coordinate axes have been chosen so that **A** is along the x axis, and the components of **A** and **B** are

$$A_x = A \cos 0 = A \qquad A_y = A \sin 0 = 0$$

$$B_x = B \cos \theta \qquad\qquad B_y = B \sin \theta$$

Then $C_x = A + B \cos \theta$ and $C_y = B \sin \theta$. From Eq. (2-7), $C = \sqrt{C_x^2 + C_y^2}$ or

$$C = \sqrt{(A + B \cos \theta)^2 + (B \sin \theta)^2}$$

$$= \sqrt{A^2 + 2AB \cos \theta + B^2 \cos^2 \theta + B^2 \sin^2 \theta}$$

$$= \sqrt{A^2 + B^2 + 2AB \cos \theta}$$

where we have used $\cos^2 \theta + \sin^2 \theta = 1$.

(b) Letting $A = 350$ m, $B = 280$ m, and $\theta = 65°$ in the law of cosines, we obtain

$$C = \sqrt{(350 \text{ m})^2 + (280 \text{ m})^2 + 2(350 \text{ m})(280 \text{ m}) \cos 65°}$$

$$= 530 \text{ m}$$

COMMENTARY: VECTORS AND J. WILLARD GIBBS

Much of the vector notation that we now use can be attributed to Josiah Willard Gibbs (1839–1903). Gibbs was a strong advocate of the use of single symbols to represent objects, such as vectors, that consist of several quantities. For example, the vector equation **A + B = C** *is a simple and concise way to summarize three ordinary equations:*

$$A_x + B_x = C_x \qquad A_y + B_y = C_y \qquad A_z + B_z = C_z$$

Willard Gibbs was born in New Haven, Connecticut, and spent most of his life at or near Yale College, where his father was a professor. Gibbs was a student at Yale and achieved distinction in mathematics and in Latin. His graduate work there earned him the first doctorate awarded in engineering in the United States.

His thesis was entitled "On the Form of the Teeth of Wheels in Spur Gearing." After several years of travel and study in Europe, Gibbs returned to New Haven and in 1871 was appointed professor of mathematical physics at Yale. No salary was provided, and Gibbs worked without pay until 1875 when he was paid at a reduced rate of $2000 a year.

Gibbs had an interest in practical devices and inventions; he held a patent on an improved air brake for railroad cars. However, his major contributions to physics were mathematical rather than experimental. His published papers were abstract and difficult to understand and consequently attracted little attention. But his work was noticed and appreciated by the brilliant Scottish physicist, James Clerk Maxwell (1831 – 1879). There was a comment on Maxwell's death that only one person (Maxwell) could understand Gibbs's work, and he was now dead.

Gibbs's major work was in thermodynamics and statistical mechanics. (Statistical mechanics provides a theoretical basis for thermodynamics.) He extended these fields to apply to mixtures of chemical substances, and he is often described as the father of physical chemistry. An important concept in statistical mechanics is phase space, a fictitious space with axes labeled by three spatial coordinates and three velocity components for each particle or molecule of a system such as a gas. The phase space for a single particle therefore has six dimensions. The phase space for a system with N particles, say a gas with 10^{22} molecules, has $6N = 6 \times 10^{22}$ dimensions. Just as we deal with a position vector that locates a point in three dimensions, Gibbs considered the motion of a point in the 6N-dimensional phase space. Many of the techniques and much of the notation that we use for vectors in three dimensions were used by Gibbs in 6N dimensions.

His work was highly mathematical, and Gibbs used mathematics to describe and understand the processes of nature. In an address on the applications of multiple algebra (vectors), Gibbs noted that since position in space is essentially a vector quantity, "Nature herself takes us by the hand, and leads us along by easy steps. . . ." Gibbs maintained that the mathematics used by physicists must always be directed toward the results of experiments. He is reputed to have said, "A mathematician may say anything he pleases, but a physicist must be at least partially sane."

For further reading, see J. Willard Gibbs by Raymond J. Seeger (Pergamon Press, New York, 1974) and Willard Gibbs by Muriel Rukeyser (Doubleday, Doran & Co., New York, 1942).

SUMMARY WITH APPLICATIONS

Section 2-2. Scalars and vectors

A scalar is specified by a single number. A vector has a magnitude and a direction and is specified by three numbers. A vector in a plane is specified by two numbers. A displacement is a vector from one point in space to another.

Distinguish between a scalar and a vector; define a displacement and describe its properties.

Section 2-3. Graphical addition of vectors

Vectors can be added graphically using the head-to-tail method or the parallelogram method. Vector addition is commutative and associative. A vector multiplied by a scalar is another vector. The vector $-\mathbf{A}$ is equal in magnitude and opposite in direction to the vector $\mathbf{A}$. Subtraction of vectors is defined by

$$\mathbf{A} - \mathbf{B} = \mathbf{A} + (-\mathbf{B}) \qquad (2\text{-}3)$$

Add and subtract vectors graphically; multiply a vector by a scalar.

Section 2-4. Unit vectors and the resolution of vectors

A unit vector is a dimensionless vector of magnitude 1. Unit vectors **i**, **j**, and **k** lie along the axes of an xyz coordinate system. A vector in a plane can be specified either by its magnitude and direction or by its components. The components are found from the magnitude and direction, using

$$C_x = C \cos \theta$$
$$C_y = C \sin \theta \qquad (2\text{-}6)$$

The magnitude and direction are found from the components, using

$$C = \sqrt{C_x^2 + C_y^2}$$
$$\tan \theta = \frac{C_y}{C_x} \qquad (2\text{-}7)$$

A vector in three dimensions is expressed in terms of its

components by $\mathbf{F} = F_x\mathbf{i} + F_y\mathbf{j} + F_z\mathbf{k}$.

Define a unit vector; describe unit vectors **i**, **j**, **k**; resolve a vector into its components; obtain the magnitude and direction of a vector from its components.

Section 2-5. Vector addition, analytical method
Vectors are added analytically using their components. If $\mathbf{C} = \mathbf{A} + \mathbf{B}$, then

$$C_x = A_x + B_x$$
$$C_y = A_y + B_y \qquad (2\text{-}8)$$
$$C_z = A_z + B_z$$

Add and subtract vectors analytically.

QUESTIONS

2-1 Can a scalar be negative? Can the magnitude of a vector be negative? Can a vector component be negative? Explain.

2-2 Consider the displacements that lie along the two diagonals of this page, one from the lower-left to the upper-right corner and the other from the lower-right to the upper-left corner. Are the magnitudes of these vectors equal? Are the vectors equal? Explain.

2-3 Is there a distinction between a position vector and a displacement? Explain.

2-4 You and a friend decide to go from the first to the third level of a department store. Leaving from a common point by the elevator, you take the elevator up, while your claustrophobic friend takes the escalator. You and your friend meet at the third-level elevator. How do your path lengths compare? How do your displacements compare? How do the magnitudes of your displacements compare?

2-5 Two vectors of equal magnitude are added. Depending on the directions of the two, what is the maximum magnitude of the resultant? What is the minimum?

2-6 Displacement **D** has magnitude 12 m, and displacement **E** has magnitude 9 m. The resultant, $\mathbf{F} = \mathbf{D} + \mathbf{E}$, has magnitude 3 m. What can you say about the directions of **D** and **E**?

2-7 If $\mathbf{A} \ne -\mathbf{B}$, is it possible for $\mathbf{A} + \mathbf{B}$ to equal zero? Explain.

2-8 Is it possible for $\mathbf{a} + \mathbf{b} + \mathbf{c}$ to equal zero if the three vectors **a**, **b**, and **c** have (a) unequal magnitudes, (b) equal magnitudes? Explain.

2-9 You overhear a classmate describing a 400-m race, "Since the finish line and the starting line are at the same point on the track, the displacement of a runner for the entire race is zero." Do you agree with this statement? Explain.

2-10 A square city block is 150 m on a side. If you take the walkway from one corner to the next, what is the mag-

nitude of your displacement? You continue around the block to the next corner diagonally opposite your initial location. What is the magnitude of this second displacement? What is the magnitude of your resultant displacement? What is the total distance traveled?

2-11 While facing east, you take a giant step that results in a displacement of magnitude 1 m. Is this displacement a unit vector? Explain.

2-12 Different cartesian coordinate systems can be chosen that have different orientations for the coordinate axes. Does the value of a scalar depend on the orientation of the axes? Do the components of a vector depend on the orientation of the coordinate axes? Does the vector depend on the orientation of the axes? Does the magnitude of the vector depend on the orientation of the axes? Explain.

2-13 The vector $\mathbf{V} = \mathbf{i} + \mathbf{j} + \mathbf{k}$ has magnitude $V = \sqrt{3}$. What are the magnitudes of the vectors $\mathbf{U} = -\mathbf{i} - \mathbf{j} - \mathbf{k}$ and $\mathbf{W} = \mathbf{i} + \mathbf{j} - \mathbf{k}$?

2-14 A position vector in the xy plane lies in the third quadrant. What is the sign of each component?

2-15 A vector $\mathbf{F} = F_x\mathbf{i} + F_y\mathbf{j} + F_z\mathbf{k}$ lies in the yz plane. What is the value of its x component F_x?

2-16 If you change from one coordinate system to another with a different orientation of axes, do the unit vectors **i**, **j**, **k** remain the same? Explain.

2-17 What are the components of the unit vector **j**?

2-18 What range of angles is returned by your calculator by the $\tan^{-1}$ routine? By the $\cos^{-1}$ routine? By the $\sin^{-1}$ routine?

2-19 Does your calculator have radians or degrees as the default unit for angles? How can you tell?

2-20 What angles have a tangent equal to $+1$, -1, 0, $+\infty$, $-\infty$?

2-21 At the end of each chapter, the final question will ask you to complete a table that contains some of the symbols used in that chapter to represent physical quantities. Fill in the table entries by stating concisely the meaning of the symbol; stating whether the quantity is a scalar, a vector, or a vector component; and giving the SI unit for the quantity. The table below contains some of the symbols for this chapter. Complete the table:

Symbol	Represents	Type	SI Unit
$|\mathbf{A}|$	Magnitude of a vector	Scalar	*
C_x		Component	*
$\mathbf{r}$	Position vector		m
$\mathbf{i}$		Vector	None

* The SI unit for this entry depends on the quantity. If $\mathbf{A}$ or $C_x\mathbf{i}$ is a displacement, then the SI unit is the meter.

EXERCISES

Section 2-2. Scalars and vectors

2-1 Determine the magnitude of the position vector that locates the point with coordinates (a) (1.0 m, 2.0 m, 0.0 m); (b) (0.0 m, 1.0 m, 2.0 m); (c) (1.0 m, 2.0 m, 3.0 m).

2-2 The origin of a coordinate system is at one corner of a rectangular room, with the coordinate axes along the three edges from that corner. A mosquito starts at the origin and crawls only along edges to reach the corner with coordinates (4.2 m, 3.8 m, 2.6 m). (a) What is the minimum path length for the mosquito? (b) What is the magnitude of the displacement for the trip? (c) What is the answer to part (b) if the mosquito flies directly from the origin to the opposite corner? (d) What is the answer to part (a) if the mosquito crawls along walls? (*Hint:* Imagine the walls to form a box which can be unfolded so that the walls lie in the same plane.)

2-3 Set up an xy coordinate system in the plane of a sheet of paper. Using a ruler and a protractor, display each of the following vectors: (a) the position vector locating the point (55 mm, 65 mm); (b) the displacement from the point (32 mm, 18 mm) to the point (87 mm, 83 mm); (c) the displacement from the point (0.0 mm, 18 mm) that has magnitude 85 mm at a 50° angle from the positive x axis. What do these vectors have in common?

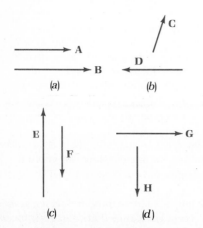

Figure 2-20. Exercise 2-4.

Section 2-3. Graphical addition of vectors

2-4 Use a ruler and protractor to transfer each pair of vectors in Fig. 2-20 to a sheet of paper and determine their sum graphically.

2-5 Five vectors, all having the same magnitude and lying in a plane, make angles with the positive x axis of 0, ±72°, and ±144°. Determine graphically the sum of these vectors.

2-6 Vectors **A**, **B**, and **C** lie in a plane as shown in Fig. 2-21.

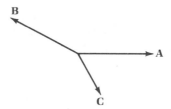

Figure 2-21. Exercise 2-6.

Using ruler and protractor, determine (a) $\mathbf{A} + \mathbf{B} + \mathbf{C}$; (b) $\mathbf{A} - \mathbf{B} - \mathbf{C}$; (c) $\mathbf{C} + \mathbf{B} + \mathbf{A}$.

2-7 On a diagram, show a pair of vectors **d** and **e** such that
(a) $\mathbf{d} + \mathbf{e} = \mathbf{f}, f = d - e, d > e$
(b) $\mathbf{d} + \mathbf{e} = \mathbf{f}, f = d + e$
(c) $\mathbf{d} - \mathbf{e} = \mathbf{f}, f = d + e$
(d) $\mathbf{d} + \mathbf{e} = \mathbf{f}, f = \sqrt{2}d, d = e$

2-8 In the parallelogram method of addition illustrated in Fig. 2-11b, the sum $\mathbf{A} + \mathbf{B}$ is represented by one diagonal of the parallelogram. Show that the other diagonal, directed from the head of **B** to the head of **A**, represents $\mathbf{A} - \mathbf{B}$.

Section 2-4. Unit vectors and the resolution of vectors

2-9 (a) On a sheet of paper, construct an xy coordinate system and display the position vector locating the point $x = 54$ mm, $y = 22$ mm. (b) Determine the magnitude and direction of this vector. (c) What are the x and y components of this vector?

2-10 Verify that Eqs. (2-6) correctly give the components C_x and C_y for a vector **C** that can lie in any one of the four quadrants of the xy plane.

2-11 A coordinate system is oriented so that **i** points east, **j** points north, and **k** points up. The entrance to Physics Hall is 340 m from the entrance to the library along the direction 49° west of north. Both entrances are at the same horizontal level. Determine the components of the displacement (*a*) from the library entrance to the Physics Hall entrance; (*b*) from the Physics Hall entrance to the library entrance; (*c*) from the library entrance to the Physics Hall wind vane, which is 35 m directly above the entrance.

2-12 (*a*) The unit vector **n** lies in the *xy* plane and makes an angle θ with the positive *x* axis. Express **n** in terms of **i**, **j**, and θ. (*b*) Show that **i** $3/\sqrt{14}$ − **j** $1/\sqrt{14}$ + **k** $2/\sqrt{14}$ is a unit vector.

2-13 The position vector $\mathbf{r} = x\mathbf{i} + y\mathbf{j}$ locates the point (*x*, *y*). (*a*) What is the magnitude *r* of this vector? (*b*) Determine the expression in component form for the unit vector $\hat{\mathbf{r}} = \mathbf{r}/r$.

2-14 A vector **v** (a velocity) has components $v_x = 34$ m/s, $v_y = -12$ m/s. Determine the magnitude and direction of the vector (*a*) **v**; (*b*) 2**v**; (*c*) − 2**v**; (*d*) (1/*v*)**v**. (*e*) If *v* and θ represent the magnitude and direction of **v**, determine the components of the vector with magnitude 2*v* and direction 2θ.

Section 2-5. Vector addition, analytical method

2-15 Given the two dimensionless vectors $\mathbf{A} = 3\mathbf{i} + 4\mathbf{j}$ and $\mathbf{B} = -2\mathbf{i} - 6\mathbf{j} + 5\mathbf{k}$, determine (*a*) **A** + **B**; (*b*) **A** − **B**; (*c*) **B** − **A**; (*d*) **B** + **A**.

2-16 Two displacements are given by $\mathbf{d} = (3$ m$)\mathbf{i} + (4$ m$)\mathbf{j} + (5$ m$)\mathbf{k}$ and $\mathbf{e} = (2$ m$)\mathbf{i} + (-6$ m$)\mathbf{j} + (-1$ m$)\mathbf{k}$. Determine (*a*) the resultant $\mathbf{f} = \mathbf{e} + \mathbf{d}$; (*b*) a vector **g** such that $\mathbf{d} - \mathbf{e} + \mathbf{g} = 0$.

2-17 The position vector $\mathbf{r}_Q = x_Q\mathbf{i} + y_Q\mathbf{j}$ locates a point *Q* with coordinates (x_Q, y_Q). (*a*) What is the expression for the position vector $\mathbf{r}_P$ that locates point *P* with coordinates (x_P, y_P)? (*b*) Determine the components of the displacement from point *P* to point *Q*. (*c*) Explain why these components do not depend on the location of the origin of the coordinate system.

2-18 Given the displacement $\mathbf{a} = (5$ m$)\mathbf{i} + 0\mathbf{j}$, find two other displacements **b** and **c**, also of magnitude 5 m and in the *xy* plane, such that $\mathbf{a} + \mathbf{b} + \mathbf{c} = 0$. Is the pair **b**, **c** unique? Explain.

2-19 A delivery truck has successive displacements of 1.37 km southeast, 0.85 km north, and 2.12 km 17° west of north. Determine the magnitude and direction of the resultant displacement.

2-20 A yacht is tacking into the wind on a zigzag path. On the first leg of the course, the yacht has a displacement of 12 km at 84° east of north. After the second leg has been completed, the yacht's resultant displacement is 15 km at 23° east of north. Determine the magnitude and direction of the second leg of the course.

2-21 Eight vectors when arranged head to tail form a regular octagon of edge 25 mm. Use the coordinate system shown in Fig. 2-22 (*a*) Determine the components of

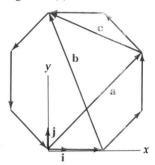

Figure 2-22. Exercise 2-21.

each of the vectors that form the octagon. (*b*) Determine the magnitude and direction of the vectors labeled **a**, **b**, and **c** in the figure.

2-22 A goose flies 120 m in a straight line, turns abruptly and flies 160 m in a straight line at 77° from the original course. (*a*) Determine the magnitude of the resultant displacement. (*Hint:* See Example 2-5.) (*b*) What is the total distance traveled by the goose?

2-23 Use the law of cosines in Example 2-5 to determine the angle between vectors **A** and **B** if $A = 23$ mm, $B = 18$ mm, and $C = 7$ mm $(\mathbf{C} = \mathbf{A} + \mathbf{B})$.

2-24 The law of cosines is sometimes expressed using the interior angle ϕ shown in Fig. 2-23 rather than the exterior angle θ. Show that this form is given by

$$C = \sqrt{A^2 + B^2 - 2AB \cos \phi}$$

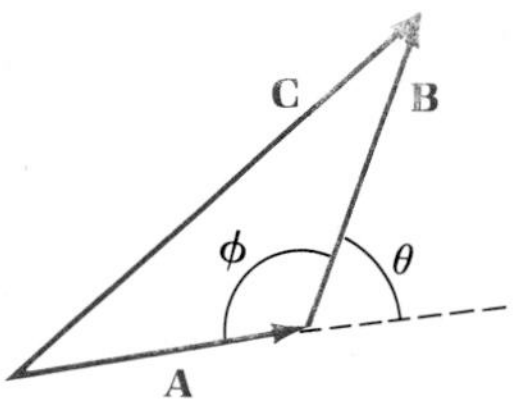

Figure 2-23. Exercise 2-24.

2-25 (*a*) If $\mathbf{C} = \mathbf{A} + \mathbf{B}$, show that $|A - B| \leqslant C \leqslant A + B$. (*b*) What is the angle between **A** and **B** if $|A - B| = C$? (*c*) If $A + B = C$?

PROBLEMS

2-1 ***Direction cosines.*** A unit vector **n** makes angles of α, β, γ with the *x*, *y*, *z* coordinate axes, as shown in Fig.

2-24. (*a*) Show that the direction cosines (cos α, cos β, cos γ) are the components of **n**. (*b*) Show that the direc-

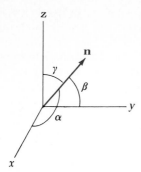

Figure 2-24. Prob. 2-1.

tion cosines satisfy the identity

$$\cos^2 \alpha + \cos^2 \beta + \cos^2 \gamma = 1$$

(c) If $\mathbf{F} = F\mathbf{n}$, express the components of $\mathbf{F}$ in terms of the direction cosines of $\mathbf{n}$ and the magnitude F.

2-2 Two displacements are given by $\mathbf{d} = (2.1 \text{ m})\mathbf{i} + (-1.3 \text{ m})\mathbf{j}$ and $\mathbf{e} = (0.8 \text{ m})\mathbf{i} + (1.6 \text{ m})\mathbf{j}$. Determine the angle between (a) $\mathbf{d}$ and $\mathbf{e}$; (b) $\mathbf{d}$ and $\mathbf{f}$ where $\mathbf{f} = \mathbf{d} + \mathbf{e}$; (c) $\mathbf{f}$ and $\mathbf{g}$ where $\mathbf{g} = \mathbf{d} - \mathbf{e}$.

2-3 Let θ represent the angle between two vectors $\mathbf{a}$ and $\mathbf{b}$ with $b = \frac{1}{2}a$. If $\mathbf{c} = \mathbf{a} - \mathbf{b}$, determine the value of θ if
(a) $c = \sqrt{a^2 + b^2} = \sqrt{5}a/2$
(b) $c = \sqrt{a^2 - b^2} = \sqrt{3}a/2$
(c) $c = 3a/2$
(d) $c = \frac{1}{2}a$

2-4 Two sets of coordinate axes and associated unit vectors are shown in Fig. 2-25. (a) Show that

$$\mathbf{i}' = \mathbf{i} \cos \phi + \mathbf{j} \sin \phi$$

$$\mathbf{j}' = -\mathbf{i} \sin \phi + \mathbf{j} \cos \phi$$

(b) A vector $\mathbf{A}$ can be expressed as $\mathbf{A} = A_x\mathbf{i} + A_y\mathbf{j}$ or as $\mathbf{A} = A_x'\mathbf{i}' + A_y'\mathbf{i}'$. Use part (a) to show that

$$A_x' = A_x \cos \phi + A_y \sin \phi$$

$$A_y' = -A_x \sin \phi + A_y \cos \phi$$

More advanced treatments of vectors use expressions such as these to define vectors.

2-5 Given a vector, say $\mathbf{A}$ of magnitude A, you can construct a unit vector with the same direction as $\mathbf{A}$. We use the symbol $\hat{\mathbf{A}}$ to denote a unit vector formed from the vector $\mathbf{A}$. Thus $\hat{\mathbf{A}} = (1/A)\mathbf{A} = \mathbf{A}/A$. (a) Prove that $\hat{\mathbf{A}}$ is a unit vector parallel to $\mathbf{A}$. (b) The position vector $\mathbf{r}$ locates the point (x, y, z) from the origin of a coordinate system. Determine the x, y, and z components of the unit vector $\hat{\mathbf{r}}$.

2-6 Four vectors $\mathbf{A}$, $\mathbf{B}$, $\mathbf{C}$, and $\mathbf{D}$ have magnitudes, in arbitrary units, of 1, 2, 3, and 4, respectively. The directions are unspecified and can be considered variable. Determine (a) the largest and (b) the smallest magnitude of the resultant $\mathbf{E} = \mathbf{A} + \mathbf{B} + \mathbf{C} + \mathbf{D}$. (c) Rework with the restriction that three of the vectors lie in a plane and the fourth vector is perpendicular to that plane.

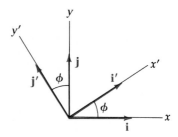

Figure 2-25. Prob. 2-4.

CHAPTER 3
MOTION IN ONE DIMENSION

3-1 INTRODUCTION

Mechanics is the study of motion. Suppose you are interested in the motion of a satellite orbiting the earth. You know the satellite's present position, its speed, and the direction in which it is traveling. You want to be able to predict the satellite's path and the time it will reach each point on its path. These are the kinds of questions that are addressed by mechanics.

A satellite orbiting the earth. (*N.A.S.A.*)

Mechanics is divided into two parts: *kinematics* and *dynamics.* Kinematics serves as the introduction for dynamics. In kinematics, we define many of the quantities that are used in mechanics, and from their definitions we establish relationships among these quantities. Dynamics, which contains the laws of motion, allows us to predict an object's motion from information about the object and its environment.

In preparation for dynamics, this chapter and the next are about kinematics. This chapter is restricted to discussions of objects moving along a straight line — that is, it deals with one-dimensional kinematics. Chapter 4 deals with motion in two dimensions.

3-2 POSITION VECTOR AND DISPLACEMENT

Definition of a particle

In these early chapters, we simplify our discussion of the motion of an object by treating the object as a particle. A *particle* is an idealized entity with no size or internal structure. Treating an extended object as a particle is a valid approximation if the object's size is irrelevant to the problem at hand. For example, in describing the orbital motion of the planets about the sun, we can treat the sun and the planets as particles. The radius of the sun and that of any of the planets is much smaller than any sun-planet separation distance. Also, the

A spiral galaxy similar in shape to our own Milky Way galaxy. (*Hale Observatories/Courtesy A.I.P. Niels Bohr Library, Physics Today Collection*)

spinning motion of the sun and of the planets has a negligible effect on the planetary orbits. Even a galaxy, which contains a billion stars the size of the sun and larger, can sometimes be treated as a particle.

To describe the motion of an object, the first step is to establish a coordinate frame, or a *frame of reference.* For motion along a straight line, this entails selecting first an origin at some point along the line and then a positive direction. Measurements are then made relative to this frame of reference. Consider a car that is traveling along a straight road that runs east-west. Any conven-

Establishing a frame of reference

iently located point can serve as the origin, such as a point adjacent to a large tree beside the road. Letting the x axis be along the road, we choose eastward as the positive direction for the unit vector $\mathbf{i}$. The car's *position vector* $\mathbf{r}$ is given by

Position vector r

$$\mathbf{r} = x\mathbf{i} \qquad (3\text{-}1)$$

The car's coordinate x is the component of its position vector. When the car is 55 m east of the origin, its position vector is $\mathbf{r} = (55 \text{ m})\mathbf{i}$. When it is 25 m west of the origin, its position vector is $\mathbf{r} = -(25 \text{ m})\mathbf{i}$.

A *displacement* $\Delta\mathbf{r}$ occurs with a change in position. It is the difference between a final position vector $\mathbf{r}_f$ and an initial position vector $\mathbf{r}_i$:

Displacement Δr

$$\Delta\mathbf{r} = \mathbf{r}_f - \mathbf{r}_i = (x_f - x_i)\mathbf{i} = \Delta x\,\mathbf{i} \qquad (3\text{-}2)$$

If the car's initial position was 25 m west of the origin and its final position was 55 m east of the origin, then its displacement was

$$\Delta\mathbf{r} = [(55 \text{ m}) - (-25 \text{ m})]\mathbf{i} = (80 \text{ m})\mathbf{i}$$

The use of the unit vector $\mathbf{i}$ is superfluous in one-dimensional kinematics. The object is always along a straight line, such as the x axis, and the sign of x tells us which side of the origin it is on. This means that we can describe motion in one dimension by using x rather than $\mathbf{r}$, and by using Δx rather than $\Delta\mathbf{r}$. However, this simplicity does not extend to two and three dimensions. Even though it is unnecessary in one-dimensional kinematics, we use this vector notation in this chapter in order to prepare you for the discussions of two- and three-dimensional motion that lie ahead.

EXAMPLE 3-1. Sometimes the solution to a dynamics problem produces an expression for the coordinate x of an object as a function of the time t, written as $x(t)$. After having found such an expression, we can use it to determine the coordinate at a particular time. Suppose a bobsled is sliding up a straight snowy slope. The sled continuously moves more slowly as it slides up the slope; it comes to a stop momentarily; and then it slides backward down the slope. An analysis of the sled's motion gives its coordinate x as a function of time t as

$$x(t) = 18 \text{ m} + (12 \text{ m/s})t - (1.2 \text{ m/s}^2)t^2$$

where x is measured along the sled's path and the positive x direction is up the slope. (a) Construct a graph of the sled's coordinate versus time from $t = 0.0$ s to $t = 8.0$ s by plotting points at each 1.0 s. (b) Determine the sled's displacement between $t_i = 1.0$ s and $t_f = 7.0$ s. (c) The distance an object travels is the total length of its path. Estimate the distance traveled by the sled between $t_i = 1.0$ s and $t_f = 7.0$ s.

SOLUTION. (a) The sled's coordinate at, say 2.0 s, is found by substituting $t = 2.0$ s into the equation for $x(t)$:

$$x = 18 \text{ m} + (12 \text{ m/s})(2.0 \text{ s}) - (1.2 \text{ m/s}^2)(2.0 \text{ s})^2 = 37 \text{ m}$$

Finding the coordinate at the other times yields the data in Table 3-1. Figure 3-1 is a graph of x versus t. Incidentally, notice the way the multiplication of the units in each term of the above equation gives the unit m. For instance, the unit of

Table 3-1

t, s	x, m
0.0	18
1.0	29
2.0	37
3.0	43
4.0	47
5.0	48
6.0	47
7.0	43
8.0	37

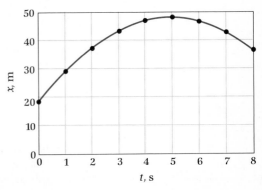

Figure 3-1. Example 3-1: Coordinate x of a bobsled versus time t. Initially sliding up the slope, the sled stopped momentarily at $t \approx 5.0$ s and then slid backward down the slope.

the third term is $(m/s^2)(s)^2 = m$. Any time you perform a calculation like this, make certain the units are consistent. (If you wish to refresh your memory about units, see Sec. 1-4.) (b) Using data from Table 3-1, we find that the displacement between $t_i = 1.0$ s and $t_f = 7.0$ s is

$$\Delta \mathbf{r} = (x_f - x_i)\mathbf{i} = (43 \text{ m} - 29 \text{ m})\mathbf{i} = (14 \text{ m})\mathbf{i}$$

(c) From the graph we can estimate the position at which the sled changed its direction of motion. Its coordinate was increasing until $x \approx 48$ m, and then it began decreasing. Beginning at $t = 1.0$ s, it traveled in the $+x$ direction a distance of about 48 m $-$ 29 m $=$ 19 m. Ending at $t = 7.0$ s, it traveled in the $-x$ direction a distance of about 48 m $-$ 43 m $=$ 5 m. The total distance traveled from $t = 1.0$ s to $t = 7.0$ s was about 19 m $+$ 5 m $=$ 24 m. Notice the distinction between displacement and distance.

3-3 VELOCITY AND SPEED

The *position* of an object tells you where the object is relative to a reference frame. The *velocity* of an object tells you how rapidly the object is moving and in what direction it is heading relative to the reference frame.

To define velocity, we first define and discuss the *average velocity*. An object's average velocity $\overline{\mathbf{v}}$ over a time interval from t_i to t_f is

Average velocity

$$\overline{\mathbf{v}} = \frac{\mathbf{r}_f - \mathbf{r}_i}{t_f - t_i} = \frac{\Delta \mathbf{r}}{\Delta t} \tag{3-3}$$

where $\mathbf{r}_f$ and $\mathbf{r}_i$ are the position vectors that locate the object at times t_f and t_i, respectively. A symbol with a bar over it, such as $\overline{\mathbf{v}}$, is the customary way to represent the average of a quantity. In one dimension, the average velocity has only one component:

$$\overline{\mathbf{v}} = \frac{(x_f - x_i)\mathbf{i}}{t_f - t_i} = \frac{\Delta x}{\Delta t}\mathbf{i} = \overline{v}_x \mathbf{i}$$

The average velocity component is

$$\overline{v}_x = \frac{x_f - x_i}{t_f - t_i} = \frac{\Delta x}{\Delta t}$$

Let us use Table 3-1 to find the average velocity component of the sled in Example 3-1 for two different time intervals. The average velocity component for the time interval from $t_i = 1.0$ s to $t_f = 4.0$ s is

$$\overline{v}_x = \frac{47 \text{ m} - 29 \text{ m}}{4.0 \text{ s} - 1.0 \text{ s}} = \frac{18 \text{ m}}{3.0 \text{ s}} = 6 \text{ m/s}$$

For the time interval from $t_i = 1.0$ s to $t_f = 3.0$ s, we have

$$\overline{v}_x = \frac{43 \text{ m} - 29 \text{ m}}{3.0 \text{ s} - 1.0 \text{ s}} = \frac{14 \text{ m}}{2.0 \text{ s}} = 7 \text{ m/s}$$

On a graph of x versus t, the average velocity component is equal to the slope of the straight line that joins two points on the graph. Figure 3-2 shows a straight line which connects the points for the interval from $t_i = 1.0$ s to $t_f = 4.0$ s. The figure shows that the slope of this line is $\overline{v}_x = 6$ m/s. Keep in mind that a graph of the coordinate versus time does not represent the path of the object. In this chapter, the path of the object is always along a straight line.

The average velocity characterizes how rapidly an object is moving and the direction it is heading *during a time interval*. We now define the velocity,

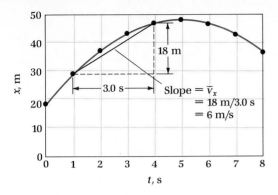

Figure 3-2. The average velocity component between t_i and t_f is equal to the slope of the straight line connecting the points at t_i and t_f on a graph of x versus t. For the bobsled in Example 3-1, $\bar{v}_x = 6$ m/s between $t_i = 1.0$ s and $t_f = 4.0$ s.

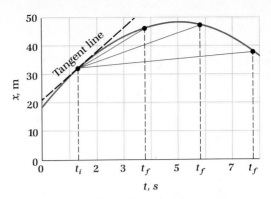

Figure 3-3. As t_f approaches t_i on a graph of x versus t, the slope of each line connecting the points at t_i and t_f approaches the slope of the line tangent to the curve at $t = t_i$.

which characterizes how rapidly an object is moving and the direction it is heading *at an instant of time.* To emphasize that the velocity pertains to an instant of time, it is sometimes called the *instantaneous velocity.*

Again consider the bobsled in Example 3-1. Suppose, in the graph of x versus t, we plot many points so that the points appear as a smooth continuous curve, as in Fig. 3-3. The slope of a line between any two points gives the average velocity component over the time interval between those points. Imagine finding the average velocity component for smaller and smaller time intervals. In each succeeding calculation, we keep t_i fixed and select t_f closer to t_i. From the figure you can see that as t_f approaches t_i, the slope of each succeeding line approaches the slope of a line tangent to the curve at t_i. The velocity component is defined such that it is equal to the slope of the line tangent to the x-versus-t curve. That is, the velocity component is the limiting value of the average velocity component as the time interval approaches zero:

$$v_x = \lim_{\Delta t \to 0} \bar{v}_x = \lim_{\Delta t \to 0} \frac{\Delta x}{\Delta t}$$

As Δt approaches zero, so does Δx. In the limit as both approach zero, their ratio approaches v_x.

The slope of a line tangent to a curve at a point is usually referred to as the *slope of the curve* at that point. This slope is given by the derivative of x with respect to t:

$$\text{Slope of curve} = \lim_{\Delta t \to 0} \frac{\Delta x}{\Delta t} = \frac{dx}{dt}$$

Thus v_x is defined as the derivative of x with respect to t:

Definition of the velocity component

$$v_x = \frac{dx}{dt}$$

Since $v_x = dx/dt$, the slope of a graph of x versus t at a particular time gives the velocity component at that time (Fig. 3-4).

The definition of the velocity component leads us to the general definition of

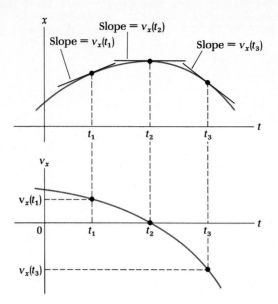

Figure 3-4. The slope of a graph of x versus t at each instant of time t gives v_x at that time.

velocity $\mathbf{v}$. The velocity is the limiting value of the average velocity as the time interval approaches zero:

$$\mathbf{v} = \lim_{\Delta t \to 0} \overline{\mathbf{v}}$$

Since $\overline{\mathbf{v}} = \Delta \mathbf{r}/\Delta t$, we have

$$\mathbf{v} = \lim_{\Delta t \to 0} \frac{\Delta \mathbf{r}}{\Delta t}$$

Definition of velocity

or

$$\mathbf{v} = \frac{d\mathbf{r}}{dt} \tag{3-4}$$

Because displacement is a vector quantity and time is a scalar quantity, velocity is a vector quantity. The SI unit of displacement is m and the SI unit of time is s, so that the SI unit for velocity is m/s.

The speed v of an object is the magnitude of its velocity:

Definition of speed

$$v = |\mathbf{v}| = \left| \frac{d\mathbf{r}}{dt} \right| \tag{3-5}$$

Since speed is the magnitude of a vector, it is a scalar quantity that is never negative. Its SI unit is the same as that for velocity, m/s. In one dimension,

$$v = |v_x \mathbf{i}| = |v_x| = \left| \frac{dx}{dt} \right|$$

Some representative speeds are listed in Table 3-2.

Table 3-2. A few speeds in m/s (approximate)

North America (relative to Europe, continental drift)	10^{-9}
Glacier (relative to earth's surface)	10^{-6}
Human walking (relative to sidewalk)	1
Jet taking off (relative to runway)	80
Earth's surface at equator (relative to center of earth)	4.6×10^2
Center of earth (relative to sun)	3.0×10^3
Solar system (relative to center of our galaxy)	2.5×10^5
Fastest known galaxy (relative to earth)	2.4×10^8
Light	3.0×10^8

EXAMPLE 3-2. (a) For the sled in Example 3-1, determine an expression for the velocity component $v_x(t)$ as a function of time. (b) Construct a graph of the velocity component versus time from $t = 0.0$ s to $t = 8.0$ s by plotting points at each 1.0 s. (c) Using data from Table 3-1, show the sled's position along its straight-line path at $t = 0.0$, 2.0, 5.0, and 8.0 s. Use arrows to represent the sled's velocity at each of these times.

SOLUTION. (a) From Example 3-1,

$$x(t) = 18 \text{ m} + (12 \text{ m/s})t - (1.2 \text{ m/s}^2)t^2$$

Since $x(t)$ is a polynomial in t, we use the rule for taking the derivative of a power of t:

$$\frac{d}{dt}t^n = nt^{n-1}$$

Therefore

$$v_x(t) = \frac{d}{dt}[18 \text{ m} + (12 \text{ m/s})t - (1.2 \text{ m/s}^2)t^2]$$

$$= 12 \text{ m/s} - 2(1.2 \text{ m/s}^2)t$$

$$= 12 \text{ m/s} - (2.4 \text{ m/s}^2)t$$

(b) The value of v_x at, say $t = 2.0$ s, is

$$v_x = 12 \text{ m/s} - (2.4 \text{ m/s}^2)(2.0 \text{ s}) = 7 \text{ m/s}$$

Finding the velocity component at the other times yields the data in Table 3-3, and these data are plotted in Fig. 3-5a. Notice that v_x passes through zero at $t = 5.0$ s. At this instant the sled is momentarily at rest before it begins its backward slide. (c) The sled's position and velocity at the four times are shown in Fig. 3-5b. The length of each arrow corresponds to the sled's speed at that instant.

Table 3-3

t, s	v_x, m/s
0.0	12
1.0	10
2.0	7
3.0	5
4.0	2
5.0	0
6.0	−2
7.0	−5
8.0	−7

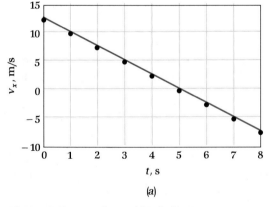

(a)

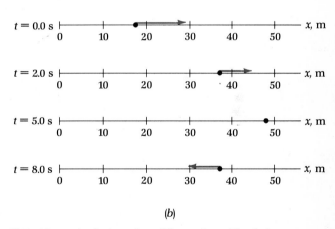

(b)

Figure 3-5. Example 3-2: (a) Velocity component versus time. (b) Position and velocity at four different times. The sled was momentarily at rest at $t = 5.0$ s.

EXAMPLE 3-3. Speedometers in cars often give the speed in the unit mi/h (miles per hour). (a) Determine the conversion factor for changing the unit of a speed from mi/h to m/s. (b) Convert a speed of 55 mi/h to m/s.

SOLUTION. (a) From App. C, 1 mi = 1.61 km. Also, 1 h = 3600 s. Thus 1 mi/1 h = 1.61 km/3600 s = 0.447 m/s, or

$$1 \text{ mi/h} = 0.447 \text{ m/s}$$

We can write the number 1 by dividing both sides by 1 mi/h:

$$1 = \frac{0.447 \text{ m/s}}{1 \text{ mi/h}} = 0.447 \text{ m h mi}^{-1} \text{ s}^{-1}$$

This way of writing the number 1 is our conversion factor. (b) Using the conversion factor from part (a), we have

$$55 \text{ mi/h} = (55 \text{ mi h}^{-1})(0.447 \text{ m s}^{-1} \text{ mi}^{-1} \text{ h})$$

$$= 25 \text{ m s}^{-1} = 25 \text{ m/s}$$

3-4   ACCELERATION

The *acceleration* of an object characterizes how rapidly its velocity is changing, both in magnitude and direction. Acceleration is the rate of change of velocity. Similar to the way we used average velocity to define velocity, we now use average acceleration to define acceleration.

An object's average acceleration $\bar{\mathbf{a}}$ over the time interval from t_i to t_f is

Average acceleration

$$\bar{\mathbf{a}} = \frac{\mathbf{v}_f - \mathbf{v}_i}{t_f - t_i} = \frac{\Delta \mathbf{v}}{\Delta t} \tag{3-6}$$

where $\mathbf{v}_f$ and $\mathbf{v}_i$ are the velocities at times t_f and t_i, respectively. In one dimension, the average acceleration has only one component. Since $\mathbf{v}_f - \mathbf{v}_i = v_{xf}\mathbf{i} - v_{xi}\mathbf{i}$, we have

$$\bar{\mathbf{a}} = \frac{(v_{xf} - v_{xi})\mathbf{i}}{t_f - t_i} = \frac{\Delta v_x}{\Delta t}\mathbf{i} = \bar{a}_x\mathbf{i}$$

where v_{xf} and v_{xi} are the velocity components at times t_f and t_i. The quantity $\bar{a}_x$ is the average acceleration component:

$$\bar{a}_x = \frac{v_{xf} - v_{xi}}{t_f - t_i} = \frac{\Delta v_x}{\Delta t}$$

To determine the acceleration, we find the limiting value of the average acceleration as the time interval approaches zero:

$$\mathbf{a} = \lim_{\Delta t \to 0} \bar{\mathbf{a}} = \lim_{\Delta t \to 0} \frac{\Delta \mathbf{v}}{\Delta t}$$

Since

$$\lim_{\Delta t \to 0} \frac{\Delta \mathbf{v}}{\Delta t} = \frac{d\mathbf{v}}{dt}$$

we define the acceleration as

Definition of acceleration

$$\mathbf{a} = \frac{d\mathbf{v}}{dt} \tag{3-7}$$

For one-dimensional motion along the x axis, $\mathbf{a} = a_x\mathbf{i}$, so that $a_x = dv_x/dt$. Also, since $v_x = dx/dt$, we have

$$a_x = \frac{dv_x}{dt} = \frac{d}{dt}\left(\frac{dx}{dt}\right) = \frac{d^2x}{dt^2}$$

Figure 3-6 shows the connection between a graph of v_x versus t and a graph of a_x versus t. Note that the relation between a_x and v_x is similar to the relation between v_x and x.

Further, the acceleration of an object can be found from a graph of x versus t. In a graph of x versus t, $v_x = dx/dt$ is the slope of the graph. The rate at which the slope v_x changes is given by $a_x = dv_x/dt = d^2x/dt^2$. Thus a_x is a measure of the rate of change of the slope. In other words, a_x is related to the bending of the graph. The tighter the bending of the graph, the larger is $|d^2x/dt^2|$ and the larger is the magnitude of the acceleration. If the graph bends upward with

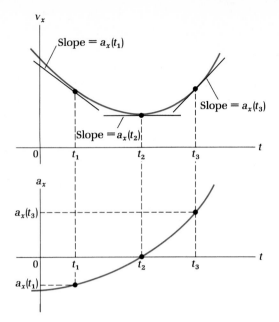

Figure 3-6. The slope of a graph of v_x versus t at each instant of time t gives a_x at that time.

Figure 3-7. (a) A graph of x versus t that is concave upward. In this case v_x is increasing with time and a_x is positive. (b) A graph of x versus t that is concave downward. In this case v_x is decreasing with time and a_x is negative. (c) A graph of x versus t that is straight. In this case v_x is constant and a_x is zero.

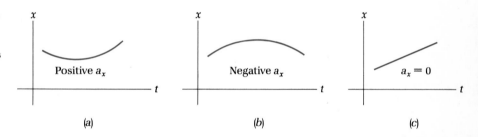

increasing t, as shown in Fig. 3-7a, then v_x is increasing with time and a_x is positive. If the graph bends downward with increasing t, as shown in Fig. 3-7b, then v_x is decreasing with time and a_x is negative. If the graph is straight, as shown in Fig. 3-7c, then v_x is constant and a_x is zero.

Since velocity is a vector quantity and time is a scalar quantity, acceleration is the ratio of a vector to a scalar. Thus acceleration is a vector quantity. The SI unit for velocity is m/s, which means that the SI unit for acceleration is m/s². Table 3-4 lists the magnitudes of a few representative accelerations.

Table 3-4. A few acceleration magnitudes in m/s² (approximate)

Solar system (relative to center of our galaxy)	2×10^{-10}
Earth's center (relative to sun)	6×10^{-3}
Earth's surface at equator (relative to earth's center)	3×10^{-2}
Object falling near earth's surface (relative to earth's surface)	10
Proton in a laboratory accelerator (relative to accelerator)	10^{14}

EXAMPLE 3-4. For the sled in Example 3-1, $x(t) = 18$ m + $(12$ m/s$)t - (1.2$ m/s²$)t^2$. (a) Determine an expression for the sled's acceleration component. (b) Construct a graph of the acceleration component versus time from $t = 0.0$ s to $t = 8.0$ s.

SOLUTION. (a) To find the acceleration component, we take the derivative of v_x with respect to t. In Example 3-2 we found the expression for v_x for the sled to be

$$v_x = 12 \text{ m/s} - (2.4 \text{ m/s}^2)t$$

Thus the acceleration component is

$$a_x = \frac{d}{dt}[12 \text{ m/s} - (2.4 \text{ m/s}^2)t] = -2.4 \text{ m/s}^2$$

In this case it turns out that the acceleration component is constant at -2.4 m/s². (b) A graph of a_x versus t is shown in Fig. 3-8. Since a_x is constant, it is represented by a horizontal straight line.

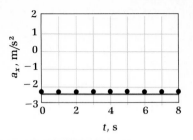

Figure 3-8. Example 3-4: A graph of a_x versus t when a_x is constant.

EXAMPLE 3-5. Suppose that the coordinate of an object is given by

$$x(t) = (4.0 \text{ m/s})t + (1.1 \text{ m/s}^3)t^3$$

Find expressions for (a) v_x and (b) a_x. (c) Construct a graph of v_x versus t in the time interval from $t = 0.0$ s to $t = 4.0$ s. (d) Determine a_x at $t = 1.0$ s, and show the line tangent to the v_x-versus-t graph whose slope is equal to this value of the acceleration.

SOLUTION. (a) Since $v_x = dx/dt$,

$$v_x = \frac{d}{dt}[(4.0 \text{ m/s})t + (1.1 \text{ m/s}^3)t^3]$$

$$= 4.0 \text{ m/s} + 3(1.1 \text{ m/s}^3)t^2$$

$$= 4.0 \text{ m/s} + (3.3 \text{ m/s}^3)t^2$$

(b) Since $a_x = dv_x/dt$,

$$a_x = \frac{d}{dt}[4.0 \text{ m/s} + (3.3 \text{ m/s}^3)t^2] = 2(3.3 \text{ m/s}^3)t$$

$$= (6.6 \text{ m/s}^3)t$$

(c) To construct the graph, we use the expression from part (a) above to evaluate v_x at each second from $t = 0.0$ s to $t = 4.0$ s. The value of v_x at, say 2.0 s, is

$$v_x(2 \text{ s}) = 4.0 \text{ m/s} + (3.3 \text{ m/s}^3)(2.0 \text{ s})^2 = 17 \text{ m/s}$$

The other values of v_x are listed in Table 3-5, and the graph of v_x versus t is shown in Fig. 3-9. (d) Using the expression for a_x

from part (b) above gives

$$a_x(1 \text{ s}) = (6.6 \text{ m/s}^3)(1.0 \text{ s}) = 6.6 \text{ m/s}^2$$

The line whose slope is equal to this value of the acceleration is tangent to the graph of v_x versus t at $t = 1.0$ s, as shown on the graph in Fig. 3-9.

Table 3-5

t, s	v_x, m/s
0.0	4.0
1.0	7.3
2.0	17
3.0	34
4.0	57

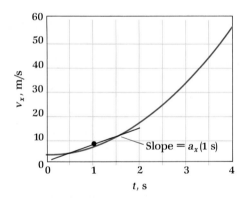

Figure 3-9. Example 3-5.

EXAMPLE 3-6. A barge equipped with an engine travels back and forth along a straight canal that is aligned east to west. Figure 3-10 is a graph of the barge's coordinate versus time where the origin is at the dock and the $+x$ direction is toward the east. Use this graph to describe the barge's motion.

SOLUTION

1 The barge remained stationary at the dock from $t = 0$ s to $t = 10$ s.
2 At $t = 10$ s the barge began accelerating. During the time interval from $t = 10$ s to $t = 30$ s, a_x was positive (the graph bends upward); the acceleration was toward the east. This means that v_x was increasing. Also, v_x was positive

(the slope of the graph is positive) so that the velocity was directed toward the east and the speed was increasing. The slope of the tangent line at $t = 24$ s shows that the velocity at that instant was $\mathbf{v} = (20 \text{ m/40 s})\mathbf{i} = (0.5 \text{ m/s})\mathbf{i}$.
3 From $t = 30$ s to $t = 50$ s, the acceleration was zero (the graph is straight) so that the velocity was constant toward the east with magnitude

$$v = \frac{26 \text{ m} - 8 \text{ m}}{50 \text{ s} - 30 \text{ s}} = 0.9 \text{ m/s}$$

4 From $t = 50$ s to $t = 80$ s, the acceleration component was negative (the graph bends downward) so that the velocity component was decreasing. At $t = 64$ s the barge was instantaneously at rest as it changed its direction of motion

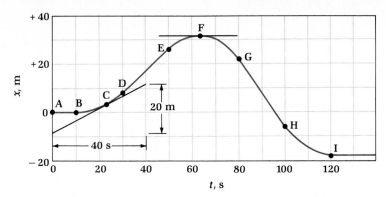

Figure 3-10. Example 3-6: A graph of x versus t for a barge.

from eastward to westward. From $t = 50$ s to $t = 64$ s the velocity component and the speed were decreasing. Between $t = 64$ s and $t = 80$ s the speed was *increasing* despite the fact that the velocity component was *decreasing*. This is because the velocity component is negative and when a negative quantity is decreasing (becoming more negative), its absolute value is increasing.

5 During the time interval from $t = 80$ s to $t = 100$ s,

the barge traveled westward at a constant speed of

$$[(22 \text{ m}) - (-6 \text{ m})]/(100 \text{ s} - 80 \text{ s}) = 1.4 \text{ m/s}.$$

6 Between $t = 100$ s and $t = 120$ s the acceleration component was positive so that the velocity component was increasing (becoming less negative) and the speed was decreasing. The barge came to rest 18 m west of the dock at $t = 120$ s.

3-5 MOTION WITH CONSTANT ACCELERATION

A simple type of motion is motion with constant acceleration. The bobsled, whose adventures we have followed in Examples 3-1, 3-2, and 3-4, moved with constant acceleration. When an object moves with constant acceleration, the acceleration is equal to the average acceleration. Thus $a_x = \bar{a}_x = \Delta v_x/\Delta t$, or $a_x = (v_{xf} - v_{xi})/(t_f - t_i)$. To find an expression for $v_x(t)$, we let $t_f = t$ and $t_i = 0$, so that $v_{xf} = v_x(t)$ and $v_{xi} = v_x(0) = v_{x0}$. This gives

$$a_x = \frac{v_x(t) - v_{x0}}{t - 0}$$

Solving for $v_x(t)$, we obtain

Velocity component as a function of time, constant a_x

$$v_x(t) = v_{x0} + a_x t \tag{3-8}$$

The object's velocity depends linearly on the time t.

We can find the expression for $x(t)$ from the definition of velocity and Eq. (3-8). Since

$$v_x(t) = \frac{d}{dt} x(t)$$

and

$$v_x(t) = v_{x0} + a_x t$$

we have

$$\frac{d}{dx} x(t) = v_{x0} + a_x t \tag{3-9}$$

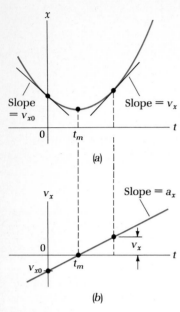

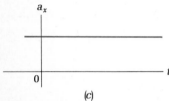

Figure 3-11. Motion with constant acceleration. For the case shown, x_0 is positive, v_{x0} is negative, and a_x is positive. (a) The graph of x versus t is a parabola whose slope at each point is v_x. (b) The graph of v_x versus t is a straight line with slope a_x. (c) The graph of a_x versus t is a horizontal straight line.

Table 3-6. Equations describing motion with constant acceleration

$$v_x(t) = v_{x0} + a_x t$$
$$x(t) = x_0 + v_{x0}t + \tfrac{1}{2}a_x t^2$$
$$v_x^2 = v_{x0}^2 + 2a_x(x - x_0)$$
$$x = x_0 + \tfrac{1}{2}(v_{x0} + v_x)$$

Velocity component as a function of x, constant a_x

That is, $x(t)$ is a function of t such that its time derivative gives $v_{x0} + a_x t$. From the rule

$$\frac{d}{dt}t^n = nt^{n-1}$$

you can see that if we take the derivative of a polynomial in t, then each exponent is reduced by 1. This means that for dx/dt to give Eq. (3-9), the time dependence of $x(t)$ must be of the form

$$x(t) = C_0 + C_1 t + C_2 t^2 \tag{3-10}$$

where C_0, C_1, and C_2 are constants. To verify that Eq. (3-10) does give the correct time dependence for x, we take its derivative and compare the result to $v_x = v_{x0} + a_x t$. Taking the derivative gives

$$\frac{d}{dt}x(t) = \frac{d}{dt}(C_0 + C_1 t + C_2 t^2) = C_1 + 2C_2 t$$

Comparing this expression with $v_{x0} + a_x t$, we have

$$v_{x0} + a_x t = C_1 + 2C_2 t$$

If we let $C_1 = v_{x0}$ and $C_2 = \tfrac{1}{2}a_x$, then the derivative of Eq. (3-10) gives Eq. (3-9).

We have verified that Eq. (3-10) has the proper time dependence to describe motion with constant acceleration, and we have determined the values of C_1 and C_2. Now we find C_0 by evaluating Eq. (3-10) at $t = 0$. This gives $x(0) = C_0$. Since we customarily designate this initial value of x as x_0, we let $C_0 = x_0$. Substituting the values for the constants into Eq. (3-10), we obtain

$$x(t) = x_0 + v_{x0}t + \tfrac{1}{2}a_x t^2 \tag{3-11}$$

Thus x depends quadratically on t.

Figure 3-11 shows graphs of x, v_x, and a_x versus t for a case where x_0 is positive, v_{x0} is negative, and a_x is positive. These graphs reveal the symmetry of the motion about the time t_m. At this time, the object is instantaneously at rest ($v_x = 0$) and it is changing its direction of travel. At any time *before* t_m, the value of x is the same as it is for the same time *after* t_m. Also, the object's speed is the same for equal times before and after t_m. Since x depends quadratically on t, the graph of x versus t in Fig. 3-11a is a parabola.

Equations (3-8) and (3-11) describe the motion in terms of the time t. A third equation can be developed from these two by eliminating t. Solving Eq. (3-8) for t, we find $t = (v_x - v_{x0})/a_x$. Inserting this result into Eq. (3-11) gives

$$x = x_0 + v_{x0}\left(\frac{v_x - v_{x0}}{a_x}\right) + \frac{1}{2}a_x\left(\frac{v_x - v_{x0}}{a_x}\right)^2$$

Rearranging and solving for v_x^2, we obtain

$$v_x^2 = v_{x0}^2 + 2a_x(x - x_0) \tag{3-12}$$

Another equation that is sometimes used in describing an object moving in one dimension with constant acceleration is

$$x = x_0 + \tfrac{1}{2}(v_{x0} + v_x)t \tag{3-13}$$

You can obtain this expression by using Eq. (3-8) to eliminate a_x in Eq. (3-11). (See Prob. 3-10.) Table 3-6 summarizes the important equations in this section.

EXAMPLE 3-7. Within his local tennis circle, Max is renowned for his hard serve. (a) Assume that the ball's acceleration is constant during Max's serve and that its speed v immediately after it leaves his racket is 50 m/s. Estimate the acceleration magnitude a of the ball during the serve. (b) Janet is to receive Max's serve. Estimate the time Janet has to react between the time the ball is served and when she must hit it.

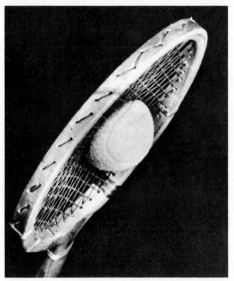

A tennis racket striking a ball. (*Dr. Harold Edgerton/M.I.T., Cambridge, Mass.*)

SOLUTION. (a) We can use Eq. (3-12) to find the acceleration magnitude by setting $v_{x0} = 0$, $v_x = v = 50$ m/s and solving for $a_x = a$. Then $x - x_0$ corresponds to the distance the ball moved while in contact with the racket. Let us estimate this distance to be 0.5 m. This gives

$$a = \frac{v^2}{2(x - x_0)} = \frac{(50 \text{ m/s})^2}{2(0.5 \text{ m})} = 2 \times 10^3 \text{ m/s}^2$$

(b) To estimate the time for the ball to get to Janet, we assume that it moves in a straight line at constant speed. That is, we use Eq. (3-11) with $a_x = 0$ and $v_{x0} = v$. This gives $x = x_0 + vt$. The length of a tennis court is about 24 m, so that $x - x_0 \approx 25$ m. Solving for t, we find

$$t = \frac{x - x_0}{v} \approx \frac{25 \text{ m}}{50 \text{ m/s}} = 0.5 \text{ s}$$

The time will actually be longer than this because air resistance will slow the ball. Janet will probably have plenty of time to notice that Max has committed a foot fault.

EXAMPLE 3-8. *Experiment with a rolling ball.* A useful device for observing the motion of an object is a stroboscope. A stroboscope is a light that briefly flashes at regular time intervals. If a stroboscope is used in conjunction with a camera whose shutter remains open, the camera records the position of an object at each successive flash. Figure 3-12 shows a stroboscopic picture of a billiard ball rolling down a straight slope. The flashes are 0.20 s apart and the scale is calibrated in meters. Let the unit vector **i** point in the direction of motion (to the right), and let $t = 0.00$ s be the time when the ball is farthest up the slope. Table 3-7 gives the coordinate of the center of the ball at each time t. (a) Assume that the ball moves with constant acceleration and find values of x_0, v_{x0}, and a_x. (b) Write the expressions for $x(t)$ and $v_x(t)$. (c) Verify that the data in Table 3-7 are consistent with constant acceleration.

Table 3-7

t, s	x, m
0.00	−0.030
0.20	0.067
0.40	0.203
0.60	0.377
0.80	0.589
1.00	0.840

SOLUTION. (a) If the ball moves with constant acceleration, the data of Table 3-7 can be given by Eq. (3-11). As you can see from the table, $x_0 = -0.030$ m. Therefore we have two unknowns to find; they are a_x and v_{x0}. Since two unknowns can be found from two equations, we can insert two data pairs from Table 3-7, call them (t_1, x_1) and (t_2, x_2), into

Figure 3-12. Example 3-8: A stroboscopic picture of a billiard ball rolling down a straight slope. (*Tom Richard*)

Eq. (3-11) and solve for the unknowns. These equations are

$$x_1 = x_0 + v_{x0}t_1 + \tfrac{1}{2}a_x t_1^2 \qquad (A)$$

$$x_2 = x_0 + v_{x0}t_2 + \tfrac{1}{2}a_x t_2^2 \qquad (B)$$

Solving Eq. (A) for v_{x0}, we find

$$v_{x0} = \frac{x_1 - x_0}{t_1} - \frac{1}{2} a_x t_1 \qquad (C)$$

Inserting this result into Eq. (B) and solving for a_x, we obtain

$$a_x = \frac{2[t_1(x_2 - x_0) - t_2(x_1 - x_0)]}{t_1 t_2^2 - t_1^2 t_2} \qquad (D)$$

We choose (0.20 s, 0.067 m) and (1.00 s, 0.840 m) as our data pairs from Table 3-7. Substituting these data into Eq. (D), we find

$$a_x = \frac{2[(0.20\text{ s})(0.870\text{ m}) - (1.00\text{ s})(0.097\text{ m})]}{(0.20\text{ s})(1.00\text{ s})^2 - (0.20\text{ s})^2(1.00\text{ s})} = 0.96\text{ m/s}^2$$

Using this value of a_x and a data pair from the table, say (0.20 s, 0.067 m), in Eq. (C), we have

$$v_{x0} = \frac{0.097\text{ m}}{0.20\text{ s}} - \frac{1}{2}(0.96\text{ m/s}^2)(0.20\text{ s}) = 0.39\text{ m/s}$$

(b) The ball's coordinate and velocity component as functions of time are

$$x(t) = -0.030\text{ m} + (0.39\text{ m/s})t + (0.48\text{ m/s}^2)t^2$$

$$v_x(t) = 0.39\text{ m/s} + (0.96\text{ m/s}^2)t$$

(c) To verify that the data in Table 3-7 are consistent with the assumption of constant velocity, we can insert each value of t from the table into our expression for $x(t)$ and see whether each calculation gives the corresponding value of x. For instance, let us check the pair (0.40 s, 0.203 m):

$$x = -0.030\text{ m} + (0.39\text{ m/s})(0.40\text{ s}) + (0.48\text{ m/s}^2)(0.40\text{ s})^2$$
$$= 0.20\text{ m}$$

This data pair is consistent with the assumption of constant acceleration. You should check some of the other data pairs in the same way.

3-6 FREE-FALL

We are all familiar with falling objects—for example, a paperweight that is accidentally knocked off the edge of a desk. Often in describing the motion of the paperweight, we can neglect air resistance. If air resistance has a negligible effect on a falling object, then it is valid to assume that the object's acceleration is due entirely to gravity. In this case the motion is called *free-fall*. Treating the motion of the paperweight as free-fall is a valid approximation as long as it does not fall too far. Even for short falls, this approximation is poor for an object such as a feather or a badminton birdie.

Galileo Galilei (1564–1642) made quantitative studies of free-fall and determined that the acceleration due to gravity is constant. (Some of Galileo's results are discussed in Prob. 3-12.) Modern measurements verify that objects in free-fall have a constant downward acceleration; the acceleration is the same at each instant during the fall. Further, this acceleration is the *same* for *different* objects (Fig. 3-13). This familiar but nevertheless intriguing result will be considered in more detail in Chap. 7.

The magnitude of this acceleration is represented by the symbol g. Although g varies slightly from place to place on the earth's surface, a value that is accurate enough for our purposes is

$$g = 9.8\text{ m/s}^2$$

We shall discuss the slight variation of g on the earth's surface in Chap. 7.

In describing free-fall, we customarily choose the y axis along the direction of motion with the unit vector **j** directed upward. Then the acceleration of a freely falling object is

$$\mathbf{a} = -g\mathbf{j}$$

A minus sign is explicitly put into the equation because the acceleration is

Definition of free-fall

Magnitude of the acceleration due to gravity

Free-fall acceleration

Galileo Galilei is regarded as the father of modern science. A brief biography of Galileo is contained in Chap. 4. (*A.I.P. Niels Bohr Library/ Physics Today Collection*)

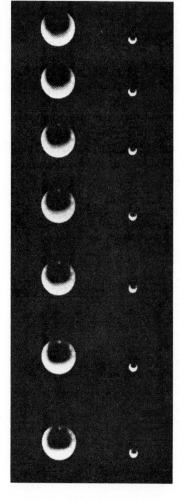

Figure 3-13. A stroboscopic photograph of two balls as they fall. The balls were released simultaneously, and, as far as can be told from the photograph, both balls fall with the same acceleration. (*Tom Richard*)

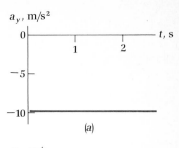

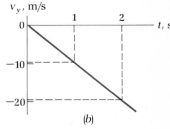

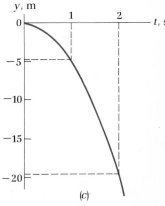

Figure 3-14. Graphs of (a) a_y, (b) v_y, and (c) y for free-fall when $v_{y0} = 0$ and $y_0 = 0$.

downward and the symbol g represents a positive number. Since free-fall is motion with constant acceleration, we can use Eqs. (3-8), (3-11), and (3-12) to describe this motion by letting $a_x = -g$ and by changing the coordinate from x to y:

Equations describing free-fall

$$v_y(t) = v_{y0} - gt \tag{3-14}$$

$$y(t) = y_0 + v_{y0}t - \tfrac{1}{2}gt^2 \tag{3-15}$$

$$v_y{}^2 = v_{y0}{}^2 - 2g(y - y_0) \tag{3-16}$$

Figure 3-14 shows graphs of a_y, v_y, and y for an object that undergoes free-fall after it is released from rest at $y = 0$.

If an object, such as a baseball, is thrown vertically upward with initial speed v_0, two quantities that can be readily measured are (i) the time t_m required for the ball to reach its maximum height and (ii) the ball's maximum height h_m. Let the origin of the coordinate frame be at the release point and let $t = 0$ correspond to the instant the ball is released: $y_0 = 0$ and $v_{y0} = v_0$. When the ball reaches its maximum height, its velocity is zero. Assuming the ball is in free-fall, we use Eq. (3-14) and find $v_y(t_m) = 0 = v_0 - gt_m$, or

Time of maximum height

$$t_m = \frac{v_0}{g} \tag{3-17}$$

The coordinate evaluated at this time is the maximum height, $h_m = y(t_m)$. Inserting t_m from Eq. (3-17) into Eq. (3-15) gives

$$y(t_m) = h_m = 0 + v_0\left(\frac{v_0}{g}\right) - \frac{1}{2}g\left(\frac{v_0}{g}\right)^2$$

Maximum height

or

$$h_m = \frac{v_0^2}{2g} \tag{3-18}$$

The same result follows from Eq. (3-16) with $v_y = 0$, $v_{y0} = v_0$, and $h_m = y - y_0$.

EXAMPLE 3-9. A rock was thrown vertically upward such that the time required for it to reach its maximum height was 1.2 s. The release point was 1.5 m above the ground. (a) Letting $t = 0$ be the instant the rock was released and $y = 0$ correspond to the ground, determine the expressions for the rock's velocity component and coordinate as functions of time. (b) Evaluate these expressions at $t = 0.0$, 0.60, 1.2, and 1.8 s. (c) Sketch the rock's position, velocity, and acceleration at each of these times. Use arrows to represent the velocity and acceleration. Neglect air resistance.

SOLUTION. (a) To find these expressions, we must determine the values of y_0 and v_{y0} and insert them into Eqs. (3-14) and (3-15). The value of y_0 is given ($y_0 = 1.5$ m), and we can find v_0 from Eq. (3-17):

$$v_0 = t_m g = (1.2\ \text{s})(9.8\ \text{m/s}^2) = 12\ \text{m/s}$$

Since the rock was thrown upward, $v_{y0} = v_0 = 12$ m/s. Thus the expressions for v_y and y are

$$v_y = 12\ \text{m/s} - (9.8\ \text{m/s}^2)t$$

$$y = 1.5\ \text{m} + (12\ \text{m/s})t - (4.9\ \text{m/s}^2)t^2$$

(b) At $t = 0.0$ s, we have $v_y = v_{y0} = 12$ m/s and $y = y_0 = 1.5$ m. At $t = 0.60$ s, we have

$$v_y = 12\ \text{m/s} - (9.8\ \text{m/s}^2)(0.60\ \text{s}) = 6.1\ \text{m/s}$$

$$y = 1.5\ \text{m} + (12\ \text{m/s})(0.60\ \text{s}) - (4.9\ \text{m/s}^2)(0.60\ \text{s})^2 = 6.9\ \text{m}$$

At $t = 1.2$ s, we have $v_y = 0.0$ m/s because $t_m = 1.2$ s. The coordinate at this time is

$$y = 1.5\ \text{m} + (12\ \text{m/s})(1.2\ \text{s}) - (4.9\ \text{m/s}^2)(1.2\ \text{s})^2 = 8.6\ \text{m}$$

At $t = 1.8$ s, we have

$$v_y = 12\ \text{m/s} - (9.8\ \text{m/s}^2)(1.8\ \text{s}) = -5.9\ \text{m/s}$$

$$y = 1.5\ \text{m} + (12\ \text{m/s})(1.8\ \text{s}) - (4.9\ \text{m/s}^2)(1.8\ \text{s})^2 = 6.8\ \text{m}$$

These values at $t = 1.8$ s could have been predicted from those at $t = 0.60$ s and from the symmetry of the motion. (c) The sketches of the rock's position, velocity, and acceleration at these times are shown in Fig. 3-15.

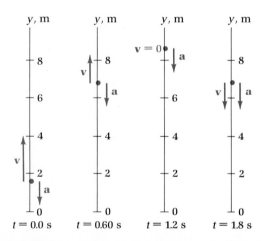

Figure 3-15. Example 3-9: A rock is thrown vertically upward. The rock's position, velocity, and acceleration are shown at four times.

EXAMPLE 3-10. A flowerpot falls from a second-floor window. What is its speed just before it hits the ground 3 m below? Neglect air resistance.

SOLUTION. Let the origin of our coordinate frame be at the ground and let $t = 0$ be the instant the pot starts to fall from rest at the window. This means that $v_{y0} = 0$ and $y_0 =$ 3 m. Since we wish to know the pot's speed at a given coordinate, namely at $y = 0$, we use Eq. (3-16). The speed $v = |v_y| = \sqrt{v_y^2}$, so that

$$v = \sqrt{v_y^2} = \sqrt{v_{y0}^2 - 2g(y - y_0)}$$

$$= \sqrt{0 - 2(9.8\ \text{m/s}^2)(0 - 3\ \text{m})} = 8\ \text{m/s}$$

🔳 3-7 VARYING ACCELERATION, NUMERICAL METHODS

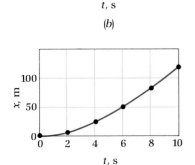

Figure 3-16. (a) (b) (c)

Figure 3-16. Graphs of the numerical results from the program of Table 3-8. A car starts from rest at $x = 0$ with an initial acceleration of $(4 \text{ m/s}^2)\mathbf{i}$.

When the acceleration is not constant, solving a kinematics problem is often difficult. Analytic solutions can be found for only a few special cases. If an analytic solution cannot be found, then we can use a numerical procedure to determine the position and velocity of an object. We do this by simply dividing the motion into many small time intervals and using the approximation that the acceleration is constant during each time interval. That is, we use constant acceleration kinematics for each time interval. We instruct a computer to calculate x and v_x at the end of each time interval Δt by using information from the previous time interval.

As an example, consider a car starting out from a stop sign. Suppose the magnitude of the car's acceleration is 4 m/s² at $t = 0$, 2 m/s² at $t = 4$ s, 1 m/s² at $t = 8$ s, and so on. That is, the magnitude of the acceleration becomes smaller by a factor of 2 every 4 s. An equation for a_x is

$$a_x(t) = a_{x0}2^{-bt} \tag{3-19}$$

where $a_{x0} = 4 \text{ m/s}^2$ and $b = 0.25 \text{ s}^{-1}$. Figure 3-16a shows a graph of a_x versus t.

Table 3-8 contains a program written in BASIC that gives x, v_x, and a_x at each second for the first 10 s, using 1000 iterations. Even though you may not be familiar with BASIC, perusal of the program will illustrate numerical methods to you. The first four statements — 100, 110, 120, and 130 — introduce the notation to the computer and give it the initial values of x, v_x, a_x, and t: X = 0, V = 0, A = 4, and T = 0. (Symbols in BASIC are printed in capital letters. Also, we express all numerical quantities in SI units.) Statement 140 gives the size of the time interval DT, and statement 200 gives the number of iterations to be performed. Statements 210, 220, 230, and 240 tell the computer how we want it to calculate a_x, v_x, x, and t for each iteration. Statement 220 corresponds to the equation $v_x(t + \Delta t) \approx v_x(t) + a_x(t)\Delta t$. Similarly, statement 230 corresponds to $x(t + \Delta t) \approx x(t) + v_x(t)\Delta t$. Statement 250 causes the computer to print the values of t, v_x, and x after each 100 iterations so that we are provided these values at each second of the motion. Statement 260 tells the computer that after it completes an iteration it is to go back and do the next one. Figure 3-16 shows graphs of the data that are produced by this program.

Notice that we have not paid attention to the rules on significant digits in this section. The reason is that computers treat all numbers as if they are exact. After the computer is through with the calculations, you should assign to the

Table 3-8. BASIC program for finding v_x and x at time t when $a_x = (4 \text{ m/s}^2)2^{-[(0.25 \text{ s}^{-1})t]}$

```
100    X=0
110    V=0
120    A=4
130    T=0
140    DT=.01
200    FOR I=1 TO 1000
210        A=4*2^(−.25*T)
220        V=V+A*DT
230        X=X+V*DT
240        T=T+DT
250        IF I=100*INT(I/100) THEN PRINT T, V, X
260    NEXT I
300    END
```

results the number of significant digits corresponding to the number of significant digits in the least precisely known input datum. Another important point is that round-off errors can accumulate and can possibly become significant. Whether this is important depends on the particular problem, the number of iterations, and the desired precision. We shall have more to say about these matters in Chap. 8.

COMMENTARY: MARCHING LOCKSTEP THROUGH PHYSICS

A textbook can be deceptive. In this textbook, you will be introduced to many laws, equations, and rules. These formulations are regarded as successful because they accurately and concisely describe many phenomena. Any theory or experiment that is now viewed as a failure will not be discussed. It is the lack of any discussion of the failures that can be deceiving. It can lead to the mistaken impression that such failures are rare, or that they never existed, or that they are without value.

Studying physics in a textbook such as this is similar to walking along a beaten path. The path has been worn smooth by those before us. There are hardly any bumps or holes which might cause us to stumble. As it exists now, the path at a particular place is nothing like it was when it was first tread. Then it was full of briars and brambles. In times past, one person or another cut a path that later turned out to be off the main trail. Textbooks avoid such diversions.

Where does this beaten path lead? It leads to the frontier of physics. The spirit of physics is at the frontier. That is where the uncertainty and the excitement are. Nearing the frontier, we find that the path becomes more obscure. Now there are lots of holes and bumps and briars and brambles. At the frontier many people are hacking straight ahead. However, real progress often is made by those who back up, step off the beaten path, and start an entirely new approach. For instance, Albert Einstein, in developing the theory of relativity (Chap. 38), returned to the most basic ideas of space and time. He showed that beyond a certain point the beaten path was leading the wrong way.

As you read this textbook, or any textbook, you should remain skeptical. But do not let your skepticism interfere with learning the material. If you are to blaze a new trail, you will probably need to start from somewhere on the beaten path.

SUMMARY WITH APPLICATIONS

Section 3-2. Position vector and displacement
The position vector **r** locates an object relative to the origin of a reference frame. In one dimension, $\mathbf{r} = x\mathbf{i}$ where x is the object's coordinate. The displacement $\Delta\mathbf{r}$ is the change in the position vector,

$$\Delta\mathbf{r} = \mathbf{r}_f - \mathbf{r}_i$$

Define position vector and displacement; evaluate expressions for $x(t)$ and construct graphs of x versus t.

Section 3-3. Velocity and speed
The average velocity of an object is the object's displacement during a time interval divided by the time interval, $\bar{\mathbf{v}} = \Delta\mathbf{r}/\Delta t$. The velocity is the limiting value of the average velocity as the time interval approaches zero:

$$\mathbf{v} = \lim_{\Delta t \to 0} \bar{\mathbf{v}} = \frac{d\mathbf{r}}{dt} \tag{3-4}$$

Speed is the magnitude of the velocity, $v = |\mathbf{v}|$.

Define average velocity, velocity, and speed; determine $v_x(t)$ from $x(t)$ and construct graphs of v_x versus t.

Section 3-4. Acceleration

The average acceleration of an object during a time interval is the change in the object's velocity divided by the time interval, $\bar{a} = \Delta v/\Delta t$. The acceleration is the limiting value of the average acceleration as the time interval approaches zero:

$$\mathbf{a} = \lim_{\Delta t \to 0} \bar{\mathbf{a}} = \frac{d\mathbf{v}}{dt} \qquad (3\text{-}7)$$

Define average acceleration and acceleration; determine $a_x(t)$ from $v_x(t)$ or $x(t)$.

Section 3-5. Motion with constant acceleration

When an object moves with constant acceleration along one dimension,

$$v_x(t) = v_{x0} + a_x t \qquad (3\text{-}8)$$

$$x(t) = x_0 + v_{x0}t + \tfrac{1}{2}a_x t^2 \qquad (3\text{-}11)$$

$$v_x{}^2 = v_{x0}{}^2 + 2a_x(x - x_0) \qquad (3\text{-}12)$$

Determine the details of the motion of an object with constant acceleration.

Section 3-6. Free-fall

Free-fall is a particular example of motion with constant acceleration. If a freely falling object moves along a vertical line (the y axis), then we use the expressions above with y as the coordinate and $-g$ as the constant acceleration component.

Describe the motion of an object along a vertical line during free-fall.

Section 3-7. Varying acceleration, numerical methods

Numerical methods can be used to describe motion with varying acceleration. Each iteration is taken over a time interval that is small enough so that the acceleration can be treated as constant.

Explain numerical procedures for describing motion with varying acceleration.

QUESTIONS

3-1   Suppose we flip a coin vertically upward. If we are interested in the maximum height of the coin, is it valid to treat the coin as a particle? If we are interested in whether the coin lands heads up or tails up, is it valid to treat the coin as a particle?

3-2   A jogger travels from $x = 0$ to $x = 50$ m between $t = 0$ and $t = 10$ s. Between $t = 10$ s and $t = 15$ s, the jogger travels from $x = 50$ m to $x = 25$ m. Is the distance traveled by the jogger equal to the magnitude of his displacement (a) between $t = 0$ and $t = 10$ s, (b) between $t = 0$ and $t = 15$ s? Explain.

3-3   The symbol $v_x(t)$ usually means "v_x as a function of time t," but it could be used to represent the product v_x times t. In the following two equations, which interpretation do you give to $v_x(t)$?
   (a) $v_x(t) = 7.3$ m
   (b) $v_x(t) = (6.1 \text{ m/s}^2)t$

3-4   While running in a race of length 24 mi, a hypothetical runner becomes increasingly tired. During the first hour of the race she runs 12 mi, during the second hour she runs 6 mi, during the third hour she runs 3 mi, and so on. Each hour she runs half the remaining distance. How long will it take her to complete the race?

3-5   In describing the motion of a car traveling west, we let the $+x$ direction be toward the east. Consider the following statements:
   (a) The velocity of the car is -32 m/s.

   (b) The velocity of the car is $(-32 \text{ m})\mathbf{i}$.
   (c) The velocity of the car is $(-32 \text{ m/s})\mathbf{i}$.
   (d) The speed of the car is -32 m/s.
   (e) The speed of the car is 32 m/s.
   (f) The velocity component of the car is -32 m/s.
   Which, if any, of these statements is meaningless? Explain what is wrong with any statement that is meaningless.

3-6   Judy says that the average speed of an object is the magnitude of the object's average velocity. Martha says that the average speed of an object is the distance traveled by the object during a time interval divided by the time interval. Will Judy and Martha always agree on the value of the average speed of an object? Describe a case where they will agree. Describe a case where they will disagree. Decide which definition you prefer and give your reasons.

3-7   Can the speed of an object be negative? Explain.

3-8   We defined speed as the magnitude of the velocity. Does a car's speedometer reading correspond to this definition? Explain.

3-9   Does a car's odometer measure distance or displacement? Explain.

3-10   A car travels along a straight east-west street. We let the unit vector $\mathbf{i}$ point toward the east. What is the sign of v_x if the car is traveling (a) toward the east, (b) toward the west? What is the sign of a_x if the car is traveling (c) toward the east and slowing down, (d) toward the east and speeding up, (e) toward the west and slowing down, (f) toward the west and speeding up?

3-11 *Deceleration* is a term that is sometimes used in describing the motion of an object. Judy says that deceleration is defined as the magnitude of the acceleration when the acceleration component is negative. Using this definition, we would describe an object as decelerating if its velocity component is decreasing. Martha says that deceleration is the magnitude of the acceleration when an object's speed is decreasing. Are these definitions the same? If they are not the same, describe a situation where their difference is evident. State the definition you prefer and give your reasons.

3-12 In describing the motion of a rock that is thrown vertically upward, we let the unit vector **j** point upward. What is the sign of the rock's velocity component v_y (a) before it reaches its maximum height, (b) at the instant it reaches its maximum height, (c) after it reaches its maximum height? (d) What is the rock's speed at the instant it reaches its maximum height? After the rock has reached its maximum height, (e) is its speed increasing, decreasing, or remaining the same? (f) Is its velocity component increasing, decreasing, or remaining the same?

3-13 For the rock in the previous question, what is the sign of the rock's acceleration component (a) before it reaches its maximum height, (b) at the instant it reaches its maximum height, (c) after it reaches its maximum height? (d) What is the magnitude of the rock's acceleration at the instant it reaches its maximum height?

3-14 A girl throws a ball vertically upward with an initial speed of 10 m/s and catches it at the same height when it returns. Neglecting air resistance, what is the ball's speed when it is caught?

3-15 Reaching out from a balcony, you throw rock A vertically upward. Then you throw rock B vertically downward from the same release point and with the same initial speed as rock A. If you neglect air resistance, which rock has the higher speed just before it hits the ground?

3-16 Two golf balls are dropped from rest from the top of a tall building. Ball 1 is dropped at $t = 0$, and ball 2 is dropped at $t = 0.5$ s. Ball 1 hits the ground at $t = 3.0$ s.

(a) Between $t = 0.5$ s and $t = 3.0$ s does the separation between the two balls increase, decrease, or remain the same? (b) When does ball 2 hit the ground?

3-17 A graph of x versus t for an object is shown in Fig. 3-17. What are the algebraic signs of v_x and a_x at times (a) t_1; (b) t_2; (c) t_3?

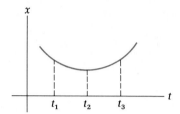

Figure 3-17. Ques. 3-17.

3-18 A graph of v_x versus t for an object is shown in Fig. 3-18. What is the algebraic sign of a_x at times (a) t_1; (b) t_2; (c) t_3?

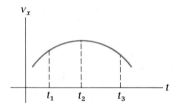

Figure 3-18. Ques. 3-18.

3-19 In each part of Fig. 3-19a through d, determine whether v_x is larger, at t_1 or at t_2. In which case is the speed v larger, at t_1 or at t_2?

3-20 A graph of x versus t for an object is shown in Fig. 3-20.

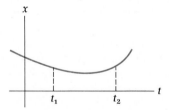

Figure 3-20. Ques. 3-20.

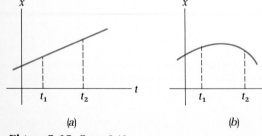

(a)   (b)   (c)   (d)

Figure 3-19. Ques. 3-19.

At which time, t_1 or t_2, is the magnitude of the acceleration larger? Explain.

3-21 Suppose the expression that gives a_x versus t is linear. What is the expression for v_x versus t?

3-22 Without using numerical values, sketch the graphs of x versus t and v_x versus t for the following cases of constant acceleration:
(a) $a_x < 0$, $v_{x0} > 0$, $x_0 > 0$
(b) $a_x > 0$, $v_{x0} < 0$, $x_0 > 0$
(c) $a_x > 0$, $v_{x0} > 0$, $x_0 > 0$

3-23 Suppose the expression for the coordinate of an object is of the form $x(t) = C_0 + C_1 t + C_3 t^3$. What is the time dependence of a_x? Is it quadratic? Linear? Constant? Something else?

3-24 Complete the following table:

Symbol	Represents	Type	SI unit
$\mathbf{r}$			m
x_0	Initial coordinate		
v_x		Component	
v			
a_x			

EXERCISES

Section 3-2. Position vector and displacement

3-1 A jogger is 16 m west of a stop sign at time t_i and is 37 m east of the stop sign at time t_f. Let the stop sign be the origin and let the unit vector $\mathbf{i}$ point east. Determine (a) x_i; (b) x_f; (c) $\mathbf{r}_i$; (d) $\mathbf{r}_f$; (e) $\Delta \mathbf{r}$.

3-2 The coordinate for a bicycle is given by the expression $x(t) = -(14 \text{ m/s})t + 74 \text{ m}$. Make a graph of x versus t from $t = 0.0$ s to $t = 6.0$ s by plotting points for each second. Sketch a curve through the points.

3-3 The coordinate of an object is given by the expression $x(t) = 52 \text{ mm sin } [(0.44 \text{ rad/s})t]$. (Recall that $2\pi \text{ rad} = 360°$. Be certain you change from degrees to radians on your calculator.) (a) Make a graph of x versus t from $t = 0.0$ s to $t = 15.0$ s by plotting points each second. Sketch a curve through the points. Between $t = 0.0$ s and $t = 10.0$ s, what is (b) the distance traveled by the object and (c) the displacement of the object?

Section 3-3. Velocity and speed

3-4 A car traveling west along a straight road is 81 m east of a manhole cover at $t_i = 15$ s and 13 m west of the cover at $t_f = 22$ s. (a) If we let the unit vector $\mathbf{i}$ point east, what is the car's average velocity component? (b) If we let the unit vector $\mathbf{i}$ point west, what is the car's average velocity component?

3-5 (a) Determine a conversion factor between ft/s and m/s. (b) Convert a speed of 25 m/s to ft/s.

3-6 One light-year (abbreviated ly) is the distance light travels in one year. (a) Given that the speed of light is about 3.0×10^8 m/s, determine a conversion factor between m and ly. The distance from earth to the star Sirius (the brightest star in the heavens, other than the sun) is about 10 ly. Determine the distance to Sirius (b) in m and (c) in mi.

3-7 The average distance from the earth to the sun is about 100 million mi (1×10^8 mi) and the speed of light is 3.0×10^8 m/s. (a) How long does it take the light from the sun to reach the earth? (b) One light-minute is the distance light travels in one minute. Determine the distance to the sun in units of light-minutes.

3-8 The speed of sound in air at ordinary temperatures is about 340 m/s. Suppose you see a lightning flash in an approaching storm and 6.0 s later you hear the thunder. (a) Estimate the distance that the storm is from you by assuming that the speed of light is infinite. (b) What sort of precision (the number of significant digits) would be required of the time measurement for the assumption in part (a) to be invalid?

3-9 Often, just about a second or two after the lights flicker in your house, you may hear the sound of a distant explosion. The sound may be due to the explosion of a nearby transformer and the flicker to the subsequent destruction of the transformer. Assuming that the electric energy propagates along the wires at an infinite speed and that the speed of sound in air is 340 m/s, estimate the distance to an exploded transformer when you hear the explosion 0.50 s after the lights flicker.

3-10 (a) A ferry boat crosses a 550-m-wide river from the east to the west shore in 1 min and 9 s. What is the boat's average velocity? (b) The boat makes the return trip in 58 s. What is the boat's average velocity for the return trip? (c) What is the boat's average velocity for the entire round-trip? Keep in mind that velocity is a vector quantity.

3-11 The equation for the coordinate of an object as a function of time is $x(t) = (2.2 \text{ m/s}^3)t^3 - 18$ m. (a) What is the object's average velocity component between $t_i = 1.0$ s and $t_f = 3.0$ s? (b) What is the object's velocity component at $t = 2.0$ s?

3-12 A graph of the coordinate versus time for an object is shown in Fig. 3-21. Determine $\bar{v}_x$ (a) between $t = 0.0$ s and $t = 4.0$ s; (b) between $t = 5.0$ s and $t = 9.0$ s. Find (c) $v_x(3.0 \text{ s})$ and (d) $v(3.0 \text{ s})$. Find (e) $v_x(8.0 \text{ s})$ and (f) $v(8.0 \text{ s})$.

3-13 Use the graph of coordinate versus time in Fig. 3-22 to find $\bar{v}_x$ between $t = 1.0$ s and $t = t_f$ when (a) $t_f = 5.0$ s;

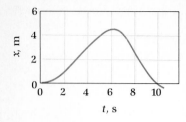

Figure 3-21. Exercise 3-12.

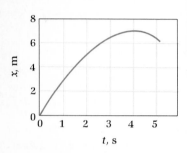

Figure 3-22. Exercise 3-13.   **Figure 3-23.** Exercise 3-14. (*Dr. Harold Edgerton/M.I.T., Cambridge, Mass.*)

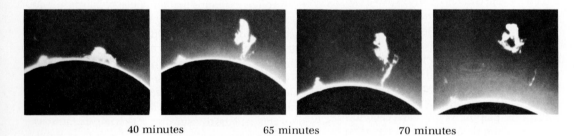

40 minutes   65 minutes   70 minutes

Figure 3-24. Exercise 3-15. (*National Center for Atmospheric Research/National Science Foundation*)

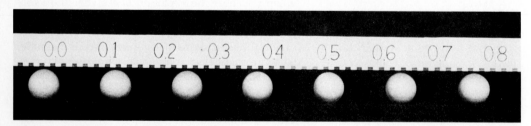

Figure 3-25. Exercise 3-17. (*Tom Richard*)

(*b*) $t_f = 4.0$ s; (*c*) $t_f = 3.0$ s; (*d*) $t_f = 2.0$ s. (*e*) Estimate $v_x(1.0 \text{ s})$.

3-14 Figure 3-23 shows a stroboscopic photograph of a golfer driving a ball off a tee. The stroboscopic light flashed 100 times per second. Estimate the speed of the ball as it left the tee.

3-15 Figure 3-24 shows sequential photographs of a burst of incandescent gas emitted from the surface of the sun. Estimate the speed of the emitted material between

each of the photographs. The radius of the sun is about 7×10^8 m.

3-16 An expression for the coordinate of an object is $x(t) = -(3.5 \text{ m/s}^3)t^3 - (1.8 \text{ m/s})t$. (*a*) Write an expression for $v_x(t)$. (*b*) What is $v_x(2.6 \text{ s})$? (*c*) What is v_{x0}?

3-17 Figure 3-25 shows a stroboscopic photograph of a puck made of dry ice as it slides across a smooth horizontal surface. The time between flashes is 0.10 s. Use a point adjacent to the left end of the meter stick as origin and let the unit vector **i** point to the right. (*a*) Assuming that the puck is moving to the right, write an expression for $x(t)$ with $t = 0.00$ s corresponding to the puck's position at the far left. (*b*) Assuming that the puck is moving to the left, write an expression for $x(t)$ with $t = 0.00$ s corresponding to the puck's position at the far right.

Section 3-4. Acceleration

3-18 Automobile magazines sometimes give the magnitude of the acceleration in units of mi h^{-1} s^{-1} (miles per hour per second). (*a*) Determine a conversion factor for converting mi h^{-1} s^{-1} to m s^{-2}. (*b*) Convert an acceleration magnitude of 12 mi h^{-1} s^{-1} to m s^{-2}.

3-19 The speed of a car increases from 18 to 23 m/s in a time interval of 5.8 s. (*a*) Let the $+x$ direction be along the direction of travel and determine the average acceleration component. (*b*) Let the $+x$ direction be opposite the direction of travel and determine the average acceleration component.

3-20 The speed of a car decreases from 23 to 18 m/s in a time interval of 5.8 s. (*a*) Let the $+x$ direction be along the direction of travel and determine the average acceleration component. (*b*) Let the $+x$ direction be opposite the direction of travel and determine the average acceleration component.

3-21 A graph of the velocity component versus time for an object is shown in Fig. 3-26. Determine $\bar{a}_x$ (*a*) between $t = 0.0$ s and $t = 3.0$ s; (*b*) between $t = 3.0$ s and $t = 9.0$ s. (*c*) Find $a_x(5.0$ s).

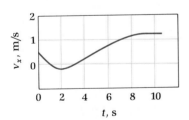

Figure 3-26. Exercise 3-21.

3-22 Use the graph of the velocity component versus time in

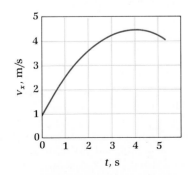

Figure 3-27. Exercise 3-22.

Fig. 3-27 to find $\bar{a}_x$ between $t = 1.0$ s and $t = t_f$ when (*a*) $t_f = 5.0$ s; (*b*) $t_f = 4.0$ s; (*c*) $t_f = 3.0$ s; (*d*) $t_f = 2.0$ s. (*e*) Estimate $a_x(1$ s).

3-23 An expression for the coordinate of an object is $x(t) = -(1.6$ m/s$^3)t^3 + (2.1$ m/s$^2)t^2 - 42$ m. (*a*) Write an expression for $a_x(t)$. (*b*) Determine $a_x(4.1$ s). (*c*) What is $a_x(0) = a_{x0}$?

3-24 An expression for the velocity component of an object is $v_x(t) = (3.2$ m/s$^3)t^2 - 6.1$ m/s. (*a*) Write an expression for $a_x(t)$. (*b*) Determine $a_x(2.7$ s). (*c*) What is $a_x(0) = a_{x0}$?

Section 3-5. Motion with constant acceleration

3-25 A 60-km footrace that was held in New York in 1983 was won with a time of about 4 h and 40 min. Assuming constant speed, what was the speed of the winner?

3-26 Major-league pitchers typically throw a baseball with a speed of about 90 mi/h. The distance between the pitcher's mound and home plate is about 20 m. Assuming the ball travels at constant speed, estimate the time required for the ball to travel from the mound to the plate.

3-27 A jogger runs with a constant velocity of 2.2 m/s toward the north. Choose the origin of the coordinate frame at an oak tree, let the unit vector **i** point north, and let $t = 0$ correspond to the instant the jogger is 15 m north of the tree. (*a*) Determine an expression for the jogger's coordinate as a function of time. (*b*) What is the jogger's coordinate at $t = 28$ s? (*c*) When will the jogger's coordinate be 51 m?

3-28 The acceleration of a sprinter at the beginning of a race can be approximated as constant. Use this approximation and an acceleration magnitude of 3.8 m/s^2 to determine (*a*) the distance traversed by the sprinter in the first 2.0 s of a race and (*b*) the sprinter's speed 2.0 s after the start of the race.

3-29 Assume that an airliner on its takeoff run moves at constant acceleration with magnitude 3.6 m/s^2. (*a*) Write an expression for the airliner's velocity component as a function of time. (*b*) What is the airliner's speed 24 s after the start of the run? (*c*) Write an expression for the airliner's coordinate as a function of time. (*d*) What is the distance traversed by the airliner during the first 24 s of the run?

3-30 An object has a constant acceleration of 4.0 m/s^2 toward the south. At a certain instant the object's velocity is 8.4 m/s toward the north, and its position is 47 m north of our origin. (*a*) Establish a convenient reference frame and starting time for describing the motion. Determine an expression for the object's (*b*) coordinate and (*c*) velocity component as functions of time. Determine the object's (*d*) coordinate and (*e*) velocity component 3.0 s after the instant mentioned above.

3-31 The motion of a particular sprinter can be approximated by constant acceleration with magnitude 3.4 m/s² for the first 40 m after she leaves the starting line. What is her speed when she has traveled (a) 20 m and (b) 40 m?

3-32 A car traveling along a straight road at a speed of 22 m/s begins to slow down with a constant acceleration of magnitude 2.9 m/s² at the instant it passes a "stop ahead" warning sign. (a) What is the car's speed 30 m beyond the sign? (b) What is the car's speed 60 m beyond the sign? (c) If the car continues its constant acceleration until it stops just at the stop sign, how far apart are the signs?

3-33 The driver of a car traveling along a straight road with a speed of 18 m/s observes a sign which gives the speed limit as 25 m/s. The sign is 85 m ahead at the instant the driver begins to accelerate the car. Determine the magnitude of the constant acceleration which will cause the car to pass the sign at the posted speed limit.

3-34 A ship is cruising at a speed of 6.3 m/s at the instant it passes a buoy. At this time it begins to increase its speed with a constant acceleration of magnitude 0.20 m/s². How far is the ship from the buoy when its speed is 8.6 m/s?

3-35 The motion of a particular sprinter during a 50-m dash can be approximated as constant acceleration of magnitude 3.7 m/s². Let $t = 0$ correspond to the beginning of the dash, and determine the time the sprinter has traversed (a) 5.0 m and (b) 10.0 m.

3-36 A car is traveling at a speed of 14 m/s at the instant it passes a sign which gives the speed limit as 20 m/s. If the car increases its speed with a constant acceleration of magnitude 1.4 m/s², how long after it passes the sign will its speed be at the speed limit?

3-37 A car is 18 m past the entrance to a restaurant and traveling at a speed of 16 m/s when the driver applies the brakes. The speed of the car decreases with a constant acceleration of magnitude 2.3 m/s². How long after the driver applies the brakes will the car be 65 m past the entrance?

3-38 Major-league pitchers typically throw a baseball with a speed of 90 mi/h. Estimate the acceleration of the ball during the throw.

3-39 The typical speed of a bullet as it leaves the muzzle of a rifle is about 700 m/s. Estimate the acceleration of the bullet while it is in the rifle's barrel.

3-40 (a) Obtain Eq. (C) in Example 3-8 by solving Eq. (A) for v_{x0}. (b) Obtain Eq. (D) in Example 3-8 by inserting Eq. (C) into Eq. (B) and solving for a_x.

3-41 Table 3-9 gives the coordinate of an object in terms of time. Assume that the acceleration is constant and determine the values of (a) x_0; (b) a_x; (c) v_{x0}. (d) Use your answers to write an expression for $x(t)$. (e) Use the expression from part (d) to verify that the data are consistent with the assumption of constant acceleration. (Hint: See Example 3-8.)

Table 3-9

t, s	x, m
0.0	3.0
1.0	7.5
2.0	15.2
3.0	26.1
4.0	40.2
5.0	57.5

3-42 Two drag racers starting from rest run the same course. Racer A gets to the finish line in half the time of racer B. Assuming constant acceleration for both racers, find the ratio of the acceleration of racer A to that of racer B.

Section 3-6. Free-fall

3-43 Sometimes it is convenient to compare an acceleration with the acceleration due to gravity. Let us define a unit of acceleration which we call the g: 1 g = 9.8 m/s² (exactly). Suppose a car increases its speed from zero to 25 m/s in 4.0 s. Assuming constant acceleration, determine the acceleration magnitude in the unit g.

3-44 A rock is released from rest at $t = 0$ from the top of an observation tower. Let the y axis be vertical with the unit vector **j** pointing upward. Make a table which lists values of a_y, v_y, and y at half-second intervals from $t = 0.0$ s to $t = 3.0$ s. Use these data to make graphs of a_y, v_y, and y versus t. Sketch the curves and compare them with Fig. 3-14.

3-45 An astronaut stands on the steps of her spaceship that is resting on the surface of planet X, and she drops a rock from a height of 3.5 m. The rock hits the surface in 0.83 s. Determine the magnitude of the acceleration due to gravity on the surface of planet X.

3-46 A flowerpot falls from rest from a window sill that is 6.2 m above the ground. (a) What is the pot's speed as it hits the ground? (b) How long does it take the pot to hit the ground? (c) How far has the pot fallen after 0.50 s? (d) What is the pot's speed after 0.50 s? (e) What is the pot's acceleration after 0.50 s?

3-47 A ball is thrown vertically upward with an initial speed of 12 m/s from a release point that is 1.8 m above the ground. Let $t = 0$ correspond to the instant of release and let the origin of the coordinate be at the ground with the unit vector **j** pointing upward. (a) Determine h_m and t_m. (b) At what time prior to t_m does the ball have a velocity component of +5.0 m/s and at what time after t_m does it have a velocity component of −5.0 m/s? (c) What are the coordinates that correspond to the two velocity components in part (b)?

3-48 A rock thrown vertically upward at $t = 0$ reaches a maximum height of 14 m above the release point. (a) What is its initial speed? (b) At what time does it pass the release point on the way down?

3-49 A ball thrown vertically upward hits a telephone wire

that is 5.1 m above the release point with a speed 0.70 m/s. What was the ball's initial speed?

Section 3-7. Varying acceleration, numerical methods

3-50 Write a BASIC program for the motion of an object

PROBLEMS

3-1   A sprinter runs the 100-m dash in 10.0 s. Approximate his motion by assuming constant acceleration over the first 15 m and then constant velocity over the remaining 85 m. Determine (a) his final speed; (b) the time required for the first 15 m; (c) the time required for the remaining 85 m; (d) the acceleration magnitude for the first 15 m.

3-2   A wad of chewing gum is stuck on the top of a wheel at time t_i, as shown in Fig. 3-28. The wheel then rolls without slipping in the $+x$ direction, and at time t_f the gum is on the bottom of the wheel. Use the coordinate frame in the figure to give the displacement $\Delta \mathbf{r}$ of the gum.

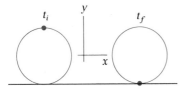

Figure 3-28. Prob. 3-2.

3-3   Car A, traveling at a constant speed of 18 m/s, passes car B, which is at rest at a stop sign. At the instant A and B are abreast, B accelerates with a constant magnitude of 4.6 m/s². Determine (a) the time required for B to catch A; (b) the distance traveled by B during the time required to catch A; (c) the speed of B as it passes A.

3-4   Consider a method of comparing the reaction times of different people. Have a friend hold her thumb and forefinger about 20 mm apart while you hold a ruler vertically so that the bottom end is between the thumb and finger. Your friend is to catch the ruler the instant she sees it released. By finding the distance the ruler falls before it is caught, we can measure a reaction time. If the ruler falls 200 mm, what is your friend's reaction time? Assume free-fall.

3-5   Suppose you are to design a runway for use by a particular type of jet. On the takeoff run, the speed of this aircraft increases with a constant acceleration of magnitude 4.0 m/s² until it becomes airborne at a speed of 85 m/s. Should the pilot be required to abort the takeoff, the jet's speed decreases with a constant acceleration of magnitude 5.0 m/s². Determine the length of the runway needed to allow the pilot to abort the takeoff at the instant the jet reaches flying speed and still not run out of pavement.

in free-fall ($a_y = -g$) with $y = 0$ and $v_y = 0$ at $t = 0$. Let the computer perform 1000 iterations for a time period from $t = 0$ to $t = 10$ s. Have the computer print t, y, and v_y at each 1-s interval and compare with the values determined from the free-fall equations $v_y = -gt$, $y = -\frac{1}{2}gt^2$.

3-6   Suppose you are to design the braking system for a jet airplane. On its takeoff run, the jet increases its speed with a constant acceleration of magnitude 3.5 m/s² until it becomes airborne at a speed of 95 m/s. The length of the runway is 2500 m. Determine the magnitude of the constant acceleration which will stop the jet at the end of the runway, assuming that the pilot aborted takeoff at the instant the jet attained takeoff speed.

3-7   (a) Show that for motion with constant acceleration $\bar{v}_x = \frac{1}{2}[v_x(t_f) + v_x(t_i)]$. [Hint: Use the definition of the average velocity component and note that $t_f^2 - t_i^2 = (t_f + t_i)(t_f - t_i)$.] (b) Consider the case where $a_x = 2.0$ m/s², $v_{x0} = 1.0$ m/s, $t_i = 1.0$ s, and $t_f = 3.0$ s. Make a graph of v_x versus t from $t = 0.0$ s to $t = 4.0$ s. Show $v_x(t_i)$, $v_x(t_f)$, and $\bar{v}_x$ on the graph.

3-8   Consider an acceleration that varies linearly with time: $a_x(t) = a_{x0} + b_x t$. Find expressions for (a) $v_x(t)$ and (b) $x(t)$. (c) What is the physical meaning of b_x?

3-9   Run the program in Table 3-10 and construct graphs of x, v_x, and a_x versus t between $t = 0.0$ s and $t = 16.0$ s. Do you recognize these curves? They describe a type of motion called *simple harmonic motion*, which will be discussed in Chap. 14.

Table 3-10. BASIC program for finding x, v_x, and a_x at time t when $a_x = -(0.25$ s$^{-2})x$, $a_{x0} = 0$, $v_{x0} = 0.5$ m/s², and $x_0 = 0$

```
100    X=0
110    V=.5
120    A=0
130    T=0
140    DT=.01
200    FOR I=1 TO 1600
210        A=-.25*X
220        V=V+A*DT
230        X=X+V*DT
240        T=T+DT
250        IF I=100*INT(I/100) THEN PRINT T, X, V, A
260    NEXT I
300    END
```

3-10 Obtain Eq. (3-13) from Eqs. (3-8) and (3-11).

3-11 A coin was flipped vertically into the air such that it rotated from heads to tails and then back to heads 10 times per second. The coin was released with heads up at a height of 0.49 m above the surface on which it landed and its maximum height above that surface was 1.13 m. Did the coin land heads up or tails up?

3-12 ***Galileo's law of odd numbers.*** An object undergoes free-fall after having been released from rest. We divide the time of fall into many equal time intervals Δt. Show that the change of coordinate during each successive time interval follows the pattern $\Delta y_2 = 3\Delta y_1$, $\Delta y_3 = 5\Delta y_1$, $\Delta y_4 = 7\Delta y_1$, . . . , $\Delta y_n = (2n - 1)\Delta y_1$. (See Fig. 3-29.)

3-13 Suppose $x(t) = A \sin \omega t$, where A and ω represent constants. Determine expressions for (a) $v_x(t)$ and (b) $a_x(t)$. (c) Show that $a_x = -\omega^2 x$. Let $A = 10.0$ mm and $\omega = 0.628$ rad/s and make graphs of (d) x; (e) v_x and a_x versus time from $t = 0.0$ s to $t = 10.0$ s. Plot points at each 1-s interval and sketch curves through the data.

3-14 ⬚ An approximate expression which accounts for air resistance during the fall of an object such as a baseball is $a_y = -g - bvv_y$, where b is a constant. (a) Write a BASIC program with $b = 0.0020$ m^{-1} for an object falling from rest for a period of 10 s. (b) Compare $y(10$ s$)$ given from your program with $y(10$ s$)$ given by assuming free-fall.

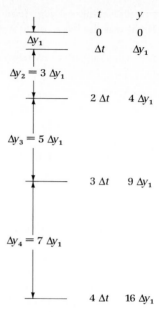

Figure 3-29. Prob. 3-12.

CHAPTER 4
MOTION IN TWO DIMENSIONS

4-1 INTRODUCTION

In Chap. 3 we defined the three kinematical quantities — position vector, velocity, and acceleration — and we used them to describe motion along a straight line. Now we apply these definitions to objects moving in two dimensions or moving in a plane. The vector nature of the velocity and acceleration is manifested more clearly by motion in two dimensions. Contrary to motion in one

A stroboscopic photograph of a bouncing golf ball. *(Dr. Harold Edgerton/M.I.T., Cambridge, Mass.)*

The planets, including the beautiful Saturn pictured here, travel around the sun in nearly circular orbits (Sec. 4-4). *(N.A.S.A.)*

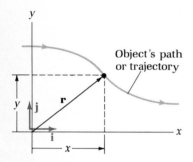

Figure 4-1. Position vector **r** in two dimensions.

Position vector

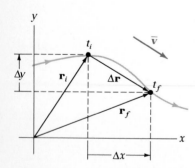

Figure 4-2. Displacement $\Delta\mathbf{r}$ and average velocity $\bar{\mathbf{v}}$; $\bar{\mathbf{v}}$ is parallel to $\Delta\mathbf{r}$. The position-vector triangle shows $\Delta\mathbf{r} = \mathbf{r}_f - \mathbf{r}_i$, or $\mathbf{r}_f = \mathbf{r}_i + \Delta\mathbf{r}$.

dimension, the velocity and acceleration are not necessarily along the same line. The further extension from two to three dimensions is straightforward and can be treated as the need arises. Besides, many of the motions that occur in nature are confined (approximately) to a plane. Two such motions which we shall describe in detail are that of an object launched or thrown into the air, such as a ball tossed from one person to another, and that of an object traveling in a circle, such as a planet orbiting the sun.

4-2 VELOCITY AND ACCELERATION

The position vector **r** locates an object relative to the origin of a reference frame (Fig. 4-1). In two dimensions,

$$\mathbf{r} = x\mathbf{i} + y\mathbf{j} \tag{4-1}$$

where x and y are the object's coordinates. Notice the difference between the graph in Fig. 4-1 and the type of graphs we used in Chap. 3. In Chap. 3 we usually discussed graphs of x or v_x versus t. Figure 4-1, which is typical of the sort of graph we use in this chapter, shows an object's path in the xy plane. An object's path is often called its *trajectory*.

The displacement, $\Delta\mathbf{r} = \mathbf{r}_f - \mathbf{r}_i$, is directed from an object's initial position to its final position, as shown in Fig. 4-2. In component form,

$$\Delta\mathbf{r} = (x_f\mathbf{i} + y_f\mathbf{j}) - (x_i\mathbf{i} + y_i\mathbf{j})$$

$$= (x_f - x_i)\mathbf{i} + (y_f - y_i)\mathbf{j}$$

Letting $\Delta x = x_f - x_i$ and $\Delta y = y_f - y_i$, we have

$$\Delta\mathbf{r} = \Delta x\mathbf{i} + \Delta y\mathbf{j}$$

Velocity. An object's average velocity $\bar{\mathbf{v}}$ for a time interval Δt is its displacement divided by the time interval, or $\bar{\mathbf{v}} = \Delta\mathbf{r}/\Delta t$:

$$\overline{\mathbf{v}} = \frac{\Delta x}{\Delta t}\mathbf{i} + \frac{\Delta y}{\Delta t}\mathbf{j} = \overline{v}_x\mathbf{i} + \overline{v}_y\mathbf{j}$$

Since $\overline{\mathbf{v}} = \Delta\mathbf{r}/\Delta t$, the direction of the average velocity is the same as $\Delta\mathbf{r}$ (Fig. 4-2).

The *velocity* is defined as the limiting value of the average velocity as the time interval approaches zero:

Velocity

$$\mathbf{v} = \lim_{\Delta t \to 0} \overline{\mathbf{v}} = \lim_{\Delta t \to 0} \frac{\Delta\mathbf{r}}{\Delta t} = \frac{d\mathbf{r}}{dt} \tag{4-2}$$

Figure 4-3 shows this limiting process on a graph of an object's path. In passing from Fig. 4-3a through c, we show $\overline{\mathbf{v}}$ for smaller and smaller time intervals as t_i is held fixed while t_f approaches t_i. As this limit is approached, $\Delta\mathbf{r}$ becomes parallel to a tangent to the path and points in the direction of motion. Therefore, *the velocity* $\mathbf{v}$, *at any point on an object's path, is directed parallel to a line tangent to the path and points in the direction of motion* (Fig. 4-3d).

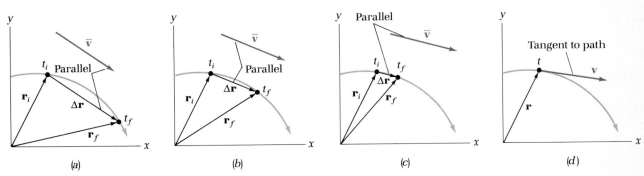

Figure 4-3. As the time interval Δt approaches zero, the average velocity $\overline{\mathbf{v}}$ approaches the velocity $\mathbf{v}$. The direction of $\mathbf{v}$ is parallel to a line tangent to the path.

There is also an analytic approach to this limiting process. Writing $\Delta\mathbf{r}$ in terms of its components, we have

$$\mathbf{v} = \lim_{\Delta t \to 0}\left(\frac{\Delta x}{\Delta t}\mathbf{i} + \frac{\Delta y}{\Delta t}\mathbf{j}\right) = \mathbf{i}\left(\lim_{\Delta t \to 0}\frac{\Delta x}{\Delta t}\right) + \mathbf{j}\left(\lim_{\Delta t \to 0}\frac{\Delta y}{\Delta t}\right) = \frac{dx}{dt}\mathbf{i} + \frac{dy}{dt}\mathbf{j}$$

Since $\mathbf{v} = v_x\mathbf{i} + v_y\mathbf{j}$, we have

Velocity components

$$v_x = \frac{dx}{dt} \quad \text{and} \quad v_y = \frac{dy}{dt} \tag{4-3}$$

If the expressions for the coordinates x and y as functions of time are known, then the velocity can be determined by taking the derivatives of the expressions $x(t)$ and $y(t)$.

The magnitude of the velocity is the speed v:

Speed

$$v = \sqrt{v_x^2 + v_y^2} \tag{4-4}$$

The direction in which the object is headed at any time may be described in terms of the angle θ between the velocity vector and the x axis. Figure 4-4 shows that

Direction of motion

$$\tan\theta = \frac{v_y}{v_x} \quad \text{or} \quad \theta = \tan^{-1}\frac{v_y}{v_x} \tag{4-5}$$

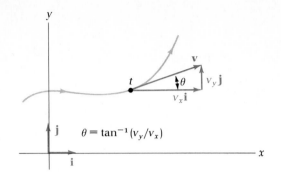

Figure 4-4. Resolving the velocity in terms of its components gives $v_x = v \cos \theta$ and $v_y = v \sin \theta$

where θ is positive when measured counterclockwise from the x axis. From the figure you can see that the velocity components are

$$v_x = v \cos \theta \quad \text{and} \quad v_y = v \sin \theta \qquad (4\text{-}6)$$

EXAMPLE 4-1. A motorboat is traveling 52° south of east at a speed of 12 m/s. Establish a coordinate frame and determine the boat's velocity components.

SOLUTION. Let $+x$ be toward the east and $+y$ be toward the north, as shown in Fig. 4-5. Since an angle measured counterclockwise is positive, we have $\theta = -52°$ in this case. From Eqs. (4-6),

$$v_x = 12 \text{ m/s} \cos(-52°) = 7.4 \text{ m/s}$$

$$v_y = 12 \text{ m/s} \sin(-52°) = -9.5 \text{ m/s}$$

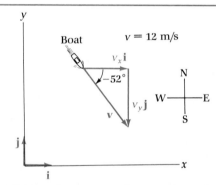

Figure 4-5. Example 4-1: A motorboat traveling 52° south of east. In this case $\theta = -52°$.

Acceleration. The average acceleration $\bar{\mathbf{a}}$ of an object for a time interval Δt is the object's velocity change divided by the time interval. That is, $\bar{\mathbf{a}} = \Delta \mathbf{v}/\Delta t$, or

$$\bar{\mathbf{a}} = \frac{\Delta v_x}{\Delta t} \mathbf{i} + \frac{\Delta v_y}{\Delta t} \mathbf{j} = \bar{a}_x \mathbf{i} + \bar{a}_y \mathbf{j}$$

The *acceleration* is defined as the limiting value of the average acceleration as the time interval approaches zero:

Acceleration

$$\mathbf{a} = \lim_{\Delta t \to 0} \bar{\mathbf{a}} = \lim_{\Delta t \to 0} \frac{\Delta \mathbf{v}}{\Delta t} = \frac{d\mathbf{v}}{dt} \qquad (4\text{-}7)$$

Since $\Delta \mathbf{v} = \Delta v_x \mathbf{i} + \Delta v_y \mathbf{j}$, we have

$$\mathbf{a} = \lim_{\Delta t \to 0} \left(\frac{\Delta v_x}{\Delta t} \mathbf{i} + \frac{\Delta v_y}{\Delta t} \mathbf{j} \right) = \mathbf{i} \left(\lim_{\Delta t \to 0} \frac{\Delta v_x}{\Delta t} \right) + \mathbf{j} \left(\lim_{\Delta t \to 0} \frac{\Delta v_y}{\Delta t} \right) = \frac{dv_x}{dt} \mathbf{i} + \frac{dv_y}{dt} \mathbf{j}$$

Writing $\mathbf{a} = a_x \mathbf{i} + a_y \mathbf{j}$, we see that

Acceleration components

$$a_x = \frac{dv_x}{dt} \quad \text{and} \quad a_y = \frac{dv_y}{dt} \qquad (4\text{-}8)$$

Further, since $v_x = dx/dt$ and $v_y = dy/dt$,

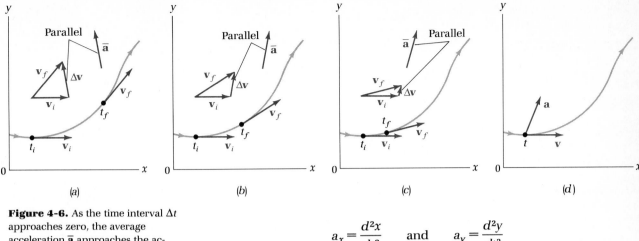

(a)   (b)   (c)   (d)

Figure 4-6. As the time interval Δt approaches zero, the average acceleration $\overline{\mathbf{a}}$ approaches the acceleration $\mathbf{a}$. Each velocity-vector triangle shows $\Delta\mathbf{v} = \mathbf{v}_f - \mathbf{v}_i$, or $\mathbf{v}_f = \mathbf{v}_i + \Delta\mathbf{v}$.

$$a_x = \frac{d^2x}{dt^2} \quad \text{and} \quad a_y = \frac{d^2y}{dt^2}$$

If expressions for the velocity components v_x and v_y, or the coordinates x and y, are known, then the acceleration can be found by taking derivatives of these expressions.

Figure 4-6 shows this limiting process graphically. In Fig. 4-6a through c, we show $\overline{\mathbf{a}}$ for smaller and smaller time intervals as t_i is held fixed while t_f approaches t_i.

The direction of $\mathbf{a}$ is given by the direction of the limiting value of $\Delta\mathbf{v}$. In Fig. 4-7, we examine the direction of $\Delta\mathbf{v}$ for an object which follows a curved path. Figure 4-7b shows a velocity-vector triangle with sides $\mathbf{v}_i$, $\mathbf{v}_f$, and $\Delta\mathbf{v}$. The expanded view in Fig. 4-7c shows $\Delta\mathbf{v}$ resolved into two vectors: $\Delta\mathbf{v}_\parallel$ and $\Delta\mathbf{v}_\perp$, which are parallel to and perpendicular to $\mathbf{v}_i$, respectively. In the limit, $\mathbf{v}_f$ approaches $\mathbf{v}_i$ and $\mathbf{v}_i$ is then designated simply as $\mathbf{v}$. Since $\mathbf{v}_f$ is directed more toward the concave side of the path than $\mathbf{v}_i$, $\Delta\mathbf{v}_\perp$ is directed toward the concave side of the path. Indeed, as an object turns, the direction of $\Delta\mathbf{v}_\perp$ is always toward the concave side of the path. Consequently, for any object following a curved path, $\mathbf{a}$ has a positive component toward the concave side of the path. That is, $\mathbf{a}$ is directed, at least partially, toward the concave side of the path. If the path is straight, then $\Delta\mathbf{v}_\perp = 0$, and $\mathbf{a}$ is parallel to a line tangent to the path.

In Fig. 4-7, $\mathbf{v}_f$ is shown with a larger magnitude than $\mathbf{v}_i$ ($v_f > v_i$), which means that the object's speed is increasing. In this case, $\Delta\mathbf{v}_\parallel$ is in the same direction as $\mathbf{v}$, and $\mathbf{a}$ has a positive component along $\mathbf{v}$ ($\mathbf{a}$ is directed partially along $\mathbf{v}$). If an object's speed is constant ($v_f = v_i$), then $\Delta\mathbf{v}_\parallel = 0$, and $\mathbf{a}$ has no component parallel to $\mathbf{v}$. If an object's speed is decreasing ($v_f < v_i$), then $\Delta\mathbf{v}_\parallel$ is directed opposite $\mathbf{v}$, and $\mathbf{a}$ has a negative component along $\mathbf{v}$.

Figure 4-7. The direction of $\mathbf{a}$ is the same as the limiting value of $\Delta\mathbf{v}$ as Δt approaches zero. (a) An object follows a curved path. (b) The velocity-vector triangle. (c) Showing $\Delta\mathbf{v} = \Delta\mathbf{v}_\parallel + \Delta\mathbf{v}_\perp$.

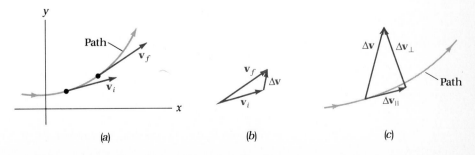

(a)   (b)   (c)

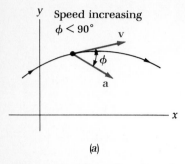

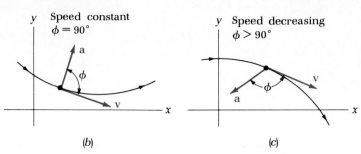

(a) (b) (c)

Figure 4-8. Relative directions of **v** and **a** for an object following a curved path when the object's speed is (a) increasing, (b) constant, and (c) decreasing.

Figure 4-8 shows three possible relationships between the velocity and acceleration of an object which follows a curved path. In Fig. 4-8a the object's speed is increasing so that the angle ϕ between **v** and **a** is less than 90°. In Fig. 4-8b the object's speed is constant so that $\phi = 90°$, and **v** and **a** are perpendicular. In Fig. 4-8c the object's speed is decreasing so that ϕ is greater than 90°.

EXAMPLE 4-2. Suppose the coordinates of an object are given by $x = (2.3 \text{ m/s}^3)t^3 - 12 \text{ m}$ and $y = (5.1 \text{ m/s})t$. Find expressions for the object's (a) velocity and (b) acceleration.

SOLUTION. (a) From Eqs. (4-3),

$$v_x = \frac{dx}{dt} = \frac{d}{dt}[(2.3 \text{ m/s}^3)t^3 - 12 \text{ m}] = (6.9 \text{ m/s}^3)t^2$$

$$v_y = \frac{dy}{dt} = \frac{d}{dt}[(5.1 \text{ m/s})t] = 5.1 \text{ m/s}$$

Thus $\mathbf{v} = [(6.9 \text{ m/s}^3)t^2]\mathbf{i} + (5.1 \text{ m/s})\mathbf{j}$

(b) Similarly, Eqs. (4-8) give

$$a_x = \frac{dv_x}{dt} = \frac{d}{dt}[(6.9 \text{ m/s}^3)t^2] = (13.8 \text{ m/s}^3)t$$

$$a_y = \frac{dv_y}{dt} = \frac{d}{dt}(5.1 \text{ m/s}) = 0$$

Consequently,

$$\mathbf{a} = [(13.8 \text{ m/s}^3)t]\mathbf{i}$$

4-3 CONSTANT ACCELERATION: PROJECTILE MOTION

The simplest case of accelerated motion is motion with constant acceleration. To find expressions for **v** and **r**, we proceed as we did for constant acceleration in one dimension (Sec. 3-5). When the acceleration is constant, it is equal to its average value: $\mathbf{a} = \bar{\mathbf{a}} = \Delta\mathbf{v}/\Delta t$. If we let $\mathbf{v}_f = \mathbf{v}$, $\mathbf{v}_i = \mathbf{v}_0$, $t_f = t$, and $t_i = 0$, then $\mathbf{a} = (\mathbf{v} - \mathbf{v}_0)/(t - 0)$, or

$$\mathbf{v} = \mathbf{v}_0 + \mathbf{a}t \qquad (4\text{-}9)$$

In terms of components,

$$\mathbf{v} = (v_{x0}\mathbf{i} + v_{y0}\mathbf{j}) + (a_x\mathbf{i} + a_y\mathbf{j})t = (v_{x0} + a_xt)\mathbf{i} + (v_{y0} + a_yt)\mathbf{j}$$

so that

$$v_x = v_{x0} + a_xt \qquad \text{and} \qquad v_y = v_{y0} + a_yt \qquad (4\text{-}10)$$

The equation for **r** can be determined by finding an expression whose derivative gives Eq. (4-9):

$$\mathbf{r} = \mathbf{r}_0 + \mathbf{v}_0t + \tfrac{1}{2}\mathbf{a}t^2 \qquad (4\text{-}11)$$

You should verify that the derivative of Eq. (4-11) gives Eq. (4-9), and that **r** evaluated at $t = 0$ yields $\mathbf{r}_0$. Separating Eq. (4-11) into its components, we find

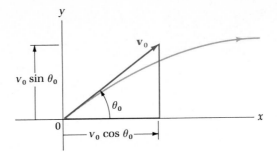

Figure 4-9. Resolving the initial velocity of a projectile into its components: $v_{x0} = v_0 \cos \theta_0$ and $v_{y0} = v_0 \sin \theta_0$, where v_0 is the initial speed and θ_0 is the angle of projection.

$$x = x_0 + v_{x0}t + \tfrac{1}{2}a_x t^2$$
$$y = y_0 + v_{y0}t + \tfrac{1}{2}a_y t^2 \qquad (4\text{-}12)$$

These equations show that the x and y motions are independent of each other. That is, the motion can be treated as two separate simultaneous one-dimensional motions with constant acceleration along perpendicular directions. This feature of motion with constant acceleration can be demonstrated with projectile motion, which we describe next.

Projectile motion. An object that is in flight after being launched or thrown is called a *projectile*. If the object has a large enough mass density (that is, like a baseball but not like a ping-pong ball), then experiments show that we can often neglect the effects of air resistance and assume that the object's acceleration is due to gravity alone. Following custom, we let the x axis be horizontal and the $+y$ direction be vertically upward. Then the acceleration is $\mathbf{a} = -g\mathbf{j}$, and

Acceleration components of a projectile

$$a_x = 0 \qquad \text{and} \qquad a_y = -g$$

where $g = 9.8$ m/s². Suppose the projectile is launched such that its initial velocity $\mathbf{v}_0$ is at an angle θ_0 with the x axis, as shown in Fig. 4-9. We call θ_0 the *angle of projection*. By resolving the initial velocity, we obtain the initial velocity components: $v_{x0} = v_0 \cos \theta_0$ and $v_{y0} = v_0 \sin \theta_0$, where v_0 is the initial speed. Substituting these values into Eqs. (4-10), we find

Velocity components of a projectile

$$v_x = v_0 \cos \theta_0$$
$$v_y = v_0 \sin \theta_0 - gt \qquad (4\text{-}13)$$

If we place the origin of our reference frame at the initial position, then $x_0 = y_0 = 0$ and Eqs. (4-12) give

Coordinates of a projectile

$$x = (v_0 \cos \theta_0)t$$
$$y = (v_0 \sin \theta_0)t - \tfrac{1}{2}gt^2 \qquad (4\text{-}14)$$

Therefore, the x motion can be regarded as one-dimensional motion with constant velocity, and the y motion can be regarded as one-dimensional motion with constant acceleration.

Figure 4-10, which is a stroboscopic photograph of the simultaneous motion of two golf balls, demonstrates the independence of the x and y parts of the motion. One ball was released from rest at the same instant the other ball was launched horizontally. The motion of the ball that was released from rest is described by Eqs. (4-14) if we set $v_0 = 0$. This gives $x = 0$ for all t and $y = -\tfrac{1}{2}gt^2$.

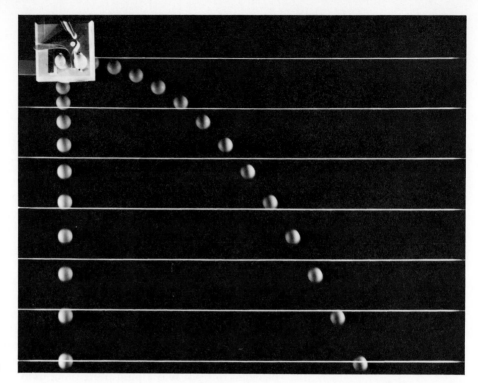

Figure 4-10. A stroboscopic picture of two golf balls. One ball was released from rest at the instant the other was launched with a horizontal velocity. The simultaneous vertical coordinates of each ball are the same. *(Dr. Harold Edgerton/M.I.T., Cambridge, Mass.)*

The motion of the ball that was launched horizontally is described by Eqs. (4-14) if we set $\theta_0 = 0$. This gives $x = v_0 t$ and $y = -\frac{1}{2}gt^2$. Thus, Eqs. (4-14) give the same y coordinate for each ball at each instant of time, and this result is verified by Fig. 4-10.

This observation was first explained by Galileo. Describing a particle projected off the edge of a horizontal surface, he wrote

> . . . then the moving particle, which we imagine to be a heavy one, will on passing over the edge of the plane acquire, in addition to its previous uniform and perpetual motion, a downward propensity due to its own weight; so that the resulting motion, which I call projection *[projectio]*, is compounded of one which is uniform and horizontal and of another which is vertical and naturally accelerated.[*]

An equation for the path or trajectory of a projectile can be found by eliminating the time between the expressions for x and y in Eqs. (4-14). Solving $x = (v_0 \cos \theta_0)t$ for the time gives $t = x/(v_0 \cos \theta_0)$. Substituting this result into the expression for y and rearranging, we obtain

Trajectory of a projectile

$$y = (\tan \theta_0)x - \frac{g}{2(v_0 \cos \theta_0)^2}x^2 \qquad (4\text{-}15)$$

We have found that if the effects of air resistance can be neglected, then the trajectory of a projectile is a parabola. In Fig. 4-11, we show this parabolic path with the velocity indicated at several points. Notice that v_x remains fixed throughout the motion, whereas v_y decreases in magnitude as the projectile is

[*] Galileo Galilei, *Two New Sciences*, Henry Crew and Alfonso de Salvio (trans.), Dover, New York, 1954, p. 244.

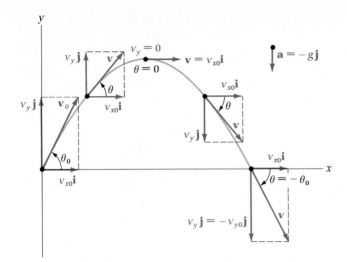

Figure 4-11. If the effects of air resistance are negligible, the trajectory of a projectile is a parabola. Note that the x component of the velocity remains fixed while the y component continually changes.

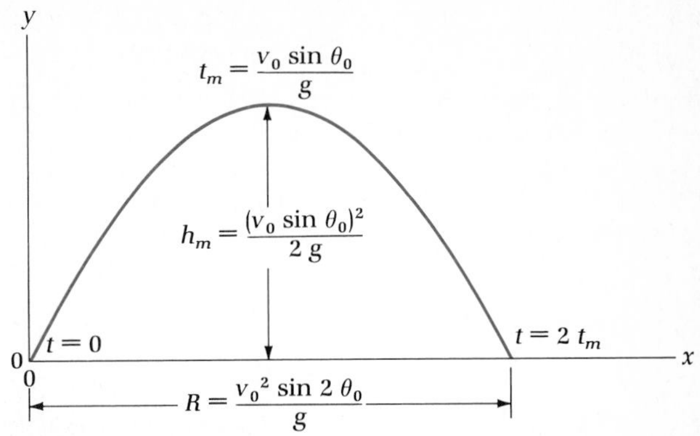

Figure 4-12. The trajectory of a projectile showing the maximum height and the horizontal range.

going up and increases in magnitude as the projectile is going down. That is, v_y continually decreases, corresponding to the fact that a_y is negative. At the instant the projectile reaches its maximum height, $v_y = 0$.

The projectile motion shown in Fig. 4-11 is consistent with our conclusions of the previous section about the direction **a**. There we showed that **a** is always directed toward the concave side of the path, and that the angle ϕ between **a** and **v** is greater than 90° when the speed is decreasing and less than 90° when the speed is increasing. In projectile motion, **a** is vertically downward, so that it is directed toward the concave side of the parabolic path. As the projectile rises, its speed decreases and $\phi > 90°$. As the projectile falls, its speed increases and $\phi < 90°$. Each of these conclusions is verified by Fig. 4-11.

Consider the time t_m when the projectile reaches its maximum height. Since $v_y = 0$ when $t = t_m$, Eq. (4-13) gives $v_y = v_0 \sin \theta_0 - g t_m = 0$, or

Time of maximum height

$$t_m = \frac{v_0 \sin \theta_0}{g} \tag{4-16}$$

The maximum height h_m is the value of y at $t = t_m$ (Fig. 4-12). Substituting $y = h_m$ and $t = t_m = v_0 \sin \theta_0/g$ into the expression for y in Eq. (4-14), we find

Maximum height of a projectile

$$h_m = \frac{(v_0 \sin \theta_0)^2}{2g} \tag{4-17}$$

The horizontal distance traversed by the projectile from its launch point to where it passes $y = 0$ on its way down is called the *horizontal range R*. By examination of the symmetry of Fig. 4-12, you can see that R is equal to x evaluated at $2t_m$. Letting $x = R$ and $t = 2t_m = 2(v_0 \sin \theta_0)/g$, we find that the expression for x in Eq. (4-14) gives

$$R = \frac{2(v_0{}^2 \sin \theta_0 \cos \theta_0)}{g}$$

This equation can be simplified by using the trigonometric identity $\sin 2\alpha = 2 \cos \alpha \sin \alpha$:

Horizontal range of a projectile

$$R = \frac{v_0{}^2 \sin 2\theta_0}{g} \tag{4-18}$$

Examination of Eq. (4-18) allows us to answer an interesting question. For a given initial speed v_0, at what projection angle should we launch a projectile such that its horizontal range is maximum? That is, what angle θ_0 makes R a maximum when v_0 is held fixed? Since $\sin 2\theta_0$ has a maximum value of 1 when $2\theta_0 = 90°$, R is maximum when $\theta_0 = 45°$. Thus the maximum horizontal range is $R_m = v_0{}^2/g$, and this maximum occurs when the projection angle is $\theta_0 = 45°$.

Table 4-1 summarizes the important equations describing projectile motion. These equations are more general than those discussed above because the initial coordinates are left unspecified as (x_0, y_0) rather than being placed at $(0, 0)$.

Table 4-1. Projectile motion

$a_x = 0$	$a_y = -g$
$v_x = v_0 \cos \theta_0$	$v_y = v_0 \cos \theta_0 - gt$
$x = x_0 + (v_0 \cos \theta_0)t$	$y = y_0 + (v_0 \sin \theta_0)t - \tfrac{1}{2}gt^2$

$$y = y_0 + (\tan \theta_0)(x - x_0) - \frac{g}{2(v_0 \cos \theta_0)^2}(x - x_0)^2$$

EXAMPLE 4-3. A rock is thrown with a speed of 17 m/s and at a projection angle of 58° above the horizontal. (a) Find an expression for the trajectory of the rock. Determine (b) the time of maximum height and (c) the maximum height above the release point. Neglect air resistance.

SOLUTION. (a) From Eq. (4-15), the expression for the trajectory is

$$y = (\tan 58°)x - \frac{9.8 \text{ m/s}^2}{2(17 \text{ m/s} \cos 58°)^2}x^2$$

$$= (1.6)x - (0.060 \text{ m}^{-1})x^2$$

(b) Using Eq. (4-16), we find

$$t_m = \frac{17 \text{ m/s} \sin 58°}{9.8 \text{ m/s}^2} = 1.5 \text{ s}$$

(c) From Eq. (4-17), the maximum height above the release point is

$$h_m = \frac{(17 \text{ m/s} \sin 58°)^2}{2(9.8 \text{ m/s}^2)} = 11 \text{ m}$$

EXAMPLE 4-4. A baseball bat hits a ball such that the ball's initial speed is 35 m/s and its projection angle is 42° above the horizontal. The outfield fence is 115 m from home plate and is 4 m high. Neglecting air resistance, determine whether the ball clears the fence. Assume that the ball was struck at a height of 1 m above the level playing surface at home plate.

SOLUTION. Letting the origin be at home plate, we have

$x_0 = 0$ and $y_0 = 1$ m. Using the equation for the trajectory in Table 4-1, we find the value of y when $x = 115$ m:

$$y = 1 \text{ m} + (\tan 42°)(115 \text{ m})$$

$$- \frac{9.8 \text{ m/s}^2}{2(35 \text{ m/s} \cos 42°)^2}(115 \text{ m})^2 = 9 \text{ m}$$

Since the fence is 4 m high, the ball clears the fence by 5 m, and the hit is a home run. We shall return to this example and consider air resistance effects in Sec. 4-6.

4-4 UNIFORM CIRCULAR MOTION

Definition of uniform circular motion

Consider a child's block as it rides on a phonograph turntable, as shown in Fig. 4-13. The path of the block is a circle and its speed v is constant. If an object follows a circular path at constant speed, the motion is called *uniform circular motion*. The word "uniform" refers to the constant speed. The block's velocity

Figure 4-13. A child's block rides on a phonograph turntable. The motion of the block is uniform circular motion. *(Tom Richard)*

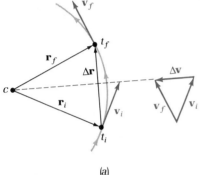

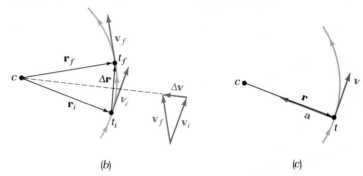

(a)   (b)   (c)

Figure 4-14. The direction of $\bar{a}$ is the same as that of Δv. (a) The direction of Δv, when placed midway between the initial and final positions, is directed toward the center of the circle. (b) As t_f approaches t_i, Δv remains directed toward the center. (c) In the limit, $\bar{a}$ becomes a, and a is directed toward the center of the circle.

at each point on its circular path is tangent to the circle and points in the direction of motion. Therefore, as the block moves around the circle, its velocity is continuously changing. Even though the block's speed is constant, it is accelerating because the direction of its velocity is changing.

In Sec. 4-2, we found that the acceleration of an object following a curved path is always directed toward the concave side of the path, and, if the speed of the object is constant, a is perpendicular to v. This is illustrated in Fig. 4-14 for the specific case of an object in uniform circular motion. Figure 4-14a shows two triangles: a position-vector triangle, made up of r_i, r_f, and Δr, and a velocity-vector triangle, composed of v_i, v_f, and Δv. Since v_f is perpendicular to r_f and v_i is perpendicular to r_i, Δv is perpendicular to Δr. Keep in mind that the direction of Δv is the same as that of $\bar{a}$. When Δv is placed on the line that bisects the angle between r_i and r_f, it is directed toward the center of the circle. Figure 4-14b shows these triangles for a smaller time interval, and Δv is again directed toward the center of the circle. In Fig. 4-14c we have passed to the limit as Δt approaches zero. In this limit, $\bar{a}$ has become a, and a is directed toward the center of the circle. Thus the acceleration of an object executing uniform circular motion is toward the center of the circle.

The magnitude of the acceleration is the limiting value of $|\Delta v|/\Delta t$ as Δt approaches zero:

$$a = \lim_{\Delta t \to 0} \frac{|\Delta v|}{\Delta t}$$

Again consider Fig. 4-14a. Since $r_i = r_f = R$ and $v_i = v_f = v$, both the position-

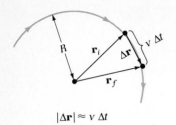

$$|\Delta \mathbf{r}| \approx v\, \Delta t$$

Figure 4-15. When $|\Delta \mathbf{r}|$ is much smaller than R, the arc length $v\,\Delta t$ is approximately equal to $|\Delta \mathbf{r}|$. In the limit as Δt approaches zero, the approximation becomes exact.

vector and velocity-vector triangles are isosceles (two sides are equal). Also, since $\mathbf{v}_i$ is perpendicular to $\mathbf{r}_i$ and $\mathbf{v}_f$ is perpendicular to $\mathbf{r}_f$, these triangles are similar. Because the triangles are similar, the ratio of base length to side length for one of the triangles is equal to that for the other triangle: $|\Delta \mathbf{v}|/v = |\Delta \mathbf{r}|/R$ or $|\Delta \mathbf{v}| = v|\Delta \mathbf{r}|/R$. Thus

$$a = \lim_{\Delta t \to 0} \frac{|\Delta \mathbf{v}|}{\Delta t} = \lim_{\Delta t \to 0} \frac{v|\Delta \mathbf{r}|/R}{\Delta t} = \frac{v}{R} \lim_{\Delta t \to 0} \frac{|\Delta \mathbf{r}|}{\Delta t}$$

where we have factored v/R out of the limit because neither v nor R depends on Δt. From Fig. 4-15, you can see that if $|\Delta \mathbf{r}|$ is small compared with R, then $|\Delta \mathbf{r}| \approx v\,\Delta t$ or $|\Delta \mathbf{r}|/\Delta t \approx v$. In the limit as Δt approaches zero, this approximation becomes exact:

$$\lim_{\Delta t \to 0} \frac{|\Delta \mathbf{r}|}{\Delta t} = v$$

Thus $a = (v/R)v = v^2/R$. Since the direction of this acceleration is toward the center of the circle, the acceleration is called the *centripetal acceleration*. "Centripetal" comes from a Greek term which means center-seeking. Accordingly, we use the symbol a_c to represent the magnitude of this acceleration:

Magnitude of the centripetal acceleration

$$a_c = \frac{v^2}{R} \tag{4-19}$$

Since v and R are constants, the magnitude of the centripetal acceleration is constant. However, as the object follows its circular path, the direction of the acceleration continuously changes because it is always directed from the object toward the center of the circle. Thus the centripetal acceleration is not constant.

EXAMPLE 4-5. A car, initially traveling west, makes a right turn, following a circular arc of radius $R = 22$ m, and finishes the turn heading north. The car's speed is constant at $v = 8.5$ m/s throughout the turn. Determine the car's acceleration (a) at the instant after it begins turning, (b) when it is halfway through the turn, and (c) at the instant before it finishes the turn.

SOLUTION. (a) During the turn the car is in uniform circular motion, so that the magnitude of its acceleration is $a_c = v^2/R = (8.5 \text{ m/s})^2/22 \text{ m} = 3.3 \text{ m/s}^2$. The car's path is shown in Fig. 4-16. As the car enters the turn, the center of the circle is to the north. Thus the acceleration is 3.3 m/s² toward the north. (b) At the instant the car is halfway through the turn, the center of the circle is toward the northeast. Consequently, the acceleration is 3.3 m/s² toward the northeast. (c) Similarly, just before the turn is completed, the accelera-

tion is 3.3 m/s² toward the east.

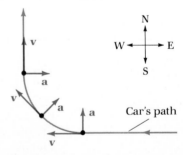

Figure 4-16. Example 4-5: A car initially traveling west makes a right turn of 90° along a circular arc. Just after the beginning of the turn, $\mathbf{v}$ is toward the west and $\mathbf{a}$ is toward the north; halfway through the turn, $\mathbf{v}$ is toward the northwest and $\mathbf{a}$ is toward the northeast; just before the end of the turn, $\mathbf{v}$ is toward the north and $\mathbf{a}$ is toward the east.

EXAMPLE 4-6. Consider an earth satellite that is in a circular orbit. Such a satellite travels at constant speed and the time required for it to complete one revolution is called its

period T. (a) Show that an expression for the magnitude of the satellite's centripetal acceleration is $a_c = 4\pi^2R/T^2$. (b) A satellite that orbits the earth at a height $h = 200$ km above the surface has a period $T = 1.47$ h $= 5.30 \times 10^3$ s. What is a_c for this satellite? The radius of the earth is $R_e = 6.37 \times 10^6$ m $= 6.37$ Mm.

SOLUTION. (a) The constant speed of the satellite is equal to the distance traveled during one revolution ($2\pi R$) divided by the time for one revolution (T): $v = 2\pi R/T$. Inserting this into Eq. (4-19), we have

$$a_c = \frac{v^2}{R} = \frac{(2\pi R/T)^2}{R} = \frac{4\pi^2 R}{T^2}$$

(b) The center of the satellite's circular path is the center of the earth so that

$$R = R_e + h = 6.37 \text{ Mm} + 200 \text{ km}$$
$$= 6.37 \text{ Mm} + 0.20 \text{ Mm} = 6.57 \text{ Mm}$$

For this satellite,

$$a_c = 4\pi^2 \frac{6.57 \text{ Mm}}{(5.30 \times 10^3 \text{ s})^2} = 9.22 \text{ m/s}^2$$

Note that the magnitude of the satellite's acceleration is smaller than g on the earth's surface.

4-5   RELATIVE MOTION

Alvin was standing on the curb on the south side of an east-west street waiting for a bus, as shown in Fig. 4-17. Bill was riding in a car traveling at a speed of 20 m/s toward the east. Just before the car passed close to Alvin, when it was northwest of him, Bill threw a banana peel out of the window with velocity components (according to Bill) of 10 m/s toward the south and 10 m/s toward the west. The banana peel hit Alvin's ear.

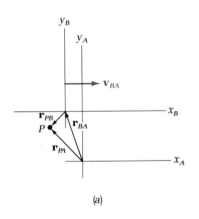

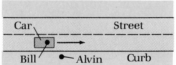

Figure 4-17. Bill was riding in a car traveling east. Alvin was standing on the curb.

Alvin and Bill met later, and Alvin accused Bill of throwing the peel at him. Bill pleaded innocent by truthfully saying that he threw the peel toward the south*west*, and at the time of release Alvin was south*east* of the release point. This episode reveals that two observers moving at constant velocity relative to one another and each measuring the velocity of an object will find that their velocity measurements yield different results.

We use Fig. 4-18 to understand this disagreement between Alvin and Bill. This figure shows two reference frames, the frame for observer A (Alvin) and the frame for observer B (Bill). Each observer is at rest in his frame. The two frames are moving at constant velocity relative to one another along their common x direction. (In the Alvin-Bill dispute, the unit vector $\mathbf{i}$ is toward the east and the unit vector $\mathbf{j}$ is toward the north.)

To distinguish measurements by different observers, we use a double-subscript notation. We let $\mathbf{r}_{PA}$ be the position vector of a particle P (the peel) according to observer A. That is, the first subscript indicates the object whose position is measured and the second subscript indicates the observer who made the measurement. In words, $\mathbf{r}_{PA}$ is the position vector of P relative to A. A similar notation is used for velocities. For example, $\mathbf{v}_{BA}$ is the velocity of observer B relative to observer A. If observer B is moving in the $+x$ direction according to A at a speed v, as shown in the figure, then $\mathbf{v}_{BA} = v\mathbf{i}$. This means that A is moving in the $-x$ direction according to B: $\mathbf{v}_{AB} = -v\mathbf{i}$. In this double-

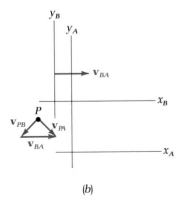

(a)

(b)

Figure 4-18. Observers in frame A and frame B measure particle P's (a) position vector and (b) velocity.

subscript notation, reversing the order of the subscripts changes the sign of the quantity: $\mathbf{v}_{BA} = -\mathbf{v}_{AB}$.

From Fig. 4-18a, the position vector $\mathbf{r}_{PA}$ of P relative to A is given by

Relative position vectors

$$\mathbf{r}_{PA} = \mathbf{r}_{PB} + \mathbf{r}_{BA} \tag{4-20}$$

where $\mathbf{r}_{PB}$ is the position vector of P relative to B and $\mathbf{r}_{BA}$ is the position vector of B relative to A. The velocity of P relative to A is found by taking the derivative of $\mathbf{r}_{PA}$ with respect to t:

$$\frac{d}{dt}\mathbf{r}_{PA} = \mathbf{v}_{PA}$$

Similarly,

$$\frac{d}{dt}\mathbf{r}_{PB} = \mathbf{v}_{PB} \quad \text{and} \quad \frac{d}{dt}\mathbf{r}_{BA} = \mathbf{v}_{BA}$$

Therefore, if we take the derivative of Eq. (4-20) with respect to t, we find

Relative velocities

$$\mathbf{v}_{PA} = \mathbf{v}_{PB} + \mathbf{v}_{BA} \tag{4-21}$$

This result is shown in Fig. 4-18b.*

In the incident involving Alvin and Bill, Bill threw the banana peel toward the southwest, $\mathbf{v}_{PB} = (-10 \text{ m/s})\mathbf{i} + (-10 \text{ m/s})\mathbf{j}$, and the car was traveling east, $\mathbf{v}_{BA} = (20 \text{ m/s})\mathbf{i}$. Therefore, the velocity of the peel relative to Alvin was

$$\mathbf{v}_{PA} = (-10 \text{ m/s})\mathbf{i} + (-10 \text{ m/s})\mathbf{j} + (20 \text{ m/s})\mathbf{i}$$

$$= (10 \text{ m/s})\mathbf{i} + (-10 \text{ m/s})\mathbf{j}$$

That is, the velocity of the peel relative to Alvin was toward the southeast. Since Alvin was southeast of the release point, the peel headed directly toward him. Despite Bill's innocence, the peel hit Alvin's ear with a speed of

$$\sqrt{(10 \text{ m/s})^2 + (-10 \text{ m/s})^2} = 14 \text{ m/s}$$

Now consider the acceleration of an object according to two observers who are in relative motion with constant velocity. The acceleration $\mathbf{a}_{PA}$ of P relative to A is found by taking the time derivative of $\mathbf{v}_{PA}$ with respect to t:

$$\frac{d}{dt}\mathbf{v}_{PA} = \mathbf{a}_{PA}$$

Similarly,

$$\frac{d}{dt}\mathbf{v}_{PB} = \mathbf{a}_{PB} \quad \text{and} \quad \frac{d}{dt}\mathbf{v}_{BA} = \mathbf{a}_{BA}$$

However, since $\mathbf{v}_{BA}$ is constant, its time derivative is zero: $\mathbf{a}_{BA} = 0$. Therefore the derivative of Eq. (4-21) with respect to t is

Relative accelerations, constant relative velocity

$$\mathbf{a}_{PA} = \mathbf{a}_{PB} \tag{4-22}$$

That is, each observer measures the particle's acceleration to be the same. Note

---

* Perhaps the most surprising thing about Eq. (4-21) is that it does not hold for relative speeds that are an appreciable fraction of the speed of light (3.0×10^8 m/s). At such high speeds, Eq. (4-21) is replaced by a result that we shall give in Chap. 38.

that this conclusion is based on the premise that the relative velocity of the observers is constant.

EXAMPLE 4-7. Charles is in an airplane flying overhead with a constant horizontal velocity relative to the ground of 75 m/s toward the east. Emily, who is standing on the ground, observes Charles as he drops a parcel out of the airplane's window, as shown in Fig. 4-19. At the instant of release, the parcel is at rest relative to Charles. Describe the motion of the parcel according to (a) Charles and (b) Emily. Let the origins for Charles and Emily be at the point of re-

lease at the instant of release and let this instant be $t = 0$. Also, let the unit vector $\mathbf{j}$ be directed vertically upward and the unit vector $\mathbf{i}$ be directed toward the east. Neglect air resistance.

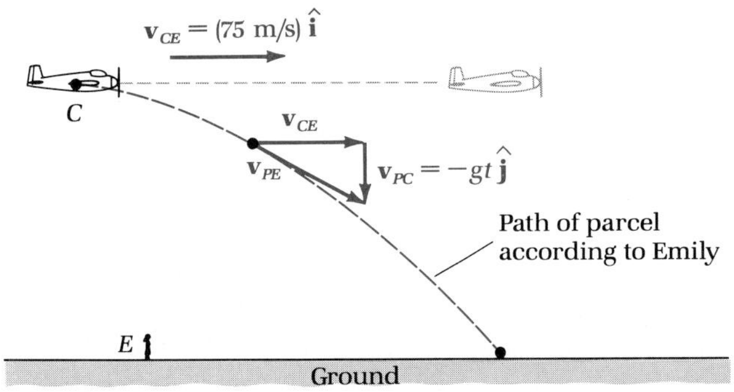

SOLUTION. (a) According to Charles, the parcel is released from rest so that it falls vertically downward in a straight line and hits the ground directly beneath the airplane. The acceleration of the parcel (P) relative to Charles (C) is $\mathbf{a}_{PC} = -g\mathbf{j}$. The parcel's x component of velocity is zero during the entire motion, and its y component of velocity is $-gt$ so that the velocity of the parcel relative to Charles is $\mathbf{v}_{PC} = -gt\mathbf{j}$. (b) Since their relative velocity is constant ($\mathbf{a}_{CE} = 0$), Emily (E) agrees with Charles about the parcel's acceleration ($\mathbf{a}_{PE} = -g\mathbf{j}$), but they measure different velocities. The velocity $\mathbf{v}_{PE}$ of the parcel relative to Emily is $\mathbf{v}_{PE} = \mathbf{v}_{PC} + \mathbf{v}_{CE}$, where $\mathbf{v}_{CE}$ is the velocity of Charles relative to Emily. The velocity of Charles relative to Emily is the same as the velocity of the airplane relative to the ground: $\mathbf{v}_{CE} = (75 \text{ m/s})\mathbf{i}$. Thus

$$\mathbf{v}_{PE} = (75 \text{ m/s})\mathbf{i} - gt\mathbf{j}$$

This velocity expression corresponds to projectile motion. According to Emily, the path of the parcel is a parabola, as shown in Fig. 4-19.

Figure 4-19. Example 4-7: Charles drops a parcel from the plane. From Emily's point of view, the path of the parcel is a parabola.

4-6 NUMERICAL METHODS: AIR RESISTANCE

As an example of numerical methods in a two-dimensional problem, we consider the effect of air resistance on the baseball in Example 4-4. The effect of air resistance on a baseball can be approximated by adding a term to the acceleration that depends on the square of the speed of the ball through the air and points in a direction opposite to the velocity. The acceleration then becomes

$$\mathbf{a} = \mathbf{g} - bv\mathbf{v}$$

where $\mathbf{g}$ is the gravitational acceleration and b is a constant. (Measurements indicate that an approximate value of b for a baseball in air is 0.002 m^{-1}.) With $+y$ vertically upward and $+x$ horizontal and in the direction of motion, $\mathbf{g} = -g\mathbf{j}$ and

$$\mathbf{a} = (-bvv_x)\mathbf{i} + (-g - bvv_y)\mathbf{j}$$

Writing $v = \sqrt{v_x{}^2 + v_y{}^2}$, we obtain

$$a_x = -bv_x\sqrt{v_x{}^2 + v_y{}^2}$$
$$a_y = -g - bv_y\sqrt{v_x{}^2 + v_y{}^2}$$

Table 4-2 contains a BASIC program for determining the coordinates of the baseball during its flight. The initial values of x, y, v_x, and v_y are taken from

Table 4-2. BASIC program for the trajectory of a baseball with air resistance included (Quantities are in SI units)

```
100    X=0
110    Y=1
120    VX=26
130    VY=23
140    T=0
150    DT=.005
200        FOR I=1 TO 1000
210        AX=-.002*VX*(VX*VX+VY*VY)^.5
220        AY=-9.8-.002*VY*(VX*VX+VY*VY)^.5
230        VX=VX+AX*DT
240        VY=VY+AY*DT
250        X=X+VX*DT
260        Y=Y+VY*DT
270        T=T+DT
280        IF I=100*INT(I/100) THEN PRINT T, X, Y
290        NEXT I
300    END
```

Example 4-4. (The initial velocity components are $v_{x0} = v_0 \cos \theta_0 = 35$ m/s $\cos 42° = 26$ m/s, and $v_{y0} = v_0 \sin \theta_0 = 23$ m/s.) We notice that the time of the flight of the ball without air resistance is about 5 s from the fact that $v_x = 26$ m/s and the range of the ball is about 120 m: 120 m/26 m/s $\approx$ 5 s. Therefore we let the time intervals be 5 ms, and in that way 1000 iterations will encompass 5 s. Statement 280 causes the computer to print the time and coordinates after every 100 iterations, that is, for each 0.5 s of the motion.

Figure 4-20. The trajectory of the baseball in Example 4-4. The curve is without air resistance; the points are with air resistance.

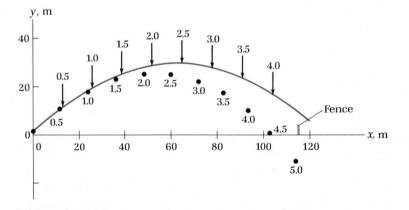

Figure 4-20 shows a graph of the data generated by this program, and a curve for the trajectory when air resistance is neglected. Times of the positions are indicated for both the case with air resistance and without air resistance. With air resistance included, our prospective home run from Example 4-4 is nothing more than a long fly ball.

COMMENTARY: GALILEO GALILEI

Galileo was born in Pisa, Tuscany (part of present-day Italy), in 1564, the year of William Shakespeare's birth and Michelangelo's death. His father, Vincenzio Galilei, was a musician and merchant with a lively interest in cultural activities. Vincenzio's ancestors were distinguished citizens of Florence, but at the time of Galileo's birth the family was in economic decline. His father sent him, at age 17,

Galileo is depicted here trying to convince two skeptical cardinals that the surface of the moon is not perfectly spherical. *(National Geographic)*

Jupiter with four of its brightest moons. Longitude was very difficult to measure in Galileo's day, and, as one of his many practical accomplishments, he devised a means for measuring longitude from observations of Jupiter's moons. *(Denis Milon)*

to the University of Pisa to study medicine, but Galileo soon became captivated by a passion for science and mathematics. He demonstrated his aptitude for experimentation and measurement when, as a medical student, he devised a pendulum-type clock for measuring pulse rates. His extraordinary abilities were apparent early, and he was appointed professor of mathematics at Pisa at the age of 26.

Since Galileo was the eldest son, his father's death left him with the family's financial burdens, but without means. He incurred huge debts to provide dowries for two of his sisters and partially supported a younger brother for many years. Throughout his life, Galileo never completely escaped the specter of poverty. He never married, but he was the father of three children by Marina Gamba, who was his affectionate companion for 10 years. Their separation was amicable and Marina subsequently married one of Galileo's friends. Galileo consigned his two daughters, Virginia and Livia, to a convent at the ages of 13 and 12, and they later became nuns. He treated his son Vincenzio with somewhat more favor than his daughters, and he eventually took action to make his son legitimate. Late in his life, his daughter Virginia became his close companion. Her death at the age of 36 was an extremely grievous event in Galileo's life.

Because of his exuberance and fiery personality, Galileo's life was filled with turbulence and controversy. He is probably more famous for his difficulties with the Roman Catholic church than for his remarkable scientific achievements. He was tried twice by the Inquisition. He supported the sun-centered, or copernican, theory of the universe, whereas church doctrine held that the earth is stationary at the center of the universe. At his second trial, in 1633, when he was 69 and feeble, Galileo was forced to recant his scientific beliefs to avoid imprisonment.

Galileo's scientific interests were so broad that they can scarcely be mentioned here. He studied mechanics, astronomy, optics, and the behavior of fluids. He was an early developer of the telescope, and was among the first to use it as an

The phases of Venus are shown here with the same magnification in each photograph. When Venus is on the opposite side of the sun from the earth, it is at its farthest distance from the earth and its illuminated side faces the earth. When it is on the same side of the sun as the earth, it is nearest the earth and its illuminated side faces away from the earth. *(Photo Researchers)*

astronomical instrument. He discovered the moons of Jupiter, the rings of Saturn, the phases of Venus, and the existence of surface features on the moon. (Because of the limited resolving power of his telescopes, he mistook the rings of Saturn to be two satellites, one on each side of the planet.) As we have noted in these two chapters on kinematics, he explained free-fall and projectile motion. The description of relative motion that we discussed in Sec. 4-5 is attributed to him and is known as galilean relativity. Many historians give Galileo credit for discovering one of the three laws of motion, the one referred to as Newton's first law, or the law of inertia (Sec. 5-3).

Because of his philosophy of science, Galileo is regarded as the father of modern science. The importance he attached to mathematics in describing physical phenomena is evident in the following passage:

> *Philosophy is written in this grand book — I mean the universe — which stands continually open to our gaze, but it cannot be understood unless one first learns to comprehend the language and interpret the characters in which it is written. It is*

Sketches by Galileo of some of the planets with their signs. Across the top is Saturn on the left, Jupiter in the middle, and Mars on the right. Across the bottom are the phases of Venus; the sun, shown as a circle with a dot in the middle, is on the far right.

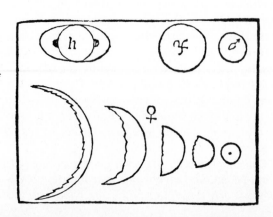

written in the language of mathematics, and its characters are triangles, circles, and other geometrical figures, without which it is humanly impossible to understand a word of it; without these, one is wandering about in a dark labyrinth.*

Galileo was primarily concerned with mathematics as the "language" of nature, and he showed little interest in pure mathematics.

After his second trial, Galileo was kept in near-seclusion for the remaining nine years of his life. Despite being sick and blind, he wrote some of his greatest works during this time. His enthusiasm was unflagging to the end. He died in 1642, the year of Isaac Newton's birth.

SUMMARY WITH APPLICATIONS

Section 4-2. Velocity and acceleration
In two dimensions the position vector is

$$\mathbf{r} = x\mathbf{i} + y\mathbf{j} \qquad (4\text{-}1)$$

and the velocity is $\mathbf{v} = \dfrac{dx}{dt}\mathbf{i} + \dfrac{dy}{dt}\mathbf{j}$

The velocity is parallel to a line tangent to the path and points in the direction of motion. The acceleration is

$$\mathbf{a} = \frac{dv_x}{dt}\mathbf{i} + \frac{dv_y}{dt}\mathbf{j}$$

For a curved path, $\mathbf{a}$ is always toward the concave side of the path. If the speed is increasing, the angle ϕ between $\mathbf{v}$ and $\mathbf{a}$ is less than 90°; but if the speed is decreasing, ϕ is greater than 90°.

Define velocity and acceleration in two dimensions; determine velocity and acceleration components from expressions of the coordinates as functions of time; describe the directions of the velocity and acceleration.

Section 4-3. Constant acceleration: projectile motion
Projectile motion with negligible air resistance is an example of motion with constant acceleration in two dimensions. The trajectory of a projectile is a parabola. Table 4-1 summarizes the equations that describe a projectile.

Determine the velocity and position of a projectile.

Section 4-4. Uniform circular motion
An object that moves in a circle at constant speed is in uniform circular motion, and its acceleration, called the centripetal acceleration, is toward the center of the circle. The magnitude of the centripetal acceleration is

$$a_c = \frac{v^2}{R} \qquad (4\text{-}19)$$

Describe uniform circular motion and determine the velocity and acceleration of an object which executes this motion.

Section 4-5. Relative motion
Two observers moving at constant velocity with respect to one another measure different values for the velocity of an object. The difference between their measurements is equal to their velocity relative to one another. These two observers measure the same acceleration for an object.

Using the velocity of one observer relative to another, determine the velocity of an object measured by one of the observers in terms of measurements made by the other observer.

🔧 Section 4-6. Numerical methods: air resistance
Numerical methods can be used to account approximately for the effects of air resistance on the motion of a projectile.

Use a program which describes projectile motion with air resistance.

QUESTIONS

4-1   What sort of relationship, if any, always holds between the directions (a) of an object's position vector and velocity, (b) of its displacement and average velocity, (c) of a line tangent to the path and the velocity, (d) of the change in velocity and the average acceleration, (e) of a line tangent to the path and the acceleration?

4-2   If an object is traveling in a straight line, what sort of

relationship, if any, always holds between the directions of the object's path and its acceleration?

4-3   If an object has a curved path, what sort of relationship, if any, always holds between the direction in which the path is curving and the direction of the object's acceleration?

4-4   Is it possible for an object to accelerate and still have

---

* Ludovico Geymonat, *Galileo Galilei*, Stillman Drake (trans.), McGraw-Hill, New York, 1965, p. 106.

(a) a constant speed, (b) a straight path, (c) a constant velocity? Explain.

4-5 If the velocity of an object is changing and becomes zero at an instant of time, must its acceleration be zero at that instant? Can its acceleration be zero at that instant? Can its acceleration be zero over a time interval that includes that instant?

4-6 Is it possible for an object's velocity to be in the direction opposite to its acceleration? If it is possible, give an example. If not, explain.

4-7 If an object is accelerating during a time interval, can its velocity be zero at an instant during this time interval? Can the velocity be zero during the entire time interval? Give examples to support your answers.

4-8 We have seen that if the acceleration of an object is constant, then the velocity varies linearly with time and the position vector varies quadratically with time. Suppose the acceleration varies linearly with time. What is the time variation of (a) the velocity and (b) the position vector?

4-9 The following list contains various objects and the range of their trajectories when they are launched with a variety of speeds into the air at an angle of 45° over flat terrain. Suppose we wish to predict the positions of the objects during their motion to an accuracy of 10 percent. For which objects is it valid to neglect air resistance?

(a) Golf ball, 5 m   (e) Badminton birdie, 3 m
(b) Golf ball, 100 m   (f) Ping-pong ball, 3 m
(c) Baseball, 5 m   (g) Frisbee, 10 m
(d) Baseball, 100 m   (h) Boomerang, 10 m

4-10 Judy says that an object traveling through the air is falling if its acceleration is downward. Martha says that such an object is falling if its velocity is downward. In what part of the trajectory of a projectile will Judy and Martha agree? In what part will they disagree? Which definition of the term "falling" do you prefer, Judy's or Martha's?

4-11 A projectile is launched with an initial velocity of $(3 \text{ m/s})\mathbf{i} + (2 \text{ m/s})\mathbf{j}$. Neglect air resistance. What is its velocity at the top of its trajectory? What is its acceleration at the top of its trajectory?

4-12 A projectile is launched with an initial velocity $\mathbf{v}_0 = v_{x0}\mathbf{i} + v_{y0}\mathbf{j}$. Neglect air resistance. Does the range of the projectile depend on (a) v_{x0}; (b) v_{y0}? Does the maximum height of the projectile depend on (c) v_{x0}; (d) v_{y0}?

4-13 A stone is thrown into the air at an angle of, say, 40° with respect to the horizontal. Is its velocity ever parallel to its acceleration at any time during its motion? If so, when? If not, explain. Is its velocity ever perpendicular to its acceleration at any time during the motion? If so, when? If not, explain.

4-14 Suppose you throw a rock at a bottle that will begin falling from rest at the instant you release the rock. To hit the bottle, should you aim above it, below it, or directly at it? Explain.

4-15 Is it possible for an object to be moving with constant

speed and be accelerating at the same time? If so, give an example of such a case. If not, explain.

4-16 If an object follows a curved path, can its velocity be constant? Can its speed be constant? Can its acceleration be constant? Can the magnitude of its acceleration be constant? If the answer to any of these questions is yes, give an example.

4-17 Suppose an object is traveling in a circle at constant speed and the origin is at the center of the circle. What is the relationship, if any, between the directions of the object's (a) position vector and velocity, (b) position vector and acceleration, (c) velocity and acceleration?

4-18 In uniform circular motion, (a) is the speed constant? (b) Is the velocity constant? (c) Is the magnitude of the acceleration constant? (d) Is the acceleration constant? Explain.

4-19 A penny on a rotating turntable executes uniform circular motion with a speed of 0.8 m/s and an acceleration magnitude of 4 m/s². The penny is repositioned on the turntable such that the radius of its circular path is halved. What is its subsequent speed and acceleration magnitude?

4-20 A penny on a rotating turntable executes uniform circular motion with a speed of 0.4 m/s and an acceleration magnitude of 2 m/s². The rotational speed of the turntable is doubled so that the period of the penny's motion is halved. What is its subsequent speed and acceleration magnitude?

4-21 *Acceleration of a pendulum bob.* A pendulum is composed of a heavy object, such as a rock, which is allowed to swing back and forth on the end of a string in a vertical plane (Fig. 4-21). The heavy object is called the *pendulum bob*, and its path is along the arc of a circle. In the figure, the bob is instantaneously at rest when it is at the far right. Suppose the bob is swinging to the left, which arrow best indicates the direction of its acceleration at each position shown? How about when it is swinging to the right?

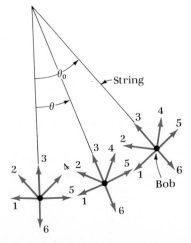

Figure 4-21. Ques. 4-21: A pendulum bob is shown at three positions as it swings back and forth in a plane.

4-22 Consider an object at point P along each trajectory shown in Fig. 4-22. (a) In Fig. 4-22a, what are the algebraic signs of v_x and v_y? (b) In Fig. 4-22b, what are the algebraic signs of a_x and a_y if the object's speed is increasing? (c) In Fig. 4-22c, what are the algebraic signs of a_x and a_y if the object's speed is decreasing?

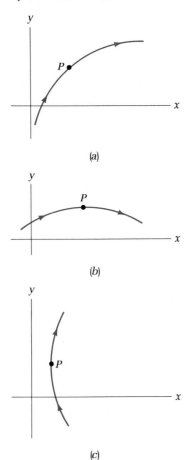

(a)

(b)

(c)

Figure 4-22. Ques. 4-22.

4-23 Suppose an object follows a spiral path while traveling at constant speed (Fig. 4-23). Is the object's velocity constant? Is its acceleration constant? Is its acceleration magnitude constant? If its acceleration magnitude is not constant, is it increasing or decreasing?

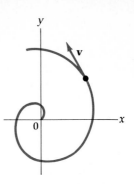

Figure 4-23. Ques. 4-23.

4-24 As you know, the earth circles the sun once each year. From our perspective on earth, the sun returns to its original position relative to the backdrop of distant stars in 1 year. How would it look to us if the sun circled the earth, instead of the other way around?

4-25 (a) Suppose two observers who are moving at constant velocity relative to one another each measure the velocity of an object. Will they find the same result? If so, explain. If not, how will they differ? (b) Suppose the observers measure the object's acceleration. Will they find the same result? If so, explain. If not, how will they differ?

4-26 When the acceleration is constant, we found that the x and y motions are independent of one another. That is, a_x has no effect on v_y or y, and a_y has no effect on v_x or x. Thus, when air resistance has a negligible effect on the motion of a projectile, the x and y motions are independent. Is this still true when air resistance is not negligible? Explain.

4-27 Did Bill intend to hit Alvin with the banana peel? (*Hint:* Bill made an A in Physics.)

4-28 Complete the following table:

Symbol	Represents	Type	SI Unit
v		Vector	
a_x			m/s²
y		Component	
v_O	Initial speed		
a_c		Scalar	
$\mathbf{v}_{BA}$			

EXERCISES

Section 4-2. Velocity and acceleration

4-1 A jogger runs around a circular track of radius 45.0 m (Fig. 4-24). Let the origin of an xy coordinate frame be at the center of the circle, with $+\mathbf{i}$ toward the east and $+\mathbf{j}$ toward the north, and let $t = 0.0$ s correspond to the instant the jogger's coordinates (x, y) are (45.0 m, 0.0 m). (a) At $t = 16.8$ s, the jogger is directly northeast of the origin. What is her position vector? (b) At $t = 33.6$ s, the jogger is due north of the origin. What is her displacement between $t = 0.0$ s and $t = 33.6$ s? (c) What is the distance she traveled between $t = 0.0$ s and $t = 33.6$ s?

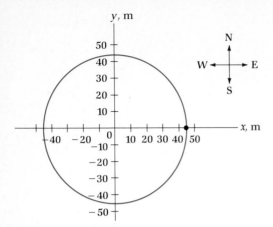

Figure 4-24. Exercise 4-1.

4-2 The jogger in the previous exercise is directly north-west of the origin at $t = 50.4$ s. (a) What is her position vector? (b) What is her displacement between $t = 0.0$ s and $t = 50.4$ s? (c) What is the distance she traveled between $t = 0.0$ s and $t = 50.4$ s?

4-3 (a) What is the average velocity of the jogger in Exercise 4-1 between $t = 0.0$ s and $t = 33.6$ s? (b) At $t = 8.4$ s her position is (41.6 m, 17.2 m), and at $t = 25.2$ s her position is (17.2 m, 41.6 m). What is her average velocity during this time interval?

4-4 The jogger in Exercise 4-1 completes one revolution in 134.4 s. (a) If she travels at constant speed, what is her speed? (b) What is her velocity at $t = 16.8$ s? Compare this answer with the answers in the previous exercise.

4-5 A car travels the horizontal path from A through K, as shown in Fig. 4-25. The paths from C to E and G to I are circular arcs of radii 200 and 300 m, respectively. The car is at rest at A, accelerates uniformly from A to C, travels at a constant speed of 23 m/s from C to I, then slows down with a constant acceleration until it is at rest at K. (a) What is the car's velocity at B? (b) What is its acceleration at B? (c) What is its velocity at D? (d) What is its average acceleration between C and E?

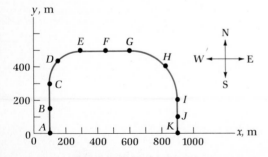

Figure 4-25. Exercise 4-5.

4-6 For the car in the previous exercise (Fig. 4-25), what is its velocity at (a) F; (b) H; (c) J? What is its acceleration at (d) F and (e) J? (f) What is its average acceleration between G and I?

4-7 The position vector of an object is $\mathbf{r} = [(3.5 \text{ m/s})t + 4.2 \text{ m}]\mathbf{i} + [(5.1 \text{ m/s})t]\mathbf{j}$. (a) Determine $\mathbf{v}$. (b) Make a graph of the object's path from $t = 0.0$ s to $t = 3.0$ s. Plot points each 0.5 s and sketch the path. Show $\mathbf{v}$ at several places on the path to indicate the direction of motion.

4-8 The coordinates of an object are given by $x = (1.9 \text{ m/s}^2)t^2$ and $y = (0.47 \text{ m/s}^3)t^3 - 5.6$ m. What are the object's (a) velocity components and (b) acceleration components?

4-9 At a particular point on a roller-coaster track, the track makes an angle of 29° with respect to the horizontal. If the roller-coaster car passes this point with a speed of 16 m/s, what are the (a) horizontal and (b) vertical components of the car's velocity?

4-10 As an airplane climbs after takeoff, the horizontal and vertical components of its velocity are 97 m/s and 22 m/s, respectively. What are (a) the airplane's speed and (b) the angle between its velocity and the horizontal?

Section 4-3. Constant acceleration: projectile motion*

4-11 A billiard ball rolls toward the east down a straight plank that makes an angle of 15° with respect to the horizontal. The magnitude of the ball's acceleration is 1.81 m/s² during the entire motion. Let the x axis be horizontal with $+\mathbf{i}$ toward the east and let $+\mathbf{j}$ point vertically upward. Let $t = 0$ correspond to the instant the ball is released at the origin. (a) Write expressions for a_x, a_y, v_x, v_y, x, and y. (b) Repeat part (a) with $\mathbf{i}$ directed down the ramp and $\mathbf{j}$ perpendicular to it. (c) Is this motion in one or two dimensions? Explain.

4-12 A projectile has an initial speed of 26 m/s and a projection angle of 48° at the launch point. At $t = 2.1$ s after launch, (a) what is the projectile's distance from the launch point? (b) What is its speed? (c) What is the direction it is heading relative to the horizontal?

4-13 A rock is thrown into the air with an initial speed of 36 m/s and at a projection angle of 62°. Let the origin be at the point of release and let $t = 0$ correspond to the instant of release. Write expressions for v_x, v_y, x, and y.

4-14 A baseball pitcher throws the ball with an initial speed of 40 m/s. At the instant of release the velocity is directed horizontally and the ball is 2.1 m above the ground and 20 m (horizontally) from home plate. (a) How long does it take to pass over the plate? (b) As it crosses the plate, what is its height above the ground?

4-15 A football thrown over a level field travels a horizontal distance of 17 m before hitting the ground. The point of release is 1.5 m above the ground and the projection angle is 16°. What is the ball's initial speed?

---

* *Note:* The effects of air resistance are neglected in the exercises in this section.

4-16 A golf ball is struck such that its initial speed is 105 m/s and the angle of projection is 34°. The fairway is level. What is the ball's (a) time of maximum height, (b) time of flight, (c) maximum height, and (d) horizontal range?

4-17 The horizontal range of a projectile is 48 m and its initial speed is 33 m/s. (a) What is its angle of projection? (b) Is there another angle of projection that is consistent with these values of R and v_0? If so, find this angle. If not, explain.

4-18 A ball is thrown from a balcony with an initial speed of 31 m/s and at a projection angle of 24°. The point of release is 8.2 m above flat terrain. (a) What is the horizontal distance from the release point to where the ball hits the ground? (b) What is the straight-line distance from the release point to where the ball hits the ground?

4-19 An air gun fires a pellet with an initial speed of 52 m/s. The gun is fired with its barrel directed 75° above the horizontal, with the end of the barrel 1.9 m above the ground. The terrain is level. (a) How long after the gun is fired will the pellet reach its maximum height? (b) What is the pellet's maximum height above the ground? (c) What is the horizontal distance traveled by the pellet from the gun barrel to the point where it hits the ground?

4-20 Make a graph of the trajectory of a projectile. Let $x_0 =$ 0.0 m, $y_0 = 0.0$ m, $v_0 = 40.0$ m/s, and $\theta_0 = 50.0°$. Plot points at each 0.5 s and label each point with its value of t. Sketch a curve through the points. Determine t_m and show **v** on the graph at $t = 0.5t_m, 1.0t_m, 1.5t_m$, and $2.0t_m$.

4-21 Figure 4-26 shows the paths of a rock and a bottle. The bottle was released from rest at the instant the rock was launched. The value of g has been taken to be 10.0 m/s² in order to deal with round numbers. Note that the initial velocity of the rock was directed straight toward the bottle. From data taken from the graph, determine v_0 and θ_0 for the rock.

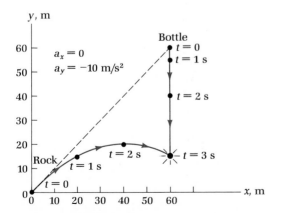

Figure 4-26. Exercise 4-21.

Section 4-4. Uniform circular motion

4-22 A car makes a circular turn of radius $R = 63$ m while its speed is constant at $v = 12$ m/s. What is the magnitude of its centripetal acceleration?

4-23 A penny rides on a phonograph turntable at a distance of 130 mm from the spindle. What is the magnitude of the penny's centripetal acceleration when the turntable rotates at (a) 33.3 rev/min (revolutions per minute) and (b) 45.0 rev/min?

4-24 The jogger in Exercise 4-1 (Fig. 4-24) runs at constant speed and completes one revolution in 134.4 s. What is the magnitude and direction of her centripetal acceleration when she is (a) north of the origin and (b) northwest of the origin? (c) Write her acceleration in terms of unit vectors in each case.

4-25 Determine the magnitude and direction of the velocity of the car in Exercise 4-5 (Fig. 4-25) at (a) D and (b) H. (c) Write its acceleration in terms of the unit vectors in each case.

4-26 An object executes uniform circular motion with the origin of an xy coordinate frame at the center of the circle. Make a graph of the circular path and show the velocity and acceleration vectors with their tails at the object's position when the object's coordinates (x, y) are (a) $(R, 0)$; (b) $(0, R)$; (c) $(-R/\sqrt{2}, R/\sqrt{2})$. The object is traveling counterclockwise. (d) Repeat with the object traveling clockwise.

4-27 A boy swings a rock tied to a string around his head in a horizontal circle. The radius of the circle is 0.96 m, and the time for one revolution is 1.1 s. What is the rock's (a) speed and (b) acceleration magnitude?

4-28 The orbit of the moon around the earth is nearly circular, with a radius of 3.85×10^8 m and a period of 27.3 days. What is the magnitude of the moon's centripetal acceleration in its motion about the earth?

4-29 (a) The radius of the earth is 6.37×10^6 m. Determine the centripetal acceleration of a point on the earth's surface at the equator relative to the center of the earth in m/s² and in g's. (b) The radius of the earth's orbit about the sun is 1.5×10^{11} m. Determine the centripetal acceleration of the earth relative to the sun in m/s² and in g's. (c) Astronomical measurements indicate that our solar system is in nearly a circular orbit about the center of the Milky Way galaxy at a radius of 2.8×10^{20} m and a speed of 2.5×10^5 m/s. Determine the centripetal acceleration of the solar system relative to the center of the galaxy in m/s² and in g's. (d) Determine the ratios of each pair of these accelerations.

4-30 In the Fermilab accelerator at Batavia, Illinois, protons travel at nearly the speed of light (3×10^8 m/s) along a circular path of radius 1 km. Find the centripetal acceleration of one of these protons in (a) m/s² and (b) in g's.

4-31 (a) Show that for an object undergoing uniform circular motion, $a_c = 2\pi v/T$. (b) A go-cart travels around a circular track once every 5.1 s at a constant speed of 11 m/s. What is the cart's centripetal acceleration?

4-32 A carnival Ferris wheel has a radius of 7.5 m and makes one revolution every 5.7 s. What are the magnitude and direction of a passenger's acceleration when the passenger is (a) at the top and (b) at the bottom?

Section 4-5. Relative motion

4-33 Becky is driving south in the right lane of a highway at a speed of 22 m/s. Suzie is in the left lane and traveling in the same direction as Becky at a speed of 28 m/s. What is Suzie's (a) speed and (b) velocity relative to Becky? What is Becky's (c) speed and (d) velocity relative to Suzie?

4-34 Observer A measures the velocity and acceleration of particle P to be $(3 \text{ m/s})\mathbf{j}$ and $(4 \text{ m/s}^2)\mathbf{i}$, respectively. Observer B moves with a constant velocity relative to A: $\mathbf{v}_{BA} = (2 \text{ m/s})\mathbf{i} + (-1 \text{ m/s})\mathbf{j}$. According to B, what is the (a) velocity and (b) acceleration of P?

4-35 A train is traveling east at a speed of 3.4 m/s. Using a compass for direction, a man on a flatcar of the train walks northeast at a speed of 1.2 m/s relative to the flatcar. What is the man's velocity relative to the ground?

4-36 An airplane's compass shows that it is headed west, and its airspeed indicator shows that its speed through the air is 175 m/s. Relative to the ground, the velocity of the wind is 42 m/s toward the north. Establish a coordinate frame and determine the velocity of the airplane relative to the ground.

4-37 The cruising speed of a ferry boat relative to the water is 7.8 m/s. The boat crosses a river to a destination on the other side that is directly north of the departure point. The distance from departure to destination is 1.8 km. The current in the river is 2.3 m/s toward the east. Let $+\mathbf{i}$ point east and $+\mathbf{j}$ point north. (a) Determine the velocity of the boat relative to the water such that the boat travels in a straight line to its destination. (b) How long does it take the boat to make the crossing? (c) Repeat with a current velocity of 4.6 m/s toward the east.

Section 4-6. Numerical methods: air resistance

4-38 ⬛ Run the program listed in Table 4-2 and tabulate the data. Make a graph of the data and compare it with Fig. 4-20.

PROBLEMS

(*Note:* Unless stated otherwise, neglect air resistance in problems dealing with projectile motion.)

4-1 The coordinates of an object are given by $x = R \cos \omega t$ and $y = R \sin \omega t$, where R and ω are constants. (a) Show that the velocity components are $v_x = -R\omega \sin \omega t$ and $v_y = R\omega \cos \omega t$. (b) Show that the acceleration components are $a_x = -R\omega^2 \cos \omega t$ and $a_y = -R\omega^2 \sin \omega t$. (c) Show that $\mathbf{a} = -\omega^2 \mathbf{r}$. (d) Make a graph of the path of the object on an xy coordinate frame for the case where $R = 45.0$ m and $\omega = 46.75$ mrad/s. Plot points at each 8.4 s between $t = 0.0$ s and $t = 134.4$ s, and sketch the curve. (e) Evaluate $\mathbf{v}$ and $\mathbf{a}$ at $t = 16.8$ s and draw the vectors on your graph with their tails at the position of the object at this instant. (f) What type of motion is this?

4-2 For an object moving with constant acceleration, show that (a) $v_x^2 = v_{x0}^2 + 2a_x(x - x_0)$ and (b) $v_y^2 = v_{y0}^2 + 2a_y(y - y_0)$ by eliminating t in Eqs. (4-10) and (4-12). (c) Combine the results of parts (a) and (b) to show that $v^2 = v_0^2 + 2[a_x(x - x_0) + a_y(y - y_0)]$. (d) For projectile motion, show that $v^2 = v_0^2 - 2g(y - y_0)$. (e) The projectile is launched at coordinates (x, y) of $(2.4 \text{ m}, 1.5 \text{ m})$ with an initial speed of 28 m/s. Use the answer from part (d) to find the projectile's speed at the position $(37.6 \text{ m}, 25.4 \text{ m})$.

4-3 (a) Show that the projection angle θ_0 for a projectile launched from the origin is given by $\theta_0 = \tan^{-1}(4h_m/R)$. (b) What is the projection angle for a projectile launched from the origin when the maximum height is 6.2 m and the horizontal range is 32 m? (c) What is the projection angle for a projectile whose maximum height is equal to its horizontal range? (d) What is the maximum height for a projectile whose range is R_m?

4-4 Show that the horizontal range of a projectile whose projection angle is $\Delta\theta$ less than 45° is the same as that for a projectile whose projection angle is $\Delta\theta$ greater than 45°, v_0 held fixed. That is, show that R is symmetric about $\theta_0 = 45°$. (*Hint:* Consider derivatives of R with respect to θ_0.)

4-5 A skier leaves the ski-jump ramp with a velocity of 34 m/s along the horizontal (Fig. 4-27). The ground is a vertical distance of 4.2 m below the launch point and the hill below makes an angle of 25° with respect to the

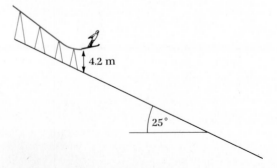

Figure 4-27. Prob. 4-5.

horizontal. Neglecting air resistance, determine the distance from the launch point to the point where the skier touches down. (*Note:* A skilled jumper holds her body such that she obtains "lift" from the air and thus lengthens her flight.)

4-6 An airplane is in a vertical dive at a speed of 174 m/s over level terrain. Assume that the plane pulls out of the dive in a circular path and that the maximum acceleration the airplane can tolerate is 8.0 g's. Determine the minimum altitude at which the plane must begin to pull out in order to avoid hitting the ground. Assume constant speed throughout the motion.

4-7 Show that for a projectile the angle between the velocity and the x axis as a function of time is

$$\theta(t) = \tan^{-1} \frac{v_{y0} - gt}{v_{x0}}$$

4-8 In Example 4-6 we showed that the magnitude of the centripetal acceleration can be written $a_c = 4\pi^2 R/T^2$, where T is the period (the time to complete one revolution). The centripetal acceleration of an earth satellite is due to the earth's gravitational attraction. An expression for this acceleration is $a_c = gR_e^2/R^2$, where R is the radius of the orbit and R_e is the earth's radius ($R_e = 6.37 \times 10^6$ m). (a) Show that the relation between a satellite's orbital radius and its period is

$$R^3 = \frac{gR_e^2}{4\pi^2} T^2 = (1.0 \times 10^{13} \text{ m}^3/\text{s}^2)T^2$$

(b) A geosychronous orbit is an orbit over the equator with a 24-h period. In such an orbit a satellite remains directly above a point on the earth's surface. Show that the height of a geosynchronous orbit above a point on the earth's surface at the equator is $h = 5.6 R_e$.

4-9 (a) Use the velocity-vector triangle in Fig. 4-14a to show that the magnitude of the average acceleration for an object in uniform circular motion can be written

$$|\bar{\mathbf{a}}| = \frac{v^2}{R} \frac{2[\sin{(\Delta\theta/2)}]}{\Delta\theta}$$

where $\Delta\theta$ is the angle between $\mathbf{v}_i$ and $\mathbf{v}_f$ expressed in radians. Use the expression in part (a) to determine $|\bar{\mathbf{a}}|$ when $\Delta\theta$ equals (b) $\pi/2$; (c) $\pi/4$; (d) $\pi/10$; (e) $\pi/1000$. (f) What is

$$\lim_{\Delta\theta \to 0} \frac{\sin{(\Delta\theta/2)}}{\Delta\theta}$$

4-10 A runner is to travel from A to B in Fig. 4-28. Because the footing is different, his speed is different on each side of the x axis. Let v_1 represent his speed above the x axis and v_2 represent his speed below the x axis. Also, let the two straight-line portions of the path be characterized by the angles θ_1 and θ_2, as shown in the figure. Show that his running time will be minimized when the relation between the angles is given by $v_2 \sin \theta_1 = v_1 \sin \theta_2$. (*Hint:* Write an expression for the time re-

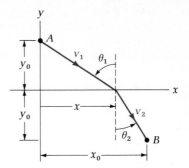

Figure 4-28. Prob. 4-10.

quired to run each straight-line portion, add these times, and take the derivative of the sum with respect to x and set it equal to zero. Following along this path minimizes the time because the runner travels a longer distance in the region where his speed is greater and a shorter distance in the region where his speed is slower.)

4-11 A batter hits a baseball such that $v_0 = 33$ m/s and $\theta_0 = 32°$ at a point 1 m above the plate. The horizontal direction of the ball's path is directly toward an outfielder who is 118 m from the plate. At 0.50 s after the ball is struck, the outfielder begins running toward the plate with constant acceleration. What must be the magnitude of his acceleration if he is to catch the ball when it is 1 m above the ground?

4-12 (a) Suppose we define $|\Delta\mathbf{r}| = |\mathbf{r}_f - \mathbf{r}_i|$ and $\Delta r = r_f - r_i$. Show that these quantities are different by writing them in terms of coordinates. Make a graph of an object executing uniform circular motion. Consider the object at two points on its path and show $|\Delta\mathbf{r}|$ and Δr. (b) Suppose we define $|\Delta\mathbf{v}| = |\mathbf{v}_f - \mathbf{v}_i|$ and $\Delta v = v_f - v_i$. Show that these quantities are different by writing them in terms of velocity components. Make a graph of an object executing uniform circular motion. Consider the object at two points on its path and show $|\Delta\mathbf{v}|$ and Δv.

4-13 A girl anchors her boat in the middle of a river (Fig. 4-29). The current in the river is 0.85 m/s toward the east. (a) Determine the time required for the girl to swim to a point 50 m east of the boat and return. The girl's swimming speed relative to the water is 1.43 m/s. (b) Determine the time required for the girl to swim to a

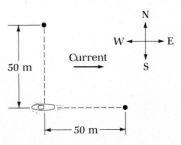

Figure 4-29. Prob. 4-13.

point 50 m north of the boat and return. (c) Which trip took the longer time and by how much?

4-14 A boy is standing on a flatcar of a train that is moving at a speed of 8.2 m/s relative to the ground. The boy throws a rock straight up (according to him) at a speed of 12.5 m/s. (a) What is the initial velocity of the rock according to a woman who is standing on the ground? The boy catches the rock when it returns to the same elevation from which it was released. What is the rock's horizontal range according to (b) the boy and (c) the woman? What is the time of flight according to (d) the boy and (e) the woman? Neglect air resistance.

4-15 When an object falls through the air (or other fluid), it asymptotically approaches a terminal speed v_t because of frictional effects. Suppose an object that is falling vertically has an acceleration component given by

$$a_y = -g + bv^2$$

where $b = 0.002$ m^{-1}. Determine v_t. (Hint: As the object's speed approaches the terminal speed, its acceleration approaches zero.)

4-16 **Artillery range-finding.** (a) By firing one shot short of the target and another shot long, an artillery gunner can zero in so that the third shot is on the mark. Suppose that an artillery shot lands a distance ΔR_1 short of the target when the cannon barrel makes an angle of θ_{01} with the horizontal and another round lands ΔR_2 past the target when the angle is θ_{02}. Show that the angle θ_0 which puts the next shot on target is

$$\theta_0 = \frac{1}{2} \sin^{-1} \frac{\Delta R_1 \sin 2\theta_{02} + \Delta R_2 \sin 2\theta_{01}}{\Delta R_2 + \Delta R_1}$$

(b) With the barrel at an angle of 15.20°, an artillery shot lands 130 m short of its target, and with the angle at 15.85°, a second shot lands 160 m long. What is the angle that will cause the third shot to land on the target?

4-17 By the time raindrops are near the surface of the earth, the combined effects of gravity and air resistance have caused them to reach a steady speed called the *termi-*

nal speed. Suppose a steady rain is falling vertically relative to the earth (there is no wind). You get in your car and while moving at a speed of 10 m/s you measure the angle of the rain with the vertical to be 50°. (a) What is the terminal speed of the raindrops relative to the earth? (b) What is the terminal speed of the raindrops relative to the moving car?

4-18 The planets travel around the sun in nearly circular orbits and all the planetary orbits are in nearly the same plane. The radius of the earth's orbit is 1.5×10^{11} m, and the radius and period of Venus's orbit are 1.1×10^{11} m and 0.61 year, respectively. What is the acceleration magnitude of Venus relative to the earth when they are (a) on the same side of the sun and (b) on opposite sides of the sun?

4-19 **A cycloid.** If a wheel rolls at a constant speed without sliding along a level surface, the coordinates of a particle on the edge of the wheel as a function of time t are

$$x = vt - R \sin \frac{vt}{R} \qquad y = R - R \cos \frac{vt}{R}$$

where R is the wheel's radius and v is the speed of the center of the wheel. The coordinate frame is fixed to the surface, with $+x$ along the surface in the direction of motion and $+y$ vertically upward. (a) Evaluate x and y at times $t = 0$, $T/4$, $T/2$, . . . , $3T/2$, where $T = 2\pi R/v$, and make a graph of the particle's trajectory. This path is called a *cycloid* and will be discussed again in Sec. 12-9. (b) Determine v_x and v_y as functions of time and show $\mathbf{v}$ on your graph at the times $t = 0$, $T/2$, T, and $3T/2$. (c) Determine a_x and a_y as functions of time and show $\mathbf{a}$ on your graph at the times $t = 0$, $T/2$, T, and $3T/2$. (d) Using a_x and a_y from part (c) above, show that $a = v^2/R$.

4-20 ▣ Write a BASIC program for the baseball in Example 4-4, where the added term to the acceleration due to air resistance is assumed to depend on the 1.7 power of the ball's speed: $\mathbf{a} = -g\mathbf{j} - cv^{0.7}\mathbf{v}$, where $c = 0.0070$ m$^{-0.7}$s$^{-0.3}$. Plot your data as shown in Fig. 4-20 and compare your results with that figure.

CHAPTER 5
NEWTON'S LAWS
OF MOTION

5-1 INTRODUCTION

Three fundamental principles, called *Newton's laws of motion*, form the basis of mechanics. Sir Isaac Newton (1642–1727) presented these principles to the world in his book *Philosophiae Naturalis Principia Mathematica (The Mathematical Principles of Natural Philosophy)*, which was published in 1686 and is often referred to as the *Principia*. We shall introduce these principles in this chapter, and use them in much of this book. Also in this chapter we discuss a familiar force, the weight of an object, and we establish procedures for finding the motion of an object.

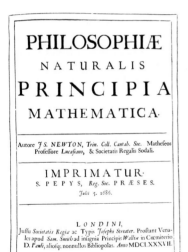

Title page of the *Principia*. (A.I.P., Niels Bohr Library)

5-2 FORCE AND MASS

Newton's laws are phrased in terms of force and mass. It is helpful to have some understanding of these two concepts before being introduced to the laws. However, because force and mass are defined with Newton's laws, we are confronted with a dilemma. How can we discuss Newton's laws without first having the definitions of force and mass well in mind? How can we define force and mass without first stating Newton's laws? We proceed by describing force and mass qualitatively, in terms of everyday experience, and by using these intuitive notions in preliminary discussions of the laws. After we have the laws, we then state the formal definitions of force and mass.

Mass. The *mass* of an object is a measure of the object's resistance to a change in its velocity. A child's wagon, coasting along a horizontal sidewalk, is more

79

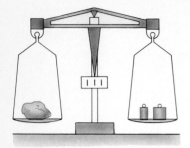

Figure 5-1. An equal-arm balance.

difficult to stop when it is loaded with bricks than when it is empty. The system, wagon plus load, is more massive in the former case than in the latter. Mass is a scalar quantity and is additive. That is, if we fasten two objects of mass m_1 and m_2 together, then the mass m_{12} of the composite system is

$$m_{12} = m_1 + m_2$$

In the laboratory, the mass of an object is often measured with an equal-arm balance by comparison with standard "weights" of known mass (Fig. 5-1). As we shall see in Sec. 5-6, an object's weight is proportional to its mass.

EXAMPLE 5-1. The mass density ρ of a substance is the mass m of a given quantity of the substance divided by the volume V occupied by that quantity: $\rho = m/V$. Water has a density such that one liter (L) of water has a mass of about one kilogram. One liter is the volume of a cube 0.1 m on a side. (a) Determine the mass density of water in SI units (kg/m^3). (b) What is the mass of the quantity of water contained in a drinking glass which has a diameter of 80 mm when it is filled to a height of 100 mm?

SOLUTION. (a) The mass density ρ of water is

$$\rho = \frac{m}{V} = \frac{1\ kg}{(0.1\ m)^3} = 1 \times 10^3\ kg/m^3$$

One cubic meter of water has a mass of 1000 kg. (b) The volume of the water in the glass is the volume V of a cylinder of radius R and height h:

$$V = \pi R^2 h = \pi (40\ mm)^2 (100\ mm) = 0.5 \times 10^{-3}\ m^3$$

The mass m of the water is

$$m = \rho V = (1 \times 10^3\ kg/m^3)(0.5 \times 10^{-3}\ m^3) = 0.5\ kg$$

Interestingly, Newton regarded mass density as an intuitively familiar concept. At the beginning of the *Principia*, he discussed mass as the product of mass density and volume.

Force. While Newton was forming his ideas about mechanics, he struggled mightily with the concept of force. From his notes, one of his early definitions was "Force is yᵉ pressure or crouding of one body upon another." In modern everyday language, a *force* is a push or a pull. If you push on an object with your hand, you exert a force on the object. Such a force is the result of direct contact between your hand and the object, and is an example of a *contact force*. Another familiar force is the *weight* of an object. The weight of an object is the *gravitational force* exerted by the earth on the object. We examine the gravitational force in detail in Chap. 7. When you take your socks out of the clothes dryer on a dry day and the socks cling to each other, you are observing the effects of *electric forces*. A *magnetic force* is responsible when you use a small magnet to hold a note on the refrigerator door. We investigate electric and magnetic forces in Chaps. 20 through 31. *Nuclear forces* are outside the realm of direct human experience.* The commentary at the end of Chap. 7 gives an overall view of the forces in nature.

Types of forces in nature

From common experience, we can point out four properties of force:

1 Since a push or a pull has both magnitude and direction, we expect that force is a vector quantity. In the next section, we shall substantiate this expectation.
2 Forces occur in pairs. If object A exerts a force on object B, then B also exerts a force on A. For example, when a golf club strikes a ball (Fig. 5-2), the club exerts a force on the ball, but the ball exerts a force on the club too.

---

* In the "extended" edition of this text, nuclear forces are discussed in Chap. 43.

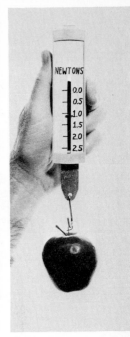

Figure 5-2. High-speed photograph of a golf ball as it is struck by a club. The ball is temporarily deformed and is accelerated. *(Dr. Harold Edgerton/M.I.T., Cambridge, Mass.)*

Figure 5-3. A spring scale. *(Tom Richard)*

3 A force can cause an object to accelerate. If you kick a soccer ball, the ball's velocity changes while your foot is in contact with it.

4 A force can deform an object. As you can see from Fig. 5-2, the ball is deformed by the force exerted on it by the club. The club is deformed too, but since it is harder than the ball, its deformation is not as noticeable.

Property 4, that a force causes an object to be deformed, is often used to measure a force. This is the principle of a spring scale (Fig. 5-3). A spring scale consists of a spring, usually contained in a housing, and a pointer which indicates the amount the spring is stretched or compressed. The magnitude of this force is proportional to the amount the spring is stretched (or compressed), and the direction of the force is along the spring. The scale may be calibrated to read in pounds (lb) or in newtons (N), which is the SI unit of force. A few representative force magnitudes are given in Table 5-1.

Finally, note that the mass of an object is a property of that object alone. In contrast, a force exerted on an object is a result of an interaction between that object and some other object. Further, an object's *environment* consists of other objects that exert forces on that object. For example, if you hold a book in

Environment of an object

Table 5-1. A few representative forces

Exerted by	Exerted on	Type	Approximate magnitude, N
Andromeda galaxy	Milky Way galaxy	Gravitational	7×10^{28}
Sun	Earth	Gravitational	3.5×10^{22}
Saturn V rockets	Apollo spacecraft	Contact	3.3×10^{7}
Earth	You	Gravitational	600
Hydrogen atom nucleus (proton)	Atom's electron	Electric	8×10^{-8}
Hydrogen atom nucleus (proton)	Atom's electron	Gravitational	4×10^{-47}

your hand, the important elements of the book's environment are your hand, which exerts an upward force on the book, and the earth, which exerts a downward force on the book (the book's weight).

EXAMPLE 5-2. In the British system of units, force is measured in pounds, and 1.00 lb = 4.45 N. (a) What is the weight of a 5.0-lb bag of sugar in newtons? (b) If an apple weighs 1.1 N, what is its weight in pounds?

SOLUTION. (a) Dividing the equation 1.00 lb = 4.45 N by 1.00 lb, we find that the number 1 can be written as 1 = 4.45 N/1.00 lb = 4.45 N/lb. Multiplying the weight of the bag of sugar by this conversion factor, we obtain

$$5.0 \text{ lb} = (5.0 \text{ lb})(4.45 \text{ N/lb}) = 22 \text{ N}$$

(b) Similarly, the conversion factor can be written as 1 = 1.00 lb/4.45 N = 0.225 lb/N, and the weight of the apple is

$$1.1 \text{ N} = (1.1 \text{ N})(0.225 \text{ lb/N}) = 0.25 \text{ lb}$$

Since an apple plays a prominent role in a famous legend about Newton, it is interesting that a small apple weighs about 1 N.

5-3 NEWTON'S FIRST LAW

As was the custom for a scholarly work in Newton's day, the *Principia* was written in Latin. A translation of Newton's first law is*

> Law I. Every body continues in its state of rest, or in uniform motion in a right [straight] line unless it is compelled to change that state by forces impressed upon it.

This law is often called the *law of inertia,* because "inertia" means resistance to a change, and the law states that an object naturally tends to maintain whatever velocity it happens to have (including a velocity of zero).

If an object is in a state of rest or in uniform motion in a straight line, then its acceleration is zero. Thus the first law can be expressed in this way: *If no forces are exerted on an object, then the object's acceleration is zero.* To test Newton's first law, we should place an object in an environment where no forces are exerted on it, and then observe whether its acceleration is zero. However, a more realistic approach is to use the vector property of forces. Since force is a vector quantity, two or more forces can be combined to give a *net force* of zero. The net force exerted on an object is the vector sum of the individual forces exerted on it. Customarily, the Greek letter Σ is used to denote a summation, so that we represent the net force as $\Sigma \mathbf{F}$:

The net force $\Sigma \mathbf{F}$ is the vector sum of the individual forces.

$$\Sigma \mathbf{F} = \mathbf{F}_1 + \mathbf{F}_2 + \mathbf{F}_3 + \cdots$$

where $\mathbf{F}_1$, $\mathbf{F}_2$, and so on are the individual forces exerted on the object. A net force of zero is equivalent to no force at all. We include this in the statement of Newton's first law, so that the law becomes

Newton's first law

If the net force on an object is zero ($\Sigma \mathbf{F} = 0$), then the object's acceleration is zero ($\mathbf{a} = 0$).

At first glance, Newton's first law seems to violate common experience. We are inclined to go along with Newton when he tells us that an object at rest tends to remain at rest. But does an object moving at constant velocity tend to maintain that velocity? Suppose you push a grocery cart (exert a force on it)

---

* Isaac Newton, *Philosophiae Naturalis Principia Mathematica* (1686), Andrew Motte (trans., 1729), University of California Press, Berkeley, 1960.

Figure 5-4. An air track. Air is blown into the hollow triangular track and escapes through small holes. The escaping air suspends the glider on a cushion of air so that frictional forces on the glider as it moves along the track are negligible. *(Dave Riban)*

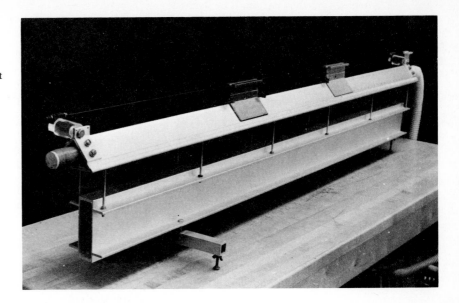

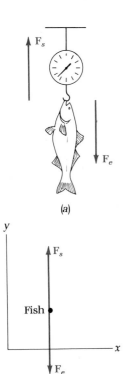

(a)

(b)

Figure 5-5. (a) A fish is suspended by a spring scale. The reading on the scale gives the magnitude F_s of the force exerted upward by the scale on the fish. (b) Free-body diagram for the fish. The fish is not accelerating so that, by Newton's first law, the net force on it is zero. Thus, the scale reads the magnitude of the fish's weight: $F_s = F_e$.

along a supermarket aisle at a constant velocity. If you release the cart (stop exerting the force), it slows down (accelerates) until it comes to rest. This seems to disagree with Newton's first law. That your experience with the cart does not contradict Newton's first law can be seen by recognizing the presence of a *frictional force* and by making a clear distinction between the *net force on the cart* and the *force you exert on it.* While you push the cart at constant velocity, the force you exert is not zero, but the net force is zero because the frictional force on the cart is equal and opposite the force you exert. In the next chapter we discuss frictional forces, and there you will see in detail how this works. When you release the cart, the net force on it is no longer zero because the frictional force continues to act on it, until it comes to rest. Your experience with the cart does not contradict Newton's first law, it is in accord with this law.

A skeptic might say that the frictional force was contrived to make these observations agree with Newton's first law. To see that this is not so, we can effectively eliminate the frictional force by performing experiments on an air track (Fig. 5-4). The glider on an air track rides on a cushion of air so that the frictional force on the glider as it moves along the track is due to air resistance only. Consequently, the frictional force is practically imperceptible, and, once the glider is set in motion, it moves along the air track with a velocity that is essentially constant.

A common application of Newton's first law is the weighing of an object. Figure 5-5a shows a fish suspended from a spring scale. In the figure, force vectors are used to represent the forces exerted on the fish. To indicate a particular force, we place a subscript on the symbol **F**, and the subscript refers to the object that exerts the force. The fish's weight F_e is the gravitational force exerted on it by the *earth* (directed downward) and F_s is the force exerted by the *scale* (directed upward).

Figure 5-5b is a *free-body diagram* for the fish. A free-body diagram is an aid we use for finding the net force on an object. In the free-body diagram we represent the fish as a dot, and place the tails of the force vectors at the dot. The fish is represented simply as a dot because we assume its extent is of no consequence, which means that we treat it as a particle. (Situations where this

Figure 5-6. Forces add vectorially. (a) A block suspended by spring scale a. (b) The same block suspended by spring scales b and c. (c) The effect of forces $\mathbf{F}_b$ and $\mathbf{F}_c$ acting together is the same as a single force which is their vector sum; $\mathbf{F}_a = \mathbf{F}_b + \mathbf{F}_c$.

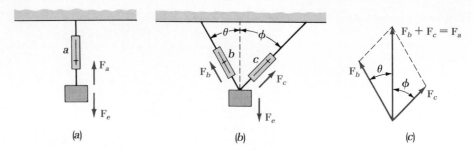

assumption is invalid will be discussed in Chaps. 11 through 13.) Using the coordinate frame in the free-body diagram, we find that the net force on the fish is

$$\Sigma\mathbf{F} = \mathbf{F}_s + \mathbf{F}_e = (F_s\mathbf{j}) + (-F_e\mathbf{j}) = (F_s - F_e)\mathbf{j}$$

Since the fish is not accelerating, Newton's first law states that the net force on it is zero. Thus $F_s = F_e$. That is, the scale reads the fish's weight. (Strictly speaking, the weight of an object has both magnitude *and* direction, because weight is a force. But since weight is directed downward always, the term "weight" often is taken loosely to mean the magnitude of the weight.)

We can use Newton's first law to verify experimentally that force is a vector. Suppose we hang a block from a spring scale and measure the force $\mathbf{F}_a$ exerted by the scale on the block (Fig. 5-6a). By Newton's first law, $\mathbf{F}_a$ is equal and opposite the block's weight. Next we suspend the block with two spring scales that make angles of θ and ϕ with the vertical and measure forces $\mathbf{F}_b$ and $\mathbf{F}_c$ (Fig. 5-6b). By Newton's first law, $\mathbf{F}_b$ and $\mathbf{F}_c$ combine to give a force that is equal and opposite the block's weight. Thus the effect of the combined forces $\mathbf{F}_b$ and $\mathbf{F}_c$ is the same as $\mathbf{F}_a$ acting alone. A vector diagram shows that the vector sum $\mathbf{F}_b + \mathbf{F}_c$ is equal to $\mathbf{F}_a$ (Fig. 5-6c). That is, the effect of both forces acting simultaneously is the same as their vector sum. The property that forces add as vectors

Principle of superposition

is sometimes called the *principle of superposition*.

You may be taken aback by our next discovery: *Newton's first law is not valid in all reference frames.* Let us apply the law to an object, say object *A*, using measurements made in different reference frames. For simplicity, suppose that object *A* is so far removed from other objects that each individual force exerted on it is effectively zero; consequently, $\Sigma\mathbf{F} = 0$. Now we measure object *A*'s acceleration relative to reference frame 1 and find that it is zero: $a_{A1} = 0$. Newton's first law states that if $\Sigma\mathbf{F} = 0$, then $\mathbf{a} = 0$, so that we conclude that the first law is valid in frame 1. Suppose reference frame 2 *accelerates* relative to frame 1. This means that object *A* must accelerate relative to frame 2: $a_{A2} \neq 0$. Since $\Sigma\mathbf{F} = 0$, Newton's first law is *not* valid in frame 2, or in any frame that accelerates relative to frame 1. Suppose frame 3 moves with *constant velocity* relative to frame 1. This means that object *A*'s acceleration relative to frame 3 is zero, $a_{A3} = 0$, and the first law is valid in frame 3. Indeed, the first law is valid in any frame that does not accelerate relative to frame 1.

Given that Newton's first law is not valid in some reference frames, one might question whether the law is useful. Actually, this very feature leads us to the utilization of this law. We now define a special type of reference frame,

Inertial reference frame

called an inertial reference frame. *An inertial reference frame is a frame in which Newton's first law is valid.* From the discussion above, we recognize that any frame that moves with constant velocity relative to an inertial reference frame is itself an inertial reference frame and that any frame that accelerates relative to an inertial reference frame is not an inertial reference frame.

A reference frame we ordinarily use for the motion of an object on or near the surface of the earth is a frame with axes that are fixed relative to the horizontal and vertical at a nearby point on the surface of the earth. We shall call such a frame an *earth frame* (Fig. 5-7). Is an earth frame an inertial reference frame? Experiments show that an earth frame is *not* inertial. As you know, the earth rotates on its axis once a day (Fig. 5-8) and revolves around the sun once a year. If we imagine looking at the earth from a reference frame that is fixed relative to the stars, then in this reference frame an earth frame moves in a circle about the earth's axis and the center of the earth orbits the sun. The centripetal acceleration about the axis is maximum for a point on the earth's surface at the equator, where $a_c = 0.034$ m/s^2, and the acceleration of the earth's center relative to the sun has a magnitude of 0.006 m/s^2. (See Exercise 4-29.) These accelerations are too small to be of significance in most terrestrial applications of the laws of motion.

It is generally assumed that an inertial reference frame is a frame with axes fixed relative to distant matter in the universe (for most purposes, fixed relative to the background of distant stars). Within the capabilities of present-day measuring techniques, this assumption is consistent with Newton's first law, and it appeals to our modern perception of the universe. Since an earth frame has a very small acceleration relative to such a frame, it is often valid to use an earth frame as an inertial reference frame.

Earth frame

Figure 5-7. An earth frame. The axes of an earth frame are fixed relative to the horizontal and vertical at a point on the earth's surface.

Figure 5-8. Time-lapse photograph of the night sky with the camera pointed toward Polaris, the North Star. As the earth rotates, the stars appear to travel in circles. *(Richard E. Hill)*

5-4 NEWTON'S SECOND LAW

Newton wrote the second law as

Law II. The change of motion is proportional to the motive force impressed; and is made in the direction of the right line in which that force is impressed.

Using modern terminology, Newton's second law states, *The acceleration of an object is proportional to the net force exerted on the object.* In equation form, this can be written as

Newton's second law

$$\Sigma \mathbf{F} = m\mathbf{a} \qquad (5\text{-}1)$$

where m is the mass of the object. The object's mass is the proportionality factor between the net force exerted on the object and the object's acceleration. For a given net force, an object with larger mass will have a smaller acceleration. Thus the mass of an object is that property of the object which causes it to resist any change in its velocity. Since inertia means resistance to a change, the mass is often referred to as the *inertial mass*.

From a comparison of Newton's first and second laws, one is tempted to view the first law as simply a particular case of the second law. Since $\Sigma \mathbf{F} = m\mathbf{a}$, it follows that $\mathbf{a} = 0$ when $\Sigma \mathbf{F} = 0$. However, we used the first law to define the type of reference frame relative to which the acceleration in Newton's second law must be measured, namely, an inertial reference frame. With this interpretation, the first law is a statement about nature that is independent of the second law. The first law states that inertial reference frames exist, and gives a procedure for determining whether a frame is inertial.

Definition of force

Newton's second law provides the definition of the concept of force: *A force is that which causes an object to accelerate. A single force acting alone on an object has the same direction as the acceleration, and the force magnitude is proportional to the acceleration magnitude.* Also, this law gives a connection between the unit of force on the one hand and the units of mass and acceleration on the other. The SI unit of force, the newton, is defined with Newton's second law:

Definition of the newton (N)

$$1 \text{ N} = 1 \text{ kg} \cdot \text{m/s}^2 \qquad (\text{exactly})$$

If an object of mass one kilogram has an acceleration of one meter/second squared relative to an inertial reference frame, then the net force exerted on the object is one newton.

EXAMPLE 5-3. At the time it was launched, the ill-fated *H.M.S. Titanic* was the most massive mobile object ever built by humans, having a mass of 6.0×10^7 kg. What would have been the magnitude of the net force required to give the *Titanic* an acceleration of magnitude of 0.1 m/s^2?

SOLUTION. Newton's second law in terms of magnitudes is $|\Sigma \mathbf{F}| = ma$. For the *Titanic* to have an acceleration magnitude of 0.1 m/s^2, the magnitude of the net force would have to have been

$$|\Sigma \mathbf{F}| = (6.0 \times 10^7 \text{ kg})(0.1 \text{ m/s}^2) = 6 \times 10^6 \text{ N} = 6 \text{ MN}$$

5-5 NEWTON'S THIRD LAW

A translation of Newton's third law is

Law III. To every action there is always opposed an equal reaction; or, the mutual actions of two bodies upon each other are always directed to contrary parts.

Figure 5-9. Newton's third law. Objects a and b exert forces on each other. By Newton's third law, these forces are equal and opposite: $\mathbf{F}_{ab} = -\mathbf{F}_{ba}$. In this figure the forces are shown as attractive forces: $\mathbf{F}_{ab}$ is toward a and $\mathbf{F}_{ba}$ is toward b.

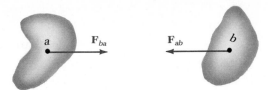

The first and second laws are statements about a single object, whereas the third law is a statement about two objects. To discuss the third law, we require two subscripts on the force symbol $\mathbf{F}$, the first subscript to denote the object that exerts the force and the second subscript to denote the object on which the force acts. Suppose objects a and b exert forces on each other (Fig. 5-9); $\mathbf{F}_{ab}$ is the force exerted by a on b, and $\mathbf{F}_{ba}$ is the force exerted by b on a. Newton's third law states that these two forces are equal and opposite, or

Newton's third law

$$\mathbf{F}_{ab} = -\mathbf{F}_{ba} \qquad (5\text{-}2)$$

Forces occur in pairs. A single force cannot exist.

When two objects exert forces on each other, we say that an *interaction* exists between the objects. Newton's third law gives the relation between the two forces that are the result of an interaction. The two forces $\mathbf{F}_{ab}$ and $\mathbf{F}_{ba}$ are often called an *action-reaction pair*. One of the forces is called the action force and the other is called the reaction force. Which force is called the action and which is called the reaction is arbitrary. Newton's third law reveals an underlying symmetry in the forces that occur in nature.

EXAMPLE 5-4. Suppose that your physics and history books are lying on your desk, with the history book on top of the physics book (Fig. 5-10). The history and physics books weigh 14 and 18 N, respectively. Identify each force on each book with a double subscript notation and determine the value of each of these forces.

SOLUTION. The free-body diagrams for the books are shown in Fig. 5-10. Since the weight of the history book is the force exerted by the *earth* on the *history* book, we represent it as $\mathbf{F}_{eh}$:

$$\mathbf{F}_{eh} = -(14 \text{ N})\mathbf{j}$$

Other than the earth, the history book interacts only with the physics book. Since the acceleration of the history book is zero, the net force on it is zero by Newton's second law:

$$\mathbf{F}_{ph} + \mathbf{F}_{eh} = 0$$

where $\mathbf{F}_{ph}$ is the force exerted by the *physics* book on the *history* book. Thus $\mathbf{F}_{ph} = -\mathbf{F}_{eh} = -[-(14 \text{ N})]\mathbf{j}$, or

$$\mathbf{F}_{ph} = (14 \text{ N})\mathbf{j}$$

We find that the physics book exerts an upward force of magnitude 14 N on the history book.

Figure 5-10. Example 5-4: (a) A history book and a physics book rest on a desk. (b) Free-body diagram for the history book. (c) Free-body diagram for the physics book.

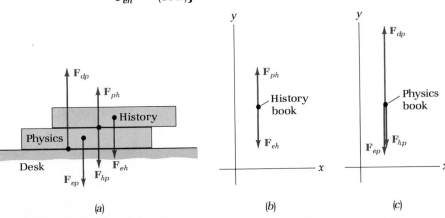

The physics book has three forces exerted on it: $\mathbf{F}_{ep}$ due to the earth, $\mathbf{F}_{hp}$ due to the *history* book, and $\mathbf{F}_{dp}$ due to the desktop. Since the physics book weighs 18 N,

$$\mathbf{F}_{ep} = -(18 \text{ N})\mathbf{j}$$

From Newton's third law, $\mathbf{F}_{hp} = -\mathbf{F}_{ph}$, so that

$$\mathbf{F}_{hp} = -(14 \text{ N})\mathbf{j}$$

Newton's second law applied to the physics book gives $\Sigma \mathbf{F} = 0$, or $\mathbf{F}_{dp} + \mathbf{F}_{ep} + \mathbf{F}_{hp} = 0$, or $\mathbf{F}_{dp} = -\mathbf{F}_{ep} - \mathbf{F}_{hp}$, so that

$$\mathbf{F}_{dp} = -[-(18 \text{ N})\mathbf{j}] - [-(14 \text{ N})\mathbf{j}] = (32 \text{ N})\mathbf{j}$$

The desk exerts an upward force of 32 N on the physics book. To arrive at the solution, we have applied Newton's second law twice and Newton's third law once.

A word of caution is in order. For the particular case in which two forces are exerted on an object with zero acceleration, Newton's second law appears deceptively similar to Newton's third law. For example, Newton's second law applied to the history book above gives $\mathbf{F}_{ph} + \mathbf{F}_{eh} = 0$, or $\mathbf{F}_{ph} = -\mathbf{F}_{eh}$; the forces are equal and opposite. The important thing to note about these two forces is that they are both applied to the *same* object, the history book. This is indicated by the fact that the second subscript on the force symbols is the same—h for *history* book. On the other hand, Newton's third law applied to the interaction between the physics book and the history book is written $\mathbf{F}_{hp} = -\mathbf{F}_{ph}$; these forces are also equal and opposite. The important thing to note about these two forces is that they are exerted on *different* objects, one on the physics book and one on the history book. This fact is indicated by the reversal of the subscripts on the force symbols. Newton's second law applies to a single object, whereas Newton's third law applies to an interaction between two objects. Note that the two forces in Newton's third law never occur in the same free-body diagram. This is because a free-body diagram shows forces acting on a single object, and the action-reaction pair in Newton's third law always act on different objects.

Now we combine Newton's second and third laws to provide a definition for the mass of an object. Suppose we have two objects, a and b, that exert forces on each other, $\mathbf{F}_{ab}$ and $\mathbf{F}_{ba}$. There may be other forces on these two objects besides $\mathbf{F}_{ab}$ and $\mathbf{F}_{ba}$, but we arrange to have the vector sum of these other forces add to zero so that the net force on object a is $\mathbf{F}_{ba}$ and the net force on object b is $\mathbf{F}_{ab}$. Newton's second law applied to each object gives

$$\mathbf{F}_{ba} = m_a \mathbf{a}_a \qquad \text{and} \qquad \mathbf{F}_{ab} = m_b \mathbf{a}_b$$

Inserting this result into Newton's third law, $\mathbf{F}_{ba} = -\mathbf{F}_{ab}$, we have

$$m_a \mathbf{a}_a = -m_b \mathbf{a}_b$$

Or, in terms of acceleration magnitudes,

$$m_a a_a = m_b a_b$$

Now we let object b be the standard kilogram (or a replica of it), and we let object a be the object whose mass m we wish to determine. Then $m_b = 1$ kg (exactly), $m_a = m$, and

Definition of mass

$$m = 1 \text{ kg} \frac{a_s}{a}$$

where a_s and a are the acceleration magnitudes of the standard kilogram and the object of mass m, respectively.

EXAMPLE 5-5. Carts *A* and *B*, each equipped with a spring bumper (Fig. 5-11a), are pushed together so that their spring bumpers are compressed. When the carts are released, the springs push the carts apart such that $a_A = 0.87$ m/s² and $a_B = 1.42$ m/s². Given that the mass of cart *B* is 1.0 kg, determine the mass of cart *A*. The mass of each cart's wheels is much less than that of its body, and the wheel bearings are well lubricated.

SOLUTION. Since the mass of each cart's wheels is much less than that of its body, the effects due to the rotation of the wheels can be neglected and each cart can be treated as a particle (see Chap. 13). Further, since the wheel bearings are well lubricated, frictional effects which tend to slow the

carts are negligible, so that the force exerted on each cart by the horizontal surface has no horizontal component. This means that each of these forces is vertically upward, as shown in the free-body diagrams in Fig. 5-11b. The vertical component of each cart's acceleration is zero, so that the force upward by the surface on each cart is equal and opposite the cart's weight. Thus the net force on each cart is the force exerted by the other cart, and, by Newton's third law, these forces are equal and opposite. This arrangement is a good approximation to the situation we described above in defining the mass of an object. The mass of cart *A* is

$$m_A = m_B \frac{a_B}{a_A} = 1.0 \text{ kg} \frac{1.42 \text{ m/s}^2}{0.87 \text{ m/s}^2} = 1.6 \text{ kg}$$

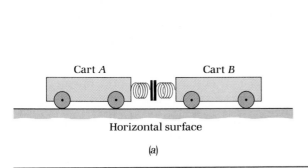

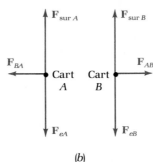

Figure 5-11. Example 5-5: (a) Carts *A* and *B*, each with a spring bumper, are pushed together and then released. (b) Free-body diagrams for the two carts immediately after they are released.

5-6 WEIGHT, THE GRAVITATIONAL FORCE BY THE EARTH

The weight $\mathbf{F}_e$ of an object is the gravitational force exerted by the earth on the object. We can develop an expression for this force by applying Newton's second law to an object in free-fall. For an object in free-fall, the frictional force due to air resistance is negligible, so that the only significant force on the object is the gravitational force by the earth. This situation can be realized experimentally by an object falling in an evacuated chamber. For such an object, the net force is

$$\Sigma \mathbf{F} = \mathbf{F}_e$$

From Chap. 3, the acceleration of any object in free-fall is $\mathbf{a} = \mathbf{g}$, with magnitude $g = 9.8$ m/s². Inserting these results into Newton's second law, $\Sigma \mathbf{F} = m\mathbf{a}$, we obtain

Weight of an object of mass *m*

$$\mathbf{F}_e = m\mathbf{g} \tag{5-3}$$

The weight of an object is proportional to its mass. For example, the mass of a typical adult human is 65 kg, so that $F_e = (65 \text{ kg})(9.8 \text{ m/s}^2) = 640$ N.

Equation (5-3) is an example of a *force law*. Actually, it is an application of a more general force law which we shall introduce in Chap. 7. This application is valid only for objects on or near the surface of the earth. Because the force is given by the product of the object's mass *m* and an acceleration **g**, Eq. (5-3) resembles Newton's second law. In spite of its appearance, Eq. (5-3) is *not* Newton's second law. It is an equation for one of perhaps several forces on an object. It often provides one term in the sum of the forces $\Sigma \mathbf{F}$ on an object when using Newton's second law. The distinction between a force law and Newton's second law will become more apparent as we introduce additional force laws.

It is customary to treat the weight of an object as an intrinsic property of the object, that is, as a property of that object alone. For example, we speak of a 20-lb pumpkin. (In SI units, it is a 90-N pumpkin.) However, the weight of an object is a force, and a force depends upon the object that exerts the force as well as upon the object on which the force acts. In the particular case of weight, the force is exerted by the earth. Therefore in principle it is invalid to treat the weight of an object as an intrinsic property of the object.

On the other hand, mass is an intrinsic property of an object; it is proper to speak of a 9-kg pumpkin. As a practical matter, we may treat the weight of an object as an intrinsic property of the object because $\mathbf{F}_e = m\mathbf{g}$ and $\mathbf{g}$ is the same for any object. However, g varies slightly with position on the earth so that the weight of an object varies in the same way as g does. As we shall see later, the variation is small, less than 1 percent over the earth's surface. A 9.00-kg pumpkin weighs $(9.00 \text{ kg})(9.80 \text{ m/s}^2) = 88.2$ N in Florida, and it weighs $(9.00 \text{ kg})(9.82 \text{ m/s}^2) = 88.4$ N in Alaska. Therefore, if we apply our measurements to a limited region on or near the surface of the earth, or if we do not require high precision, then we may treat the weight of an object as a property of that object alone.

EXAMPLE 5-6. *An accelerating elevator.* Consider a person standing on a spring scale in an elevator (Fig. 5-12a). Before the elevator begins to move, the scale reads 651 N, and, as the elevator accelerates upward, the scale reads 733 N. (This larger reading on the scale corresponds to the feeling of being pushed down when the elevator accelerates upward.) Determine (a) the person's mass, (b) the net force on the person as the elevator accelerates upward, and (c) the person's (and the elevator's) acceleration.

SOLUTION. (a) Before the elevator starts to move, the acceleration of the person relative to an earth frame is zero. We assume an earth frame is the same as an inertial frame, so that $\mathbf{a} = 0$ in Newton's second law. Thus $\Sigma \mathbf{F} = 0$. Consequently, the scale reading at that time gives the person's weight: $F_e = 651$ N. From Eq. (5-3),

$$m = \frac{F_e}{g} = \frac{651 \text{ N}}{9.8 \text{ m/s}^2} = 66 \text{ kg}$$

(b) As the elevator accelerates upward, the force $\mathbf{F}_s$ exerted by the scale is larger than the person's weight ($F_s = 733$ N). From the free-body diagram in Fig. 5-12b, the net force on the person is

$$\Sigma \mathbf{F} = F_s\mathbf{j} - F_e\mathbf{j} = (733 \text{ N})\mathbf{j} - (651 \text{ N})\mathbf{j} = (82 \text{ N})\mathbf{j}$$

(c) Solving Newton's second law for the acceleration gives

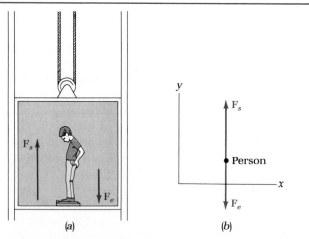

Figure 5-12. Example 5-6: (a) A person standing on a spring scale in an elevator. (b) Free-body diagram for the person as the elevator accelerates upward.

$$\mathbf{a} = \frac{\Sigma \mathbf{F}}{m} = \frac{(82 \text{ N})\mathbf{j}}{66 \text{ kg}} = (1.2 \text{ m/s}^2)\mathbf{j}$$

We find that an acceleration can be determined without measuring distances traveled and time intervals. Instead, we measure the stretch of a spring and use Newton's second law. When used in this way, the scale is an *accelerometer*, a device that measures an acceleration.

It is instructive to review the previous example using measurements made relative to a reference frame fixed to the elevator. In this elevator frame, the person's acceleration is zero whether the elevator is accelerating relative to an earth frame (assumed inertial) or not. While the elevator is accelerating relative to an earth frame, the net force on the person is not zero. Thus $\Sigma \mathbf{F} \neq 0$, and $\mathbf{a} = 0$ in the elevator frame. Newton's first law is not valid in the elevator frame while the elevator is accelerating relative to an earth frame. In agreement with our discussion in Sec. 5-3, the elevator frame is not an inertial frame.

Incidentally, when an object is placed on a scale, the scale reading is often called the *apparent weight* of the object. If the object (and the scale) remains at rest or moves with constant velocity relative to an inertial frame, then the apparent weight is equal to the weight. If the object (and the scale) accelerates relative to an inertial frame, then the apparent weight is not equal to the weight.

Apparent weight

5-7 SOLVING MECHANICS PROBLEMS

In the previous sections you have seen a few examples of mechanics problems. Now we list some procedures for solving such problems and then reinforce these procedures with more examples. Newton's second law, $\Sigma \mathbf{F} = m\mathbf{a}$, provides the fundamental principle for solving a problem. Since the second law is a vector relation, we can separate it into components:

$$\Sigma F_x = ma_x \qquad \Sigma F_y = ma_y \qquad \Sigma F_z = ma_z \qquad (5\text{-}4)$$

Newton's second law, component form

Each component provides an equation which may be used in a problem.

The procedures for solving a problem can be divided into three parts:

1 Draw a sketch of the system and identify the object (or objects) to which you will apply the second law. On your sketch, show force vectors that represent the forces on the object. Introduce a symbol for each quantity by using a notation that helps bring the quantity to mind. For example, if the mass of a block is given, write $m_b = 2.3$ kg, or if an angle is given, write $\theta = 25°$. These are *known quantities*. Also write a symbol for each *unknown quantity* that is to be found. If the problem asks for the acceleration of an object, write $\mathbf{a} = ?$, so that the unknown quantity is clearly stated at the outset.
2 Draw a free-body diagram (or diagrams) with coordinate axes on it. These axes should be oriented so that subsequent calculations will be simplified. Usually this is done by placing the axes along as many of the forces as possible, or by placing one axis along the acceleration, if its direction is known. This step requires judgment and there is no right way or wrong way of doing it, just one or two easy ways and many difficult ways. Good judgment comes with practice.
3 Using the free-body diagram, write the components of Newton's second law in terms of the known and unknown quantities. Solve these equations for each unknown quantity in terms of the known quantities. Finally, substitute the numerical values of the known quantities (including their units) and calculate each unknown quantity.

EXAMPLE 5-7. *Tension in a rope.* A bucket with mass $m = 8.4$ kg is suspended by two light ropes, a and b, as shown in Fig. 5-13a. By a "light" rope, we mean one with a mass that is small enough such that the weight of the rope is much less than the force it exerts. With this approximation, we may assume that the rope is straight. When a rope (or string or cable) is attached to an object, the magnitude of the force exerted by the rope is called the *tension* in the rope. Determine the tension in ropes a and b.

SOLUTION. The free-body diagram for the bucket is shown in Fig. 5-13b. The forces by the ropes on the bucket are represented as $\mathbf{F}_a$ and $\mathbf{F}_b$, and the angles they make with the horizontal are shown as θ and ϕ. Since the bucket remains at rest, its acceleration is zero. Thus Newton's second law gives $\Sigma F_x = 0$, or

$$-F_a \cos \theta + F_b \cos \phi = 0 \qquad \text{(A)}$$

and $\Sigma F_y = 0$, or

$$F_a \sin \theta + F_b \sin \phi - mg = 0 \qquad \text{(B)}$$

where F_a and F_b are the tensions in the ropes, and we have used $F_e = mg$. Equations (A) and (B) represent two equations in two unknowns; the unknowns are F_a and F_b. If we solve Eq. (A) for F_b,

$$F_b = \frac{F_a \cos \theta}{\cos \phi} \qquad \text{(C)}$$

and substitute this result into Eq. (B), then we obtain

$$F_a \sin \theta + \frac{F_a \cos \theta \sin \phi}{\cos \phi} - mg = 0$$

Now we have an equation which contains only one unknown. Solving for F_a gives

$$F_a = \frac{mg}{\sin \theta + \cos \theta \tan \phi} \qquad \text{(D)}$$

To obtain a similar expression for F_b, we insert F_a from Eq. (D) into Eq. (C), which gives

$$F_b = \frac{mg}{\sin \phi + \cos \phi \tan \theta} \qquad \text{(E)}$$

[Given Eq. (D), could you have predicted Eq. (E) from symmetry?] Inserting the numerical values of the known quantities, we find

$$F_a = \frac{(8.4 \text{ kg})(9.8 \text{ m/s}^2)}{\sin 27° + \cos 27° \tan 55°} = 48 \text{ N}$$

and

$$F_b = \frac{(8.4 \text{ kg})(9.8 \text{ m/s}^2)}{\sin 55° + \cos 55° \tan 27°} = 74 \text{ N}$$

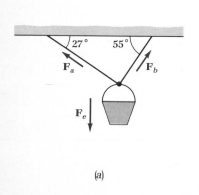

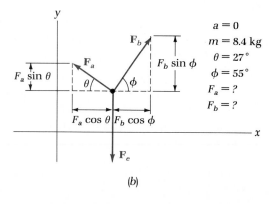

$a = 0$
$m = 8.4$ kg
$\theta = 27°$
$\phi = 55°$
$F_a = ?$
$F_b = ?$

Figure 5-13. Example 5-7: (a) A bucket suspended by two ropes. (b) Free-body diagram for the bucket.

(a)   (b)

EXAMPLE 5-8. A cart with small wheels and well-lubricated bearings is released from rest at $t = 0$ on a sloping surface, as shown in Fig. 5-14a. The cart's mass is $m = 1.3$ kg. (a) Determine the magnitude of the force exerted by the surface on the cart. (b) Determine the magnitude of the cart's acceleration. At $t = 1.5$ s, determine (c) the cart's speed and (d) the distance traveled.

SOLUTION. We neglect the effect of the rotation of the small wheels and treat the cart as a particle. Since the bearings are well lubricated, we neglect frictional forces that tend to slow the cart. That is, we assume that the force exerted on the cart by the surface does not have a component parallel to the surface. Therefore this force is normal to

the surface and represented as $\mathbf{F}_N$ in the cart's free-body diagram (Fig. 5-14b). We let the y axis be perpendicular to the surface because there is no motion in that direction. Thus $a_y = 0$ and the y component of the second law gives $\Sigma F_y = 0$, or

$$F_N - mg \cos \theta = 0 \qquad \text{(A)}$$

where we have used $F_e = mg$. The x component of the second law, $\Sigma F_x = ma_x$, gives

$$mg \sin \theta = ma \qquad \text{(B)}$$

where $a = |a_x| = a_x$ is the acceleration magnitude. (a) From Eq. (A), we have

$$F_N = mg \cos \theta = (1.3 \text{ kg})(9.8 \text{ m/s}^2) \cos 32° = 11 \text{ N}$$

(b) Solving Eq. (B) for a gives

$$a = g \sin \theta = (9.8 \text{ m/s}^2) \sin 32° = 5.2 \text{ m/s}^2$$

(c) Since the acceleration is constant and the cart started from rest, its speed at $t = 1.5$ s is

$$v = at = (5.2 \text{ m/s}^2)(1.5 \text{ s}) = 7.8 \text{ m/s}$$

(d) The distance traveled after 1.5 s is

$$d = \tfrac{1}{2}at^2 = \tfrac{1}{2}(5.2 \text{ m/s}^2)(1.5 \text{ s})^2 = 5.8 \text{ m}$$

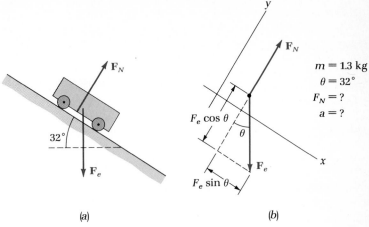

(a)

(b)

Figure 5-14. Example 5-8: (a) A cart on a sloping surface. (b) Free-body diagram for the cart.

EXAMPLE 5-9. A cart (mass $m_C = 1.8$ kg) with small wheels and well-lubricated bearings is connected to a block (mass $m_B = 0.50$ kg) by a string which passes over a pulley, as shown in Fig. 5-15a. Assume that the pulley rotates freely and that its mass is small enough such that the effect of its rotation is insignificant. That is, the pulley's only effect is to change the direction of the string. Consequently, the tension is the same throughout the string, and the magnitudes of the forces exerted by the string on the cart and on the block are both equal to the tension. Determine (a) the acceleration magnitude of the cart (and the block) and (b) the tension in the string.

SOLUTION. The free-body diagrams for the cart and for the block are shown in Fig. 5-15b and c, respectively. Because the cart and the block are connected by the string, they have the same acceleration magnitude a. The coordinate frames are oriented so that the acceleration of each object is in the $+x$ direction of its frame. The x component of the second law applied to the cart gives

$$F_T = m_C a \qquad \text{(A)}$$

where F_T is the tension in the string. For the block, the x component of the second law is

$$m_B g - F_T = m_B a \qquad \text{(B)}$$

Equations (A) and (B) are two equations in two unknowns; the unknowns are a and F_T. (a) If we add Eq. (A) to Eq. (B), F_T is eliminated and we obtain

$$m_B g = m_B a + m_C a$$

Solving for a gives

$$a = \frac{m_B}{m_C + m_B} g = \frac{0.50 \text{ kg}}{1.8 \text{ kg} + 0.50 \text{ kg}} \; 9.8 \text{ m/s}^2 = 2.1 \text{ m/s}^2$$

(b) Inserting the expression above for a into Eq. (A), we find

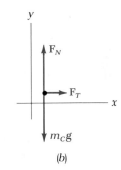

(a)

(b)

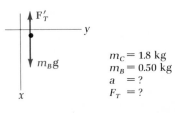

$m_C = 1.8$ kg
$m_B = 0.50$ kg
$a \;\; = ?$
$F_T \;\; = ?$

(c)

Figure 5-15. Example 5-9: (a) A cart being pulled along a horizontal surface by a string tied to a falling block. (b) Free-body diagram for the cart. (c) Free-body diagram for the block.

$$F_T = \frac{m_C m_B}{m_C + m_B} g = \frac{(1.8 \text{ kg})(0.50 \text{ kg})}{1.8 \text{ kg} + 0.50 \text{ kg}} \; 9.8 \text{ m/s}^2 = 3.8 \text{ N}$$

COMMENTARY: CLASSICAL MECHANICS AND DETERMINISM

Now that you have been introduced to Newton's laws of motion, let us stand back and view them in perspective.

1 *The first law defines an inertial reference frame, the reference frame for measuring **a** in the second law.*
2 *The second law, $\Sigma F = m\mathbf{a}$, connects the forces exerted on an object to the object's acceleration. The second law is often called the* equation of motion.
3 *The third law, $F_{ab} = -F_{ba}$, expresses the relation between the forces that two interacting objects exert on each other.*

Force laws

We apply Newton's second law to determine the motion of an object. To find the net force ΣF, we need some way to obtain the individual forces exerted on the object. We need force laws. A force law *is an expression or a rule for determining the force on an object in terms of properties of the object and its environment. Equation (5-3), which gives the weight of an object on or near the surface of the earth, is an example of a force law. Other force laws will follow. In the next chapter we give a force law for frictional forces; in Chap. 7 we develop the gravitational force law; in Chap. 20 we introduce the electric force law; and so on. The combination of the force laws with Newton's laws of motion is called* newtonian mechanics, *or* classical mechanics.

Definition of classical mechanics

The procedure for predicting the motion of any object is now clear. From properties of the object and its environment, we use the force laws to obtain the individual forces on the object, and we add the forces to find the net force. Then we determine the acceleration of the object with Newton's second law: $\mathbf{a} = \Sigma F/m$. If we also know the position and velocity of the object at some instant, we can use the methods of kinematics to calculate the velocity and position as functions of time. In principle, if all the forces are known, then the motion can be determined exactly.

Newton's laws of motion imply that an object's future conditions are completely determined by its present conditions, and its present conditions were completely determined by its past conditions. This may be said for every object in the universe. Newton's laws suggest that the evolution of events in the universe is an unfolding of conditions that were determined from some beginning. This idea has had a great influence on philosophy, religion, and the concept of free will. After Newton presented the laws of motion to the world, there arose a branch of philosophical thought called mechanistic determinism. *This view of the universe was summarized in the words of Pierre Simon de Laplace (1749–1827):*

> *If an intellect were to know, for a given instant, all the forces that animate nature and the conditions of all the objects that compose her, and were also capable of subjecting these data to analysis, then this intellect would encompass in a single formula the motions of the largest bodies in the universe as well as those of the smallest atom; and the future as well as the past would be present before its eyes.*

Indeed, classical mechanics is generally regarded as one of the most successful theories in all of science. Using this theory, engineers have placed astronauts on the moon and sent space probes to the outer reaches of the solar system. With split-second accuracy, astronomers can predict celestial events decades in advance. However, classical mechanics does have limitations. It is not applicable to small objects, those as small as atoms and smaller. Then we must use quantum

A sequence of photos of a total solar eclipse. Astronomers use classical mechanics to predict such events centuries into the future, or to tell us when they occurred in the distant past. *(Photo Researchers)*

mechanics (Chap. 39)* With quantum mechanics, we can no longer predict all mechanical quantities to any desired precision, not even in principle. The basis for mechanistic determinism evaporates.

Another limitation of classical mechanics occurs for an object traveling at a speed near the speed of light or an event near a massive body, such as a large, dense star. For such cases, we use Einstein's theory of relativity (Chap. 38).

During the 1970s, the 1980s, and to the present time, a new field of study has arisen which bears upon the concept of mechanistic determinism; it is called chaos. Chaos may become a new branch of science, somewhere between mathematics and physics. Its birth and growth have been accompanied by the expanding use of computers in science, and is largely a byproduct of the computer revolution. Chaos has shown us that a deterministic equation, such as Newton's second law, can produce nondeterministic results. Because it provides a new way to use Newton's laws to attack important problems, chaos is causing a renewed interest in classical mechanics at the cutting edge of physics research.

SUMMARY WITH APPLICATIONS

Section 5-2. Force and mass
Mass is a scalar quantity. An object's mass is proportional to its weight. Force is a push or a pull. It is a vector quantity that can be measured with a spring scale.

Qualitatively describe the concepts of force and mass.

Section 5-3. Newton's first law
Newton's first law states that if $\Sigma \mathbf{F} = 0$ for an object, then $\mathbf{a} = 0$. Newton's first law is used to define an inertial reference frame.

State and discuss Newton's first law; define an inertial reference frame; describe an earth frame.

Section 5-4. Newton's second law
The motion of an object is determined with Newton's second law,

$$\Sigma \mathbf{F} = m\mathbf{a} \qquad (5\text{-}1)$$

Force is defined as that which causes an object to accelerate.

State and discuss Newton's second law; define the concept of force.

* In some cases, quantum mechanics is also applied to macroscopic systems. In the "extended" edition of this text, quantum mechanics is dealt with more fully in Chaps. 40 through 43.

Section 5-5. Newton's third law

Newton's third law states that when two objects exert forces on each other, these forces are equal and opposite:

$$\mathbf{F}_{ab} = -\mathbf{F}_{ba} \tag{5-2}$$

If an object interacts with the standard kilogram, and the net force on the object and the standard kilogram is given by their interaction force only, then the mass m of the object is defined as

$$m = 1 \text{ kg} \frac{a_s}{a}$$

where a_s and a are the accelerations of the standard kilogram and the object, respectively.

State and discuss Newton's third law; define the concept of mass.

Section 5-6. Weight, the gravitational force by the earth

The weight $\mathbf{F}_e$ of an object is the gravitational force exerted by the earth on the object. For an object on or near the surface of the earth,

$$\mathbf{F}_e = m\mathbf{g} \tag{5-3}$$

Define weight and discuss its relation to mass.

Section 5-7. Solving mechanics problems

The procedures for solving a mechanics problem are (i) draw a sketch, (ii) draw a free-body diagram, and (iii) apply Newton's second law.

Use free-body diagrams and Newton's second law to solve mechanics problems.

QUESTIONS

5-1   As a corollary to the laws of motion, Newton stated:

> Corollary I. A body, acted on by two forces simultaneously, will describe the diagonal of a parallelogram in the same time it would describe the sides by those forces separately.

In modern terms, what property of force was Newton describing? Explain.

5-2   By continuously measuring the velocity of an object, can you tell whether the net force on the object is zero? Explain.

5-3   Is it possible for an object to follow a curved path when the net force on it is zero? Explain.

5-4   Suppose you are riding in a car at constant velocity when the driver suddenly slams on the brakes so that you are "pushed" forward. Was this "push" exerted on you by some other object? If so, identify the object. If no object exerted the push, then how do you account for your acceleration relative to the car?

5-5   Suppose you are riding on a steadily rotating merry-go-round and you place a skate on the floor such that it is aligned with its back end toward the center of the merry-go-round and its front end away from the center. When you release the skate from rest (relative to you), it accelerates forward, radially away from the merry-go-round's center. Is there a force on the skate that is directed radially outward? If so, identify the object that exerts this force. If not, explain why the skate accelerates.

5-6   A block of ice slides down a curved chute, as shown in Fig. 5-16, and then onto a horizontal floor. When the block exits the chute, will it continue its curved path or will it change to a straight path? Explain.

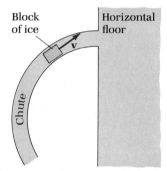

Figure 5-16. Ques. 5-6.

5-7   Suppose you drop objects a and b from a second-floor window. Each object is released from rest at the same instant, and $m_a > m_b$. Assume that at each instant of the time during the fall the force due to air resistance on object a is equal to that on object b. Which object reaches the ground first? Explain.

5-8   What object exerts the force that holds a compass needle in its north-south orientation?

5-9   When the driver of a car slams on the car's brakes, what object exerts the force that slows the car? Suppose this happened when the street is covered with ice?

5-10 Must the acceleration in Newton's second law be measured relative to any particular type of reference frame? If so, what type of reference frame must be used? Are there a limited number of these reference frames? Explain.

5-11 In the British system of units, mass is measured in sl (slugs), length in ft (feet), and force in lb (pounds), such that 1 lb = (1 sl)(1 ft/s²). What is your mass in sl?

5-12 A friend tells you that Newton's third law cannot be correct because it predicts that an object cannot be moved. The friend says: "Suppose I push on a cart. By Newton's third law the force exerted on me by the cart is equal and opposite the force I exert on the cart. Consequently, the net force is zero and the third law predicts that the cart cannot be moved." Explain what is wrong with this reasoning.

5-13 Two strings, *a* and *b*, can sustain the same maximum tension before breaking. But a force smaller than this maximum tension causes string *a* to stretch much more than *b*. If each string has one end tied to a rigid support and the other end is given a quick jerk, which string is more likely to break? Explain.

5-14 In a free-body diagram, why is it often convenient to orient the axes horizontally and vertically? In Example 5-8, why was it preferable to orient the axes parallel and perpendicular to the surface?

5-15 Suppose a friend argues that Newton's first law is not needed to define an inertial reference frame. The friend says that an inertial reference frame is simply a frame that is either at rest or is moving with constant velocity. Explain why this definition is inadequate.

5-16 Suppose that while standing on a rotating merry-go-round, you hold a rock suspended from the end of a string. Does the string hang vertically downward? Is the net force on the rock zero? Is your frame of reference an inertial frame?

5-17 Suppose that you drop a marble of mass *m* into a jar of honey. As the marble sinks, its speed is effectively constant. What is the net force on the marble as it sinks? What are the magnitude and direction of the force exerted by the honey on the marble?

5-18 If string *b* in Fig. 5-17 is pulled downward, while the force is gradually increased, string *a* eventually breaks. However, if string *b* is given a sharp jerk downward, string *b* is more likely to break. Explain.

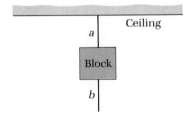

Figure 5-17. Ques. 5-18.

5-19 The force vectors in Fig. 5-18 each have the same magnitude. When exerted on an object, which combinations of these forces, if any, would result in a net force of zero on the object?

5-20 The strings and the spring scales in Fig. 5-19 have negligible weights, each block weighs 25 N, and the pulleys

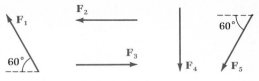

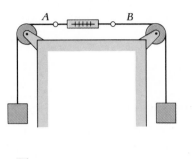

Figure 5-18. Ques. 5-19.

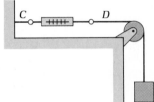

Figure 5-19. Ques. 5-20.

are essentially frictionless. What is the tension in each string? What is the reading on each spring scale?

5-21 A rope is stretched tightly between two trees, and a brick is hung by a short string from the middle of the rope. Is it possible to stretch the rope tightly enough so that the rope is straight?

5-22 A horse is pulling a cart toward town (toward the north) by exerting a horizontal force of magnitude *F*. What are the magnitude and direction of the force exerted by the cart on the horse?

5-23 Is there any directional relation between the net force on an object and the object's velocity? If so, what is this relation?

5-24 What are the magnitude and direction of the gravitational force you exert on the earth?

5-25 Suppose you are standing on a spring scale in an elevator. In which of the following situations is your apparent weight greatest and in which is it least? The elevator is (*a*) traveling upward with constant speed, (*b*) traveling downward with constant speed, (*c*) traveling upward with increasing speed, (*d*) traveling upward with decreasing speed.

5-26 If we were on another planet, we would regard the weight of an object as the gravitational force exerted by that planet on the object. Would you expect your weight to be different on another planet? Would you expect your mass to be different on another planet?

5-27 Write the dimension of mass $[M]$ in terms of force $[F]$, length $[L]$, and time $[T]$.

5-28 Ecologists are fond of the adage "You can never do just one thing." Discuss the connection between this axiom and Newton's third law. Which do you regard as the more fundamental statement, the adage above or Newton's third law? Explain.

5-29 Complete the following table:

Symbol	Represents	Type	SI Unit
ΣF		Vector	
F_{ab}			N
F_T	Tension in a rope		
F_e			
m			

EXERCISES

Section 5-2. Force and mass

5-1 The unit of mass in the British system is the slug (sl), and $1.000 \text{ sl} = 14.59$ kg. What is the mass of a 72-kg person in sl?

5-2 The density of water is about 1000 kg/m³. (a) The tonne (t) is a unit of mass defined to be equal to 1000 kg. What is the density of water in t/m³? (b) What is the density of water in units of g/cm³?

5-3 The ton is a unit of force defined to be equal to 2000 lb. (a) Convert a force of 1.6 tons to N. (b) Convert a force of 5.6 MN to tons.

5-4 The dyne (dyn) is the unit of force in the cgs (centimeter-gram-second) system of units, and is defined to be equal to 1×10^{-5} N. (a) Convert a force of 34 mN to dyn. (b) Convert a force of 630 dyn to N. (c) Estimate your weight in dyn.

Section 5-3. Newton's first law

5-5 Two forces, $\mathbf{F_1} = -(2.4 \text{ N})\mathbf{i} + (6.1 \text{ N})\mathbf{j}$ and $\mathbf{F_2} = (8.5 \text{ N})\mathbf{i} - (9.7 \text{ N})\mathbf{j}$, are exerted on an object. (a) What is the magnitude of each of these forces? (b) What is the angle between each of these forces and the x axis? (c) Draw a free-body diagram showing these forces. (d) Determine the magnitude and direction of the net force on the object.

5-6 Two forces, $\mathbf{F_1}$ and $\mathbf{F_2}$, act on an object. If $\mathbf{F_1} = -(6.1 \text{ N})\mathbf{i} + (5.6 \text{ N})\mathbf{j} - (4.7 \text{ N})\mathbf{k}$ and the net force on the object is $\Sigma \mathbf{F} = -(4.1 \text{ N})\mathbf{i} - (2.4 \text{ N})\mathbf{j} + (1.1 \text{ N})\mathbf{k}$, what is $\mathbf{F_2}$?

5-7 While sliding a large crate across a floor, Alvin and Bill exert horizontal forces $\mathbf{F_A}$ and $\mathbf{F_B}$ on it. Force $\mathbf{F_A}$ is toward the north with magnitude 130 N and $\mathbf{F_B}$ is 32° east of north with magnitude 180 N. What are the magnitude and direction of the single force that has the same effect as these two forces acting together?

5-8 In the free-body diagram shown in Fig. 5-20, $F_1 = 22$ N, $F_2 = 18$ N, and $F_3 = 16$ N. (a) Determine the components of each of these forces. (b) Determine each component, ΣF_x and ΣF_y, of the net force. (c) Determine the net force $\Sigma \mathbf{F}$ in terms of unit vectors. (d) Determine the magnitude and direction of the net force.

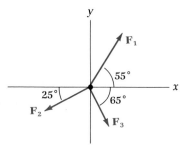

Figure 5-20. Exercise 5-8.

5-9 Shortly after jumping out of an airplane, a skydiver, whose weight is 720 N, reaches a velocity that is essen-

A skydiver. Jose A. Fernandez.
(Woodfin Camp & Associates)

tially constant. In this situation, there are two significant forces exerted on the skydiver. (a) What exerts each of these forces? (b) What are the magnitude and direction of each of these forces?

5-10 A box is pulled along a horizontal floor at constant velocity with a spring scale. There are three significant forces on the box: the force by the scale, which is 15 N and horizontal; the weight of the box, which is 25 N;

and the force exerted by the floor. Determine the magnitude and direction of the force exerted by the floor.

Section 5-4. Newton's second law

5-11 An 830-kg car starts from rest and reaches a speed of 22 m/s after 10 s. Assuming that this acceleration is uniform, determine the magnitude of the net force on the car.

5-12 A cathode-ray tube (such as a TV tube) contains an element, called an electron gun, which emits a beam of electrons. Suppose that in an electron gun an electron is accelerated from rest to a speed of 2×10^7 m/s over a distance of 10 mm. Estimate the net force on an electron in this electron gun. [*Hint:* Use Eq. (3-12) to determine an electron's acceleration. The mass of the electron is given on the inside front cover.]

5-13 The nucleus of an atom is very small, about 10^{-14} m across. Suppose that in a nuclear reaction a neutron with a speed of 1×10^7 m/s impinges upon a nucleus and comes to rest inside it. (a) Estimate the net force on the neutron during the reaction. [*Hint:* Use Eq. (3-12) to find the acceleration of the neutron. The mass of the neutron is given on the inside front cover.] (b) Estimate the time interval of the reaction.

5-14 When a tennis ball is served, the ball accelerates from rest (nearly) to a speed of about 50 m/s. The mass of a tennis ball is about 0.06 kg. Estimate the force exerted by the racket on the ball, assuming that the acceleration is uniform over a distance of 1 m. [*Hint:* Use Eq. (3-12) to find the ball's acceleration.]

5-15 Estimate the force exerted on a softball ($m = 0.3$ kg) by the pitcher during a typical pitch.

5-16 Let us make the (unfounded) assumption that the only force on the Milky Way galaxy is the gravitational force by the Andromeda galaxy. Given that the mass of the Milky Way galaxy is 7×10^{41} kg, determine the magnitude of the Milky Way's acceleration. (See Table 5-1.) What is a reference frame in which this acceleration would be measured?

5-17 A baseball bat strikes a 0.15-kg baseball such that it reverses the ball's velocity from 48 m/s horizontal and eastward to 81 m/s horizontal and westward in a time interval of 0.01 s. Estimate the force by the bat on the ball, assuming the force is uniform and neglecting all other forces on the ball.

5-18 Estimate the force exerted on a bullet by the expanding gases in a rifle barrel during a shot. The barrel is 0.5 m long, the bullet exits the barrel at a speed of 400 m/s, and the mass of the bullet is 2 g. Assume that the force is constant during the shot and neglect all other forces on the bullet.

Section 5-5. Newton's third law

5-19 Using Table 5-1, determine the magnitude of (a) the

gravitational force exerted by the Milky Way galaxy on the Andromeda galaxy and (b) the gravitational force exerted by the earth on the sun.

5-20 A 2200-kg truck collides with a 550-kg sports car, and during the collision the net force on each vehicle is essentially the force exerted by the other. If the magnitude of the truck's acceleration is 10 m/s², what is the magnitude of the sports car's acceleration?

5-21 Carts 1 and 2, each with mass 1.0 kg, are equipped with spring bumpers similar to the carts in Fig. 5-11 (Example 5-5). A block of unknown mass m is fastened to cart 1 and the carts are pushed together, compressing their spring bumpers, and released. The acceleration magnitudes of the carts are $a_1 = 0.51$ m/s² and $a_2 = 1.14$ m/s². The carts have small wheels and well-lubricated bearings. Determine m. State any assumptions that you make.

5-22 A chemistry book whose weight is 13 N is placed on top of the history book in Fig. 5-10 (Example 5-4) making it a stack of three, not two. Identify each force on each book with an appropriate double-subscript notation and determine the magnitude and direction of each of these forces. How many times do you apply Newton's third law and how many times do you apply Newton's second law in finding these forces?

5-23 (a) Two carts, 1 and 2, are being pushed along by an externally applied force $\mathbf{F}_{a1}$, which is exerted on cart 1, as shown in Fig. 5-21a. Treat each cart as a particle and neglect the frictional forces which tend to slow each cart. Given that $F_{a1} = 12$ N, $m_1 = 4.0$ kg, and $m_2 = 2.0$ kg, determine the magnitude and direction of each of the interaction forces $\mathbf{F}_{12}$ and $\mathbf{F}_{21}$. (b) Now suppose force $\mathbf{F}_{a1}$ is taken away and an externally applied force $\mathbf{F}_{a2}$ is exerted on cart 2, as shown in Fig. 5-21b, where

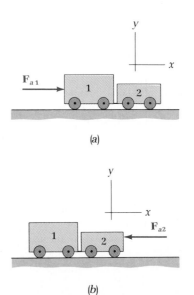

(a)

(b)

Figure 5-21. Exercise 5-23.

$F_{a2} = 12$ N. Determine the magnitude and direction of each of the interaction forces in this case. (c) Explain why the magnitude of the interaction forces is different in the two cases.

Section 5-6. Weight, the gravitational force by the earth

5-24 If we were on another planet, such as Mars, we would define the weight of an object as the gravitational force by that planet on the object. On Mars, the acceleration of an object in free-fall is 3.8 m/s². What is the weight of a 68-kg person on Mars?

5-25 While on the surface of the planet Illocorb, a space traveler stands on a spring scale and the scale reads 950 N. If the space traveler's mass is 71 kg, what is the acceleration of an object in free-fall on Illocorb?

5-26 A person whose mass is 58 kg stands on a spring scale in an elevator. What are the magnitude and direction of the elevator's acceleration at an instant when the scale reads (a) 570 N; (b) 420 N; (c) 710 N?

5-27 (a) Determine the weight of an electron. (The mass of the electron is given on the inside front cover.) (b) Compare your answer with the net force on an electron in the electron gun of the cathode-ray tube described in Exercise 5-12.

5-28 (a) Determine the weight of a neutron. (The mass of the neutron is given on the inside front cover.) (b) Compare your answer with the net force on a neutron as it is absorbed by the nucleus in the reaction described in Exercise 5-13.

5-29 A 77-kg person is standing on a spring scale in an elevator. What is the person's apparent weight while the elevator is (a) accelerating upward at 2.8 m/s², (b) accelerating downward at 3.1 m/s², (c) traveling upward at a constant speed of 4.4 m/s?

Section 5-7. Solving mechanics problems

5-30 A 52-kg skier slides down a straight slope that makes an angle of 24° with the horizontal. (a) Neglecting frictional forces, determine the skier's acceleration magnitude. (b) What is the skier's speed 1.0 s after starting from rest? (c) How far did the skier travel in 1.0 s?

5-31 A 24-kg box resting on the floor has a rope secured to its top. The maximum tension the rope can withstand without breaking is 310 N. What is the minimum amount of time in which the box can be lifted a vertical distance of 4.6 m by pulling on the rope?

5-32 Determine the tension in the supporting cable of a 1500-kg elevator while the elevator is accelerating (a) upward at 2.1 m/s² and (b) downward at 2.1 m/s². Neglect forces other than the cable tension and the weight of the elevator.

5-33 A 32-kg sled is being pulled along a horizontal icy surface by a rope, as shown in Fig. 5-22. The constant tension in the rope is 140 N and frictional forces are negligible. (a) Draw a free-body diagram for the sled. (b) What are the magnitude and direction of the force exerted by the surface on the sled? (c) What is the sled's acceleration magnitude? (d) If it starts from rest, how far does the sled travel in 1.3 s?

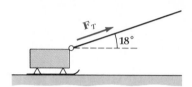

Figure 5-22. Exercise 5-33.

5-34 A 1430-kg car accelerates in the same direction as its velocity along a straight horizontal road, and $a = 1.95$ m/s². (a) What is the magnitude of the net force on the car? (b) Suppose air friction exerts a force of 513 N on the car, directed opposite the velocity. Determine the horizontal and vertical components of the force by the road on the car.

5-35 The cart in Fig. 5-23 has a mass of 2.4 kg and remains at rest. The cart's axles are well lubricated so that the force exerted on it by the surface has a negligible component parallel to the surface. (a) Determine the magnitude of the force by the surface. (b) Determine the tension in the string.

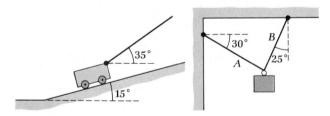

Figure 5-23. Exercise 5-35.   **Figure 5-24.** Exercise 5-36.

5-36 The mass of the suspended block in Fig. 5-24 is 45 kg. Determine the tension in each rope.

5-37 Sphere A is suspended from a light string and sphere B is attached to a thin rod (Fig. 5-25). Each sphere is given

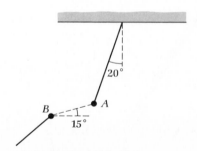

Figure 5-25. Exercise 5-37.

an electric charge that causes them to attract each other. That is, the force by B on A is directly toward B. If sphere B is held near A, such that the spheres are positioned as shown in the figure, then A remains at rest. The mass of sphere A is 0.62 g. Determine (a) the magnitude of the electrical force exerted by the spheres on each other and (b) the tension in the string.

5-38 The cart-block system shown in Fig. 5-15 (Example 5-9) is released from rest with block B 1.2 m above the floor. How long will it take for the block to hit the floor?

5-39 A bird with mass $m = 26$ g perches at the middle of a stretched string (Fig. 5-26). (a) Show that the tension in

the string is given by $F_T = mg/(2 \sin \theta)$. Determine the tension when (b) $\theta = 5°$ and (c) $\theta = 0.5°$. Assume that each half of the string is straight.

5-40 A girl pushes a 31-kg box sled at constant speed up a straight snowy slope by exerting a horizontal force on the sled, as shown in Fig. 5-27. Neglect the frictional force by the surface on the sled by assuming that the force exerted by the surface on the sled has no component parallel to the surface. Determine the magnitude of the force exerted (a) by the girl and (b) by the surface.

Figure 5-27. Exercise 5-40.

Figure 5-26. Exercise 5-39.

PROBLEMS

5-1 When the moon is directly overhead at sunset, the force $\mathbf{F}_{em}$ by the earth on the moon is essentially at 90° to the force $\mathbf{F}_{sm}$ by the sun on the moon, as shown in Fig. 5-28. Given that $F_{em} = 1.98 \times 10^{20}$ N, $F_{sm} = 4.36 \times 10^{20}$ N, all other forces on the moon are negligible, and the mass of the moon is 7.35×10^{22} kg, determine the magnitude of the moon's acceleration. Is this the acceleration of the moon relative to the earth? If not, then relative to what reference frame is this acceleration measured?

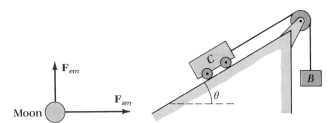

Figure 5-28. Prob. 5-1. **Figure 5-29.** Prob. 5-2.

5-2 In the cart-block system in Fig. 5-29, the cart has mass m_C and the block has mass m_B. Determine an expression for (a) the acceleration magnitude a of the cart, (b) the tension F_T in the string, (c) the force $\mathbf{F}_N$ exerted by the surface on the cart. State the assumptions you must make to work the problem. (d) Evaluate $a, F_T,$ and F_N when $\theta = 30°, m_C = 4.0$ kg, and $m_B = 2.5$ kg. (e) Repeat part (d) except with $m_B = 2.0$ kg. (f) Repeat part (d) except with $m_B = 1.5$ kg.

5-3 **A hot-air balloon.** The force which keeps a lighter-than-air aircraft, such as a hot-air balloon or a dirigible, aloft is called a *buoyant force* $\mathbf{F}_B$. This force is related to

the displacement of air by the lighter-than-air aircraft. Suppose a hot-air balloon of mass M has a downward acceleration of magnitude a. (a) Show that the mass m

A hot-air balloon.

of ballast that must be dropped overboard to cause the balloon to accelerate upward with magnitude a is $m = 2Ma/(g + a)$. What assumptions must you make to work the problem? (b) Evaluate m for the case where $M = 400$ kg and $a = 0.2$ m/s².

5-4   A 12-kg monkey climbs a light rope, as shown in Fig. 5-30. The rope passes over a pulley and is attached to a 16-kg bunch of bananas. Mass and friction in the pulley are negligible so that the pulley's only effect is to reverse the direction of the rope. What is the maximum acceleration the monkey can have without lifting the bananas?

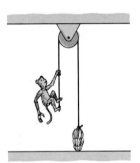

Figure 5-30. Prob. 5-4.

5-5   **Atwood's machine.** Atwood's machine, shown in Fig. 5-31, can be used to measure g. If the two blocks have nearly the same mass, then the acceleration of the system is small and g can be determined without the need to measure short time intervals. Assume that mass and friction in the pulley are negligible (so that the pulley's only effect is to reverse the direction of the light string). Show that g can be determined from the expression

$$g = \frac{a(m_2 + m_1)}{m_2 - m_1}$$

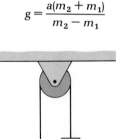

Figure 5-31. Prob. 5-5: Atwood's machine.

In this expression, a is the acceleration magnitude of the blocks, and we have let the mass m_2 of block 2 be greater than the mass m_1 of block 1. (b) Suppose you are sent to the planet Norc to measure the magnitude g of the acceleration of free-fall on its surface. Using Atwood's machine with $m_2 = 4.85$ kg and $m_1 = 4.65$ kg,

you release the blocks from rest and find that they move a distance of 0.50 m in 2.5 s. What is g on Norc?

5-6   A boy of mass m places one foot in a loop at the end of a light rope that passes over a pulley, and pulls himself upward at constant speed by pulling on the other end of the rope (Fig. 5-32). Neglecting mass and friction in the pulley and the mass of the rope, determine the force exerted on the rope by (a) the boy's hands and (b) the boy's foot.

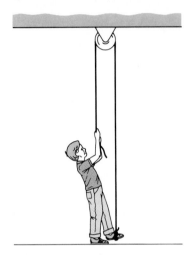

Figure 5-32. Prob. 5-6.

5-7   Three air-track gliders, connected together by strings, are being pulled along a track by a horizontally applied force **F** such that the acceleration magnitude of the system is 2.0 m/s² (Fig. 5-33). Neglecting friction, determine the tension in each string. The masses of the gliders are $m_a = 2.0$ kg, $m_b = 1.0$ kg, and $m_c = 2.0$ kg.

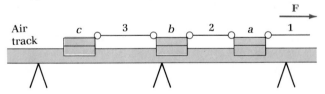

Figure 5-33. Prob. 5-7.

5-8   Determine an expression for the acceleration of block B in Fig. 5-34 in terms of m_C, m_B, and g. Assume that the cart's wheels are small and have well-lubricated bearings. Neglect mass and friction in the pulleys and neglect the mass of the rope.

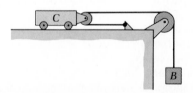

Figure 5-34. Prob. 5-8.

5-9 The wedge-shaped block in Fig. 5-35 has an accelera-tion to the right such that the cart does not roll up or down its sloping face. The cart's wheels are small and its bearings are well lubricated. (a) Show that $a = g \tan \theta$. (b) What happens if $a > g \tan \theta$?

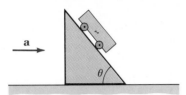

Figure 5-35. Prob. 5-9.

5-10 In football, a 130-kg offensive lineman is blocking a 110-kg defensive linebacker. The acceleration of both players is 0.11 m/s² horizontally toward the north, in the direction the lineman is pushing. The horizontal component of the force exerted by the lineman on the ground is 1335 N. Determine the magnitude and direc-tion of the following forces: (a) by the lineman on the linebacker, (b) by the linebacker on the lineman, (c) by the linebacker on the ground, (d) by the ground on the linebacker.

5-11 A 54-kg girl on ice skates on a frozen lake pulls with a constant force on a light rope that is tied to a 41-kg sled. The sled is initially 22 m from the girl, and both the sled and the girl start from rest. Neglecting friction, deter-mine the distance the girl travels to the point where she meets the sled.

5-12 (a) Show that the tension in the rope in Atwood's ma-chine (Fig. 5-31) is

$$F_T = \frac{2m_1 m_2 g}{m_1 + m_2}$$

(b) For the case where $m_2 > m_1$, show that $m_1 g < F_T < m_2 g$.

CHAPTER 6
APPLICATIONS OF
NEWTON'S LAWS
OF MOTION

6-1 INTRODUCTION

Newton's second law is the equation of motion. If we have some way to determine the forces on an object, then, given the object's initial position and velocity, we can apply the second law and determine its subsequent motion. In some cases we reverse this procedure. That is, from measurements of an object's motion, we determine the forces exerted on it. In this chapter we use this method to investigate the nature of contact forces. We also consider the dynamics of uniform circular motion. Finally we discuss how motion is often described by an observer in a noninertial frame.

6-2 CONTACT FORCES: THE NORMAL FORCE
AND THE FRICTIONAL FORCE

Contact forces are so pervasive in our lives that an understanding of their behavior is useful to any person, whether the person is a scientist or an engineer or a worker of almost any kind. One obvious effect of contact forces is to prevent objects from interpenetrating. The fundamental interaction that is responsible for these forces is the electromagnetic force between atoms and molecules, which operates at the level of their constituents, electrons and nuclei. At this microscopic level, contact forces involve many particles and are very complex and incompletely understood. Fortunately, the macroscopic behavior of these forces is much simpler, and we consider contact forces only at this level.

There is a particularly convenient way to describe contact forces between the flat surfaces of two solid objects. The method involves resolving a contact force into two forces, one parallel to the surface of contact and the other perpendicular, and then treating each of these as a separate force. The force

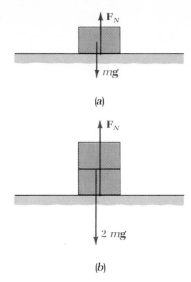

Figure 6-1. (a) A block of mass m at rest on a surface. The normal force $\mathbf{F}_N$ is exerted by the surface on the block: $F_N = mg$. (b) When another block of mass m is placed on top of the first block, the normal force doubles: $F_N = 2\,mg$.

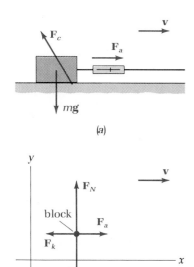

Figure 6-2. (a) A block of mass m being pulled at constant velocity to the right. (b) Free-body diagram for the block. The contact force is represented as two forces, the normal force $\mathbf{F}_N$ perpendicular to the surface and the kinetic frictional force $\mathbf{F}_k$ parallel to the surface and opposite $\mathbf{v}$.

Contact forces are the way we keep in touch with our environment. *(Randy Matusow)*

parallel to the surface is called the *frictional force* and the force perpendicular to the surface is called the *normal force.*

The normal force. Suppose a block of mass m is at rest on a horizontal surface, with only its weight and the contact force by the surface exerted on it, as shown in Fig. 6-1a. The force by the surface supports the block, holding it at rest. Since the block's acceleration is zero, the net force on it is zero, which means that the contact force is equal and opposite the block's weight. This contact force is the *normal force* $\mathbf{F}_N$, because it is directed perpendicular, or normal, to the surface. For the case shown in Fig. 6-1a, $F_N = mg$. Now suppose we place another block of mass m on top of our original block forming a composite block of mass $2m$ (Fig. 6-1b). The weight is now doubled, and, to support the composite block, the normal force also doubles: $F_N = 2mg$. That is, the normal force adjusts itself to keep the block from accelerating perpendicular to the surface.

The kinetic frictional force. In Fig. 6-2a we show a block of mass m being pulled at constant velocity by a spring scale along a horizontal surface. There are three forces on the block: $\mathbf{F}_a$, the applied force by the scale; $\mathbf{F}_e = m\mathbf{g}$, the block's weight; and $\mathbf{F}_c$, the contact force by the surface. In the block's free-body diagram (Fig. 6-2b), the contact force is represented by two forces: $\mathbf{F}_k$, the frictional force (parallel to the surface and opposite the velocity), and $\mathbf{F}_N$, the normal force (perpendicular to the surface). The subscript on $\mathbf{F}_k$ stands for "kinetic," and $\mathbf{F}_k$ is called the *kinetic frictional force.* ("Kinetic" is a Greek term which means motion, and the subscript k refers to the motion between the two surfaces.) Since the block's acceleration is zero, Newton's second law applied to the block gives $\Sigma F_x = 0$ and $\Sigma F_y = 0$. Therefore, $F_k = F_a$ and $F_N = mg$, so that the scale reading gives the value of F_k, and F_N equals the block's weight.

To investigate the relation between the normal force and the kinetic frictional force, we fasten another block of mass m on top of the sliding block and determine the forces on the composite block of mass $2m$. The normal force exerted by the surface is now double its previous value, $F_N = 2mg$. From the reading on the spring scale, we find that the applied force required to slide the block at constant velocity also doubles, as does F_k, since $F_k = F_a$. Experiments such as this show that, to a good approximation, F_k is proportional to F_N, or

Kinetic frictional force

$$F_k = \mu_k F_N \qquad (6\text{-}1)$$

where the proportionality constant μ_k is a dimensionless number and is called the *coefficient of kinetic friction*. Notice that Eq. (6-1) connects only the magnitudes of $\mathbf{F}_k$ and $\mathbf{F}_N$. These forces have perpendicular directions and $\mathbf{F}_k$ is opposite $\mathbf{v}$.

Further experiments show that

Table 6-1. A few representative values of coefficients of friction

Surface	μ_k	μ_s
Copper on steel	0.36	0.53
Copper on cast iron	0.29	1.05
Rubber on concrete	0.8	0.9
Wood on leather	0.4	0.5
Steel on ice	0.06	0.10

1 F_k depends on the nature and condition of the two surfaces, and μ_k usually falls in the range from about 0.1 to about 1.5. (See Table 6-1.)
2 F_k (or μ_k) is nearly independent of speed for low relative speeds of the surfaces, decreasing slightly as the speed increases. We shall use the approximation that F_k is independent of the speed.
3 F_k (or μ_k) is nearly independent of the area of contact for a wide range of areas.

The near independence of μ_k on the area of contact can be demonstrated by sliding a block that has sides with different areas (Fig. 6-3). The surface of each side should consist of the same type of material and should be in the same condition. When the applied force required to slide the block at a given speed on different sides is measured, it is found to be nearly the same. Since F_N is the same in each case, we conclude that μ_k is approximately independent of the area.

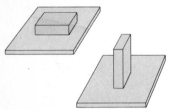

Figure 6-3. A block on a horizontal surface. Upon sliding the block, the frictional force is found to be nearly independent of whether it slides on a face with large area or a face with small area. This demonstrates that, with F_N the same, F_k is nearly the same.

A close look at the surface of an object gives an indication of why our description of frictional forces is imprecise. Figure 6-4 shows a photograph, taken with the aid of a scanning electron microscope, of a highly polished surface.

The famous Italian artist, Leonardo da Vinci (1452–1519), was also a scientist, mathematician, engineer, and architect. He studied frictional forces and understood many of their properties. *(Photo Researchers)*

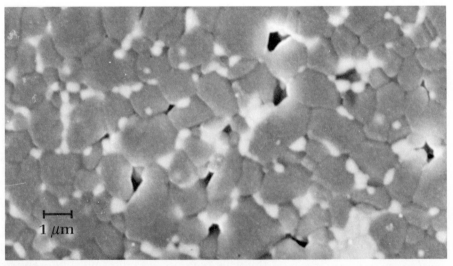

Figure 6-4. Scanning-electron-microscope photograph of a highly polished metal surface. A distance of 1 μm is indicated in the figure. *(Joan Hudson)*

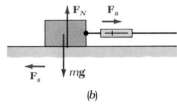

Figure 6-5. (a) through (c) The applied force is gradually increased, and in response the static frictional force $\mathbf{F}_s$ gradually increases. (d) Just before sliding begins $F_s = F_{s,\text{max}} = \mu_s F_N$.

(a)

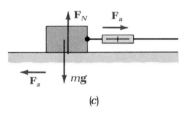

The static frictional force. A frictional force can also exist between two objects when there is no relative motion. Such a force is called a *static frictional force* $\mathbf{F}_s$. In Fig. 6-5a through d, the applied force by the spring scale on the block is gradually increased, but the block remains at rest. Since the acceleration is zero in each case, the applied force $\mathbf{F}_a$ by the scale is equal and opposite the static frictional force $\mathbf{F}_s$ by the surface. The maximum static frictional force $F_{s,\text{max}}$ occurs just as the block is about to slide. Experiment shows that, to a good approximation, $F_{s,\text{max}}$ is proportional to F_N, or

(b)

$$F_{s,\text{max}} = \mu_s F_N \qquad (6\text{-}2)$$

where the proportionality constant μ_s is called the *coefficient of static friction*. Therefore, up to a limit, the static frictional force adjusts to keep one surface from sliding across the other:

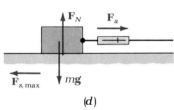

$$F_s \leq \mu_s F_N \qquad (6\text{-}3)$$

Similar to μ_k, the coefficient μ_s depends on the condition and nature of the two surfaces and is nearly independent of the area of contact. Table 6-1 lists μ_k and μ_s for a few representative pairs of surfaces. Normally, for a given pair of surfaces, μ_s is noticeably larger than μ_k.

(c)

A way to reduce frictional effects while transporting a load is to use a wheeled vehicle. Ordinarily, it is much easier to move something in a cart than it is in a sledge because the sliding surfaces are at the wheel bearings and can be lubricated. The frictional forces which tend to slow a wheeled vehicle can be treated as kinetic friction—namely, by introducing a coefficient of *rolling friction*.

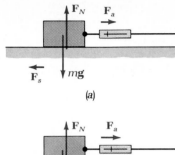

(d)

EXAMPLE 6-1. A spring scale is used to exert a horizontal force on a block, as in Figs. 6-2 and 6-5. The block is initially at rest. Let the coefficients of friction be $\mu_s = 0.80$ and $\mu_k = 0.60$ and let the mass of the block be $m = 0.51$ kg. On the same graph, plot F_s and F_k (as appropriate) versus F_a as F_a is increased from 0.0 to 7.0 N in increments of 1.0 N. Sketch a line through the points for F_s versus F_a and F_k versus F_a. Determine the block's approximate acceleration for each value of F_a.

SOLUTION. The surface is horizontal so that $F_N = mg = (0.51 \text{ kg})(9.8 \text{ m/s}^2) = 5.0$ N. Therefore, $F_{s,\text{max}} = \mu_s F_N = (0.80)(5.0 \text{ N}) = 4.0$ N. At each value of F_a up to this limit, $F_s = F_a$, as shown in the graph in Fig. 6-6, and for each of these values both the velocity and the acceleration of the block are zero.

For the values of F_a greater than 4.0 N, the block slides on the surface and $F_k = \mu_k F_N = (0.60)(5.0 \text{ N}) = 3.0$ N. Since $F_a > F_k$, there is a net horizontal force of magnitude $F_a - F_k$. In the case where $F_a = 5.0$ N, the acceleration magnitude is

$$a = \frac{F_a - F_k}{m} = \frac{5.0 \text{ N} - 3.0 \text{ N}}{0.51 \text{ kg}} \approx 4 \text{ m/s}^2$$

Similarly, when $F_a = 6.0$ N,

$$a = \frac{6.0 \text{ N} - 3.0 \text{ N}}{0.51 \text{ kg}} \approx 6 \text{ m/s}^2$$

and when $F_a = 7.0$ N

$$a = \frac{7.0 \text{ N} - 3.0 \text{ N}}{0.51 \text{ kg}} \approx 8 \text{ m/s}^2$$

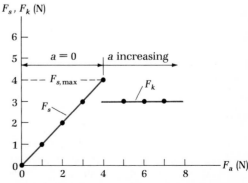

Figure 6-6. Example 6-1: Graph of F_s and F_k versus F_a for a 0.51-kg block on a horizontal surface where $\mu_s = 0.80$ and $\mu_k = 0.60$.

EXAMPLE 6-2. A girl pushes a sled along a snowy horizontal road. When the sled's speed is $v = 2.5$ m/s (Fig. 6-7a), the girl releases it and it slides a distance $d = 6.4$ m before coming to rest. Determine μ_k between the sled runners and the snowy surface.

SOLUTION. The free-body diagram for the sled, after being released by the girl, is shown in Fig. 6-7b. Since the sled has no vertical acceleration, $\Sigma F_y = 0$ so that $F_N = mg$, where m is the sled's mass. From the free-body diagram, $\Sigma F_x = -F_k$. Using Eq. (6-1), we find $F_k = \mu_k F_N = \mu_k mg$, and the x component of Newton's second law, $\Sigma F_x = ma_x$, gives $-\mu_k mg = ma_x$. Or,

$$a_x = -\mu_k g \qquad (A)$$

Since a_x is constant, but unknown, we use Eq. (3-12) to find another expression for a_x:

$$v_x^2 - v_{x0}^2 = 2a_x(x - x_0)$$

If we let x_0 be the coordinate where the girl released the sled and x be the coordinate where the sled came to rest, then $x - x_0 = d$, $v_{x0} = v$, and $v_x = 0$, so that $-v^2 = 2a_x d$, or

$$a_x = \frac{-v^2}{2d} \qquad (B)$$

Combining Eqs. (A) and (B) gives

$$-\mu_k g = \frac{-v^2}{2d}$$

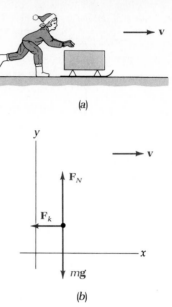

(a)

(b)

Figure 6-7. Example 6-2: (a) A girl releases a sled while it is traveling with speed v. (b) Free-body diagram for the sled after it is released.

Solving for μ_k, we obtain

$$\mu_k = \frac{v^2}{2gd} = \frac{(2.5 \text{ m/s})^2}{2(9.8 \text{ m/s}^2)(6.4 \text{ m})} = 0.050$$

EXAMPLE 6-3. *Critical angle for sliding to begin.* A convenient way to measure the coefficient of static friction between a block and a plank is to place the block on the plank and gradually tilt the plank. The angle between the plank and the horizontal just before the block begins to slide is called the *critical angle* θ_s for static friction. Determine μ_s in terms of θ_s.

SOLUTION. Consider the block at rest on the plank when the plank is tilted at an angle θ, where $\theta < \theta_s$ (Fig. 6-8). Since the block remains at rest, the components of Newton's second law give $\Sigma F_x = 0$ and $\Sigma F_y = 0$, or

$$F_s - mg \sin \theta = 0 \quad \text{and} \quad F_N - mg \cos \theta = 0$$

Note that in this case the normal force is not equal and opposite the weight because the weight is not perpendicular to the surface. Solving for F_s and F_N, we have

$$F_s = mg \sin \theta \qquad (A)$$

$$F_N = mg \cos \theta \qquad (B)$$

As the angle θ is gradually increased, the component of the weight down the plane, $mg \sin \theta$, increases and F_s also increases, keeping the block at rest. The component of the weight perpendicular to the surface, $mg \cos \theta$, decreases as θ increases. When $\theta = \theta_s$, the static frictional force attains its

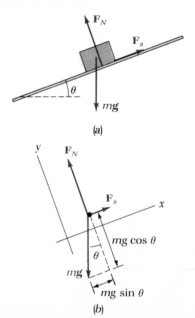

(a)

(b)

Figure 6-8. Example 6-3: (a) A block on a plank tilted at an angle θ. (b) Free-body diagram for the block.

maximum value, $F_s = F_{s,\text{max}} = \mu_s F_N$, so that Eqs. (A) and (B) become

$$\mu_s F_N = mg \sin \theta_s \qquad \text{(C)}$$

$$F_N = mg \cos \theta_s \qquad \text{(D)}$$

When we divide Eq. (C) by Eq. (D), F_N and mg cancel out and we obtain

$$\mu_s = \tan \theta_s$$

Suppose $\theta_s = 38°$ for a block and a plank. Then

$$\mu_s = \tan 38° = 0.78$$

Similarly, you can show that

$$\mu_k = \tan \theta_k$$

where θ_k is the angle between the plank and the horizontal such that the block slides with constant velocity (see Exercise 6-10).

EXAMPLE 6-4. A man slides a 45-kg crate at constant velocity across a horizontal floor by pulling on a rope attached to the crate, as shown in Fig. 6-9a. The angle θ between the rope and the horizontal is 33° and the coefficient of kinetic friction between the crate and the floor is 0.63. Determine the tension F_T in the rope.

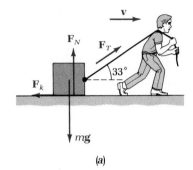

SOLUTION. The free-body diagram for the crate is shown in Fig. 6-9b. Because the crate's velocity is constant, the components of Newton's second law applied to the crate give $\Sigma F_x = 0$ and $\Sigma F_y = 0$, or

$$F_T \cos \theta - \mu_k F_N = 0$$

$$F_T \sin \theta + F_N - mg = 0$$

where we have used $F_k = \mu_k F_N$. Note that in this case $\mathbf{F}_N$ is not equal and opposite the weight because the weight is partially balanced by the vertical component of the force exerted by the rope. The two equations above contain two unknowns, F_N and F_T. As an exercise, you should eliminate F_N and solve for F_T. The result is

$$F_T = \frac{\mu_k mg}{\cos \theta + \mu_k \sin \theta} = \frac{(0.63)(45 \text{ kg})(9.8 \text{ m/s}^2)}{\cos 33° + 0.63 \sin 33°} = 240 \text{ N}$$

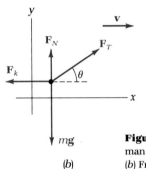

Figure 6-9. Example 6-4: (a) A man slides a crate across a floor. (b) Free-body diagram for the crate.

Frictional forces due to fluids. When a solid object, such as a rock, moves in a fluid, such as air or water, the fluid exerts a frictional force on the object. The behavior of this force depends on many things, including the shape of the object, the velocity of the object relative to the fluid, and the nature of the fluid. The property of a fluid responsible for the force is called *viscosity*, and the force is called a *viscous force*, or a *drag force*, or a *retarding force*. To illustrate numerical methods, we described the effect of such a force on a baseball traveling in air in Sec. 4-6.

Because we wish to show a few of the characteristics of motion in a fluid without becoming bogged down with complicating factors, we shall assume a particularly simple form for the drag force $\mathbf{F}_d$:

$$\mathbf{F}_d = -b\mathbf{v}$$

where b is a proportionality constant. That is, we assume $\mathbf{F}_d$ is directed opposite the object's velocity with a magnitude that increases linearly with the speed. This expression is approximately valid when v is not large.

Now suppose we release some object, such as a marble of mass m, from rest

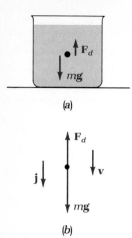

Figure 6-10. (a) A marble falls through oil. (b) Free-body diagram for the marble.

in some fluid, such as oil (Fig. 6-10). To deal mostly with positive quantities, we let the $+y$ direction be downward (not upward), so that

$$\Sigma F_y = mg - bv$$

(For simplicity, we have neglected a force that is significant in liquids, the *buoyant force*. Since the buoyant force is constant, it does not alter the qualitative features of the motion we describe here. See Sec. 15-5.) As the marble falls, its weight acts as a constant force downward and the fluid exerts a varying force upward. From Newton's second law, $\Sigma F_y = ma_y = ma$, so that

$$a = \frac{mg - bv}{m}$$

Since $a = dv/dt$,

$$\frac{dv}{dt} = g - \frac{b}{m}v$$

This equation, which contains v and its derivative dv/dt, is called a *differential equation*. In later chapters, we shall encounter differential equations similar to this, and there we shall proceed to solve them. Here we simply describe the solution.

Figure 6-11 shows a graph of the marble's speed v versus time t as the marble falls. Keep in mind that the slope of this graph at any time gives the acceleration magnitude a. At the instant the marble is released ($v = 0$ at $t = 0$), $a = g - (b/m)(0) = g$, as indicated by the slope of the dashed line. As v increases, F_d increases, causing the net force to decrease. Consequently, a decreases, approaching zero as t becomes large. As a approaches zero, v approaches an asymptotic value called the *terminal speed* v_t. When v approaches v_t, F_d approaches mg, so that

$$bv_t = mg$$

or,

$$v_t = \frac{mg}{b}$$

As an example, suppose the factor b for a marble of mass $m = 0.015$ kg falling in oil is $b = 8$ N $\cdot$ s/m. Then

$$v_t = \frac{(0.015 \text{ kg})(9.8 \text{ m/s}^2)}{8 \text{ N} \cdot \text{s/m}} = 0.02 \text{ m/s}$$

6-3 DYNAMICS OF UNIFORM CIRCULAR MOTION

Circular motion, or nearly circular motion, is common in nature and in mechanical devices. For example, the planets move in nearly circular paths

Figure 6-11. A graph of v versus t for the marble. The slope of the graph gives a. At $t = 0$, $v = 0$ and $a = g$. As t becomes large, v approaches v_t and a approaches zero.

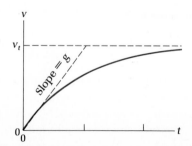

around the sun, and gears, pulleys, and wheels involve circular motion.

Recall from Chap. 4 that an object moving in a circle is accelerating even though the object's speed may be constant. There must be an acceleration during circular motion because the velocity is continuously changing direction. If the speed v of the object is constant, then the motion is called *uniform circular motion*. In this motion the acceleration vector points toward the center of the circle, and its magnitude is $a_c = v^2/R$, where R is the radius of the circle. This acceleration toward the center of the circle is called the *centripetal acceleration*.

In the light of Newton's second law, we see that an object in uniform circular motion must have a net force toward the center of the circle. Since $\Sigma\mathbf{F} = m\mathbf{a}$ and $\mathbf{a}$ points toward the center of the circle with magnitude v^2/R, $\Sigma\mathbf{F}$ must also point toward the center of the circle, and

Centripetal force

$$|\Sigma\mathbf{F}| = \frac{mv^2}{R}$$

This net force toward the center of the circle is called the *centripetal force*. Note that the term "centripetal force" does not refer to a type of interaction, like a gravitational force or an electrical force. This term simply indicates that the net force is directed toward the center of the circular motion, without reference to how the force is provided.

EXAMPLE 6-5. A car travels at a constant speed v on a horizontal road while rounding a circular turn of radius R, as shown in Fig. 6-12a and b. (a) The coefficient of static friction between the tires and the road surface is μ_s. Determine an expression for the maximum speed v_m that the car can have without beginning to slide. (b) Determine v_m for the case where $\mu_s = 1.2$ and $R = 150$ m.

SOLUTION. (a) The car's free-body diagram is shown in Fig. 6-12c. Since the vertical acceleration is zero, the normal force and the gravitational force are equal and opposite: $F_N = mg$. The net force is horizontal: $\Sigma\mathbf{F} = \mathbf{F}_s$. The static frictional force $\mathbf{F}_s$ (rather than the kinetic frictional force $\mathbf{F}_k$) provides the centripetal force because the car's tire tread does not slide on the road. From Newton's second law, $|\Sigma\mathbf{F}| = F_s = ma = mv^2/R$, and we have

$$F_s = \frac{mv^2}{R}$$

Thus F_s is larger when v is larger, but F_s cannot exceed $F_{s,\text{max}}$. The maximum speed v_m corresponds to $F_s = F_{s,\text{max}}$:

$$\frac{mv_m^2}{R} = F_{s,\text{max}} = \mu_s F_N = \mu_s mg$$

Solving for v_m, we obtain

$$v_m = \sqrt{\mu_s gR}$$

Should the car exceed this speed, sliding will begin and the car will no longer travel in a circle. Note that v_m is independent of the mass of the car, but depends on the coefficient of friction and the radius of the curve. (b) When $\mu_s = 1.2$ and $R = 150$ m,

$$v_m = \sqrt{(1.2)(9.8 \text{ m/s}^2)(150 \text{ m})} = 42 \text{ m/s}$$

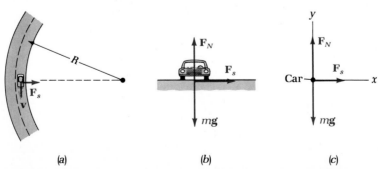

(a)   (b)   (c)

Figure 6-12. Example 6-5: A car rounding a curve. (a) Top view. (b) Front view. (c) Free-body diagram for the car.

EXAMPLE 6-6. *Banking a curve on a racetrack.* In the design of a racetrack, as well as a highway, the appropriate angle to bank a curve is such that the horizontal component of the normal force exerted by the pavement provides the centripetal force on a car traveling at the design speed v_d. For a car at this speed, a frictional force is not needed to provide the centripetal force, and the car will not tend to slide off the track when the coefficient of friction is reduced by smooth tires or water on the pavement. (a) Determine the banking angle for a racetrack curve of radius R such that a car rounding the curve with speed v_d will experience no frictional force perpendicular to its velocity. (b) Determine the banking angle for a curve of radius 280 m designed for a speed of 35 m/s.

SOLUTION. (a) Figure 6-13a shows a sketch of the system where θ_b is the banking angle of the racetrack surface relative to the horizontal. Figure 6-13b is a free-body diagram for a car traveling at speed v_d. Since there is no frictional force, the horizontal component of $\mathbf{F}_N$ provides the centripetal force on the car, and the horizontal component of the second law gives

$$F_N \sin \theta_b = \frac{mv_d^2}{R}$$

Since there is no vertical acceleration, the vertical component of $\mathbf{F}_N$ is equal to the car's weight:

$$F_N \cos \theta_b = mg$$

We have two equations with two unknowns; the unknowns are F_N and θ_b. The unwanted unknown, F_N, is eliminated by

taking the ratio of these equations:

$$\frac{F_N \sin \theta_b}{F_N \cos \theta_b} = \frac{mv_d^2/R}{mg} \qquad \text{or} \qquad \tan \theta_b = \frac{v_d^2}{Rg}$$

Solving for θ_b gives

$$\theta_b = \tan^{-1} \frac{v_d^2}{Rg}$$

This expression is consistent with our expectations; it predicts that θ_b should be made larger for a larger value of v_d, and θ_b should be made smaller for a curve with a larger radius of curvature R. (b) For a curve with $R = 280$ m designed for $v_d = 35$ m/s,

$$\theta_b = \tan^{-1} \frac{(35 \text{ m/s})^2}{(280 \text{ m})(9.8 \text{ m/s}^2)} = 24°$$

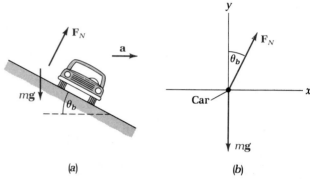

(a)   (b)

Figure 6-13. Example 6-6: Banking a racetrack curve. (a) Car rounding the curve at the design speed v_d. (b) Free-body diagram for the car.

EXAMPLE 6-7. *The conical pendulum.* A pendulum is composed of a dense object, such as a rock of mass m, suspended from a string of length L. The rock is called the pendulum bob. If the bob is swung in a horizontal circle of radius R, as shown in Fig. 6-14a, the system is called a *conical pendulum* because the string sweeps out a cone. The time required for the bob to make one complete revolution is

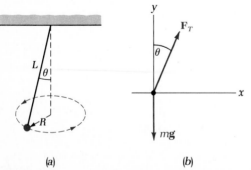

(a)   (b)

Figure 6-14. Example 6-7: (a) A conical pendulum. (b) Free-body diagram for the bob.

called the *period T.* Newton used a conical pendulum to measure g. Previously, he had accepted a value of g determined by Galileo, but he had reason to believe that Galileo's value was not very accurate. Following Newton, develop an expression for g in terms of T, L, and the angle θ between the string and the vertical.

SOLUTION. The period T is related to the constant speed v of the bob. Since the bob travels a distance $2\pi R$ during one period, $v = 2\pi R/T$. A connection between v and g can be found by applying Newton's second law. The free-body diagram for the bob is shown in Fig. 6-14b. The vertical acceleration is zero so that the second law gives $\Sigma F_y = 0$, or

$$F_t \cos \theta = mg \qquad (A)$$

where F_t is the tension in the string. Since the bob travels in a horizontal circular path, the horizontal acceleration is v^2/R. The centripetal force is the horizontal component of the tension in the string, so that the horizontal component of the second law gives

$$F_t \sin \theta = \frac{mv^2}{R} \qquad (B)$$

Dividing Eq. (B) by Eq. (A), we find

$$\tan \theta = \frac{v^2}{Rg}$$

Substituting $v = 2\pi R/T$ and $R = L \sin \theta$, and then solving for g, we obtain

$$g = \frac{4\pi^2 L \cos \theta}{T^2}$$

Newton swung a pendulum with $L = 81$ inches while keeping $\theta = 45°$ and measured the period. He arrived at a value of g that was accurate to within 4 percent. You should try this experiment and determine the accuracy of your results. It will probably cause you to have great respect for Newton's skill as an experimentalist.

EXAMPLE 6-8. *Apparent weight.* In Chap. 5 we defined the weight of an object as the gravitational force $\mathbf{F}_e$ exerted by the earth, and we defined the apparent weight according to the force $\mathbf{F}_s$ measured with a spring scale. Because the earth rotates, the apparent weight determined by a scale at rest relative to the earth's surface is, in general, not equal to the weight. This effect of the earth's rotation does not exist at the poles, which are on the axis of rotation, but it is maximum at the equator. Determine the relation between the weight $F_e = mg$ and the apparent weight F_s at the equator.

SOLUTION. Figure 6-15a shows a sketch of a person at the equator holding a fish suspended from a spring scale. The view is from above the north pole looking along the earth's axis of rotation. Relative to a frame with axes fixed to the stars (an inertial reference frame), the fish is in uniform circular motion with speed $v = 2\pi R_e/T_e$, where R_e is the earth's radius (6.37×10^6 m $= 6.37$ Mm) and T_e is the period of the earth's rotation (8.616×10^4 s ≈ 24 h). The fish's centripetal acceleration is $v^2/R_e = 4\pi^2 R_e/T_e^2$. From the free-body diagram for the fish (Fig. 6-15b), the magnitude of the net force is $mg - F_s$ so that Newton's second law gives

$$mg - F_s = \frac{m 4\pi^2 R_e}{T_e^2} \qquad \text{(A)}$$

Solving for F_s, we obtain

$$F_s = mg \left(1 - \frac{4\pi^2 R_e}{g T_e^2} \right)$$

Inserting the numerical values of R_e, T_e, and g gives

$$F_s = mg(1 - 0.0035) = (0.9965)mg$$

The effect of the earth's rotation on the apparent weight of an object is small, even at the equator where the effect is maximum.

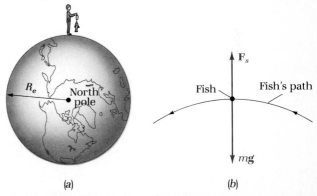

Figure 6-15. Example 6-8: (a) A person holding a fish suspended from a spring scale at the equator. (b) Free-body diagram for the fish. The difference between the magnitudes of the two forces is greatly exaggerated for purposes of illustration.

6-4 MOTION RELATIVE TO NONINERTIAL FRAMES

Jim is on a rotating merry-go-round that has a smooth horizontal floor. When he places a roller skate on the floor such that its wheels are directed along a line from the center of the merry-go-round, the roller skate begins to move toward the outside of the merry-go-round. That is, the skate accelerates relative to Jim even though there are no horizontal forces on it before it begins to move. This result is expected by anyone who has been a passenger in a car as it turns a corner.

Why does the skate seem to violate Newton's second law in this way, accelerating in a direction in which there is no net force? The answer is that the merry-go-round is not an inertial reference frame. Newton's second law is not valid for measurements made with respect to noninertial reference frames. In Newton's second law, $\Sigma \mathbf{F} = m\mathbf{a}$, the acceleration must be measured with respect to an inertial reference frame.

Jim insists on using Newton's second law, even though it is not valid in his

Centrifugal force

frame. So we ask Jim: Why does the skate accelerate toward the outside of the merry-go-round? He tells us there is a force toward the outside of the merry-go-round called a *centrifugal force*. Centrifugal means "proceeding in a direction *away* from a center."

To hold the skate stationary with respect to the merry-go-round, Jim exerts a force on the skate toward the center of the merry-go-round. Jim tells us that the skate is not accelerating. The horizontal force he exerts is equal and opposite the centrifugal force, and the net force on the skate is zero.

Mary is standing on the ground and watching Jim and the skate go around on the merry-go-round. She tells us that the skate is accelerating; it has a centripetal acceleration toward the center of the merry-go-round. She tells us that Jim is exerting a centripetal force on the skate that is causing it to move in a circle. Mary does not even mention a centrifugal force.

Fictitious force

The centrifugal force that Jim speaks of is an example of a fictitious force. He introduced this fictitious force in order to make Newton's second law seem to be valid in his frame of reference. A *fictitious force* is a force invoked by an observer in a noninertial frame of reference in order to make Newton's second law seem to be valid in the noninertial reference frame. Fictitious forces, such as the centrifugal force, are sometimes called *pseudo* forces or *inertial* forces. Recall that from Newton's third law, forces always occur in pairs; a pair of forces is called an *action-reaction pair*. One indication that a force may be fictitious is when the other member of the pair cannot be identified. A fictitious force is not the result of an interaction between two objects. Consequently, the missing member of the action-reaction pair does not exist.

Figure 6-16. Free-body diagram for the fish in Example 6-8, using an earth frame. The magnitude F_{cen} of the centrifugal force is greatly exaggerated for purposes of illustration.

In Example 6-8, we applied Newton's second law to a fish on a spring scale in order to determine the effect of the earth's rotation on the apparent weight of an object at the equator. Let us take Jim's point of view and pretend that Newton's second law is valid in the rotating earth frame. Using an earth frame as the reference frame in the fish's free-body diagram (Fig. 6-16), we find that the x component of Newton's second law gives

$$mg - F_s - F_{\text{cen}} = 0$$

where $\mathbf{F}_{\text{cen}}$ is the centrifugal force we introduce in order to make Newton's second law seem valid in our earth frame. Comparison with Eq. (A) in Example 6-8 shows that

$$F_{\text{cen}} = \frac{m 4\pi^2 R_e}{T_e^2} = 0.0035 mg$$

Using this centrifugal force, we can pretend that our earth frame at the equator is an inertial reference frame. The fact that this centrifugal force turns out to be such a small fraction of an object's weight means that it can often be neglected and an earth frame can be treated as an inertial frame.

Coriolis force

The centrifugal force is just one example of a fictitious force. Another example of such a force is the Coriolis force. If an object is *moving* relative to some frame of reference, and if this reference frame is rotating relative to an inertial frame, then a fictitious force called the *Coriolis force* is invented in order to compensate partially for the acceleration of the reference frame. The Coriolis force depends on the speed of the object relative to the noninertial frame, and the direction of this fictitious force is perpendicular to the object's velocity. The Coriolis force due to the earth's rotation has a major effect on the earth's air

Figure 6-17. A hurricane in the North Atlantic photographed from an earth satellite. The counterclockwise direction of the winds around a region of low pressure in the northern hemisphere is due to the Coriolis force. *(Photo Researchers)*

currents (winds), ocean currents, and weather patterns (Fig. 6-17). It is beyond our scope to discuss the Coriolis force in detail.

COMMENTARY: ISAAC NEWTON

The list in Table 6-2 provides some idea of the enormous influence Isaac Newton has had on science and mathematics. His major discoveries include the laws of motion, the law of gravity, and the calculus. Any one of these achievements would be sufficient to grant its discoverer acclaim as a genius of historical proportions.

Newton's father, also named Isaac, was illiterate but moderately wealthy. The Newton clan had been rising socially and economically for several generations when Newton's father married his mother, and the marriage represented another step forward. Newton's mother, Hannah Ayscough Newton, could read

Table 6-2. Some of Newton's discoveries

Discovery or invention	Field
Laws of motion	Mechanics
Law of gravity	Mechanics
Law of hydrodynamic resistance	Hydrodynamics
Newtonian fluid	Hydrodynamics
Law of cooling	Thermodynamics
Newton's rings	Optics
Emission theory	Optics
Newtonian telescope	Optics
The calculus	Mathematics
Binomial series	Mathematics
Newton's method	Mathematics
Newton-Cotes formula	Mathematics
Formula for interpolation	Mathematics

A portrait of Newton at age 46 by Sir Godfrey Kneller. In the words of biographer Richard Westfall: ". . . an arresting presence, instinct with intelligence, caught when his capacities stood at their height. Without difficulty, we recognize the author of the *Principia*." *(Courtesy of Lord Portsmouth and the Trustees of the Portsmouth Estates.)*

and write, which was unusual for a woman in those times. However, there is no hint of latent genius to be found in Newton's pedigree.

Newton was born in Woolsthorpe, England, on Christmas day in 1642, within a year of Galileo's death. His father had died the previous October, only six months after he had married Hannah. When Isaac was 3 years old, his mother married Barnabas Smith, an elderly but wealthy rector at a nearby village. Part of the marriage agreement was that young Isaac would be left in the care of his grandmother Ayscough in Woolsthorpe while his mother and stepfather lived some 10 mi away. There is no record of affection between Isaac and his grandmother, and some historians suspect that none existed. When Isaac was 10 years old, his stepfather died, and his mother returned to resume care of Isaac at Woolsthorpe. Many biographers of Newton have speculated on the psychological damage done to the fatherless boy by the absence of his mother during those formative years. By his own admission, young Isaac was a peevish and obstinate boy, and by most accounts he developed into an introspective and sometimes petulant adult.

At 18 years of age, Newton entered Trinity College of Cambridge University. The social structure of Cambridge reflected contemporary English society. An entering student was classified as either a pensioner or a sizar. A pensioner was privileged and given the better accommodations. A sizar performed menial tasks, often as a servant for a pensioner. Newton was a sizar, despite the fact that his mother, who grudgingly allowed him to attend college, easily could have afforded to make him a pensioner. It is disconcerting to imagine the young student, soon to become the intellectual titan of his times, waiting on tables and emptying chamber pots.

Newton's advancement at Cambridge, from sizar to scholar to fellow to Lucasian Professor of Mathematics, played a critical role in his later accomplishments. Residency at Cambridge meant a steady income with few duties, although celibacy was a requirement. These positions gave Newton the freedom to pursue studies of mechanics, optics, mathematics, astronomy, alchemy, and theology. Although his contributions to physics and mathematics account for his enduring fame, he spent a majority of his time and effort on alchemy and theology.

Newton was a solitary scholar. His ability to concentrate on a problem is legendary. He often became so engrossed in his work that he was oblivious to his own human needs, reputedly going for days without food or sleep. When asked on one occasion how he made his discoveries, he said, "By always thinking unto them." On another occasion he said, "I keep the subject constantly before me and wait till the first dawnings open little by little into the full light."

Newton certainly did not suffer fools gladly, and he was an exacting taskmaster toward himself. He was exceedingly cautious about anything he said or wrote, always fearful of a mistake. He explained his reluctance to publish as "fear that disputes and controversies may be raised against me by ignoramuses." It has been said that discoveries by Newton had two phases: he made the discovery and then someone pried it from him so that the rest of the world could share it.

Newton's masterpiece, the Principia, *was pried from him by Edmund Halley, the astronomer for whom Halley's comet is named. The great unsolved problem at that time was the force on the planets by the sun. Halley, Christopher Wren (the famous architect), Robert Hooke, and possibly others had surmised that the force varies inversely as the square of the separation distance, a so-called inverse-square force (Chap. 7). However, no one was able to prove it. With tongue in cheek, Wren offered a prize worth 40 shillings to the person who could solve the problem. (To these proud and competitive men, the accomplishment itself was worth far more than any prize.) In 1684, Halley visited Newton and asked him what sort of path would be followed by a planet if the force by the sun was an inverse-square force. Newton replied immediately that the path would be an ellipse. Halley was "struck with joy & amazement," and he asked Newton how he knew it. Newton returned a crushingly terse reply: "I have calculated it." With these simple words, Newton announced that he had solved the problem of the centuries. Indeed, Newton was probably the only person of his time who had both the physical insight and the mathematical muscle to solve such a problem. Several months later, Newton sent Halley, who was clerk to the Royal Society (Britain's scientific organization), a treatise which contained the mathematical solution. In those days, only a handful of people would have had the ability to understand this treatise, but fortunately, Halley was one of those people. Halley recognized the monumental significance of Newton's work, and he immediately began to press him to publish a book. With Halley as midwife, the Principia was born in 1686.*

Newton's reluctance to publish caused him to share the credit for some of his discoveries; the most significant example is the calculus. From his notes and letters, we know that Newton developed the calculus about 10 years before it was published by Gottfried Leibniz in 1684. Possibly, had someone like Halley prodded Newton in the 1670s to publish his findings, Leibniz would not now be considered the codiscoverer of the calculus.

In 1696, Newton moved to London to accept the position of warden of the mint. He played a major role in the revision of the coinage during his term (1696 to 1699), and in 1699 he was appointed master of the mint. He resigned his professorship at Cambridge in 1701 and was elected a member of Parliament that year. In 1703 he was elected president of the Royal Society and held that post until his death in 1726. In 1705 he was knighted. Upon his death at age 83, he was given a national funeral and buried in Westminster Abbey. Alexander Pope wrote a fitting tribute:

> *Nature and Nature's Laws lay hid by night;*
> *God said, Let Newton be! And all was light.*

For further reading see Never at Rest *by Richard Westfall (Cambridge University Press, New York, 1980) or* A Portrait of Isaac Newton *by F. E. Manuel (Harvard University Press, Cambridge, Mass., 1968).*

SUMMARY WITH APPLICATIONS

Section 6-2. Contact forces: The normal force and the frictional force

A contact force exerted by one solid object on another is resolved into a normal force and a frictional force. The kinetic frictional force on an object as it slides on a surface is

$$F_k = \mu_k F_N \qquad (6\text{-}1)$$

Up to a maximum value of $F_{s,\text{max}} = \mu_s F_N$, the static frictional force on an object at rest on a surface adjusts itself to keep the object from sliding, so that

$$F_s \leq \mu_s F_N \qquad (6\text{-}3)$$

When a solid object falls in a fluid, the fluid exerts a retarding or drag force on the object such that the object's acceleration approaches zero and its speed approaches a maximum value called the terminal speed v_t.

Use the frictional force laws in Newton's second law to solve problems; describe the behavior of a solid object falling in a fluid.

Section 6-3. Dynamics of uniform circular motion

For an object to execute uniform circular motion, a net force of constant magnitude, called a centripetal force, must be exerted toward the center of the circle:

$$|\Sigma\mathbf{F}| = \frac{mv^2}{R}$$

Apply Newton's second law to an object in uniform circular motion.

Section 6-4. Motion relative to noninertial frames

Often an observer in a noninertial frame will invoke a fictitious force in order to use Newton's second law, with the acceleration measured relative to the noninertial frame. When this fictitious force is incorporated into Newton's second law, the law seems to be valid in the noninertial frame. Fictitious forces that allow us to treat an earth frame as an inertial frame are the centrifugal force and the Coriolis force.

Explain why and how a fictitious force is used; explain how to determine whether a force is fictitious.

QUESTIONS

6-1 Why is it useful to separate a contact force into a normal force and a frictional force? Give at least two reasons.

6-2 Suppose you wish to prop open a screen door that has a strong closing spring. A brick resting on the floor in front of the door will not keep it from closing; the door simply slides the brick along. However, a wedge-shaped piece of wood can hold the door open if it is sandwiched between the bottom of the door and the floor, even though its weight is much less than the brick's. Explain.

6-3 You are asked to slide a crate across a horizontal floor. The crate's weight is a few newtons larger than your weight, and the coefficient of friction between the crate and the floor is slightly larger than that between your shoes and the floor. Can you slide the crate by exerting a horizontal force on it? If not, how should you direct the force you exert in order to slide the crate?

6-4 Suppose you attempted to measure a coefficient of static friction between the surface of water and a block of wood floating on the water. What do you think you would find?

6-5 Consider a toy boat set in motion across the surface of water in a tub. Suppose we attempt to measure a coefficient of kinetic friction between the boat and the water, using the analysis developed in Example 6-2 for the sled sliding along a snow-covered road. Do you think our value of μ_k would be independent of the initial speed of the boat? If not, do you think that this concept of a coefficient of friction is useful?

6-6 A crate is placed at the center of a flatbed truck, and as the truck accelerates so does the crate. What type of force exerts the accelerating force on the crate? If the truck's acceleration is larger than a certain maximum value, the crate will slide. Will this maximum acceleration depend on the mass of the crate? Explain.

6-7 A sidewalk covered with melting ice is much more slippery than one covered with ice that is very cold and not melting. Explain.

6-8 You may have seen the trick where a tablecloth is jerked from a table, leaving the dishes that were on the cloth-covered table in nearly their original positions. To successfully perform this trick, should the cloth be made of thick burlap or thin silk? Should the dishes have large mass or small mass? Is it better to pull the cloth with a large force or pull it with a gentle and steady force?

6-9 Cross-country skiers apply a special wax to their skis to allow them to push off with one ski while the other ski slides easily along. What can you say about the ratio μ_s/μ_k between the wax and snow?

6-10 If you want to stop a car in a minimum distance, why is it better *not* to press so hard on the brakes that the tires slide on the pavement?

6-11 A carpenter's level placed on the dashboard of a car has the bubble in the center when the car is at rest on a horizontal surface. This indicates that the dashboard is parallel to the surface. Consider observing the bubble as the car makes a right turn on a road banked for cars traveling at speed v_d. Is the bubble centered, right of center, or left of center when the car's speed v is (a) $v = v_d$; (b) $v > v_d$; (c) $v < v_d$?

6-12 A panel truck is traveling at constant velocity along a horizontal street. A skate, which is aligned with the truck's length, is at rest on the floor and a helium-filled balloon is at rest against the ceiling. Describe the motion of the skate and the balloon when the driver applies the brakes.

6-13 Given the same initial speed, can a heavier car come to a stop in a shorter distance than a lighter one? Explain.

6-14 When deciding on the angle at which a highway curve should be banked, does the engineer need to take the mass of the cars into account? Explain.

6-15 Why is a drag-racing car designed so that most of its mass is over the drive wheels, which are at the rear of the car? (See Fig. 6-18.)

Figure 6-18. Ques. 6-15: A drag racer. *(Michael Simonet/ Photo Researchers)*

6-16 Explain why a pilot banks an airplane when making a turn.

6-17 A turn-and-slip indicator is an instrument used by a pilot in an airplane. One part of this instrument is a small ball that can roll in a glass tube (Fig. 6-19). The glass tube is circular and oriented in a vertical plane perpendicular to the length of the airplane. The ball rests in the bottom of the tube when the plane is at rest on a horizontal runway, and this position is marked on the tube and called the center position. When the airplane turns, the proper angle of bank is maintained by keeping the ball centered. Suppose the plane is turning right and the ball is left of center. Should the banking angle be increased or decreased? Explain.

Figure 6-19. Ques. 6-17: A ball that can roll in a circular glass tube is part of a turn-and-slip indicator on the instrument panel of an airplane.

6-18 When a jet airliner rapidly accelerates during takeoff, the passengers are "forced" back against their backrests. Is this a fictitious force? If so, what is the noninertial reference frame? If not, identify the object that exerts the force.

6-19 We have defined the weight of an object as the gravitational force exerted by the earth on the object. Suppose we decide to change the definition to include the centrifugal force due to the earth's rotation. That is, we define the weight of an object as the gravitational force plus the centrifugal force. Is an object's weight still proportional to its mass? Explain.

6-20 A string supports a plumb bob suspended from a surveyor's tripod. Is the string aligned along the direction of the gravitational force on the bob (*a*) at the equator, (*b*) at the poles, (*c*) at a latitude of 45°? If the string is not

along the direction of the force at any of these latitudes, then describe its relation to that direction.

6-21 The planet Noino orbits its star with the same period and separation distance as the earth orbits the sun. Noino has twice the radius of the earth, and a day on Noino is 48 earth-hours. Is a coordinate frame at rest on Noino's equator more nearly an inertial frame than a frame at rest on earth's equator? Justify your answer.

6-22 While exploring the planet Otatop, you are captured and confined to a dungeon. From your cell you cannot see the sky, but you have a spring scale that measures apparent weight very precisely. To pass the time, you place a rock on the scale every day and record the reading. One day you find that the reading is less than before. (*a*) One of your guards tells you that Otatop has changed its rotational speed. If this is true, then is the planet spinning faster or slower? (*b*) Another guard tells you that Otatop has not changed its rotational speed—rather, the gravitational force has somehow become weaker. Can you tell which guard is correct? If you could make your apparent weight measurement at a different latitude, could you tell which guard is correct? Explain.

6-23 In Example 6-5 we stated that the centripetal force exerted on the car rounding a curve on a horizontal road is provided by the static frictional force $\mathbf{F}_s$. Note that $\mathbf{F}_k$ cannot be a centripetal force because $\mathbf{F}_k$ is directed opposite the relative velocity of the surfaces, and, in uniform circular motion, the velocity is tangent to the circle and perpendicular to $\mathbf{a}$. If the tires should slide on the road, then the car no longer travels in a circle because $\mathbf{F}_k$ cannot have a component perpendicular to the velocity. What is the car's path if its tires should begin to slide?

6-24 What is the terminal acceleration of an object falling in a fluid?

6-25 A man is riding inside a boxcar on a train that runs so smoothly that he cannot detect any vibrations. The boxcar has no windows so that he cannot see outside. After awakening from a nap, the man notices that the string supporting a plumb bob from the ceiling of the boxcar is not perpendicular to the floor (Fig. 6-20), even though the boxcar floor was measured to be horizontal when the train was at rest on a horizontal track. Should the man conclude that the train is (*a*) on a hill so that the

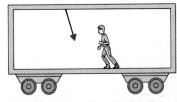

Figure 6-20. Ques. 6-25: Man and a plumb bob in a boxcar. Is the boxcar on a hill that slopes upward to the left, or is the boxcar accelerating to the left?

floor is not horizontal or (b) accelerating on level ground so that the floor is horizontal? Are either of these conclusions warranted? Are both warranted? Explain.

6-26 Complete the following table:

Symbol	Represents	Type	SI unit
F_N		Scalar	
F_k	Kinetic frictional force		
μ_k			None
F_{cen}			

EXERCISES

Section 6-2. Contact forces: The normal force and the frictional force

6-1 A 37-kg crate is at rest on a horizontal floor. A rope is attached to the top of the crate, and the rope pulls vertically upward on the crate. What is the normal force exerted on the crate by the floor when the tension in the rope is (a) 52 N; (b) 170 N; (c) 360 N?

6-2 A 940-kg car is parked on a hill such that the street surface makes an angle of 16° with the horizontal. Determine the normal force and the static frictional force exerted on the car.

6-3 A 41-kg sofa is to be moved across the room, and $\mu_s = 0.46$ and $\mu_k = 0.39$ between the sofa's legs and the floor. (a) What is the minimum horizontal force that will start the sofa sliding? (b) What horizontal force is required to keep the sofa sliding at constant velocity?

6-4 A cord is attached to a 3.9-kg box, and the cord pulls upward on the box at an angle of 32° relative to the horizontal. The tension in the cord is 21 N, but the box remains at rest on a horizontal surface. Determine the magnitudes of (a) the normal force, (b) the static frictional force, (c) the contact force on the box by the surface.

6-5 A horizontal force of 28 N is required to start a 2.6-kg block sliding across a horizontal surface. (a) What is μ_s between the block and the surface? (b) If a horizontal force of 19 N keeps the block sliding at constant velocity, then what is μ_k between the block and the surface?

6-6 The angle between a plank and the horizontal such that a block just begins to slide down the plank is 26°. What is μ_s between the block and the plank?

6-7 The speed limit along a certain road is 25 m/s. To stop at a red light, the driver of a car slammed on the brakes and the car slid 57 m before coming to a stop. The coefficient μ_k is 0.80 between the tires and the road. Was the driver exceeding the speed limit?

6-8 Construct a graph of the minimum stopping distance d versus the speed v of a car at the instant the brakes are applied. Let μ_s between the tires and the pavement be 0.90, and plot v horizontally from zero to 35 m/s in increments of 5 m/s. What is the percent increase in stopping distance for a 20 percent increase in v from 25 to 30 m/s?

6-9 If the coefficient μ_k is 0.12 between a shuffleboard and

a disk, how far will the disk slide when released with an initial speed of 5.2 m/s?

6-10 (a) Show that if a block slides at constant velocity down a plank that makes an angle θ_k with the horizontal, then the coefficient of kinetic friction between the block and the plank is

$$\mu_k = \tan \theta_k$$

(b) What is μ_k between a plank and a block when $\theta_k = 29°$?

6-11 (a) Show that the expression for the magnitude of the normal force exerted by the floor in Example 6-4 (Fig. 6-9) is

$$F_N = \frac{mg \cos \theta}{\cos \theta + \mu_k \sin \theta}$$

(b) Show that the magnitude F_c of the contact force by the floor is

$$F_c = \frac{mg \cos \theta}{\cos \theta + \mu_k \sin \theta} \sqrt{1 + \mu_k^2}$$

(c) Using the data from Example 6-4 ($m = 45$ kg, $\theta = 33°$, and $\mu_k = 0.63$), evaluate F_N and F_c.

6-12 The coefficient μ_s between a sprinter's shoes and the running track is 0.92. What is the sprinter's maximum acceleration?

6-13 Given that μ_s between the pavement and the tires of a car is 0.85, determine the maximum acceleration of the car on a horizontal road. Assume that half the car's weight is supported by the drive wheels.

6-14 A 3.4-kg block slides down a sloping surface, as shown in Fig. 6-21. The coefficient μ_k between the block and the surface is 0.37. Determine the magnitudes of (a) the normal force on the block, (b) the frictional force on the block, (c) the block's acceleration.

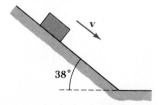

Figure 6-21. Exercise 6-14.

6-15 A boy pulls a sled up a snow-covered slope, as shown in Fig. 6-22. The mass of the sled is $m = 26$ kg, and μ_s and μ_k between the sled runners and the snow are 0.096 and 0.072, respectively. Determine the magnitude of the force exerted by the boy (a) to start the sled sliding and (b) to slide the sled at constant velocity.

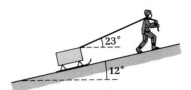

Figure 6-22. Exercise 6-15.

6-16 The applied force exerted on the sliding crate shown in Fig. 6-23a, b, and c has the same magnitude in each case, $F_a = 380$ N. The crate's mass is $m = 43$ kg and $\mu_k = 0.47$. Determine the crate's acceleration magnitude in each case. Explain why the acceleration is different in each case even though F_a is the same.

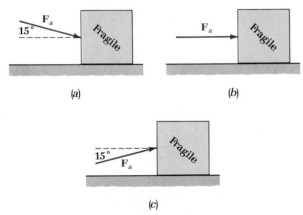

(a)   (b)

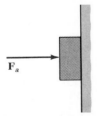

(c)

Figure 6-23. Exercise 6-16.

6-17 In Fig. 6-24, what is the magnitude of the minimum applied force that will keep the block from sliding down the vertical wall? The mass of the block is $m = 6.4$ kg and μ_s between the block and the wall is 0.76.

Figure 6-24. Exercise 6-17.

6-18 A cart coasts at constant velocity down a straight incline that makes an angle of 3.1° with the horizontal. What is the coefficient of rolling friction μ_r between the

cart and the incline's surface?

6-19 The coefficient of rolling friction μ_r between a cart and a plank is 0.062. What is the cart's acceleration when the cart is placed on the plank and the plank is tilted to an angle of 5.0° relative to the horizontal?

6-20 A marble with mass $m = 0.012$ kg is found to have a terminal speed of 0.072 m/s when falling in a clear syrup. Assume a drag force of the form $\mathbf{F}_d = -b\mathbf{v}$ and neglect the buoyant force (as we did in the text). (a) Determine b. (b) Determine the magnitude of the net force on the marble when its speed is 0.050 m/s.

6-21 The drag force on a 0.081-kg rock falling in oil is given by the expression $\mathbf{F}_d = -(13 \text{ N} \cdot \text{s/m})\mathbf{v}$. What is the rock's terminal speed v_t? Neglect any buoyant forces, as we did in the text.

Section 6-3. Dynamics of uniform circular motion

6-22 What is the maximum speed a car can have while making a turn of radius 130 m on a horizontal road? The coefficient μ_s between the tires and the pavement is 0.91.

6-23 You are designing a highway in a section where it is to make a turn of radius $R = 310$ m. If cars are expected to travel at a speed of 25 m/s along this section of the highway, what should you make the angle of bank?

6-24 When Newton used a conical pendulum to determine g, he stated his value by saying that an object released from rest will fall 200 inches in 1 s. Determine Newton's value of g from this statement. Determine the percent error in this value of g.

6-25 If an aircraft is properly banked during a turn in level flight at constant speed, the force $\mathbf{F}_a$ exerted by the air on the aircraft is directed perpendicular to a plane which contains the aircraft's wings and fuselage (Fig. 6-25). Draw a free-body diagram for such an aircraft. (*Hint:* Note the similarity to the conical pendulum in Example 6-7.) An aircraft traveling at a speed of $v = 75$ m/s makes a properly banked turn at a banking angle of 28°. What is the radius of curvature of the turn?

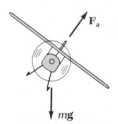

Figure 6-25. Exercise 6-25.

6-26 What is the period of a conical pendulum with $L = 1.00$ m, swung at an angle $\theta = 30°$?

6-27 An 875-kg car turns a corner with a radius of curvature $R = 15$ m. The car's speed is $v = 7.5$ m/s, and the street is horizontal. Determine the magnitudes of (a) the car's acceleration, (b) the frictional force on the car, (c) the normal force on the car, (d) the contact force on the car. (e) Determine the angle between the contact force and the vertical.

6-28 Show that two conical pendulums 1 and 2, with different lengths L_1 and L_2, have the same period T if the pendulums are swung such that the vertical distance between the point of suspension and the plane occupied by the circular path of a bob is the same.

6-29 The period of a phonograph turntable (when set at $33\frac{1}{3}$ rpm) is $T = 1.8$ s. A penny is placed on a phonograph record, and the turntable is switched on. If the penny is placed at a distance of 0.092 m from the spindle, or less, it stays on the record and travels around in a circle. But if the penny is placed at a distance greater than 0.092 m, it slides off. What is μ_s between the penny and the phonograph record?

6-30 A bicyclist makes a turn with a radius of curvature of 65 m. The road is banked at an angle of 14°, and the speed of the bicycle is 18 m/s. The combined mass of the bicycle and the bicyclist is 92 kg. Determine the magnitudes of (a) the normal force, (b) the frictional force, (c) the contact force.

6-31 An interesting trick is to swing a bucket of water in a vertical circle such that the water does not pour out of the bucket while the bucket is inverted at the top of the circle. To successfully perform this trick, the speed of the bucket must be larger than a certain minimum value. (a) Determine an expression for the minimum speed v_m of the bucket at the top of the circle in terms of the radius R of the circle. (b) Evaluate v_m when $R = 1.0$ m.

6-32 A car tops a hill as it travels along a road. The road is straight horizontally, but, because of the hill, the road follows the arc of a vertical circle of radius R. (a) Determine an expression for the maximum speed v_m the car can have such that its tires remain in contact with the pavement at the crest of the hill. (b) Evaluate v_m when $R = 140$ m.

6-33 A 62-kg girl rides a steadily rotating Ferris wheel. At the top of her circular path, her apparent weight is 210 N. The distance between the wheel's axis and the seats is 7.1 m. (a) What is the girl's apparent weight at the bottom of her circular path? (b) What is her speed? (c) What is the period of the motion?

6-34 The planet Cilrag, which orbits the star Nikpmup, has a radius of 7.46 Mm and a period of 1.21×10^4 s. While exploring Cilrag you measure the weight of a replica of the standard kilogram to be 8.4 N at one of Cilrag's poles. (a) What is g on Cilrag? (b) What is the apparent weight of the replica measured at Cilrag's equator? (c) Is it a good approximation to treat a frame with axes fixed relative to the horizontal and vertical at Cilrag's equator as an inertial reference frame? Neglect the effects of Cilrag's orbital motion around Nikpmup.

6-35 While exploring the planet Egabbac, which orbits the star Torrac, you use a spring scale to measure the apparent weight F_s of a replica of the standard kilogram. At one pole $F_s = 12.8$ N and at the equator $F_s = 10.1$ N. The period of Egabbac's rotation about its axis is 8.7×10^3 s. Determine (a) g on Egabbac and (b) Egabbac's radius.

Section 6-4. Motion relative to noninertial frames

6-36 Determine the magnitude of the centrifugal force on the replica of the standard kilogram while it is (a) on Cilrag's equator (see Exercise 6-34) and (b) on Egabbac's equator (see Exercise 6-35).

6-37 The merry-go-round Jim is riding on (Sec. 6-4) has a period of 8.2 s and Jim is 3.8 m from the center. The skate he is keeping from rolling radially outward has a mass of 0.69 kg. (a) What are the magnitude and direction of the centrifugal force on the skate according to Jim? (b) If Jim were to hold a plumb bob, what would be the angle between the string and vertical?

PROBLEMS

6-1 Two blocks, 1 and 2, are sliding down a plank, as shown in Fig. 6-26. Each block has the same mass m,

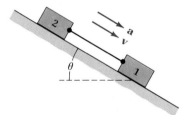

Figure 6-26. Prob. 6-1.

but the coefficients of kinetic friction between the blocks and the surface are different, with $\mu_2 > \mu_1$. The system accelerates down the slope and the string between blocks remains taut. (a) Show that the tension in the string is

$$F_T = \tfrac{1}{2}(\mu_2 - \mu_1)mg \cos \theta$$

(b) Show that the magnitude a of the system's acceleration is

$$a = g[\sin \theta - \tfrac{1}{2}(\mu_2 + \mu_1) \cos \theta]$$

(c) Show that the system slides down the slope with constant velocity when $\theta = \theta_k$, where

$$\theta_k = \tan^{-1}[\tfrac{1}{2}(\mu_2 + \mu_1)]$$

6-2 A flatbed truck transports a crate, as shown in Fig. 6-27. The crate is not fastened to the bed, but the coefficient μ_s between the crate and the bed is 0.70. When the

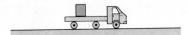

Figure 6-27. Prob. 6-2.

truck starts out from a red light on a horizontal street, what is the maximum acceleration it can have such that the crate will not slide backward relative to the bed?

6-3 In Fig. 6-28, block B has mass m, cart C has mass M, and the coefficient of static friction between the block and the cart is μ_s. Neglect frictional effects, which tend to slow the cart, and the rotational effects of the wheels. Determine an expression for the minimum value of F_a such that the block will not slide.

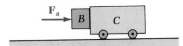

Figure 6-28. Prob. 6-3.

6-4 ***A rotor.*** A rotor is an amusement park ride which consists of a cylindrical room that rotates about a vertical axis (Fig. 6-29). The passengers enter and place their backs to the wall, and the room begins to rotate. The rotational speed gradually increases, and, when it reaches a certain minimum value, the floor is taken away, exposing the passengers to the (supposed) hazard of falling into a pit below. (a) In terms of the coefficient μ_s between the passengers and the wall, and the radius R of the room, determine an expression for the minimum speed v_m of the passengers in their circular path such that they will not slide down the wall. (b) Determine an expression for the maximum period of the motion which corresponds to speed v_m.

Figure 6-29. Prob. 6-4.

6-5 A crate is pulled along a horizontal surface at constant velocity by an applied force $\mathbf{F}_a$ that makes an angle θ with the horizontal, as shown in Fig. 6-30. The coefficient of kinetic friction between the crate and the surface is μ_k. (a) Show that the magnitude F_a is minimum when the angle $\theta = \theta_m$, where

$$\theta_m = \tan^{-1} \mu_k$$

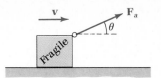

Figure 6-30. Prob. 6-5.

(*Hint:* Find an expression for F_a in terms of θ and take its derivative to find θ_m.) (b) Show that the minimum value of F_a is

$$F_{a,min} = \frac{\mu_k mg}{\sqrt{1 + \mu_k^2}}$$

(*Hint:* Determine $\cos \theta_m$ and $\sin \theta_m$ by constructing a right triangle with sides equal to 1 and μ_k so that $\tan \theta_m = \mu_k$.) (c) What is the minimum applied force required to slide a 51-kg crate across a horizontal floor at constant velocity when $\mu_k = 0.70$? (d) At what angle relative to the horizontal must the force in part (c) be directed? (e) Compare your answer in part (c) with the magnitude of the horizontally applied force that slides the crate at constant velocity.

6-6 In Fig. 6-31, the mass of block B is m and the mass of cart C is M. Show that the maximum applied force $F_{a,max}$ such that the block does not slide has a magnitude

$$F_{a,max} = \mu_s mg \left(1 + \frac{m}{M}\right)$$

Neglect frictional forces, which tend to slow the cart, and neglect the rotational effects of the cart's wheels.

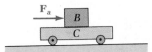

Figure 6-31. Prob. 6-6.

6-7 A crate is placed in the middle of the bed of a flatbed truck and is not strapped down. The coefficient μ_s between the bed and the crate is 0.75. If the truck is traveling at a speed of $v = 22$ m/s along a horizontal street, what is the minimum stopping distance such that the crate will not slide?

6-8 Consider the effect of the earth's rotation on the apparent weight of an object. For simplicity, we neglect the effect of the earth's orbital motion about the sun, and we assume that the earth is spherically symmetric. (See Chap. 7.) In Fig. 6-32a we show a person holding a fish with a spring scale at latitude λ. (a) Using a frame with axes fixed relative to the stars (an inertial reference frame), show that the centripetal acceleration of the fish is

$$a_c = \frac{4\pi^2 R_e \cos \lambda}{T_e^2}$$

where T_e is the period of the earth's rotation about its

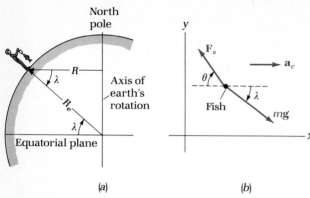

(a) (b)

Figure 6-32. Prob. 6-8: The apparent weight of an object measured on the earth's surface. (a) A fish is held suspended by a spring scale at latitude λ. (b) Free-body diagram for the fish. Because of the earth's centripetal acceleration, the force $\mathbf{F}_s$ by the scale is neither equal in magnitude nor opposite in direction to the weight $m\mathbf{g}$.

axis ($T_e = 8.616 \times 10^4$ s) and R_e is the earth's radius ($R_e = 6.37$ Mm). (b) In the fish's free-body diagram (Fig. 6-32b), the x axis is parallel to the equatorial plane and is directed toward the earth's axis. Note that the force $\mathbf{F}_s$ is *not* equal and opposite the weight $m\mathbf{g}$ because of the centripetal acceleration. Show that

$$F_s \cos \theta = mg(1 - \alpha) \cos \lambda$$

and

$$F_s \sin \theta = mg \sin \lambda$$

where $\alpha = 4\pi^2 R_e / gT_e^2$ for brevity. (c) Use the answer to part (b) to show that

$$F_s = mg[1 - (2\alpha - \alpha^2) \cos^2 \lambda]^{1/2}$$

(*Hint:* Eliminate θ by squaring each equation, adding them, and using the identity $\sin^2 \theta + \cos^2 \theta = 1$.) (d) Show that

$$\tan \theta = \frac{\tan \lambda}{1 - \alpha}$$

(e) Using the numerical data, show that $\alpha = 3.5 \times 10^{-3}$. (f) Since $\alpha \ll 1$, show that

$$F_s \approx mg(1 - \alpha \cos^2 \lambda)$$

(g) Evaluate F_s and θ at $\lambda = 45°$.

6-9 In Fig. 6-33, $m_A = m_B = 5.0$ kg, and μ_k between block A and the surface is 0.40. Block A is sliding up the slope.

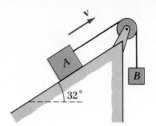

Figure 6-33. Prob. 6-9.

Determine (a) the acceleration magnitude of the system and (b) the tension in the string. Neglect friction and rotational effects in the pulley.

6-10 In Fig. 6-34, μ_k is the same between each block and the surface, and $\mu_k = 0.25$. The system is sliding as shown, and $m_A = 7.0$ kg and $m_B = 9.0$ kg. Determine (a) the acceleration of the system and (b) the tension in the string. Neglect friction and rotational effects in the pulley.

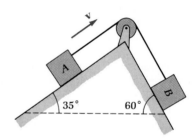

Figure 6-34. Prob. 6-10.

6-11 Consider an airplane as it ascends, reaches a maximum altitude, and then descends such that it follows the arc of a vertical circle of radius R while traveling at a constant speed v. The airplane's speed is just right so that at the maximum altitude the pilot is "weightless." (In contradiction to the term, the pilot is weightless when the only force on him is his weight.) Show that the magnitude F_s of the force by the airplane on the pilot (mostly due to contact with the seat) is $F_s = 2mg \sin \frac{1}{2}\theta$ where m is the pilot's mass and θ is the angle between the plane's velocity and the horizontal.

6-12 ⌨ Write a BASIC program for the marble falling in oil discussed in Sec. 6-2. Using about 10 data points, construct a graph of v versus t from $v = 0$ to $v \approx (0.95)v_t$.

CHAPTER 7
NEWTON'S LAW
OF UNIVERSAL
GRAVITATION

7-1 INTRODUCTION

According to legend, the seed of the theory of gravity was planted in the mind of Isaac Newton when he saw an apple fall from a tree in Woolsthorpe in Lincolnshire, England, in 1666. Newton recognized the connection between the acceleration of falling objects on earth and that of orbiting celestial bodies. For example, an apple falls from a tree and the moon orbits the earth (Fig. 7-1). Each of these seemingly unrelated phenomena is caused by the earth's gravitational force of attraction, and in each case the force is given by the same mathematical expression, Newton's law of universal gravitation. "Why does the apple fall?" and "Why does the moon orbit the earth?" are not two separate mysteries. They are different examples of the same mystery, the gravitational force.

    The gravitational force is universal. It not only holds us firmly to the surface of the earth, but it also holds the planets in their orbits around the sun. It holds the sun and other stars together in a swirling system of stars which we call the Milky Way galaxy (Fig. 7-2). It holds galaxies together in clusters of galaxies (Fig. 7-3). The gravitational force is attractive. If you trip on a curb, you fall down, not up. Because of this force, each object in the universe attracts every other object.

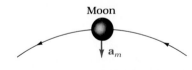

Figure 7-1. The moon and the apple both accelerate toward the center of the earth because of the gravitational attraction of the earth.

7-2 THE LAW OF UNIVERSAL GRAVITATION

By using some intuition and some experimental information about the solar system, we now develop the law of universal gravitation. Because the solar

Figure 7-2. Our own galaxy, the Milky Way, is a spiral galaxy shaped much like the one shown on page 28. This photograph shows a view of the sky in the plane of the Milky Way. *(Allan E. Morton)*

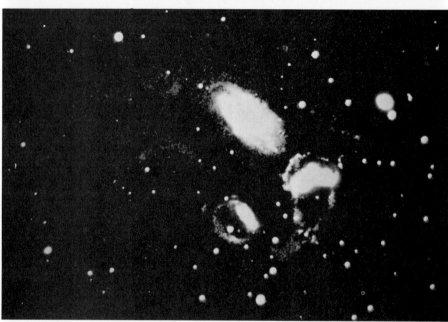

Figure 7-3. A cluster of galaxies. This cluster of four galaxies is called Stephan's Quartet. There is a fifth galaxy in the photograph, but it is much nearer the earth and belongs to another, less compact galaxy cluster. The individual stars seen scattered about in this photograph are within our own galaxy. *(Photo Researchers)*

system can be described with a simple model, it is almost ideal for the study of the gravitational force. Also, because the nine planets are at greatly different distances from the sun, they provide a broad sampling of the distance dependence of the gravitational force.

Model of the solar system. Our model of the solar system involves four principal assumptions.

1 The sun and planets are considered to be particles. Despite their large sizes, the sun and planets may be regarded as particles because their separations are much greater than their sizes (Fig. 7-4).

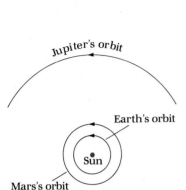

Saturn's orbit

Jupiter's orbit

Earth's orbit

Sun

Mars's orbit

Figure 7-4. A few representative orbits of planets, shown to scale. On this scale the sun's radius is less than one-tenth the thickness of this page.

2 The rest frame of the sun is an inertial reference frame. Presently we shall apply Newton's second law, $\Sigma\mathbf{F} = m\mathbf{a}$, to a planet, and the acceleration in Newton's second law must be measured relative to an inertial reference frame (Sec. 5-4). Employing this feature of the model, we use the planet's acceleration measured relative to the sun.

3 Each planet moves around the sun in a circular orbit. As we shall see (Secs. 7-7 and 7-8), the planetary orbits are elliptical. However, the orbits turn out to be nearly circular. For a circular orbit of radius R about the sun, the acceleration of the planet relative to the sun is the centripetal acceleration, $a_c = v^2/R$.

4 The only significant force on a planet is the gravitational force due to the sun. To a high degree of accuracy, each planet's orbit is unaffected by the positions of other planets. Therefore, we assume that the only force on a planet is the gravitational force by the sun and use it as the net force.

Distance dependence. Now we utilize this model to find the distance dependence of the gravitational force. Columns (1) and (2) in Table 7-1 give the periods T and the radii R of the planetary orbits about the sun. Using these data, we can find the acceleration of each planet. Since the speed of an object traveling in a circle of radius R with period T is $v = 2\pi R/T$, the object's centripetal acceleration is

$$a_c = \frac{v^2}{R} = \frac{(2\pi R/T)^2}{R} = \frac{4\pi^2 R}{T^2}$$

Inserting T and R for each planet gives the accelerations listed in column (3). As an example, the earth's acceleration relative to the sun is

$$a_c = \frac{4\pi^2(1.496 \times 10^{11} \text{ m})}{(3.156 \times 10^7 \text{ s})^2} = 5.929 \times 10^{-3} \text{ m/s}^2$$

Column (4) of Table 7-1 presents the data that are crucial to our investigation. The product $a_c R^2$ (or $4\pi^2 R^3/T^2$) for each of the planets is nearly the same. Each value is within 1 percent of the average value. Within the realm of our approximations, we can state that the product $a_c R^2$ is the same for each planet. That is,

$$a_c R^2 = k_s$$

Table 7-1. Solar system data

Body	(1) Period T, 10^7 s	(2) Average orbital radius R, 10^{11} m	(3) Average orbital acceleration $a_c = 4\pi^2 R/T^2$, 10^{-3} m/s²	(4) Acceleration × orbital radius squared $a_c R^2 = 4\pi^2 R^3/T^2$, 10^{20} m³/s²	(5) Mass, 10^{24} kg
Sun					1,990,000
Mercury	0.760	0.579	39.6	1.33	0.335
Venus	1.94	1.08	11.3	1.32	4.89
Earth	3.156	1.496	5.929	1.327	5.97
Mars	5.94	2.28	2.55	1.33	0.646
Jupiter	37.4	7.78	0.219	1.33	1900
Saturn	93.5	14.3	0.0646	1.32	569
Uranus	264	28.7	0.0163	1.34	87.3
Neptune	522	45.0	0.00652	1.32	103
Pluto	782	59.1	0.00382	1.33	5.4

where k_s (subscript s for $s$un) is a constant that is the same for each planet ($k_s = 1.33 \times 10^{20}$ m³/s²). Solving for a_c gives

$$a_c = \frac{k_s}{R^2}$$

If we let F_{sp} be the magnitude of the force by the sun on a planet and m_p be the mass of the planet, then Newton's second law gives $F_{sp} = m_p a_c$, or

$$F_{sp} = m_p \left(\frac{k_s}{R^2}\right) = \frac{k_s m_p}{R^2} \tag{7-1}$$

Thus the gravitational force decreases with increasing distance R as $1/R^2$. A force that depends on distance in this fashion is called an *inverse-square force*.

An inverse-square force

Mass dependence. In the *Principia*, Newton used the third law of motion to arrive at the mass dependence of the gravitational force law, as indicated by the following passage:

> And since the action of centripetal force upon the attracted body, at equal distances, is proportional to the matter in this body, it is reasonable, too, that it is also proportional to the matter in the attracting body. For the action is mutual, and causes the bodies by mutual endeavor (by law 3) to approach each other, and accordingly it ought to be similar to itself in both bodies. One body can be considered as attracting and the other as attracted, but this distinction is more mathematical than natural. The attraction is really that of either of the two bodies toward the other, and thus is of the same kind in each of the bodies.[*]

Let us follow Newton's reasoning step by step. From Eq. (7-1), the gravitational force by the sun on a planet is proportional to the mass of the planet. Also, from Newton's third law, if the sun exerts a force $\mathbf{F}_{sp}$ on a planet, then the planet exerts a force $\mathbf{F}_{ps}$ on the sun, and the magnitudes are equal: $F_{sp} = F_{ps}$. If a single mathematical expression (or law) is to provide both of these forces, then m_s must enter the expression in the same way as m_p. That is, since $F_{sp} \propto m_p$, we expect that $F_{ps} \propto m_s$. Therefore, we let $k_s = Gm_s$, where G is a proportionality constant independent of either mass, and Eq. (7-1) becomes

$$F_{sp} = \frac{Gm_s m_p}{R^2}$$

The expression for F_{ps} is found by exchanging p for s and s for p:

$$F_{ps} = \frac{Gm_p m_s}{R^2}$$

Since these expressions give $F_{ps} = F_{sp}$, they agree with Newton's third law, and the mass of each object enters each expression the same way.

Gravitational force law for particles. To generalize our results, we let $\mathbf{F}_{12}$ represent the gravitational force exerted by particle 1 on particle 2. Since the force is attractive, it is directed from 2 toward 1. The customary way to show

[*] I. Bernard Cohen, "Newton's Discovery of Gravity," *Scientific American*, March 1981.

this direction is to use a unit vector $\hat{\mathbf{r}}$, which is directed from 1 toward 2, as shown in Fig. 7-5. Thus we have

$$\mathbf{F}_{12} = -\frac{Gm_1 m_2}{r^2}\hat{\mathbf{r}} \tag{7-2}$$

where m_1 and m_2 are the masses of the particles and r is the distance between them. The minus sign indicates that the direction of the force is opposite $\hat{\mathbf{r}}$. This is Newton's law of universal gravitation. The symbol G represents a universal constant, and is referred to as "big G" in conversations. Capital "G" is used in order to avoid confusion with the magnitude of the acceleration of gravity near the earth's surface, represented by g and sometimes called "little g."

The magnitude of the force exerted by particle 1 on particle 2 is equal to the magnitude of the force exerted by particle 2 on particle 1: $F_{12} = F_{21} = Gm_1 m_2/r^2$. Because of this, we often refer to the force *between* particles 1 and 2. Such wording is common, but it misleadingly implies that there is no distinction between the force by 1 on 2 and the force by 2 on 1. This is true only for the *magnitudes* of the forces by Newton's third law. When using such wording you should keep in mind that you are talking about two different forces on two separate particles, and that these two forces are opposite in direction.

Force between extended objects. Equation (7-2) applies to objects that are separated far enough such that they can be regarded as particles. How do we determine the gravitational force between objects that are not small compared with their separation? For example, how do we find the gravitational force between the earth and a chair near the surface of the earth? To answer this question, Newton applied his newly invented integral calculus. The answer is that we imagine the two objects to consist of a large number of small pieces, each piece being small enough to be regarded as a particle. Then, using integral calculus, we add vectorially the forces due to each piece. The sum (or integral) gives the total gravitational force.

Showing this procedure is beyond our present scope (see Chaps. 20 and 21), but the answer for objects with a spherical distribution of mass, such as a billiard ball and a ping-pong ball, is remarkably simple. Consider two spherically symmetric objects, A and B, as shown in Fig. 7-6. The gravitational force between A and B is the same as it would be if A and B were particles with all the mass of each object concentrated at its center. If you wish to find the gravitational force between two objects with spherical symmetry, such as a billiard ball and the earth, or a billiard ball and a basketball, use Eq. (7-2) with r as the distance between centers and $\hat{\mathbf{r}}$ directed along the line between centers. However, the two objects must be outside of one another. If the billiard ball is inside the basketball, then Eq. (7-2) is invalid.

This result for objects with spherical symmetry is a consequence of two features of the gravitational force: (i) the force is directed along the line joining the particles and (ii) the force is an inverse-square force. The electric force between two charged particles has these same two features. We shall return to this problem of the force between objects with spherical symmetry when discussing electric forces in Chap. 21.

Now consider the gravitational force on a chair near the surface of the earth. A chair is shaped nothing like a sphere. What force law do we use in this case? We still use Eq. (7-2). The chair does not have spherical symmetry, but the earth

Newton's law of universal gravitation

Figure 7-5. Newton's law of universal gravitation. The gravitational force $\mathbf{F}_{12}$ exerted by particle 1 on particle 2 is directed toward particle 1.

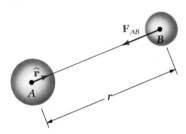

Figure 7-6. Gravitational force $\mathbf{F}_{AB}$ by object A with spherical symmetry on object B with spherical symmetry. Each object interacts gravitationally as a particle with all the mass of the object located at its center.

Gravitationally, an object with spherical symmetry behaves as a particle with all its mass located at its center.

does. In describing the interaction, the earth may be treated as a particle with mass m_e located at the center of the earth. Since the distance from the chair to the center of the earth is $R_e = 6.37 \times 10^6$ m, the separation r between the chair and the "earth-treated-as-a-particle" is large compared with the dimensions of the chair (≈ 1 m). This means that the chair may be treated as a particle too. Thus the gravitational force $\mathbf{F}_e$ exerted by the earth on an object of mass m at the surface of the earth is

Weight of an object near the surface of the earth

$$\mathbf{F}_e = -\left(\frac{Gmm_e}{R_e^2}\right)\hat{\mathbf{r}}$$

where m_e is the mass of the earth, R_e is the radius of the earth, and $\hat{\mathbf{r}}$ is a unit vector directed away from the center of the earth. This force is the weight of the object, which we have expressed as

$$\mathbf{F}_e = m\mathbf{g}$$

A comparison of these equations for the weight of an object provides us with an expression for the magnitude g of the acceleration due to gravity. Since $Gmm_e/R_e^2 = mg$, we have

$$g = \frac{Gm_e}{R_e^2} \tag{7-3}$$

Newton's law of universal gravitation shows why all objects falling freely near the surface of the earth have the same acceleration. The acceleration depends on properties of the earth (m_e and R_e) and is independent of any property of the falling object.

7-3 THE GRAVITATIONAL CONSTANT G

An accurate measurement of the gravitational constant G eluded scientists for many years. The constant cannot be evaluated from the radii and periods of the planetary orbits without first knowing the mass of the sun. We can see why this is so by applying Newton's second law, $\Sigma\mathbf{F} = m\mathbf{a}$, to a planet: $Gm_sm_p/R^2 = m_pa_c$. Solving for G, we have

$$G = \frac{a_cR^2}{m_s}$$

As we have seen, the radii and periods of the orbits of the planets give $a_cR^2 \approx 1.33 \times 10^{20}$ m^3/s^2 for each planet (Table 7-1). However, without knowing the mass of the sun, we cannot determine G.

Another way to try to find G is from the measured values of g and R_e. Solving Eq. (7-3) for G gives

$$G = \frac{gR_e^2}{m_e}$$

However, without first knowing the mass of the earth, we cannot determine G.

This problem of finding the value of G can be solved by measuring the magnitude F_{12} of the force between two spherically shaped objects of known masses m_1 and m_2 that are a known distance r apart. Solving Eq. (7-2) for G, we have

$$G = \frac{F_{12}r^2}{m_1 m_2} \qquad (7\text{-}4)$$

The values of the measurements can then be inserted into Eq. (7-4). However, an accurate measurement of G is very difficult to make. The difficulty is that if m_1 and m_2 are of ordinary size, say a few kilograms, then F_{12} is exceedingly small.

It was in 1798, 71 years after Newton's death, that Henry Cavendish (1731–1810) made the first reasonably accurate measurement of G with a device now called a Cavendish balance (Fig. 7-7). He used four lead balls: balls a and b were of equal mass and balls A and B were of equal mass but different from a and b. Balls a and b were placed on each end of a light rod to form a dumbbell, which was suspended by a thin fiber. Balls A and B were placed near a and b on opposite sides, as seen in the figure, so that the gravitational attraction between a and A and between b and B caused the thin fiber to twist by a measurable amount. A mirror was attached to the rod so that a beam of light reflected from the mirror to a scale gave a precise measure of the equilibrium orientation of the rod. Then A and B were repositioned as shown by the dashed circles in the figure. In this second configuration, the gravitational attraction between the balls caused the fiber to twist in the opposite sense. The new equilibrium orientation of the rod was then recorded. From a separate measurement of the forces on a and b which twist the fiber a given amount, the gravitational forces were calculated.

Cavendish described his experiment as "weighing the earth." Indeed, once G is known, the mass of the earth can be determined. For that matter, the mass of the other planets and the mass of the sun can also be found. The presently accepted value of G is

$$G = 6.670 \times 10^{-11}\ \text{N} \cdot \text{m}^2/\text{kg}^2$$

Besides finding the value of G, the Cavendish balance has also been used to confirm the mass and distance dependence in Newton's law of universal gravitation.

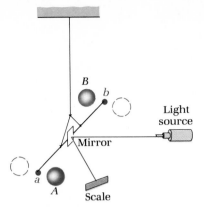

Figure 7-7. A schematic drawing of a Cavendish balance. The balance can be used to measure G and to provide experimental verification of the distance and mass dependence in Newton's law of universal gravitation.

The value of G

EXAMPLE 7-1. Determine the magnitude of the gravitational force between a billiard ball of mass 0.2 kg and a basketball of mass 0.6 kg when they are separated by a distance of 0.5 m between their centers.

SOLUTION. From Newton's law of universal gravitation, Eq. (7-2), the magnitude of the force is

$$F_{12} = \frac{Gm_1 m_2}{r^2} = \frac{(6.67 \times 10^{-11}\ \text{N} \cdot \text{m}^2/\text{kg}^2)(0.2\ \text{kg})(0.6\ \text{kg})}{(0.5\ \text{m})^2}$$

$$= 3 \times 10^{-11}\ \text{N}$$

This is a very small force magnitude, not enough to noticeably affect either ball.

EXAMPLE 7-2. Using the value of G and the data of Table 7-1, determine the mass of the sun.

SOLUTION. From Table 7-1 we have $a_c R^2 =$ $1.33 \times 10^{20}\ \text{m}^3/\text{s}^2$, and we previously noted that $G = a_c R^2 / m_s$. Therefore,

$$m_s = \frac{a_c R^2}{G} = \frac{1.33 \times 10^{20}\ \text{m}^3/\text{s}^2}{6.67 \times 10^{-11}\ \text{N} \cdot \text{m}^2/\text{kg}^2} = 1.99 \times 10^{30}\ \text{kg}$$

EXAMPLE 7-3. Determine the mass of the earth from the radius of the earth ($R_e = 6.37 \times 10^6\ \text{m} = 6.37\ \text{Mm}$), the magnitude of the acceleration due to gravity at the earth's surface ($g = 9.8\ \text{m/s}^2$), and G.

SOLUTION. Solving Eq. (7-3), $g = Gm_e/R_e^2$, for m_e, we have

$$m_e = \frac{gR_e^2}{G} = \frac{(9.8\ \text{m/s}^2)(6.37\ \text{Mm})^2}{6.670 \times 10^{-11}\ \text{N} \cdot \text{m}^2/\text{kg}^2} = 6.0 \times 10^{24}\ \text{kg}$$

EXAMPLE 7-4. Construct a graph of the distance dependence of the magnitude of the gravitational force by the earth on a 1.00-kg object in the range of distances from R_e to $4R_e$ from the earth's center. Determine the force magnitude at R_e, $2R_e$, $3R_e$, and $4R_e$; plot the points; and then sketch a curve between the points.

SOLUTION. Let e represent the earth and b the object. At R_e,

$$F_{eb} = \frac{Gm_e m_b}{R_e^2}$$

$$= \frac{(6.67 \times 10^{-11}\ \text{N} \cdot \text{m}^2/\text{kg}^2)(5.97 \times 10^{24}\ \text{kg})(1.00\ \text{kg})}{(6.37\ \text{Mm})^2} = 9.81\ \text{N}$$

At $2R_e$,

$$F_{eb} = \frac{Gm_e m_b}{(2R_e)^2} = \frac{9.81\ \text{N}}{2^2} = \frac{9.81\ \text{N}}{4} = 2.45\ \text{N}$$

At $3R_e$,

$$F_{eb} = \frac{Gm_e m_b}{(3R_e)^2} = \frac{9.81\ \text{N}}{3^2} = \frac{9.81\ \text{N}}{9} = 1.09\ \text{N}$$

Similarly, at $4R_e$,

$$F_{eb} = \frac{Gm_e m_b}{(4R_e)^2} = \frac{9.81\ \text{N}}{4^2} = \frac{9.81\ \text{N}}{16} = 0.613\ \text{N}$$

The graph is shown in Fig. 7-8.

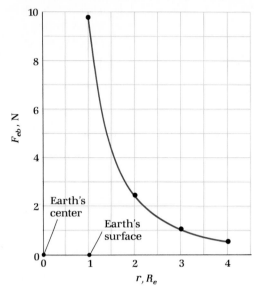

Figure 7-8. Example 7-4: The magnitude F_{eb} of the gravitational force by the earth on object b ($m_b = 1.00$ kg) versus distance r from the center of the earth.

EXAMPLE 7-5. As with other forces, gravitational forces add vectorially. Consider a spacecraft traveling from the earth to the moon along a straight line between the center of the earth and the center of the moon. At what distance from the center of the earth is the force $\mathbf{F}_{es}$ by the earth on the spacecraft equal and opposite the force $\mathbf{F}_{ms}$ by the moon on the spacecraft? The mass of the moon is $m_m = 7.35 \times 10^{22}$ kg, and the radius of the moon's orbit about the earth is $r_{em} = 3.84 \times 10^8$ m = 384 Mm.

SOLUTION. Figure 7-9 shows a coordinate frame, with the center of the earth at the origin and the x axis extending to the moon. Since any gravitational force is attractive, the point P where $\mathbf{F}_{es}$ and $\mathbf{F}_{ms}$ are equal and opposite must be on this axis and between the earth and the moon. In the figure we show this point at a distance x from the center of the earth and a distance $r_{em} - x$ from the center of the moon. Setting the magnitudes of the two forces equal, we have

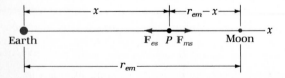

Figure 7-9. Example 7-5: Finding the distance x from the center of the earth to the point P where the gravitational forces on a spaceship due to the earth ($\mathbf{F}_{es}$) and due to the moon ($\mathbf{F}_{ms}$) are equal and opposite.

$$\frac{Gm m_e}{x^2} = \frac{Gm m_m}{(r_{em} - x)^2}$$

where m is the mass of the spaceship. Rearranging gives

$$\left(1 - \frac{m_m}{m_e}\right)x^2 - (2r_{em})x + r_{em}^2 = 0$$

This equation for x is a quadratic equation. Using the solution to a quadratic equation (App. M), we find

$$x = \frac{r_{em}}{1 \pm \sqrt{m_m/m_e}}$$

The plus or minus sign indicates that there are two points on the x axis where the force magnitudes are equal. For the minus sign, $x > r_{em}$. This corresponds to a point on the opposite side of the moon from the earth. At this point the two forces are equal in magnitude and in the *same* direction. Since we want the point where the forces are equal in magnitude and *opposite* in direction, we discard the solution with the minus sign. For the plus sign, $x < r_{em}$. This corresponds to a point between the earth and the moon and is the point of interest in this example. The ratio of the mass of the moon to the mass of the earth (see Table 7-1) is

$$\frac{m_m}{m_e} = \frac{0.0735 \times 10^{24}\ \text{kg}}{5.97 \times 10^{24}\ \text{kg}} = 0.0123$$

so that

$$x = \frac{384 \text{ Mm}}{1 + \sqrt{0.0123}} = (0.900)(384 \text{ Mm}) = 346 \text{ Mm}$$

The point between the earth and the moon where the two forces cancel is 90 percent of the way to the moon.

7-4 GRAVITATIONAL AND INERTIAL MASS

From Chap. 5 we know that the mass m of an object is the proportionality factor between the net force $\Sigma \mathbf{F}$ exerted on the object and the object's acceleration $\mathbf{a}$, or $\Sigma \mathbf{F} = m\mathbf{a}$. Thus *the mass of an object is that property of the object which causes it to resist a change in its velocity.* For that reason we often call the mass the *inertial mass.* Suppose a runaway grocery cart loaded with groceries is rolling out of control down a supermarket aisle and you must stop the cart before it crashes into a stack of cans. The force required to stop the cart depends on its inertial mass.

Inertial mass

In this chapter we have seen that the mass of an object also appears in Newton's law of universal gravitation. The magnitude F of the gravitational force on an object of mass m due to another object of mass M is $F = GmM/r^2$. (We assume that the two objects may be treated as particles.) In this expression *the mass of the object is that property of the object that causes it to be attracted to another object by the gravitational force.* For that reason, the mass that appears in Newton's law of universal gravitation often is called the *gravitational mass.* Suppose you are holding a bag of groceries while waiting for your roommate. The force you must exert while holding the bag depends on the gravitational mass of the bag of groceries.

Gravitational mass

The difficulty you encounter in stopping the runaway cart has nothing to do with its gravitational mass. The effort you expend in holding the bag of groceries has nothing to do with its inertial mass. The term "mass of an object" characterizes two different properties of the object. On the one hand, it is a measure of an object's resistance to a change of velocity (inertial mass), and on the other hand, it is a measure of an object's gravitational attraction to other objects in its environment (gravitational mass). For the purpose of this discussion, let us distinguish the inertial mass from the gravitational mass by using the symbol m_I for the former and m_G for the latter.

Mass characterizes two different properties of matter.

Why are these two different properties of matter, the inertial mass and the gravitational mass, both called "mass"? Because experiment shows that they are proportional to one another. One such experiment is the measurement of the acceleration of different objects during free-fall. During free-fall, all forces on an object are negligible except for the force of gravity; the net force on the object is the gravitational force due to the earth. Consider a golf ball in free-fall near the surface of the earth and let the $+y$ direction be vertically upward. Then $\Sigma F_y = -Gm_G m_e/R_e^2$, where m_G is the gravitational mass of the ball. The y component of Newton's second law gives

$$-\frac{Gm_G m_e}{R_e^2} = m_I a_y$$

where m_I is the inertial mass of the golf ball. Solving for a_y, we have

$$a_y = -\left(\frac{Gm_e}{R_e^2}\right)\left(\frac{m_G}{m_I}\right)$$

The factor (Gm_e/R_e^2) is independent of the object whose motion we are describing (the golf ball), but m_G and m_I depend on this object. As you know, all freely falling objects have the same acceleration: $a_y = -g$. If we drop a rock instead of a golf ball, then $a_y = -g$ for the rock. Thus a_y is independent of the object. This means that the ratio (m_G/m_I) must be independent of the object. In other words, our experiment shows that m_G must be proportional to m_I for each object. Since m_I is proportional to m_G, we may choose our units in such a way that they are made equal. This was tacitly done when G was evaluated from the results of the Cavendish experiment. Thus $m_I = m_G$.

Experiment shows that m_I is proportional to m_G, and our units are chosen such that $m_I = m_G$.

The statement that the inertial mass is the same as the gravitational mass is an experimental statement. The validity of the statement depends on the accuracy of the experiments. Modern experiments have shown that the statement is valid to at least three parts in 10^{11}.

7-5 THE VARIATION OF g ON THE EARTH'S SURFACE

Newton's law of universal gravitation helps us understand why the earth (as well as the other planets and the sun) is spherical. The earth's own gravitational force tends to shape it as a sphere. Each part of the earth is attracted to every other part. The way to pack all the parts together so that they are as close to each other as possible is to pack them in the shape of a sphere.

However, the earth is not exactly spherical. It is more nearly shaped as an oblate spheroid, slightly flattened at the poles, similar to a beach ball that is compressed by someone sitting on it. This oblateness is a result of the spinning of the earth about its axis. Like a pot being formed on a potter's wheel, the earth bulges slightly around its middle (near the equator). The distance from the center of the earth to one of the poles is about 6.36 Mm, and the distance from the center of the earth to the equator is about 6.38 Mm. A measure of the earth's oblateness is given by

The earth is slightly oblate.

$$\frac{6.38 \text{ Mm} - 6.36 \text{ Mm}}{6.37 \text{ Mm}} = 0.003$$

Therefore the earth is nearly spherical. If a basketball had the same degree of oblateness as the earth, its radius the long way would be $\frac{1}{2}$ mm larger than the short way. There probably are not many basketballs that are as nearly spherical as the earth.

Because of the earth's oblateness and other irregularities, the gravitational acceleration g varies with latitude on the earth's surface. Since a point at sea level near the poles is closer to the earth's center than a similar point at the equator, g is a few tenths of a percent larger at the poles. At midlatitudes, g ranges between its value at the equator and the poles. This slight variation of g causes the magnitude mg of the weight of an object to depend slightly on latitude. As discussed in Chap. 6, because of the earth's rotation about its axis, there is also a dependence on latitude of the apparent weight of an object.

EXAMPLE 7-6. Assume that the earth has exact spherical symmetry, with radius $R_e = 6.37$ Mm, which is the distance from the center of the earth to sea level at midlatitudes.

(a) Develop an expression for $g(h)$ where h is the height of a point above the earth's (assumed) spherical surface. Use the expression from part (a) to evaluate g (b) at sea level ($h = 0$)

and (c) at the top of Mount Everest ($h = 8.9$ km ≈ 0.01 Mm).

SOLUTION. (a) If the earth has exact spherical symmetry, then at the earth's surface $mg = Gmm_e/R_e^2$ so that

$$g = \frac{Gm_e}{R_e^2}$$

A point at a distance h above the earth's surface is a distance $r = R_e + h$ from the earth's center so that

$$g(h) = \frac{Gm_e}{(R_e + h)^2}$$

(b) At sea level,

$$g = \frac{(6.67 \times 10^{-11}\ \text{N} \cdot \text{m}^2/\text{kg}^2)(5.97 \times 10^{24}\ \text{kg})}{(6.37\ \text{Mm})^2} = 9.81\ \text{m/s}^2$$

(c) At the top of Mount Everest,

$$g = \frac{(6.67 \times 10^{-11}\ \text{N} \cdot \text{m}^2/\text{kg}^2)(5.97 \times 10^{24}\ \text{kg})}{(6.37\ \text{Mm} + 0.01\ \text{Mm})^2}$$

$$= 9.78\ \text{m/s}^2$$

This result indicates that in midlatitudes the acceleration due to gravity is about 0.3 percent smaller on top of Mount Everest than it is at sea level.

7-6 THE GRAVITATIONAL FIELD

Often a convenient way to deal with gravitational forces is to use the concept of a gravitational field. The *gravitational field* $\mathbf{g}$ at a point P is defined as the gravitational force $\mathbf{F}$ on a particle located at P divided by the mass m of the particle:

Definition of the gravitational field

$$\mathbf{g} = \frac{\mathbf{F}}{m} \tag{7-5}$$

Thus the gravitational field is the gravitational force per unit mass.

We previously called $\mathbf{g}$ the acceleration due to gravity. More specifically, it was used to represent the quantity $-(9.8\ \text{m/s}^2)\mathbf{j}$, where $\mathbf{j}$ is directed upward (away from the center of the earth). Now we see that this is a particular value of a more general concept; it is the value of the gravitational field at a point near the surface of the earth.

Consider the gravitational field of a particle. From Eq. (7-2), the gravitational force on particle 2 due to particle 1 is $\mathbf{F}_{12} = -(Gm_2m_1/r^2)\hat{\mathbf{r}}$. Let us write this as

$$\mathbf{F}_{12} = m_2\mathbf{g}_1 \tag{7-6}$$

Gravitational field of a particle

where

$$\mathbf{g}_1 = -\frac{Gm_1}{r^2}\hat{\mathbf{r}} \tag{7-7}$$

The quantity $\mathbf{g}_1$ is the gravitational field of particle 1 at the point P, where P is a distance r from the particle and $\hat{\mathbf{r}}$ is directed from the particle to P (Fig. 7-10).

Equations (7-6) and (7-7) taken together give the same information as Eq. (7-2), so that we have not added anything. The convenience comes about because we have divided the calculation of the force on particle 2 into two parts. Equation (7-6) states that the force on 2 is the mass of 2 multiplied by the gravitational field due to particle 1. Equation (7-7) shows how to determine the gravitational field due to particle 1. Therefore, in determining the force by 1 on 2, we can start off by calculating the gravitational field due to 1 while forgetting about 2. Then we find the force on 2 by multiplying the mass of 2 by the value of the field at 2's position. By introducing the gravitational field, we have broken the problem into two parts, which we can then solve one at a time. In dealing with two particles this procedure is of little use, but in more complex problems it is very helpful.

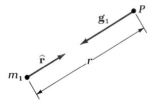

Figure 7-10. Gravitational field $\mathbf{g}_1$ of particle 1 at point P. The field has magnitude $g_1 = Gm_1/r^2$ and is directed toward particle 1.

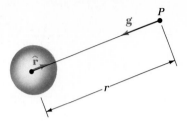

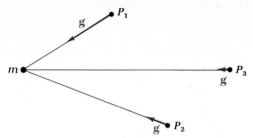

Figure 7-11. Gravitational field **g** of an object with spherical symmetry at a point P outside the object.

Figure 7-12. The gravitational field of a particle of mass m is shown at three representative points. The field is directed toward the particle at each point and decreases with distance r as $1/r^2$. Point P_3 is twice as far from the particle as P_1, so that the field at P_3 has one-fourth the magnitude it has at P_1.

A spherically symmetric object behaves gravitationally as a particle at points outside the object. Thus the gravitational field of a spherically symmetric object of mass m and radius R is

Gravitational field of an object with spherical symmetry

$$\mathbf{g} = -\frac{Gm}{r^2}\,\hat{\mathbf{r}} \qquad (r > R) \tag{7-8}$$

where r is the distance from the center of the object to the point P where the field is evaluated, and $\hat{\mathbf{r}}$ is a unit vector directed away from the center of the object and toward P (Fig. 7-11).

The concept of a gravitational field introduces more than simply a convenient procedure for calculating gravitational forces; it also provides an alternative view of the gravitational interaction. Now we regard space as being modified by the presence of an object; the object *produces* a gravitational field. We associate a physical quantity, the gravitational field, with each point in space (Fig. 7-12). Later, when we study electricity and magnetism, we shall find that the concept of a field is a central feature of our inquiry.

A gravitational field is viewed as a condition established in space by an object with mass.

From Eq. (7-5), $\mathbf{g} = \mathbf{F}/m$, the dimension of $\mathbf{g}$ is force divided by mass. Previously, when we viewed $\mathbf{g}$ as an acceleration, we gave its dimension as length divided by time squared. From Newton's second law, these two dimensions are the same. When we write $\mathbf{g}$'s dimension as length/(time)^2, we are treating it as an acceleration, but when we write $\mathbf{g}$'s dimension as force/mass, we are treating it as a gravitational field.

EXAMPLE 7-7. Since gravitational forces add vectorially, gravitational fields add vectorially too. (a) Determine the resultant gravitational field **g** due to the individual fields of the earth ($\mathbf{g}_e$) and of the sun ($\mathbf{g}_s$) at a point P along a straight line between the earth and the sun. The distance from the earth to P is the same as the radius of the moon's orbit around the earth. The radius of the moon's orbit about the earth is 3.84×10^8 m, and the remaining data are given in Table 7-1. (b) Determine the force on the moon due to both the earth and the sun when the moon is at P. The moon's mass is 7.35×10^{22} kg.

SOLUTION. (a) Between the earth and the sun the contribution to the gravitational field due to the earth is opposite that due to the sun. The field of the earth is toward the earth, and the field of the sun is toward the sun. If we let the unit vector **i** be directed from the earth toward the sun, the resultant field is

$$\mathbf{g} = \mathbf{g}_e + \mathbf{g}_s = -\frac{Gm_e}{r_{eP}^2}\,\mathbf{i} + \frac{Gm_s}{r_{sP}^2}\,\mathbf{i}$$

where r_{eP} is the distance from the earth to P and r_{sP} is the distance from the sun to P:

$$r_{eP} = 3.84 \times 10^8 \text{ m}$$

and

$$r_{sP} = 1.496 \times 10^{11} \text{ m} - 3.84 \times 10^8 \text{ m} = 1.492 \times 10^{11} \text{ m}$$

Thus

$$\mathbf{g} = -\frac{(6.67 \times 10^{-11} \text{ N} \cdot \text{m}^2/\text{kg}^2)(5.97 \times 10^{24} \text{ kg})}{(3.84 \times 10^8 \text{ m})^2} \mathbf{i}$$

$$+ \frac{(6.67 \times 10^{-11} \text{ N} \cdot \text{m}^2/\text{kg}^2)(1.99 \times 10^{30} \text{ kg})}{(1.492 \times 10^{11} \text{ m})^2} \mathbf{i}$$

$$= -(2.70 \times 10^{-3} \text{ N/kg})\mathbf{i} + (5.96 \times 10^{-3} \text{ N/kg})\mathbf{i}$$

$$= (3.26 \times 10^{-3} \text{ N/kg})\mathbf{i}$$

The resultant field is directed toward the sun because the contribution to the field by the sun is larger than that by the earth. (b) Using the field we determined in part (a), we find that the force **F** on the moon is

$$\mathbf{F} = m_m \mathbf{g} = (7.35 \times 10^{22} \text{ kg})(3.26 \times 10^{-3} \text{ N/kg})\mathbf{i}$$

$$= (2.40 \times 10^{20} \text{ N})\mathbf{i}$$

At point P, the force due to both the earth and the sun is directed toward the sun and away from the earth. If you find this result surprising, you may wish to pursue it by working Exercise 7-3 and Prob. 7-6.

7-7 ☙ ORBITS, NUMERICAL METHODS

To understand how a satellite continually moves in its orbit, consider launching a projectile horizontally from the top of a high mountain. Because we are interested in satellite motion, we neglect air friction. The distance the projectile travels before hitting the ground depends on the launching speed: the greater the speed, the greater the distance. The distance the projectile travels before hitting the ground is also affected by the curvature of the earth, as illustrated in Fig. 7-13. This figure, used by Newton in the *Principia*, shows different trajectories for different launching speeds. As the launching speed is made greater, a speed is reached whereby the projectile's path follows the curvature of the earth. This is the launching speed which places the projectile in a circular orbit. Thus an object in circular orbit may be regarded as falling, but as it falls its path is concentric with the earth's spherical surface and the object maintains a fixed distance from the earth's center. Since this motion may continue indefinitely, we may say that the orbit is *stable*.

Let us find the speed v of a satellite of mass m in circular orbit around the earth. We assume that the rest frame of the earth may be treated as an inertial reference frame and that the gravitational force by the earth is the only significant force on the satellite. These assumptions are valid if the radius of the orbit

Figure 7-13. A figure used by Newton in the *Principia* to illustrate the trajectory of a projectile launched horizontally from the top of a tall mountain (V). (We neglect friction.) As the projectile's launching speed is increased, its range is increased and its landing point is farther from the mountain (from D to E to F to G). If the launching speed is made large enough, the projectile's path follows the curvature of the earth. (*A.I.P., Niels Bohr Library*)

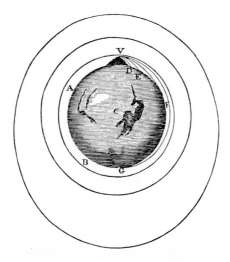

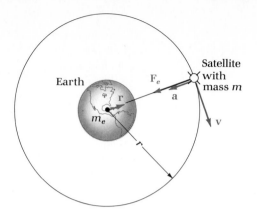

Figure 7-14. A satellite in circular orbit around the earth. The net force on the satellite is the gravitational force due to the earth, $\mathbf{F}_e = -(Gmm_e/r^2)\hat{\mathbf{r}}$. The acceleration $\mathbf{a}$ is parallel to $\mathbf{F}_e$, with magnitude v^2/r. The velocity $\mathbf{v}$ is perpendicular to $\mathbf{F}_e$ and $\mathbf{a}$, and $v = \sqrt{Gm_e/r}$.

is not too large. Newton's second law, $\Sigma\mathbf{F} = m\mathbf{a}$, applied to the satellite gives

$$\frac{Gmm_e}{r^2} = m\left(\frac{v^2}{r}\right)$$

where the speed v is relative to the center of the earth. The direction of the force and the acceleration are toward the center of the earth, as shown in Fig. 7-14. Solving for v, we have

$$v = \sqrt{\frac{Gm_e}{r}}$$

A satellite with this speed continually moves in its circular orbit of radius r.

Numerical methods. In Chap. 4, we developed a program for the trajectory of a baseball (Table 4-2). By modifying this program, we can use it to describe the circular orbit of a satellite. To proceed, we (1) select a consistent set of initial conditions, (2) determine the equations for the x and y components of the acceleration, and (3) find a convenient time interval for the iterations.

1 Let the orbital radius be, say three earth radii: $r = 3R_e = (3)(6.37\ \text{Mm}) = 19.1\ \text{Mm}$. Then the speed of the satellite is

$$v = \sqrt{\frac{Gm_e}{r}} = \sqrt{\frac{(6.67 \times 10^{-11}\ \text{N} \cdot \text{m}^2/\text{kg}^2)(5.97 \times 10^{24}\ \text{kg})}{19.1\ \text{Mm}}} = 4.56\ \text{km/s}$$

We use the coordinate frame shown in Fig. 7-15. The center of the earth is at the origin and the initial position of the satellite is at $x_0 = 0$ and $y_0 = 19.1$ Mm. Since the velocity $\mathbf{v}$ must be perpendicular to a line from the center of the earth to the satellite, we let the initial components of $\mathbf{v}$ be $v_{x0} = 4.56$ km/s and $v_{y0} = 0$.

2 To determine the acceleration of the satellite, we find the net force on it and use Newton's second law. Figure 7-16 shows the x and y components of the force on the satellite. The x component is

$$F_{ex} = -F_e \cos\theta = -F_e\left(\frac{x}{r}\right) = -\left(\frac{Gm_e m}{r^2}\right)\left(\frac{x}{r}\right) = -\frac{Gm_e mx}{r^3}$$

From Newton's second law, $a_x = \Sigma F_x/m = F_{ex}/m$. Therefore, the x component of the satellite's acceleration is $a_x = -Gm_e x/r^3$. Since $r = \sqrt{x^2 + y^2}$, the expression for a_x in cartesian coordinates is

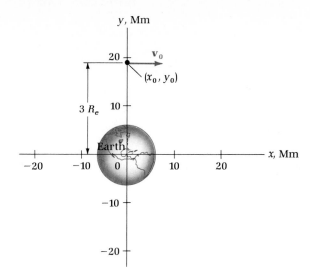

Figure 7-15. Initial conditions used in the program in Table 7-2 for an earth satellite.

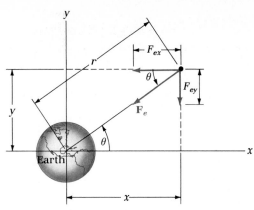

Figure 7-16. Finding the x and y components of the force on a satellite in an earth orbit: $F_{ex} = -F_e(x/r)$ and $F_{ey} = -F_e(y/r)$.

$$a_x = -\frac{Gm_e x}{(x^2 + y^2)^{3/2}}$$

Inserting the numerical values of G and m_e gives

$$a_x = -\frac{(3.98 \times 10^{14} \text{ m}^3/\text{s}^2)x}{(x^2 + y^2)^{3/2}}$$

Similarly,

$$a_y = -\frac{(3.98 \times 10^{14} \text{ m}^3/\text{s}^2)y}{(x^2 + y^2)^{3/2}}$$

3 To determine a convenient time interval for the iterations, we find the period T of the orbit. For uniform circular motion, $v = 2\pi r/T$, or $T = 2\pi r/v$. Inserting $r = 19.1$ Mm and $v = 4.56$ km/s, we find that $T = 2.63 \times 10^4$ s. A convenient procedure is to let the computer perform 1000 iterations with time intervals of 26.3 s. In that way the program will encompass one complete revolution.

Table 7-2 gives a BASIC program which produces coordinates for 20 posi-

Table 7-2. BASIC program for an object in circular orbit around the earth (Note that E+7 means 10^7.)

```
100     X=0
110     Y=1.91E+7
120     VX=4.56E+3
130     VY=0
140     T=0
150     DT=26.3
200         For I=1 TO 1000
210         AX=-3.98E+14*X/(X*X+Y*Y)^1.5
220         AY=-3.98E+14*Y/(X*X+Y*Y)^1.5
230         VX=VX+AX*DT
240         VY=VY+AY*DT
250         X=X+VX*DT
260         Y=Y+VY*DT
270         T=T+DT
280         IF I=50*INT(I/50) THEN PRINT T, X, Y
300         NEXT I
310     END
```

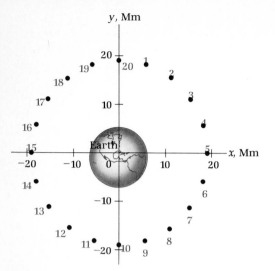

Figure 7-17. A graph of the orbit of an earth satellite. Data taken from the program in Table 7-2.

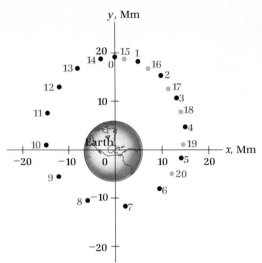

Figure 7-18. A graph of the orbit of the earth satellite after editing the program of Table 7-2 so that $v_0 = (4.00 \text{ km s}^{-1})\mathbf{i}$. The orbit is an ellipse, with the center of the earth at one focus.

tions. Figure 7-17 shows a graph of the orbit. To show that the orbit is a circle, we can substitute the coordinates at each position into the expression $x^2 + y^2 = r^2$. When this is done we find that $r = 19.1$ Mm at each position. Within the accuracy of our data, the orbit is a circle.

Elliptical orbits. We can use this same program in Table 7-2 to find out what happens if the initial speed is not the right value for a circular orbit. Suppose we edit statement 120 so that the initial velocity is, say (4.00 km/s)$\mathbf{i}$:

$$120 \text{ VX} = 4\text{E} + 3$$

A graph of the resulting data is given in Fig. 7-18. An analysis of this graph shows that the orbit is an *ellipse,* with the center of the earth at one focus. The point where the orbit is farthest from the earth is called the *apogee,* and the point where the orbit is nearest the earth is called the *perigee.* From the figure, we estimate that the distance from the center of the earth to the apogee is about 19 Mm, and the distance from the center of the earth to the perigee is about 12 Mm.

Notice that the spacing between positions is smaller near the apogee than near the perigee. Since there are equal time intervals between these positions, this means that the satellite is traveling slower near the apogee and faster near the perigee. Also, notice that the second revolution is tracing out the same path as the first.

It is instructive to try a few other initial velocities. How small can you make the initial velocity and still have the satellite miss the earth? That is, try to find the value of v_{x0} that gives the distance from the center of the earth to the perigee to be R_e.

We stated above that the orbital path is an ellipse when the velocity does not have just the right value for a circular orbit. This is true as long as the speed is not too great. If the speed is much greater, great enough so that the satellite is

Apogee and perigee

Nicolaus Copernicus *(A.I.P., Niels Bohr Library)*

Tycho Brahe *(A.I.P., Niels Bohr Library)*

Johannes Kepler *(A.I.P.)*

just barely able to escape the earth and never return, then the path is a parabola. If the velocity is greater still, then the path is a hyperbola. These types of curves are called *conic sections.* To prove that orbital paths are always one of these conic sections, we would be required to use analytical methods beyond the scope of this book. Such a proof provides an example of some of the advantages of analytical methods as compared with numerical methods. One cannot show with numerical methods that all orbits are conic sections.

7-8 THE DISCOVERY OF THE LAW OF GRAVITATION

The way the law of universal gravitation was discovered is often considered the paradigm of modern scientific technique. The major steps involved were (1) the hypothesis about planetary motion given by Nicolaus Copernicus (1473–1543); (2) the careful experimental measurements of the positions of the planets and the sun by Tycho Brahe (1546–1601); (3) analysis of the data and the formulation of empirical laws by Johannes Kepler (1571–1630); and (4) the development of a general theory by Isaac Newton.

1 Although a sun-centered, or heliocentric, model of the solar system had been proposed by Aristarchus in the third century B.C., for many centuries the western world believed that the earth remains fixed while the sun and planets circle it. This earth-centered, or geocentric, model required elaborate geometrical schemes to account for the observed motion of the planets. In his book *De Revolutionibus Orbium Coelestium (On the Revolution of the Heavenly Spheres)*, Copernicus asserted that the geocentric model was not "sufficiently pleasing to the mind." He proposed a system using the following assumptions: (*a*) the earth rotates on its axis once per day, (*b*) the earth revolves around the sun (along with the other planets), and (*c*) the stars are at a much greater distance from the earth than are the sun and the planets.
2 The work of Tycho Brahe exemplifies the fundamental basis of experimental research: *If you want to know how something works, carefully measure its behavior.* He spent the last half of his life, more than 20 years, precisely measuring the positions of the sun and planets. His measurements provided the data for those who followed to solve the mysteries of the motion of celestial objects. During his final years Brahe acquired Johannes Kepler as his assistant.
3 Kepler possessed great mathematical and computational abilities. He used these skills and Brahe's measurements to determine the orbits of the planets, especially those of the earth and Mars. He condensed his findings into three laws:

All planets move in elliptical orbits with the sun at one focus (Fig. 7-19).

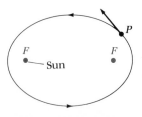

Figure 7-19. Kepler's first law. The orbit of a planet is an ellipse, with the sun at one focus. For the sake of illustration, the eccentricity of the ellipse shown is much greater than that of any of the actual planetary orbits.

Kepler's laws of planetary motion

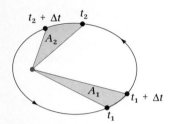

Figure 7-20. Kepler's second law. The time intervals Δt are the same for the two cases shown. Kepler's second law states that $A_1 = A_2$.

A line joining any planet to the sun sweeps out equal areas in equal time intervals (Fig. 7-20).

The square of the period of any planet is proportional to the cube of the planet's average distance from the sun.

With his three laws, Kepler introduced more than a precise characterization of the solar system. He also initiated a new way of describing natural phenomena. The description takes the form of brief, concentrated, broadly applicable statements, which we now call "laws." Kepler fostered the tenet of modern science that the proper description of natural phenomena is the simplest one that complies with the experimental data. Uncommon for his day, Kepler insisted that a successful theory must conform to the strict details of experimental measurements. Kepler would have greatly appreciated the further generalizations by Newton.

4 By introducing the laws of motion and the law of universal gravitation, Newton provided a general theory that unified the astronomical laws of Kepler and terrestrial experience. One of the tests to which Newton subjected his laws was that they give elliptical orbits for the planets, and thus agree with Kepler's first law. We saw an example of this in the previous section. In Sec. 13-6 we will show that Kepler's second law can be developed from Newton's laws.

We now show that Kepler's third law follows from Newton's second law and the law of universal gravitation applied to a planet in a circular orbit. Newton's second law applied to a planet gives $F_{sp} = m_p a_c$, where F_{sp} is the magnitude of the force on the planet by the sun, m_p is the mass of the planet, and a_c is the magnitude of the centripetal acceleration of the planet around the sun. Since $F_{sp} = Gm_s m_p / r^2$ and $a_c = 4\pi^2 r/T^2$, we have

$$\frac{Gm_s m_p}{r^2} = \frac{m_p 4\pi^2 r}{T^2}$$

Solving for T^2 gives

$$T^2 = \left(\frac{4\pi^2}{Gm_s}\right) r^3$$

The factor in the parentheses is a constant, independent of the planet, so that the square of the period T is proportional to the cube of the distance r to the sun. This is Kepler's third law for the case of a circular orbit.

Kepler's three laws of planetary motion can be derived from Newton's second and third laws in combination with Newton's law of universal gravitation. In retrospect, Kepler's empirical laws represent a first step toward the understanding of natural phenomena that is typical of scientific progress. Newton recognized this when he said: "If I have seen farther than others, it is because I stand on the shoulders of giants."

COMMENTARY: FUNDAMENTAL FORCES AND UNIFICATION

In recent years exciting discoveries have been made in physics, discoveries that have revolutionized the way we view matter and the forces that determine the behavior of matter. Physicists are attempting to find an ultimate force law which explains all of the many interactions we observe in nature. This quest to unify all

*forces into one force is based on the concept of a fundamental force. A funda-
mental force is the result of a basic interaction between particles. Such a force
explains many phenomena that cannot be attributed to some other force. For
example, contact forces between macroscopic objects are not regarded as fundamental forces. These forces are a complex manifestation of the more fundamental electromagnetic force (discussed below). By contrast, the gravitational
force is not simply an effect that can be explained as one example of some other
force. The gravitational force is a fundamental force. Or is it? How can we be
certain? Whether a force is regarded as fundamental at a particular time depends on what we know at that time.*

*To be specific, let us place ourselves in the year 1967 and list the fundamental
forces known then. There are four such forces:*

1 *The gravitational force*
2 *The electromagnetic force*
3 *The strong nuclear force*
4 *The weak nuclear force*

*We are already familiar with the gravitational force. After we briefly describe the
other three forces and make a comparison of the four fundamental forces, we
shall discuss progress toward the unification of the fundamental forces.*

*The electromagnetic force is important in many ways. As mentioned above, it
is the underlying cause of the contact forces we experience at the macroscopic
scale, such as friction. This interaction gives rise to the electric shock you feel
when you touch a metal part of a car after sliding across the seat on a cold and
dry winter day. Because it produces electric currents in wires, the electromagnetic force is the basis of a large part of our modern technology. It is regarded as
a fundamental force because it is responsible for interactions between some of
the elementary particles that compose matter. For example, it provides the
attractive force which holds an atom's electrons near the nucleus of the atom. As
the name implies, the electromagnetic force includes both electric and magnetic
forces. These two forces are intimately connected; both are the result of the
same property of matter, the electric charge.*

*The strong nuclear force is the force that binds protons and neutrons together
to form an atomic nucleus. Within a nucleus the protons and neutrons are
confined to a very small space, about 5×10^{-15} m across. Because of their
electric charge, protons repel each other through the electromagnetic force. If it
were not for the dominance of the strong nuclear force, the repulsion between
the protons would make the nucleus unstable; the protons would fly apart and
the nucleus could not exist.*

*The weak nuclear force acts between elementary particles and is responsible
for some nuclear reactions. For example, in radioactive decay a nucleus will
spontaneously disintegrate into several fragments. The weak nuclear force
causes a particular radioactive decay which is called beta decay. In addition, the
weak nuclear force is important in controlling the rate of some of the nuclear
reactions that occur in stars such as the sun. The lifetime of the sun is determined by the characteristics of this force.*

*A comparison of the fundamental forces is given in Table 7-3. Consider the
distance over which each force acts, or the range of the force. The gravitational
and the electromagnetic forces are inverse-square forces. The magnitudes of
these forces weaken with distance but never become zero. The range of these*

Table 7-3. Comparison of the fundamental forces

	Gravitational	Electromagnetic	Strong nuclear	Weak nuclear
Example interactions	Binds stars together to form galaxies	Binds electrons to nuclei to form atoms	Binds protons and neutrons together to form nuclei	Responsible for nuclear beta decay
Range	Infinite	Infinite	10^{-15} m	$\ll 10^{-16}$ m
Relative strength	10^{-39}	10^{-2}	1	10^{-5}

two forces is infinite. The strong nuclear force has a very short range; its effects are imperceptible beyond a separation distance of about 10^{-15} m. The range of the weak nuclear force is smaller still, less than 10^{-16} m.

The relative strength of a force is gauged by the magnitude of the force between elementary particles that are within the range of the force. On a strength scale where the strong nuclear force has a value of 1, the electromagnetic force has a value of 10^{-2}, the weak nuclear force a value of 10^{-5}, and the gravitational force a value of 10^{-39}. The gravitational force is by far the weakest of the fundamental forces. Since the gravitational force is often the dominant force on objects you regularly encounter, this may surprise you. In the case of the strong and weak nuclear forces, objects in the macroscopic world of direct human experience are beyond their range. The direct effects of these forces are seen in

Figure 7-21. The Stanford Linear Accelerator Center (SLAC) is one of several large accelerators where experiments are performed on elementary particles. Particles are accelerated along the 2-mi beam tube to very high energies, and then they collide with other particles. Accelerators such as this one help provide the experimental data for the search for an ultimate force law. *(Stanford Linear Accelerator)*

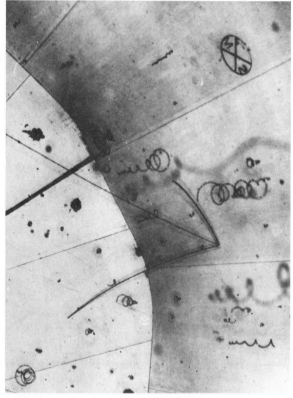

Figure 7-22. The interactions between high-energy elementary particles are revealed in bubble-chamber photographs. As the particles pass through a liquid, such as liquid hydrogen, bubbles are formed along their paths. *(Argonne National Laboratory)*

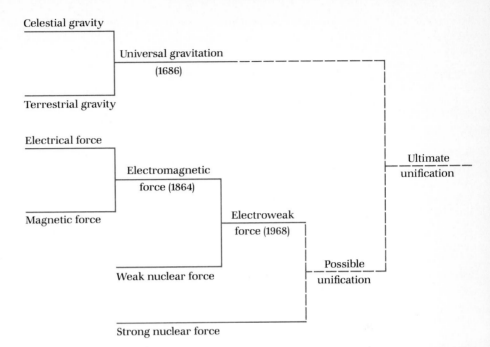

Figure 7-23. Progress toward unification.

experiments using high-energy accelerators that probe deeply into matter (Figs. 7-21 and 7-22). In the case of the electromagnetic force, the electric charge on macroscopic objects is often too small to produce noticeable electric forces. Macroscopic objects consist of elementary particles that have both negative and positive charge. Normally the amount of negative charge is almost exactly the same as the amount of positive charge so that the object is nearly electrically neutral and experiences an insignificant electric force.

The historical trend toward unification is shown in Fig. 7-23. As we have seen in this chapter, Newton unified celestial forces with gravitational forces on earth when he discovered the law of universal gravitation. Experimental work during the nineteenth century unified electrical and magnetic phenomena and culminated with the theory of electromagnetism developed by James Clerk Maxwell. A recent advance toward unification was accomplished independently by Steven Weinberg and Abdus Salam, who showed the underlying connection between the electromagnetic force and the weak nuclear force. This unification gave rise to the so-called electroweak force. An approach similar to that of Weinberg-Salam may bring about the unification of the electroweak force with the strong nuclear force in the near future. In Fig. 7-23, we have dared to speculate on the occurrence of an ultimate unification. Does this most fundamental force exist? If it does exist, is it simple enough to be knowable by humans? The search for unification is based on our belief that, after removing the cloak of complexity, we shall find that nature laid bare is beautifully simple.

SUMMARY WITH APPLICATIONS

Section 7-2. The law of universal gravitation

Newton's law of universal gravitation is a fundamental force law in nature:

$$\mathbf{F}_{12} = -\frac{Gm_1m_2}{r^2}\,\hat{\mathbf{r}} \qquad (7\text{-}2)$$

The gravitational force is always attractive. Since the force depends on the inverse of the square of the separation distance r, the force is called an inverse-square force.

Explain how the periods and the radii of the planetary orbits around the sun lead to Newton's law of universal gravitation; explain why, in the gravitational interaction between the earth and objects near the earth's surface, each object can be treated as a particle.

Section 7-3. The gravitational constant G

The development of Newton's law of universal gravitation was completed with the measurement of G by Cavendish: $G = 6.670 \times 10^{-11}$ N $\cdot$ m²/kg². Gravitational forces could then be calculated.

Describe the Cavendish experiment; use Newton's law of universal gravitation to calculate gravitational forces.

Section 7-4. Gravitational and inertial mass

Mass characterizes two different properties of an object, its resistance to a change in its velocity and its gravitational interaction with other objects. Experiment shows that these two properties are proportional, and our choice of units makes them equal.

Explain why the inertial mass and the gravitational mass can be treated as a single property of an object.

Section 7-5. The variation of g on the earth's surface

Because the earth does not have exact spherical symmetry, g varies on the surface of the earth.

Discuss the variation of g on the earth's surface.

Section 7-6. The gravitational field

The solution to complex problems involving gravitational forces can be facilitated by using the gravitational field, $\mathbf{g} = \mathbf{F}/m$. The gravitational field is viewed as a condition in space produced by an object with mass.

Use Newton's law of universal gravitation to calculate gravitational fields.

Section 7-7. Orbits, numerical methods

A satellite in a circular earth orbit has its velocity directed perpendicular to a line to the center of the earth with magnitude $v = \sqrt{Gm_e/r}$. In general, the path of a satellite is an ellipse.

Explain how a satellite can have a stable orbit; describe the properties of orbital motion.

Section 7-8. The discovery of the law of gravitation

The discovery of the law of gravitation involved the work of many great men over a span of hundreds of years. It is a paragon of scientific endeavor.

Discuss the discovery of the law of universal gravitation.

QUESTIONS

7-1 Consider the following three prospective force laws for the gravitational force $\mathbf{F}_{sp}$ by the sun on a planet: (a) $F_{sp} = Km_s m_p^2/r^2$; (b) $F_{sp} = Km_s^2 m_p/r^2$; and (c) $F_{sp} = Km_s m_p/r^3$, where K is a factor independent of m_s, m_p, or r. Using the periods and orbital radii of the planets as your data base, which of these prospective force laws (if any) can be shown to be inconsistent with the data? Which (if any) are consistent with the data?

7-2 Two spherically symmetric objects, each of mass m_0, exert a gravitational force of magnitude F_0 on each other when their centers are a distance r_0 apart. What are the magnitudes of these forces when they are separated by (a) $2r_0$; (b) $3r_0$; (c) $4r_0$?

7-3 Two spherically symmetric objects, each of mass m_0, exert a gravitational force of magnitude F_0 on each other when their centers are a distance r_0 apart. What would the magnitudes of these forces be if each had a mass of (a) $2m_0$; (b) $3m_0$; (c) $4m_0$?

7-4 If the gravitational force on an object depends linearly on its mass, why is the acceleration of a freely falling object independent of its mass?

7-5 The inside of a satellite orbiting the earth is often called a *weightless environment*. Is the gravitational force by the earth on objects in this environment zero? How do you account for the zero reading when an astronaut attempts to weigh herself on a spring scale?

7-6 Describe the way the mass of an astronaut and the gravitational force on the astronaut vary during a trip from the earth to the moon.

7-7 Suppose you are communicating with an intelligent being from another solar system. Which concept do you think you could define more clearly for this being, mass or weight? Explain.

7-8 If you are buying gold from a dealer who uses a spring scale to measure the amount of gold, and you wish to get the most gold for your money, do you want the measurement to be made at the equator or at the poles?

7-9 The planet Egabbac (in another solar system) has a radius twice that of the earth's, but an average mass density which is the same as the earth's. Would the weight of an object on Egabbac's surface be the same as on the earth's, greater than on the earth's, or less than on the earth's? If greater or less than on the earth's, then by how much?

7-10 Suppose an artificial satellite has a circular orbit around the earth, and we measure its radius and period. Can we use this information and Newton's laws to determine the mass of the satellite? Can we use it to find the mass of the earth?

7-11 In the British system of units, the foot (ft) is a unit of length, the second (s) is a unit of time, and the slug (sl) is a unit of mass. What is the unit of G in the British system?

7-12 Figure 7-24 is a photograph of a planetary nebula. The star at the center is surrounded by a shell of material that was ejected from the star. (The material appears as a ring because its line-of-sight thickness is greater at the edges than in the middle.) Using the approximation that the shell has spherical symmetry, what is the gravitational force on the star due to the shell? Explain.

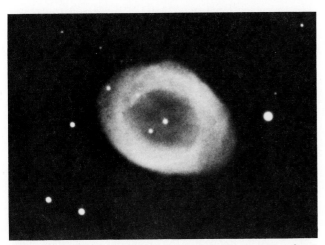

Figure 7-24. Ques. 7-12: A planetary nebula. *(Photo Researchers)*

7-13 Suppose an artificial satellite is in a circular orbit around the earth at a distance r_0 from the center of the earth. A short burst is fired from its rocket engine in a direction such that its speed quickly increases (but not enough to take it out of earth orbit). (a) What is the subsequent path of the satellite? (b) Will its perigee distance be greater than, less than, or equal to r_0? (c) Will its apogee distance be greater than, less than, or equal to r_0? (d) Will its period increase or decrease?

7-14 Suppose that the rocket engine of the satellite in the previous question is fired in a direction such that the satellite's speed quickly decreases (but not enough to cause the satellite to hit the earth), and rework your answers to that question.

7-15 Consider two artificial satellites B and C in circular orbits around the earth. The radius of C's orbit is twice that of B's: $r_C/r_B = 2$. What is the ratio of their (a) accelerations, (b) periods, (c) speeds?

7-16 In its elliptical orbit around the sun, with the sun at one focus, a planet comes closest to the sun at the point called its *perihelion;* at the point called its *aphelion,* a planet is farthest from the sun. At which point is the speed of the planet higher and at which point is it lower?

7-17 The sun's speed relative to the earth (as measured with respect to background stars) is highest at around January 4 each year and lowest around July 4. When is the earth closest to the sun and when is it farthest from the sun? Does this effect tend to make summers and winters more severe or less severe in (a) the northern hemisphere, (b) the southern hemisphere?

7-18 The magnitude of the force on the moon due to the sun is more than twice the magnitude of the force on the moon due to the earth. Would it be more accurate to say that the moon orbits the sun rather than the moon orbits the earth? Explain.

7-19 If an artificial satellite is orbiting the earth, is it possible for the plane of the orbit to not pass through the center of the earth? On what property of the gravitational force is your answer based?

7-20 Which planet falls farther toward the sun in 1 s, the earth or Venus?

7-21 An apple is dropped from rest. An ant on the ground states that the apple accelerates toward the earth and strikes it. A worm in the apple states that the earth accelerates toward the apple and strikes it. Which statement do you consider more appropriate from a dynamical point of view and why?

7-22 A *geosynchronous orbit* is an orbit in which the satellite remains fixed directly over a point on the earth's surface. (a) What must be the period of a geosynchronous orbit? (b) Is there a particular plane in which the orbit must be contained? If so, identify the plane.

7-23 If an object at a distance h above the earth's surface is released from rest, it plummets to the earth's surface. If an object at a distance h above the earth's surface is launched horizontally with a speed $v = \sqrt{Gm_e/(R_e + h)}$, it moves in a stable circular orbit (assuming h is large enough so that air friction is negligible). Explain.

7-24 Complete the following table:

Symbol	Represents	Type	SI unit
G		Scalar	
g	Gravitational field		
g			m/s²
m_I			
m_G			

EXERCISES

Section 7-2. The law of universal gravitation

7-1   Use the data in columns (1) and (2) of Table 7-1 to calculate (a) a_c and (b) $a_c R^2$ for Mars and for Neptune.

7-2   Consider developing Newton's law of universal gravitation by using the data in Table 7-4. This table gives the periods and orbital radii of the four largest moons of Jupiter. (a) Determine a_c for each of these moons around Jupiter. (b) Determine $k_J = a_c R^2$ for each of the moons. (c) If you assume that Jupiter is at rest in an inertial reference frame and that the only significant force on each of the moons is the gravitational force by Jupiter, what can you say about the distance dependence of the force? (d) What can you say about the dependence of the force on the mass of each moon? (e) What can you say about the dependence of the force on the mass of Jupiter?

Table 7-4. The moons of Jupiter

Name	Orbital radius, Mm	Period, days
Io	421.6	1.769
Europa	670.8	3.551
Ganymede	1070	7.155
Callisto	1882	16.689

7-3   (a) Determine the acceleration of the moon relative to the earth. The period and the radius of the moon's orbit around the earth are $T_m = 2.36 \times 10^6$ s and $r_{em} = 384$ Mm, respectively. (b) Determine $a_c r_{em}^2$. (c) Determine $g R_e^2$, where g is the acceleration of free-fall on the earth's surface and R_e is the radius of the earth. (d) Note that the answers to parts (b) and (c) are equal to each other (within the precision of the data). Assuming that the earth's frame of reference is an inertial frame and that the only significant force on the moon is the gravitational force due to the earth, what can you say about the dependence of the gravitational force due to the earth on distance from the center of the earth? (When applied to the moon, each of these assumptions is invalid; see Example 7-7. However, because the earth-moon system is much farther from the sun than the earth is from the moon, the error caused by one of these assumptions almost exactly cancels the error caused by the other; see Prob. 7-6.)

Section 7-3. The gravitational constant G

7-4   Determine the magnitude of the gravitational force between two billiard balls of mass 0.16 kg when the distance between their centers is 450 mm.

7-5   Determine the magnitude of the gravitational force between a bowling ball of mass 5.2 kg and a baseball of mass 0.15 kg when the distance between their centers is 640 mm.

7-6   Determine the magnitude of the gravitational force on the earth (a) due to the sun (F_{se}) and (b) due to the moon (F_{me}). (c) Find the ratio F_{se}/F_{me}. (See Table 7-1 and Example 7-5 for data.)

7-7   What is the distance between centers of a baseball of mass 0.145 kg and a bowling ball of mass 5.5 kg such that the gravitational force between them is 1.3×10^{-10} N?

7-8   A billiard ball of mass 0.16 kg exerts a force of 6.2×10^{-10} N on a bowling ball when the distance between their centers is 0.37 m. What is the mass of the bowling ball?

7-9   At what distance from the center of the earth will a 1-kg object have a weight of 1 N? If released from rest at this distance, what will its initial acceleration be?

7-10 Use the data of Table 7-4 to determine the mass of Jupiter. What assumptions must you make about the forces on the moons of Jupiter and Jupiter's reference frame?

7-11 Estimate the magnitude of the gravitational force between the earth and Mars when (a) Mars is in the west at sunrise, (b) Mars is in the east at sunrise, (c) Mars is overhead at sunrise. (See Table 7-1.)

7-12 (a) Using the data of Table 7-1, determine the magnitudes of the forces on the sun due to each of the planets. (b) Assuming that all the planets are lined up such that the forces they exert on the sun are all in the same direction, determine the magnitude of the total force on the sun due to the planets. (c) From the answer to part (b), determine the maximum acceleration of the sun if the only significant forces on the sun are due to the planets. Compare your answer with the accelerations given in Table 7-1.

7-13 The radius of Mars is 3.4 Mm and the acceleration of a freely falling object on its surface is 3.7 m/s². Determine the mass of Mars.

7-14 (a) Determine the dimension of G. (b) Find the value of G in the British system of units. (See App. C.)

7-15 Suppose we invent a unit of mass which we shall call the cavendish (C). One cavendish of mass is defined such that $G = 1.0000$ (AU)³/(yr² · C). Our unit of length is the astronomical unit (AU), the earth-sun distance— 1 AU = 1.496×10^{11} m—and our unit of time is the year (yr). (a) Determine the conversion factor between C and kg. (b) Find the mass of the sun in C.

7-16 Estimate the magnitude of the gravitational force on a 1-kg object on the surface of the earth due to (a) the sun and (b) the moon. (c) Compare the forces you find in parts (a) and (b) with the force on the object due to the earth's gravity.

7-17 A solar probe is rocketed from earth toward the sun in such a way that it is always between the earth and the sun. At what distance from the center of the earth will the probe be when the force on it due to the sun is equal and opposite the force on it due to the earth? What percentage of the earth-sun distance is this?

7-18 Reconsider the solar probe of the previous problem. Taking into account the force on the probe due to the moon as well as to the sun and the earth, determine the magnitude of the net force on the probe when it is 300 Mm from the earth for various phases of the moon: (*a*) new moon, (*b*) full moon, (*c*) first quarter. (*Hint:* The angle between the moon and the sun at the earth is 90° at first quarter.)

7-19 A lunar probe is rocketed from earth directly toward the moon in such a way that it is always between the earth and the moon. The probe narrowly misses the moon and continues to travel beyond it on an extension of the line segment described above. At what distance from the center of the earth will the force due to the earth be equal to the force due to the moon?

7-20 Solve the quadratic equation for x in Example 7-5 and show that $x = 1/(1 \pm \sqrt{m_m/m_e})$. [*Hint:* $1 - u^2 = (1 + u)(1 - u)$.]

7-21 Determine the ratio of the magnitude of the force by Venus on the earth to that by the sun on the earth at the time when the earth and Venus are nearest each other.

7-22 Phobos, a satellite of Mars, has a period of 7 h and 39 min and has an orbital radius of 9.4 Mm. From these data determine the mass of Mars. State any assumptions that you make.

7-23 In Fig. 7-25, three particles, each of mass m, occupy the corners of an equilateral triangle of side a. Determine an expression for the magnitude of the force on each particle.

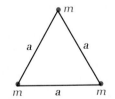

Figure 7-25. Exercise 7-23.

7-24 A neighboring galaxy to our Milky Way is the Andromeda galaxy at a distance of 2.1×10^{22} m. The mass of the Milky Way galaxy is 7×10^{41} kg and the mass of Andromeda is 6×10^{41} kg. (*a*) Treating these galaxies as particles, determine the magnitude of the force by Andromeda on the Milky Way. (*b*) Suppose that the magnitude of the net force on our galaxy is equal to the magnitude of the force on it by Andromeda. What is the magnitude of the acceleration of our galaxy relative to an inertial reference frame?

Section 7-5. The variation of g on the earth's surface

7-25 Assuming that the earth has exact spherical symmetry, with $R_e = 6.37$ Mm and $m_e = 5.97 \times 10^{24}$ kg, determine g at a height of 0.02 Mm above its surface.

7-26 We have traveled to another solar system in order to investigate the planet Yrelec. We measured the gravitational field at Yrelec's poles to be 7.69 m/s² and at its equator to be 7.52 m/s². Assuming this difference is due to the planet's oblateness, estimate the ratio of the distances between the center and the poles and the center and the equator.

7-27 Determine the fractional reduction of the acceleration of gravity due to an increase in elevation of 10 km near the earth's surface.

Section 7-6. The gravitational field

7-28 (*a*) Using the radius (1.74 Mm) and the mass (7.35×10^{22} kg) of the moon, determine the gravitational field on the surface of the moon. (*b*) If an object's earth weight is 714 N, what is its weight on the surface of the moon?

7-29 (*a*) Using the radius (3.4 Mm) and the mass (6.46×10^{23} kg) of Mars, determine the gravitational field on the surface of Mars. (*b*) An object has an earth weight of 689 N; what is its weight on Mars?

7-30 Three particles, A, B, and C, each have a mass of 1.9 kg and are placed on the corners of the square shown in Fig. 7-26. (*a*) What is the gravitational field at the empty corner (point P)? Give your answer in terms of unit vectors **i** and **j**. (*b*) What is the gravitational force on a particle of mass 2.3 kg placed at the empty corner?

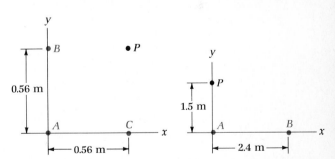

Figure 7-26. Exercise 7-30.   **Figure 7-27.** Exercise 7-31.

7-31 In Fig. 7-27, particle A has a mass of 1.4 kg and particle B has a mass of 3.1 kg. What is the gravitational field at point P?

7-32 Two planets, Egabbac and Ecuttel, orbit the star Torrac. Curiously, both Egabbac and Ecuttel have a radius twice that of earth, Egabbac has a mass the same as earth, and Ecuttel has an average mass density the same as earth. What is g on the surface (a) of Egabbac and (b) of Ecuttel?

Section 7-7. Orbits, numerical methods

7-33 An earth satellite is in a circular orbit with $r = 7.19$ Mm. (a) What is the satellite's speed? (b) What is the period of the orbit?

7-34 Show that the speed of an earth satellite in circular orbit is given by the expression

$$v = \sqrt{\frac{Gm_e}{R_e + h}}$$

where h is the height of the satellite above the earth's surface.

7-35 ⚙ Consider an artificial satellite in a circular lunar orbit of radius $1.5r_m$, where r_m is the radius of the moon. (a) What is the speed of the satellite? (b) Write a program that generates the coordinates of 20 positions of the satellite in one revolution.

7-36 ⚙ Estimate the x and y components of the force on the object orbiting the earth in Fig. 7-17 when it is at (a) position 12 and (b) position 18. Take the mass of the object to be 500 kg and determine distances and angles as best you can from the figure. (c) Check your answers

remains fixed. The orbit is contained in the equatorial plane and has a period of 24 h traveling eastward. Determine (a) the radius of the orbit, (b) the speed of the satellite relative to the center of the earth, (c) the acceleration of the satellite relative to the center of the earth.

7-38 (a) An artificial satellite is placed in a circular orbit traveling eastward in the equatorial plane such that its height above the surface is 14×10^6 m. What is the time interval that the satellite remains above the horizon for an observer stationed at the equator? (b) Suppose that the satellite is traveling westward, and repeat part (a).

Section 7-8. The discovery of the law of gravitation

7-39 The four largest moons of Jupiter have nearly circular orbits, and their periods and orbital radii are given in Table 7-4. Show that the comparison of these orbits conforms to Kepler's third law.

7-40 Use the data from Table 7-1 to show that a comparison of the orbits of earth and Venus conforms to Kepler's third law.

7-41 The radius of the orbit of Mars is 1.52 that of the earth's. Use this information in Kepler's third law to find the period of the orbit of Mars in years.

PROBLEMS

7-1 (a) Estimate G by assuming that the average mass density ρ_e of the earth is approximately the same as that of rocks on the surface of the earth (2.7×10^3 kg/m³). Use $g = 9.8$ m/s² and $R_e = 6.37$ Mm. (b) Using $m_e = 5.97 \times 10^{24}$ kg, determine the average mass density of the earth.

7-2 Consider the net force on the moon due to the earth and due to the sun when they are at right angles to the moon, as shown in Fig. 7-28. (Notice the different scales on the axes.) (a) Assuming these are the only significant forces on the moon, write a vector equation for the net force. (b) Draw a free-body diagram of the moon showing the net force and the two individual forces. (c) Determine the magnitude of the moon's acceleration relative to an inertial reference frame.

7-3 While investigating the planet Norc in another solar system, we find that the radius of Norc is 9.54×10^6 m and that the period of a satellite put in circular orbit of radius 1.476×10^7 m is 8.09×10^3 s. Determine (a) the mass of Norc, (b) the average mass density of Norc, (c) the value of the gravitational field on the surface of Norc. (d) If the period of Norc's rotation about its axis is

7-37 A communications satellite is put in a circular orbit such that its position relative to the surface of the earth

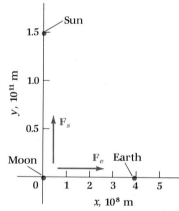

Figure 7-28. Prob. 7-2.

1.04×10^4 s, what will be the reading on a spring scale (calibrated on earth) supporting a 1.0-kg object at Norc's equator?

7-4 Consider the gravitational field produced by two particles, particle B of mass m_B at the origin of coordinates and particle C of mass m_C at position x_C on the x axis (Fig. 7-29). Develop equations for the gravitational field at points along the x axis for three regions: (a) region 1, $x < 0$; (b) region 2, $0 < x < x_C$; (c) region 3, $x > x_C$. In

with your computer by letting it find a_x and a_y at those positions.

each case write the field in terms of the unit vector **i**.

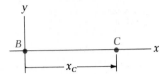

Figure 7-29. Prob. 7-4.

7-5 (a) For the situation described in the previous problem, develop an equation for the position where the field is zero (the null position). (b) Find the null position for the case where $m_B = 2$ kg, $m_C = 8$ kg, and $x_C = 6$ m. (c) Plot a graph of the gravitational field for this case in the region -6 m $< x < +12$ m.

7-6 If we assume that the rest frame of the sun is an inertial reference frame and that the only significant forces on the moon are those due to the sun and the earth, then Newton's second law applied to the moon gives

$$\mathbf{F}_{sm} + \mathbf{F}_{em} = m_m \mathbf{a}_{ms}$$

where $\mathbf{F}_{sm}$ is the force by the sun on the moon, $\mathbf{F}_{em}$ is the force by the earth on the moon, m_m is the mass of the moon, and $\mathbf{a}_{ms}$ is the acceleration of the moon relative to the sun. Using the fact that r_{es} (the earth-sun distance) is nearly equal to r_{ms} (the moon-sun distance), show that this reduces to

$$\mathbf{F}_{em} \approx m_m \mathbf{a}_{me}$$

where $\mathbf{a}_{me}$ is the acceleration of the moon relative to earth. (Hint: From Sec. 4-5, $\mathbf{a}_{ms} = \mathbf{a}_{me} + \mathbf{a}_{es}$.)

7-7 ⏱ Edit the program in Table 7-2 so that it prints the value of $r = \sqrt{x^2 + y^2}$ at each position. Since this value is the same at each position (there will be some differences due to round-off error), the orbit is a circle.

7-8 ⏱ The concept of mechanical energy will be introduced in Chap. 8. The mechanical energy E of a satellite of mass m_s orbiting a planet of mass m_p is

$$E = \tfrac{1}{2}m_s v^2 - \frac{Gm_p m_s}{r}$$

where r is the radius of the orbit and v is the speed of the satellite. (a) Modify the program of Table 7-2 so that this quantity is printed at each of the 20 positions and

note that it is the same at all positions. (There will be slight differences due to round-off error.) (b) Similarly verify that E is constant when the initial speed is 4.00 km/s.

7-9 ⏱ The concept of angular momentum will be introduced in Chap. 13. The magnitude of the angular momentum L of a satellite of mass m_s is

$$L = m_s(x v_y - y v_x)$$

where x and y are the coordinates of the satellite and v_x and v_y are the components of its velocity. (a) Modify the program of Table 7-2 so that this quantity is printed at each of the 20 positions, and note that it is the same at each one. (There will be slight differences due to round-off error.) (b) Verify that L is also constant when the initial speed is 4.00 km/s.

7-10 Suppose you are at the equator and are observing an artificial satellite in a circular orbit in the equatorial plane. The satellite passes over you from east to west, and you measure a time interval of 1.055×10^4 s between consecutive sightings of the satellite directly overhead. (a) What is the period of the satellite? (b) What is the radius of the orbit? (c) What is the speed of the satellite? (d) What is the acceleration of the satellite? (Hint: Be sure to take account of the earth's rotation.)

7-11 Assuming that the earth has exact spherical symmetry, show that g at a height h above the surface can be written

$$g \approx \left(\frac{Gm_e}{R_e^2}\right)\left(1 - \frac{2h}{R_e}\right)$$

where $h \ll R_e$.

7-12 Measurements indicate that our solar system is in nearly a circular orbit about the center of the Milky Way galaxy at a radius of 2.8×10^{20} m and a speed of 2.5×10^5 m/s. (a) Determine the period of the motion. (b) Determine the acceleration of our solar system relative to the center of the galaxy. (c) Estimate the mass of that part of the galaxy that is inside the orbit of our solar system. State any assumptions that you make. (d) Astronomers estimate the mass of the galaxy to be 7×10^{41} kg. Assuming that the sun is a typical star, estimate the number of stars in the galaxy.

CHAPTER 8
WORK AND ENERGY

8-1 INTRODUCTION

In the preceding chapters, we have developed a straightforward method for finding the motion of a particle. For example, we can determine how the position of a planet, say Venus, varies with time. The law of gravitation gives the force acting on the planet, and Newton's second law connects the net force to the acceleration. Given the initial position and velocity of Venus, we can then solve for its motion. One method for solving this kind of problem was illustrated in Sec. 7-7. This procedure can be applied to determine the motion of each particle in a complicated system of many particles. That is, we can determine the position of each particle at any instant. Often we are not concerned with such a detailed description. Instead we desire a description that tells us in a broader sense how a system evolves.

In these next two chapters, we introduce the concepts of work and energy, which will provide a new and useful perspective on the motion of objects. After defining work, we shall develop the work-energy theorem, the central focus of this chapter. In the following chapter, we discuss one of the fundamental laws of nature, the law of conservation of energy.

8-2 WORK DONE BY A CONSTANT FORCE

We introduce the idea of work by considering a constant force acting on an object that moves in a straight line. The more general case of a variable force, and a path that can be curved, is treated in Sec. 8-4.

Suppose that you pull a crate in a straight line across a floor so that it has a displacement $\Delta \mathbf{r} = \boldsymbol{\ell}$ from one point on the line to another, as shown in Fig. 8-1. Let $\mathbf{F}$ represent the force you apply to the crate. Although there are other forces acting on the crate, we are concerned for the moment with only the one

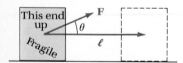

Figure 8-1. A constant force acts on a crate as it undergoes a displacement. The work done by the force is $W = F\ell \cos \theta$.

force **F**. Assume that the magnitude of the force is constant and its direction makes a fixed angle θ with respect to the displacement. The work W done by a constant force **F** on an object as it undergoes the displacement $\Delta \mathbf{r} = \boldsymbol{\ell}$ is defined by

Definition of work

$$W = F\ell \cos \theta \qquad (8\text{-}1)$$

where F and ℓ are the magnitudes of the vectors **F** and $\boldsymbol{\ell}$. The SI unit of work is the newton-meter (N · m), to which we assign the name "joule," abbreviated J and pronounced as $\overline{\text{jool}}$. This unit is named after James Prescott Joule (1818–1889), whose experiments helped to clarify the relationship between work and heat.

The SI unit of work is the joule (J).

For work to be done, a force **F** must act on an object, and the object must move. The work done on the crate described above is consistent with the everyday sense of work. You provide the muscular effort (the force **F**) required to move the crate (the displacement $\boldsymbol{\ell}$). On the other hand, if an object does not move, then $W = 0$ because $\ell = 0$ in Eq. (8-1). Suppose that you push very hard against a wall, but the wall does not move. In this case, our definition results in zero work being done on the wall, even though you may feel tired after pressing hard against this immobile object.

No work is done unless the object moves.

It is essential to understand that work depends on the relative directions of the force and displacement. This dependence is contained in the factor $\cos \theta$ in Eq. (8-1). For example, the work done by a force which is parallel to the displacement ($\theta = 0$) is just the product $F\ell$, since $\cos \theta = \cos 0 = 1$. If you push horizontally on a book with a constant force of magnitude 20 N and move it 0.5 m across a tabletop, as seen in Fig. 8-2a, then the work done on the book by the force pushing it is $W = (20 \text{ N})(0.5 \text{ m}) \cos 0 = 10 \text{ J}$.

Work depends on angle θ between **F** and $\boldsymbol{\ell}$.

Suppose instead that a force on an object is perpendicular to its displacement. Then the factor $\cos 90° = 0$, and the work done on the object by the force is zero: *The work done by a force whose direction is perpendicular to the displacement is zero.* When you carry a book across a room, the supporting force you exert to balance the weight of the book is vertical, while the displacement is horizontal and perpendicular to that force, as shown in Fig. 8-2b. The supporting force does no work on the book.

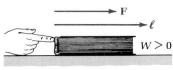

(a)

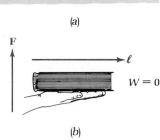

(b)

If the angle between the force and displacement vectors is greater than 90°, then $\cos \theta$ is negative and the work done by that force is negative. As you gently lower a 30-N book (Fig. 8-2c), the force you exert on the book is upward, opposite to a 0.5-m downward displacement of the book. In this case, the work that you do is $(30 \text{ N})(0.5 \text{ m}) \cos 180° = -15 \text{ J}$. You do negative work on the book because the force that you exert is opposite to the direction of the book's motion.

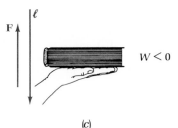

(c)

Figure 8-2. (a) A force does positive work on a book. (b) No work is done on the book because **F** and $\boldsymbol{\ell}$ are perpendicular. (c) The force does negative work on the book because **F** and $\boldsymbol{\ell}$ are opposite.

We see then that the work done by a force can be positive, zero, or negative, depending on the angle between force and displacement. Even though the work done by the force that you exert on an object may be zero or negative, the muscular fatigue that you experience may seem much the same as when you do positive work on the object. Thus muscular fatigue is not a good indicator of the sign or the amount of work that you do on an object.

So far we have looked at the work done by one force acting on an object. If more than one force is present, we can calculate the work done by each force separately as the object undergoes a displacement. The second example below illustrates such a calculation.

EXAMPLE 8-1. A constant force of magnitude 17 N is exerted by a rope on a box as it slides 2.0 m across the floor in a straight line. How much work is done by the force if the rope makes an angle with the displacement of (a) 25°, (b) 90°, and (c) 120°?

SOLUTION. (a) Applying Eq. (8-1), we have

$$W = (17 \text{ N})(2.0 \text{ m}) \cos 25° = 31 \text{ J}$$

The rope does positive work on the box because cos 25° > 0. (b) Since $\theta = 90°$, the two vectors are perpendicular and

$$W = (17 \text{ N})(2.0 \text{ m}) \cos 90° = 0$$

(c) Equation (8-1) gives in this case

$$W = (17 \text{ N})(2.0 \text{ m}) \cos 120° = -17 \text{ J}$$

The rope does negative work because the angle between **F** and ℓ is greater than 90°.

EXAMPLE 8-2. A 48-kg crate is pulled 8.0 m up a 30.0° ramp by a rope with constant tension $F_r = 540$ N, as shown in Fig. 8-3. The coefficient of kinetic friction is $\mu_k = 0.40$. Determine the work done by each force acting on the crate.

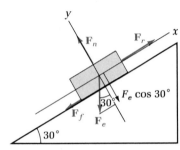

Figure 8-3. Example 8-2.

SOLUTION. Using methods from Chaps. 5 and 6, we resolve forces along coordinate axes, as shown in Fig. 8-3. The

force exerted by the rope has magnitude $F_r = 540$ N, while the magnitude of the weight is $F_e = mg = 470$ N. Since there is no motion perpendicular to the plane of the ramp, the normal force must balance the component of weight acting perpendicular to the ramp, $F_n = F_e \cos 30° = 410$ N. The magnitude of the frictional force is then $F_f = \mu_k F_n = 160$ N.

Now we calculate the work done by each force acting on the crate as it moves up the ramp. For the rope force,

$$W_r = (540 \text{ N})(8.0 \text{ m}) \cos 0° = 4.3 \text{ kJ}$$

The work done by the gravitational force, or weight, is

$$W_e = (470 \text{ N})(8.0 \text{ m}) \cos 120° = -1.9 \text{ kJ}$$

The normal force does no work since its direction is perpendicular to the displacement: $W_n = 0$ J. Finally, the work done by the frictional force is

$$W_f = (160 \text{ N})(8.0 \text{ m}) \cos 180° = -1.3 \text{ kJ}$$

8-3 THE DOT PRODUCT

The definition of work is expressed in Eq. (8-1) as a product of the magnitudes F and ℓ of the force and the displacement and the cosine of the angle between their directions: $W = F\ell \cos \theta$. An elegant and useful way to write this expression is in terms of the *dot product* of two vectors. Using this product streamlines our notation and simplifies the calculation of work.

In Chap. 2, we concentrated on adding and subtracting vectors. Here we consider one way of multiplying two vectors. The dot product of any two vectors **A** and **B** is defined as

The dot product of two vectors

$$\mathbf{A} \cdot \mathbf{B} = AB \cos \theta \tag{8-2}$$

where θ is the angle between the two vectors, as shown in Fig. 8-4a. The

Figure 8-4. (a) The dot product of two vectors is a scalar, $\mathbf{A} \cdot \mathbf{B} = AB \cos \theta$. (b) $B \cos \theta$ is the projection of vector **B** onto vector **A**. (c) $A \cos \theta$ is the projection of vector **A** onto vector **B**.

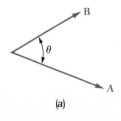

(a)

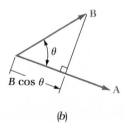

(b)

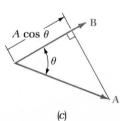

(c)

right-hand side of Eq. (8-2) is the product of three scalars, the magnitudes A and B and the cosine. Therefore, the dot product of two vectors is a scalar quantity. Each of the vectors $\mathbf{A}$ and $\mathbf{B}$ has a direction, but the dot product itself does not. Since it is a scalar quantity, the dot product is often called the *scalar product*.

For a force $\mathbf{F}$ and a displacement $\boldsymbol{\ell}$, the dot product is $\mathbf{F} \cdot \boldsymbol{\ell} = F\ell \cos \theta$, which is the work done by the force. Thus the work done by a force $\mathbf{F}$ on an object that moves in a straight line with a displacement $\boldsymbol{\ell}$ is the dot product of these two vectors:

Work as a dot product

$$W = \mathbf{F} \cdot \boldsymbol{\ell} \tag{8-3}$$

The dot product of two vectors can be interpreted geometrically in terms of the projection of one vector onto the other vector. Writing Eq. (8-2) as $\mathbf{A} \cdot \mathbf{B} = A(B \cos \theta)$ and using Fig. 8-4b, we see that $\mathbf{A} \cdot \mathbf{B}$ is the product of the magnitude of $\mathbf{A}$ and the component of $\mathbf{B}$ along $\mathbf{A}$. Alternatively, we can write $\mathbf{A} \cdot \mathbf{B} = B(A \cos \theta)$ and use Fig. 8-4c. The equality of these two results expresses the commutativity of the dot product of two vectors; the value is independent of the order of the vectors in the product:

Commutative and distributive properties of the dot product

$$\mathbf{A} \cdot \mathbf{B} = \mathbf{B} \cdot \mathbf{A}$$

The dot product is also distributive:

$$\mathbf{A} \cdot (\mathbf{B} + \mathbf{C}) = \mathbf{A} \cdot \mathbf{B} + \mathbf{A} \cdot \mathbf{C}$$

Another property of the dot product is $\mathbf{A} \cdot (s\mathbf{B}) = s(\mathbf{A} \cdot \mathbf{B})$, where s is a scalar. (Exercise 8-10 considers a graphical demonstration of these last two results.)

Since vectors are often specified by their components, let us express the dot product of two vectors in terms of their components. Suppose that vectors $\mathbf{A}$ and $\mathbf{B}$ are written in component form as $\mathbf{A} = A_x\mathbf{i} + A_y\mathbf{j} + A_z\mathbf{k}$ and $\mathbf{B} = B_x\mathbf{i} + B_y\mathbf{j} + B_z\mathbf{k}$. Then

$$\mathbf{A} \cdot \mathbf{B} = (A_x\mathbf{i} + A_y\mathbf{j} + A_z\mathbf{k}) \cdot (B_x\mathbf{i} + B_y\mathbf{j} + B_z\mathbf{k})$$

In multiplying out the parentheses in this last expression, we see that nine products appear in the sum:

$$\mathbf{A} \cdot \mathbf{B} = A_xB_x\mathbf{i} \cdot \mathbf{i} + A_xB_y\mathbf{i} \cdot \mathbf{j} + A_xB_z\mathbf{i} \cdot \mathbf{k}$$
$$+ A_yB_x\mathbf{j} \cdot \mathbf{i} + A_yB_y\mathbf{j} \cdot \mathbf{j} + A_yB_z\mathbf{j} \cdot \mathbf{k}$$
$$+ A_zB_x\mathbf{k} \cdot \mathbf{i} + A_zB_y\mathbf{k} \cdot \mathbf{j} + A_zB_z\mathbf{k} \cdot \mathbf{k}$$

Since $\mathbf{i}$, $\mathbf{j}$, and $\mathbf{k}$ are mutually perpendicular unit vectors, we can easily evaluate all such products by using Eq. (8-2), the definition of the dot product of any two vectors. For example, $\mathbf{i} \cdot \mathbf{i} = (1)(1) \cos 0 = 1$; $\mathbf{i} \cdot \mathbf{j} = (1)(1) \cos 90° = 0$; and there are similar results for the others. We have

$$\mathbf{i} \cdot \mathbf{i} = \mathbf{j} \cdot \mathbf{j} = \mathbf{k} \cdot \mathbf{k} = 1$$
$$\mathbf{i} \cdot \mathbf{j} = \mathbf{j} \cdot \mathbf{k} = \mathbf{k} \cdot \mathbf{i} = 0$$
$$\mathbf{j} \cdot \mathbf{i} = \mathbf{k} \cdot \mathbf{j} = \mathbf{i} \cdot \mathbf{k} = 0$$

Of the nine products in the equation above for $\mathbf{A} \cdot \mathbf{B}$, only three are nonzero. Thus in terms of the components of $\mathbf{A}$ and $\mathbf{B}$, the dot product is

The dot product in component form

$$\mathbf{A} \cdot \mathbf{B} = A_xB_x + A_yB_y + A_zB_z \tag{8-4}$$

There are two equivalent ways to evaluate the dot product. If you know or can determine the magnitude of each vector and the angle between them, then you can evaluate the dot product by using Eq. (8-2). Alternatively, if the components of each vector are known, then Eq. (8-4) is simpler to use.

As a special case of Eq. (8-4), suppose that $\mathbf{A} = \mathbf{B}$. Using Eq. (8-2) first and then Eq. (8-4), we have

$$\mathbf{A} \cdot \mathbf{A} = (A)(A) \cos 0 = A^2$$

and

$$\mathbf{A} \cdot \mathbf{A} = A_x A_x + A_y A_y + A_z A_z$$

Combining these results yields

$$A^2 = A_x{}^2 + A_y{}^2 + A_z{}^2$$

We have used the dot product to obtain a familiar result: The square of the magnitude of a vector is equal to the sum of the squares of its components. This is the three-dimensional form of the pythagorean theorem.

EXAMPLE 8-3. An object moves in a straight line with a displacement given by $\boldsymbol{\ell} = (3.0 \text{ m})\mathbf{i} + (4.0 \text{ m})\mathbf{j}$. Determine the work done on the object by the constant force $\mathbf{F} = (8.0 \text{ N})\mathbf{i} + (-8.0 \text{ N})\mathbf{j}$. These vectors are shown in Fig. 8-5.

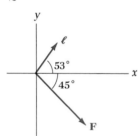

Figure 8-5. Example 8-3.

SOLUTION. Since the components of the vectors are given (note that $F_z = 0$ and $\Delta z = 0$), we use Eq. (8-4) to evaluate Eq.

(8-3) for the work:

$$W = \mathbf{F} \cdot \boldsymbol{\ell} = F_x \, \Delta x + F_y \, \Delta y$$
$$= (8.0 \text{ N})(3.0 \text{ m}) + (-8.0 \text{ N})(4.0 \text{ m}) = -8.0 \text{ J}$$

The dot product can also be evaluated by finding the magnitude of each vector and the angle between the two. Using

$$F = \sqrt{F_x{}^2 + F_y{}^2} = 11 \text{ N}$$
$$\ell = \sqrt{\Delta x^2 + \Delta y^2} = 5.0 \text{ m}$$

and

$$\theta = \tan^{-1}\left(\frac{\Delta y}{\Delta x}\right) - \tan^{-1}\left(\frac{F_y}{F_x}\right) = 53° - (-45°) = 98°$$

we have

$$W = F\ell \cos \theta = (11 \text{ N})(5.0 \text{ m}) \cos 98° = -8.0 \text{ J}$$

EXAMPLE 8-4. Determine the work done by the constant force $\mathbf{F} = (2 \text{ N})\mathbf{i} + (3 \text{ N})\mathbf{j} - (5 \text{ N})\mathbf{k}$ as it pushes an object whose displacement is $\boldsymbol{\ell} = (9 \text{ m})\mathbf{i} + (4 \text{ m})\mathbf{j} + (6 \text{ m})\mathbf{k}$.

SOLUTION. To find the work, we evaluate the dot product

in component form:

$$W = \mathbf{F} \cdot \boldsymbol{\ell} = (2 \text{ N})(9 \text{ m}) + (3 \text{ N})(4 \text{ m}) + (-5 \text{ N})(6 \text{ m}) = 0$$

Since the work is zero, we conclude that the force and displacement are perpendicular.

8-4 WORK DONE BY A VARIABLE FORCE

So far we have considered the work done by constant forces. Many of the forces we encounter are not constant. For example, the force exerted on an object by a spring depends on the amount of stretch or compression of the spring. Consider a variable force acting on an object that moves along a straight line, say the x axis, and assume that the force component $F_x(x)$ depends only on the coordinate x. Figure 8-6a shows a typical graph of $F_x(x)$ versus x. How much

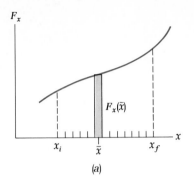

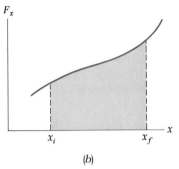

Figure 8-6. (a) The area of the rectangle approximately equals the work done for the small displacement, $\Delta W = F_x(\bar{x}) \, \Delta x$. (b) The work done for the displacement from x_i to x_f equals the area bounded by the curve and the x axis.

Work done by a varying force in one dimension

Work equals the area under the graph of $F_x(x)$.

work is done by such a force as the object moves from x_i to x_f? The work done by the varying force for the full displacement from x_i to x_f can be approximated by adding the work done in each of a large number of small displacements. Each subinterval is taken to be small enough so that the force changes insignificantly as x changes by Δx. We approximate the work ΔW done by the force for the displacement $\Delta \boldsymbol{\ell} = \Delta x \, \mathbf{i}$ by evaluating the force component $F_x(x)$ at the midpoint $\bar{x}$ of the subinterval and writing

$$\Delta W \approx \mathbf{F} \cdot \Delta \boldsymbol{\ell} = [F_x(\bar{x})\mathbf{i}] \cdot (\Delta x \, \mathbf{i}) = F_x(\bar{x}) \, \Delta x$$

since $\mathbf{i} \cdot \mathbf{i} = 1$. From Fig. 8-6a this value of ΔW is equal to the area of the shaded rectangular region of height $F_x(\bar{x})$ and base Δx.

Adding such contributions for each incremental displacement Δx for the entire displacement from x_i to x_f, we arrive at an approximation for the work done:

$$W \approx \Sigma \, F_x(\bar{x}) \, \Delta x$$

Suppose N is the number of subintervals into which we have divided the interval $x_f - x_i$; then $N \, \Delta x = x_f - x_i$. If we make N larger and Δx correspondingly smaller, the accuracy of the approximation for the work will improve because the force $F_x(x)$ varies even less over a smaller subinterval.

We imagine a sequence of such choices of larger N and smaller Δx so that in the limit, as $N \to \infty$ and $\Delta x \to 0$, the result becomes exact. This limiting process allows us to express the work as an integral. Since

$$\lim_{\substack{N \to \infty \\ \Delta x \to 0}} \Sigma \, F_x(\bar{x}) \, \Delta x = \int_{x_i}^{x_f} F_x(x) \, dx$$

we obtain for the work done by the variable force as the object is displaced from x_i to x_f,

$$W = \int_{x_i}^{x_f} F_x(x) \, dx \tag{8-5}$$

The integral for work came from the limiting case of summing the work done for each small step, $\Delta W = F_x(\bar{x}) \, \Delta x$. Since $F_x(\bar{x}) \, \Delta x$ is the area of the rectangular region in Fig. 8-6a, we can give a graphical interpretation to the integral. Between the limits x_i and x_f, the integral for work is equal to the area under the graph of $F_x(x)$. It is the area bounded by the curve and the x axis, as shown in Fig. 8-6b. In that figure the sense of the displacement is to the right and the curve lies above the axis. Such an area is positive. If the curve were below the axis (force is opposite displacement), then the work (or area) would be negative. A brief summary of results of integral calculus is given in App. I.

As a simple example of using Eq. (8-5) to calculate the work done by a force, consider a constant force of magnitude F acting in the direction of motion of an object, such as a rope pulling a crate across a floor. As the crate moves from x_i to x_f, the force is directed in the positive x direction so that the x component of the force is $F_x(x) = F$. Substituting into Eq. (8-5), we have

$$W = \int_{x_i}^{x_f} F_x(x) \, dx = \int_{x_i}^{x_f} F \, dx = F \int_{x_i}^{x_f} dx = F(x_f - x_i)$$

This work for a constant force is the same as that obtained by using Eq. (8-1)

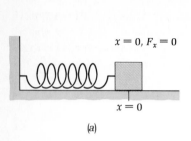

$x = 0, F_x = 0$

$x = 0$

(a)

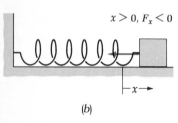

$x > 0, F_x < 0$

$\leftarrow x \rightarrow$

(b)

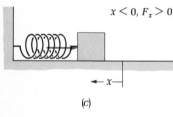

$x < 0, F_x > 0$

$\leftarrow x \rightarrow$

(c)

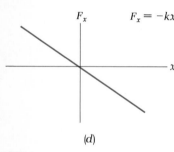

F_x $F_x = -kx$

x

(d)

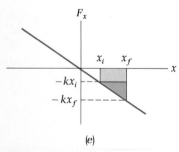

F_x

x_i x_f

x

$-kx_i$

$-kx_f$

(e)

Figure 8-8. (a), (b), (c) A spring exerts a restoring force on the block. (d) The restoring force is proportional to the displacement but in the opposite direction, $F_x(x) = -kx$. (e) The area representing the work done by the spring equals the sum of the area of the rectangle and the area of the triangle.

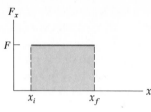

F_x

F

x_i x_f

x

Figure 8-7. A constant force does work on an object. The work done equals the area of the rectangle, $W = F(x_f - x_i)$.

with $\ell = x_f - x_i$ and $\theta = 0$. Notice that $W = F(x_f - x_i)$ equals the area of the shaded rectangle in Fig. 8-7.

Now we consider a force that does vary with x. A spring is fastened at one end to a fixed support. Attached at the other end is a block that can slide on a horizontal surface. In Fig. 8-8a the spring is neither stretched nor compressed; it is in its relaxed state. We let x denote the position of the block from this equilibrium position. Then x is also the amount of stretch of the spring, as shown in Fig. 8-8b. For many springs, the magnitude of the force is proportional to the extension x of the spring, as described by *Hooke's law:*

$$F_x(x) = -kx$$

Here F_x is the x component of the force exerted by the spring on the block and k is the *spring constant* of the spring.* The stiffer the spring, the larger the spring constant and the greater the force exerted by the spring on an object attached to it. The SI unit for the spring constant is N/m.

The spring exerts no force on the block with $x = 0$ in Fig. 8-8a since $F_x = -k(0) = 0$. This is the equilibrium position for the block if no other horizontal forces are acting. If the spring is extended, so that x is positive, as in Fig. 8-8b, then F_x is negative and the spring force tends to return or restore the block to the equilibrium position. Similarly, if the spring is compressed, as in Fig. 8-8c, then x is negative and F_x is positive. Again the spring force tends to restore the block to $x = 0$. Since the spring exerts a force on the block that is opposite in direction to the displacement of the block, the force is often called a *restoring force.* This behavior for a spring obeying Hooke's law is shown graphically in Fig. 8-8d. For most springs the linear dependence of F_x on x is valid for displacements from equilibrium that are small compared with the length of the spring. Large displacements may even cause a spring to become permanently deformed.

We now determine the work done by the spring on the block as it moves from x_i to x_f. Substituting into the integral in Eq. (8-5), we have

$$W = \int_{x_i}^{x_f} F_x(x)\, dx \int_{x_i}^{x_f} (-kx)\, dx = -k \int_{x_i}^{x_f} x\, dx$$

where $-k$ has been factored out of the integral because it is constant. Since $\int x\, dx = \frac{1}{2}x^2$, we obtain

$$W = -\tfrac{1}{2}k(x_f^2 - x_i^2) \tag{8-6}$$

Note that the negative sign occurs because the spring force is opposite to the displacement of the block.

The work done by the spring can also be found graphically. From Hooke's

* Newton's contemporary, Robert Hooke (1635–1703), is credited with first showing that the spring force is proportional to the displacement.

law we see that the force component is negative if x is positive. This is shown explicitly in Fig. 8-8e. The work, equal to the area bounded by the curve, is negative for an outward displacement since the curve lies below the axis. The area is easily calculated from the figure as the sum of the area of the rectangle, $-[kx_i \cdot (x_f - x_i)]$, and the area of the triangle, $-\{\frac{1}{2}[k(x_f - x_i)](x_f - x_i)\}$:

$$W = -\{kx_i \cdot (x_f - x_i) + \frac{1}{2}[k(x_f - x_i)](x_f - x_i)\} = -\frac{1}{2}k(x_f^2 - x_i^2)$$

which is Eq. (8-6).

EXAMPLE 8-5. A block is attached to a spring of spring constant $k = 2200$ N/m and slides on a horizontal surface. Calculate the work done by the spring force on the block as it moves (a) from the equilibrium position $x_i = 0$ to $x_f = 0.15$ m and (b) from $x_i = 0.15$ m to $x_f = 0.30$ m.

SOLUTION. From Eq. (8-6) the work done by the spring

force is given by $-\frac{1}{2}k(x_f^2 - x_i^2)$. Substituting the numerical values, we obtain

(a) $W = -\frac{1}{2}(2200 \text{ N/m})[(0.15 \text{ m})^2 - (0)^2] = -25$ J

(b) $W = -\frac{1}{2}(2200 \text{ N/m})[(0.30 \text{ m})^2 - (0.15 \text{ m})^2] = -74$ J

Notice that the block moves equal distances in parts (a) and (b), but the work done by the spring is different because the force depends on x.

The general expression for work. In addition to dealing with a force that varies as the object moves along a straight line, we must consider a path which is curved rather than straight. A smooth curved path is illustrated in Fig. 8-9a. While the figure appears to be in the plane of the paper, it could also represent a general curved path which the object traces in three dimensions. To evaluate the work done by a force that can vary in magnitude and direction, we again imagine dividing the path into a number of segments. A given segment can be approximated by a small displacement $\Delta\mathbf{r}$, as shown in Fig. 8-9b. We suppose each displacement is so small that the force vector can be considered unchanging and the path straight as the object undergoes such a minute displacement. For each segment, the element of work done by the force is $\Delta W = \mathbf{F} \cdot \Delta\mathbf{r}$. We add these contributions for each of the segments that form the path from point i to point f. That sum gives an approximation for the work, $W \approx \sum \mathbf{F} \cdot \Delta\mathbf{r}$.

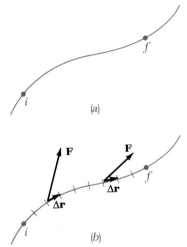

Figure 8-9. (a) An object can move along a general path from an initial point i to a final point f. (b) The path is divided into small segments. The work done by the force for a small displacement is $\Delta W = \mathbf{F} \cdot \Delta\mathbf{r}$. Notice that the force can vary along the path.

The same type of limiting process is invoked as in the last section. We consider the limit of such sums as the number of segments tends to infinity while the length of each displacement approaches zero. The limit of that sequence of sums is defined as a *line integral*, $\int_i^f \mathbf{F} \cdot d\mathbf{r}$. This gives the general expression for the work done by a force on an object as it moves along a path from i to f:

$$W = \int_i^f \mathbf{F} \cdot d\mathbf{r} \tag{8-7}$$

The interpretation of this line integral is that the work done during an infinitesimal displacement $d\mathbf{r}$ is $dW = \mathbf{F} \cdot d\mathbf{r}$. The work W is obtained by integrating along the path from an initial point i to a final point f. In Exercise 8-19, you are asked to show that our previous expressions for work, Eqs. (8-1) and (8-5), are special cases of the general expression above.

Evaluating the line integral in Eq. (8-7) is not always an easy task. If the components of the force are known, then

$$\mathbf{F} \cdot d\mathbf{r} = (F_x\mathbf{i} + F_y\mathbf{j} + F_z\mathbf{k}) \cdot (dx\,\mathbf{i} + dy\,\mathbf{j} + dz\,\mathbf{k}) = F_x\,dx + F_y\,dy + F_z\,dz$$

and we can express Eq. (8-7) as

Using the components to express
the line integral for work

$$W = \int_i^f (F_x\, dx + F_y\, dy + F_z\, dz) \qquad (8\text{-}8)$$

Each component of the force may depend on the coordinates (x, y, z), which vary as the path is traced out.

A simple but important example is to determine the work done by the weight $\mathbf{F}_e$ of an object as it moves along an arbitrary path from the point (x_i, y_i, z_i) to the point (x_f, y_f, z_f). Both points are near the earth's surface and the y axis is chosen vertically upward. A representative path for this calculation is sketched in Fig. 8-10, which shows the weight acting on the object as it undergoes a displacement $d\mathbf{r}$. Other forces are also acting on the object, but we consider just the work done by the gravitational force. In using Eq. (8-8) we note that the gravitational force has only a y component, $F_{ey} = -mg$ and $F_{ex} = F_{ez} = 0$; then $\mathbf{F}_e \cdot d\mathbf{r} = (0)\, dx + F_{ey}\, dy + (0)\, dz = (-mg)\, dy$. Since the force has only one component and it is constant, the integral in Eq. (8-8) reduces to a simple one-dimensional one:

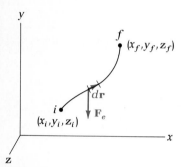

Figure 8-10. An object moves along an arbitrary path from i to f. The work done by the weight for an infinitesimal displacement is $\mathbf{F}_e \cdot d\mathbf{r}$.

$$W = \int_i^f \mathbf{F}_e \cdot d\mathbf{r} = \int_{y_i}^{y_f} F_{ey}\, dy = \int_{y_i}^{y_f} (-mg)\, dy = -mg \int_{y_i}^{y_f} dy$$
$$= -mg(y_f - y_i)$$

Since the gravitational force acts down, it does negative work on an object that goes to a higher elevation ($y_f > y_i$) and positive work on an object that goes to a lower elevation ($y_f < y_i$).

In the above calculation, we did not specify the path in detail. The result holds for any path connecting the two endpoints i and f. In other words, *the work done by the gravitational force is independent of the path connecting i and f.* In the next chapter, we shall see how this feature of the work done by the gravitational force is related to gravitational potential energy. For the present we just note that the work done by the gravitational force as an object near the earth's surface moves from i to f is independent of the path and is given by

Work done by the gravitational
force is independent of the path:
$W = -mg(y_f - y_i)$

$$W = -mg(y_f - y_i) \qquad (8\text{-}9)$$

From now on we shall use Eq. (8-9) to evaluate the work done by the weight of an object near the surface of the earth.

In determining the work done by the constant gravitational force, it was convenient to use Eq. (8-8) since the force had only a y component and the resulting integral was simple. In other cases, as in the example below, the direct use of Eq. (8-7) for the work can be simpler. There is no clear procedure for determining whether to use Eq. (8-7) or Eq. (8-8) in a particular problem. If the calculation seems exceedingly complex using one of the forms, you should try using the other. Of course, there is no guarantee that either equation will be easy to apply.

EXAMPLE 8-6. A 0.40-kg puck moves in a circular path of radius 0.50 m on a horizontal tabletop, as shown in Fig. 8-11. The coefficient of kinetic friction is $\mu_k = 0.24$. Determine the work done by the frictional force as the puck moves through one-quarter of a revolution.

SOLUTION. The normal force exerted by the tabletop on the puck balances the weight of the puck, $F_n = mg$. The magnitude of the frictional force is constant and given by $F_f = \mu_k F_n = \mu_k mg$. The direction of the frictional force changes continuously, always being opposite the velocity of

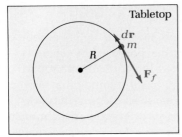

Figure 8-11. Example 8-6: A puck moves counterclockwise in a circle on a horizontal tabletop. The frictional force acts tangent to the circle and opposite to the velocity.

the puck. For an infinitesimal displacement $d\mathbf{r}$ tangent to the circular path, we have

$$\mathbf{F}_f \cdot d\mathbf{r} = F_f \, dr \cos 180° = -\mu_k mg \, dr$$

where dr is the magnitude of the displacement. We use Eq. (8-7) to evaluate the work:

$$W = \int_i^f \mathbf{F} \cdot d\mathbf{r} = \int_i^f (-\mu_k mg) \, dr = -\mu_k mg \int_i^f dr$$

The integral

$$\int_i^f dr = \tfrac{1}{4}(2\pi R) = \tfrac{1}{2}\pi R$$

is the distance along the circular arc for one-quarter of a revolution. Thus

$$W = -\mu_k mg\tfrac{1}{2}\pi R = -(0.24)(0.40 \text{ kg})(9.8 \text{ m/s}^2)\tfrac{1}{2}\pi(0.50 \text{ m})$$

$$= -0.74 \text{ J}$$

The work done by the frictional force is negative because the frictional force is opposite the displacement in each incremental displacement.

8-5 THE WORK-ENERGY THEOREM AND KINETIC ENERGY

How do we use work? What is its value in mechanics? In this section we develop a theorem that relates work to kinetic energy, the energy of motion. This work-energy theorem provides a powerful method that connects a particle's speed with its position, no matter how complicated the motion.

First we consider the special case of an object moving along a straight line, say the x axis, with a constant net force acting on it. From Newton's second law, the acceleration component $a_x = \Sigma F_x/m$ is also constant. As the object moves from x_i to x_f, its speed changes from v_i to v_f. From Chap. 3, we have $v_f^2 - v_i^2 = 2a_x(x_f - x_i)$, or

$$a_x(x_f - x_i) = \tfrac{1}{2}v_f^2 - \tfrac{1}{2}v_i^2$$

We now consider the work W_{net} done by the *net* force on the object. Since the motion is along the x axis and the net force is constant, the net work is $W_{\text{net}} = (\Sigma F_x)(x_f - x_i)$. Using Newton's second law, $ma_x = \Sigma F_x$, we find that

$$W_{\text{net}} = (\Sigma F_x)(x_f - x_i) = (ma_x)(x_f - x_i) = m(\tfrac{1}{2}v_f^2 - \tfrac{1}{2}v_i^2)$$

or

Work-energy theorem

$$W_{\text{net}} = \tfrac{1}{2}mv_f^2 - \tfrac{1}{2}mv_i^2 \qquad (8\text{-}10)$$

This result is called the *work-energy theorem.*

The left-hand side of the work-energy theorem is the work done by the net force, or the net work. We can think of calculating this net work by adding all the forces acting on an object to get the net force and then determining the work done by the net force. Equivalently, we can determine the work done by each force separately and add these individual contributions to get the net work.

The right side of Eq. (8-10) is the difference of the quantity $\tfrac{1}{2}mv^2$ evaluated at initial and final points of the path. *We define $\tfrac{1}{2}mv^2$ as the kinetic energy K of an object of mass m with velocity* **v**:

$$K = \tfrac{1}{2}mv^2 \tag{8-11}$$

Kinetic energy is the energy of motion. From Eq. (8-11), an object at rest has zero kinetic energy; a moving object has positive kinetic energy. Kinetic energy cannot be negative since its expression contains the square of the speed. According to Eq. (8-10), kinetic energy has the same dimension as work, and the SI unit of energy is the joule, the same as the unit of work.

Phrasing the work-energy theorem in words shows the connection between work and kinetic energy: *The work done by the net force acting on an object is equal to the change in the kinetic energy of that object,* or

$$W_{\text{net}} = \Delta K = K_f - K_i$$

The kinetic energy increases if the net force on the object does positive work. The kinetic energy decreases if the net force does negative work. If the net work is zero, the kinetic energy does not change.

Because the net work equals the change in kinetic energy, it is often convenient to think of the net work as the measure of the kinetic energy transferred to an object. For example, if you throw a ball, the net work done on the ball (due mostly to the force exerted by your hand) is positive and the ball gains kinetic energy. Your hand has given energy to the ball. If you catch a ball, the net work done on the ball is negative, and the ball loses kinetic energy. Your hand has taken energy from the ball.

It is not surprising that the work done by the net force on an object is related to the change in kinetic energy; the kinetic energy depends on the velocity, a quantity which describes the motion of the object. It is the net force, after all, which determines the motion through Newton's second law. As time progresses, the path is traced out and work is done by the net force. The velocity also changes in response to the net force, and the kinetic energy of the object changes. The work-energy theorem equates the change in kinetic energy to the net work done on the object.

The examples at the end of this section illustrate the problem-solving capabilities of the work-energy theorem. With it we are able to treat situations which would otherwise require great computational effort. It should be pointed out, however, that the description of motion obtained from the theorem is a partial one. It essentially connects values of speeds with positions along the path. There is no explicit reference to time in this approach. That is, we cannot determine the time dependence of the velocity and position by using the work-energy theorem alone. Even though the description is a partial one, it can increase our understanding of the motion of a system both quantitatively and qualitatively.

General derivation of the work-energy theorem. We obtained the work-energy theorem in Eq. (8-10) for the special case of one-dimensional motion with constant acceleration. The result is generally valid in an inertial reference frame, as we shall see. Recalling that the acceleration of a particle is determined by the net force acting on it, we start with Newton's second law,

$$\Sigma \mathbf{F} = m\mathbf{a}$$

Now we form the dot product of each side of this equation with an infinitesimal displacement $d\mathbf{r}$ along the path taken by the object. This gives $(\Sigma \mathbf{F}) \cdot d\mathbf{r}$, the work done by the net force for the infinitesimal displacement. Next we integrate along the path from an initial point where the velocity is $\mathbf{v}_i$ to a final point where the velocity is $\mathbf{v}_f$:

$$\int_i^f (\Sigma \mathbf{F}) \cdot d\mathbf{r} = \int_i^f m\mathbf{a} \cdot d\mathbf{r} \qquad (8\text{-}12)$$

The left side of this equation is the work done by the net force W_{net}.

We now show that the integral on the right side is the change in kinetic energy. The dot product $\mathbf{a} \cdot d\mathbf{r}$ in component form is $\mathbf{a} \cdot d\mathbf{r} = a_x\, dx + a_y\, dy + a_z\, dz$. Consider just the first term, $a_x\, dx$. Let dt be the differential time element in which x changes by dx; then since $v_x = dx/dt$, we can write $dx = v_x\, dt$. The acceleration component is the derivative of the velocity component, $a_x = dv_x/dt$, and these substitutions give

$$a_x\, dx = \frac{dv_x}{dt} v_x\, dt = v_x \left(\frac{dv_x}{dt} \right) dt$$

The right-hand side, which contains the product of the velocity component v_x and its derivative dv_x/dt, can be written as the derivative of $\frac{1}{2}v_x^2$. That is,

$$\frac{d}{dt} \left(\tfrac{1}{2}v_x^2 \right) = \tfrac{1}{2} \cdot 2v_x \left(\frac{dv_x}{dt} \right) = v_x \left(\frac{dv_x}{dt} \right)$$

Thus

$$a_x\, dx = v_x \left(\frac{dv_x}{dt} \right) dt = \tfrac{1}{2} \frac{d}{dt} (v_x^2)\, dt$$

Multiplying by the mass m, we have

$$m a_x\, dx = \tfrac{1}{2}m \frac{d}{dt} (v_x^2)\, dt$$

The y and z parts of $m\mathbf{a} \cdot d\mathbf{r} = m(a_x\, dx + a_y\, dy + a_z\, dz)$ in Eq. (8-12) can be treated in the same way. Adding the contributions from the three component parts, we have

$$m\mathbf{a} \cdot d\mathbf{r} = \tfrac{1}{2}m \left[\frac{d}{dt} (v_x^2) + \frac{d}{dt} (v_y^2) + \frac{d}{dt} (v_z^2) \right]$$

$$= \tfrac{1}{2}m \frac{d}{dt} [v_x^2 + v_y^2 + v_z^2] = \tfrac{1}{2}m \frac{d}{dt} (v^2)$$

where $v^2 = v_x^2 + v_y^2 + v_z^2$. Then Eq. (8-12) becomes

$$\int_i^f (\Sigma \mathbf{F}) \cdot d\mathbf{r} = \int_{t_i}^{t_f} \tfrac{1}{2}m \frac{d}{dt} (v^2)\, dt = \tfrac{1}{2}m \int_{t_i}^{t_f} \frac{d}{dt} (v^2)\, dt$$

The integral on the right side is just the quantity v^2, evaluated at t_f and at t_i; that is,

$$\int_{t_i}^{t_f} \frac{d}{dt} (v^2)\, dt = v_f^2 - v_i^2$$

Thus we arrive at the work-energy theorem once again, Eq. (8-10):

Again, the work-energy theorem

$$W_{\text{net}} = \tfrac{1}{2}mv_f^2 - \tfrac{1}{2}mv_i^2$$

Now that we have established the work-energy theorem in general, we can apply the result to determine something about the motion of an object. For example, if we know the initial speed of an object and can determine the net work done as the object moves from point i to point f, we can calculate the speed at point f. Conversely, if we know the speed of an object at each of two points in its motion, we can evaluate the work done by the net force. These approaches will be illustrated by the following examples.

EXAMPLE 8-7. A roller-coaster car starts from rest at the top and moves down the curved track, as shown in Fig. 8-12. Determine its speed as it reaches the bottom. Assume that the work done by frictional forces is negligible.

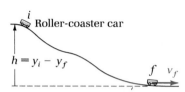

Figure 8-12. Example 8-7: A roller-coaster car moves down a frictionless track.

SOLUTION. Since frictional effects are neglected, we consider only two forces acting on the car. One is the gravitational force exerted by the earth; the other force is the normal force exerted by the track that constrains the car to move along the track. The value of the normal force cannot be easily determined since the track is not straight. However, the normal force performs no work in this situation. For any infinitesimal displacement $d\mathbf{r}$ of the car tangent to the surface, the normal force $\mathbf{F}_n$ is perpendicular to that

displacement, $\mathbf{F}_n \cdot d\mathbf{r} = F_n\, dr \cos 90° = 0$. Only the weight of the car does work in this case. Rather than calculating this work explicitly, we recall Eq. (8-9) and the discussion surrounding it. The work done by the gravitational force, $W_g = -mg(y_f - y_i)$, is independent of the path. It depends only on the vertical separation $y_f - y_i$ of the initial and final points. The net work is just the work done by the weight of the car, $W_{\text{net}} = -mg(y_f - y_i)$. Since the car started from rest, $v_i = 0$ and the work-energy theorem gives

$$-mg(y_f - y_i) = \tfrac{1}{2}mv_f^2 - \tfrac{1}{2}m(0)^2 = \tfrac{1}{2}mv_f^2$$

Noting from the figure that the height of the track is $h = y_i - y_f$, we can solve for v_f^2:

$$v_f^2 = -2g(y_f - y_i) = 2gh$$

and
$$v_f = \sqrt{2gh}$$

Note that the final speed at the bottom is independent of the shape of the curved track. In fact, the speed would be the same if there were no track at all and the car were released from rest to fall straight down from a height h. The time required to reach bottom and the direction of the velocity, however, do depend on the shape of the track.

EXAMPLE 8-8. The driver of a 1200-kg automobile cruising at 18 m/s on a level avenue suddenly brakes. The wheels lock and the automobile skids, coming to a stop after traveling 25 m. (a) What work is done on the automobile by the frictional force exerted by the road surface? (b) Determine the value of the frictional force, assuming it to be constant.

SOLUTION. From the work-energy theorem, we can immediately determine the net work:

$$W_{\text{net}} = \tfrac{1}{2}mv_f^2 - \tfrac{1}{2}mv_i^2 = \tfrac{1}{2}m(0)^2 - \tfrac{1}{2}mv_i^2$$
$$= -\tfrac{1}{2}(1200 \text{ kg})(18 \text{ m/s})^2 = -190 \text{ kJ}$$

The three relevant forces are the weight, the normal force,

and the frictional force. Of these, only the frictional force does work in this case. (Be sure that you understand why the other two forces do no work!) (a) The net work is done by friction, and

$$W_f = W_{\text{net}} = -190 \text{ kJ}$$

(b) For a constant frictional force and a displacement along a straight path, the work is

$$W_f = \mathbf{F}_f \cdot \Delta\mathbf{r} = F_f(25 \text{ m}) \cos 180° = F_f(25 \text{ m})(-1)$$

Then,

$$F_f = -\frac{W_f}{25 \text{ m}} = -\frac{-190 \text{ kJ}}{25 \text{ m}} = 7.8 \text{ kN}$$

EXAMPLE 8-9. A child's sled starts from rest at the top of an icy hill, as shown in Fig. 8-13. The portion of the path from f to q is circular, with radius R. Neglect any frictional effects. (a) Determine the speed of the sled at f, the lowest point in the path. (b) What normal force is exerted by the ice on the sled at this point? (c) What are the speed and normal force at point q?

SOLUTION. First we consider the work done by the force exerted by the frictionless icy surface on the sled. That work is zero since the normal force $\mathbf{F}_n$ is perpendicular to a infinitesimal displacement $d\mathbf{r}$ of the sled tangent to the path, $\mathbf{F}_n \cdot d\mathbf{r} = 0$. The only other force is the weight of the sled. Its work is given by Eq. (8-9) and is independent of the path. (a) For the motion from i to f, $W_{\text{net}} = W_g = -mg(y_f - y_i)$ and

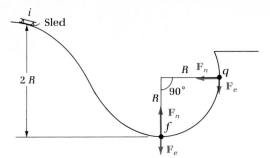

Figure 8-13. Example 8-9: A sled slides on a frictionless icy surface.

the difference $y_f - y_i = -2R$. The work-energy theorem gives

$$-mg(-2R) = \tfrac{1}{2}mv_f^2 - \tfrac{1}{2}m(0)^2 = \tfrac{1}{2}mv_f^2$$

Solving for v_f, we obtain

$$v_f = \sqrt{4gR}$$

(b) From the figure we can see that the net force on the sled at position f has magnitude $F_n - F_e = F_n - mg$ and is di-

rected toward the center of the circle. This net force is the centripetal force, and from Newton's second law, its magnitude must be mv_f^2/R. (Recall the discussion of circular motion in Chap. 6.) We have then $F_n - mg = mv_f^2/R$, or

$$F_n = mg + \frac{mv_f^2}{R}$$

From part (a) above, $v_f^2 = 4gR$ so that $mv_f^2/R = 4mg$. At the bottom of the hill, the normal force exerted on the sled is

$$F_n = mg + 4mg = 5mg$$

or five times the weight of the sled! (c) As the sled slides from i to q, the work done by the net force is again due only to the gravitational force and is $-mg(y_q - y_i) = mgR$. Applying the work-energy theorem as before gives $mgR = \tfrac{1}{2}mv_q^2$ so that $v_q = \sqrt{2gR}$. When the sled passes through position q, the normal force alone provides the centripetal force since the weight is tangential at this point, $F_n = mv_q^2/R$. Since $v_q = \sqrt{2gR}$ and $v_q^2 = 2gR$, we have

$$F_n = \frac{mv_q^2}{R} = \frac{m(2gR)}{R} = 2mg$$

8-6 POWER

"Power" is another of those commonly used words which have a much stricter meaning in physics than in everyday conversation. We often hear expressions such as "a powerful influence" or "a powerful aroma." The usage is considerably different in physics. Power relates work to the time interval in which it is done. *Power is the time rate at which work is performed.* In a machine, work is often done at a steady rate, so that the machine is conveniently characterized by its power.

Suppose you do 200 J of work on a box as you slide it across the floor. If the displacement occurs in a time interval $\Delta t = 5$ s, the average rate at which you perform work is 200 J/5 s $= 40$ J/s. We define the *average power* $\overline{P}$ for a time interval Δt during which work ΔW is performed as

Average power

$$\overline{P} = \frac{\Delta W}{\Delta t} \tag{8-13}$$

The SI unit of power is the watt (W), with 1 W $= 1$ J/s. The watt is named after James Watt (1736–1819), who made significant improvements to the steam engine. Watt introduced the idea of the horsepower as a unit of power to characterize the rate at which these engines performed work. The horsepower (hp) is now defined as 1 hp $= 746$ W. In the simple calculation above, the average power is 40 W $= 0.05$ hp.

Rather than talking of average power, we often talk of power itself, defined as the limit of Eq. (8-13) as Δt approaches zero:

Definition of power

$$P = \frac{dW}{dt} \tag{8-14}$$

The *power P* is the instantaneous rate at which work is performed.

An alternative expression for power can be developed in terms of the force which does the work and the velocity of the object. Suppose in a small time interval Δt, a force $\mathbf{F}$ acts on an object as it is displaced by $\Delta\mathbf{r}$. Since $\Delta W = \mathbf{F} \cdot \Delta\mathbf{r}$, the average power is given by

$$\overline{P} = \frac{\mathbf{F} \cdot \Delta\mathbf{r}}{\Delta t} = \mathbf{F} \cdot \frac{\Delta\mathbf{r}}{\Delta t}$$

Power in terms of force and velocity

We take the limit as Δt approaches zero and note that $\Delta\mathbf{r}/\Delta t \rightarrow \mathbf{v}$, the velocity of the object. This gives the power as the dot product of the force and the velocity:

$$P = \mathbf{F} \cdot \mathbf{v} \tag{8-15}$$

Most electrical devices have a power rating. This rating is the rate of conversion of electric energy under normal operating conditions. We can determine from the power rating the consumption of electric energy during a given time interval; the energy used, ΔE, is the product of the power with the time interval: $\Delta E = P \Delta t$. A useful energy unit can be introduced here. Suppose the power is expressed in kilowatts (kW) and the time interval in hours (h). The product $P \Delta t$ has the dimension of work or energy and the unit kilowatt-hour, abbreviated kW · h. It is the energy unit commonly used by electric utilities.

The energy unit, kW · h

EXAMPLE 8-10. An elevator cable pulls a fully loaded elevator upward at a constant speed of 0.75 m/s. The power delivered by the cable is 23 kW. What is the tension in the cable?

SOLUTION. The force $\mathbf{F}_c$ exerted by the cable on the elevator is parallel to the velocity $\mathbf{v}$. Then the dot product in Eq.

(8-15) is just the product of the magnitudes:

$$P = \mathbf{F}_c \cdot \mathbf{v} = F_c v \cos 0 = F_c v$$

Solving for F_c, we obtain

$$F_c = \frac{P}{v} = \frac{23 \text{ kW}}{0.75 \text{ m/s}} = 31 \text{ kN}$$

EXAMPLE 8-11. A 1.0-hp electric motor (1 hp = 746 W) operates a pump continuously. How much work is performed by the motor in one day and at what cost? Let the cost rate for electric energy be $0.12 per kW · h.

SOLUTION. Since 1 hp = 0.746 kW, the work performed

in a 24-h time interval is

$$\Delta W = (0.746 \text{ kW})(24 \text{ h}) = 18 \text{ kW} \cdot \text{h}$$

The cost for one day's operation is

$$(18 \text{ kW} \cdot \text{h})(\$0.12 \text{ kW}^{-1} \text{ h}^{-1}) = \$2.10.$$

8-7 ⬛ INTEGRATION, NUMERICAL METHODS

We have used the concept of the integral in evaluating the work done by a variable force. In simple cases we can perform the integration analytically, as in Sec. 8-4, perhaps with help from App. I. We also must consider integrals that are not so easy to do.

Some integrals can only be evaluated by numerical methods. A simple technique for the numerical evaluation of an integral can be developed by following the discussion of the integral in Sec. 8-4. There we divided the interval into a large number of small subintervals, each of extent Δx. The function $F_x(x)$ to be integrated is evaluated at the midpoint of each subinterval and multiplied by Δx. Adding such contributions, we have an approximation to the integral:

$$\int_{x_i}^{x_f} F_x(x) \, dx \approx \Sigma F_x(\bar{x}) \, \Delta x \tag{8-16}$$

The approximation should improve as Δx is made smaller. Such a sum of terms can be easily evaluated using a computer. The following problem can be solved in this way:

EXAMPLE 8-12. The rubber band shown in Fig. 8-14 exerts a restoring force given by $F_x(x) = -kx \tanh |x/a|$, with $k = 1100$ N/m and $a = 0.050$ m. The hyperbolic tangent function is

$$\tanh z = \frac{\sinh z}{\cosh z} = \frac{e^z - e^{-z}}{e^z + e^{-z}}$$

Calculate the work done by this force on your finger as it stretches the band from $x = 0$ to $x = 0.10$ m.

SOLUTION. We divide the interval from 0 to 0.10 m into 50 subintervals of length 0.0020 m. The function is to be evaluated at the midpoint of each subinterval and then multiplied by Δx and summed. Table 8-1 displays a BASIC program to calculate this sum. Lines 100–130 initialize the work to zero, set the subinterval size to 0.0020 m, and assign values to the

quantities k and a. Line 200 begins a loop by setting x at the midpoint of each subinterval. The exponential function EXP is used in line 220 to calculate E1 $= e^{x/a}$. Note that E2 $= e^{-x/a} = 1/e^{x/a} = 1/E1$ in line 230. The force component is evaluated in line 240. Line 260 causes each contribution F * DX to be added to the sum. When run, the program determines the work to be -4.5 J.

One way to assess the accuracy of our numerical evaluation of the integral is to modify the program to use a larger number of smaller subintervals. If the resulting answer is not significantly different from the previous one, you may be satisfied with the approximation. If the program is modified so that the subinterval size is 0.0010 m, the calculated value of the work again gives -4.5 J. This result indicates that our initial subinterval size of 0.0020 m was sufficiently small to achieve accuracy to two significant figures.

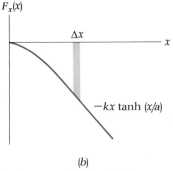

$F_x(x)$

$-kx \tanh (x/a)$

Table 8-1. BASIC program to evaluate the integral of $-kx \cdot \tanh (x/a)$.

```
100   W=0
110   DX=.002
120   K=1100
130   A=.05
200       FOR X=.001 TO .1 STEP .002
220       E1=EXP(X/A)
230       E2=1/E1
240       F=-K*X*(E1-E2)/(E1+E2)
260       W=W+F*DX
280       NEXT X
300   PRINT ''WORK='',W
310   END
```

(a) (b)

Figure 8-14. Example 8-12: (a) The rubber band exerts a force on the finger. (b) A graph of the force exerted by the rubber band. (*Tom Richard*)

COMMENTARY: WORK AND ENERGY

What is energy? What is work? Can you give a rigorous, one-sentence definition of each of these? Good definitions are not easy to formulate, and seldom is a good definition also a good description. There is the old story of Plato's attempt to define a man as "a two-legged animal without feathers." The inadequacy of this definition became obvious when Diogenes displayed a plucked chicken as an example of Plato's man.

In elementary science books, we often see energy defined as "the ability to do work," and work as "a force acting through a distance." Like Plato's definition of a man, these definitions are descriptive, but they are hardly incisive. We can immediately think of examples, like plucked chickens, that cause us to put aside such definitions. We should not expect the definition of a quantity, such as work, also to serve as a description of it or to give us an intuitive feeling for the concept. Rather, our understanding comes with practice; we apply a rigorous definition to a variety of situations. With each application, the concept becomes clearer — it matures.

Take work, for example. The general expression for work is given by the rather formidable integral in Eq. (8-7). By looking at some simple cases, such as a constant force and a straight path, we see how work depends on the relative directions of force and displacement; the value of the work can be positive, negative, or zero. We find that the work done by the weight of an object is positive if the object moves downward, negative if it moves upward, and zero if it moves horizontally. With these and similar calculations, the concept of work becomes more familiar, a part of our experience.

The real understanding of work comes when we see its connection with kinetic energy, through the work-energy theorem. Here we relate work done by the net force to a change in the object's kinetic energy. For example, if the kinetic energy decreases, then negative work is done by the net force on the object. As the object slows, it can do positive work on some agent in its environment. In a hydroelectric generator, water slows as it does work in turning a turbine blade. In this sense the kinetic energy of an element of water represents its "ability to do work."

We have just begun our look at energy by identifying and defining kinetic energy, an energy of motion. There are other kinds of energy, and we shall identify some of them in the next chapter. It will take some time and effort to develop a good understanding of energy, but the payoff is enormous. The concept of energy extends to all the natural sciences, and, like the common denominator in fractions, allows us to combine and simplify our descriptions of diverse phenomena.

SUMMARY WITH APPLICATIONS

Sections 8-2 and 8-4. Work done by a constant force and by a variable force

The work done on an object by a force acting on it as the object moves along its path is defined in general as the line integral,

$$W = \int_i^f \mathbf{F} \cdot d\mathbf{r} \tag{8-7}$$

In the simple case of a constant force and a displacement $\Delta\mathbf{r}$ along a straight-line path, the work is given by $\mathbf{F} \cdot \Delta\mathbf{r}$. For a variable force in one dimension,

$$W = \int_{x_i}^{x_f} F_x(x)\, dx \tag{8-5}$$

The work done by the weight of an object near the surface of the earth is

$$W_g = -mg(y_f - y_i) \tag{8-9}$$

and is independent of the path connecting the initial and final points. A stretched or compressed spring exerts a restoring force given by Hooke's law, $F_x = -kx$. The work done by the spring is

$$W = -\tfrac{1}{2}k(x_f^2 - x_i^2) \tag{8-6}$$

Define work and explain the concept of a line integral; evaluate the work for a constant force and a straight path; evaluate the work for a variable force in one dimension; determine the work done by the gravitational force; determine the force exerted by a spring and the work done by the spring.

Section 8-3. The dot product

The dot product of any two vectors is defined as a scalar quantity:

$$\mathbf{A} \cdot \mathbf{B} = AB \cos\theta \tag{8-2}$$

where θ is the angle between the directions of $\mathbf{A}$ and $\mathbf{B}$. The dot product can be expressed in terms of the components of the vectors as

$$\mathbf{A} \cdot \mathbf{B} = A_x B_x + A_y B_y + A_z B_z \tag{8-4}$$

Define and evaluate the dot product of two vectors; express work using the dot product.

Section 8-5. The work-energy theorem and kinetic energy

The kinetic energy of an object of mass m with speed v is $K = \frac{1}{2}mv^2$. It is the energy of motion. The work-energy theorem equates the work done by the net force acting on an object to the change in its kinetic energy,

$$W_{\text{net}} = \frac{1}{2}mv_f^2 - \frac{1}{2}mv_i^2 \qquad (8\text{-}10)$$

Define and evaluate the kinetic energy of an object; apply the work-energy theorem to relate the speed of an object to its position.

Section 8-6. Power

Power is the rate at which work is performed by a force:

$P = dW/dt$. The power of a force doing work on an object with velocity $\mathbf{v}$ is $P = \mathbf{F} \cdot \mathbf{v}$.

Use power to express the rate at which work is done.

Section 8-7. Integration, numerical methods

An integral can be approximated by a sum,

$$\int_{x_i}^{x_f} F_x(x)\, dx \approx \Sigma F_x(\bar{x})\, \Delta x \qquad (8\text{-}16)$$

which can be evaluated numerically.

Evaluate integrals numerically.

QUESTIONS

8-1 An object slides on a stationary surface. Can the work done on that object by the kinetic frictional force be positive? Negative? Zero? Does your answer depend on your reference frame? Explain.

8-2 Can a static frictional force acting on some object perform work? If so, under what circumstances? If not, why not?

8-3 Can the normal force exerted by a surface on an object do work on that object? If so, under what circumstances?

8-4 Suppose a crate is pushed across a warehouse floor from one end to the other at constant speed. How does the work done by the frictional force on the crate, if it moves in a straight path, compare with the work for a curved path?

8-5 If $\mathbf{A} \cdot \mathbf{B} = 0$, is it necessary either that $A = 0$ or that $B = 0$? Explain.

8-6 Suppose that $-AB < \mathbf{A} \cdot \mathbf{B} < 0$. What can you conclude about the directions of $\mathbf{A}$ and $\mathbf{B}$?

8-7 Can a force do any work on an object if the force is always perpendicular to the velocity of that object? Explain.

8-8 Can a force do any work on an object if the force is always perpendicular to the acceleration of that object? (Is it possible for a force to be perpendicular to the acceleration?) Explain.

8-9 Suppose that the speed of a baseball is doubled when struck by a bat. By what factor does the ball's kinetic energy change?

8-10 Is it possible for an object to have a negative value of kinetic energy? Explain.

8-11 A satellite moves in a circular orbit about the earth's center. The gravitational force of the earth provides the centripetal force on the satellite. How much work is done by the gravitational force on the satellite?

8-12 A satellite moves in an elliptical orbit about the earth. The gravitational force of the earth on the satellite is directed toward the center of the earth. Does the kinetic energy of the satellite change? Explain.

8-13 Is the work-energy theorem consistent with Newton's first law? Can you expect the work-energy theorem to be valid in a noninertial reference frame? Explain.

8-14 You may take either the escalator or an elevator from the first to the second floor of a department store. For these two routes, compare the values of the work done on you by the gravitational force.

8-15 In a British system of units, the foot (ft) is a unit of length and the pound (lb) is a unit of force. What is a unit of work in this system? What is a unit of kinetic energy in this system?

8-16 If object A exerts a force on object B, then B exerts an equal but opposite force on A (Newton's third law). How can any net work be done on an object if $\mathbf{F}_{BA} = -\mathbf{F}_{AB}$?

8-17 How much work is done by a spring on the connected block in Fig. 8-8 if the block returns to its starting point? Explain.

8-18 The horsepower (1 hp = 746 W) is a unit of power that was based on an estimate of the rate at which a horse could do work. While a horse cannot steadily maintain such a power, you can maintain about 5 percent of that for an hour or so. Suppose that we call 37 W a "manpower." Is this how the word is used in commerce? Explain.

8-19 Does an electric utility sell power or energy, or both? Instead of being called a power bill, should it be called an energy bill? If you don't pay the bill, will the electric utility cut off power or energy, or both?

8-20 Complete the following table:

Symbol	Represents	Type	SI Unit
W			
K			
$\mathbf{A} \cdot \mathbf{B}$			—
W_{net}	Work done by net force		
P		Scalar	
ℓ			m

EXERCISES

Section 8-2. Work done by a constant force

8-1   Suppose that you lift a 4-kg book from the floor to a shelf 2 m high. (a) What force must you apply to move the book at constant velocity? (b) What work is done by this force?

8-2   (a) What force must you apply to a 4-kg book to carry it slowly at constant velocity from one shelf to an adjoining one 3 m away but at the same level? (b) How much work is done by this force?

8-3   Show that the joule is equivalent to $kg \cdot m^2 \cdot s^{-2}$.

8-4   A 16-kg sled is pulled by a rope, as shown in Fig. 8-15, over wet snow for a horizontal distance of 3.2 m. The tension in the rope remains constant at 5.8 N, and the rope is at $37°$ from the horizontal. Determine the work done by the rope on the sled.

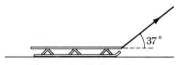

Figure 8-15. Exercise 8-4.

8-5   Suppose that the sled in the previous exercise is moving with constant velocity. Determine (a) the work done by the frictional force on the sled and (b) the coefficient of kinetic friction at the snow-sled interface.

8-6   A tow plane uses a light cable to pull a glider along a straight path at a constant speed of 280 km/h. If the tension in the cable is 1400 N, how much work is done by the cable force on the glider during 24 min of flight?

Section 8-3. The dot product

8-7   Prove the inequality, $-AB \leqslant \mathbf{A} \cdot \mathbf{B} \leqslant AB$, where $\mathbf{A}$ and $\mathbf{B}$ are any two vectors.

8-8   An object moves 4.2 m along a straight line while a constant force of magnitude 9.8 N acts on it. The work done on the object by this force is -31 J. What is the angle between the force and displacement vectors?

8-9   An object moving in a straight line has a displacement $(2\ m)\mathbf{i} + (3\ m)\mathbf{j} - (5\ m)\mathbf{k}$ while a constant force $(7\ N)\mathbf{i} - (7\ N)\mathbf{j} - (2\ N)\mathbf{k}$ acts. Evaluate (a) the work done by this force and (b) the angle between the two vectors.

8-10   By using the projective interpretation of the dot product, (a) construct a graphical or geometric illustration of its distributive property, $\mathbf{A} \cdot (\mathbf{B} + \mathbf{C}) = \mathbf{A} \cdot \mathbf{B} + \mathbf{A} \cdot \mathbf{C}$. (b) If s is a scalar, show $\mathbf{A} \cdot (s\mathbf{B}) = s(\mathbf{A} \cdot \mathbf{B})$.

8-11   Two vectors are arranged head to tail, as shown in Fig. 8-16, with an angle θ between their directions. Let $\mathbf{C} = \mathbf{A} + \mathbf{B}$, form $\mathbf{C} \cdot \mathbf{C}$, and prove one form of the law of cosines:

$$C = \sqrt{A^2 + B^2 + 2AB \cos \theta}$$

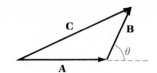

Figure 8-16. Exercise 8-11.

8-12   **Direction cosines.** A vector in three dimensions is expressed in component form, $\mathbf{F} = F_x\mathbf{i} + F_y\mathbf{j} + F_z\mathbf{k}$. (a) Find the projection of $\mathbf{F}$ onto each of the coordinate axes by showing that $\mathbf{i} \cdot \mathbf{F} = F_x$, $\mathbf{j} \cdot \mathbf{F} = F_y$, $\mathbf{k} \cdot \mathbf{F} = F_z$. (b) These dot products can also be expressed in terms of the angles that $\mathbf{F}$ makes with the x, y, and z coordinate axes — call them α, β, and γ, respectively. That is, $\mathbf{i} \cdot \mathbf{F} = F \cos \alpha$, etc. Prove the identity: $\cos^2 \alpha + \cos^2 \beta + \cos^2 \gamma = 1$. The quantities $\cos \alpha$, $\cos \beta$, and $\cos \gamma$ are called the *direction cosines* of the direction of the vector $\mathbf{F}$ and serve to determine its direction.

Section 8-4. Work done by a variable force

8-13   A block is attached to a spring of spring constant $k = 2100$ N/m and moves from the equilibrium position out to $x = 0.14$ m. (a) How much work is done by the spring force? (b) Determine the minimum and maximum magnitudes of the spring force exerted on the block for this motion.

8-14   An automobile spring is compressed 15 mm by applying a force of magnitude 450 N. (a) What is the compression if a force of magnitude 2250 N is applied? (b) Determine the spring constant of this spring. (c) How much work is done by the spring if it is compressed 15 mm from its relaxed length? (d) What additional work is done by the spring if it is compressed an additional 60 mm? (e) On what object is work done by the spring?

8-15   Let the y axis be vertical so that the weight of an object has only a y component, $F_y = -mg$. An object moves along the y axis from y_i to y_f. Show that the work done by the weight is $W_g = -mg(y_f - y_i)$. Compare with Eq. (8-9).

8-16   A particle moving along the x axis is subjected to a force given by $F_x(x) = F_0 (e^{x/a} - 1)$, where F_0 and a are constants. (a) Determine an expression for the work done by this force as the particle moves from the origin to the point x_1. (b) Let $F_0 = 2.5$ N and $a = 0.20$ m. Evaluate the work done if $x_1 = 0.50$ m.

8-17   Suppose that an object moving along the z axis is acted on by a force given by $F_z(z) = -C/z^2$, where C is a constant. Taking both z_i and z_f as positive, obtain the expression for the work done by this force as the object moves from z_i to z_f.

8-18   The graph of a coordinate dependent force is shown in Fig. 8-17. Determine from the graph the work done by that force on a particle that moves from 0 to 2.0 m.

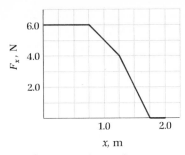

Figure 8-17. Exercise 8-18.

8-19 Apply Eq. (8-7) to two special cases: (a) If the force **F** is constant, show that the line integral gives Eqs. (8-3) and (8-1). (b) If the path is along the x axis, show that Eq. (8-5) results.

8-20 A 1.5-kg ball attached to a light string is whirled in a *horizontal* circle of radius 0.75 m. (a) How much work is done by the earth's gravitational force on the ball as it moves halfway around the circle? (b) How much work is done by the tension force in the string?

8-21 A 1.5-kg ball attached to a light string is whirled in a *vertical* circle of radius 0.75 m. (a) Evaluate the work done by the earth's gravitational force as the ball moves from the highest point to the lowest point in the circle. (b) How much work is done by the tension force in the string?

Section 8-5. The work-energy theorem and kinetic energy

8-22 From $K = \frac{1}{2}mv^2$, show that the SI unit of kinetic energy is the joule.

8-23 What is the kinetic energy of (a) a 1100-kg automobile traveling at 45 km/h, (b) a 550-kg subcompact at 90 km/h?

8-24 A 95-kg crate, given an initial speed of 3.5 m/s, slides across a warehouse floor and comes to rest after traveling 2.3 m. (a) Determine the work done by the frictional force. Assume a constant frictional force and determine (b) its magnitude and (c) the coefficient of kinetic friction.

8-25 A 0.015-kg marble is loaded into a spring gun, as shown in Fig. 8-18. The spring has a spring constant $k = 120$ N/m and is compressed by 0.12 m. When the spring is released, the marble is shot from the barrel. Neglecting all frictional effects, determine the speed of the marble as it leaves the barrel.

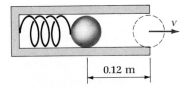

Figure 8-18. Exercise 8-25.

8-26 A skydiver falls straight down through the air at a constant speed of 140 km/h. During a time interval of 120 s, what work is done by (a) the net force, (b) the gravitational force, (c) the air-resistance force?

8-27 One end of a light string is slipped around a peg fixed in a horizontal tabletop, while the other end is tied to a 0.50-kg puck. The puck is given an initial velocity of magnitude 3.4 m/s so that it moves in a horizontal circle of radius 0.75 m. The object comes to rest after completing 2.5 revolutions. (a) For the entire motion, what work is done by the frictional force? (b) Assume that the magnitude of the frictional force is constant and determine the coefficient of kinetic friction at the interface. (c) Determine the tension in the string at the instant that the puck completes the first revolution. (d) How much work is done by the tension force in the string?

8-28 A 1.5-g bullet with speed 420 m/s penetrates 0.14 m into a stationary wooden block. (a) What work is done by the block in stopping the bullet? (b) Estimate the magnitude of the stopping force exerted on the bullet by the wooden block.

8-29 A 0.37-kg ball is thrown straight up with an initial velocity of 14 m/s. It rises to a maximum height of 8.4 m. (a) What work is done by air resistance on the ball? (b) Assume that air resistance does about the same work on the downward trip. Estimate the speed of the ball as it returns to its starting point.

8-30 A 0.35-kg ball, attached to a light string, is initially at position I in Fig. 8-19. It is given an initial downward velocity of magnitude 5.0 m/s and swings in a circular arc of radius $R = 0.80$ m in a vertical plane. Neglecting frictional effects, determine the speed of the ball and the tension in the string at position (a) A; (b) B; (c) C.

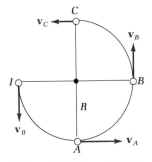

Figure 8-19. Exercise 8-30.

8-31 What minimum initial speed must the ball in the previous exercise be given so that it completes the circle in its motion? (*Hint:* The string will just become slack when the ball reaches the highest point in the circle.)

8-32 A 15-kg toolbox rests on the horizontal bed of a pickup truck. The truck and toolbox begin moving with a constant acceleration of 2.5 m/s² while covering a distance of 18 m. (a) Evaluate the kinetic energy of the toolbox at the end of this period. (*b*) What work was done by the static frictional force on the toolbox? (*c*) What is the minimum value of the coefficient of static friction for these surfaces?

8-33 Suppose that the truck in the previous exercise has a smoother bed. As the truck accelerates from rest at 2.5 m/s², the toolbox slides with a coefficient of kinetic friction of 0.20. It starts from rest at the front and slides until it hits the tailgate of the 2.0-m bed. What work is done by the frictional force on the toolbox for this part of the motion? Use an inertial reference frame at rest relative to the road. (*Caution:* With respect to this roadside reference frame, the displacement of the toolbox is not 2.0 m.)

Section 8-6. Power

8-34 Show that 1 kW · h = 3.6 MJ.

8-35 A log is pulled across a level forest floor at a constant speed of 2.3 m/s by a horizontal cable connected to a winch. If the power delivered by the cable is 940 W, what is the tension in the cable?

8-36 An electric motor performs work on a large compressor at the rate 1.5 kW. (*a*) How much work is done in 1 month if the motor runs continuously? (*b*) If the electric utility charges $0.12 per kW · h, estimate the cost of operation for 1 month.

PROBLEMS

8-1 A 15-kg block is projected up a 30.0° ramp, with an initial speed of 4.6 m/s at the bottom of the ramp. The coefficient of kinetic friction for this pair of surfaces is 0.34. Determine the work done on the block as it slides to its highest point on the ramp by (*a*) the net force, (*b*) the weight of the block, (*c*) the normal force, (*d*) the frictional force. (*e*) How far up the ramp does the block slide before coming momentarily to rest?

8-2 Suppose the block in Prob. 8-1 slides back down the ramp. (*a*) Determine the net work done on the block as it moves to the bottom of the ramp. (*b*) What is its speed as it reaches the bottom?

8-3 A ball of mass *m* is attached to a light string of length *L* and suspended vertically. A constant horizontal force, whose magnitude F_a equals the weight of the ball, is

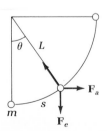

Figure 8-21. Prob. 8-3.

8-37 Assume that the drag force exerted by the water on a barge is proportional to the speed of the barge relative to the water. A tug delivers 230 hp to the barge when they travel at a constant speed of 0.25 m/s. (*a*) What power is required to move the barge at 0.75 m/s? (*b*) What force does the tug exert on the barge at the lower speed? (*c*) At the higher speed?

8-38 A horse draws a barge on a canal, as shown in Fig. 8-20. Suppose that the horse does work on the barge at a rate of 0.3 hp (1 hp = 746 W) when the barge has a steady velocity parallel to the canal bank, with a magnitude of 0.7 m/s. (*a*) What is the tension in the (straight) tow rope which makes a 34° angle with the velocity? (*b*) How can the barge move parallel to the bank?

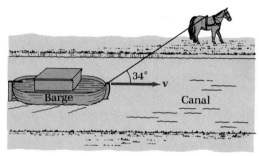

Figure 8-20. Exercise 8-38: A horse pulls a barge along a canal.

applied, as shown in Fig. 8-21. Determine the speed of the ball as it reaches the 90° level in terms of *L* and *g*. Note that as the ball moves along the circular arc, the distance moved along the arc is $s = L\theta$, and so $ds = L d\theta$. Neglect any frictional effects.

8-4 As a particle moves in the *xy* plane, it is acted on by a force whose components are functions of the coordinates of the particle, $F_x = (8.0 \text{ N/m}^2)xy$, $F_y = (6.0 \text{ N/m}^2)y^2$. (*a*) Evaluate the work done by this force as the particle moves from the origin to the point (2.0 m, 2.0 m) along the path $y = x$. (*b*) Repeat the calculation using the path $y = (0.50 \text{ m}^{-1})x^2$. Is the work done by this force independent of path?

8-5 Suppose that you are a 60.0-kg passenger in an elevator. The elevator accelerates upward from rest at 1.0 m/s² for 2.0 s, moves at the resulting velocity for 10.0 s, and then decelerates at −1.0 m/s² for 2.0 s. (*a*) For the entire trip, what is the work done by the normal force exerted on you by the elevator floor? (*b*) By your weight? (*c*) What average power is delivered by the normal force for the full 14.0 s? (*d*) What instantaneous power is delivered by the normal force at 7.0 s? (*e*) At 13.0 s?

8-6 One end of a light string is attached to a 1.2-kg puck which can slide with negligible friction on a 37° ramp. The other end of the string is fixed to a point on the ramp, and the puck moves in a circular path of radius 0.75 m, as seen in Fig. 8-22. At the lowest position, the tension in the string is 110 N. Determine (a) the speed of the puck at this lowest point, (b) the speed of the puck at the highest point in the circle, (c) the tension in the string for this highest position.

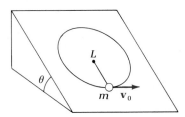

Figure 8-22. Prob. 8-6.

8-7   Suppose that the puck in the preceding problem has speed v_0 at the lowest position. (a) Determine the minimum value of v_0 such that the puck can complete the circular path. (*Hint:* The tension in the string will be

zero at the highest position.) (b) Determine for these conditions the tension in the string at the lowest position. (c) Describe the motion qualitatively if the puck has this value v_0 at the lowest position, but frictional effects, while small, are not negligible.

8-8   ▯ Modify the BASIC program in Table 8-1 to use a larger number of smaller subintervals. For example, try doubling the number of steps while halving the increment DX. Perform this doubling/halving several times to see if a limiting value of the sum is apparent.

8-9   ▯ Suppose that the force exerted by the rubber band in Example 8-12 is the net force acting on a 2.0-kg block. The block starts from rest at $x = 0$ and moves out to $x = 0.10$ m. The work-energy theorem can be applied at any point in the motion to calculate the speed of the object at that point. Modify the program in Table 8-1 to calculate the speed of the block at each increment of x. Print values of x and v at each step. (*Hint:* The square root of a variable A can be taken by using the BASIC statement, B = SQR(A).

8-10 ▯ Further modify the program discussed in Prob. 8-9 so that it will calculate and print the power supplied by the force at each step of the calculation.

CHAPTER 9
CONSERVATION OF ENERGY

9-1 INTRODUCTION

In this chapter you will encounter the first of the great conservation laws, the *law of conservation of energy*. When we say that a quantity is "conserved," we mean that the value of that quantity does not change with time. Its value at some initial instant is the same as its value at some final instant, and at all times in between. If energy is conserved for a system, then the total amount of energy remains the same, although some of the energy may change its form or type. Conservation of energy is similar to the conservation of a fixed amount of financial assets. The form or type may change from money in a checking account to money in a cookie jar, but the total assets remain the same.

A conserved quantity is constant in time.

9-2 ONE-DIMENSIONAL CONSERVATIVE SYSTEMS

The main ideas in energy conservation can be developed for the case of a particle that moves along a straight line. We restrict our attention to this case in this section and generalize the results in Secs. 9-4 and 9-5.

To begin, we classify the forces that do work on an object into *conservative* forces and *nonconservative* forces. Suppose that an object undergoes a round-trip so that its ending point is the same as its beginning point. *A force is conservative if it does no net work on an object for any round-trip.* The gravitational force is an example of a conservative force. As an object moves up, such as the ball in Fig. 9-1a, the gravitational force does negative work (displacement is opposite to force). In Fig. 9-1b, as the ball returns downward to its starting

Definition of a conservative force

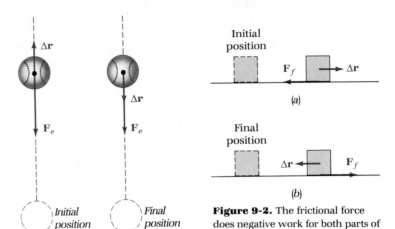

Figure 9-1. The earth's gravitational force does (a) negative work on a ball going up and (b) positive work on a ball going down.

(a)   (b)

Figure 9-2. The frictional force does negative work for both parts of a round-trip. The work for the round-trip is not zero.

Gravitational force is conservative.

point, the gravitational force does positive work. The positive work and negative work add to zero and no work is done for the round-trip. You can also get this result from Eq. (8-9), $W = -mg(y_f - y_i)$. Thus $W = 0$ for a round-trip because $y_f = y_i$.

In one dimension, a force is conservative if it depends only on the coordinate that locates the object. An example of such a force is the elastic spring force, $F_x(x) = -kx$, and $W = -\frac{1}{2}k(x_f^2 - x_i^2)$ from Eq. (8-6). For a round-trip, $x_f = x_i$, so that $W = 0$. The positive and negative contributions to the work cancel for a round-trip. This cancellation occurs because the spring force depends only on where the object is (through x) and not on which way it is moving.

In contrast, the work done by the kinetic frictional force usually depends on which way the object moves. If an object slides on a stationary surface, the direction of the frictional force is always opposite to the velocity of the object, as illustrated in Fig. 9-2. The frictional force does negative work on the object throughout its motion, and the work cannot be zero for a round-trip. If nonzero work is done by a force on an object as it makes a round-trip, then the force is *nonconservative*. A nonconservative force is a force that is *not* conservative. The kinetic frictional force is a nonconservative force.

Frictional force is nonconservative.

A conservative system is one in which only conservative forces do work.

The forces doing work on an object are exerted by other parts of a *system* that consists of the object and its surroundings. For example, if a packing box slides down a ramp, then the system consists of the box, the ramp, and the earth (through its gravity). If only conservative forces do work on an object, the system is called a *conservative system*.

For a conservative system, there is a simple connection between the work done by the conservative forces and the conservation of energy. As a simple illustration of this connection, consider a ball moving vertically up or down in free-fall. We neglect air-resistance effects, so that only the conservative gravitational force does work on the ball: $W_{net} = -mg(y_f - y_i)$ from Eq. (8-9). This work is equal to the change in kinetic energy of the ball from the work-energy theorem, $K_f - K_i = W_{net}$. We obtain

$$\tfrac{1}{2}mv_f^2 - \tfrac{1}{2}mv_i^2 = -mg(y_f - y_i)$$

The subscripts i for $i$nitial and f for $f$inal refer to any two points in the motion. Placing everything that pertains to the final point on one side of the equation and the terms that refer to the initial point on the other side of the equation gives

$$\tfrac{1}{2}mv_f^2 + mgy_f = \tfrac{1}{2}mv_i^2 + mgy_i \qquad (9\text{-}1)$$

This equality expresses the conservation, or constancy, of the quantity $\tfrac{1}{2}mv^2 + mgy$. The value of this quantity at time t_f equals its value at another time t_i. We are already familiar with the kinetic energy $K = \tfrac{1}{2}mv^2$, which depends on the speed of the ball. The term $U = mgy$ is defined as the *gravitational potential energy*, which depends on the position of the ball. Each of these energies will change during the ball's motion; however, their sum, $\tfrac{1}{2}mv^2 + mgy$, remains constant throughout this motion.

> *The sum of kinetic and potential energies is conserved.*

The sum of the kinetic energy K and the potential energy U is defined as the *mechanical energy E*:

> *Definition of mechanical energy*

$$E = K + U$$

In the example above, the mechanical energy does not change during the motion; that is, *mechanical energy is conserved*. A decrease in the kinetic energy of the ball on its way up is accompanied by an equal increase in the potential energy. Potential energy is sometimes considered to be "stored energy," since it has the "potential" of being converted into kinetic energy. As the ball falls down, the kinetic energy increases by the same amount that the potential energy decreases. Thus kinetic and potential energies are transformed into each other during the motion such that the mechanical energy remains unchanged.

> *A decrease of potential energy is offset by an equal gain of kinetic energy and vice versa.*

The expression for conservation of mechanical energy, Eq. (9-1), can be written simply as

$$E_f = E_i \qquad (9\text{-}2)$$

where $E_f = K_f + U_f$ and $E_i = K_i + U_i$. Since the kinetic energy depends on speed and the potential energy depends on position, Eq. (9-2) can be used to connect the speed of an object with its position. It provides us with a partial description of the motion of the object. We can determine how fast the object is moving when it is at a particular position, without explicit reference to the time. Equation (9-2) cannot, however, provide us with the direction of motion or with the time at which the object is at a certain position.

EXAMPLE 9-1. A 2.0-kg stone is thrown straight up with an initial speed $v_i = 8.0$ m/s, as shown in Fig. 9-3. Air-resistance effects may be neglected, so that the system consists of the stone and the earth's gravity. (a) Evaluate the mechanical energy of the system. (b) How high does the stone rise and what is the potential energy at that position? (c) What is the speed of the stone when it reaches one-half the maximum height? (d) Describe the changes in kinetic and potential energies during this motion.

SOLUTION. Since only the conservative gravitational force does appreciable work, mechanical energy is conserved. For convenience, we measure vertical positions from the initial location of the stone, so $y_i = 0$.

(a) At the initial point in the motion, $v_i = 8.0$ m/s and $y_i = 0$. The initial kinetic and potential energies are

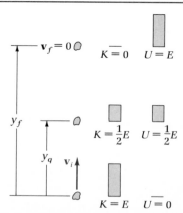

Figure 9-3. Example 9-1: A stone is projected upward. Kinetic energy is converted into potential energy as the stone rises.

$$K_i = \tfrac{1}{2}(2.0 \text{ kg})(8.0 \text{ m/s})^2 = 64 \text{ J}$$

$$U_i = mgy_i = mg(0) = 0$$

The mechanical energy of this system at the initial point, and throughout the motion, is

$$E = E_i = 64 \text{ J} + 0 = 64 \text{ J}$$

(b) Let y_f represent the maximum height of the stone. At this position the speed $v_f = 0$, so that the kinetic energy $K_f = \tfrac{1}{2}mv_f^2 = 0$. The conserved mechanical energy, $E = K_f + U_f$, must still have the value 64 J, however. So at the maximum height, the potential energy $U_f = 64$ J, and

$$y_f = \frac{U_f}{mg} = \frac{64 \text{ J}}{(2.0 \text{ kg})(9.8 \text{ m/s}^2)} = 3.3 \text{ m}$$

(c) Let $y_q = \tfrac{1}{2}y_f$ represent the y coordinate at half the maximum height. There the mechanical energy is part kinetic energy and part potential energy. The mechanical energy is

still 64 J. We have $\tfrac{1}{2}mv_q^2 + mgy_q = 64$ J. Inserting numerical values gives

$$\tfrac{1}{2}(2.0 \text{ kg})v_q^2 = 64 \text{ J} - (2 \text{ kg})(9.8 \text{ m/s}^2)\tfrac{1}{2}(3.3 \text{ m})$$

$$v_q^2 = 32 \text{ m}^2/\text{s}^2 \quad \text{and} \quad v_q = 5.7 \text{ m/s}$$

There are two possible velocities for the stone since the stone has this position on the way up ($v_{yq} = +5.7$ m/s) and on the return-trip down ($v_{yq} = -5.7$ m/s). (d) During the entire free-fall motion, the mechanical energy is conserved. Initially, when $y_i = 0$, the mechanical energy is entirely kinetic. As the stone moves up, the kinetic energy decreases as the potential energy increases. Halfway up or down, at point q, the kinetic and potential energies become equal. At the highest position, the mechanical energy is entirely potential since $v_f = 0$ there. The division of the constant mechanical energy into kinetic and potential is suggested in the figure at several points in the motion by the bars labeled by the symbols K and U.

Potential energy and conservation of mechanical energy. In the free-fall example, the change in gravitational potential energy was expressed as the negative of the work done by the conservative gravitational force. By introducing this potential energy, we saw that a change in the kinetic energy was balanced by a change of opposite sign in potential energy so that the mechanical energy remained the same. We can proceed similarly by introducing a potential energy for any conservative force in one dimension. Let $F_x(x)$ represent such a force acting on an object. From Eq. (8-5), the work done by this force is

$$W = \int_{x_i}^{x_f} F_x(x) \, dx$$

Change in potential energy in one dimension

We define the change in potential energy $U_f - U_i$ due to a conservative force as the negative of the work done by the force:

$$U_f - U_i = -\int_{x_i}^{x_f} F_x(x) \, dx \tag{9-3}$$

The negative sign is used so that an increase in potential energy corresponds to a decrease in kinetic energy. For example, the gravitational force does negative work on an object as it goes up, which corresponds to an increase of potential energy and a decrease of kinetic energy.

For any conservative system, conservation of mechanical energy is obtained by combining the definition of potential-energy change with the work-energy theorem. If work is done only by a conservative force, then $W_{\text{net}} = W = -(U_f - U_i)$ and

$$K_f - K_i = W_{\text{net}} = -(U_f - U_i)$$

Conservation of mechanical energy

On rearranging, we have $K_f + U_f = K_i + U_i$, or with $E = K + U$,

$$E_f = E_i \tag{9-4}$$

The mechanical energy of a conservative system is conserved.

Gravitational potential energy. As an object of mass m moves from a point with vertical coordinate y_i to a point with vertical coordinate y_f, the change in gravitational potential energy is

$$U_f - U_i = mgy_f - mgy_i$$

This is the negative of the work done by the gravitational force on the object (its weight).

It is important to notice that only changes or differences in potential energy are relevant. The potential energy can be set equal to zero at a point of our choice, called the *reference point*. For example, we usually select the reference point or level for gravitational potential energy at $y = 0$; that is, $U = 0$ at $y = 0$. Having selected the reference point, where $U = 0$, we can then refer to a value of the potential energy at any point as the difference between the potential energy at that point and the reference point. With our choice of the reference point at $y = 0$, the gravitational potential energy for an object at a point with vertical coordinate y is

Gravitational potential energy

$$U = mgy \tag{9-5}$$

Although the value of the potential energy depends on the choice of the origin ($y = 0$), changes in potential energy do not, as the following example shows.

EXAMPLE 9-2. Calculate the gravitational potential energy of a 2.1-kg book on the floor and on a shelf 2.0 m above the floor and evaluate the difference in potential energy of the book between the floor and the shelf. Perform these calculations twice: (a) with the origin at the floor and (b) with the origin at the shelf.

SOLUTION. Let y_i be the vertical coordinate of the book when on the floor and y_f its coordinate when on the shelf.

(a) If the origin is at the floor, then $y_i = 0$ and $y_f = 2.0$ m. Using Eq. (9-5), we obtain

$$U_i = mgy_i = 0$$

and

$$U_f = mgy_f = (2.1 \text{ kg})(9.8 \text{ m/s}^2)(2.0 \text{ m}) = 41 \text{ J}$$

The difference in potential energy is

$$U_f - U_i = 41 \text{ J} - 0 = 41 \text{ J}$$

(b) With the origin at the level of the shelf, the coordinate of the floor level is $y_i = -2.0$ m, and the shelf is at $y_f = 0$. The values of potential energy at these two locations are different from those in part (a) because the origin of coordinates is different. At floor level, the potential energy of the book is

$$U_i = mgy_i = (2.1 \text{ kg})(9.8 \text{ m/s}^2)(-2.0 \text{ m}) = -41 \text{ J}$$

On the shelf the book's potential energy is $U_f = mgy_f = 0$. The difference or change in potential energy is

$$U_f - U_i = 0 - (-41 \text{ J}) = 41 \text{ J}$$

the same as in part (a).

Elastic potential energy. Hooke's law for an ideal spring, $F_x(x) = -kx$, provides another example of a one-dimensional conservative force. The potential energy associated with this force is called the *elastic potential energy* of the spring. Figure 9-4a shows a typical arrangement of a spring with one end attached to a rigid support and the other end to a movable block. The origin of coordinates is chosen so that $x = 0$ when the spring is relaxed, neither stretched nor compressed. In Fig. 9-4b, the x coordinate gives the amount by which the spring is stretched or compressed.

The work done by the spring was determined in Chap. 8 and is given by Eq. (8-6), $W = -\frac{1}{2}k(x_f^2 - x_i^2)$. From Eq. (9-3), $U_f - U_i = -W$, and we have

$$U_f - U_i = \frac{1}{2}kx_f^2 - \frac{1}{2}kx_i^2 \tag{9-6}$$

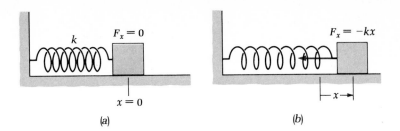

Figure 9-4. Example 9-3: A block is connected to a spring. (a) The spring is relaxed. (b) The spring exerts a restoring force.

By choosing the reference point at $x = 0$, we identify U_f with $\frac{1}{2}kx_f^2$ and U_i with $\frac{1}{2}kx_i^2$. The elastic potential energy of the spring, stretched or compressed by an amount x, is given by

$$U = \tfrac{1}{2}kx^2 \tag{9-7}$$

The elastic potential energy of a spring is nonnegative.

This potential energy is never negative because it is proportional to the square of x. If the spring is compressed, making x negative, the potential energy is again positive. The elastic potential energy is zero only if $x = 0$, corresponding to a relaxed spring.

EXAMPLE 9-3. A 2.5-kg block is attached to the free end of a spring of constant $k = 1100$ N/m, as seen in Fig. 9-4. The block is pulled from $x = 0$ to $x = 0.15$ m and released from rest at an initial instant. The block slides on the surface with negligible friction. (a) Evaluate the initial potential energy of this system. (b) Determine an expression for the speed of the block as a function of its coordinate. (c) What is the speed of the block as it reaches the equilibrium position? (d) By how much is the spring compressed as the block comes to rest momentarily to the left of the equilibrium position?

SOLUTION. (a) The initial potential energy is

$$U_i = \tfrac{1}{2}kx_i^2 = \tfrac{1}{2}(1100 \text{ N/m})(0.15 \text{ m})^2 = 12 \text{ J}$$

The block is released from rest at this position, so that $K_i = 0$, and the mechanical energy is $E = 12$ J.

(b) Since frictional effects are negligible, only the conservative spring force does work and mechanical energy is con-served. Applying Eq. (9-4), we have

$$\tfrac{1}{2}mv_f^2 + \tfrac{1}{2}kx_f^2 = \tfrac{1}{2}kx_i^2$$

Simplifying, we obtain $v_f^2 = (k/m)(x_i^2 - x_f^2)$, or

$$v_f = \sqrt{\frac{k}{m}(x_i^2 - x_f^2)}$$

Where the values of k, m, and x_i are known.

(c) As the block passes through the equilibrium position, $x_f = 0$, and the speed of the block is

$$v_f = \sqrt{\frac{k}{m}}\, x_i = \sqrt{\frac{1100 \text{ N/m}}{2.5 \text{ kg}}}\, 0.15 \text{ m} = 3.1 \text{ m/s}$$

(d) Now we let f label the point of maximum compres-sion of the spring corresponding to $v_f = 0$. Then we have $x_i^2 - x_f^2 = 0$, or $x_f = \pm x_i$. The negative sign is selected be-cause the spring is compressed at this instant: $x_f = -0.15$ m.

9-3 GRAPHICAL ANALYSIS OF CONSERVATIVE SYSTEMS

For a one-dimensional conservative system, the division of the conserved me-chanical energy into changing amounts of kinetic and potential energies can be displayed graphically. As a simple example we consider a familiar system, a block connected to a spring as shown in Fig. 9-5a. Suppose the block slides with negligible friction on the horizontal surface; its position is determined by the coordinate x with the spring relaxed for $x = 0$. The elastic potential energy of the spring is given by Eq. (9-7): $U = \tfrac{1}{2}kx^2$. The mechanical energy of this system is conserved because only the spring force performs work and it is a conserva-tive force.

Figure 9-5b shows the x dependence of the potential energy. The curve is a

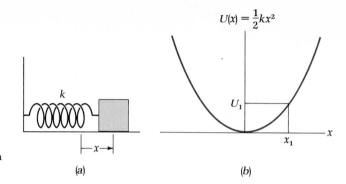

Figure 9-5. (a) A block is connected to a spring. The coordinate of the block, x, gives the stretch or the compression of the spring. (b) The elastic potential energy of a spring: $U = \frac{1}{2}kx^2$.

parabola since the potential energy is proportional to the square of x. From the graph we can determine the value of potential energy U_1 corresponding to the coordinate value x_1. Note that this potential-energy function is positive both for extension and for compression of the spring.

Suppose we set the system in motion by pulling the block out a distance x_m and releasing it from rest. In the subsequent motion, the mechanical energy is conserved. The value of the mechanical energy can be expressed in terms of the initial situation. Since the kinetic energy is zero at the initial instant, the mechanical energy is entirely potential energy, $E = U_m = \frac{1}{2}kx_m^2$. Later in the motion, that mechanical energy is divided into kinetic and potential energy, $E = K + U$. For example, suppose the block is at position x_1 in Fig. 9-5b, moving either to the right or to the left. Part of the mechanical energy is potential energy U_1, and the remainder is kinetic energy K_1, with $E = K_1 + U_1$. This division is shown explicitly in Fig. 9-6. The length of the line up to the curve at point x_1 represents the potential energy U_1. Then the line length from this curve up to E represents the kinetic energy K_1. This graphical construction corresponds to $E = K_1 + U_1$.

We can follow the motion of this object using the graphical construction outlined in Fig. 9-6. Starting with the initial configuration of this system, we evaluate the mechanical energy. On the vertical axis we mark this value of energy and draw the horizontal line whose height represents the fixed value of the mechanical energy. This line intersects the potential-energy curve at $\pm x_m$. For any value of x between $\pm x_m$, the values of kinetic and potential energies are represented by the line lengths above and below the potential-energy curve, just as at point x_1. Thus, as the block passes through the equilibrium position at $x = 0$, the potential energy is zero and the kinetic energy $K = E$. The mechanical energy is entirely kinetic energy at this point. As a consequence, the speed of the block is greatest at this position. At either of the points x_m and $-x_m$, the mechanical energy is entirely potential energy, and the kinetic energy is (momentarily) zero as the velocity changes direction. These points are called *turning points* for the motion. A turning point is located graphically by the intersection of the potential-energy curve with the horizontal line corresponding to the value of the mechanical energy of the system.

We can also use the potential-energy curve to obtain information about the conservative force acting on the object. Equation (9-3) defines the change in potential energy between two points as the negative of the integral of the conservative force. Because integration is the operation inverse to differentiation, we must have $F_x(x) = -dU/dx$, a purely mathematical fact. More physi-

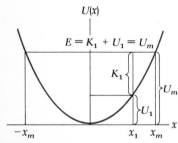

Figure 9-6. The conserved mechanical energy is part kinetic energy and part potential energy: $E = K + U$.

A conservative force is a negative derivative of the potential energy.

cally we can consider the negative of the work done by the conservative force $F_x(x)$ for a infinitesimal displacement dx. The corresponding infinitesimal change in potential energy is $dU = -F_x(x)\, dx$, or

$$F_x(x) = -\frac{dU}{dx} \qquad (9\text{-}8)$$

The one-dimensional conservative force is the negative of the derivative of the potential-energy function. To see how this works, consider two examples for which we already know the force. For an ideal spring, $U(x) = \frac{1}{2}kx^2$ and $F_x(x) = -d(\frac{1}{2}kx^2)/dx = -kx$. For gravitational potential energy, $U(y) = mgy$ and $F_y(y) = -d(mgy)/dy = -mg$.

Recall from Chap. 3 the graphical interpretation of the derivative of a function, which we now apply to the graph of the potential-energy function. At some point x_1 the derivative of $U(x)$, dU/dx, is equal to the slope of the tangent line to the graph at that point. The force is then the negative of the slope of the tangent line. This interpretation is illustrated in Fig. 9-7 for the mass-spring system we have been discussing. At x_1 the slope of the tangent line is positive and $F_x(x_1)$ is negative; that is, the force is opposite the displacement of the block. At x_2 the slope is negative and $F_x(x_2)$ is positive. Again, the force is opposite the displacement. At the origin, of course, the slope of the tangent line is zero, consistent with the force being zero there.

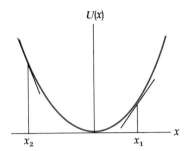

U(x)

x_2 x_1 x

Figure 9-7. The force component is the negative of the slope of the tangent line to the curve: $F_x(x) = -dU/dx$.

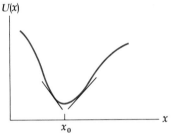

U(x)

x_0 x

Figure 9-8. The force is zero at x_0, a point of stable equilibrium.

Stable equilibrium

Equilibrium and stability. *An equilibrium position of an object is a point at which the net force on the object is zero.* We use the graphical analysis of one-dimensional conservative systems to illustrate two types of equilibrium. These kinds of equilibrium are classified according to ideas of *stability*.

A graph of a hypothetical potential-energy function is shown in Fig. 9-8. The point x_0 is a point of *stable equilibrium*. It is an equilibrium point because F_x, equal to the negative slope of the tangent line to the curve, is zero there. Suppose the object, initially at rest at point x_0, is given a small displacement to the right. The force can be estimated from the slope of the tangent line there. The direction of the force is to the left, tending to return the object to the equilibrium position. A similar conclusion results if we displace the object by a small amount to the left of the equilibrium position. The direction of the force is to the right, again to return the object to the equilibrium point. *A point of equilibrium is stable if, for any small displacement of the object from that point, the force tends to return the object to the equilibrium point.* It should be clear from Fig. 9-8 that a minimum of the potential-energy function corresponds to a point of stable equilibrium for a one-dimensional conservative system.

Point x_1 in Fig. 9-9 is also an equilibrium point; the force on the object is zero there. For this point, however, the force on the object, if displaced slightly to

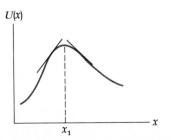

U(x)

x_1 x

Figure 9-9. The force is zero at x_1, a point of unstable equilibrium.

Unstable equilibrium

either side of x_1, tends to remove the object farther from the equilibrium point. This equilibrium point is *unstable*. *A point of equilibrium is unstable if, for any small displacement of the object from that point, the force tends to move the object away from the equilibrium point.* For a one-dimensional conservative system, a maximum of the potential-energy function is a point of unstable equilibrium.

We have classified two types of equilibrium for one-dimensional conservative systems. The classification can be extended, however, to more general types of systems. For example, a roller coaster at the highest point of the track is at a point of unstable equilibrium with respect to motion along the track. As another example, suppose a marble can roll on the inside of a round-bottomed bowl. The lowest point on that surface is a point of stable equilibrium for the marble. If displaced slightly from that position, the marble tends to return to that point.

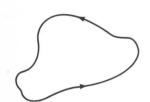

Figure 9-10. A curve that closes on itself forms a closed path.

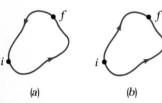

Figure 9-11. The work done by a conservative force is (a) zero for a closed path and (b) the same for alternative paths going from *i* to *f*.

Definition of a conservative force

9-4 CONSERVATIVE FORCES AND POTENTIAL ENERGY IN THREE DIMENSIONS

Our discussion of conservative forces, potential energy, and the conservation of mechanical energy has been confined to one-dimensional systems. We need to extend these concepts to systems in two and three dimensions. In this section we shall expand our definitions of conservative force and potential energy.

Conservative force. We classified forces in one dimension in terms of the work done for a round-trip. For a conservative force, the work is zero for any round-trip; and a nonconservative force is, in short, a force that is not conservative. A round-trip in one dimension is out and back along a given line. In two or three dimensions, a round-trip can be any *closed path*, that is, a path that closes on itself, as seen in Fig. 9-10. We extend the definition of a conservative force to include such paths. *The work done by a conservative force is zero for any closed path.* Positive work done by a conservative force for part of a closed path is exactly canceled by negative work done for another part of the path, and this cancellation occurs for *any closed path*.

The definition of a conservative force can be expressed as an integral. Recall from Chap. 8 that the work done by a force **F** for an infinitesimal displacement *d***r** is **F** · *d***r**. The integral ∫ **F** · *d***r** for the work done along a path represents the sum of the contributions for each infinitesimal displacement along the path. To indicate a closed path, we put a circle on the integral sign: ∮. Thus the work done by a force **F** for a closed path is denoted by ∮ **F** · *d***r**. For a conservative force, this work is zero for any closed path, or

For a conservative force, $\oint \mathbf{F} \cdot d\mathbf{r} = 0$.

$$\oint \mathbf{F} \cdot d\mathbf{r} = 0 \qquad \text{any closed path} \qquad (9\text{-}9)$$

Instead of using a closed path, we can consider the work done by a conservative force along alternative paths connecting two endpoints, say *i* and *f*, as shown in Fig. 9-11*a*. Since the work done by a conservative force for a closed path is zero, then the work done along one path from *i* to *f* must exactly cancel the work done along the reurn path from *f* back to *i*. In Fig. 9-11*b*, the sense of the return path has been reversed so that both paths go from i to f. Reversing the sense of a path is equivalent to replacing $d\mathbf{r}$ with $-d\mathbf{r}$ and so changing the sign of the integral. That is,

$$\int_f^i \mathbf{F} \cdot d\mathbf{r} = -\int_i^f \mathbf{F} \cdot d\mathbf{r}$$

So along any two paths connecting points i and f, a conservative force does the same work. Therefore, *the work done by a conservative force is independent of the path connecting the endpoints.* This is an alternative and convenient definition of a conservative force.

We saw in Chap. 8 that the work done by the gravitational force is independent of the path. Thus this force is conservative according to our extended definition. The work done by a frictional force does depend on the path generally and so is nonconservative.

EXAMPLE 9-4. Compare the work done by the kinetic frictional force on a 50-kg crate which is pushed horizontally (a) around a semicircle of diameter 4 m and (b) straight along a diameter. Take $\mu_k = 0.3$.

SOLUTION. Since the crate is pushed horizontally, the normal force must balance the weight, $F_n = mg$. The magnitude of the frictional force is then $F_f = \mu_k mg$. For either path, the force F_f is opposite an infinitesimal displacement of magnitude ds along the path, and $dW = -F_f ds$ is the ele-

ment of work done. On integrating we obtain $W = -F_f s = -\mu_k mgs$, where s is the total path length.

(a) For the path around the semicircle, the length is $s = \frac{1}{2}\pi(4\text{ m})$ and the work is

$$W = -\mu_k mgs = -(0.3)(50\text{ kg})(9.8\text{ m/s}^2)(\tfrac{1}{2}\pi)(4\text{ m}) = -900\text{ J}$$

(b) For the straight path along the diameter, the length is $s = 4$ m, and the work done is $W = -600$ J. Work done by the frictional force is different along these two paths, showing that the kinetic frictional force is nonconservative.

Potential energy. The work done by a conservative force, $W = \int_i^f \mathbf{F} \cdot d\mathbf{r}$, is independent of the path connecting the endpoints. Since the work does not depend on the path, it can only depend on the two endpoints. This kind of dependence on the endpoints can be seen in the case of the conservative gravitational force $\mathbf{F}_e$ on an object where $F_e = mg$. Using Eq. (8-9), we write

$$\int_i^f \mathbf{F}_e \cdot d\mathbf{r} = -mg(y_f - y_i) = -(mgy_f - mgy_i)$$

That is, the work done by the conservative force can be written as the difference of a quantity, $-mgy$ in this case, evaluated at the endpoints. The equation above is the definition of the negative of the change in gravitational energy.

The potential energy for any conservative force is defined in the same way as above. *The change in potential energy is the negative of the work done by the conservative force.* This is the same definition as for a one-dimensional system in Eq. (9-3), except that the integral for the work done by the conservative force can be along any path connecting the points i and f. Thus the change in potential energy, $U_f - U_i$, for a conservative force $\mathbf{F}$ is given by

$$U_f - U_i = -\int_i^f \mathbf{F} \cdot d\mathbf{r} \tag{9-10}$$

The expressions for the potential energies that we have used so far remain the same. For an object of mass m close to the earth's surface, the gravitational potential energy is $U = mgy$. For a spring stretched or compressed in a straight line, the elastic potential energy of the spring is $U = \frac{1}{2}kx^2$, where x is the extension or the compression of the spring.

9-5 CONSERVATION OF MECHANICAL ENERGY

We can obtain conservation of mechanical energy for an object moving in two or three dimensions just as we did for motion in one dimension. From the work-energy theorem, the change in the kinetic energy of the object equals the work done by the net force on the object: $K_f - K_i = W_{net}$. Suppose that only conservative forces are performing work on the object. The work done by a conservative force is independent of the path and is equal to the negative of the change in potential energy. Combining these results, we have $K_f - K_i = W_{net} = -(U_f - U_i)$. Rearranging this last expression gives $K_f + U_f = K_i + U_i$, or

$$E_f = E_i \qquad (9\text{-}11)$$

If only conservative forces do work, mechanical energy is conserved.

where $E = K + U$ is the mechanical energy of the system. The mechanical energy is conserved because the only forces performing work are conservative, and the net work done can then be written as the negative change in potential energy. *If only conservative forces perform work, the mechanical energy of the system is conserved.*

Equation (9-11) expresses the conservation of mechanical energy of a system in one, two, or three dimensions. It connects the speed of the object with its position. Throughout the motion, both the kinetic energy and the potential energy can change, but their sum, $E = K + U$, does not change.

Often a normal force is exerted on an object by a stationary surface on which the object slides. However, this normal force performs no work because the normal force $\mathbf{F}_n$ is perpendicular to any infinitesimal displacement $d\mathbf{r}$ of the object, and $\mathbf{F}_n \cdot d\mathbf{r} = 0$. Although the normal force in this case is not zero, the work done by the normal force is zero. It is the *work* performed by the force, and not the force itself, which is important for conservation of mechanical energy.

EXAMPLE 9-5. A 2.1-kg block is held against a light spring (of negligible mass) of spring constant $k = 2400$ N/m, which is compressed by 0.15 m. The spring projects the block up the 25° ramp, as shown in Fig. 9-12. The block comes to rest momentarily at point f. Frictional forces are negligible. Assume that the block loses contact with the spring when the spring is relaxed. (a) How far up the ramp from point i is

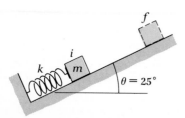

Figure 9-12. Example 9-5: A spring projects a block up a smooth ramp.

point f? (b) As the block slides back down the ramp, what is its speed halfway between f and i?

SOLUTION. There are three forces acting on the block. Of these three, the spring force and the weight are conservative. The normal force performs no work since the displacement of the block is perpendicular to the normal force. Since only conservative forces perform work, mechanical energy is conserved. There are two contributions to the potential energy, the elastic potential energy of the spring and the gravitational potential energy. We measure the vertical coordinate y from the initial position i, so that $y_i = 0$. The initial value of elastic potential energy is $\frac{1}{2}(2400$ N/m$)(0.15$ m$)^2 = 27$ J.

(a) The block is released from rest at i and comes to rest at f; the kinetic energy is zero at both points. Let y_f be the vertical coordinate of point f; the gravitational potential energy there is mgy_f. The elastic potential energy is zero for point f

since the relaxed spring has been left behind. Conservation of mechanical energy gives $mgy_f = 27\text{ J} + mgy_i = 27\text{ J}$. Inserting numerical values, we obtain $y_f = 1.3$ m for the vertical coordinate of point f. Measured along the ramp, the distance s is related to y_f by $y_f = s \sin \theta$, or

$$s = \frac{1.3\text{ m}}{\sin 25°} = 3.1\text{ m}$$

EXAMPLE 9-6. A small ice cube of mass m slides with negligible friction on a "loop-the-loop" track, as shown in Fig. 9-13. The ice starts from rest at a point $y_i = 4R$ above the

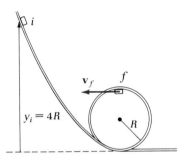

Figure 9-13. Example 9-6: A loop-the-loop track.

level of the lowest part of the track. (a) What is the speed of the ice cube at point f, the highest point on the circular loop? (b) What normal force is exerted on the ice at this point?

SOLUTION. In any infinitesimal displacement of the ice cube along the track, the normal force does no work since it is perpendicular to the displacement. Neglecting frictional effects, we see that only the weight of the ice cube performs work, and it is a conservative force. Mechanical energy is conserved in this motion.

(a) At point i the speed v_i is zero and $y_i = 4R$. At point f the speed v_f is to be determined and $y_f = 2R$. Applying Eq.

(b) As the block comes halfway down on the return trip, the spring remains relaxed, and the 27 J of mechanical energy is divided into kinetic energy and gravitational potential energy. Let h label this point; then

$$\tfrac{1}{2}mv_h^2 + mgy_h = 27\text{ J}$$

with $y_h = \tfrac{1}{2}y_f = \tfrac{1}{2}(1.3\text{ m})$. Solving for v_h gives $v_h = 3.6$ m/s.

(9-11), we equate the mechanical energy at points i and f:

$$K_f + U_f = K_i + U_i$$

or,

$$\tfrac{1}{2}mv_f^2 + mg(2R) = 0 + mg(4R)$$

The kinetic energy at point f is then

$$\tfrac{1}{2}mv_f^2 = 2mgR$$

and the speed is $v_f = \sqrt{4gR}$.

(b) At point f both the normal force exerted by the track and the weight of the ice cube are directed downward. Together these provide the centripetal force, of magnitude mv^2/R, necessary for the circular path. From Newton's second law, $\Sigma \mathbf{F} = m\mathbf{a}$:

$$F_n + mg = \frac{mv_f^2}{R}$$

From part (a) we have

$$\tfrac{1}{2}mv_f^2 = 2mgR$$

or $mv_f^2 = 4mgR$ and $mv_f^2/R = 4mg$. The centripetal force here is 4 times the weight! Substituting this value and solving for the normal force gives $F_n = 4mg - mg = 3mg$. In arriving at our answer we can see that the lower the release point i, the slower the speed at point f and the smaller the normal force exerted by the track. An interesting question is: From what minimum height can the ice cube be released and still remain in contact with the track at point f? See Prob. 9-6.

9-6 NONCONSERVATIVE FORCES AND INTERNAL WORK

In each of the examples in the last section, we were careful to note that only conservative forces were performing work. If a nonconservative force, such as a frictional force, does work on an object, then mechanical energy is not conserved. In this case the mechanical energy can change during the motion of the object.

Nonconservative forces. To see how the mechanical energy can change, we begin with the work-energy theorem, $K_f - K_i = W_{\text{net}}$, which is valid for all forces, nonconservative and conservative. We separate the net work done by all the forces acting on the object into two contributions, $W_{\text{net}} = W_{\text{con}} + W_{\text{non}}$. One contribution is the work done by the conservative forces, which equals the negative of the change in potential energy: $W_{\text{con}} = -(U_f - U_i)$. The other

Work done by a nonconservative force depends on the path.

contribution is the work done by the nonconservative forces W_{non}. We cannot evaluate this work in general because its value depends on the details of the motion of the object. To evaluate W_{non}, we must know both the path and how the force varies along the path.

By dividing W_{net} into the conservative and nonconservative parts, we can write

$$K_f - K_i = W_{net} = W_{con} + W_{non} = -(U_f - U_i) + W_{non}$$

We rearrange the equation to get $K_f + U_f$ on the left side of the equation and $K_i + U_i$ on the right side:

$$K_f + U_f = K_i + U_i + W_{non}$$

Since $E_f = K_f + U_f$ is the mechanical energy at point f and $E_i + K_i + U_i$ is the mechanical energy at point i, then

Modified work-energy theorem

$$E_f = E_i + W_{non} \tag{9-12}$$

which is a modified form of the work-energy theorem. From this equation, we see that the change in mechanical energy, $E_f - E_i$, is equal to the work done by the nonconservative forces along the path from i to f. Notice as a special case that if $W_{non} = 0$ (no work performed by nonconservative forces), then $E_f = E_i$, and the conservation of mechanical energy is recovered.

The modified work-energy theorem provides a description of the motion of the object if we can evaluate the work done by the nonconservative forces in a specific case. By relating changes in kinetic and potential energies, the theorem connects the values of speed and position of the object. Alternatively, if we know the speed of the object at each of two positions i and f, we can evaluate the work done by the nonconservative forces. The following example illustrates this approach.

EXAMPLE 9-7. A 17-kg child starts from rest at the top of a 2.0-m slide, as shown in Fig. 9-14. Her speed at the bottom is 4.2 m/s. How much work is done by frictional forces?

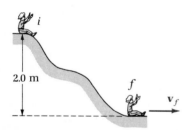

Figure 9-14. Example 9-7: A child on a slide.

SOLUTION. The forces acting on the child are her weight, which is conservative; a normal force exerted by the slide surface, which performs no work; and the nonconservative frictional forces from the slide surface and air-resistance effects. In applying Eq. (9-12), we let $y_f = 0$ and $v_f = 4.2$ m/s so that $y_i = 2.0$ m and $v_i = 0$. This gives, since $U_f = 0$ and $K_i = 0$,

$$W_{non} = E_f - E_i = K_f - U_i$$

$$= \tfrac{1}{2}(17 \text{ kg})(4.2 \text{ m/s})^2 - (17 \text{ kg})(9.8 \text{ m/s}^2)(2.0 \text{ m})$$

$$= -180 \text{ J}$$

The negative work done by friction corresponds to the decrease in the mechanical energy of the system.

Internal work. In applying methods of work and energy, we have restricted our attention to the case of a single, inert object acted on by external forces. In the situation illustrated by Fig. 9-12, for example, the object we describe is the block. The external forces are exerted by the earth, by the spring, and by the ramp surface. Except for changing its position and speed, the block remains unchanged; it is treated as a particle.

We can also consider more complicated objects, however, which undergo changes in their makeup or composition or shape. Suppose that an athlete climbs hand over hand up a stationary, vertical rope at a steady speed. The athlete's gravitational potential energy, $U = mgy$, is increasing. Since the kinetic energy is constant, the mechanical energy, $E = K + U$, is also increasing. Yet the rope does no work on the athlete. Although the rope exerts a force on a hand, the hand *does not move* while grasping the rope.

What is responsible for increasing the mechanical energy of the athlete? What provides the work? In this case, the athlete's contracting muscles perform work. That is, the arms do work in raising the rest of the athlete. These forces are internal to the object or system rather than external. The work done by internal forces exerted by one part of a system on another part is called *internal work*. In considering changes in the mechanical energy of a system, we must account for the internal work done by such internal forces.

Internal work can be done by internal forces.

9-7 THE LAW OF CONSERVATION OF ENERGY

Having considered a number of examples for which mechanical energy is conserved, we may have become accustomed to thinking of energy as a conserved quantity generally. If the mechanical energy of a system is not conserved, because nonconservative forces perform the work, then we tend to account for its change. For example, if the mechanical energy increases, we look for the source of this increase. If the mechanical energy decreases, we look for this energy in another form or in another place.

Suppose a crate is given a push so that it slides across a horizontal floor with an initial speed v_i. The initial mechanical energy is $E_i = K_i = \frac{1}{2}mv_i^2$. Because of frictional effects, the crate slows and comes to rest; its mechanical energy has been reduced to zero. We understand that loss of mechanical energy in terms of the work done by the nonconservative frictional force, $E_f - E_i = W_{non}$ from Eq. (9-12). We can also interpret the decrease of mechanical energy of the crate as an energy-conversion process, mechanical energy being converted into some other kind of energy. With this interpretation, the total amount of energy remains unchanged; only its form changes. What name do we give to this new kind of energy? From our everyday experiences with frictional forces, we expect that the transformed energy is associated with changes of the crate and floor. In particular, measurement shows that the temperature of these surfaces has increased. This energy is called the *internal energy* of the system consisting of crate and floor. The increase in internal energy is equal to the decrease in mechanical energy. The total energy of this system is conserved in this way. The internal energy of a system and its connection to temperature and "heat" will be discussed further in Chap. 17. For now we can think of the internal energy of a system as kinetic and potential energy of the molecules of that system.

Internal energy of a system: kinetic and potential energy of molecules

Internal energy, energy at the molecular level, has a different character from the kinetic and potential energy of an object such as a ball. It is a simple matter to convert the potential energy of a ball into kinetic energy; we just let it fall. It is also easy to convert mechanical energy into internal energy of the ball-floor system. After the ball bounces a few times, it comes to rest. Its initial mechanical energy has been converted into internal energy of the ball and floor. The reverse process, converting internal energy into mechanical energy, is not simple, however. We do not expect a ball initially at rest on the floor spontaneously to lower its internal energy and rise from the floor. The conversion from mechanical energy to internal energy as described above is associated with work done by nonconservative forces such as friction. These processes have a one-way character and are often called *dissipative processes,* since the mechanical energy is dissipated into the more inaccessible internal energy of a system.

Frictional effects are dissipative.

We generalize the ideas suggested above. Consider a *closed,* or *isolated, system,* one on which no work is done by anything external to the system. No exchange of energy occurs between the system and its environment. We identify the various kinds of energy in the system. There is the kinetic energy of each moving macroscopic component of the system. There may be potential energy present because of elastic springs and gravitational forces. We have already seen the need to include the internal energy of various parts of the system. Other identifiable contributions to the total energy may include acoustic energy, electric energy, chemical energy, nuclear energy, and so on. In short, we should include all energies that could be changing with time. We add together all of these contributions evaluated at a certain time, calling that sum the *total energy* of the system. The *law of conservation of energy* states that *the total energy of an isolated system is conserved.* The various contributions to the total energy can change with time, transforming from one type to another, but their sum does not change.

The law of conservation of energy

We have not proved the law of conservation of energy. It is a law in the same sense that Newton's second law is a law of nature. We accept it as true or valid so long as no violation is observed. To our knowledge, no violation has ever occurred. Indeed, our acceptance of the law is so strong that when apparent violations are observed, we search for a previously unidentified form of energy to enter into the balance. It was in this way that the existence of the neutrino, a subatomic particle, was proposed.

EXAMPLE 9-8. A 2.5-kg ball of sticky clay is dropped from a height of 2.0 m above a stationary floor. On hitting the floor, the clay sticks to the floor. Account for energy transformations in the motion.

SOLUTION. We take the clay, the floor, and the earth and its atmosphere as the isolated system. Since the clay is released from rest, $K_i = 0$ and $U_i = mgy_i$. We measure y_i from floor level, and

$$E_i = U_i = (2.5 \text{ kg})(9.8 \text{ m/s}^2)(2.0 \text{ m}) = 49 \text{ J}$$

On coming to rest ($v_i = 0$) on the floor ($y_f = 0$), the clay has zero mechanical energy. We must account for the 49 J of mechanical energy that has been transformed into other kinds of energy of the system. A small amount of the energy is acoustic; we should hear the clay hitting the floor. Because of the dissipative effects of air resistance and the deformation of the clay, most of the 49 J appears as an increase in the internal energy manifested by temperature increases in parts of the system.

9-8 SATELLITE MOTION AND ESCAPE SPEED

For an object of mass m close to the earth's surface, where the weight is approximately constant, we have used $U = mgy$ to evaluate the gravitational potential energy. For an object such as a satellite or an interplanetary probe, which is not near the surface, we must use a more general expression for gravitational potential energy.

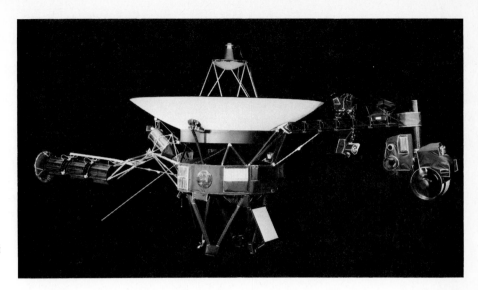

The Voyager spacecraft returned video images during its voyage past the planets Jupiter, Saturn, and Uranus. (N.A.S.A. photograph)

Newton's law of universal gravitation determines the attractive force exerted by one particle on another particle. The force has the same form for two objects that have size if they are spherically symmetric and nonintersecting, as shown in Fig. 9-15 for objects of mass m and M. From Eq. (7-2), the magnitude of the force is

$$F = G \frac{Mm}{r^2}$$

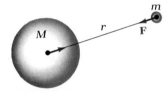

Figure 9-15. Two spherically symmetric objects exert gravitational forces on each other.

where r is the separation of their centers. To determine the gravitational potential energy, we need to calculate the work done by this force on one of the objects as it moves with respect to the other object.

First we note that the gravitational force is conservative, that the work done by this force is independent of path. Figure 9-16a shows a small displacement $\Delta \mathbf{s}$ (exaggerated for clarity), with the force on the body of mass m directed along the line joining the objects. Figure 9-16b shows that the displacement $\Delta \mathbf{s}$ changes the separation of the two bodies from r to $r + \Delta r$ where

$$\Delta r = |\Delta \mathbf{s}| \cos (\pi - \phi) = -|\Delta \mathbf{s}| \cos \phi$$

The work done by $\mathbf{F}$ for this displacement is $\mathbf{F} \cdot \Delta \mathbf{s} = F|\Delta \mathbf{s}| \cos \phi = -F \Delta r$. The work done for this displacement depends then only on the separation distance r and the change Δr in that separation distance, but not at all on the distance moved perpendicular to the line joining the two bodies. It is this feature that makes the work path-independent. (See Prob. 9-5.) For a general path the work done is the integral

Figure 9-16. (a) An object of mass m moves along an arbitrary path connecting i and f. (b) The change in the separation distance r is $\Delta r = |\Delta \mathbf{s}| \cos (180° - \phi) = -|\Delta \mathbf{s}| \cos \phi$.

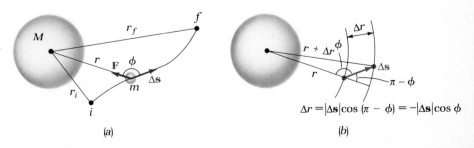

$$W = \int_i^f \mathbf{F} \cdot d\mathbf{s} = -\int_{r_i}^{r_f} G\frac{Mm}{r^2}\,dr = -GMm\int_{r_i}^{r_f}\frac{1}{r^2}\,dr = GMm\left(\frac{1}{r_f} - \frac{1}{r_i}\right)$$

The change in gravitational potential energy of this system is just the negative of the work done by the gravitational force, $U_f - U_i = -W$, from Eq. (9-10). If the separation of the two objects changes from r_i to r_f, then the potential energy difference is

Gravitational potential energy difference

$$U_f - U_i = -GMm\left(\frac{1}{r_f} - \frac{1}{r_i}\right) \qquad (9\text{-}13)$$

Since the separation r of the two objects can be arbitrarily large, it is conventional to choose the potential energy to be zero for an infinite separation. With this choice, the gravitational potential energy for the two objects separated by a distance r is

Gravitational potential energy for objects separated by a distance r

$$U(r) = -\frac{GMm}{r} \qquad (9\text{-}14)$$

Notice from Eq. (9-14), shown graphically in Fig. 9-17, that as the separation r of the objects tends to infinity, the potential energy $U(r)$ approaches zero. Since the zero of potential energy has been chosen to correspond to infinite separation of the two objects, the potential energy for a finite separation is less than zero, or negative. The potential energy $U(r)$ increases as the separation r increases. See Exercise 9-40 to relate Eqs. (9-13) and (9-14) to the special case of mgy for an object close to the earth's surface.

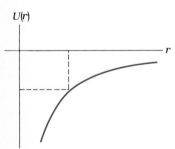

Figure 9-17. Gravitational potential energy $U = -GMm/r$ is negative, approaching zero for infinite separation. As r increases, U increases.

Consider a satellite of mass m in orbit about the earth. Assume that the satellite can be treated as a particle and that the earth is spherically symmetric, with mass m_e. The gravitational potential energy is given by Eq. (9-14) with $M = m_e$, $U(r) = -Gm_em/r$. If the orbit is elliptical, then r and $U(r)$ will be changing. Since mechanical energy is conserved (only the gravitational force acts on the satellite), $K + U = E$, or

$$\tfrac{1}{2}mv^2 + \left(-\frac{Gm_em}{r}\right) = E$$

As r increases, the potential energy increases and the kinetic energy decreases. The satellite moves more slowly when farther from the earth, more rapidly when closer to the earth.

For the special case of a circular orbit, the potential energy and the kinetic energy each remain fixed. We can determine the values of the kinetic energy and the mechanical energy for a circular orbit. The centripetal force is provided by the gravitational force. Newton's second law, $ma = \Sigma \mathbf{F}$, gives

$$\frac{mv^2}{r} = \frac{Gm_em}{r^2}$$

On multiplying this equation by $\tfrac{1}{2}r$, we obtain

$$\tfrac{1}{2}mv^2 = \frac{\tfrac{1}{2}Gm_em}{r}$$

The kinetic energy of the satellite is one-half the magnitude of the potential energy, $K = \tfrac{1}{2}(-U)$. The mechanical energy is $E = K + U = \tfrac{1}{2}Gm_em/r + (-Gm_em/r)$, or

Energy of a satellite in a circular orbit

$$E = -\frac{\frac{1}{2}Gm_em}{r} \qquad (9\text{-}15)$$

The negative sign is a consequence of the convention of having the zero of potential energy correspond to infinite separation of the two objects. The mechanical energy of a satellite in orbit is less than zero. Compare this for an object free of the earth's influence, as $r \to \infty$. Since $U \to 0$ and $K \geqslant 0$ for the free object, the mechanical energy $E = K + U \geqslant 0$. Thus a satellite in orbit has less energy than if free and so is *bound* to the earth. The absolute value of its mechanical energy is called the *binding energy* of the satellite. That much energy would have to be provided to free the satellite from the earth's gravitational influence. For a circular orbit, the binding energy is $|E| = \frac{1}{2}Gm_em/r$.

A satellite's binding energy

Suppose we give an object sufficient energy to escape from the earth. Depending on its initial location, there is a minimum speed, or *escape speed*, that the object must have. We can determine the escape speed using conservation of mechanical energy, $E_f = E_i$. To escape, the object can just come to rest ($K_f = 0$) on achieving infinite separation from the earth ($U_f = 0$). That is, its mechanical energy $E_f = K_f + U_f$ must be at least zero to escape. The object initially at distance r_i ($U_i = -Gm_em/r_i$) from the earth has escape speed v_i ($K_i = \frac{1}{2}mv_i^2$) at that point if $E_i = \frac{1}{2}mv_i^2 + (-Gm_em/r_i) = 0$. Thus

Escape speed from the earth

$$v_i = \sqrt{\frac{2Gm_e}{r_i}} \qquad (9\text{-}16)$$

is the escape speed from that position. Notice that the escape speed depends on the mass of the earth but not on the mass of the escaping object.

EXAMPLE 9-9. A 150-kg satellite is in circular orbit of radius 7.3 Mm about the earth. Evaluate (*a*) the potential, kinetic, and mechanical energies and (*b*) the orbital speed. (*c*) What is the escape speed from this altitude?

SOLUTION. (*a*) The potential energy, $U = -Gm_em/r$, is

$$U = -\frac{(6.67 \times 10^{-11} \text{ N m}^2 \text{ kg}^{-2})(5.98 \times 10^{24} \text{ kg})(150 \text{ kg})}{7.3 \text{ Mm}}$$

$$= -8.2 \times 10^9 \text{ J} = -8.2 \text{ GJ}$$

The kinetic energy is one-half the magnitude of the potential energy, $K = \frac{1}{2}(-U) = 4.1$ GJ. The mechanical energy is

$$E = K + U = 4.1 \text{ GJ} + (-8.2 \text{ GJ}) = -4.1 \text{ GJ}$$

(*b*) From the kinetic energy, we can calculate the orbital speed: $v = \sqrt{2K/m} = 7.4$ km/s.

•(*c*) The escape speed from this distance from the earth's center is obtained from Eq. (9-16):

$$v_i = \sqrt{\frac{2Gm_e}{r_i}} = 10 \text{ km/s}$$

COMMENTARY: WHAT IS A LAW?

If you violate one of society's laws, say a law dealing with fraud, you could face a prison term or a fine or both. The usual role of criminal and civil law in a community is to protect its citizens. What is the role of a law in physics? What happens if you violate one of nature's laws? Is it even possible to break a law of nature?

So far we have encountered five basic laws: Newton's three laws of motion, Newton's law of universal gravitation, and, in this chapter, the law of conservation of energy. We can broaden our understanding of the nature of physical laws by describing some of their general features.

First of all, a law is a fundamental statement that helps form the foundation of a

conceptual framework. In this sense, a law is similar to a postulate in plane geometry. In geometry, a postulate is accepted without proof, and various consequences are derived (theorems are proved) from a set of postulates. Similarly in mechanics, Newton's third law is accepted as a fundamental statement about the way forces occur as action-reaction pairs. Newton's third law serves as a postulate.

There is an important difference between a postulate in geometry and a law in physics, however. A mathematical postulate in geometry is not subject to validation. That is, its truth or validity is not open to question: It cannot be tested because mathematics is a pure abstraction and does not have a physical basis. A law in physics does have a physical basis; it should always be regarded as "on trial." Its truth is tested by our insistence that the law, and its consequences, be fully in accord with experiment. If an experiment shows that a new effect is contrary to a law, then the law is abandoned, or at least modified to include the new effect. Thus the laws of physics are not necessarily immutable; they must change in response to newly discovered phenomena. For example, the law of conservation of energy was modified by Einstein to include mass energy, a previously unrecognized form of energy (described in Chap. 38). In doing so, Einstein merged what had been two separate, unrelated conservation laws — conservation of energy and conservation of mass — into a single, more general law.

Despite the word "law" in its name, Hooke's law for a spring, $F_x = -kx$, is not a law in the sense that we are using the term. That is, Hooke's law is not a fundamental statement or principle. Instead, it is a simple and useful rule that characterizes how a material, such as spring steel, responds to an extension or a compression. Hooke's law is an example of an empirical law, a rule that summarizes our experience over a limited range of conditions. In contrast, Newton's law of universal gravitation gives the gravitational force between any two particles; and this forms the basis for describing gravitational phenomena, such as the structure of the solar system.

Can you willfully violate one of nature's laws? With what penalty? Suppose that you could devise an ingenious exxperiment with a result that conflicted with a law. Strangely enough, the penalty could be a Nobel Prize! Violations of nature's laws are richly rewarded. C. N. Yang and T. D. Lee received the 1957 Nobel physics award for suggesting the possibility of observing a violation of what had been accepted as the law of conservation of parity. (Parity has to do with how a description of a system changes if one of the coordinate axes, say the x axis, is inverted through the origin as if it were reflected in a mirror.) The confirming observation was subsequently made by C. S. Wu. She demonstrated that parity is not conserved in certain nuclear decay processes. So go ahead and break a law of physics — if you can.

SUMMARY WITH APPLICATIONS

Section 9-2. One-dimensional conservative systems

A force is conservative if the work it does is zero for a round-trip. In a one-dimensional conservative system, only conservative forces perform work and mechanical energy, $E = K + U$, is conserved. Potential energy is an energy of position. Two types of potential energy are gravitational potential energy,

$$U = mgy \tag{9-5}$$

and elastic potential energy of a stretched or compressed

spring,

$$U = \tfrac{1}{2}kx^2 \tag{9-7}$$

Distinguish between conservative and nonconservative forces; apply conservation of mechanical energy to one-dimensional conservative systems using gravitational and elastic potential energies.

Section 9-3. Graphical analysis of conservative systems

Motion for an object can be displayed on a graph of the potential-energy function. Turning points and equilibrium points can be located on the graph.

Use a graph of a potential-energy function to describe the motion of an object in one dimension; identify turning points and points of equilibrium from the graph.

Section 9-4. Conservative forces and potential energy in three dimensions

In general, a force is conservative if its work is independent of the path connecting the endpoints i and f. The change in potential energy is the negative of the work done by the conservative force.

Define conservative force and change in potential energy for forces in two and three dimensions.

Section 9-5. Conservation of mechanical energy

If only conservative forces do work, then the mechanical energy of the system is conserved. Conservation of mechanical energy can be used to determine features of the motion of the system.

Use conservation of mechanical energy to determine features of motion in two and three dimensions.

Sections 9-6. Nonconservative forces and internal work; 9-7. The law of conservation of energy

Work done by nonconservative forces and forces internal to a system can cause the mechanical energy to change. The total energy of a system is the sum of various types of energy, including kinetic, potential, and internal energies. Transformations of energy obey the law of conservation of energy: For an isolated system, the total energy is conserved.

Account for work done by nonconservative forces and internal forces when mechanical energy changes; use the law of conservation of energy to account for energy transformations.

Section 9-8. Satellite motion and escape speed

The gravitational potential energy for two spherically symmetric objects separated by a distance r is given by

$$U(r) = -\frac{GMm}{r} \tag{9-14}$$

where M and m are the masses. A satellite is bound to the earth and its mechanical energy is negative. An object escaping from the earth must have a minimum speed, which is called the escape speed.

Determine gravitational potential energy for spherically symmetric objects; apply conservation of mechanical energy to satellites and to escaping objects.

QUESTIONS

9-1   Is something conserved by a conservative force? Explain.

9-2   Is the static frictional force conservative or nonconservative? Explain.

9-3   What are the differences in meaning of the phrase "conservation of energy" as used in this text and as used in the news media in connection with energy shortages?

9-4   Under what circumstances can a normal force, exerted by a surface on some object, perform work? Is this work path-dependent? Explain.

9-5   Consider an automobile traveling at constant speed on a level road surface. What relevant energy transformations are occurring?

9-6   As an automobile begins moving, how does it get its kinetic energy?

9-7   A parachutist leaves a plane at an altitude of 3000 m and immediately opens the parachute. What becomes of her potential energy as she drifts downward at a relatively low speed?

9-8   If 1.0 kg of water changes its temperature by $1.0\,°C$, its internal energy changes by about 4.2 kJ. Through what vertical height would the 1.0 kg of water have to fall to change its gravitational potential energy by that amount?

9-9   Can you start a fire by rubbing two sticks together? (Neither stick is a match.) Comment on the energy transformations involved in the attempt.

9-10 Why is potential energy defined with a negative sign, as in Eq. (9-3)? Suppose it were positive instead. What important consequences would result?

9-11 How can the gravitational potential energy (a) be positive (mgy) for an object above but close to the earth's surface and (b) be negative ($-Gm_e m/r$) for an object above the earth's surface?

9-12 For an object close to the earth's surface, the y component of the force is always negative, $F_y = -mg$, while the potential energy may be positive or negative, $U = mgy$. What corresponding statements can be made for an object connected to a spring obeying Hooke's law?

9-13 Mechanical energy is conserved if only conservative forces perform work. Suppose no forces perform work. Is mechanical energy conserved? Explain.

9-14 Potential energy is often said to be stored energy, as in the gravitational potential energy of the water behind a dam. Can kinetic energy be considered as stored energy? Explain.

9-15 Gravitational potential energy and kinetic energy can be transformed into each other. Elastic potential energy of a spring and kinetic energy can be transformed into each other. Can elastic potential energy be transformed directly into gravitational potential energy? Explain.

9-16 Estimate the change in your gravitational potential energy in going from the first to the second floor of a department store by (a) riding the escalator, (b) riding the elevator, (c) running at top speed up the stairs.

9-17 Identify in each case posed in the previous question the energy transformations which lead to the increase in gravitational potential energy.

9-18 Develop an analogy between transformations of energy and financial transactions involving coins, currency, checks, loans, and other forms of assets and liabilities.

9-19 Consider a satellite in each of several possible circular orbits of different radii. To have the satellite speed increase, must its mechanical energy increase or decrease? Explain.

9-20 How far from the earth must an object move before it is *effectively* free of the earth's influence? What do you mean by *effectively* free? Do your answers depend on the location of the object relative to other objects in the solar system? Explain.

9-21 Consider two satellites of mass m in circular orbits of radii r_1 and r_2, with $r_1 < r_2$. Which satellite has the larger (a) kinetic energy, (b) potential energy, (c) mechanical energy, (d) binding energy?

9-22 The expression for gravitational potential energy in Eq. (9-14) is based on the assumption that both objects are spherically symmetric. Assume that the earth is spherically symmetric. Is a typical satellite spherically symmetric? What about the moon? Explain why the shape of an artificial satellite is not important when considering potential energy.

9-23 Complete the following table:

Symbol	Represents	Type	SI Unit
U			J
$U_f - U_i$			
E			
$\oint \mathbf{F} \cdot d\mathbf{r}$			
mgy	Gravitational potential energy		
$-GMm/r$		Scalar	
$\frac{1}{2}kx^2$			

EXERCISES

Section 9-2. One-dimensional conservative systems

9-1 A 0.55-kg stone is thrown straight up with an initial speed of $v_i = 14$ m/s. Air-resistance effects may be neglected. (a) Evaluate the mechanical energy of this system. (b) What is the potential energy as the stone reaches the highest point in its motion? (c) How high is this point?

9-2 A 0.22-kg pebble is thrown straight down with an initial speed of 12 m/s from a bridge 15 m above the water surface. Neglect air-resistance effects. (a) Determine the mechanical energy of this system. (b) With what speed does the pebble reach the water?

9-3 A 0.75-kg block is connected to a spring of spring constant $k = 2100$ N/m, as shown in Fig. 9-4, and the block is set in motion with a mechanical energy of 47 J. Neglecting frictional effects, determine (a) the maximum displacement of the block from its equilibrium position, (b) the maximum speed of the block, (c) the displacement of the block when its speed is 5.6 m/s.

9-4 Show that mgy and $\frac{1}{2}kx^2$ have dimensions of energy.

9-5 A 12,000-kg railroad car rolls at 4.3 m/s with negligible friction on a horizontal track, as shown in Fig. 9-18.

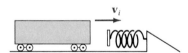

Figure 9-18. Exercise 9-5.

Near the end of the track, the car hits and compresses a bumper spring by 0.23 m and comes momentarily to rest. Assuming that only the conservative spring force performs work on the car, determine the spring constant of the spring.

9-6 Suppose the force exerted on an object in one dimension is given by $F_x(x) = -\alpha x^3$ where α is a constant with units of N/m³. Determine the expression for the potential energy corresponding to this conservative force. Let $U = 0$ at $x = 0$.

9-7 A freight elevator and a 75-kg carton on the elevator floor accelerate upward from rest with a constant acceleration, $a_y = 2.4$ m/s². On reaching the next floor 3.8 m above, the elevator and carton go into free-fall because of an elevator-cable failure. (a) What work is done by the normal force exerted on the carton by the elevator floor as they accelerate upward? (b) Is this normal force conservative? Explain. (c) With what final speed does the carton pass its starting point on the way down?

9-8 Consider the arrangement shown in Fig. 9-19a. Suppose that both springs are relaxed when the block is at $x = 0$. In Fig. 9-19b the block is displaced so that x is the amount of stretch for one spring and the amount of compression for the other. Assume that friction is negligible and determine expressions for (a) the force component $F_x(x)$ acting on the block and (b) the potential energy of this system.

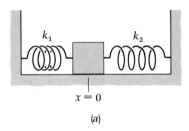

$x = 0$

(a)

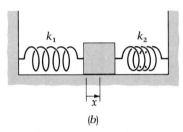

x

(b)

Figure 9-19. Exercise 9-8.

9-9 The mass of the block in the previous exercise is 5.0 kg and the springs have constants $k_1 = 1200$ N/m and $k_2 = 1800$ N/m. The block is pulled out and released from rest at $x = 0.20$ m. (a) Determine the maximum kinetic energy of the block. Determine the speed of the block at (b) $x = 0.0$ and (c) $x = -0.10$ m.

9-10 The block in Example 9-3 is set in motion so that its maximum speed is v_m. (a) Show that when the block is at position x, its speed is

$$v = \sqrt{v_m^2 - \frac{k}{m}x^2}$$

Let $k = 1100$ N/m, $m = 2.5$ kg, and $v_m = 3.0$ m/s. Determine (b) the maximum distance x_m of the block from equilibrium, (c) the speed at $x = -\frac{1}{2}x_m$, (d) the position of the block when $v = \frac{1}{2}v_m$.

Section 9-3. Graphical analysis of conservative systems

9-11 The gravitational-potential-energy function $U(y) = mgy$ is graphed in Fig. 9-20 for a 10.2-kg object close to the earth's surface; $y = 0$ corresponds to ground level. Suppose the mechanical energy of the system is 0.20

kJ. From the graph determine (a) the maximum height of the object, (b) the maximum kinetic energy and the point where the object has that maximum kinetic energy, (c) the location of the object when its kinetic energy equals the potential energy, (d) the force on the object at that instant.

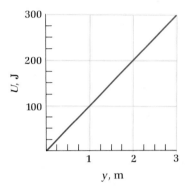

Figure 9-20. Exercise 9-11.

9-12 In a one-dimensional model of an atom vibrating in a molecule, the potential-energy function is given by

$$U = \tfrac{1}{4}\alpha x^4 - \tfrac{1}{2}kx^2$$

with $\alpha = 16 \times 10^{20}$ N/m³ and $k = 4.0$ N/m. (a) Construct a graph of this function for -0.10 nm $\leqslant x \leqslant 0.10$ nm (1 nm $= 10^{-9}$ m). Suppose a 2.3×10^{-26}-kg atom has this potential energy and moves with a maximum displacement of 0.08 nm from the origin. Using the graph, determine (b) the speed of the atom at $x = 0$, (c) the speed of the atom at $x = 0.05$ nm, (d) the force on the atom at $x = -0.05$ nm.

9-13 For the potential-energy function in the previous exercise, suppose that the atom is instantaneously at rest at $x_i = -0.02$ nm. (a) Determine from the graph the maximum kinetic energy of the atom. (b) The initial point is one turning point in the motion; locate the other turning point in the motion. (c) How is the motion for $E < 0$ (in this exercise) fundamentally different from the motion for $E > 0$ (in Exercise 9-12)?

9-14 A simple model of a hydrogen molecule uses a one-dimensional potential energy $U(x) = U_0(e^{-2x/a} - 2e^{-x/a})$, where $U_0 = 7.5 \times 10^{-19}$ J and $a = 7.0 \times 10^{-11}$ m. (a) Construct a graph of $U(x)$ versus x for $-1.5 \leqslant x/a \leqslant 3$. From the graph, determine the turning points of the motion if (b) $E = -2.5 \times 10^{-19}$ J and (c) $E = +2.5 \times 10^{-19}$ J.

Section 9-4. Conservative forces and potential energy in three dimensions

9-15 Estimate the work done on you by the gravitational force if you (a) climb a ladder from the ground to a rooftop 3 m above and (b) jump from roof level to the ground and walk back to the bottom of the ladder.

(c) How much work is done on you by the gravitational force for the round-trip?

9-16 Consider a constant force $\mathbf{F} = (3\text{ N})\mathbf{i} + (4\text{ N})\mathbf{j}$ which acts on an object moving in the xy plane. Show that the work done by this force as the object moves from the point (x_i, y_i) to the point (x_f, y_f) is independent of path. Note that $\mathbf{F} \cdot d\mathbf{r} = F_x\,dx + F_y\,dy$ and evaluate the integral without specifying the path.

9-17 The force in the previous exercise is conservative. (Why?) (a) Determine the expression for the difference in potential energy between points (x_i, y_i) and (x_f, y_f). (b) Choose the origin $(0, 0)$ as the reference point at which $U = 0$. What is the potential-energy function $U(x, y)$? Evaluate the potential energy at the point (c) (8 m, 6 m) and (d) (−8 m, 6 m).

Section 9-5. Conservation of mechanical energy

9-18 Neglecting air resistance, show that the speed of a projectile as it reaches an altitude y depends on the initial speed v_i but is independent of the angle of projection. See Fig. 9-21.

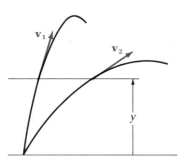

Figure 9-21. Exercise 9-18: Identical projectiles are fired with the same initial speed but at different angles.

9-19 A 0.25-kg ball is thrown so that it travels a horizontal distance of 37 m in 2.0 s and reaches a maximum height of 18 m. Air resistance is negligible, so the horizontal velocity component is constant. Determine (a) the mechanical energy of the ball, (b) the initial speed of the ball, (c) the maximum potential energy of the ball.

9-20 A projectile of mass m is fired with initial speed v_i at an angle of θ_i from the horizontal, as shown in Fig. 9-22.

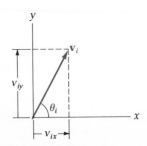

Figure 9-22. Exercise 9-20.

Neglect effects of air resistance and use conservation of mechanical energy to determine (a) the maximum altitude reached and (b) the speed of the projectile on returning to ground level. Remember that the x component of the velocity does not change in this motion.

9-21 A simple pendulum is formed by attaching a ball to one end of a light string; the other end of the string is held fixed, and the ball can swing in a vertical plane. Suppose the ball is released from rest from the position shown in Fig. 9-23 with $\ell = 450$ mm and $\theta = 30.0°$. Determine (a) the speed of the ball and (b) the tension in the string when the ball passes through its lowest position.

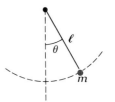

Figure 9-23. Exercise 9-21.

9-22 A ball of mass m is attached to a light string and moves in a vertical circle of radius r. It is given an initial velocity of magnitude v_0 at point O, as shown in Fig. 9-24. Determine, in terms of m, g, v_0, and r, the speed of the ball and the string tension at (a) point A and (b) point B.

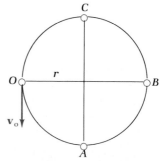

Figure 9-24. Exercise 9-22.

9-23 What minimum speed must the ball in the previous exercise be given at point O so that the string does not go slack before the ball reaches point C? See Fig. 9-24.

9-24 A light spring of constant $k = 1600$ N/m is compressed by 15 mm. A 75-g marble is placed against the spring,

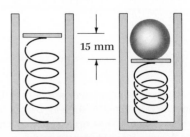

Figure 9-25. Exercise 9-24.

as shown in Fig. 9-25. The marble is fired upward when the spring is released. Assume that the marble leaves the spring behind in its relaxed configuration and that frictional effects are negligible. (a) What maximum height is attained by the marble? (b) With what speed does the marble leave the spring?

9-25 A spring gun similar to that in the previous exercise is used to fire a 75-g marble horizontally from a countertop that is 1.2 m above the floor, as shown in Fig. 9-26. If the spring is compressed by 25 mm, the marble hits the floor 4.2 m from the bottom of the counter, as measured along the floor. Neglect all frictional effects. (a) Determine the mechanical energy of the marble in its trajectory. (b) Determine the spring constant of the spring. (c) How far will the marble travel horizontally if the spring is compressed by 37 mm?

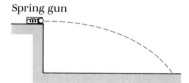

Figure 9-26. Exercise 9-25.

9-26 A child sits at the top of a cylindrical tank of radius R, as shown in Fig. 9-27. The surface is very smooth and the child begins to slide with negligible friction. Determine the value of the angle at which the child loses contact with the cylindrical surface.

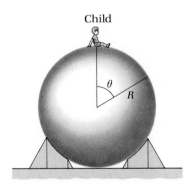

Figure 9-27. Exercise 9-26.

Section 9-6. Nonconservative forces and internal work

9-27 Consider the crate in Example 9-4. Suppose it is pushed horizontally so that its path traces out a full circle of radius 4.5 m. (a) Evaluate the work done by the kinetic frictional force for this path. (b) Explain how this calculation shows that the frictional force is nonconservative.

9-28 A 0.25-kg rubber ball is released from rest at a height of 1.5 m above the floor. After hitting the floor, the ball rises to a maximum height of 0.8 m. Estimate (a) the

work done by the floor on the ball and (b) the speed of the ball just before and just after it comes into contact with the floor.

9-29 Suppose that you walk up a flight of stairs at constant speed while changing your vertical coordinate by 10 m. (a) Estimate the change in your mechanical energy. (b) Explain why the normal force exerted on your shoes by the steps performs no work. (c) How do you account for the change in your mechanical energy? What forces perform work?

Section 9-7. The law of conservation of energy

9-30 (a) Estimate the running speed of a pole vaulter who clears the bar at 4 m. (b) Describe the energy transformations that occur and explain why the pole is necessary.

9-31 An automobile coasts down a 5 percent grade at 36 km/h. (a) Estimate the magnitude of the net retarding force due to air resistance, friction, and so on. (b) Estimate the minimum power provided by the engine if the automobile travels up the grade at a steady 36 km/h.

9-32 Suppose that frictional effects are not negligible in Example 9-3. The block is released from rest at $x_i = 0.15$ m and after a few seconds comes to rest and remains at $x_f = -0.02$ m. (How can it remain at rest there?) (a) Describe the energy transformations that occur for this motion. (b) Determine the change in internal energy of the system of spring, block, and surface. State any assumptions you make in the calculation.

9-33 A 0.33-kg ball is projected upward with an initial speed of $v_i = 23$ m/s. On reaching a level of $y_f = 14$ m, its speed is $v_f = 13$ m/s. Consider the system of projectile, atmosphere, and earth to be isolated. (a) Account quantitatively for energy transformations between these two points in the motion by determining the changes in kinetic, potential, and internal energies. (b) What can you say about the speed of the projectile as it returns to the 14-m level on its descent?

Section 9-8. Satellite motion and escape speed

9-34 Show $U = -GMm/r$ has dimensions of energy.

9-35 Evaluate the (a) potential, (b) kinetic, and (c) mechanical energies of a 30-Mg space laboratory in a circular orbit of radius 70 Mm about the earth. (d) Which, if any, of these energies would increase if the radius of the orbit were smaller?

9-36 A 125-kg communications satellite is first "parked" in a circular earth orbit of radius 7000 km. Later it is moved to a geosynchronous orbit with a period of 24 h, so that as the earth rotates on its axis, the satellite is always above the same spot on the equator. (a) Determine the radius of the geosynchronous orbit. (b) What additional energy must be supplied to move the satellite from the parking orbit to the geosynchronous orbit?

9-37 The planet Mercury has mass 3.3×10^{23} kg and moves in an approximately circular orbit of radius 5.8×10^{10} m about the sun, which has a mass of 2.0×10^{30} kg. (a) Determine the mechanical energy of the Mercury-sun system. (b) Suppose Mercury were moved to a circular orbit of radius 15×10^{10} m, equal to that of the earth about the sun. How much energy would have to be provided?

9-38 The mass of the earth is 81 times the mass of the moon. The earth's radius is 3.7 times the moon's radius. Compare the escape speeds of an object from the surfaces of these bodies. Does this comparison help explain why the moon has no atmosphere?

9-39 A satellite is in an elliptical orbit about the earth. The separation of the satellite from the center of the earth ranges from a minimum at perigee of 7.2 Mm, where its speed is 8.0 km/s, to a maximum of 9.9 Mm at apogee. Determine the speed of the satellite when (a) at apogee and (b) at a separation of 8.4 Mm from the earth's center.

9-40 For an object close to the earth's surface, the difference in gravitational potential energy is given by $U_f - U_i = mg(y_f - y_i)$. Alternatively, Eq. (9-13) can be used by letting $r_i = R + y_i$ and $r_f = R + y_f$, where R is the earth's radius. Show that Eq. (9-13) approximately reduces to $U_f - U_i = mg(y_f - y_i)$. [Hint: Remember that $g = Gm_e/R^2$ and that $(1 + z)^{-1} \approx 1 - z$ for $|z| \ll 1$.]

PROBLEMS

9-1 A 0.73-kg block begins sliding from the top of a ramp, as shown in Fig. 9-28. At the bottom of the ramp is a light spring of constant $k = 1200$ N/m. Neglect frictional effects. (a) By how much is the spring compressed as the block comes to rest? (b) What is the speed of the block as it reaches the spring?

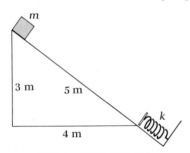

Figure 9-28. Prob. 9-1.

9-2 Take kinetic frictional effects into account in the situation posed in the previous problem. Let $\mu_k = 0.10$ and determine (a) the speed as the block reaches the spring and (b) the maximum compression of the spring.

9-3 A light spring is suspended vertically, as shown in Fig.

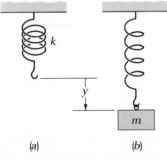

(a)   (b)

Figure 9-29. Prob. 9-3.

9-29a. A block of mass m is attached and set in vertical motion. Let y denote the position of the block as seen in Fig. 9-29b so that $y = 0$ corresponds to the position where the spring is relaxed. (a) Write down the potential-energy function as the sum of elastic and gravitational contributions. (b) Determine the net force acting on the block as a function of the coordinate y. (c) At what value of y, call it y_1, is the net force zero? (d) Show that the potential-energy function found in part (a) can be written as $\frac{1}{2}k(y - y_1)^2 +$ a constant term. (e) By resetting the origin at the equilibrium point, $y - y_1 \rightarrow y$, and resetting the zero of potential energy at this equilibrium point, show that the potential energy of a block connected to a vertical spring can be expressed as $U = \frac{1}{2}ky^2$.

9-4 The potential energy of interaction between neutral atoms is sometimes approximated by the "12-6" potential-energy function:

$$U(x) = V_0\left[\left(\frac{a}{x}\right)^{12} - 2\left(\frac{a}{x}\right)^6\right]$$

where x is the separation between centers of the atoms and V_0 and a are constants. (a) Construct a graph of this function with $a = 0.30$ nm and $V_0 = 3.2 \times 10^{-21}$ J for 0.24 nm $\leq x \leq 0.36$ nm. (b) Determine from the graph the equilibrium separation where $F_x = 0$. (c) Check this value by using the connection $F_x(x) = -dU/dx$. (d) Suppose one turning point in the motion is at $x = 0.28$ nm; locate the other turning point. (e) Determine the mechanical energy for the motion between these turning points.

9-5 If a force on an object is always directed along a line from the object to a given point, which we take as the origin in three dimensions, and the magnitude of the force depends only on the separation of the object from the origin, the force is said to be a *central force.* After reviewing the discussion preceding Eq. (9-13), show that any central force is a conservative force.

9-6   In Example 9-6, a small ice cube slides without friction on a "loop-the-loop" track. Determine the minimum height above the bottom of the circular track from which the cube can be released and still remain in contact with the track at the highest point.

9-7   Two blocks are connected by a light string which passes over a small pulley, as shown in Fig. 9-30. They are released from rest, and frictional effects may be neglected. (a) Show that the sum of the work done by the string force on the blocks is zero. (b) Using energy methods, determine the common speed of the blocks when m_1 has fallen a distance h. Express your answer in terms of m_1, m_2, g, and h.

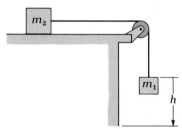

Figure 9-30. Prob. 9-7.

9-8   Reconsider the previous problem, but include friction; let μ_k represent the coefficient of kinetic friction. Determine the speed after m_1 has fallen a distance h.

9-9   Construct graphs of (a) the force component $F_x(x)$ from the potential-energy graph in Fig. 9-31a and (b) the potential-energy function $U(x)$ from the force component graph in Fig. 9-31b. Take $U(0) = 0$.

9-10   Suppose that the block in Exercise 9-8 is in equilibrium at $x = 0$, but that neither spring is relaxed; one spring is stretched by an amount a_1, while the other is stretched by a_2 when $x = 0$. (a) By requiring the net force on the block to be zero at $x = 0$, show that $k_1a_1 = k_2a_2$. Determine expressions for (b) the elastic potential energy $U(x)$ of this system and (c) the force component $F_x(x)$ acting on the block.

9-11   ▣ Modify the program in Table 7-2 to determine the orbit of the satellite in Exercise 9-39. (a) Print values of the speed along with distance from the earth to check the values calculated in that exercise. Take as initial conditions: X = 0,   Y = 7.2E + 6,   VX = 8.0E + 3, VY = 0. (b) Redo the program and print values of the kinetic, potential, and mechanical energies at each iteration. Is mechanical energy conserved?

9-12   ▣ The program in the previous problem can be adapted to investigate escape speeds. For simplicity, take the initial velocity to be directed away from the earth. The initial conditions are X = 0, Y = initial distance from center of earth, VX = 0, and VY = your estimate of the escape speed. If you underestimate the escape-speed value, the velocity component VY will eventually become negative, indicating that the object is returning to earth. You may have to use more than 1000 iterations. Determine numerically the escape speed of an object initially at 7 Mm from the earth's center and compare your answer with that given by Eq. (9-16).

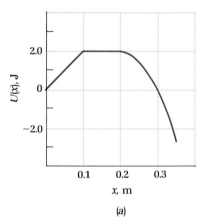

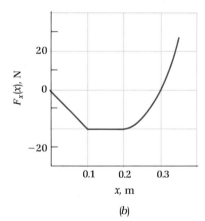

(a)   (b)

Figure 9-31. Prob. 9-9.

CHAPTER 10
MOMENTUM AND
THE MOTION
OF SYSTEMS

10-1 INTRODUCTION

When the study of mechanics was developing during the seventeenth century, two concepts vied for the central place. They were called the "amount of motion" of an object (equal to the mass of the object times its velocity) and the "vis viva" of an object. We now call the former the *momentum* and the latter the *kinetic energy*. Both of these quantities are important, but sometimes one is more useful. Just as we found the concept of energy to be particularly useful in the solution of problems involving conservative forces, we shall find the concept of momentum to be particularly useful in problems involving collisions. In fact, the concept of momentum has proved so useful that the term has been stolen from physics and applied to such things as the "momentum" of a basketball team, having to do with the rate at which points are scored rather than with the physical motion of the team!

10-2 CENTER OF MASS

In this chapter we will no longer treat objects as if they were particles, as if they had no extent. Although this was a good approximation up to now, there are many situations in which we must consider the extended nature of the objects. Furthermore, we wish to describe *systems* of objects that interact with each other, such as the solar system, the atoms that form a molecule, and the system composed of two cars that collide.

In considering the motion of an extended object or a system of particles, we often find it useful to fix our attention on a single representative point. The point that is most convenient is an average position of the mass of the system, called the *center of mass*. A wrench will balance on your finger if you position its center of mass directly above your finger. The position $\mathbf{r}_{cm}$ of the center of mass of a system of particles is defined quantitatively as

Definition of the center of mass

$$\mathbf{r}_{cm} = \frac{\Sigma m_i \mathbf{r}_i}{\Sigma m_i} \qquad (10\text{-}1)$$

where $\mathbf{r}_i$ is the position, m_i is the mass of the ith particle of the system, and the sum is over all the particles in the system (Fig. 10-1). Since Σm_i is the total mass M of the system, we have $\mathbf{r}_{cm} = (\Sigma m_i \mathbf{r}_i)/M$. In component form this becomes

$$x_{cm} = \frac{\Sigma m_i x_i}{M} \qquad y_{cm} = \frac{\Sigma m_i y_i}{M} \qquad z_{cm} = \frac{\Sigma m_i z_i}{M} \qquad (10\text{-}2)$$

where x_{cm}, y_{cm}, and z_{cm} are the coordinates locating the center of mass, and x_i, y_i, and z_i are the coordinates that locate the ith particle.

Often the system of particles will not consist of discrete particles for which a sum can be done. It may be that the system is a continuous object. Although we realize that, on a microscopic scale, objects may be made up of discrete particles, an extended object, such as this book, can be treated as continuous when viewed on a scale commensurate with its size. In such a case the sum in Eq. (10-1) is replaced by an integral: $\mathbf{r}_{cm} = \int \mathbf{r}\, dm / \int dm$, or

Center of mass of an extended object

$$\mathbf{r}_{cm} = \frac{1}{M} \int \mathbf{r}\, dm \qquad (10\text{-}3)$$

where $M = \int dm$ is the total mass of the system.

To integrate means, in a limiting sense, to sum an infinite number of infinitesimal pieces. Here we sum the vectors $\mathbf{r}$ for all the infinitesimal increments of mass dm that make up the object. It is usually convenient to break this vector equation into its components to do the actual integration. Thus the coordinates of the center of mass of a continuous object are

$$x_{cm} = \frac{1}{M} \int x\, dm \qquad y_{cm} = \frac{1}{M} \int y\, dm \qquad z_{cm} = \frac{1}{M} \int z\, dm \qquad (10\text{-}4)$$

To evaluate the integrals in Eqs. (10-4) we must express dm, the increment of mass, in terms of the coordinates of the object. The mass dm of a differential volume element dV is $\rho\, dV$, where ρ is the mass density (mass per unit volume) of the object. Then Eqs. (10-4) become

$$x_{cm} = \frac{1}{M} \int x\rho\, dV \qquad y_{cm} = \frac{1}{M} \int y\rho\, dV \qquad z_{cm} = \frac{1}{M} \int z\rho\, dV \qquad (10\text{-}5)$$

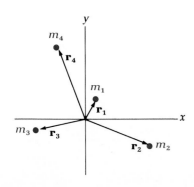

Figure 10-1. Each particle is located by its position vector.

EXAMPLE 10-1. Find the coordinates of the center of mass of the system of three particles that lie in the plane of Fig. 10-2.

SOLUTION. Using the coordinates given in Fig. 10-2 in Eq. (10-2), we find, approximately

$$x_{cm} = \frac{(3 \text{ g})(11 \text{ mm}) + (4 \text{ g})(-8 \text{ mm}) + (5 \text{ g})(10 \text{ mm})}{12 \text{ g}} = 4 \text{ mm}$$

$$y_{cm} = \frac{(3 \text{ g})(9 \text{ mm}) + (4 \text{ g})(2 \text{ mm}) + (5 \text{ g})(-3 \text{ mm})}{12 \text{ g}} = 2 \text{ mm}$$

$$z_{cm} = 0$$

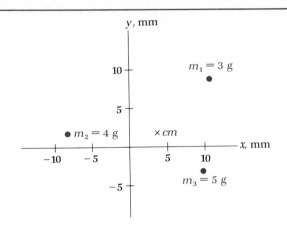

Figure 10-2. Example 10-1.

EXAMPLE 10-2. Find the center of mass of a long, thin rod with uniform density.

SOLUTION. Let the rod have length ℓ, cross-sectional area A, and mass M. To write dm in terms of the position x along the rod , we divide the rod into many thin slices, as shown in Fig. 10-3. Each slice is thin enough that the x coordinate of all of each slice is essentially the same. Because the rod is uniform, with volume ℓA, its density is $\rho = M/\ell A$. The volume element is $dV = A\, dx$. Thus

$$x_{cm} = \frac{1}{M} \int_0^\ell x \left(\frac{M}{\ell A}\right) A\, dx$$

where the limits of integration are the ends of the rod at $x = 0$ and $x = \ell$:

$$x_{cm} = \frac{1}{M}\frac{M}{\ell} \int_0^\ell x\, dx = \frac{1}{\ell}\frac{x^2}{2}\Big|_0^\ell = \frac{\ell}{2}$$

As you may have guessed from symmetry, the center of mass is at the midpoint of the rod.

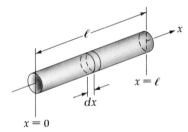

Figure 10-3. Example 10-2.

10-3 MOTION OF THE CENTER OF MASS

Consider the motion of a wrench thrown upward, as shown in the strobe photograph of Fig. 10-4. If you try to follow the motion of an end of the wrench, you find the path is a complicated combination of circular and parabolic motions. The complicated nature of the path is not unexpected because a particle at the end of the wrench is subject not only to the force of gravity, but also to the forces exerted on it by the rest of the wrench. The motion of the center of mass, marked with a cross, is a simple parabola. We now show that the motion of the center of mass is due solely to the forces exerted by agents external to the system.

The position of the center of mass of a system is given by Eq. (10-1), which we write as $\mathbf{r}_{cm} = (\Sigma m_i \mathbf{r}_i)/M$. The velocity and acceleration of the center of mass are obtained by differentiation:

$$\mathbf{v}_{cm} = \frac{d}{dt}\mathbf{r}_{cm} = \frac{1}{M}\Sigma m_i \frac{d\mathbf{r}_i}{dt}$$

or

$$\mathbf{v}_{cm} = \frac{1}{M}\Sigma m_i \mathbf{v}_i \qquad (10\text{-}6)$$

Figure 10-4. Multiflash photograph of a wrench thrown upward and outward. Although the motion of most parts of the wrench is quite complex, the motion of the center of mass, which is marked by a cross, is a simple parabola. The parabola is the same path that a particle would follow if it had the same forces and initial velocity. *(Danny Overcash)*

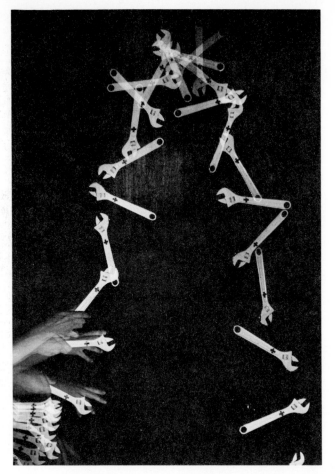

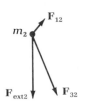

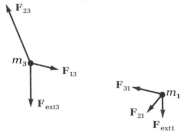

Figure 10-5. Three particles form a system. Each particle exerts a force on the other two particles as shown. $\mathbf{F}_{21}$ is the force that particle 2 exerts on particle 1. There are also forces from sources external to the system, such as that exerted on particle 1, $\mathbf{F}_{ext1}$.

Similarly,

$$\mathbf{a}_{cm} = \frac{d}{dt}\,\mathbf{v}_{cm} = \frac{1}{M}\,\Sigma m_i\,\frac{d^2\mathbf{r}_i}{dt^2}$$

or

$$\mathbf{a}_{cm} = \frac{1}{M}\,\Sigma m_i\mathbf{a}_i \qquad (10\text{-}7)$$

To show that the acceleration of the center of mass depends only on the forces exerted by agents external to the system, we must distinguish between internal and external forces. *Internal forces* are forces exerted on particles within the system by other particles within the system, whereas *external forces* are forces exerted on particles within the system by agents external to the system. To make this distinction clear, we let $\mathbf{F}_{ij}$ be the force exerted by particle i on particle j, where both i and j are within the system. We let $\mathbf{F}_{extj}$ be the force exerted by objects external to the system on particle j.

The acceleration of the center of mass is defined by Eq. (10-7). To determine its value for a given system, we first find the accelerations of the individual particles using Newton's second law, and then add these accelerations. Consider the three-particle system shown in Fig. 10-5. The acceleration of the center of mass is given by $M\mathbf{a}_{cm} = m_1\mathbf{a}_1 + m_2\mathbf{a}_2 + m_3\mathbf{a}_3$. The acceleration of each of the individual particles is given by Newton's second law:

$$m_1\mathbf{a}_1 = \Sigma\mathbf{F}_1 = \mathbf{F}_{21} + \mathbf{F}_{31} + \mathbf{F}_{ext1}$$

$$m_2\mathbf{a}_2 = \Sigma\mathbf{F}_2 = \mathbf{F}_{12} + \mathbf{F}_{32} + \mathbf{F}_{\text{ext2}}$$

$$m_3\mathbf{a}_3 = \Sigma\mathbf{F}_3 = \mathbf{F}_{13} + \mathbf{F}_{23} + \mathbf{F}_{\text{ext3}}$$

Thus

$$M\mathbf{a}_{cm} = (\mathbf{F}_{21} + \mathbf{F}_{31} + \mathbf{F}_{\text{ext1}}) + (\mathbf{F}_{12} + \mathbf{F}_{32} + \mathbf{F}_{\text{ext2}}) + (\mathbf{F}_{13} + \mathbf{F}_{23} + \mathbf{F}_{\text{ext3}})$$

But Newton's third law states that $\mathbf{F}_{ij} = -\mathbf{F}_{ji}$, so the internal forces cancel in pairs in the sum. For example, $\mathbf{F}_{31} = -\mathbf{F}_{13}$. Therefore, the sum of all the forces on the particles is equal to the sum of the external forces only. Letting $\Sigma\mathbf{F}_{\text{ext}} = \mathbf{F}_{\text{ext1}} + \mathbf{F}_{\text{ext2}} + \mathbf{F}_{\text{ext3}}$, we have

$$M\mathbf{a}_{cm} = \mathbf{F}_{\text{ext1}} + \mathbf{F}_{\text{ext2}} + \mathbf{F}_{\text{ext3}} = \Sigma\mathbf{F}_{\text{ext}}$$

The motion of the center of mass is due to external forces.

The acceleration of the center of mass is determined by the external forces only.

The same result follows for any number of particles. The mass of the system times the acceleration of the center of mass is determined by the sum of the accelerations of the individual particles times their masses:

$$M\mathbf{a}_{cm} = \Sigma m_i\mathbf{a}_i$$

When the accelerations of the particles are expressed in terms of the forces on them (by Newton's second law), the internal forces cancel in pairs in the summation (by Newton's third law), and the acceleration of the center of mass is determined by just the external forces:

$$M\mathbf{a}_{cm} = \sum_i \left(\mathbf{F}_{\text{ext},i} + \sum_j \mathbf{F}_{ij} \right) = \sum_i \mathbf{F}_{\text{ext},i}$$

It is not important to know on which particle the external force is exerted, so we can drop the i subscript and write

Newton's second law for the motion of the center of mass of a system

$$\Sigma\mathbf{F}_{\text{ext}} = M\mathbf{a}_{cm} \tag{10-8}$$

Now we can see why the cross that indicates the center of mass of the wrench in Fig. 10-4 has a simple parabolic path. It moves as if all the mass of the wrench were concentrated there and only the external forces (in this case gravitational) were applied there.

Although the internal forces do not affect the acceleration of the center of mass, they can still do work. Thus there is not a general work-energy theorem relating the sum of the work done by the external forces and the kinetic energy of the system. Although energy is still conserved, the change in kinetic energy of the system may not be simply related to the work done by just the external forces. For example, if you push yourself away from the wall, the force exerted by the wall does no work because its point of application does not move. The acceleration of your center of mass is given by the force the wall exerts on you divided by your total mass, but only internal forces (exerted by your muscles on your bones) do work.

EXAMPLE 10-3. A spacecraft is far enough away from any other body so that no appreciable external forces are exerted on it. (a) What is the path of its center of mass? (b) The spacecraft then extends its antenna to talk to earth. What is the path of the center of mass during this maneuver?

SOLUTION. (a) Since there are no external forces on the spacecraft, its center of mass has zero acceleration, and therefore it travels at constant speed along a straight line. (b) The forces that extend the antenna are internal to the spacecraft. There are still no external forces, so the center of mass of the spacecraft continues to move at constant speed along the same straight line.

The centers of mass of the two subsystems consisting of (i) the antenna and (ii) the rest of the spacecraft will each accelerate briefly during the time the arm is being extended. The center of mass of the whole spacecraft will not accelerate, since all forces are internal to the whole spacecraft system.

EXAMPLE 10-4. A pair of figure skaters of masses 45 and 80 kg join hands while at rest on ice. An external force $\mathbf{F}_a = (100\ \mathrm{N})\mathbf{i}$ is applied to the smaller skater. Assume that the skaters have no horizontal forces exerted on them by the ice, so that $\mathbf{F}_a$ is the sole external horizontal force. (a) What is the acceleration of the center of mass of the pair? (b) The skaters let go of each other, but $\mathbf{F}_a$ is still applied to the smaller skater. What is the acceleration of the center of mass of the pair now?

SOLUTION. (a) The motion of the pair of skaters is complex, involving both translation of the center of mass and movement with respect to the center of mass. The acceleration of the center of mass is simple:

$$\Sigma \mathbf{F}_{\mathrm{ext}} = M\mathbf{a}_{cm}$$

$$\mathbf{a}_{cm} = \left(\frac{100\ \mathrm{N}}{125\ \mathrm{kg}}\right)\mathbf{i} = (0.8\ \mathrm{m/s^2})\mathbf{i}$$

It would be difficult (although not impossible) to find the acceleration of an individual skater. (b) The forces that the skaters exert on each other are internal to the system consisting of the pair of skaters. Since internal forces do not affect the motion of the center of mass, the acceleration of the center of mass is, as before, $(0.8\ \mathrm{m/s^2})\mathbf{i}$.

10-4 MOMENTUM

In a midair collision in a football game between a 75-kg ball carrier and a 110-kg defender, what counts? What determines which way the players will go after the collision? Does mass count? Does speed count? Which is more important? How do you find the direction they go after the collision? Solving problems such as this one leads to the concept of momentum.

Momentum of a particle. The momentum $\mathbf{p}$ of a particle of mass m and velocity $\mathbf{v}$ is defined by

Momentum of a particle

$$\mathbf{p} = m\mathbf{v} \tag{10-9}$$

Momentum is a vector because in the product $m\mathbf{v}$, m is a scalar and $\mathbf{v}$ is a vector. The direction of the momentum of a particle is the direction of the velocity of the particle, and the magnitude of the momentum is $p = mv$. Momentum has the dimension of mass times length divided by time and the SI unit of kg · m/s. The momentum of a 0.75-kg ball with a velocity of 15 m/s in the x direction is $\mathbf{p} = m\mathbf{v} = (0.75\ \mathrm{kg})(15\ \mathrm{m/s})\mathbf{i} = (11\ \mathrm{kg \cdot m/s})\mathbf{i}$.

Newton originally gave the second law in a form that in our notation becomes

$$\Sigma \mathbf{F} = \frac{d\mathbf{p}}{dt} \tag{10-10}$$

This is equivalent to the form for the law we used in Chap. 5, $\Sigma \mathbf{F} = m\mathbf{a}$:

$$\Sigma \mathbf{F} = m\mathbf{a} = m\frac{d\mathbf{v}}{dt} = \frac{d(m\mathbf{v})}{dt} = \frac{d\mathbf{p}}{dt}$$

where we have assumed that the mass is constant.

Momentum of a system of particles. The total momentum $\mathbf{P}$ of a system of particles is defined to be

$$P = \sum_i p_i \qquad (10\text{-}11)$$

where the sum is over all the objects that are defined to be part of the system.

The momentum of a system that has forces applied to it may change. The rate of change in the momentum is given by

$$\frac{d\mathbf{P}}{dt} = \frac{d(\Sigma \mathbf{p}_i)}{dt} = \frac{d(\Sigma m_i \mathbf{v}_i)}{dt}.$$

But $\Sigma m_i \mathbf{v}_i = M\mathbf{v}_{cm}$, or $\mathbf{P} = M\mathbf{v}_{cm}$. Thus

$$\frac{d\mathbf{P}}{dt} = M\frac{d\mathbf{v}_{cm}}{dt} = M\mathbf{a}_{cm}$$

In Sec. 10-3 we saw that the motion of the center of mass was affected only by external forces: $\Sigma \mathbf{F}_{ext} = M\mathbf{a}_{cm}$. From this we have *the momentum of a system* $\mathbf{P}$ *is affected by external forces only*:

$$\Sigma \mathbf{F}_{ext} = \frac{d\mathbf{P}}{dt} \qquad (10\text{-}12)$$

Both internal and external forces may change the momenta of individual particles in the system, but Newton's third law shows that the change in the total momentum $\mathbf{P}$ due to internal forces is always zero. The change in the total momentum of the system is due solely to external forces. You cannot raise yourself by your own bootstraps!

EXAMPLE 10-5. A 15-Mg (15,000-kg) Kenworth truck is hauling logs north at 110 km/h on Pine Street, and a 32-Mg Mack truck is hauling hogs east at 73 km/h on Constitution Street. What are the magnitude and direction of the momentum of the system of the two trucks?

SOLUTION. Each truck can be considered a particle, since all of the mass of each truck has the same velocity. Then, choosing east to be the positive x direction and north to be the positive y direction, as in Fig. 10-6,

$\mathbf{P} = \mathbf{P}_M + \mathbf{P}_K$

$\quad = (32 \text{ Mg})(73 \text{ km/h})\mathbf{i} + (15 \text{ Mg})(110 \text{ km/h})\mathbf{j}$

$\quad = (6.5 \times 10^5 \text{ kg} \cdot \text{m/s})\mathbf{i} + (4.6 \times 10^5 \text{ kg} \cdot \text{m/s})\mathbf{j}$

or $\quad P = 7.9 \times 10^5 \text{ kg} \cdot \text{m/s}$

with a direction 35° above the x axis (35° north of east).

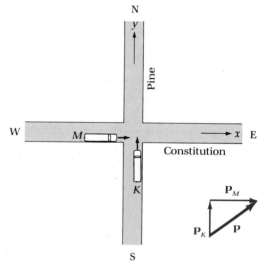

Figure 10-6. Example 10-5.

10-5 CONSERVATION OF MOMENTUM

Newton's first law states that if the net force on a particle is zero, then the particle travels in a straight line at constant speed (in an inertial reference frame). If $\mathbf{v}$ is constant in time, then $\mathbf{p} = m\mathbf{v}$ is also constant in time. In other words, when the net force on a particle is zero, the particle's momentum **p** is conserved.

Newton's second law for a system of particles, expressed in Eq. (10-12), shows that if $\Sigma \mathbf{F}_{ext}$ is zero, then $d\mathbf{P}/dt = 0$ and the system's total momentum **P** does not change in time. This result is called the law of conservation of momentum: *When the net external force on a system is zero, the total momentum of the system is conserved.* Put another way, the momentum of an isolated system does not change in time. Suppose a system has no net external force on it. Let $\mathbf{P}_i$ be the initial momentum of the system and $\mathbf{P}_f$ be the momentum of the system at any later time; conservation of momentum is then expressed as

Conservation of momentum of a system

$$\mathbf{P}_i = \mathbf{P}_f$$

Notice the similarity and the difference between this law and the law of conservation of mechanical energy. In both cases there is a condition on the forces, but for energy conservation *all* forces that perform work must be conservative, whereas for momentum conservation there must be *no net external force.* A further difference is that since momentum is a vector, when **P** is conserved **P** stays the same in both magnitude and direction, whereas energy is a scalar so that it has only magnitude to be conserved.

Momentum is conserved when $\Sigma \mathbf{F}_{ext} = 0$.

The momentum of individual particles may be changing even if the momentum of the whole system is conserved. The forces internal to the system can change the momenta of the individual particles, but the total momentum of the system cannot be changed by internal forces.

The law of conservation of momentum is particularly helpful in relating the initial and final states of an isolated system. Although the system may change its internal structure, the total momentum of the system remains constant.

EXAMPLE 10-6. Two skaters move horizontally across the ice, without appreciable friction, directly toward each other, as seen in Fig. 10-7. One has a mass of 50 kg and a speed of 3.0 m/s and the other a mass of 75 kg and a speed of 2.5 m/s. They push off each other and go back along their original paths. If the 75-kg skater leaves with a speed of 4.0 m/s, with what velocity component does the other skater leave?

Figure 10-7. Example 10-6.

SOLUTION. The momentum of the system of the two skaters must be the same after they push off as it was before they met, since the only appreciable outside forces on the skaters are those of the earth and the normal forces, and these add to zero. Horizontal frictional forces from the ice are negligible. If we choose the system to consist of the two skaters, the external forces sum to zero. Thus the initial momentum of the system is equal to the final momentum of the system:

$$\mathbf{P}_i = \mathbf{P}_f$$

Since all velocities lie along one horizontal direction, we can work with only the components in that direction:

$$(50 \text{ kg})(3.0 \text{ m/s}) + (75 \text{ kg})(-2.5 \text{ m/s})$$
$$= (50 \text{ kg})v_{xf} + (75 \text{ kg})(4.0 \text{ m/s})$$

$$v_{xf} = \frac{-340 \text{ kg m/s}}{50 \text{ kg}} = -6.8 \text{ m/s}$$

10-6 IMPULSE

Suppose a tennis ball is hit with a racket, as seen in Fig. 10-8. The force exerted by the racket on the ball, $\mathbf{F}_{rb}$, changes the momentum of the ball. During the

Figure 10-8. A tennis ball in the act of being hit by a tennis racket. The distortion of the tennis ball indicates that the force exerted on it by the tennis racket is quite large. Forces such as this that are exerted over a brief time are called *impulsive forces. (Dr. Harold Edgerton/M.I.T., Cambridge, Mass.)*

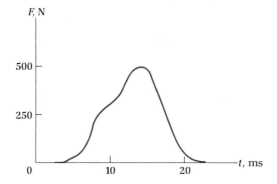

Figure 10-9. A graph of how the impulsive force exerted on the tennis ball in Fig. 10-8 might vary in time.

time the racket is in contact with the ball, the force that the racket exerts on the ball is very large compared with any other force on the ball. Figure 10-9 shows how the force exerted by the racket in such an event might vary in time. Notice that the force is exerted for only about 10 milliseconds.

Forces which are exerted over a limited time are called *impulsive forces*. Often the magnitude of an impulsive force is so large that its effect is appreciable, even though its duration is short. During the short time such an impulsive force is exerted on an object, the effects of other forces can often be neglected, because these other forces are not large enough to have a significant effect in this short time. In such a case, we need consider only the impulsive force during the time it is exerted.

When only one force **F** is significant, we may write Newton's second law as

$$\Sigma \mathbf{F} = \mathbf{F} = \frac{d\mathbf{p}}{dt} \qquad \text{or} \qquad d\mathbf{p} = \mathbf{F}\, dt$$

Integrating this equation, we have

$$\Delta \mathbf{p} = \mathbf{p}_f - \mathbf{p}_i = \int_{t_i}^{t_f} \mathbf{F}\, dt$$

Impulse of a force

The right side of the equation is called the *impulse* of a force and is given the symbol **J**:

$$\mathbf{J} = \int_{t_i}^{t_f} \mathbf{F}\, dt$$

The impulse of the net force is related to an object's change of the momentum by

The impulse is equal to the change in momentum.

$$\mathbf{J} = \Delta \mathbf{p} \tag{10-13}$$

Impulse has the same dimension as momentum. The SI unit of impulse is N · s.

Sometimes we know the change in the momentum of a body on which an impulsive force acted, but not what the force was as a function of time. To characterize such an impulsive force, we compare it with the constant average force $\overline{\mathbf{F}}$ which would deliver the same impulse (and therefore the same change in momentum) if it acted over the same time as the impulsive force. Figure 10-10 shows this graphically. The relation between **J** and $\overline{\mathbf{F}}$ is

$$\mathbf{J} = \int_{t_i}^{t_f} \mathbf{F}\, dt = \overline{\mathbf{F}}\, \Delta t$$

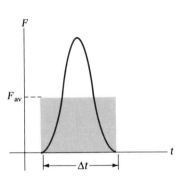

Figure 10-10. The time-averaged force exerted in an event is defined as the constant force which, if exerted over the same time period as the actual force, would have the same impulse as the actual force. In the graph, the area under the actual force is equal to the area of the rectangle formed by $\mathbf{F}_{av}$ and the time interval Δt.

EXAMPLE 10-7. Estimate the average force that you exert on a nail when you drive it into a board with a hammer.

SOLUTION. The hammer exerts an impulsive force on the nail because it is in contact with the nail for only a short time but the effect on the nail is large. We will need to estimate the change in momentum of the hammerhead, and the time over which the change occurred. From this we can calculate the average force on the hammer (and through Newton's third law, the average force the hammer exerts on the nail). Let us estimate the time the hammer and nail are in contact.

A second is about the time it takes to say "one-one thousand," and the hammerhead isn't in contact with the nail for even a tenth of that time. Consequently, we shall take $\Delta t \approx 0.01$ s. The mass of a hammerhead is about 0.3 kg. The speed of the hammer before it hits the nail can be estimated from the acceleration you give a hammer, perhaps 4 times the acceleration of gravity, or 40 m/s², and the time you take to swing the hammer, about $\frac{1}{2}$ s. This gives $v = at \approx 20$ m/s.

The speed of the hammer after the collision depends somewhat on the hammer, nail, board, etc. Suppose the hammer rebounds with half the speed it had before the collision. Choose the direction of motion of the hammer just before it hits the nail as the positive y direction. Then the impulse on the hammer is

$$J_y = P_{fy} - P_{iy}$$
$$= (0.3 \text{ kg})(-10 \text{ m/s}) - (0.3 \text{ kg})(20 \text{ m/s})$$
$$= -9 \text{ kg} \cdot \text{m/s} = -9 \text{ N} \cdot \text{s}$$

We estimated that this takes place over 0.01 s. The average force component on the hammer is $\overline{F}_y = J_y/\Delta t$, or -900 N. This force is exerted on the hammer by the nail. An equal and opposite force is exerted on the nail by the hammer. It is quite a large force, more than you could exert with a steady push. As shown in Fig. 10-10, the actual force at its peak might be about twice as large as the average force, possibly several thousand N.

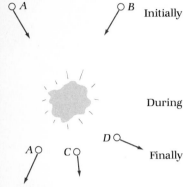

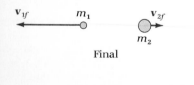

Figure 10-11. In a collision, particles interact only during a limited time and place. During this time many complicated forces may be exerted, but often we are only interested in the outcome of the collision. In this case we examine only the initial and final states.

10-7 COLLISIONS

Conservation of momentum is a particularly useful concept when examining collisions. A *collision* is an interaction between two or more objects that takes place in a limited region of time and space (Fig. 10-11). One or more objects come into a region and interact. The interaction occurs quickly and in a limited region of space, and then one or more objects leave the region. The forces between the objects during the collision may be large, but we do not examine these forces in detail. We only examine what goes into the collision and what comes out of the collision. We assume that during the limited time of the collision, forces external to the system (which consists of the interacting objects) produce negligible impulse and thus have a negligible effect on the momentum of the system. Because the effect of external forces is negligible, *the momentum of the system is conserved, and the total momentum of the system before the collision is equal to the total momentum of the system after the collision.*

In studying collisions, one of our goals is to be able to relate the incoming and outgoing velocities of the objects. In atomic collisions, for example, the velocities of the outgoing particles are often used to study the interaction of the incoming particles. Consider a collision in which two particles enter and two particles leave. If we know the incoming velocities and we want to know the outgoing velocities, conservation of momentum gives one vector equation relating the incoming and outgoing velocities. But there are six unknowns (we want to know the three components of the velocity of each outgoing particle), and conservation of momentum gives only the three equations that result from each component of the vector equation. With more unknowns than equations, the problem is in general unsolvable. Even if the collision takes place in one dimension, such as on a railroad track, conservation of momentum gives one equation for the two unknown outgoing velocity components.

Other information can help. Energy is always conserved, but since energy can take many forms, that may not be much help. There are collisions in which kinetic energy by itself is conserved. We call such a collision an *elastic* collision. On the other hand, a collision in which kinetic energy is not conserved is called *inelastic*. Collisions on an atomic level are often elastic, but on a macroscopic level, collisions always involve some inelasticity. Many macroscopic collisions transform so little kinetic energy into other forms of energy, however, that they may be considered elastic within the precision to which measurements are made. Collisions between steel balls at low speeds, for example, transform so little kinetic energy that we can treat them as elastic in almost all cases.

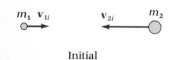

Initial

Final

$$\longrightarrow x$$

Figure 10-12. In a one-dimensional elastic collision, the final velocity components $\mathbf{v}_{1f}$ and $\mathbf{v}_{2f}$ are determined by the initial velocity components $\mathbf{v}_{1i}$ and $\mathbf{v}_{2i}$.

Elastic collisions in one dimension. Consider a one-dimensional elastic collision in which an object of mass m_1 and initial velocity component along the x axis v_{1i} collides with an object of mass m_2 and initial velocity component along the x axis v_{2i}, as shown in Fig. 10-12. (For brevity, we temporarily drop the x subscript on the symbols for the velocity components.) After the collision, their velocity components along the x axis are v_{1f} and v_{2f}. Conservation of momentum gives

$$m_1 v_{1i} + m_2 v_{2i} = m_1 v_{1f} + m_2 v_{2f} \tag{10-14}$$

and conservation of kinetic energy gives

$$\tfrac{1}{2}m_1 v_{1i}{}^2 + \tfrac{1}{2}m_2 v_{2i}{}^2 = \tfrac{1}{2}m_1 v_{1f}{}^2 + \tfrac{1}{2}m_2 v_{2f}{}^2 \tag{10-15}$$

The final state of a one-dimensional elastic collision is determined by the initial state.

If the masses and initial velocity components are given, then the final velocity components can be found, and the final state of the system can be determined.

Before considering some special cases, we derive a useful relation. First we rewrite Eqs. (10-14) and (10-15):

$$m_1(v_{1i} - v_{1f}) = m_2(v_{2f} - v_{2i}) \tag{10-16}$$

$$m_1(v_{1i}{}^2 - v_{1f}{}^2) = m_2(v_{2f}{}^2 - v_{2i}{}^2) \tag{10-17}$$

Dividing Eq. (10-17) by Eq. (10-16) gives

$$v_{1i} + v_{1f} = v_{2f} + v_{2i}$$

which we rewrite as

$$v_{1i} - v_{2i} = -(v_{1f} - v_{2f}) \tag{10-18}$$

This relation shows that the relative velocity components of the objects before and after a one-dimensional elastic collision are reversed, but the relative speeds of the objects remain the same. (See Fig. 10-13.)

Consider now a one-dimensional elastic collision in which object 2 is initially at rest, $v_{2i} = 0$. We need two equations to solve for the two final velocity components. Conservation of momentum gives

$$m_1 v_{1i} = m_1 v_{1f} + m_2 v_{2f}$$

For the other relation we could use either conservation of kinetic energy or Eq. (10-18). It is easier to solve Eq. (10-18) for v_{2f}, getting $v_{2f} = v_{1i} + v_{1f}$, and put this into the momentum conservation equation:

$$m_1 v_{1i} = m_1 v_{1f} + m_2(v_{1i} + v_{1f})$$

Solving for the final velocity components, we obtain

Final velocity components in a one-dimensional collision with one object initially stationary

$$v_{1f} = v_{1i} \left(\frac{m_1 - m_2}{m_1 + m_2} \right) \tag{10-19}$$

$$v_{2f} = v_{1i} \left(\frac{2m_1}{m_1 + m_2} \right) \tag{10-20}$$

Thus if a bowling ball (1) hits a stationary pin (2) straight on, the pin goes off with a speed equal to the ratio $2m_1/(m_1 + m_2)$ times the incoming speed of the bowling ball (v_{1i}).

We now consider some special cases of one-dimensional elastic collisions.

1 Equal masses. (a) If object 2 is initially stationary, setting $m_1 = m_2$ in these equations gives $v_{1f} = 0$ and $v_{2f} = v_{1i}$. If a moving ball strikes an identical

Figure 10-13. In a one-dimensional elastic collision, the relative velocity component $v_1 - v_2$ changes sign but keeps the same magnitude.

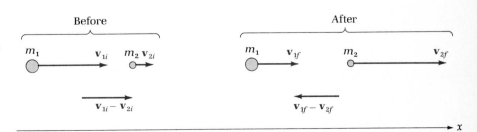

Before

After

Figure 10-14. In a one-dimensional elastic collision between two particles of the same mass, one at rest, the particle in motion ends up at rest, and the particle at rest ends up with the motion of the other particle.

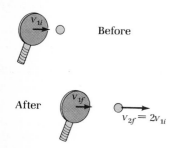

Before

After

Figure 10-15. A ping-pong ball hit by a much heavier paddle leaves at twice the speed of the paddle.

stationary ball, the initially stationary ball moves off with the same speed the incoming ball had, and the incoming ball comes to a dead stop. As illustrated in Fig. 10-14, the balls have exchanged velocities! (We ignore the possible spins of the balls.) (b) If object 2 is not initially stationary, we can use conservation of momentum directly, dividing out the equal masses:

$$v_{1i} + v_{2i} = v_{1f} + v_{2f}$$

Adding and subtracting this from Eq. (10-18) gives

$$v_{1i} = v_{2f} \quad \text{and} \quad v_{2i} = v_{1f}$$

In other words, if the masses of the objects are equal, they exchange velocities in a one-dimensional (or head-on) elastic collision.

2 Object 2 initially at rest and $m_1 \gg m_2$. We need only specialize Eqs. (10-19) and (10-20):

$$v_{1f} \approx v_{1i} \left(\frac{m_1}{m_1} \right) = v_{1i}$$

$$v_{2f} \approx v_{1i} \left(\frac{2m_1}{m_1} \right) = 2v_{1i}$$

The velocity of the incoming, large-mass object is practically unchanged, while the small-mass object moves off at twice the velocity of the incoming object. Suppose a ping-pong ball initially at rest is struck with a much heavier paddle. The ball leaves the paddle with twice the incoming speed of the paddle, and the paddle follows through at essentially the same speed it had before it hit the ball. See Fig. 10-15.

3 Object 2 initially at rest and $m_1 \ll m_2$. Again we need only specialize Eqs. (10-19) and (10-20):

$$v_{1f} \approx v_{1i} \left(\frac{-m_2}{m_2} \right) = -v_{1i}$$

$$v_{2f} \approx v_{1i} \left(\frac{2m_1}{m_2} \right) \approx 0$$

where $v_{2f} \approx 0$ because $m_1/m_2 \approx 0$. The large-mass object is nearly undisturbed, while the small-mass object bounces back with essentially the same speed with which it entered. If you throw a ping-pong ball at a bowling ball, the bowling ball will barely move, whereas the ping-pong ball will bounce back with nearly its incoming speed (Fig. 10-16).

If both objects have initial velocity components, then Eqs. (10-14) and (10-15) must be solved simultaneously for the two unknown final velocity

Before

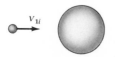

After

Figure 10-16. A ping-pong ball thrown at a bowling ball has its velocity reversed, while the bowling ball is barely moved.

Final velocity components in a general one-dimensional elastic collision

components v_{2f} and v_{1f}. The algebra is straightforward but tedious. You are asked to do it in Prob. 10-2. The result is

$$v_{1f} = \frac{m_1 - m_2}{m_1 + m_2} v_{1i} + \frac{2m_2}{m_1 + m_2} v_{2i} \qquad (10\text{-}21)$$

$$v_{2f} = \frac{m_2 - m_1}{m_2 + m_1} v_{2i} + \frac{2m_1}{m_2 + m_1} v_{1i} \qquad (10\text{-}22)$$

EXAMPLE 10-8. In a nuclear reactor, it turns out that a neutron released in one fission event must be slowed down before it is likely to cause another nucleus to fission. Neutrons are slowed down by collisions with other nuclei, in a process called *moderating*. This process is similar to the way the cue ball is slowed down by collisions with the numbered balls on a pool table. In some reactors the hydrogen in water is used as the moderator, and in other reactors carbon is used. Assume that such a collision is elastic, and that the target is initially stationary. By what fraction is the kinetic energy of the neutron reduced in a head-on collision with each of these nuclei? The masses of the neutron, the hydrogen nucleus, and the carbon nucleus have ratios of about 1 : 1 : 12, respectively.

SOLUTION. The target nucleus is essentially stationary. Using subscripts n for the neutron and t for the target nucleus, we have, from Eq. (10-19),

$$v_{nf} = \frac{m_n - m_t}{m_n + m_t} v_{ni}$$

$$K_{nf} = \tfrac{1}{2} m_n v_{nf}^2$$

$$= \tfrac{1}{2} m_n \left(\frac{m_n - m_t}{m_n + m_t}\right)^2 v_{ni}^2 = \left(\frac{m_n - m_t}{m_n + m_t}\right)^2 K_{ni}$$

Thus a head-on elastic collision with a hydrogen nucleus will stop the neutron, since $m_t \approx m_n$. In a similar collision with a carbon nucleus, $K_{nf} \approx (11/13)^2 K_{ni}$ and the kinetic energy of the neutron is reduced by only the fraction $1 - (11/13)^2 = 0.28$.

Inelastic collisions. If a collision is not elastic, calculating the final velocities in terms of the initial velocities is not usually easy. The amount of energy lost depends on how inelastic the collision is. A special inelastic collision, in which the objects stick together after the collision, is called *completely inelastic*.

If a one-dimensional collision is completely inelastic, there is only one final velocity v_f, and it can be found from conservation of momentum:

$$m_1 v_{1i} + m_2 v_{2i} = (m_1 + m_2) v_f$$

$$v_f = \frac{m_1 v_{1i} + m_2 v_{2i}}{m_1 + m_2}$$

Note that although momentum is conserved in all collisions (because we neglect external forces), kinetic energy is *not* conserved in an inelastic collision.

EXAMPLE 10-9. The speed of a bullet as it leaves the muzzle of a gun is called the "muzzle velocity." A ballistic pendulum is a device for measuring this speed. Figure 10-17 shows the arrangement of the device. Suppose a 13.6-g bullet is fired into a 5.42-kg wooden block that forms the pendulum bob of a pendulum of length $L = 372$ mm. The bullet delivers an impulsive force to the bob. The bob, with the bullet in it, then swings out through an arc of 26.7°. What is the muzzle velocity of the bullet?

SOLUTION. We take the block and the bullet as the system. In the first part of the process, the bullet and the wood block collide in a completely inelastic fashion, the bullet sticking in

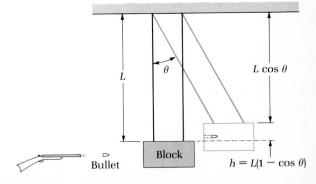

Figure 10-17. Example 10-9.

the block. The collision is also impulsive; it takes place over a time interval so short that the block does not rise appreciably during the collision and external forces have negligible effect during the collision. The collision is inelastic, so that kinetic energy is not conserved during the collision. Thus momentum is conserved but not kinetic energy during the collision.

In the second part of the process, the block (with the bullet in it) swings out after the collision, the external force of gravity gradually slowing it down. During this time period, mechanical energy is conserved (only the gravitational force does work), but not momentum. Gravity and the support string provide external forces that affect the system during the comparatively long duration of the outward swing.

We analyze the two parts of the process separately. First the collision: Let the mass of the bullet be m_1, its initial velocity component v_{1i}, the mass of the block m_2, and the final velocity component v_f. For the inelastic collision,

$$v_f = \frac{m_1 v_{1i} + m_2 v_{2i}}{m_1 + m_2}$$

$$= \frac{(13.6 \text{ g})v_{1i} + 0}{5.43 \text{ kg}} = (2.50 \times 10^{-3})v_{1i}$$

Second, the outward swing: We relate v_f to the maximum height h reached by the block and bullet by applying conservation of mechanical energy during the swing:

$$K_f + U_f = K_i + U_i$$

$$0 + (m_1 + m_2)gh = \tfrac{1}{2}(m_1 + m_2)v_f^2 + 0$$

$$v_f^2 = 2gh$$

Notice that v_f is both the final velocity of the collision and the initial velocity for the swing outward. The height the bob rises is the difference in the distances below the support of the bob at the top and bottom of its swing. From Fig. 10-17,

$$h = L - L \cos 26.7° = 372 \text{ mm } (1 - \cos 26.7°) = 39.7 \text{ mm}$$

Thus

$$v_f = \sqrt{2gh} = \sqrt{2(9.80 \text{ m/s})(0.0397 \text{ m})} = 0.882 \text{ m/s}$$

and

$$v_{1i} = \frac{0.882 \text{ m/s}}{2.50 \times 10^{-3}} = 352 \text{ m/s}$$

Thus the speed of the bullet just before it collides with the bob is 352 m/s.

10-8 COLLISIONS IN TWO AND THREE DIMENSIONS

Conservation of momentum and energy do not completely determine the outcome of a 2-dimensional or 3-dimensional collision.

Initial state

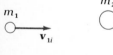

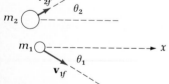

Final state

Figure 10-18. Symbols used for a two-dimensional collision. Particle 1, with initial velocity $\mathbf{v}_{1i}$, is incident on particle 2, which is initially stationary. After the collision the particles have velocities $\mathbf{v}_{1f}$ and $\mathbf{v}_{2f}$.

Consider a collision between two particles that takes place in two dimensions. Even if we know that the collision is elastic, conservation of momentum plus conservation of energy yield but three equations, one for conservation of each component of momentum and one for conservation of energy. But each final velocity has two components, so there are four unknowns. For example, consider the two-dimensional collision sketched in Fig. 10-18. Before the collision, particle 1 is going in the x direction with speed v_{1i} and particle 2 is at rest. After the collision, particle 1 is going in a direction θ_1 below the x direction, with speed v_{1f}, and particle 2 is going in a direction θ_2 above the x axis, with speed v_{2f}. Conservation of momentum gives two equations, one for the x direction:

$$m_1 v_{1i} = m_1 v_{1f} \cos \theta_1 + m_2 v_{2f} \cos \theta_2$$

and one for the y direction:

$$0 = m_1 v_{1f} \sin \theta_1 - m_2 v_{2f} \sin \theta_2$$

If in addition the collision is elastic, energy conservation gives another equation:

$$\tfrac{1}{2} m_1 v_{1i}^2 = \tfrac{1}{2} m_1 v_{1f}^2 + \tfrac{1}{2} m_2 v_{2f}^2$$

If we knew the initial state of the system (m_1, m_2, and v_{1i}) we would need four equations to solve for the final state (v_{1f}, v_{2f}, θ_1, and θ_2). Unless we have some other information, the final state cannot be found. This is an expression of the fact that the outcome of a two- or three-dimensional elastic collision is not determined by the conservation laws alone.

How can the additional information needed to determine the final outcome of such a collision be obtained? In the experimental study of two-dimensional collisions, the direction in which one of the particles leaves the collision is often measured. This additional information completely determines the final states of both particles. Collision experiments are important because the distribution of these final states gives information about the forces between the particles.

EXAMPLE 10-10. Consider the collision between two billiard balls shown in Fig. 10-19. The photograph was taken with a strobe light which flashed 30 times a second. The distance between the images of the incoming ball is 0.108 m. (a) What is the ratio of the masses of the balls? (b) Is kinetic energy conserved in the collision? Measure the velocities from the photograph.

SOLUTION. (a) The speed of the incoming ball is 0.108 mm/($\frac{1}{30}$ s) = 3.24 m/s. The distances between successive images for the incident and target balls are 0.442 and 0.860 that of the incoming ball. Thus the outgoing speeds are 1.43 m/s for the incident ball and 2.79 m/s for the target ball. The upper outgoing track and the lower outgoing track make angles of 59° and 26° with the incoming track. For convenience we pick the x axis to lie along the direction of the velocity of the incoming ball. The sum of the y components of momentum is zero before and, therefore, after the collision. The y components of the outgoing velocities are

$$v_{y1} = (1.43 \text{ m/s}) \sin 59° = 1.23 \text{ m/s}$$

$$v_{y2} = (2.79 \text{ m/s}) \sin(-26°) = -1.22 \text{ m/s}$$

Within the precision of our measurements these have the same magnitude, so in order for the y component of the momentum to be zero, the masses of the balls must be equal. (b) Before the collision the kinetic energy was

$$\tfrac{1}{2}mv_{1i}^2 = \tfrac{1}{2}m(3.24 \text{ m/s})^2 = \tfrac{1}{2}m(10.5 \text{ m}^2/\text{s}^2)$$

and after the collision the kinetic energy is

$$\tfrac{1}{2}mv_{1f}^2 + \tfrac{1}{2}mv_{2f}^2 = \tfrac{1}{2}m(1.43 \text{ m/s})^2 + \tfrac{1}{2}m(2.79 \text{ m/s})^2$$
$$= \tfrac{1}{2}m(9.83 \text{ m}^2/\text{s}^2)$$

Thus we see that kinetic energy does not quite seem to be conserved. If you look carefully at the collision you will see that the balls are rotating after the collision. This takes up energy in a way that will be described in Chap. 12. Further, there may have been impulsive forces on the balls by the table on which they were rolling.

Note that we were able to discover some things about the objects in the collision from these results: Their masses are equal and they can take up energy internally. Such measurements of collisions between elementary particles have enabled us to learn quite a bit about the nature of the submicroscopic world.

Figure 10-19. Example 10-10. *(Bernice Abbott/Photo Researchers)*

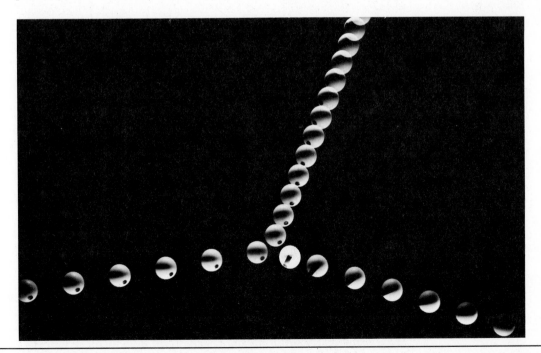

10-9 ROCKET MOTION

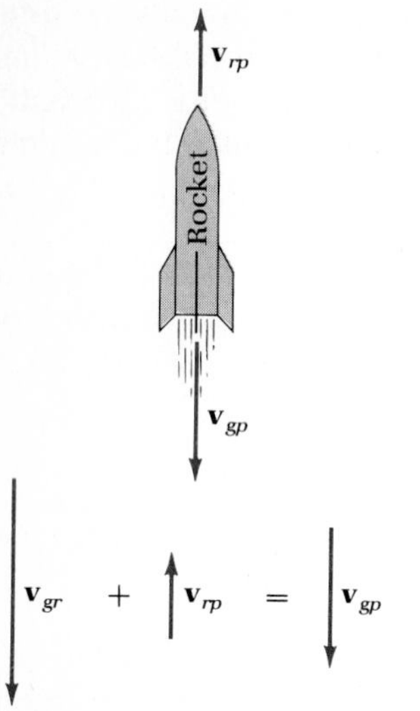

The problem of the motion of a rocket is somewhat different from the problems we have considered so far in that as the rocket accelerates, it throws mass backwards. Thus the rocket does not have a constant mass. First let us consider changes in momenta in the system of the rocket and its exhaust gases.

At some initial instant, let the velocity of the rocket with respect to an observer on the launchpad be $\mathbf{v}_{rp}$, the mass of the rocket be m, the amount of fuel fired backward in a small time Δt be ΔM, and the velocity of the exhaust gases with respect to the rocket be $\mathbf{v}_{gr}$ (Fig. 10-20). The initial momentum of the system with respect to the ground observer is

$$\mathbf{P}_i = m\mathbf{v}_{rp}$$

After the time interval Δt, the mass of the rocket is $m - \Delta M$, the velocity of the rocket $\mathbf{v}_{rp} + \Delta\mathbf{v}_{rp}$, the mass of the gases exhausted ΔM, and the velocity of the exhaust gases with respect to an inertial reference frame (the launchpad) $\mathbf{v}_{gp}$. Thus at time $t + \Delta t$ the momentum of the system is

$$\mathbf{P}_f = (m - \Delta M)(\mathbf{v}_{rp} + \Delta\mathbf{v}_{rp}) + (\Delta M)\mathbf{v}_{gp}$$

The velocity of the exhaust gases with respect to the launchpad is related to the known velocity of the exhaust gases with respect to the rocket, $\mathbf{v}_{gr}$, by

$$\mathbf{v}_{gp} = \mathbf{v}_{gr} + \mathbf{v}_{rp}$$

Note that this is a vector equation, and since $\mathbf{v}_{gr}$ is usually in a direction opposite to $\mathbf{v}_{rp}$, $|\mathbf{v}_{gp}|$ is usually less than $|\mathbf{v}_{gr}|$ (Fig. 10-20). Combining the last two equations gives

$$\mathbf{P}_f = (m - \Delta M)(\mathbf{v}_{rp} + \Delta\mathbf{v}_{rp}) + (\Delta M)(\mathbf{v}_{gr} + \mathbf{v}_{rp})$$

or

$$\mathbf{P}_f = m\mathbf{v}_{rp} + (m - \Delta M)\Delta\mathbf{v}_{rp} + (\Delta M)\mathbf{v}_{gr}$$

From Newton's second law, $\Sigma\mathbf{F}_{\text{ext}} = d\mathbf{P}/dt \approx (\mathbf{P}_f - \mathbf{P}_i)/\Delta t$, so that

$$\Sigma\mathbf{F}_{\text{ext}} = \frac{m\,\Delta\mathbf{v}_{rp} - (\Delta M)(\Delta\mathbf{v}_{rp}) + (\Delta M)\mathbf{v}_{gr}}{\Delta t}$$

We now take the limit as Δt goes to zero. The term $(\Delta M)(\Delta\mathbf{v}_{rp})/\Delta t$ goes to zero as it contains two infinitesimals in the numerator. Since ΔM is the mass leaving the rocket and m is the mass of the rocket, $\Delta M = -\Delta m$ and the limit as Δt goes to zero of $\Delta M/\Delta t$ is $-dm/dt$. Thus

$$\Sigma\mathbf{F}_{\text{ext}} = m\frac{d\mathbf{v}_{rp}}{dt} - \mathbf{v}_{gr}\frac{dm}{dt}$$

or

The rocket equation

$$m\frac{d\mathbf{v}_{rp}}{dt} = \Sigma\mathbf{F}_{\text{ext}} + \mathbf{v}_{gr}\frac{dm}{dt} \tag{10-23}$$

The magnitude of $\mathbf{v}_{gr}\,dm/dt$ is called the *thrust* of the rocket and has the dimensions of force.

Newton's second law for a system, $\Sigma\mathbf{F}_{\text{ext}} = d\mathbf{P}/dt$, was derived assuming the mass of the system to be constant. So far we have considered the rocket plus the

Figure 10-20. Symbols used in the rocket problem. The rocket has velocity $\mathbf{v}_{rp}$ with respect to the launchpad, an inertial reference frame. The exhaust gases have velocity $\mathbf{v}_{gp}$ with respect to this reference frame. The velocity of the exhaust gases with respect to the rocket, $\mathbf{v}_{gr}$, plus the velocity of the rocket with respect to the launchpad, $\mathbf{v}_{rp}$, gives the velocity of the exhaust gases with respect to the launchpad, $\mathbf{v}_{gp}$, as discussed in Sec. 4-5.

exhaust gases to be the system. But we are not interested in the exhaust gases after they leave the rocket. In order to focus on the rocket, we continually change what we consider to be the system, deleting the fuel from the system as it leaves in the form of exhaust gases. In this continually changing system, $\mathbf{v}_{rp}$ is the velocity of the rocket at time t, and m the mass of the rocket at time t.

For simplicity, we now assume that the rocket is in interstellar space, where $\Sigma\mathbf{F}_{ext}$ is zero, and that the rocket engine keeps the thrust constant. We may then rewrite Eq. (10-23) as

$$d\mathbf{v}_{rp} = \mathbf{v}_{gr}\,\frac{dm}{m}$$

and integrate it to get

$$\int d\mathbf{v}_{rp} = \mathbf{v}_{gr}\int \frac{dm}{m}$$

or, on integrating,

$$(\mathbf{v}_{rp})_f - (\mathbf{v}_{rp})_i = \mathbf{v}_{gr}\left(\ln\frac{m_f}{m_i}\right) \tag{10-24}$$

Equation (10-24) gives the change in velocity of the rocket and shows that the larger the exhaust speed $\mathbf{v}_{gr}$, the better the rocket propulsion.

EXAMPLE 10-11. A practical upper limit for v_{gr} using chemical fuels is around 2.5 km/s. If such a chemical rocket in outer space, starting from rest in an inertial reference frame, burns four-fifths of its mass, what is its final velocity?

SOLUTION. Take the component of Eq. (10-24) along the direction of motion of the rocket and suppose that the exhaust gases are directed opposite to the direction of motion of the rocket. Let the initial velocity component of the rocket be $v_i = 0$, the final velocity component of the rocket be v_f, and the velocity component of the exhaust gases with respect to the rocket be $-V = -v_{gr}$. Then

$$v_f = -V\left(\ln\frac{m/5}{m}\right) = V\ln 5$$

$$v_f = (2.5\text{ km/s})\ln 5 = 4\text{ km/s}$$

You can see from the logarithm in Eq. (10-24) that it is difficult to achieve high speeds with a single rocket. For example, if we wish v_f to be $10V$, then

$$\ln\frac{m_i}{m_f} = \frac{v_f - v_i}{V} = \frac{10V}{V} = 10$$

$$m_i = m_f e^{10} = 2.2\times 10^4\, m_f$$

and less than 0.1 percent of the initial rocket (payload + fuel) is payload. Building the rocket in stages helps, and this is considered in Prob. 10-8.

COMMENTARY:
SYMMETRY AND THE CONSERVATION PRINCIPLES

Newton's laws have led us to two conservation principles. In Chap. 9, Newton's laws were used to show that the mechanical energy of a system is conserved when only conservative forces do work, and a generalized principle was stated: The total energy of an isolated system is conserved. In this chapter, Newton's laws were used to prove the principle of momentum conservation: The total momentum of a system is conserved if only internal forces are effective — that is, if the system is isolated.

Newton's laws explain most of the mechanical behavior of our ordinary world, but when high speeds or small sizes are involved, the predictions of Newton's laws do not agree with the results of experiments, and relativistic or quantum theories are necessary. These theories give the same results as newtonian physics in the realm of ordinary experience. When high speeds or small sizes are involved, these theories give results which differ from the predictions of newtonian physics, but are in agreement with experiment. Both of these newer theories lead to conservation principles, including conservation of momentum and energy. It seems that conservation of momentum and energy are more general than any of these theories. Accordingly, we expect that any new theory that might arise as we extend the boundaries of knowledge would also include these conservation principles.

Is there then a more fundamental basis for these conservation principles? Is there a way to get them that does not involve first assuming Newton's laws (or the laws of relativity or of quantum theory)? One conjecture is that the conservation principles are due to the symmetries of the universe. It states that because the universe has certain symmetries, certain conservation principles must exist in any theory.

What symmetries does the universe possess? In isolated systems far away from matter — for example, in deep space — the laws of physics and the dynamics of a system are the same if you are displaced in any direction and are the same as time progresses. Put another way, space is homogeneous and we may choose the origin of a coordinate system wherever we please. Similarly, time is uniform and we may choose any instant as the zero of time. You may remember that the formulas for accelerated motion involved things like $x_2 - x_1$ rather than the absolute positions x_1 or x_2 alone. It is the distance or time interval that mattered, not the absolute distance or time. The independence of the dynamics of a system on its absolute position leads to the conservation of momentum for an isolated system, and the independence of the dynamics on the zero of time leads to the conservation of energy. If the dynamics of an isolated system were to depend on where it is in the universe, then we would not expect the momentum of an isolated system to be conserved, and if the dynamics of identical isolated systems were different at differing times, we would not expect energy to be conserved.

Are there any more conservation principles? If so, what symmetry of the universe is responsible for them? The dynamics of an isolated system does not depend on its orientation in space, and hence we expect that there is another conservation law associated with that symmetry, the isotropy of space. The quantity that is conserved is called angular momentum *and will be discussed in Chap. 13.*

At one time it was also thought that the dynamics of a system is independent of "handedness," that is, of whether the system was right- or left-handed. Thus if you built the mirror image of a system, you might expect it to behave in the same manner as the original system would if viewed in a mirror. The quantity that was thought to be conserved was called parity. *Experiments showed, however, that parity was not always conserved. A consequence is that if you view some experiments in a mirror you will see something that does not occur in reality. Nuclei which spin counterclockwise may preferentially emit particles upward; when viewed in a mirror it looks as if clockwise-spinning nuclei emit particles preferentially upward, and that is not seen in reality.*

Thus the symmetries of the universe in position, time, and orientation lead to the conservation of momentum, energy, and angular momentum. However, there is a definite handedness to our universe, and the conservation principle associated with mirror reflections is not always obeyed.

Theories of the early universe, near the time of the "big bang," often assume that there were other symmetries which were obeyed when the universe was young, but are not always obeyed now in our larger, cooler universe. The use of the conservation principles associated with these symmetries lets one predict many properties of the early universe without knowing what the complete laws of physics were in the extreme circumstances of that time.

SUMMARY WITH APPLICATIONS

There are two main points to this chapter:

1 The center of mass of a system of particles moves as if it were a particle, with the mass of the whole system subject to the forces external to the system.
2 The total momentum of a system of particles is conserved if no net external force is applied.

Section 10-2. Center of mass
The position of the center of mass of a system of particles is defined by

$$\mathbf{r}_{cm} = \frac{\Sigma m_i \mathbf{r}_i}{M} \qquad (10\text{-}1)$$

For a continuous system, we have

$$M\mathbf{r}_{cm} = \int \rho \mathbf{r}\, dV$$

Calculate the position of the center of mass.

Section 10-3. Motion of the center of mass
The velocity and acceleration of the center of mass of a system are

$$\mathbf{v}_{cm} = \frac{\Sigma m_i \mathbf{v}_i}{M}$$

$$\mathbf{a}_{cm} = \frac{\Sigma m_i \mathbf{a}_i}{M}$$

From Newton's second and third laws, we have

$$\Sigma \mathbf{F}_{ext} = M\mathbf{a}_{cm}$$

Find the motion of the center of mass.

Section 10-4. Momentum
The momentum of a particle is defined to be

$$\mathbf{p} = m\mathbf{v}$$

Newton's second law can be written

$$\Sigma \mathbf{F} = \frac{d\mathbf{p}}{dt}$$

The total momentum **P** of a system of particles is related to

the external forces applied to the system by

$$\Sigma \mathbf{F}_{ext} = \frac{d\mathbf{P}}{dt} \qquad (10\text{-}12)$$

Define the momentum of a particle and of a system.

Section 10-5. Conservation of momentum
When the net external force is zero, momentum is conserved.

Section 10-6. Impulse
The impulse of a force is defined as

$$\mathbf{J} = \int_{t_i}^{t_f} \mathbf{F}\, dt$$

When a single impulsive force is applied to an object, the change in momentum of the object is

$$\mathbf{J} = \mathbf{p}_f - \mathbf{p}_i \qquad (10\text{-}13)$$

Define impulse and relate it to momentum change.

Section 10-7. Collisions
Collisions in which kinetic energy is conserved are called elastic. Collisions in which kinetic energy is not conserved are called inelastic.

Apply momentum conservation to collisions; apply energy conservation to elastic collisions

Section 10-8. Collisions in two and three dimensions
In two and three dimensions, conservation of momentum and kinetic energy do not determine the results of an elastic collision between two objects; supplementary data must be obtained to determine the final states of the colliding objects.

Show momentum is conserved in two- and three-dimensional collisions.

Section 10-9. Rocket motion
The equation of motion of a rocket is

$$m \frac{d\mathbf{v}_{rp}}{dt} = \Sigma \mathbf{F}_{ext} + \mathbf{v}_{gr} \frac{dm}{dt} \qquad (10\text{-}23)$$

Find the motion of a rocket.

QUESTIONS

10-1 Estimate the maximum magnitude of momentum you have ever had. In what reference frame?

10-2 Is there any connection between Newton's first law and the conservation-of-momentum law for a single particle? Explain.

10-3 Must there be a particle at the center of mass of a system of particles? Explain.

10-4 Draw a picture of a continuous object which has no mass at its center of mass.

10-5 Where is the center of mass of a basketball? Of a hula hoop? Of a doughnut? Of this book? Of a horseshoe?

10-6 Where is the center of mass of a uniform sphere? Of a cube? Of a regular tetrahedron? Of any regular solid polyhedron?

10-7 What can you say without calculation about the center of mass of a uniform hemisphere? About a D-shaped cylinder? About an isosceles triangle?

10-8 A truck driver carrying chickens to market is stopped at a weighing station. He bangs on the side of the truck to frighten the chickens so that they will fly up and make the truck lighter. Will his scheme work? Does it make any difference if the truck is open or closed? Explain.

10-9 Is it possible to conserve kinetic energy but not momentum? Explain. Is it possible to conserve momentum but not kinetic energy? Explain.

10-10 Is potential energy conserved in an elastic collision? Is it conserved all during the collision, or is the potential energy just the same at the finish as it was at the start?

10-11 Is it necessary that the forces that do work during an elastic collision be conservative? Is it sufficient that they are conservative for the collision to be elastic?

10-12 Why are pile drivers used to set piles in the ground rather than just pushing the piles slowly into the ground?

10-13 How do the air wrenches that mechanics use to remove wheels from your car work? Why do they make a clattering sound?

10-14 Most of the skid marks left at the scene of an automobile accident are left by the car tires after the collision occurs. How can measuring the direction and length of these skid marks after the collision reveal whether either of the cars involved was speeding before the collision?

10-15 You are standing still in the middle of a frictionless, flat, iced-over lake. Now how do you get off? Remember that, lacking a net external horizontal force, momentum is conserved.

10-16 A fat man walks from one end of a light canoe to the other end. If you watch from shore, the man hardly moves at all, but the canoe moves approximately its own length. Why?

10-17 Make a rough estimate of how long it takes to stop an oceangoing oil tanker. What provides the external force to stop the tanker?

10-18 Why do energy-absorbing bumpers reduce the death rate in collisions?

10-19 It has been claimed that a skillful high jumper clears the bar even though her center of mass passes *under* the bar. Show with a diagram that this is possible.

10-20 An hourglass with a valve that starts the flow of sand is being weighed on a sensitive balance. Compare the momentum of the sand before the valve is turned, when sand is being dropped in a steady stream from the upper to the lower half, and when all the sand is in the bottom. What are the scale readings at these three times? Does the scale read differently when the momentum of the sand is changing?

10-21 Would a completely inelastic head-on collision between two identical cars with equal but opposite velocities be more or less damaging than a completely inelastic collision between a car and an immovable wall? Explain.

10-22 Devise a method of experimentally determining the location of the center of mass of an extended object without knowing the mass of any part of the object.

10-23 Does doubling the thrust of a rocket by doubling the rate at which mass is thrown backwards double the final speed of the rocket? Why or why not?

10-24 Does doubling the speed at which a rocket throws mass backward double its final speed? Why or why not?

10-25 A cart rolling along a track hits another cart which is initially stationary. The stationary cart has a compressed spring bumper that releases when hit. Why can such a collision be called superelastic?

10-26 Complete the following table:

Symbol	Represents	Type	SI unit
$\mathbf{P}$			
$\mathbf{p}$			kg · m/s
$\mathbf{J}$		Vector	
$\mathbf{v}_{rp}$	Velocity of rocket with respect to pad		
$\mathbf{v}_{gr}$			

EXERCISES

Section 10-2. Center of mass

10-1 Find the coordinates of the center of mass of the particles of Fig. 10-21.

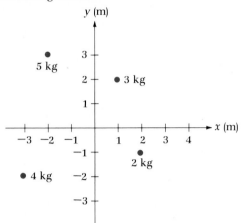

Figure 10-21. Exercise 10-1.

10-2 Where is the center of mass of the water molecule shown in Fig. 10-22? The relative masses of hydrogen and oxygen are as $1:16$.

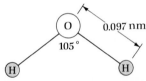

Figure 10-22. Exercise 10-2: Schematic drawing of a water molecule.

10-3 Find the coordinates of the center of mass of the particles of Fig. 10-23. Each particle has a mass of 0.041 kg, and the edge of each square in the grid of the figure represents 0.010 m.

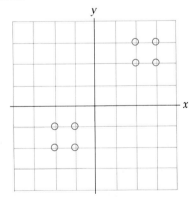

Figure 10-23. Exercise 10-3.

10-4 A hula hoop of uniform density and radius R is cut into two identical semicircles. Find the center of mass of one of the half-hoops.

10-5 Find the center of mass of a hemisphere of uniform density.

10-6 Find the center of mass of a uniform right circular cone of bottom diameter 0.430 m and height 0.526 m.

Section 10-3. Motion of the center of mass

10-7 A 42-kg girl walks along a stationary uniform beam of mass 21 kg. She walks with a speed of 0.75 m/s. What is the speed of the center of mass of the system of girl plus beam?

10-8 A 125-kg satellite contains two astronauts, Tony and Ben. Tony has a mass of 48 kg and Ben a mass of 52 kg. If the satellite has a velocity of (32 m/s)$\mathbf{j}$, Ben has a velocity of (30 m/s)$\mathbf{i}$, and Tony has a velocity *with respect to the satellite* of (2 m/s)$\mathbf{i}$, what is the velocity of the center of mass of the system of satellite plus astronauts?

10-9 A 1.0-kg block slides down an inclined plane of mass 3.2 kg, as shown in Fig. 10-24. If the plane is fixed and the 1.0-kg block slides without friction, find the acceleration of the center of mass of the system of the block and inclined plane.

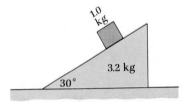

Figure 10-24. Exercise 10-9.

10-10 An 85-kg man is at the stern of a 12-m-long, 200-kg barge that is free to move in the water (Fig. 10-25). The barge has its center of mass 6 m from either end. (*a*) Where is the center of mass of the system of barge plus man? (*b*) By how much does the center of mass of the system move if the man walks to the bow of the barge? (*c*) By how much has the man moved with respect to the shore? (*d*) By how much has the barge moved with respect to the shore?

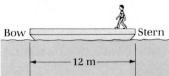

Figure 10-25. Exercise 10-10.

10-11 Consider the Atwood machine shown in Fig. 10-26. Neglect friction. (*a*) What are the external forces acting on the system inside the dashed lines? (*b*) If the string has negligible mass, where is the center of mass of the system? (*c*) Neglecting the retarding effects of the pulley, what is the acceleration of the center of mass of the system?

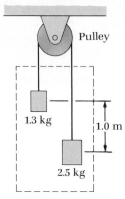

Figure 10-26. Exercise 10-11.

10-12 A 1.56-kg fireworks mortar shell is fired straight up, with an initial speed of 31 m/s. It explodes at the peak of its path, breaking into three pieces of different color. The pieces all start out moving horizontally. A 0.78-kg piece lands 212 m north of the mortar, and a 0.26-kg piece lands 68 m east of the mortar. If frictional forces and the wind can be neglected, where does the third piece land?

Section 10-4. Momentum

10-13 What are the magnitude and direction of the momentum of the earth (as seen from the sun)?

10-14 What is the magnitude of the momentum of a 1.25-Mg car going 55 mi/h?

10-15 A 4-Mg truck going straight north at 24 m/s makes a 90° right turn, keeping its speed constant. What is the change in its momentum (magnitude and direction)?

10-16 A 1.35-kg basketball bounces off a backboard. Initially it was going 12 m/s horizontally directly toward the backboard. It bounces straight back with its speed unchanged. What is its change in momentum?

Section 10-5. Conservation of momentum

10-17 Two carts, initially at rest, are free to move in the x direction. Cart A has mass 4.52 kg and cart B mass 2.37 kg. They are tied together, compressing a spring in between them, as shown in Fig. 10-27. When the string holding them together is burned in two, cart A moves off with a speed of 2.11 m/s. (a) With what speed does cart B leave? (b) How much energy was stored in the spring before the string was burned?

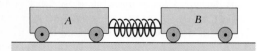

Figure 10-27. Exercise 10-17.

10-18 A 62-kg astronaut in free space pushes a 94-kg astro-

naut. If they were originally stationary, and the 94-kg astronaut leaves with a velocity of (1.7 m/s)**j** with respect to an inertial reference frame, what is the velocity of the 94-kg astronaut with respect to the 62-kg astronaut?

10-19 A 45-kg girl dives off a 1000-kg boat. She leaves the boat with horizontal speed 5.2 m/s. Assume the boat is originally at rest and free to move in the water. With what speed does the boat start to move off?

10-20 John and Mary dive off a raft with equal speeds. John has a mass of 75 kg and dives eastward; Mary has a mass of 52 kg and dives southward. In what direction does the raft take off?

10-21 Two pucks of mass m_1 and m_2 rest on a frictionless air table. They are connected by a stretched, light, elastic cord and then released. What is the ratio of their speeds after they are let go?

10-22 Two boys on ice skates throw a ball back and forth. They throw it so that its speed with respect to the thrower is 3 m/s. The boys each have a mass of 47 kg, and the ball a mass of 0.25 kg. If the boys are initially stationary, after how many tosses of the ball will they be receding from each other with a speed of 1.0 m/s? (Such a model of particle exchange seems to work well in the description of forces on the microscopic level, but in that case the force may be either attractive or repulsive.)

Section 10-6. Impulse

10-23 A pile driver has a 413-kg block that is lifted 1.4 m and then dropped onto the pile being driven into the ground. Suppose that the block takes 24 ms to stop when it hits the pile. What is the average force exerted on the pile by the pile driver?

10-24 The force that a bat exerts on a 0.20-kg ball as a function of time is shown in Fig. 10-28. If the ball is thrown toward the bat with a speed of 25 m/s, and leaves in the opposite direction, how fast with respect to the ground does it leave the bat?

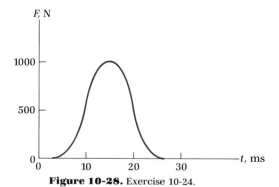

Figure 10-28. Exercise 10-24.

10-25 A machine gun fires 40-g bullets at a speed of 500 m/s. The gunner, holding the machine gun in his hands, can exert a maximum force of magnitude 200 N against the gun. Determine the maximum number of bullets he can fire per minute.

10-26 A handball of mass 100 g hits and bounces off a wall, as shown in Fig. 10-29. (*a*) What is the change in momentum of the ball? Assume the ball leaves the collision with the same speed it entered. (*b*) If the collision takes place in 30 ms, what is the average force exerted on the handball by the wall? (*c*) On the wall by the handball?

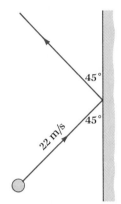

Figure 10-29. Exercise 10-26.

Section 10-7. Collisions

10-27 A boxcar of mass 14.2 Mg, with a speed of 1.8 m/s, hits and couples to a stationary flatcar of mass 23.5 Mg on a straight and level track. What is the speed of the two cars after the collision? By how much does the kinetic energy of the system change in this collision?

10-28 A nucleus at rest decays into an alpha particle and a smaller nucleus. The original nucleus has a mass 59 times larger than that of the alpha particle. What will the speed of the recoiling nucleus be if the speed of the alpha particle is 5.8×10^6 m/s?

10-29 Two meteoroids have a close encounter. Long before their encounter, meteoroid *A*, of mass 1.5×10^{12} kg, has a velocity of 0.25 m/s in the *x* direction, and meteoroid *B*, of mass 2.2×10^{12} kg, has a velocity of 0.34 m/s in the negative *x* direction. Long after the encounter, meteorite *A* is observed to have a velocity of 0.35 m/s in the *y* direction. What velocity does meteorite *B* have after the encounter? Neglect outside forces from the sun and other bodies.

10-30 A 100-kg fullback trying to make a touchdown dives directly forward. At the peak of his trajectory he is 1.2 m above the ground and 1.1 m from the goal line, and he has a speed of 4.2 m/s. At that point a 110-kg linebacker at the peak of *his* trajectory, going 2.3 m/s in the opposite direction, hits and holds the fullback tightly. Does the fullback cross the goal and land in the end zone?

10-31 Astronaut Ann wishes to go from the right side of her spaceship to the left side. She pushes against the wall and floats over. Astronaut Bob, floating freely outside the ship, watches and sees Ann going across with a speed of 1.00 m/s (Fig. 10-30). Ann has a mass of 51 kg, Bob a mass of 80 kg, and the spaceship a mass of 501 kg. If the spaceship is 5.0 m long, then how long does it take Ann to get to the left side?

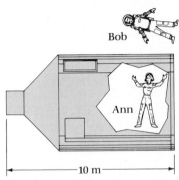

Figure 10-30. Exercise 10-31.

10-32 A 3.2-kg object with a speed of 15 m/s has a completely inelastic collision with a 4.8-kg object initially at rest. Find the final speed of the combination.

10-33 A boy throws a 3.3-kg beach ball to a 48-kg girl on roller skates who is initially stationary. After catching the ball, she starts moving at 0.32 m/s. How fast was the beach ball going when she caught it?

10-34 A 3.2-kg object with a speed of 15 m/s has a head-on elastic collision with a 4.8-kg object initially at rest. Find the speeds of the objects after the collision.

10-35 An alpha particle (of mass 4 u, where 1 u is approximately the mass of a proton) with a speed of 3.5×10^6 m/s has a head-on elastic collision with an initially stationary uranium nucleus (of mass 235 u). What is the recoil speed of the uranium nucleus?

10-36 A bob of mass $2m$ on a pendulum of length *L* is pulled back to an angle of 14.5° and let go. It makes an elastic collision with a ball of mass *m* at the bottom of its swing (Fig. 10-31). If this ball is also the bob of a pendulum of length *L*, how far does it swing out?

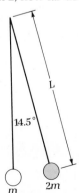

Figure 10-31. Exercise 10-36.

10-37 A pistol shoots a 4.5-g bullet into the 1.5-kg block of a ballistic pendulum. The block and bullet then rise 80 mm. What is the muzzle velocity of the bullet fired by this pistol?

10-38 A 50-g bullet is shot clear through a 1-kg wooden block suspended on a string 2 m long. The center of mass of the block is observed to rise to a maximum height of 50 mm. Find the speed of the bullet as it emerges from the block if its initial speed is 500 m/s. Neglect the loss of mass of the block due to the penetrating bullet.

10-39 Two carts, each of mass 2.2 kg, collide on a frictionless track. Before the collision, A has a velocity of 3.1 m/s east and B a velocity of 5.4 m/s west. The collision is elastic. What are the velocities of the carts after the collision?

10-40 Rework the previous problem, but assume that 9.2 J of kinetic energy is lost in the collision.

10-41 In a completely inelastic head-on collision between two objects A and B, with B initially at rest, show that the ratio of the kinetic energy before the collision to the kinetic energy after the collision is $(m_A + m_B)/m_A$.

10-42 Show that in an elastic head-on collision between two objects A and B, if B is initially at rest, the ratio of the kinetic energy of B after the collision (K_{Bf}) to the kinetic energy of A before the collision (K_{Ai}) is

$$\frac{K_{Bf}}{K_{Ai}} = \frac{4m_A m_B}{(m_A + m_B)^2}$$

Section 10-8. Collisions in two and three dimensions

10-43 A 1-Mg car going eastward on Main Street at 30 km/h collides with an 8-Mg truck crossing Main Street in a southward direction at 20 km/h. If the vehicles become entangled, how fast and in what direction will they start to move after the collision?

10-44 Figure 10-32 shows the positions at equal intervals of time of two frictionless pucks colliding in two dimensions on a horizontal air table. The pucks were

Figure 10-32. Exercise 10-44: Strobe photo of a collision between two pucks riding on a surface with negligible friction. Each image of the puck is formed during a flash of the strobe. The flashes come at equal intervals of 1.4 ms.

launched from the right. Find the ratio of the masses of the pucks. Is the collision elastic?

10-45 Show that if two objects collide to form a third object, all velocities in the problem lie in one plane.

10-46 Show that for an elastic collision between two particles of equal mass in which one particle is initially at rest, the velocities of the particles after the collision are at right angles to each other. What happens if the collision is head-on?

Section 10-9. Rocket motion

10-47 A stationary fire truck pumps 400 L of water a minute from its tank in a horizontal stream. One liter of water has a mass of 1 kg. By how many kg · m/s is the momentum of the system of fire truck plus water changing every second? What outside force must be exerted on the fire truck to keep it stationary?

10-48 A fire hose carrying 450 L of water per minute goes through a right-angle turn, as shown in Fig. 10-33. Consider the system outlined on the drawing. A liter of water has a mass of 1 kg. What momentum enters the system per second? What momentum leaves the system per second? What force must be applied to this section of hose to keep it stationary?

Figure 10-33. Exercise 10-48.

10-49 Water enters a turbine at the rate of 60 kg/s and a speed of 18 m/s, and leaves at a right angle to the direction it came in at a speed of 3 m/s. (a) What force must the bearings exert on the turbine shaft? (b) Assuming mechanical energy is conserved, how much power is given to the turbine by the water?

10-50 Ten tons of sand are dumped vertically downward into a 6-ton railway gondola car coasting along a flat track. If the car was going 3.8 m/s before the sand was dumped in, how fast is it going after the sand is dumped in? Is the vertical component of momentum of the system of sand and gondola conserved? Why or why not?

10-51 A 10-Mg spaceship has positioning jets that move it around in space. The jet has an exhaust speed of

2 km/s and uses 10 g/s of gas. (a) What is the thrust of the jet? (b) How long must it be on to change the speed of the spaceship by 20 m/s? (c) How much gas would be used in this maneuver?

10-52 A rocket in interstellar space uses its engines to accel-erate from rest to a speed of 5 km/s. The engine pro-duces exhaust gases that leave the rocket with a rela-tive velocity of 2 km/s. What fraction of the mass of the rocket is burned up and exhausted by the en-gines?

PROBLEMS

10-1   A system of particles is made up of two subsystems, A and B. Show that the center of mass of the system $\mathbf{r}_{cm}$ is given by

$$M\mathbf{r}_{cm} = M_A\mathbf{r}_A + M_B\mathbf{r}_B$$

where M is the mass of the whole system, M_A and M_B are the masses of the subsystems, and $\mathbf{r}_A$ and $\mathbf{r}_B$ locate the centers of mass of the subsystems.

10-2   Derive Eqs. (10-21) and (10-22) from conservation of momentum and conservation of kinetic energy.

10-3   A block of mass m slides down a frictionless curved ramp, as shown in Fig. 10-34. The ramp, of mass M, sits on a frictionless horizontal table. (a) If the block starts at a height h above the table, show that when the block leaves the ramp, the ramp has a speed

$$V = \sqrt{\frac{2m^2gh}{M(m + M)}}$$

(b) What is the speed v of the block at this instant?

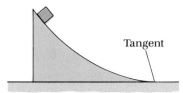

Figure 10-34. Prob. 10-3.

10-4   If the ramp of the last problem is straight rather than curved (Fig. 10-35), show that when the block reaches the bottom, the ramp has a speed of

$$V = \sqrt{\frac{2m^2gh\cos^2\phi}{(M + m)(M + m\sin^2\phi)}}$$

where ϕ is the angle the ramp makes with the hori-zontal.

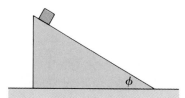

Figure 10-35. Prob. 10-4.

10-5   A cart of mass 2m is moving along a track toward a second stationary cart of mass m. A distance ℓ farther on down the track, there is a third cart, of mass 2m. If all collisions are elastic, show that the second cart collides with the first cart twice, and that the time between collisions is $(12/7)\,(\ell/v_0)$, where v_0 is the ini-tial speed of the first cart.

10-6   A 20-Mg railway car stands 10 m up a hill with its brakes set. When the brakes are released, it rolls down the hill, collides with a 10-Mg car resting at the bottom, and couples to this car. The two cars together roll up the next hill. (a) If friction along the tracks is negligible, how high up the next hill do the two cars go? (b) Is mechanical energy conserved for the whole process?

10-7   In Example 10-9 we assumed that the block did not rise during the collision. Estimate the error in our answer. Assume that the bullet stops halfway through the 105-mm-long block and is uniformly de-celerated by the block. What significant external forces act during this time?

10-8   (a) An isolated single-stage rocket has a total mass of 11 Mg, of which 9.7 Mg is fuel. Its exhaust speed is 2 km/s. If it starts from rest in an inertial system and burns all its fuel, what is the final speed of the rocket? (b) A two-stage rocket has the same amount of fuel and total mass as the rocket of part (a), but is divided into a first stage with 10-Mg mass, of which 9 Mg is fuel, and a second stage with 1-Mg mass, of which 0.7 Mg is fuel. Its engines also have an exhaust speed of 2 km/s. The second stage separates from the first stage after the fuel of the first stage is used up, and then the second-stage rocket commences firing. What is the final speed of the second stage?

10-9   Frame of reference A has a system of n particles with masses $m_1, m_2, \ldots$ and velocities $\mathbf{v}_1, \mathbf{v}_2, \ldots$. (a) Prove that if the total momentum is conserved in frame A, then it is also conserved in frame of refer-ence B moving at constant velocity with respect to A. (b) Is the physical quantity momentum invariant be-tween frames?

10-10 A jet of water with a speed of 35 m/s and a mass flow of 500 kg/s is incident on a cone, as seen in Fig. 10-36. What force must be applied to the cone to keep it in place? Assume the water splays out uniformly from the cone.

10-11 Two objects of mass m and M are initially at rest a long way apart from each other. They exert gravitational forces on each other. Show that as they approach

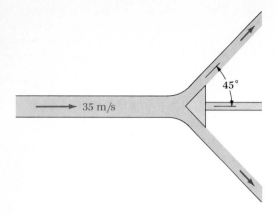

each other the speed v of the object with mass m is $\sqrt{(2GM^2)/[(m + M)r]}$.

10-12 ☕ Write a program to calculate the final speed of a rocket fired from the earth's surface toward free space. Remember that the force of gravity will be a function of the distance from the earth's center. Let the speed $\mathbf{v}_{gr}$ of the exhaust gases be 2.7 km/s, the initial mass of the rocket be 1 Gg, and the final mass be 10 Mg. Make the thrust of the rocket equal 3.2 times the initial weight of the rocket and neglect air resistance.

Figure 10-36. Prob. 10-10.

CHAPTER 11
STATIC EQUILIBRIUM
OF A RIGID BODY

11-1 INTRODUCTION

Just over a century ago, the Brooklyn Bridge linking Manhattan and Brooklyn was completed. At that time it was the longest suspension bridge on earth. And while it may have been surreptitiously sold many times, it remains in place as a graceful example of an extended object in static equilibrium.

What is the value of studying an extended object in static equilibrium? After all, its motion is trivially simple: It remains at rest. But as we shall see, analysis reveals information about some of the forces acting on the object. This knowledge is essential when selecting the materials and components of a structure.

A view of the Brooklyn Bridge.
(Peter Miller/Photo Researchers)

227

Many engineering students take one or more courses in statics. Such courses are based on the principles introduced in this chapter. We shall focus our attention on simple situations which illustrate how these principles are used to analyze a "statics" problem.

11-2 STATIC EQUILIBRIUM OF A RIGID BODY

If a particle, a point object, remains at rest in an inertial reference frame, its acceleration is zero, and, from Newton's second law, the net force on the particle is zero, $\Sigma\mathbf{F} = 0$. This is the necessary (and sufficient) condition for the static equilibrium of a particle, as we recall from Chap. 5. But in the real world, we must deal with extended objects instead of particles. What do we mean by static equilibrium for an extended object? *An extended object is in static equilibrium if every point of the object is at rest and remains at rest.* Of course, if the object is in static equilibrium in one inertial reference frame, every point on the object moves with a common, constant velocity in a different inertial reference frame. We shall choose the reference frame in which the object is at rest to discuss static equilibrium.

> In static equilibrium every point on an object remains at rest.

Some extended objects, such as bread dough, a spring, or a pencil eraser, are flexible and can change their shape or size in response to applied forces. On the other hand, a mechanic's wrench remains rigid and nondeformable under ordinary circumstances. We restrict our attention in this chapter to *rigid bodies* in static equilibrium. *A rigid body is one for which the distance between any pair of points on the object remains fixed.* If an object changes its shape or size, then the distance between some pairs of points will change. Hence a rigid body retains its shape and size under the application of forces. The concept of a rigid body is an idealization, however. Every material object undergoes some deformation in response to externally applied forces (see Chap. 15). But if these changes are negligible, we consider the object to be a rigid body.

> A rigid body retains its shape and size.

In Chap. 10 we saw that the motion of the center of mass is determined by the external forces, $M\mathbf{a}_{cm} = \Sigma\mathbf{F}_{ext}$, where M is the mass of the object. The object is said to be in *translational equilibrium* if the acceleration of the center of mass is zero. If $\mathbf{a}_{cm} = 0$, then

> In translational equilibrium, $\mathbf{a}_{cm} = 0$.

$$\Sigma\mathbf{F}_{ext} = 0 \qquad (11\text{-}1)$$

This is the condition for translational equilibrium.

Even if the center of mass of a rigid body remains at rest, the object is not necessarily in static equilibrium. It could be changing its spatial orientation by *rotating* about the stationary center of mass. For example, a pulley mounted on a shaft can rotate about an axis passing through its center of mass. Points on the pulley are moving, although the center of mass remains at rest. An object which does not rotate (or which rotates steadily about an axis, as discussed in the next chapter) is in *rotational equilibrium*. A rigid body in static equilibrium neither translates nor rotates and is, therefore, in translational and rotational equilibrium.

> In rotational equilibrium, a rigid body has a fixed orientation.

Consider a revolving door as viewed from above, shown in Fig. 11-1a. The door can rotate about a vertical axis which passes through its center of mass. The bearings along the axis will exert a force $\mathbf{F}_b$ (not shown in the figures) on the shaft of the door so that $\Sigma\mathbf{F}_{ext} = 0$ to keep the door in translational equilibrium. Suppose that two pedestrians are in opposite quadrants, exerting equal

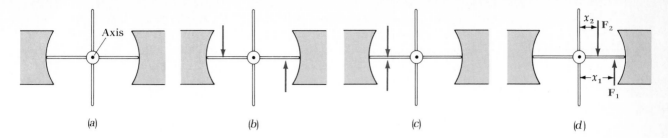

(a)   (b)   (c)   (d)

Figure 11-1. A revolving door viewed from above.

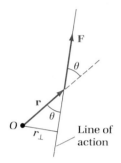

Figure 11-2. A force **F** is applied at a point located by the position vector **r**.

but opposite forces on the door, as seen in Fig. 11-1*b*. The net external force is still zero, but our experience shows that the door is not in rotational equilibrium. The door actually starts rotating when the pedestrians begin pushing in this way. In Fig. 11-1*c*, however, the door is in static equilibrium. Here the net external force is zero and, by symmetry, the door is in rotational equilibrium.

Experiment shows that the door in Fig. 11-1*d* is also in static equilibrium if the magnitudes of the forces F_1 and F_2 are inversely proportional to the distances from the axis of their points of application: $F_1/F_2 = x_2/x_1$. This result can also be written as

$$x_1F_1 - x_2F_2 = 0 \qquad (11\text{-}2)$$

Although $\mathbf{F}_1$ and $\mathbf{F}_2$ do not add to zero, the condition $\Sigma \mathbf{F}_{\text{ext}} = 0$ is still satisfied because of the force exerted by the bearings. The force $\mathbf{F}_1$ tends to cause the door to rotate in a counterclockwise sense, while $\mathbf{F}_2$ tends to produce a clockwise rotation. These two tendencies balance, or cancel out, for static equilibrium. We shall soon recognize Eq. (11-2) as the application of a condition for rotational equilibrium. The general conditions of static equilibrium of a rigid body will be stated in Sec. 11-4.

EXAMPLE 11-1. One pedestrian exerts a 40-N force F_1 on a revolving door at a point 0.3 m from the axis, as shown in Fig. 11-1*d*. What force F_2 must be exerted at 0.2 m from the axis to keep the door stationary?

SOLUTION. From Eq. (11-2) we have $x_2F_2 = x_1F_1$, so that

$$F_2 = \frac{F_1x_1}{x_2} = \frac{(40 \text{ N})(0.3 \text{ m})}{0.2 \text{ m}} = 60 \text{ N}$$

11-3 TORQUE ABOUT AN AXIS

In considering the equilibrium of an object such as a door that can rotate about an axis, we have seen [Eq. (11-2)] the importance of the point of application of a force. The quantity which takes this feature into account is called the *torque*. Torque is produced by a force about an axis; it is the torque which tends to cause an object to rotate.

To define torque, we consider a force **F** applied at a point on an object, as indicated in Fig. 11-2. The point *O* represents the intersection of a perpendicular axis with the plane containing the vectors **F** and **r**; the vector **r** locates the point of application of the force from this axis. We construct the *line of action* of this force by extending the line along which **F** lies. The perpendicular distance from the axis to the line of action of the force is $r_\perp = r \sin \theta$, where θ is the angle between the directions of **r** and **F**. The magnitude of the torque about axis *O* produced by this force is defined as

Line of action of a force

Magnitude of torque about an axis

$$\tau = r_\perp F = (r \sin \theta)F \qquad (11\text{-}3)$$

Moment arm and moment of a force

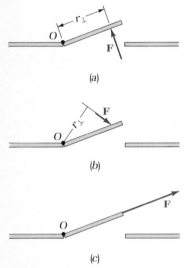

(a)

(b)

(c)

Figure 11-3. Forces applied to a door, as viewed from above.

The magnitude of the torque is the product of the force and the perpendicular distance from the axis to the line of action of the force. Often the perpendicular distance $r_\perp$ is called the *moment arm* of the force, and the torque $r_\perp F$ is called the *moment of the force* about the axis. Notice from Fig. 11-2 that $r_\perp$ would be the same if the force was applied at any point along the line of action of the force. You can imagine sliding the force vector along that line of action; the magnitude of the torque would be unchanged.

The dimension of torque is [force] × [length], the same as the dimension of work and energy. The SI unit of torque is N · m and that of work is J = N · m. Torque is a very different kind of quantity from work, however, and we express the SI unit of torque as N · m and reserve the unit J for work and for energy.

To see how torque tends to produce a rotation about an axis, consider a door which can rotate about a vertical axis passing through the hinges. Figure 11-3a shows the door viewed from above, with a horizontal force applied perpendicular to the face. The magnitude of the torque is $\tau = r_\perp F$. Our everyday experience indicates that the door tends to rotate in a counterclockwise sense (that is, it opens). Similarly, in Fig. 11-3b the magnitude of the torque is $\tau = r_\perp F$, but the door tends to rotate with a clockwise sense (that is, it closes). However, in Fig. 11-3c the moment arm $r_\perp = 0$, so the magnitude of the torque is zero. Our experience in this case is that the door tends neither to open nor to close if we apply a force in the direction shown. From the situation illustrated in Fig. 11-3c, we can extract the following useful result: *If the line of action of a force passes through the axis, the torque about that axis is zero.*

EXAMPLE 11-2. Evaluate the magnitude of the torque about axis O for each force shown in Fig. 11-4. Take $F_1 =$ $F_2 = F_3 = 110$ N   and $r_1 = 110$ mm, $r_2 = 160$ mm, $r_3 = 210$ mm.

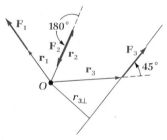

Figure 11-4. Example 11-2: Three forces are applied to an object. Only $\mathbf{F}_3$ causes a torque about axis O.

SOLUTION. As the figure indicates, force $\mathbf{F}_1$ is parallel to $\mathbf{r}_1$. The line of action of $\mathbf{F}_1$ passes through the axis. The magnitude of the torque produced by $\mathbf{F}_1$ about axis O is zero, $\tau_1 = 0$.

The angle between the direction of $\mathbf{r}_2$ and the direction of $\mathbf{F}_2$ is $180°$. The line of action of $\mathbf{F}_2$ passes through the axis; therefore, $\tau_2 = 0$.

The line of action of $\mathbf{F}_3$ does not pass through the axis. From the figure we have $r_{3\perp} = r_3 \sin 45° = 150$ mm. Thus

$$\tau_3 = r_{3\perp}F_3 = (0.15 \text{ m})(110 \text{ N}) = 16 \text{ N} \cdot \text{m}$$

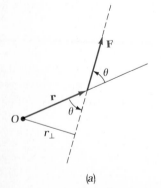

(a)

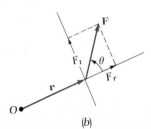

(b)

In calculating torques, it is sometimes convenient to use an alternative form of Eq. (11-3), which can be obtained from the construction in Fig. 11-5. From Fig. 11-5a and Eq. (11-3) we have $\tau = r_\perp F = (r \sin \theta)F$. The factor $\sin \theta$ can be

Figure 11-5. (a) $r_\perp$ is the perpendicular distance from the axis to the line of action of the force. (b) The force is resolved into components along directions parallel and perpendicular to $\mathbf{r}$.

associated with the force F rather than with the distance r. In Fig. 11-5b the force vector is resolved into a component F_r, parallel to $\mathbf{r}$, and a component F_t, perpendicular to $\mathbf{r}$. Denoting the magnitude of this perpendicular component by $F_\perp = |F_t| = F \sin \theta$, we have for the magnitude of the torque about axis O,

$$\tau = rF_\perp \tag{11-4}$$

The magnitude of the torque about an axis is the product of the magnitude of the vector $\mathbf{r}$ locating the point of application of the force from the axis and the magnitude of the component of the force perpendicular to $\mathbf{r}$.

Three equivalent expressions for τ Equations (11-3) and (11-4) are equivalent expressions. They are just different ways of expressing the quantity $rF \sin \theta$

$$rF \sin \theta = r_\perp F = rF_\perp$$

Any one of these three forms may be used to evaluate the magnitude of the torque. Choose the one that seems easiest to apply.

EXAMPLE 11-3. Part of a steel I beam extends 8.0 m beyond a wall, as shown in Fig. 11-6. Assume that the weight of this uniform section acts at the center of the section, with magnitude 2100 N. Determine the magnitude and direction of the torque about the axis O.

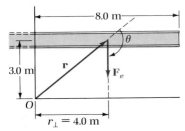

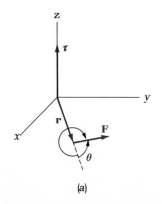

Figure 11-6. Example 11-3: The weight of a section of a cantilevered beam exerts a torque about O.

SOLUTION. From the information provided in the figure, we see that the torque can be evaluated most easily from Eq. (11-3):

$$\tau_e = r_\perp F_e = (4.0 \text{ m})(2.1 \text{ kN}) = 8.4 \text{ kN} \cdot \text{m}$$

With somewhat more effort, the expression $rF \sin \theta$ can be applied. The angle θ is given by

$$\theta = 90° + \tan^{-1} \frac{3.0}{4.0} = 127°$$

and $r = \sqrt{(3.0 \text{ m})^2 + (4.0 \text{ m})^2} = 5.0 \text{ m}$

Then

$$\tau_e = rF_e \sin \theta = (5.0 \text{ m})(2100 \text{ N}) \sin 127° = 8.4 \text{ kN} \cdot \text{m}$$

You can similarly show that Eq. (11-4) gives the same result.

Torque will be generally defined as a vector quantity in Sec. 11-6. Equation (11-3) gives the magnitude of the torque about an axis. We must also specify its direction. For now it is sufficient to choose the z axis to be parallel to the axis of rotation, with the xy plane containing the vectors $\mathbf{r}$ and $\mathbf{F}$, as seen in Fig. 11-7a. The direction of the torque is along the z axis. The torque τ has only a z component τ_z, and the magnitude of the torque is $\tau = |\tau_z| = r_\perp F$. The sign of the component τ_z is determined by the sense of rotational motion of the object (clockwise or counterclockwise when viewed from a point on the positive z

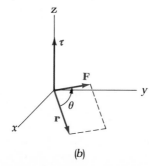

(a)   (b)

Figure 11-7. (a) Vectors $\mathbf{r}$ and $\mathbf{F}$ lie in the xy plane, and the torque is along the z axis. (b) The sense is determined by the rotation that takes $\mathbf{r}$ into $\mathbf{F}$ through the smaller angle θ.

The sense of rotation determines the sign of τ_z.

axis) that the torque tends to cause. *If the sense of rotation is counterclockwise, τ_z is positive; if the sense of motion is clockwise, τ_z is negative.* The sense is determined by the rotation that would carry the direction of **r** into the direction of **F**. Figure 11-7a indicates two such rotations; we always perform the rotation through the smaller of the two angles between **r** and **F** placed tail to tail, as shown in Fig. 11-7b. In this case the rotation is through angle θ with a counterclockwise sense. The z component of torque about axis O is positive. Since the sign of τ_z is determined by the sense of rotation, a positive τ_z is often called a *counterclockwise torque* and a negative τ_z is called a *clockwise torque*.

EXAMPLE 11-4. For each force shown in Fig. 11-8, determine the sign of the z component of torque about the axis O. The z axis comes perpendicularly out of the plane of the page.

SOLUTION. The sense of the rotation that carries $\mathbf{r}_1$ into $\mathbf{F}_1$ is counterclockwise through angle θ_1. The sign of τ_{1z} is positive. The direction of the torque vector $\boldsymbol{\tau}_1$ is perpendicularly out of the page. A clockwise rotation through θ_2 carries the direction of $\mathbf{r}_2$ into $\mathbf{F}_2$. The component τ_{2z} is therefore negative, and $\boldsymbol{\tau}_2$ points into the page. Similarly, τ_{3z} is negative and $\boldsymbol{\tau}_3$ points into the page.

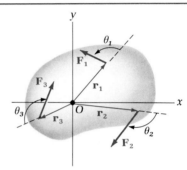

Figure 11-8. Example 11-4: Three forces exert torques about axis O.

11-4 CONDITIONS FOR STATIC EQUILIBRIUM

The condition for translational equilibrium of an object is given by Eq. (11-1), $\Sigma \mathbf{F}_{\text{ext}} = 0$. For a rigid body to be in static equilibrium, we must require it to be in rotational as well as translational equilibrium. The condition for rotational equilibrium is stated in terms of the torques produced by the external forces acting on the rigid body. From our previous discussion of torques, we should expect that rotational equilibrium requires the balancing of tendencies to rotate clockwise and counterclockwise about any axis because of torques about that axis. We can express this condition as a vector equation:

Condition for rotational equilibrium

$$\Sigma \boldsymbol{\tau}_{\text{ext}} = 0 \qquad (11\text{-}5)$$

This condition for rotational equilibrium of a rigid body is a special case of the more general consideration of rotational dynamics to be developed from Newton's laws in Chap. 13.

Together Eqs. (11-1) and (11-5) constitute the conditions for static equilibrium of a rigid body. *For a rigid body in static equilibrium, the net external force must be zero and the net external torque must be zero:*

Conditions for static equilibrium

$$\Sigma \mathbf{F}_{\text{ext}} = 0 \qquad \Sigma \boldsymbol{\tau}_{\text{ext}} = 0 \qquad (11\text{-}6)$$

These conditions are often referred to as the *first* ($\Sigma \mathbf{F}_{\text{ext}} = 0$) and *second* ($\Sigma \boldsymbol{\tau}_{\text{ext}} = 0$) conditions of equilibrium of a rigid body.

Each of these two vector equations has x, y, and z components, for a total of six equations. However, in many situations, all external forces effectively lie in a given plane, say the xy plane. These forces are said to be *coplanar,* and we shall confine our attention to the case of coplanar forces. Then the external

Coplanar forces lie in a plane.

forces have only x and y components, and the external torques have only z components. These torque components correspond to clockwise and counterclockwise torques about some axis perpendicular to the xy plane. The conditions for static equilibrium become

$$\Sigma F_{x,\text{ext}} = 0 \qquad \Sigma F_{y,\text{ext}} = 0 \qquad \Sigma \tau_{z,\text{ext}} = 0 \qquad (11\text{-}7)$$

Equations (11-7) can be solved for at most three unknowns. The equations contain forces, distances, and angles. Up to three of these quantities can be determined by solving the equations simultaneously. In many simple situations, the number of unknown quantities will be three or less. There are also cases in which the number of unknowns is greater than three. In such cases, additional information would have to be provided to determine the unknowns.

A useful procedure, consisting of several steps, may be followed in solving the typical statics problem. These steps are

1 Sketch the situation showing the rigid body which is in static equilibrium.
2 Construct the free-body diagram by drawing in all external force vectors acting on the rigid body and indicate the magnitude, the direction, and the point of application of each force. Some of these quantities will be unknown; for example, you may not know the direction of a force or the point at which it is applied.
3 Select a set of coordinate axes along which to resolve the forces. Usually, a judicious choice of the orientation of the coordinate axes simplifies this resolution.
4 Make a choice of an axis about which to evaluate torques. Choosing the axis to pass through the intersection of the lines of action of two or more forces is often convenient because the moment arm of each of these forces is zero.
5 Apply the conditions of static equilibrium, Eqs. (11-7).
6 Solve these equations for up to three unknowns.

One of the forces which acts on a rigid body close to the earth's surface is the weight of the body. Its point of application in the examples to follow is assumed to be at the center of mass (Sec. 10-2) of the object. We shall discuss this assumption in the next section.

EXAMPLE 11-5. A uniform 48-N board of length 3.6 m rests horizontally on two sawhorses, as shown in Fig. 11-9a. What normal forces are exerted on the board by the sawhorses?

SOLUTION. Since the board is uniform, the weight is assumed to act at the center of mass, 1.8 m from each end. Figure 11-9b shows the free-body diagram for the board. The sawhorses exert vertical normal forces of magnitude F_P and F_Q on the board at points P and Q. These two normal forces are the unknowns. Since the board is in static equilibrium, we can apply the conditions of static equilibrium, Eqs. (11-7). Take the x axis as horizontal and the y axis as vertically upward. Then $\Sigma F_{x,\text{ext}} = 0$ is automatically satisfied because

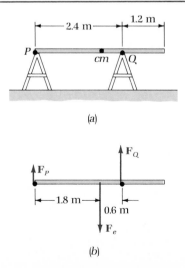

(a)

(b)

Figure 11-9. Example 11-5: (a) A board rests on two sawhorses. (b) The free-body diagram of the board.

all the forces act vertically. Requiring $\Sigma F_{y,\text{ext}} = 0$, we have $F_P + F_Q - F_e = 0$, or

$$F_P + F_Q = F_e$$

The sum of the two normal forces must balance the weight. We must now select an axis about which to calculate torques. Any axis will do, but a convenient choice is the axis through point P because $\mathbf{F}_P$ exerts no torque about this axis. The weight exerts a clockwise torque, and $\mathbf{F}_Q$ exerts a counterclockwise torque about the axis through P. With the z axis perpendicularly out of the page, applying $\Sigma \tau_{z,\text{ext}} = 0$ gives $(2.4 \text{ m})F_Q - (1.8 \text{ m})F_e = 0$, or

$$(2.4 \text{ m})F_Q = (1.8 \text{ m})(48 \text{ N})$$

$$F_Q = 36 \text{ N}$$

The other normal force can be determined immediately since $F_P + F_Q = 48$ N, or $F_P = 12$ N. Try reworking this example for a different choice of axis, such as through point Q or through the center of mass.

EXAMPLE 11-6. A uniform boom supports a load weight of magnitude $F_L = 1100$ N, as shown in Fig. 11-10a. The boom is attached to the wall by a pin which exerts a force $\mathbf{F}_p$ on the boom. The weight of the boom acts at its midpoint and has magnitude 200 N. Determine the horizontal and vertical components of $\mathbf{F}_p$ and the tension in the guy wire.

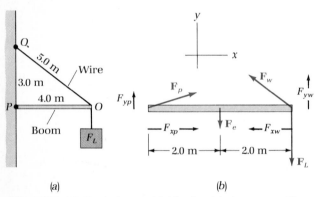

(a)   (b)

Figure 11-10. Example 11-6: (a) A load weight is supported by a boom. (b) The free-body diagram of the boom.

SOLUTION. We take the boom as a rigid body in static equilibrium and display its free-body diagram in Fig. 11-10b. Notice that the load is in equilibrium so that the tension in the vertical wire attached to the load must also be F_L. Neither the magnitude nor the direction of the pin force $\mathbf{F}_p$ is known, but let us assume that it has x and y components as shown. If F_{xp} and F_{yp} come out as positive in our solution, then our assumption about the direction of $\mathbf{F}_p$ is correct. If one or both of the components have negative values, then

we can correct the direction of $\mathbf{F}_p$ accordingly. The three unknowns are F_{xp}, F_{yp}, and the guy-wire tension F_w. The tension force can be resolved into x and y components from similar triangles. Thus $F_{yw}/F_w = 3.0 \text{ m}/5.0 \text{ m}$, or $F_{yw} = \frac{3}{5}F_w$. Similarly $F_{xw} = -\frac{4}{5}F_w$. Applying the conditions for translational equilibrium, we have

$$F_{xp} - \tfrac{4}{5}F_w = 0$$

$$F_{yp} + \tfrac{3}{5}F_w - F_e - F_L = 0$$

It is convenient to choose the axis at point O at the right end of the boom. The lines of action of F_w, F_L, and F_{xp} all pass through this axis, and therefore these forces exert no torque about O. The force component F_{yp} causes a clockwise torque, and F_e a counterclockwise torque about this axis. For rotational equilibrium then, $(2.0 \text{ m})F_e - (4.0 \text{ m})F_{yp} = 0$, so

$$F_{yp} = \tfrac{1}{2}F_e = 100 \text{ N}$$

Substituting this into the second of the conditions above gives $\frac{3}{5}F_w = F_e + F_L - 100$ N, or

$$F_w = 2000 \text{ N}$$

F_{xp} is obtained from the first condition above:

$$F_{xp} = \tfrac{4}{5}F_w = 1600 \text{ N}$$

What is the practical value of this calculation? From the solution we see that the guy-wire tension is 2000 N. We must use a wire substantial enough to support this tension without significant stretching. Similarly, we can see that there are forces exerted on the boom which tend to compress it and to bend it. The boom must be stiff enough to sustain these forces without appreciable deformation.

We have stated that the choice of axis about which to compute torques is arbitrary. It is instructive to make different choices of axis to evaluate the torques in the previous example, using the now-determined force values. For example, suppose we calculate the torques about an axis through point P at the pin seen in Fig. 11-10a. The pin force exerts no torque about this axis. Clockwise torques are exerted by the forces F_e and F_L. The counterclockwise torque is caused by the vertical component, $F_{yw} = \frac{3}{5}F_w = 1200$ N. Adding the z components of the torques about axis P, we obtain

$$(4.0 \text{ m})(1200 \text{ N}) - (2.0 \text{ m})(200 \text{ N}) - (4.0 \text{ m})(1100 \text{ N}) = 0$$

The sum of the external torque components about axis P is also zero. A similar calculation about axis Q in Fig. 11-10a shows zero net external torque about that axis. This is what we expect because the rigid body is in static equilibrium.

In an alternative approach to a statics problem, we can obtain three equations in three unknowns by applying the condition $\Sigma\tau_{z,\text{ext}} = 0$ about three appropriately chosen axes. These equations are not independent of the three conditions in Eqs. (11-7), but are sometimes easier to apply, as the following example shows.

EXAMPLE 11-7. Reconsider the previous example by requiring $\Sigma\tau_{z,\text{ext}} = 0$ about axes through O, P, and Q.

SOLUTION. About axis O we have, as before,

$$(2.0 \text{ m})F_e - (4.0 \text{ m})F_{yp} = 0$$

$$F_{yp} = 100 \text{ N}$$

About axis P, we obtain

$$(4.0 \text{ m})\tfrac{3}{5}F_w - (2.0 \text{ m})F_e - (4.0 \text{ m})F_L = 0$$

$$\tfrac{3}{5}F_w = \tfrac{1}{2}F_e + F_L = 1200 \text{ N}$$

$$F_w = 2000 \text{ N}$$

And about axis Q, $\mathbf{F}_w$ exerts no torque so we have

$$(3.0 \text{ m})F_{xp} - (2.0 \text{ m})F_e - (4.0 \text{ m})F_L = 0$$

$$F_{xp} = \tfrac{2}{3}F_e + \tfrac{4}{3}F_L = 1600 \text{ N}$$

In the examples considered so far, the conditions of static equilibrium, Eqs. (11-7), have been sufficient to determine all of the unknown quantities. There are many situations, however, in which those conditions alone will not determine all of the unknowns. For example, there may be more than three unknown forces, but only three equations connect them. The additional information that must be provided to solve this type of problem often comes from considering the mechanical properties of materials. We shall not pursue this approach, but the following examples will illustrate this type of problem.

EXAMPLE 11-8. A uniform door of dimensions 0.82 m by 2.04 m and weight of magnitude 210 N is hung by two hinges placed symmetrically 1.60 m apart, as shown in Fig. 11-11a. (a) Determine the horizontal component of the force exerted by each hinge on the door. (b) Determine the vertical component of the force exerted by each hinge on the door.

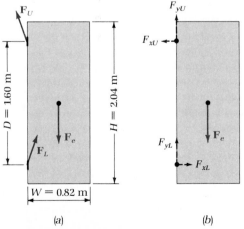

(a)   (b)

Figure 11-11. Example 11-8: (a) A door is supported by two hinges. (b) The free-body diagram of the door.

Comment on the difficulty encountered.

SOLUTION. (a) The free-body diagram is shown in Fig. 11-11b, with the forces exerted by the upper and lower hinges resolved into horizontal and vertical components. The weight of the uniform door acts at the midpoint of the door. Requiring the x and y components of the external forces to add to zero gives

$$F_{yU} + F_{yL} - F_e = 0$$

$$F_{xU} + F_{xL} = 0$$

So the sum of the vertical components of the hinge forces balances the weight, and the horizontal components of the hinge forces balance each other. Choose an axis through the upper hinge position and perpendicular to the plane of the figure. The weight of the door produces a clockwise torque about this axis. The only other nonzero torque is caused by the component F_{xL}, and it exerts a counterclockwise torque about the axis. Then

$$DF_{xL} - \tfrac{1}{2}WF_e = 0$$

$$(1.60 \text{ m})F_{xL} = (0.41 \text{ m})(210 \text{ N})$$

$$F_{xL} = 54 \text{ N}$$

The upper hinge force compoment balances this, so

$$F_{xU} = -54 \text{ N}$$

(b) We have determined two unknowns, F_{xU} and F_{xL}, and have only a single equation connecting the other two unknown force components:

$$F_{yU} + F_{yL} = 210 \text{ N}$$

From the information provided we cannot determine how this 210-N load is shared by the two hinges. Notice that F_{yU} and F_{yL} have the same line of action and therefore exert the same net torque about an axis, no matter how the 210-N total is shared. Additional information is required to determine F_{yU} and F_{yL}, and that information depends in detail on how the hinges are mounted and aligned.

EXAMPLE 11-9. A uniform ladder leans against a wall, as shown in Fig. 11-12a. What minimum value of the coefficient of static friction at the floor-ladder interface will prevent the ladder from slipping?

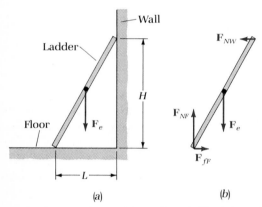

Figure 11-12. Example 11-9: (a) A uniform ladder is in static equilibrium. (b) The free-body diagram of the ladder. The frictional force at the wall is negligible.

SOLUTION. There are four unknown forces in this problem. Normal forces are exerted on the ladder by the floor and by the wall. Static frictional forces are also exerted on the ladder by the two surfaces. Let us assume that the wall surface is very smooth and that the frictional force there is negligible. This assumption reduces the number of unknown forces to three. The free-body diagram is shown in Fig. 11-12b. We choose the axis to pass through the point of contact of the ladder and floor. Applying the conditions of static equilibrium gives for the magnitudes of these forces:

$$F_{fF} = F_{NW} \qquad F_{NF} = F_e \qquad HF_{NW} - \tfrac{1}{2}LF_e = 0$$

These equations are easily solved for the unknown forces:

$$F_{NW} = \frac{L}{2H} F_e \qquad F_{fF} = \frac{L}{2H} F_e \qquad F_{NF} = F_e$$

Since F_{fF} is a static frictional force, we must require that its value not exceed the maximum value of the static frictional force, $F_{fF} \leq \mu_s F_{NF}$ from Eq. (6-3). Imposing this condition gives $(L/2H)F_e \leq \mu_s F_e$ or, on simplifying,

$$\mu_s \geq \frac{L}{2H}$$

11-5 CENTER OF GRAVITY

We have taken the effective point of application of the weight of an object to be at the center of mass of that object. What is the justification for this assumption? In what sense is there a single point at which we can consider the full weight of the object to be acting? What is the full weight of the object?

Since we can regard an object as composed of a large number of small parts, the weight of the object, $\mathbf{F}_e$, is just the sum of the weights of these parts. For an object of ordinary size close to the earth's surface, the weight of each part is directed downward and we can easily add them. Letting m_i represent the mass of one of those elements, we have

> The weight of an object is the sum of the weights of its parts.

$$F_e = \Sigma m_i g = (\Sigma m_i)g = Mg \tag{11-8}$$

where $M = \Sigma m_i$ is the total mass of the object and g is the acceleration due to gravity. Adding together the weights of the individual pieces of the object gives, according to Eq. (11-8), the full weight of the object, independent of the question of points of application of these forces.

The point of application of each force is important when calculating torques.

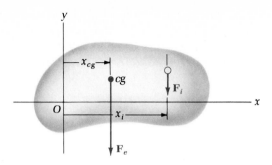

Figure 11-13. The full weight of an object acts at the center of gravity. The weight of one part of the object has magnitude $F_i = m_i g$.

The weight of each part of the body will exert a torque about some axis, as shown in Fig. 11-13. For the force of magnitude $F_i = m_i g$, the torque component τ_{zi} is

$$\tau_{zi} = -(x_i)(m_i g)$$

The overall torque is the sum of the torques due to the weight of each part.

where x_i is the x coordinate of that part of the object and the negative sign accounts for the clockwise sense of the torque. If we add these contributions from each piece of the body, we obtain the torque component due to the full gravitational force acting on the object:

$$\tau_z = \Sigma\,[-(x_i)(m_i g)] \tag{11-9}$$

From this expression we can see that the torque due to the weight of an object depends on how the parts of the object are distributed spatially. We can find an effective point on the object, the *center of gravity*, at which the full weight of the object can be considered to act so as to cause the same torque given by Eq. (11-9). If x_{cg} is the x coordinate of that point, the torque component due to the full weight, of magnitude $F_e = \Sigma m_i g$, is

$$\tau_z = -x_{cg}F_e = -x_{cg}\Sigma m_i g \tag{11-10}$$

The x coordinate of the center of gravity is determined by equating the right-hand sides of Eqs. (11-9) and (11-10):

$$x_{cg} = \frac{\Sigma(x_i)(m_i g)}{\Sigma m_i g}$$

The center of gravity is that point at which the weight of an object can be considered to act and is given by

$$x_{cg} = \frac{\Sigma x_i m_i g}{\Sigma m_i g} \tag{11-11}$$

In most cases of interest, the value of g is the same for every part of the object and can be divided out of the expressions in Eq. (11-11). After dividing out the common factor g, we have

$$x_{cg} = \frac{\Sigma x_i m_i}{\Sigma m_i}$$

We recognize the right-hand side as the x coordinate of the center of mass of the object. *If the acceleration due to gravity is the same for each part of the object, then the center of gravity and the center of mass coincide.*

The center of gravity of a rigid body can be determined experimentally by suspending the object from two or more points, as shown in Fig. 11-14. If the

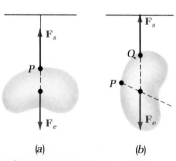

(a)   (b)

Figure 11-14. The center of gravity must lie directly below the point of suspension.

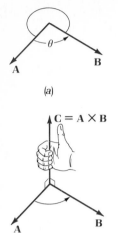

(a)

C = A × B

(b)

Figure 11-15. (a) Two vectors lie in a plane, with θ the smaller of the angles between them. (b) Vector $\mathbf{C} = \mathbf{A} \times \mathbf{B}$ is perpendicular to both $\mathbf{A}$ and $\mathbf{B}$, with a sense given by the right-hand rule.

Definition of the cross product

The right-hand rule

The cross product is noncommutative.

Vectors $\mathbf{A} \times \mathbf{B}$ and $\mathbf{B} \times \mathbf{A}$ have equal magnitude and opposite direction.

object is suspended by a string at point P, the conditions of static equilibrium require that $F_e = F_s$ and that the two forces have the same line of action. The center of gravity must lie directly below point P. Similarly, the center of gravity must lie directly below point Q, another point of suspension. The center of gravity is at the intersection of these two lines.

11-6   TORQUE AND THE CROSS PRODUCT OF VECTORS

The direction of the torque produced by a force has been taken to be along an axis perpendicular to the plane containing the force $\mathbf{F}$ and the vector $\mathbf{r}$ that locates the point of application of the force. If that plane is the xy plane, then the torque vector is along the z axis, and we refer to the torque component τ_z as the torque about the z axis. It is desirable to consider the torque as a vector, without reference to a particular coordinate system. We shall generalize the definition of torque by introducing a *vector product,* or *cross product of vectors.*

The cross product. The dot product or scalar product of two vectors was defined in Chap. 8. We now consider an entirely different kind of product of two vectors. As the names imply, the vector product, or cross product of two vectors, yields another vector, and the product is denoted by a cross ($\times$) between the factors. Consider two vectors $\mathbf{A}$ and $\mathbf{B}$, as shown in Fig. 11-15a, where the angle θ is the smaller of the angles between the two vectors. *The cross product $\mathbf{A} \times \mathbf{B}$ is defined as a vector $\mathbf{C} = \mathbf{A} \times \mathbf{B}$; the direction of $\mathbf{C}$ is given by the right-hand rule and the magnitude C is given by*

$$C = AB \sin \theta \tag{11-12}$$

The phrase "right-hand rule" stands for the following convention for obtaining the direction of the vector $\mathbf{C} = \mathbf{A} \times \mathbf{B}$:

Vector $\mathbf{C}$ is perpendicular to the plane containing vectors $\mathbf{A}$ and $\mathbf{B}$. Curl the fingers of the right hand in the sense that would rotate the first factor $\mathbf{A}$ into the second factor $\mathbf{B}$. The extended thumb gives the direction of $\mathbf{C}$.

The rotation that would carry $\mathbf{A}$ into $\mathbf{B}$ is through the smaller of the two angles between them. The right-hand rule is illustrated in Fig. 11-15b, where $\mathbf{C}$ is perpendicular to both $\mathbf{A}$ and $\mathbf{B}$. The definition of the cross product $\mathbf{C} = \mathbf{A} \times \mathbf{B}$ consists of two parts: Both the magnitude and the direction of $\mathbf{C}$ must be specified. Equation (11-12) gives the magnitude, and the right-hand rule gives the direction.

The cross product of two vectors is *noncommutative:* $\mathbf{A} \times \mathbf{B} \neq \mathbf{B} \times \mathbf{A}$. Let us change the order of the factors in the cross product; consider the vector $\mathbf{D} = \mathbf{B} \times \mathbf{A}$, with $\mathbf{A}$ and $\mathbf{B}$ the same vectors as before. The magnitude is again given by Eq. (11-12), $D = BA \sin \theta$. Applying the right-hand rule, however, requires us to imagine rotating $\mathbf{B}$ into $\mathbf{A}$, as indicated in Fig. 11-16a. The direction of $\mathbf{D} = \mathbf{B} \times \mathbf{A}$ is opposite the direction of $\mathbf{C} = \mathbf{A} \times \mathbf{B}$, as shown in Fig. 11-16$b$. The magnitudes of $\mathbf{C}$ and $\mathbf{D}$ are the same, $C = D = AB \sin \theta$. Hence,

$$\mathbf{B} \times \mathbf{A} = -\mathbf{A} \times \mathbf{B} \tag{11-13}$$

Reversing the order of the factors reverses the direction of the cross product. Although noncommutative, the cross product does obey the distributive rule:

$$\mathbf{A} \times (\mathbf{B} + \mathbf{C}) = \mathbf{A} \times \mathbf{B} + \mathbf{A} \times \mathbf{C}$$

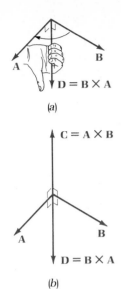

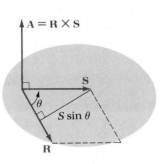

Figure 11-17. The area vector $\mathbf{A} = \mathbf{R} \times \mathbf{S}$ is perpendicular to the plane containing displacements $\mathbf{R}$ and $\mathbf{S}$, and the magnitude A equals the area of the parallelogram.

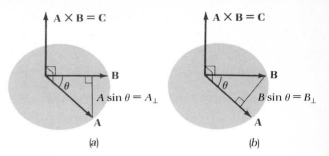

Figure 11-18. The magnitude of the cross product can be expressed as either (a) $|\mathbf{A} \times \mathbf{B}| = A_\perp B$ or (b) $|\mathbf{A} \times \mathbf{B}| = AB_\perp$.

Figure 11-16. (a) The direction of $\mathbf{D} = \mathbf{B} \times \mathbf{A}$ is given by the right-hand rule. (b) The cross product is noncommutative: $\mathbf{B} \times \mathbf{A} = -\mathbf{A} \times \mathbf{B}$.

Definition of vector area

Magnitude $|\mathbf{A} \times \mathbf{B}| = A_\perp B = AB_\perp$.

Special cases of the cross product

There is an interesting and useful geometric interpretation of the cross product of two displacements. The displacements $\mathbf{R}$ and $\mathbf{S}$ in Fig. 11-17 define a parallelogram whose area is $A = RS \sin \theta$, the product of the base and height. From Eq. (11-12) this area is the magnitude of the cross product of $\mathbf{R}$ and $\mathbf{S}$: $A = |\mathbf{R} \times \mathbf{S}| = RS \sin \theta$.

We define an oriented area element as a vector $\mathbf{A} = \mathbf{R} \times \mathbf{S}$ whose magnitude is the area of the parallelogram formed by $\mathbf{R}$ and $\mathbf{S}$ and whose direction is perpendicular to the plane of $\mathbf{R}$ and $\mathbf{S}$. In this way we specify the orientation of an element of surface area.

A geometric interpretation can also be applied to the magnitude of the cross product of any two vectors. In Eq. (11-12), the factor $\sin \theta$ can be associated with the magnitude of either $\mathbf{A}$ or $\mathbf{B}$. For example, $A \sin \theta$ is the magnitude of the component, $A_\perp = A \sin \theta$, which is perpendicular to $\mathbf{B}$ as shown in Fig. 11-18a. Thus the magnitude $C = |\mathbf{A} \times \mathbf{B}| = A_\perp B$. Similarly, the construction in Fig. 11-18b shows that $C = AB_\perp$. *The magnitude of the cross product of vectors $\mathbf{A}$ and $\mathbf{B}$ is the product of the magnitude of one vector and the magnitude of the perpendicular component of the other vector.* It is often convenient to use this result to calculate the magnitude of the cross product.

There are some special cases that deserve our attention. Suppose two vectors $\mathbf{A}$ and $\mathbf{B}$ are perpendicular. Then since $\sin 90° = 1$, $|\mathbf{A} \times \mathbf{B}| = AB$. At the other extreme we can consider two vectors that are either parallel ($\theta = 0$) or opposite ($\theta = 180°$). In either case the factor $\sin \theta = 0$ and the magnitude of the cross product $|\mathbf{A} \times \mathbf{B}| = 0$; thus $\mathbf{A} \times \mathbf{B} = 0$, the null vector. *The cross product of two vectors which are either parallel or opposite is zero.*

EXAMPLE 11-10. A surveyor marks off two displacements from a pin: $\mathbf{A}$ of magnitude $A = 204.56$ m due east and $\mathbf{B}$ of magnitude $B = 188.32$ m at $74.82°$ north of east. Determine the area of the parallelogram formed by these displacements.

SOLUTION. Rather than using Eq. (11-12) directly, we find the component of $\mathbf{A}$ perpendicular to $\mathbf{B}$:

$$A_\perp = (204.56 \text{ m}) \sin 74.82° = 197.4 \text{ m}$$

Then the magnitude of the area $|\mathbf{A} \times \mathbf{B}|$ is

$$A_\perp B = (197.4 \text{ m})(188.32 \text{ m}) = 37{,}180 \text{ m}^2$$

Alternatively, we can find that $B_\perp = 181.7$ m, and

$$AB_\perp = (204.56 \text{ m})(181.7 \text{ m}) = 37{,}180 \text{ m}^2$$

The direction of the vector area $\mathbf{A} \times \mathbf{B}$ is given by the right-hand rule and is upward in this case. What is the direction of $\mathbf{B} \times \mathbf{A}$?

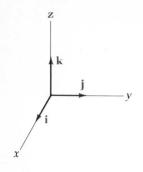

Figure 11-19. A right-handed coordinate system with $\mathbf{i} \times \mathbf{j} = \mathbf{k}$.

Cross product in component form. The cross product of two vectors can be evaluated in terms of the components of the two vectors. To do so, we must consider cross products of the unit vectors. Let us evaluate $\mathbf{i} \times \mathbf{i}$. The result is zero, or the null vector, because these two vectors are parallel ($\sin \theta = 0$). For the same reason, $\mathbf{j} \times \mathbf{j} = \mathbf{k} \times \mathbf{k} = 0$. To evaluate $\mathbf{i} \times \mathbf{j}$, refer to Fig. 11-19, which shows the unit vectors on an *xyz*-coordinate system. The magnitude of each unit vector is 1, or unity, and so the magnitude of $\mathbf{i} \times \mathbf{j}$ is also 1: $|\mathbf{i} \times \mathbf{j}| = (1)(1) \sin 90° = 1$. The direction of $\mathbf{i} \times \mathbf{j}$ is given by the right-hand rule and, from Fig. 11-19, is along the positive z axis. Thus $\mathbf{i} \times \mathbf{j}$ is a vector of magnitude 1 directed along the z axis; but this is just the unit vector $\mathbf{k}$. We have $\mathbf{i} \times \mathbf{j} = \mathbf{k}$. Simply reversing the order of the factors gives $\mathbf{j} \times \mathbf{i} = -\mathbf{k}$.

The coordinate system shown in Fig. 11-19 is called a *right-handed coordinate system*. The unit vectors $\mathbf{i}, \mathbf{j}, \mathbf{k}$ associated with the x, y, z axes, in that order, are connected by the right-hand rule: $\mathbf{i} \times \mathbf{j} = \mathbf{k}$. We shall use only right-handed coordinate systems in this text.

The cross products of the remaining pairs of unit vectors can be evaluated as above. There are a total of nine such products, and you should convince yourself of the following results:

$$\mathbf{i} \times \mathbf{i} = \mathbf{j} \times \mathbf{j} = \mathbf{k} \times \mathbf{k} = 0$$

$$\mathbf{i} \times \mathbf{j} = \mathbf{k} = -\mathbf{j} \times \mathbf{i} \qquad \mathbf{j} \times \mathbf{k} = \mathbf{i} = -\mathbf{k} \times \mathbf{j} \qquad \mathbf{k} \times \mathbf{i} = \mathbf{j} = -\mathbf{i} \times \mathbf{k} \qquad (11\text{-}14)$$

Consider now two vectors $\mathbf{A}$ and $\mathbf{B}$ given in terms of their components:

$$\mathbf{A} = A_x\mathbf{i} + A_y\mathbf{j} + A_z\mathbf{k} \qquad \mathbf{B} = B_x\mathbf{i} + B_y\mathbf{j} + B_z\mathbf{k}$$

We form the cross product $\mathbf{C} = \mathbf{A} \times \mathbf{B}$, expressing $\mathbf{A}$ and $\mathbf{B}$ in terms of their components:

$$\mathbf{A} \times \mathbf{B} = (A_x\mathbf{i} + A_y\mathbf{j} + A_z\mathbf{k}) \times (B_x\mathbf{i} + B_y\mathbf{j} + B_z\mathbf{k})$$

The distributive property allows us to multiply out the parentheses, giving nine terms involving cross products of pairs of unit vectors. For example, the terms $A_xB_x\mathbf{i} \times \mathbf{i}$ and $A_zB_y\mathbf{k} \times \mathbf{j}$ appear. We evaluate the cross products using Eqs. (11-14) and obtain

$$\mathbf{A} \times \mathbf{B} = (A_yB_z - A_zB_y)\mathbf{i} + (A_zB_x - A_xB_z)\mathbf{j} + (A_xB_y - A_yB_x)\mathbf{k} \quad (11\text{-}15)$$

Another way to express the result is

$$\mathbf{A} \times \mathbf{B} = \mathbf{C} = C_x\mathbf{i} + C_y\mathbf{j} + C_z\mathbf{k}$$

and, by comparison with Eq. (11-15), the components of $\mathbf{C}$ are given by

$$C_x = A_yB_z - A_zB_y \qquad C_y = A_zB_x - A_xB_z \qquad C_z = A_xB_y - A_yB_x$$

A right-handed coordinate system

Cross products of unit vectors

The cross product in component form

EXAMPLE 11-11. Determine the vector representing the area measured by the surveyor in Example 11-10 by evaluating the cross product in component form. Use a coordinate system with $\mathbf{i}$ directed east and $\mathbf{j}$ directed north; then $\mathbf{k}$ is directed vertically upward.

SOLUTION. From Example 11-10, we determine the components of the displacements: $A_x = 204.56$ m, $A_y = 0$,

$A_z = 0$ and $B_x = (188.32 \text{ m}) \cos 74.82° = 49.31$ m, $B_y = (188.32 \text{ m}) \sin 74.82° = 181.7$ m, $B_z = 0$. Let $\mathbf{C}$ represent the vector area, $\mathbf{C} = \mathbf{A} \times \mathbf{B}$. From Eq. (11-15), the components of $\mathbf{C}$ are

$$C_x = A_yB_z - A_zB_y = (0)(0) - (0)(181.7 \text{ m}) = 0$$

$$C_y = A_zB_x - A_xB_z = (0)(49.31 \text{ m}) - (204.56 \text{ m})(0) = 0$$

$C_z = A_x B_y - A_y B_x$

$= (204.56 \text{ m})(181.7 \text{ m}) - (0)(49.31 \text{ m}) = 37{,}180 \text{ m}^2$

The area measured by the surveyer is represented by

$$\mathbf{C} = (37{,}180 \text{ m}^2)\mathbf{k}$$

Torque as a cross product. The cross product can be used to give a general definition of torque as a vector quantity. Suppose a force $\mathbf{F}$ is applied to an object at a point located by a position vector $\mathbf{r}$ relative to some origin or reference point O, as shown in Fig. 11-20. *The torque exerted by force $\mathbf{F}$ about reference point O is the cross product,*

Torque about a point as a cross product, $\tau = \mathbf{r} \times \mathbf{F}$

$$\boldsymbol{\tau} = \mathbf{r} \times \mathbf{F} \tag{11-16}$$

The magnitude of the cross product is $\tau = rF\sin\theta$, and the direction is given by the right-hand rule to be perpendicular to the plane containing $\mathbf{r}$ and $\mathbf{F}$. If we choose this plane to be the xy plane, then the torque has only a z component and is the same as the torque about this z axis, as defined in Sec. 11-3. For some other choice of a coordinate system, the torque $\boldsymbol{\tau}$ would have components τ_x, τ_y, τ_z. The component τ_x is the torque about the x axis, τ_y is the torque about the y axis, and τ_z is the torque about the z axis.

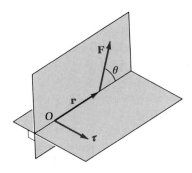

Figure 11-20. A position vector $\mathbf{r}$ locates the point of application of a force $\mathbf{F}$ from a reference point O. The torque about O is defined as $\boldsymbol{\tau} = \mathbf{r} \times \mathbf{F}$.

EXAMPLE 11-12. A 12-kg block of ice in the shape of a cube of edge 0.24 m lies in the first octant of a coordinate system, as shown in Fig. 11-21. Evaluate the torque due to the weight of the block about the corner at the origin.

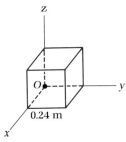

Figure 11-21. Example 11-12: A cubic block of ice has edge 0.24 m. The z axis is vertically upward and the weight is directed downward.

SOLUTION. The center of gravity of the cubic block is halfway along the body diagonal and is located by

$$\mathbf{r}_{cg} = (0.12 \text{ m})\mathbf{i} + (0.12 \text{ m})\mathbf{j} + (0.12 \text{ m})\mathbf{k}$$

The weight has only a z component (vertical) and is

$$\mathbf{F}_e = -mg\mathbf{k} = (-120 \text{ N})\mathbf{k}$$

Using Eq. (11-16), we form the cross product $\boldsymbol{\tau} = \mathbf{r}_{cg} \times \mathbf{F}_e$. Expressing the cross product in component form, we have

$$\tau_x = y_{cg}F_{ez} - z_{cg}F_{ey} = -14 \text{ N} \cdot \text{m}$$

$$\tau_y = z_{cg}F_{ex} - x_{cg}F_{ez} = 14 \text{ N} \cdot \text{m}$$

$$\tau_z = x_{cg}F_{ey} - y_{cg}F_{ex} = 0$$

or

$$\boldsymbol{\tau} = (-14 \text{ N} \cdot \text{m})\mathbf{i} + (14 \text{ N} \cdot \text{m})\mathbf{j}$$

COMMENTARY: CABLES AND BRIDGES

In a suspension bridge such as the Brooklyn Bridge or the Golden Gate Bridge, the graceful curve of a main cable is an essential feature that attracts and holds the eye. These bridges are acknowledged as works of art as well as engineering marvels. Cable-supported bridges can span long distances. For example, the Golden Gate Bridge has two main pylons, or towers, with a central span of 1280 m between them. When such lengths must be spanned, a suspension bridge is often the only feasible type.

The deck, or roadway, is typically connected to the curved main cable by smaller, usually vertical, cables. Some bridges have staying cables, or stays, that

Figure 11-22. The Brooklyn Bridge. Stays radiate fanlike from the pylon. Vertical cables connect the deck to the curved main cables. *(Charles Colby/Photo Researchers)*

are essentially straight and are used instead of curved main cables to support the deck. In other cases, stays are used in addition to curved main cables. A portion of the cable structure of the Brooklyn Bridge is shown in Fig. 11-22. The stays radiate fanlike from the pylon and appear to cross the vertical cables that descend from the curved main cable. According to the designer, John Roebling, "The supporting power of the stays alone will be 15,000 tons, ample to hold up the floor. If the [vertical] cables were removed, the bridge would sink in the center but would not fall."

In treating a cable (or a rope or a string) in this text, we have made the simplifying assumption that the weight of the cable is negligible compared with the tension in it. Hence an ideal cable is assumed to be straight, with the same tension everywhere. In a real cable, the tension varies along its length, and the tension and the curvature are determined by the distribution of the load weight. The weight of the cable itself may be a significant part of the total load. The shape is determined mathematically by requiring each element of the cable to be in static equilibrium. For a uniform, flexible cable supporting only its own weight, the curve is called a common catenary. *This problem was first solved in 1691, largely through the efforts of James Bernoulli. Adding the weight of the deck and including the effects of the rigidity of the spanning truss greatly increase the complexity of the problem. Sophisticated computer programs are now used to perform numerical analyses for building bridges and other structures.*

Since a cable must safely support a large load, special requirements are imposed on cable materials and sizes. A typical cable is composed of steel wires that have a composition different from the steel used for structural beams. As a result, cable steel can support, before breaking, about twice the load, for the same cross-sectional area, as high-strength structural steel. A cable with a large cross section is composed of many steel wires. Typically, a main cable is formed from wires of 5 mm diameter. These wires may be strung one or several at a time along the entire span as the cable is assembled in place during the construction of the bridge. Many passes are required for a large main cable. For example, each main cable of the Golden Gate Bridge contains more than 27,000 wires. The total length of wire used was about 80,000 mi, enough to circle the earth more than three times.

For further reading, see Cable-Supported Bridges *by Niels J. Gimsing (John Wiley & Sons, New York, 1983).*

SUMMARY WITH APPLICATIONS

Section 11-2. Static equilibrium of a rigid body
An extended object is in static equilibrium if every point of that object remains at rest. A rigid body is an object for which the distance between any pair of points on the object remains fixed.

Define static equilibrium; define a rigid body.

Section 11-3. Torque about an axis
Let $\mathbf{r}$ locate the point of application of a force $\mathbf{F}$ on a body. If the plane containing $\mathbf{r}$ and $\mathbf{F}$ is taken as the xy plane, the torque about the z axis is τ_z. The magnitude of the torque is given by $\tau = r_\perp F$. The torque component τ_z is positive if it tends to produce a counterclockwise rotation of the object when viewed from the positive z axis, and τ_z is negative if the tendency of rotation is clockwise.

Determine the torque about an axis due to a force; use the right-hand rule to relate the sign of the torque component τ_z with the sense of the rotation that it tends to cause.

Section 11-4. Conditions for static equilibrium
For a rigid body to be in static equilibrium, both the condition for translational equilibrium, $\Sigma \mathbf{F}_{\text{ext}} = 0$, and the condition for rotational equilibrium about any point, $\Sigma \tau_{\text{ext}} = 0$, must be satisfied. For coplanar forces, these conditions reduce to

$$\Sigma F_{x,\text{ext}} = 0 \qquad \Sigma F_{y,\text{ext}} = 0 \qquad \Sigma \tau_{z,\text{ext}} = 0 \quad (11\text{-}7)$$

where the coplanar forces lie in the xy plane. These equations can be solved for up to three unknowns.

State the conditions for static equilibrium of a rigid body; apply the conditions for the case of coplanar forces.

Section 11-5. Center of gravity
The center of gravity of an extended object is that point at which the full gravitational force on the object can be considered to act. The center of gravity and the center of mass coincide for objects of ordinary size close to the earth's surface.

Define the center of gravity of an object and determine its location.

Section 11-6. Torque and the cross product of vectors
The cross product of two vectors $\mathbf{A}$ and $\mathbf{B}$ is also a vector, $\mathbf{C} = \mathbf{A} \times \mathbf{B}$. The magnitude of $\mathbf{C}$ is $C = AB \sin \theta$, with θ the smaller angle between $\mathbf{A}$ and $\mathbf{B}$. The direction of $\mathbf{C}$ is given by the right-hand rule and is perpendicular to both $\mathbf{A}$ and $\mathbf{B}$. The cross product in component form is

$$\mathbf{A} \times \mathbf{B} = (A_y B_z - A_z B_y)\mathbf{i} + (A_z B_x - A_x B_z)\mathbf{j} + (A_x B_y - A_y B_x)\mathbf{k}$$
$$(11\text{-}15)$$

Torque about a point O is defined as the cross product.

$$\tau = \mathbf{r} \times \mathbf{F} \qquad\qquad (11\text{-}16)$$

Define and evaluate the cross product of two vectors; express the cross product in component form; use the cross product to define the torque about a point.

QUESTIONS

11-1   Give some examples of objects that are rigid bodies, of objects that are not rigid bodies.

11-2   Consider a block of gelatin at rest in a bowl. Does the distance between any pair of points in the block remain the same? What happens if you press on it with a spoon? Is the gelatin a rigid body?

11-3   Because of the load it supports, a steel post has its length shortened by 0.1 percent. Is this post a rigid body?

11-4   Explain how and why an *equal*-arm balance can be used to compare weights. Can it compare masses?

11-5   Explain how and why an *unequal*-arm balance can be used to compare weights.

11-6   Archimedes claimed to be capable of moving the earth, given a lever and a place to stand. Explain the principle behind his claim. Is it a practical claim?

11-7   A playground seesaw has a total length of 3 m and is pivoted at its midpoint. Where and with what force should Uncle press on the board to balance 20-kg Baby at one end of the board?

11-8   Consider an 18-wheel tractor-trailer at rest on a level surface. Is the normal force on each wheel the same for all 18 wheels? What is the sum of the normal forces on the wheels?

11-9   Trucks are weighed at a highway weigh station by adding the scale reading when the front half of the truck is on the scale to the reading when the back half is on the scale. Does this procedure give an accurate measure of the truck's weight? Explain.

11-10   In reference to the preceding question, should a truck be at rest when the scale readings are taken? Should the scale be on level terrain? Explain.

11-11   Suppose you suspend an object from the ceiling by using two wires. One wire is attached to each end of the object, and the wires may have any orientation when attached to the ceiling. What orientation of the wires corresponds to a minimum in the tension of each?

11-12   In Example 11-9, the floor exerts a normal force and a frictional force on the ladder. These two forces can be added to obtain the resultant force $\mathbf{F}_F$ exerted on the ladder by the floor. Is this force directed along the ladder?

11-13   From the equation $\mathbf{A} \times \mathbf{B} = 0$, can you conclude that either $\mathbf{A} = 0$ or $\mathbf{B} = 0$? Explain.

11-14   Suppose that $\mathbf{R}$ and $\mathbf{S}$ are displacements. If $\mathbf{A} = \mathbf{R} \times \mathbf{S}$

is an oriented area element, as shown in Fig. 11-17, what is the interpretation of $\mathbf{S} \times \mathbf{R}$?

11-15   Can a rigid body be in translational equilibrium and rotational equilibrium but not in static equilibrium? Explain.

11-16   Must there be any matter at the center of gravity of an object?

11-17   Give an example of a situation in which the center of gravity and the center of mass of an object do not coincide.

11-18   Does the phrase "center of gravity of the earth" have meaning? Explain.

11-19   The torque exerted by a force about some axis depends on the choice of axis. How can the condition, $\Sigma \tau_{z,\text{ext}} = 0$, be satisfied for *any* choice of axis?

11-20   What are the units of torque and of work in a British system of units in which the lb (pound), the ft (foot), and the s (second), are the basic units?

11-21   Complete the following table:

Symbol	Represents	Type	SI unit
τ_z		Component	
τ			
$\Sigma \tau_{\text{ext}}$			
$\mathbf{A} \times \mathbf{B}$	Cross product of vectors		———
$r_\perp$			m

EXERCISES

Section 11-3. Torque about an axis

11-1   Before finger holes are drilled, a uniform bowling ball of radius 120 mm has its weight of magnitude 65 N acting at its center. Determine the magnitude and direction of the torque exerted by this force about an axis perpendicular to the plane of Fig. 11-23 and passing through point (a) A; (b) B; (c) C; (d) O.

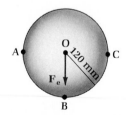

Figure 11-23. Exercise 11-1: A uniform bowling ball.

11-2   Show that the SI unit of torque can be expressed as $\text{kg} \cdot \text{m}^2 \cdot \text{s}^{-2}$.

11-3   Suppose that you hold a 20-kg stone in your hand with your arm extended horizontally from your side. (a) What force does the stone exert on your hand? (b) Estimate the torque due to this force on your hand

about a horizontal axis through your nose and perpendicular to your arm.

11-4   A force $\mathbf{F}$ acts on an object at a point with coordinates (x, y), as shown in Fig. 11-24. Evaluate the torque produced about the z axis by adding the torque components produced separately by F_x and F_y. In this way show that $\tau_z = xF_y - yF_x$.

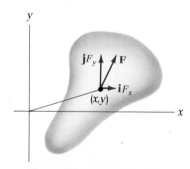

Figure 11-24. Exercise 11-4.

Section 11-4. Conditions for static equilibrium

11-5   A uniform 325-g meter stick is in balance in Fig. 11-25, with the knife edge directly below the midpoint. The

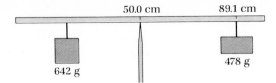

Figure 11-25. Exercise 11-5.

478-g mass is suspended by a light string at the 89.1-cm mark. (*a*) From what point is the 642-g mass suspended? (*b*) What force does the knife edge exert on the stick? (*c*) Would the answers be different if this apparatus were on the moon? In interstellar space?

11-6 Suppose that you weigh 500 N and that you are standing on the board in Example 11-5. Determine the upward normal forces on the board if you are standing (*a*) at the middle of the board and (*b*) at the left-hand end. (*c*) How close can you stand to the right-hand end without tipping the board?

11-7 Estimate the force you must apply to the lever in Fig. 11-26 to move the 2000-N boulder.

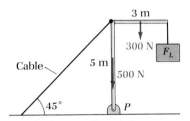

Figure 11-26. Exercise 11-7.

11-8 A load weight $F_L = 900$ N is supported by the boom shown in Fig. 11-27. A pin exerts a force with vertical and horizontal components at *P*. The weight of each section of the structure acts at the midpoint of that section. (*a*) Determine the components of the force exerted by the pin and the tension value in the cable. (*b*) What maximum load F_L can be supported if the cable tension is not to exceed 2500 N?

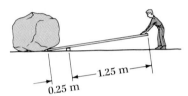

Figure 11-27. Exercise 11-8.

11-9 An 8.0-m horizontal boom supports a 20.0-kN load, as shown in Fig. 11-28. A pin exerts a force on the boom at the left-hand end. (*a*) Neglecting the weight of the boom itself, find the vertical and horizontal components of the pin force and the tension in the cable. (*b*) What is the direction of the pin force?

11-10 Rework the preceding exercise, taking the boom's weight of magnitude 4.0 kN to be acting at its midpoint. Again determine the direction of the pin force

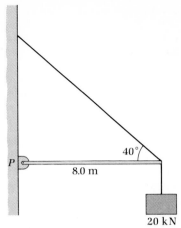

Figure 11-28. Exercise 11-9.

and explain any differences from the earlier result.

11-11 A 30-kN truck-crane on level ground supports a 20-kN load, as shown in Fig. 11-29. (*a*) Determine the normal forces exerted on the front and rear wheels by the ground. (*b*) What minimum load would cause the crane to tip?

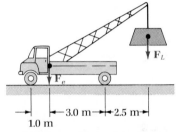

Figure 11-29. Exercise 11-11.

11-12 Rework the preceding exercise, but orient the truck-crane to face uphill on a 20° slope. Explain your assumptions concerning the frictional forces exerted on the wheels.

11-13 A 480-N gate is fastened by two hinges to a post, as shown in Fig. 11-30. The guy wire is drawn up such that the horizontal component of the force exerted by

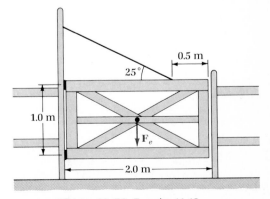

Figure 11-30. Exercise 11-13.

the upper hinge is zero. Evaluate the horizontal component of the force exerted by the lower hinge, the tension in the wire, and the sum of the vertical components of the hinge forces.

11-14 A 4.0-m, 15-kg ladder leans against a smooth wall; the ladder's lower end touches the floor 1.0 m from the wall. The weight of the ladder acts at its midpoint. A 52-kg painter stands on the ladder at a point 1.5 m from its top. Determine (a) the (horizontal) force exerted by the wall, (b) the normal and frictional forces exerted by the floor, and (c) the minimum coefficient of friction needed at the ladder-floor interface to keep the ladder from sliding.

11-15 A uniform disk of radius R rests in contact with a curb of height $h = \frac{1}{2}R$, as shown in Fig. 11-31. A horizontal pull force of magnitude $F_p = F_e/3$ is applied at the center of the disk. Determine in terms of F_e (a) the normal force exerted by the floor and (b) the horizontal and vertical components of the force exerted by the corner on the disk. (c) What is the direction of the force exerted by the corner?

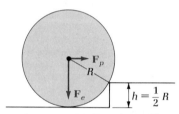

Figure 11-31. Exercise 11-15.

11-16 For the conditions given in the previous exercise, determine the minimum magnitude of the horizontal force F_p necessary to raise the disk over the curb. Express this force in terms of F_e. (*Hint:* What happens to the magnitude of the normal force just as the disk leaves the floor surface?)

11-17 A rigid rod is in static equilibrium as seen in Fig. 11-32, with a horizontal force applied at the midpoint. The weight of the rod may be neglected. The floor exerts normal and frictional forces on the rod. (a) Assuming the rod does not slip, determine the tension in the cable, the static frictional force, and the normal force, all in terms of the value of F_a. (b) Determine the minimum value of μ_s for which the rod does not slip.

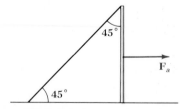

Figure 11-32. Exercise 11-17.

11-18 A 2.5-m footbridge is supported by a pier at each end. The center of gravity of the 120-kg bridge is at its

midpoint. A 60-kg man moves steadily across the bridge. Determine the magnitudes of the upward forces exerted by the piers on the bridge as functions of the position of the man as he moves from one end of the bridge to the other.

Section 11-5. Center of gravity

11-19 Locate the center of gravity of the inverted L-shaped structure shown in Fig. 11-27.

11-20 A uniform, square metal plate of edge 25.0 mm has a square section of edge 5.0 mm cut out, as shown in Fig. 11-33. Locate the center of gravity of this plate.

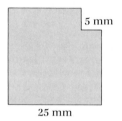

5 mm

25 mm

Figure 11-33. Exercise 11-20.

11-21 A uniform cubic block is placed on a very rough surface so that when the surface is slowly tilted, the block does not slide. At what angle of the ramp will the block tip over?

Section 11-6. Torque and the cross product of vectors

11-22 With respect to a coordinate system centered at point O, a force acts at a point located on the y axis. The torque exerted by this force about point O lies in the xz plane. What can you determine about the direction of this force?

11-23 A force $\mathbf{F} = (174\ \mathrm{N})\mathbf{i} + (203\ \mathrm{N})\mathbf{j} + (-166\ \mathrm{N})\mathbf{k}$ is exerted on an object at a point located by the position vector $\mathbf{r} = (1.35\ \mathrm{m})\mathbf{i} + (-2.22\ \mathrm{m})\mathbf{j}$ from a reference point O. Evaluate the torque exerted by this force about point O.

11-24 Consider three displacements $\mathbf{a}$, $\mathbf{b}$, $\mathbf{c}$, as shown in Fig. 11-34. Show that $\mathbf{a} \cdot (\mathbf{b} \times \mathbf{c})$ equals the volume of the parallelepiped formed by these vectors.

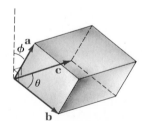

Figure 11-34. Exercise 11-24.

11-25 A tetrahedron has one vertex at the origin and the other three vertices at points (1, 0, 0), (1, 1, 0), and

(1, 1, 1), where all distances are in meters. Determine the volume of the tetrahedron. (*Hint:* See the previous exercise.)

11-26 For each face of the tetrahedron in the previous exercise, find a vector perpendicular to that face and directed out of the enclosed volume.

11-27 (*a*) Using the rules for evaluating an ordinary determinant, show that $\mathbf{A} \times \mathbf{B}$ can be obtained by evaluating

$$\begin{vmatrix} \mathbf{i} & \mathbf{j} & \mathbf{k} \\ A_x & A_y & A_z \\ B_x & B_y & B_z \end{vmatrix}$$

(*b*) Evaluate the cross product for the case $\mathbf{A} = \mathbf{i} + 2\mathbf{j} + 3\mathbf{k}$ and $\mathbf{B} = 2\mathbf{i} - \mathbf{j} - \mathbf{k}$.

11-28 (*a*) Establish the so-called BAC-CAB rule:

$$\mathbf{A} \times (\mathbf{B} \times \mathbf{C}) = \mathbf{B}(\mathbf{A} \cdot \mathbf{C}) - \mathbf{C}(\mathbf{A} \cdot \mathbf{B})$$

(*Hint:* Evaluate the products in terms of components.)
(*b*) If $\mathbf{A}$ is perpendicular to both $\mathbf{B}$ and $\mathbf{C}$, show that $\mathbf{A} \times (\mathbf{B} \times \mathbf{C}) = 0$.

11-29 Consider two nonparallel vectors $\mathbf{A}$ and $\mathbf{B}$ and their cross product $\mathbf{C} = \mathbf{A} \times \mathbf{B}$. If a and b are any two scalars, show that $a\mathbf{A} + b\mathbf{B}$ is perpendicular to $\mathbf{C}$. What is the geometrical interpretation of this result?

11-30 Verify Eqs. (11-14) by evaluating all nine cross products.

11-31 A *couple* consists of two forces that are equal in magnitude F and opposite in direction, with a perpendicular distance d between the lines of action, as shown in Fig. 11-35. Show that the sum of the torques due to the couple about any point is the same for any choice of reference point and is of magnitude Fd.

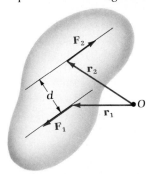

Figure 11-35. Exercise 11-31.

11-32 Suppose that the condition for translational equilibrium of a rigid body is satisfied, $\Sigma\mathbf{F}_{ext} = 0$. Show that the net external torque $\Sigma\boldsymbol{\tau}_{ext}$ is independent of the reference point about which torques are evaluated. This proves that if $\Sigma\boldsymbol{\tau}_{ext} = 0$ about one point, then $\Sigma\boldsymbol{\tau}_{ext} = 0$ about any point, so long as $\Sigma\mathbf{F}_{ext} = 0$.

PROBLEMS

11-1 A uniform 350-N, 8.0-m ladder leans against a smooth wall, with the ladder's lower end on the floor 2.5 m from the wall. The coefficient of static friction at the floor is $\mu_s = 0.21$. A painter weighing 440 N begins climbing the ladder slowly. How far up the ladder can she climb before the ladder begins to slide?

11-2 The normal force exerted on an object by a surface is actually a sum of a large number of such forces distributed over the area of contact of the two surfaces. The effective point of application of the full normal force is such that the torque is the same as that produced by the distributed normal forces. A horizontal force of magnitude $F_p = \frac{1}{3}F_e$ is applied at the top of the uniform cubic block shown in Fig. 11-36. (*a*) Locate the effective point of application of the normal

force, assuming that the block does not slide. (*b*) What is the minimum value of the coefficient of static friction?

11-3 Rework the previous problem, but suppose that the magnitude F_p of the horizontal force is increased. Assuming that the block does not slide, determine the value of F_p that will cause the block to tip over. What is the minimum value of the coefficient of static friction to keep the block from sliding?

11-4 The irregularly shaped object of length L and weight of magnitude F_e shown in Fig. 11-37 is in static equilibrium, with two light strings attached as indicated.

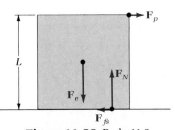

Figure 11-36. Prob. 11-2.

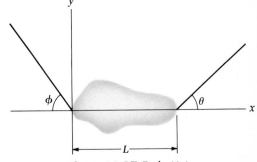

Figure 11-37. Prob. 11-4.

Determine the x coordinate of the center of gravity of the object and the tension in each string in terms of F_e, L, θ, and ϕ.

11-5 Two uniform boards are hinged together at one end to form a right angle as shown in Fig. 11-38. One board has length 3.0 m and weight of magnitude 120 N, and the other board has length 4.0 m and weight of magnitude 160 N. The combination rests in contact with a smooth floor and a light, horizontal cable is strung between the boards at a height of 1.0 m from the floor. Determine (*a*) the normal force exerted by the floor on each board, (*b*) the tension in the cable, (*c*) the force that one board exerts on the other at the hinged apex A.

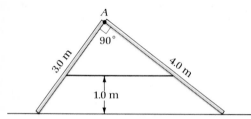

Figure 11-38. Prob. 11-5.

11-6 Figure 11-39 shows a horizontal forearm supporting a 100-N stone. Using your own arm as a model for numerical values, estimate the force exerted on the forearm by (*a*) the biceps muscle and (*b*) the upper arm bone at the elbow. (*c*) How sensitive are your answers to your estimates of where the biceps is attached, where the center of gravity of the hand-forearm is located, and the weight of the hand-forearm?

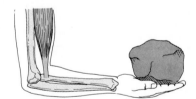

Figure 11-39. Prob. 11-6.

11-7 A simple crane is shown supporting a 15-kN load in Fig. 11-40. The center of gravity of the 7.5-m, 2.5-kN boom is 3.0 m, as measured along the boom from the lower end, which is pinned at P. Cable C can be drawn up by a winch to change the elevation angle of the boom. (*a*) Determine the tension in cable C and the components of the pin force at P on the boom for

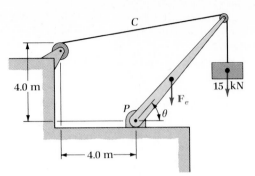

Figure 11-40. Prob. 11-7.

$\theta = 30°$. (*b*) Repeat for $\theta = 60°$ and compare the answers for these two angles.

11-8 ***The law of sines.*** Consider the triangle formed by vectors **A**, **B**, and $\mathbf{C} = \mathbf{A} + \mathbf{B}$, as seen in Fig. 11-41. By forming the cross products $\mathbf{A} \times \mathbf{C}$ and $\mathbf{B} \times \mathbf{C}$, prove the *law of sines*:

$$\frac{\sin \alpha}{A} = \frac{\sin \beta}{B} = \frac{\sin \gamma}{C}$$

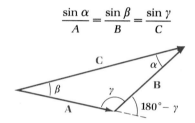

Figure 11-41. Prob. 11-8.

11-9 Prove the identity $\mathbf{A} \cdot (\mathbf{B} \times \mathbf{C}) = (\mathbf{A} \times \mathbf{B}) \cdot \mathbf{C}$.

11-10 Consider the three vectors **u**, **v**, **w** with

$$\mathbf{u} = \frac{\mathbf{i} + \mathbf{j}}{\sqrt{2}} \qquad \mathbf{v} = \frac{-\mathbf{i} + \mathbf{j}}{\sqrt{2}} \qquad \mathbf{w} = \mathbf{k}$$

(*a*) Show that each of these is a unit vector. (*b*) Show that the three vectors are mutually perpendicular. (*c*) Evaluate the cross product of each pair of these vectors. (*d*) If an *xyz*-coordinate system is set up with *x*, *y*, *z* axes along the directions of **u**, **v**, **w**, in that order, is this coordinate system right-handed?

11-11 A schematic diagram of the Cavendish balance, used for measuring the gravitational constant G, is shown in Fig. 7-7. Estimate the torque about the suspension-fiber axis due to the gravitational force between the pairs of spheres. Assume that the distance between spheres a and b is 15 cm, that spheres a and b have mass 0.25 kg and radius 2 cm, and that spheres A and B have mass 2.0 kg and radius 3.5 cm.

CHAPTER 12
ROTATION I

12-1 INTRODUCTION

In our everyday activities, we often encounter objects that rotate—such as a door on its hinges, a pulley on its axle, or a phonograph record on a turntable. The earth is involved in two rotational motions: It spins on its axis once a day and it orbits the sun once a year. At the level of atoms and molecules, both spin and orbital motion play important roles in the properties of matter. When we discuss these properties in later chapters, an understanding of rotational motion is crucial. We now begin a two-chapter sequence about the rotation of rigid objects. This chapter is mostly about *rotational kinematics,* and the next chapter discusses *rotational dynamics.*

The earth spins on its axis and orbits the sun. This photograph was taken from Apollo 17 during its voyage to the moon. *(N.A.S.A.)*

Riding an escalator. These people are undergoing translational motion. *(F. Keller)*

12-2 TRANSLATION AND ROTATION OF A RIGID OBJECT

Before discussing rotation, it is helpful to clearly state what is meant by translational motion. An example of translational motion is the motion of the body of a car as the car travels along a straight road. A rigid object executes *translational motion* when each particle of the object has the same displacement in the same time interval.

Definition of translational motion

An example of rotational motion is the motion of a door being opened or closed, and a line along the hinges is the axis of rotation. A rigid object executes *rotational motion* when each particle of the object (except those on the axis of rotation) travels in a circle (Fig. 12-1). The *axis of rotation* is a straight line that consists of the centers of the circular motion of the particles. For a rotating rigid object, a line drawn perpendicular to the axis of rotation to any particle sweeps out the same angle in the same time interval as any other such line.

Definitions of rotational motion and axis of rotation

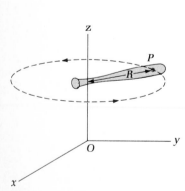

Figure 12-1. Each particle in a rotating rigid object travels in a circle centered at the axis of rotation, except those particles that are on the axis.

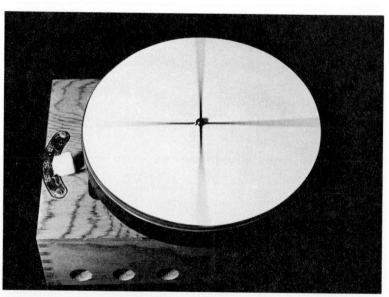

This phonograph turntable is undergoing rotational motion. *(Tom Richard)*

An example of translational and rotational motion combined is the motion of a moving car's wheel relative to a coordinate frame fixed to the earth. Relative to this frame the axis of rotation of the wheel (along the wheel's axle) executes translational motion along the road. If the road is straight, the orientation of the wheel's axis remains fixed relative to this coordinate frame.

A completely general motion of a rigid object involves changes in the orientation of the axis of rotation as well as translation of this axis. An example is a wobbly pass of a football. The ball rotates about an instantaneous axis, but since the throw is wobbly, the orientation of the axis, as well as its position, changes. In this chapter, we restrict our discussions to the rotation of a rigid object about an axis that maintains a fixed orientation.

12-3 ANGULAR MEASUREMENT

You are familiar with measuring angles in degrees. However, a more convenient unit to use for rotational motion is the SI unit, the radian (rad). In Fig. 12-2, the angle θ in rad between the x axis and the line segment OP is defined as the ratio s/R, where s is measured along the arc from the x axis to P and R is the radial distance from O to P:

Definition of angle θ in radians

$$\theta = \frac{s}{R} \qquad (12\text{-}1)$$

where s and R are measured in the same unit of length.

For a full circle, s is the circle's circumference, so that $s = 2\pi R$. Therefore,

$$\theta(\text{full circle}) = \frac{2\pi R}{R} = 2\pi \text{ rad}$$

Since $\theta(\text{full circle}) = 360°$, we have

$$2\pi \text{ rad} = 360° \qquad \text{or} \qquad \pi \text{ rad} = 180°$$

Thus 1 rad $= 180°/\pi \approx 57.3°$. As an example, let us convert an angle of 64° to rad:

$$64° = 64° \frac{\pi \text{ rad}}{180°} = 1.1 \text{ rad}$$

Another way to measure an angle is in terms of revolutions (rev), cycles, or rotations. All three terms refer to one full circle: 1 rev = 1 cycle = 1 rotation. Thus

$$1 \text{ rev} = 360° = 2\pi \text{ rad} \qquad \text{(exactly)}$$

Revolutions are often used when discussing angular speeds. For example, we refer to a 45-rpm (rev/min) phonograph turntable. Converting 64° to rev, we have

$$64° = 64° \frac{1 \text{ rev}}{360°} = 0.18 \text{ rev}$$

Although angular measurements have these three commonly used units (rad, °, and rev), angle is a dimensionless quantity. It is defined in terms of the ratio of lengths. When performing calculations with angular quantities, you will find it useful to write the angular unit along with the numerical value, as we have been doing for other quantities.

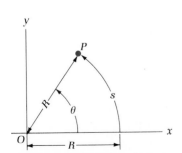

Figure 12-2. Definition of angular measure in rad. The same length unit is used to measure both s and R.

12-4 ANGULAR COORDINATE, VELOCITY, AND ACCELERATION

The quantities we use to describe the rotational motion of a rigid object about a fixed axis are the object's angular coordinate θ, angular velocity ω, and angular acceleration α. As we define these angular quantities, you will find it helpful to recall the analogous linear quantities. As you shall see, the kinematics of a rigid object rotating about a fixed axis is mathematically similar to that of a particle moving along a straight line (Chap. 3).

Angular coordinate θ. The *angular coordinate* of a garden gate can be measured as shown in Fig. 12-3. We let the z axis be along the hinges and let the xy plane be the plane of the ground, with the x axis along the fence and the y axis perpendicular to the fence. The angular coordinate θ of the gate is measured from the x axis to the gate. When the gate is closed, $\theta = 0$. When the gate is open, its angular coordinate is measured in a counterclockwise sense from the x axis when viewed from the positive z direction (that is, from above). Hence, an angle measured counterclockwise is positive, and an angle measured clockwise is negative. A right-hand rule gives the positive sense for θ (Fig. 12-4). If you imagine grasping the z axis with your right hand so that your thumb points in the $+z$ direction, your fingers curl in the positive θ sense.

A major distinction between the angular coordinate θ and the linear coordinate x is that θ is cyclic. That is, the angular coordinates θ and $\theta + 2\pi$ represent the same angular position (Fig. 12-5). More generally, if n is any positive or negative integer, then θ and $\theta + n(2\pi)$ represent the same angular position. Ordinarily values of θ are adjusted so that they fall in the range from 0 to 2π rad or from $-\pi$ rad to π rad.

Angular speed and angular velocity. The *angular speed* ω is the magnitude of the rate of change of the angular coordinate:

$$\omega = \left| \frac{d\theta}{dt} \right|$$

The *angular velocity* ω is a vector whose magnitude is the angular speed and whose direction gives the sense of the rotation. The right-hand rule provides

The right-hand rule gives the positive θ sense.

Angle θ is cyclic.

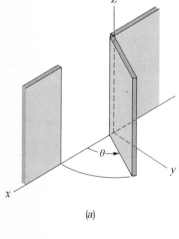

(a)

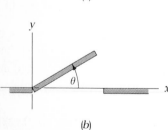

(b)

Figure 12-3. (a) Angular coordinate θ of a garden gate. (b) View from above, looking down onto the xy plane from the $+z$ direction. Angular coordinate θ is positive for counterclockwise rotation and negative for clockwise rotation.

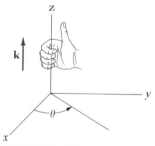

Figure 12-4. The right-hand rule. When you grasp the z axis with your right hand such that your thumb points in the $+z$ direction, your fingers curl in the positive sense for θ.

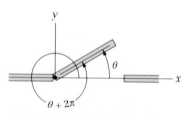

Figure 12-5. The angular coordinate is cyclic; the coordinates θ and $\theta + n(2\pi)$ rad represent the same angular position, where n is any positive or negative integer.

the connection between the sense of the rotation and the direction of $\boldsymbol{\omega}$. If you imagine grasping the axis of rotation with your right hand such that your fingers curl in the sense of the rotation, then your thumb points in the direction of $\boldsymbol{\omega}$. Again, looking down on the gate in Fig. 12-3, $\boldsymbol{\omega}$ is toward $+z$ if the rotation is counterclockwise, and $\boldsymbol{\omega}$ is toward $-z$ if the rotation is clockwise. This means that for an object rotating about the z axis, $\boldsymbol{\omega} = \omega_z\mathbf{k}$, and ω_z is positive for counterclockwise rotation and negative for clockwise rotation. Thus ω_z is positive when θ is increasing and negative when θ is decreasing. Therefore,

Definition of the angular velocity component

$$\omega_z = \frac{d\theta}{dt} \tag{12-2}$$

Particles move in planes perpendicular to $\boldsymbol{\omega}$.

Notice that when an object is rotating about a fixed axis, as shown in Fig. 12-3, none of the particles in the rotating object moves along the axis of rotation, which, by our definition, is the direction we have chosen for $\boldsymbol{\omega}$. Rather, the motion of the particles is contained in planes perpendicular to $\boldsymbol{\omega}$. Why should we assign the direction of $\boldsymbol{\omega}$ to be along a direction in which no particles move? The answer is that the axis of rotation provides a direction in space that can be uniquely associated with the motion. As a particle circles the axis of rotation, all directions in the plane of its motion are equivalent, so that no direction contained in this plane can be used to describe the motion. Thus $\boldsymbol{\omega}$ is taken to be perpendicular to the plane of motion, or parallel to the axis of rotation. We then have a choice between the two opposite directions along the axis for assigning the positive direction of $\boldsymbol{\omega}$. By custom, the positive direction of $\boldsymbol{\omega}$ is determined by the right-hand rule.

Since the angular coordinate θ is dimensionless, angular velocity $\boldsymbol{\omega}$ has the dimension time^{-1}, and since the SI unit for θ is the rad, the SI unit for $\boldsymbol{\omega}$ is rad/s.

EXAMPLE 12-1. Figure 12-6 shows a phonograph turntable rotating steadily at 45 rev/min in the clockwise sense

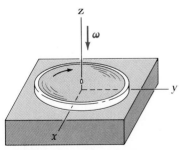

Figure 12-6. Example 12-1: A rotating phonograph turntable. The z axis passes through the spindle with $+z$ upward, and the x and y axes are fixed relative to the desktop. Viewed from above, the turntable rotates in the clockwise sense so that ω_z is negative.

when viewed from above. The z axis is along the axis of rotation, with $+z$ upward. The x and y axes are horizontal and fixed relative to the desk on which the turntable mechanism rests. Using this coordinate frame, determine ω_z in units of rad/s.

SOLUTION. Converting $\boldsymbol{\omega}$ from rev/min to rad/s, we have

$$\omega = 45 \text{ rev/min} \frac{2\pi \text{ rad/rev}}{60 \text{ s/min}} = 4.7 \text{ rad/s}$$

Using the right-hand rule (Fig. 12-4), we see that the turntable is rotating such that the direction of $\boldsymbol{\omega}$ is downward. That is, if you grasp the axis of rotation with your right hand such that your fingers curl in the sense of the rotation, then your thumb points downward. Thus ω_z is negative, so that

$$\omega_z = -4.7 \text{ rad/s}$$

Angular acceleration. Immediately after a phonograph turntable is switched on (or off), the angular velocity of the turntable changes and it has an angular acceleration $\boldsymbol{\alpha}$. The angular acceleration is a vector whose direction is along the axis of rotation. If the z axis is chosen as the axis of rotation, then the angular acceleration has only one component, $\boldsymbol{\alpha} = \alpha_z\mathbf{k}$. The angular acceleration component is defined as the time rate of change of the angular velocity component:

Definition of the angular acceleration component

$$\alpha_z = \frac{d\omega_z}{dt} = \frac{d^2\theta}{dt^2} \tag{12-3}$$

Thus α_z is positive when ω_z is increasing, and α_z is negative when ω_z is decreasing. The magnitude of the angular acceleration is $\alpha = |\boldsymbol{\alpha}| = |\alpha_z|$. Angular acceleration has the dimension of time^{-2}, and the SI unit rad/s^2.

Each particle of a rotating rigid
object has the same values of ω_z
and α_z.

Although we have defined the angular kinematical quantities (θ, $\boldsymbol{\omega}$, and $\boldsymbol{\alpha}$) by considering a rotating rigid object, these quantities can be used to describe the motion of a particle traveling in a circle. In a rotating rigid object, each particle of the object (except those on the axis of rotation) travels in a circle, and each particle has the same $\boldsymbol{\omega}$ and $\boldsymbol{\alpha}$.

Notice that the relationships involving θ, ω_z, and α_z for a rotating rigid object are analogous to those of x, v_x, and a_x for a particle moving along a straight line.

12-5 KINEMATICS OF ROTATION ABOUT A FIXED AXIS

As we have seen, the quantities that describe the motion of a rigid object rotating about a fixed axis are mathematically similar to those for a particle moving along a straight line. We now discuss two special cases: constant angular velocity and constant angular acceleration. The equations we develop in this section are analogous to those developed in Sec. 3-5.

Constant angular velocity. Consider an object, such as the turntable seen in Fig. 12-6, rotating with a constant angular velocity. From Eq. (12-2), we have

$$\frac{d\theta}{dt} = \omega_z$$

Integrating from an initial time zero to a final time t gives θ as a function of t:

$$\theta - \theta_0 = \int_0^t \omega_z \, dt' = \omega_z \int_0^t dt' = \omega_z t$$

where ω_z is factored out of the integral because it is constant. Thus

Angle θ as a function of time,
constant ω_z

$$\theta(t) = \theta_0 + \omega_z t \tag{12-4}$$

EXAMPLE 12-2. (a) Give the equation that describes the angular position of the turntable in Fig. 12-6 when it is rotating at a constant speed of 45 rev/min. The initial angular coordinate is $\theta_0 = 1.2$ rad. (b) Determine θ at $t = 2.4$ s.

SOLUTION. (a) From Example 12-1, we have $\omega_z =$ -4.7 rad/s. Substituting this value and $\theta_0 = 1.2$ rad into Eq. (12-4), we have

$$\theta(t) = 1.2 \text{ rad} - (4.7 \text{ rad/s})t$$

(b) At $t = 2.4$ s,

$$\theta = 1.2 \text{ rad} - (4.7 \text{ rad/s})(2.4 \text{ s}) = -10 \text{ rad}$$

Constant angular acceleration. Suppose an object, such as the garden gate in Fig. 12-3, rotates with a constant angular acceleration as it swings open. From Eq. (12-3),

$$\frac{d\omega_z}{dt} = \alpha_z$$

Integrating from an initial time zero to a final time t gives ω_z as a function of t:

$$\omega_z - \omega_{z0} = \int_0^t \alpha_z \, dt' = \alpha_z \int_0^t dt' = \alpha_z t$$

where α_z is factored out of the integral because it is constant. Thus

$$\omega_z(t) = \omega_{z0} + \alpha_z t \qquad (12\text{-}5)$$

Angular velocity component ω_z as a function of time, constant α_z

Substituting this value of ω_z into Eq. (12-2), we have

$$\frac{d\theta}{dt} = \omega_z = \omega_{z0} + \alpha_z t$$

Integrating from an initial time zero to a final time t gives θ as a function of t:

$$\theta - \theta_0 = \int_0^t (\omega_{z0} + \alpha_z t')dt' = \omega_{z0}\int_0^t dt' + \alpha_z \int_0^t t' \, dt'$$

where ω_{z0} and α_z are factored out of the integrals. (Why?) The integration gives $\theta - \theta_0 = \omega_{z0}t + \frac{1}{2}\alpha_z t^2$, or

$$\theta(t) = \theta_0 + \omega_{z0}t + \tfrac{1}{2}\alpha_z t^2 \qquad (12\text{-}6)$$

Angle θ as a function of time, constant α_z

By eliminating the time t between Eqs. (12-5) and (12-6) (see Exercise 12-16), you can show that

$$\omega_z{}^2 = \omega_{z0}{}^2 + 2\alpha_z(\theta - \theta_0) \qquad (12\text{-}7)$$

Angular velocity component ω_z as a function of θ, constant α_z

Table 12-1 lists the equations which describe rotation with constant angular velocity and constant angular acceleration. Also given in the table are the analogous expressions for a particle moving along a straight line. This comparison shows the similarity between these two types of motion.

Table 12-1. Analogy between translation and rotation

Translation (one dimension)	Rotation (fixed axis)
Constant linear velocity	Constant angular velocity
$x = x_0 + v_x t$	$\theta = \theta_0 + \omega_z t$
Constant linear acceleration	Constant angular acceleration
$v_x = v_{x0} + a_x t$	$\omega_z = \omega_{z0} + \alpha_z t$
$x = x_0 + v_{x0}t + \frac{1}{2}a_x t^2$	$\theta = \theta_0 + \omega_{z0}t + \frac{1}{2}\alpha_z t^2$
$v_x{}^2 = v_{x0}{}^2 + 2a_x(x - x_0)$	$\omega_z{}^2 = \omega_{z0}{}^2 + 2\alpha_z(\theta - \theta_0)$

EXAMPLE 12-3. Suppose that after being switched off, the turntable in Example 12-1 slows to a stop in a time interval of 1.7 s. (a) Find an equation for the turntable's angular coordinate as a function of time while it is slowing to a stop, assuming that the angular acceleration is constant. Let $t = 0$ correspond to the instant the turntable is turned off, and let θ_0 be zero. (b) Through what angular coordinate does the turntable rotate while coming to a stop?

SOLUTION. (a) Using Eq. (12-5) to find α_z gives

$$\alpha_z = \frac{\omega_z - \omega_{z0}}{t}$$

Since the turntable comes to rest in 1.7 s, $\omega_z = 0$ when $t = 1.7$ s, and from Example 12-1, $\omega_{z0} = -4.7$ rad/s. Therefore,

$$\alpha_z = \frac{0 - (-4.7 \text{ rad/s})}{1.7 \text{ s}} = 2.8 \text{ rad/s}^2$$

Substituting into Eq. (12-6) gives

$$\theta(t) = -(4.7 \text{ rad/s})t + (1.4 \text{ rad/s}^2)t^2$$

(b) Since $\theta_0 = 0$ and the turntable stops in 1.7 s, the angle through which the turntable rotates in coming to a stop is

$$\theta(1.7 \text{ s}) = -(4.7 \text{ rad/s})(1.7 \text{ s}) + (1.4 \text{ rad/s}^2)(1.7 \text{ s})^2$$
$$= -3.9 \text{ rad}$$

12-6 RELATIONS BETWEEN ANGULAR AND LINEAR VELOCITY AND ANGULAR AND LINEAR ACCELERATION

Consider a gate swinging open as shown in Fig. 12-7. Imagine that the gate consists of many small pieces, each small enough to be considered a particle. Because the gate is rigid, each particle has the same angular velocity ω and angular acceleration α. Thus ω and α characterize the motion of the entire gate. However, particles with different distances from the axis of rotation have different linear velocities **v** and linear accelerations **a**. We now establish the connection between the angular velocity and angular acceleration of the gate on the one hand, and the linear velocity and linear acceleration of a particle P in the gate on the other.

As before, we let the ground compose the xy plane and place the origin directly below the hinges, so that the z axis is the axis of rotation (Fig. 12-8). Particle P travels in a circle of radius R, and can be located relative to the x axis by the *arc coordinate s* measured along the arc. The sign convention for s is the same as for θ: Viewed from above, s is positive in the counterclockwise sense and negative in the clockwise sense. We define the *tangential component of the velocity* of P as

$$v_t = \frac{ds}{dt}$$

Thus v_t is positive when s increases with time (counterclockwise rotation) and is negative when s decreases with time (clockwise rotation). With this definition, v_t has the same algebraic sign as ω_z. Further, since $s = R\theta$, we have

$$v_t = \frac{ds}{dt} = \frac{d(R\theta)}{dt} = R\frac{d\theta}{dt}$$

Or,
$$v_t = R\omega_z \tag{12-8}$$

Since particle P travels in a circle, its velocity **v** has a tangential component only and its speed v is $v = |\mathbf{v}| = |v_t| = R|\omega_z|$, or

$$v = R\omega \tag{12-9}$$

For a given angular speed ω, the linear speed of a particle is proportional to its distance R from the axis of rotation. Suppose the gate is rotating at an angular speed of 0.5 rad/s. A particle 0.2 m from the axis of rotation has a linear speed of (0.2 m)(0.5 rad/s) = 0.1 m/s, and a particle 0.4 m from the axis of rotation has a linear speed of (0.4 m)(0.5 rad/s) = 0.2 m/s.

Now we resolve the linear acceleration **a** into tangential and radial components, as shown in Fig. 12-9. The tangential component a_t of the linear accelera-

Tangential velocity component

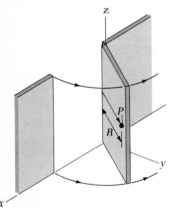

Figure 12-7. A garden gate is swinging open. Each particle in the gate has the same angular velocity and angular acceleration, but particles with different distances from the axis of rotation have different linear velocities and linear accelerations.

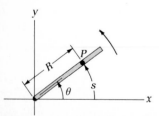

Figure 12-8. Top view of the gate in Fig. 12-7. A particle at radius R can be located with the arc coordinate s. The sign convention for s is similar to that for θ, so $s = R\theta$.

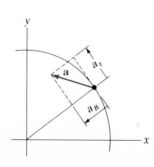

Figure 12-9. Tangential and radial components of the linear acceleration. The radial component $a_R = v^2/R$ corresponds to the projection of **a** along the radial line. This projection is always inward. The tangential component a_t corresponds to the projection of **a** tangent to the circle. This projection may be counterclockwise $(a_t > 0)$ or clockwise $(a_t < 0)$.

tion of a particle traveling in a circle is defined as the time derivative of the tangential component of the linear velocity:

Tangential acceleration component

$$a_t = \frac{dv_t}{dt} = \frac{d}{dt}(R\omega_z) = R\frac{d\omega_z}{dt}$$

Since $\alpha_z = d\omega_z/dt$, we have $\qquad a_t = R\alpha_z$ (12-10)

Similar to v_t, a_t for the particle is proportional to its distance R from the axis of rotation.

In Sec. 4-4 we found that a particle traveling in a circle at constant speed v has an acceleration of magnitude v^2/R directed toward the center of the circle (along a radial line). This is the centripetal acceleration. In the present case, where the speed may vary, the quantity v^2/R represents one component of the linear acceleration, the component which corresponds to the projection of **a** toward the center of the circle (Fig. 12-9). We call this component the *radial*

Radial acceleration component

component a_R of the linear acceleration, $a_R = v^2/R$. We can write a_R in terms of the angular speed ω by using Eq. (12-9) to substitute for v: $a_R = v^2/R = (R\omega)^2/R$, or

$$a_R = R\omega^2$$ (12-11)

As with v_t and a_t, a_R for a particle is proportional to the particle's distance R from the axis of rotation.

Since a_t and a_R are components of **a** along perpendicular directions (Fig. 12-9), the pythagorean theorem gives

$$a = \sqrt{a_t^2 + a_R^2}$$

Using Eqs. (12-10) and (12-11), we have $a_t^2 = R^2\alpha_z^2 = R^2\alpha^2$ and $a_R^2 = R^2\omega^4$, so

$$a = \sqrt{R^2\alpha^2 + R^2\omega^4} = R\sqrt{\alpha^2 + \omega^4}$$

Thus the magnitude a of the linear acceleration of a particle is proportional to the particle's distance R from the axis of rotation.

Figure 12-10 shows the linear velocity and linear acceleration for the case where ω_z (and v_t) is positive. In Fig. 12-10a, α_z (and a_t) is positive; in Fig. 12-10b, α_z (and a_t) is zero; and in Fig. 12-10c, α_z (and a_t) is negative. You may wish to draw the corresponding figures for the case where ω_z is negative.

When using Eqs. (12-8), (12-9), and (12-11), be certain that you insert the

Figure 12-10. The directional relationships between **v**, **a**, ω, and α for a particle in circular motion about the z axis when $\omega_z > 0$; (a) $\alpha_z > 0$; (b) $\alpha_z = 0$; (c) $\alpha_z < 0$.

values of ω and ω_z in the SI unit rad/s, and not in °/s or rev/s. These equations are based on the expression $s = R\theta$. If the same unit is used to measure s and R, then θ is in rad. Similarly, when using Eq. (12-10), you should insert α_z in the SI unit rad/s².

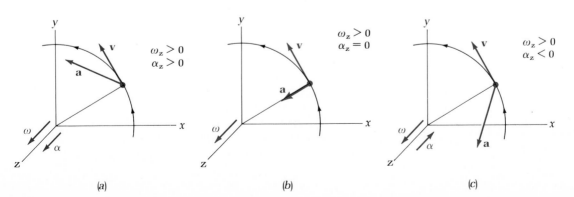

(a)   (b)   (c)

EXAMPLE 12-4. A child is riding on a playground merry-go-round at a distance of 2.1 m from the vertical axis of rotation. At a particular instant the merry-go-round is rotating clockwise when viewed from above, with an angular speed of 0.42 rad/s and this angular speed is decreasing such that $\alpha = 0.14$ rad/s². For the child, determine (a) v_t, (b) a_t, (c) a_R, and (d) a. Let the xy plane be horizontal, and let the z axis be along the axis of rotation with +z upward.

SOLUTION. (a) Since the merry-go-round is rotating clockwise, ω_z is negative: $\omega_z = -0.42$ rad/s. Thus

$$v_t = R\omega_z = (2.1 \text{ m})(-0.42 \text{ rad/s}) = -0.88 \text{ m/s}$$

(b) To find a_t, we need α_z. We know that $\alpha = |\alpha_z| =$ 0.14 rad/s², but we must find the sign of α_z. The angular speed ω is decreasing, and ω_z is negative. Thus ω_z is increasing, because a negative quantity is increasing when its magnitude is decreasing. Since α_z is positive when ω_z is increasing, $\alpha_z = 0.14$ rad/s². From Eq. (12-10),

$$a_t = R\alpha_z = (2.1 \text{ m})(0.14 \text{ rad/s}^2) = 0.29 \text{ m/s}^2$$

(c) From Eq. (12-11)

$$a_R = \omega^2 R = (0.42 \text{ rad/s})^2(2.1 \text{ m}) = 0.37 \text{ m/s}^2$$

(d) The magnitude a of the child's acceleration is

$$a = R\sqrt{\alpha^2 + \omega^4} = 2.1 \text{ m }\sqrt{(0.14 \text{ rad/s}^2)^2 + (0.42 \text{ rad/s})^4}$$

$$= 0.47 \text{ m/s}^2$$

12-7 ROTATIONAL KINETIC ENERGY: MOMENT OF INERTIA

When a wheel rotates, there is kinetic energy associated with the rotation. The wheel consists of many small particles, and the kinetic energy of a particle, say particle i with mass m_i and speed v_i, is $\frac{1}{2}m_i v_i^2$. The kinetic energy K of the entire wheel is the sum of the kinetic energies of all the particles that compose the wheel:

$$K = \Sigma \tfrac{1}{2}m_i v_i^2$$

Particles that are different distances from the axis of rotation have different linear speeds v_i, but, because the wheel is rigid, each particle has the same angular speed ω. (This fact is indicated by the lack of a subscript i on the ω.) Using $v_i = R_i\omega$, we can write the kinetic energy of the wheel as

$$K = \Sigma \tfrac{1}{2}m_i R_i^2 \omega^2$$

Two factors contained in this sum are the same for every term; they are the 1/2 and the ω^2. Therefore, we can take these factors outside of the summation:

$$K = \tfrac{1}{2}\omega^2(\Sigma m_i R_i^2)$$

The quantity $\Sigma m_i R_i^2$ is called the *moment of inertia I*:

Definition of the moment of inertia
$$I = \Sigma m_i R_i^2 \tag{12-12}$$

The moment of inertia has the dimension (mass)(length)², and its SI unit is kg · m². We shall discuss the moment of inertia in more detail in the next section.

In terms of the moment of inertia, the kinetic energy of a rotating object is

Rotational kinetic energy
$$K = \tfrac{1}{2}I\omega^2 \tag{12-13}$$

If we compare the expression for rotational kinetic energy with $K = \frac{1}{2}mv^2$ for translation, then I is the rotational analog of the mass m, and ω is the rotational analog of the speed v. As a brief example, suppose a door, whose moment of inertia I about its hinges is $I = 8.2$ kg · m², is rotating with an angular speed of $\omega = 0.71$ rad/s. The door's rotational kinetic energy is

$$K = \tfrac{1}{2}(8.2 \text{ kg} \cdot \text{m}^2)(0.71 \text{ rad/s})^2 = 2.1 \text{ kg} \cdot \text{m}^2/\text{s}^2 = 2.1 \text{ J}$$

12-8 MOMENT OF INERTIA

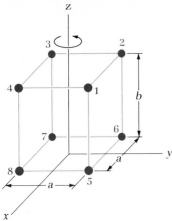

Figure 12-11. An array of eight particles, each with mass m, held together by rigid rods of negligible mass. The z axis passes through the center of the array and is parallel to the edges of length b. About the z axis, $I = 4ma^2$, and about an axis through particles 3 and 7, $I = 8ma^2$. The moment of inertia depends on how the mass is distributed relative to the axis of rotation.

Before proceeding further, we should strengthen our understanding of this new concept, the moment of inertia. We can discover some general features of the moment of inertia by considering the array of eight particles shown in Fig. 12-11. Each particle has the same mass m, and they are held fixed, relative to each other, by rods of negligible mass. First we determine the moment of inertia about an axis through the center of the array and parallel to the side with dimension b, shown as the z axis in the figure:

$$I = \Sigma m_i R_i^2 = m_1 R_1^2 + m_2 R_2^2 + \cdots + m_8 R_8^2$$

Each particle is the same distance from the axis of rotation:

$$R = \sqrt{(\tfrac{1}{2}a)^2 + (\tfrac{1}{2}a)^2} = \frac{a}{\sqrt{2}}$$

Thus

$$I = m\left(\frac{a}{\sqrt{2}}\right)^2 + m\left(\frac{a}{\sqrt{2}}\right)^2 + \cdots + m\left(\frac{a}{\sqrt{2}}\right)^2 = 8m\left(\frac{a}{\sqrt{2}}\right)^2 = 4ma^2$$

Next consider the moment of inertia of this array about an axis parallel to the z axis that passes through particles 3 and 7. The distance from this axis to particles 1 and 5 is $R_1 = R_5 = \sqrt{a^2 + a^2} = \sqrt{2}a$; to particles 2, 4, 6, and 8 is $R_2 = R_4 = R_6 = R_8 = a$; and to particles 3 and 7 is $R_3 = R_7 = 0$. Thus

$$I = \Sigma m_i R_i^2 = 2m(\sqrt{2}a)^2 + 4m(a)^2 + 2m(0)^2 = 8ma^2$$

For rotation about the axis through the center, $I = 4ma^2$, but for rotation about the axis through particles 3 and 7, $I = 8ma^2$. We have found that, unlike the mass, the moment of inertia is not an intrinsic property of a system. Rather, it depends on the mass of the system *and* on the location of the axis of rotation. Notice that I depends strongly on the distribution of mass perpendicular to the axis; if a is doubled, I is quadrupled. However, I is independent of the mass distribution parallel to the axis; it is independent of the dimension b in the array in Fig. 12-11.

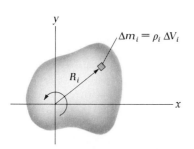

Figure 12-12. Moment of inertia of a continuous object about the z axis. The $+z$ direction is out of the page.

Moment of inertia of a continuous object. In finding the moment of inertia of a continuous object, such as a pulley or a wheel, we imagine the object to consist of many small pieces, each small enough to be considered a particle (Fig. 12-12). The mass of each piece is $\Delta m_i = \rho_i \Delta V_i$, where ρ_i is the mass density of the material and ΔV_i is the small volume occupied by the piece. Thus

$$I = \Sigma \, \Delta m_i R_i^2 = \Sigma \rho_i \, \Delta V_i R_i^2$$

As the volume ΔV_i approaches an infinitesimal dV, the sum transforms into an integral:

$$I = \lim_{\Delta V_i \to 0} \Sigma \rho_i \, \Delta V_i R_i^2 = \int_V \rho R^2 \, dV$$

Thus the moment of inertia of a continuous object is

Moment of inertia of a continuous object

$$I = \int_V \rho R^2 \, dV \tag{12-14}$$

where the integration is over the volume of the object. If the density is uniform, then ρ can be taken out of the integral:

$$I = \rho \int_V R^2 \, dV$$

EXAMPLE 12-5. (a) Find the moment of inertia of a door of uniform mass density ρ about an axis along its hinges. The door has mass M, height h, width w, and thickness b. Assume that the thickness of the door is much smaller than its width. (b) Evaluate this moment of inertia for a door of mass 27.3 kg and width 0.95 m.

SOLUTION. (a) The door is shown in Fig. 12-13. We choose as our element of volume a thin strip of height h, thickness b, and infinitesimal width dx. This element of volume is chosen because all of the mass within such a strip is approximately the same distance x from the axis through the hinges. This approximation is valid because the door's thickness is small compared with its width. Substituting $dV = hb \, dx$, and $R^2 = x^2$ into Eq. (12-14) and factoring the constants ρ, h, and b out of the integral, we have

$$I = \rho h b \int_0^w x^2 \, dx$$

Performing the integration gives

$$I = \frac{\rho h b w^3}{3}$$

Since $\rho = M/V = M/hbw$, we have $\rho hbw = M$. Thus

$$I = \frac{M w^2}{3}$$

The height of the door does not appear in the final answer. Thus this answer is valid for a door of any height. For that matter, it is also the expression for the moment of inertia of a stick of length w about an axis perpendicular to the stick and

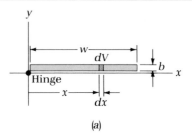

(a)

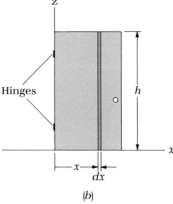

(b)

Figure 12-13. Example 12-5: (a) Top view of the door. The $+z$ direction is out of the page. (b) Front view of the door. Since $w \gg b$, nearly all the mass in dV is the same distance from the axis.

passing through one end. (b) Substituting $M = 27.3$ kg and $w = 0.95$ m, we have

$$I = \frac{(27.3 \text{ kg})(0.95 \text{ m})^2}{3} = 8.2 \text{ kg} \cdot \text{m}^2$$

EXAMPLE 12-6. Find the moment of inertia of a hollow right circular cylinder for rotation about its symmetry axis. Let the cylinder have inner radius R_1, outer radius R_2, height h, and uniform mass density ρ, as shown in Fig. 12-14.

SOLUTION. We choose as our element of volume a thin cylindrical shell of height h, circumference $2\pi R$, and infinitesimal thickness dR (Fig. 12-14), $dV = h2\pi R \, dR$. This element is chosen because all the mass within such an element is essentially the same distance from the axis of rotation. Substituting this value of dV into Eq. (12-14) and factoring constants out of the integral gives

$$I = 2\pi \rho h \int_{R_1}^{R_2} R^3 \, dR$$

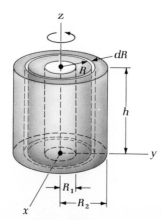

Figure 12-14. Example 12-6: Calculating the moment of inertia of a hollow cylinder. The mass within the volume element $dV = 2\pi Rh \, dR$ is essentially all at a distance R from the z axis. All the mass of the cylinder is contained between the values R_1 and R_2 of the integration variable R.

The limits on the integral are determined by the value of R within which the mass is contained. Performing the integration gives

$$I = \tfrac{1}{2}\pi\rho h(R_2{}^4 - R_1{}^4)$$

We wish to express this in terms of the mass of the cylinder, so we rewrite I as

$$I = \tfrac{1}{2}\pi\rho h(R_2{}^2 - R_1{}^2)(R_2{}^2 + R_1{}^2)$$

The volume V of the hollow cylinder is the product of its height times the area of its base:

$$V = h\pi(R_2{}^2 - R_1{}^2)$$

Its mass M is

$$M = \rho V = \rho h\pi(R_2{}^2 - R_1{}^2)$$

Therefore,

$$I = \tfrac{1}{2}M(R_2{}^2 + R_1{}^2)$$

The moment of inertia for objects with two other shapes can be found from the answer to the above example.

1. The moment of inertia of a solid cylinder of radius R_0 for rotation about its symmetry axis is found by setting the inner radius R_1 equal to zero and setting the outer radius R_2 equal to R_0. This gives

$$I = \tfrac{1}{2}MR_0{}^2$$

This equation is also valid for a disk-shaped object such as a phonograph record (neglecting the hole) and for a long thin object such as a log with uniform radius.

2. The moment of inertia of a thin cylindrical shell of radius R_0 for rotation about its symmetry axis is found by using the approximation that $R_1 \approx R_0$ and $R_2 \approx R_0$. This gives

$$I = MR_0{}^2$$

This equation is valid both for a hula hoop, and for a thin-walled pipe.

Table 12-2 gives moments of inertia for objects with various shapes about axes that pass through the center of mass.

Table 12-2. Some representative moments of inertia. In each case the density is uniform and the axis of rotation is through the center of mass. (a) Thin-walled cylinder. (b) Thin-walled cylinder. (c) Thin-walled hollow sphere. (d) Solid cylinder. (e) Solid cylinder. (f) Solid sphere. (g) Thick-walled hollow cylinder. (h) Long, thin rod. (i) Rectangular plate.

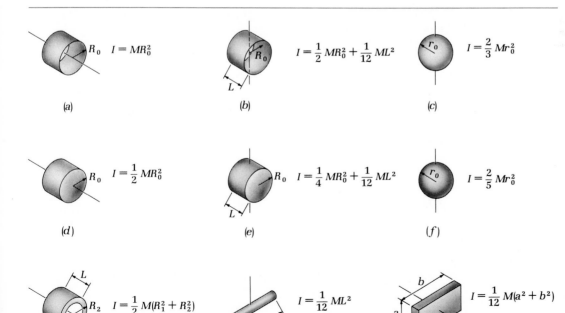

(a) $R_0 \quad I = MR_0^2$

(b) $R_0 \quad I = \dfrac{1}{2}MR_0^2 + \dfrac{1}{12}ML^2$

(c) $r_0 \quad I = \dfrac{2}{3}Mr_0^2$

(d) $R_0 \quad I = \dfrac{1}{2}MR_0^2$

(e) $R_0 \quad I = \dfrac{1}{4}MR_0^2 + \dfrac{1}{12}ML^2$

(f) $r_0 \quad I = \dfrac{2}{5}Mr_0^2$

(g) $R_2, R_1 \quad I = \dfrac{1}{2}M(R_1^2 + R_2^2)$

(h) $I = \dfrac{1}{12}ML^2$

(i) $b, a \quad I = \dfrac{1}{12}M(a^2 + b^2)$

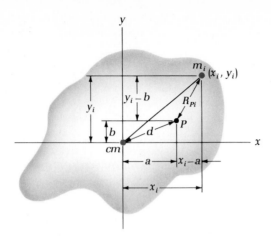

Figure 12-15. The parallel-axis theorem. The z axis passes through the center of mass and is parallel to the rotational axis that passes through point P (the $+z$ direction is out of the page). The moment of inertia I_P about the axis through P is $I_P = I_{cm} + Md^2$, where d is the distance between the axes.

Parallel-axis theorem. Calculating the moment of inertia of an object about an axis that is not an axis of symmetry can be very complex. Fortunately, there is an easily applicable theorem that helps do this, the *parallel-axis theorem*. This theorem provides a relation between the moment of inertia I_P about an axis through an arbitrary point P and the moment of inertia I_{cm} about a parallel axis through the object's center of mass.

Consider the moment of inertia of the arbitrarily shaped object shown in Fig. 12-15 about an axis that passes through the point P. In this figure, the z axis passes through the center of mass and is parallel to the rotational axis through P. Since the z axis passes through the center of mass, $x_{cm} = 0$ and $y_{cm} = 0$. The distance between the two parallel axes is $d = \sqrt{a^2 + b^2}$. From Eq. (12-12), the moment of inertia I_P about an axis through P is

$$I_P = \Sigma m_i R_{Pi}{}^2 = \Sigma m_i[(x_i - a)^2 + (y_i - b)^2]$$

where R_{Pi} is the distance from the axis (through P) to particle i. Multiplying out the squared terms gives

$$I_P = \Sigma m_i(x_i{}^2 + y_i{}^2) - 2a\Sigma m_i x_i - 2b\Sigma m_i y_i + (a^2 + b^2)\Sigma m_i$$

where we have factored out of the summations the quantities that are the same in each term of the sums. In the above equation, the term $\Sigma m_i(x_i{}^2 + y_i{}^2)$ is the moment of inertia I_{cm} of the object about the axis through the center of mass (the z axis) because x_i and y_i are measured relative to the axis through the center of mass:

$$I_{cm} = \Sigma m_i(x_i{}^2 + y_i{}^2)$$

From Sec. 10-2, the center of mass is defined such that $\Sigma m_i x_i = Mx_{cm}$ and $\Sigma m_i y_i = My_{cm}$. This means that our choice of coordinate frame causes the second and third terms to be zero: $\Sigma m_i x_i = Mx_{cm} = 0$ and $\Sigma m_i y_i = My_{cm} = 0$. The fourth term, $(a^2 + b^2)\Sigma m_i$, equals Md^2 because $\Sigma m_i = M$ and $a^2 + b^2 = d^2$. Therefore,

The parallel-axis theorem

$$I_P = I_{cm} + Md^2 \tag{12-15}$$

which is the parallel-axis theorem.

EXAMPLE 12-7. Table 12-2 gives the moment of inertia of a uniform thin rod about an axis through the center of mass and perpendicular to the rod's long axis. Determine the moment of inertia of the rod about an axis parallel to the axis described above and passing through a point P at one end, as shown in Fig. 12-16.

SOLUTION. Using Eq. (12-15),we have

$$I_P = I_{cm} + Md^2 = \frac{ML^2}{12} + M\left(\frac{L}{2}\right)^2 = \frac{ML^2}{3}$$

Compare this result with the solution in Example 12-5.

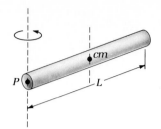

Figure 12-16. Example 12-7: Using the parallel-axis theorem to find the moment of inertia of a uniform thin rod about an axis perpendicular to the rod's length and passing through one end (P).

12-9 ROLLING OBJECTS

So far we have discussed objects that rotate about a fixed axis only. Now we consider an object that rolls, such as a wheel or a ball. For simplicity, we consider an object with a circular cross section that rolls without sliding along a straight line. In this case the axis of rotation undergoes translation, but it maintains a fixed orientation.

When an object rolls without sliding, there is a simple connection between the linear speed v of its center and the rotational speed ω about an axis through its center. Figure 12-17 shows a rolling wheel of radius R at a time t_i and a later time t_f. The distance Δx moved by the center of the wheel in a given time interval Δt is equal to the distance Δs moved by the point of contact along the wheel's edge: $\Delta x = \Delta s$. If v is the linear speed of the center of the wheel and ω is the angular speed about the axis of rotation, then

$$v = \frac{\Delta x}{\Delta t} = \frac{\Delta s}{\Delta t} = R\frac{\Delta \theta}{\Delta t} = R\omega$$

Rolling without sliding

For rolling without sliding, we have

$$v = R\omega \tag{12-16}$$

Now we find the kinetic energy of a rolling object. Figure 12-18 shows that such an object rotates about an axis that passes through the point of contact P between the object and the surface on which it is rolling. This axis has a fixed

Figure 12-17. Rolling without sliding. In the time interval Δt, the center of the wheel moves a distance Δx, which is equal to the distance Δs that the point of contact moves along the wheel's edge: $\Delta x = \Delta s$. Thus $v = \Delta x/\Delta t = \Delta s/\Delta t = R\,\Delta\theta/\Delta t = R\omega$.

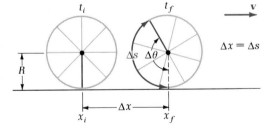

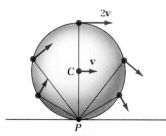

Figure 12-18. A rolling object at any instant is rotating about an axis through the point of contact P. The linear velocity of any particle is perpendicular to a line from P to the particle, and the particle's linear speed is proportional to the length of that line.

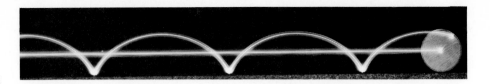

orientation parallel to the surface and perpendicular to the direction of motion. Since no sliding occurs, the point of contact P is *instantaneously* at rest, and the axis of rotation of the object instantaneously passes through that point (Fig. 12-19). In Fig. 12-18, the velocities of several points on the object are shown. The velocities are directed perpendicular to a line from P and have magnitudes proportional to the lengths of those lines. For example, the velocity of the point at the top of the object is $2\mathbf{v}$, twice the velocity of the center.

Note that the angular speed ω_P about an axis through P is equal to the angular speed ω_C about an axis through C, because the speed of C relative to P is $\omega_P R$ and the speed of P relative to C is $\omega_C R$. Thus $\omega_P R = \omega_C R$, and consequently we drop the subscripts: $\omega = \omega_P = \omega_C$.

The kinetic energy of the object is

$$K = \tfrac{1}{2}I_P\omega^2$$

where I_P is the moment of inertia of the object about an axis perpendicular to the direction of motion, parallel to the surface, and through P. If the object has a symmetric distribution of mass about an axis through C, then C corresponds to the center of mass, and the parallel-axis theorem gives

$$K = \tfrac{1}{2}(I_{cm} + Md^2)\omega^2$$

where I_{cm} is the moment of inertia of the object about an axis perpendicular to the direction of motion, parallel to the surface, and through C. The distance d between these two axes is the radius R. Since the object rolls without sliding, $v = \omega R$, or $\omega = v/R$. This gives $K = \tfrac{1}{2}I_{cm}\omega^2 + \tfrac{1}{2}M(R)^2(v/R)^2$, or

Kinetic energy of a rolling object

$$K = \tfrac{1}{2}I_{cm}\omega^2 + \tfrac{1}{2}Mv^2 \qquad (12\text{-}17)$$

Thus the kinetic energy of a rolling object can be expressed as the sum of two terms: One term corresponds to rotation about the center of mass, and the other corresponds to translation of the center of mass.

The velocity of a particle in a rolling object may also be regarded as being the result of a combination of pure translation and pure rotation of the object, as illustrated in Fig. 12-20. In particular, notice how the velocity of the particle at point A on the rolling object is the vector sum of the velocities at A due to pure translation and pure rotation.

We should mention that Eq. (12-17) is valid when the object rolls with partial sliding, even though we developed it assuming no sliding. However, in this

Figure 12-20. The linear velocity of a particle of a rolling object may be regarded as a combination of a linear velocity that is the same as that of the axis (pure translation) and a linear velocity due to the particle's rotation about the axis (pure rotation).

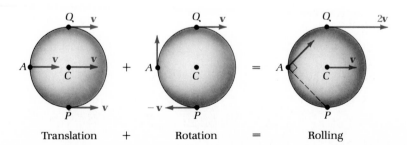

Translation   +   Rotation   =   Rolling

case $v \neq \omega R$. The only restriction on Eq. (12-17) is that the axis of rotation must maintain a fixed orientation.

EXAMPLE 12-8. (*a*) Develop an equation for the speed of an object that rolls from rest down a hill without sliding, as shown in Fig. 12-21. Assume that nonconservative forces, such as air resistance, are negligible. (*b*) Using the answer from part (*a*), find the speed of a basketball after it rolls from rest down a hill. The ball's vertical drop is $h = 2.3$ m.

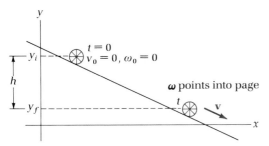

Figure 12-21. Example 12-8: An object rolling from rest down a straight slope.

SOLUTION. (*a*) Since nonconservative forces are negligible, we use conservation of mechanical energy (Sec. 9-5):

$$K_f + U_f = K_i + U_i$$

$$\tfrac{1}{2}Mv_f^2 + \tfrac{1}{2}I_{cm}\omega_f^2 + Mgy_f = \tfrac{1}{2}Mv_i^2 + \tfrac{1}{2}I_{cm}\omega_i^2 + Mgy_i$$

Since the object starts from rest, $v_i = 0$ and $\omega_i = 0$. Also, we let $v_f = v$, $\omega_f = \omega$, and $y_i - y_f = h$. Rearranging terms gives

$$Mgh = \tfrac{1}{2}Mv^2 + \tfrac{1}{2}I_{cm}\omega^2$$

This equation states that the decrease in potential energy, as the object rolls down the hill, is equal to its increase in ki-

netic energy. Substituting $\omega = v/R$ and solving for v, we obtain

$$v = \sqrt{\frac{2gh}{1 + I_{cm}/MR^2}}$$

From Sec. 3-6, the speed of a particle after falling a vertical distance h from rest, neglecting friction, is $v = \sqrt{2gh}$. Similarly, this is the expression for the speed of a block sliding down a slope without friction. Therefore, since part of the kinetic energy of a rolling object is rotational kinetic energy, its speed after a given vertical drop is less than that of an object that has only a translational part to its kinetic energy. The amount that the speed is decreased due to the rolling depends on the ratio I_{cm}/MR^2: The larger this ratio, the smaller will be the speed for a given vertical drop h. For the objects listed in Table 12-2 that have spherical or cylindrical symmetry, this ratio is independent of both M and R, because I_{cm} about the symmetry axes of these objects is proportional to MR^2. Therefore, the speed of such a rolling object is independent of either its mass or its radius, but depends only on how its mass is distributed about an axis perpendicular to the direction of motion, parallel to the surface, and through the center of mass.

(*b*) A basketball can be treated approximately as a spherical shell (Table 12-2). Substituting $I_{cm} = 2Mr_0^2/3 = 2MR^2/3$ gives

$$v = \sqrt{\frac{6gh}{5}} = \sqrt{\frac{6(9.8 \text{ m/s}^2)(2.3 \text{ m})}{5}} = 5.2 \text{ m/s}$$

What would be the speed of the basketball if it slid without friction down the slope?

COMMENTARY: THE USE OF MODELS IN PHYSICS

The word "model" evokes a vision of a dollhouse or a scaled-down replica of an airplane. But to a physicist, a model is an idealized mental picture of a physical system or natural phenomenon. We have already used several models in this book. For example, when we discussed projectile motion in Sec. 4-3, we treated a ball launched into the air as a particle and neglected the effect of air resistance. In Chap. 7 we developed a model of the solar system. In this chapter, we treated a rolling ball as a rigid object and neglected frictional effects, which dissipate energy.

A good model has three desirable attributes: simplicity, agreement with experiment, and generality. To ensure simplicity, we comply with a rule of parsimony: In developing a model, use the simplest conceivable assumptions that are consistent with observation and logic. Therefore, a model builder must glean all nonessential details from the description of a phenomenon — the de-

tails which would cause the calculations to become unwieldy or overly complex. The key to constructing a good model is determining which details are nonessential.

A model is created by using approximations that are valid within some realm. Ordinarily, the validity of a model begins to break down as the model is extended beyond the realm of its origin. Indeed, a model's usefulness depends greatly on how far it can be extended.

Often it is more important for a model to give the correct functional dependence of one physical quantity on another than for it to provide precise numerical results. For example, in Sec. 4-3 we found that the projectile model neglecting air resistance predicted that the range is maximum when the angle of projection θ_0 is 45°; decreasing θ_0 when $\theta_0 < 45°$ decreases the range, and increasing θ_0 when $\theta_0 > 45°$ also decreases the range. For a thrown baseball, the angle for maximum range is somewhat less than 45°. However, an angle θ_{0m} for maximum range of a thrown baseball does exist. The success of this prediction is more important than the precision of the numerical value.

Some important models you will see in subsequent chapters are a model of a gas, a model of a metal, a model of light, a model of an atom, and a model of a nucleus.

SUMMARY WITH APPLICATIONS

Section 12-2. Translation and rotation of a rigid object

In translational motion, all the particles in a rigid object have the same displacement in the same time interval. In rotational motion, all the particles in a rigid object execute circular motion about the axis of rotation.

Compare and contrast translational and rotational motion.

Section 12-3. Angular measurement

The SI unit of angle, the rad, is defined as $\theta = s/R$, where s and R are measured with the same length unit.

Define the rad as the SI unit of angle.

Section 12-4. Angular coordinate, velocity, and acceleration

Angular kinematical quantities are the angular coordinate θ, the angular velocity component $\omega_z = d\theta/dt$, and the angular acceleration component $\alpha_z = d\omega_z/dt$. The right-hand rule is used to define the positive sense for rotation.

Define the angular kinematic quantities.

Section 12-5. Kinematics of rotation about a fixed axis

The kinematics of a rigid object rotating about a fixed axis is analogous to that of a particle moving in a straight line. The equations which describe constant angular velocity and constant angular acceleration are listed in Table 12-1.

Determine the expressions that describe rotation with constant angular velocity and rotation with constant angular acceleration.

Section 12-6. Relations between angular and linear velocity and angular and linear acceleration

For a particle in a rotating rigid object, the relation between the linear and angular velocity components are

$$v_t = R\omega_z \qquad (12\text{-}9)$$

The linear acceleration components are

$$a_t = R\alpha_z \qquad (12\text{-}10)$$

$$a_R = R\omega^2 \qquad (12\text{-}11)$$

Determine the relation between the linear kinematic quantities and the angular kinematic quantities for a particle in a rotating rigid object.

Section 12-7. Rotational kinetic energy: moment of inertia

The rotational kinetic energy of a rigid object is

$$K = \tfrac{1}{2}I\omega^2 \qquad (12\text{-}13)$$

where the moment of inertia is

$$I = \Sigma m_i R_i^2 \qquad (12\text{-}12)$$

Determine the expression for rotational kinetic energy and define the moment of inertia.

Section 12-8. Moment of inertia

The moment of inertia of a continuous object is

$$I = \int_V \rho R^2 \, dV \qquad (12\text{-}14)$$

The moment of inertia of an object about an axis parallel to an axis through the center of mass is given by the parallel-axis theorem:

$$I_P = I_{cm} + Md^2 \qquad (12\text{-}15)$$

Use the definition of the moment of inertia to develop expressions for moments of inertia; use the parallel-axis theorem.

Section 12-9. Rolling objects

The axis of rotation of a rolling object undergoes translation. The kinetic energy of a rolling object can be written

$$K = \tfrac{1}{2}I_{cm}\omega^2 + \tfrac{1}{2}Mv^2 \qquad (12\text{-}17)$$

Use rotational and translational quantities to describe the motion of a rolling object.

QUESTIONS

12-1 When is it particularly useful to measure angles in rad? When is the angular unit of measure unimportant?

12-2 Are all angular measurements dimensionless, regardless of the units?

12-3 What is the path of a particle in a rigid object rotating about a fixed axis?

12-4 How would you define a fixed axis of rotation of a rigid object in terms of the motion of the particles that compose the object?

12-5 If a rigid object has only translational motion (for example, the body of a car traveling in a straight line on a flat road), are there any points within the object that always have the same velocity as the center of mass? If so, which ones?

12-6 If a rigid object has only rotational motion about a fixed axis (for example, a swinging door), are there any points within the object that always have the same velocity as the center of mass? If so, which ones?

12-7 If a rigid object moves with both translation and rotation about an axis with a fixed orientation (for example, a rolling wheel), are there any points within the object that always have the same velocity as the center of mass? If so, which ones?

12-8 If a rigid object moves with both translation and rotation about an axis that is not fixed (for example, a football during a wobbly pass), are there any points within the object that always have the same velocity as the center of mass? If so, which ones?

12-9 Suppose you have a meter stick and a dime. How would you measure the angle subtended by the moon at the earth? Does it require less arithmetic to find the angle in degrees or in rad? Which angular unit would you say is easier to use in this case?

12-10 If we imagine looking down on the solar system from Polaris (the North Star), both the earth's orbital motion around the sun and its rotation on its axis are in a counterclockwise sense. When is your linear speed with respect to the sun the greater, at night or during the day?

12-11 What is the direction of the angular velocity of a rigid object rotating about a fixed axis? What is the direction of the linear velocity of a particle in a rigid object rotating about a fixed axis?

12-12 A rigid object rotating about a fixed axis has nonzero angular velocity and angular acceleration. Particle *A* in the object is twice as far from the axis of rotation as particle *B*. What is the ratio of the following quantities for *A* and *B*: (*a*) the angular speeds, (*b*) the linear speeds, (*c*) the magnitudes of the angular accelerations, (*d*) the tangential components of the accelerations, (*e*) the radial components of the accelerations, (*f*) the magnitudes of the linear accelerations?

12-13 Do the angular velocities of the hands of a wall clock point into the wall or out of the wall? At the instant the clock is unplugged, do the angular accelerations of the hands point into the wall or out of the wall?

12-14 Consider a particle on the end of the second hand of a wall clock at the instant the hand passes the 12 just after the clock is plugged in (such that the hand's angular speed is increasing). Let the origin of coordinates be at the center of the clock, with the *z* axis pointing out of the wall along the axis of rotation, the *x* axis pointing horizontally toward the 3, and the *y* axis pointing vertically upward toward the 12. Which cartesian components of the linear velocity and linear acceleration of the particle are zero? What is the algebraic sign of the nonzero components? Which cartesian components of the angular velocity and angular acceleration are zero? What is the algebraic sign of the nonzero components?

12-15 A car is moving forward and slowing down. Is the direction of the angular velocity of the wheels toward the driver's left or right? What is the direction of the angular acceleration of the wheels?

12-16 Can an object have more than one moment of inertia? Other than an object's shape and mass, what information must be given to find its moment of inertia?

12-17 One side of a door (Fig. 12-22) is made of material with a larger mass density than the other side. To minimize the moment of inertia about an axis of rotation along the hinges, should the hinges be placed at the heavier side or the lighter side? Explain.

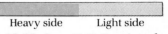

Heavy side   Light side

Figure 12-22. Ques. 12-17: Top view of a door.

12-18 Consider three rods made of the same material and with the same length and mass, but with different cross-sectional shapes (Fig. 12-23). Which of the three has the largest moment of inertia about an axis through the center of mass and along the rod's long axis? Which rod has the smallest moment of inertia about that axis?

Figure 12-23. Ques. 12-18: Cross section of three rods.

12-19 Is it possible to find an axis of rotation (call the axis *A*) about which the moment of inertia for an object is smaller than the moment of inertia about an axis through the center of mass and parallel to *A*?

12-20 Suppose you allow the following objects, starting from rest, to roll down the same straight slope at the same instant: a basketball, a billiard ball, a hollow can with the ends removed, a soccer ball, and a bowling ball. Which do you expect will reach the bottom first? Which do you expect will reach the bottom last? Do you expect any ties? Assume that mechanical energy is conserved.

12-21 Suppose you are designing a cart for coasting down a hill. To maximize your coasting speed, should you design the wheels so that their moments of inertia about their rotation axes are large or small, or does it matter? Keeping the moment of inertia of the wheels fixed, will the cart's speed be increased or decreased by increasing the mass of the cart's body? Assume that mechanical energy is conserved.

12-22 Two similar barrels *A* and *B* with the same radius and mass roll down the same slope starting at the same instant. Barrel *A* is filled with liquid water, and barrel *B* is filled with ice of equal mass. (Barrel *B* is slightly longer than barrel *A* to compensate for the slightly larger density of liquid water.) Which barrel reaches the bottom of the slope first? Explain.

12-23 Complete the following table:

Symbol	Represents	Type	SI unit
θ			
ω		Vector	
ω_z		Component	
α_z			
v_t			m/s
a_t			
a_R			
I	Moment of inertia		

EXERCISES

Section 12-3. Angular measurement

12-1 Determine the angle between the 12 and the 4 on the face of a clock in (*a*) rad, (*b*) degrees, and (*c*) revolutions.

12-2 The diameter of the sun subtends an angle of 0.53° at the earth. (*a*) Convert this angle to rad. (*b*) Given that the radius of the earth's orbit is 1.5×10^{11} m, estimate the diameter of the sun.

12-3 The knob of a door is 0.84 m from an axis through the hinges. (*a*) Determine the distance the knob moves when the door rotates through an angle of 35°. (*b*) Determine the distance the knob moves when the door rotates through an angle of 0.61 rad.

12-4 When a dime (diameter = 18 mm) is held at a distance of 2 m from one's eye, it just barely obscures one's view of the moon. What is the angle subtended by the moon's diameter at the earth in (*a*) rad and (*b*) degrees? (*c*) During a lunar eclipse, the shadow of the earth is cast on the moon. From observations of such eclipses, the ancient Greeks knew that the moon's diameter is about 1/4 that of the earth's. Using this information, estimate the earth-moon distance in units of earth radii.

12-5 Determine the distance the earth's center of mass travels relative to the sun in 1 day. The radius of the earth's orbit is 1.5×10^{11} m.

Section 12-4. Angular coordinate, velocity, and acceleration

12-6 In the following list of angular coordinates, which, if any, corresponds to the same angular position? 48.69 rad, −27.38 rad, 36.20 rad, 67.54 rad.

12-7 Find the angular speed of a 78-rev/min turntable in rad/s.

12-8 A Ferris wheel rotating steadily makes 1 revolution every 7.6 s. The riders face west and are moving forward when at the top. What is the wheel's angular velocity (magnitude and direction)?

12-9 Suppose $\theta(t) = -(1.4 \text{ rad/s}^3)t^3 + (6.8 \text{ rad})$. Find (*a*) $\omega_z(t)$; (*b*) $\omega_z(2.1 \text{ s})$; (*c*) $\omega(2.1 \text{ s})$; (*d*) $\theta(2.1 \text{ s})$.

12-10 Suppose $\omega_z(t) = (2.3 \text{ rad/s}^4)t^3 - (7.5 \text{ rad/s}^3)t^2$. Find (*a*) $\alpha_z(t)$; (*b*) $\alpha_z(1.6 \text{ s})$; (*c*) $\alpha(1.6 \text{ s})$; (*d*) $\omega_z(1.6 \text{ s})$; (*e*) $\omega(1.6 \text{ s})$.

Section 12-5. Kinematics of rotation about a fixed axis

12-11 Write an equation for $\theta(t)$ for a phonograph turntable rotating steadily at 33 rev/min. Use the ordinary coordinate frame with $+\mathbf{k}$ upward and the xy plane horizontal, and let $\theta_0 = 0$.

12-12 A gear begins rotating from rest with a constant angular acceleration of magnitude 0.21 rad/s². What is its angular speed after completing (*a*) 1 rev, (*b*) 2 rev, (*c*) 4 rev?

12-13 A wheel rotates about a fixed horizontal axis that is aligned east-west. If the $+\mathbf{k}$ direction is toward the west, the wheel's angular velocity component is given by

$$\omega_z(t) = 5.8 \text{ rad/s} - (2.2 \text{ rad/s}^2)t$$

(*a*) What is the angular acceleration component? (*b*) Write an equation for $\theta(t)$, with θ_0 set equal to zero. (*c*) Find the time t_q at which the angular velocity is zero. (*d*) What is the direction of a particle's linear velocity at the top of the wheel before t_q and after t_q. (*e*) Write an equation for $\omega_z{}^2$ as a function of θ.

12-14 A wheel with a fixed axis of rotation along the vertical rotates with constant angular acceleration. At $t = 0$ the wheel is rotating at 17 rev/s in the counterclockwise direction when viewed from above, and 6.2 s later it is rotating at 11 rev/s in the counterclockwise direction when viewed from above. Develop equations for (*a*) $\omega_z(t)$ and (*b*) $\theta(t)$ using a coordinate frame with the z axis as the axis of rotation and $+\mathbf{k}$ upward. (*c*) Develop an equation for $\omega_z{}^2$ as a function of θ. Use SI units.

12-15 The front door of a north-facing house swings inward, and the hinges are on the west side of the door frame. The door is opened starting from rest at the closed position such that its angular acceleration is constant and its angular speed is 1.4 rad/s at the instant it is opened an angle of 0.72 rad. Letting $+\mathbf{k}$ point upward along the hinges and $\theta = 0$ correspond to the closed position, develop equations for (*a*) $\omega_z(t)$, (*b*) $\theta(t)$, and (*c*) $\omega_z{}^2$ as a function of θ.

12-16 Develop Eq. (12-7) by eliminating the time t between Eqs. (12-5) and (12-6).

Section 12-6. Relations between angular and linear velocity and angular and linear acceleration

12-17 The tip of the second hand on a clock is 93 mm from the axis of rotation. What is the linear speed of the tip?

12-18 (*a*) Determine the earth's angular speed about the sun in rad/s. (*b*) Determine the linear speed of the center of the earth relative to the sun. The earth-sun distance is 1.5×10^{11} m.

12-19 A child riding on a merry-go-round is 1.4 m from the axis of rotation. (*a*) Determine the magnitudes of the tangential and radial components of the child's linear acceleration at the instant the merry-go-round's angular speed is 0.34 rad/s and its angular acceleration has a magnitude of 0.18 rad/s². (*b*) What is the child's linear speed and the magnitude of his linear acceleration?

12-20 Wheels A and C are connected by belt B which does not slip (Fig. 12-24); $R_A = 250$ mm and $R_C = 410$ mm. Find the angular speed of wheel A at the instant the angular speed of wheel C is 1.7 rad/s.

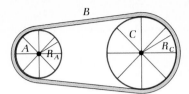

Figure 12-24. Exercise 12-20: Wheels A and C connected by belt B.

Section 12-7. Rotational kinetic energy: Moment of inertia

12-21 Show that the quantity $\frac{1}{2}I\omega^2$ has (*a*) the dimension of energy and (*b*) the SI unit of J (joule).

12-22 The moment of inertia of a grindstone about its axis of rotation is 0.11 kg · m². (*a*) What is the kinetic energy of the grindstone when rotating at an angular speed of 28 rad/s? (*b*) What is the kinetic energy if the speed is doubled to 56 rad/s?

12-23 A wheel rotating about a fixed axis has a kinetic energy of 29 J when its angular speed is 13 rad/s. What is the wheel's moment of inertia about the axis of rotation?

12-24 A stone of mass m (= 0.68 kg) is tied to a string of negligible mass and swung in a horizontal circle of radius R (= 0.84 m) such that the period of the motion is T (= 0.39 s). Determine the kinetic energy of the stone two ways: (*a*) Treat the stone as a particle of mass m and linear speed v (= $2\pi R/T$). (*b*) Treat the stone as a rotating system of moment of inertia I (= mR^2) and angular speed ω (= $2\pi/T$). (*c*) Compare your answers.

Section 12-8. Moment of inertia

12-25 Consider the array of four particles shown in Fig. 12-25. The particles are contained in the xy plane and are connected by rods of negligible mass. Determine the moment of inertia about (*a*) the x axis (I_x), (*b*) the y axis (I_y), and (*c*) the z axis (I_z). (Notice that $I_z = I_x + I_y$. This equation is called the *plane-figure theorem*. As the name implies, the theorem is valid only if the system is of negligible thickness so that it can be con-

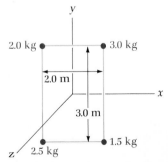

Figure 12-25. Exercise 12-25: The particles are contained in the xy plane, and the rectangle is centered at the origin.

tained in a plane, such as the xy plane. The array in Fig. 12-25 satisfies this criterion and obeys the plane-figure theorem. See Prob. 12-6.)

12-26 Find the moment of inertia of the array in Fig. 12-11 about an axis that passes through (a) particles 3 and 8 and (b) particles 2 and 8.

12-27 A door has a height of 2.1 m, a width of 1.1 m, a thickness of 42 mm, and a uniform density of 0.88×10^3 kg/m³. What is the moment of inertia of the door about an axis along its hinges?

12-28 (a) Estimate the moment of inertia about a vertical axis through the center of mass of a man standing erect with arms at his sides. The man is 1.8 m tall and has a mass of 73 kg. Treat the man as a right circular cylinder with density 1.0×10^3 kg/m³. (b) Estimate the man's moment of inertia about the same axis if he holds his arms out horizontally; treat his arms as thin rods.

12-29 Find the moment of inertia of the thin, triangular-shaped slab of uniform density shown in Fig. 12-26 about the z axis in terms of its mass M and dimensions a and b.

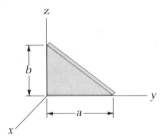

Figure 12-26. Exercise 12-29.

12-30 Find the moment of inertia of the solid right circular cylinder of uniform density shown in Fig. 12-27 about the z axis in terms of its mass M and radius R.

12-31 Using Table 12-2, find the moment of inertia of a solid sphere of uniform density, mass M, and radius r_0 about an axis that passes a distance of $\frac{1}{2}r_0$ from the center. Give your answer in terms of M and r_0.

12-32 (a) Determine the mass density of the earth ($m_e = 6.0 \times 10^{24}$ kg, $R_e = 6.4$ Mm), assuming that its density is uniform, and compare your answer with the average density of rocks on the earth's surface ($\rho = 2.7 \times 10^3$ kg/m³). (b) Estimate the earth's moment of

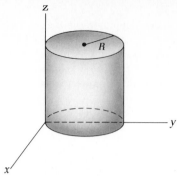

Figure 12-27. Exercise 12-30.

inertia about an axis through its center by assuming it has a uniform mass density. (c) Based on your answer to part (a), is your estimate in part (b) an overestimate or an underestimate? Explain.

Section 12-9. Rolling objects

12-33 A wheel of radius 340 mm rolls in a straight line without sliding. At the instant the center of the wheel has a linear speed of 1.4 m/s, determine (a) the wheel's angular speed about its center and (b) the linear speed of a particle at the top of the wheel.

12-34 (a) What is the kinetic energy of an 8.2-kg bowling ball that is rolling without sliding when the linear speed of its center is 1.7 m/s? (b) What fraction of the kinetic energy corresponds to rotation about the center of mass and what fraction corresponds to translation of the center of mass?

12-35 Find (a) the linear speed and (b) the angular speed of a hollow cylinder that rolls from rest a distance of 6.7 m down a straight slope that makes an angle of 12° with the horizontal. The cylinder has an outer radius of 96 mm, an inner radius of 75 mm, and a mass of 0.83 kg. Neglect frictional effects, which tend to slow the cylinder.

12-36 The following objects are rolling without sliding. In each case, find the ratio of the rotational kinetic energy about the center to the total kinetic energy: (a) a hollow cylinder, (b) a solid cylinder, (c) a hollow sphere, (d) a solid sphere. Assume uniform densities.

12-37 Estimate the kinetic energy of a thrown Frisbee immediately after release. What fraction of your estimate is due to its spinning about its center of mass?

PROBLEMS

12-1 A wheel rotating about the z axis with constant angular acceleration has the following angular coordinates: $\theta = 0.0$ at $t = 0$; $\theta = -3.8$ rad at $t = 1.0$ s; and $\theta = -5.0$ rad at $t = 2.0$ s. (a) Find α_z and ω_{z0}. (b) Write equations for the $\omega_z(t)$ and $\theta(t)$.

12-2 (a) Estimate the linear speed and the magnitude of the

linear acceleration of a tree relative to the earth's axis due to the earth's rotation. The tree's latitude is 55° and the radius of the earth is 6.37 Mm. (b) If we arrange a coordinate frame with its origin at the tree, and $+\mathbf{i}$, $+\mathbf{j}$, and $+\mathbf{k}$ pointing eastward, northward, and upward, respectively, determine the cartesian components of the linear velocity and linear acceleration.

12-3   Consider dividing the earth's kinetic energy relative to the sun into two parts: one part for the orbital motion of the center of mass and the other part for the rotation about its axis. Calculate and compare these two energies, assuming the earth's mass density is uniform. The earth's mass and radius are 6.0×10^{24} kg and 6.4×10^6 m, respectively. The radius of the earth's orbit is 1.5×10^{11} m.

12-4   One end of a uniform plank of length L is held fixed by a frictionless hinge (Fig. 12-28). The plank is given a slight push from the vertical position such that it swings down under the influence of gravity. At the instant the plank's orientation passes through the horizontal, find (a) its angular speed, (b) the linear speed of its center, (c) the radial component of the linear acceleration of its center, (d) the linear speed of its free end. Find your answers in terms of L and g.

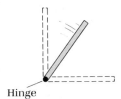

Hinge

Figure 12-28. Prob. 12-4.

12-5   **Radius of gyration.** The radius of gyration k of an object about an axis is defined as

$$k = \sqrt{\frac{I}{M}}$$

where I is the moment of inertia of the object about the axis and M is its mass. That is, if the entire mass of the object were concentrated at the distance from the axis given by the radius of gyration, the resulting moment of inertia would be the same as that of the object. (a) Determine the radii of gyration for the objects with the shapes and axes given in Table 12-2. (b) Write the equation for the speed of the rolling object in Example 12-8 in terms of its radius of gyration rather than its mass and moment of inertia.

12-6   **Plane-figure theorem.** Consider an object of negli-

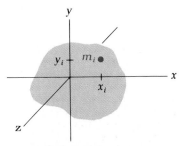

Figure 12-29. Prob. 12-6.

gible thickness contained in the xy plane, as shown in Fig. 12-29. Show that

$$I_z = I_x + I_y$$

where I_x, I_y, and I_z are the moments of inertia of the object about the x, y, and z axes, respectively.

12-7   Find the moment of inertia of a thin circular disk with uniform density about an axis along a diameter in terms of the disk's mass and radius. Do the calculation two ways: (a) by direct integration of Eq. (12-14) and (b) by using the plane-figure theorem (Prob. 12-6).

12-8   Recall that the moment of inertia of a uniform door of height h, width w, and mass M (neglecting its thickness) about an axis along the hinges is $Mw^2/3$. Use the parallel-axis theorem and the plane-figure theorem (Prob. 12-6) to find the door's moment of inertia about an axis through its center and perpendicular to its face. (See Table 12-2.)

12-9   A uniform sphere of radius 26 mm and mass 0.175 kg rolls from rest without sliding down a straight slope. After the sphere has undergone a vertical drop of 130 mm, the linear speed of its center is 1.3 m/s. What is the moment of inertia of the sphere about a diameter?

12-10 Find the linear speed v, in terms of a vertical drop h, of a cart as it coasts down a hill from a standing start. The cart's body has a mass M_b, each of its four wheels has a mass m, and the total mass of the cart is $M = M_b + 4m$. Neglect frictional effects, which tend to reduce the cart's mechanical energy. The wheels roll without sliding and may be treated as uniform disks. (a) Determine the linear speed in terms of the ratio m/M. (b) Compare the linear speed when m/M is 0.05 and 0.15.

12-11 A block of mass m is tied to a string of negligible mass that is wrapped around a uniform cylinder of mass M and radius R_0 (Fig. 12-30). The cylinder is free to rotate, with negligible friction, about a fixed horizontal axis through its center. After the block has dropped a vertical distance h from rest, find (a) the linear speed of the center of the block and (b) the angular speed of the cylinder about its axis of rotation.

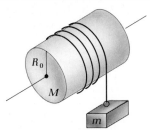

Figure 12-30. Prob. 12-11.

12-12 Estimate the linear speed of the center of a yo-yo of mass M and radius R_2 after it has fallen from rest a distance h while attached to a string (Fig. 12-31). The

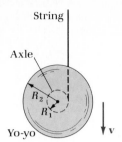

Figure 12-31. Prob. 12-12.

string is of negligible mass and thickness and is wound around an axle of radius R_1. Neglect the moment of inertia of the axle, and treat the body of the yo-yo as a uniform disk. Compare your answer for the case where $R_2/R_1 = 5$ with the speed of free-fall from the same height.

12-13 Consider a roller-coaster car at the instant it is halfway up a loop, as shown in Fig. 12-32. The linear velocity of the car is 13 m/s upward, the radius of the loop is 5.3 m, and frictional forces, which tend to reduce the car's mechanical energy, are negligible. Determine the magnitude and direction of the car's (a) angular velocity, (b) angular acceleration, (c) linear acceleration.

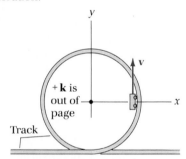

Figure 12-32. Prob. 12-13.

12-14 ***Choking up on a bat.*** In the next chapter we shall show that the moment of inertia is a measure of the resistance of an object to a change in its angular velocity. A way for a baseball player to increase his ability to swing a bat rapidly is to reduce the bat's moment of inertia. This can be done by "choking up," or grasping the bat nearer to its center of mass. (a) Treat a bat as a uniform rod of mass M and length ℓ, and consider rotation about an axis perpendicular to the length and passing through a point which is a distance h from one end (Fig. 12-33). Show that $I = M(\ell^2/3 - \ell h + h^2)$. (b) Make a graph of I versus h for values of h from zero to $\frac{1}{2}\ell$. Plot about six points and sketch a curve through them.

Figure 12-33. Prob. 12-14.

12-15 Suppose a hemispherical bowl of radius r_0 is rotating with constant angular velocity ω about its vertical axis of symmetry (Fig. 12-34). If a marble placed on the

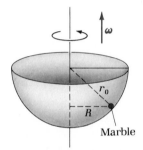

Figure 12-34. Prob. 12-15.

inside surface of the bowl is at rest relative to the surface at a distance R from the axis, the marble remains at rest relative to the surface. Show that

$$R = \sqrt{r_0^2 - \frac{g^2}{\omega^4}}$$

CHAPTER 13
ROTATION II

13-1 INTRODUCTION

Electrons, nuclei, and molecules — wheels, gears, and pulleys — planets, stars, and galaxies — all rotate. What causes a wheel to begin to rotate? After the wheel is rotating, what causes it to stop? A torque exerted on the wheel causes its angular velocity to change just as a force causes the linear velocity of an object to change.

Once a wheel is set in rotation, it tends to continue rotating. Eventually torques due to friction in the bearings and air resistance slow the wheel, bringing it to rest. That the wheel tends to continue to rotate is evidence that there is momentum associated with rotational motion — angular momentum. Angular momentum plays a central role in our study of rotational dynamics. We begin with the angular momentum of a single particle.

Carnival rides often use rotational effects to amuse and delight people. This Coney Island Ferris wheel is one of the largest in the world. *(Randy Matusow)*

Definition of angular momentum

13-2 ANGULAR MOMENTUM OF A PARTICLE

In Sec. 10-4 we defined the linear momentum of a particle as $\mathbf{p} = m\mathbf{v}$, where m is the particle's mass and $\mathbf{v}$ is its velocity. We found this concept to be very useful, especially when extended to systems of particles and continuous objects. The analogous rotational quantity, the *angular momentum*, is similarly useful.

Definition of angular momentum. We define the angular momentum $\boldsymbol{\ell}$ of a particle about a reference point O as

$$\boldsymbol{\ell} = \mathbf{r} \times \mathbf{p} \tag{13-1}$$

where $\mathbf{r}$ is the particle's position vector measured from O and $\mathbf{p}$ is its linear momentum, as shown in Fig. 13-1. Since it is defined as a cross product, the angular momentum is a vector quantity. It is perpendicular to the plane con-

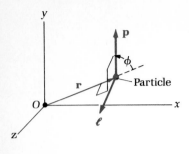

Figure 13-1. The angular momentum of a particle about the origin O is $\boldsymbol{\ell} = \mathbf{r} \times \mathbf{p}$, where $\mathbf{r}$ is the particle's position vector and $\mathbf{p} = m\mathbf{v}$ is its linear momentum. Thus $\boldsymbol{\ell}$ is perpendicular to the plane that contains $\mathbf{r}$ and $\mathbf{p}$.

taining $\mathbf{r}$ and $\mathbf{p}$, with its direction given by the right-hand rule (Sec. 11-6). The dimension of angular momentum is (mass)(length)^2(time)$^{-1}$, and its SI unit is kg · m^2/s. The magnitude ℓ of the angular momentum can be written a number of equivalent ways:

Magnitude of angular momentum

$$\ell = rp \sin \phi = rmv \sin \phi = r_\perp p = rp_\perp \qquad (13\text{-}2)$$

where ϕ is the angle between $\mathbf{r}$ and $\mathbf{p}$ (or $\mathbf{v}$), and where $r_\perp = r \sin \phi$ and $p_\perp = p \sin \phi$.

Since the definition of $\boldsymbol{\ell}$ contains $\mathbf{r}$, the value of $\boldsymbol{\ell}$ depends on the point O about which it is calculated. Selecting this point is an important part of making the angular momentum a useful quantity. Any time an angular momentum is discussed, the point about which it is calculated should be kept clearly in mind.

Particle traveling in a circle. A simple and important case to consider is a particle traveling in a circle of radius R. We determine the angular momentum about the center of the circle so that $r = R$ (Fig. 13-2). Since in circular motion $\mathbf{v}$ is perpendicular to $\mathbf{r}$ at each point along the path, $\phi = 90°$ at each point. From Eq. (13-2),

$$\ell = Rmv \sin 90° = Rmv$$

The magnitude of angular momentum for a particle in circular motion

For motion in a circle, $v = \omega R$, so $\ell = Rm(\omega R)$, or

$$\ell = mR^2\omega$$

The direction of $\boldsymbol{\ell}$ depends on the sense of the rotation. In Fig. 13-2, vectors $\mathbf{r}$ and $\mathbf{p}$ are contained in the xy plane, which means that $\boldsymbol{\ell}$ is along the z axis. Which way $\boldsymbol{\ell}$ points along the z axis, toward $+z$ or $-z$, is determined with the right-hand rule. If you curl the fingers of your right hand in the sense that would rotate $\mathbf{r}$ into $\mathbf{p}$, then your extended thumb gives the direction of $\boldsymbol{\ell}$. When the motion is counterclockwise (viewed from the $+z$ direction), $\boldsymbol{\ell}$ is toward $+z$ (ℓ_z is positive), and when the motion is clockwise, $\boldsymbol{\ell}$ is toward $-z$ (ℓ_z is negative). Since this also corresponds to the sign convention for ω_z, we can write $\boldsymbol{\ell}$ as

Angular momentum of a particle in circular motion

$$\boldsymbol{\ell} = \ell_z \mathbf{k} = mR^2 \omega_z \mathbf{k} \qquad (13\text{-}3)$$

If the motion is uniform circular motion, ω_z is constant, and consequently $\boldsymbol{\ell}$ is constant.

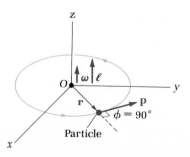

Figure 13-2. For a particle in circular motion about the origin in the xy plane, the angular momentum relative to the origin is $\boldsymbol{\ell} = mR^2\omega_z\mathbf{k}$.

EXAMPLE 13-1. Determine the magnitude and direction, relative to the sun, of the earth's angular momentum due to its orbital motion around the sun. The earth's orbital radius is $R = 1.5 \times 10^{11}$ m, and its mass is $m_e = 6.0 \times 10^{24}$ kg.

SOLUTION. The earth completes one revolution (2π rad) per year ($T = 365$ days), so that its angular speed $\omega = 2\pi/T$ about the sun is

$$\omega = \frac{2\pi}{(365 \text{ day})(24 \text{ h/day})(3600 \text{ s/h})} = 2.0 \times 10^{-7} \text{ rad/s}$$

The magnitude ℓ of the earth's orbital angular momentum about the sun is

$$\ell = m_e R^2 \omega$$
$$= (6.0 \times 10^{24} \text{ kg})(1.5 \times 10^{11} \text{ m})^2 (2.0 \times 10^{-7} \text{ rad/s})$$
$$= 2.7 \times 10^{40} \text{ kg} \cdot \text{m}^2/\text{s}$$

If you imagine looking down on the solar system from Polaris (the North Star), the earth travels counterclockwise around the sun. Thus the direction of ℓ is perpendicular to the plane of the orbit and in the approximate direction of Polaris.

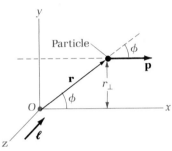

Figure 13-3. For a particle traveling in a straight line, ℓ relative to O is $\ell = r_\perp mv$, where $r_\perp$ is the perpendicular distance from the particle's path to O.

Particle traveling in a straight line. Strange as it may seem at first thought, a particle traveling in a straight line has angular momentum. Figure 13-3 shows a particle in the xy plane moving in a straight line parallel to the x axis. From Eq. (13-2), the magnitude of the particle's angular momentum relative to origin O is

$$\ell = rp \sin \phi = mvr_\perp \qquad (13\text{-}4)$$

where $r_\perp$ is the perpendicular distance from the particle's path to O. Thus a particle with a straight-line path has a nonzero angular momentum about any point that is not on its path. If the particle's speed is constant, its angular momentum is constant, but if the particle accelerates along a straight line, the angular momentum changes with time. By the right-hand rule, the direction of ℓ for the particle in Fig. 13-3 is in the $-z$ direction.

EXAMPLE 13-2. Suppose you are standing in an orchard and an apple of mass $m = 0.17$ kg falls from a tree from a height of 2.6 m and lands 3.1 m from where you are standing. (a) Using the coordinate frame in Fig. 13-4, determine the falling apple's angular momentum relative to an origin at your feet. (b) Evaluate ℓ at the instant before the apple hits the ground. Let $t = 0$ correspond to when the apple begins falling and neglect air resistance.

SOLUTION. (a) From Fig. 13-4, the right-hand rule gives ℓ in the $-z$ direction. Since $t = 0$ corresponds to when the apple starts falling, $v = gt$, and

$$\ell = -(r_\perp mv)\mathbf{k} = -(r_\perp mgt)\mathbf{k}$$
$$= -[(3.1 \text{ m})(0.17 \text{ kg})(9.8 \text{ m/s}^2)t]\mathbf{k} = -[(5.2 \text{ kg} \cdot \text{m}^2/\text{s}^2)t]\mathbf{k}$$

(b) The apple hits the ground at the time t_1 such that $h = \frac{1}{2}gt_1^2$, or

$$t_1 = \sqrt{\frac{2h}{g}} = \sqrt{\frac{2(2.6 \text{ m})}{(9.8 \text{ m/s}^2)}} = 0.73 \text{ s}$$

At the instant before the apple hits,

$$\ell = -[(5.2 \text{ kg} \cdot \text{m}^2/\text{s}^2)(0.73 \text{ s})]\mathbf{k} = -(3.8 \text{ kg} \cdot \text{m}^2/\text{s})\mathbf{k}$$

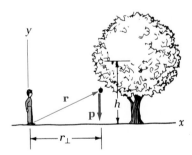

Figure 13-4. Example 13-2: An apple falls from a tree. The $+z$ direction is out of the page.

Relation between angular momentum and torque. In Sec. 10-4, we wrote Newton's second law for a particle in terms of its linear momentum $\mathbf{p}$: $\Sigma \mathbf{F} = d\mathbf{p}/dt$, where $\Sigma \mathbf{F}$ is the net force on the particle. Now we develop the analogous rotational expression between the net torque $\Sigma \boldsymbol{\tau}$ acting on a particle and the particle's angular momentum $\boldsymbol{\ell}$.

The time derivative of the angular momentum is

$$\frac{d\boldsymbol{\ell}}{dt} = \frac{d}{dt}(\mathbf{r} \times \mathbf{p})$$

Using the product rule for differentiation gives

$$\frac{d\boldsymbol{\ell}}{dt} = \frac{d\mathbf{r}}{dt} \times \mathbf{p} + \mathbf{r} \times \frac{d\mathbf{p}}{dt}$$

The first of the two cross products on the right-hand side of this equation is zero because $d\mathbf{r}/dt = \mathbf{v}$ and $\mathbf{p} = m\mathbf{v}$. The vectors $\mathbf{v}$ and $m\mathbf{v}$ are parallel, so their cross product must be zero. Therefore,

$$\frac{d\boldsymbol{\ell}}{dt} = \mathbf{r} \times \frac{d\mathbf{p}}{dt}$$

Using Newton's second law for a particle, $\Sigma\mathbf{F} = d\mathbf{p}/dt$, we have

$$\frac{d\boldsymbol{\ell}}{dt} = \mathbf{r} \times \Sigma\mathbf{F}$$

The quantity $\mathbf{r} \times \Sigma\mathbf{F}$ is the net torque $\Sigma\boldsymbol{\tau}$ exerted on the particle about the origin (Sec. 11-6): $\Sigma\boldsymbol{\tau} = \mathbf{r} \times \Sigma\mathbf{F}$. Thus

Rotational analog of Newton's
second law for a single particle

$$\Sigma\boldsymbol{\tau} = \frac{d\boldsymbol{\ell}}{dt} \tag{13-5}$$

In Newton's second law, $\Sigma\mathbf{F} = d\mathbf{p}/dt$, $\mathbf{p}$ must be measured relative to an inertial reference frame. Thus for Eq. (13-5) to be valid, $\boldsymbol{\ell}$ must be measured relative to an inertial reference frame.

EXAMPLE 13-3. Separately determine both the left-hand side and the right-hand side of Eq. (13-5) for the apple in Example 13-2, and thus show that the equation is valid for this case.

SOLUTION. First we evaluate the left-hand side of Eq. (13-5) for this case. The magnitude of the net force on the falling apple (neglecting air resistance) is mg, and the moment arm of this force relative to the origin is $r_\perp$ (see Fig. 13-4). The magnitude of the net torque is $r_\perp mg$, and the

right-hand rule gives its direction as $-\mathbf{k}$. Therefore,

$$\Sigma\boldsymbol{\tau} = -(r_\perp mg)\mathbf{k}$$

Now we evaluate the right-hand side of Eq. (13-5). From Example 13-2, $\boldsymbol{\ell} = -(r_\perp mgt)\mathbf{k}$, so that

$$\frac{d\boldsymbol{\ell}}{dt} = \frac{d}{dt}[-(r_\perp mgt)\mathbf{k}] = -(r_\perp mg)\mathbf{k}$$

which is the same result we obtained for the left-hand side.

13-3 ANGULAR MOMENTUM OF A SYSTEM OF PARTICLES

Equation (13-5) states that the net torque on a single particle relative to some point is equal to the rate of change of the particle's angular momentum relative to that point. Now we apply this equation to a system of particles.

The total angular momentum $\mathbf{L}$ of a system of n particles relative to a point is defined as *the vector sum of the individual angular momenta of all the particles relative to that same point:*

Total angular momentum

$$\mathbf{L} = \boldsymbol{\ell}_1 + \boldsymbol{\ell}_2 + \cdots + \boldsymbol{\ell}_n = \Sigma\boldsymbol{\ell}_i \tag{13-6}$$

where $\boldsymbol{\ell}_i$ is the angular momentum of particle i. From the sum rule for differentiation, the time derivative of the total angular momentum is

$$\frac{d\mathbf{L}}{dt} = \Sigma \frac{d\boldsymbol{\ell}_i}{dt} \qquad (13\text{-}7)$$

We now use Eq. (13-5) to substitute for $d\boldsymbol{\ell}_i/dt$, but with a slight change of notation. Previously we used the symbol $\Sigma\boldsymbol{\tau}$ for the net torque (the vector sum of the torques on a single particle). In Eq. (13-7) we are summing over particles, so we write the net torque on particle i simply as $\boldsymbol{\tau}_i$ to avoid confusion. This gives

$$\frac{d\mathbf{L}}{dt} = \Sigma\boldsymbol{\tau}_i \qquad (13\text{-}8)$$

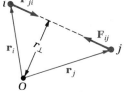

Figure 13-5. The torques due to the interaction of a pair of particles are equal and opposite because the forces of interaction obey Newton's third law.

The sum of the net torques for all the particles of a system, $\Sigma\boldsymbol{\tau}_i$, can be divided into two parts: the sum of the torques on the particles within the system due to the forces they exert on each other (the *net internal torque*) and the sum of the torques on the particles within the system due to forces exerted on them by objects external to the system (the *net external torque*). We now show that Newton's third law requires that the net internal torque be zero. For the interaction between particles i and j (Fig. 13-5), Newton's third law states that $\mathbf{F}_{ij} = -\mathbf{F}_{ji}$, and that *the direction of the two forces is along the line between them*. That is, the two forces are equal and opposite and have the same line of action. Since the line of action of each force is the same, each has the same moment arm $r_\perp$ about point O, and each torque magnitude is the same. If you use the right-hand rule to find the direction of the torques in Fig. 13-5, you will find that they are opposite each other: $\boldsymbol{\tau}_{ij} = -\boldsymbol{\tau}_{ji}$. If the two torques are added, their sum is zero. This is true for any reference point we wish to use. So it goes for all pairs of torques due to interactions between all pairs of particles within the system. Therefore, $\Sigma\boldsymbol{\tau}_i$ in Eq. (13-8) involves torques due to *external* forces only:

Rotational analog of Newton's second law for a system of particles

$$\Sigma\boldsymbol{\tau}_{\text{ext}} = \frac{d\mathbf{L}}{dt} \qquad (13\text{-}9)$$

where we have dropped the subscript i for brevity. Also for the sake of brevity, we often drop the subscript "ext" from $\Sigma\boldsymbol{\tau}_{\text{ext}}$. You should keep in mind that *only external torques can change a system's angular momentum.*

As an example, the planets and the sun in the solar system exert forces on one another, and the torques from these forces about any point cancel in pairs. The angular momentum of the solar system relative to any point is unaffected by the torques due to forces between planets or between the sun and any planet.

The translational analog of Eq. (13-9) is $\Sigma\mathbf{F}_{\text{ext}} = d\mathbf{P}/dt$. Similar to what we did above, we used Newton's third law in the development of this equation.

The torques and the angular momentum in Eq. (13-9) may be measured about any point as long as the same point is used for all measurements, and as long as the point is fixed in an inertial reference frame. Although we shall not prove it here, this equation is even more general than that. *The equation is valid if the reference point is at the center of mass of the system, even when the center of mass accelerates relative to an inertial reference frame.* Often this makes it convenient to separate the motion of a system into two parts: the translational motion of the center of mass, in which $\Sigma\mathbf{F}_{\text{ext}} = d\mathbf{P}/dt$ is used, and the rotational motion about the center of mass, in which $\Sigma\boldsymbol{\tau}_{\text{ext}} = d\mathbf{L}/dt$ is used.

EXAMPLE 13-4. In Fig. 13-6 we show an array of four particles at the corners of a square of side $a = 2.3$ m, centered at the origin and contained in the xy plane. Each particle has mass $m = 1.8$ kg, and the array is held together by rigid rods of negligible mass. The array is rotating about the z axis such that its angular coordinate θ is given by

$$\theta = 0.8 \text{ rad} - (5.1 \text{ rad/s})t + (1.6 \text{ rad/s}^2)t^2$$

Determine (a) the array's total angular momentum about the origin and (b) the net external torque on the array about the origin. (c) The external forces on the array are force $\mathbf{F}_2 = -F\mathbf{i}$ exerted on particle 2 and force $\mathbf{F}_4 = F\mathbf{i}$ exerted on particle 4. Determine the magnitude F of these forces.

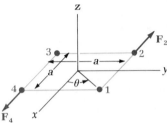

Figure 13-6. Example 13-4: An array of four particles contained in the xy plane and centered at the origin rotates about the z axis.

SOLUTION. We recognize the equation for the array's angular coordinate as motion with constant angular acceleration (Sec. 12-5), where $\omega_{z0} = -5.1$ rad/s and $\alpha_z = 3.2$ rad/s². Therefore,

$$\omega_z = \omega_{z0} + \alpha_z t = -5.1 \text{ rad/s} + (3.2 \text{ rad/s}^2)t$$

(a) Since the array is rigid, each particle travels in a circular path, and each has the same angular velocity and acceleration. Also, each particle has the same mass and the same distance from the origin [$r = \sqrt{(\tfrac{1}{2}a)^2 + (\tfrac{1}{2}a)^2} = a/\sqrt{2}$], so that for each particle,

$$\ell_z = mr^2\omega_z = m\left(\frac{a}{\sqrt{2}}\right)^2 \omega_z = \tfrac{1}{2}ma^2\omega_z$$

Since there are four particles, $L_z = 4\ell_z$, or

$$L_z = 4(\tfrac{1}{2}ma^2\omega_z) = 2ma^2\omega_z = 2ma^2(\omega_{z0} + \alpha_z t)$$
$$= 2(1.8 \text{ kg})(2.3 \text{ m})^2[(-5.1 \text{ rad/s}) + (3.2 \text{ rad/s}^2)t]$$

Thus

$$\mathbf{L} = [-97 \text{ kg} \cdot \text{m}^2/\text{s} + (61 \text{ kg} \cdot \text{m}^2/\text{s}^2)t]\mathbf{k}$$

(b) The z component $\Sigma\tau_z$ of the net external torque is the time derivative of L_z:

$$\Sigma\tau_z = \frac{d}{dt}[2ma^2(\omega_{z0} + \alpha_z t)] = 2ma^2\alpha_z = 61 \text{ N} \cdot \text{m}$$

Thus

$$\Sigma\boldsymbol{\tau} = (61 \text{ N} \cdot \text{m})\mathbf{k}$$

(c) Since $\mathbf{r}_2 = (-\tfrac{1}{2}a\mathbf{i} + \tfrac{1}{2}a\mathbf{j})$ and $\mathbf{r}_4 = (\tfrac{1}{2}a\mathbf{i} - \tfrac{1}{2}a\mathbf{j})$, the torques on particles 2 and 4 about the origin are

$$\boldsymbol{\tau}_2 = (-\tfrac{1}{2}a\mathbf{i}) + \tfrac{1}{2}a\mathbf{j}) \times (-F\mathbf{i}) = \tfrac{1}{2}aF\mathbf{k}$$
$$\boldsymbol{\tau}_4 = (\tfrac{1}{2}a\mathbf{i} - \tfrac{1}{2}a\mathbf{j}) \times (F\mathbf{i}) = \tfrac{1}{2}aF\mathbf{k}$$

where we have used $\mathbf{i} \times \mathbf{i} = 0$ and $\mathbf{j} \times \mathbf{i} = -\mathbf{k}$. Adding these torques gives

$$\Sigma\tau_z = \tau_{2z} + \tau_{4z} = \tfrac{1}{2}aF + \tfrac{1}{2}aF = aF$$

Thus

$$F = \frac{\Sigma\tau_z}{a} = \frac{61 \text{ N} \cdot \text{m}}{2.3 \text{ m}} = 26 \text{ N}$$

13-4 ROTATIONAL DYNAMICS OF A RIGID OBJECT ABOUT A FIXED AXIS

The rotation of a rigid object about a fixed axis is of great practical interest. We now investigate the angular momentum of such an object and develop its equation of motion.

Angular momentum. Consider the relation between the angular momentum **L** of a rigid object relative to a point O on the axis of rotation and the object's angular velocity $\boldsymbol{\omega}$ about the axis. As we proceed, we must take care to distinguish between a distance r from a point (origin O in Fig. 13-7) and a distance R from an axis (z axis in Fig. 13-7). The angular momentum **L** is referred to a *point* (such as O), whereas the angular velocity $\boldsymbol{\omega}$ is referred to an *axis* (such as the z axis).

The z (or axial) component of an object's angular momentum is $L_z = (\Sigma\boldsymbol{\ell}_i)_z = \Sigma\ell_{iz}$. To find L_z, we first find ℓ_{iz} for particle i. In Fig. 13-7a, θ_i is the angle between $\mathbf{r}_i$ and the z axis, so $R_i = r_i \sin\theta_i$. The angular momentum of particle i,

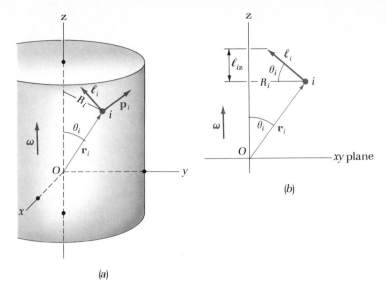

(a)

(b)

Figure 13-7. (a) As a rigid object rotates about the z axis, particle i moves in a circle centered on the axis. The distance from origin O to i is r_i, and the distance from the axis to i is $R_i = r_i \sin \theta_i$. (b) Relative to O, the axial component of $\boldsymbol{\ell}_i$ is $\ell_{iz} = \ell_i \sin \theta_i = m_i R_i^2 \omega_z$.

$\boldsymbol{\ell}_i = \mathbf{r}_i \times \mathbf{p}_i$, has both an axial and a radial component. As shown in the figure, $\mathbf{r}_i$ is perpendicular to $\mathbf{p}_i$ so that $\ell_i = r_i p_i \sin 90° = r_i m_i v_i$. Since $v_i = R_i \omega$, $\ell_i = r_i m_i R_i \omega$. From Fig. 13-7b, the z component of particle i's angular momentum is

$$\ell_{iz} = r_i m_i R_i \omega_z \sin \theta_i = m_i R_i (r_i \sin \theta_i) \omega_z = m_i R_i^2 \omega_z$$

Note that since R_i and ω_z are referred to the axis, ℓ_{iz} is independent of where the origin is located on the axis. *Therefore, this expression is valid for any origin as long as the origin is on the axis.*

Adding ℓ_{iz} for each particle in the object gives

$$L_z = \Sigma m_i R_i^2 \omega_z = \omega_z \Sigma m_i R_i^2$$

where we have factored ω_z out of the sum because it does not depend on i. (ω_z is the same for each particle.) We recognize the quantity $\Sigma m_i R_i^2$ as the moment of inertia I of the object about the axis of rotation (Sec. 12-8). Thus

The axial component of the angular momentum of a rigid object about any point on the axis of rotation

$$L_z = I \omega_z \qquad (13\text{-}10)$$

Equation (13-10) is valid for any rigid object, but it refers only to the axial component of **L**. It turns out that when an object has sufficient symmetry about the axis, **L** is parallel to the axis. For example, suppose particle i is on the opposite side of the axis from particle j and $m_i = m_j$ (Fig. 13-8). Then the radial component of $\boldsymbol{\ell}_i$ is equal and opposite that of $\boldsymbol{\ell}_j$. If we have this pairwise cancellation of the radial components of the angular momenta of particles over the entire object, then the sum of the radial components is zero, and $\mathbf{L} = L_z \mathbf{k}$. Besides this pairwise cancellation, there are other ways that an object with sufficient symmetry can have **L** parallel to the axis. Since $\boldsymbol{\omega}$ is parallel to the axis ($\boldsymbol{\omega} = \omega_z \mathbf{k}$), **L** and $\boldsymbol{\omega}$ are parallel to each other for an object with sufficient symmetry about its axis of rotation, and

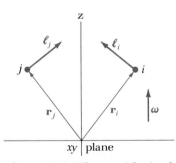

Figure 13-8. When particles i and j, which are on opposite sides of the axis, have the same mass ($m_i = m_j$), the radial components of $\boldsymbol{\ell}_i$ and $\boldsymbol{\ell}_j$ are equal and opposite. The radial components of $\boldsymbol{\ell}$ for the particles cancel when forming $\mathbf{L} = \Sigma \boldsymbol{\ell}_i$, then $\mathbf{L} = L_z \mathbf{k}$ and **L** is parallel to $\boldsymbol{\omega}$.

$$\mathbf{L} = I\boldsymbol{\omega} \qquad \text{(sufficient symmetry only)} \qquad (13\text{-}11)$$

If an object does not have sufficient symmetry about the axis such that **L** is parallel to the axis, then the direction of **L** will rotate as the object rotates. An example is a car's wheel that is "out of balance." Such a wheel tends to wobble, and the torque required to maintain the rotation about the axle is exerted by the bearings in the axle.

The translational analog of Eq. (13-11) for a system of particles is $\mathbf{P} = M\mathbf{v}_{cm}$, where $\mathbf{P}$ is the total linear momentum, M is the total mass, and $\mathbf{v}_{cm}$ is the velocity of the center of mass (Sec. 10-4).

Equation of motion. Newton's second law for a rigid object undergoing translational motion is $\Sigma\mathbf{F}_{ext} = M\mathbf{a}_{cm}$. To find the rotational analog of this equation, we take the time derivative of Eq. (13-10):

$$\frac{dL_z}{dt} = \frac{d}{dt}\,I\omega_z = I\,\frac{d\omega_z}{dt} = I\alpha_z$$

We have factored I out of the derivative (because it is constant for a rigid body rotating about a fixed axis), and we have used $d\omega_z/dt = \alpha_z$. The z component of Eq. (13-9) is $\Sigma\tau_z = dL_z/dt$. From the expression above, we can replace dL_z/dt with $I\alpha_z$ to give

$$\Sigma\tau_z = I\alpha_z \qquad (13\text{-}12)$$

The equation of motion for a rigid object rotating about a fixed axis

This is the equation of motion for a rigid object constrained to rotate about a fixed axis, and is a consequence of Newton's laws.

Finding the axial torque due to an applied force

Now consider the way to find the axial torque τ_z exerted on a rigid object relative to a point on the object's axis of rotation. We are guided by experience in opening a door. The effectiveness of a force in opening a door depends on two things: (i) the perpendicular distance R from a line along the hinges (the axis) to the point P of application of the force (at the knob) and (ii) the component of the force perpendicular to the door's face (called the *tangential component F_t* because it is tangent to the circular path of the door's particles).

In Fig. 13-9a, we show an arbitrarily directed force $\mathbf{F}$ exerted at point P on an object which can rotate about the z axis. (For clarity, only point P on the object is shown.) The axial component τ_z of the torque due to $\mathbf{F}$ relative to origin O is

$$\tau_z = (\mathbf{r} \times \mathbf{F})_z$$

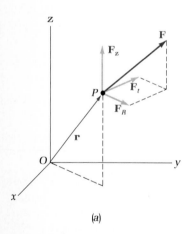

We decompose $\mathbf{F}$ into three mutually perpendicular forces: $\mathbf{F}_z$ parallel to the axis, $\mathbf{F}_R$ radially away from the axis, and $\mathbf{F}_t$ tangent to the circular path of the particle at P. Now we write τ_z as

$$\tau_z = [\mathbf{r} \times (\mathbf{F}_z + \mathbf{F}_R + \mathbf{F}_t)]_z = (\mathbf{r} \times \mathbf{F}_z)_z + (\mathbf{r} \times \mathbf{F}_R)_z + (\mathbf{r} \times \mathbf{F}_t)_z$$

If you apply the right-hand rule to $\mathbf{r} \times \mathbf{F}_z$ and $\mathbf{r} \times \mathbf{F}_R$ in Fig. 13-9a, you will see that they are both parallel to the xy plane: $(\mathbf{r} \times \mathbf{F}_z)_z = 0$ and $(\mathbf{r} \times \mathbf{F}_R)_z = 0$. Only $\mathbf{F}_t$ contributes to τ_z. Further, Fig. 13-9b shows that $(\mathbf{r} \times \mathbf{F}_t)_z = RF_t$, or

$$\tau_z = RF_t$$

We find that τ_z depends on (i) the perpendicular distance R from the axis to P and (ii) only the tangential component F_t of force $\mathbf{F}$. Since τ_z depends on R instead of r, the value of τ_z is the same for any origin as long as the origin is on the axis. For rotation about a fixed axis, it is proper to speak of the "torque about the axis." Finally, for τ_z to have the proper algebraic sign, our sign convention for F_t must be similar to that for s, v_t, and a_t; F_t is positive if it tends to cause

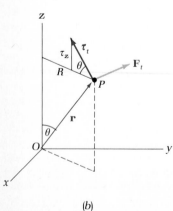

Figure 13-9. (a) In finding τ_z due to an arbitrarily directed force $\mathbf{F}$, we decompose $\mathbf{F}$ into three mutually perpendicular forces, $\mathbf{F} = \mathbf{F}_z + \mathbf{F}_R + \mathbf{F}_t$, and note that $(\mathbf{r} \times \mathbf{F}_z)_z = 0$ and $(\mathbf{r} \times \mathbf{F}_R)_z = 0$ by the right-hand rule. Only $\mathbf{F}_t$ contributes to τ_z. (b) The torque due to $\mathbf{F}_t$ is τ_t, and since $\mathbf{r}$ and $\mathbf{F}_t$ are perpendicular, $\tau_t = rF_t$. Thus $\tau_z = \tau_t \sin\theta = rF_t \sin\theta = (r\sin\theta)F_t = RF_t$.

counterclockwise rotation and negative if it tends to cause clockwise rotation.

Moment of inertia revisited. We introduced the moment of inertia in Chap. 12 in connection with the rotational kinetic energy, and noted at that time that it is the rotational analog of the mass of an object. The development of Eqs. (13-10) and (13-12) provides an alternative introduction for the moment of inertia. In this latter case, the reason for the term "inertia" in its name is more apparent. Equation (13-12) shows that the moment of inertia is the measure of an object's resistance to a change in its angular velocity. For a given net external torque, an object with a larger moment of inertia will have a smaller angular acceleration. The moment of inertia is sometimes referred to as the *rotational inertia*.

EXAMPLE 13-5. Determine the earth's angular momentum magnitude, due to its daily rotation. We call this angular momentum the earth's *spin angular momentum* $\mathbf{L}_s$. Assume that $\mathbf{L}_s$ is parallel to the earth's axis and that the earth's mass density is uniform. The mass of the earth is 6.0×10^{24} kg and its radius is 6.4 Mm.

SOLUTION. The moment of inertia of a uniform sphere about an axis along a diameter is $2Mr_0^2/5$ (Table 12-2), so the earth's moment of inertia (assuming its density is uniform) is

$I = [2(6.0 \times 10^{24} \text{ kg})(6.4 \text{ Mm})^2]/5 = 9.8 \times 10^{37} \text{ kg} \cdot \text{m}^2$. The angular speed of the earth's daily rotation is

$$\omega = \frac{2\pi}{T} = \frac{2\pi}{(24 \text{ h})(3600 \text{ s/h})} = 7.3 \times 10^{-5} \text{ rad/s}$$

The magnitude of the earth's spin angular momentum is

$$L_s = I\omega = (9.8 \times 10^{37} \text{ kg} \cdot \text{m}^2)(7.3 \times 10^{-5} \text{ rad/s})$$
$$= 7.2 \times 10^{33} \text{ kg} \cdot \text{m}^2/\text{s}$$

EXAMPLE 13-6. Two forces are exerted on a uniform door, as shown in Fig. 13-10. The door is initially rotating in the sense shown with an angular speed of 0.45 rad/s. Assuming the torques due to these forces remain constant, determine the door's (a) angular acceleration component, (b) angular velocity component as a function of time, and (c) angular coordinate as a function of time. Neglect the torque due to friction in the hinges. The door's mass is $M = 38$ kg, and its width is $w = 0.88$ m. Other data are $\phi = 63°$, $F_b = 15$ N, and $F_c = 12$ N.

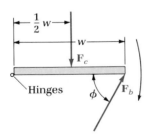

Figure 13-10. Example 13-6: The z axis is perpendicular to the page (along the hinges), and $+z$ is out of the page.

SOLUTION. (a) We let the z axis in Fig. 13-10 be along the hinges, with $+z$ pointing out of the page. The z component of the net torque about any point on the axis is

$$\Sigma\tau_z = wF_b \sin\phi - \tfrac{1}{2}wF_c$$

Solving Eq. (13-12) for α_z gives $\alpha_z = \Sigma\tau_z/I$, where $I = Mw^2/3$ (Example 12-5). Substituting $\Sigma\tau_z$ from above gives

$$\alpha_z = \frac{3(F_b \sin\phi - \tfrac{1}{2}F_c)}{Mw}$$
$$= \frac{3[15 \text{ N} \sin 63° - \tfrac{1}{2}(12 \text{ N})]}{(38 \text{ kg})(0.88 \text{ m})} = 0.66 \text{ rad/s}^2$$

(b) The right-hand rule applied to the initial direction of rotation shown in Fig. 13-10 gives $\boldsymbol{\omega}_0$ into the page so that ω_{z0} is negative: $\omega_{z0} = -0.45$ rad/s. Using the result from part (a) and the expression $\omega_z = \omega_{z0} + \alpha_z t$, we have

$$\omega_z = -0.45 \text{ rad/s} + (0.66 \text{ rad/s}^2)t$$

(c) Using the expression $\theta = \theta_0 + \omega_{z0}t + \tfrac{1}{2}\alpha_z t^2$ and letting the door's initial angular position θ_0 be zero, we have

$$\theta = -(0.45 \text{ rad/s})t + (0.33 \text{ rad/s}^2)t^2$$

EXAMPLE 13-7. A crate is tied to a rope that is wrapped around a windlass and the crate is released (Fig. 13-11a). The mass of the crate is $M_C = 35$ kg, and the mass and radius of the windlass are $M_W = 94$ kg and $R_0 = 83$ mm. Determine (a) the magnitude a of the crate's linear acceleration and

(b) the tension F_T in the rope. The windlass may be treated as a uniform cylinder of radius R_0, and the torque due to friction in the bearings and the mass of the rope both may be neglected.

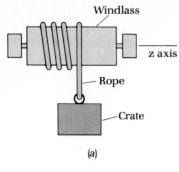

Windlass

z axis

Rope

Crate

(a)

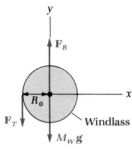

y

$\mathbf{F}_B$

x

R_0

$\mathbf{F}_T$

Windlass

$M_W\mathbf{g}$

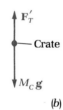

$\mathbf{F}_T'$

Crate

$M_C\mathbf{g}$

(b)

Figure 13-11. Example 13-7: (a) Front view. The z axis is in the plane of the page (along the axle). (b) Free-body diagrams. The z axis is perpendicular to the page, with +z out of the page.

SOLUTION. The free-body diagrams of the crate and the windlass are shown in Fig. 13-11b, where $M_W\mathbf{g}$ is the weight

of the windlass, $M_C\mathbf{g}$ is the weight of the crate, $\mathbf{F}_T$ is the force by the rope on the windlass, $\mathbf{F}_T'$ is the force by the rope on the crate, and $\mathbf{F}_B$ is the force by the bearings on the windlass. We choose a coordinate system oriented as shown in the figure, with +z along the windlass's axis and out of the page. Since the rope's mass is negligible, $|\mathbf{F}_T| = |\mathbf{F}_T'| = F_T$. (a) The vertical component of Newton's second law applied to the crate gives

$$F_T - M_Cg = -M_Ca \qquad \text{(A)}$$

The axial component of the torque exerted on the windlass by the rope relative to any point on the axis is $\tau_z = F_TR_0$. The torques due to $\mathbf{F}_B$ and $M_W\mathbf{g}$ are zero because the line of action of each of these forces passes through the axis. Thus $\Sigma\tau_z = F_TR_0$. The rotational analog of Newton's second law, Eq. (13-12), gives

$$F_TR_0 = I\alpha_z = I\alpha \qquad \text{(B)}$$

The magnitudes of the linear acceleration of the crate and the angular acceleration of the windlass are related by $a = \alpha R_0$. Also, since the windlass is a uniform cylinder, $I = \frac{1}{2}M_WR_0^2$. Substituting into Eq. (B) and dividing both sides by R_0, we obtain

$$F_T = \tfrac{1}{2}M_Wa \qquad \text{(C)}$$

Inserting F_T from Eq. (C) into Eq. (A), and solving for a gives

$$a = \frac{M_Cg}{M_C + \tfrac{1}{2}M_W} = \frac{(35\text{ kg})(9.8\text{ m/s}^2)}{35\text{ kg} + \tfrac{1}{2}(94\text{ kg})} = 4.2\text{ m/s}^2$$

Notice that a is less than g. Why is this so? (b) Substituting the above value of a into Eq. (C) gives

$$F_T = \frac{\tfrac{1}{2}M_WM_Cg}{M_C + \tfrac{1}{2}M_W} = \frac{\tfrac{1}{2}(94\text{ kg})(35\text{ kg})(9.8\text{ m/s}^2)}{35\text{ kg} + \tfrac{1}{2}(94\text{ kg})} = 200\text{ N}$$

Notice that the tension in the rope is less than the weight of the crate. Why is this so?

13-5   ROTATIONAL WORK AND POWER FOR A RIGID OBJECT

When a force causes a torque on a rotating object, work is done by the agent that exerts the force. In Fig. 13-12, we consider the work done by a force $\mathbf{F}$ during a time interval in which a door's angular position changes by an amount $d\theta$. The work dW done by $\mathbf{F}$ is

$$dW = \mathbf{F} \cdot d\mathbf{s} = F_t(R\,d\theta)$$

where F_t is the tangential component of $\mathbf{F}$. Since $\tau_z = F_tR$,

$$dW = \tau_z\,d\theta \qquad \text{(13-13)}$$

The work W done by torque τ_z when the door rotates from θ_i to θ_f is

Work done on a rigid object rotating about a fixed axis

$$W = \int_{\theta_i}^{\theta_f} \tau_z\,d\theta \qquad \text{(13-14)}$$

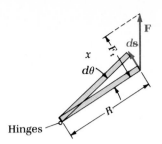

Figure 13-12. Work done in rotating a door. The z axis is perpendicular to the page (along the hinges), and +z is out of the page.

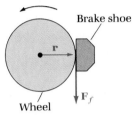

Figure 13-13. A brake shoe slowing the rotation of a wheel. The z axis is perpendicular to the page (along the wheel's axle), with +z out of the page.

For a constant torque, τ_z can be taken out of the integral, and

$$W = \tau_z(\theta_f - \theta_i) = \tau_z\,\Delta\theta \tag{13-15}$$

The translational analog of Eq. (13-14) is $W = \int F_x\,dx$ for one-dimensional motion.

The work done by a torque may be negative. Figure 13-13 shows a rotating wheel being slowed by the torque due to a brake shoe. With the z axis along the axle and +z out of the page, the angular displacement of the wheel is positive ($\Delta\theta > 0$), and by the right-hand rule τ_z due to the force $\mathbf{F}_f$ is negative. Therefore, τ_z and $\Delta\theta$ have opposite signs, which makes W negative. What are the algebraic signs of $\Delta\theta$, τ_z, and W when the wheel rotates in the opposite sense with the brakes on?

The work-energy theorem gives the relation between the net work on an object and the change in the object's kinetic energy (Sec. 8-5). We now develop the rotational counterpart of the work-energy theorem for a rigid object rotating about a fixed axis. Combining Eqs. (13-12) and (13-13), we obtain

$$dW_{\text{net}} = \Sigma\tau_z\,d\theta = I\alpha_z\,d\theta = I\,\frac{d\omega_z}{dt}\,\omega_z\,dt$$

Since

$$\frac{d}{dt}\left(\tfrac{1}{2}\omega_z{}^2\right) = \omega_z\,\frac{d\omega_z}{dt}$$

we have

$$dW_{\text{net}} = I\,\frac{d}{dt}\left(\tfrac{1}{2}\omega_z{}^2\right)dt = \tfrac{1}{2}I\,\frac{d}{dt}\left(\omega_z{}^2\right)dt = \tfrac{1}{2}I\,\frac{d}{dt}\left(\omega^2\right)dt$$

This gives

$$W_{\text{net}} = \tfrac{1}{2}I\int_{t_i}^{t_f}\frac{d}{dt}\left(\omega^2\right)dt$$

The rotational work-energy theorem for a rigid object rotating about a fixed axis

where we have taken I out of the integral because the object is rigid and the axis is fixed. Performing the integration gives

$$W_{\text{net}} = \tfrac{1}{2}I\omega_f{}^2 - \tfrac{1}{2}I\omega_i{}^2 \tag{13-16}$$

The power P delivered to a rotating rigid object by a torque is the rate at which work is done by the torque. Using Eq. (13-13), we have

Power delivered to a rigid object rotating about a fixed axis

$$P = \frac{dW}{dt} = \tau_z\,\frac{d\theta}{dt} = \tau_z\omega_z \tag{13-17}$$

As with the work, the power due to a torque may be negative. If a torque tends to slow the rotation, then τ_z has the opposite sign from ω_z and P is negative. Such an energy transfer tends to decrease the object's rotational energy.

EXAMPLE 13-8. (a) Find the work done on the windlass by the force due to the rope in Example 13-7 (Fig. 13-11) during the time interval in which it rotates through an angle of 45°. (b) Assuming the windlass is at rest at the beginning of the 45° rotation, determine its angular speed at the end of the rotation. (c) Find the power delivered to the windlass by the rope at the instant the 45° rotation is completed.

SOLUTION. (a) From Example 13-7, the torque due to the rope is constant, $\tau_z = F_T R_0$, so that Eq. (13-15) may be used:

$W = F_T R_0 \, \Delta\theta$. Since 45° corresponds to $\pi/4$ rad,

$$W = (200 \text{ N})(0.083 \text{ m})(\pi/4 \text{ rad}) = 13 \text{ J}$$

(b) Since the torque due to the rope is the net torque about the axis of rotation, the solution from part (a) above gives $W_{net} = 13$ J. Also, the initial angular velocity was zero, so that $W_{net} = \frac{1}{2}I\omega^2$, or

$$\omega = \sqrt{\frac{2W_{net}}{I}} = \sqrt{\frac{2W_{net}}{\frac{1}{2}MR_0^2}}$$

$$= \sqrt{\frac{2(13 \text{ J})}{\frac{1}{2}(94 \text{ kg})(0.083 \text{ m})^2}} = 9.0 \text{ rad/s}$$

(c) Using the coordinate frame of Fig. 13-11b (+z out of the page), τ_z due to the rope is positive:

$$\tau_z = F_T R_0 = (200 \text{ N})(0.083 \text{ m}) = 17 \text{ N} \cdot \text{m}$$

and ω_z at the end of the 45° rotation is positive: $\omega_z = 9.0$ rad/s. Thus

$$P = \tau_z \omega_z = (17 \text{ N} \cdot \text{m})(9.0 \text{ rad/s}) = 150 \text{ W}$$

13-6 CONSERVATION OF ANGULAR MOMENTUM

In Chaps. 9 and 10, we introduced the principles of conservation of energy and conservation of linear momentum, respectively. Now we present a third conservation principle, the principle of *conservation of angular momentum*.

Suppose the net external torque on a system of particles is zero: $\Sigma\tau = 0$. From Eq. (13-9), $\Sigma\tau = d\mathbf{L}/dt$, so that

$$\frac{d\mathbf{L}}{dt} = 0 \qquad \text{or} \qquad \frac{d}{dt}(\Sigma\boldsymbol{\ell}_i) = 0$$

If the time derivative (or rate of change) of a quantity is zero, then the quantity remains constant. Therefore, when the net external torque on a system is zero, we have

$$\mathbf{L} = \Sigma\boldsymbol{\ell}_i = \text{constant}$$

Although the individual angular momenta of the particles that compose the system may change when $\Sigma\tau = 0$, their sum cannot change. Another way to express this result is

Total angular momentum is conserved when $\Sigma\tau = 0$.

$$\mathbf{L}_i = \mathbf{L}_f \tag{13-18}$$

The principle of conservation of angular momentum

where $\mathbf{L}_i$ and $\mathbf{L}_f$ are the initial and final total angular momenta of the system. Thus the principle of conservation of angular momentum is: *If the net torque on a system of particles relative to some point is zero, then the total angular momentum of the system relative to that same point is constant.*

EXAMPLE 13-9. A boy of mass m running with speed v jumps onto the outer edge of a playground merry-go-round that is initially at rest (Fig. 13-14a). What is the angular speed ω of the merry-go-round after the boy is at rest relative to the merry-go-round? Assume the torque due to friction in the axle of the merry-go-round is negligible.

SOLUTION. We treat the boy as a particle, and arrange our coordinate system as shown in Fig. 13-14b. We take the system to be the boy and the merry-go-round. Since the torque due to friction in the axle is negligible, there are no external torques on the system, and its total angular momentum is conserved. The boy and the merry-go-round exert forces and torques on each other, but these forces and torques are internal; they are equal and opposite, so their sum is zero.

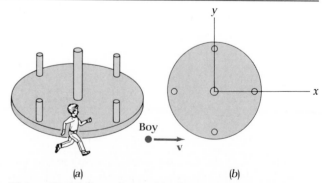

Figure 13-14. Example 13-9: (a) A boy jumps onto a playground merry-go-round. (b) Top view (+z is out of the page).

Since the merry-go-round is initially at rest, the initial

angular momentum of the system about the axle (the z axis) is entirely due to the boy:

$$L_{zi} = mvR$$

where R is the radius of the merry-go-round. If I is the moment of inertia of the merry-go-round, then the moment of inertia of the system after the boy is at rest relative to the merry-go-round is $I + mR^2$. Therefore,

$$L_{zf} = (I + mR^2)\omega_z$$

Conservation of angular momentum gives

$$mvR = (I + mR^2)\omega_z$$

Thus the angular speed is

$$\omega = \frac{mvR}{I + mR^2}$$

A changing moment of inertia. A particularly interesting application of the principle of conservation of angular momentum is to a system whose moment of inertia changes. If the object can be regarded as a rigid body rotating about the z axis before and after (but not during) the change in moment of inertia, then the z component of Eq. (13-18) can be written

$$I_i \omega_{zi} = I_f \omega_{zf} \qquad (13\text{-}19)$$

If the moment of inertia of a system changes while no external torques are exerted, the angular velocity must also change in order for the angular momentum to remain fixed. When this happens, the kinetic energy of the system changes, so that work must be done.

EXAMPLE 13-10. A physics professor is seated on a stool rotating about a vertical axis with an angular speed ω_i, as shown in Fig. 13-15a. The professor's arms are outstretched, and she is holding a dumbbell in each hand such that the moment of inertia of the system (professor, stool seat, and dumbbells) is I_i. She quickly pulls the dumbbells in to her sides so that the final moment of inertia of the system is one-third the initial: $I_f = I_i/3$ (Fig. 13-15b). (a) What is her final angular speed? (b) Compare the final and initial kinetic energies of the system. Neglect the torque due to friction in the stool's axle during the time interval in which the system's moment of inertia changes.

SOLUTION. (a) Since the torque due to friction in the stool's axle is negligible, there are no external torques on the system and its angular momentum is conserved:

$$I_i \omega_i = I_f \omega_f = \frac{I_i}{3} \omega_f$$

Solving for ω_f, we have

$$\omega_f = 3\omega_i$$

Thus conservation of angular momentum requires that the angular speed increase by the same factor by which the moment of inertia decreases. (b) The final kinetic energy of the system is

$$K_f = \tfrac{1}{2} I_f \omega_f^2 = \frac{1}{2}\left(\frac{I_i}{3}\right)(3\omega_i)^2$$

$$= 3(\tfrac{1}{2} I_i \omega_i^2) = 3K_i$$

Thus conservation of angular momentum requires that the kinetic energy of the system increase by the same factor by which the moment of inertia decreases. From where did this additional kinetic energy come?

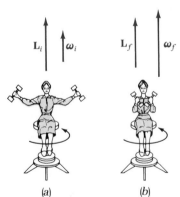

L_i ω_i L_f ω_f

(a)   (b)

Figure 13-15. Example 13-10: A physics professor on a rotating stool. (a) Large I, small ω. (b) Small I, large ω.

Conservation of angular momentum and central forces. The angular momentum of a system is conserved when the net torque on the system is zero. The net torque on a system is always zero when the net force on the system is zero. However, it is possible to have a zero net torque even with a nonzero net force. This is the case when the net torque is measured relative to a point that is

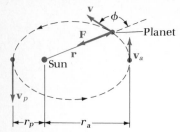

Figure 13-16. The elliptical orbit of a planet around the sun.

contained in the line of action of the net force. An example of this case is the torque on a planet, relative to the sun, due to the sun's gravitational force on the planet.

Consider a planet or comet of mass m in an elliptical orbit about the sun, as shown in Fig. 13-16. We regard the planet alone (excluding the sun) as the system. The gravitational force on the planet due to the sun is directly toward the sun. The moment arm of this force relative to the position of the sun is zero, so that the torque about the sun due to this force is zero. Therefore, the orbital angular momentum of the planet relative to the sun is constant, or conserved:

$$mvr \sin \phi = \text{constant}$$

All three quantities v, r, and ϕ vary as the planet moves in its elliptical orbit, but $mvr \sin \phi$ does not vary.

At two positions in the orbit—position a (for aphelion) where the planet is farthest from the sun, and position p (for perihelion) where the planet is nearest the sun—v is perpendicular to r, which means that $\phi = 90°$ and $\sin \phi = 1$. Applying conservation of momentum to these two points gives

$$mv_a r_a = mv_p r_p \qquad \text{or} \qquad v_a r_a = v_p r_p$$

This requires that $v_a < v_p$ because $r_a > r_p$. As the planet orbits the sun, its speed increases in going from a to p and then decreases in going from p to a. You may recall that our numerical solution of an elliptical orbit in Sec. 7-7 provided an example of this effect. We also reached similar conclusions using the principle of conservation of mechanical energy in Chap. 9.

In Chap. 7 we indicated that there are two important characteristics of the gravitational force: It is an inverse-square force, and it is an attractive force which is directed along the line between the interacting objects. In the case of the planets orbiting the sun, the sun is so much more massive than the planets that the planets effectively orbit a fixed point at the center of the sun. If a force on an object is always directed along a line from the object to a central point, and the magnitude of the force depends only on the distance to this point, then the force is called a *central force*. The gravitational force by the sun on the planets is an example of a central force. *The angular momentum of an object moving under the action of a central force, when measured relative to the origin at which the force is directed, is conserved.*

Definition of a central force

EXAMPLE 13-11. Prove Kepler's second law (Sec. 7-8).

SOLUTION. Kepler's second law states that *a line joining any planet to the sun sweeps out equal areas in equal time intervals.* Figure 13-17 shows an infinitesimal area dA which is swept out in an infinitesimal time interval dt. The area is that of a triangle of height $|d\mathbf{r}| \sin \phi$ and base r:

$$dA = \tfrac{1}{2}(r)(|d\mathbf{r}|\sin \phi) = \tfrac{1}{2}(r)(v \, dt \sin \phi)$$

where we have used $|d\mathbf{r}| = v \, dt$. Dividing both sides by dt and multiplying and dividing the right-hand side by m gives

$$\frac{dA}{dt} = \frac{mvr \sin \phi}{2m}$$

We recognize the numerator on the right-hand side as the magnitude of the planet's orbital angular momentum, which is constant. Thus $dA/dt = \text{constant}$, which is a mathematical statement of Kepler's second law.

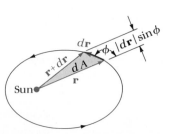

Figure 13-17. Example 13-11: Kepler's second law: The line connecting a planet to the sun sweeps out equal areas in equal time intervals.

13-7 MOTION OF A GYROSCOPE

So far we have applied Eq. (13-9), $\Sigma \tau = d\mathbf{L}/dt$, to only a few special cases. In specific examples, we have discussed rigid objects that are symmetric about an axis of rotation that has a fixed orientation. In such cases, $\Sigma \tau$ (and $d\mathbf{L}/dt$) is in the same direction as $\mathbf{L}$; both quantities are along the axis, and the problem is essentially one-dimensional. The study of gyroscopic motion affords us the opportunity to consider a more general case, where $\Sigma \tau$ and $\mathbf{L}$ are not along the same line. This provides a clear demonstration of the vector nature of torque and angular momentum.

Gyroscopic motion can be exhibited with a top or with a toy gyroscope. The usual demonstration of this motion in the physics classroom is with a bicycle wheel that is spinning rapidly with angular speed ω_s about an axle. One end of the axle (end P in Fig. 13-18) forms a ball-and-socket joint, with the top of a stand so that the axle pivots freely. When end A of the axle is released, an astonishing thing happens. The spinning wheel seems to defy gravity. It does not fall to the floor as it would if it were not spinning. Instead, the wheel and axle rotate about a vertical axis, turning out the path shown in Fig. 13-18. This rotation of the axle and wheel is called *precession*, and we let ω_p represent the angular speed of precession. For precession to occur, we must have $\omega_s \gg \omega_p$.

As you can see from the figure, there is more to this motion than we have mentioned so far. When first released, end A bobs up and down as the wheel precesses. This bobbing motion is called *nutation*, and it becomes damped out due to friction in the pivot. We shall ignore the nutation by considering the motion after the nutation has become negligible.

In Fig. 13-19 we show a coordinate frame with the origin at the pivot, the y axis vertical, and the xz plane horizontal. We let the axle be horizontal for simplicity, and consider the motion at the instant the axle is along the z axis. There are two external forces on the wheel and its axle (which we regard as the system). They are the weight $\mathbf{F}_e$ acting downward at the center of the wheel and the force $\mathbf{F}_p$, due to the stand, acting at the pivot P. We neglect the torque due to friction in the pivot. The net external torque on the system about P is

$$\Sigma \tau = F_e D\mathbf{i} = MgD\mathbf{i}$$

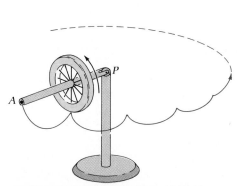

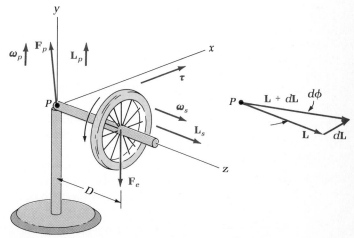

Figure 13-18. A bicycle wheel precesses around a vertical axis. When first released, the wheel also exhibits a nutational motion.

Figure 13-19. Viewing the wheel at the instant the axle is along the z axis.

That is, only the weight contributes to the torque about P because the line of action of $\mathbf{F}_p$ passes through P. Therefore, the infinitesimal change $d\mathbf{L}$ in total angular momentum about P during an infinitesimal time interval dt is

$$d\mathbf{L} = \Sigma\boldsymbol{\tau}\,dt = (MgD\,dt)\mathbf{i}$$

The total angular momentum $\mathbf{L}$ of the system about P is the sum of the angular momentum $\mathbf{L}_s$ due to the spinning wheel and the angular momentum $\mathbf{L}_p$ due to the precession of the wheel and axle:

$$\mathbf{L} = \mathbf{L}_s + \mathbf{L}_p$$

The spin angular momentum is

$$\mathbf{L}_s = I_s\omega_s\,\mathbf{k}$$

where I_s is the moment of inertia of the wheel about its axle. The precessional angular momentum is

$$\mathbf{L}_p = I_p\omega_p\mathbf{j}$$

where I_p is the moment of inertia of the wheel and axle about the y axis. This gives

$$\mathbf{L} = I_s\omega_s\mathbf{k} + I_p\omega_p\mathbf{j}$$

Note that $\mathbf{L}$ is perpendicular to $d\mathbf{L}$, which means that $\mathbf{L}$ will not change in magnitude but will change in direction.

Now we assume ω_s is much larger than ω_p, so that the total angular momentum is very nearly equal to the spin angular momentum. With this simplification, we can see from the triangle in Fig. 13-19 that the infinitesimal precession angle $d\phi$ swept out in time interval dt is

$$d\phi = \frac{dL}{L} = \frac{MgD\,dt}{I_s\omega_s}$$

Since $\omega_p = d\phi/dt$,
$$\omega_p = \frac{MgD}{I_s\omega_s} \tag{13-20}$$

Thus, using reasonable assumptions, we have developed an equation for the angular speed of precession. The equation indicates that as friction in the axle causes ω_s to decrease, ω_p will increase, a feature of the motion that is easily noticeable.

Let us now try to understand why the wheel does not fall if it is spinning, but does fall if it is not spinning. First we describe, in terms of torque and angular momentum, the way a nonspinning wheel does fall. Suppose the wheel in Fig. 13-19 is not spinning, so that $\mathbf{L}_s$ does not exist. The net torque $\Sigma\boldsymbol{\tau}$ and $d\mathbf{L}$ are both along the x axis. Since the wheel is *not* spinning when released, the angular momentum is initially zero; after the wheel is released, the angular momentum increases in magnitude, while always pointing along the x axis. That is, the wheel and axle rotate about the x axis. If you place your thumb along the x axis, your fingers will curl in the direction of the rotation, showing you that the wheel rotates downward or falls.

Now suppose the wheel is initially spinning. In this case $d\mathbf{L}$ (along the x axis) adds to the existing $\mathbf{L}_s$ (along the z axis) to form a new vector $\mathbf{L} + d\mathbf{L}$ that makes an angle $d\phi$ with the z axis. This means that after time dt the axle has precessed by an angle $d\phi$. This rotation is about the vertical z axis rather than the horizontal x axis. Since the axle has rotated by an angle $d\phi$ from the z axis, the net torque now makes an angle $d\phi$ with the x axis. Both vectors, $\Sigma\boldsymbol{\tau}$ and $\mathbf{L}$, continuously rotate about the vertical, with $\Sigma\tau$ staying $90°$ ahead of $\mathbf{L}$. The torque does not maintain a fixed direction when the wheel is spinning, whereas it does when the wheel is not spinning. The torque causes a spinning wheel to precess, and it causes a nonspinning wheel to fall.

SUMMARY WITH APPLICATIONS

Section 13-2. Angular momentum of a particle

The angular momentum ℓ of a particle about a point O is

$$\ell = \mathbf{r} \times \mathbf{p} \tag{13-1}$$

where $\mathbf{r}$ is measured relative to O and $\mathbf{p} = m\mathbf{v}$. From Newton's second law, the relation between ℓ and the net torque $\Sigma\tau = \mathbf{r} \times \Sigma\mathbf{F}$ is

$$\Sigma\tau = \frac{d\ell}{dt} \tag{13-5}$$

Determine the angular momentum of a particle traveling in a circle and of a particle traveling in a straight line; determine the rate of change of the angular momentum of a particle from the net torque exerted on it.

Section 13-3. Angular momentum of a system of particles

The total angular momentum of a system of particles is the vector sum of the angular momenta of the particles that compose the system:

$$\mathbf{L} = \Sigma\ell_i \tag{13-6}$$

Using Eq. (13-5) and Newton's third law, we find

$$\Sigma\tau_{\text{ext}} = \frac{d\mathbf{L}}{dt} \tag{13-9}$$

where $\Sigma\tau_{\text{ext}}$ is the net external torque on the system.

Determine the total angular momentum of a system of particles; use Newton's laws to show that internal torques do not contribute to the rate of change of the total angular momentum.

Section 13-4. Rotational dynamics of a rigid object about a fixed axis

For the case of a rigid object rotating about a fixed axis,

$$L_z = I\omega_z \tag{13-10}$$

and

$$\Sigma\tau_z = I\alpha_z \tag{13-12}$$

Relative to any point on the axis, a torque's axial component is

$$\tau_z = RF_t$$

Use the rotational analog of Newton's second law to determine the rotational motion of a rigid object rotating about a fixed axis.

Section 13-5. Rotational work and power for a rigid object

The work done by a torque on a rigid object rotating about a fixed axis is

$$W = \int_{\theta_i}^{\theta_f} \tau_z \, d\theta \tag{13-14}$$

Work done by the net torque changes the rotational kinetic energy:

$$W_{\text{net}} = \tfrac{1}{2}I\omega_f^2 - \tfrac{1}{2}I\omega_i^2 \tag{13-16}$$

The power to a rotating rigid object is

$$P = \tau_z\omega_z \tag{13-17}$$

Determine the work done by a torque; use the principle of conservation of energy to describe rotational motion; determine the power delivered to a rotating object by a torque.

Section 13-6. Conservation of angular momentum

If the net external torque on a system is zero, the total angular momentum of the system is conserved:

$$\mathbf{L}_i = \mathbf{L}_f \tag{13-18}$$

Use the principle of conservation of angular momentum to determine rotational motion.

Section 13-7. Motion of a gyroscope

The motion of a gyroscope provides an example of rotational motion where the rotating object is not constrained to rotate about an axis with fixed orientation.

Describe the motion of a gyroscope.

Table 13-1 summarizes the mathematical similarity between translational motion in one dimension and rotational motion about a fixed axis.

Table 13-1. Analogy between rotation and translation

Translation (one dimension)		Rotation (fixed axis)	
Coordinate	x	Coordinate	θ
Velocity component	v_x	Velocity component	ω_z
Acceleration component	a_x	Acceleration component	α_z
Mass	M	Moment of inertia	I
Force component	F_x	Torque component	τ_z
Momentum	P_x	Momentum	L_z
$\Sigma F_{\text{ext},x} = Ma_x$		$\Sigma\tau_{\text{ext},z} = I\alpha_z$	
$P_x = Mv_x$		$L_z = I\omega_z$	
$W = \int F_x \, dx$		$W = \int \tau_z \, d\theta$	
$W_{\text{net}} = \tfrac{1}{2}Mv_f^2 - \tfrac{1}{2}Mv_i^2$		$W_{\text{net}} = \tfrac{1}{2}I\omega_f^2 - \tfrac{1}{2}I\omega_i^2$	
$P = F_x v_x$		$P = \tau_z\omega_z$	

QUESTIONS

13-1   What is the angle between a particle's linear velocity and its angular momentum?

13-2   If a particle is traveling in a straight line, are there any points about which its angular momentum is zero? Explain.

13-3   A particle is moving along a straight line with increasing speed, and point P is not on its line of motion. Is the direction of its angular momentum about P constant? Is the magnitude of its angular momentum about P constant?

13-4   If a particle is in uniform circular motion, is either the direction or the magnitude of the angular momentum about the center of its motion constant? If the particle's speed is changing as it travels in a circle, is either the direction or the magnitude of the angular momentum constant?

13-5   If the net torque exerted on a particle is in the same direction as the particle's angular momentum, is there a change in the direction of the particle's angular momentum? Is there a change in the magnitude of the particle's angular momentum?

13-6   If the net torque on a particle is perpendicular to the particle's angular momentum, is there a change in the direction of the particle's angular momentum? Is there a change in the magnitude of the particle's angular momentum?

13-7   Consider an isolated system of two particles a and b that interact with each other such that $\mathbf{F}_{ab} = -\mathbf{F}_{ba}$, but the direction of the forces is perpendicular to the line joining the particles, as shown in Fig. 13-20. What happens to this system as time goes on? Is total linear momentum conserved? Is total angular momentum conserved? Is such a system possible? Explain.

Figure 13-20. Ques. 13-7.

13-8   Explain why heavily muscled calves can be a disadvantage to a sprinter.

13-9   Explain why it is often advisable for a batter to "choke up" on the bat (Fig. 13-21) when facing a pitcher who can throw a baseball at a very high speed.

13-10 When a billiard ball rolls down a slope without sliding, what force is responsible for the torque that causes the angular acceleration about an axis through the center of mass? What force is responsible for the torque that causes the angular acceleration about an axis through the point of contact with the surface?

13-11 Legend has it that a cat always lands on its feet. High-speed cameras have shown that when a cat begins a

Figure 13-21. Ques. 13-9: Choking up on a bat. *(Tom Richard)*

fall with its feet up, its tail rotates rapidly and the cat's body also rotates, so that it does, in fact, land on its feet. Explain the motion in terms of conservation of angular momentum. Include in your explanation a comparison of the sense of the rotation of the cat's body with that of its tail. How do you think a bobtailed cat might do in a fall that begins with its feet up?

13-12 A small satellite orbiting the earth has only one window for the astronaut, and the window is facing away from the earth. Explain how the astronaut can rotate the satellite so he can view the earth and not use any rocket fuel in the process.

13-13 A spinning ice skater rapidly extends his arms. (Neglect friction during the time interval the arms are extended.) Is his kinetic energy conserved? Is his potential energy conserved? Is his mechanical energy conserved? Is his angular momentum conserved? If any of these quantities are not conserved, tell whether they increase or decrease.

13-14 A yo-yo with half the string wound on its axle is placed on its edge on the floor, as shown in Fig. 13-22. Consider pulling gently on the string in the three different directions indicated by $\mathbf{F}_a$, $\mathbf{F}_b$, and $\mathbf{F}_c$ in the figure. The force in each case is gentle enough so that the yo-yo does not slide. In which case, if any, does

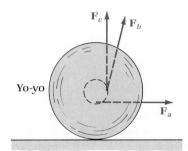

Figure 13-22. Ques. 13-14.

the string wind onto the yo-yo, and in which case, if any, does the string wind off the yo-yo?

13-15   A particle moves in a straight line at constant speed, and origin O is not on the particle's path. Does the line between O and the particle sweep out equal areas in equal times? Explain.

13-16   Consider the angular momentum $\mathbf{L}$ of a uniform door relative to origin O on the axis through the hinges. Let the z axis be along the hinges and let ω_z be positive. Describe qualitatively the direction of $\mathbf{L}$ when O is (a) midway between the top and bottom of the door, (b) at the top, (c) at the bottom. Reconsider the question, with ω_z negative.

13-17   For the case considered in Fig. 13-8, ω_z is positive so that $\mathbf{p}_i$ is into the page and $\mathbf{p}_j$ is out of the page. Draw the figure for the case where ω_z is negative. With $m_i = m_j$, are the radial components of $\boldsymbol{\ell}_i$ and $\boldsymbol{\ell}_j$ still equal and opposite?

13-18   A pencil that was balanced on its eraser end falls over such that the eraser does not slide (Fig. 13-23). Consider the contact force $\mathbf{F}_c$ exerted by the surface on the pencil. (a) Is the x component of $\mathbf{F}_c$ positive or

negative? Explain. (b) Is the y component of $\mathbf{F}_c$ equal to mg, less than mg, or greater than mg? (c) Sketch Fig. 13-23 on a scratch sheet and show $\mathbf{F}_c$ and $m\mathbf{g}$ on your sketch.

13-19   Why is it easier to balance a spinning basketball on the end of your finger than a nonspinning basketball?

13-20   Suppose the angular momentum of a system about a particular point is zero. Must the net external torque on the system about that point be zero? Must the net external force on the system be zero?

13-21   Suppose we assume that the axle-wheel system in Sec. 13-7 is constructed such that the mass of the axle is much less than the mass of the wheel. In this case, if we double the mass of the wheel, what will be the approximate effect on the angular speed of precession?

13-22   Consider the bicycle wheel in Fig. 13-19 spinning in the opposite direction from that shown. What are the directions of $\boldsymbol{\omega}_p$, $\mathbf{L}$, $d\mathbf{L}$, and $\Sigma \boldsymbol{\tau}_{\text{ext}}$ in this case?

13-23   You hand a porter a suitcase, inside of which is a large spinning rotor. What happens when the porter turns a corner?

13-24   Complete the following table:

Symbol	Represents	Type	SI unit
$\boldsymbol{\ell}$		Vector	
$\mathbf{L}$			kg · m²/s
$\Sigma \boldsymbol{\tau}_{\text{ext}}$			
r	Distance from a point		
R			
P			

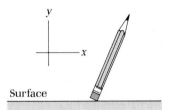

Figure 13-23. Ques. 13-18: A falling pencil.

EXERCISES

Section 13-2. Angular momentum of a particle

13-1   An observer stands 125 m south of an east-west road, and a 1340-kg automobile is traveling east along the road. (a) What are the magnitude and direction of the angular momentum of the automobile relative to the observer at the instant it is directly north of the observer and moving at a speed of 36.4 m/s? (b) What is the angular momentum after the car has traveled 325 m beyond the position in part (a) and is still moving at 36.4 m/s?

13-2   Determine the magnitude of the orbital angular momentum of Mars relative to the sun, assuming a circular orbit of radius 2.28×10^{11} m. The mass of Mars is 6.46×10^{23} kg, and the period of its orbit is 5.94×10^7 s.

13-3   What is the angular momentum relative to the origin for a 4.1-kg particle at the instant its position is $\mathbf{r} = (-3.5 \text{ m})\mathbf{i} + (1.4 \text{ m})\mathbf{j}$ and its velocity is $\mathbf{v} = (-2.0 \text{ m/s})\mathbf{i} + (-6.3 \text{ m/s})\mathbf{j}$?

13-4   A 3.6-kg particle is moving in the xy plane. What is its angular momentum (magnitude and direction) relative to the origin at the instant it crosses the x axis at $x = +4.6$ m and at a speed of 2.4 m/s? The angle between $\mathbf{i}$ and $\mathbf{v}$ at that instant is $+0.76$ rad.

13-5   A 72-g bead slides without friction on a vertically oriented circular wire of radius 0.93 m, as shown in Fig.

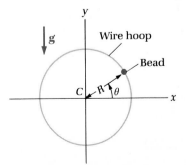

Figure 13-24. Exercise 13-5.

13-24. If the bead is released from rest at $\theta = 0.87$ rad, what is the angular momentum of the bead relative to C at the instant it passes the x axis?

13-6   Recall that the kinetic energy of a particle may be written $K = \frac{1}{2}p^2/m$, where $p = mv$. Show that the kinetic energy of a particle moving in a circle of radius R can be written $K = \frac{1}{2}\ell^2/I$, where $I = mR^2$ and ℓ is measured relative to the center of the circle.

Section 13-3. Angular momentum of a system of particles

13-7   A system consists of three particles which have angular momenta, relative to the origin, of $\boldsymbol{\ell}_a = (2.4 \text{ kg m}^2/\text{s})\mathbf{i}$, $\boldsymbol{\ell}_b = (-6.1 \text{ kg m}^2/\text{s})\mathbf{k}$, and $\boldsymbol{\ell}_c = (-4.8 \text{ kg m}^2/\text{s})\mathbf{i} + (1.6 \text{ kg m}^2/\text{s})\mathbf{j}$. What is the total angular momentum of the system relative to the origin?

13-8   Two particles A and B exert forces on one another of magnitude 14 N, as shown in Fig. 13-25. (a) Determine the magnitude and direction of the torque exerted by B on A about the origin. (b) Determine the magnitude and direction of the torque exerted by A on B about the origin. (c) Determine the net torque on the two particles due to their interaction.

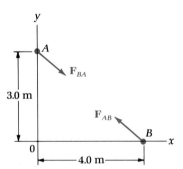

Figure 13-25. Exercise 13-8: The $+z$ direction is out of the page.

13-9   Two particles of equal mass m move in opposite directions along straight-line paths with the same speed v. The paths of the particles are parallel and separated a distance D. Show that the magnitude of the total angular momentum of the two particles is mvD about any point.

13-10 Two particles of mass M_1 and M_2 are connected to each other and to the axis of rotation by a rigid rod of negligible mass, as shown in Fig. 13-26. The two parti-

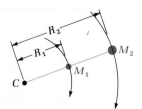

Figure 13-26. Exercise 13-10.

cles have an angular speed ω and are at distances of R_1 and R_2 from the axis. Write an expression for the total angular momentum in terms of M_1, M_2, R_1, R_2, and ω.

Section 13-4. Rotational dynamics of a rigid object about a fixed axis

13-11 What is the angular momentum, relative to the center of the record, of an 85-g phonograph record of radius 150 mm when it is rotating on a 33.33-rev/min turntable.

13-12 (a) What is the z component of the net external torque on a uniform door of mass 22 kg and width 0.95 m at the instant its z component of angular acceleration is 8.2 rad/s²? The z axis is along the hinges and $+z$ is upward. (b) If the net torque component in part (a) is entirely due to a force perpendicular to the face of the door and applied at the knob, which is 0.89 m from the axis through the hinges, what is the magnitude of this force?

13-13 A grinding wheel with a moment of inertia about its axle of 0.15 kg · m² has a constant net torque of magnitude 18 N · m exerted on it about its axle. Assuming it starts from rest at $t = 0$, develop equations for the wheel's angular acceleration, angular velocity, and angular position as functions of time.

13-14 A bicycle wheel with a moment of inertia about its axle of 0.25 kg · m² and an initial angular speed of 12 rad/s slows to a stop because of friction in the bearings in a time interval of 320 s. Determine the magnitude of the torque due to friction, assuming it is constant.

13-15 (a) The pulley in Fig. 13-27a has a moment of inertia of 0.085 kg · m² about its axle and a radius of 170 mm. The string wrapped around the pulley exerts a constant force of magnitude 32 N. Neglecting the torque due to friction in the bearings, determine the pulley's angular acceleration magnitude. (b) The same pulley now has a 32-N block tied to the string and is released (Fig. 13-27b). Determine the pulley's angular acceleration magnitude. (c) Explain why the answers to parts (a) and (b) are different. What would you do to cause the force to be constant at 32 N, as in part (a)?

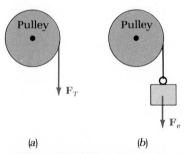

(a)   (b)

Figure 13-27. Exercise 13-15.

13-16 A pulley with a radius of 120 mm has a 7.3-kg block tied to a string that is wrapped around the pulley, similar to the arrangement shown in Fig. 13-27b. The block falls from rest a distance of 450 mm in 0.33 s. Find the moment of inertia of the pulley about its axle, assuming frictional effects are negligible. What can you say about the way the mass of the pulley is distributed about its axis?

13-17 Rework the previous exercise, taking friction in the pulley bearings into account. Using the procedure of Exercise 13-14, we find that the torque due to friction between the pulley and its bearings is 0.23 N · m. Compare your answer with that of the previous exercise.

13-18 Blocks B and C are tied to a string that passes over a pulley P, as shown in Fig. 13-28. Neglecting friction between the pulley and its bearings, neglecting the mass of the string, and assuming that the string does not slip, determine (a) the magnitude of the linear acceleration of the blocks, (b) the tension in the part of the string connected to B, (c) the tension in the part of the string connected to C, (d) the magnitude of the force on the pulley due to its bearings. (e) Compare the answer in part (d) with the total weight of the blocks and the pulley, and explain why these two results differ. Treat the pulley as a uniform disk of radius R_0 and use these data: $R_0 = 78$ mm, $m_P = 0.74$ kg, $m_B = 0.83$ kg, and $m_C = 0.57$ kg.

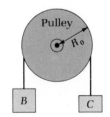

Figure 13-28. Exercise 13-18.

13-19 Blocks B and C are tied together by a light string that passes over a pulley, as shown in Fig. 13-29. Friction between block B and the table and friction in the pulley are negligible. Assuming the string does not slip,

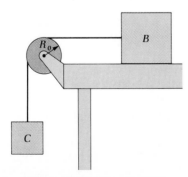

Figure 13-29. Exercise 13-19.

determine (a) the magnitude of the linear acceleration of the blocks, (b) the tension in the string between block B and the pulley, (c) the tension in the string between block C and the pulley. Find your answers in terms of m_B, m_C, I, R_0, and g.

13-20 A 4.5-kg block is tied to a string that is wrapped around a pulley, and the block slides down a slope as shown in Fig. 13-30. The coefficient of kinetic friction between the block and the slope is 0.30, and there is a constant torque due to friction, of magnitude 1.3 N · m acting on the pulley. The moment of inertia of the pulley about its axle is 0.016 kg · m². Other data are $\theta = 0.73$ rad and $R_0 = 85$ mm. Determine (a) the magnitude of the block's acceleration and (b) the tension in the string.

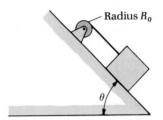

Figure 13-30. Exercise 13-20.

13-21 Find the force on the windlass of Example 13-7 that is caused by its bearings.

Section 13-5. Rotational work and power for a rigid object

13-22 (a) What is the work done by the frictional torque at the bearings of a bicycle wheel of moment of inertia 0.22 kg · m² when the wheel slows to a stop from an angular speed of 14 rad/s? (b) The wheel comes to rest in a time interval of 86 s. Assuming the frictional torque is constant, what is the magnitude of the angular acceleration? (c) Find the power delivered to the wheel as a function of time where $t = 0$ corresponds to the instant its angular speed was 14 rad/s.

13-23 Show that the kinetic energy of a rigid body rotating about a fixed axis may be written $K = \frac{1}{2}L^2/I$.

13-24 What is the power delivered to the pulley by the rope in Fig. 13-27a at the instant its angular speed is 2.9 rad/s and $F_T = 32$ N?

13-25 Determine the linear speed of the two blocks in Fig. 13-28 at the instant block B has fallen 12 mm after being released from rest.

13-26 The pulley P in Fig. 13-31 is rotated clockwise until the

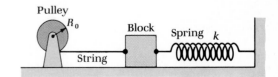

Figure 13-31. Exercise 13-26.

spring is stretched 52 mm, and then released from rest. Determine (a) the speed of the block when it passes through the position at which the spring is unstretched and (b) the power delivered to the block by the spring when it passes through the position at which the spring is unstretched. Neglect friction between the block and the surface and in the pulley bearings. The data are $m_B = 4.3$ kg, $I_P = 0.016$ kg · m², $R_0 = 73$ mm, and $k = 230$ N/m.

Section 13-6. Conservation of angular momentum

13-27 An ice skater spins about a vertical axis at an angular speed of 15 rad/s with outstretched arms, then quickly pulls her arms in to her sides in a time interval so small that the effect of frictional forces due to the ice are negligible. Her initial moment of inertia about the axis of rotation is 1.72 kg · m², and her final moment of inertia is 0.61 kg · m². (a) What is her resultant angular speed? (b) What is the change in her kinetic energy? (c) Explain this change in kinetic energy.

13-28 A 22-kg child stands halfway between the center and the edge of a merry-go-round that is rotating freely at an angular speed of 1.8 rad/s. (a) What is the angular speed of the merry-go-round after the child walks to its edge? (b) What is the change in the kinetic energy of the system (child plus merry-go-round)? The radius of the merry-go-round is 3.0 m, and its moment of inertia, when empty, is 610 kg · m². Neglect friction in the axle during the time interval in which the child moves.

13-29 An open door of mass M is at rest when struck by a thrown ball of mass m ($m \ll M$) at a point that is a distance D from an axis through the hinges, as shown in Fig. 13-32. Just before the ball strikes the door, its path is perpendicular to the door face, and, since $m \ll M$, its path is still nearly perpendicular just after the collision. The door has a uniform density and width w. Let v_i and v_f represent the initial and final speeds of the ball. Neglect friction in the hinges during the time interval of the collision. (a) Taking the system to be the ball and the door, explain why the total linear momentum of the system is not conserved. (b) Is the angular momentum of the system about any axis conserved? If so, identify the axis. (c) Use the approximation discussed above and deter-

mine an expression for the resulting angular speed ω of the door in terms of the quantities introduced. (d) Evaluate ω when $m = 1.1$ kg, $M = 35$ kg, $w = 73$ cm, $D = 62$ cm, $v_i = 27$ m/s, and $v_f = 16$ m/s. (This collision is considered further in Prob. 13-19.)

13-30 The door described in the previous exercise is at rest when struck by a ball of putty of mass m, as shown in Fig. 13-33. The initial velocity of the putty is horizontal and makes an angle θ with a normal to the door, and the putty sticks to the door after the collision. (a) Find the resulting angular speed of the door. (b) Find the change in kinetic energy of the system (door plus putty). (c) Evaluate the answers to parts (a) and (b) when $m = 1.1$ kg, $M = 35$ kg, $w = 73$ cm, $D = 62$ cm, $\theta = 0.38$ rad, and $v = 27$ m/s.

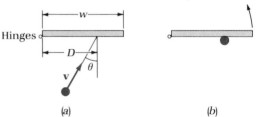

(a)   (b)

Figure 13-33. Exercise 13-30: Top view of the door: (a) before the collision; (b) after the collision.

13-31 A block of mass m moves in a circle of radius R_i with speed v_i, while sliding without friction on a horizontal tabletop. The block is tied to a string that passes through a hole in the table, as shown in Fig. 13-34, and there is no frictional force between the table and the string. The end of the string under the table is displaced downward so that after the displacement the block moves in a circle of radius R_f. (a) Show that the ratio of the tension in the string after the displacement to that before the displacement equals $(R_i/R_f)^3$. (b) Determine the tension in the string after the displacement for the case where the tension before the displacement is 3.4 N and $R_f = \frac{1}{2}R_i$.

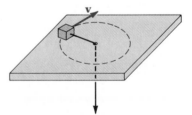

Figure 13-34. Exercise 13-31.

13-32 Disk B rotates freely with angular velocity ω_B and has a rod that projects along its axis of rotation. A hole in the center of disk C is fitted over the rod, as shown in Fig. 13-35, and disk C, initially at rest, is dropped onto disk B. (a) Determine the angular velocity of the sys-

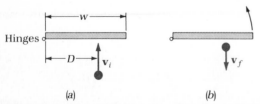

(a)   (b)

Figure 13-32. Exercise 13-29: Top view of the door: (a) before the collision; (b) after the collision.

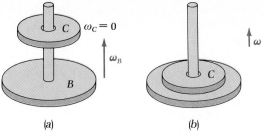

Figure 13-35. Exercise 13-32: Wheel B is connected to the shaft and wheel C fits loosely over the shaft: (a) before C is dropped; (b) after C is dropped.

tem after the frictional interaction between B and C brings them to a common angular velocity. (b) What is the change in kinetic energy of the system? Find your answers in terms of ω_B, I_B, and I_C. (c) Evaluate your answers to parts (a) and (b) when $I_B = 0.20$ kg $\cdot$ m², $I_C = 0.10$ kg $\cdot$ m², and $\omega_B = 6.2$ rad/s.

13-33 Two ice skaters of equal mass m skate in straight lines

toward each other on parallel paths with the same speed v. The lines of motion of the skaters are a distance D apart, which is a little more than an arm's length. When the skaters are abreast, they clasp arms and rotate in a circle of diameter D. (a) Determine the resulting angular speed of the skaters in terms of the quantities introduced above. (b) Find the change, if any, in the kinetic energy of the system.

Section 13-7. Motion of a gyroscope

13-34 A bicycle-wheel gyroscope is precessing without nutation, with its axle horizontal (Fig. 13-19). The wheel is spinning at 58 rad/s about its axle. The moment of inertia of the wheel about its axle is 0.23 kg $\cdot$ m², and the moment of inertia of the wheel and axle about the pivot is 0.14 kg $\cdot$ m². The axle is 280 mm long and the wheel is centered on the axle. (a) Find the angular speed of precession, assuming $L_s \gg L_p$. (b) Determine L_s and L_p and justify the assumption in part (a).

PROBLEMS

13-1 Consider a particle moving in a circle. Show that the equation $\mathbf{v} = \boldsymbol{\omega} \times \mathbf{r}$ gives the correct magnitude and direction for $\mathbf{v}$, where $\mathbf{r}$ is the position of the particle relative to the center of the circle.

13-2 Consider a particle at position $\mathbf{r} = x\mathbf{i} + y\mathbf{j} + z\mathbf{k}$, with linear momentum $\mathbf{p} = p_x\mathbf{i} + p_y\mathbf{j} + p_z\mathbf{k}$ that has force $\mathbf{F} = F_x\mathbf{i} + F_y\mathbf{j} + F_z\mathbf{k}$ exerted on it. (a) Determine the components of the angular momentum $\boldsymbol{\ell}$ and torque $\boldsymbol{\tau}$ relative to the origin. (b) Show that $d\ell_z/dt = v_x p_y - v_y p_x + xF_y - yF_x$. (c) Show that the first two terms in the previous equation add to zero so that $d\ell_z/dt = \tau_z$.

13-3 To start a billiard ball of radius r_0 rolling without sliding on a horizontal frictionless surface, a horizontal force is exerted on the ball such that its line of action is a distance h above the center of the ball (Fig. 13-36). Find h in terms of r_0. (Hint: Consider both the translational and rotational motion of the ball.)

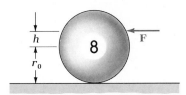

Figure 13-36. Prob. 13-3.

13-4 Consider a billiard ball rolling without sliding down a straight slope that makes an angle θ with the horizontal. (a) Show that the magnitude of the linear acceleration of the ball is $(5g \sin \theta)/7$. (b) Show that the minimum value for the coefficient of friction between a

ball and the surface in order for the ball to roll down the slope without sliding is $(2 \tan \theta)/7$. (Hint: Consider both the translational and rotational motion of the ball.)

13-5 A billiard ball of radius r_0 is initially sliding without rolling at linear speed v_0 on a horizontal surface; the coefficient of friction between the ball and the surface is μ. Show that, at the instant the ball begins to roll without sliding, (a) its linear speed is $5v_0/7$; (b) the time elapsed is $2v_0/7\mu g$; (c) the distance traveled is $12v_0{}^2/49\mu g$. (Hint: During the time the ball is both rolling and sliding, the surface exerts a constant force μmg at the point of contact. Also, the equations $v = \omega r_0$ and $a = \alpha r_0$ are valid at the instant rolling without sliding begins.)

13-6 Consider the force $\mathbf{F}_a$ exerted on the yo-yo of Fig. 13-22. (a) Assuming the yo-yo does not slide, find the magnitude of its linear acceleration in terms of its mass M, its radius R_2, the radius of its axle R_1, and F_a. Assume $I = \frac{1}{2}MR_2{}^2$. (b) Show that the maximum value F_a can have such that the yo-yo does not slide is $3\mu MgR_2/(R_2 + 2R_1)$, where μ is the coefficient of friction between the yo-yo and the surface.

13-7 A billiard ball of radius r_0 rolls without sliding from rest at the top of a loop-the-loop track having a loop of radius R_0, as shown in Fig. 13-37. What is the minimum height h from which the ball can be released and have it not leave the track as it passes the top of the loop? Assume $r_0 \ll R_0$.

13-8 A basketball of radius r_0 rolls without sliding down the side of a circular track of radius R_0, as shown in

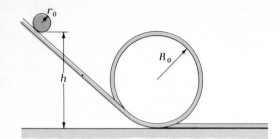

Figure 13-37. Prob. 13-7.

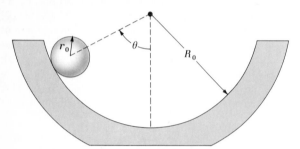

Figure 13-38. Prob. 13-8.

Fig. 13-38. The ball is released from rest at angle θ. What is its speed as it reaches the bottom?

13-9   A uniform trapdoor of mass M and length h rotates without friction about a horizontal axis through its hinges, as shown in Fig. 13-39. Show that the angular speed of the door at position θ, after beginning the fall from a vertical orientation and with a negligible initial speed, is $\sqrt{3g(1-\cos\theta)/h}$.

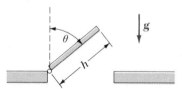

Figure 13-39. Prob. 13-9: Side view of a trapdoor.

13-10 Two wheels B and C rotate without friction about axles that are parallel but displaced, as shown in Fig. 13-40. The wheels have the same mass M, radius R_0, and moment of inertia I. Wheel C has angular velocity $\omega_0\mathbf{k}$, and wheel B is at rest when their edges are brought into contact. After a while, their angular speeds are the same as a result of their frictional interaction: $\omega_C = \omega\mathbf{k}$ and $\omega_B = -\omega\mathbf{k}$. (a) If we take the two wheels (excluding the axles) as the system, is the kinetic energy of the system conserved? (b) Is the angular momentum of the system conserved? (c) Show that the torque on either wheel is $-FR_0\mathbf{k}$ about any axis parallel to the axles, where F is the magnitude of the vertical component of the frictional force of interaction. (d) Show that $\omega = \frac{1}{2}\omega_0$. (e) What is the ratio of the final to the initial kinetic energy? (f) What is the

final angular momentum of the system? (*Hint:* Be sure to take account of the force on the wheels due to their axles.)

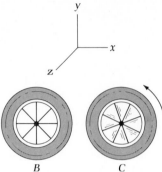

Figure 13-40. Prob. 13-10: The $+z$ direction is out of the page.

13-11 Reconsider the block of Exercise 13-31 (Fig. 13-34). Suppose the string is pulled down very slowly so that the block can be considered to be nearly moving in a circle of radius R at any instant. (a) Show that the tension in the string varies with R as $mv_i^2R_i^2/R^3$, where i refers to the initial values. (b) Use your answer from part (a) to find the work done on the block by the tension in the string in changing the radius of the block's circular path from R_i to R_f. (c) Show that your answer from part (b) equals the change in kinetic energy of the block.

13-12 A student is sitting on a stool that can rotate about a vertical axis, and she is holding a bicycle wheel such that the axle is vertical, as shown in Fig. 13-41. The moment of inertia of the wheel about its axle is 0.21 kg $\cdot$ m², and the moment of inertia of the student plus wheel plus stool seat about the stool's axle is 2.8 kg $\cdot$ m². The initial angular velocity of the wheel about its axle is $(61$ rad/s$)\mathbf{k}$, and the initial angular velocity of the student about the stool's axle is zero, where we take $\mathbf{k}$ as vertically upward. The student rotates the wheel's axle $180°$ such that it is again vertical and the angular velocity of the wheel is $(-61$ rad/s$)\mathbf{k}$. (a) Determine the resulting angular velocity of the student about the stool's axle. (b) Determine the work done by the student. Neglect friction in the stool's axle.

Figure 13-41. Prob. 13-12: The $+z$ direction is vertically upward.

13-13 Suppose the axle of a steadily precessing bicycle wheel is not horizontal, as it was shown to be in Fig. 13-19; rather, the axle makes an angle θ with the xz plane. Using the assumptions given in Sec. 13-7, show that the angular speed of precession is independent of θ.

13-14 Find I_p for the bicycle-wheel gyroscope in Fig. 13-19 with the wheel centered on the axle. Assume $I_s = M_W R_0^2$, where M_W is the mass of the wheel (tire and rim) and R_0 is its radius. That is, treat the wheel as a hoop. Use the plane-figure theorem (Prob. 12-6) and the parallel-axis theorem to show that $I_p = \frac{1}{2} M_W R_0^2 + M_W D^2 + 4mD^2/3$, where m is the mass of the axle and $2D$ is its length.

13-15 (a) Show that the horizontal component of the force due to the pivot on the bicycle-wheel gyroscope described in Sec. 13-7 is $Mg[M^2gD^3/(I_s\omega_s)^2]$. (b) Determine the magnitude of the force due to the pivot. (c) Determine the angle between the vertical and the direction of the force due to the pivot.

13-16 The earth's axis of rotation precesses because the earth is not a perfect sphere. The earth can be considered as a perfect sphere plus a "belt" (Fig. 13-42). (a) Show that if we further approximate the belt as a dumbbell, with spheres of mass Δm at the positions shown in the figure, then the magnitude τ_s of the torque exerted by the sun about the center of the earth is

$$\tau_s = \frac{2\,GM_s\,\Delta m R_e^2\,\sin 23°\,\cos 23°}{R_0^3}$$

where M_s is the mass of the sun, R_e is the radius of the earth, and R_0 is the earth-sun distance. (b) Averaging over the actual bulge and over the year gives an average torque of 3/8 the above result. Also, comparison of the earth's circumference around the poles and around the equator gives Δm as 8/3000 the mass of the earth. Show that this leads to a precession of the earth's axis with a period of about 80,000 years. (Effects of the moon bring the precessional period down to about 26,000 years.)

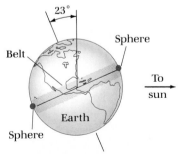

Figure 13-42. Prob. 13-16.

13-17 Consider a system in which $\boldsymbol{\omega}$ and $\mathbf{L}$ are not parallel. Two spheres of equal mass M are connected by a rod

of negligible mass and rotate on an axle, as shown in Fig. 13-43. Show that at the instant the spheres are in the yz plane: (a) the angular momentum about the origin is

$$\mathbf{L} = 2Mr^2\omega\,\sin\theta\,[(\sin\theta)\mathbf{k} + (\cos\theta)\mathbf{j}]$$

(b) the torque on the axle due to the bearings about the origin is

$$\boldsymbol{\tau}_b = -(2Mr^2\omega^2\sin\theta\cos\theta)\mathbf{i}$$

(Hint: Consider the projection of $\mathbf{L}$ and $d\mathbf{L}$ onto the xy plane similar to Fig. 13-19.) (c) the horizontal component of the force exerted on the axle by the upper bearing is

$$F_b = \frac{Mr^2\omega^2}{D}\cos\theta\,\sin\theta$$

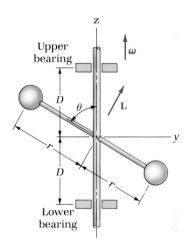

Figure 13-43. Prob. 13-17: The $+x$ direction is out of the page.

13-18 The particle of mass m in Fig. 13-44 is traveling in uniform circular motion about the point $(a, 0)$. (a) Show that the magnitude of its angular momentum about the origin is

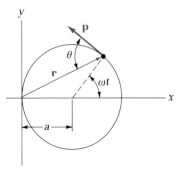

Figure 13-44. Prob. 13-18.

$$\ell = ma^2\omega(1 + \cos \omega t)$$

where ω is its angular speed and $t = 0$ corresponds to the instant the particle is at $(2a, 0)$. (b) Make a graph of ℓ versus t from $t = 0$ to $t = 2\pi/\omega$.

13-19 Consider the collision between the ball and the door discussed in Exercise 13-29 (Fig. 13-32). (a) Assume that the collision is elastic (the kinetic energy of the system is conserved) and show that

$$v_f = v_i \frac{Mw^2 - 3mD^2}{Mw^2 + 3mD^2}$$

$$\omega = v_i \frac{6mD}{Mw^2 + 3mD^2}$$

(b) Use the above expressions and the values from Exercise 13-29 to evaluate v_f and ω. Was the collision discussed in Exercise 13-29 elastic?

CHAPTER 14
OSCILLATIONS

14-1 INTRODUCTION

A type of motion common in nature is *oscillatory motion,* or *periodic motion.* Many effects are periodic; examples are the heartbeat of an animal, the seasons of the year, the swinging of the pendulum in a grandfather clock, the vibrations of atoms in solids, the electric current in the wires of the light bulb that illuminates this page, and on and on. On the grandest scale of all, some cosmologists believe that the entire universe may be oscillating with a time interval of tens of billions of years between oscillations.

Two types of motion that are closely associated with oscillatory motion are circular (or nearly circular) motion and wave motion. The average temperature in your town changes periodically as the seasons change, and these changes are associated with the earth's circular motion about the sun. As waves of water pass a dock, the water level on the dock pilings oscillates up and down. When we study waves in Chap. 32, we shall find that their description is based largely on the concepts learned in this chapter.

14-2 KINEMATICS OF SIMPLE HARMONIC MOTION

The simplest type of oscillatory motion is called *simple harmonic motion,* or *SHM* for brevity. Suppose you suspend a metal block from a spring attached to the ceiling. If you raise the block slightly from its equilibrium position and release it, the block oscillates up and down. This motion is an example of SHM. An important part of learning about SHM is becoming familiar with the jargon and the mathematical symbols. Therefore, we begin by introducing the equations and the terminology associated with SHM.

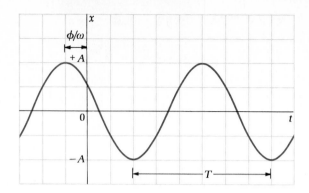

Figure 14-1. Coordinate x versus time t for an object executing SHM.

We define SHM as the motion of an object whose coordinate x as a function of time t is

Coordinate x of an object executing SHM

$$x = A \cos (\omega t + \phi) \qquad (14\text{-}1)$$

Definitions of amplitude A, angular frequency ω, phase constant ϕ, and phase $(\omega t + \phi)$

As the object oscillates back and forth, x varies sinusoidally with time (as a sine or cosine) between $x = A$ and $x = -A$ (Fig. 14-1). Thus A is called the *amplitude* because it is the maximum distance between the object and the central position at $x = 0$. The symbol ω represents the *angular frequency*, and, as we shall see, its value depends on the rate of the oscillations. The parameter ϕ is called the *phase constant* and is selected by our choice of when we begin the measurement ($t = 0$). The entire quantity in parentheses, the argument of the cosine, is called the *phase, $\omega t + \phi$*. In the next section we shall present a dynamical description of SHM that leads to Eq. (14-1).

Definition of the period T

A distinguishing feature of any oscillatory motion, including SHM, is that the motion repeats itself after a characteristic time interval, which is called the *period T*. That is, *the object undergoes a complete cycle of its motion during the time interval T*, as shown in Fig. 14-1. Thus, for a full cycle, the phase $(\omega t + \phi)$ increases by 2π rad while the time t increases by T, or

$$\omega(t + T) + \phi = (\omega t + \phi) + 2\pi$$

Subtracting $\omega t + \phi$ from each side gives $\omega T = 2\pi$, or

Relationship between T and ω

$$T = \frac{2\pi}{\omega} \qquad (14\text{-}2)$$

The period T is inversely proportional to ω; the larger the angular frequency, the smaller the period and the more quickly the object completes a cycle.

Besides T and ω, there is a third quantity that is used to specify the rate of the oscillations, the *frequency ν*:

Definition of frequency ν

$$\nu = \frac{1}{T} \qquad (14\text{-}3)$$

Since T is the time per cycle, ν is the number of cycles per unit of time. Substituting $T = 2\pi/\omega$ into Eq. (14-3), we find $\nu = \omega/2\pi$, or

$$2\pi\nu = \omega$$

Radians and cycles are dimensionless, so ν and ω have the same dimension, namely time^{-1}. The SI units for these closely related quantities are different: rad/s in the case of ω, and Hz (hertz) in the case of ν.* As an example, suppose

* A frequency of 1 cycle/s = 1 Hz. The hertz is named for H. R. Hertz (1857–1894), whose contributions are discussed in Sec. 34-7.

an object executing SHM has a period $T = 2$ s. Then the frequency is $\nu = 1/(2 \text{ s}) = 0.5 \text{ s}^{-1} = 0.5$ Hz, and the angular frequency is $\omega = 2\pi(0.5 \text{ Hz}) = \pi$ rad/s.

We can find the velocity and the acceleration of an object executing SHM by applying the procedures of kinematics from Chap. 3: Given an expression for x, we determine $v_x = dx/dt$ and $a_x = dv_x/dt = d^2x/dt^2$. Differentiating x in Eq. (14-1) with respect to t (see App. D), we find

Velocity component during SHM

$$v_x = \frac{dx}{dt} = -\omega A \sin(\omega t + \phi) \tag{14-4}$$

Differentiating a second time gives

Acceleration component during SHM

$$a_x = \frac{d^2x}{dt^2} = -\omega^2 A \cos(\omega t + \phi) \tag{14-5}$$

The derivative of a sinusoidally varying function is itself a sinusoidally varying function with the same frequency. Thus v_x and a_x oscillate with the same frequency as x, as shown in Fig. 14-2. Note that each differentiation changes the multiplicative factor by the factor ω; x oscillates between A and $-A$, v_x oscillates between ωA and $-\omega A$, and a_x oscillates between $\omega^2 A$ and $-\omega^2 A$. Therefore, the maximum speed of the object is $v_{\max} = \omega A$, and its maximum acceleration magnitude is $a_{\max} = \omega^2 A$.

Another effect of each differentiation is a change in phase by $\frac{1}{2}\pi$ rad, or 90°. From a comparison of the graphs of x and v_x in Fig. 14-2, you can see that v_x

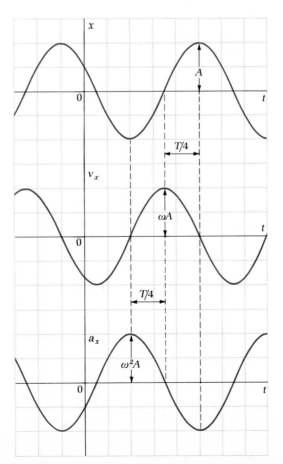

Figure 14-2. The relationships between x, v_x, and a_x for an object executing SHM: x and v_x are out of phase by $\frac{1}{2}\pi$ rad, or 90°; v_x and a_x are out of phase by 90°; and x and a_x are out of phase by 180°.

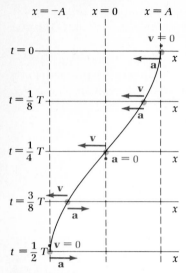

Figure 14-3. An object moving with SHM is shown at five different times during half of a cycle. Note the magnitude and direction of the velocity and acceleration at each time.

Acceleration and displacement are opposite in direction, and their magnitudes are proportional.

A simple harmonic oscillator is a system that undergoes SHM.

passes through each maximum and minimum one-fourth of a period before x. Since one-fourth of a period corresponds to a phase change of $\frac{1}{2}\pi$ rad, or $90°$, we sometimes describe this by saying, "v_x leads x by $90°$." Similarly, as you can see from the figure, a_x leads v_x by $90°$, and a_x leads x by $180°$.

In Fig. 14-3 we show an object at five different times during half a period of its motion from $t = 0$ to $t = T/2$. We have set $\phi = 0$ so that the figure shows the motion occurring between $x = A$ and $x = -A$. As an example of how the figure was constructed, let us determine x, v_x, and a_x at $t = 3T/8$. Substituting $t = 3T/8$ into the phase, we find $\omega t + \phi = (2\pi/T)(3T/8) + 0 = 3\pi/4$, so that $x = A \cos 3\pi/4 \approx -0.7A$; $v_x = -\omega A \sin 3\pi/4 \approx -0.7\omega A$; and $a_x = -\omega^2 A \cos 3\pi/4 \approx 0.7\omega^2 A$. At $t = 3T/8$, the figure shows the object at $x = -0.7A$, with $\mathbf{v} = -0.7v_{max}\mathbf{i}$ and with $\mathbf{a} = 0.7a_{max}\mathbf{i}$. You should check the values at the other times shown in the figure.

For an object executing SHM, there is a direct relation between the object's displacement ($x\mathbf{i}$) and its acceleration ($a_x\mathbf{i}$). Since

$$a_x = \frac{d^2x}{dt^2} = -\omega^2 A \cos(\omega t + \phi)$$

and

$$x = A \cos(\omega t + \phi)$$

we have

$$a_x = -\omega^2 x \qquad (14\text{-}6)$$

The object's acceleration and displacement are in opposite directions, and their magnitudes are proportional. This relation is used to identify a system that undergoes SHM. In the next several sections, we shall apply Newton's second law to a variety of systems. For each system, we shall find that the acceleration and displacement are opposite in direction and proportional in magnitude. Consequently, we shall conclude that each system undergoes SHM. A system that undergoes SHM is called a *simple harmonic oscillator*.

EXAMPLE 14-1. An object executes SHM with an amplitude of 0.17 m and a period of 0.84 s. Determine (a) the frequency and (b) the angular frequency of the motion. Write expressions for the time dependence of (c) the coordinate, (d) the velocity component, and (e) the acceleration component.

SOLUTION. (a) The frequency is $\nu = 1/T = 1/(0.84\text{ s}) = 1.2$ Hz.

(b) The angular frequency is $\omega = 2\pi/T = 2\pi/(0.84\text{ s}) = 7.5$ rad/s.

(c) From Eq. (14-1), $x = A \cos(\omega t + \phi)$. The value of A is given and ω was found in part (b). To use this expression, we must determine a value for ϕ. Since nothing in this problem requires otherwise, let us choose $\phi = 0$ for simplicity. Thus

$$x = (0.17\text{ m}) \cos[(7.5\text{ rad/s})t]$$

(d) From Eq. (14-4),

$$v_x = -\omega A \sin(\omega t + \phi)$$
$$= -(7.5\text{ rad/s})(0.17\text{ m}) \sin[(7.5\text{ rad/s})t]$$
$$= -(1.3\text{ m/s}) \sin[(7.5\text{ rad/s})t]$$

Notice that $v_{max} = 1.3$ m/s.

(e) From Eq. (14-5),

$$a_x = -\omega^2 A \cos(\omega t + \phi)$$
$$= -(7.5\text{ rad/s})^2(0.17\text{ m}) \cos[(7.5\text{ rad/s})t]$$
$$= -(9.5\text{ m/s}^2) \cos[(7.5\text{ rad/s})t]$$

Notice that $a_{max} = 9.5$ m/s^2.

Finding ϕ and A from the initial conditions. Often, when dealing with a system that undergoes SHM, the values of ϕ and A are not directly measured, but the values of x_0 and v_{x0} are known. The quantities x_0 and v_{x0} are called the *initial conditions*. We now show how to determine ϕ and A from the initial conditions. Setting $t = 0$ in Eqs. (14-1) and (14-4), we find

$$x_0 = A \cos \phi \qquad \text{and} \qquad v_{x0} = -\omega A \sin \phi \qquad (14\text{-}7)$$

These equations give x_0 and v_{x0} in terms of ϕ and A, but we want ϕ and A in terms of x_0 and v_{x0}. First we find ϕ by eliminating A. Dividing the second of these equations by the first, we have $v_{x0}/x_0 = (-\omega A \sin \phi)/(A \cos \phi) = -\omega \tan \phi$. Solving for ϕ, we obtain

Phase constant ϕ in terms of x_0 and v_{x0}

$$\phi = \tan^{-1} \frac{-v_{x0}}{\omega x_0} \qquad (14\text{-}8)$$

Next we find A by eliminating ϕ. Squaring each of Eqs. (14-7) and forming the sum $\sin^2 \phi + \cos^2 \phi = 1$, we have $(v_{x0}/\omega A)^2 + (x_0/A)^2 = 1$, or

Amplitude A in terms of x_0 and v_{x0}

$$A = \sqrt{x_0{}^2 + \frac{v_{x0}{}^2}{\omega^2}} \qquad (14\text{-}9)$$

A simple example is to determine ϕ and A for the case where the object starts from rest. Then $v_{x0} = 0$ so that Eq. (14-8) gives $\phi = \tan^{-1}(0) = 0$, and Eq. (14-9) gives $A = \sqrt{x_0{}^2 + 0} = |x_0|$. This corresponds to the case shown in Fig. 14-3.

14-3 DYNAMICS OF SIMPLE HARMONIC MOTION

Now that we have learned how to describe simple harmonic motion, let us investigate what causes it. As our representative simple harmonic oscillator, we use a block of mass m connected to a light spring with spring constant k (Fig. 14-4). In this idealized system, the block slides along the horizontal surface with negligible friction so that the force due to the surface is equal and opposite the block's weight, and the net force on the block is the force $\mathbf{F}_s$ due to the spring: $\Sigma \mathbf{F} = \mathbf{F}_s$. From Sec. 8-4, the force due to the spring is

$$\mathbf{F}_s = -(kx)\mathbf{i} \qquad (14\text{-}10)$$

where x is the coordinate of the block measured from the position where the spring is relaxed, that is, it is neither stretched nor compressed. This type of force is called a *linear restoring force*. It is called "linear" because it is linearly proportional to the displacement $x\mathbf{i}$, and it is called "restoring" because the force is directed opposite the displacement. If x is positive, the force is toward

The spring force is a linear restoring force.

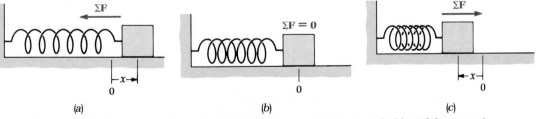

Figure 14-4. A block attached to a spring. In this idealized system, friction is negligible and the mass of the spring is insignificantly small compared with the mass of the block. The net force on the block is due to the spring, $\Sigma \mathbf{F} = \mathbf{F}_s = -kx\mathbf{i}$. (a) The block is displaced to the right, and $\Sigma \mathbf{F}$ is directed to the left. (b) The block is at the equilibrium position, $\Sigma \mathbf{F} = 0$. (c) The block is displaced to the left, and $\Sigma \mathbf{F}$ is directed to the right. If the block is displaced from equilibrium and released, it executes SHM.

−x, and if x is negative, the force is toward +x. The force tends to restore the object to the central position ($x = 0$), and the larger the displacement, the larger the force.

Since the spring force provides the net force on the block, Newton's second law, $\Sigma\mathbf{F} = m\mathbf{a}$, gives

Newton's second law

$$-kx = ma_x$$

Writing a_x as d^2x/dt^2 and rearranging, we have

Differential equation for coordinate x

$$\frac{d^2x}{dt^2} = -\frac{k}{m}x \qquad (14\text{-}11)$$

Newton's second law becomes a differential equation for the coordinate x. A solution to the equation is an expression for x as a function of time which satisfies the equation. What function of time has its second derivative proportional to the negative of the function itself? We are familiar with such a function from the last section. The second derivative of a cosine function is proportional to the negative of the cosine function. (This is also true for a sine function. See Exercise 14-12.) Thus the solution to Eq. (14-11) can be written

$$x = A\cos(\omega t + \phi) \qquad (14\text{-}1)$$

As we have seen, the second derivative of x with respect to t is

$$\frac{d^2x}{dt^2} = -\omega^2 A\cos(\omega t + \phi)$$

Substitution into Eq. (14-11) gives

$$-\omega^2 A\cos(\omega t + \phi) = -\frac{k}{m}A\cos(\omega t + \phi)$$

Thus Eq. (14-1) is a solution to Eq. (14-11), provided $\omega^2 = k/m$. This means that the block executes SHM, and that the angular frequency is

Angular frequency in terms of the spring constant k and the mass m

$$\omega = \sqrt{\frac{k}{m}} \qquad (14\text{-}12)$$

For a strong spring (large k) or small mass, the oscillations are rapid, and for a weak spring (small k) or large mass, the oscillations are slow. These predictions agree with common experience with oscillating systems involving springs. We have found what causes simple harmonic motion. It is caused by a net force that is a linear restoring force.

Our conclusion that the block-spring system executes SHM with angular frequency $\omega = \sqrt{k/m}$ can also be seen by comparing Eq. (14-11) with Eq. (14-6), $a_x = -\omega^2 x$. If we write Eq. (14-11) with d^2x/dt^2 replaced by a_x, this comparison is

$$a_x = -\frac{k}{m}x \qquad \text{and} \qquad a_x = -\omega^2 x$$

With $\omega^2 = k/m$, these equations are the same.

EXAMPLE 14-2. Suppose the block in Fig. 14-4 has a mass of 0.31 kg and the spring constant of the spring is 63 N/m. The block is pulled aside such that the spring is stretched 0.074 m and then released at $t = 0$. (a) Determine ω, T, and ν. (b) Write expressions for x, v_x, and a_x.

SOLUTION. (a) The angular frequency is

$$\omega = \sqrt{\frac{k}{m}} = \sqrt{\frac{63 \text{ N/m}}{0.31 \text{ kg}}} = 14 \text{ rad/s}$$

The period is

$$T = \frac{2\pi}{\omega} = 2\pi \sqrt{\frac{m}{k}} = 2\pi \sqrt{\frac{0.31 \text{ kg}}{63 \text{ N/m}}} = 0.44 \text{ s}$$

The frequency is

$$\nu = \frac{\omega}{2\pi} = \frac{1}{2\pi} \sqrt{\frac{k}{m}} = \frac{1}{2\pi} \sqrt{\frac{63 \text{ N/m}}{0.31 \text{ kg}}} = 2.3 \text{ Hz}$$

(b) Since the block was released from rest with the spring stretched 0.074 m, $x_0 = 0.074$ m and $v_{x0} = 0$. Therefore, $\phi = 0$ and

$$x = (0.074 \text{ m}) \cos [(14 \text{ rad/s})t]$$

We have $v_{max} = \omega A = (14 \text{ rad/s})(0.074 \text{ m}) = 1.1$ m/s so that

$$v_x = -(1.1 \text{ m/s}) \sin [(14 \text{ rad/s})t]$$

Also, $a_{max} = \omega^2 A = (14 \text{ rad/s})^2(0.074 \text{ m}) = 15$ m/s² so that

$$a_x = -(15 \text{ m/s}^2) \cos [(14 \text{ rad/s})t]$$

14-4 THE ENERGY OF A SIMPLE HARMONIC OSCILLATOR

In Chap. 9 we found that the force due to a spring is a conservative force and that the expression for the potential energy of a spring is $U = \frac{1}{2}kx^2$. Using Eq. (14-1), we find that the potential energy of our idealized block-spring harmonic oscillator in Fig. 14-4 is $U = \frac{1}{2}kx^2 = \frac{1}{2}k[A \cos (\omega t + \phi)]^2$, or

Potential energy of a simple harmonic oscillator

$$U = \tfrac{1}{2}kA^2 \cos^2 (\omega t + \phi) \tag{14-13}$$

Similarly, we can use Eq. (14-4) to find the kinetic energy of the block-spring system: $K = \frac{1}{2}mv^2 = \frac{1}{2}m[-\omega A \sin (\omega t + \phi)]^2$, or

Kinetic energy of a simple harmonic oscillator

$$K = \tfrac{1}{2}m\omega^2 A^2 \sin^2 (\omega t + \phi) \tag{14-14}$$

The maximum value of the square of a sine or cosine function is 1, so we can express these energies as

$$U = U_{max} \cos^2 (\omega t + \phi)$$

$$K = K_{max} \sin^2 (\omega t + \phi)$$

where $U_{max} = \frac{1}{2}kA^2$ and $K_{max} = \frac{1}{2}m\omega^2 A^2$. Since $\omega^2 = k/m$, $K_{max} = \frac{1}{2}m\omega^2 A^2 = \frac{1}{2}m(k/m)A^2 = \frac{1}{2}kA^2$, or

$$K_{max} = U_{max}$$

In our block-spring oscillator system, only the spring force does work. Consequently, the mechanical energy E of the oscillator is

$$E = K + U = K_{max} \sin^2 (\omega t + \phi) + U_{max} \cos^2 (\omega t + \phi)$$

Using $K_{max} = U_{max}$ and $\sin^2 \theta + \cos^2 \theta = 1$, we have $E = K_{max} = U_{max}$, or

Mechanical energy of a simple harmonic oscillator

$$E = \tfrac{1}{2}m\omega^2 A^2 = \tfrac{1}{2}kA^2 \tag{14-15}$$

The mechanical energy of the oscillator is constant; the simple harmonic oscillator is a conservative system.

Graphs of K and U versus time are shown in Fig. 14-5 ($\phi = 0$ for simplicity). Each function oscillates between zero and E. The energy of the oscillator continuously changes from potential energy to kinetic energy, then back to potential energy, and on and on.

Equations (14-13) and (14-14) give the potential and kinetic energies as functions of time. Now consider these energies as functions of the coordinate x. The equation for potential energy as a function of x is $U = \frac{1}{2}kx^2$. We use conserva-

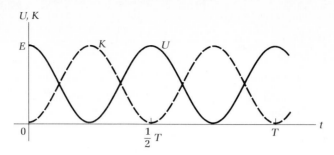

Figure 14-5. Potential energy U and kinetic energy K versus time t for a simple harmonic oscillator ($\phi = 0$). Note that $E = U_{\text{max}} = K_{\text{max}}$.

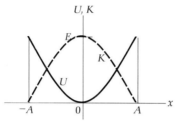

Figure 14-6. Potential energy U and kinetic energy K versus coordinate x for a simple harmonic oscillator.

tion of energy to find K as a function of x: $E = K + U = K + \frac{1}{2}kx^2$, or

$$K = E - \tfrac{1}{2}kx^2 = \tfrac{1}{2}kA^2 - \tfrac{1}{2}kx^2 = \tfrac{1}{2}k(A^2 - x^2)$$

In Fig. 14-6 we show graphs of U and K versus x. Each curve is a parabola centered at $x = 0$. Consider finding the point at which the two curves cross. At this point $U = K$ or $\frac{1}{2}kx^2 = \frac{1}{2}kA^2 - \frac{1}{2}kx^2$. Solving for x, we find $x = \pm A/\sqrt{2} \approx \pm 0.7A$.

EXAMPLE 14-3. Suppose our block-spring system has $k = 18$ N/m and $m = 0.71$ kg. The system is oscillating, with an amplitude $A = 54$ mm. (a) Determine the angular frequency of the oscillations. (b) Develop an expression for the speed v of the block as a function of x and use the expression to find v at $x = 34$ mm. (c) Develop an expression for the block's distance $|x|$ from the central point as a function of the speed v and use the expression to find $|x|$ when $v = 0.18$ m/s.

SOLUTION. (a) The angular frequency is

$$\omega = \sqrt{\frac{k}{m}} = \sqrt{\frac{18 \text{ N/m}}{0.71 \text{ kg}}} = 5.0 \text{ rad/s}$$

(b) Using conservation of energy with $E = \frac{1}{2}kA^2$, we have

$$\tfrac{1}{2}kA^2 = \tfrac{1}{2}mv^2 + \tfrac{1}{2}kx^2$$

Solving for v gives $v = \omega\sqrt{A^2 - x^2}$

where we have used $\omega = \sqrt{k/m}$. The speed at $x = 34$ mm is

$$v = (5.0 \text{ rad/s})\sqrt{(0.054 \text{ m})^2 - (0.034 \text{ m})^2} = 0.21 \text{ m/s}$$

(c) From conservation of energy with $E = \frac{1}{2}m\omega^2A^2$,

$$\tfrac{1}{2}m\omega^2A^2 = \tfrac{1}{2}mv^2 + \tfrac{1}{2}kx^2$$

Solving for $\sqrt{x^2} = |x|$, we obtain

$$|x| = \sqrt{A^2 - \left(\frac{v}{\omega}\right)^2}$$

Thus, when $v = 0.18$ m/s,

$$|x| = \sqrt{(0.054 \text{ m})^2 - \left(\frac{0.18 \text{ m/s}}{5.0 \text{ rad/s}}\right)^2} = 40 \text{ mm}$$

14-5 EXAMPLES OF SIMPLE HARMONIC MOTION

As our main example of SHM, we considered an object connected to a light horizontal spring and moving on a horizontal surface. The net force was due to the spring, and dissipative effects of friction were assumed to be negligible. The acceleration of the object was proportional to its displacement but in the opposite direction. There are many other systems that move such that the

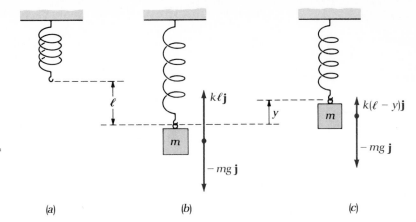

Figure 14-7. (a) A light spring is suspended vertically. (b) The block is in equilibrium, with $\mathbf{j}(k\ell - mg) = 0$. (c) The spring is stretched by $\ell - y$, and the net force is $[k(\ell - y) - mg]\mathbf{j} = -ky\mathbf{j}$, which tends to restore the block to its equilibrium position.

(a)   (b)   (c)

acceleration is essentially proportional to but opposite the displacement, so that simple harmonic motion occurs. We consider here some examples of such systems.

An object on a vertical spring. Suppose that a light spring with spring constant k is suspended vertically from a support, as shown in Fig. 14-7a. Initially the spring is neither stretched nor compressed. Now a block of mass m is attached to the other end of the spring, and the block is gently lowered until it comes to equilibrium, as shown in Fig. 14-7b. In this configuration the spring is stretched by an amount ℓ and exerts an upward force of magnitude $k\ell$ on the block. The block is in equilibrium at this position, and the spring force balances the downward weight of the block of magnitude mg:

$$k\ell = mg \qquad (14\text{-}16)$$

If the block is displaced vertically from this equilibrium position, the spring force will not balance the weight and the block will be accelerated. Let us determine the acceleration. We choose the origin of the y axis at the equilibrium position, as shown in Fig. 14-7c, which also shows the two forces acting on the block when its coordinate is y. Notice that y gives the displacement of the block from the equilibrium position. However, the spring is stretched by an amount $\ell - y$, so that the spring exerts an upward force of magnitude $k(\ell - y)$. The weight of the block is downward and of magnitude mg. Therefore the net force has a y component given by $\Sigma F_y = k(\ell - y) - mg$. Applying Newton's second law gives

$$\Sigma F_y = k(\ell - y) - mg = ma_y$$

Equation (14-16) determines the stretch ℓ of the spring when the block is in equilibrium, so that $k\ell - mg = 0$. Thus the expression above simplifies to $-ky = ma_y$, or

$$a_y = -\frac{k}{m}\,y \qquad (14\text{-}17)$$

Displacement of the block from its equilibrium position is given by y.

The acceleration of the block is proportional to but opposite its displacement from equilibrium.

Compare Eq. (14-17) with the standard form for SHM in Eq. (14-6), $a_x = -\omega^2 x$. Except for the use of y instead of x for the coordinate, the equations are

A block on a vertical spring moves with SHM.

the same if $\omega^2 = k/m$. That is, the motion of the block connected to the vertical spring is SHM with angular frequency $\omega = \sqrt{k/m}$. The displacement of the block from equilibrium is given by [we just replace x with y in Eq. (14-1)]

$$y = A \cos{(\omega t + \phi)} \qquad \left(\omega = \sqrt{\frac{k}{m}}\right) \qquad (14\text{-}18)$$

EXAMPLE 14-4. One end of a light vertical spring is attached to a rigid support, as seen in Fig. 14-7. A 5.0-kg block is attached to the other end of the spring and gently lowered to its equilibrium position. The stretch of the spring is measured to be 180 mm. The block is then pulled down an additional 75 mm and released from rest. Determine (a) the spring constant of the spring, (b) the amplitude of the motion, and (c) the period of the motion. (d) Determine the elastic potential energy of the spring at the instant the block is released.

SOLUTION. (a) From Eq. (14-16), which applies to the equilibrium configuration, we have

$$k = \frac{mg}{\ell} = \frac{(5.0 \text{ kg})(9.8 \text{ m/s}^2)}{0.18 \text{ m}} = 270 \text{ N/m}$$

(b) Since the block is released from rest at $y = -75$ mm, it

will oscillate between ± 75 mm, as in Eq. (14-18), with $A = 75$ mm.

(c) Since $\omega = \sqrt{k/m}$, the period $T = 2\pi/\omega$ is

$$T = 2\pi \sqrt{\frac{m}{k}} = 2\pi \sqrt{\frac{5.0 \text{ kg}}{270 \text{ N/m}}} = 0.85 \text{ s}$$

(d) The elastic potential energy of the spring depends on the stretch of the spring. At the instant the block is released, the spring is stretched from its relaxed length by 180 mm plus the additional 75 mm, or by 255 mm. The elastic potential energy U_s is

$$U_s = \tfrac{1}{2}(270 \text{ N/m})(0.255 \text{ m})^2 = 8.8 \text{ J}$$

Mechanical energy is conserved in this motion, and there is a continual interchange of kinetic energy, gravitational potential energy, and elastic potential energy. (See Exercise 14-25.)

The simple pendulum. The periodic motion of a pendulum has long been used in pendulum clocks to regulate the mechanism that causes the hands to move around the dial. We shall see that, for small displacements from equilibrium, a pendulum undergoes SHM. Here we consider a *simple pendulum*, a pendulum with all the mass concentrated at one end and suspended about the other end, such as the ball-and-cord pendulum in Fig. 14-8. The ball forms the "bob" of the pendulum whose length is L.

A simple pendulum has its mass concentrated at one end.

The pendulum bob is shown at rest at its equilibrium position in Fig. 14-8a. The force $\mathbf{F}_c$ exerted by the cord on the bob is balanced by the weight $\mathbf{F}_e$ of magnitude mg. Suppose the bob is pulled aside slightly and released. Figure 14-8b shows the bob at one point as it swings along the circular arc. The

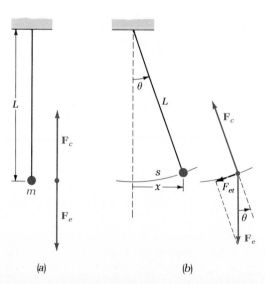

Figure 14-8. (a) The pendulum bob is at rest and $\mathbf{F}_c + \mathbf{F}_e = 0$. (b) For $x \ll L$, the arc length $s \approx x$. The tangential force component F_{et} has magnitude $F_e \sin{\theta} = mgx/L$.

(a)   (b)

tangential component of the net force, $\Sigma F_t = -F_e \sin \theta$, causes the tangential component of acceleration a_t and is responsible for restoring the bob to its equilibrium position along the arc. From Newton's second law,

$$\Sigma F_t = -mg \sin \theta = ma_t$$

We shall consider only small displacements from equilibrium, so that the arc length s is very small compared with L. As a consequence, the vertical displacement of the bob is very small compared with its horizontal displacement. Thus the arc length s nearly coincides with the coordinate x, and $a_t \approx a_x$. The tangential force component can also be expressed in terms of x, $-mg \sin \theta = -mgx/L$, since $\sin \theta = x/L$ from the figure. Making these substitutions in Newton's second law above, we have

$$-\frac{mgx}{L} = ma_x$$

A pendulum bob undergoes SHM for small displacements.

or

$$a_x = -\frac{g}{L} x \qquad (14\text{-}19)$$

Since a_x is proportional to $-x$ for small displacements from equilibrium, the pendulum bob moves with SHM.

Comparing Eq. (14-19) with Eq. (14-6), $a_x = -\omega^2 x$, we find that the angular frequency of the motion of the simple pendulum is $\omega = \sqrt{g/L}$. The motion of the bob is given by

$$x = A \cos (\omega t + \phi) \qquad \left(\omega = \sqrt{\frac{g}{L}} \right) \qquad (14\text{-}20)$$

The period $T = 2\pi/\omega$ of a simple pendulum is given by

The period of a simple pendulum is determined by its length.

$$T = 2\pi \sqrt{\frac{L}{g}} \qquad (14\text{-}21)$$

Notice that the period is independent of the mass of the bob; it depends only on the length of the pendulum and g. If the period of a pendulum is determined by precise time measurements, the pendulum can be used to measure g. Precision measurements made with a physical pendulum, described below, are capable of determining local variations in g due to density variations in the earth's upper surface and are useful in locating deposits of natural resources.

EXAMPLE 14-5. A moon explorer sets up a simple pendulum of length 860 mm and measures its period for small displacements to be 4.6 s. Determine the acceleration due to gravity at this location on the surface of the moon.

SOLUTION. Solving Eq. (14-21) for g, we obtain

$$g = \frac{4\pi^2 L}{T^2} = \frac{4\pi^2 (0.86 \text{ m})}{(4.6 \text{ s})^2} = 1.6 \text{ m/s}^2$$

The physical pendulum. A *physical pendulum* is a rigid body pivoted to rotate about a fixed, horizontal axis, as shown in Fig. 14-9. The equilibrium orientation of the pendulum is shown in Fig. 14-9a, with the center of gravity a distance L directly below the axis. In this configuration, the torque component τ_z about the axis of rotation is zero.

If the pendulum is displaced from equilibrium, as seen in Fig. 14-9b, the torque component τ_z due to the weight tends to cause a clockwise rotation so as to restore the pendulum to the equilibrium orientation. For the situation shown in the figure, $L \sin \theta$ is the perpendicular distance from the axis to the line of action of the weight $\mathbf{F}_e$. With the z axis out of the plane of the figure, the

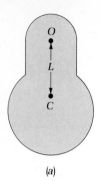

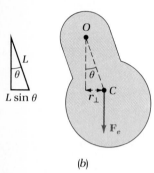

(b)

Figure 14-9. (a) A rigid body is in rotational equilibrium, with the center of gravity C directly below the axis of rotation O. (b) The torque component due to the weight $\mathbf{F}_e$ is $\tau_z = -r_\perp F_e = -(L \sin \theta)(mg)$. The positive z axis passes through O and comes out of the plane of the figure.

A physical pendulum undergoes SHM

torque component is $\tau_z = -mgL \sin \theta$. Let $\alpha_z = d^2\theta/dt^2$ represent the angular acceleration component of the rigid body with moment of inertia I about the axis of rotation. We apply Newton's second law for angular motion, Eq. (13-12). We neglect any frictional effects, so that the only torque is due to the weight. Thus

$$\Sigma\tau_z = -mgL \sin \theta = I\alpha_z$$

Dividing this equation by I, we obtain

$$\alpha_z = -\frac{mgL}{I} \sin \theta \qquad (14\text{-}22)$$

for the rotational motion.

We now compare Eq. (14-22) with Eq. (14-6) for SHM: $a_x = -\omega^2 x$. The left-hand sides are analogous; $\alpha_z = d^2\theta/dt^2$ is an angular acceleration component and $a_x = d^2x/dt^2$ is a linear acceleration component. The right-hand sides will likewise correspond if we restrict the motion to small displacements from equilibrium. Then $\sin \theta \approx \theta$, where θ is expressed in rad measure. [For example, if $\theta = 0.100$ rad (or $5.73°$), $\sin 0.100$ rad $= 0.0998 \approx 0.100$. Compare the values of $\sin \theta$ and θ for larger and smaller θ. Remember to set your calculator to rad measure for angles.] Replacing $\sin \theta$ with θ in Eq. (14-22), we obtain

$$\alpha_z = -\frac{mgL}{I} \theta$$

which is completely analogous to $a_x = -\omega^2 x$, with $\omega^2 = mgL/I$. Thus the angular coordinate of the physical pendulum for small displacements is

$$\theta = A \cos (\omega t + \phi) \qquad \left(\omega = \sqrt{\frac{mgL}{I}}\right) \qquad (14\text{-}23)$$

Since θ is an angular coordinate, some of the symbols in Eq. (14-23) must be interpreted with care. The amplitude A represents the maximum *angular* coordinate θ_{max}. The *angular frequency* of the oscillatory motion is $\omega = \sqrt{mgL/I}$. It must be distinguished from the *angular velocity* component, $\omega_z = d\theta/dt$, of the rigid body. Taking the derivative of θ in Eq. (14-23), we obtain

$$\omega_z = -\omega A \sin (\omega t + \phi)$$

This expression for the angular velocity component of the pendulum is analogous to $v_x = -\omega A \sin (\omega t + \phi)$ for the linear velocity component for linear motion. In each expression, $\omega = 2\pi/T$ is the angular frequency of the oscillation.

EXAMPLE 14-6. A thin, uniform rod of mass m and length D is pivoted to rotate freely about a horizontal axis at one end. Determine the period of this pendulum for small displacements from equilibrium.

SOLUTION. For small displacements from equilibrium, the rod oscillates in SHM with angular frequency $\omega = \sqrt{mgL/I}$. Since L represents the distance from the axis to the center of gravity, located at the center of the uniform rod, $L = \frac{1}{2}D$. The moment of inertia of the rod of length D about

an axis through one end is $mD^2/3$. (See Example 12-7, but note that L is used there for the length of the rod.) Making these substitutions, we have

$$\omega = \sqrt{\frac{mgL}{I}} = \sqrt{\frac{mg\frac{1}{2}D}{mD^2/3}} = \sqrt{\frac{3g}{2D}}$$

The period is

$$T = \frac{2\pi}{\omega} = 2\pi \sqrt{\frac{2D}{3g}}$$

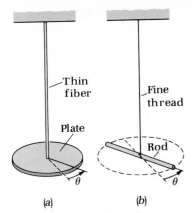

Thin fiber

Plate

Fine thread

Rod

θ

θ

(a)

(b)

Figure 14-10. A fiber twisted through angle θ exerts a restoring torque on (a) a horizontal plate and (b) a horizontal rod.

A torsion pendulum undergoes SHM.

The torsional pendulum. Two examples of a *torsional pendulum* are shown schematically in Fig. 14-10. A vertical fiber is attached to a rigid object such as a plate or a rod. The plate in Fig. 14-10a can rotate in a horizontal plane about an axis along the vertical fiber. The angle θ gives the orientation of the plate from its equilibrium orientation. At equilibrium, $\theta = 0$ and the fiber is not twisted. When twisted through angle θ, the fiber exerts a restoring torque on the plate that tends to return the plate to its equilibrium orientation. For many fibers this restoring torque is proportional to the angle of twist θ. Let the z axis be vertically up along the fiber. Then

$$\tau_z = -\kappa\theta \tag{14-24}$$

gives the torque component, where κ is called the *torsion constant* of the fiber.

Suppose that only the fiber exerts a torque on the plate, $\Sigma\tau_z = -\kappa\theta$. If I is the moment of inertia of the plate about the fiber axis, then Eq. (13-12) gives $-\kappa\theta = I\alpha_z$, or

$$\alpha_z = -\frac{\kappa}{I}\theta$$

Since this has the form $\alpha_z = -\omega^2\theta$, the plate undergoes SHM in the angular coordinate θ and $\omega^2 = \kappa/I$:

$$\theta = A\cos(\omega t + \phi) \qquad \left(\omega = \sqrt{\frac{\kappa}{I}}\right) \tag{14-25}$$

EXAMPLE 14-7. A fine thread is attached to the midpoint of a 10-g pencil of length $L = 200$ mm, as shown in Fig. 14-10b. The system is set in motion as a torsional pendulum and the period is observed to be 4 s. (a) Estimate the torsion constant of the thread. (b) If the amplitude of the motion is 3 rad, determine the maximum magnitude of the restoring torque on the pencil.

SOLUTION. (a) Since $\omega = \sqrt{\kappa/I}$ for a torsional pendulum, we have $\kappa = \omega^2 I = 4\pi^2 I/T^2$, where $T = 2\pi/\omega$ is the period. From Table 12-2, the pencil has a moment of inertia $I = mL^2/12$.

$$\kappa = \frac{4\pi^2 mL^2}{12T^2} = \frac{m\pi^2 L^2}{3T^2}$$

$$= \frac{(0.01\ \text{kg})\pi^2(0.2\ \text{m})^2}{(3)(4\ \text{s})^2} = 8\times10^{-5}\ \text{N}\cdot\text{m}\cdot\text{rad}^{-1}$$

(b) The amplitude is the maximum value of θ: $\theta_{\max} = A = 3$ rad. (Such a torsional pendulum can undergo SHM even if the angle θ is not small.) From Eq. (14-24),

$$\tau_{\max} = |\tau_z|_{\max} = \kappa\theta_{\max} = (8\times10^{-5}\ \text{N}\cdot\text{m}\cdot\text{rad}^{-1})(3\ \text{rad})$$

$$= 2\times10^{-4}\ \text{N}\cdot\text{m}$$

14-6 SIMPLE HARMONIC MOTION AND UNIFORM CIRCULAR MOTION

There is an intimate connection between the simple harmonic motion of an object moving along a line, such as the x axis, and the motion of a particle at constant speed in a circle. Exploring this connection may help us to understand each type of motion better and to see how some other types of motion are related to SHM.

Consider a particle or reference point Q that moves at constant speed v around a circle of radius A, as shown in Fig. 14-11a. The radial line OQ from the origin to the point Q makes an angle θ with the positive x axis. Since point Q moves with constant speed, the angle θ changes uniformly, and $d\theta/dt = \omega_z$. (See Sec. 12-6.) For the case shown in the figure, ω_z is positive and we shall drop the z subscript and use the angular speed $\omega = v/A$. Since ω is constant,

Figure 14-11. Point Q moves counterclockwise, around a circle of radius A, with constant angular speed ω so that $\theta = \omega t + \phi$. (a) The x coordinate of Q and of P is $x = A \cos \theta = A \cos (\omega t + \phi)$. (b) The x component of the velocity of Q and of P is $v_x = v \cos (\theta + \pi/2) = -\omega A \sin (\omega t + \phi)$. (c) The x component of the acceleration of Q and of P is $a_x = a \cos (\theta + \pi) = -\omega^2 A \cos (\omega t + \phi)$.

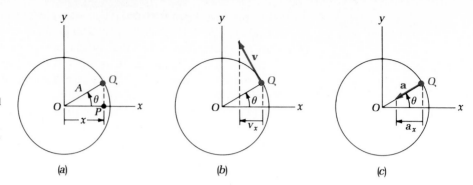

(a)   (b)   (c)

we have $\theta = \omega t + \phi$, where the phase constant ϕ is the initial value of θ.

Now we determine the x coordinate of the reference point Q. This is also the x coordinate of point P on the x axis. From the figure we have $x = A \cos \theta$, or with $\theta = \omega t + \phi$,

$$x = A \cos (\omega t + \phi)$$

which is Eq. (14-1) for SHM. Thus as point Q moves around the circle at constant speed, point P moves along the x axis in SHM.

We can think of point P as the *projection* of point Q onto the x axis. The projection can be realized by using light from a distant slide projector to observe on a screen the shadow of a particle moving in a circle. Such an arrangement is shown schematically in Fig. 14-12.

We can also look at the x components of the velocity and acceleration of point Q in its uniform circular motion. The velocity is tangent to the circular path, as shown in Fig. 14-11b. The angle between the velocity and the positive x axis is $\theta + \pi/2$. The velocity component is

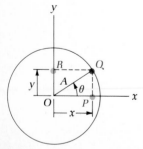

Light from a slide projector

Shadow of Q

Screen

Figure 14-12. Light from a slide projector illuminates an object Q rotating on a turntable at constant angular speed. The shadow of Q on a screen moves along a line in SHM.

$$v_x = v \cos \left(\theta + \frac{\pi}{2} \right) = -v \sin \theta$$

But $v = \omega A$ and $\theta = \omega t + \phi$, so that

$$v_x = -\omega A \sin (\omega t + \phi)$$

which is Eq. (14-4) for the velocity component of a point P in SHM.

The acceleration for uniform circular motion is the centripetal acceleration. It is directed toward the center, and its magnitude is $a = v^2/A = \omega^2 A$, from Sec. 12-6. Notice from Fig. 14-11c that the direction of the acceleration is opposite the direction of the position vector from O to Q. Therefore $\mathbf{a}$ makes an angle $\theta + \pi$ with the positive x axis. The acceleration component is $a_x = a \cos (\theta + \pi) = -a \cos \theta$. Substituting $a = \omega^2 A$ and $\theta = \omega t + \phi$ gives

$$a_x = -\omega^2 A \cos (\omega t + \phi)$$

which is Eq. (14-5) for the acceleration component of a point P in SHM.

In terms of the coordinate, velocity, and acceleration, the x part of the motion of a particle in a circle of radius A with constant angular speed ω is equivalent to the simple harmonic motion of a particle with amplitude A and angular frequency ω. Similar conclusions hold for the y part of the motion. For example, the y coordinate of point Q in Fig. 14-13 is

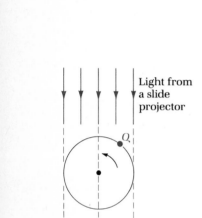

Figure 14-13. Point P is the projection of Q onto the x axis, and point R is the projection of Q onto the y axis.

$$y = A \sin (\omega t + \phi)$$

which is also the y coordinate of point R, the projection of point Q onto the y

axis. This motion along the y axis is also SHM, with amplitude A and angular frequency ω. The use of a sine for y and a cosine for x means that the x and y parts of the motion have a phase difference of $\pi/2$.

We have seen that SHM is equivalent to the projection of uniform circular motion onto the x axis or onto the y axis, or onto any diameter of the circle. We can also reverse the equivalence. Thus uniform circular motion is equivalent to compounded simple harmonic motions along perpendicular diameters (say on the x and y axes). The two motions must have the same amplitude and angular frequency and must have a phase difference of $\pi/2$. That is, a particle moving in a circular path of radius A with constant angular speed ω has coordinates given by

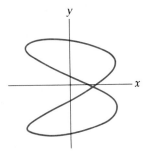

$$x = A \cos (\omega t + \phi) \qquad y = A \sin (\omega t + \phi) \qquad (14\text{-}26)$$

More complicated motions can also be compounded from simple harmonic motions. Interesting two-dimensional figures, called *Lissajous figures,* can be generated by combining motions of the form in Eqs. (14-26). One or more of the amplitudes, angular frequencies, or the phase difference must be changed to obtain noncircular figures. One such example is shown in Fig. 14-14 for which the frequency of the x part of the motion is twice the frequency of the y part.

The complicated vibrations of atoms in a crystal can also be represented by compounding simple harmonic motions. In the simplest model, an atom moves with three simple harmonic motions, one each along three mutually perpendicular directions. We shall use this idea in Chap. 18 to understand the response of a substance to a change in its temperature.

Figure 14-14. A Lissajous figure with ω for the x part of the motion twice that for the y part of the motion.

Uniform circular motion is compounded from two simple harmonic motions.

14-7 DAMPED HARMONIC MOTION

In our discussion of oscillations, we have neglected dissipative effects such as those due to frictional forces. These effects are almost always present, and often they cannot be neglected. Suppose that a pendulum is set in motion. Although it may swing through many cycles before we notice a decrease in its amplitude, the motion will eventually cease or be "damped out" unless we replenish the mechanical energy dissipated by friction.

Consider a block connected to a spring and oscillating vertically about the equilibrium position at $y = 0$. As we saw in Sec. 14-5, the net force component is $\Sigma F_y = -ky$ and the motion is SHM if we neglect dissipative forces. We can investigate the effects of dissipation by adding a damping mechanism, as shown schematically in Fig. 14-15. A vane, a part of the oscillating object, is in a fluid which exerts a resistive or damping force on the vane. This force will act in a direction opposite the velocity of the object. By varying the shape of the vane and by using different fluids, this damping force can be made large or small.

A simple model for the damping force is one that is proportional to the velocity of the block but with the opposite direction: $\mathbf{F}_D = -b\mathbf{v}$, where b is a constant that depends on the fluid and the shape of the vane. Since the force is opposite the velocity, it does negative work for every displacement of the block. That is, this force causes the mechanical energy of the oscillator to decrease.

Including this force in Newton's second law for the block, we have

$$\Sigma F_y = -ky - bv_y = ma_y$$

Mechanical energy is dissipated by friction, and the motion is damped.

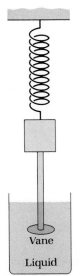

Figure 14-15. A damping vane is attached to an oscillating block. The liquid exerts a damping force on the moving vane.

Vane

Liquid

or $$a_y = -\frac{k}{m}y - \frac{b}{m}v_y \qquad (14\text{-}27)$$

This is the equation of motion for the *damped harmonic oscillator*. Obtaining the solution of this equation involves mathematical techniques beyond the level of this course. We quote the solution, which you can verify as outlined in Exercise 14-43, for the case of relatively small damping:

Solution for the underdamped oscillator

$$y = e^{-\gamma t} A \cos(\omega_D t + \phi) \qquad (14\text{-}28)$$

where $\gamma = b/2m$ and $\omega_D = \sqrt{k/m - (b/2m)^2}$. This solution is valid for $(b/2m)^2 < k/m$. Except for the exponential factor $e^{-\gamma t}$, the solution would be SHM with an angular frequency ω_D that is less than the "natural" angular frequency $\omega = \sqrt{k/m}$, the frequency with no damping (if $b = 0$). The exponential factor decreases continuously and approaches zero as t increases. In effect, the oscillation has a continuously decreasing amplitude. The motion is said to be *underdamped*. An example is shown graphically in Fig. 14-16 for a case with $(b/2m)^2 = 0.0050k/m$ so that $\gamma = 0.071\omega_D$.

The solution of Eq. (14-27) is qualitatively different for large damping. If $(b/2m)^2 > k/m$, then the damping force effectively prevents oscillations, and the motion is called *overdamped*. As shown in Fig. 14-17, an overdamped oscillator initially displaced from equilibrium slowly approaches the equilib-

Solution for the overdamped oscillator

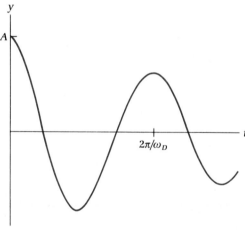

Figure 14-16. The solution for an underdamped harmonic oscillator with $(b/2m)^2 = 0.005k/m$ so that $\gamma = 0.07\omega_D$. The oscillator is released from rest at $t = 0$, with $y_0 = A$.

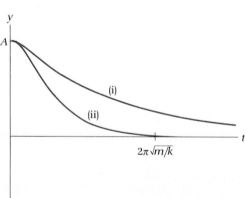

Figure 14-17. An oscillator is released from rest with $y = A$ at $t = 0$. Two cases are shown: (i) overdamped motion with $(b/2m)^2 = 6k/m$ and (ii) critically damped motion with $(b/2m)^2 = k/m$.

rium position without passing through it. The form of the overdamped solution is considered in Exercise 14-44.

If $(b/2m)^2 = k/m$, then the motion is called *critically damped.* As suggested in Fig. 14-17, a critically damped oscillator does not oscillate but approaches the equilibrium position more rapidly than the overdamped oscillator. The form of the critically damped solution is considered in Exercise 14-45.

Solution for the critically damped oscillator

EXAMPLE 14-8. For the underdamped motion shown in Fig. 14-16, determine the ratio of the coordinate at $t = T_D = 2\pi/\omega_D$ to the coordinate at $t = 0$.

SOLUTION. The underdamped solution is given by Eq. (14-28), and the motion in Fig. 14-16 cooresponds to $\gamma = 0.071\omega_D$. The sinusoidal part of the equation,

$A \cos (\omega_D t + \phi)$, has the same value at $t = 0$ and at $t = T_D$ because $\cos (\omega_D T_D + \phi) = \cos (2\pi + \phi) = \cos \phi$. Therefore, the ratio of the coordinates at these times is given by the ratio of the exponential parts:

$$\frac{e^{-\gamma T_D}}{e^{-\gamma \cdot 0}} = \frac{e^{-\gamma 2\pi/\omega_D}}{1} = e^{-2\pi(0.071)} = 0.64$$

14-8 FORCED OSCILLATIONS AND RESONANCE

Forced oscillations are driven by an external agent.

A damped oscillator will eventually come to rest as its mechanical energy is dissipated, unless mechanical energy is supplied by a driving force. For example, a child on a swing can swing for hours if a parent gives the swing an occasional push in the direction of its velocity. Most of the oscillations that occur in machinery and in electric circuits are *forced oscillations,* oscillations that are created and sustained by an external force or influence.

The simplest driving force is one that itself oscillates as a sine or a cosine. Suppose such an external force $\mathbf{F}_E$ is applied to an oscillator that moves along the x axis, such as a block connected to a spring. We write the external force component as

An external driving force with angular frequency ω_E

$$F_{Ex} = F_0 \cos \omega_E t \tag{14-29}$$

where F_0 is the maximum magnitude of the force and the force component oscillates sinusoidally with angular frequency ω_E. The frequency of the external force is generally different from the natural angular frequency $\omega = \sqrt{k/m}$ of the oscillator, which is its angular frequency only if there is no damping and no driving force.

If we include the force component in Eq. (14-29) in Newton's second law for a damped harmonic oscillator, we have

$$\Sigma F_x = F_0 \cos \omega_E t - kx - bv_x = ma_x$$

That is, three forces are acting: an external force, a restoring force, and a damping force. Dividing by the mass, we obtain the equation of motion,

$$a_x = -\omega^2 x - 2\gamma v_x + \left(\frac{F_0}{m}\right) \cos \omega_E t \tag{14-30}$$

where $\omega^2 = k/m$ and $\gamma = b/2m$ as before.

The transient solution damps out and leaves only the steady-state solution.

The techniques for solving Eq. (14-30) are beyond the scope of this course, but we shall describe some interesting features of the solution. The general solution consists of the sum of two terms. One of these is called the *transient solution,* and it is the solution for a damped harmonic oscillator discussed in the last section. This solution depends in detail on the initial conditions but will be damped out eventually. That leaves the other term, which is called the *steady-state solution*. It is the solution due to the external driving force and persists after the transient solution has died away. We suppose the motion began in the distant past so that for $t \geq 0$, only the steady-state solution remains.

The steady-state solution oscillates sinusoidally with the same frequency as the external force. It has a steady or fixed amplitude A_0 and has a definite phase difference ϕ_E with the external force. This solution, which you can verify in Prob. 14-10, is

$$x = A_0 \cos (\omega_E t - \phi_E) \qquad (14\text{-}31)$$

where

$$A_0 = \frac{F_0/m}{\sqrt{(\omega_E^2 - \omega^2)^2 + 4\gamma^2\omega_E^2}}$$

$$\tan \phi_E = \frac{2\gamma\omega_E}{\omega^2 - \omega_E^2}$$

The amplitude of the motion A_0 is proportional to the amplitude of the driving force F_0.

The amplitude also depends on the driving frequency ω_E. That is, the oscillator responds differently to a driving force of the same magnitude but a different driving frequency. To understand this response, think of the natural frequency ω as fixed and the driving frequency ω_E as variable. For each value of ω_E, we can determine the amplitude A_0 of the motion. This dependence is shown in Fig. 14-18 for an oscillator with small damping. Notice that the amplitude of the motion is small if ω_E is either much larger or much smaller than the natural angular frequency ω. The amplitude is largest if $\omega_E \approx \omega$. In this case the driving force is approximately in phase with the velocity, so that positive work is done by this force on the block during most of the cycle. Thus the oscillator can obtain more energy from the driving force and the amplitude is large.

The dramatic increase in the amplitude of the motion for $\omega_E \approx \omega$ is called *resonance*. Resonance also can occur when any oscillating system is driven by or coupled to another oscillating system, if their frequencies are about the same. In effect, the coupling between the systems is enhanced if the frequencies are equal. Depending on the circumstances, resonance can be desirable or undesirable. For example, the characteristic shape of a guitar allows a resonant coupling between the vibrating string and the vibrating air in the sound box of

Maximum amplitude occurs if $\omega_E \approx \omega$.

Resonance occurs between coupled systems with nearly equal frequencies.

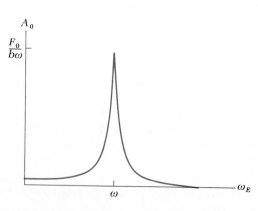

Figure 14-18. The amplitude A_0 of a driven oscillator is shown for small damping, $(b/2m)^2 = 0.005\omega^2$. The resonance peak corresponds to $A_0 = F_0/b\omega$ at $\omega_E = \omega$.

Figure 14-19. High, turbulent winds drove the Tacoma Narrows bridge at resonance to a destructively large amplitude. *(Reuters/ Bettman News Photo)*

the instrument. A radio or television receiver is tuned to be in resonance with the frequency of the signals to be received. On the undesirable side, unwanted vibrations in a mechanical system may occur with a large amplitude if the system is driven at resonance. A spectacular example is the collapse of the Tacoma Narrows bridge in 1940 (see Fig. 14-19). The destructively large amplitude vibration resulted from a resonant coupling due to high winds.

EXAMPLE 14-9. Show, as indicated in Fig. 14-18, that the amplitude of oscillation for resonance at $\omega_E = \omega$ is given by $A_0 = F_0/b\omega$.

SOLUTION. The frequency dependence of the amplitude A_0 is given by the expression just after Eq. (14-31),

$$A_0 = \frac{F_0/m}{\sqrt{(\omega_E{}^2 - \omega^2)^2 + 4\gamma^2\omega_E{}^2}}$$

At $\omega_E = \omega$, the denominator becomes

$$\sqrt{(0)^2 + 4\gamma^2\omega^2} = 2\gamma\omega$$

Thus

$$A_0 = \frac{F_0/m}{2\gamma\omega} = \frac{F_0/m}{(b/m)\omega} = \frac{F_0}{b\omega}$$

Notice that a smaller value of b, which corresponds to less damping, leads to a larger value of the amplitude A_0 at resonance.

COMMENTARY: THE TIDE IN THE BAY OF FUNDY

The Bay of Fundy is a large bay—it has an area of 1.5×10^{10} m²—located between Maine and New Brunswick on its north side and Nova Scotia on its south side. The height of the tide in this bay is the largest in the world, reaching an astonishing vertical range of more than 15 m at the head of the bay. The mouth of the bay opens onto the Gulf of Maine, which has a tide with a vertical range of about 3 m.

How can a tide at the head of a bay become 5 times greater than at the bay's

High and low tides on the Bay of Fundy. *(Clyde H. Smith/Peter Arnold)*

mouth? The answer is found in our study of resonance. This type of resonance is associated with wave behavior and is discussed more fully in Chap. 32. But you can understand this tide qualitatively from your present knowledge of resonance. Suppose you partially fill a rectangular trough with water. If you quickly raise and then lower one end of the trough, the water will slosh back and forth along the trough's length with a characteristic or natural period. As it turns out, theory and observation give the period as $T \approx 2L/\sqrt{gd}$, where L is the length of the trough, g is the gravitational acceleration, and d is the water depth. If you repeatedly raise and lower one end of the trough with a period that is nearly T, then the amplitude of the sloshing will become large because you will be driving the system near resonance.

Suppose we regard the Bay of Fundy as one-half of a trough, with the mouth of the bay corresponding to the middle of the trough and the head of the bay corresponding to one end of the trough. Applying the above expression for T to the bay, we set d equal to the depth of the bay and L equal to twice the length of the bay. The length and depth of a bay, such as the Bay of Fundy, are nebulous quantities, but we can use approximate values. The calculation yields $T \approx 12$ h, which is about the same as the period of the tide. Thus the tide in the bay is being driven at nearly the same period as its natural period of oscillation. The huge tide in the Bay of Fundy is a resonance phenomenon on a grand scale. A number of other bays around the world have a natural period that is nearly 12 h, and these bays also exhibit resonance effects. Such an example is Long Island Sound.

SUMMARY WITH APPLICATIONS

Section 14-2. Kinematics of simple harmonic motion
For an object undergoing SHM,

$$x = A \cos (\omega t + \phi) \tag{14-1}$$

$$v_x = -\omega A \sin (\omega t + \phi) \tag{14-4}$$

$$a_x = -\omega^2 A \cos (\omega t + \phi) \tag{14-5}$$

The angular frequency ω, the frequency ν, and the period T are related by

$$\omega = 2\pi \nu = \frac{2\pi}{T}$$

SHM can be identified by the relation

$$a_x = -\omega^2 x \tag{14-6}$$

Describe the kinematic quantities for an object undergoing SHM; use the initial conditions to find A and ϕ.

Section 14-3. Dynamics of simple harmonic motion
SHM is caused by a net force that is a linear restoring force. Newton's second law applied to such an object can be cast as a differential equation:

$$\frac{d^2x}{dt^2} = -\frac{k}{m}x \qquad (14\text{-}11)$$

A solution to this equation is $x = A \cos(\omega t + \phi)$, with $\omega = \sqrt{k/m}$.

Show that a net force which is a linear restoring force causes SHM; determine the equations which describe the motion in terms of the spring constant and the mass.

Section 14-4. The energy of a simple harmonic oscillator

The potential and kinetic energies of a simple harmonic oscillator are

$$U = \tfrac{1}{2}kA^2 \cos^2(\omega t + \phi) \qquad (14\text{-}13)$$

$$K = \tfrac{1}{2}m\omega^2 A^2 \sin^2(\omega t + \phi) \qquad (14\text{-}14)$$

and the mechanical energy is constant:

$$E = \tfrac{1}{2}m\omega^2 A^2 = \tfrac{1}{2}kA^2 \qquad (14\text{-}15)$$

Determine the potential, kinetic, and mechanical energies of a simple harmonic oscillator.

Section 14-5. Examples of simple harmonic motion

Systems which were shown to undergo SHM are (i) a block suspended from a vertical spring, $\omega = \sqrt{k/m}$; (ii) a simple pendulum, $\omega = \sqrt{g/L}$; (iii) a physical pendulum, $\omega = \sqrt{mgL/I}$; and (iv) a torsional pendulum, $\omega = \sqrt{\kappa/I}$.

Describe various systems that are expected to exhibit SHM and find the angular frequencies of the oscillations.

Section 14-6. Simple harmonic motion and uniform circular motion

For a particle executing uniform circular motion in the xy plane, the x and y components of the motion are each simple harmonic motion.

Show the relation between uniform circular motion and SHM.

Section 14-7. Damped harmonic motion

The equation of motion for a damped harmonic oscillator is

$$a_y = -\frac{k}{m}y - \frac{b}{m}v_y \qquad (14\text{-}27)$$

For the underdamped case

$$y = e^{-\gamma t} A \cos(\omega_D t + \phi) \qquad (14\text{-}28)$$

The amplitude of the oscillations decreases exponentially with time. If the oscillator is critically damped or over-damped, no oscillations occur.

Describe the effect of dissipative forces on an oscillator.

Section 14-8. Forced oscillations and resonance

The equation of motion for a forced oscillator is

$$a_x = -\omega^2 x - 2\gamma v_x + \left(\frac{F_0}{m}\right)\cos \omega_E t \qquad (14\text{-}30)$$

The amplitude of the oscillations is

$$A_0 = \frac{F_0/m}{\sqrt{(\omega_E^2 - \omega^2)^2 + \gamma^2 \omega_E^2}}$$

The amplitude is maximum when resonance occurs: $\omega_E \approx \omega$.

Describe the effect of an external driving force on a damped oscillator; determine the amplitude of the oscillations.

QUESTIONS

14-1 Give three examples of oscillating systems. Are any of these systems simple harmonic oscillators? If not, why not?

14-2 What is the distance traveled during one period by an object executing SHM with amplitude A?

14-3 Suppose the angular frequency ω of a simple harmonic oscillator is doubled. By what factor does this change (a) the frequency ν, (b) the period T, (c) the amplitude A, (d) the phase constant ϕ?

14-4 Suppose the amplitude A of a simple harmonic oscillator is doubled. By what factor does this change (a) the angular frequency ω, (b) the frequency ν, (c) the period T, (d) the maximum speed v_{max}, (e) the maximum acceleration magnitude a_{max}, (f) the mechanical energy E?

14-5 During SHM, are the displacement and velocity ever in the same direction? The velocity and acceleration? The displacement and the acceleration?

14-6 An astronaut is to stay in earth orbit for several months. Devise a procedure for keeping track of the astronaut's mass.

14-7 In finding $\omega = \sqrt{k/m}$ for the block-spring system, we neglected the mass of the spring. Suppose we used a spring with significant mass. Describe its effect on the motion of the system.

14-8 Can you find the amplitude or the phase constant for a simple harmonic oscillator if you know the initial coordinate but not the initial velocity? If you know the initial velocity but not the initial coordinate? Explain.

14-9 A block of mass m is suspended from two light springs in two different ways (Fig. 14-20). Each spring has the same spring constant k and same unstretched length. What is the angular frequency of the oscillations, in terms of k and m, when the springs are side by side, as in Fig. 14-20a? What is the angular frequency when the springs are end to end, as in Fig. 14-20b?

14-10 A block-spring simple harmonic oscillator has $E = 4$ J when $x = A$. At $x = A$, what are (a) U and (b) K? At

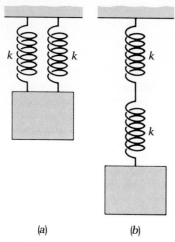

(a)   (b)

Figure 14-20. Ques. 14-9.

$x = 0$, what are (c) E; (d) U; (e) K? At $x = -A$, what are (f) E; (g) U; (h) K?

14-11 Estimate the spring constant of the springs of an automobile by estimating its mass and its period of oscillation if the springs are pushed down and released.

14-12 Why do automobiles have shock absorbers? Estimate a value of γ in Eq. (14-28) from the way a typical automobile bounces.

14-13 Two common lengths for a pendulum in pendulum clocks are about 1 m and about $\frac{1}{4}$ m. What is the advantage of each of these lengths?

14-14 Would a pendulum clock have the same period at the equator as at one of the poles? What about a windup watch that uses a torsional pendulum? Expain.

14-15 Does the period of a pendulum depend on its temperature? Did you think of this in answering the previous question?

14-16 A child on a swing is swinging very high, almost to the point where the ropes are horizontal. If the child stops pumping and lets the amplitude of the swing die down, how will the period of the swing change?

14-17 If you drive an automobile with a tire out of balance, you feel a large vibration at a certain speed. Why does the amplitude of the vibration decrease if you speed up or slow down?

14-18 Why do soldiers break the cadence of their march when crossing a bridge? It is sometimes said that a cat can cause a bridge to collapse. Is that possible? Explain.

14-19 The earth moves about the sun in an almost circular orbit. Is this motion compounded of two simple harmonic motions? If so, what are the angular frequencies?

14-20 Figure 14-21 shows a conical pendulum with the bob swinging in a horizontal circle, say in the xy plane. How are the period and the amplitude of the x motion related to the period and the amplitude of the y mo-

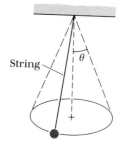

String

θ

Figure 14-21. Ques. 14-20.

tion? What are some other figures that can be traced out by such a pendulum? Try it.

14-21 Complete the following table:

Symbol	Represents	Type	SI unit
ω			
T		Scalar	
ν			
A			
ϕ			rad
κ	Torsion constant		
ω_E			

EXERCISES

Section 14-2. Kinematics of simple harmonic motion

14-1 The angular frequency of an object undergoing SHM is 5.8 rad/s. Determine the period and the frequency of the motion.

14-2 (a) Show that the dimension of ωA is the same as velocity, (length)(time)$^{-1}$. (b) Show that the dimension of $\omega^2 A$ is the same as acceleration, (length)(time)$^{-2}$.

14-3 An object executes SHM with $A = 63$ mm, $\omega = 4.1$ rad/s, and $\phi = 0$. (a) Write expressions for x, v_x, and a_x. (b) Determine x, v_x, and a_x at $t = 1.7$ s.

14-4 The coordinate of an object is given by $x = (0.057 \text{ m}) \cos [(3.9 \text{ rad/s})t]$. (a) What are A, ω, ν, T, and ϕ? (b) Write expressions for v_x and a_x. (c) Determine x, v_x, and a_x at $t = 2.3$ s.

14-5 The velocity component of an object is given by $v_x = (1.8 \text{ m/s}) \sin [(7.1 \text{ rad/s})t]$. (a) What are ω, A, ν, T, and ϕ? (b) Write expressions for x and a_x. (c) Determine x, v_x, and a_x at $t = 0.25$ s.

14-6 The acceleration component of an object is given by $a_x = -(16.8 \text{ rad/s}^2)x$. The object's initial coordinate is $x_0 = 24$ mm and its initial velocity component is $v_{x0} = 0.71$ m/s. Determine expressions for the object's (a) coordinate, (b) velocity component, (c) acceleration component as functions of time.

14-7 An object executes SHM with $a_{max} = 13$ m/s^2, $T = 0.94$ s, and $\phi = \frac{1}{2}\pi$. (a) Write expressions for x, v_x, and a_x. (b) Determine x, v_x, and a_x at $t = 0.54$ s.

14-8 An object is executing SHM with a period $T = 1.8$ s, an initial coordinate $x_0 = 0$, and an initial velocity component $v_{x0} = -0.33$ m/s. (a) Write expressions for x, v_x, and a_x as functions of time. (b) Make graphs of x, v_x, and a_x versus time from $t = 0$ to $t = 3.0$ s.

14-9 An object undergoes SHM with a frequency $\nu = 0.42$ Hz. The initial coordinate is $x_0 = 0.021$ m, and the initial velocity component is $v_{x0} = 1.3$ m/s. Determine A, v_{max}, and a_{max}.

Section 14-3. Dynamics of simple harmonic motion

14-10 Show that the dimension of $\sqrt{k/m}$ is time^{-1}.

14-11 A block-spring simple harmonic oscillator has $k = 45$ N/m and $m = 0.88$ kg. Determine (a) ω; (b) ν; (c) T.

14-12 (a) Show that $x = A \sin(\omega t + \delta)$ is a solution to Eq. (14-11),

$$\frac{d^2x}{dt^2} = -\frac{k}{m}x$$

(b) Determine the relation between δ in the expression above and ϕ in Eq. (14-1), $x = A \cos(\omega t + \phi)$.

14-13 The period of a block-spring simple harmonic oscillator is $T = 0.87$ s. If the mass of the block is 0.62 kg, what is the spring constant of the spring?

14-14 A block-spring simple harmonic oscillator has $k = 27$ N/m and $m = 0.46$ kg. Assuming the block was released from rest at $x = 29$ mm, write expressions for x, v_x, and a_x as functions of time.

14-15 The frequency of a block-spring harmonic oscillator is 1.4 Hz. If the spring constant of the spring is 26 N/m, what is the mass of the block?

14-16 A block of mass 1.4 kg oscillates with SHM due to a net force exerted by a spring. The amplitude of the motion is $A = 0.14$ m, and the maximum speed of the block is $v_{max} = 2.3$ m/s. What is the spring constant of the spring?

Section 14-4. The energy of a simple harmonic oscillator

14-17 A block-spring harmonic oscillator has a force constant $k = 22$ N/m and oscillates with an amplitude $A = 87$ mm. What is the mechanical energy of the oscillator?

14-18 The mass of the block in a block-spring harmonic oscillator is $m = 0.49$ kg. If the oscillator has a period $T = 0.91$ s and an amplitude $A = 62$ mm, what is the mechanical energy of the oscillator?

14-19 For a block-spring harmonic oscillator, the spring constant of the spring is $k = 31$ N/m and the mass of

the block is $m = 0.74$ kg. The block is released from rest at $t = 0$ and $x_0 = 39$ mm. Write expressions for (a) U and (b) K as functions of time. (c) On the same sheet of graph paper, plot U and K versus t for one period of the motion.

14-20 A block-spring harmonic oscillator oscillates such that the block's amplitude is A and its maximum speed is v_{max}. (a) At what distance from the central point, in terms of A, is the block when its speed is $\frac{1}{2}v_{max}$? (b) What is the block's speed, in terms of v_{max}, when its distance from the central point is $\frac{1}{2}A$?

14-21 A block-spring harmonic oscillator with $k = 23$ N/m and $m = 0.47$ kg has a mechanical energy of 25 mJ. (a) What is the amplitude of the motion? (b) What is the maximum speed of the block? (c) What is the block's speed when $x = 11$ mm? (d) What is the block's distance from the central point when its speed is 0.25 m/s?

Section 14-5. Examples of simple harmonic motion

14-22 A 2.0-kg block is attached to a light vertical spring and gently lowered, so that the block is in equilibrium after the spring extends by 450 mm. The same block is then attached to the unstretched spring and released from rest. Determine (a) the period and (b) the amplitude of the resulting vertical oscillation.

14-23 When a standard 1.000-kg mass is connected to a vertical spring of negligible mass, the period of oscillations is 1.43 s. When an object of unknown mass replaces the standard, the period is 1.85 s. Determine (a) the unknown mass and (b) the spring constant of the spring.

14-24 A 3.0-kg block is attached to a light vertical spring of spring constant 2400 N/m. The system oscillates vertically, and the maximum speed of the block is 4.8 m/s. Determine for this motion (a) the amplitude, (b) the period, and (c) the maximum magnitude of the acceleration of the block. (d) How much is the spring stretched if the block is at rest at the equilibrium position?

14-25 A 5.0-kg block is attached to a 1200-N/m spring and gently lowered to its equilibrium position at $y = 0$. Take the potential energy of the unstretched spring to be zero and the gravitational potential energy of the block to be zero at $y = 0$. (a) What is the mechanical energy of the system in this configuration? (b) The block is pulled down an additional 25 mm and released from rest. Determine the initial mechanical energy of the system. (c) Where is the block when its speed is maximum and what is this maximum speed? (d) What is the maximum value of the gravitational potential energy for this motion?

14-26 The periods for simple, physical, and torsional pendula are given by $2\pi\sqrt{L/g}$, $2\pi\sqrt{I/mgL}$ and $2\pi\sqrt{I/\kappa}$.

Show that each of these expressions has dimensions of time.

14-27 A 20-kg child swings on a 3-m swing with a 0.2-m amplitude. Determine (a) the period and the frequency ν and (b) the maximum speed of the child for this motion.

14-28 Tarzan swings from one tree to another on a vine that is joined to a branch 15 m above his head and midway between the two trees. (a) Estimate the time interval for his swing if he just lets go of one tree and swings on the vine to the next. (b) Does the answer depend on the distance between the trees? (c) Would the time interval be different if Tarzan pushed off from one tree with an initial speed? Explain.

14-29 A uniform meter stick is pivoted about a horizontal axis at one end. (a) Determine the period of small oscillations of this stick. (b) Estimate the period of small oscillations if the stick is suspended at a small hole drilled through the 250-mm mark.

14-30 Two small, identical 1.0-kg balls are attached at each end of a 1.0-m rigid rod of negligible mass. Determine the period of small oscillations of this pendulum if it is suspended at (a) one end, (b) the other end, (c) one-third of the way from one end to the other, (d) the midpoint.

14-31 A mechanical windup clock is timed by the period of a torsional pendulum called a balance wheel. The balance wheel has moment of inertia 4.20×10^{-8} kg $\cdot$ m^2 and is designed to oscillate with a period of 0.250 s. (a) Determine the torsion constant of the spiral spring that acts as a torsional fiber. (b) What is the maximum magnitude of the angular acceleration of the wheel if the amplitude of the oscillation is 0.45 rad?

14-32 A uniform circular disk of radius 180 mm and mass 0.75 kg is attached to a thin fiber of torsion constant $\kappa = 24$ N $\cdot$ m/rad, as seen in Fig. 14-10. The disk is turned through 1.5 rad from its equilibrium orientation and released from rest. Determine (a) the period, (b) the angular frequency, (c) the maximum angular speed, (d) the maximum rotational kinetic energy of the disk for the motion.

14-33 A 150-mm-long, 25-g pencil is suspended as seen in Fig. 14-10b. If equal but opposite horizontal forces of magnitude 2.2 mN are applied at each end perpendicular to the pencil, the pencil is in a new equilibrium position that is rotated by $\pi/4$ rad from its original equilibrium position. Determine (a) the period of oscillation and (b) the maximum rotational kinetic energy of the pencil after the forces are removed.

Section 14-6. Simple harmonic motion and uniform circular motion

14-34 A particle moves with constant speed $v = 12$ m/s in a circular path of radius $A = 0.50$ m. For the motion of its projection onto the x axis, determine (a) the period,

(b) the amplitude, (c) the maximum speed, (d) the maximum magnitude of acceleration.

14-35 The object Q in Fig. 14-12 is 150 mm from the center of a turntable that rotates at $33\frac{1}{3}$ rev/min. Consider the motion of its shadow on the screen. Write expressions as functions of time t for x, v_x, and a_x. Assume that x is a maximum at $t = 0$.

14-36 As the bob of the conical pendulum in Fig. 14-21 traces out a circular path, the light string of length L sweeps out a cone of half-angle θ. Show that the period of the circular motion of the bob is given by $2\pi \sqrt{(L/g)} \cos \theta$.

14-37 Suppose that the circle traced out by the bob in the previous exercise is in the xy plane, with the center at the origin. (a) Show that the x and y coordinates undergo SHM. (b) Determine the amplitude and the angular frequency for the x and y motions.

Section 14-7. Damped harmonic motion

14-38 Determine the SI units of (a) the damping constant b that appears in Eq. (14-27) and (b) the constant $\gamma = b/2m$ in Eq. (14-28).

14-39 A block attached to a spring is set in oscillation, with an initial amplitude of 120 mm. After 2.4 min the amplitude has decreased to 60 mm. (a) When will the amplitude be 30 mm? (b) Determine the value of γ for this motion.

14-40 A 2.5-kg block is connected to a 1250-N/m spring. The block is released from rest at $t = 0$ at 28 mm from the equilibrium position, and the motion is damped with $b = 50$ kg/s. (a) Determine the angular frequency ω_D of the damped harmonic motion. (b) Determine the initial amplitude A and the phase constant ϕ in Eq. (14-28) for this motion. (Caution: ϕ is not zero.) (c) Determine x, v_x, and a_x at $t = \pi/5$ s.

14-41 The pendulum of a clock normally swings through an arc of length 135 mm. The mechanism, which is driven by a falling weight, stops if the arc length is less than 50 mm. After the weight reaches the bottom of the clock at the time 9:17, the arc length of the pendulum decreases to 95 mm at 9:22. (a) What is the constant γ for this damped harmonic motion? (b) What time does the clock stop?

14-42 A steady force of 120 N is required to push a 700-kg boat through the water at a constant speed of 1.0 m/s. Assume that the damping force exerted by the water is given by $\mathbf{F}_D = -b\mathbf{v}$. (a) Determine the value of b. (b) The boat is fastened by springs to two posts, as shown in Fig. 14-22, and held at 2.0 m from its equilibrium position by a 450-N horizontal force. Write the expression for the motion of the boat after it is released at $t = 0$.

14-43 By direct substitution, show that Eq. (14-28) is a solution of Eq. (14-27). [Hint: The functions $\cos (\omega_D t + \phi)$ and $\sin (\omega_D t + \phi)$ are independent. That is,

Figure 14-22. Exercise 14-42: The boat is displaced 2.0 m to the right from its equilibrium position and released from rest.

$C \cos{(\omega_D t + \phi)} + D \sin{(\omega_D t + \phi)} = 0$ if and only if $C = D = 0$.]

14-44 Verify by direct substitution that the solution of Eq. (14-27) for the case of the overdamped oscillator is given by

$$y = e^{-\gamma t}(Ae^{pt} + Be^{-pt})$$

where $\gamma = b/2m$ and $p = \sqrt{(b/2m)^2 - k/m}$ and A and B are constants.

PROBLEMS

14-1 In terms of the period T, determine the time required for a simple harmonic oscillator to travel from $x = A$ to $x = \frac{1}{2}A$.

14-2 Consider a block-spring simple harmonic oscillator with $k = 200$ N/m and $m = 2.4$ kg. The initial conditions of the oscillator are $x_0 = 0.15$ m and $v_{x0} = 0.45$ m/s. Determine the position of the block at $t = 3.0$ s.

14-3 A clock regulated by a simple pendulum with period 0.11 s is placed in an elevator. (a) What is the period when the elevator is accelerating upward with magnitude $\frac{1}{2}g$? (b) What is the period when the elevator is traveling upward at a steady speed of 5.1 m/s? (c) What is the period when the elevator is accelerating downward with magnitude $\frac{1}{2}g$? (d) At the start of the day, the pendulum clock is on the elevator at the lobby level and is set to the same time as the lobby clock. The pendulum clock and the lobby clock are calibrated such that they keep the same time if they remain stationary. After many trips up and down in the elevator during the day, the pendulum clock is back in the lobby. Do the clocks agree? If not, which one reads the earlier time?

14-4 A clock regulated by a simple pendulum is accurate when its temperature remains fixed at 20°C. The pendulum increases its length by 0.0010 percent for each 1.0°C increase in temperature. What is the temperature if the clock loses 2.0 s in 1 day?

14-5 When we found that the angular frequency of the oscillations of the idealized block-spring system was $\omega = \sqrt{k/m}$, we neglected the mass of the spring. Let us now take account of the mass m_s of the spring. Assume that the extension of the spring is uniform over its length ℓ and that its linear mass density μ is uniform. With these assumptions, $\mu = m_s/\ell$, and the relation between the speed v of the block and the speed v_ξ of an element of the spring located at ξ (see Fig. 14-23) is $v_\xi = (\xi/\ell)v$. (a) Show that the kinetic energy K_s of the spring is

$$K_s = \frac{m_s v^2}{6}$$

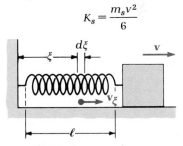

Figure 14-23. Prob. 14-5.

(b) Write the expression for the mechanical energy of the block-spring system, including the kinetic energy of the spring. By comparison with the expression for the mechanical energy of a block-spring system having a spring of negligible mass, $E = \frac{1}{2}mv^2 + \frac{1}{2}kx^2$, show that the angular frequency taking the spring's mass into account is

$$\omega = \sqrt{\frac{k}{m + m_s/3}}$$

14-6 (a) A uniform meter stick swings freely from one end.

14-45 For critical damping, $b/2m = \sqrt{k/m} = \omega$. Verify that the critically damped solution of Eq. (14-27) is given by

$$y = e^{-\omega t}(A + Bt)$$

where A and B are constants.

Section 14-8. Forced oscillations and resonance

14-46 Show that the meter is the SI unit of A_0 in the expression following Eq. (14-31).

14-47 The block in Exercise 14-40 is subjected to a sinusoidal driving force of angular frequency $\omega_E = 25$ rad/s and maximum magnitude $F_0 = 12$ N. Determine (a) the amplitude A_0 and (b) the phase constant ϕ_E for the steady-state motion. (c) Determine the amplitude if the system is driven at resonance.

14-48 Construct graphs similar to that in Fig. 14-18 for $b/2m = $ (a) 0.07ω; (b) 0.10ω; and (c) 0.70ω. Show all three cases on the same graph and comment on the effect of increased damping.

What is the period for small oscillations? (b) A lump of wax whose mass is 12 percent of the mass of the meter stick is placed at the 500-mm mark. What is the period for small oscillations now? (c) Where could the lump be placed on the stick such that the period is not affected?

14-7   A small, slippery ice cube is placed near the bottom of a bowl with radius of curvature $R = 140$ mm. What is the period of small oscillations of the ice cube?

14-8   A 100.0-g "weight" holder is attached to a light spring and oscillates vertically with a period of 0.33 s. (See Fig. 14-24.) Suppose a 10.0-g weight is put on the holder. What is the maximum amplitude of oscillation of this system such that the 10-g weight remains in contact with the holder throughout the motion?

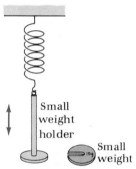

Small weight holder

Small weight

Figure 14-24. Prob. 14-8.

14-9   If an external force $\mathbf{F}_E$ is applied to an object, the rate at which work is done by the force is $P = \mathbf{F}_E \cdot \mathbf{v}$, where $\mathbf{v}$ is the velocity of the object. (See Sec. 8-6.) (a) Determine an expression for the power delivered by the driving force to an oscillator described by Eq. (14-31). (b) Your answer to part (a) should contain the term $\cos \omega_E t \sin (\omega_E t - \phi_E)$. The average of this term over one cycle is

$$-\tfrac{1}{2} \sin \phi_E = \frac{-\gamma \omega_E}{\sqrt{(\omega^2 - \omega_E{}^2)^2 + 4\gamma^2 \omega_E{}^2}}$$

Show that the average power $\bar{P}$ is a maximum if $\omega_E = \omega$.

14-10   Verify that Eq. (14-31) is a solution of Eq. (14-30). Note that

$$\cos (\omega_E t - \phi_E) = \cos \omega_E t \cos \phi_E + \sin \omega_E t \sin \phi_E$$

and

$$\sin (\omega_E t - \phi_E) = \sin \omega_E t \cos \phi_E - \cos \omega_E t \sin \phi_E$$

14-11   A damping force can be represented as a force with a direction opposite to the velocity and proportional to the square of the speed: $F_x = -c|v_x|v_x$ where c is a positive quantity. Using such a force in Newton's second law for an oscillator leads to the equation of motion,

$$a_x = -\frac{c}{m}|v_x|v_x - \frac{k}{m}x$$

A solution can be found numerically by adapting the program in Table 4-2. Let $c/m = 1.0$ m^{-1}; $k/m = 39.48$ s^{-2}; $x_0 = 0.50$ m; and $v_{x0} = 0$. Determine x at intervals $\Delta t = 0.05$ s from $t = 0$ to $t = 2$ s and construct a graph of x versus t. Repeat for $c/m = 5.0$ m^{-1}.

14-12   All springs have some degree of nonlinear behavior, so that the restoring force is not strictly proportional to x. Consider a spring force component of the form

$$F_x = -kx - \alpha x^2$$

Adapt the program in Table 4-2 (or from the previous problem) to determine the motion of an undamped oscillator subject to this force. Let $m = 1.0$ kg; $k = 39.48$ N/m; $\alpha = 400$ N/m^2; $v_{x0} = 0$; $\Delta t = 0.05$ s. Consider the motion from $t = 0$ to $t = 2.0$ s for three cases: (a) $x_0 = 0.020$ m; (b) $x_0 = 0.05$ m; (c) $x_0 = 0.15$ m. Is the period independent of the amplitude? Explain.

CHAPTER 15
SOLIDS AND FLUIDS

15-1 INTRODUCTION

Most of the substances that exist in the world can be classified into one of three *phases:* solid, liquid, or gas. When acted on by outside forces, solids tend to keep their volume and shape, liquids tend to keep their volume but not their shape, and gases tend to keep neither their volume nor their shape.

The dividing lines between solids, liquids, and gases are not sharp, and many objects cannot be definitively categorized. Glass gradually changes from what is clearly a liquid into what is clearly a solid as it is cooled through the narrow range of temperatures in which it hardens. The "solid" rocks that make up the mantle of the earth slowly change shape in response to the forces that have separated the Americas from Africa and Europe. Bread dough and Silly Putty flow like liquid if acted upon by small forces but fracture in response to large forces. By suitable changes of pressure and temperature, it is possible to gradually change a liquid into a gas, with no sharp dividing line to mark the change of phase. Further, some people speak of a fourth phase of matter, the plasma phase, which has properties distinct from liquids, gases, and solids.

Despite these ambiguities, the classification of solids, liquids and gases is a useful system. A crystal of salt and a diamond are typical solids, water is a typical liquid, and the air we breathe a typical gas.

15-2 PROPERTIES OF SOLIDS

Solids resist changes in shape. Suppose we apply forces to a solid, keeping the solid in translational and rotational equilibrium. Although the solid will not change its size or shape much, it will deform slightly. A force applied to the pointed end of a stake causes more deformation than the same force applied to the blunt end. This is because the deformation depends on the force per unit area rather than on just the force itself. Consequently, we define a quantity

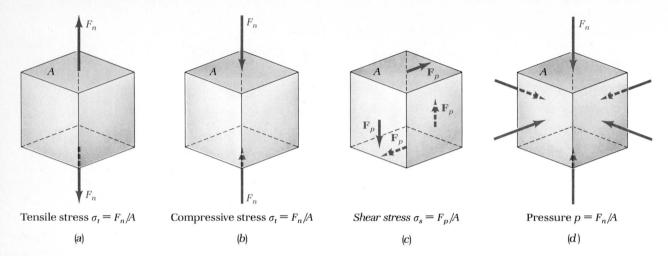

Tensile stress $\sigma_t = F_n/A$

(a)

Compressive stress $\sigma_t = F_n/A$

(b)

Shear stress $\sigma_s = F_p/A$

(c)

Pressure $p = F_n/A$

(d)

Figure 15-1. Stress is defined as the force per unit area on a surface. (a) and (b) If the force is normal to the surface, the stress is a tensile or compressive stress. (c) If the force is parallel to the surface, the stress is a shear stress. (d) If the same force is applied normal to all surfaces, it is called a pressure.

called the *stress* σ as the magnitude of the force divided by the area on which it is applied.

Consider the solid cube of Fig. 15-1. When equal forces of magnitude F_n are applied normal to two opposite faces, the resulting stress is called a *normal stress*. The forces in Fig. 15-1a are directed away from the solid, and the resulting normal stress is called *tensile*. The forces in Fig. 15-1b are directed which is in effect a negative tension. For both cases the magnitude of the normal stress is

$$\sigma_t = \frac{F_n}{A} \qquad (15\text{-}1)$$

where A is the area on which F_n is applied. The dimension of stress is force divided by area, and its SI unit is N/m², which is given the name pascal (Pa). In the British system the unit of pressure is pounds per square inch, abbreviated either lb/in² or psi (1 lb/in² is equal to 6.9 kPa).

If the forces applied to a solid cube have a component parallel to the faces, then at least four forces must be applied to keep the solid in equilibrium (Fig. 15-1c). The stress that results from these force components is called a *shear stress* σ_s:

Shear stress

$$\sigma_s = \frac{F_p}{A} \qquad (15\text{-}2)$$

where F_p is the component of the force parallel to the surface.

If the same force per unit area is applied perpendicularly inward on all faces of the solid, as shown in Fig. 15-1d, then the stress is called *pressure p*:

Pressure

$$p = \frac{F_n}{A}$$

where F_n is the force component which is applied normal to each surface. The earth's atmosphere applies 1 atm, or 1.01×10^5 Pa, of pressure at sea level.

When stress is applied to a solid, the solid will deform. The way it deforms depends not only on the stress, but also on the solid. An anisotropic solid, such as wood, behaves differently if a tensile stress is applied along the grain than if the stress is applied perpendicular to the grain. An isotropic material, such as

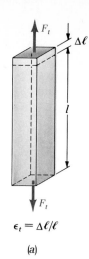

$$\epsilon_t = \Delta\ell/\ell$$

(a)

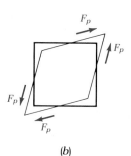

(b)

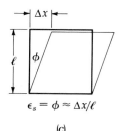

$$\epsilon_s = \phi \approx \Delta x/\ell$$

(c)

Figure 15-2. *(a)* The tensile strain is defined as the increase, due to the applied forces, in length $\Delta\ell$, divided by the unstressed length ℓ. *(b)* When shear stresses are applied, the body deforms. *(c)* Rotating the stressed body so that one side is coincident with the position of the unstressed body allows the shear stress to be defined as the angle ϕ. For usual shear strains, $\phi \approx \Delta x/\ell$.

glass, behaves the same for all orientations of the material. For simplicity we will treat only isotropic materials here.

The deformation of an isotropic solid in response to tensile stress is shown in Fig. 15-2a. The dimension ℓ of the solid elongates by an amount $\Delta\ell$. The *tensile strain* ϵ_t is defined as

$$\epsilon_t = \frac{\Delta\ell}{\ell} \tag{15-3}$$

Since the strain is a ratio of lengths, it is dimensionless. It is unfortunate that the terms "stress" (the force per unit area) and "strain" (the fractional change in length) are so similar. *Compressive strain* is defined as the ratio of the decrease in length to the original length.

The response of a uniform isotropic solid to a shear stress is called a *shear strain* and is defined as

$$\epsilon_s = \phi \approx \frac{\Delta x}{\ell} \tag{15-4}$$

where Δx is the displacement of the cube corner from its right-angle position, as shown in Fig. 15-2c. The shear strain is also dimensionless.

How is the strain in a solid related to the applied stress? This is a question that only experiment can answer. The magnitude of the strain as a function of the applied stress for a common material, such as copper, is shown in Fig. 15-3. For strains less than about $\frac{1}{2}$ percent, the strain is proportional to the stress within experimental accuracy. This behavior is known as *Hooke's law*. (Note that Hooke's law does not have the same generality as Newton's laws; it merely expresses a property of many, but not all, materials.) At higher strains, experiments show that the strain is not exactly proportional to the stress. The value of the stress at which this becomes noticeable is called the *proportional limit* and is shown at A in Fig. 15-3.

If the stress is large enough, the solid will be permanently deformed. The value of the stress at which this occurs is called the *elastic limit*, or the *yield point*, and is shown at B in Fig. 15-3. The region between the yield point and fracture is called the *plastic region*.

The elastic properties of an isotropic solid are described by two quantities, one for normal stress and one for shear stress. In the proportional region of the

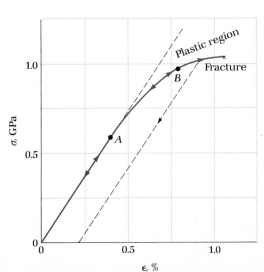

Figure 15-3. A stress-strain curve that might be measured for a typical solid. For stresses larger than that at point A, the stress-strain curve can no longer be considered linear. This point is called the proportional limit. If the stress is released after having been higher than that at point B, called the elastic limit, the solid is permanently elongated; as the stress is released, a line such as the dashed one is followed.

stress-strain curve, the ratio of the stress to the strain is a constant whose value depends on the material of the solid. *Young's modulus Y* expresses this linear relation between normal stress and strain for a solid:

Young's modulus

$$Y = \frac{\sigma_t}{\epsilon_t} = \frac{F_n/A}{\Delta\ell/\ell}$$

or $\sigma_t = Y\epsilon_t$. Young's modulus has the dimensions of force per unit area and SI units of Pa. A steel wire has a large value of Y, while a soft rubber band stretches easily and has a small value of Y. See Table 15-1.

The *shear modulus S* expresses the relation between the shear stress and shear strain:

Shear modulus

$$S = \frac{\sigma_s}{\epsilon_s} = \frac{F_p/A}{\Delta x/\ell}$$

or $\sigma_s = S\epsilon_s$. The shear modulus also has dimensions of force per unit area and SI units of Pa. A solid which strongly resists twisting has a large value of S. As you can see in Table 15-1, large values of Y and S usually occur in the same solid.

The *bulk modulus B* relates the fractional change in volume to the change in the applied pressure:

Bulk modulus

$$B = -V\frac{dp}{dV} \approx -\frac{\Delta p}{\Delta V/V}$$

It measures how much pressure is required to compress a substance by a given fraction. Notice in Table 15-1 that solids and liquids have much higher values of B than do gases.

Table 15-1. Approximate elastic constants for a few materials

Material	Y, GPa	S, GPa	B, GPa
Aluminum	70	30	70
Brass	91	36	61
Copper	110	44	140
Iron, cast	100	40	90
Lead	15	5.6	7.7
Steel	200	84	160
Tungsten	390	150	200
Bone	15	80	
Brick	14		
Concrete	25		
Diamond	1120	450	540
Glass	55	23	31
Ice	14	3	8
Nylon	5		
Rock	50		40
Rubber (vulcanized)	14		
Wood			
(∥ grain)	10		
(⊥ grain)	1		
Ethyl alcohol	0	0	0.9
Glycerine	0	0	4.8
Mercury	0	0	27
Water	0	0	2.2
Most gases at constant room temperature and atmospheric pressure	0	0	10^{-4}

EXAMPLE 15-1. A steel logging wire is wrapped around a log and then pulled by a tractor. The wire is 12.5 mm in diameter and is 10.5 m long between the tractor and the log. A force of 9500 N is necessary to pull the log. (*a*) What is the stress in the wire? (*b*) What is the strain in the wire? (*c*) How much does the wire stretch when the log is pulled?

SOLUTION. (*a*) From the definition of normal stress:

$$\sigma_t = \frac{F_n}{A} = \frac{9500 \text{ N}}{\pi(6.25 \times 10^{-3} \text{ m})^2} = 7.74 \times 10^7 \text{ Pa}$$

(*b*) The strain can be found from the value of Young's modulus in Table 15-1:

$$\epsilon_t = \frac{\sigma_t}{Y} = \frac{7.74 \times 10^7 \text{ Pa}}{200 \times 10^9 \text{ Pa}} = 3.87 \times 10^{-4}$$

(*c*) The change in length of the wire can be found from the definition of strain, $\epsilon_t = \Delta\ell/\ell$:

$$\Delta\ell = \epsilon_t\ell = (3.87 \times 10^{-4})(10.5 \text{ m}) = 4.06 \text{ mm}$$

Although the change in length is measurable, it is not enough to be noticeable to the logger.

15-3 DENSITY

When we say that iron is "heavier" than aluminum, what do we mean? We do not mean that every piece of iron weighs more than every piece of aluminum; we mean that given equal volumes of iron and of aluminum, the iron weighs more and thus has more mass. This is quantified in the mass per unit volume, or *density* ρ, of a substance:

Density

$$\rho = \frac{m}{V}$$

where m is the mass and V the volume. The dimension of density is mass divided by volume, and the SI unit is kg/m³. Approximate densities of a few materials are given in Table 15-2. As we will see in the next section, the pressure in a fluid at a given depth is determined by the density of the fluid.

Because water plays such a large role in ordinary life, it is common to compare the density of a material with the density of water by dividing the former by the latter and calling the ratio the *specific gravity* of the material.*

* Specific gravity is actually a misnomer, since it has nothing to do with gravity.

Table 15-2. Approximate density of a few materials*

Material	Density ρ (kg/m⁻³)	Material	Density ρ (kg/m⁻³)
Aluminum	2.7×10^3	Wood	0.7×10^3
Brass	8.4×10^3		
Copper	8.9×10^3	Blood	1.05×10^3
Gold	19.3×10^3	Ethyl alcohol	0.81×10^3
Iridium	22.6×10^3	Glycerine	1.26×10^3
Iron or steel	7.8×10^3	Mercury	13.6×10^3
Lead	11.3×10^3	Water	1.00×10^3
Platinum	21.4×10^3	Seawater	1.03×10^3
Tungsten	19.3×10^3		
		Air	1.29
Bone	1.8×10^3	Helium	0.179
Brick	$1.4–2.2 \times 10^3$	Hydrogen	0.090
Concrete	2.4×10^3	Steam (100°C)	0.6
Diamond	3.5×10^3	Uranium hexafluoride	15
Glass	2.6×10^3		
Ice	0.92×10^3	Interstellar space	3×10^{-22}
Nylon	1.1×10^3	Sun (average)	1.4×10^3
Rock (average)	2.8×10^3	Earth (average)	5.5×10^3
Rubber (hard)	1.2×10^3	Neutron star	10^{17}

* At room temperature and atmospheric pressure, except as noted and for extraterrestrial locations.

Because the specific gravity is the ratio of two quantities with the same dimension, it is dimensionless. Specific gravity is used more in commerce than in science. The condition of battery fluid and of wine is commonly characterized by specific gravity.

Weight density

In the British system, the *weight density* is often given, since the unit for weight is more common than the unit for mass in the British system. The weight density is given by ρg, and is thus

$$\frac{\text{Weight}}{\text{Volume}} = \frac{mg}{V}$$

The unit of weight density in the British system is pounds per cubic foot (lb/ft^3).

EXAMPLE 15-2. A rectangular block of silicon is 120 mm by 165 mm by 255 mm and has a mass of 11.8 kg. (*a*) What is the density of silicon? (*b*) What is the specific gravity of silicon?

SOLUTION. (*a*) The volume of the silicon is

$$V = (0.120 \text{ m})(0.165 \text{ m})(0.255 \text{ m}) = 5.05 \times 10^{-3} \text{ m}^3$$

Thus the density of silicon is

$$\rho = \frac{V}{m} = \frac{11.8 \text{ kg}}{5.05 \times 10^{-3} \text{ m}^3} = 2.34 \times 10^3 \text{ kg/m}^3$$

(*b*) The specific gravity of silicon is the ratio of the density of silicon to the density of water, or

$$\text{sp. gr.} = \frac{2.34 \times 10^3 \text{ kg/m}^3}{1.00 \times 10^3 \text{ kg/m}^3} = 2.34$$

15-4 PRESSURE IN A STATIC FLUID

A gas or a liquid will not come to equilibrium when acted on by a shear stress, but will continually deform. We call such substances *fluids*. Under static conditions then, there cannot be a shear stress in a fluid. It follows that the force on any surface bounding a fluid at rest is normal to the surface.

The pressure in a fluid at rest is independent of the orientation of the surface on which it acts. By way of illustration, suppose a small piece of tubing bent into a circular arc is suspended horizontally in a fluid, as seen in Fig. 15-4. If there were any difference in the pressure at the two ends, the fluid would flow, contrary to our supposition that the fluid was static. Since the ends of the tube may have any orientation, we conclude that the fluid pressure at a given level is the same in all directions.

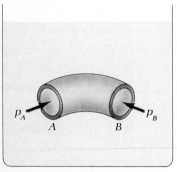

Figure 15-4. If a short, hollow, bent tube is immersed in a static fluid, no flow occurs. This implies that the pressure is equal at the ends of the horizontal tube and that the pressure is the same in all directions in a fluid.

Pressure as a function of depth. Now let us consider the effects of the gravitational force of the earth on the vertical pressure variation in a fluid. Take a small element of fluid of weight dF_e, as shown in Fig. 15-5. The forces on the sides of the element add to zero as above. Let p represent the pressure at level y, and $p + dp$ represent the pressure at level $y + dy$. The forces on the top and bottom must be slightly different in order that the sum of the vertical components of the force on the element be zero:

$$pA - (p + dp)A - dF_e = 0$$

But $dF_e = (dm)g = (\rho \, dV)g = \rho g A \, dy$ and thus

$$dp = -\rho g \, dy \qquad (15\text{-}5)$$

The cause of this pressure difference is the necessity of holding the element of fluid up against the force of gravity; the pressure difference supports the

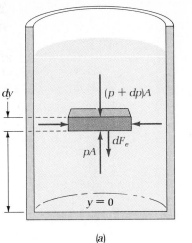

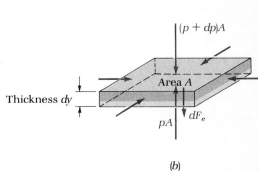

Figure 15-5. Forces on an element of fluid in equilibrium.

(a)　　　　　　　　　　　　　　　(b)

weight of the element of fluid. The negative sign indicates that the pressure decreases as the height above the bottom increases. We can integrate Eq. (15-5) to obtain the pressure as a function of height in the fluid:

$$\int_{p_1}^{p_2} dp = -\int_{y_1}^{y_2} \rho g \, dy'$$

From Table 15-1, we can see that most liquids have a large value of B and are thus nearly incompressible. For example, to cause a 1 percent change in the volume of water takes a pressure of 2.2×10^7 Pa, or 200 atm. Thus the density ρ of most liquids is nearly independent of y, and ρ can be taken out of the integral. The integration then yields

$$p_2 - p_1 = -\rho g(y_2 - y_1)$$

If the top of the liquid is at $y_2 = h$ and the pressure at the top surface of the liquid is p_0, then at a depth $h = y_2 - y_1$, the pressure p is given by $p_0 - p = -\rho g h$, or

$$p = p_0 + \rho g h \tag{15-6}$$

Static pressure in an incompressible fluid

Thus the pressure increases linearly with depth in an incompressible fluid.

EXAMPLE 15-3. What is the pressure at the bottom of the ocean in a place where it is 3 km deep? The pressure at the top of the ocean is atmospheric pressure, or 1.01×10^5 Pa.

SOLUTION. From Table 15-2, the density of seawater is 1.03×10^3 kg/m³. Thus from Eq. (15-6),

$p = 1.01 \times 10^5$ Pa

$+ (1.03 \times 10^3 \text{ kg/m}^3) (9.80 \text{ N/kg})(3 \times 10^3 \text{ m}) = 3.0 \times 10^7$ Pa

or about 300 times atmospheric pressure. The density of water 3 km deep in the ocean is about $1\frac{1}{2}$ percent higher than at the top, and thus our results, which assume an incompressible fluid, are slightly off. That is why we have rounded off the answer to two places.

If the pressure at the surface of the liquid p_0 is increased by Δp, then Eq. (15-6) shows that the pressure at an arbitrary point a distance h below the surface also increases by Δp. This result is called *Pascal's principle*:

Pascal's principle

Pressure applied to an enclosed incompressible static fluid is transmitted undiminished to all parts of the fluid.

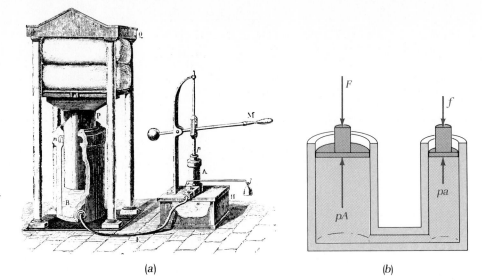

Figure 15-6. The hydraulic press. (a) An illustration of a cotton press. *(From Ganot's Physics, 9th ed., 1879.)* (b) A schematic drawing of the press.

(a)   (b)

The hydraulic press illustrates Pascal's principle nicely. Figure 15-6a, from a nineteenth-century physics text, shows a press for cotton bales. A large pressure can be created at A with a small force, because the area at A is small. The same pressure is applied to every surface of the fluid, including the piston P. Since the area of P is large, the total force on P is large. The ratio of the force applied at r to the force on the cotton bale at P is equal to the ratio of the areas of the pistons at r and P.

Compressible fluids. If the fluid is noticeably compressible, the relation between the density and the height in the fluid must be known before Eq. (15-5) can be integrated. For many gases, such as air, there is a relation between the pressure p and the density ρ when the temperature is constant: $p/p_0 = \rho/\rho_0$, where p_0 and ρ_0 are the pressure and density at a reference point, say at $y = 0$. Equation (15-5) can then be written $dp = -\rho g\, dy = (p\rho_0/p_0)g\, dy$, or

$$\frac{dp}{p} = -\frac{\rho_0 g}{p_0}\, dy$$

This expression can be integrated from the reference level $y = 0$ to a level h:

$$\ln p(h) - \ln p_0 = -\frac{\rho_0 g}{p_0}(h - 0)$$

or

$$\ln \frac{p(h)}{p_0} = -\frac{\rho_0 g}{p_0} h$$

or

$$p(h) = p_0 e^{-(\rho_0 g/p_0)h} \tag{15-7}$$

Static pressure in a compressible fluid

The pressure decreases exponentially with height.

EXAMPLE 15-4. (a) What is the pressure difference between the floor and the ceiling of a 4.0-m-high room? (b) How high above the earth's surface is the pressure half that at the surface? Assume that the temperature of the atmosphere is constant.

SOLUTION. (a) From Table 15-2

$$\frac{\rho_0 g}{p_0} = \frac{(1.29 \text{ kg/m}^3)(9.8 \text{ N/kg})}{1.01 \times 10^5 \text{ Pa}} = 1.25 \times 10^{-4} \text{ m}^{-1}$$

Thus

$p(\text{ceiling}) = p(\text{floor})e^{-(1.25\times 10^{-4} \text{ m}^{-1})(4 \text{ m})} = 0.99950p(\text{floor})$

or $p(\text{floor}) - p(\text{ceiling}) = (5.0 \times 10^{-4})p(\text{floor}) = 50$ Pa. [Another method is to note that $e^{-x} \approx 1 - x$ when $x \ll 1$, so that for small height differences, $p - p_0 = p_0(1 - \rho_0 g/h) = 50$ Pa.] Since the density of air is low, this pressure difference is small, but a good aneroid barometer can show it.

(b) Solving Eq. (15-7) for h,

$$h = -\frac{p_0}{\rho_0 g} \ln \frac{p}{p_0} = (-8.0 \times 10^3 \text{ m}) \ln 0.5 = 5540 \text{ m}$$

Airplanes routinely fly above this height, which is why oxygen masks are necessary if the cabin pressurization should fail. Actually, the temperature of the air decreases slightly with height in this range, and the pressure at 5500 m is about 15 percent lower than this estimate.

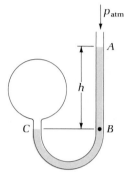

Figure 15-7. A manometer.

Manometers. The pressure of a gas inside a vessel can be measured with a manometer such as that shown in Fig. 15-7. The U-shaped tube contains a liquid, such as mercury (Hg), which rises to different levels on either side. The pressure at point A is atmospheric pressure p_{atm}, since the tube is open above A. From Eq. (15-6), the pressure in the liquid of the manometer at B is $p_{\text{atm}} + \rho gh$, where ρ is the density of the fluid in the manometer. The pressure at point C is the same as the pressure at point B, since they are at the same level. Thus the pressure p in the bulb of Fig. 15-7 is

$$p = p_{\text{atm}} + \rho gh$$

The total pressure p is called the *absolute pressure*, while $p_g = p - p_{\text{atm}} = \rho gh$ is called the *gauge pressure*.

EXAMPLE 15-5. A mercury manometer is connected to an air tank, as shown in Fig. 15-8. What is the gauge pressure at points a and b and inside the air tank?

SOLUTION. At point a, the pressure is that of the atmosphere, and thus the gauge pressure is zero. At point b, the pressure is $p_b = p_{\text{atm}} + \rho gh$, and the gauge pressure p_{bg} (or ρgh) is

$$p_{bg} = (13.6 \times 10^3 \text{ kg/m}^3)(9.8 \text{ N/kg})(0.044 \text{ m}) = 5.9 \text{ kPa}$$

Inside the tank, the pressure is essentially the same as it is at b, because the density of air is so small.

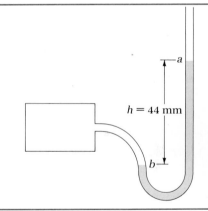

Figure 15-8. Example 15-5.

Barometers. A barometer is a device for measuring the pressure of the atmosphere. One kind of barometer can be made by taking a tube at least 800 mm long and closed at one end and filling it with mercury. The open end is then covered with the thumb, the tube is inverted, the open end placed in a reservoir of mercury, and the thumb removed, as illustrated in Fig. 15-9. When the thumb is removed, the mercury level drops until the top of the column is a height h above the reservoir. At sea level the height h is 760 mm on average, depending upon the weather. Since there is nothing above the mercury, the pressure at the top of the mercury column is zero. (We neglect the pressure of the mercury vapor in this region; it is less than a millionth of an atmosphere.) Equation (15-6) shows that the pressure at the bottom of the column is $\rho_{\text{Hg}} gh$. But this is also the pressure that the atmosphere exerts on the mercury in the bowl, hence $p_{\text{atm}} = \rho_{\text{Hg}} gh$. That is, the pressure of the atmosphere is directly proportional to the height of the mercury column. Put another way, the weight of the column of mercury is equal to the weight of a column of the

A barometer measures the pressure exerted by the atmosphere.

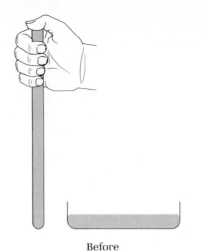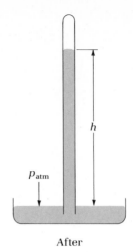

Figure 15-9. A barometer. A tube is filled with mercury, the bottom of the tube immersed in mercury, and the thumb released. The mercury level in the tube falls to height h, which depends on the pressure of the atmosphere.

Before   After

atmosphere of the same cross section, extending to the top of the earth's atmosphere. Because pressures were often measured in this way, they are sometimes given in mmHg or torr, by which is meant the height in millimeters of a column of mercury that the pressure can support. Blood pressures are routinely measured in mmHg.

EXAMPLE 15-6. (a) What is the absolute pressure at the bottom of a 6.2-m-deep freshwater lake? (b) What is the gauge pressure at the bottom? (c) What is the gauge pressure at the bottom measured in the non-SI unit torr?

SOLUTION. (a) The absolute pressure p is

$$p = p_{atm} + \rho gh = 1.01 \times 10^5 \text{ Pa}$$
$$+ (1.00 \times 10^3 \text{ kg/m}^3)(9.8 \text{ m/s}^2)(6.2 \text{ m}) = 1.62 \times 10^5 \text{ Pa}$$

It is worth noting that ρg for water is about 10^4 N/m³, so that

for every extra 10 m of depth of water, the pressure increases by 10^5 Pa, or about 1 atm. (b) The gauge pressure p_g is the absolute pressure minus the atmospheric pressure: $p = p_g - p_{atm} = 6.1 \times 10^4$ Pa. (c) The gauge pressure in torr is the height h (in mm) of the column of mercury the gauge pressure will support:

$$h = \frac{p}{\rho_{Hg} g} = \frac{6.1 \times 10^4 \text{ Pa}}{(13.6 \times 10^3 \text{ kg/m}^3)(9.8 \text{ N/kg})} = 460 \text{ mm}$$

Thus the gauge pressure can also be expressed as 460 torr.

EXAMPLE 15-7. A dam has a height H of 15 m and a width W of 40 m, as seen in Fig. 15-10. (a) What is the total horizontal force component F_h exerted on the dam by the water behind it? (b) What is the torque τ, exerted by the water on the dam, about an axis through the bottom of the dam along its width?

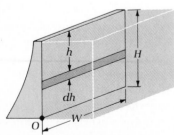

Figure 15-10. Example 15-7.

SOLUTION. We will use the gauge pressure of the water to calculate F_h and τ because atmospheric pressure is exerted

on both sides of the dam. Since the pressure varies with depth, an integral is necessary. The magnitude of the force component dF_h on a narrow strip of incremental depth dh, width W, located at depth h is $dF_h = p_g\, dA = (\rho gh)(W\, dh)$ and thus the total force component is

$$F_h = \int_0^H \rho gh W\, dh = \rho gW \int_0^H h\, dh = \rho gW(\tfrac{1}{2}H^2)$$

Notice that the force is porportional to the square of the height of the dam. For the case at hand,

$$F_h = \tfrac{1}{2}(10^3 \text{ kg/m}^3)(9.8 \text{ N/m})(40 \text{ m})(15 \text{ m})^2 = 40 \text{ MN}$$

(b) The magnitude of the torque about a horizontal axis through the point O, due to the force on the narrow strip, is $d\tau = (H - h)dF = (H - h)(\rho gh)(W\, dh)$, and the total torque exerted by the water has magnitude

$$\tau = \rho gW \int_0^H (H - h)h\, dh = \rho gW(\tfrac{1}{2}H^3 - \tfrac{1}{3}H^3) = \frac{\rho gWH^3}{6}$$

Notice that the magnitude of the torque is proportional to the cube of the height of the dam. Counter torques are exerted on the sides of the dam and on the base by the surrounding ground to keep the dam in equilibrium. For the case at hand,

$$\tau = \frac{(10^3 \text{ kg/m}^3)(9.8 \text{ N/kg})(40 \text{ m})(15 \text{ m})^3}{6} = 0.2 \text{ GN} \cdot \text{m}$$

The center of pressure is defined as the place where a single horizontal force could be applied with the same effect as the total force applied by the water. Can you see why the center of pressure is not at the center of the dam?

15-5 ARCHIMEDES' PRINCIPLE

According to a story, Hiero, the king of Syracuse, ordered a new crown. On receiving the crown, he wasn't satisfied. He suspected the goldsmith of adulterating the gold in the crown with silver. The king asked his mathematician friend, Archimedes, if it were possible to determine if the crown were pure gold without cutting into it. Archimedes was contemplating the problem as he went to his bath. As he stepped into the full tub, he recognized that the water which he displaced was equal to the volume of his body under the water. In the story, Archimedes shouted, "Eureka!" ("I found it!"), jumped out of the bath, and ran down the street. What he had discovered was that the volume of the irregularly shaped crown could be found by immersing it in water. By comparing the weight of the crown with the weight of an equal volume of pure gold, he could determine if the crown were pure gold. According to the legend, the goldsmith had cheated and was executed! Although the story may not be true, Archimedes did go on to write Περι Οχονμενων (On Floating Bodies), which established the general principles of hydrostatics.

The principle which is named after Archimedes is this:

Archimedes' principle

A body that is partly or entirely submerged in a fluid is buoyed up by a force equal in magnitude to the weight of the displaced fluid and directed upward along a line through the center of gravity of the displaced fluid.

For the proof of this principle from Newton's laws, consider an object in equilibrium while immersed in a fluid, as shown in Fig. 15-11. If we replace the object with an equal volume of fluid (the displaced fluid), the displaced fluid is also in translational and rotational equilibrium. The force the fluid exerts on the object and the forces that it exerted on the displaced fluid are the same; thus the force applied by the surrounding fluid on the object must be equal to the weight of the displaced fluid and be directed upward through the center of gravity of the displaced fluid. Since the weight of the displaced fluid is equal to the mass of the displaced fluid ρV times the acceleration of gravity, the magnitude of the buoyant force F_B is

Figure 15-11. The buoyant force on an object is equal to the force on the fluid that the object displaces.

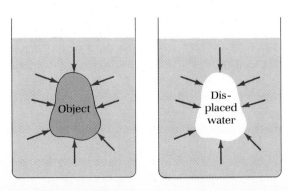

$$F_B = \rho g V$$

Notice that ρ is the density of the displaced fluid and V the volume of the displaced fluid.

EXAMPLE 15-8. A box of treasure with a mass of 92 kg and a volume of 0.031 m³ lies at the bottom of the ocean. How much force is needed to lift it?

SOLUTION. As seen in Fig. 15-12, the magnitude of the force F necessary to lift the box is equal to its weight minus the buoyant force:

$F = mg - \rho g V = (92\ \text{kg})(9.8\ \text{N/kg})$

$\quad\quad - (1.03 \times 10^3\ \text{kg/m}^3)(9.8\ \text{N/kg})(0.031\ \text{m}^3) = 590\ \text{N}$

Since 590 N is the weight of 60 kg (in air), it would be like lifting a 60-kg box that was above water.

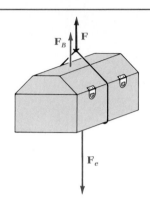

Figure 15-12. Example 15-8.

EXAMPLE 15-9. What volume of helium is needed to float a balloon if the empty balloon and its equipment have a mass of 390 kg?

SOLUTION. The buoyant force on the balloon due to the displaced air must be equal and opposite to the weight of the balloon and equipment plus the helium. Thus $F_B = (390\ \text{kg} + m_{He})g = \rho_{air}gV$. But the mass of the helium de-

pends on the volume of the balloon: $m_{He} = \rho_{He}V$. Notice that we have assumed that the volume of the empty balloon and equipment is negligible. Thus $\rho_{air}gV = (390\ \text{kg} + \rho_{He}V)g$, or

$$V = \frac{390\ \text{kg}}{\rho_{air} - \rho_{He}} = 351\ \text{m}^3$$

where the air and helium are assumed to be at atmospheric pressure.

15-6 BERNOULLI'S EQUATION

Fluids in motion are much more complex than fluids at rest. It is difficult to apply Newton's laws to a single "particle" of fluid, following the motion of the particle through a complicated system. Instead we use Newton's second law to find the properties of the fluid at each point of the system, while the particles of the system flow through. A description of the motion of the fluid then consists of finding the density, pressure, and velocity of the fluid at all points.

Figure 15-13 shows the shape of smoke rising from a cigarette. The smoke pattern starts out with a shape which is constant in time and then, higher up, changes to a more complicated pattern which varies in time. This time-varying regime is called *turbulent.* A complete understanding of turbulent motion does not yet exist. Therefore we start with the assumption of nonturbulent flow, and further restrict ourselves to steady-state conditions, so that the density ρ, pressure p, and velocity $\mathbf{v}$ of the fluid at any given point are constant. In this case, lines of flow of the fluid particles are smooth, as in the lower region of the cigarette-smoke pattern (Fig. 15-13a), and can be drawn as in Fig. 15-14, or made experimentally observable as in Fig. 15-15. These lines are called *streamlines.* They are drawn everywhere parallel to the velocity of the fluid. Since the particles move along streamlines, no fluid crosses a surface made up of streamlines.

In steady state, flow streamlines

Lines of flow can be drawn so that they enclose a *tube of flow,* which is a bundle of neighboring streamlines, as seen in Fig. 15-16. Though we visualize

Figure 15-13. The flow of smoke from a cigarette. (*a*) At first the flow is smooth and steady. (*b*) As the smoke rises, the flow becomes unstable and forms vortices that vary in time. *(Tom Richard)*

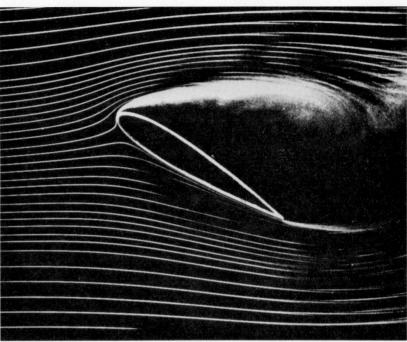

(*a*)

Figure 15-15. (*a*) Lines of flow around an airfoil. [Illustrated Experiments in Fluid Mechanics *(The NCFMF Book of Film Notes) National Committee for Fluid Mechanics Films, Educational Development Center, Inc., M.I.T. Press, Cambridge, Mass., 1972.*] (*b*) Streamline flow around a series of cylinders. The flow lines are composed of fluid that has been dyed. *(Tecquipment Ltd., Nottingham, England.)*

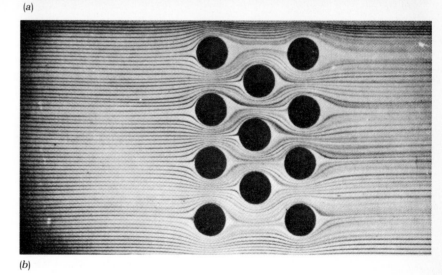

(*b*)

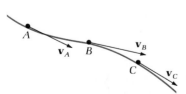

Figure 15-14. A streamline in a moving fluid. At each point the streamline points in the direction of the velocity of the fluid.

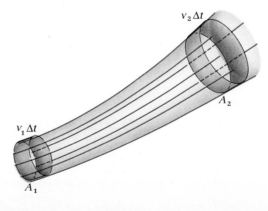

Figure 15-16. A tube of flow is surrounded by streamlines.

A tube of flow is bounded by
streamlines.

the bundle as being fixed in time and space, its confining wall is not a solid tube, but rather a bounding surface also made of streamlines. We consider the region in the tube to be thin enough so that the pressure p, density ρ, and speed v are uniform across any cross-sectional area A.

The mass of fluid having a small volume ΔV passing any cross-sectional area A in a short time Δt is $\Delta m = \rho \Delta V = \rho A v \Delta t$. Thus the rate of flow of mass is $\Delta m/\Delta t = \rho A v$. If we have a steady flow, this must be the same for all times and at all places throughout the tube, as whatever flows across one cross section must flow across all cross sections—nothing accumulates in the tube and nothing crosses its boundaries. Thus we have

Equation of continuity

$$\rho_1 v_1 A_1 = \rho_2 v_2 A_2 \tag{15-8}$$

This is called the *equation of continuity*. It expresses conservation of mass in a steady flow.

Further, if we assume that the fluid is incompressible or, equivalently, that the density is constant, then $\rho_1 = \rho_2$ and

Equation of continuity for an
incompressible fluid

$$v_1 A_1 = v_2 A_2 \tag{15-9}$$

This is a good assumption for water, and even works fairly well for airflow around wings or in heating and cooling ducts, where the pressure changes are small. The product vA gives the volume flow rate, which is given the symbol Q.

EXAMPLE 15-10. (a) A water line necks down from a pipe with a 12.5-mm radius to a pipe with a 9-mm radius. If the speed of the water in the 12.5-mm pipe is 1.8 m/s, what is the speed in the smaller pipe? See Fig. 15-17. (b) What is the volume flow rate? (c) What is the mass flow rate?

SOLUTION. (a) Using the equation of continuity,

$$v_2 = \frac{v_1 A_1}{A_2} = v_1 \frac{r_1^2}{r_2^2} = 3.5 \text{ m/s}$$

(b) The volume flow rate Q is

$$v_1 A_1 = v_2 A_2 = [\pi(12.5 \times 10^{-3} \text{ m})^2](1.8 \text{ m/s})$$
$$= 8.8 \times 10^{-4} \text{ m}^3/\text{s}$$

(c) The mass flow rate is

$$\rho v_1 A_1 = \rho v_2 A_2 = (1.0 \times 10^3 \text{ kg/m}^3)(8.8 \times 10^{-4} \text{ m}^3/\text{s})$$
$$= 0.88 \text{ kg/s}$$

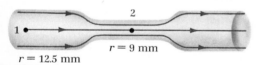

$r = 12.5$ mm

$r = 9$ mm

Figure 15-17. Example 15-10.

We have been able to derive the equation of continuity under the assumption that the flow is steady and to show that vA is a constant in the steady flow of an incompressible fluid. If, in addition, the work done by nonconservative forces is negligible, mechanical energy is conserved. We consider this case next, and in the following section discuss the case where the work done by nonconservative forces is not negligible.

The speed of flow, the height of the fluid, and the pressure may differ along a flow line, such as at 1 and 2 in Fig. 15-18. We now show how the work-energy theorem relates these quantities for points along the flow lines.

First we find the work done in a short time interval Δt on the fluid initially in the region bounded by A_1, A_2, and the flow tube. The force exerted on the boundary A_1 by the fluid behind it is $p_1 A_1$. The work done by this force in time Δt is the product of this force and the distance through which it moves, $v_1 \Delta t$. Thus $W_1 = p_1 A_1 v_1 \Delta t$. Similarly at A_2, the pressure does work $W_2 = -p_2 A_2 v_2 \Delta t$. Note that at A_1 there is work done *on* the fluid, while at A_2 there is work done *by* the fluid; hence the difference in sign. The net work $W = W_1 +$

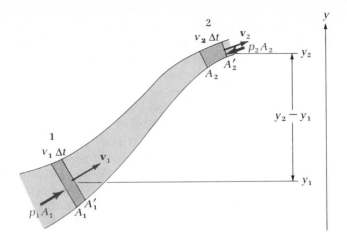

Figure 15-18. Flow along a tube of flow. Volumes ΔV in the shaded regions are equal: $\Delta V = A_1 v_1 \Delta t = A_2 v_2 \Delta t$. The mass of each shaded region is $\Delta m = \rho \, \Delta V$.

W_2 done on the fluid is

$$W = p_1 A_1 v_1 \, \Delta t - p_2 A_2 v_2 \, \Delta t$$

From the equation of continuity for an incompressible fluid, $v_1 A_1 = v_2 A_2$. Thus $\Delta V = v_1 A_1 \, \Delta t = v_2 A_2 \, \Delta t$ is the volume between A_1 and A_1' or between A_2 and A_2'. It is the volume of fluid entering one end and leaving the other end of the tube in the time interval Δt. The net input work on the fluid can now be written $W = (p_1 - p_2)\Delta V$.

The work-energy theorem shows that this work is equal to the change in the mechanical energy of the fluid initially bounded by A_1 and A_2. Since the flow is steady, the properties of the fluid in the region between A_1' and A_2 are constant. There is a change in mechanical energy in the newly occupied region between A_2 and A_2' and in the region between A_1 and A_1', which is left behind. Since the volume of each of these regions is ΔV and the density is constant, the mass contained in either region is $\Delta m = \rho \, \Delta V$. The potential energy is given by $(\Delta m)gy$ and the kinetic energy by $\frac{1}{2}(\Delta m)v^2$. The change in mechanical energy is thus

$$\Delta E = (\Delta m)gy_2 + \tfrac{1}{2}(\Delta m)v_2{}^2 - [(\Delta m)gy_1 + \tfrac{1}{2}(\Delta m)v_1{}^2]$$

The work-energy theorem then reads

$$(p_1 - p_2)\Delta V = [(\Delta m)gy_2 + \tfrac{1}{2}(\Delta m)v_2{}^2] - [(\Delta m)gy_1 + \tfrac{1}{2}(\Delta m)v_1{}^2]$$

or, dividing by ΔV with $\rho = \Delta m/\Delta V$, we find

$$p_1 - p_2 = \rho gy_2 + \tfrac{1}{2}\rho v_2{}^2 - \rho gy_1 - \tfrac{1}{2}\rho v_1{}^2$$

Collecting terms so that the same subscript appears on each side of the equation, we obtain

$$p_1 + \rho gy_1 + \tfrac{1}{2}\rho v_1{}^2 = p_2 + \rho gy_2 + \tfrac{1}{2}\rho v_2{}^2 \tag{15-10}$$

Bernoulli's equation

This is known as *Bernoulli's equation* and was originally stated in his *Hydrodynamica* in 1738. Note that we have assumed steady, nonturbulent, energy-conserving flow of an incompressible liquid in the derivation of Bernoulli's equation.

Although our derivation of Eq. (15-10) relates the pressure, speed, and height along a flow line, it is shown in more advanced texts that if the flow is "irrotational," Bernoulli's equation holds even across flow lines. You can visualize what "irrotational" means by imagining a small paddle wheel inserted in the

Bernoulli's equation holds throughout the fluid

fluid. If the paddle wheel does not have a tendency to rotate, then the flow is irrotational.

Notice that if the speed v is zero, then Bernoulli's equation, Eq. (15-10), reduces to Eq. (15-6), as we would expect.

EXAMPLE 15-11. Water (treated as an incompressible fluid whose viscosity is negligible) flows through the horizontal pipe of Fig. 15-17. At point 1 the gauge pressure is 51 kPa and the speed 1.8 m/s. What are the speed and gauge pressure at point 2?

SOLUTION. The speed at point 2 can be found from the equation of continuity for an incompressible fluid:

$$v_2 A_2 = v_1 A_1$$

$$v_2 = v_1 \frac{\pi r_1^2}{\pi r_2^2} = 3.5 \text{ m/s}$$

The pressure at point B can then be found from Bernoulli's equation. Since $y_1 = y_2$,

$$p_2 = p_1 + \tfrac{1}{2}\rho v_1^2 - \tfrac{1}{2}\rho v_2^2$$

$= 5.1 \times 10^4$ Pa

$\quad + \tfrac{1}{2}(1.00 \times 10^3 \text{ kg/m}^3)[(1.8 \text{ m/s})^2 - (3.5 \text{ m/s})^2]$

$= 4.7 \times 10^4$ Pa

At first it may seem a paradox that the pressure at 2 is lower than that at 1. But if you consider that the fluid must be accelerated between 1 and 2, it is clear that the pressure at 1 must be higher than the pressure at 2. Even if the fluid has a small viscosity, the forces due to viscosity may be small compared with the forces necessary to accelerate the fluid, and p_2 may be less than p_1. We see from this example that when the height is constant, higher speed in the fluid implies lower pressure, and lower speed implies higher pressure.

EXAMPLE 15-12. A vertical glass cylinder has a 150-mm inner diameter and a hole punched in its side near the bottom. It is filled with water until the water level is 350 mm above the hole. A horizontal jet of water 5 mm in diameter flows out of the hole. What is the speed of the water in the jet?

SOLUTION. The pressure at the top of the water in the cylinder *and* in the jet is the pressure of the atmosphere. Thus Bernoulli's equation becomes

$$\tfrac{1}{2}(v_1^2 - v_2^2) = g(h_2 - h_1)$$

where the subscript 1 is for the jet and the subscript 2 is for the top of the water in the cylinder. The equation of continuity relates the speeds in the jet and in the cylinder:

$$v_2 = \frac{A_1}{A_2} v_1$$

Thus $\quad v_1^2 = \dfrac{2g(y_2 - y_1)}{1 - (A_1/A_2)^2} = \dfrac{2(9.8 \text{ m/s}^2)(350 \text{ mm})}{1 - (5 \text{ mm}/150 \text{ mm})^2}$

$$= \frac{6.9 \text{ m}^2/\text{s}^2}{0.999}$$

Notice that to two-place accuracy the denominator is 1.0. Taking the square root, we obtain

$$v_1 = 2.6 \text{ m/s}$$

If the cylinder is large enough that the speed at the top can be neglected, then the speed of the water in the jet is the same as the speed it would have if dropped a distance $y_2 - y_1$.

EXAMPLE 15-13. A water-supply system uses a water tank for storage so that water will be available when needed. If the water level in the tank in Fig. 15-19 is 12 m above the water main at point A, and the speed in the main at point B is 16 m/s, what is the gauge pressure at points A and B?

SOLUTION. At point A, the gauge pressure is zero, because the tank is open to the atmosphere. Applying Bernoulli's equation at A and B,

$$p_B + \rho g y_B + \tfrac{1}{2}\rho v_B^2 = p_A + \rho g y_A + \tfrac{1}{2}\rho v_A^2$$

The speed of water in the large tank v_A is essentially zero

Figure 15-19. Example 15-13.

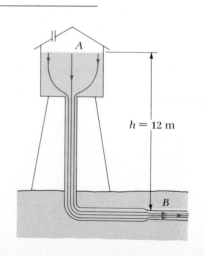

(can you show why?), and $y_A - y_B = 12$ m. Thus

$$p_B = \rho g h - \tfrac{1}{2} \rho v_B^2$$

$$= (1.00 \times 10^3 \text{ kg/m}^3)[(9.8 \text{ N/kg})(12 \text{ m}) - \tfrac{1}{2}(16 \text{ m/s})^2]$$

$$= -1.0 \times 10^4 \text{ Pa}$$

The gauge pressure in the line is negative! This means the

absolute pressure in the line is less than atmospheric pressure. (The absolute pressure is not less than zero, however.) In the design of water systems, such situations are to be avoided, since if there were a hole in the pipe, contaminated groundwater might be sucked in. In real water systems the flow is often turbulent, and water seldom has speeds over 3 m/s.

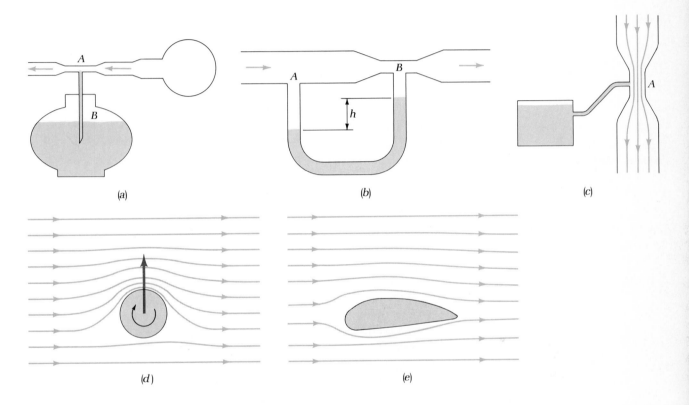

(a)   (b)   (c)

(d)   (e)

Figure 15-20. Illustrations of Bernoulli's principle.

Many practical devices are applications of Bernoulli's equation. Figure 15-20a shows a perfume atomizer. Similar devices are used to spray paint or insecticide. When the bulb in the atomizer is squeezed, air rushes through the narrow neck of the atomizer. If the perfume has the density of water, an air-speed of about 17 m/s in the narrow channel will lower the pressure at point A so that atmospheric pressure will push the perfume 2 cm up the tube leading to the narrow channel. The suction tube that dentists use to clear the mouth of saliva uses a narrow channel with a high speed of water to create a pressure lower than atmospheric.

This lowering of pressure due to the speed of the fluid is the basis for the venturi meter shown in Fig. 15-20b. The pressure difference between A and B is a measure of the speed of the fluid. Many automobile carburetors have a narrow channel called the venturi tube, shown in Fig. 15-20c. Its purpose is to lower the pressure at point A so that gasoline will enter the airflow leading to the combustion chambers of the engine.

In storms and high winds, the air rushing by a building leads to a lower pressure on the outside of the building than in the still air inside the building. This can cause windows to pop out of the building. Note that windows are almost always blown *out*, not *in*! Similarly, chimneys usually have a small draft even without a fire because the air at the top of the chimney usually has at least a small speed, while the air inside the house is stationary. If you watch a fireplace on a windy night, you can easily see the Bernouilli effect.

Figure 15-20*d* shows a rotating cylinder in a moving fluid. If the cylinder drags some fluid around with it, the net flow of fluid is as shown. This makes the speed of the air higher above the cylinder than below it, and pressure lower above the cylinder than below it. Thus there is a net force on the cylinder perpendicular to the flow direction of the fluid (up the page in this case). This is called the *Magnus effect.* Ships have been built with rotating cylinders rather than sails, and although the effect works, the ships have not been of lasting practical use (Fig. 15-21).

An airplane wing gets its "lift," the upward force that keeps the airplane up, in large part from the difference in pressure between the top of the wing and the bottom of the wing. The lower pressure above the wing is due to the higher speed of the air above the wing than below it, as seen in Fig. 15-20*e.* The actual determination of the amount of lift is a complicated problem because the viscosity of the air is of importance and turbulence is present.

15-7 VISCOSITY

Often the nonconservative forces in a fluid cannot be neglected as we have done thus far in this chapter. These forces dissipate the mechanical energy of the fluid into internal energy of the fluid, much as frictional forces dissipate the energy of the sliding block into internal energy of the block and surface. A fluid with such forces is called *viscous.* If the viscosity of a fluid is not negligible, then mechanical energy is not conserved, and Bernoulli's equation is not satisfied. When a viscous fluid flows in a horizontal uniform pipe, the pressure decreases along a line of flow, as indicated in Fig. 15-22.

The arrangement in Fig. 15-23 can be used to study the viscosity of fluids. The upper plate is moved at a constant low speed across the top of the fluid.

Viscous forces dissipate energy.

Figure 15-21. A Flettner ship. The two tall cylinders were rotated and in a wind drove the ship forward. *(Wolf D. Seufert.)*

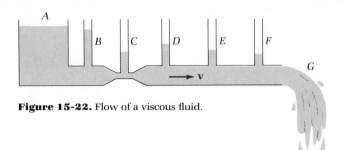

Figure 15-22. Flow of a viscous fluid.

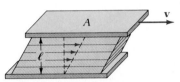

Figure 15-23. When the upper plate is pulled slowly, the viscous fluid between the plates flows in laminae whose speed is proportional to their distance from the stationary plate at the bottom, as indicated by the length of the arrows in the figure.

Experiment shows that, for most fluids, the speed of the fluid at points between the two plates of Fig. 15-23 varies linearly with the distance away from the moving plate. Fluids for which the horizontal force component required to move the plate is proportional to the speed of the plate are called *newtonian fluids*. Water and air are examples of nearly newtonian fluids. Certain plastics and suspensions such as blood and water-clay mixtures are examples of quite nonnewtonian fluids, in which the magnitude of the force required to move the plate might be proportional to the square of the speed. At high speeds, the flow becomes turbulent and very complex in all fluids.

The magnitude of the force F on the moving plate is found experimentally to depend not only on the speed v of the moving plate, but also to be proportional to the area of the plate A and inversely proportional to the distance ℓ between the moving plate and the stationary plate:

Viscous force

$$F = \frac{\eta A v}{\ell} \qquad (15\text{-}11)$$

where η is a constant of proportionality called the *viscosity*. The SI unit of viscosity is $N \cdot s \cdot m^{-2}$. A common non-SI unit for viscosity is the P (poise), equal to $0.1\ N \cdot s \cdot m^{-2}$. The viscosities of a few materials are shown as a function of temperature in Fig. 15-24.

In laminar flow, the layers of fluid do not mix.

The pattern of motion of the fluid shown in Fig. 15-23 is called *laminar flow*. Each layer (lamina) of fluid exerts a force on the layer beside it, but since the flow is not turbulent, the layers do not mix.

The flow rate Q, due to a pressure difference Δp, of a viscous fluid through a circular pipe of radius R and length ℓ can be shown to be

$$Q = \frac{\pi(\Delta p)R^4}{8\eta\ell} \qquad (15\text{-}12)$$

The derivation of this result is indicated in Prob. 15-14.

EXAMPLE 15-14. Suppose that arteriosclerosis decreases the radius of the channel in an artery in the heart by a factor of 2. By what factor must the heart increase the pressure gradient in the artery to keep the flow constant? Assume that blood is a newtonian fluid and that the flow is laminar.

SOLUTION. Since the flow is proportional to the fourth power of the radius, decreasing the radius by a factor of 2 decreases the flow by a factor of 2^4, or 16. The flow is proportional to the first power of the pressure, and thus the heart must increase the pressure by a factor of 16.

Since blood is not, in fact, a newtonian fluid and the flow of blood is not without turbulence, this result cannot be exact. Nevertheless, it illustrates the difficulties imposed by arteriosclerosis.

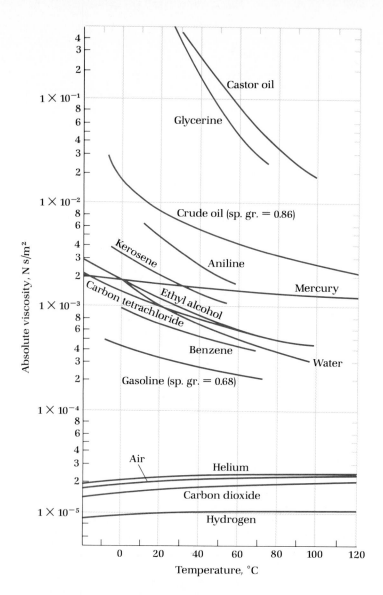

Figure 15-24. Viscosities of certain fluids. *(Adapted from V. L. Streeter,* Fluid Mechanics, *5th ed., McGraw-Hill, New York, 1971)*

COMMENTARY: ARCHIMEDES

The story of Archimedes jumping out of his bath with the solution to Hiero's problem is part of the story of the origins of modern science. Archimedes was born about 287 B.C. and died in the sack of his native Syracuse by the Romans under Marcellus in 212 B.C.

When Rome threatened the Greek-speaking settlements in southern Italy and Sicily, Archimedes helped defend Syracuse by devising military applications of his scientific knowledge. According to some accounts, he designed mirrors that set fire to part of a Roman fleet as it approached the city. For their part, the Romans admired the abilities of Archimedes, and Marcellus directed that he be unharmed when the city fell. But legend says that a Roman soldier, coming upon Archimedes in deep study over some mathematical figures and being brushed off by the preoccupied man, peremptorily drew his sword and ran the mathematician through.

In this chapter we have seen that buoyant forces are associated with Archimedes. But he is also credited with a device for pumping water, Archimedes' screw, and he constructed an organ which used water to force air across pipes. His father may have been an astronomer; in any case, Archimedes wrote a text on the construction of spheres, and his descriptions were used in making astronomical models. One of these models used water power to simulate the earth and other planets going around the sun, a model proposed by his friend Eratosthenes. When Syracuse fell, Marcellus took one of the planetary spheres in his share of the booty.

Archimedes shunned fame for his engineering prowess. Plutarch wrote that Archimedes thought that "every kind of act connected with daily needs was ignoble and vulgar," and much preferred pure mathematics. He derived expressions for the volume of figures such as spheres and cones and for the center of gravity of circular cones and figures of revolution generated by hyperbolas. In establishing such proofs, he used a process not far removed from the calculus that Newton invented.

Among his mathematical proofs is one that showed that the area of a circle is equal to πr^2. We can give the flavor of Archimedes' work with a quick and dirty version of this proof. Consider the hexagon inscribed inside the circle of Fig. 15-25. The area of the hexagon is the area of 12 right triangles congruent to triangle COM, and thus the area of the hexagon is equal to that of a right triangle in which the two sides about the right angle are equal to (i) the apothem OC (the perpendicular distance from the center of the circle to the side of the hexagon) and (ii) the perimeter of the hexagon. Similarly, a polygon of n sides inscribed in the circle has an area equal to that of a right triangle in which the sides about the right angle are the apothem and the perimeter of the polygon. Now as n becomes large, the apothem approaches the radius of the circle and the perimeter of the polygon approaches the circumference of the circle. In the limit of large n, the area of the polygon is equal to that of the circle (Archimedes was more careful here), and the area of the circle is equal to the area of a right triangle in which the sides are equal to the circle's radius r and to its circumference $2\pi r$. Thus the area of the circle is $\frac{1}{2}(r)(2\pi r) = \pi r^2$. (The limiting process of calculus was foreshadowed by the limit in which the polygon approaches a circle.) Archimedes' proof involved polygons which circumscribed as well as inscribed the circle, and by working with polygons of up to 96 sides, he was able to show that $(3 + 10/71) < \pi < (3 + 1/7)$, or $3.1408 < \pi < 3.1429$.

The importance of Archimedes' work in the history of science can scarcely be exaggerated. When Alexandria was conquered by the Arabs and the library burned, much of his work was lost. But the Arabs preserved and expanded some of it, and other parts were preserved in the Byzantine empire. When Europe emerged from the dark ages, Archimedes' work was translated into Latin and greatly influenced the beginnings of the scientific revolution. Galileo mentions Archimedes over 100 times, using such expressions as superhumanus Archimedes, inimitabilis Archimedes, and divinissimus Archimedes. The connection between mathematics and the description of experiment that is the core of modern science was nascent in the work of this great mathematician and inventor.

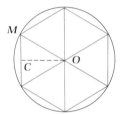

Figure 15-25. The area of a circle is approximated by the area of an inscribed hexagon. Line OC is called the apothem.

SUMMARY WITH APPLICATIONS

Section 15-2. Properties of solids

The force per unit area on a solid is called the stress σ, and the resulting deformation of the solid is called the strain ϵ. Stress and strain are classified as normal or shear depending on whether the forces applied to the solid are perpendicular to the surfaces (normal) or tangential to the surface (shear). The stress and strain in a solid are related to each other by Hooke's law:

$$\sigma_t = Y\epsilon_t$$

$$\sigma_s = S\epsilon_s$$

where Y is called Young's modulus and S is called the shear modulus. The change in volume is related to the change in the applied pressure by the bulk modulus B:

$$\Delta p = -B\left(\frac{\Delta V}{V}\right)$$

Relate the stress and strain in an object.

Section 15-3. Density
The density ρ of an object is its mass m divided by its volume V.

Section 15-4. Pressure in a static fluid
The pressure in a fluid acts normally to any surface. It varies with vertical position in an incompressible fluid by

$$p = p_0 + \rho gh \qquad (15\text{-}6)$$

In most gases, when the temperature is constant, the pressure is given as a function of height of

$$p(h) = p(0)e^{-(\rho_0 g/p_0)h} \qquad (15\text{-}7)$$

Calculate the pressure in a fluid.

Section 15-5. Archimedes' principle
Archimedes discovered the principle behind buoyant forces: A body which is partly or entirely submerged in a fluid is buoyed up by a force equal in magnitude to the weight of the displaced fluid and directed upward along a line through the center of gravity of the displaced fluid.

Find the buoyant force on an object in a fluid.

Section 15-6. Bernoulli's equation
The equation of continuity expresses conservation of mass for a fluid flowing in a tube of variable area A:

$$\rho_1 v_1 A_1 = \rho_2 v_2 A_2 \qquad (15\text{-}8)$$

For an incompressible nonviscous fluid, conservation of mechanical energy leads to Bernoulli's equation along a streamline:

$$p_1 + \rho gy_1 + \tfrac{1}{2}\rho v_1^2 = p_2 + \rho gy_2 + \tfrac{1}{2}\rho v_2^2 \quad (15\text{-}10)$$

Relate the pressure, height, and speed in a flowing fluid.

Section 15-7. Viscosity
For newtonian fluids the viscous force F_v on a surface of area A is related to the velocity gradient v/ℓ in the fluid by

$$F_v = \frac{\eta A v}{\ell} \qquad (15\text{-}11)$$

Applying this to the flow in a pipe shows that the total flow rate in the pipe is

$$Q = \frac{\pi(\Delta p)R^4}{8\eta\ell} \qquad (15\text{-}12)$$

Find the viscous force; find the flow rate of a viscous fluid in a circular pipe.

QUESTIONS

15-1   Classify the following as solid, liquid, gas, or other: ice, a glacier, gelatin, water vapor, fog, a cloud, taffy, bread dough, sugar, honey.

15-2   Give an example of a substance that could be considered a solid or a liquid, depending on the time scale of the experiment.

15-3   Two blocks are glued together to form a cube, as shown in Fig. 15-26, where the colored diagonal line represents the glue joint. If forces are applied as shown, is the stress on the glue joint tensile or shear, or a combination of both? If a combination, what is the ratio of the tensile stress to the shear stress?

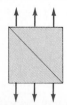

Figure 15-26. Ques. 15-3.

15-4   When we say a substance is "strong," do we usually mean that it has a high Young's modulus or a high yield point or a high shear modulus? Is a wooden rod stronger than a glass rod?

15-5   For very high "strength" applications, composite solids such as fiberglass-epoxy are often used. Can you explain why in terms of Young's modulus and the yield point?

15-6   Is it true that the higher an element is in the periodic chart, the higher its density?

15-7   What is the least dense gas (at atmospheric pressure and room temperature)? What is the most dense substance at atmospheric pressure and room temperature?

15-8   In which vertical tube of the apparatus shown in Fig. 15-27 will a fluid rise highest when the fluid is at rest? Ignore any effects of surface tension.

15-9   How does the "cartesian diver" of Fig. 15-28 work? When the membrane at the top is pushed down, the diver descends, when the membrane is released the diver ascends. If the diver is stationary in the middle of the apparatus, what is its overall density? What properties of a fluid are important in operating the diver?

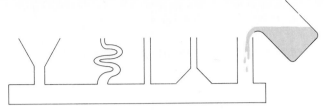

Figure 15-27. Ques. 15-8.

Figure 15-28. Ques. 15-9: Cartesian diver.

15-10 Why is it easier to swim in seawater than in fresh water?

15-11 After oil tankers discharge their cargo of oil, they put water in their tanks for the return voyage, even though water isn't needed at their destination. Why?

15-12 A block is lowered into water as shown in Fig. 15-29. What is the reading of the bottom scale in Fig. 15-29*b* after the block is immersed in the water?

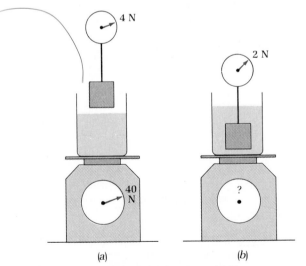

Figure 15-29. Ques. 15-12.

15-13 If you look at the stream of water issuing from a faucet, you will see that it narrows as it descends. Relate this effect to the equation of continuity.

15-14 How high will the jet of water in Fig. 15-30 go? Explain.

15-15 What is wrong with the Escher print in Fig. 15-31? (Physically, not aesthetically!)

Figure 15-30. Ques. 15-14.

Figure 15-31. Ques. 15-15: *Waterfall*, a lithograph by Escher. *(Art Resources)*

15-16 If you blow between two sheets of paper, will the sheets tend to separate or to come toward each other? Try it! Explain your results.

15-17 When a car with a convertible top travels at high speed, the top always seems to bulge out. Why?

15-18 In the pitot tube of Fig. 15-32, the pressure at point *A* is

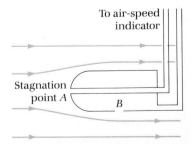

To air-speed indicator

Stagnation point *A*

B

Figure 15-32. Ques. 15-18: A pitot tube.

higher than at point *B*. Why? How can this device be used to measure the airspeed of an airplane?

15-19 How does the temperature dependence of the viscosity of gases differ from that of liquids? (See Fig. 15-24.)

15-20 Is viscous flow in a pipe irrotational?

15-21 The apparatus of Fig. 15-33 is used in an experiment on waterflow, and the water levels are as shown. Show that the value of $p + \rho g h + \frac{1}{2}\rho v^2$ is not the same at points A and B. What is the reason for this disagreement with Bernoulli's equation?

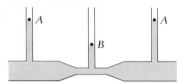

Figure 15-33. Ques. 15-21.

15-22 In tornadoes, the walls of houses are often blown outward, not inward. Why?

15-23 If a large truck passes you on the highway, does the airflow blow your car toward or away from the truck? Explain.

15-24 A glass of water is full to the brim, and an ice cube floats in the water. When the ice cube melts, does the glass run over, is the water level lowered, or does the water level stay the same? Explain.

15-25 The device of Fig. 15-34 has been proposed as a perpetual motion machine. The buoyant force on the rope in the water forces the rope to go up on the left side. If all frictional forces are negligible, why won't it work? Explain (beyond citing conservation of energy).

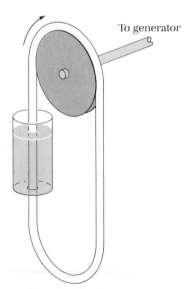

Figure 15-34. Ques. 15-25.

15-26 The perpetual motion machine of Fig. 15-35 has also been proposed. On the arms are cups with pistons that seal in air but are free to move in and out along the cups. When the cups face down, the pistons fall downward, and the cups displace more water than on the side where they face upward. The buoyant force is therefore greater on the left side than on the

right side and the device turns as indicated. What's wrong with this analysis?

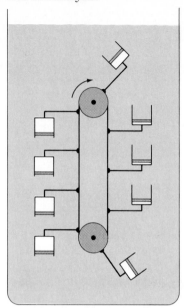

Figure 15-35. Ques. 15-26.

15-27 A "suction" pump, which operates by lowering the pressure in a pipe that extends to the bottom of a well, can only pump water from a well 10 m deep or less. Why?

15-28 Explain how the siphon of Fig. 15-36 is able to transfer water from A to B. Why doesn't the water in the tube merely run back into the two reservoirs? What is the maximum value that h can have if the siphon is to work?

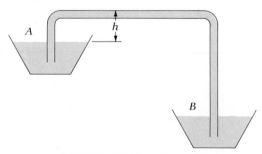

Figure 15-36. Ques. 15-28.

15-29 Complete the following table:

Symbol	Represents	Type	SI unit
σ			Pa
ϵ	Strain		
p		Scalar	
Y			
B			
K			
ρ			
η			

EXERCISES

Section 15-2. Properties of solids

15-1 A 12.7-mm cube of copper is put into a vise and squeezed by a force of 215 N exerted by either side of the vise. What is the stress in the copper cube?

15-2 An object of mass 13.4 kg is held up by a 1.33-m-long steel wire of cross section 1.63 mm². What is the stress in the wire?

15-3 A 22.4-kg block is hung from a brass cube by a 91-mm-diameter aluminum wire that is 750 mm long; the cube has 85.0-mm-long sides (Fig. 15-37). What is the stress (a) in the aluminum and (b) in the brass? Assume that the brass is under a pure shear stress.

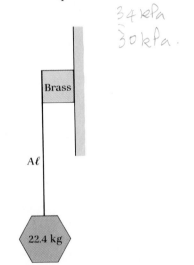

34 kPa
30 kPa.

Figure 15-37. Exercise 15-3.

15-4 A 130-Mg building is on a foundation of 160 concrete blocks, each of effective cross section 6000 mm². Estimate the stress in the concrete blocks.

15-5 (a) What is the strain in the copper cube of Exercise 15-1? By how much does the side of the copper cube decrease?

15-6 (a) What is the strain in the wire of Exercise 15-2? (b) What is the increase in length of the wire as the weight is attached?

15-7 The block of Exercise 15-3 is attached to the wire but held up entirely by your hand. (a) When you remove your hand, what is the strain in the brass cube? (b) By how much is the angle between the sides of the brass cube changed? (c) How far downward does the block move?

8·4×10⁻⁷
8·4×10⁻⁷
0·43 μm

15-8 The highest steady pressure available in the laboratory is about 20 GPa in a diamond anvil. If liquid mercury stayed in the same phase when this much pressure was applied, by what fraction would its volume be decreased as this pressure was applied?

Section 15-3. Density

15-9 A 73.0-mm-radius sphere of plutonium has a mass of 32.3 kg. What is the density of plutonium?

15-10 In the past, the meter was defined by the length of a platinum bar of rectangular cross section 25.3 mm × 4.0 mm. What is the mass of this old standard?

15-11 What is the density of water at the bottom of the sea where the pressure is 30 MPa? What is the density of lead at the bottom of the sea?

15-12 When a tensile stress is applied to an object, not only is the object's length increased along the direction of the applied force, its width is decreased perpendicular to the direction of the applied force. For many substances the ratio of the fractional contraction perpendicular to the applied force to the fractional elongation parallel to the applied force is nearly 1/3. This ratio is called the Poisson ratio ν. Assuming ν is 1/3 for steel, by what fraction does the density of a 15-mm steel cube change when a tensile stress of 1 GPa is applied?

Section 15-4. Pressure in a static fluid

15-13 The deepest parts of the ocean are about 10 km below the surface. What is the pressure there?

15-14 Pressures in air ducts are frequently given in "inches of water." What is the conversion between the pressure measured in inches with a water manometer and the pressure measured in pascals?

15-15 The highest mountains are about 8 km high. What is the pressure at the top? Assume the atmosphere has a constant temperature.

15-16 What is the force on a circular eardrum of diameter 7 mm if the inside of the ear is at the pressure at sea level and the outside of the ear at the pressure inside an airplane, that of the atmosphere 1500 m above sea level? (This force causes the pain that occurs when you cannot equalize the pressure on the two sides of the eardrum through the eustachian tube that connects the inside of the ear to the atmosphere.)

15-17 In Fig. 15-38, how much force must be exerted at A to raise the 0.85-Mg automobile at B? The piston at A has a diameter of 17 mm and the piston at B a diameter of 300 mm.

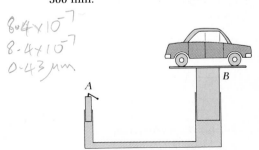

Figure 15-38. Exercise 15-17.

Section 15-5. Archimedes' principle

15-18 An iceberg has a mass of 13 Gg. What volume of water does it displace?

15-19 An iceberg has 100 m³ of its volume above water level. How much water does it displace?

15-20 A crown is weighed as in Fig. 15-39. In air it weighs 28.24 N, and in water it weighs 26.36 N. What is the density of the crown?

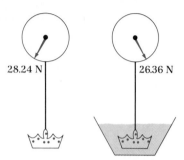

28.24 N   26.36 N

Figure 15-39. Exercise 15-20.

15-21 Estimate the volume of your body without making any length measurements or assumptions.

15-22 Suppose a submarine has a cross section which is a section of a cylinder, as seen in Fig. 15-40. (a) Where is the center of gravity of the displaced water? (b) Suppose the submarine carries ballast fixed in the bottom of its hold so that the center of gravity of the submarine is at point A, $3r/4$ below the center of the cylinder. If the submarine rolls over by 10°, what is the magnitude of the restoring torque about the center of mass that tends to right the submarine? Give the torque in terms of the mass of the submarine m, the density of water ρ, the radius of the cylindrical section r, and the acceleration of gravity g.

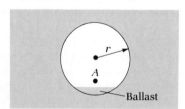

r

A

Ballast

Figure 15-40. Exercise 15-22. A submarine with ballast submerged in water.

15-23 When you weigh yourself, your true weight w is greater than the reading of the scale w', due to the buoyant force of the air. Determine the size of the correction factor f in $w = fw'$. Assume your density to be that of water.

Section 15-6. Bernoulli's equation

15-24 At point A of Fig. 15-41, the gauge pressure is 50 kPa and the speed of the water flowing in the circular pipe is 2.4 m/s. The pipe is horizontal. (a) What is the

flow rate at points A and B? (b) What is the speed at point B? (c) What is the gauge pressure at point B? Assume streamline flow.

•A   •B

51 mm   25 mm
diameter   diameter

Figure 15-41. Exercise 15-24.

15-25 At point A of Fig. 15-42 the gauge pressure is 75 kPa and the speed of the water flowing in this 50-mm-diameter pipe is 1.7 m/s. The pipe splits into two smaller pipes, each of 25 mm diameter. (a) What are the flow rates at A and at B? (b) What is the speed at point B? (c) What is the gauge pressure at point B? Assume streamline flow and constant height.

•B

•A

Figure 15-42. Exercise 15-25.

15-26 Part of an air-distribution system with square ducts is shown in Fig. 15-43. If at A the gauge pressure is 320 Pa and the flow rate is 2.2 m³/s, what is the air pressure at B? Assume incompressible streamline flow.

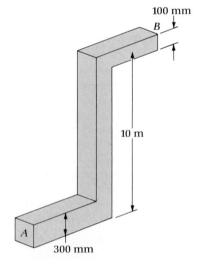

100 mm
B

10 m

A

300 mm

Figure 15-43. Exercise 15-26.

15-27 Show that Bernoulli's equation reduces to Eq. (15-6) when the flow speed is the same at both points.

15-28 A fire truck has a pump which must supply enough pressure to enable the water to reach the top floor of a 30-m-high building in a uniform hose at a speed of 10 m/s. Ignoring viscosity, what is the minimum gauge pressure the pumper must supply? What is the minimum power?

15-29 An automobile engine has a displacement of 1.6 L. Each time the engine makes two complete revolutions, an amount of air approximately equal to the displacement is sent through the engine. At highway speeds the engine turns at 3500 rev/min. The venturi tube of the engine's carburetor has a diameter of 9.1 mm. What is the gauge pressure in the venturi under these conditions?

15-30 The insecticide sprayer of Fig. 15-44 has a pump with a diameter of 60 mm. The insecticide level is 90 mm below the inlet tube at A. The tube at A has a diameter of 2 mm. Estimate the minimum speed with which the plunger should be pushed if the air jet at the end is to contain insecticide. Assume that the insecticide has the density of water and that the airflow is incompressible and streamline.

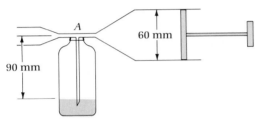

Figure 15-44. Exercise 15-30.

15-31 Water flows steadily from a holding tank, as seen in Fig. 15-45. The cross section of the pipe at point A is 0.055 m², at point B it is 0.040 m², and the cross section of the discharge stream at C is 0.025 m². Neglect viscosity and turbulence. (a) What is the speed at C? (b) What is the flow rate? (c) What are the gauge pressures at points A and B?

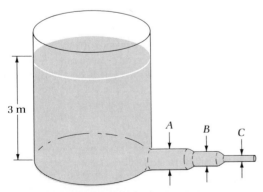

Figure 15-45. Exercise 15-31.

15-32 A window of area 5.0 m² has still air on its inside and air of speed 15 m/s on its outside. If you suppose that the flow is irrotational so that the two sides can be connected by Bernoulli's equation, how much force would be exerted on the window? In which direction?

Section 15-7. Viscosity

15-33 A flat-bottomed canal boat with a bottom area of 30 m² is dragged along a canal at 1.5 m/s. The bottom of the boat is 140 mm above the bottom of the canal. The canal water is at 20° C. What is the viscous force on the boat? (Normally the forces that waves exert on a canal boat are much greater than the viscous force.)

15-34 A cylindrical viscometer is shown in Fig. 15-46. When the inner cylinder is rotated at constant speed, the stationary outer cylinder experiences a torque. The magnitude of the torque on the outer cylinder is a measure of the viscosity of the fluid between the cylinders. When the distance between the cylinders ΔR is small compared with the radius R_1 and R_2 of either cylinder, then the force applied to the outer cylinder by the fluid is

$$F = \frac{\eta A v}{\ell} \approx \eta(2\pi RL) \frac{v}{\Delta R}$$

where $R = \frac{1}{2}(R_1 + R_2)$ and v is the tangential speed of the inner cylinder. (a) What is the torque applied to the outer cylinder? (b) A cylindrical viscometer has radii of 92 and 93 mm and a length of 170 mm. When the inner cylinder is rotated at a constant angular speed of 20 rev/min, the stationary outer cylinder experiences a torque of 0.54 N · m. What is the viscosity of the fluid in the viscometer? If the temperature is 30°C, what might the substance in the viscometer be?

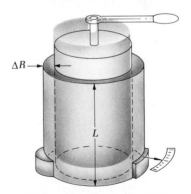

Figure 15-46. Exercise 15-34.

15-35 Oil of specific gravity 0.765 and viscosity 2.5 × 10⁻³ Pa · s is sent through a small oil hole of length 10 mm to lubricate a bearing. If the pressure drop along the tube is 0.305 MPa and the hole diameter is 0.843 mm, what volume of oil will pass through the bearing in an hour? Assume laminar flow.

PROBLEMS

15-1 Three bars are welded together end to end to form a single bar. The first bar is 0.55 m long, has a cross section of 420 mm², and is made of copper. The second section is 0.75 m long, has a cross section of 390 mm², and is made of cast iron. The third bar is 0.45 m long, has a cross section of 405 mm², and is made of aluminum. (*a*) What is the mass of the complete bar? (*b*) What is its average density? (*c*) If tensile forces of 10 kN are applied at either end of the complete bar, by how much does it elongate?

15-2 A cork of density ρ_c has a cylindrical cross section of radius r and length ℓ. It is floating in water of density ρ. Show that, if it is given a small push down into the water from its equilibrium floating position and then released, it will vibrate up and down with a period $2\pi \sqrt{\rho_c \ell/(\rho g)}$.

15-3 Oil of density $\rho_0 < \rho_{H_2O}$ floats on water. The cork described in the previous problem has density $\rho_c > \rho_0$ and floats between the two layers so that its top is in oil and its bottom in water. What fraction of the cork is below the water? Give your answer in terms of ρ_0, ρ_c, and ρ_{H_2O}.

15-4 The standard kilogram is made of an alloy that is 90 percent platinum and 10 percent iridium. What is the magnitude of the buoyant-force correction (because of the atmosphere) that must be made when the standard kilogram is weighed?

15-5 The maximum compressive strain that concrete can safely withstand is about 0.1 percent. What is the maximum height of a concrete building of constant cross section? Using the same criterion, what is the maximum height of a constant-cross-section steel building?

15-6 The viscous force F_v on a small sphere of radius r in motion through a fluid of viscosity η (with laminar flow) and with a speed v can be shown to follow Stokes' law: $F_v = 6\pi r \eta v$. Show that the terminal speed v_t of a sphere of density ρ_s falling through a fluid of density ρ_0 is

$$v_t = \frac{2(\rho_s - \rho_0)r^2 g}{9\eta}$$

15-7 A large tank has a pipe that leads out of its bottom. (See Fig. 15-47.) Along the pipe is a constriction that has a diameter one third the diameter of the rest of the pipe. In this constriction is a tube which leads to a second tank containing the same fluid as the first tank. When liquid flows out of the first tank, to what height h_2 does the fluid rise in the tube? Express your answer in terms of h_1. Assume laminar flow of a non-viscous fluid.

15-8 Several holes are drilled in a cylindrical tube containing water. Water issues from the holes horizontally, as seen in Fig. 15-48. At what height should a hole be

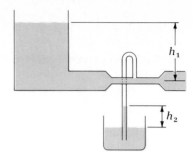

Figure 15-47. Prob. 15-7.

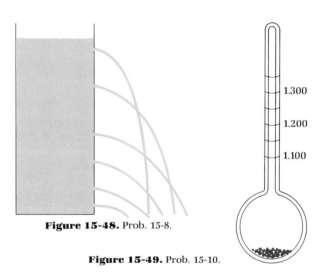

Figure 15-48. Prob. 15-8.

Figure 15-49. Prob. 15-10.

drilled so that water spewing from it hits the ground farthest from the cylinder? Assume the fluid is non-viscous.

15-9 A keg of beer may be approximated by a cylinder 750 mm high and 250 mm in radius. If a hole is drilled near the bottom, and a 1.0-m-long tube with inner diameter 3.8 mm is attached, how long will it take for half the beer to drain out? There is a hole in the top of the keg to keep the top of the beer at atmospheric pressure. Assume that beer has the density and viscosity of water and is kept at 5°C.

15-10 A hydrometer is made of glass with a hollow spherical bottom of radius r and an upright tube of radius R, as shown in Fig. 15-49. It is to measure specific gravity in the range from 1.100 to 1.300, the specific gravity being given by the depth to which the hydrometer sinks in the fluid. The hydrometer's mass is adjusted by adding lead shot. Find the total mass m of the hydrometer and the length ℓ of the tube to measure this range of specific gravities. Give your answer in terms of r, R, and the density of water ρ.

15-11 A steel wire of cross section A and Young's modulus Y is stretched horizontally between two posts. Initially the tension in the wire is negligible. An object of mass m is hung from the middle of the wire, causing it to sag as seen in Fig. 15-50. (a) Show that the wire stretches until θ is given by the transcendental equation

$$2 \sin \theta (\sec \theta - 1) = \frac{mg}{YA}$$

(b) What is the value of θ when $mg/YA = 1$ percent? (c) How much energy E_w is stored in the stretched wire? How much does the gravitational energy E_g of the object decrease as it descends? Why aren't these energies equal? Show that for small θ, $E_w = \frac{1}{2} E_g$.

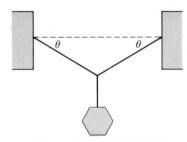

Figure 15-50. Prob. 15-11.

15-12 The flow of water over a weir or spillway is illustrated in Fig. 15-51. Assuming negligible viscosity, show that the rate of flow Q of water over the weir is

$$Q = \tfrac{2}{3} w \sqrt{2gy^3}$$

where y is the height of the water level above the weir. Actual flows are about one-half of this because of viscosity and the drop in level of the water between the reservoir and the weir.

15-13 (a) Show that the magnitude of the viscous force on the colored cylinder of Fig. 15-52 is $F = \eta(2\pi R\ell)(dv/dR)$. (b) Show that the speed gradient

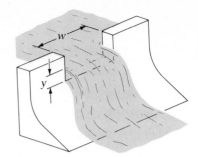

Figure 15-51. Prob. 15-12.

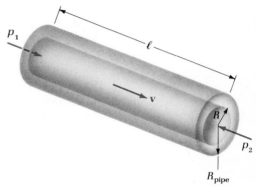

Figure 15-52. Prob. 15-13.

$dv/dR = -[(p_1 - p_2)R]/(2\eta\ell)$. (c) Integrate this expression from $R = R_{pipe}$ to R' and show that the speed of the fluid a distance R' from the center is:

$$v(R') = \frac{|p_1 - p_2|}{4\eta\ell} (R_{pipe}^2 - R'^2)$$

15-14 Show that Eq. 15-12 follows from the results of Prob. 15-13 by integrating the flow rate,

$$dQ = v(R)dA = v(R)(2\pi R\ dR)$$

from $R = 0$ to $R = R_{pipe}$.

CHAPTER 16
TEMPERATURE AND HEAT TRANSFER

16-1 INTRODUCTION

Suppose an ice cube is taken from a freezer and placed on a level table. For a short time, the response of this object to its surroundings can be described by the methods of mechanics. It is in static equilibrium and the net force acting on the ice cube is zero: The earth exerts a downward gravitational force on the ice cube which is balanced by the upward normal force exerted by the table (along with a small buoyant force due to the atmosphere). Before long, however, the ice begins to melt, and eventually we see a puddle of water on the table.

We are not able to describe or understand this melting process on the basis of mechanics alone. Some new concepts, independent of mechanics, must be developed to discuss situations of this sort. In these next four chapters, we shall develop some of the ideas that are central to *thermodynamics* and to *statistical mechanics*. The concepts of *temperature* and of *heat transfer* are introduced in this chapter.

16-2 MICROSCOPIC AND MACROSCOPIC DESCRIPTIONS

A microscopic description is at the molecular level.

Suppose that a fixed amount of a gas, say 5 g of oxygen, occupies a container. A *microscopic description* of this system would begin with the recognition that the gas consists of molecules. Is it reasonable to attempt to determine the motion of each molecule by applying Newton's laws? With a large, high-speed computer, a very small system consisting of several thousand molecules can be simulated to provide useful information. In these simulations the motion of each molecule is followed in detail. Any property of the system which depends on the positions and velocities of the molecules can be calculated. This approach is known as *molecular dynamics*.

However, the number of molecules in 5 g of oxygen is of the order of 10^{23}, far too large to be treated by molecular dynamics. Just listing the instantaneous values of the position and the velocity of each individual molecule would be an overwhelming task. That amount of information is too vast to assimilate and, therefore, would be of little value in describing this system and its interaction with its environment. Instead, it is more useful to consider averages. The molecular dynamics approach also evaluates quantities which involve averages over molecular motions. The methods of *statistical mechanics* connect averages of molecular properties to quantities such as temperature and pressure that are part of our everyday world. We shall see connections of this sort in Chap. 18.

| Thermodynamics is the larger-scale, or macroscopic, description. | A *macroscopic description* deals with properties on a scale much larger than the molecular one. On this larger scale there is no direct reference to the molecular properties of the system. The macroscopic description of the interaction of a system with its surroundings is called *thermodynamics*. Although thermodynamics does not depend on our knowledge of the molecular structure of matter, interpreting the thermodynamic description in terms of molecular averages often helps us to visualize what is going on. |

We have already encountered some of the macroscopic quantities which are used in thermodynamics. Thus the *pressure p* of a gas (Chap. 15) is the force per unit area exerted by the gas on a surface. The gas occupies a *volume V*. The amount of gas can be specified by the *number of moles n*. For example, O_2 has a molar mass of about 32 g/mol, and the mass of 3.0 mol of O_2 is (3.0 mol)(32 g/mol) $= 96$ g $= 0.096$ kg. Additional quantities, which will be defined later, include *temperature T*, *internal energy U*, and *entropy S*. These properties are the variables of the system and are called *variables of state*. The variables of state of a system are, in fact, variable: Their values generally change in response to interactions with the surroundings of the system. For example, we can decrease the volume *V* of a gas in a balloon by squeezing (carefully) the balloon.

Variables of state include p, V, n, T, U, and S.

EXAMPLE 16-1. A gas occupies a cylindrical container with circular cross section of radius $R = 0.22$ m and length $L = 0.35$ m. The pressure of the gas is 2.00 atm, or 2.02×10^5 Pa. Determine (a) the volume in liters occupied by the gas and (b) the force exerted by the gas on one of the circular faces of the cylinder. (c) Suppose the gas is He and its mass is 0.0072 kg. What is the number of moles n?

SOLUTION. (a) The volume of the cylinder is given by the product of its length L and its cross-sectional area πR^2:

$$V = \pi R^2 L = 0.053 \text{ m}^3 = 53 \text{ L}$$

(b) The force exerted on an area $A = \pi R^2$ is

$$F = pA = (202 \text{ kPa})(0.15 \text{ m}^2) = 31 \text{ kN}$$

(c) The molecular mass of He is $M_0 = 4.0$ g/mol. The number of moles is

$$n = \frac{m}{M_0} = \frac{7.2 \text{ g}}{4.0 \text{ g/mol}} = 1.8 \text{ mol}$$

16-3 THERMAL EQUILIBRIUM AND THE ZEROTH LAW OF THERMODYNAMICS

In the equilibrium state, the variables of state are constant.

A variable of state, such as the pressure, is assumed to have the same value throughout the system. In this way a single value of the pressure applies to the entire system. We also suppose that each of the variables of state of a system is

Figure 16-1. Two systems are separated (a) by a stationary adiabatic wall which inhibits their interaction and (b) by a stationary diathermic wall which allows them to interact.

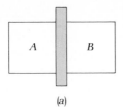

(a)

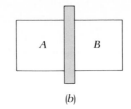

(b)

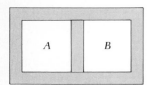

Figure 16-2. Two systems interact through a diathermic wall. The adiabatic cover insulates A and B from the outside.

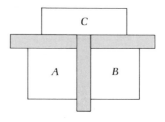

Figure 16-3. An adiabatic wall separates A and B. Each interacts with C through a diathermic wall.

constant in time. The system is then said to be in an *equilibrium state.* As long as the variables of state remain constant, the system remains in this equilibrium state.

The variables of state of one system can be changed by interaction with another system. Often we wish to "insulate" one system from another. To do so, we can place a barrier between the systems which will inhibit their interaction. An idealized version of such a stationary barrier is called an *adiabatic wall.* Two systems separated by an adiabatic wall, shown schematically by the shaded, gray layer in Fig. 16-1a, do not influence each other. Each can remain in its equilibrium state. An adiabatic wall can be approximated by a thick layer of insulating material such as Styrofoam. In contrast, a *diathermic wall* facilitates the thermal interaction of the two systems. It is represented in Fig. 16-1b by the shaded, colored wall. A thin layer of metal, such as copper, behaves approximately as a diathermic wall.

> An adiabatic wall insulates one system from another.

> A diathermic wall allows two systems to interact.

Suppose two systems A and B are allowed to interact through a diathermic wall, as seen in Fig. 16-2. The enclosing adiabatic wall prevents any thermal contact with systems outside the enclosure. As a result of the interaction between A and B, some of the variables of each system will change. Eventually, however, these variables will settle down to constant values, and each system will achieve an equilibrium state. The two systems A and B are then said to be in *thermal equilibrium. Two systems are in thermal equilibrium if, when put in contact through a diathermic wall, their variables of state do not change.*

> Thermal equilibrium of two systems

Two systems can be in thermal equilibrium even if they are not in direct contact. Figure 16-3 shows an adiabatic wall separating systems A and B, though each is in contact with a third system C through a diathermic wall. After a sufficiently long time, the variables of each system become constant. Therefore, systems A and C are in thermal equilibrium, and systems B and C are in thermal equilibrium. Experiment indicates that systems A and B are also in thermal equilibrium. This result is contained in the statement of the *zeroth law of thermodynamics: Two systems in thermal equilibrium with a third system are in thermal equilibrium with each other.* This statement may seem trivially obvious. That it is not logically necessary is suggested by the lovers' triangle: Heathcliff loves Shirley and Garfield loves Shirley, but Heathcliff and Garfield do not love each other. The need for the zeroth law was recognized only after the first law of thermodynamics had been given its name. The

> The zeroth law of thermodynamics

unusual term "zeroth" was therefore used to indicate that this law precedes the first law.

In the next section, we shall define temperature by specifying a procedure for its measurement. However, it is often helpful to think of the temperature of a system as a quantity that is related to the random motion of the molecules of the system. This relation will be developed in Chap. 18. For now, we just associate an increase in the temperature of a system with an increase in the average molecular speed and in the average molecular kinetic energy.

Temperature and thermal equilibrium

The concept of temperature is intimately related to the state of thermal equilibrium of two systems. *Two systems in thermal equilibrium have the same temperature.* If two systems are placed in contact and their variables change, then the systems are not at the same temperature, but they will come to a common temperature as thermal equilibrium is achieved. Suppose that one of these systems is a thermometer used to measure the temperature. After the thermometer comes to thermal equilibrium with the other system, the thermometer has the same temperature as the other system. We actually measure the temperature of the thermometer! The other system has the same temperature because it is in thermal equilibrium with the thermometer. The thermometer can also be used in conjunction with the zeroth law of thermodynamics to determine if two separated systems A and B are in thermal equilibrium. If A and B have the same temperature, as determined by the thermometer, then they are in thermal equilibrium, but systems A and B are not in thermal equilibrium if their temperatures are different.

16-4 THERMOMETERS AND THE IDEAL GAS TEMPERATURE SCALE

Temperature is described subjectively by terms such as "hot," "warm," and "cold." That is, "hot" corresponds to a higher temperature than "cold." These terms do not have consistent objective meaning. For example, suppose that you are served a bowl of hot soup and a glass of cold water. After they have been sitting for a while, you complain that your soup is cold and that your water is warm. Even so, a thermometer will show that the soup still has a higher temperature than the water.

Temperatures are expressed quantitatively using a scale that is established arbitrarily by specifying the procedure by which the temperature measurement is performed—in short, by specifying what thermometer is used.

Thermometers. A thermometer is any device or system that is used to connect a value of one of its variables to the temperature. There are some desirable features that a thermometer should possess. It should have a property, such as a length, a pressure, or an electrical resistance, which varies with temperature in an easily measured way. Its readings should be reproducible. Its construction should be easily duplicated so that like thermometers can be used throughout the world. The sensitivity of its readings should not depend on the specific materials used in its construction. It should be capable of reading temperatures over a wide range. Real thermometers have these features in varying degrees.

Some desirable properties of a thermometer

Mercury thermometer

A familiar example of a thermometer is the *mercury-in-glass thermometer* in which the length of the column of mercury in the glass capillary indicates the temperature. The temperature is taken to have a linear dependence on the

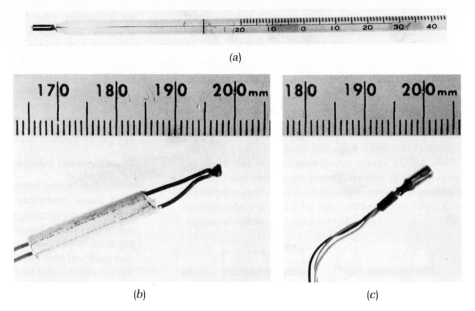

(a)

(b)   *(c)*

Three different types of thermometers are shown: (a) a mercury-in-glass thermometer, (b) a thermocouple with a junction of different metals, and (c) a silicon resistance thermometer.

length of the mercury column. Graduations can be marked at equal-length intervals on the glass to indicate values of temperature between two fixed points. The normal melting point and normal boiling point of water, for example, could be chosen as the fixed points. (The adjective "normal" implies that the system is at normal atmospheric pressure of 101 kPa.)

Thermocouple thermometer

A *thermocouple* is another type of thermometer. It consists of two junctions of two different metallic wires. If one junction is maintained at a reference temperature (such as in a liquid-water-and-ice bath) and the other junction is at another temperature, then an electric potential difference, or voltage (to be discussed in Chap. 22), exists between the junctions. This potential difference is used to measure the temperature. Another type of electrical thermometer is a *resistance thermometer*. The electrical resistance of the thermometer varies with temperature and is used to indicate the temperature.

Resistance thermometer

Temperature is proportional to pressure in a constant-volume gas thermometer.

Below we look in detail at a *constant-volume gas thermometer*. It consists of a bulb containing a gas with a mechanism for ensuring that the volume occupied by the gas remains constant—hence the name "constant-volume gas thermometer." The pressure of the gas is measured and is used to determine the temperature by choosing the temperature to be proportional to the pressure of the gas.

Suppose that the thermometers listed above are calibrated to give identical readings at some fixed point, and then the thermometers are used to measure the temperature of some other system. It is likely that each thermometer would give a slightly different reading. In such a case, the value of the measured temperature depends on the thermometer used to measure it, and this is an unsatisfactory result. In Chap. 19 we shall define a temperature, called the *thermodynamic temperature*, which is independent of the properties of any material. Until then, we work with temperatures as measured with a constant-volume gas thermometer. As we shall see, the use of this thermometer will lead to a temperature measurement which is virtually independent of which gas is used in these thermometers.

Constant-volume gas thermometer. Suppose we compare the temperatures of two systems *A* and *B* with a constant-volume gas thermometer. First we put the thermometer in contact with system A and allow it to come to thermal equilibrium with A. System A and the gas in the thermometer then have the same temperature, call it T_A. The pressure of the gas *in the thermometer bulb* is measured; let p_A denote its value. Next the thermometer is allowed to come to thermal equilibrium with system B. The temperature T_B corresponds to the value p_B of the gas pressure of the thermometer. Since the temperature has been chosen to be proportional to the pressure of the gas in the thermometer, we have

$$\frac{T_B}{T_A} = \frac{p_B}{p_A}$$

For example, if the pressure ratio is $p_B/p_A = 2.1$, then the temperature of system B is 2.1 times the temperature of system A. Note, however, that we do not have a value for either temperature. The scale has not yet been established.

To establish a temperature scale, a numerical value of the temperature is assigned to some fixed point, a definite state of some system. By convention, the *triple point of water* is chosen as that fixed point. We are all familiar with a system consisting of ice and liquid water. Two phases, solid and liquid, can coexist in equilibrium at a temperature called the *melting point*. Similarly, the liquid and vapor (steam) phases are in equilibrium at the *boiling point*. The *sublimation point* corresponds to the solid and vapor phases in equilibrium. The temperatures of these points depend on the pressure of the liquid or vapor phases, as indicated in Fig. 16-4, which shows temperatures on the Celsius scale. Lowering the pressure lowers the temperature of the boiling point, for example. There is a unique temperature of the system of water at which all three phases are in equilibrium. *For this state the melting point, boiling point, and sublimation point all coincide. This state is the triple point of water.* It occurs at a vapor pressure of 610 Pa and at a temperature of 0.01°C on the familiar Celsius scale.

The temperature scale obtained from the constant-volume gas thermometer corresponds to an arbitrary but convenient choice of the triple-point temperature. The triple-point temperature T_3 is chosen to be

$$T_3 = 273.16 \text{ K} \tag{16-1}$$

where the unit abbreviation "K" stands for kelvin, the SI unit of temperature. The convenience of this particular numerical value, $T_3 = 273.16$ K, is that a temperature interval of 1 K corresponds to one division, or degree, on the Celsius scale. Thus the Celsius degree and the Kelvin "degree" are the same

Solid, liquid, and vapor phases are in equilibrium at the triple point.

Triple-point temperature

The kelvin (K) and the Celsius degree have the same size.

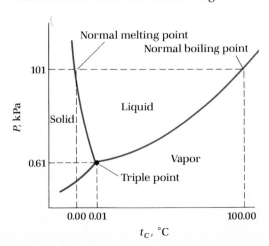

Normal melting point
Normal boiling point

Figure 16-4. A portion of the phase diagram for water is shown. The scales are *not* linear. At the triple point the solid, liquid, and vapor phases are all in equilibrium.

size. The normal melting point of water on the Kelvin scale is 273.15 K (0.00°C), and the normal boiling point is 100 K higher at 373.15 K (100.00°C).

To calibrate the constant-volume gas thermometer at the triple point of water, we allow the thermometer to come to thermal equilibrium with water at its triple point. The pressure p_3 of the gas in the thermometer is measured at this temperature T_3. To measure the temperature of some system, we allow the thermometer to come to thermal equilibrium with that system. Letting T denote the temperature of that system and p denote the pressure of the gas in the thermometer at that temperature, we have from Eq. (16-1)

$$\frac{T}{T_3} = \frac{p}{p_3}$$

or
$$T = (273.16 \text{ K}) \frac{p}{p_3} \qquad (16\text{-}2)$$

Once the pressure of the gas has been determined when it is in thermal equilibrium with a system of water at its triple point, the temperature of some other system is determined from Eq. (16-2) by measuring the pressure of the gas when it is in thermal equilibrium with that system.

EXAMPLE 16-2. When in thermal equilibrium at the triple point of water, the pressure of He in a constant-volume gas thermometer is 1020 Pa. The pressure of the He is 288 Pa when the thermometer is in thermal equilibrium with liquid nitrogen at its normal boiling point. What is the normal boiling point of nitrogen as measured using this thermometer?

SOLUTION. Substituting the pressure values into Eq. (16-2) gives

$$T = (273.16 \text{ K}) \frac{288}{1020} = 77.1 \text{ K}$$

Ideal gas temperature. A lower pressure of the gas in the thermometer corresponds to a lower temperature (reflecting lower average speed and lower average kinetic energy for the molecules). Equation (16-2) suggests that, as p tends to zero, the temperature also tends to zero, the *absolute zero of temperature.* At this lowest of temperatures, the pressure of a gas presumably becomes zero. As a practical matter, however, every real gas either liquefies or solidifies before this point is reached. Because of this property of real gases, the constant-volume gas thermometer cannot be used to measure temperatures below about 1 K.

There is another technical problem with the constant-volume gas thermometer: Identically constructed thermometers give different temperature readings if different gases or different amounts of the same gas are used. These differences in temperature readings are usually very small. To assign a single value of the temperature, an extrapolation technique is employed. Suppose that measurements are made with a set of constant-volume gas thermometers containing smaller and smaller amounts of gas. A smaller amount of gas corresponds to a smaller value of the pressure p_3 of the gas at the triple point. The results of measuring a temperature with this set of thermometers are shown graphically in Fig. 16-5. The thermometers are distinguished by the type of gas and by the amount of gas as indicated by the value of p_3. If we extrapolate the measurements for a given gas down to a zero value of p_3, these extrapolations yield the same value of temperature, independent of the type of gas. *In the limit of infinitely dilute gas ($p_3 \rightarrow 0$), the temperature determined by the constant-vol-*

The absolute zero is the lowest temperature.

Real gases change phase above the absolute zero.

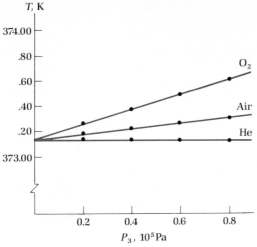

Figure 16-5. The temperature of the normal boiling point of water is measured with a set of constant-volume gas thermometers. The thermometers contain different gases or different amounts of a given gas. Each thermometer is characterized by the pressure of its gas p_3 at the triple point. By extrapolation to $p_3 = 0$, the temperature is found to be 373.15 K.

ume gas thermometer is the same for all gases. We modify Eq. (16-2) to include this result: The *ideal gas temperature* is defined by

Ideal gas temperature

$$T = \lim_{p_3 \to 0} \left(\frac{p}{p_3} \right) (273.16 \text{ K}) \qquad (16\text{-}3)$$

where the limit is taken by performing the extrapolation process described above. Over the temperature range in which the gas thermometer can be used, the ideal gas temperature is independent of any particular gas and is identical with the thermodynamic temperature that we discuss later.

In this dilute limit, real gases occupying the same volume have the same dependence of temperature on pressure: T and p are proportional, with the same constant of proportionality for all gases at a constant volume. It is useful to consider a fictitious gas whose proportional dependence of temperature on pressure holds not only in the dilute case but at any pressure. The *ideal gas* is the name given to this imaginary gas. We shall learn more about the ideal gas in the next three chapters. For now we note that its properties are approximated by real dilute gases and that a temperature scale, based on the common properties of dilute gases, bears its name.

The ideal gas

16-5 OTHER TEMPERATURE SCALES

Historically the Celsius temperature scale was based on the properties of water. The temperature of the normal melting point corresponded to 0°C and that of the normal boiling point to 100°C. Now this scale is defined by

Celsius temperature

$$t_C = T - 273.15 \text{ K} \qquad (16\text{-}4)$$

where the Celsius temperature is denoted by t_C. Notice from Eq. (16-4) that the Celsius and Kelvin scales differ only in their zero point. The absolute zero ($T = 0$ K) is at $t_C = -273.15$°C. The normal melting point of water ($t_C = 0.00$°C) is at $T = 273.15$ K. Since the size of the "degree" is the same on the two scales, temperature differences have the same numerical value. For example, a temperature difference of 5.7 C° (read as 5.7 Celsius degrees*) corresponds to a

* Notice that for a temperature *difference*, the degree symbol (°) follows the Celsius abbreviation, such as a difference of 5.7 C°. For a *value* of the temperature, the degree symbol precedes the abbreviation; for example, the human body temperature is 37°C.

difference of 5.7 K (read as 5.7 kelvins). Conventionally, the degree symbol (°) is not used when expressing temperatures or temperature differences on the Kelvin scale.

The Rankine temperature scale has the same zero point as the Kelvin scale, but the size of the degree is smaller. With T_R representing a temperature on the Rankine scale, its connection with the Kelvin temperature is

Rankine temperature

$$T_R = \tfrac{9}{5} T \tag{16-5}$$

For example, the normal boiling point of water on the Rankine scale is $T_R = (9/5)(373\ \text{K}) = 671\,°\text{R}$.

The Rankine and the Fahrenheit scales are still in use in the United States and in Great Britain. The Fahrenheit scale has the same degree size as the Rankine scale but a different zero point. A commonly used conversion changes Fahrenheit temperature readings to Celsius and vice versa:

Fahrenheit temperature

$$t_F = \tfrac{9}{5} t_C + 32\,°\text{F}$$
$$t_C = \tfrac{5}{9}\,(t_F - 32\,°\text{F}) \tag{16-6}$$

The normal melting and normal boiling points of water are at 32 and 212°F on the Fahrenheit scale. The four temperature scales are displayed in Fig. 16-6, which shows the temperatures of several fixed points.

16-6 THERMAL EXPANSION

Most substances expand with increasing temperature and contract with decreasing temperature. This *thermal expansion* is usually quite small, but it can be an important effect. Suppose the length of a solid rod is L_0 at some reference temperature T_0. If the temperature is changed by an amount $\Delta T = T - T_0$, then the length changes by an amount $\Delta L = L - L_0$. Experiment shows that under usual circumstances the change in length is proportional to the temperature change, at least for a small temperature change. We expect that the change in length should be proportional to the reference length L_0. That is, if

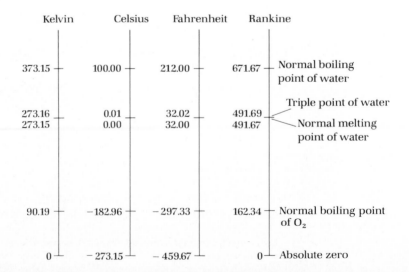

Figure 16-6. A comparison of some temperature values on four temperature scales.

Table 16-1. Some expansion coefficient values

Linear expansion		Volume expansion	
Substance (solid)	α, 10^{-5} C$^{\circ-1}$	**Substance (liquid)**	β, 10^{-5} C$^{\circ-1}$
Aluminum	2.4	Methanol	113
Copper	1.8	Glycerin	49
Steel	1.1	Mercury	18
Glass	0.1–1.3	Turpentine	90
Concrete	0.7–1.4	Acetone	132

the change in length of a rod 2 m long is 0.4 mm, then the change in length of a 1-m rod should be 0.2 mm. The change in length also depends on the type of material. For example, copper and iron rods of equal length at one temperature have different lengths at other temperatures.

These features can be put into equation form by introducing a coefficient which is characteristic of the material. The average *coefficient of linear expansion* is denoted by α. The change in length ΔL for a temperature change ΔT is given by

Coefficient of linear expansion α

$$\Delta L = \alpha L_0 \, \Delta T \qquad (16\text{-}7)$$

Although α depends on the temperature interval ΔT and the reference temperature T_0, that dependence is usually negligible for moderate temperature changes. The coefficient α does not depend on the length L_0. The dimension of α is reciprocal temperature, and the commonly used unit is the reciprocal Celsius degree C$^{\circ-1}$. Note that this unit is the same as the SI unit K^{-1}, reciprocal kelvin, because we are using temperature changes. Table 16-1 lists the values of α for several common substances.

Our discussion of thermal expansion has been based on the change in length of a rod, but Eq. (16-7) applies to any linear dimension such as the diameter of a cylinder or even the radius of a circular hole in a plate. You can think of thermal expansion as analogous to a photographic enlargement in which every linear feature of an isotropic substance changes proportionally. (An isotropic substance has the same properties in all directions.)

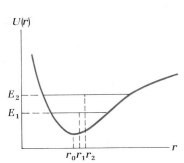

$U(r)$

E_2
E_1

$r_0 r_1 r_2$ r

Figure 16-7. The potential energy of interaction of two neighboring atoms is asymmetric about the minimum at r_0. The average separation is r_1 when the vibrational energy is E_1. The average separation increases to r_2 if the vibrational energy increases to E_2 because of a temperature increase.

We can understand on a microscopic level why a typical solid expands with an increase in temperature. In a solid, neighboring atoms exert springlike forces on each other and undergo vibrational motions. At a given temperature, a typical molecule oscillates about its average position as indicated schematically in Fig. 16-7. An effective-potential-energy function of two adjacent atoms separated by a distance r is shown. This function is asymmetric about its minimum, and the average separation depends on the energy of the molecule. We associate an increase in temperature with an increase in the average molecular energy. With an increase in energy, the average separation of molecules increases. This effect, when applied to the atoms in a solid, gives rise to thermal expansion.

For liquids, as well as for solids, it is convenient to consider volume changes that correspond to temperature changes. If V_0 is the volume of a substance at a reference temperature T_0, then the change in volume ΔV which accompanies a temperature change ΔT is given by

$$\Delta V = \beta V_0 \, \Delta T \qquad (16\text{-}8)$$

Coefficient of volume expansion β

where β is the average *coefficient of volume expansion*. Its value is characteristic of the particular substance. Values of β for some liquids are listed in Table 16-1.

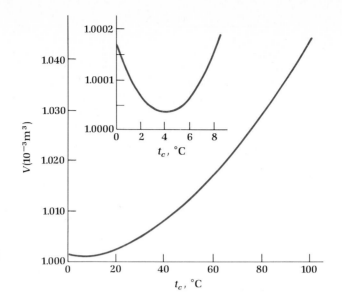

Figure 16-8. The temperature dependence of the volume of 1.000 kg of water is shown. The inset shows the region around 4°C where the density of water is a maximum.

Since the product of three linear dimensions gives a volume, it is not surprising that linear expansion and volume expansion are related. The result of Prob. 16-2 shows that $\beta = 3\alpha$ for an isotropic substance.

Notable by its absence from Table 16-1 is liquid water. The positive values of α and β for the substances in that table indicate that they expand with increasing temperature. Water also expands (but not linearly) with a temperature increase in the temperature range from about 4 to 100°C. However, between 0°C and about 4°C, water contracts with a temperature increase. This behavior is shown in Fig. 16-8, in which the volume of 1 kg of water is plotted versus temperature. The inset shows the region of smallest volume (largest density) around 4°C. This variation of volume or of density with temperature is responsible for the stratification that sometimes occurs in large bodies of fresh water. The anomalous thermal expansion of water is ultimately due to the interaction of the unusually shaped water molecules.

EXAMPLE 16-3. A concrete slab has length of 12 m at $-5°C$ on a winter day. What change in length occurs from winter to summer, when the temperature is 35°C?

SOLUTION. From Table 16-1, the coefficient of linear expansion for concrete is around 1×10^{-5} C$°^{-1}$. Using Eq. 16-7, we have

$$\Delta L = \alpha L_0 \, \Delta T$$
$$= (1 \times 10^{-5} \text{ C}°^{-1})(12 \text{ m})(40 \text{ C}°)$$
$$= 5 \text{ mm}$$

Adjacent slabs in highways and in sidewalks are often separated by pliable spacers to allow for this kind of expansion.

EXAMPLE 16-4. An aluminum sphere has a radius R of 3.000 mm at 100.0°C. What is its volume at 0.0°C?

SOLUTION. The volume of the sphere $(4\pi R^3/3)$ at 100°C is $V = 113.1$ mm^3. From Table 16-1, $\alpha = 2.4 \times 10^{-5}$ C$°^{-1}$ and $\beta = 3\alpha = 7.2 \times 10^{-5}$ C$°^{-1}$. Applying Eq. (16-8), we obtain

$$\Delta V = (7.2 \times 10^{-5} \text{ C}°^{-1})(113.1 \text{ mm}^3)(-100 \text{ C}°)$$

$$= -0.81 \text{ mm}^3$$

The volume at 0°C is 113.1 mm^3 − 0.8 mm^3 = 112.3 mm^3.

An alternative approach is to evaluate the radius of the sphere (a linear dimension) at 0°C and calculate the volume from $V = 4\pi R^3/3$. (In Exercise 16-21, you will be asked to show that you get the same answer this way.)

16-7 HEAT TRANSFER

Suppose we wish to increase the temperature of a flask of water. The procedure would be, in everyday language, to "heat it up." We could, for example, apply a flame to the flask, or we could drop a hot object into the water. In either case there is a transfer of energy to the water, and that energy transfer occurs because there is a temperature difference between the water and some part of its surroundings. This observation is the basis of our definition of the term "heat." *Heat is the energy transferred between a system and its surroundings due solely to a temperature difference between that system and some part of its surroundings.* The reference to a temperature difference is an essential part of the definition of heat because energy can also be transferred in other ways (to be described in the next chapter). In order to qualify as heat, the energy added to or removed from a system must have been transferred directly and solely because of a difference of temperature between the system and its environment.

How is this energy transferred at the molecular level? In the process of *heat conduction,* described more fully below, the energy is transferred in the collisions of the randomly moving molecules of a substance. Consider a rod with a temperature difference between its ends. Molecules at the higher temperature end will be moving faster on average than molecules at the lower temperature end. In a typical collision, the slower molecule will gain energy, and the faster molecule will lose energy. Averaged over many collisions involving the molecules all along the rod, there is a net transfer of energy — heat — because of this temperature difference.

The proper use of the term "heat" is as an amount of energy transferred to or from a system. It is not an energy that resides in a system or belongs to a system as potential energy does. It is, therefore, *incorrect* to speak of the "heat in a system" or the "heat of a system." Rather we speak of the "heat added to a system" or the "heat extracted from a system." We use the symbol Q to represent heat. As an energy transfer, heat has dimensions of energy. The SI unit of heat is the J (joule). Other heat units are also in common usage, and we shall introduce them as the need arises.

How is heat transferred between a system and its environment or, for simplicity, between two systems? The processes by which heat is transferred are classified into three categories: *conduction, convection,* and *radiation.* In some situations, only one of these mechanisms may be significantly operative. But often, two or all three processes may be contributing significantly. We shall discuss them separately, beginning with heat conduction.

Heat conduction. In the conduction process, heat is transferred between two systems through a connecting medium. We assume that no part of the medium is moving. Thus the medium must be a rigid solid, or if fluid, it must have no circulating currents. Consider the situation shown schematically in Fig. 16-9. A uniform rod of cross-sectional area A and length L is the medium separating two systems maintained at temperatures T_1 and T_2. Heat is transferred through the medium from the higher temperature, say T_2, to the lower temperature T_1. An adiabatic wall covering the lateral surface of the rod prevents any flow of heat from that surface.

We can expect the temperature to vary along the length of the rod. The

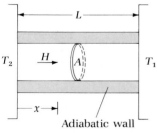

Figure 16-9. A uniform rod conducts heat from a higher temperature T_2 to a lower temperature T_1. The lateral surface of the rod is insulated.

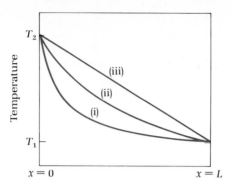

Figure 16-10. Temperature profiles are shown at different times for the rod of Fig. 16-9. Profile (i) is for shortly after the heat conduction begins and profile (ii) is somewhat later. After a sufficiently long time, the steady-state profile (iii) is achieved.

temperature should be T_2 at the left end ($x = 0$) and T_1 at the other end ($x = L$). At an intermediate point in the rod, located by x, the temperature should be between T_1 and T_2 and generally is changing with time. Some temperature profiles are sketched in Fig. 16-10. Experiment shows that after *steady-state* conditions are achieved (the temperature at any given point no longer is changing), the temperature varies linearly along the length of the rod if T_1 and T_2 are not greatly different.

For steady-state heat flow in the rod, the heat Q flowing through a cross section of the rod in a time interval t is the same all along the rod. Thus, under steady-state conditions, the energy is transferred through the medium, and no part of the medium is gaining or losing energy. We let the *heat current* H be the heat per unit time flowing through a cross section:

$$H = \frac{Q}{t}$$

The steady-state heat current H then has the same value everywhere along the uniform rod. From experiment we find that the steady-state heat current H in the rod is (i) proportional to the temperature difference $T_2 - T_1$, (ii) proportional to the cross-sectional area A, (iii) inversely proportional to the length L, and (iv) dependent on the material. These features are summarized by the expression

$$H = kA\,\frac{T_2 - T_1}{L} \tag{16-9}$$

where k is the *thermal conductivity* characteristic of the material (but not the size or shape) of the rod. The temperature dependence of the thermal conductivity of most substances is usually slight. The SI unit of heat current is the watt (W), and the SI unit of thermal conductivity is $W \cdot m^{-1} \cdot K^{-1}$. Table 16-2 lists values of the thermal conductivity for some common materials.

From Eq. (16-9), we see that the heat current can be large for a material with a

Marginal notes: Steady-state heat flow · Heat current · Thermal conductivity

Table 16-2. Some values of thermal conductivity and some R-values

Substance	k, $W \cdot m^{-1} \cdot K^{-1}$	Material	R-value, $F° \cdot ft^2 \cdot h \cdot Btu^{-1}$
Aluminum	237	Asphalt shingles	0.44
Copper	401	Plasterboard, $\frac{1}{2}$ inch	0.45
Concrete	0.9–1.3	Plywood, $\frac{3}{4}$ inch	0.9
Wood	0.05–0.36	Brick veneer	0.6–1.3
Fiberglass batt	0.04	Styrofoam panel, $\frac{3}{4}$ inch	6.3
Air	0.02	Fiberglass roll, 3.5 inch	11
Styrofoam	0.01		

A good heat conductor has a large thermal conductivity; a good insulator has a small thermal conductivity.

large value of thermal conductivity. Such a substance is called a "good" heat conductor and can be used to approximate a diathermic wall. Metals typically are good heat conductors; copper is one of the best. In contrast, a substance with a small value of thermal conductivity would be a poor heat conductor and a good insulator. A thick insulating layer approximates an adiabatic wall. Styrofoam is an excellent insulator (below its melting point of course).

Equation (16-9) can be generalized to describe heat conduction in nonsteady-state conditions and in a variety of geometries. At a point in a medium characterized by thermal conductivity k, let H represent the instantaneous heat current through a small area element A. If x is a coordinate perpendicular to the plane of the area and the temperature varies with that coordinate, then dT/dx is the *temperature gradient* at that position. These quantities are related by

Temperature gradient

Heat-conduction equation

$$H = -kA\frac{dT}{dx} \qquad (16\text{-}10)$$

The negative sign in Eq. (16-10) corresponds to the fact that heat flows from higher to lower temperature. Thus, if the temperature is decreasing in the direction of increasing x, then $-dT/dx$ is positive and heat flows in the positive x direction.

EXAMPLE 16-5. Estimate the heat current in the Styrofoam insulation in the walls of a kitchen refrigerator. How much heat flows through these walls in an hour?

SOLUTION. The total wall area of a refrigerator is around 4 m² and the temperature difference between inside and outside is about $25°C - 5°C = 20$ C°. We estimate the Styrofoam thickness at 30 mm. Using the thermal conductivity of

Styrofoam from Table 16-2, we have from Eq. (16-9),

$$H = \frac{(0.01\ \text{W} \cdot \text{m}^{-1} \cdot \text{K}^{-1})(4\ \text{m}^2)(20\ \text{C}°)}{0.03\ \text{m}}$$

$$= 30\ \text{W}$$

In an hour the heat would be

$$Q = Ht = (30\ \text{W})(3600\ \text{s}) = 100\ \text{kJ}$$

EXAMPLE 16-6. Evaluate the temperature gradient in the Styrofoam insulation of Example 16-5.

SOLUTION. Select the positive x axis to be perpendicular to one of the walls and directed from outside the refrigerator to the inside. The temperature profile for this steady-state heat flow is illustrated by line (iii) in Fig. 16-10. The temperature

gradient is the slope of the straight line in the figure:

$$\frac{dT}{dx} = \frac{-20\ \text{C}°}{0.03\ \text{m}} = -700\ \text{C}° \cdot \text{m}^{-1}$$

Since $dT/dx < 0$, the heat current is in the positive x direction, or into the refrigerator.

In the building-construction industry, the insulating value of materials under conditions of steady-state heat conduction is expressed as the "R-value," or R. We apply Eq. (16-9) to a slab of thickness $\Delta x = L$ with a (positive) temperature difference of $\Delta T = T_2 - T_1$ across it:

$$H = \frac{kA\,\Delta T}{\Delta x}$$

We solve for the temperature difference ΔT in terms of the heat current per unit area H/A:

$$\Delta T = \frac{H}{A}\frac{\Delta x}{k}$$

R-value

The R-value is defined as $\Delta x/k$, and the equation above becomes

$$\Delta T = \frac{H}{A} R \qquad (16\text{-}11)$$

British thermal unit

In a system of units used in the building industry in the United States, the unit of heat is the Btu (British thermal unit), and 1 Btu = 1055 J; the unit of area is ft^2; the unit of time is the hour (h); the unit of length (for the thickness) is the inch; and temperature difference is expressed in F°. The unit of R-value, whether explicitly expressed or just understood, is F° · ft^2 · h · Btu^{-1}. For example, if a roll of fiberglass insulation has "R 11" stamped on it, the R-value is 11 F° · ft^2 · h · Btu^{-1}. We shall often follow the convention of omitting this unwieldy unit when quoting an R-value. R-values for some building materials are listed in Table 16-2.

The R-value for a composite equals the sum of R-values for the layers.

The usefulness of Eq. (16-11) and the R-value is in determining heat conduction through composite slab-type structures such as walls or floorings. Under steady-state conditions, the heat current per unit area is the same all along the thickness (why?), the temperature difference across the composite is the sum of temperatures across the individual layers, and the effective R-value of the composite is simply the sum of R-values of the layers.

EXAMPLE 16-7. A wall consists of $\frac{1}{2}$-inch plasterboard, $3\frac{1}{2}$ inches of fiberglass insulation, and $\frac{3}{4}$-inch plywood. (*a*) Determine the effective R-value of the composite wall. If the inside temperature is 70°F and the outside temperature is 10°F, evaluate (*b*) the heat current per unit area in the wall and (*c*) the temperature distribution in the wall.

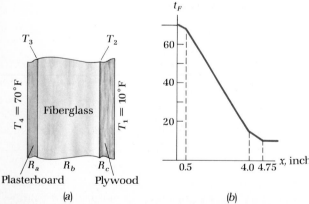

Figure 16-11. Example 16-7: (*a*) A composite wall in cross section consists of three layers: $\frac{1}{2}$-inch plasterboard, $3\frac{1}{2}$-inch fiberglass roll, and $\frac{3}{4}$-inch plywood. (*b*) The temperature profile for the wall is shown. The largest temperature drop is across the fiberglass insulation.

SOLUTION. The composite wall is shown in cross section in Fig. 16-11*a*, with temperatures at the interfaces between layers indicated. Applying Eq. (16-11) to each layer in turn, we have

$$T_2 - T_1 = \frac{H}{A} R_c$$

$$T_3 - T_2 = \frac{H}{A} R_b$$

$$T_4 - T_3 = \frac{H}{A} R_a$$

The heat current per unit area (H/A) is the same in all layers under steady-state conditions, and there is no net gain or loss of energy in any layer. The sum of these three equations is

$$T_4 - T_1 = \frac{H}{A} (R_a + R_b + R_c)$$

$$= \frac{H}{A} R_{\text{eff}}$$

So the effective R-value R_{eff} is the sum of the individual R-values. From Table 16-2, we obtain

$$R_{\text{eff}} = 0.45 + 11 + 0.95 = 12.4 \text{ F}° \cdot \text{h} \cdot \text{ft}^2 \cdot \text{Btu}^{-1}$$

(*b*) Using this value, we can evaluate the heat current per unit area:

$$\frac{H}{A} = \frac{T_4 - T_1}{R_{\text{eff}}} = 4.8 \text{ Btu} \cdot \text{h}^{-1} \cdot \text{ft}^{-2}$$

(*c*) The temperature values T_2 and T_3 can now be determined from the first two equations above:

$$T_2 = T_1 + \frac{H}{A} R_c$$

$$= 10°\text{F} + (4.8)(0.95) \text{ F}° = 15°\text{F}$$

In a similar way, T_3 can be determined to be 68°F. The temperature profile is shown in Fig. 16-11b. Note that the largest temperature drop is across the fiberglass insulation, the component with the largest R-value.

Convection currents

An object emits energy from its surface.

Heat convection and radiation. In convection, heat is transferred by macroscopic movement of matter in the form of convection currents. Such currents can occur spontaneously in fluids whose density varies with temperature. In air, for example, because of the earth's gravitational field, convection currents are established as higher-temperature (lower-density) air rises and lower-temperature (higher-density) air sinks. Forced convection is produced using blowers. Calculations of heat flow by convection are complex and will not be treated here.

Radiation is the third mechanism of heat transfer. It can be the dominant mechanism of heat transfer in some situations. All objects emit energy from their surfaces. A portion of this radiant energy may be seen easily if the surface is at a high-enough temperature (such as a glowing ember). Even at much lower temperatures, a surface still emits energy, although an insignificant amount is visible. You can feel the radiation coming from a warm stove, for example.

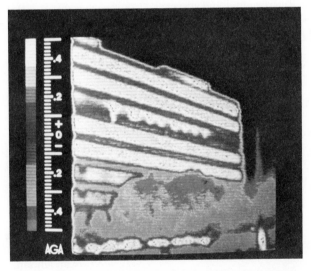

Special film was used to show heat losses from a structure. *(BL Thermographic Surveys/Photo Researchers.)*

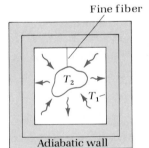

Fine fiber

T_2

T_1

Adiabatic wall

Figure 16-12. An insulated object at temperature T_2 is surrounded by walls at temperature T_1. Both surfaces absorb and emit energy.

The Stefan-Boltzmann law

The Stefan-Boltzmann constant

A surface at temperature T (on the Kelvin scale) will emit radiant energy at a rate which is proportional to the surface area A and to the fourth power of the temperature. The expression for the radiated power P is called the *Stefan-Boltzmann law:*

$$P = e\sigma A T^4 \tag{16-12}$$

where e is the *emissivity,* which characterizes the emitting properties of the particular surface ($0 \leq e \leq 1$), and σ is the *Stefan-Boltzmann constant,* $\sigma = 5.67 \times 10^{-8}$ W $\cdot$ m^{-2} $\cdot$ K^{-4}, which is the same for all objects.

Surfaces absorb as well as emit radiation. Consider an object at temperature T_2 surrounded by walls at temperature T_1, as seen in Fig. 16-12. Experiment shows that the temperatures will become equal. Then the surface of the enclosed object and the surrounding wall surface must each emit and absorb energy at the same rate at that temperature in order to maintain thermal equilibrium. That is, the surface of the enclosed object at temperature T must emit and absorb energy at the same rate. Thus a good absorbing surface is also a good emitting surface ($e \approx 1$), and a poor absorbing (but a good reflecting) surface is a poor emitting surface ($e \approx 0$).

Suppose the object in the enclosure is maintained at a somewhat higher temperature than the surrounding walls: $T_2 > T_1$. Then its rate of energy emission is greater than its absorption rate, and the net rate of heat transfer (or heat current) H is given by

$$H = e\sigma A(T_2{}^4 - T_1{}^4) \tag{16-13}$$

Since the contributions to the heat-transfer rate depend on the fourth power of temperature, the effect can be large at high temperatures and for large temperature differences.

EXAMPLE 16-8. Estimate the rate of heat transfer between the bare head of a bald man (at 37°C) and the surroundings at (a) 20°C and (b) −40°C.

SOLUTION. Approximate the head by a sphere of radius $a = 120$ mm and of emissivity $e = 1$. Since $0 \leqslant e \leqslant 1$, we are assuming that the skin is an excellent emitter and absorber. The surface area is then $A = 4\pi a^2 = 0.2$ m². The temperatures must be expressed on the Kelvin scale. Equation (16-13) gives

$H = (1)(5.67 \times 10^{-8} \text{ W} \cdot \text{m}^{-2} \cdot \text{K}^{-4})(0.2 \text{ m}^2)[(310 \text{ K})^4 - T_1{}^4)]$

(a) With $T_1 = 293$ K, we obtain

$H = (1 \times 10^{-8} \text{ W} \cdot \text{K}^{-4})[(310 \text{ K})^4 - (293 \text{ K})^4]$

$= 20$ W

(b) For $T_1 = 233$ K, a similar calculation gives

$H = 60$ W

SUMMARY WITH APPLICATIONS

Section 16-2. Microscopic and macroscopic descriptions
The macroscopic description of a system uses thermodynamic variables of state such as pressure, volume, and temperature.

Describe the thermodynamic variables of state.

Section 16-3. Thermal equilibrium and the zeroth law of thermodynamics
Two systems in contact are in thermal equilibrium if their properties are no longer changing. The zeroth law of thermodynamics states that two systems in thermal equilibrium with a third system are in thermal equilibrium with each other. If two systems are in thermal equilibrium, they have the same temperature.

Explain the concept of thermal equilibrium; state the zeroth law of thermodynamics.

Section 16-4. Thermometers and the ideal gas temperature scale
The ideal gas temperature is defined by a limiting process using real dilute gases in constant-volume gas thermometers. The scale is set by assigning to the triple point of water the temperature 273.16 K.

Define the ideal gas temperature scale; describe the triple point.

Section 16-5. Other temperature scales
Temperatures can be expressed on different scales. The relation between the Celsius and Kelvin scales is

$$t_C = T - 273.15 \text{ K} \tag{16-4}$$

Express and convert temperatures on different scales.

Section 16-6. Thermal expansion
The length L_0 of an object changes with a change in temperature ΔT by an amount

$$\Delta L = \alpha L_0 \Delta T \tag{16-7}$$

Volume changes are described by

$$\Delta V = \beta V_0 \Delta T \tag{16-8}$$

Calculate changes in length, area, and volume due to temperature changes.

Section 16-7. Heat transfer
Heat Q is defined as the energy transferred between a system and its surroundings solely because of a temperature difference between the system and its surroundings. Heat conduction is one of the mechanisms of heat transfer and is described by the heat-conduction equation:

$$H = -kA\frac{dT}{dx} \tag{16-10}$$

Convection is a mechanism of heat transfer in which macroscopic convection currents are present. For heat transferred by radiation, the radiated power from a surface is given by the Stefan-Boltzmann law

$$P = e\sigma A T^4 \qquad (16\text{-}12)$$

Define heat; solve steady-state heat-conduction problems; apply the Stefan-Boltzmann law to heat transfer by radiation.

QUESTIONS

16-1 Describe some situations in a typical kitchen for which it would be desirable to use (a) an adiabatic wall and (b) a diathermic wall.

16-2 A liquid is a fluid and a gas is a fluid. How are liquids and gases different? How are they similar?

16-3 Is pressure a variable of state for a liquid? For a solid? Explain.

16-4 What is the mass of 1 mol of diatomic hydrogen H_2? How many molecules are in 1 mol? How many atoms are in 1 mol? Answer these same questions for He and for CO_2.

16-5 In a constant-volume gas thermometer, the pressure increases with increasing temperature. How does volume vary with temperature in a constant-pressure gas thermometer?

16-6 If both glass and mercury expand with increasing temperature, how does a mercury-in-glass thermometer work?

16-7 What difficulties are encountered in measuring very low temperatures with a constant-volume gas thermometer? What about very high temperatures?

16-8 Suppose a nice round number like 300 were assigned as the triple-point temperature. What changes would occur in the ideal gas temperature scale? Explain the advantage of choosing the triple-point temperature to be 273.16 K.

16-9 If two systems are in thermal equilibrium, they have the same temperature. Is the converse true? That is, if two systems have the same temperature, are they in thermal equilibrium? What can you say about two systems that have different temperatures?

16-10 Is it possible for a container of water to be freezing and boiling at the same time? Explain.

16-11 The outside diameter of a hollow aluminum sphere increases with increasing temperature. What happens to the inside diameter? Explain.

16-12 Describe the temperature variation with depth of the water in a lake (a) in summer and (b) in winter.

16-13 Pressure, volume, and temperature are variables of state for a thermodynamic system. Is heat a variable of state? Explain.

16-14 As a practical matter, there is always a temperature difference between a system and some part of its environment, however remote. Must there always be some heat transferred because of that temperature difference? Explain.

16-15 Suppose a wooden rod and a metal rod are both at room temperature. Which one feels cooler to the touch and why?

16-16 Explain why a copper teakettle is commonly fitted with a wooden handle.

16-17 What is the SI unit of R-value?

16-18 What are the significant mechanisms of heat transfer for a single-pane window? For a double-pane window?

16-19 Glass has a relatively high thermal conductivity. Account for the good insulating properties of fiberglass batts or rolls.

16-20 A thermos is double-walled, with the space between walls evacuated. What is the advantage of this construction?

16-21 Why are the walls of a thermos silvered, that is, highly reflecting?

16-22 Why are nights with clear skies usually colder than nights with cloudy skies during the same season?

16-23 Complete the following table:

Symbol	Represents	Type	SI unit
p	Pressure		
V			
n			
T			K
t_C			
α			
β			
Q		Scalar	
H			
k			
R			
σ			

EXERCISES

Section 16-2. Microscopic and macroscopic descriptions

16-1 Suppose that the instantaneous values of the position and velocity of a molecule in a system can be determined from an application of Newton's laws to the system, and that the calculation time per molecule is

1 ns on a high-speed computer. Estimate the time in years that would be required to calculate the positions and velocities for all of the molecules (10^{23}) of that system.

16-2 An amount 2.4 mol of He gas occupies a volume of 82 L (1 L = 10^{-3} m³). (a) What is the mass of the gas? (b) How many molecules are in this system? (c) Estimate the average separation between molecules and compare that with the size of a helium atom (about 50 pm).

16-3 One mole of a gas at standard temperature and pressure (STP corresponds to $T = 273$ K and $p = 101$ kPa) occupies a volume of 22.5 L. Suppose the container is in the shape of a cube. (a) Determine the length of the cube edge. (b) What force is exerted by the gas on each face of the container?

Section 16-4. Thermometers and the ideal gas temperature scale

16-4 Suppose that the gas in Exercise 16-3 comes to thermal equilibrium with water at its normal boiling point. If the volume is fixed at 22.5 L, (a) what is the pressure of the gas and (b) what force does the gas exert on each face of the container?

16-5 Helium gas in a constant-volume thermometer is at pressure 1439 Pa when in thermal equilibrium with water at its triple point. (a) What is the pressure of this gas when in thermal equilibrium with zinc at its normal melting point (693 K)? (b) The pressure of the gas is 406 Pa when in thermal equilibrium with a liquid at its normal boiling point. What is the temperature of this boiling point?

16-6 Four constant-volume gas thermometers are used to measure the temperature of the normal melting point of zinc. Each thermometer contains a different amount of the same gas, and these gases have different pressures at the triple point of water, as shown in the table below. The pressure readings when in thermal equilibrium with zinc at its melting point are also shown in the table. From these data, construct a graph similar to Fig. 16-5 and perform the extrapolation to determine the ideal gas temperature of the normal melting point of zinc.

Thermometer	1	2	3	4
p_3, kPa	217.12	123.01	84.09	49.83
p, kPa	551.01	312.08	213.31	126.39

16-7 The pressure of the gas in a constant-volume gas thermometer is 24.5 mmHg when in thermal equilibrium with water at its normal boiling point. What is the pressure (in mmHg) when the gas is in thermal equilibrium with water at (a) its triple point, (b) its normal melting point, (c) 37°C?

16-8 Temperatures can be determined using a resistance thermometer in which the electrical resistance is measured. Suppose the temperature of the thermometer is proportional to its resistance. [The unit of resistance is the ohm (Ω), defined in Chap. 24.] The thermometer is calibrated by measuring the resistance to be 100.000 Ω at the triple point of water and to be 104.783 Ω at the normal boiling point of water. What is the resistance-thermometer temperature if the resistance is (a) 102.445 Ω? (b) 98.729 Ω? (c) What is the resistance at the normal melting point of water?

16-9 The length of a column of mercury in a glass capillary is 43 mm when in thermal equilibrium with the underside of a healthy person's tongue (37°C). For a person with "two degrees of fever" (39°C), the length is 67 mm. What is the temperature of a tepid bath for which the length of the column is 16 mm? State any assumptions that you make.

Section 16-5. Other temperature scales

16-10 Express the normal body temperature of 37°C on (a) the Fahrenheit scale, (b) the Kelvin scale, (c) the Rankine scale.

16-11 At what temperature (if any) are the readings the same on (a) the Celsius and Fahrenheit scales, (b) the Kelvin and Fahrenheit scales, (c) the Kelvin and Rankine scales, (d) the Kelvin and Celsius scales?

16-12 The normal boiling point of helium is 4.2 K; a comfortable room temperature is 295 K; the surface of the sun is at about 6000 K; the interior of a star is about 10 MK. Express these temperatures on (a) the Celsius scale, (b) the Fahrenheit scale, (c) the Rankine scale.

Section 16-6. Thermal expansion

16-13 A steel rule is calibrated at 22°C against a standard so that the distance between numbered divisions is 10.00 mm. (a) What is the distance between these divisions when the rule is at −5°C? (b) If a nominal length of 1 m is measured with the rule at this lower temperature, what percent error is made? (c) What absolute error is made for a 100-m length?

16-14 A copper plate at 0°C has thickness of 5.00 mm and a circular hole of radius 75.0 mm. Its temperature is raised to 220°C. Determine the values at this temperature of (a) the thickness of the plate, (b) the radius of the hole, (c) the circumference of the boundary of the circular hole, (d) the area of the hole in the plate.

16-15 A steel shaft has diameter 42.51 mm at 28°C. It is to be fitted to a steel pulley with a circular hole of diameter 42.50 mm at that temperature. (a) By how much must the temperature of the shaft be reduced so that it can fit in the hole? (b) Suppose the temperature of the entire structure is reduced to −5°C after the shaft has been fitted. Will the shaft come loose? Explain.

16-16 Rework Exercise 16-15, with an aluminum pulley replacing the steel pulley.

16-17 A simple pendulum consists of a bob attached to a fine steel wire so that the length of the pendulum is

0.2482 m at 27°C. (a) What is the change in the period of the pendulum (Sec. 14-5) if its temperature is changed by −5 C°? (b) If this pendulum is used as a clock, accurate at 27°C, how many seconds does the clock gain or lose in one day because of this temperature change?

16-18 The density of aluminum is 2692 kg/m³ at 20°C. (a) What is the mass of an aluminum sphere ($V = 4\pi R^3/3$) whose radius R at this temperature is 25.00 mm? (b) What is the mass of the aluminum at 100.0°C? (c) What is the density of aluminum at 100.0°C? (d) What are the answers to parts (b) and (c) if the aluminum is in the shape of a cube?

16-19 A glass ($\beta = 2.2 \times 10^{-5}$ C°⁻¹) bulb is completely filled with 176.2 mL of mercury ($\beta = 18 \times 10^{-5}$ C°⁻¹) at 0.0°C. The bulb is fitted, as illustrated in Fig. 16-13, with a glass tube of inside diameter 2.5 mm at 0.0°C. How high does the mercury rise in the tube if the temperature of the system is raised to 50.0°C? The change in diameter of the glass tube may be neglected. Why?

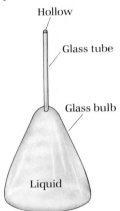

Hollow

Glass tube

Glass bulb

Liquid

Figure 16-13. Exercise 16-19.

16-20 Suppose the glass bulb of Exercise 16-19 is filled with an oil, occupying the 176.2-mL volume at 0.0°C. At a temperature of 8.0°C, the oil has risen in the glass tube to a height of 190 mm. Evaluate the volume coefficient of expansion for this liquid.

16-21 Work Example 16-4 as suggested there by determining the radius of the sphere at 0.0°C and calculating the volume at that temperature.

16-22 A certain type of plastic with $\beta = 2 \times 10^{-7}$ C°⁻¹ remains at rest if released when completely immersed in water at 6°C. What happens to the plastic if it is released when completely immersed in water at (a) 8°C, (b) 4°C, (c) 1°C? See Fig. 16-8.

Section 16-7. Heat transfer

16-23 An aluminum pot contains water which is kept steadily boiling (100°C). The bottom surface of the pot, which is 12 mm thick and 1.5×10^4 mm² in area, is maintained at a temperature of 102°C by an electric heating unit. The remaining part of the surface is well insulated from the surroundings. Evaluate the heat current entering the water through the bottom surface.

16-24 Determine the SI units of R-value and use those units to express the R-value of a roll of fiberglass insulation of thickness 3.5 inch (90 mm).

16-25 A piece of wood, in the shape of a 350-mm by 350-mm slab of thickness 15 mm, conducts heat through this thickness under steady-state conditions. The heat current in the slab is measured to be 14.3 W when a temperature difference of 25 C° is maintained across the slab. (a) Evaluate the temperature gradient in the slab. (b) Determine the thermal conductivity of this wood. (c) Would this material be classified as a good heat conductor or as a good heat insulator?

16-26 Approximate the living space of a residence by a box having a 40-ft by 40-ft floor and ceiling and 8-ft-high walls. Suppose the interior is maintained at 70°F, while the exterior surfaces of walls and ceilings are exposed to a steady 10°F and the exterior surface of the floor remains at 40°F. The wall structure has an effective R-value $R_w = 10$, the ceiling has $R_c = 15$, and the floor has $R_f = 8$, all in building-industry units. Evaluate the heat current in (a) ceiling, (b) walls, (c) floor. (d) Suppose these conditions are maintained for a 24-h period. What is the heat loss to the outside in this period? (e) The inside temperature is maintained by consuming fuel costing $0.05 per 1000 Btu. What is the heating cost for the 24-h period?

16-27 The R-value of a building material is determined experimentally by constructing a box from the material and measuring the electric power input to a heater inside the box which maintains the inside at a given temperature. Suppose a box of total area 96 ft² is constructed of ¾-inch-thick particleboard and that a power input of 1100 W will maintain a temperature difference of 30 F° between inside and outside. (a) What is the total heat current in the walls in units of Btu · h⁻¹? (b) Calculate the R-value of this particleboard. (c) What is the thermal conductivity of particleboard in SI units?

16-28 Two rods of the same area and R-values R_1 and R_2 are joined in series end to end, as shown in Fig. 16-14a. The lateral surfaces are insulated and opposite ends

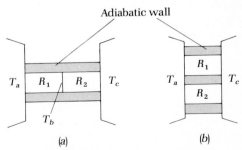

Adiabatic wall

T_a R_1 R_2 T_c T_a R_1 T_c

T_b R_2

(a)   (b)

Figure 16-14. Exercises 16-28 and 16-29.

are maintained at different temperatures. For steady-state heat conduction, (a) show that the series combination has an effective R-value R_{eff} given by

$$R_{eff} = R_1 + R_2$$

(b) Suppose $R_1 < R_2$; which rod has the larger temperature drop across its length?

16-29 Suppose the two rods from the previous exercise are arranged in parallel, as shown in Fig. 16-14b. For steady-state heat conduction, show that the parallel combination has an effective R-value R_{eff} given by

$$\frac{2}{R_{eff}} = \frac{1}{R_1} + \frac{1}{R_2} \quad \text{or} \quad R_{eff} = \frac{2R_1R_2}{R_1 + R_2}$$

Note that the combined heat current $H = H_1 + H_2$.

16-30 A wall consists of two layers: plasterboard with R-value $R_p = 0.45$ and brick veneer with R-value $R_b = 1.2$. If a temperature difference of 50 F° exists across the wall, determine (a) the heat current per unit area in the wall and (b) the temperature at the plasterboard-brick interface if the inside temperature is 70°F and the outside temperature is 20°F.

16-31 A 250-mm-long wooden ($k = 0.19 \text{ W} \cdot \text{m}^{-1} \cdot \text{K}^{-1}$) tube has circular cross section with inner radius $a = 10$ mm and outer radius $b = 20$ mm. Fitting snugly

within the tube is a circular aluminum rod of the same length. A temperature difference of 150 C° is maintained across the ends of this compound bar, and heat loss at the lateral surface is negligible. For steady-state conditions, (a) what is the total heat current in the compound bar and (b) how much energy is transferred through the bar in an hour?

16-32 A metal sphere of radius 150 mm has a surface of emissivity 0.40. (a) At what rate does it emit energy if its temperature is maintained at 900°C? (b) Suppose the sphere at 900°C is in an evacuated enclosure whose walls are maintained at 500°C. At what rate must energy be supplied to the sphere under these steady conditions?

16-33 Compare the radiated power per unit area emitted by the surface of (a) the sun at 6000 K, (b) the earth at 300 K, (c) the dark side of the moon at 200 K, (d) a neutron star at 3 K. For simplicity, take the emissivity of each surface to be 1.

16-34 Consider a body of emissivity e at temperature T_2 which is surrounded by walls at temperature T_1. Suppose that the temperature difference $\Delta T = T_2 - T_1$ is small compared with T_1. Show that $T_2{}^4 - T_1{}^4 \approx 4T_1{}^3 \Delta T$ and that the net heat current H is

$$H = 4e\sigma A T_1{}^3 \Delta T$$

PROBLEMS

16-1 Consider a rectangular plate of length L_0 and width W_0 at some reference temperature T_0. The area of the plate at this temperature is $A_0 = L_0 W_0$. With a change in temperature ΔT, each linear dimension changes by an amount determined by the coefficient of linear expansion α. Show that the change in area ΔA is given by

$$\Delta A = 2\alpha A_0 \, \Delta T$$

where the small area element $\Delta L \, \Delta W$ is neglected.

16-2 A rectangular block at temperature T_0 has dimensions of L_0, W_0, and H_0 and a volume of V_0. Show that the coefficient of volume expansion $\beta = 3\alpha$. What approximations have been made? What would be the relation between β and α for a sphere?

16-3 Apply the heat-conduction equation, Eq. (16-10), to steady-state radial heat flow corresponding to cylindrical symmetry, as shown in Fig. 16-15a. Suppose a long inner cylinder of radius a is maintained at temperature T_a. Surrounding the inner cylinder is a cylindrical medium of thermal conductivity k and outer radius b. The outer surface is maintained at a lower temperature T_b. The radial coordinate r is the perpendicular distance from the axis to a cylindrical surface, and we consider a length L of the cylinder. The area A through which the heat flows is $2\pi r L$. (a) By

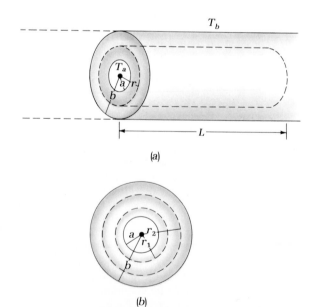

(a)

(b)

Figure 16-15. Prob. 16-3.

requiring that energy be conserved, show that the heat current H has the same value through concentric cylinders of radii r_1 and r_2 (see Fig. 16-15b). (b) Show that the temperature gradient at distance r from the axis is given by

$$\frac{dT}{dr} = \frac{-H}{2\pi r L k}$$

(c) Integrate this equation to obtain the temperature distribution

$$T(r) = \left(\frac{H}{2\pi L k}\right) \ln r + \text{constant}$$

(d) The constant of integration and the heat-current value are determined from the temperature values at the boundaries. Show that

$$H = \frac{2\pi k L (T_a - T_b)}{\ln (b/a)}$$

$$T(r) = T_a + \frac{(T_b - T_a) \ln (r/a)}{\ln (b/a)}$$

16-4 Consider a medium between two concentric *spheres* of radius a at temperature T_a and radius b at temperature T_b. Using the previous problem as a guide (but now r is the radial distance from the center of the sphere), show that

$$\frac{dT}{dr} = \frac{-H}{4\pi r^2 k}$$

and that

$$H = \frac{4\pi a b k (T_a - T_b)}{b - a}$$

$$T = \frac{b T_b - a T_a}{b - a} + \frac{a b (T_a - T_b)}{(b - a) r}$$

16-5 A cylindrical metal pipe of outside radius 12 mm carries high-pressure steam at temperature 140°C. It is in contact with and surrounded by a cylindrical insulating sleeve of outside radius 28 mm and of thermal conductivity $k = 0.11 \ \text{W} \cdot \text{m}^{-1} \cdot \text{K}^{-1}$. The outside surface is exposed to a fixed temperature of 35°C. For each meter of length, determine (a) the heat current and (b) the temperature distribution in the insulating medium. (c) Construct a graph of T versus r to show the temperature distribution. (d) Evaluate the temperature gradient at a point 20 mm from the axis. (*Hint:* See Prob. 16-3.)

16-6 A radioactive copper sphere of radius 25 mm is insulated from its 25°C surroundings by a spherical Styrofoam blanket of inner radius 25 mm and of thickness 15 mm. If the heat current into the surroundings is 600 mW (equal to the power provided by the radioactivity), determine (a) the temperature of the copper sphere and (b) the temperature distribution in the Styrofoam insulation. (c) Show the temperature distribution graphically. (d) Explain why the copper

sphere can be considered to have the same temperature throughout. (*Hint:* See Prob. 16-4.)

16-7 A bimetallic strip consists of two metal strips with different coefficients of linear expansion α_1 and α_2, each of thickness d and length L_0 at T_0. They are bonded together and, with a change in temperature ΔT, will curve in a circular arc, as shown in Fig. 16-16. Show that the radius of curvature R is given approximately by

$$R = \frac{d}{(\alpha_2 - \alpha_1) \, \Delta T}$$

(*Hint:* Let $R_1 = R - \frac{1}{2}d$ and $R_2 = R + \frac{1}{2}d$ represent the mean radii of the two strips and equate the angles subtended by each strip.)

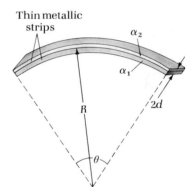

Figure 16-16. Prob. 16-7.

16-8 A 90-mm-thick roll of fiberglass insulation separates two wall surfaces whose temperatures are 290 and 270 K. (a) Determine the heat current per unit area (in SI units). (b) Compare with the net heat current per unit area that would be transferred between these surfaces by radiation if the space between these walls were evacuated. Take the emissivity of each wall to be 0.5. (c) Repeat the above calculations, taking the surfaces temperatures to be 490 and 470 K. (d) Repeat for surface temperatures of 90 and 70 K. Assume that the thermal conductivity and the emissivities are independent of temperature.

16-9 ***Laplace's equation.*** For steady-state heat conduction in one dimension, the temperature distribution $T(x)$ is the solution of *Laplace's equation* for a medium with no sources of heat:

$$\frac{d^2 T}{dx^2} = 0$$

This equation is to be solved [integrated to determine $T(x)$] with the temperature specified at the boundaries. At $x = 0$, the temperature is T_2; at $x = L$, the temperature is T_1. Solve Laplace's equation for the situation illustrated in Fig. 16-9.

16-10 For problems with cylindrical symmetry, Laplace's

equation (see Prob. 16-9) is

$$\frac{d}{dr}\left(r\frac{dT}{dr}\right) = 0$$

Solve this equation subject to the boundary conditions:

$$T = T_a \quad \text{at} \quad r = a$$

$$T = T_b \quad \text{at} \quad r = b$$

Compare the solution with the one displayed in Prob. 16-3.

16-11 Laplace's equation (see the previous two problems) for problems with spherical symmetry is

$$\frac{d}{dr}\left(r^2\frac{dT}{dr}\right) = 0$$

Show that the temperature distribution displayed in Prob. 16-4 is a solution of Laplace's equation.

16-12 The sun's radius is 7×10^8 m, its surface temperature is 6000 K, and its emissivity is almost 1. (a) Calculate the radiated power from the surface. (b) Assume that the radiated energy spreads out uniformly in all directions and that equal amounts pass through concentric spheres of different radii in equal time intervals. Evaluate the radiated power per unit area at the earth's distance from the sun, 1.5×10^{11} m.

CHAPTER 17
THE FIRST LAW OF THERMODYNAMICS

17-1 INTRODUCTION

The origins of thermodynamics and its laws are in the very practical inventions of the industrial revolution, particularly the steam engine. These inventions eventually replaced the labor performed by human and beast with the mechanical work performed by heat engines. Obtaining mechanical work from an engine, such as a steam engine, required the burning of fuel and the accompanying heat transfer between the flame and the working substance in the engine (usually water).

Not until the second half of the last century did it become widely recognized that heat and mechanical work are energy transfers and that energy is a conserved quantity. Among those who contributed to the gradual development of these ideas were Benjamin Thompson (1753–1814) and James Joule (1818–1889). It was Thompson (see the Commentary) who recognized the inadequacy of treating heat as a fluid, called "caloric," that could flow from one body to another. From his observations of the high temperatures produced in the boring of cannon, he proposed a connection between heat and the work done by friction. Joule, after whom the SI unit of energy is named, in a series of experiments determined the amount of mechanical work that is equivalent to heat in raising the temperature of water. These were crucial steps in arriving at the statement of the first law of thermodynamics.

17-2 EQUATIONS OF STATE

What determines the value of a variable of state, say the pressure p of a gas? Suppose we put a certain amount of gas (n moles) in a container of fixed size (volume V) and maintain it at a constant temperature T. Experimentally, we find that the pressure of the gas cannot now be adjusted; fixing the values of n,

The equation of state is an equation that relates the variables of state.

V, and T determines the pressure. However, if one or more of n, V, and T are changed, then the pressure p may also change to a value that is determined by the new values of the other variables. That is, these variables of state are related by a mathematical equation. This relation is called the *equation of state* of that substance. Using the equation of state, we can evaluate any one of the variables of state, the pressure for example, in terms of the values of the remaining variables of state. The equation of state of some substance can be an extremely complicated function of the variables of state. But measurement can give their interdependence over all experimentally accessible conditions. We can, for example, hold n and T fixed and determine how the pressure p of a gas varies with its volume V.

Experiments of this sort for gases at low densities lead to the following conclusions:

1. For fixed n and T, p and V are inversely proportional. Thus, if the volume is doubled, the pressure is halved. This relationship, long known as *Boyle's law*, can also be written as

$$pV = \text{constant} \qquad (n, T \text{ fixed})$$

2. For fixed n and V, p and T (on the Kelvin scale) are proportional. This result is evident from our discussion of the constant-volume gas thermometer in the last chapter. The mathematical relation is

$$\frac{p}{T} = \text{constant} \qquad (n, V \text{ fixed})$$

3. For fixed V and T, p and n are proportional. Injecting an additional amount of gas into the container increases the pressure proportionately,

$$\frac{p}{n} = \text{constant} \qquad (V, T \text{ fixed})$$

All of these results, along with the results of varying other pairs of variables, are summarized in the relation

$$\frac{pV}{nT} = \text{constant}$$

where the constant in this expression is essentially independent of the variables p, V, n, and T so long as the density of the gas is low. From experiment the constant is found to have about the same value for all gases. In the limit of dilute gases, or for the ideal gas, the value of the constant is the same for all gases and is called the *universal gas constant R*. Its value in SI units is

Universal gas constant

$$R = 8.31 \text{ J} \cdot \text{mol}^{-1} \cdot \text{K}^{-1}$$

Thus the variables of state of a real dilute gas are related by an equation of state which is the same for all such gases. It is called the *ideal gas equation of state:*

Ideal gas equation of state

$$pV = nRT \qquad (17\text{-}1)$$

The ideal gas equation of state is obeyed approximately by a real gas whose pressure is not too large and whose temperature is not too low — that is, a dilute gas. Equation (17-1) can be used only for a real gas of this sort. (See Prob. 17-2 for an example of another equation of state.)

EXAMPLE 17-1. (a) What is the pressure of $n = 0.85$ mol of He occupying a volume V of 0.012 m³ at a temperature T of 273 K? (b) What is the volume of this gas at that same pressure but at temperature $T = 580$ K?

SOLUTION. (a) From the ideal gas equation of state, Eq. (17-1), we have

$$p = \frac{nRT}{V}$$

$$= \frac{(0.85 \text{ mol})(8.31 \text{ J} \cdot \text{mol}^{-1} \cdot \text{K}^{-1})(273 \text{ K})}{0.012 \text{ m}^3} = 160 \text{ kPa}$$

(b) Often we find it convenient to form ratios of state variables for each of two states. Let the state of the gas in part (a) be denoted by a and the state for part (b) be denoted by b. The variables for each state satisfy (n remains the same)

$$p_a V_a = nRT_a \quad \text{and} \quad p_b V_b = nRT_b$$

Dividing one equation by the other and canceling the common factors n and R, we obtain

$$\frac{p_b V_b}{p_a V_a} = \frac{T_b}{T_a}$$

Or, since $p_a = p_b$,

$$V_b = V_a \frac{T_b}{T_a}$$

Because we are dealing with ratios here, we may express the volume in any unit. Let us use the liter (1 L = 0.001 m³) as a convenient unit of volume. Then

$$V_b = 12 \text{ L} \frac{580 \text{ K}}{273 \text{ K}} = 25 \text{ L}$$

The p-V diagram. The ideal gas equation of state allows us to determine the value of one of the variables of state of a gas in terms of the others. If we deal with a fixed amount of gas (n remains the same), then any two of the remaining variables serve to determine the third. For convenience in displaying certain kinds of information, we often select p and V to be the independent variables; then the value of T is determined from Eq. (17-1). In this way the values of p and V determine the state of the gas.

A state of a system such as a gas can be represented on a *p-V diagram*. The axes in Fig. 17-1 are scaled to indicate values of pressure and volume, and a point in the plane corresponds to definite values of p and V. Each point on the p-V diagram represents a state of the system with a specified number of moles n. From the values of p and V, we can evaluate the temperature T for that state. Thus a value of the temperature is associated with each point on the p-V diagram. The state labeled a in Fig. 17-1, for example, has temperature $T_a = 300$ K.

There is a set of states on the p-V diagram (and of the system) that have the same temperature. The state labeled b in Fig. 17-1 has twice the pressure and half the volume of state a, but it has the same temperature. The set of all states with that value of the temperature forms a curve on a p-V diagram called an *isotherm*. The 300-K isotherm is shown as the curve containing points a and b in Fig. 17-1. Also shown is the 900-K isotherm.

A point on a p-V diagram represents a state of a system.

States with the same temperature lie on an isotherm.

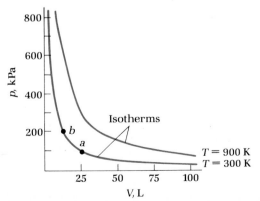

Figure 17-1. State a and state b, represented by points on a p-V diagram, have the same temperature. The 300- and 900-K isotherms are shown.

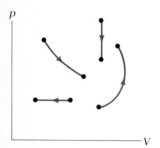

Figure 17-2. Several quasi-static
processes are shown on a *p-V*
diagram.

A *p-V* diagram is also useful in representing processes in which the state of
the system changes. We usually consider *quasi-static* processes which occur
slowly enough so that the system can be considered to be in an equilibrium
state at any instant during the process. In particular, the values of *p* and *V* are
well defined at each instant. A quasi-static process can be represented on the
p-V diagram by a curve corresponding to the succession of pressure and
volume values taken on by the system. Some illustrative processes are shown
on the *p-V* diagram in Fig. 17-2. Notice that each point on a process curve
represents a *different* state of the system. The direction or sense in time of each
process is indicated by the arrowhead.

Not all processes are quasi-static. A system can undergo processes, rapidly or
even violently for example, in which the system does not pass through a
succession of equilibrium states. Such processes cannot be represented by
curves on the *p-V* diagram. The system may begin in an initial equilibrium state
and end in a final equilibrium state, each represented by a point on the *p-V*
diagram. But no curve can be drawn connecting these two states to represent a
process which is not quasi-static.

17-3 SPECIFIC HEAT AND LATENT HEAT

In the last chapter, we defined heat as the energy transferred between a system
and its surroundings due to the temperature difference between them. What
happens to the temperature of the system as heat is added to it from its
surroundings? Our everyday experience suggests that the temperature of the
system can increase as a result. For example, suppose that we monitor the
temperature of water in a pot placed on the burner of a stove. A graph showing
how the temperature of the water changes with time is shown schematically in
Fig. 17-3. As heat is transferred from the burner to the water, the temperature
of the water increases steadily. However, when the water is at its boiling point,
its temperature no longer changes, even though heat is still being added. In the
first case, the heat added causes a temperature change, which corresponds to
the molecules moving faster on average. In the second case, the added heat
produces a change in phase from liquid to vapor without changing the temperature. At the molecular level, such a phase change corresponds to increasing
the average separation of the molecules and decreasing their interaction.

Specific heat. Suppose we measure the temperature change ΔT of a system
of mass m when an amount of heat Q has been added. For the moment we
assume that the system is kept at a fixed pressure and that no phase change
occurs. For small temperature changes we expect, and experiment shows, the
heat added and the temperature change to be proportional. Further, to cause a

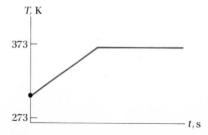

Figure 17-3. The temperature of
a sample of water rises to the
boiling point as heat is added. Heat
is added to the water after it
reaches the boiling point, but the
temperature does not change.

given temperature change, the amount of heat added is proportional to the mass of the system. For example, the heat that must be added to 2 kg of water is twice the heat that must be added to 1 kg of water to cause the same temperature change. Thus the heat added to a system is proportional both to the mass of the system and to the temperature change: $Q \propto m \, \Delta T$. This relationship can be put into equation form by introducing a quantity characteristic of the substance. The *specific heat capacity* at constant pressure c_p is defined in the limiting case of infinitesimal temperature changes as

Specific heat capacity

Definition of specific heat

$$dQ = mc_p \, dT \qquad (17\text{-}2)$$

It is customary to drop the word "capacity" and shorten the phrase to "specific heat." From Eq. (17-2), the SI units of specific heat are $J \cdot kg^{-1} \cdot K^{-1}$. Remember that a temperature *change* expressed in K is the same as the change expressed in C°, so the unit of specific heat can also be expressed as $J \cdot kg^{-1} \cdot C^{\circ -1}$.

The subscript on c_p is a reminder that heat is added at constant pressure. If heat is added while keeping the volume constant, we must use the specific heat at constant volume c_V:

Specific heat at constant volume

$$dQ = mc_V \, dT \qquad (17\text{-}3)$$

For many substances, and particularly for gases, these two specific heats have significantly different values. That is, producing the same temperature change in a given amount of a substance requires a different amount of heat added at constant pressure than at constant volume. Under ordinary conditions for most solids and liquids, c_p and c_V are approximately equal. Some specific heat values are listed in Table 17-1.

The specific heat c_p is defined in the limiting case of infinitesimal temperature changes and is a function of temperature. For small temperature changes, however, the specific heat of many substances may be considered as independent of temperature. In these cases, Eq. (17-2) can be written as

Specific heat connects heat added and temperature change.

$$Q = mc_p \, \Delta T \qquad (17\text{-}4)$$

This equation connects the heat added to a system at constant pressure and the accompanying temperature change. We avoid using the symbol Δ with heat Q since heat is an energy transfer and not the change in a quantity. In contrast, the temperature change is denoted by ΔT.

Table 17-1. Some specific-heat and molar-heat-capacity values at 25°C and atmospheric pressure

Substance	c_p		C_p,
	$J \cdot kg^{-1} \cdot K^{-1}$	$cal \cdot g^{-1} \cdot C^{\circ -1}$	$J \, mol^{-1} \, K^{-1}$
Aluminum	910	0.215	24.4
Copper	386	0.092	24.5
Iron	447	0.107	25.0
Lead	128	0.031	26.8
Mercury	140	0.033	28.0
Tungsten	136	0.032	25.0
Helium	5200	1.24	20.8
Nitrogen	1040	0.25	29.1
Oxygen	920	0.22	29.4
Carbon (diamond)	509	0.121	6.1
Water	4180	0.998	75.3
Ice ($-10°C$)	2100	0.50	38
Alcohol (ethyl)	2500	0.60	91.5
Glass (crown)	67	0.016	

EXAMPLE 17-2. How much heat must be added to a 2-kg cast-iron skillet to raise its temperature by 120 C°?

$$Q = (2 \text{ kg})(447 \text{ J} \cdot \text{kg}^{-1} \cdot \text{C}^{\circ -1})(120 \text{ C}^{\circ})$$
$$= 100 \text{ kJ}$$

SOLUTION. The specific heat of iron, from Table 17-1, is $c_p = 447 \text{ J} \cdot \text{kg}^{-1} \cdot \text{K}^{-1}$. Equation (17-4) gives

This represents the minimum heat required, assuming no losses to other parts of the environment.

Molar heat capacity. Instead of specifying the mass m of a system, we often specify the number of moles present, $n = m/M$, where M is the gram molecular weight of the substance. (A periodic table of the elements appears in App. P.) Instead of the specific heat c_p, we use the *molar heat capacity* C_p, defined by

Molar heat capacity

$$dQ = nC_p \, dT \qquad (17\text{-}5)$$

The molar heat capacity at constant volume C_V is similarly defined: $dQ = nC_V \, dT$. The SI unit of molar heat capacity is $\text{J} \cdot \text{mol}^{-1} \cdot \text{K}^{-1}$. Some molar heat capacity values are listed in Table 17-1.

The specific heat of water and the calorie. The *calorie* (cal) is a unit of energy that was originally based on the properties of water. It was defined as the amount of heat required to raise the temperature of 1 g of water by 1 C°. Thus the specific heat of water would be $c_p = 1 \text{ cal} \cdot \text{g}^{-1} \cdot \text{C}^{\circ -1}$ exactly. The specific heat of liquid water actually depends very slightly on temperature between 0 and 100°C. The calorie is now defined in terms of the joule. The conversion is

Definition of the calorie

$$1 \text{ cal} = 4.186 \text{ J} \qquad (17\text{-}6)$$

The calorie is a convenient energy unit to use for a system of liquid water, since $c_p = 1.00 \text{ cal} \cdot \text{g}^{-1} \cdot \text{C}^{\circ -1}$ to three significant figures over the 100 C° range.

British thermal unit, Btu

Another similar unit of heat is the Btu (British thermal unit). It was originally defined such that 1 Btu raised the temperature of 1 lb of water by 1 F°. The conversion is 1 Btu = 1055 J.

Latent heat. At atmospheric pressure, the temperature of the melting point of water (ice) is 0.00°C. As water melts, changing its phase from solid to liquid, heat must be added, even though the temperature remains fixed. Similarly, as the liquid freezes to the solid phase, heat must be removed. The amount of heat per unit mass which is added to or removed from a substance undergoing a phase change is called the *latent heat L*:

Latent heat

$$Q = mL \qquad (17\text{-}7)$$

The SI unit of latent heat is J/kg. The latent heat for a substance undergoing a

Table 17-2. Some latent-heat values at atmospheric pressure

Substance	L_f (fusion), $\text{MJ} \cdot \text{kg}^{-1}$	L_v (vaporization), $\text{MJ} \cdot \text{kg}^{-1}$
Aluminum	0.400	12.3
Copper	0.205	4.80
Iron	0.275	6.29
Lead	0.023	0.87
Mercury	0.011	0.29
Tungsten	0.192	4.35
Nitrogen	—	0.20
Oxygen	—	0.21
Water	0.335	2.260
Alcohol (ethyl)	—	1.1

liquid-solid phase change is denoted by L_f, called the *latent heat of fusion*. For a liquid-vapor phase change, the *latent heat of vaporization* is denoted by L_v. Some latent-heat values for fusion and vaporization are listed in Table 17-2. We note that in addition to the type of phase changes described here, there are different types of phase changes which involve no latent heat.

EXAMPLE 17-3. How much heat must be added at atmospheric pressure to 0.50 kg of water in the form of ice at $0°C$ to convert it to steam (vapor) at $100°C$?

SOLUTION. There are three contributions — heat added to melt the ice, heat added to raise the temperature of the liquid from 0 to $100°C$, and heat added to change the phase from liquid to vapor. The specific-heat and latent-heat values are taken from Tables 17-1 and 17-2:

$$Q = (0.50 \text{ kg})(0.335 \text{ MJ/kg})$$
$$+ (0.50 \text{ kg})(4180 \text{ J} \cdot \text{kg}^{-1} \cdot \text{C}°^{-1})(100 \text{ C}°)$$
$$+ (0.50 \text{ kg})(2.26 \text{ MJ/kg})$$
$$= 0.17 \text{ MJ} + 0.21 \text{ MJ} + 1.1 \text{ MJ} = 1.5 \text{ MJ}$$

Note the large contributions to the total heat added to the water that are made during the phase changes.

17-4 WORK

Energy which is transferred between a system and its environment because of a temperature difference between them is heat. There is another type of energy transfer between the system and its environment. It is called *work*.

Work done by a system

Work is the energy transferred between a system and it surroundings by means independent of the temperature difference between them. Energy can be transferred as work by electric and magnetic forces, but we shall be concerned primarily with the mechanical work done by the forces that the system exerts on its surroundings. Since work is a product of a force and a displacement [Eq. (8-3)], the work done by the system is always connected with the motion of some part of the surroundings. Note that we consider the work done by the system on its surroundings rather than the work done by the surroundings on the system. Our convention has its roots in the practical importance of the work performed by a steam (the system) engine on the moving mechanical parts (the surroundings). This work is positive if energy is transferred from the system to the surroundings.

Work is connected with motion of the surroundings.

A simple example of the work done by a system is the mechanical work done on a moving wall of a container by the force due to the pressure of a fluid. Suppose the fluid (which is the system) undergoes an infinitesimal expansion as the movable piston (a part of the surroundings) in Fig. 17-4 is displaced by an amount dx. If the piston has a face area of A and the pressure of the fluid is p, then the fluid exerts a force $F_x = pA$ on the piston. The work done by this force is $F_x \, dx = pA \, dx$, or, since $A \, dx$ is the infinitesimal change dV in the volume of the system, the work dW done by the system is

Infinitesimal work done by a system

$$dW = p \, dV \tag{17-8}$$

For an expansion or volume increase $(dV > 0)$, the force exerted by the fluid is

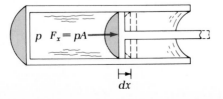

Figure 17-4. A cutaway view shows a cylinder with a movable piston. The fluid with pressure p exerts a force of magnitude $F = pA$ on the piston of face area A.

dx

in the same direction as the displacement, and the work done by the system is positive $(dW > 0)$. If the volume of the fluid decreases in a compression $(dV < 0)$, then the force exerted by the fluid is opposite the displacement of the piston, and the work done by the system is negative $(dW < 0)$. For a constant-volume, or *isochoric*, process $(dV = 0)$, the work done is zero; no part of the surroundings moves, and the system does no mechanical work $(dW = 0)$.

In an isochoric process, volume is constant and $dW = 0$.

For a finite process in which the volume changes quasi-statically from V_i to V_f, Eq. (17-8) must be integrated to determine the work done for the process:

$$W_{if} = \int_{V_i}^{V_f} p \, dV \tag{17-9}$$

To evaluate the integral, we must know how the pressure changes with the volume during the process. As a simple example, consider a constant-pressure, or *isobaric*, process in which the pressure is maintained at its initial value p_i. The integral is easily done since the pressure is constant:

In an isobaric process, pressure is constant and $W_{if} = p_i \, \Delta V$.

$$W_{if} = p_i \int_{V_i}^{V_f} dV = p_i \, (V_f - V_i)$$

or, with $\Delta V = V_f - V_i$,

$$W_{if} = p_i \, \Delta V \tag{17-10}$$

This isobaric process is illustrated on the p-V diagram in Fig. 17-5a. The work done by the system is equal to the area under the process curve, as indicated. For the expansion illustrated there, the volume change ΔV is positive, so the work done by the system is also positive. For a compression, the volume change would be negative, corresponding to negative work done by the system.

The graphical interpretation of the integral as the work being the area under the curve can be applied to any quasi-static process on a p-V diagram. The work done by the system for the process shown in Fig. 17-5b equals the shaded area under the curve. For an expansion the area is positive. For a compression, or decrease in volume, as illustrated in Fig. 17-5c, the area would be negative, corresponding to a negative value of the work.

In an isothermal process, temperature is constant.

An *isothermal*, or constant-temperature, process for an ideal gas is shown in Fig. 17-6. The isotherm corresponding to temperature T is shown on the p-V diagram for reference, and the gas expands from an initial volume V_i to a final volume V_f while the temperature is fixed. An isothermal process such as this

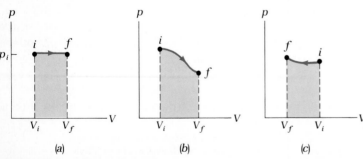

Figure 17-5. (a) The work done by the system for an isobaric process is $p_i(V_f - V_i)$, the area of the rectangle. (b) The work done by the system for a quasi-static process equals the area under the curve. (c) The area, or the work done by the system, is negative for a compression.

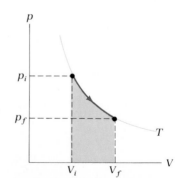

Figure 17-6. An isothermal expansion for an ideal gas.

can be performed by having the system remain in good thermal contact with surroundings that are maintained at the desired temperature. For example, a metal cylinder containing a gas can be immersed in a fluid bath at a temperature slightly above T during the expansion. Heat is conducted from the bath to the gas through the cylinder walls so that the temperature of the gas remains the same.

To evaluate the work done by the gas as it expands, which is equal to the area under the curve on the p-V diagram, we use the ideal gas equation of state, Eq. (17-1): $pV = nRT$. We solve for the pressure as a function of the volume (T is constant for an isothermal process) and substitute in Eq. (17-9):

$$W_{if} = \int_{V_i}^{V_f} \frac{nRT}{V} \, dV = nRT \int_{V_i}^{V_f} \frac{dV}{V} = nRT(\ln V_f - \ln V_i)$$

Since $\ln V_f - \ln V_i = \ln (V_f/V_i)$, we have

Work done by an ideal gas for an isothermal process

$$W_{if} = nRT \left(\ln \frac{V_f}{V_i} \right) \tag{17-11}$$

If $V_f > V_i$, then $\ln (V_f/V_i) > 0$, and the work is positive. But if $V_f < V_i$, $\ln (V_f/V_i) < 0$, and W_{if} is negative.

Another process for which the work can be easily calculated is an adiabatic process for an ideal gas. (This process is discussed in parts of the next two chapters.) For an adiabatic process (no heat is transferred to or from the system), there is a relation between the pressure and volume that depends on a parameter γ, where $\gamma = C_p/C_V$ for the ideal gas. The calculation of the work done by an ideal gas for an adiabatic process is outlined in Exercise 17-22; try it. We quote the result here for convenience:

Work done by an ideal gas for an adiabatic process

$$W = \frac{p_i V_i}{\gamma - 1} \left[1 - \left(\frac{V_i}{V_f} \right)^{\gamma - 1} \right]$$

where p_i and V_i are the pressure and volume of the initial state and V_f is the volume of the final state of the gas.

EXAMPLE 17-4. Helium gas at 310 K is contained in a cylinder fitted with a movable piston. The gas is initially at 2 atm of pressure (202 kPa) and occupies a volume of 48 L. The gas expands isothermally until the volume is 106 L. Then the gas is compressed isobarically at that final pressure back to the original volume of 48 L. Evaluate the work done by the gas for (a) the isothermal expansion, (b) the isobaric compression, (c) the entire process. (d) What is the final temperature of the He? The quasi-static process is illustrated on the p-V diagram in Fig. 17-7.

SOLUTION. (a) The work done by the gas for the isothermal expansion is given by Eq. (17-11). From the ideal gas equation of state, the value of nRT is

$$nRT = p_i V_i = (202 \text{ kPa})(48 \times 10^{-3} \text{ m}^3) = 9.7 \text{ kJ}$$

and the work is

$$W = (9.7 \text{ kJ}) \left(\ln \frac{106}{48} \right) = 7.7 \text{ kJ}$$

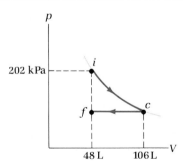

Figure 17-7. Example 17-4: An isothermal expansion is followed by an isobaric compression.

(b) The pressure at the end of the isothermal expansion and during the isobaric compression is

$$p_f = p_c = \frac{p_i V_i}{V_c} = 202 \text{ kPa} \, \frac{48}{106} = 91 \text{ kPa}$$

From Eq. (17-10),

$$W = (91 \text{ kPa})(0.048 \text{ m}^3 - 0.106 \text{ m}^3) = -5.3 \text{ kJ}$$

The work done by the gas during the isobaric compression is negative because the volume decreases. (c) For the entire process the work done is simply the sum of the two contributions from parts (a) and (b):

$$W = 7.7 \text{ kJ} + (-5.3 \text{ kJ}) = 2.4 \text{ kJ}$$

(d) The final temperature can be obtained using the ideal gas equation of state and comparing the initial and final states, which have the same volume:

$$T_f = T_i \frac{p_f}{p_i} = 310 \text{ K} \frac{91}{202} = 140 \text{ K}$$

17-5 THE FIRST LAW OF THERMODYNAMICS

We have identified the two types of energy transfer between a system and its surroundings: heat and work. Our sign conventions for heat and work are illustrated schematically in Fig. 17-8, in which the positive transfer of energy is represented by the sense of the arrow. Heat Q is positive if energy is added to a system from its surroundings, as seen in Fig. 17-8a and c. Heat Q is negative if heat is extracted from the system, as shown in Fig. 17-8b and d. The work W done by the system is positive if energy is transferred to the surroundings, as shown in Fig. 17-8a and b. Work W is negative if the transferred energy is from the surroundings to the system, as seen in Fig. 17-8c and d. During some process for which work W is performed by the system and heat Q is added to the system, the *net* energy transferred to the system from the surroundings is $Q - W$.

Whether an energy transfer is heat or work can depend on what we choose to be the system. For example, suppose that the temperature of a container of water is raised using a resistive "heating" element which is immersed in the water. The resistive element is connected to a battery which supplies energy. If we choose the system to be the water and make the resistive element a part of the surroundings, then energy is transferred solely as a result of the temperature difference between the element and the water. The energy transferred is heat. On the other hand, if we choose the system to consist of both the water and the element, then the energy is transferred to this enlarged system through electric forces and not because of a temperature difference between the battery and the system. In this case the energy transfer is work. This example shows the great importance of carefully defining the system and distinguishing it from its surroundings.

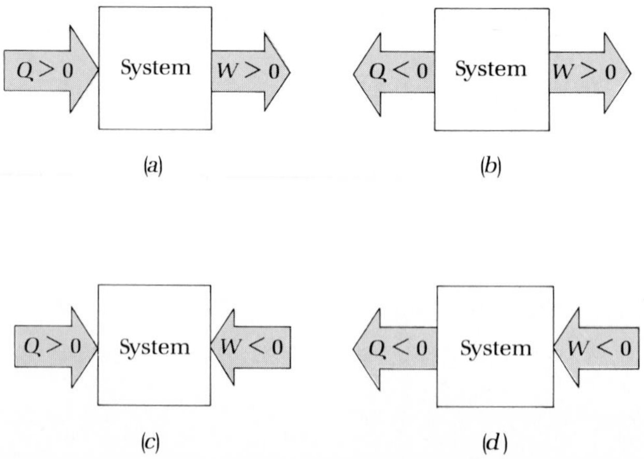

Net energy transferred to a system is $Q - W$.

Figure 17-8. The arrows illustrate the sense of energy transfers between a system and its surroundings. In (a) for example, positive energy enters the system as heat, and positive energy leaves the system as work.

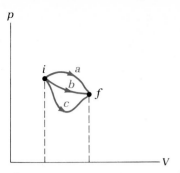

Figure 17-9. Three different processes are shown connecting an initial and a final state of a system. The work done by the system depends on the process.

The value of the work done by the system depends not only on the initial and final states of a system but also on how the process is performed. This result is evident from Fig. 17-9, which shows three different processes connecting the same initial and final states on a p-V diagram for some substance. For each process, the work done by the system — equal to the area under the process curve — has a different value. Labeling the processes by a, b, and c, we have

$$W_a \neq W_b \neq W_c$$

The work done by a system which undergoes a process from an initial state to a final state depends on the details of that process.

Measurements show that the heat added to the system also depends on how the process is performed. For the three processes displayed in Fig. 17-9, the heat added has different values (although this result is not obvious from the figure). Using the same labels as before, we have

$$Q_a \neq Q_b \neq Q_c$$

Heat added to a system which undergoes a process from an initial state to a final state depends on the details of that process.

We can also consider the net energy transferred to the system for each of these processes. For process a, the net energy added is $Q_a - W_a$. The value of this *net* energy transferred to the system is measured to be the same for all three processes that connect the initial state and the final state of the system. That is,

$$Q_a - W_a = Q_b - W_b = Q_c - W_c$$

The generalization, based on many experiments, is that while the heat added depends on the process and the work done depends on the process, their difference, $Q - W$, does not depend on the process. That difference depends only on the initial and final states of the system.

The above result is a consequence of the *first law of thermodynamics: For a process in which heat Q is added to a system and work W is done by the system, the net energy transferred to the system equals the change in the internal energy of the system* ΔU. In equation form, the first law of thermodynamics is written

$$Q - W = \Delta U = U_f - U_i \qquad (17\text{-}12)$$

The first law introduces internal energy and expresses the conservation of energy in the sense that the net energy transferred to a system changes the internal energy by that amount. But there is more to the first law than conservation of energy. Included in the statement of the first law is the understanding that the change in internal energy, $\Delta U = U_f - U_i$, depends only on the initial and final states and not at all on the process connecting them.

The internal energy of a system can be interpreted on the molecular level. For a dilute gas, or for an ideal gas, the potential energy of interaction of the molecules with each other is negligible. The internal energy is simply the sum of the kinetic energy of each molecule in the system. An increase in internal energy of an ideal gas corresponds to an increase in the total kinetic energy of the molecules (and an increase in the temperature). For a denser gas, the potential energy of interaction of the molecules with each other contributes to the internal energy. Other contributions to the internal energy become significant for more complicated systems.

The change in internal energy of a system depends only on the initial and

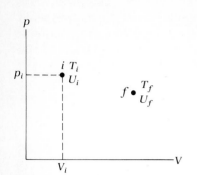

Figure 17-10. A value of the internal energy of a system can be assigned to a point on a p-V diagram.

final states. Therefore, we can assign a value of the internal energy to a state of the system. Consider the state labeled by i with pressure and volume values p_i and V_i seen in Fig. 17-10. The temperature of the system in that state is T_i, and we arbitrarily assign a value of internal energy U_i to that state. The internal energy of any other state of the system, say state f, can then be determined by applying a process to take the system from i to f. For any process which takes the system from state i to state f, the change in internal energy is $U_f - U_i$, independent of the process. Thus the internal energy of state f depends only on the state and not on how the system came to be in that state. The internal energy is, therefore, a variable of state. Once the state of a system is specified, by values of p and V for example, the values of the other variables of state are determined. Thus, in the same sense that we assign a value of the temperature to a point on the p-V diagram, we can assign a value of the internal energy to a point on the diagram. *Any* process which takes the system from i to f will correspond to a change in internal energy of the system of $U_f - U_i$.

In contrast, heat and work are *not* variables of state. The heat added for a process connecting states i and f depends in detail on how the process is performed. The work done by the system for the process likewise depends on the process. For any process the net energy transferred to the system, $Q - W$, equals the difference of internal energy values for the initial and final states, $U_f - U_i$. These ideas form the content of the first law of thermodynamics.

EXAMPLE 17-5. (a) The temperature of 0.25 kg of water is gradually raised from 1.1 to 7.7°C at atmospheric pressure with a resistance heater. During this process, the volume of the water changes insignificantly. Determine the change in internal energy of the water. (b) An amount 0.25 kg of water initially at 1.1°C in a thermos is vigorously stirred until the temperature rises to 7.7°C. The initial and final pressures are atmospheric. Determine the change in internal energy of the water and the work done by the water.

SOLUTION. (a) For this process, the heat added to the water at constant pressure is given by

$$Q = mc_p \, \Delta t = (0.25 \text{ kg})(4180 \text{ J} \cdot \text{kg}^{-1} \cdot \text{C}^{°-1})(6.6 \text{ C}°)$$

$$= 6.9 \text{ kJ}$$

where we have assumed that the specific heat of water from Table 17-1 is essentially constant over this temperature range. Since the volume change is negligible, the work done

by the water in this quasi-static process is also negligible, $W = 0$. The first law of thermodynamics, Eq. (17-12), gives

$$U_f - U_i = Q - W = 6.9 \text{ kJ} - 0 = 6.9 \text{ kJ}$$

(b) In this second process, which is not quasi-static, the initial state and the final state are the same as for the process in part (a). The change in internal energy must also be the same, because it depends only on the initial and final states and not on the process:

$$U_f - U_i = 6.9 \text{ kJ}$$

Since this process occurs with the system insulated by the thermos, the heat added is negligible, $Q = 0$. The first law applied to this process gives

$$U_f - U_i = Q - W$$

$$6.9 \text{ kJ} = 0 - W$$

or $W = -6.9$ kJ. The water does negative (why?) work on the stirring mechanism.

17-6 SOME APPLICATIONS OF THE FIRST LAW

The first law of thermodynamics describes the energy exchanges for any process which takes a system from an initial equilibrium state to a final equilibrium state. We apply the first law here to several types of processes. In each case we evaluate two of the three quantities — Q, W, ΔU — and use the first law to determine the third quantity.

Isochoric process. An *isochoric process* is one in which the volume of the system remains fixed; it is a constant-volume process. In each step of a quasi-static, constant-volume process, $dW = p\,dV$ and $dV = 0$. So no work is done by the system: $W = \int p\,dV = 0$. Applying the first law of thermodynamics, we have for an isochoric process

$$\Delta U = Q - W = Q - 0 = Q$$

That is, the heat added equals the change in internal energy because $W = 0$.

EXAMPLE 17-6. The temperature of 2.50 mol of He is raised at constant volume from 275.0 to 325.0 K. The initial state is at atmospheric pressure, and the molar heat capacity of He is $C_V = 12.5$ J $\cdot$ mol^{-1} $\cdot$ K^{-1} over this range of temperatures and pressures. Evaluate the change in internal energy of this gas.

SOLUTION. Since the volume remains fixed, the heat added to the system is, from Sec. 17-3,

$$Q = nC_V\,\Delta T = (2.50\text{ mol})(12.5\text{ J}\cdot\text{mol}^{-1}\cdot\text{K}^{-1})(50.0\text{ K})$$

$$= 1.56\text{ kJ}$$

Since the process occurs at constant volume, $W = 0$. The first law gives for the change in internal energy,

$$U_f - U_i = Q - W = 1.56\text{ kJ} - 0 = 1.56\text{ kJ}$$

In an adiabatic process, no heat is transferred to the system.

Adiabatic process. An *adiabatic process* is one in which no heat is added to the system. In each infinitesimal stage of the process, $dQ = 0$; for the entire adiabatic process, $Q = 0$. One way to prevent heat transfer between the system and its surroundings is to insulate the system with adiabatic walls. Or the process may be performed rapidly enough so that a negligible amount of heat is transferred. For example, the compression stroke in an automobile engine is essentially an adiabatic compression of the air-fuel mixture. It occurs too rapidly for appreciable heat transfer to take place. Application of the first law to an adiabatic process gives

$$\Delta U = Q - W = 0 - W = -W$$

EXAMPLE 17-7. During the compression stroke for a cylinder in an experimental engine, the volume decreases by a factor of 8 (the compression ratio). The work done by the air-fuel mixture for this compression is measured to be $W = -200$ J. Evaluate the change in internal energy of the air-fuel mixture.

SOLUTION. Because the compression occurs quickly, this process can be considered to be adiabatic: $Q = 0$. The work done by the mixture is $W = -200$ J and is negative since the volume decreased. Applying the first law, we obtain for the change in internal energy

$$U_f - U_i = Q - W = 0 - (-200\text{ J}) = 200\text{ J}$$

Isobaric process. For an *isobaric*, or *constant-pressure*, *process*, both types of energy transfer may occur between the system and its surroundings. The work done by the system for a quasi-static isobaric process is given by Eq. (17-10). The heat added to the system can be evaluated using specific-heat or latent-heat data.

EXAMPLE 17-8. The volume occupied by 1.00 kg of water at 100°C and atmospheric pressure changes from 1.0 L in the liquid phase to 1700 L in the vapor (steam) phase. Evaluate the difference in internal energy of 1.00 kg of water vapor and 1.00 kg of liquid water at the normal boiling point.

SOLUTION. Consider a process in which heat is added at constant atmospheric pressure to convert 1.00 kg of water from liquid at 100°C to vapor at 100°C. The water is contained in a cylinder fitted with a piston which moves outward to keep the pressure fixed. The volume change is

$1700 \text{ L} - 1 \text{ L} = 1.7 \text{ m}^3$. From Eq. (17-10) the work done by the system is

$$W = p \, \Delta V = (101 \text{ kPa})(1.7 \text{ m}^3) = 170 \text{ kJ}$$

The heat added during the process is evaluated using the latent heat of vaporization from Table 17-2:

$$Q = mL_v = (1.00 \text{ kg})(2260 \text{ kJ/kg}) = 2260 \text{ kJ}$$

The difference in internal energy for these two states of water is

$$U_f - U_i = Q - W = 2260 \text{ kJ} - 170 \text{ kJ} = 2090 \text{ kJ} \approx 2100 \text{ kJ}$$

The calculation shows that of the 2260 kJ of heat added to the system, about 170 kJ of work is performed by the system, and the remainder, about 2100 kJ, appears as an increase in internal energy. Although we used a specific process to calculate the difference in internal energy of these two states of water, note that the 2100-J difference in internal energy is independent of the process.

Free expansion. Consider a gas which initially occupies one compartment of a two-chambered container as illustrated in Fig. 17-11. A membrane separates the two chambers, and the one on the right is evacuated. The entire assembly is insulated from the exterior. The initial state of the gas is characterized by the values of some of its variables of state: p_i, V_i, T_i, and U_i. Suppose now that the membrane separating the two chambers spontaneously breaks and the gas expands freely to fill the entire container. This process is called a *free expansion*. During the free expansion, the gas is not in equilibrium, so the process is not quasi-static and cannot be represented on a p-V diagram. But the gas will eventually come to a final equilibrium state in which the variables of state have values p_f, V_f, T_f, and U_f. How have these final values changed from the initial values? Certainly the volume has increased, and measurement shows that the pressure has decreased. The temperature change can also be measured (although not easily for a very small change).

The change in the internal energy of the gas can be calculated by applying the first law of thermodynamics to the free-expansion process. The process is adiabatic because of the insulation, so $Q = 0$. No part of the surroundings moves (we consider the rupturing membrane to be an inert part of the system), so the system does no work on its surroundings: $W = 0$. Therefore, the internal energy does not change:

$$U_f - U_i = Q - W = 0 - 0 = 0 \tag{17-13}$$

The initial and final states of this gas have the same internal energy.

It is customary to think of the internal energy of a gas as a function of the independent variables V and T: $U(V, T)$. Experiments in which a gas undergoes a free expansion give information about this functional dependence. If, in a free expansion, the volume changes from V_i to V_f and the temperature changes from T_i to T_f, then Eq. (17-13) gives

$$U(V_f, T_f) = U(V_i, T_i) \tag{17-14}$$

For real gases, measurements show that the temperature changes slightly in a free expansion. Thus Eq. (17-14) indicates a dependence of internal energy on the volume. However, in the limit of dilute gases or for an ideal gas, the

Free expansion

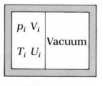

(a)

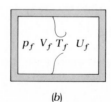

(b)

Figure 17-11. (a) A thin membrane confines a gas to one side of an insulated container. (b) The membrane ruptures spontaneously, and the gas expands freely to occupy the entire region.

temperature drop tends to zero for a free expansion. Let $T_i = T_f = T$; then Eq. (17-14) gives

$$U(V_f, T) = U(V_i, T)$$

which implies that the internal energy of an ideal gas does not depend on the volume at all. The free-expansion process has led us to the following conclusion: *The internal energy U(T) of an ideal gas depends only on the temperature.*

U depends only on T for an ideal gas.

Isothermal process. In an *isothermal process* the temperature remains fixed. An example of an isothermal process is one in which a substance changes phase, say from solid to liquid, quasi-statically. Heat is added to the system and the system may do work on its surroundings, but the temperature does not change. Example 17-8 dealt with a phase change at constant pressure from liquid to vapor. That process was not only isobaric, it was isothermal as well.

EXAMPLE 17-9. A metal cylinder fitted with a movable piston contains 0.24 mol of N_2 gas at an initial pressure of 140 kPa. The piston is slowly withdrawn until the volume has doubled. The cylinder remains in good thermal contact with its surroundings at 310 K during the process. How much heat is added to the gas for this process?

SOLUTION. In experiments at these temperature and pressure values, nitrogen behaves as an ideal gas. The process is isothermal at 310 K, and the internal energy of the

gas, depending only on T, does not change: $\Delta U = 0$. The work done by an ideal gas for an isothermal expansion is given by Eq. (17-11): $W = nRT \ln (V_f/V_i)$. Applying the first law to the process, we have

$$Q = \Delta U + W = 0 + nRT \left(\ln \frac{V_f}{V_i} \right)$$

$$= (0.24 \text{ mol})(8.31 \text{ J} \cdot \text{mol}^{-1} \cdot \text{K}^{-1})(310 \text{ K})(\ln 2)$$

$$= 430 \text{ J}$$

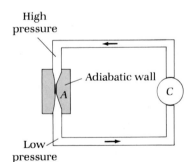

High pressure

Adiabatic wall

A

C

Low pressure

Figure 17-12. In a continuous throttling process, gas at higher pressure streams through a valve A to the low-pressure side. The pressure difference is maintained by the compressor C.

$\Delta U = 0$ for a cycle.

Throttling process. The *throttling process* is of practical importance because it is used in most refrigeration cycles. The process occurs when a fluid at higher pressure streams through a porous wall or through a small valve into a region of lower pressure. Usually the process is a continuous one, as illustrated in Fig. 17-12, with the pressure difference across the valve maintained by a pump or compressor and the valve region insulated. Problem 17-5 shows that as a given amount of gas undergoes the throttling process, the quantity $U + pV$, called the *enthalpy*, remains fixed.

If the fluid on the high-pressure side is a liquid close to evaporating and is partially vaporized on the low-pressure side, then the temperature is substantially lowered on the low-pressure side. It is this property which is used in many refrigeration systems.

Cyclic process. A *cycle* is a process in which the system is returned to the same state from which it started. That is, the initial and final states are the same in a cyclic process. The cycle has great practical importance, and we shall consider these practical aspects in Chap. 19. A general cycle is sketched on the p-V diagram in Fig. 17-13a. Any point may be chosen as the initial state of the system; the essential feature is that the system returns to that state at the conclusion of the cycle. The cycle may be repeated any number of times.

When a system completes a cycle, the change in the internal energy of the system for the cycle must be zero. The internal energy of the final state is the same as the internal energy of the initial state because the final state is the same

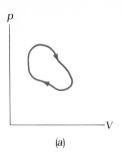
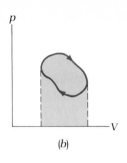

Figure 17-13. (a) A cycle is represented by a closed curve on a p-V diagram. (b) The net work done by the system for a cycle equals the area enclosed by the cycle on a p-V diagram.

as the initial state. The heat added to the system and the work done by the system during a cycle need not be zero. In Fig. 17-13b, a cycle is divided into an expansion phase, in which the system does positive work, and a compression phase, in which the system does negative work. The net work done by the system equals the area enclosed by the cycle. It is positive for the case shown in the figure. Let W represent the net work done for the cycle and Q represent the net heat added for the cycle. Applying the first law to the cycle, we have $Q - W = \Delta U = 0$, or

$$W = Q$$

Thus for a cycle, the net work done by the system equals the net heat added to the system.

COMMENTARY: BENJAMIN THOMPSON, COUNT RUMFORD

Benjamin Thompson, Count Rumford. *(Culver Pictures)*

The flow of heat from a body at a higher temperature to one at a lower temperature is somewhat analogous to the flow of a fluid, say water, from a higher to a lower elevation. It is not surprising that the early theory of heat flow treated heat as a fluidlike substance called caloric. As a body lost caloric, its temperature would drop, and the temperature of a body gaining caloric would increase. While many features of heat flow can be explained with the idea of such a fluid, the caloric theory turned out to be inconsistent with experiment.

Credit for seriously challenging the concept of caloric is usually given to Benjamin Thompson, also known as Count Rumford of Bavaria. Fearing the spread of the French Revolution, the ruling elector of Bavaria assigned Count Rumford to overseeing the construction of cannons for the defense of the borders. As a cannon was bored, Rumford noticed that the cannon stock, the metal chips, and the boring tool all had an increase in temperature. That is, heat seemed to be continuously generated instead of being conserved as the caloric theory supposed.

Rumford conducted quantitative experiments by measuring the temperature change that occurred when a blunt tool was used in the boring process. In one experiment, water was used to cool the boring tool and the cannon stock. Rumford measured the increasing temperature of the water and noted "the surprise and astonishment expressed in the countenances of the by-standers, on seeing so large a quantity of cold water heated, and actually made to boil without any fire." He concluded that heat was not a material substance since there seemed to be no limit to it. Rather, it was the result of friction, or of the work done by friction.

Count Rumford was born Benjamin Thompson in Woburn, Massachusetts, in 1753. His early life showed little promise of eventual nobility. He served two unfulfilled apprenticeships with shopkeepers. One shopkeeper complained to Thompson's mother that Benjamin spent more time under the counter making little machines and reading science books than he did behind the counter serving customers. Thompson's fortunes improved when, at age 19, he married a wealthy 33-year-old widow in Concord, New Hampshire, a region that was also known as Rumford.

Thompson was a loyalist in the disputes between Britain and her American colonies. He served as a major in a company of militia. When his loyalist sentiments became known, a group of colonists, dressed as Indians, arrived at his doorstep, threatening a tar-and-feathers treatment. Thompson escaped to Boston with a horse, $20, and his life.

By his own account, Thompson served the British as a courageous and inventive officer during the American Revolution. After one of his horses drowned crossing a river, he invented a cork life preserver for a horse carrying a cannon on its back. He also designed a gun carriage that could be carried by three horses and could be assembled and fired in 75 seconds.

After being knighted by England's King George III, Thompson was introduced to the court of Theodor, Elector of Bavaria. There he conducted experiments on the properties of silk, an important product of Bavaria at the time. He entertained the court with calculations such as, "If a silk gown worn by a lady weighs 28 ounces, it is very certain that she carries upon her back upwards of 2000 miles in length of silk, as spun by the worm. . . ."

Appointed a major general by the elector, Thompson improved the lot of the Bavarian soldiers. While investigating materials that could provide the greatest warmth for his soldiers, he discovered the great insulating value of a layer of entrapped air. Thompson also provided opportunities for the soldiers that would allow them to earn money for necessities. In experiments to determine the best lighting conditions for workhouses for the poor, Thompson established the candle as a standard for measuring illumination.

Thompson's benefactor, the Elector Theodor, enjoyed a brief reign as vicar of the Holy Roman Empire between the death of Emperor Leopold II and the coronation of Emperor Francis II. As vicar, Theodor had limited powers, but he did have the privilege of elevating a person to the nobility. Thus, on May 9, 1792, Theodor exercised this privilege, and Benjamin Thompson became Count Rumford.

The Count established two large awards for scientific discoveries in the subjects of heat and light. The awards were to be medals of silver or gold equal in value to the interest that had accrued on the original principal. One of the awards was to be handled by the Royal Society in London. When no medal was awarded after six years, Count Rumford had himself appointed to the selecting committee, and in 1802 he became the first recipient of the Rumford Medal. His accomplishments were not recognized by his contemporaries, however, and when he died of "nervous fever" in 1814, few people witnessed his burial.

For further reading, see Benjamin Thompson, Count Rumford *by Sanborn C. Brown (M.I.T. Press, Cambridge, Mass., 1979).*

SUMMARY WITH APPLICATIONS

Section 17-2. Equations of state

The variables of state p, V, T, and n for a substance are connected by a mathematical equation called the equation of state. For an ideal gas, or a real dilute gas, the equation of state is $pV = nRT$. An equilibrium state of a system such as a gas can be represented by a point on the p-V diagram. A quasi-static process, in which the system passes through a succession of equilibrium states, is represented by a curve on a p-V diagram.

Determine values of variables of state of dilute gases using the ideal gas equation of state; represent states and quasi-static processes on a p-V diagram.

Section 17-3. Specific heat and latent heat

The heat added to a system at constant pressure is related to the temperature change by the specific heat

$$dQ = mc_p\, dT \qquad (17\text{-}2)$$

if the mass m is specified, or by the molar heat capacity

$$dQ = nC_p\, dT \qquad (17\text{-}5)$$

if the number of moles n is specified. The specific heat at constant volume c_V and the molar heat capacity at constant volume C_V are similarly defined. The heat added to a system of mass m undergoing a phase change is

$$Q = mL \qquad (17\text{-}7)$$

where L is the latent heat for the phase change.

Determine the heat added to a system using specific-heat and latent-heat data.

Section 17-4. Work

Work is an energy transfer between a system and its surroundings because of the motion of some part of the surroundings. The work done by a fluid on its surroundings is

$$W = \int_{V_i}^{V_f} p\, dV \qquad (17\text{-}9)$$

The work done by the system is positive if energy is transferred from the system to the surroundings.

Evaluate the work done by a system for quasi-static processes.

Section 17-5. The first law of thermodynamics

The first law of thermodynamics gives the relation between the energy transferred between a system and its surroundings and the change in internal energy of the system:

$$Q - W = U_f - U_i \qquad (17\text{-}12)$$

The heat added to the system and the work done by a system depend on the details of the process. The internal energy is a variable of state; the change in internal energy $U_f - U_i$ depends only on the two states and not on the process connecting them.

State the first law of thermodynamics; describe the fundamental differences between the energy transfers, heat and work, and the variable of state, internal energy.

Section 17-6. Some applications of the first law

The first law of thermodynamics can be easily applied to some special processes such as the isochoric, adiabatic, isobaric, isothermal, throttling, and cyclic processes. From free-expansion experiments on dilute gases, the first law implies that the internal energy of an ideal gas depends only on temperature.

Define the isochoric, adiabatic, isobaric, isothermal, throttling, cyclic, and free-expansion processes; apply the first law to these and to other processes.

QUESTIONS

17-1   Are there any circumstances in which the equation of state $pV = nRT$ correctly describes He in (a) its gaseous phase? (b) A liquid phase? Explain.

17-2   Are there any circumstances in which the equation of state $pV = nRT$ correctly describes H_2O in (a) its liquid phase? (b) One of its solid phases? Explain.

17-3   Air at ordinary temperatures and pressures is a mixture of several different gases, principally nitrogen and oxygen. Is its equation of state given by $pV = nRT$? What is the meaning of n in this case?

17-4   What is the value of the universal gas constant R in units of cal $\cdot$ mol^{-1} $\cdot$ K^{-1}?

17-5   Can a process which is not quasi-static be shown on a p-V diagram? Explain.

17-6   Heat can be added to a system while holding the pressure fixed. Heat can also be added at constant volume. Can heat be added while holding the temperature fixed? Explain.

17-7   Work can be done by a system while holding the pressure fixed or while holding the temperature fixed. Can work be done by the system while holding the volume fixed? Explain.

17-8   Must the internal energy of a system increase if heat is added to the system? Explain.

17-9   Must the internal energy of a system increase if its temperature increases? Explain.

17-10 Suppose that a system does work W on its surroundings in a process. How much work is done by the surroundings on the system? Can you think of any exceptions to your answer?

17-11 The outside surface of a metallic container of gas is buffed vigorously by a polishing wheel. Is the energy transferred to the gas inside the container called heat or work? Explain.

17-12 A gas in a cylinder expands as the piston is withdrawn. A frictional force acts between the piston and the walls of the cylinder. Is the energy transferred to the gas due to the friction heat or work? Explain.

17-13 Can you "heat up" a bowl of soup without adding heat? Must the temperature of a system change if heat is added?

17-14 Suppose a system undergoes a process in which the final state has the same volume as the initial state. Can you determine how much work the system has done?

Use a p-V diagram to explain your answer.

17-15 An ice cube is placed in a well-insulated beaker of lukewarm water. Take the system to consist of the ice cube and the water. The ice melts, and the final state of this system is liquid water at some final lower temperature. Is this process adiabatic? What provided the energy to melt the ice?

17-16 Explain why your skin would be more severely burned if put in contact with 1 g of steam at 100°C than with 1 g of liquid water at 100°C.

17-17 Work can be represented conveniently on a p-V diagram. What useful information can be shown on a p-T diagram? (See Chap. 16.)

17-18 Show an isobaric process on a p-T diagram. Show an isothermal process on a p-T diagram. Show, for an ideal gas, an isochoric process on a p-T diagram.

17-19 Given the initial and final states of a system on a p-V diagram and the value of the change in internal energy, can you determine how much heat was added and how much work was done? Explain.

17-20 In a cycle the final state of the system is the same as the initial state. Given the heat added in a cycle, can you determine how much work is done by the system? Explain.

17-21 From the properties or condition of a system undergoing a cycle, can you determine how many cycles have been performed previously? Explain.

17-22 A small magnet immersed in a liquid stirs the liquid by being driven by an external rotating magnet. Explain why this energy transfer to the liquid is work even though there is no change in volume.

17-23 Which, if any, of the following types of processes must be quasi-static? Explain your answer.

(a) Isobaric

(b) Isothermal

(c) Isochoric

17-24 An electric water heater has resistive elements immersed in the water in the tank. (a) If the system is considered to be the whole unit, is the energy transferred to the system heat or work? (b) If the system is considered to be just the water, is the energy transferred to the system heat or work? (c) In each case above, what happens to the internal energy of the system?

17-25 Draw an analogy between the first law of thermodynamics and your personal finances, using the three concepts: income q, expenditures w, and cash on hand u. Does it make sense to speak of the amount of expenditures on hand? What equation connects the three quantities q, w, u? Why is the analogy imperfect?

17-26 Nutritionists (and dieters) work with the "large Calorie," 1 Calorie = 1 kcal. Suppose that you are on a strict 1600-Calorie-a-day diet. At what average rate in J per day does your body metabolize your food? Express this rate in W also.

17-27 Complete the following table:

Symbol	Represents	Type	SI unit
R		Scalar	
c_p			
c_V			
C_V			
L	Latent heat		
W			
ΔU			J
U			

EXERCISES

Section 17-2. Equations of state

17-1 An ideal gas undergoes a process in which the temperature is doubled and the pressure is tripled. (a) By what factor is the volume changed? (b) Show the initial and final states on a p-V diagram.

17-2 Determine the volume in liters (1 L = 10^{-3} m^3) occupied by 1 mol of an ideal gas at atmospheric pressure (101 kPa) and 0.0°C.

17-3 Helium gas initially is in a state characterized by $p = 0.73$ kPa, $V = 12$ L, and $T = 320$ K. (a) Determine the amount of gas present. (b) The gas expands isothermally until the volume is 18 L. Determine the pressure of the He in this state. (c) Show the process on a p-V diagram.

17-4 An ideal gas is initially in the state labeled by p_i, V_i, T_i. It undergoes an isothermal expansion to an intermediate state m in which the pressure is $p_m = \frac{1}{2}p_i$. The gas is then compressed to a final state f at that constant value of pressure p_m until the volume is returned to its initial value. (a) Show these processes on a p-V diagram. (b) Determine the values of the variables p, V, T for states m and f. Express these in terms of the values for the initial state.

17-5 Gas pressure is often expressed in atmospheres (1 atm = 101 kPa) and volume in liters. Determine the value of the universal gas constant in units of L · atm · mol^{-1} · K^{-1}. [*Note:* (1 Pa)(1 m^3) = 1 J.]

17-6 A cylinder contains 2.54 mol of O$_2$ at 113 kPa and 325 K. The gas is compressed isothermally to half its original volume. The moving piston does not fit tightly, and 0.26 mol escapes in the process. (a) Determine the final pressure of the gas. (b) Can this process be represented meaningfully on a p-V diagram? Explain.

17-7 Determine the number of molecules per m³ for an ideal gas at standard conditions of 1.0 atm and 0.0°C.

17-8 The coefficient of volume expansion (see Chap. 16) for a gas at constant pressure is defined by $\beta = (1/V)(dV/dT)$, where the derivative is taken with the pressure regarded as a constant. (a) Show that $\beta = 1/T$ for an ideal gas. (b) Evaluate β at 0.0°C for an ideal gas.

Section 17-3. Specific heat and latent heat

17-9 How much heat must be added at constant pressure to a 3-g iron nail to raise its temperature by 20 C°?

17-10 How much heat must be added at constant pressure to 1.5 mol of iron to raise its temperature from 280 to 320 K?

17-11 An insulated vessel contains 0.75 kg of water at 20°C, and 1.24 kg of lead, initially at 95°C, is added. (a) Assuming no energy exchanges with the surroundings, determine the final temperature of the water-lead system. (b) Considering only the water as the system, how much heat was added to the water in the process?

17-12 Suppose that the water-lead system in the previous exercise is initially at 15°C and that 1800 J of heat is added using an immersion heater. (a) What is the final temperature of the system? (b) How much heat is added to the lead?

17-13 How much water, initially at 25°C, must be added to 0.35 kg of ice at 0.0°C to completely melt the ice? The final state consists of liquid at 0.0°C.

17-14 A 0.35-kg lump of ice at 0.0°C is placed in an insulated container of water initially at 25°C. (a) If the original amount of water is 2.0 kg, determine the final temperature and composition of the system. (b) Repeat the calculation for 1.0 kg of water present initially.

17-15 The temperature of 1.2 kg of H_2O is measured with a thermometer of mass 0.033 kg and of specific heat 1070 $J \cdot kg^{-1} \cdot C^{\circ -1}$. The thermometer reads 23.5°C before it is inserted in the water. After coming to thermal equilibrium with the water, the thermometer reads 57.9°C. (a) Neglecting other energy exchanges with the surroundings, determine the temperature of the water before the thermometer is inserted. (b) Suppose this thermometer is used to measure the temperature of 0.012 kg of water. Comment on the effect of the measurement process on the measured value.

17-16 The specific heat of Si is measured by dropping a 1.50-kg Si slug, initially at 40.0°C, into 3.00 kg of water, initially at 25.0°C. The system comes to a final temperature of 26.2°C. Neglecting energy transfers to the outside, determine the specific heat of Si from these data.

Section 17-4. Work

17-17 A fluid expands at constant atmospheric pressure

(101 kPa) from an initial volume of 0.344 m³ to a final volume of 0.424 m³. (a) Determine the work done by the fluid. (b) Determine the work done by the fluid if the first process is reversed — that is, the fluid is compressed at atmospheric pressure back to the original volume.

17-18 A cylinder with a movable piston contains 96 g of O_2 initially at 150 kPa pressure and at 290 K. (a) Determine the volume occupied by the gas. (b) The gas expands at constant pressure, performing 7.2 kJ of work in the process. What is the volume of the final state? (c) The pressure is then increased isochorically to 300 kPa. How much work is done by the gas for the entire process?

17-19 An ideal gas undergoes a process, shown in Fig. 17-14, which consists of an isobaric expansion followed by an isothermal compression. Determine the work done by the gas for (a) the isobaric expansion, (b) the isothermal compression, (c) the entire process. (d) Check your answers by estimating areas under the process curves in the figure.

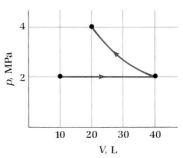

Figure 17-14. Exercise 17-19.

17-20 It is possible to have a process similar to that shown in Fig. 17-14 for which the net work is zero. Suppose the isobaric process is as shown and the isothermal compression takes the system to some final volume V_f. Determine V_f such that $W = 0$ for the entire process.

17-21 An ideal gas is initially in the state specified by p_i, V_i. It undergoes a process in which the pressure changes linearly with volume to the final state specified by p_f, V_f, as shown in Fig. 17-15. (a) Determine the work done by the gas for this process in terms of the initial

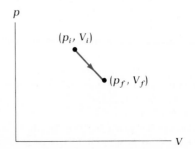

Figure 17-15. Exercise 17-21.

and final pressure and volume values. (b) Evaluate the work done by the gas for this process if $p_i = 140$ kPa, $V_i = 0.064$ m³, $p_f = 108$ kPa, $V_f = 0.096$ m³. (c) Determine the temperatures of the initial and final states if the system consists of 3.0 mol of gas.

17-22 For an ideal gas undergoing a quasi-static adiabatic process (no heat is added to the system), the pressure changes with the volume such that pV^γ is constant. (We shall see that $\gamma = C_p/C_V$ in the next chapter.) If p_i and V_i refer to the initial state, then at volume V the pressure is

$$p = \frac{p_i V_i^\gamma}{V^\gamma}$$

Show that the work done by the ideal gas for a quasi-static adiabatic process is given by

$$W = \frac{p_i V_i}{\gamma - 1} \left[1 - \left(\frac{V_i}{V_f} \right)^{\gamma - 1} \right]$$

17-23 The value of γ (see the previous exercise) for air is 1.4. Suppose that 1.0 mol of air is initially at 202 kPa and occupies a volume of 45 L; it expands adiabatically to a final volume of 65 L. Determine (a) the work done by the air, (b) the final pressure, (c) the initial and final temperatures of the system.

Section 17-5. The first law of thermodynamics

17-24 A system undergoes a process in which 27 J of heat is added to the system while it performs 8 J of work. (a) What is the change in internal energy of the system? (b) If the internal energy of the initial state is 304 J, what is the internal energy of the final state? (c) Suppose the system is taken from the same initial state to the same final state by a different process in which the system performs 12 J of work. What is the internal energy of the final state and how much heat is added?

17-25 A fluid undergoes the process iaf shown in Fig. 17-16. For the isobaric part of the process $Q_{ia} = 11$ kJ, and $Q_{af} = 12$ kJ for the isochoric part. Given that the internal energy of the initial state i is $U_i = 2.0$ kJ, deter-

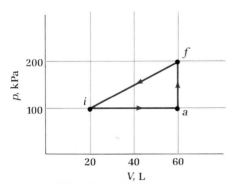

Figure 17-16. Exercise 17-25.

mine the internal energy of (a) state a and (b) state f. (c) Suppose the system is returned to state i from state f along the straight-line path (process) shown in the figure. How much heat must be extracted from the system?

17-26 A nail is placed in a water bath and both are initially at 20°C. The water and the nail are gradually heated to 90°C. The internal energy of the nail increases by 45 J. An identical nail initially at 20°C is quickly withdrawn from a wooden block by a hammer. As a result, the temperature of the nail is 90°C. For each of the two processes, state whether heat was added or work was done. By how much did the internal energy of the nail change in the second process?

Section 17-6. Some applications of the first law

17-27 One mole of He undergoes the process iaf shown in Fig. 17-16. The molar heat capacity values are $C_V = 12.5$ J·mol^{-1}·K^{-1} and $C_p = 20.8$ J·mol^{-1}·K^{-1}. Evaluate the difference in internal energy between (a) states i and a, (b) states a and f, (c) states i and f.

17-28 At atmospheric pressure and 0.0°C, the volume of 1.00 kg of ice is $V_S = 0.917$ L, while the volume of the same mass of liquid water is $V_L = 1.000$ L. Evaluate for 1.00 kg of water the difference in internal energy of the liquid and solid states, $U_L - U_S$.

17-29 Determine the difference in internal energy for 1 mol of H_2O between liquid at the normal melting point and liquid at the normal boiling point. The small changes in the volume of liquid water as its temperature is changed at atmospheric pressure may be neglected.

17-30 Consider the cycle $iafi$ for a substance shown in Fig. 17-16. For the entire cycle evaluate (a) the work done by the system, (b) the change in internal energy of the system, (c) the heat added to the system.

17-31 For each process listed in the table below, supply the sign (+, −, or 0) for each missing entry:

Process description	Q	W	ΔU
Isochoric pressure drop			−
Isobaric compression of an ideal gas			
Adiabatic expansion			
Isothermal expansion of an ideal gas			
Isothermal compression of an ideal gas			
Free expansion of a gas			
Cyclic process		+	

17-32 Each kg of water drops about 50 m at Niagara Falls. By how much does the temperature of the water rise as a result? Assume that the increase in internal energy of the water in the process is due to the change in its gravitational potential energy.

PROBLEMS

17-1   The molar heat capacity C_p for Al changes nearly linearly with temperature from 24.4 J $\cdot$ mol^{-1} $\cdot$ K^{-1} at 300 K to 28.1 J $\cdot$ mol^{-1} $\cdot$ K^{-1} at 600 K. (a) Construct a mathematical expression for C_p of the form $C_p = A + BT$ by evaluating the constants A and B from the given data. (b) Construct a graph showing this temperature dependence of the molar heat capacity. (c) Determine the amount of heat added at constant pressure to 2.50 mol of Al as its temperature is raised from 300 to 500 K.

17-2   The *van der Waals equation of state* for 1 mol of a gas is

$$\left(p + \frac{a}{V^2}\right)(V - b) = RT$$

where a and b are constants that are experimentally determined for a particular gas. The equation describes gases at high densities and pressures more accurately than does the ideal gas equation of state. Use this equation of state to evaluate the work done by 1 mol of a gas for a quasi-static isothermal process at temperature T from an initial state p_i, V_i to a final state p_f, V_f. Express the answer in terms of V_i, V_f, T, and the constants a and b.

17-3   The isothermal compressibility of a substance is defined as (see Chap. 15) $-(1/V)(dV/dp)$, with the understanding that T is held fixed. Evaluate the isothermal compressibility for (a) an ideal gas and (b) a van der Waals gas (see the previous problem). (c) In the latter case, show that as the parameters a and b approach zero, the answer to part (a) is obtained.

17-4   The internal energy of a system can be considered as a function of V and T: $U(V, T)$. (a) Use the first law of thermodynamics to show that

$$c_V = \frac{1}{m}\frac{dU}{dT}$$

where V is held fixed in taking the derivative with respect to T. (b) Explain why a corresponding expression does not hold for c_p; that is,

$$c_p \neq \frac{1}{m}\frac{dU}{dT}$$

where the derivative is taken with p fixed.

17-5   A continuous throttling process is sketched in Fig. 17-17a in which a fluid streams adiabatically through a valve from a high-pressure side (p_2) to a low-pressure side (p_1). For a given amount of fluid, the process can be simulated by the process illustrated in Fig. 17-17b and c. The pistons on either side of the valve move in such a way that an amount of fluid at pressure p_2 is forced through the valve to the region at pressure p_1. Evaluate the work done by the fluid,

apply the first law, and show that the enthalpy $U + pV$ is constant for the process: $U_2 + p_2V_2 = U_1 + p_1V_1$.

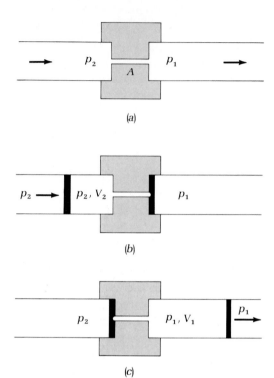

Figure 17-17. Prob. 17-5: (a) A throttling process is simulated by (b, c) the motion of the two pistons.

17-6   At low temperatures the molar heat capacity of a solid such as NaCl has a temperature dependence given approximately by

$$C_V = 234\ R\left(\frac{T}{\Theta}\right)^3$$

where R is the universal gas constant and Θ is the Debye temperature, a parameter characteristic of the material. For NaCl the Debye $\Theta = 300$ K, and the above expression is valid for T small compared with Θ. Determine the amount of heat added at constant volume to 1.0 mol of NaCl in raising its temperature from 1.0 to 9.0 K.

17-7   An ideal gas undergoes a quasi-static adiabatic process. For such a process, show that (a) $TV^{\gamma-1} = $ constant and (b) $p^{\gamma-1}/T^\gamma = $ constant. See Exercise 17-22.

17-8   One mole of an ideal gas is initially at 300 K and occupies a volume of 24 L. It undergoes an isothermal expansion in which the volume doubles, followed by an adiabatic compression in which the temperature rises to 600 K. Take $C_p = 2.5R$ and $C_V = 1.5R$ for this gas. (a) Evaluate the final volume and pressure of the gas. (b) Show the process on a p-V diagram. (c) Evaluate the heat added for the entire process. (d) Evaluate the work done by the gas for the entire process (see Exercise 17-22). (e) What is the change in internal energy of the gas? (See the previous problem also.)

17-9 An ideal gas undergoes the quasi-static cycle consisting of two adiabatic and two isothermal processes, as shown in Fig. 17-18. Using only the first law and the fact that the internal energy of an ideal gas depends only on the temperature, show that the work done by the gas for the two adiabatic processes is related by $W_{41} = -W_{23}$.

17-10 ⬛ One model of a polyatomic gas has the following temperature dependence of the molar heat capacity:

$$C_V = R \left[\frac{5}{2} + \frac{(\Theta/T)^2 e^{\Theta/T}}{(e^{\Theta/T} - 1)^2} \right]$$

where R is the universal gas constant and Θ is a parameter characterizing this gas. Adapt the integrating program from Table 8-1 to determine for a particular gas ($\Theta = 85$ K) the difference in internal energy between two states of 1.0 mol of this gas having the same

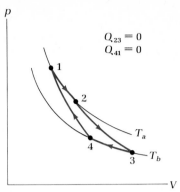

Figure 17-18. Prob. 17-9: An ideal gas undergoes a cycle consisting of two isothermal (at T_a and T_b) and two adiabatic processes.

volume but at temperatures $T_i = 10$ K and $T_f = 200$ K. Since $C_V = (1/n)(dU/dT)$, note that

$$U_f - U_i = \int_{T_i}^{T_f} n C_V(T) \, dT$$

CHAPTER 18
KINETIC THEORY
OF GASES

18-1 INTRODUCTION

"Your chances of winning the jackpot are 1 in 2,300,000,000." "There is safety in numbers." "If at first you don't succeed, try, try again." These clichés express the conventional wisdom which comes from averaging over the large numbers of entities in a complex system. In a similar way, we seek to relate the macroscopic behavior of a system such as a gas to its constituents, a large number of molecules.

The number of molecules in a typical system is indeed large. A coin such as a penny contains about 10^{23} atoms. Even the "vacuum" of interstellar space may

Slot machine. *(Leif Scoogfoots/ Woodfin Camp & Assoc.)*

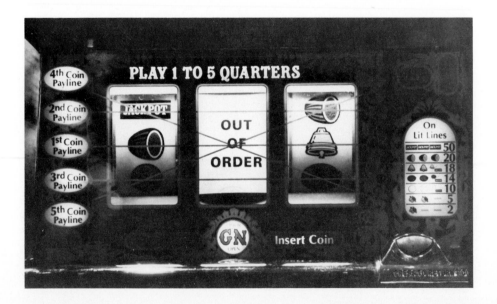

have 10^8 molecules in 1 m³. Because of these large numbers, we do not attempt to follow the motion of individual molecules, but consider averages over molecular motions instead. *Kinetic theory*, a special branch of statistical mechanics, allows us to express some of the macroscopic quantities in terms of averages over molecular motions. A much deeper understanding of the thermodynamic properties of a system comes in this way.

18-2 MOLECULAR MODEL OF AN IDEAL GAS

To formulate a microscopic or molecular model of an ideal gas, we make several simplifying assumptions about the behavior of molecules in the gas and the system that they form:

1. *Large numbers.* The gas consists of N molecules, where N is a very large number. Each molecule has mass m and a size which is negligible compared with the average distance between molecules.

2. *Mechanics.* The motions of the individual molecules are adequately described by newtonian mechanics.

3. *Collisions.* A molecule moves freely, with negligible forces acting on it, except when it contacts and collides with another molecule or with a wall of the container. All collisions are elastic, and in the case of a collision of a molecule with a wall, only the velocity component perpendicular to the wall changes. That component changes its sign on collision but not its magnitude.

4. *Randomness.* The molecules of the gas are in random motion, and the gas is in equilibrium. The methods of elementary probability theory may be applied to the system.

Some of these assumptions are more restrictive than is really necessary. However, the connections between the microscopic and the macroscopic descriptions that we seek are more easily obtained using the assumptions. Also, for simplicity, we consider the gas to be enclosed in a stationary, rectangular box with edges L_1, L_2, L_3, and of volume $V = L_1 L_2 L_3$. Our final results are independent of the shape of the container.

Averages and probability. In what sense do we speak of the "average motion of a molecule"? To illustrate, we consider some simple but useful averages over molecular motions, beginning with the average velocity. Since the molecules are moving randomly, a given molecule is equally likely to be moving in any direction and can have almost any speed. We use a coordinate system with axes parallel to the edges of the box and select the x component of the velocity of a molecule of the system, as shown in Fig. 18-1. We label this molecule with an index j and denote its velocity component by v_{jx}. Now we average over all N molecules in the system:

$$\langle v_x \rangle = \frac{\Sigma v_{jx}}{N} \tag{18-1}$$

where the symbol $\langle \ \rangle$ denotes the average or mean value and the sum is over all the molecules of the system. Since a component of the velocity can have negative as well as positive values, there is a molecule with a negative value of v_x for each molecule with a positive value of v_x. Positive and negative contributions to the sum in Eq. (18-1) occur with the same frequency, or *with the same*

Assumptions about the molecular model of an ideal gas

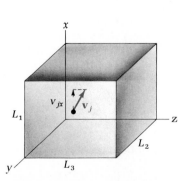

Figure 18-1. One of the molecules of a gas is shown in a container of volume $V = L_1 L_2 L_3$. This molecule has velocity $\mathbf{v}_j$, with x component v_{jx}.

The average molecular velocity is zero, but the average speed is *not* zero.

probability. Thus the sum Σv_{jx} is zero and $\langle v_x \rangle = 0$. The same reasoning applies to the y and z components of velocity, and we have

$$\langle v_x \rangle = \langle v_y \rangle = \langle v_z \rangle = 0$$

That is, the average molecular velocity is zero:

$$\langle \mathbf{v} \rangle = \langle v_x \rangle \mathbf{i} + \langle v_y \rangle \mathbf{j} + \langle v_z \rangle \mathbf{k} = 0$$

Although the average velocity (a vector) is zero, this result does *not* mean that the molecules are at rest! Indeed the average molecular speed (a scalar) is not zero. Consider the square of the speed. For the molecule labeled by j,

$$v_j^2 = v_{jx}^2 + v_{jy}^2 + v_{jz}^2$$

The average of this quantity, called the *mean square speed* $\langle v^2 \rangle$, will be of primary importance to us. It is the average of the square of the molecular speed and is given by

$$\langle v^2 \rangle = \frac{\Sigma v_j^2}{N}$$

Later we shall see how $\langle v^2 \rangle$ is related to the temperature of a gas.

The mean square speed can be expressed in terms of the average of the square of one of the components. Since the x, y, and z directions are equivalent, we have

$$\langle v_x^2 \rangle = \langle v_y^2 \rangle = \langle v_z^2 \rangle$$

and $\langle v^2 \rangle = \langle v_x^2 \rangle + \langle v_y^2 \rangle + \langle v_z^2 \rangle$, or

$$\langle v^2 \rangle = 3 \langle v_x^2 \rangle \tag{18-2}$$

The factor of 3 corresponds to the three equivalent spatial directions, and for later convenience we have chosen to use the square of the x component.

We have discussed averages involving the velocity and speed. Now consider averages of position. What is the average value $\langle x \rangle$ of the x coordinate for the molecules of the system? From Fig. 18-1 we can see that $\langle x \rangle = (\Sigma x_j)/N$ must have a value between 0 and L_1. Consistent with the random molecular motion, a gas in equilibrium is spatially homogeneous. That is, all values of x between 0 and L_1 are equally likely, and the average value of x is $\frac{1}{2}L_1$:

$$\langle x \rangle = \frac{\Sigma x_j}{N} = \tfrac{1}{2}L_1$$

Probability that an x coordinate is in a range ℓ_1

Put another way, the probability, or chance, is $1/2$ that a particular molecule is in one side, say $0 \leqslant x \leqslant \frac{1}{2}L_1$, of the box. It is equally likely to be in either half. More generally, the probability that a given molecule has an x coordinate within a range ℓ_1 is given by the fraction that distance is of the total range L_1 of x. That probability P is

$$P = \frac{\ell_1}{L_1} \tag{18-3}$$

This result is a consequence of the spatial uniformity of the gas, and we use it below to consider the pressure.

Calculation of the pressure. A gas at pressure p exerts a force of magnitude $F = pA$ on a wall of area A. This force, from the microscopic point of view, is caused by collisions of the molecules with the wall. Take the molecule with velocity component $v_{jx} > 0$ shown in Fig. 18-1. What contribution will it make,

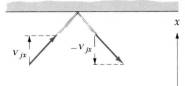

Figure 18-2. A molecule collides elastically with a wall. The velocity component perpendicular to the wall changes from v_{jx} before the collision to $-v_{jx}$ after the collision.

in some selected time interval Δt, to the force exerted on the upper wall? There are two aspects to consider: whether it actually hits the wall in the time interval and, if so, what impulse, $\mathbf{J} = \overline{\mathbf{F}} \, \Delta t$, it delivers to the wall in the collision (see Sec. 10-6).

Suppose that the molecule does collide with the wall. According to our assumptions, the x component of the velocity only changes sign. So the x component of the molecule's velocity changes from v_{jx} initially to $-v_{jx}$ after the collision. The x component of the momentum change is, as seen from Fig. 18-2 (and Chap. 10),

$$\Delta p_{jx} = p_{jx}{}^{(f)} - p_{jx}{}^{(i)} = m(-v_{jx}) - m(v_{jx}) = -2mv_{jx}$$

The x component of the impulse J'_{jx} of the force exerted by the wall on the molecule is

$$J'_{jx} = \Delta p_{jx} = -2mv_{jx}$$

A molecule delivers an impulse to the wall.

The impulse delivered to the wall by this molecule is, by Newton's third law, equal but opposite to the impulse delivered to the molecule. We denote by J_{jx} the x component of the impulse on the wall due to this collision, and $J_{jx} = -J'_{jx}$, or

$$J_{jx} = 2mv_{jx} \tag{18-4}$$

But this molecule may not reach the wall with this velocity. It could suffer a collision with another molecule first. We should therefore multiply Eq. (18-4) by the probability that the molecule will hit the wall in the selected time interval Δt. Let us choose this time interval to be sufficiently small so that the molecule will (almost) surely not collide with another molecule. Then this molecule will hit the wall if it is headed toward the wall (the probability is 1/2 that $v_{jx} > 0$) rather than away from the wall and if it is within a perpendicular distance $v_{jx} \Delta t$ from that wall. That is, the probability that the molecule will hit the wall is one-half the probability that it is within a distance $v_{jx} \, \Delta t$ of the wall at the beginning of the time interval. From Eq. (18-3) with $\ell = v_{jx} \, \Delta t$, we obtain

Probability that the molecule will hit the wall

$$p = \frac{\frac{1}{2} v_{jx} \, \Delta t}{L_1} \tag{18-5}$$

where v_{jx} is assumed positive and the factor of 1/2 accounts for the probability that the molecule is initially moving toward the wall rather than away from it.

The expected or average value of the impulse delivered to the wall by a molecule is just the probability P of a collision times the impulse for such a collision. Multiplying Eqs. (18-4) and (18-5), we obtain

$$\langle J_{jx} \rangle = 2mv_{jx} \frac{\frac{1}{2} v_{jx} \, \Delta t}{L_1} = \frac{mv_{jx}{}^2 \, \Delta t}{L_1}$$

We now sum this expression over all the molecules of the system. The x component of the total impulse delivered to the wall in a time interval Δt by collisions of molecules with the wall is given by

$$\langle J_x \rangle = \frac{\Delta t\, m}{L_1} \Sigma v_{jx}^2$$

The average force component $\bar{F}_x$ exerted on this wall (averaged for the time interval Δt) is the impulse divided by the time interval:

$$\bar{F}_x = \frac{\langle J_x \rangle}{\Delta t} = \frac{m}{L_1} \Sigma v_{jx}^2$$

To obtain the pressure, we divide this force by the area $L_2 L_3$ of the upper wall:

$$p = \frac{\bar{F}_x}{L_2 L_3} = \frac{m \Sigma v_{jx}^2}{L_1 L_2 L_3}$$

or, with volume $V = L_1 L_2 L_3$,

$$pV = m\Sigma v_{jx}^2 \tag{18-6}$$

The sum that appears in Eq. (18-6) is closely related to the mean square speed through Eq. (18-2), $\langle v^2 \rangle = 3\langle v_x^2 \rangle$. By multiplying and dividing the sum by the number of molecules in the system, we have

$$\Sigma v_{jx}^2 = N \frac{\Sigma v_{jx}^2}{N} = N\langle v_x^2 \rangle = \frac{N\langle v^2 \rangle}{3}$$

Equation (18-6) then becomes

Pressure is proportional to mean square speed.

$$pV = \frac{Nm\langle v^2 \rangle}{3} \tag{18-7}$$

which shows that for a given volume, *the pressure of a gas is proportional to the mean square speed of the molecules.* The faster the molecules move, the larger their mean square speed and the greater the pressure. By averaging over the molecular motions, we have obtained the connection between a macroscopic quantity, the pressure, and a microscopic quantity, the mean square speed of the molecules. This is the central point of this section.

EXAMPLE 18-1. The pressure of 1.0 mol of He occupying 22.5 L is 101 kPa. Determine the mean square speed of the molecules.

SOLUTION. The molecular weight of He is $M = 4.0$ g/mol,

so that 1.0 mol has a total mass $Nm = 4.0$ g. Using Eq. (18-7), we have

$$\langle v^2 \rangle = \frac{3pV}{Nm} = \frac{3(101\ \text{kPa})(22.5\ \text{L})}{0.0040\ \text{kg}}$$

$$= 1.7 \times 10^6\ \text{m}^2/\text{s}^2$$

18-3 THE MICROSCOPIC INTERPRETATION OF TEMPERATURE

The mean square speed $\langle v^2 \rangle$ of the N molecules of the ideal gas is defined by $\langle v^2 \rangle = (\Sigma v_j^2)/N$, and Eq. (18-7) shows how the pressure of the gas is related to the mean square speed. The internal energy of the gas and its temperature can also be interpreted in terms of the mean square speed.

In a monatomic gas, a molecule has only one atom.

Consider a *monatomic* ideal gas whose molecules consist of single atoms. The "noble gases"—He, Ne, Ar, Kr, Xe, and Rn—are monatomic under ordinary circumstances. We assume that the molecules behave as point particles

The internal energy of an ideal gas is the kinetic energy of the molecules.

and that the potential energy of their interaction may be neglected. For point molecules, there is no rotation or vibration to consider. The mechanical energy of the system consists solely of the translational kinetic energy of the molecules. That is, the internal energy U is the sum of the kinetic energies of the molecules:

$$U = \Sigma \tfrac{1}{2}mv_j^2 \tag{18-8}$$

Equivalently, the average kinetic energy $\langle K \rangle$ of a molecule of this system is given by

$$\langle K \rangle = \frac{\Sigma \tfrac{1}{2}mv_j^2}{N} = \tfrac{1}{2}m \frac{\Sigma v_j^2}{N} = \tfrac{1}{2}m\langle v^2 \rangle$$

Thus the average molecular kinetic energy is proportional to the mean square speed, as is the internal energy of a monatomic ideal gas: $U = N\langle K \rangle$, or

$$U = \tfrac{1}{2}Nm\langle v^2 \rangle \tag{18-9}$$

Since the pressure of the gas, from Eq. (18-7), and the internal energy are both proportional to the mean square speed, they are proportional to each other. Combining Eqs. (18-7) and (18-9), we have

$$pV = \tfrac{1}{3}Nm\langle v^2 \rangle = \tfrac{2}{3}(\tfrac{1}{2}Nm\langle v^2 \rangle)$$

or

$$pV = \tfrac{2}{3}U \tag{18-10}$$

We now compare Eq. (18-10), obtained from kinetic theory, with the ideal gas equation of state, Eq. (17-1), $pV = nRT$. Equating the right-hand sides of these two expressions for pV, we obtain

$$\tfrac{2}{3}U = nRT$$

The internal energy of a monatomic ideal gas is proportional to T.

or

$$U = \tfrac{3}{2}nRT \tag{18-11}$$

The internal energy of an ideal gas is proportional to the Kelvin temperature. For the monatomic ideal gas, the proportionality factor is $\tfrac{3}{2}nR$.

The result expressed in Eq. (18-11) can be phrased in molecular terms using Eq. (18-9). Note that a system of n moles contains N molecules with $n = N/N_A$, where N_A is Avogadro's number, the number of molecules in 1 mol. Equation (18-11) becomes

$$U = \frac{3N}{2N_A} RT$$

The average molecular translational kinetic energy is given by

$$\langle K \rangle = \frac{U}{N} = \frac{(3N/2N_A)\,RT}{N} = \frac{3R}{2N_A}\,T$$

or

Average translational kinetic energy

$$\langle K \rangle = \tfrac{3}{2}kT \tag{18-12}$$

We have introduced in Eq. (18-12) the *Boltzmann constant,*

Boltzmann constant k

$$k = \frac{R}{N_A} = 1.38 \times 10^{-23} \text{ J/K}$$

The gas constant R refers to 1 mol of a substance, as does Avogadro's number N_A. The Boltzmann constant $k = R/N_A$ is therefore independent of the concept of the mole and refers to the molecule. We can think of the Boltzmann constant k as the gas constant *per molecule.*

Equation (18-12) gives the molecular interpretation of temperature: *The average molecular translational kinetic energy and the temperature are proportional.* The higher the temperature of a system, the greater, proportionally, is the average translational kinetic energy of the molecules of that system. Equation (18-12) was obtained from considering a monatomic ideal gas. The result for the average *translational* kinetic energy, $\langle K \rangle = \frac{3}{2}kT$, turns out to be valid for any gas. The connection $U = N\langle K \rangle$, however, applies just to a monatomic ideal gas, for which the internal energy consists only of translational kinetic energy.

If the temperature of a system increases, then the molecules move faster on the average. We can phrase this in terms of speed by using the *root-mean-square speed* v_{rms},

$$v_{rms} = \sqrt{\langle v^2 \rangle} \tag{18-13}$$

The root-mean-square speed is one of the quantities that characterize the distribution of molecular speeds, which we discuss later in Sec. 18-7. It is not the average speed but is the square root of the mean square speed. To see how v_{rms} depends on temperature, we use $\langle K \rangle = \frac{1}{2}mv^2$ so that Eq. (18-12) becomes

$$\tfrac{1}{2}m\langle v^2 \rangle = \tfrac{3}{2}kT$$

Solving for $\langle v^2 \rangle$ and taking a square root gives

$$v_{rms} = \sqrt{\frac{3kT}{m}} \tag{18-14}$$

Thus the root-mean-square speed is proportional to the square root of the Kelvin temperature and inversely proportional to the square root of the molecular mass.

Equations (18-12) and (18-14) imply incorrectly that molecular motion ceases as $T \rightarrow 0$. One of our assumptions, on which these results are based, becomes invalid for a system of molecules at sufficiently low temperatures: Newton's laws do not adequately describe the motion of a molecule under these conditions, and the methods of quantum statistical mechanics must be used. These quantum effects are important in the behavior of systems such as electrons in condensed matter and the superfluid phases of liquid He.

EXAMPLE 18-2. A system consists of 2.21 mol of Ar at 273 K. Determine for this gas (a) the average molecular kinetic energy, (b) the internal energy, and (c) the root-mean-square speed. (d) What is v_{rms} for He at the same temperature?

SOLUTION. (a) The average molecular kinetic energy is given by Eq. (18-12):

$$\langle K \rangle = \tfrac{3}{2} (1.38 \times 10^{-23} \text{ J/K})(273 \text{ K})$$

$$= 5.65 \times 10^{-21} \text{ J}$$

(b) The internal energy of this monatomic ideal gas can be calculated using Eq. (18-11). Alternatively, we can determine

the number of molecules in the system:

$$N = nN_A = (2.21 \text{ mol})(6.02 \times 10^{23} \text{ mol}^{-1}) = 1.33 \times 10^{24}$$

The internal energy is then

$$U = N\langle K \rangle = (1.33 \times 10^{24})(5.65 \times 10^{-21} \text{ J}) = 7.52 \text{ kJ}$$

(c) The mass of an Ar atom is $m = M/N_A$, where M is the molar mass. From the periodic chart in App. P, $M = 39.9$ g/mol and

$$m = \frac{0.0399 \text{ kg/mol}}{6.02 \times 10^{23} \text{ mol}^{-1}}$$

$$= 6.63 \times 10^{-26} \text{ kg}$$

The root-mean-square speed for Ar at this temperature is

from Eq. (18-14):

$$v_{\text{rms}} = \sqrt{\frac{(3)(1.38 \times 10^{-23} \text{ J/K})(273 \text{ K})}{6.63 \times 10^{-26} \text{ kg}}}$$

$$= 413 \text{ m/s}$$

(d) The root-mean-square speed for He at the same temperature can be calculated in the same way. But since v_{rms} is inversely proportional to the square root of the molecular mass, we can write for He,

$$v_{\text{rms}} = 413 \text{ m/s } \sqrt{\left(\frac{m_{\text{Ar}}}{m_{\text{He}}}\right)}$$

and the mass ratio is $m_{\text{Ar}}/m_{\text{He}} = 39.9/4.00 = 9.98$. Thus, for He,

$$v_{\text{rms}} = 1300 \text{ m/s}$$

Notice that the smaller mass molecules of He are moving faster, in a root-mean-square sense, than the more massive molecules of Ar at the same temperature.

18-4 EQUIPARTITION OF ENERGY

According to Eq. (18-12), the average translational molecular kinetic energy for a system at temperature T is given by

$$\langle K \rangle = \tfrac{1}{2}m\langle v^2 \rangle = \tfrac{3}{2}kT \qquad (18\text{-}12)$$

It is useful to trace back through the last two sections to determine the origin of the factor of 3 in this expression. The first appearance of this factor is in Eq. (18-2) for the mean square speed $\langle v^2 \rangle$. It came about because of the equivalence of the three spatial directions, or the equivalence of the average of square velocity components:

$$\langle v^2 \rangle = \langle v_x^2 \rangle + \langle v_y^2 \rangle + \langle v_z^2 \rangle = 3\langle v_x^2 \rangle$$

Because of this equivalence, which has its roots in the fact that the properties of the system do not depend on our choice of orientation for the xyz-coordinate system, we can write

$$\tfrac{1}{2}m\langle v_x^2 \rangle = \tfrac{1}{2}m\langle v_y^2 \rangle = \tfrac{1}{2}m\langle v_z^2 \rangle = \tfrac{1}{2}kT$$

The sum of these three equal contributions gives Eq. (18-12).

Degrees of freedom

The factor of 3 is connected to the three translational *degrees of freedom* of a monatomic molecule. For our purposes, each degree of freedom corresponds to the ability of a molecule to participate in a one-dimensional motion which contributes to the mechanical energy of that molecule. This is best illustrated by a translational degree of freedom: A molecule can have a velocity component in the x direction with a contribution to the mechanical energy of $\tfrac{1}{2}mv_x^2$. [Note that although we can speak of a one-dimensional contribution to the kinetic energy, the kinetic energy of a molecule is $\tfrac{1}{2}m(v_x^2 + v_y^2 + v_z^2)$.] Since there are three spatial directions in which the molecule can move, the monatomic ideal gas has three degrees of freedom, and the average molecular mechanical energy $\langle E \rangle = \langle K \rangle$ is

$$\langle E \rangle = 3(\tfrac{1}{2}kT)$$

Equipartition of energy theorem

A general statement of this result is referred to as the *equipartition of energy theorem. For a system of molecules at temperature T, with each molecule having ν degrees of freedom, the average molecular mechanical energy $\langle E \rangle$ is*

$$\langle E \rangle = \nu(\tfrac{1}{2}kT) \qquad (18\text{-}15)$$

Equation (18-15) implies that, on the average, an amount $\tfrac{1}{2}kT$ of mechanical energy is associated with each degree of freedom. For the monatomic ideal gas

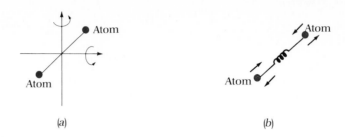

Figure 18-3. (a) A linear diatomic molecule may rotate about perpendicular axes through the center of mass. (b) The relative motion of two atoms is vibrational.

once again, there are only the three translational degrees of freedom, $\nu = 3$, and Eq. (18-12) results.

Molecules of diatomic or polyatomic (more than two atoms per molecule) gases may have additional degrees of freedom corresponding to additional contributions to the mechanical energy of a molecule. Consider the rotation of a diatomic molecule such as H_2, depicted schematically in Fig. 18-3a. There are three translational degrees of freedom for the motion of the center of mass. The molecule can also rotate about either of the two perpendicular axes through the center of mass and perpendicular to the line joining the two atoms. (Since we think of each atom as a particle, we do not include rotation about the line joining the two atoms.) There is a rotational kinetic energy contribution for each of these two axes and thus two rotational degrees of freedom. If all five degrees of freedom (three translational and two rotational) contribute on the average to the mechanical energy of the diatomic molecule, then the average molecular mechanical energy for the diatomic gas at temperature T is

$$\langle E \rangle = 5(\tfrac{1}{2}kT)$$

Vibrational degrees of freedom may also have to be considered. A diatomic molecule, in addition to translating and rotating, can have a vibrational motion in which the two atoms have a relative motion, as illustrated in Fig. 18-3b. You may think of the two atoms as being joined by a spring and having a potential energy of interaction. A more advanced analysis shows that a potential energy of the form $\tfrac{1}{2}kx^2$ contributes one degree of freedom. Note that this potential energy is internal to the molecule. We still assume no potential energy of interaction between the molecules of the gas. There are two vibrational degrees of freedom; one is associated with the kinetic energy of the relative motion, and the other with the potential energy of interaction of the two atoms in the molecule. Thus a diatomic molecule may have up to seven degrees of freedom contributing to the mechanical energy: three translational, two rotational, and two vibrational. We shall consider how the number of participating degrees of freedom is related to the molar heat capacity in the next section.

EXAMPLE 18-3. Each molecule of a certain polyatomic gas at 1200 K has three translational, three rotational, and four vibrational degrees of freedom contributing to its mechanical energy. Determine (a) the average molecular mechanical energy and (b) the internal energy of 1.0 mol of this ideal gas.

SOLUTION. (a) With $\nu = 3 + 3 + 4 = 10$ degrees of freedom, the average molecular mechanical energy is

$$\langle E \rangle = (10)(\tfrac{1}{2})(1.38 \times 10^{-23} \text{ J/K})(1200 \text{ K})$$
$$= 8.3 \times 10^{-20} \text{ J}$$

(b) The internal energy consists of the total mechanical energy of the molecules:

$$U = N\langle E \rangle = nN_A\langle E \rangle$$
$$= (1.0 \text{ mol})(6.02 \times 10^{23} \text{ mol}^{-1})(8.3 \times 10^{-20} \text{ J}) = 50 \text{ kJ}$$

18-5   HEAT CAPACITIES OF IDEAL GASES AND ELEMENTAL SOLIDS

When heat is added to a system at constant volume, as shown in Fig. 18-4a, no work is done ($dW = p\,dV = 0$). According to the first law of thermodynamics, the heat dQ added goes entirely into increasing the internal energy: $dQ = dU$. The amount of heat added at constant volume can be expressed in terms of the molar heat capacity at constant volume C_V. That is, $dQ = nC_V\,dT$, where n is the number of moles for the system and dT is the resulting temperature change. Since $dU = dQ = nC_V\,dT$, we have

$$C_V = \frac{1}{n}\frac{dU}{dT} \tag{18-16}$$

with the understanding that the derivative $\dfrac{dU}{dT}$ is taken with the volume constant. Since we know the temperature dependence of the internal energy of an ideal gas from kinetic theory, we can evaluate the molar heat capacity C_V of the system from Eq. (18-16).

Consider C_V for a monatomic ideal gas. The expression from kinetic theory for the internal energy of a monatomic ideal gas is given by Eq. (18-11):

$$U = \tfrac{3}{2}nRT$$

Using Eq. (18-16), we take the derivative $\dfrac{dU}{dT}$ at constant volume (U is independent of V for the ideal gas) to get

Molar heat capacity C_V for a monatomic ideal gas

$$C_V = \frac{1}{n}\frac{d}{dT}\left(\tfrac{3}{2}nRT\right) = \tfrac{3}{2}R$$

The molar heat capacity at constant volume is a constant, $\tfrac{3}{2}R$, for any monatomic ideal gas.

When heat is added to a gas at *constant pressure,* as illustrated in Fig. 18-4b, not only does the internal energy change but also work is performed by the gas. As a consequence, the molar heat capacity at constant pressure C_p is larger than C_V. Calculating the value of C_p is not quite so straightforward. For an ideal gas, however, we can determine C_p relative to C_V in the following way: Two infinitesimal processes are shown (exaggerated) for an ideal gas on a p-V diagram in Fig. 18-4c, one at constant volume and one at constant pressure. Both processes have the same temperature change dT. They also have the same change in internal energy dU because the internal energy of an ideal gas

Figure 18-4. (a) The piston remains fixed and heat is added to a gas at constant volume. (b) Heat is added to a gas at constant pressure. The piston moves upward so that p is constant. (c) Process 1→2 corresponds to the constant-volume process in part (a). Process 1→3 corresponds to the constant-pressure process in part (b).

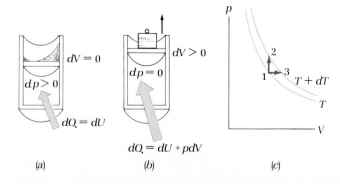

depends only on temperature. Thus, for the same temperature change, the change in internal energy of an ideal gas is the same for constant pressure and for constant volume, and from Eq. (18-16),

$$dU = nC_V\, dT$$

The work $p\, dV$ done by the gas for the constant-pressure process can be expressed in terms of the temperature change by taking the differential of the ideal gas equation of state, $pV = nRT$:

$$p\, dV + V\, dp = nR\, dT$$

But $V\, dp = 0$ for a constant-pressure process, and

$$p\, dV = nR\, dT \qquad \text{(constant-pressure process)}$$

Inserting these expressions for dU and $p\, dV$ in the first law of thermodynamics, $dQ = dU + p\, dV$, gives

$$dQ = nC_V\, dT + nR\, dT$$

Since $dQ = nC_p\, dT$ for the constant-pressure process, we have

$$nC_p\, dT = nC_V\, dT + nR\, dT$$

Solving for C_p gives

$$C_p = C_V + R \qquad\qquad (18\text{-}17)$$

For an ideal gas, $C_p - C_V = R$.

Thus for an ideal gas, C_p and C_V differ by the universal gas constant, $C_p - C_V = R$. If we know C_V from calculation, then C_p is obtained by adding R to C_V. For the monatomic ideal gas, $C_V = \frac{3}{2}R$; therefore, $C_p = \frac{3}{2}R + R = \frac{5}{2}R$.

Diatomic and polyatomic gases. The molar heat capacities of some diatomic and polyatomic gases can be evaluated by using the equipartition of energy theorem. Suppose that the molecules of a gas have ν degrees of freedom; then from Eq. (18-15), the average molecular mechanical energy is

$$\langle E \rangle = \nu(\tfrac{1}{2}kT)$$

and the internal energy of a gas with $N = nN_A$ molecules is

$$U = N\langle E \rangle = nN_A\nu(\tfrac{1}{2}kT) = n\nu(\tfrac{1}{2}N_A kT) = n\nu(\tfrac{1}{2}RT)$$

where $N_A k = R$. The molar heat capacity C_V is, from Eq. (18-16),

$$C_V = \frac{1}{n}\frac{d}{dT}(n\nu\tfrac{1}{2}RT) = \tfrac{1}{2}\nu R$$

and $C_p = C_V + R$. Thus the heat capacities of an ideal gas can be predicted from the number of active degrees of freedom of the molecules.

How well do the predicted values of molar heat capacities agree with experiment? Some comparisons between measured and calculated values are given for several gases in Table 18-1. The first gases listed are monatomic, followed by diatomic and then by polyatomic gases. Listed are the measured values of C_V, $C_p - C_V$, and the ratio of heat capacities $\gamma = C_p/C_V$. Calculated values from kinetic theory appear, where appropriate, in brackets.

For the monatomic gases, the agreement is good. The calculated values, corresponding to the three translational degrees of freedom, are $C_V = 3R/2 = 12.5 \text{ J} \cdot \text{mol}^{-1} \cdot \text{K}^{-1}$, $C_p - C_V = R = 8.31 \text{ J} \cdot \text{mol}^{-1} \cdot \text{K}^{-1}$, and $\gamma = (5R/2)/(3R/2)$

Table 18-1. Some molar-heat-capacity values for gases at 25°C

Gas	C_V, J·mol^{-1}·K^{-1}	$C_p - C_V$, J·mol^{-1}·K^{-1}	$\gamma = C_p/C_V$
He	12.8	8.04	1.63
Ne	12.7	8.12	1.64
Ar	12.6	8.20	1.65
Kr	12.3	8.49	1.69
Theory	[12.5]	[8.31]	[1.67]
H_2	20.6	8.25	1.40
N_2	20.8	8.33	1.40
O_2	21.1	8.33	1.40
Cl_2*	25.7	8.46	1.33
Theory	[20.8]	[8.31]	[1.40]
CO_2	28.5	8.50	1.30
NH_3	28.5	8.79	1.31
C_2H_6	43.1	8.58	1.20
Theory	[24.9]	[8.31]	[1.33]

* At 15°C.

$= 5/3 = 1.67$. We conclude that kinetic theory may be applied satisfactorily to describe the heat capacities of monatomic gases at moderate temperatures.

The listings for diatomic and polyatomic gases show less regularity, although the agreement with kinetic theory is adequate for some of these gases. The calculated values for diatomic gases are based on the assumption of five active degrees of freedom, three translational and two rotational. Thus $C_V = 5R/2$, $C_p - C_V = R$, and $\gamma = (7R/2)/(5R/2) = 7/5 = 1.40$. For the polyatomic gases, the calculated values are based on six active degrees of freedom, three translational and three rotational. The calculated values are $C_V = 6R/2$, $C_p - C_V = R$, and $\gamma = 8/6 = 1.33$. Vibrational degrees of freedom are assumed to be "inactive" in all cases at this temperature.

The lack of agreement between experiment and the predictions of kinetic theory is related to the idea of "active" and "inactive" degrees of freedom. At a given temperature, some of the degrees of freedom (vibrational, for example) do not participate effectively in the sharing of energy transferred between molecules in collisions. This nonparticipation has no basis in newtonian, or classical, physics. A proper understanding of the heat capacity of ideal gases can only come with the application of quantum statistical mechanics. The main features, however, can be expressed in terms of a temperature dependence of the number of active degrees of freedom.

This temperature dependence is illustrated graphically for diatomic H_2 in Fig. 18-5. At low temperatures only the three translational degrees of freedom are active, and $C_V = 3R/2$. At higher temperatures, two of the rotational degrees of freedom "thaw" and become active as C_V rises to $5R/2$. At still higher

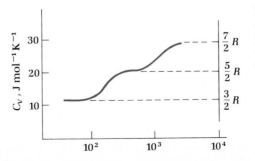

Figure 18-5. The molar heat capacity for H_2 increases with temperature. Note the logarithmic temperature scale. Molecular hydrogen dissociates at about 3200 K.

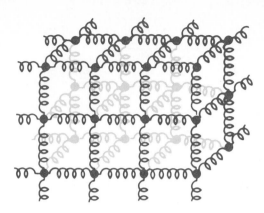

Figure 18-6. A simple model of an elemental solid has identical atoms connected by springs.

temperatures, the vibrational degrees of freedom are beginning to participate, but the molecules dissociate before these additional degrees of freedom become fully active.

Notice that $C_p - C_V$ is fairly close to its predicted value of R for all the gases listed in Table 18-1. The result, $C_p - C_V = R$, was developed using the first law of thermodynamics, the ideal gas equation of state, and the dependence on temperature only of the internal energy of the ideal gas. The result is independent of the number of degrees of freedom. The deviations from $C_p - C_V = R$ in the table occur where the gases are nonideal.

Molar heat capacity of a solid. The equipartition of energy theorem can be applied to a simple model of a solid to evaluate the molar heat capacity. In this model the individual atoms are assumed to vibrate about their equilibrium positions as if they were connected by ideal springs, as illustrated schematically in Fig. 18-6. (We consider for simplicity only elemental solids with one atom per molecule.) For each atom there are three translational degrees of freedom and three vibrational degrees of freedom for independent vibrations along the three directions. The internal energy of the solid with N atoms consists of the kinetic and potential energies of the vibrating molecules, each with six degrees of freedom:

$$U = N\langle E \rangle = N\nu(\tfrac{1}{2}kT) = N \cdot 6(\tfrac{1}{2}kT) = 3NkT$$

Or, since $Nk = nN_A k = nR$,

$$U = 3nRT$$

The molar heat capacity at constant volume is obtained by applying Eq. (18-16):

$$C_V = \frac{1}{n}\frac{d}{dT}(3nRT) = 3R$$

Our calculation predicts that the molar specific heat C_V of elemental solids is the same for all such solids, its value being $3R = 24.9 \text{ J} \cdot \text{mol}^{-1} \cdot \text{K}^{-1}$. Table 18-2 lists some molar-heat-capacity values at about room temperature. For typical solids, the heat capacities C_p and C_V have almost the same value, and C_p is usually measured. (Why is it easier to measure C_p than C_V for a solid or a liquid?) With a few exceptions, the molar heat capacity of each solid is close to the value $3R$, independent of temperature, in accord with our conclusions above. This empirical result is known as the Dulong-Petit law.

The heat capacity of a solid also shows a temperature dependence at lower

Table 18-2. Molar-heat-capacity values for some elemental solids at 25°C (J · mol⁻¹ · K⁻¹)

Solid	C_p	Solid	C_p
Al	24.4	Pb	26.7
Sb	25.2	K	29.6
Ba	26.4	Se	25.4
C (diamond)	8.6	Ag	25.5
Cu	24.5	S	22.6
Au	25.4	W	24.4
Fe	25.0	Zn	25.4

The Dulong-Petit law, $C_p = 3R$

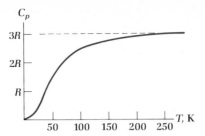

Figure 18-7. The molar heat capacity of Ag has an approximate T^3 dependence at low temperatures. It approaches the Dulong-Petit value of $3R$ at higher temperatures. There is also an electronic contribution to the molar heat capacity which is significant below about 4 K.

temperatures where some of the degrees of freedom become inactive. The typical temperature dependence of the molar heat capacity of an elemental solid due to atomic vibrations is shown in Fig. 18-7. At low temperatures, C_p is approximately proportional to T^3 and approaches zero as T goes to zero. At higher temperatures, the molar heat capacity levels out to the Dulong-Petit value of $3R$.

EXAMPLE 18-4. Estimate the molar heat capacity C_p for (a) Ne gas, (b) N_2 gas, and (c) solid Pb, all at 400 K.

SOLUTION. (a) Neon is a monatomic gas with three translational degrees of freedom. Its molar heat capacity C_V is therefore $3R/2$ and

$$C_p = C_V + R = \frac{5R}{2} = 21 \text{ J} \cdot \text{mol}^{-1} \cdot \text{K}^{-1}$$

(b) For the diatomic N_2 gas, we assume that there are two rotational degrees of freedom in addition to the three translational degrees of freedom. Then $C_V = 5R/2$, and

$$C_p = C_V + R = \frac{7R}{2} = 29 \text{ J} \cdot \text{mol}^{-1} \cdot \text{K}^{-1}$$

(c) Solid Pb at this temperature should have the asymptotic value of $3R$:

$$C_p = 3R = 25 \text{ J} \cdot \text{mol}^{-1} \cdot \text{K}^{-1}$$

18-6 ADIABATIC PROCESS FOR AN IDEAL GAS

Many important processes occur rapidly enough so that negligible heat is added (adiabatic process). For example, the compression of a fuel-air mixture in an automobile engine is approximately adiabatic. The variations in density and pressure in a gas because of a sound wave are adiabatic (see Prob. 18-4). If an ideal gas undergoes a quasi-static adiabatic process, then the gas passes through a succession of equilibrium states represented by a curve on a p-V diagram. This curve depends on the value of $\gamma = C_p/C_V$ for the gas (see Table 18-1). We shall show that the pressure and volume values of this set of states satisfy the relation

Equation for an adiabatic process for an ideal gas

$$pV^\gamma = K \tag{18-18}$$

where K is a constant determined by the initial state of the system.

To obtain Eq. (18-18) from the properties of the ideal gas, consider an infinitesimal step in the adiabatic process. We wish to find the connection between changes in the pressure dp and in the volume dV by eliminating reference to the change in temperature dT. Applying the first law to the adiabatic process, we have

$$dQ = 0 = dU + p \, dV$$

We use Eq. (18-16) to express $dU = nC_V \, dT$ in terms of the temperature change dT, so that $0 = nC_V \, dT + p \, dV$. We solve this expression for dT:

$$dT = -\frac{p\,dV}{nC_V} \qquad \text{(adiabatic process)}$$

Another expression for dT can be obtained from the ideal gas equation of state $pV = nRT$ by taking its differential, $p\,dV + V\,dp = nR\,dT$, or

$$dT = \frac{p\,dV + V\,dp}{nR} \qquad \text{(ideal gas)}$$

On eliminating dT (and n) from these two expressions, we get

$$p\,dV + V\,dp = -\frac{R}{C_V}p\,dV = -\frac{C_p - C_V}{C_V}p\,dV$$

$$= -(\gamma - 1)p\,dV$$

where we have used both $R = C_p - C_V$ and $\gamma = C_p/C_V$. Rearranging the equation gives

$$V\,dp = -\gamma p\,dV$$

or

$$\frac{dp}{p} = -\gamma\frac{dV}{V}$$

for the infinitesimal adiabatic process. For larger changes in p and V, we integrate (using the indefinite integral with a constant of integration):

$$\int \frac{dp}{p} = -\int \gamma\frac{dV}{V} + \text{constant}$$

or

$$\ln p + \gamma \ln V = \text{constant}$$

where we have assumed that γ does not change over the range of integration. The properties of the logarithm allow us to write this as

$$\ln pV^\gamma = \text{constant}$$

or

$$pV^\gamma = K$$

where K is a constant. This is Eq. (18-18).

During an adiabatic process, the pressure and volume of the ideal gas change, but in such a way that Eq. (18-18) is satisfied. We may select any two states of the system connected by an adiabatic process — let one of them be the initial state i — and apply Eq. (18-18), $pV^\gamma = K = p_iV_i^\gamma$, or

$$pV^\gamma = p_iV_i^\gamma$$

This equation may be solved for one of the variables, p for example:

$$p = \frac{p_iV_i^\gamma}{V^\gamma} \qquad (18\text{-}19)$$

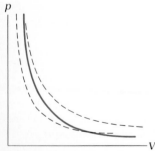

Figure 18-8. The solid curve represents a quasi-static, adiabatic process for an ideal gas. Also shown as dashed lines are two isotherms.

This expression shows how the pressure of the ideal gas varies with its volume for a quasi-static adiabatic process. This expression is represented by a curve on a p-V diagram, as shown in Fig. 18-8 for a gas with $\gamma = 1.40$. Also shown for reference are two isotherms ($pV = nRT =$ constant for an isothermal process). The adiabatic curve at a point on the diagram is steeper than an isotherm at that point (see Prob. 18-1).

EXAMPLE 18-5. In one cylinder of a diesel engine, air initially at atmospheric pressure and 310 K occupies a volume of 0.420 L. It is compressed, quasi-statically and adiabatically, to a volume of 0.028 L (a compression ratio of 15). Determine the final (*a*) pressure and (*b*) temperature.

SOLUTION. (*a*) Using Eq. (18-19) and the value of $\gamma = 1.40$ for air (see the entries for N_2 and O_2 in Table 18-1), we obtain

$$p_f = p_i \left(\frac{V_i}{V_f}\right)^{\gamma}$$

$$= (101 \text{ kPa}) \left(\frac{0.420}{0.028}\right)^{1.40}$$

$= 4500 \text{ kPa}$

(*b*) The temperature can be determined using the ideal gas equation of state:

$$T_f = T_i \frac{p_f V_f}{p_i V_i}$$

$$= 310 \text{ K} \frac{(4500 \text{ kPa})(0.028 \text{ L})}{(101 \text{ kPa})(0.420 \text{ L})} = 920 \text{ K}$$

Notice that the temperature of the gas increases for the adiabatic compression. What happens for an adiabatic expansion?

EXAMPLE 18-6. For the adiabatic compression in the preceding example, find (*a*) the work done by the air and (*b*) the change in internal energy of the air.

SOLUTION. (*a*) The work done by the gas for a quasi-static adiabatic process is evaluated using Eq. (18-19):

$$W = \int p \, dV = \int_{V_i}^{V_f} \frac{p_i V_i^{\gamma}}{V^{\gamma}} \, dV$$

$$= p_i V_i^{\gamma} \frac{1}{1-\gamma} \left(\frac{1}{V_f^{\gamma-1}} - \frac{1}{V_i^{\gamma-1}}\right)$$

$$= p_i V_i \frac{1}{1-\gamma} \left(\frac{V_i^{\gamma-1}}{V_f^{\gamma-1}} - \frac{V_i^{\gamma-1}}{V_i^{\gamma-1}}\right)$$

$$= \frac{p_i V_i}{\gamma - 1} \left[1 - \left(\frac{V_i}{V_f}\right)^{\gamma-1}\right]$$

$$= \frac{(101 \text{ kPa})(0.42 \text{ L})}{0.40} \left[1 - \left(\frac{0.42}{0.028}\right)^{0.40}\right]$$

$$= -210 \text{ J}$$

(*b*) The change in internal energy is, from the first law,

$$\Delta U = Q - W = 0 - (-210 \text{ J}) = 210 \text{ J}$$

Alternatively, *n* can be found from the ideal gas equation of state $p_i V_i = nRT_i$, $n = 0.016$ mol, and

$$\Delta U = n C_V \, \Delta T$$

$$= (0.016 \text{ mol})(21 \text{ J} \cdot \text{mol}^{-1} \cdot \text{K}^{-1})(610 \text{ K}) = 200 \text{ J}$$

The value of C_V was taken from Table 18-1 for N_2 and O_2. During the adiabatic compression, the system does negative work as the internal energy increases. Can you explain why these (calculated) answers for ΔU are slightly different?

18-7 THE DISTRIBUTION OF MOLECULAR SPEEDS

The mean square speed $\langle v^2 \rangle$ and its square root, the root-mean-square speed v_{rms}, have been related to the macroscopic properties of gases. We have considered average or mean values because experiment shows that there is a distribution of speeds for the molecules of a gas. Some molecules have speeds less than v_{rms}, while others have speeds greater than v_{rms}. There exists a range of speeds from zero up to rather large values.

The distribution of speeds is described by a *distribution function* $f(v)$. It is defined so that, of the N molecules in the system, the number ΔN which have a value of the speed between v and $v + \Delta v$ is given by

The distribution function $f(v)$ gives the distribution of molecular speeds.

$$\Delta N = f(v) \, \Delta v$$

That is, $f(v)$ is the number of molecules per unit speed range. Since we usually consider the total number of molecules to be very large, we work in the limit as Δv tends to zero, so that

$$dN = f(v)\,dv$$

is the number of molecules with speed between v and $v + dv$. Integrating over all speeds yields the total number of molecules:

$$N = \int_0^\infty f(v)\,dv$$

Distribution of molecular speeds
for an ideal gas

The distribution function for molecular speeds was first obtained by James Clerk Maxwell (1831–1879), who applied statistical concepts to the random motion of gas molecules. (See the Commentary in Chap. 19 and in Chap. 27.) That distribution of molecular speeds turns out to be

$$f(v) = Av^2 \exp \frac{-\frac{1}{2}mv^2}{kT} \tag{18-20}$$

where k is the Boltzmann constant and m is the molecular mass. The factor A is independent of the molecular speed v:

$$A = 4\pi N \left(\frac{m}{2\pi kT}\right)^{3/2}$$

(Problem 18-6 considers one experimental technique for measuring the distribution of molecular speeds.)

The form of the distribution function is shown graphically in Fig. 18-9a for Ar at 200 K and at 600 K in Fig. 18-9b. At either temperature the number of molecules with very low speeds is small. Nor are there many molecules with very high speeds. With increasing temperature, the distribution shifts to higher speeds and broadens. The area under the entire curve, equal to the integral of $f(v)$ over all speeds, is the total number of molecules N. Thus the area is the same for both graphs in Fig. 18-9; it corresponds to a choice of $N = 10^{23}$ molecules, about 1/6 of a mol.

The broadening of the distribution with increasing temperature comes from the factor T in the denominator in the argument of the exponential function, $\exp(-\frac{1}{2}mv^2/kT)$. A smaller value of the molecular mass in the numerator of the argument would have the same result on the appearance of the distribution function as an increase in temperature. That is, the distribution of molecular speeds is broader for a gas with smaller molecular mass than for a gas with larger molecular mass at the same temperature. For example, Fig. 18-9b could

Figure 18-9. The distribution of molecular speeds is shown for Ar at (a) 200 K and (b) 600 K. The total number of molecules is 1×10^{23}.

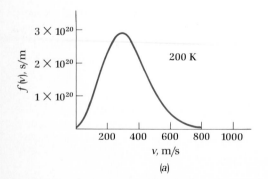

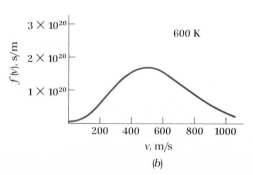

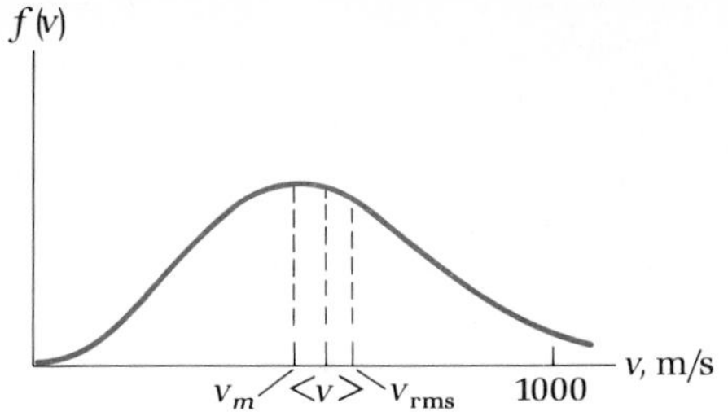

$f(v)$

Figure 18-10. Three characteristic speeds are shown for the case of Fig. 18-9b. The values are $v_m = 500$ m/s, $\langle v \rangle = 560$ m/s, $v_{rms} = 610$ m/s.

also describe the distribution of speeds for He, with 1/10 the molecular mass of Ar, at a temperature of 60 K.

The value of the root-mean-square speed v_{rms} is indicated on the graph in Fig. 18-10. We have already determined its value in terms of the molecular mass m and the temperature, Eq. (18-14):

$$v_{rms} = \sqrt{\langle v^2 \rangle} = \sqrt{\frac{3kT}{m}}$$

Its value can also be obtained by using the distribution function to average the square of the speed. Since $f(v)\,dv$ is the number of molecules with speed v in the range dv, the mean square speed (the average of v^2) is given by

$$\langle v^2 \rangle = \frac{\int_0^\infty v^2 f(v)\,dv}{N}$$

Root-mean-square speed: $v_{rms} = \sqrt{3kT/m}$

Integrals of this sort can be found in most tables of integrals after making the change of variables $x = \frac{1}{2}mv^2/kT$. The result is $\langle v^2 \rangle = 3kT/m$, so that $v_{rms} = \sqrt{3kT/m}$ as expected.

We identify two other characteristic speeds. One is the mean speed $\langle v \rangle$. Notice that the (scalar) mean *speed* $\langle v \rangle$ is different from the (vector) mean *velocity* $\langle \mathbf{v} \rangle$, which is zero. We obtain the mean speed by averaging the speeds of the molecules. Each value of the speed v is multiplied by the number of molecules with that speed, $f(v)\,dv$. The result is then summed or integrated and then divided by the total number of molecules:

$$\langle v \rangle = \frac{\int_0^\infty v f(v)\,dv}{N}$$

The integral can be evaluated from tables, with the result,

Mean speed: $\langle v \rangle = \sqrt{8kT/\pi m}$

$$\langle v \rangle = \sqrt{\frac{8kT}{\pi m}}$$

Comparing the mean speed $\langle v \rangle$ with $v_{rms} = \sqrt{3kT/m}$, we find that $\langle v \rangle < v_{rms}$, since $8/\pi < 3$.

The third characteristic speed is called the most probable speed v_m, which corresponds to the peak, or maximum value, of the distribution function. More molecules have this speed than any other value of the speed. Its value is obtained by differentiating the distribution function $f(v)$ and setting the derivative equal to zero. The result is (see Exercise 18-35)

Most probable speed: $v_m = \sqrt{2kT/m}$

$$v_m = \sqrt{\frac{2kT}{m}}$$

All three of the speeds are indicated on the graph in Fig. 18-10. They are always ordered as

$$v_m < \langle v \rangle < v_{rms}$$

EXAMPLE 18-7. Air is a mixture of gases, chiefly N_2 and O_2 with smaller amounts of other gases. Each component gas at temperature T has a distribution function given by Eq. (18-20). (a) Determine the most probable speed, the mean speed, and the root-mean-square speed of O_2 molecules in air at 300 K. (b) Repeat for H_2.

SOLUTION. (a) The mass of an O_2 molecule is $m = M/N_A$ where $M = 32$ g/mol is the molecular weight:

$$m = \frac{0.032 \text{ kg/mol}}{6.02 \times 10^{23} \text{ mol}^{-1}}$$

$$= 5.3 \times 10^{-26} \text{ kg}$$

The combination kT/m is needed for all three speeds:

$$\frac{kT}{m} = \frac{(1.38 \times 10^{-23} \text{ J/K})(300 \text{ K})}{5.3 \times 10^{-26} \text{ kg}} = 7.8 \times 10^4 \text{ m}^2/\text{s}^2$$

Then

$$v_m = \sqrt{2\left(\frac{kT}{m}\right)} = 390 \text{ m/s}$$

$$\langle v \rangle = \sqrt{\frac{8}{\pi}\left(\frac{kT}{m}\right)} = 450 \text{ m/s}$$

$$v_{\text{rms}} = \sqrt{3\left(\frac{kT}{m}\right)} = 480 \text{ m/s}$$

(b) For H_2 we only need to use the correct mass, about 1/16 the mass of the O_2 molecule. Since the speeds are proportional to the inverse square root of the molecular mass, the speeds for H_2 are 4 times those for O_2:

$$v_m = 1.6 \text{ km/s}$$

$$\langle v \rangle = 1.8 \text{ km/s}$$

$$v_{\text{rms}} = 1.9 \text{ km/s}$$

SUMMARY WITH APPLICATIONS

Section 18-2. Molecular model of an ideal gas
A molecular model of an ideal gas includes the following assumptions: there are a large number of molecules, the molecules behave as particles, Newton's laws apply to molecular motions, collisions are elastic, and the molecules move randomly.

The mean square speed is defined by $\langle v^2 \rangle = \Sigma v_j^2/N$ and is related to the pressure of the gas by

$$pV = \tfrac{1}{3}Nm\langle v^2 \rangle \tag{18-7}$$

State important assumptions for a molecular model of an ideal gas.

Define mean square speed and use its relation to the pressure of the gas.

Section 18-3. The microscopic interpretation of temperature
The internal energy of a monatomic ideal gas is given by

$$U = \tfrac{3}{2}nRT \tag{18-11}$$

Temperature is interpreted at the molecular level in terms of the average translational kinetic energy of molecules:

$$\langle K \rangle = \tfrac{3}{2}kT \tag{18-12}$$

The root-mean-square speed, $v_{\text{rms}} = \sqrt{\langle v^2 \rangle}$, depends on the temperature and the molecular mass:

$$v_{\text{rms}} = \sqrt{\frac{3kT}{m}} \tag{18-14}$$

Determine the internal energy, the average molecular kinetic energy, and the root-mean-square speed for a monatomic gas.

Section 18-4. Equipartition of energy
The average energy of a molecule with ν active degrees of freedom is

$$\langle E \rangle = \nu \tfrac{1}{2}kT \tag{18-15}$$

On the average, $\tfrac{1}{2}kT$ of energy is associated with each degree of freedom.

Use the equipartition of energy theorem to obtain the average molecular energy.

Section 18-5. Heat capacities of ideal gases and elemental solids
The molar heat capacities C_V and C_p for an ideal gas with ν active degrees of freedom are given by

$$C_V = \tfrac{1}{2}\nu R \qquad C_p = C_V + R$$

At higher temperatures, the molar heat capacity of an elemental solid is given by a simple model to be $C_V = 3R$, and $C_p \approx C_V$. This model assumes three translational and three vibrational degrees of freedom for each atom.

Calculate molar heat capacities of ideal gases, given the number of active degrees of freedom.

Calculate the molar heat capacity of an elemental solid at higher temperatures.

Section 18-6. Adiabatic process for an ideal gas
An ideal gas undergoing a quasi-static adiabatic process takes on pressure and volume values satisfying

$$pV^\gamma = K \tag{18-18}$$

where K is a constant and $\gamma = C_p/C_V$.

Determine pressure and volume values for an ideal gas undergoing an adiabatic process.

Section 18-7. The distribution of molecular speeds
The distribution of molecular speeds for an ideal gas is

$$f(v) = Av^2 \exp\left(-\tfrac{1}{2}mv^2/kT\right) \qquad (18\text{-}20)$$

where $A = 4\pi N(m/2\pi kT)^{3/2}$. Three speeds which help characterize the distribution are the most probable speed, $v_m = \sqrt{2kT/m}$; the mean speed, $\langle v \rangle = \sqrt{8kT/\pi m}$; and the root-

mean-square speed, $v_{\text{rms}} = \sqrt{3kT/m}$.

Describe the distribution of molecular speeds for an ideal gas; determine the most probable, the mean, and the root-mean-square speeds.

QUESTIONS

18-1 Explain how $\langle v \rangle$ can be different from zero while $\langle v_x \rangle = \langle v_y \rangle = \langle v_z \rangle = 0$, and so $\langle \mathbf{v} \rangle = 0$.

18-2 For an ideal gas, $\langle v \rangle < v_{\text{rms}}$, or $\langle v \rangle^2 < \langle v^2 \rangle$. That is, the *square of the mean speed* is less than the *mean square speed*. Is it possible for $\langle v \rangle^2$ to equal or exceed $\langle v^2 \rangle$ under any circumstances? Explain.

18-3 In a pure gas, all molecules are identical and have the same mass. Is the average translational kinetic energy still given by $\tfrac{3}{2}kT$ for a mixture of gases such as air? Explain.

18-4 Show that the ideal gas equation of state can be written as $pV = NkT$ and identify N in this equation.

18-5 The walls of a container of gas also consist of molecules. Thus a gas molecule colliding with a wall having the same temperature as the gas actually collides with one or more molecules. How can we justify, in an average sense, our assumption that the perpendicular component of velocity of a molecule merely reverses on a collision with the wall?

18-6 Can the gravitational potential energy of interaction of the molecules of a gas with the earth be neglected in comparison with the kinetic energy of the molecules? What about the gravitational potential energy of interaction of the molecules with each other? Explain.

18-7 Consider the air in a basketball during a game. Is (the vector) $\langle \mathbf{v} \rangle = 0$ for the air? Explain.

18-8 A molecule in a liquid must have a minimum, characteristic amount of kinetic energy in order to escape. How can a liquid such as water in an open container cool on evaporation?

18-9 Why must C_p be greater than C_V for a gas? Is this result true for liquids and solids as well? Explain.

18-10 If a molecule can change its speed on colliding with another molecule, can the distribution function $f(v)$ be independent of time? Explain.

18-11 If the distribution function is time-dependent, $f(v, t)$, can the gas be in equilibrium? Explain.

18-12 What happens to the temperature of an ideal gas if the gas is compressed adiabatically?

18-13 How can the temperature of a gas change during an adiabatic process, since no heat is exchanged with the surroundings? (*Hint:* Consider the change in velocity of a molecule colliding with a moving wall.)

18-14 Suppose that an opposite pair of walls of a container of gas are maintained at different temperatures. By what mechanism involving molecular collisions is

heat conducted through this gas? Note that the gas is not at a uniform temperature.

18-15 Why is it improper to speak of the temperature of a molecule? Of a system of 100 molecules? How many molecules must a system have before we can speak meaningfully of the temperature of that system?

18-16 Imagine a huge interstellar spaceship with billions of humans drifting randomly through the interior of the ship. The humans occasionally collide with each other and with the walls of the ship. Is it meaningful to speak of a gas of humans (anthropogas)? If so, estimate the human v_{rms}.

18-17 To what values do the differences $v_{\text{rms}} - \langle v \rangle$ and $\langle v \rangle - v_m$ tend as the temperature of a gas drops? Describe the change in appearance of the graph of the distribution function as the temperature drops.

18-18 The speed of sound in He is greater than the speed of sound in air at the same temperature and pressure. How can this be understood at the molecular level?

18-19 Molecular speeds range in value from zero to arbitrarily high values (but less than the speed of light). Explain on this basis why the distribution of molecular speeds can be asymmetric about the most probable speed.

18-20 Use features of the distribution of molecular speeds to give a possible explanation of the fact that the moon has virtually no atmosphere. Why is there almost no He in the earth's atmosphere?

18-21 Radon is a (radioactive) monatomic gas. Predict the values of C_V and C_p for this gas.

18-22 Complete the following table:

Symbol	Represents	Type	SI unit
$\langle v^2 \rangle$	Mean square speed		
v_{rms}			
$\langle v \rangle$		Scalar	
v_m			
$\langle K \rangle$			
k			J/K
ν			
C_p			
C_V			
γ			
$f(v)$			

EXERCISES

Section 18-2. Molecular model of an ideal gas

18-1 The following numbers, in units of m/s, represent a small sample of 10 molecular speeds: 290, 47, 182, 439, 330, 268, 302, 372, 344, 410. Determine for this sample (a) the mean speed $\langle v \rangle$ and (b) the mean square speed $\langle v^2 \rangle$. (c) Compare the values of $\langle v^2 \rangle$ and $\langle v \rangle^2$.

18-2 Estimate the average spacing between the molecules of 1 mol of a gas at atmospheric pressure and 300 K. Compare this with the size of an O_2 molecule (about 0.2 nm).

18-3 Consider a pure gas consisting of identical molecules of mass m. Show that the velocity components of the center of mass of this gas are related to the average velocity components of the molecules by

$$(v_{cm})_x = \langle v_x \rangle \qquad (v_{cm})_y = \langle v_y \rangle \qquad (v_{cm})_z = \langle v_z \rangle$$

In what reference frame is our description of the ideal gas based?

18-4 On a coin toss the probability of a heads is 1/2 and the probability of a tails is 1/2. What is the probability of getting (a) three heads in a row? (b) Heads, tails, tails, in that order, in three tosses? (c) One head (and one tail) in two tosses? (d) Two heads in four tosses? (Hint: List all 16 possible outcomes and find the fraction which result in two heads.)

18-5 Suppose a coin is tossed 1000 times. What is the expected number of heads? Do you *really* expect to get precisely that number of heads? See the previous exercise.

18-6 Estimate the impulse exerted on your skin by a collision with a typical molecule of the air at room temperature. Assume that $\langle v^2 \rangle = 2 \times 10^5$ m²/s².

18-7 Show that Eq. (18-7) can be written as

$$pV = \frac{nM\langle v^2 \rangle}{3}$$

where M is the molar mass.

18-8 One mole of a gas at $p = 101$ kPa occupies a volume $V = 28.8$ L. Determine the mean square speed if the gas is (a) He, (b) H_2, (c) CO_2, (d) UF_6.

Section 18-3. The microscopic interpretation of temperature

18-9 Determine the root-mean-square speed for each of the following molecular species in air at 300 K: (a) N_2, (b) O_2, (c) CO_2. (d) What is the average molecular translational kinetic energy for each of these species?

18-10 Show that Eq. (18-14) can be written in terms of the molar mass M as

$$v_{rms} = \sqrt{\frac{3RT}{M}}$$

18-11 By what factor must the temperature of a gas change

so that its root-mean-square speed changes by (a) 10 percent, (b) −10 percent, (c) 50 percent?

18-12 A gas mixture of 0.80 mol of He and 0.15 mol of Ne is at 400 K. Evaluate (a) the root-mean-square speed for each type of molecule, (b) the average translational kinetic energy for each type, (c) the internal energy of this mixture.

18-13 The electron volt (eV) is a convenient energy unit to use for atoms and molecules. The conversion is

$$1 \text{ eV} = 1.60 \times 10^{-19} \text{ J}$$

Express the average translational kinetic energy in eV for molecules of a gas at (a) 90 K (normal boiling point of O_2), (b) 300 K (temperature of the earth's surface), (c) 6000 K (temperature of the sun's surface).

18-14 Justify the following statement: The value of kT for a system at room temperature is $\frac{1}{40}$ eV. (See the previous exercise.)

18-15 A sealed tank car moves by you on a railroad track at 80 km/h in the positive x direction. It contains N_2 gas at 300 K. (a) What are the values of $\langle v_x \rangle$, $\langle v_y \rangle$, and $\langle v_z \rangle$ for this gas? (See Exercise 18-3.) (b) What are the values according to the railroad engineer? (c) Is the expression $\langle K \rangle = \frac{3}{2}kT$ for the average translational kinetic energy valid in every reference frame? Explain.

Section 18-4. Equipartition of energy

18-16 A nonlinear polyatomic gas at 650 K has molecules with 12 active degrees of freedom. (a) Evaluate the average molecular mechanical energy. (b) What is the value of v_{rms}? (c) How many vibrational degrees of freedom are active?

18-17 The temperature of 2.2 mol of O_2 is raised from 10°C to 140°C. (a) Assuming that vibrational degrees of freedom are not active over this temperature range, calculate the change in internal energy of the gas. (b) Can you determine how much heat was added and how much work was done? Explain.

Section 18-5. Heat capacities of ideal gases and elemental solids

18-18 Show that both the universal gas constant R and the Boltzmann constant k have dimensions of molar heat capacity. Note that the mole is dimensionless.

18-19 (a) Suppose that the process in Exercise 18-17 occurred at constant volume. How much heat was added to the gas and how much work was done by the gas? (b) What is the value of C_p for this range of temperatures? (c) What are the answers to part (a) if the temperature change occurred at constant pressure?

18-20 Given that F_2 is diatomic and gaseous at room temperature, estimate the values of C_V, C_p, and γ for F_2 at 25°C. Compare with the values in the next exercise.

18-21 The measured values of C_p and γ for F_2 at 25°C are $C_p = 31.4$ J · mol⁻¹ · K⁻¹ and $\gamma = 1.36$. (a) Determine the value of C_V. (b) Are the vibrational degrees of freedom active at this temperature? Explain.

18-22 From the graph in Fig. 18-5, estimate the number of active degrees of freedom for H_2 at (a) 100 K, (b) 600 K, (c) 2000 K. (d) Estimate the value of C_p at 600 K.

18-23 Estimate the value of γ for H_2 at each of the three temperatures listed in the previous exercise.

18-24 A cylinder with a movable piston contains 18 g of Ar at $p_i = 180$ kPa, $V_i = 12.0$ L. The gas is compressed to a final state given by $p_f = 480$ kPa, $V_f = 6.0$ L. (a) Determine the initial and final temperatures. (b) What is the change in internal energy?

18-25 The Ar gas in the previous exercise undergoes the process shown in Fig. 18-11. (a) Determine the net heat added to the gas, using values of C_p and C_V. (b) Calculate the work done by the gas by finding the area under the curve. (c) Check this answer by using the first law and the result of the previous exercise.

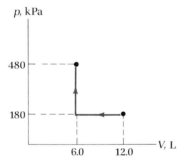

Figure 18-11. Exercise 18-25.

18-26 (a) Estimate the molar heat capacity of solid KCl at room temperature. Note that 1 mol consists of $2N_A$ atoms. (b) Estimate the value of c_V, the specific heat at constant volume, for KCl at room temperature.

Section 18-6. Adiabatic process for an ideal gas

18-27 A monatomic ideal gas with $\gamma = 1.67$ undergoes an adiabatic expansion from the initial state $p_i = 320$ kPa, $V_i = 12$ L to a final volume $V_f = 18$ L. (a) Determine the final pressure of the gas. (b) Determine the initial and final temperatures, given that $n = 1.4$ mol. (c) Show the process on a p-V diagram.

18-28 (a) Evaluate the work done by the gas for the adiabatic expansion described in the previous exercise by performing the integral $\int p \, dV$. (b) Check the result by determining the change in internal energy of the gas and using the first law.

18-29 Prove for an ideal gas that $T_i V_i^{\gamma-1} = T_f V_f^{\gamma-1}$ for a quasi-static adiabatic process. What is the corresponding expression for an isobaric process?

18-30 Helium is initially at $p_i = 101$ kPa in a cylinder of volume $V_i = 2.25$ L and in equilibrium with surroundings which remain at 300 K. The gas is quasi-statically, but quickly (adiabatically), compressed to $V_f = 1.64$ L and held at that volume as it comes to equilibrium with the surroundings. (a) Evaluate the highest temperature and highest pressure attained by the He. (b) Show the process on the p-V diagram for the He. For the entire process, determine (c) the work done by the He and (d) the heat added to the He.

18-31 The temperature of 64 g of O_2 is raised from 15°C to 45°C. What is the change in the internal energy of the O_2 if the process is (a) isochoric, (b) isobaric, (c) adiabatic? Assume that the gas is ideal.

18-32 The O_2 in the previous exercise is initially at atmospheric pressure. For each of the three quasi-static processes set forth above, determine the heat added to the gas and the work done by the gas.

18-33 One mole of an ideal gas is initially at $p_i = 200$ kPa, $V_i = 20$ L. On the same p-V diagram, show the quasi-static adiabatic process leading to a final volume $V_f = 30$ L if the ideal gas is (a) He, (b) Ne, (c) O_2, (d) CO_2.

18-34 Show that the number of active degrees of freedom ν is related to γ by $\nu = 2/(\gamma - 1)$.

Section 18-7. The distribution of molecular speeds

18-35 Using the distribution function for molecular speeds, show that the most probable speed is given by

$$v_m = \sqrt{\frac{2kT}{m}}$$

18-36 Evaluate the speeds v_m, $\langle v \rangle$, v_{rms} for (a) H_2 at 300 K and (b) O_2 at 300 K.

18-37 A small sample of molecular speeds is given in the table below, where ΔN is the number of molecules with a speed within a range of $\Delta v = 100$ m/s about v. That is, one molecule has speed between 0 and 100 m/s, two molecules have speeds between 100 and 200 m/s, and so on. Determine for this sample (a) the mean speed, (b) the root-mean-square speed, (c) the most probable speed.

ΔN	v, m/s
1	50
2	150
4	250
3	350
1	450

18-38 The speed of sound v_s in an ideal gas is given by (see Sec. 33-2 and also Prob. 18-4)

$$v_s = \sqrt{\frac{\gamma RT}{M}}$$

where $\gamma = C_p/C_V$ and M is the molar mass. Calculate the speed of sound at 300 K in (a) He, (b) N_2, (c) air.

18-39 Prove that the speed of sound in a gas (see previous exercise) is related to the mean speed by

$$\frac{v_s}{\langle v \rangle} = \sqrt{\frac{\gamma \pi}{8}}$$

Evaluate this ratio for He and for air.

PROBLEMS

18-1 Consider a process represented by a curve on a p-V diagram, as shown in Fig. 18-12. At a given point (V, p) the slope of a line tangent to the curve is dp/dV. Evaluate dp/dV at a point for an ideal gas undergoing (a) an isobaric process, (b) an isothermal process, (c) an adiabatic process. (d) Which process has the steepest slope?

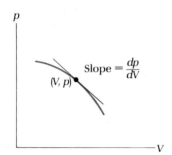

Figure 18-12. Prob. 18-1.

18-2 Using a table of integrals or otherwise, show that the mean value of v^n, $\langle v^n \rangle$, is given by (n is a positive integer)

$$\langle v^n \rangle = B_n \left(\frac{2kT}{m} \right)^{n/2}$$

where B_n depends on whether n is even or odd and is given by

$$B_1 = \frac{2}{\sqrt{\pi}}$$

$$B_2 = \frac{3}{2}$$

$$B_n = \frac{n+1}{2} \frac{n-1}{2} \cdots (2)(1) \frac{2}{\sqrt{\pi}} \qquad n \text{ odd}, n > 1$$

$$= \frac{n+1}{2} \frac{n-1}{2} \cdots \frac{3}{2} \qquad n \text{ even}, n > 2$$

18-3 The escape speed v_i of a molecule from above the earth's surface was calculated in Chap. 9. Its square is given by

$$v_i^2 = \frac{2GM_e}{r_i}$$

where M_e is the mass of the earth and r_i is the initial separation of the molecule from the center of the earth. The temperature of the earth's upper atmo-

sphere can be 1000 K at an altitude of about 150 km during a period of maximum sunspot activity. (a) Determine the mean square speed of an N_2 molecule under these conditions. (b) Determine the ratio of the number of molecules at this location that have the escape speed to the number that have the root-mean-square speed. (c) Would this ratio be different for H_2? Explain.

18-4 Ordinary sound waves in a gas have a speed v_s given in terms of the density ρ and the bulk modulus B (see Chap. 15) by

$$v_s = \sqrt{\frac{B}{\rho}}$$

The pressure and density variations that constitute the sound wave occur so rapidly that the adiabatic bulk modulus, $B = -V(dp/dV)$, is to be used, and the derivative is taken appropriate to an adiabatic process. Show that the speed of sound in an ideal gas is given by

$$v_s = \sqrt{\frac{\gamma RT}{M}}$$

18-5 Oxygen nuclei in an O_2 molecule are about 0.2 nm apart, and virtually all of the mass of the molecule is concentrated in the two nuclei. (a) Estimate the moment of inertia of the molecule about an axis which is a perpendicular bisector of the line joining the two nuclei. (b) Estimate the root-mean-square angular speed ω_{rms} about this axis for O_2 at 400 K.

18-6 One method of measuring molecular speeds is to use a rotating-drum apparatus, shown schematically in Fig. 18-13. Molecules escaping from an oven at temperature T enter the drum only when the slit S passes. The molecules stick on a glass plate G on the opposite side, with a spatial distribution along the plate de-

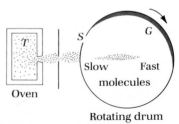

Figure 18-13. Prob. 18-6: Silver atoms from an oven pass through a slit in a rotating drum.

pending on the molecular speed distribution. Suppose the drum is 120 mm in diameter and rotates at 1200 rev/min and that Ag atoms emerge from the oven maintained at 1000 K. Determine the distance along the plate G between points struck by atoms with speeds $\frac{1}{2}v_{\text{rms}}$ and $\frac{3}{2}v_{\text{rms}}$.

18-7 *Einstein model of vibrations in a solid.* In the Einstein model of an elemental solid, all atoms are assumed to vibrate with the same frequency ν_0. Each atom can oscillate along each of the three spatial directions, and the (quantum) average mechanical energy of each oscillator is given by

$$\langle E \rangle = \frac{h\nu_0}{e^{h\nu_0/kT} - 1}$$

where $h = 6.63 \times 10^{-34}$ J $\cdot$ s is Planck's constant (see Chap. 39). (a) Show that the molar heat capacity from this model is

$$C_V = 3R \frac{(h\nu_0/kT)^2 \, e^{h\nu_0/kT}}{(e^{h\nu_0/kT} - 1)^2}$$

(b) Construct a graph of this function for T ranging from 1 to 300 K, taking $\nu_0 = 10^{12}$ Hz as a typical frequency. (c) What value does C_V approach as T becomes large?

18-8 Estimate the specific heat c_p of water vapor at low pressure. Assume three translational and three rotational degrees of freedom. Compare with the measured value $c_p = 2000$ J $\cdot$ kg^{-1} $\cdot$ K^{-1} at room temperature. Are vibrational degrees of freedom active? Explain.

18-9 *Dalton's law of partial pressures.* Consider a mixture of several gases with N_1 molecules of mass m_1. N_2 molecules of mass m_2, ... By extending the development in Sec. 18-2, prove Dalton's law of partial pressures: *The total pressure of a mixture of gases is equal to the sum of the partial pressures of the component gases.* The *partial pressure* is the pressure of a gas if it alone were present.

18-10 ⬛ The fraction of molecules with speed v within dv is the distribution function in Eq. (18-20) divided by the total number of molecules in the system:

$[f(v)\, dv]/N$. The fraction with speeds between v_1 and v_2 is therefore given by the integral

$$\frac{1}{N} \int_{v_1}^{v_2} f(v)\, dv$$

This integral must be evaluated numerically. (a) Write or adapt a program to do this, choosing an interval size for Δv which is appropriate for O_2 at 300 K. (b) Determine the fraction of molecules with speeds between 0 and v_m, between v_m and $\langle v \rangle$, and between $\langle v \rangle$ and v_{rms}.

18-11 ⬛ ***The median speed.*** Use the program developed in the preceding problem to determine the *median* speed, the speed such that half the molecules have speeds below this value and the other half have speeds above this value. Note that you must integrate the distribution function from $v = 0$ out to a speed such that half the molecules are accounted for. Compare the median speed with the most probable, the mean, and the root-mean-square speeds.

18-12 ⬛ The BASIC function RND(1) returns a (pseudo) random number whose value lies between 0 and 1. Develop a program to generate N random numbers within this range, calculate the mean of these numbers, and calculate the root-mean-square value. Do this for $N = 10, 100$, and 1000. What do you expect for the mean of these randomly distributed numbers?

18-13 ⬛ ***The gaussian distribution.*** A different kind of distribution of numbers can be obtained by using the random-number function from the previous problem. Consider a number obtained from the following expression:

$$v = 300 + \sum_{i=1}^{50} 10*(RND(1) - .5)$$

That is, added to 300 is the sum of 50 random numbers, each lying between -5 and $+5$. Write a program to generate $N = 100$ values for v of this type. Choose $\Delta v = 5$ and count the number of values that lie between v and $v + \Delta v$. Inspect these values and construct a graph of values similar to that in Fig. 18-9. This approximates a *normal*, or *gaussian, distribution.*

CHAPTER 19
THE SECOND LAW OF THERMODYNAMICS

19-1 INTRODUCTION

Occasionally we see a film clip or a videotape which is being run backward. It is amusing to see the customary order of a sequence of events reversed: Views of people walking backwards, water flowing uphill, or a previously demolished building arising from the rubble all accentuate our bias toward a one-way perception of time, flowing from past to future. Of the laws of nature that we have encountered so far — Newton's laws, the law of gravitation, the conservation laws, the first law of thermodynamics — none depends on the sense or direction of time. That is, these laws remain the same if time t is replaced by $-t$. The motion of a ball up and down in free-fall (no friction), for example, would look the same if time were reversed. If all of these laws are obeyed, why then does a time-reversed sequence of some events seem unnatural, improbable, even impossible to us? Indeed some processes *are* impossible, and it is the *second law of thermodynamics* which states that such processes do not occur.

There are many different but equivalent ways to phrase the second law. Much of the language reflects the law's origins in attempts to improve the efficiency of steam engines. We shall consider several statements of the second law of thermodynamics in this chapter and see that it applies to much more than just steam engines.

19-2 HEAT ENGINES AND THE SECOND LAW

The first law of thermodynamics, $\Delta U = Q - W$, deals with energy transfers between a system and its environment. In a typical process, heat Q is added to the system and work W is done by the system. We can regard the process as one which transforms energy: Energy enters the system as heat and leaves the

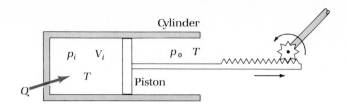

Figure 19-1. A compressed gas ($p_i > p_0$) expands isothermally, converting heat into work.

system as work. A gas expanding at constant pressure in a cylinder is a simple example. Or in a different process, the transformation or conversion of energy can be in the opposite sense, with energy entering the system as work and leaving the system as heat.

The conversion of work into heat occurs spontaneously when work is done by dissipative forces such as friction. In an automobile-braking mechanism for example, energy enters the disk as work done by frictional forces between brake pads and rotating disk. The temperature of the disk increases, and because of the temperature difference, energy is transferred to the surroundings as heat.

The opposite process, the conversion of heat into work, is highly desirable from an economic point of view. Energy transferred as work can be put to such practical uses as lifting a weight or turning a shaft to operate machinery or an electric generator. Energy transferred as heat cannot be directly used to lift a weight or turn a shaft. Simply burning gasoline to transfer energy as heat to an automobile will not propel the automobile. It is necessary first to convert heat into work.

Consider the process illustrated in Fig. 19-1: A metallic cylinder fitted with a movable piston contains a compressed ideal gas in an initial state characterized by p_i, V_i, with a temperature T the same as the surroundings. The gas is allowed to expand isothermally, with heat entering the gas from the surroundings. The gas does work on the moving piston as the volume of the gas increases. Since the process is isothermal and the system is an ideal gas, the change in internal energy $\Delta U = 0$. From the first law, $\Delta U = 0 = Q - W$. In this process, an amount of heat Q has been converted to work W, and $W = Q$.

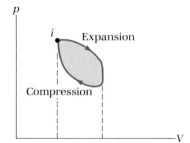

Figure 19-2. In a cycle the net work done by the system equals the area enclosed on a p-V diagram.

As a practical method for converting heat to work, the single expansion process is not very satisfactory: It is a one-time affair. Once the pressure of the gas drops to atmospheric pressure, no further expansion will occur. We were only able to convert heat into work with this process because the gas was originally compressed. To return the gas to its initial state would require that some work be done *on the gas* to compress it. Part of the work obtained during the expansion must be reinvested to prepare the gas for a subsequent expansion. Suppose that we return the gas to its initial state by a different path, one with lower pressure values so that less work has to be done on the gas. Then the net result is that (i) heat has been added to the gas; (ii) the gas has been returned to its initial state, ready for another expansion; and (iii) more work was done by the gas during the expansion than was reinvested to complete the cycle. Thus we are led to the idea of a cycle operating as a *heat engine,* a device for repeatedly converting heat into work.

The cycle as a heat engine to convert heat into work

In a cycle the system returns to its initial state, and the cycle may be repeated any number of times. This repetitive feature makes the cycle attractive as a heat engine. We shall usually analyze a single cycle so that all quantities refer to one cycle of operation. A general, quasi-static cycle is shown in Fig. 19-2 on a p-V diagram. For convenience the initial state has been chosen to correspond to the

Figure 19-3. A modern steam-plant cycle is shown schematically. High-pressure steam is generated in the boiler by heat from the fuel. The steam does work in turning the blades of the turbine. Lower pressure is maintained on the other side of the turbine by extracting heat and condensing the steam. The heat is exhausted into cooling water, often from a river or a lake. The pump forces water back into the high-pressure boiler.

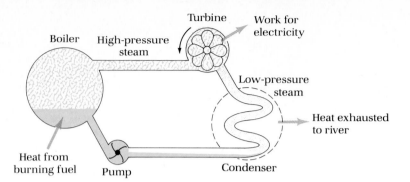

The net work for a cycle equals the enclosed area on a p-V diagram.

beginning of an expansion. The system does positive work on its surroundings during the expansion. The system does negative work on the surroundings during the compression as the system is returned to the initial state. The net work W done by the system for the entire cycle is equal to the area enclosed by the cycle on the p-V diagram, as we saw in Chap. 17. It is positive if the cycle proceeds in the clockwise sense because the work done during the expansion is greater than the magnitude of the negative work done during the compression. Let Q represent the net heat added to the system for the entire cycle. Since $\Delta U = 0$ for a cycle, the first law gives

For a cycle, $\Delta U = 0$ and $W = Q$.

$$W = Q \tag{19-1}$$

That is, the net work done for the cycle equals the net heat added for the cycle because the system is returned to its initial state ($\Delta U = 0$).

In a modern steam engine, such as one used in the generation of electric energy, work is done in turning a steam turbine rather than in moving a piston. As shown in Fig. 19-3, heat from fossil or nuclear fuel is added to water to form high-pressure steam, which performs work by expanding against the turbine blades. To be compressed at low pressure, the steam is condensed, which requires the extraction or the exhaust of heat from the water. This heat exchange is accomplished in cooling towers or by using cooling water from a large reservoir such as a river. Of the amount of heat obtained from the burning of fuel in a modern power plant, 60 percent or more is exhausted in completing the cycle. Thus 40 percent, at most, of the heat provided by the fuel is converted to mechanical work (and subsequently to electric energy, with small losses).

The efficiency of heat engines. All cyclic heat engines have in common some of the features described above for the steam engine. Some substance, called the *working substance*, undergoes a cyclic process. Heat is exchanged with the surroundings by the working substance at at least two different temperatures. Heat is added to the system at the higher temperature and must be exhausted from the system at the lower temperature to complete the cycle. It is the *net* heat added which equals the work for the cycle.

The working substance in a heat engine undergoes a cycle.

For simplicity we restrict our attention to cycles operating between only two heat reservoirs. That is, heat exchanges occur at only two temperatures of the surroundings, T_H and T_C (H for hot and C for cold). We let Q_H represent the heat added in each cycle to the system at the higher temperature T_H and Q_C the heat extracted in each cycle from the system at the lower temperature T_C. By our convention, the heat actually added to a system is positive, so $Q_H > 0$. Heat

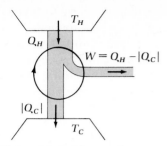

Figure 19-4. A heat engine operates between two reservoirs. The values of Q_H, $|Q_C|$, and W are proportional to the widths of the connecting pathways.

extracted from a system corresponds to a negative value of heat added to the system, so $Q_C < 0$. It is convenient to work with only positive values of the energy transfers. Therefore we use the (positive) absolute value $|Q_C| = -Q_C$ of the negative quantity Q_C: The net heat added for the cycle is

$$Q = Q_H + Q_C = Q_H - |Q_C|$$

Thus Eq. (19-1), which is the first law of thermodynamics applied to the cycle, becomes

$$W = Q_H - |Q_C| \tag{19-2}$$

In an idealized version of the steam plant, for example, heat Q_H is added to the water in the boiler and heat $|Q_C|$ is extracted from the water in the condensing coils.

The energy transfers and the cycle are represented schematically in Fig. 19-4. The circle represents the cycle as a heat engine operating between two reservoirs at temperatures T_H and T_C. The values of Q_H, $|Q_C|$, and W are proportional to the widths of the connecting pathways on the diagram, graphically illustrating Eq. (19-2).

We regard Q_H as the input of energy and W as the useful output of energy for each cycle. The exhausted heat $|Q_C|$ is therefore considered as wasted energy. The *efficiency* η of the heat engine is defined as the ratio of output to input:

The efficiency of a heat engine equals the output W divided by the input Q_H.

$$\eta = \frac{W}{Q_H} \tag{19-3}$$

The efficiency can also be expressed in terms of the two heat-exchange values. Substituting Eq. (19-2) into Eq. (19-3) gives $\eta = (Q_H - |Q_C|)/Q_H$, or

$$\eta = 1 - \frac{|Q_C|}{Q_H} \tag{19-4}$$

From this form, we see that the efficiency of a heat engine increases as $|Q_C|$ is reduced relative to Q_H.

EXAMPLE 19-1. A modern electric power plant has an efficiency of about 35 percent and produces electric energy at a rate of $P = 10^9$ W $= 1$ GW. Estimate the heat exchanges in the boiler and in the condenser for 1 h of operation.

SOLUTION. Although the symbols W, Q_H, and $|Q_C|$ refer to one cycle, the values for any particular number of cycles will be in the same proportion. Thus we let W, Q_H, and $|Q_C|$ represent in this case the values for 1 h of operation. We express energy in GW·h (gigawatt-hours), where 1 GW·h $= 3.6 \times 10^{12}$ J. The work done is

$$W = Pt = (1 \text{ GW})(1 \text{ h}) = 1 \text{ GW·h}$$

From Eq. (19-3), the heat Q_H is

$$Q_H = \frac{W}{\eta} = \frac{1 \text{ GW·h}}{0.35} = 3 \text{ GW·h}$$

and from the first law

$$Q_H - |Q_C| = W$$

$$|Q_C| = Q_H - W = 3 \text{ GW·h} - 1 \text{ GW·h} = 2 \text{ GW·h}$$

The second law of thermodynamics (Kelvin-Planck statement). Equation (19-4) combines the definition of efficiency and the first law of thermodynamics applied to a cycle. The maximum efficiency that would be allowed *mathematically* from that equation is 1, or 100 percent, corresponding to $|Q_C| = 0$. Imagine a cycle with no heat exhausted or wasted: $|Q_C| = 0$; then the first law would give $W = Q_H$. The working substance, having completed a

428   THE SECOND LAW OF THERMODYNAMICS

cycle, would be unchanged, and an amount of heat extracted from a reservoir at a single temperature would have been completely converted to work.

There have been many attempts to construct a heat engine with 100 percent efficiency. All attempts have failed. That a 100 percent efficient heat engine is impossible is one way of stating the second law of thermodynamics: *There exists no cycle which extracts heat from a reservoir at a single temperature and completely converts it into work.* This form of the second law is called the *Kelvin-Planck statement* of the law. It is important to recognize that the 100 percent efficient heat engine would obey the first law of thermodynamics. It is the second law that denies the possibility of a cycle with no heat exhausted at a lower temperature. Imagine, for example, a cycle which extracts heat Q_H from the ocean at a single temperature T_H and converts it completely into work W (to propel a ship). The first law would require $W = Q_H$, but the second law denies the existence of such a cycle.

The second law is not a strictly quantitative law. The Kelvin-Planck statement is qualitative. It states the impossibility of certain types of processes. Nevertheless, the second law is just as rigorous as the first law and has equal standing with the first law. As we encounter other ways of phrasing the second law, we shall see that it applies to other processes in addition to those suggested by the Kelvin-Planck statement.

The second law of thermodynamics (Kelvin-Planck statement)

19-3 REFRIGERATORS AND THE SECOND LAW

The Kelvin-Planck statement of the second law of thermodynamics is expressed in terms appropriate to a heat engine. The second law can also be stated in a way that relates to the operation of a refrigerator.

A refrigerator is a device operating in a cycle which is designed to extract heat from its interior so as to achieve or to maintain a lower temperature inside. During the refrigeration cycle, heat is exhausted to the outside, which is usually at a higher temperature than the inside. A net amount of work, provided typically by an electric motor, is done on the system for a cycle. A common refrigeration cycle uses a throttling process as described in Sec. 17-6. Work is done on the working substance, a fluid such as freon, by a compressor C, as shown in Fig. 19-5. The compressor maintains a high pressure difference across the throttling valve A. As the liquid evaporates on the low-pressure, low-temperature side, heat Q_C is added to the fluid from the inside of the refrigerator, which causes the inside temperature to drop. On the high-pressure, high-temperature side, heat $|Q_H|$ is exhausted from the fluid to the outside as the fluid condenses.

The energy transfers taking place in a refrigeration cycle are shown sche-

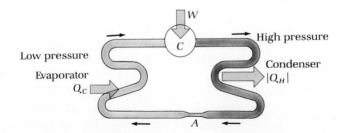

Figure 19-5. A mechanical refrigeration cycle uses a throttling process. Heat Q_C is added to the refrigerant on the low-pressure, low-temperature side. Heat $|Q_H|$ is exhausted from the refrigerant on the high-pressure, high-tempera-ture side as vapor is converted to liquid in the condenser.

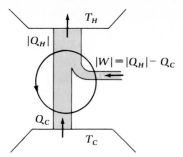

Figure 19-6. A refrigerator operates between two reservoirs.

matically in Fig. 19-6. Heat Q_C is added to the system from the low-temperature reservoir, representing the inside of the refrigerator, at T_C. A positive amount of heat $|Q_H|$ is exhausted to the high-temperature reservoir, representing the outside surroundings, at T_H. Negative work W is done by the system, or positive work $|W|$ is done on the system by the compressor motor. The first law of thermodynamics applied to the cycle gives $W = Q_H + Q_C$ or (on multiplying by -1). $-W = -Q_H - Q_C$. The result can be written in terms of positive quantities, $|W| = -W$ and $|Q_H| = -Q_H$:

$$|W| = |Q_H| - Q_C \qquad (19\text{-}5)$$

A comparison of Eqs. (19-5) and (19-2) and of Figs. 19-6 and 19-4 suggests that a refrigerator is like a heat engine running backward. The energy transfers are reversed for the heat engine and refrigerator cycles. But we should not expect the magnitudes of Q_C, Q_H, and W to be the same for the two cycles. There are usually mechanical constraints which actually prevent a particular heat engine from being run backward.

One characteristic of a refrigeration cycle (similar to the efficiency of a heat engine) is its *coefficient of performance K*. It is defined by

Coefficient of performance K for a refrigerator.

$$K = \frac{Q_C}{|W|} \qquad (19\text{-}6)$$

It is the ratio of the useful quantity for a refrigerator, the heat extracted from the inside, to the cost, the work performed by the motor.

The heat pump. The refrigeration cycle extracts heat Q_C from a low-temperature reservoir (inside a refrigerator) which tends to reduce the inside temperature. The cycle exhausts heat $|Q_H|$ to the outside, and the outside temperature tends to increase. In effect, heat is "pumped" by the refrigeration cycle from lower- to higher-temperature regions.

A heat pump "pumps" heat from lower to higher temperatures.

The *heat pump*, which is essentially a refrigerator, is in common use in moderate climates for space heating and cooling. For space heating, the evaporator heat exchanger is outside the structure, as shown in Fig. 19-7a, and extracts heat Q_C from surrounding air. The condenser heat exchanger is inside the structure, and heat $|Q_H|$ is exhausted to the inside air. The cycle pumps heat from outside to the inside. For cooling, the inside heat exchanger becomes the evaporator and the outside heat exchanger becomes the condenser, as seen in Fig. 19-7b. Heat is pumped from inside to the outside. In either case, the cycle

Figure 19-7. A heat pump pumps heat (a) from outside to inside in winter and (b) from inside to outside in summer. The compressor is not shown.

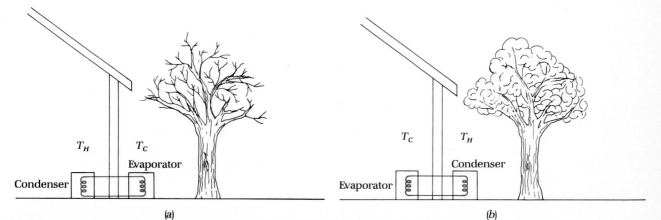

(a)

(b)

can pump heat from a lower-temperature reservoir to a higher-temperature one.

A heat pump used for space heating can be characterized by a coefficient of performance different from that of a refrigerator. The useful quantity for heating purposes is $|Q_H|$, the heat exhausted to the inside. The quantity we pay for is still the work $|W|$. The heat-pump coefficient of performance K_{hp} is defined as

Coefficient of performance K_{hp} for a heat pump.

$$K_{hp} = \frac{|Q_H|}{|W|} \qquad (19\text{-}7)$$

EXAMPLE 19-2. A refrigerator with a 480-W compressor motor is rated by a coefficient of performance $K = 2.8$. Estimate the rate of heat exchange at the condenser and at the evaporator.

SOLUTION. For a steadily running refrigerator, the rate of an energy transfer (energy transferred per second) is proportional to the energy transfer for each cycle. From Eq. (19-6),

$$K = \frac{Q_C}{|W|} = \frac{dQ_C/dt}{d|W|/dt}$$

or

$$\frac{dQ_C}{dt} = K \frac{d|W|}{dt} = (2.8)(480 \text{ W}) = 1.3 \text{ kW}$$

From the first law, $|Q_H| = Q_C + |W|$, so that

$$\frac{d|Q_H|}{dt} = \frac{dQ_C}{dt} + \frac{d|W|}{dt} = 1.3 \text{ kW} + 0.48 \text{ kW}$$

$$= 1.8 \text{ kW}$$

EXAMPLE 19-3. During an hour of operation, a heat pump uses 1.4 kW·h of electric energy while supplying 1.1×10^4 Btu to the inside of a home. Determine (a) the coefficient of performance and (b) the heat extracted from the outside in an hour.

SOLUTION. We first express the energy transfers in the same unit, converting Btu to kW·h:

$$|Q_H| = \frac{(1.1 \times 10^4 \text{ Btu})(1055 \text{ J} \cdot \text{Btu})}{3.6 \times 10^6 \text{ J} \cdot \text{kW}^{-1} \cdot \text{h}^{-1}}$$

$$= 3.2 \text{ kW} \cdot \text{h}$$

(a) The coefficient of performance is

$$K_{hp} = \frac{|Q_H|}{|W|} = \frac{3.2 \text{ kW} \cdot \text{h}}{1.4 \text{ kW} \cdot \text{h}} = 2.3$$

(b) The heat extracted from the outside in 1 h is obtained using the first law, applying it to the operation of the heat pump for this time period:

$$Q_C = |Q_H| - |W|$$

$$= 3.2 \text{ kW} \cdot \text{h} - 1.4 \text{ kW} \cdot \text{h} = 1.8 \text{ kW} \cdot \text{h}$$

The second law of thermodynamics (Clausius statement)

The second law of thermodynamics (Clausius statement). From the last two examples, and generally from Eqs. (19-6) and (19-7), we see that a coefficient of performance can have a value greater than 1. Indeed, for refrigerating or heating purposes, larger values of a coefficient of performance mean greater economy. Mathematically, a larger value of a coefficient of performance is achieved by decreasing $|W|$ relative to Q_C or $|Q_H|$. The value could be increased without bound by having $|W|$ approach zero. If $|W| = 0$, then the first law applied to the cycle would give $|Q_H| = Q_C$, and the net result would be the transfer of heat from a reservoir at lower temperature to one at higher temperature, with no change in any other system. No such process has ever been observed. Its impossibility is another way to phrase the second law of thermodynamics. *No process is possible whose sole, net result is the transfer of heat from lower to higher temperature.* This form of the second law is called the *Clausius statement.* The second law does not prohibit the operation of a refrigerator or a heat pump. That is, heat can be transferred from lower to higher

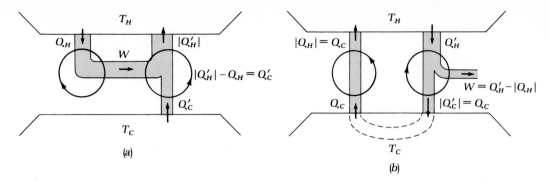

Figure 19-8. (a) A hypothetical 100 percent efficient heat engine runs a refrigerator, violating both statements of the second law of thermodynamics. (b) A hypothetical refrigerator violating the Clausius statement of the second law is combined with a heat engine. Since no *net* heat is exhausted by the combination at the low-temperature reservoir, the combination also violates the Kelvin-Planck statement of the second law.

temperature by a cycle for which work is provided. The second law does prohibit the operation of a refrigeration cycle with *no* work provided. Also prohibited is the spontaneous flow of heat from lower to higher temperature.

The Clausius statement of the second law deals with heat transfer from lower to higher temperature. The Kelvin-Planck statement deals with the conversion of heat into work. How can these very differently phrased statements correspond to one and the same law of nature? They are equivalent statements because any process prohibited by one statement can also be shown to be prohibited by the other statement. Figure 19-8 illustrates this equivalence. Suppose, as seen in Fig. 19-8a, that there were a 100 percent efficient heat engine (a violation of the Kelvin-Planck statement). Then the work from that engine could be used to run a refrigeration cycle. Taking the two cycles together, the net and only result would be a transfer of heat from lower to higher temperature (a violation of the Clausius statement). Thus a process forbidden by the Kelvin-Planck statement is also forbidden by the Clausius statement.

In a similar way, the converse is illustrated in Fig. 19-8b. A refrigeration cycle violating the Clausius statement could be run in conjunction with a heat engine. The combination constitutes a cycle which could extract heat at a single temperature and completely convert it into work, thus violating the Kelvin-Planck statement.

Alternative, equivalent statements of the second law have equal stature in thermodynamics. It is mainly for convenience (and a consequence of the history of the development of the second law) that we have more than one statement. We may find it much easier to apply one statement of the second law, rather than the other, to some proposed process.

19-4 REVERSIBILITY AND THE CARNOT CYCLE

The second law of thermodynamics tells us that no heat engine can be 100 percent efficient [$|Q_C|$ cannot be zero in Eq. (19-4)] and that no refrigerator can have an infinite coefficient of performance [$|W|$ cannot be zero in Eq. (19-6)]. But the second law does not tell us how great the efficiency of a heat engine or the coefficient of performance of a refrigerator can be. Still, our experience suggests that frictional effects and heat transfer through large temperature differences, for example, tend to reduce the efficiency of engines.

Reversible and irreversible processes. The flow of heat from a body at higher temperature to one at lower temperature is an example of an irreversible process. It is irreversible in the sense that the reversed process, one with the order of events reversed in time, is impossible according to the second law. Here is an instance of the connection between the second law and the sense or direction of time. The time-reversed process, the spontaneous flow of heat from lower to higher temperature, does not occur. Heat can be transferred from lower to higher temperature only by making substantial changes in the arrangement, such as by operating a heat pump between the two bodies.

We use this idea — significant changes in the surroundings to reverse the process — to classify processes as either reversible or irreversible. *A reversible process for a system is one which can be reversed by making only infinitesimal changes in the surroundings.* In a reversible process, heat transfer must occur because of infinitesimal temperature differences between a system and its surroundings. Heat is added to a system reversibly by having it in contact with a reservoir whose temperature is negligibly higher than that of the system. To reverse that heat transfer, the reservoir must have a temperature negligibly below that of the system. By similarly making only infinitesimal changes in external forces or constraints on a system, we can reverse any motion for a reversible process. Thus no frictional forces can perform work for a reversible process.

If a process is not reversible, then it is an irreversible process. Consequently, a process is irreversible if heat transfer occurs through a finite temperature difference, or if frictional forces perform work, or generally if finite changes in the surroundings must occur to reverse the process.

A process must be quasi-static in order to be reversible. The converse is not true: A process can be quasi-static but not reversible. For example, heat can be added quasi-statically to a system through an insulating layer with a temperature difference that is not negligible. The transfer of heat through a significant temperature difference makes the process irreversible.

A little reflection shows that every *real* process is irreversible. A reversible process is a useful idealization, similar in spirit to a frictionless interface or a spherically symmetric earth or a massless string in mechanics. A particular process can be considered nearly reversible to the extent that only very small changes in the surroundings of the system will reverse the process. The smaller the required changes, the more nearly reversible the process. We classify a process as reversible in this limiting sense. We assume that a process can be found or developed, which is as close to being reversible as desired, to connect any two states of a system. The concept of a reversible process plays an essential role in our further analysis of heat engines.

The Carnot cycle. Consider all conceivable heat engines operating between two reservoirs at temperatures T_H and T_C. Each engine has an efficiency less than 100 percent, according to the second law. Which of these engines has the greatest efficiency? The answer to this theoretical question that has practical importance was first obtained by the French engineer Sadi Carnot (1796–1832). Carnot considered an idealized heat engine that would achieve the maximum efficiency for engines working between temperatures T_H and T_C. The cycle is called the *Carnot cycle* and constitutes the *Carnot engine*.

The Carnot cycle is idealized in that it is a reversible cycle. The cycle can be reversed (from operating as an engine to operating as a refrigerator) by making only infinitesimal changes in external conditions. The cycle, operating as an engine, consists of the following four steps (note the emphasis on *reversible* for the Carnot cycle):

Reversible process defined (margin note)

Irreversible process defined (margin note)

A reversible process is an idealization. (margin note)

The Carnot cycle is a reversible cycle. (margin note)

Steps in the Carnot engine cycle (margin note)

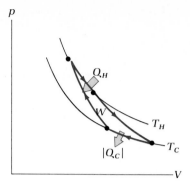

Figure 19-9. The Carnot engine cycle for an ideal gas has the following reversible steps: (i) Heat is added during the isothermal expansion at T_H. (ii) The temperature drops from T_H to T_C as the gas expands adiabatically. (iii) Heat $|Q_C|$ is extracted from the gas during the isothermal compression at T_C. (iv) The temperature increases from T_C to T_H as the gas is compressed adiabatically back to the initial state. The net work, $W = Q_H - |Q_C|$, for the cycle equals the enclosed area.

1 A reversible isothermal expansion at T_H: Heat Q_H is added to the system.
2 A reversible adiabatic process: The temperature of the system drops from T_H to T_C.
3 A reversible isothermal compression at T_C: Heat $|Q_C|$ is exhausted from the system.
4 A reversible adiabatic process to complete the cycle: The temperature of the system increases from T_C back to T_H.

The Carnot engine cycle is shown on a p-V diagram in Fig. 19-9 for the case of an ideal gas as the working substance. The energy transfers are shown schematically, with the net work W equal to the area enclosed by the cycle.

The Carnot engine is a special case of a more general heat engine called a *reversible engine*, a cycle consisting entirely of reversible steps. It is the reversible engine, *any* reversible engine, which is the most efficient heat engine operating between two reservoirs. This result is contained in *Carnot's theorem: All reversible engines operating between temperatures T_H and T_C have the same efficiency, and no engine operating between these temperatures can have a greater efficiency than this.*

Carnot's theorem contains two conclusions:

1. The efficiency of a reversible engine operating between the two reservoirs is independent of the nature of the working substance or of the details of the mechanism. All reversible engines have the same efficiency when operating between these two temperatures.

2. The efficiency of a reversible engine is the maximum efficiency for engines operating between these two temperatures. The efficiency of any engine operating between these reservoirs must be less than or equal to that of a reversible engine.

For our purposes, the distinction between the general reversible engine and the Carnot engine is unimportant. We shall use the Carnot engine, because of its simplicity, as a particular type of reversible engine.

The proof of Carnot's theorem consists in showing that if Carnot's theorem were not true, then the second law of thermodynamics could be violated. (Carnot's theorem can be taken as yet another way to phrase the second law of thermodynamics.) We briefly sketch the proof of the first part of Carnot's theorem by assuming that two Carnot engines CC and CC' have different efficiencies, η and η', when operating between the same two reservoirs. Specifically, assume that $\eta' > \eta$. Then, as seen in Fig. 19-10, we can use the more efficient one, CC', to drive the other, CC, as a refrigerator (it is reversible), having as a net result the transfer of heat from lower to higher temperature. This result is impossible according to the second law; thus our assumption that $\eta' > \eta$ is false. By interchanging the roles of the two cycles, we can show that the assumption $\eta > \eta'$ is also false. Therefore, $\eta = \eta'$. The proof of Carnot's theorem is further addressed in Prob. 19-3.

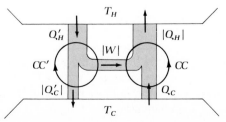

Figure 19-10. One Carnot cycle CC' is used to run a Carnot refrigerator CC. If $\eta' > \eta$, then $|Q_H| > Q_H'$ and $Q_C > |Q_C'|$. The *net* result is the transfer of heat from T_C to T_H, which violates the Clausius statement of the second law.

We shall use the two conclusions of Carnot's theorem in the next section to obtain some useful and remarkable results.

19-5 THE KELVIN, OR THERMODYNAMIC, TEMPERATURE

The reversible engine is the most efficient heat engine operating between two reservoirs at temperatures T_H and T_C. We now determine the value of this highest efficiency. Since all reversible engines operating between these reservoirs have the same efficiency, we choose a Carnot engine whose working substance is an ideal gas. This choice makes the calculation simple, but the result is the same for any working substance in any reversible engine.

Consider n moles of an ideal gas undergoing a Carnot cycle between reservoirs at T_H and T_C, as shown in Fig. 19-11. We need to evaluate the heat exchanges Q_H and $|Q_C|$ to determine the efficiency from Eq. (19-4). For the isothermal process connecting states a and b, the change in internal energy is zero ($\Delta U = 0$ for the ideal gas because $\Delta T = 0$). From the first law and the ideal gas equation of state,

$$Q_H = W_{ab} = \int_a^b p \, dv$$

$$= \int_{V_a}^{V_b} \frac{nRT_H}{V} \, dV = nRT_H \ln \frac{V_b}{V_a}$$

In a similar way, $|Q_C|$ is evaluated for the isothermal compression from c to d:

$$|Q_C| = nRT_C \ln \frac{V_c}{V_d}$$

The efficiency of the cycle is given by Eq. (19-4), $\eta = 1 - |Q_C|/Q_H$, or

$$\eta = 1 - \frac{nRT_C \ln (V_c/V_d)}{nRT_H \ln (V_b/V_a)} \tag{19-8}$$

This result can be simplified by considering the volume changes for the adiabatic processes in the cycle. For an ideal gas, pV^γ is a constant for a quasi-static adiabatic process. Using $pV = nRT$, we write this as $pV^\gamma = pVV^{\gamma-1} = nRTV^{\gamma-1}$, so that $TV^{\gamma-1}$ is also a constant. Thus $T_H V_b^{\gamma-1} = T_C V_c^{\gamma-1}$ for the adiabatic expansion, and $T_H V_a^{\gamma-1} = T_C V_d^{\gamma-1}$ for the adiabatic compression. On dividing the first of these equations by the second, we obtain $(V_b/V_a)^{\gamma-1} = (V_c/V_d)^{\gamma-1}$, or

$$\frac{V_b}{V_a} = \frac{V_c}{V_d}$$

The logarithms in Eq. (19-8) are therefore equal. On canceling common factors in Eq. (19-8), we have for the efficiency of the Carnot cycle operating between T_H and T_C,

Efficiency of a Carnot cycle

$$\eta = 1 - \frac{T_C}{T_H} \tag{19-9}$$

The efficiency of this heat engine (an ideal gas operating in a Carnot cycle) depends only on the ideal gas temperatures of the reservoirs. According to Carnot's theorem, the efficiency is the same for all reversible engines operating between these reservoirs.

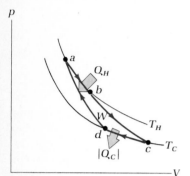

Figure 19-11. An ideal gas undergoes a Carnot cycle between reservoirs at T_H and T_C.

The thermodynamic temperature. Suppose some other reversible engine operates between these same two reservoirs. Perhaps the working substance is a very complex material; it can even change phase during part of the cycle. Carnot's theorem assures us that the efficiency of this cycle has exactly the same value as that for the ideal gas Carnot cycle. All reversible engines operating between these reservoirs have the same efficiency. The only common features of the set of all reversible engines operating between the two reservoirs are the reservoirs themselves and the ratio of heat exchanges of the cycle with these reservoirs. That is, since $\eta = 1 - |Q_C|/Q_H$, the ratio $|Q_C|/Q_H$ has the same value for all reversible engines operating between this pair of reservoirs. This observation forms the basis of our final definition of temperature.

The *thermodynamic,* or *Kelvin, temperature* is defined by the operation of a reversible engine between two reservoirs or systems. The ratio of the temperatures of these two systems is defined to be equal to the ratio of heat exchanges of a reversible engine operated between these systems:

$$\frac{T_H}{T_C} = \left| \frac{Q_H}{Q_C} \right| \tag{19-10}$$

Just as described in Chap. 16, the Kelvin scale is established by choosing 273.16 K as the temperature of the triple point of water. The temperature T of some system is obtained by measuring the heat Q exchanged with this system by a reversible engine operating between this system and a reservoir of water at the triple point. If Q_3 is the heat exchanged by the reversible engine at the triple point, then the temperature of the system is

Definition of thermodynamic, or Kelvin, temperature

$$T = 273.16 \text{ K} \left| \frac{Q}{Q_3} \right| \tag{19-11}$$

Since any substance may be used in a reversible engine and the ratio Q/Q_3 is the same for all reversible engines operating between these two systems, this definition of temperature is independent of the properties of any substance.

From Eq. (19-10), $|Q_C/Q_H| = T_C/T_H$, the efficiency $\eta = 1 - |Q_C/Q_H|$ of any reversible engine operating between two reservoirs is given by

Efficiency of any reversible engine operating between T_C and T_H

$$\eta = 1 - \frac{T_C}{T_H} \tag{19-12}$$

This same result appears in Eq. (19-9), but there the temperature is the ideal gas temperature. We conclude that over the range in which a gas thermometer can be used, the definition of the ideal gas temperature coincides with the definition of the thermodynamic temperature. We therefore continue to use the same symbol (T) for temperature on the Kelvin scale.

EXAMPLE 19-4. A Carnot cycle operates between water at its triple point and liquid N_2 at its normal boiling point. In each cycle the heat exchanged with the N_2 is $|Q_b| = 0.0401$ J, while the heat exchanged with water at the triple point is $|Q_a| = 0.1422$ J. From these heat-exchange values, determine the normal boiling point of N_2.

SOLUTION. Since one of the systems is water at its triple point, we use Eq. (19-11):

$$T = \frac{(273.16 \text{ K})(0.0401 \text{ J})}{0.1422 \text{ J}} = 77.0 \text{ K}$$

Estimating efficiencies. The first part of Carnot's theorem — all reversible engines operating between two reservoirs have the same efficiency — has led us to the definition of the thermodynamic temperature. The second part of the theorem — no engine can be more efficient than a reversible engine — allows us to determine an upper bound on the efficiencies of real engines.

An analysis of the operation of a real heat engine shows that, while heat may be added and extracted from the working substance over a range of temperatures, the engine operates between two extreme temperatures. There is a highest temperature T_H of the working substance during the cycle, and there is a lowest temperature T_C of the working substance. According to Eq. (19-12), the efficiency of a Carnot engine (a reversible engine) operating between these extreme temperatures depends only on the temperatures, $\eta = 1 - T_C/T_H$. The efficiency of the real engine cannot be greater than this Carnot efficiency. In this way the upper limit on the efficiency of a real engine is set by the temperature extremes attained by the working substance. As a practical matter, a real engine will have a lesser efficiency because of losses such as those due to frictional effects.

A Carnot engine gives an upper limit on efficiency.

The efficiency of the Carnot engine, $\eta = 1 - T_C/T_H$, shows the advantage of adding heat to a cycle from a reservoir at very high temperature and exhausting heat to a reservoir at very low temperature. Greater efficiency is achieved for the Carnot engine by decreasing T_C and increasing T_H.

Greater efficiency for higher T_H and lower T_C

In estimating efficiencies, we can also use Eq. (19-12), with T_C and T_H representing the temperatures of two reservoirs rather than the extreme temperatures of the working substance in some real engine. In this estimate, the Carnot efficiency is the upper limit on the efficiency of real engines operating between the reservoirs.

We can similarly analyze the performance of a refrigerator or a heat pump. The coefficient of performance of a real refrigerator cannot exceed that of a Carnot cycle operating as a refrigerator between the two extreme temperatures. For the Carnot cycle this is, from the definition of temperature,

$$K = \frac{Q_C}{|W|} = \frac{Q_C}{|Q_H| - Q_C} = \frac{T_C}{T_H - T_C}$$

The coefficient of performance of a typical real refrigerator is significantly smaller than that of the Carnot cycle.

EXAMPLE 19-5. Estimate the efficiency of the cycle used in a modern steam engine. The steam reaches a temperature of 550°C in the boiler, and the water in the condenser drops to 60°C.

SOLUTION. The efficiency of the steam engine cannot exceed the efficiency of a Carnot cycle operating between the highest and lowest temperatures available. The temperatures in Eq. (19-12) *must* be expressed on the Kelvin scale. Thus $T_H = 273\ \text{K} + 550°\text{C} = 823\ \text{K}$ and $T_C = 333\ \text{K}$. The Car-

not efficiency is

$$\eta = 1 - \frac{333\ \text{K}}{823\ \text{K}} = 60 \text{ percent}$$

The efficiency of the real cycle cannot exceed 60 percent. It turns out that the real cycle has an efficiency of around 35 to 45 percent, depending on the details. Since not all of the energy from the burning fuel is added to the cycle, the overall efficiency is limited to about 40 percent at best.

EXAMPLE 19-6. Estimate the power requirements for a heat pump which is to provide 3×10^4 Btu/h = 9 kW to a home in a temperate climate. For effective heat exchange outside and inside, assume the working fluid has extreme temperatures of $-23°\text{C}$ and $47°\text{C}$.

SOLUTION. A Carnot heat pump operating between these temperature extremes would have a coefficient of performance of

$$K_{hp} = \frac{|Q_H|}{|W|} = \frac{T_H}{T_H - T_C} = \frac{320\ \text{K}}{70\ \text{K}} = 4.6$$

Since the ratio of the time rate of energy transfers is the same as the ratio of energy transfers for a cycle, we write (P represents the power provided to the cycle), $K_{hp} = 9 \text{ kW}/P$, or

$$P = \frac{9 \text{ kW}}{K_{hp}} = \frac{9 \text{ kW}}{4.6} = 2 \text{ kW}$$

A real heat pump with this input power would exhaust heat to the inside at a lower rate than specified, and its coefficient of performance would be less than 4.6.

19-6 ENTROPY

The second law of thermodynamics has been phrased in terms describing practical devices such as heat engines and refrigerators. There is a way of stating the second law in which no reference is made to a particular type of device or practical process. This statement is in terms of a more abstract quantity, the *entropy* of a system. We shall define entropy in this section and show how to calculate changes in the entropy of a system. In the next section, the connection between entropy, irreversibility, and the second law of thermodynamics will be considered.

Entropy as a variable of state. Recall that a system in an equilibrium state can be characterized by the values of its variables of state. Some of the variables of state which we have encountered are those represented by the familiar symbols p, V, T, n, U. The change in a variable of state for a cycle, such as that represented by the closed path in Fig. 19-12, is zero because the system returns to its initial state in a cycle. Thus

The change in a variable of state is zero for any cycle.

$$\Delta U = 0 \qquad \text{(for a cycle)} \qquad (19\text{-}13)$$

This result follows from the fact that the internal energy U is a variable of state. A corresponding relation holds for any variable of state for a cycle. We can write, for example,

$$\Delta p = 0 \qquad \Delta T = 0 \qquad \Delta V = 0 \qquad \text{(for a cycle)}$$

In contrast, the net heat and net work contributions for a cycle (such as a heat engine) are not generally zero:

$$Q \neq 0 \qquad W \neq 0 \qquad \text{(for a cycle)}$$

If a quantity obeys a relation of the form of Eq. (19-13) for any cycle, then that quantity is a variable of state of the system.

We now introduce a new variable of state, the entropy of a system. Suppose that a system at temperature T undergoes an infinitesimal process in which heat dQ is added *reversibly* to the system. *The change in entropy of the system dS is defined as*

Definition of entropy

$$dS = \frac{dQ}{T} \qquad (19\text{-}14)$$

The integrated form of Eq. (19-14) defines *the entropy difference between two states of the system, i and f:*

$$\Delta S = S_f - S_i = \int_i^f \frac{dQ}{T} \qquad (19\text{-}15)$$

where the integral is evaluated for a *reversible* process connecting the two

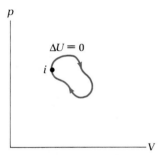

Figure 19-12. The change in a variable of state, such as the internal energy, is zero for any cycle.

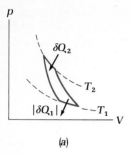

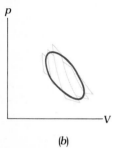

(a)

(b)

Figure 19-13. (a) A Carnot cycle operates between T_1 and T_2, and $T_1/T_2 = |\delta Q_1/\delta Q_2|$. (b) A reversible cycle is approximated by a set of Carnot cycles.

For any Carnot cycle, $\Delta S = 0$.

A general reversible cycle is approximated by a set of Carnot cycles.

Entropy is a variable of state.

states of the system. Entropy has dimensions of energy divided by thermodynamic temperature, and the SI unit is J/K.

Notice that the difference or change in entropy is defined by using a reversible process to connect the two states. An irreversible process cannot be used in applying the definition. However, *any* reversible process which connects states i and f may be used. For processes represented on a p-V diagram, any path connecting the initial and final states may be used. This independence of path corresponds to the fact that entropy is a variable of state.

We can see that the entropy of a system is a variable of state by showing that

$$\Delta S = 0 \quad \text{(for a cycle)}$$

First consider a Carnot cycle operating as a heat engine between temperatures T_1 and T_2, as shown schematically on a p-V diagram in Fig. 19-13a. Heat δQ_2 is added at temperature T_2, and heat $|\delta Q_1|$ is exhausted at T_1. From Eq. (19-10), we have $|\delta Q_2/\delta Q_1| = T_2/T_1$, or

$$\frac{\delta Q_2}{T_2} = \frac{|\delta Q_1|}{T_1}$$

Since the cycle operates as an engine, δQ_2 is positive and δQ_1 is negative ($\delta Q_1 = -|\delta Q_1|$). This result can be expressed more generally without the absolute value signs as

$$\frac{\delta Q_2}{T_2} + \frac{\delta Q_1}{T_1} = 0 \qquad (19\text{-}16)$$

That is, for any Carnot cycle, the sum of the quantity $\delta Q/T$ is zero where δQ is the heat added reversibly at temperature T.

Notice that Eq. (19-16) represents a calculation of the entropy change for that Carnot cycle. The entropy change for the reversible isothermal process at T_2 is $\delta Q_2/T_2$ and is $\delta Q_1/T_1$ for the reversible isothermal process at T_1. There is no contribution for the reversible adiabatic processes because $\delta Q = 0$ for each of them. Thus for any Carnot cycle, $\Delta S = 0$.

Now consider the general reversible cycle shown in Fig. 19-13b. The cycle can be approximated by a set of reversible isothermal and adiabatic processes which are grouped together to form a large number of Carnot cycles, as suggested schematically in the figure. Since an equation of the form of Eq. (19-16) holds for each of the Carnot cycles approximating the actual cycle, we can write

$$\Sigma \frac{\delta Q}{T} = 0$$

The sum is over the entire set of Carnot cycles used to approximate the actual cycle. In the limit of an infinite number of approximating Carnot cycles, the result becomes exact and

$$\Delta S = 0 \quad \text{(for a cycle)}$$

Since the change in entropy of a system is zero for any cycle, entropy is a variable of state.

Evaluating entropy changes. When a system undergoes a process, the change in entropy of the system depends only on the initial and final states. The actual process can be reversible or irreversible; it can be quasi-static or explosive. However, it is *essential* to use a reversible process to evaluate an

The entropy difference between two states is evaluated using any reversible process.

entropy change with Eq. (19-15). We usually devise or imagine some reversible process which connects the given initial and final states of the system. The integral in Eq. (19-15) is evaluated for this reversible process. The answer, the difference in entropy of the two states, is the same no matter what process actually occurred. *Only for the calculation must we use a reversible process.*

We consider now several examples of calculating the change in entropy of a system for initial and final states that are connected by an actual, irreversible process. In each case, we devise a reversible process connecting these states to evaluate the entropy change.

EXAMPLE 19-7. *A phase change.* A 0.120-kg lump of ice at 0.00°C is placed in liquid water of the same temperature. The combination is exposed to surroundings at room temperature and stirred so that the temperature remains at 0.00°C as the ice melts. Determine the difference in entropy between 0.120 kg of ice at 0.00°C and 0.120 kg of liquid water at 0.00°C.

SOLUTION. Heat and work are transferred irreversibly in the actual process. But to find the difference in entropy of these two states, or phases, of water at the freezing point, we devise a simple reversible process to melt the ice. Using a reservoir whose temperature is negligibly higher than that of the ice, we add heat to the ice reversibly at the normal

melting point (273 K). The heat added is determined from the heat of fusion; $L_f = 0.335$ MJ/kg from Table 17-2:

$$Q = mL_f = (0.120 \text{ kg})(0.335 \text{ MJ/kg}) = 40.2 \text{ kJ}$$

For this reversible process, the integral in Eq. (19-15) can be evaluated easily because the temperature remains fixed:

$$\Delta S = S_{\text{liquid}} - S_{\text{solid}} = \int_i^f \frac{dQ}{T}$$

$$= \frac{1}{T} \int_i^f dQ = \frac{Q}{T}$$

$$= \frac{40.2 \text{ kJ}}{273 \text{ K}} = 147 \text{ J/K}$$

EXAMPLE 19-8. *A temperature change.* Determine the change in entropy of 1.0 kg of H_2O which is heated from 10 to 95°C at atmospheric pressure on a stove.

SOLUTION. To raise the temperature of the system reversibly, we must use a succession of heat reservoirs, each at a temperature negligibly higher than the current temperature of the water. If c_p is the (constant) specific heat of water, then $dQ = mc_p \, dT$ is the amount of heat added to change

the temperature by dT. Using Eq. (19-15), we have

$$\Delta S = \int_{T_i}^{T_f} \frac{dQ}{T} = \int_{T_i}^{T_f} \frac{mc_p \, dT}{T} = mc_p \int_{T_i}^{T_f} \frac{dT}{T} = mc_p \ln \frac{T_f}{T_i}$$

$$= (1.0 \text{ kg})(4.2 \text{ kJ kg}^{-1} \text{ K}^{-1}) \left(\ln \frac{368 \text{ K}}{283 \text{ K}} \right)$$

$$= 1100 \text{ J/K}$$

EXAMPLE 19-9. *A volume change.* In Sec. 17-6, we applied the first law to the free-expansion process. In that process a gas confined to one side of an insulated, two-chambered vessel expands freely when the partition ruptures. For the free expansion, $Q = 0$, $W = 0$, and the first law gives $\Delta U = 0$. For an ideal gas, U depends only on T, and thus $\Delta T = 0$. What about ΔS? An ideal gas initially at temperature T occupies a volume V_i. It undergoes a free expansion to a larger volume V_f. Determine the change in entropy.

SOLUTION. A free expansion is obviously irreversible. A small change in external conditions will not reverse the expansion. So even though $Q = 0$ for the irreversible free expansion, we should not expect the entropy to be unchanged. We devise a reversible process to take n moles of an ideal gas from the state specified by (V_i, T) to the state (V_f, T). Since the initial and final states have the same temperature, we use a reversible, isothermal expansion from V_i

to V_f. The heat added in an infinitesimal step is, from the first law,

$$dQ = dU + dW = 0 + p \, dV = p \, dV$$

where $dU = 0$ for an ideal gas because $dT = 0$. Using the ideal gas equation of state, $pV = nRT$, we have

$$\frac{dQ}{T} = \frac{p \, dV}{T} = \frac{nRT}{V} \frac{dV}{T} = \frac{nR \, dV}{V}$$

From Eq. (19-15),

$$\Delta S = \int_{V_i}^{V_f} \frac{nR \, dV}{V} = nR \int_{V_i}^{V_f} \frac{dV}{V} = nR \ln \frac{V_f}{V_i}$$

Since the volume increases on a free expansion, the logarithm is positive, and the final state has a greater entropy than the initial state. That is, the entropy increases on a free expansion.

EXAMPLE 19-10. *Entropy of mixing.* Entropy is an additive quantity in the sense that the entropy change of a system equals the sum of the entropy changes of its subsystems. Consider a system of water which consists of two parts: 0.30 kg initially at 90°C and another 0.70 kg initially at 10°C. Suppose the two are mixed together in an insulated container and come to equilibrium (an irreversible process). Determine the change in entropy of the system of 1.00 kg of water.

SOLUTION. The final equilibrium temperature T_f of the system is obtained by requiring that the heat extracted in lowering the temperature of the hotter water equal the heat added in raising the temperature of the cooler water. Thus

$$(0.30 \text{ kg})c_p(90°\text{C} - T_f) = (0.70 \text{ kg})c_p(T_f - 10°\text{C})$$

The final temperature is $T_f = 34°\text{C} = 307 \text{ K}$. We calculate separately the entropy change of each subsystem by reversibly changing its temperature to T_f. For the hotter water, call it subsystem 1:

$$\Delta S_1 = \int_i^f \frac{dQ}{T} = m_1 c_p \int_{T_1}^{T_f} \frac{dT}{T} = m_1 c_p \ln \frac{T_f}{T_1}$$

$$= (0.30 \text{ kg})(4.2 \text{ kJ} \cdot \text{kg}^{-1} \cdot \text{K}^{-1}) \left(\ln \frac{307 \text{ K}}{363 \text{ K}} \right)$$

$$= -210 \text{ J/K}$$

The entropy of the hotter water decreases on cooling, and the minus sign comes from the logarithm. The entropy of the cooler water increases, according to a similar calculation:

$$\Delta S_2 = (0.70 \text{ kg})(4.2 \text{ kJ} \cdot \text{kg}^{-1} \cdot \text{K}^{-1}) \left(\ln \frac{307 \text{ K}}{283 \text{ K}} \right)$$

$$= 240 \text{ J/K}$$

The entropy change for the system is the sum of these two contributions:

$$\Delta S = \Delta S_1 + \Delta S_2 = -210 \text{ J/K} + 240 \text{ J/K}$$

$$= 30 \text{ J/K}$$

Notice that the entropy of the system increases. This result is generally valid for a mixing process. While the entropy of part of a system can decrease, the entropy of the other part increases by a greater amount.

19-7 ENTROPY AND THE SECOND LAW

What is entropy? What is its conceptual value in increasing our understanding of thermodynamics? These questions can be addressed in part by evaluating entropy changes, such as we did in several examples in the last section. We can see from Example 19-10 that, unlike energy, the entropy of an isolated system is not necessarily conserved. The entropy of one part of the system described in that example decreased while the entropy of the other part increased by a greater amount; the entropy of the isolated system increased. Let us generalize this observation.

Any process can be described in terms of the changes in the system of interest to us and the changes in the surroundings of that system. Together our system and the relevant part of the surroundings form a larger, isolated system which we call the *universe*. Consider the entropy changes that occur for a process. We denote the change in entropy of our system by ΔS_{sys} and the change in entropy of its surroundings by ΔS_{sur}. The sum of these changes is the change in entropy of the universe ΔS_{univ}:

A system and its surroundings are called the universe.

$$\Delta S_{univ} = \Delta S_{sys} + \Delta S_{sur}$$

In every calculation, we find that the entropy of the universe either increases or remains the same. The entropy of the universe never decreases. This result is in accord with yet another statement of the second law of thermodynamics: *For any process, the entropy of the universe either increases (if the process is irreversible) or remains the same (if the process is reversible):*

The second law of thermodynamics (entropy statement)

$$\Delta S_{univ} \geq 0 \qquad\qquad (19\text{-}17)$$

Since it is expressed in terms of entropy, we call this the *entropy statement* of

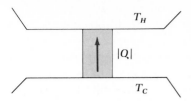

Figure 19-14. The spontaneous flow of heat from lower to higher temperatures does not occur. The entropy of the universe would decrease in violation of the second law.

the second law. Recall that a reversible process is an idealization; all real processes are irreversible. For any real process, the entropy of the universe increases.

A process for which the entropy of the universe decreases is an impossible process according to this statement. For example, consider the spontaneous flow of heat $|Q|$ from lower temperature T_C to higher temperature T_H, as shown in Fig. 19-14. This is an impossible process because it violates the Clausius statement of the second law. If it could occur, the entropy changes, ΔS_C and ΔS_H, of the low- and high-temperature reservoirs would be

$$\Delta S_C = \frac{-|Q|}{T_C} \qquad \Delta S_H = \frac{|Q|}{T_H}$$

The entropy change of the universe would be the sum of these:

$$\Delta S_{\text{univ}} = \frac{-|Q|}{T_C} + \frac{|Q|}{T_H} = -|Q|\left(\frac{1}{T_C} - \frac{1}{T_H}\right)$$

The quantity in parentheses is positive because $T_C < T_H$, and the entropy change of the universe would be negative. Thus the spontaneous flow of heat from lower to higher temperature also violates the entropy statement of the second law.

The spontaneous transfer of heat from higher to lower temperature does not violate the second law. By a calculation similar to that above, you can show that the entropy of the universe increases for this commonly occurring process. Thus the second law allows the spontaneous flow of heat from higher to lower temperature but forbids the reverse process. Indeed, the flow of heat is irreversible.

Other irreversible processes can be analyzed with the same result. Suppose the second law allows a process to occur (increasing the entropy of the universe). But the reverse process does not occur because it would violate the second law (decreasing the entropy of the universe). The second law, or the increase in entropy of the universe, explains in this way the one-way nature of macroscopic processes. The "arrow of time" is in a sense, or direction, corresponding to increasing entropy. That is, the procession of events in time is always toward states of the universe with equal or greater entropy.

Another connection between irreversibility, increasing entropy, and the second law concerns the idea of "loss of opportunity to do work" or the "unavailability of work." Consider the irreversible, spontaneous flow of heat from higher to lower temperature. As a result of this flow, the opportunity is lost to use that heat to perform work by operating a heat engine between the two temperatures. If the flow of heat continues until the two bodies come to the same temperature, then no work can be done (according to the Kelvin-Planck statement of the second law). Of the work that could have been performed by operating a heat engine between the two bodies at different temperatures, none can be obtained after they have come to the same temperature. The opportunity has been lost because of the irreversible heat flow. None of that work is available any longer.

Entropy and the second law can also be interpreted at the microscopic level. There the description is in statistical terms. Instead of forbidding a particular process, the second law describes the process as very highly improbable. For example, the probability is virtually zero that all of the gas molecules are in one part of a container. After the (irreversible) free expansion in Example 19-9 has

Heat flows irreversibly from higher to lower temperature.

The "arrow of time" is toward increasing entropy.

Work becomes unavailable as entropy increases.

occurred, it is highly unlikely that the gas will spontaneously return to the initial state, with all of the molecules occupying one side of the container.

Increasing entropy can be interpreted at the microscopic level as corresponding to a change from a more orderly situation or configuration to a less orderly one. That is, natural processes lead to a more disorderly or chaotic state of the universe. It is often easy to decide which of two configurations is the more disordered. For example, a liquid phase of a substance, with molecules moving about, is usually more disordered than the solid phase, with the molecules arranged on a lattice (Example 19-7). A gas confined to a smaller volume becomes more disordered if it expands freely into a larger volume (Example 19-9). An isolated system with parts at different temperatures is more ordered than that system when all parts have come to the same temperature (Example 19-10). In this last example, a heat engine can be run between parts at different temperatures, but not between parts at the same temperature.

Considerations of this sort can lead to speculation on the ultimate fate of the universe. In every natural (irreversible) process, the entropy of the universe increases. The universe evolves from more highly ordered states to more disordered ones. The so-called heat death of the universe would correspond to that maximum entropy state of uniform composition and temperature, with no opportunity to perform work. On a less cosmological level, we can comprehend (perhaps imperfectly) the aging process, the spontaneous flow of heat, the inevitable deterioration of any machine, and the inability of any machine to spontaneously repair itself.

Increasing entropy corresponds to increasing disorder.

Heat death of the universe

COMMENTARY: MAXWELL'S DEMON

Our understanding of a subtle concept can often be sharpened by constructing and considering a paradox. The second law of thermodynamics provides sufficient subtlety, so there is ample opportunity for sharpening our understanding. A paradox is often stated in an amusing way, perhaps with the use of caricatures, talking animals, or the like. In one well-known paradox, described below, the principal character is Maxwell's demon.

James Clerk Maxwell (see the biographical sketch in the Commentary in Chap. 27) introduced most of the ideas of probability that we used in the last chapter to describe a system at the molecular level. Seeking to make the use of statistical methods respectable, Maxwell noted its practicality by saying, "This branch of Mathematics, which is generally thought to favor gambling, dicing, and wagering, and therefore highly immoral, is the only 'Mathematics for Practical Men,' as we ought to be."

Maxwell helped in developing a bridge of understanding between macroscopic and microscopic aspects of the second law of thermodynamics. At the macroscopic level, the second law deals with irreversibility by using terms such as "heat," "temperature differences," and "friction." In contrast, the second law is expressed in statistical terms at the microscopic level. There, irreversibility is seen as the likely outcome of virtually countless random processes that involve vast numbers of molecules.

Consider this simple situation: An insulated container has two identical chambers that are separated by a fixed wall. Identical samples of gas occupy the two chambers, and they are each in equilibrium at temperature T. No work is done on any part of the system and no heat is added to it. According to the second law of thermodynamics, no temperature difference between the two

gases can spontaneously develop. Put another way, the entropy of the isolated system of two gases cannot decrease.

Maxwell, in his text, Theory of Heat, *introduced a paradox along with a tiny creature who has become known as Maxwell's demon. The demon is stationed at the wall separating the two gases described above. A small trapdoor is fitted into the wall, and the demon can open or close it with negligible work being done. The demon can determine a molecule's speed as it approaches the trapdoor, and his quick reflexes enable him to open and close the trapdoor selectively, allowing faster molecules to pass from the left-hand chamber to the right-hand chamber and slower molecules to pass the other way. As a result, without any work being done, a temperature difference develops between the two gases, and the entropy of the system of two gases decreases. Thus Maxwell's demon has paradoxically brought about a violation of the second law.*

Often a paradox is resolved by a new discovery or a broadened interpretation. Maxwell's paradox stimulated much critical thinking, and its resolution involved phenomena that are described in later chapters. For example, Brillouin (1854– 1948) argued that the enclosures are bathed in a background of thermal (or blackbody) radiation, as described in Chap. 39. Because of this background, the demon would not be able to distinguish individual molecules or sort them according to their speeds. Brillouin also developed a connection between entropy and information. If information about a system is assembled by some process, then the degree of disorder of the system (and its entropy) is correspondingly reduced. If the demon used some device to sort out the speeds of the molecules, say a light not in equilibrium with the remainder of the system, then the decrease in entropy of the gases would be more than offset by the increase in entropy of the demon and his apparatus. In other words, taking all entropy changes into account, the total entropy would not decrease.

For further reading, see James Clerk Maxwell — A Biography *by Ivan Tolstoy (University of Chicago Press, Chicago, 1981); "Maxwell's Demon" in* Mr. Tompkins in Paperback *by G. Gamow (Cambridge University Press, New York, 1965); and "Demons, Engines and the Second Law" by Charles H. Bennett in* Scientific American, *November 1987.*

SUMMARY WITH APPLICATIONS

Section 19-2. Heat engines and the second law
The efficiency η of a heat engine is

$$\eta = \frac{W}{Q_H} \qquad (19\text{-}3)$$

According to the Kelvin-Planck statement of the second law of thermodynamics, there exists no cycle which extracts heat from a reservoir at a single temperature and completely converts it into work.

Determine the efficiency of a heat engine; express and apply the Kelvin-Planck statement of the second law of thermodynamics.

Section 19-3. Refrigerators and the second law
The coefficient of performance of a refrigerator is

$$K = \frac{Q_C}{|W|} \qquad (19\text{-}6)$$

and of a heat pump is

$$K_{hp} = \left| \frac{Q_H}{W} \right| \qquad (19\text{-}7)$$

According to the Clausius statement of the second law, no process is possible whose sole, net result is the transfer of heat from lower to higher temperature.

Determine coefficients of performance for refrigerators and heat pumps; express the Clausius statement of the second law of thermodynamics.

Section 19-4. Reversibility and the Carnot cycle
A reversible process is one which can be reversed by making only infinitesimal changes in the surroundings of a system. If a process is not reversible, it is an irreversible process. A Carnot engine is a reversible engine and obeys Carnot's theorem: All reversible engines operating between temper-

atures T_H and T_C have the same efficiency and no engine can have a greater efficiency than this.

Define a reversible process; list the steps in a Carnot cycle; state Carnot's theorem.

Section 19-5. The Kelvin, or thermodynamic, temperature

The thermodynamic temperature T of a system is defined by

$$T = 273.16 \text{ K} \left| \frac{Q}{Q_3} \right| \qquad (19\text{-}11)$$

where Q and Q_3 are the heat exchanges of a Carnot cycle operating between the system and water at its triple point. The efficiency of a Carnot engine operating between T_C and T_H is given by

$$\eta = 1 - \frac{T_C}{T_H}$$

and is the upper limit on the efficiency of real engines operating between these temperatures.

Define the thermodynamic temperature; determine the efficiency of any reversible engine operating between two temperatures.

Section 19-6. Entropy

Entropy is a variable of state. The difference in entropy of two states of a system is determined by

$$\Delta S = S_f - S_i = \int_i^f \frac{dQ}{T} \qquad (19\text{-}15)$$

where the integral is for any reversible process connecting the two states.

Define entropy; determine the difference in entropy for two states of a system.

Section 19-7. Entropy and the second law

The change in entropy of the universe is the sum of the entropy changes of a system and of its surroundings. According to the entropy statement of the second law, for any process the entropy of the universe either increases (if the process is irreversible) or remains the same (if the process is reversible). The increase in entropy of an isolated system for an irreversible process is connected to the loss of an opportunity of the system to perform work. On the microscopic level, the irreversible process is from a more ordered state to a more disordered state.

Express and apply the entropy statement of the second law of thermodynamics; explain the connections between increasing entropy and (i) the unavailability of work and (ii) the progression from order to disorder.

QUESTIONS

19-1 What are some advantages of a cycle as a heat engine? Are there any disadvantages? Explain.

19-2 Is every cycle a heat engine? Does every heat engine operate in a cycle? Explain.

19-3 Is it possible to cool a room, such as a kitchen, by leaving the refrigerator door open? Explain.

19-4 In what sense does a heat pump pump heat? Is there a useful analogy with a water pump? Describe similarities and differences.

19-5 What are some factors that cause real heat engines to have efficiencies lower than the Carnot efficiency?

19-6 To increase the efficiency of a Carnot engine, is it more effective to increase T_H by an amount ΔT or decrease T_C by ΔT? Explain.

19-7 Describe some processes that are nearly or approximately reversible. Describe some that are highly irreversible.

19-8 How can the gasoline internal-combustion engine be considered as a cycle when fresh air is taken in at each intake stroke?

19-9 What plays the role of the high-temperature reservoir in the gasoline engine? What plays the role of the low-temperature reservoir?

19-10 In a hydroelectric plant, electric energy is generated when falling water turns a turbine. Is a heat engine involved in this energy conversion process? Explain. Is there an upper limit on the efficiency of this pro-

cess? If so, what is that limit? If not, why not?

19-11 Consider the following two processes performed on identical ice cubes initially at 0°C:

1 You hold the ice tightly in your hand. The ice melts and the liquid comes to thermal equilibrium at body temperature.

2 You first smash the ice with a hammer and then you hold the pieces tightly in your hand. The pieces melt and the liquid comes to thermal equilibrium at body temperature.

Is either of these processes reversible? How do the entropy changes of the system (H_2O) compare for the two processes?

19-12 Does the entropy of a gas increase, decrease, or remain the same if its expands (a) reversibly and isothermally, (b) reversibly and adiabatically?

19-13 Does the entropy of a gas increase, decrease, or remain the same if it is compressed (a) reversibly and isothermally, (b) reversibly and adiabatically?

19-14 Explain the distinction between a quasi-static process and a reversible process.

19-15 Which is a more orderly state of matter — liquid or vapor? Which has the greater entropy at the boiling point? Must heat be added to change from liquid to vapor or from vapor to liquid?

19-16 Explain why the loss of opportunity for work as a

result of an irreversible process does not violate the first law of thermodynamics.

19-17 Many living organisms are characterized by growth and development to highly differentiated (ordered) structures. Explain why this feature of life is not in conflict with the second law.

19-18 Suppose that you spend the weekend cleaning your room, making it neat and orderly. Has the entropy of the universe increased, decreased, or remained the same? Explain.

19-19 On freezing, a substance changes from a liquid to a solid, a more orderly structure, and the entropy of the substance decreases. Explain why this process does not violate the second law.

19-20 Consider the following two statements: "You can't get something for nothing," and "You can't even break even." Discuss the sense of these statements in relation to the first and second laws of thermodynamics.

19-21 How can you increase the entropy of 1 kg of water?

How can you decrease the entropy of 1 kg of water?

19-22 The term "quality" is sometimes used to describe the heat extracted from a reservoir and is related to the potential for economically converting it to work. Of the heat extracted from a variety of reservoirs at different temperatures, which do you think has the highest quality? Where would mechanical energy be placed on this quality scale?

19-23 Complete the following table:

Symbol	Represents	Type	SI unit
Q_H			
Q_C			
T_H			K
η	Efficiency of a heat engine		
K			
K_{hp}			
S		Scalar	

EXERCISES

Section 19-2. Heat engines and the second law

19-1 In each cycle of operation, a heat engine takes in 440 J of heat and performs work at 28 percent efficiency. Determine for a cycle (a) the work done, (b) the heat exhausted from the engine, (c) the change in internal energy of the working substance.

19-2 A heat engine operating steadily between two reservoirs has a heat input of 20 MJ and a heat exhaust of 14 MJ each hour. (a) What is the efficiency of this engine? (b) How much work is done in 1 h? (c) What is the output power?

19-3 In one cycle of operation, a heat engine takes in 2200 J of heat and performs 620 J of work. (a) What is the efficiency of this engine? (b) How much heat is exhausted in each cycle? (c) If the engine completes a cycle each 0.033 s, then at what rate is heat added, heat exhausted, work done?

19-4 Electric energy is produced at a steam plant at a rate of 500 MW, with an overall efficiency of 34 percent. At what rate is (a) energy released from the burning coal and (b) heat added to the river water used for cooling? (c) The heat of combustion of coal is about 3×10^{10} J/ton. Estimate the amount of coal burned each day at this plant.

19-5 One mole of He, considered to be an ideal gas, is the working substance in a heat engine which operates in the cycle shown in Fig. 19-15. State a has pressure and volume values $p_a = 101$ kPa, $V_a = 22.4$ L. (a) Determine the temperatures of states a, b, c, and d. (b) How much heat is added in one cycle? (c) How much work is done in one cycle? (d) How much heat is exhausted in one cycle? (e) What is the efficiency of this engine?

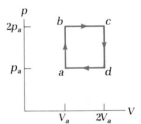

Figure 19-15. Exercise 19-5.

19-6 A heat engine carries 2.2 mol of air ($\gamma = 1.4$) through the cycle shown in Fig. 19-16, where process bc is adiabatic. State a has pressure $p_a = 150$ kPa and volume $V_a = 38$ L. Determine (a) the pressure of state b and the temperatures of b and of c, (b) the heat added to the air in one cycle, (c) the heat extracted from the air in one cycle, (d) the efficiency of the engine. Assume the air is an ideal gas.

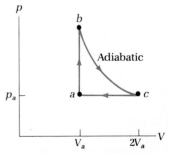

Figure 19-16. Exercise 19-6.

Section 19-3. Refrigerators and the second law

19-7 A refrigeration cycle exhausts 250 J of heat to a room

while the motor provides 80 J of work. (a) How much heat is extracted from the interior of the refrigerator? (b) What is the coefficient of performance of the refrigerator?

19-8 A refrigerating unit at a food-processing plant cools food by extracting 2×10^8 J of heat each hour. It operates with a coefficient of performance of 4.3. Determine for each hour of operation (a) the work done on the refrigerator and (b) the heat exhausted to the outside. (c) What power is required by the refrigerator?

19-9 A heat pump operates with a coefficient of performance $K_{hp} = 2.2$. Work is provided by an electric motor rated at 3.5 kW. At what rate is heat (a) exhausted at the higher temperature and (b) extracted at the lower temperature? (c) What is the cost for 1 h of operation if electric energy costs $0.10 per kW · h?

19-10 On a typical winter night, the rate of heat loss from the inside of a house averages 6 kW. Suppose that these losses are balanced by a heat pump with a 3-kW motor which runs about 30 min each hour. (a) What is the coefficient of performance of the heat pump under these conditions? (b) At what rate is heat extracted from the outside? (c) Estimate the cost for a full day of operation under these conditions. Assume electric energy costs $0.10 per kW · h.

Section 19-4. Reversibility and the Carnot cycle

19-11 On a p-V diagram, carefully sketch a Carnot cycle for air (an ideal gas with $\gamma = 1.4$) operating between 250 and 350 K. Take $n = 1.0$ mol and the isothermal expansion at 350 K to be from 22 to 32 L. Estimate the work done in a cycle from the area enclosed on the diagram.

19-12 Consider the Carnot cycle described in the previous exercise. Determine by direct calculation for one cycle (a) the heat added at 350 K, (b) the heat exhausted at 250 K, (c) the work done from the first law (compare with the estimate from the graph). (d) What is the efficiency of this engine?

Section 19-5. The Kelvin, or thermodynamic, temperature

19-13 Suppose a reversible cycle, with He as the working substance, operates between water at its normal melting point and water at its normal boiling point. (a) What is the ratio of heat exchanges at these two reservoirs? (b) If 0.0125 J of heat is extracted from the higher-temperature water in one cycle, how much is exhausted at the lower temperature? (c) Would the above answers be different if a Carnot cycle with freon as a working substance was operated between the two reservoirs? Explain.

19-14 A nearly reversible cycle is operated between Hg at its triple point and water at its triple point. Suppose the heat exchanges with these two reservoirs are $|Q_{Hg}| =$ 22.1 μJ and $|Q_3| = 25.8$ μJ. Determine the temperature of the triple point of Hg.

19-15 Show that the coefficient of performance of a reversible heat pump operating between reservoirs at T_H and T_C is given by

$$K_{hp} = \frac{T_H}{T_H - T_C}$$

What happens if $T_H = T_C$? Explain.

19-16 Suppose a Carnot engine operates between $T_C = 300$ K and $T_H = 400$ K. (a) Determine the efficiency of the engine. If $Q_H = 0.160$ J for each cycle, what are the values of (b) $|Q_C|$ and (c) W? (d) Would the answers change if a reversible, but non-Carnot engine was used? Explain.

19-17 Consider the engine in the previous exercise. Determine the change in efficiency of the reversible engine that would result if (a) T_C was decreased by 20 K and (b) if T_H was increased by 20 K. (c) Reconsider parts (a) and (b) for a 10 percent change (rather than a 20-K change) in each temperature. (d) What general conclusion do you draw from these calculations?

19-18 Suppose that the average temperature of the burning fuel in a steam plant is 1500 K and that of the cooling water in a lake is 300 K. (a) What is the upper limit on the efficiency of heat engines operating between these temperatures? (b) The overall efficiency of a real steam plant is around 40 percent. Explain why this differs from the answer to part (a).

19-19 A heat engine has been proposed to generate electricity by operating between the ocean surface and the ocean depths. Suppose that these temperatures are around 25°C and 10°C. (a) Estimate the efficiency of such an engine. (b) If work is to be performed at a rate of 2 MW, at what rate must heat be extracted from the surface water? (c) At what volume rate (m³/s) must surface water be processed if the heat is to be extracted by lowering the temperature by 1 C°?

19-20 Estimate, for an inside temperature of 20°C and an outside temperature of −5°C, the power requirements for the compressor of a heat pump used to provide heat to the inside of a dwelling at a rate of 20 kW. Is your estimate an overestimate or an underestimate? Explain.

19-21 Estimate the power requirements for the compressor of a heat pump used to cool the inside of a dwelling at a rate of 20 kW. Assume reasonable values for inside and outside temperatures. Is your estimate an overestimate or an underestimate? Explain.

19-22 Consider the following claim: "This heat pump will provide heat to your home at a rate of 40,000 Btu/h, while using only 1 kW of electric power. These figures assume an inside temperature of 70°F and an outside temperature of 20°F." Would you purchase this heat pump? Support your answer by calculation.

Section 19-6. Entropy

19-23 Heat Q is added reversibly and isothermally to a system at temperature T. (a) Determine an expression for the change in entropy of the system. (b) What is the value of ΔS if $Q = 30$ J and $T = 300$ K?

19-24 One mole of He is initially at $p_i = 101$ kPa, $V_i = 22.4$ L. It undergoes a reversible isobaric expansion to twice the initial volume. Determine the change in (a) temperature, (b) internal energy, (c) entropy of this (ideal) gas. (d) Reconsider your answers, supposing that the same final state results from an *irreversible* process that begins from the same initial state.

19-25 Determine the difference in entropy between the liquid and vapor (steam) phases of 1.0 kg of H_2O at $100°C$. Which phase has the higher entropy?

19-26 Suppose that 4200 J of heat is extracted reversibly and isobarically from 50 g of liquid H_2O initially at 300 K. (a) What is the final temperature of the water? (b) Evaluate the change in entropy of the water. (c) Explain why the answer to part (b) can also be obtained approximately from -4200 J/300 K $= -14$ J/K.

19-27 The initial state of a composite system corresponds to 250 g of ice at $0.0°C$ and 950 g of liquid water at $85°C$. The two parts are mixed in an insulated container and come to equilibrium. Neglect energy exchanges with the surroundings. (a) What is the final temperature of the water? (b) What is the change in entropy of each of the two parts of the system? (c) What is the entropy change of the entire system? (d) Is this process reversible or irreversible? Explain.

Section 19-7. Entropy and the second law

19-28 Consider the steady-state flow of 400 J of heat from a reservoir at $150°C$ to one at $75°C$. Evaluate the change in entropy of (a) the lower-temperature reservoir, (b) the higher-temperature reservoir, (c) the universe.

19-29 In a real heat engine, heat Q_H is transferred through a finite temperature difference ΔT from a reservoir at T_H to the working substance at $T_H - \Delta T$. (a) Show that

PROBLEMS

19-1 A Carnot engine operates between reservoirs at T_H and T_C, with heat exchanges Q_H and Q_C. For each of the four steps of the engine, determine an expression for the change in entropy of the working substance.

19-2 A heat-engine cycle can be represented conveniently on a T-S diagram with T as the ordinate and S as the abscissa (see Fig. 19-18). (a) Show a Carnot cycle operating as an engine (as in the previous problem) on a T-S diagram. (b) What is the interpretation of the area under each isothermal process on the diagram? (c) What is the interpretation of the area enclosed by the cycle?

the entropy change of the universe is positive for this irreversible process. (b) Show that there is also an increase in the entropy of the universe for the heat transfer through a temperature difference of ΔT at the other reservoir. (c) What can you say about the change in entropy of the universe for each cycle of a real heat engine?

19-30 Show that the entropy change of the universe is (a) zero for a reversible adiabatic process and (b) positive for an irreversible adiabatic process.

19-31 One mole of air ($\gamma = 1.4$) is initially at $p_i = 210$ kPa, $V_i = 24$ L. It undergoes an irreversible process, ending in the final state at $p_f = 146$ kPa, $V_f = 31$ L. (a) Use the reversible process shown in Fig. 19-17 to determine the difference in entropy of these two states. Treat air as an ideal gas. What can you say about the value of the change in entropy (b) of the air and (c) of the universe for the actual irreversible process?

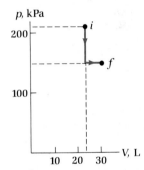

Figure 19-17. Exercise 19-31.

19-32 A geothermal power plant uses steam from the earth at 400 K and cooling water at 300 K. (a) What is the maximum efficiency value? (b) Suppose that the actual efficiency is 18 percent and that the plant generates electric energy at a 200-MW rate. How much work becomes unavailable each day? (c) How much entropy (ΔS_{univ}) is created each day?

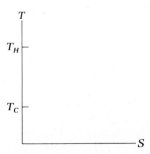

Figure 19-18. Prob. 19-2.

19-3 Prove the second part of Carnot's theorem — no engine operating between two temperatures can be more efficient than a reversible engine. Do this by assuming that some irreversible engine has a greater efficiency than a reversible one and then showing that this assumption leads to a violation of the second law. Why can you not reverse the roles of the two engines, as in the proof of the first part of Carnot's theorem?

19-4   Suppose that the heat exhaust from one engine is used as the heat input for another engine, as shown schematically in Fig. 19-19. One engine operates between T_H and T_I with efficiency η, while the other engine operates between T_I and T_C with efficiency η'. The overall efficiency is $\eta_{net} = (W + W')/Q_H$. (a) Show that $\eta_{net} = \eta + (1 - \eta)\eta'$. (b) Suppose that each engine is reversible; show that $\eta_{net} = 1 - T_C/T_H$.

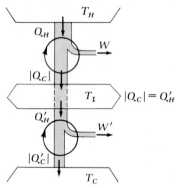

Figure 19-19. Prob. 19-4.

19-5   ***The gasoline engine and the Otto cycle.*** A useful approximation to the cycle for the gasoline internal-combustion engine is provided by an idealized cycle called the *Otto cycle*, shown in Fig. 19-20. The working substance in a real gasoline engine is mostly air with a small admixture of gasoline vapor. The Otto cycle has air as the working substance and utilizes the same air over and over. Starting at point *a* on the *p*-*V* diagram, the air is compressed adiabatically, corresponding to the compression stroke, from volume V_1 to volume V_2 at point *b*. The compression ratio $r = V_1/V_2$ characterizes the engine and is determined by the motion of the piston in the cylinder. The pressure increases at constant volume from *b* to *c*, corresponding to the rapid burning of fuel which is ignited by a spark. An adiabatic expansion, corresponding to the power stroke, follows from *c* to *d*, and the pressure is reduced at constant volume from *d* back to *a*, completing the cycle. The intake and exhaust strokes for the gasoline engine are not shown for the Otto cycle. (a) Show that the efficiency of the Otto cycle is given in terms of the compression ratio by

$$\eta = 1 - \frac{1}{r^{\gamma-1}}$$

(b) The compression ratio for a typical automobile engine is around $r = 8$ and $\gamma = 1.4$ for air. Evaluate the Otto-cycle efficiency for this case. The efficiency of a real engine is more like 20 percent.

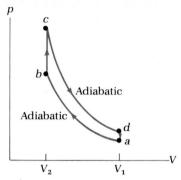

Figure 19-20. Prob. 19-5: The Otto cycle approximates an internal-combustion engine. The compression ratio $r = 3$ for this figure.

19-6   ***The diesel engine and the air-standard cycle.*** The operation of a diesel engine can be approximated by the *air-standard diesel cycle*, shown schematically in Fig. 19-21. The adiabatic compression *ab* corresponds to the compression stroke of the air. This stroke is characterized by the compression ratio $r_C = V_a/V_b$. The isobaric expansion *bc* corresponds to the burning of injected fuel and is followed by the adiabatic expansion *cd*, with an expansion ratio $r_E = V_d/V_c$. The isochoric process *da* completes the cycle. (a) Show that the efficiency of the air-standard diesel cycle is given by

$$\eta = 1 - \frac{r_E^{-\gamma} - r_C^{-\gamma}}{\gamma(r_E^{-1} - r_C^{-1})}$$

(b) Estimate the efficiency of a diesel engine with $r_C = 15$ and $r_E = 5$. Assume $\gamma = 1.4$. Do you expect a real diesel engine to have this efficiency? Explain.

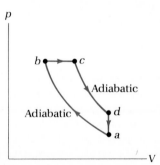

Figure 19-21. Prob. 19-6: The air-standard diesel cycle.

19-7   An irreversible engine operates between reservoirs at $T_H = 550$ K and $T_C = 350$ K, with an efficiency of 25 percent. In each cycle, heat $Q_H = 1200$ J is extracted from the reservoir at T_H and added to the working substance in the engine. Heat $|Q_C|$ is exhausted from the engine into the reservoir at T_C. (a) Determine the change in entropy of the universe for one cycle of operation. (b) How much more work could a reversible engine operating between these reservoirs perform with the same heat input for each cycle? (c) Show that for each cycle the amount of work that is unavailable because of the irreversible process is equal to $T_C \, \Delta S_{univ}$.

19-8   A system undergoes an infinitesimal, reversible process with $dW = p \, dV$. (a) Show that the *first* law of thermodynamics applied to the process can be written

$$T \, dS = dU + p \, dV$$

(b) What is the corresponding integrated form for a reversible process? (c) Is either of these expressions valid for an irreversible process? Explain.

19-9   Determine for 1.0 mol of He the entropy difference between the state with $V = 22$ L, $T = 280$ K and the state with $V = 44$ L, $T = 1120$ K. Treat He as an ideal gas.

19-10   An ideal gas is the working substance for an engine operating in the cycle shown in Fig. 19-22. Determine the efficiency of this cycle in terms of the temperatures T_H and T_C. Notice that heat exchanges occur for all four processes that make up the cycle. This engine is an idealized version of the (irreversible) Stirling engine.

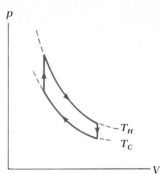

Figure 19-22. Prob. 19-10.

19-11   Consider the model of a polyatomic gas described in Prob. 17-10. Adapt the integrating program used in that problem to determine the difference in entropy for that gas ($\Theta = 85$ K) between two states of 1.0 mol having the same volume but at temperatures $T_i = 10$ K and $T_f = 200$ K. Note that

$$S_f - S_i = \int_{T_i}^{T_f} \frac{n C_V(T) \, dT}{T}$$

where $dQ = n C_V \, dT$ is the heat added reversibly at constant volume for an infinitesimal step in the isochoric process.

CHAPTER 20
COULOMB'S LAW AND THE ELECTRIC FIELD

20-1   INTRODUCTION

Electromagnetic interactions hold electrons and nuclei together to form atoms, atoms together to form molecules, and molecules together to form macroscopic objects. The constituents of your body, its atoms and molecules, are held together by electromagnetic forces. Many of the effects we see going on around us are, at root, the result of electromagnetic forces. For example, green

Lightning is a common but spectacular example of an electrical phenomenon. This awesome display was associated with the volcanic birth of the island of Surtsey near Iceland in November 1963. (*Sigurd Jonasson*)

450

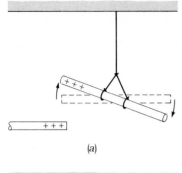

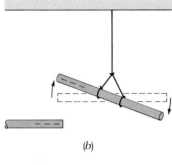

(a)

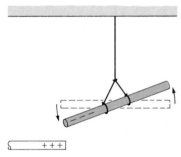

(b)

(c)

Figure 20-1. Suspended charged rods. (a) Two glass rods charged by rubbing with silk repel each other. (b) Two plastic rods charged by rubbing with fur repel each other. (c) A charged plastic rod is attracted to a charged glass rod.

plants absorb sunlight, an electromagnetic wave, and convert the energy to electromagnetic potential energy in the form of carbohydrate molecules, the basis of nearly all of the life on earth.

You may wonder why we use the word "electromagnetic" here, always combining "electric" with "magnetic." The reason is that both electric and magnetic effects involve the same property of matter, a property we call *electric charge.* Although electric and magnetic effects are intimately connected, they are not inseparably connected. If we confine our study to charges in static equilibrium (electrostatics), then we can separate electricity from magnetism. This we shall do in these beginning chapters.

20-2 ELECTRIC CHARGE AND MATTER

When the weather is cool and dry, it is easy to "charge" an object. For example, you can pass a plastic comb through your hair and then pick up tiny bits of paper with the comb. Or you can rub a balloon on your sweater and the balloon will adhere to the wall, or possibly to the ceiling. If you slide across a car seat and then touch some metallic part of the car, you can give yourself quite a shock. Products are sold at supermarkets that are supposed to remove "static cling" from articles taken out of a clothes dryer. These effects, sometimes entertaining and sometimes annoying, are manifestations of one of the fundamental forces in nature, the electric force.

Electric charge. Suppose we rub the end of a glass rod with a piece of silk cloth and suspend the rod with string. The rubbed end of the rod is shown in Fig. 20-1a, with plus signs on it. Next we rub the end of another glass rod with a piece of silk and bring the rubbed end of the second rod near that of the first. As shown in the figure, the first rod swings away from the second, indicating a force of repulsion between them. Rods treated in this fashion are said to be "electrically charged" or to "possess electric charge," and the force they exert on one another is called the *electric force.*

A similar experiment using plastic rods rather than glass and a piece of fur rather than silk gives similar results (Fig. 20-1b). In this case the rubbed ends of the rods are shown with minus signs. When the rubbed ends of the plastic rods are brought near one another, the suspended rod swings away; the rods repel.

If the rubbed end of the glass rod is brought near the rubbed end of the suspended plastic rod, the plastic rod swings toward the glass rod (Fig. 20-1c), indicating a force of attraction. Furthermore, a glass rod that has been charged by rubbing with a silk cloth is attracted by the cloth. That is, the silk cloth is charged as well as the glass rod. Similarly, a plastic rod that has been charged by rubbing with fur is attracted by the fur.

Suppose we perform such experiments with rods made of many different materials and rubbed with many different types of cloth. We learn two important results from these experiments. First, if rods A and B attract, then all other rods fall into one of two categories: (i) those that repel A and attract B, or (ii) those that repel B and attract A. Any rod in the first category repels any other rod in the same category and attracts any rod in the second category. Similarly, any rod in the second category repels any other rod in the same category and attracts any rod in the first category. We conclude that there are two types of charge: Rods in the first category have one type of charge and rods in the second have the other, or opposite type.

The second important result of these experiments is that when a rod is charged by rubbing with a cloth, the type of charge the rod obtains is opposite to the type of charge the cloth obtains. Quantitative measurements show that the amount of these opposite types of charge is the same. Thus, if one object becomes charged, another object also becomes charged, but with the opposite type of charge.

The model. We now present a model that "explains" these electrical effects:

1. Matter contains two types of electric charge, called *positive* and *negative*. Uncharged objects have equal amounts of each type of charge, and when objects are charged by rubbing, electric charge is transferred from one object to the other. After the charging process is completed, one of the objects has excess positive charge and the other has excess negative charge.
2. Objects that are charged with like sign repel.
3. Objects that are charged with unlike sign attract.

This model is nearly the same as that proposed by the American printer, statesman, and scientist, Benjamin Franklin (1706–1790). We anticipated this model when we put the plus signs on the glass rod and the minus signs on the plastic rods in Fig. 20-1. Inherent in the model is the *law of conservation of charge: Electric charge can neither be created nor destroyed; it can only be transferred.* When an object is referred to as "possessing charge," we mean that it possesses *excess* charge.

The law of conservation of charge

Atomic structure. Our present view of atomic structure contains Franklin's model of electricity. In addition, our model of atoms has features that are the result of other experiments that we discuss in later chapters. The results of these experiments show that atoms consist of three types of particles: electrons, protons, and neutrons. Electrons and protons possess charge, but neutrons are electrically neutral. The magnitude of an electron's charge is the same as that of a proton, but of the opposite sign. In the neutral atom there are equal numbers of protons and electrons. Franklin's choice of sign for charged objects was adopted worldwide, and survives to this day. This choice assigns negative charge to electrons and positive charge to protons.

The protons and neutrons of an atom are held together in a small nucleus, which is surrounded by an electron cloud (Fig. 20-2). A nucleus can contain from 1 to about 100 protons, depending on the chemical element, and usually contains about the same number of neutrons. For example, the nucleus of an aluminum atom contains 13 protons and 14 neutrons. A proton and a neutron have about the same mass, and each has about 2000 times the mass of an electron. Therefore, an atom's nucleus usually has a mass that is about 4000 times the mass of its electrons.

The size of the nucleus of an atom is much less than the extent of the electron cloud, as shown in Fig. 20-2. A nucleus is typically about 5×10^{-15} m across, whereas the electron cloud has a diameter of about 2×10^{-10} m. Thus the linear dimension of an atom is about 40,000 times that of its nucleus.

An aspect of electric charge contained in our atomic model is the *quantization of charge*. When something is said to be "quantized," it means that the something comes in lumps, or units of discrete size, and cannot be divided into

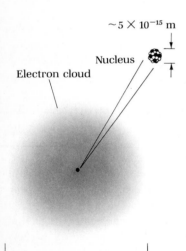

Figure 20-2. Model of the atom. The extent of the electron cloud and an enlarged view of the nucleus are shown.

Charge is quantized.

smaller and smaller pieces. For example, cash is quantized in units of one penny in the monetary system in the United States. If charge is possessed by particles—electrons and protons—and if these particles cannot be divided into smaller pieces, then charge cannot be divided into smaller pieces either. We will have more to say about this and other features of our atomic model in later chapters.

20-3 INSULATORS AND CONDUCTORS

Most materials can be classified as one of two types—as a *conductor* or as an *insulator*. A conductor is a material that readily allows charge to flow through it, and an insulator is a material that does not readily allow charge to flow. Metals are usually good conductors (and poor insulators), and nonmetals are usually good insulators (and poor conductors).

We can demonstrate the contrasting electrical behavior of conductors and insulators by performing an experiment that relies on this behavior. Figure 20-3a shows a conducting sphere supported by an insulating stand. In Fig. 20-3b a negatively charged rod has been brought close to the sphere. While the charged rod is near the sphere, the sphere is "grounded," as shown schematically in Fig. 20-3c. By "grounding," we mean that we provide a conducting path between the sphere and the earth. This is often done by connecting a wire between the sphere and a water faucet, but in this case a sufficient grounding procedure is simply to touch the sphere with your finger because your body is an adequate conductor for this purpose. With the rod still nearby, the ground connection is taken away (Fig. 20-3d). Finally, when the rod is taken away, we find that the sphere is left with excess charge (Fig. 20-3e). We can verify that the sphere is charged and determine the sign of its charge by bringing it near a charged suspended rod of known sign, as shown in Fig. 20-1. This procedure is called *charging by induction* because the sphere is charged without actually coming in contact with the charged rod.

The way charging by induction works is illustrated in Fig. 20-3 with the plus and minus signs. When the charged rod is near the sphere (Fig. 20-3b), the side of the sphere nearest the rod has excess positive charge and the side farthest from the rod has excess negative charge because (i) unlike charges attract and like charges repel and (ii) because charge is able to move readily through the conducting sphere. When the sphere is grounded (Fig. 20-3c), the negative charges can move still farther from the negatively charged rod by passing through the grounding wire. After the wire is removed, the excess positive charge remains on the sphere because charge will not readily flow through the insulating stand; the excess charge is trapped. Of course, the surrounding air must also be an insulator. Air is a reasonably good insulator, depending on weather conditions; dry air is a better insulator than humid air. For charging by induction to work, the sphere must be a good conductor and the stand must be a good insulator, and for it to work well, the humidity must be low.

Ordinarily, when charge moves through a material, it is electrons that do the

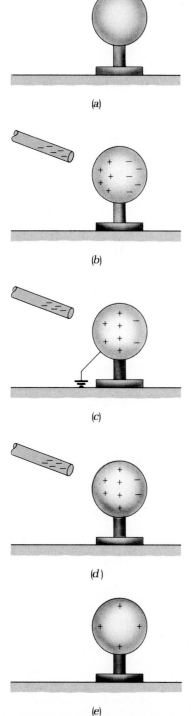

(a)

(b)

(c)

(d)

(e)

Figure 20-3. Charging by induction. (a) A neutral conducting sphere on an insulating stand. (b) A negatively charged rod is brought near the sphere. (c) The sphere is grounded. (d) The ground connection is taken away while the charged rod is still nearby. (e) After the charged rod is taken away, excess positive charge remains trapped on the sphere.

Ordinarily electrons are the charge carriers in a conductor.

moving. We say that the electrons are the *charge carriers.* A conducting material, such as a metal, can be thought of as an array of fixed positive ions* interspersed with "free" electrons capable of moving through the material. The number of free electrons in a conductor depends on the material, but is on the order of one per atom. An insulator is a material in which there are almost no free electrons. An electron in an insulator is held near the position of a particular atom or molecule and is not allowed to pass from one molecular site to the next.

In a conducting fluid, such as salt water, there are practically no free electrons, but the fluid can still be an excellent conductor. In this case the salt dissolves in the water as positive and negative ions, and the ions, which are capable of moving through the fluid, become the charge carriers.

20-4 COULOMB'S LAW

The SI unit of charge is the coulomb (C).

The force law for stationary charged particles was determined in 1784 by Charles Augustin Coulomb (1736–1806). Using a torsion balance (Fig. 20-4), he established the distance and charge dependence of the electric force. In recognition of his work, the SI unit of charge is called the *coulomb* (C).

To describe the electrical interaction between two particles a and b, which possess charge q_a and q_b, we use the coordinate frame shown in Fig. 20-5. Particle a is at the origin a distance r from b, and a unit vector $\hat{\mathbf{r}}$ points away from a along the line joining a and b. Experiment shows that the expression for the force $\mathbf{F}_{ab}$ exerted by a on b is

Coulomb's law

$$\mathbf{F}_{ab} = \frac{1}{4\pi\epsilon_0} \frac{q_a q_b}{r^2} \hat{\mathbf{r}} \tag{20-1}$$

where $1/4\pi\epsilon_0$ is a proportionality constant which is independent of the separation distance and of the amount of charge on either particle. Equation (20-1) is

* An ion is an atom with a deficiency (positive ion) or an excess (negative ion) of one or more electrons.

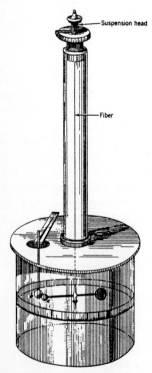

Figure 20-4. Coulomb's torsion balance. *a* and *b* are charged spheres.

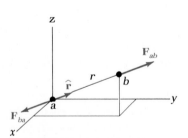

Figure 20-5. If particles *a* and *b* have charge of like sign (which is the case shown), then the force $\mathbf{F}_{ab}$ by *a* on *b* is directly away from *a*. The force $\mathbf{F}_{ba}$ by *b* on *a* is directly away from *b*, in agreement with Newton's third law. On a scratch sheet, draw a similar figure for the case where the particles have charge of opposite sign.

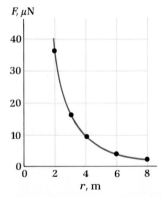

Figure 20-6. Distance dependence of the electric force between two charged particles. The force is an inverse-square force. Data from this graph are used in Example 20-1.

called *Coulomb's law*. Note that the electric force between charged particles is an inverse-square force: $F_{ab} \propto 1/r^2$. If the distance between the particles is doubled, then the magnitude of the force is reduced by a factor of 4 (Fig. 20-6). You are familiar with an inverse-square force from our discussion of Newton's law of universal gravitation (Chap. 7).

Coulomb's law contains the result that particles of like sign repel and particles of unlike sign attract.If q_a and q_b have the same sign, then the product $q_a q_b$ is positive and the direction of $\mathbf{F}_{ab}$ in Eq. (20-1) is the same as $\hat{\mathbf{r}}$; the equation says that b is repelled by a. If q_a and q_b have opposite signs, then the product $q_a q_b$ is negative and $\mathbf{F}_{ab}$ is directed opposite $\hat{\mathbf{r}}$, which describes attraction between b and a. The magnitude of the force depends on the magnitude of the product of the charges: $F_{ab} \propto |q_a q_b|$. That is, the force magnitude depends linearly on the magnitude of each charge.

As with other forces, the electric force is found from experiment to be a vector quantity. The effect of two or more electric forces acting simultaneously on a particle is determined by adding the forces vectorially. In addition, the electrical interaction obeys Newton's third law. If $\mathbf{F}_{ab}$ is the force by a on b, then the force $\mathbf{F}_{ba}$ by b on a is $\mathbf{F}_{ba} = -\mathbf{F}_{ab}$, as shown in Fig. 20-5.

The proportionality constant in Coulomb's law, $1/4\pi\epsilon_0$, appears complex, but it is nevertheless only a proportionality constant. The factor 4π is contained in this constant in order to simplify other equations which we encounter in the next chapter. The factor ϵ_0 represents a constant called the *permittivity* of free space, or vacuum. The measured value of ϵ_0 is

Permittivity of free space

$$\epsilon_0 = 8.854 \times 10^{-12} \ \text{C}^2/\text{N} \cdot \text{m}^2$$

This gives
$$\frac{1}{4\pi\epsilon_0} = 8.987 \times 10^9 \ \text{N} \cdot \text{m}^2/\text{C}^2 \approx 9 \times 10^9 \ \text{N} \cdot \text{m}^2/\text{C}^2$$

The proportionality factor $1/4\pi\epsilon_0$ is a large number because the coulomb is a large unit of charge. Suppose two particles, each with charge 1 C, are separated a distance of 1 m. From Coulomb's law, the magnitude F of the force between them is

$$F = \frac{1}{4\pi\epsilon_0} \frac{|q_a q_b|}{r^2} = (9 \times 10^9 \ \text{N} \cdot \text{m}^2/\text{C}^2) \frac{(1 \ \text{C})(1 \ \text{C})}{(1 \ \text{m})^2} = 9 \times 10^9 \ \text{N}$$

The magnitude of this force is huge, equivalent to the weight of about 15 million adult humans. This calculation shows that 1 C is a very large amount of charge. A rod charged by rubbing, as we described in Sec. 20-2, will typically possess a charge of about 10 nC (10^{-8} C). Measuring the charge on a glass rod rubbed with silk in units of C is similar to measuring the thickness of this page in units of km. The C is defined by an experimental procedure involving the measurement of a magnetic force (Chap. 30), and its size is a consequence of this definition.

We have mentioned that a proton and an electron have equal and opposite charge. The magnitude of this fundamental amount is represented by the symbol e, and its value is

A proton charge is $+1.6 \times 10^{-19}$ C.

An electron charge is -1.6×10^{-19} C.

$$e = 1.60207 \times 10^{-19} \ \text{C}$$

The charge of a proton is $+e$, and the charge of an electron is $-e$. If N_e is the number of electrons in an object and N_p is the number of protons, then the charge q on the object is

$$q = (N_p - N_e)e$$

Thus $N_p > N_e$ for a positively charged object, $N_p = N_e$ for a neutral object, and $N_p < N_e$ for a negatively charged object.

EXAMPLE 20-1. Suppose the graph in Fig. 20-6 corresponds to an interaction between two baseballs with equal positive charge. For each baseball, (a) determine the charge, (b) determine the number of missing electrons, and (c) estimate the fraction of missing electrons.

SOLUTION. (a) Since each baseball has the same charge, we let q represent both q_a and q_b in Eq. (20-1) and solve for q:

$$q = \sqrt{4\pi\epsilon_0 r^2 F}$$

We may select values of F and r from any of the points on the curve in Fig. 20-6; suppose we choose $F = 9.0 \ \mu$N and $r = 4.0$ m:

$$q = \sqrt{\frac{(4.0 \text{ m})^2 (9.0 \ \mu\text{N})}{9.0 \times 10^9 \text{ N} \cdot \text{m}^2/\text{C}^2}} = 130 \text{ nC}$$

(b) Letting n represent the number of electrons missing from each baseball ($n = N_p - N_e$), we have $q = ne$, or

$$n = \frac{q}{e} = \frac{130 \text{ nC}}{1.6 \times 10^{-19} \text{ C}} = 7.9 \times 10^{11} \text{ electrons}$$

For a macroscopic object to have a significant charge, the number of missing or extra electrons must be very large because the charge of a single electron is very small. (c) The fraction of electrons missing is n/N_p because N_p (the number of protons) is equal to the number of electrons in a neutral object. A baseball has a mass of about 0.15 kg, and about half the mass is attributed to protons and about half to neutrons. Dividing the mass of a baseball by the mass of a proton-neutron pair gives an estimate of N_p:

$$N_p \approx \frac{M}{m_p + m_n} = \frac{0.15 \text{ kg}}{2(1.67 \times 10^{-27} \text{ kg})} \approx 5 \times 10^{25} \text{ protons}$$

Thus

$$\frac{n}{N_p} \approx \frac{7.9 \times 10^{11} \text{ missing electrons}}{5 \times 10^{25} \text{ protons}} \approx 2 \times 10^{-14}$$

This means that about one out of every 5×10^{13} [or $1/(2 \times 10^{-14})$] electrons is missing from each baseball. For comparison, the earths' human population is about 5×10^9, so that 5×10^{13} is about 10,000 times the earth's population of humans. You can see that a very tiny imbalance in the electron population causes a macroscopic object to have a significant charge.

EXAMPLE 20-2. *Comparison with gravitation.* From Chap. 7 we know that the gravitational force between two particles is an attractive inverse-square force that depends on the product of the masses of the particles. Compare the magnitudes of the electric and gravitational forces between an electron and a proton by calculating the ratio of these forces.

SOLUTION. The magnitudes of the electric force and the gravitational force between a proton (charge $= e$, mass $= m_p$) and an electron (charge $= -e$, mass $= m_e$) are

$$F_E = \frac{1}{4\pi\epsilon_0} \frac{e^2}{r^2} \quad \text{and} \quad F_G = G\frac{m_p m_e}{r^2}$$

respectively. The ratio is

$$\frac{F_E}{F_G} = \frac{1}{4\pi\epsilon_0 G} \frac{e^2}{m_p m_e}$$

Since both forces are inverse-square forces, r^2 cancels out of the ratio. This means that the comparison is valid at any separation distance:

$$\frac{F_E}{F_G} = \frac{(9.0 \times 10^9 \text{ N} \cdot \text{m}^2/\text{C}^2)(1.6 \times 10^{-19} \text{ C})^2}{(6.7 \times 10^{-11} \text{ N} \cdot \text{m}^2/\text{kg}^2)(1.7 \times 10^{-27} \text{ kg})(9.1 \times 10^{-31} \text{ kg})}$$

$$\approx 2 \times 10^{39}$$

Between an electron and a proton, the gravitational force is negligible in comparison with the electric force.

EXAMPLE 20-3. Determine the force on particle c in Fig. 20-7 due to particles a and b. The charges on the particles are $q_a = 3.0 \ \mu$C, $q_b = -6.0 \ \mu$C, and $q_c = -2.0 \ \mu$C.

SOLUTION. Using Coulomb's law, we find that the force on particle c due to particle a is

$$\mathbf{F}_{ac} = \frac{1}{4\pi\epsilon_0} \frac{q_c q_a}{r_a^2} \hat{\mathbf{r}}_a$$

From the figure, $r_a = 3.0$ m. Also, our coordinate system has been arranged such that the unit vector $\hat{\mathbf{r}}_a$ that points from a to c is $\mathbf{k}$. Thus

$$\mathbf{F}_{ac} = (9.0 \times 10^9 \text{ N} \cdot \text{m}^2/\text{C}^2)\frac{(-2.0 \ \mu\text{C})(3.0 \ \mu\text{C})}{(3.0 \text{ m})^2} \mathbf{k}$$

$$= (-6.0 \times 10^{-3} \text{ N})\mathbf{k} = -(6.0 \text{ mN})\mathbf{k}$$

The direction of the force is attractive because q_a and q_c

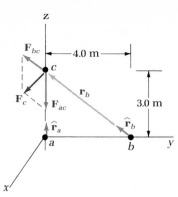

Figure 20-7. Example 20-3: Finding the force on charged particle c due to charged particles a and b.

have opposite signs. Similarly, the force on particle c due to particle b is

$$\mathbf{F}_{bc} = \frac{1}{4\pi\epsilon_0} \frac{q_c q_b}{r_b^2} \hat{\mathbf{r}}_b$$

From the figure, $r_b = \sqrt{(3.0 \text{ m})^2 + (4.0 \text{ m})^2} = 5.0 \text{ m}$. The unit vector $\hat{\mathbf{r}}_b$ is found by dividing the vector $\mathbf{r}_b$, which extends from b to c by its length r_b. Since $\mathbf{r}_b = (-4.0 \text{ m})\mathbf{j} + (3.0 \text{ m})\mathbf{k}$,

we have

$$\hat{\mathbf{r}}_b = \frac{\mathbf{r}_b}{r_b} = \frac{(-4.0 \text{ m})\mathbf{j} + (3.0 \text{ m})\mathbf{k}}{5.0 \text{ m}} = -(0.80)\mathbf{j} + (0.60)\mathbf{k}$$

Substituting these values into the equation for $\mathbf{F}_{bc}$ gives

$$\mathbf{F}_{bc}$$
$$= \left(9.0 \times 10^9 \frac{\text{N} \cdot \text{m}^2}{\text{C}^2}\right) \frac{(-2.0 \ \mu\text{C})(-6.0 \ \mu\text{C})}{(5.0 \text{ m})^2} (-0.80\mathbf{j} + 0.60\mathbf{k})$$

$$\mathbf{F}_{bc} = (-3.5 \text{ mN})\mathbf{j} + (2.6 \text{ mN})\mathbf{k}$$

The net force $\mathbf{F}_c$ on the particle c is the sum of the two individual forces:

$$\mathbf{F}_c = \mathbf{F}_{ac} + \mathbf{F}_{bc} = (-6.0 \text{ mN})\mathbf{k} + [(-3.5 \text{ mN})\mathbf{j} + (2.6 \text{ mN})\mathbf{k}]$$

$$= (-3.5 \text{ mN})\mathbf{j} + (-3.4 \text{ mN})\mathbf{k}$$

The magnitude of the force is

$$F_c = \sqrt{(-3.5 \text{ mN})^2 + (-3.4 \text{ mN})^2} = 4.9 \text{ mN}$$

The vectors $\mathbf{F}_{ac}$, $\mathbf{F}_{bc}$, and $\mathbf{F}_c$ are shown in Fig. 20-7. Examine the figure to verify that the components calculated above are consistent with the graphical results. It is often useful to check your numerical results with a reasonably accurate diagram.

20-5 THE ELECTRIC FIELD

A *field* is a physical quantity that can be associated with position. For example, the temperature of the air in a room has a specific value at each point in the room. If we let T represent the temperature, then there exists a function $T(x, y, z)$ that gives the temperature at each point (x, y, z). Further, the temperature may change with time t, in which case it is a function of t as well, $T(x, y, z, t)$. Since temperature is a scalar quantity, $T(x, y, z, t)$ is an example of a scalar field.

In addition to scalar fields, there are vector fields—that is, vector quantities that exist at points in space. Wind in the earth's atmosphere is an example of a vector field. At each point in the earth's atmosphere there is a velocity $\mathbf{v}$ of the air. The three components of this vector field are functions of position and time. Using cartesian coordinates, we can write these components as $v_x(x, y, z, t)$, $v_y(x, y, z, t)$, and $v_z(x, y, z, t)$.

In Chap. 7 we introduced the gravitational field $\mathbf{g} = \mathbf{F}/m$, where $\mathbf{F}$ is the gravitational force on an object of mass m. At each point near its surface, the earth produces a gravitational field of magnitude 9.8 N/kg that points toward the center of the earth. If a 3.6-kg object is near the earth's surface, then there is a force of magnitude $F = mg = (3.6 \text{ kg})(9.8 \text{ N/kg}) = 35 \text{ N}$ exerted on it because of the earth's gravitational field. The gravitational field is an example of a vector field.

The definition of the electric field is similar to that of the gravitational field. Suppose a charged particle, which we call a *test particle,* is placed at a point P near a group of charged particles (Fig. 20-8). The electric field $\mathbf{E}$ at P due to the group of charged particles is defined as the electric force $\mathbf{F}$ exerted by the group on the test particle divided by the test particle's charge q_0:

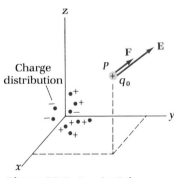

Figure 20-8. At point P the electric field $\mathbf{E}$ due to a distribution of charge is defined as the electric force $\mathbf{F}$ exerted by the distribution on a test particle placed at P divided by the charge q_0 of the test particle: $\mathbf{E} = \mathbf{F}/q_0$.

$$E = \frac{F}{q_0} \qquad \text{(small } q_0\text{)} \qquad\qquad (20\text{-}2)$$

The force $\mathbf{F}$ is the vector sum of the individual forces $\mathbf{F}_i$ due to each particle in the group: $\mathbf{F} = \Sigma\mathbf{F}_i$. Since each force $\mathbf{F}_i$ exerted on the test particle is proportional to q_0, the force $\mathbf{F}$ is proportional to q_0. Thus the ratio $\mathbf{F}/q_0$ is independent of q_0. This means that the value of the field which we measure by using a test particle is independent of the charge on the test particle.

The electric field due to a group of charged particles depends on (i) the value of the charge on each particle and how the particles are arranged in space, which we call the *charge distribution,* and (ii) the position P at which the field is measured. We view the electric field as a condition set up in space by the presence of the charge distribution. We assume that this electric field exists whether or not a test particle is there to measure it, just as the temperature exists at each position in a room whether or not a thermometer is there to measure it.

Since force $\mathbf{F}$ is a vector quantity and $\mathbf{E} = \mathbf{F}/q_0$, $\mathbf{E}$ is a vector field and obeys the principle of superposition. The direction of $\mathbf{E}$ is the same as the direction of the force on a positively charged test particle, or opposite the force on a negatively charged test particle. The dimension of the electric field is force divided by electric charge, and its SI unit is newtons per coulomb (N/C).

Suppose a test particle with charge $q_0 = 81$ nC has a force $\mathbf{F} = (2.7\ \mu\text{N})\mathbf{i} + (1.1\ \mu\text{N})\mathbf{j} + (1.3\ \mu\text{N})\mathbf{k}$ exerted on it by a charged object (Fig. 20-9). Then the electric field $\mathbf{E}$ produced by the object at the position of the test particle is found to be

$$\mathbf{E} = \frac{\mathbf{F}}{q_0} = \frac{(2.7\ \mu\text{N})\mathbf{i} + (1.1\ \mu\text{N})\mathbf{j} + (1.3\ \mu\text{N})\mathbf{k}}{81\ \text{nC}}$$

$$= (33\ \text{N/C})\mathbf{i} + (14\ \text{N/C})\mathbf{j} + (16\ \text{N/C})\mathbf{k}$$

When an electric field is measured, the magnitude of the charge on the test particle must be small enough so that it does not significantly disturb the charge distribution which produces the field. That is why we require the charge on the test particle to be small, as indicated beside Eq. (20-2). If the charge on the test particle is not small, then its presence may cause some of the particles in the charge distribution to move, altering the charge distribution, which will change the electric field produced by the distribution. This matter is especially important when measuring the electric field near a charged conductor because charge carriers can readily move through a conductor.

If $\mathbf{E}$ is known at a point, then the force on a particle with charge q_0 placed at

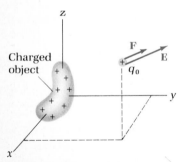

Figure 20-9. Force on a charged particle due to the electric field produced by a charged object.

Figure 20-10. Electric field due to a point charge at the origin. (a) Positive q. (b) Negative q.

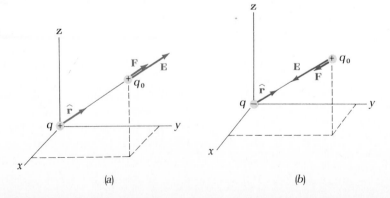

(a)   (b)

that point is found by solving Eq. (20-2) for $\mathbf{F}$:

$$\mathbf{F} = q_0\mathbf{E} \qquad (20\text{-}3)$$

Suppose a particle with charge $q_0 = -1.0$ nC is placed at a point where $\mathbf{E} = (56 \text{ N/C})\mathbf{i} + (-37 \text{ N/C})\mathbf{j} + (14 \text{ N/C})\mathbf{k}$. The electric force on the particle is

$$\mathbf{F} = q_0\mathbf{E} = (-1.0 \text{ nC})[(56 \text{ N/C})\mathbf{i} + (-37 \text{ N/C})\mathbf{j} + (14 \text{ N/C})\,\mathbf{k}]$$

$$= (-56 \text{ nN})\mathbf{i} + (37 \text{ nN})\mathbf{j} + (-14 \text{ nN})\mathbf{k}$$

Note that the force on the negatively charged particle is directed opposite $\mathbf{E}$.

20-6 CALCULATING THE ELECTRIC FIELD

The electric field due to a charge distribution can be found from Coulomb's law and the principle of superposition.

The electric field due to charged particles. Consider the force $\mathbf{F}$ exerted on a test particle with charge q_0 due to another particle with charge q located at the origin of coordinates, as shown in Fig. 20-10. From Coulomb's law,

$$\mathbf{F} = \frac{1}{4\pi\epsilon_0}\frac{q\,q_0}{r^2}\,\hat{\mathbf{r}}$$

Dividing by q_0 gives the electric field at the position of q_0:

Electric field due to a point charge

$$\mathbf{E} = \frac{1}{4\pi\epsilon_0}\frac{q}{r^2}\,\hat{\mathbf{r}} \qquad (20\text{-}4)$$

A charged particle is often called a *point charge*, and Eq. (20-4) is the field produced by a point charge q. The important features of this field are

1 E is proportional to $|q|$.
2 E is proportional to $1/r^2$. If $E = 80$ N/C at $r = 10$ cm, then at $r = 20$ cm, $E = (80 \text{ N/C})/2^2 = 20$ N/C.
3 $\mathbf{E}$ points directly away from a positive charge (Fig. 20-10a) or directly toward a negative charge (Fig. 20-10b).

Now consider the electric field due to two or more point charges. When the electric force $\mathbf{F}$ on a test charge q_0 located at point P is due to two or more point charges, we have

$$\mathbf{F} = \frac{1}{4\pi\epsilon_0}\frac{q_0 q_1}{r_1{}^2}\,\hat{\mathbf{r}}_1 + \frac{1}{4\pi\epsilon_0}\frac{q_0 q_2}{r_2{}^2}\,\hat{\mathbf{r}}_2 + \cdots$$

$$= \frac{q_0}{4\pi\epsilon_0}\left(\frac{q_1}{r_1{}^2}\,\hat{\mathbf{r}}_1 + \frac{q_2}{r_2{}^2}\,\hat{\mathbf{r}}_2 + \cdots\right)$$

$$= \frac{q_0}{4\pi\epsilon_0}\sum\frac{q_i}{r_i{}^2}\,\hat{\mathbf{r}}_i$$

where q_i is the charge on particle i, r_i is the distance from particle i to point P, and $\hat{\mathbf{r}}_i$ is a unit vector that points from particle i to point P. Dividing by q_0 gives the field at P:

Electric field due to two or more point charges

$$\mathbf{E} = \frac{1}{4\pi\epsilon_0}\sum\frac{q_i}{r_i{}^2}\,\hat{\mathbf{r}}_i \qquad (20\text{-}5)$$

The electric field due to two or more point charges is the vector sum of the individual contributions to the field produced by each charge separately.

Finding the electric field due to a distribution of point charges is essentially a problem of vector addition. We show two procedures in our examples, one using unit vectors and one using components. The two are equivalent. Example 20-3 has already provided an illustration of the first procedure, and the following example shows the second procedure.

EXAMPLE 20-4. Two particles 1 and 2, with charges $q_1 = +16$ nC and $q_2 = +28$ nC, are at positions (x, y, z) of $(0, 0, 0)$ and $(0, -2.0$ m, $0)$, respectively (Fig. 20-11). Find $\mathbf{E}$ (a) at point P_a $(0, 1.0$ m, $0)$ and (b) at P_b $(0, 0, 1.5$ m$)$.

SOLUTION. (a) The magnitudes of the two contributions to $\mathbf{E}$ at P_a are

$$E_1 = (9.0 \times 10^9 \text{ N} \cdot \text{m}^2/\text{C}^2) \frac{16 \text{ nC}}{(1.0 \text{ m})^2} = 140 \text{ N/C}$$

$$E_2 = (9.0 \times 10^9 \text{ N} \cdot \text{m}^2/\text{C}^2) \frac{28 \text{ nC}}{(3.0 \text{ m})^2} = 28 \text{ N/C}$$

Since $\mathbf{E}_1$ and $\mathbf{E}_2$ are both in the y direction at P_a, we have

$$\mathbf{E} = \mathbf{E}_1 + \mathbf{E}_2 = (140 \text{ N/C})\mathbf{j} + (28 \text{ N/C})\mathbf{j} = (170 \text{ N/C})\mathbf{j}$$

(b) Before finding the field at P_b, it is convenient to note that the distance from q_2 to P_b is $\sqrt{(1.5 \text{ m})^2 + (2.0 \text{ m})^2} = 2.5$ m. The magnitudes of the two contributions to $\mathbf{E}$ at P_b are

$$E_1 = (9.0 \times 10^9 \text{ N} \cdot \text{m}^2/\text{C}^2) \frac{16 \text{ nC}}{(1.5 \text{ m})^2} = 64 \text{ N/C}$$

$$E_2 = (9.0 \times 10^9 \text{ N} \cdot \text{m}^2/\text{C}^2) \frac{28 \text{ nC}}{(2.5 \text{ m})^2} = 40 \text{ N/C}$$

In this case the two contributions to the field are not parallel: $\mathbf{E}_1 = E_1\mathbf{k}$ and $\mathbf{E}_2 = (E_2 \cos\theta)\mathbf{j} + (E_2 \sin\theta)\mathbf{k}$. From the fig-

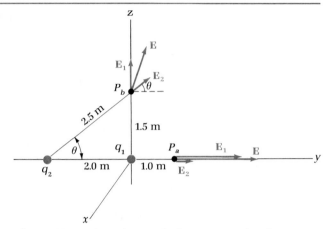

Figure 20-11. Example 20-4: Finding $\mathbf{E}$ at P_a and P_b due to charged particles 1 and 2.

ure, $\cos\theta = 2.0$ m$/2.5$ m $= 0.80$ and $\sin\theta = 1.5$ m$/2.5$ m $= 0.60$. (Notice that $\cos\theta$ and $\sin\theta$ are the components of the unit vector $\hat{\mathbf{r}}_2$ that points from q_2 to P_b, $\hat{\mathbf{r}}_2 = 0.80\mathbf{j} + 0.60\mathbf{k}$.) The field at P_b is

$$\mathbf{E} = \mathbf{E}_1 + \mathbf{E}_2 = (64 \text{ N/C})\mathbf{k} + [(40 \text{ N/C})(0.80)\mathbf{j}$$
$$+ (40 \text{ N/C})(0.60)\mathbf{k}]$$
$$= (32 \text{ N/C})\mathbf{j} + (88 \text{ N/C})\mathbf{k}$$

The electric dipole. An important charge distribution is an electric dipole. A dipole consists of two point charges of equal magnitude and opposite sign. Ordinarily, the symbol q representing the charge on an object may be positive or negative. But when referring to a dipole, we customarily let q represent the magnitude of either charge so that one particle has charge $+q$ and the other has charge $-q$. In Fig. 20-12, the particle with positive charge is at position $(0, 0, a)$ and the particle with negative charge is at $(0, 0, -a)$. The *electric dipole moment* $\mathbf{p}$ is a vector whose magnitude is the product of the charge magnitude q and the separation distance $2a$: $p = 2aq$. The direction of the dipole moment

Definition of the electric dipole moment p

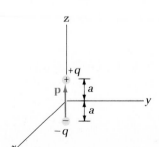

Figure 20-12. An electric dipole at the origin and pointing in the $+z$ direction. The dipole moment of this dipole is $\mathbf{p} = (2aq)\mathbf{k}$.

is from the particle with negative charge and toward the particle with positive charge. In the case shown in the figure, $\mathbf{p} = (2aq)\mathbf{k}$.

EXAMPLE 20-5. Determine the electric field in the perpendicular bisector plane of a dipole at distances that are large compared with the separation of the two point charges.

SOLUTION. Consider the electric field at a point P on the y axis, as shown in Fig. 20-13. The two contributions to the field are $\mathbf{E}_+$ due to the positive charge and $\mathbf{E}_-$ due to the negative charge:

$$\mathbf{E}_+ = \frac{1}{4\pi\epsilon_0}\frac{q}{r_+{}^2}\,\hat{\mathbf{r}}_+ \quad \text{and} \quad \mathbf{E}_- = \frac{1}{4\pi\epsilon_0}\frac{-q}{r_-{}^2}\,\hat{\mathbf{r}}_-$$

In the equation for $\mathbf{E}_-$, the negative sign for the charge has been explicitly included because q is a positive number. The distance r_+ from $+q$ to P is the same as r_- from $-q$ to P; $r_+ = r_- = r = \sqrt{y^2 + a^2}$. The vector $\mathbf{r}_+$ from $+q$ to P is $(y\mathbf{j} - a\mathbf{k})$ so that the unit vector $\hat{\mathbf{r}}_+ = (y\mathbf{j} - a\mathbf{k})/r$. This gives

$$\mathbf{E}_+ = \frac{1}{4\pi\epsilon_0}\frac{q}{r^2}\frac{y\mathbf{j}-a\mathbf{k}}{r} = \frac{q}{4\pi\epsilon_0 r^3}(y\mathbf{j}-a\mathbf{k})$$

Similarly,

$$\mathbf{E}_- = \frac{1}{4\pi\epsilon_0}\frac{-q}{r^2}\frac{y\mathbf{j}+a\mathbf{k}}{r} = \frac{q}{4\pi\epsilon_0 r^3}(-y\mathbf{j}-a\mathbf{k})$$

When we add $\mathbf{E}_+$ and $\mathbf{E}_-$ to form $\mathbf{E}$, the y components cancel, and the z components give

$$\mathbf{E} = \mathbf{E}_+ + \mathbf{E}_- = \frac{1}{4\pi\epsilon_0}\frac{-2aq}{r^3}\mathbf{k}$$

Since we are interested in the field only when $y \gg a$, we have $r = \sqrt{y^2 + a^2} \approx \sqrt{y^2}$. Also we note that the field must

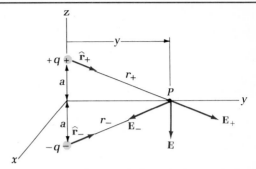

Figure 20-13. Example 20-5: Finding $\mathbf{E}$ in the perpendicular bisector plane of a dipole. The two contributions to the field are $\mathbf{E}_+$ and $\mathbf{E}_-$.

have azimuthal symmetry about the z axis, so that E is the same at all points in the xy plane that are the same distance R from the origin, where $R = \sqrt{x^2 + y^2}$. Therefore, we can generalize the result to include any point in the xy plane by replacing r ($\approx \sqrt{y^2}$) with R:

$$\mathbf{E} \approx \frac{1}{4\pi\epsilon_0}\frac{-(2aq)\mathbf{k}}{R^3} = \frac{1}{4\pi\epsilon_0}\frac{-\mathbf{p}}{R^3}$$

where $\mathbf{p} = (2aq)\mathbf{k}$ is the dipole moment. In the perpendicular bisector plane of a dipole, (i) the direction of $\mathbf{E}$ is opposite $\mathbf{p}$, (ii) E is proportional to p, and (iii) E falls off as $1/R^3$ (when $R \gg a$). If $E = 80$ N/C at $R = 10$ cm, then at $R = 20$ cm, $E \approx (80 \text{ N/C})/2^3 = 10$ N/C. We will be returning to the investigation of a dipole from time to time because it has important practical significance.

The electric field due to continuous charge distributions. The charge on macroscopic objects, such as the charged rods discussed earlier, is due to an imbalance of electron and proton populations. Since the charge on the electron or on the proton is small compared with ordinary-sized macroscopic charges, such a charge must comprise a large number of extra or missing electrons. Therefore, we may treat the charge as a continuous distribution of infinitesimal charge elements dq. Applying Eq. (20-4) to such a situation, we have that the infinitesimal electric field $d\mathbf{E}$ due to dq is

Infinitesimal electric field $d\mathbf{E}$ due to charge element dq

$$d\mathbf{E} = \frac{1}{4\pi\epsilon_0}\frac{dq}{r^2}\,\hat{\mathbf{r}} \tag{20-6}$$

where r is the distance from the element of charge dq to the point P at which the electric field is evaluated and $\hat{\mathbf{r}}$ is a unit vector that points from dq to P. The electric field $\mathbf{E}$ due to all charge elements is found by integration: $\mathbf{E} = \int d\mathbf{E}$, or

Electric field due to a continuous charge distribution

$$\mathbf{E} = \frac{1}{4\pi\epsilon_0}\int \frac{dq}{r^2}\,\hat{\mathbf{r}} \tag{20-7}$$

where the limits on the integral are determined by the extent of the charge distribution.

EXAMPLE 20-6. *A line charge.* When a charge distribution is long and narrow, as it is when charge is spread along a long, thin wire, it is called a *line charge*. A line charge is characterized by its *linear charge density* λ, which, for a uniform line charge, is the charge Q divided by the length L: $\lambda = Q/L$. Determine **E** in the perpendicular bisector plane of a long, straight, uniformly charged wire by treating the charge distribution as a uniform line charge.

SOLUTION. Figure 20-14 shows the wire centered at the origin and oriented along the z axis. It is convenient to designate the length as 2ℓ, which means that $\lambda = Q/2\ell$. The element of length dz has charge dq, and since the charge is uniformly distributed, $dq/Q = dz/2\ell$, or $dq = (Q/2\ell)dz = \lambda\,dz$. The infinitesimal electric field $d\mathbf{E}$ due to dq is

$$d\mathbf{E} = dE_y\mathbf{j} + dE_z\mathbf{k} = (dE\cos\theta)\mathbf{j} - (dE\sin\theta)\mathbf{k}$$

where the magnitude of $d\mathbf{E}$ is

$$dE = \frac{1}{4\pi\epsilon_0}\frac{\lambda\,dz}{(y^2 + z^2)}$$

From the figure we see that $\cos\theta = y/\sqrt{y^2 + z^2}$ and $\sin\theta = z/\sqrt{y^2 + z^2}$. [Notice that a unit vector $\hat{\mathbf{r}}$ that points from dz to P is $\hat{\mathbf{r}} = (\cos\theta)\mathbf{j} - (\sin\theta)\mathbf{k}$.]

First consider the y component of the field:

$$E_y = \int dE_y = \frac{\lambda y}{4\pi\epsilon_0}\int_{-\ell}^{+\ell}\frac{dz}{(y^2 + z^2)^{3/2}}$$

where the constants λ and y have been taken out of the integral. You may be surprised that y is regarded as a constant here, but keep in mind that the integral corresponds to adding up the infinitesimal electric fields $d\mathbf{E}$ due to all the infinitesimal charge elements dq along the z axis. During this procedure y, the coordinate of P, is held fixed. The limits on the integral from $-\ell$ to $+\ell$ correspond to the region occupied by the charge. From integral tables,

$$\int_{-\ell}^{+\ell}\frac{dz}{(y^2 + z^2)^{3/2}} = \frac{z}{y^2\sqrt{y^2 + z^2}}\Bigg|_{-\ell}^{+\ell} = \frac{2\ell}{y^2\sqrt{y^2 + \ell^2}}$$

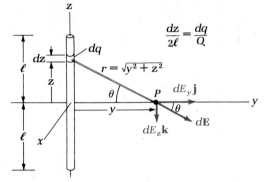

Figure 20-14. Example 20-6: Electric field **E** in the perpendicular bisector plane of a straight uniform line charge. By symmetry, the axial component is zero, or $E_z = 0$, so that in the xy plane the field is radial. We show later that if the charge distribution is very long, $\ell \gg R$, then $E \approx \lambda/2\pi\epsilon_0 R$, where $R = \sqrt{x^2 + y^2}$.

Substituting this into our expression for E_y gives

$$E_y = \frac{1}{2\pi\epsilon_0}\frac{\lambda}{y}\frac{\ell}{\sqrt{\ell^2 + y^2}}$$

Performing the integration of the z component of **E** gives $E_z = 0$ (Exercise 20-27). This result is expected from the symmetry of the charge distribution with respect to the xy plane. For every element of charge with a positive z coordinate there is a corresponding element with a negative z coordinate, and their contributions to E_z cancel.

We may generalize our result to include any point in the xy plane by noting that E must have azimuthal symmetry about the z axis, similar to that of the dipole in Example 20-5. Thus

$$E = \frac{1}{2\pi\epsilon_0}\frac{\lambda}{R}\frac{\ell}{\sqrt{\ell^2 + R^2}}$$

where $R = \sqrt{x^2 + y^2}$. The direction of **E** at any point in the xy plane is directly away from the origin (assuming λ is positive).

EXAMPLE 20-7. Determine **E** at points along the axis of a charged circular ring of radius a and charge Q. The charge on the ring is distributed uniformly and is narrow enough to be considered a line charge, similar to the way the mass is distributed on a hula hoop.

SOLUTION. Figure 20-15 shows the ring centered at the origin and contained in the yz plane. The infinitesimal electric field $d\mathbf{E}$ due to charge dq can be divided into two components, dE_x parallel to the x axis and $dE_\perp$ perpendicular to

the x axis. The symmetry of the charge distribution requires that $\int dE_\perp = 0$ because elements of charge on opposite sides of the circle produce infinitesimal components of electric field $dE_\perp$ that cancel one another. That is, the electric field must point along the x axis. The field's axial component is

$$E_x = \int dE_x = \int dE\cos\theta = \frac{1}{4\pi\epsilon_0}\int\frac{dq}{r^2}\cos\theta$$

The factor $\cos\theta/r^2$ can be factored out of the integral be-

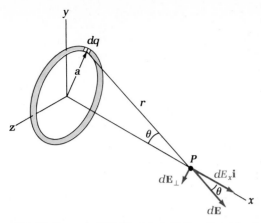

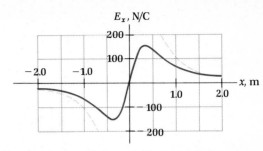

Figure 20-16. Example 20-7: Field component E_x versus x on the axis of the charged ring shown in Fig. 20-15, with $Q = 11.1$ nC and $a = 0.50$ m. The dashed curve is E_x for a charged particle with the same charge as the ring and located at the origin. These two field components approach the same value as $|x|$ becomes large compared with a.

Figure 20-15. Example 20-7: Electric field $\mathbf{E}$ on the axis of a uniformly charged ring. The ring is centered at the origin and contained in the yz plane. By symmetry, the component of $\mathbf{E}$ perpendicular to the x axis is zero.

cause θ and r are the same for each charge element dq. This gives

$$E_x = \frac{\cos\theta}{4\pi\epsilon_0 r^2} \int dq = \frac{Q\cos\theta}{4\pi\epsilon_0 r^2}$$

where we have used $\int dq = Q$. We can write E_x in terms of x and a by noting that from the figure, $\cos\theta = x/\sqrt{x^2 + a^2}$ and $r^2 = x^2 + a^2$. Thus

$$E_x = \frac{Qx}{4\pi\epsilon_0(x^2 + a^2)^{3/2}}$$

Figure 20-16 shows a graph of E_x versus x for the case where $a = 0.50$ m and $Q = +11.1$ nC. Are you surprised to see E_x negative when x is negative? The reason E_x is positive for positive x and negative for negative x is that the field is directed away from the positively charged ring. Note that the field is zero at the center of the ring. For comparison, we also show E_x for a point charge of $+11.1$ nC at the origin. The field of the ring approaches that of the point charge when $|x|$ becomes much greater than a.

EXAMPLE 20-8. A surface charge. Sometimes the charge on an object is spread over the object's surface as a thin layer, like a coat of paint. Such a charge distribution is called a *surface charge*. The *surface charge density* σ of a uniform surface charge is the charge Q divided by the area A of the surface on which the charge resides: $\sigma = Q/A$. Use the result of the previous example to find $\mathbf{E}$ on the axis of a thin, disk-shaped charge distribution of radius R_0. The charge distribution is uniform, similar to the mass distribution for a phonograph record (without the hole).

SOLUTION. Since the charge distribution is uniform and shaped as a thin disk, we treat it as a surface charge with $\sigma = Q/\pi R_0^2$, where πR_0^2 is the area of the disk. We divide the disk into rings with infinitesimal width da (Fig. 20-17), so that the area of a ring of radius a and width da is its circumference $2\pi a$ times da, and its charge is $dq = \sigma 2\pi a\, da$. From the result of the previous example, dE_x on the axis of a ring with radius a and charge $dq = \sigma 2\pi a\, da$ is

$$dE_x = \frac{(\sigma 2\pi a\, da)x}{4\pi\epsilon_0(x^2 + a^2)^{3/2}}$$

Integrating this expression from $a = 0$ to $a = R_0$ adds all the contributions to E_x due to each ring from radius $a = 0$ to

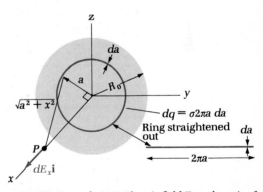

Figure 20-17. Example 20-8: Electric field $\mathbf{E}$ on the axis of a uniformly charged disk. The disk is centered at the origin and contained in the yz plane. The field is the sum of the infinite number of infinitesimal fields due to charged rings, with $dq = \sigma 2\pi a\, da$. We show later that if the radius of the disk is large compared with the distance from its center to P, $R_0 \gg |x|$, then $E \approx \sigma/2\epsilon_0$.

$a = R_0$:

$$E_x = \frac{2\pi\sigma x}{4\pi\epsilon_0} \int_0^{R_0} \frac{a\, da}{(x^2 + a^2)^{3/2}}$$

Evaluating the integral gives

$$E_x = \frac{\sigma x}{2\epsilon_0} \left(\frac{1}{\sqrt{x^2}} - \frac{1}{\sqrt{x^2 + R_0{}^2}} \right)$$

Since $1/\sqrt{x^2}$ is always larger than $1/\sqrt{x^2 + R_0{}^2}$, the algebraic sign of E_x is the same as x (assuming σ is positive). Thus E_x is positive for positive x and negative for negative x. That is, **E** points away from a positively charged disk.

Some useful approximations can be developed from the solutions to Examples 20-6 and 20-8. First, from Example 20-6, E in the bisector plane of a uniform line charge is

$$E = \frac{1}{2\pi\epsilon_0} \frac{\lambda}{R} \frac{\ell}{\sqrt{\ell^2 + R^2}}$$

Consider the field due to a very long line charge at a point near the charge but far from its ends. Then $\ell \gg R$, so that $\ell/\sqrt{\ell^2 + R^2} \approx \ell/\sqrt{\ell^2} = 1$, and

Electric field near a long, straight line charge, far from its ends

$$E \approx \frac{1}{2\pi\epsilon_0} \frac{\lambda}{R} \tag{20-8}$$

The field is directed away from the line charge (assuming λ is positive). An important feature of this field is that it falls off as $1/R$. If $E = 80$ N/C at $R = 10$ cm, then at $R = 20$ cm, $E \approx 40$ N/C.

Similarly, the solution to Example 20-8 can be used to find the approximate field near a large plane sheet with uniform surface charge density by finding E_x at points where $|x| \ll R_0$. In Exercise 20-33, you are asked to show that this gives

$$E_x \approx \frac{\sigma}{2\epsilon_0} \frac{x}{\sqrt{x^2}}$$

In this expression, the factor $x/\sqrt{x^2}$ is $+1$ for $x > 0$ and -1 for $x < 0$. This means that for positive σ, E_x is positive when x is positive and E_x is negative when x is negative, or **E** points away from a positively charged sheet. The approximate field magnitude near the sheet is

Electric field near a large plane sheet of charge, far from its edges

$$E \approx \frac{\sigma}{2\epsilon_0} \tag{20-9}$$

Thus the field is almost uniform near a large plane sheet of charge. If $E = 80$ N/C at $x = 10$ cm, then at $x = 20$ cm, $E \approx 80$ N/C.

20-7 LINES OF THE ELECTRIC FIELD

Lines of the electric field provide an aid for visualizing the field; they are essentially a map of the field. Although we draw field lines on a two-dimensional sheet of paper or a blackboard, we imagine their existence in three-dimensional space. Later we shall use field lines to describe magnetic fields as well. The concept was originated by the great British experimental physicist, Michael Faraday (1791–1867).

Figure 20-18 shows electric field lines for a few cases. A line is drawn such that **E** is tangent to the line at each point on the line, and arrowheads indicate the direction of the field. For example, near a point charge the lines are radial (Fig. 20-18a and b); they are directed away from a positive charge and toward a negative charge. To illustrate how **E** is tangent to field lines, **E** is shown at two points on the field lines of a dipole in Fig. 20-18c.

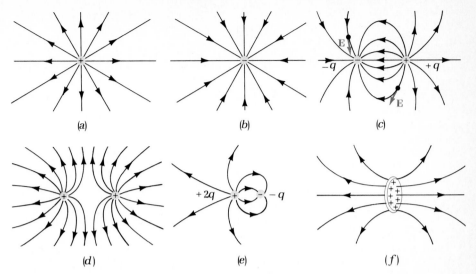

Figure 20-18. Electric field lines. (a) Particle with positive charge. (b) Particle with negative charge. (c) Dipole. (d) Two particles with equal positive charge. (e) Two particles with charges $+2q$ and $-q$. (f) Uniformly charged disk.

In a given drawing, the spacing of the lines indicates the magnitude of the field. In regions where the lines are close together, or dense, E is large, and where they are far apart, E is small. As it turns out, the density of lines is proportional to E, a fact which can be proved with Gauss's law, the subject of the next chapter.

Since the density of lines is proportional to E, the number of lines directed away from a positive charge or directed toward a negative charge is proportional to $|q|$. As an exercise, count the lines directed away from and directed toward each particle in Fig. 20-18e. Are the numbers of these lines correct for the stated values of the charges?

A uniform field is represented by field lines that are equally spaced, straight, and parallel. In the previous section we found that the field near a uniformly charged disk, but not near its edges, is almost uniform. The field lines of a uniformly charged disk are shown in Fig. 20-18f, and you can see that near the disk and away from its edges the lines are drawn so that they appear approximately equally spaced, straight, and parallel.

20-8 CHARGED PARTICLE IN A UNIFORM ELECTRIC FIELD

In Sec. 20-6 we determined the electric field produced by several charge distributions. Once the field is known, we can use Eq. (20-3), $\mathbf{F} = q\mathbf{E}$, to examine the effect of the field on a particle. If the electric force is the only significant force on the particle, then $q\mathbf{E}$ is the net force and Newton's second law gives

$$q\mathbf{E} = m\mathbf{a} \quad \text{or} \quad \mathbf{a} = \frac{q\mathbf{E}}{m}$$

We consider two specific cases: (1) a particle that is initially at rest in a uniform field and (2) a particle that is projected with velocity $\mathbf{v}_0$ into a uniform field, with $\mathbf{v}_0$ perpendicular to $\mathbf{E}$.

1. A charged particle released from rest in a uniform electric field will move with constant acceleration along a line parallel to $\mathbf{E}$ in the same way a rock released from rest in a uniform gravitational field falls vertically downward along a line parallel to $\mathbf{g}$. If we place the origin at the release point with the x

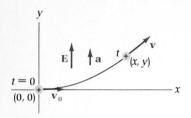

Figure 20-19. A charged particle in a uniform electric field travels in a parabolic path. The particle shown has a positive charge.

axis in the direction of **E** and set $t = 0$ when $x = 0$, then the procedures of kinematics (Chap. 3) give

$$a_x = \frac{qE}{m} \qquad v_x = \frac{qE}{m}t \qquad x = \frac{1}{2}\frac{qE}{m}t^2$$

Eliminating t in the equations for v_x and x, we also find

$$v_x^2 = \frac{2qE}{m}x \tag{20-10}$$

2. Now consider a particle with velocity $\mathbf{v_0}$ entering a region of uniform field **E**, with $\mathbf{v_0}$ perpendicular to **E**. The motion is similar to that of a ball thrown horizontally in the earth's uniform gravitational field (Sec. 4-3). In Fig. 20-19, we let the y axis be along **E** and show a positively charged particle with velocity $v_0\mathbf{i}$ at the origin at $t = 0$. Again, from the procedures of kinematics, we have

$$a_y = \frac{qE}{m} \qquad\qquad a_x = 0 \qquad a_z = 0$$

$$v_y = \left(\frac{qE}{m}\right)t \qquad v_x = v_0 \qquad v_z = 0$$

$$y = \frac{1}{2}\left(\frac{qE}{m}\right)t^2 \qquad x = v_0t \qquad z = 0$$

Thus the motion is contained in the xy plane. Eliminating t in the equations for y and x gives the parabolic path of the particle:

$$y = \frac{1}{2}\frac{qE}{mv_0^2}x^2 \tag{20-11}$$

The path shown in Fig. 20-19 is that of a particle with positive charge. If the charge is negative, then a_y is negative and the path curves downward rather than upward.

EXAMPLE 20-9. Determine the speed of an electron that travels a distance of 8.3 mm after starting from rest in a uniform field of 4.0×10^3 N/C.

SOLUTION. We let the x axis point along **E** so that $\mathbf{E} = E\mathbf{i}$. From Eq. (20-10), the speed v is

$$v = \sqrt{v_x^2} = \sqrt{\frac{2qE}{m}x}$$

In this equation, x is negative because $q\ (= -e)$ is negative. The direction of the force on the negatively charged electron is opposite the field direction. Since the electron started at rest from the origin, its x coordinate is negative throughout the motion. Substituting the numerical values gives

$$v = \sqrt{\frac{2(-1.6 \times 10^{-19}\text{ C})(4.0 \times 10^3\text{ N/C})}{9.1 \times 10^{-31}\text{ kg}}(-8.3\text{ mm})}$$

$$= 3.4 \times 10^6\text{ m/s}$$

EXAMPLE 20-10. An electron traveling horizontally with a speed of 3.4×10^6 m/s enters a region of uniform electric field that is directed upward, with $E = 520$ N/C. The field extends horizontally for a distance of about 45 mm (Fig. 20-20). Determine (a) the vertical displacement and (b) the velocity of the electron as it emerges from the region of the field.

SOLUTION. (a) Figure 20-20 shows the origin of coordinates at the point where the electron enters the field, and it leaves the field at $x = \ell$, where $\ell = 45$ mm. Using Eq. (20-11), we find that the electron's y coordinate as it emerges from

the field is

$$y = \frac{\frac{1}{2}qE\ell^2}{mv_0^2} = \frac{\frac{1}{2}(-1.6 \times 10^{-19}\text{ C})(520\text{ N/C})(45 \times 10^{-3}\text{ m})^2}{(9.1 \times 10^{-31}\text{ kg})(3.4 \times 10^6\text{ m/s})^2}$$

$$= -8.0 \times 10^{-3}\text{ m} = -8.0\text{ mm}$$

The electron is deflected downward 8.0 mm by the electric field. (b) The x component of the velocity remains constant at 3.4×10^6 m/s, but the y component changes. The time t_1 required for the electron to pass through the field is given by

$$\ell = v_0t_1 \qquad \text{or} \qquad t_1 = \frac{\ell}{v_0}$$

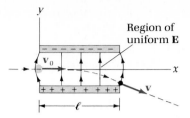

Figure 20-20. Example 20-10: An electron is deflected downward while passing through a region of uniform **E** that points upward.

Substituting this into the equation for v_y gives

$$v_y = \frac{qEt_1}{m} = \frac{qE\ell}{mv_0} = \frac{(-1.6 \times 10^{-19}\text{ C})(520\text{ N/C})(4.5 \times 10^{-2}\text{ m})}{(9.1 \times 10^{-31}\text{ kg})(3.4 \times 10^6\text{ m/s})}$$

$$= -1.2 \times 10^6\text{ m/s}$$

Therefore,

$$\mathbf{v} = v_x\mathbf{i} + v_y\mathbf{j} = (3.4 \times 10^6\text{ m/s})\mathbf{i} + (-1.2 \times 10^6\text{ m/s})\mathbf{j}$$

The electron emerges from the electric field with a downward component to its velocity, so that its downward displacement increases as it travels beyond the region of the field in a straight line.

Cathode-ray tube. Figure 20-21 shows schematically a device called a cathode-ray tube (CRT). In a CRT, electrons are first accelerated (as in Example 20-9) and then deflected (as in Example 20-10). A CRT is used for the video display in television sets, computer monitors, oscilloscopes, and so forth.

The electrons are emitted from a heated filament and accelerated by a horizontal electric field set up by charged plates in the "electron gun." The electrons emerging from a hole in one of the plates form a beam, like bullets projected from the muzzle of a machine gun. The beam then passes through a region of uniform electric field perpendicular to the beam direction. This deflecting field is produced by charged metal plates called *deflection plates.* The deflecting field directs the beam to the intended point on the face of the fluorescent screen, producing a luminous spot. The deflection plates shown in the figure are the vertical deflection plates; they control the vertical position of the luminous spot. Similarly, there are horizontal deflection plates, which are not shown. Some CRTs, such as those used in television sets, deflect the beam with a magnetic field rather than an electric field. We discuss magnetic deflection in Chap. 26.

Figure 20-21. Schematic diagram of a CRT, showing the electron gun and a set of deflection plates.

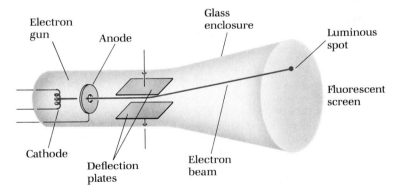

SUMMARY WITH APPLICATIONS

Section 20-2. Electric charge and matter

Electric charge is a fundamental property of matter. The charge of a proton is $+e$ and the charge of the electron is $-e$, where $e = 1.602 \times 10^{-19}$ C. A macroscopic object possesses charge q if it has an imbalance in its proton and electron populations: $q = (N_p - N_e)e$.

Describe and explain electrostatic charging experiments in terms of the charge on electrons and protons.

Section 20-3. Insulators and conductors

Most materials can be categorized as either conductors or insulators. A conductor readily allows charge carriers to flow, while an insulator does not readily allow charge carriers to flow.

Explain the distinction between a conductor and an insulator.

Section 20-4. Coulomb's law

Coulomb's law gives the electric force $\mathbf{F}_{ab}$ exerted by charged particle a on charged particle b:

$$\mathbf{F}_{ab} = \frac{1}{4\pi\epsilon_0} \frac{q_a q_b}{r^2} \hat{\mathbf{r}} \qquad (20\text{-}1)$$

This force is an inverse-square force that is attractive if the charges have opposite sign and repulsive if the charges have the same sign.

Use Coulomb's law to determine the force between charged particles.

Section 20-5. The electric field

The electric field $\mathbf{E}$ due to a charge distribution is the electric force $\mathbf{F}$ exerted by the distribution on a test particle divided by the charge of the test particle:

$$\mathbf{E} = \frac{\mathbf{F}}{q_0} \qquad \text{(small } q_0) \qquad (20\text{-}2)$$

Describe the concept of a field; define the electric field.

Section 20-6. Calculating the electric field

For a point charge,

$$\mathbf{E} = \frac{1}{4\pi\epsilon_0} \frac{q}{r^2} \hat{\mathbf{r}} \qquad (20\text{-}4)$$

where $\hat{\mathbf{r}}$ is a unit vector directed from q to the point P at which $\mathbf{E}$ is evaluated. The field due to a continuous distribution of charge is

$$\mathbf{E} = \frac{1}{4\pi\epsilon_0} \int \frac{dq}{r^2} \hat{\mathbf{r}} \qquad (20\text{-}7)$$

Determine the electric field due to a distribution of charged particles; describe and use expressions for the field due to continuous charge distributions.

Section 20-7. Lines of the electric field

The spatial characteristics of an electric field can be illustrated with electric field lines. By their direction and spacing, field lines indicate both the direction and magnitude of the field.

Sketch and use electric field lines for describing a field qualitatively.

Section 20-8. Charged particle in a uniform field

If the electric force is the only significant force on a particle, then Newton's second law gives $\mathbf{a} = q\mathbf{E}/m$. When a charged particle moves in a uniform field, its motion is described by constant-acceleration kinematics.

Describe the motion of a charged particle in a uniform electric field.

QUESTIONS

20-1   Suppose the magnitudes of the charge on the electron and proton were not the same, but differed by, say, 0.1 percent. Would the world be much different? Explain.

20-2   Suppose the signs of the charge on the proton and electron were reversed, positive for the electron and negative for the proton. Would the world be much different? Explain.

20-3   If you charge a balloon by rubbing it with wool, it will adhere to a wall. Why? Is there a net charge on the wall? (*Hint:* Examine Fig. 20-3.) The balloon will eventually fall. Why?

20-4   The net charge on the sphere in Fig. 20-3b is zero. Is there a net electric force on the sphere? If so, explain why.

20-5   The sphere in Fig. 20-3b is said to have an induced dipole moment. Explain why this name is appropriate.

20-6   In the charging-by-induction procedure illustrated in Fig. 20-3, suppose the rod were positively charged. What would be the sign of the charge on the sphere after the procedure? Draw figures similar to those in Fig. 20-3 to support your answer.

20-7   After two pairs of socks are taken out of a clothes dryer, pair A sticks together for a long time but pair B does not. Which pair is made of a material that is the better conductor?

20-8   Compare the mass in Newton's law of universal gravitation with the charge in Coulomb's law. How are they similar and how are they different?

20-9   Suppose you have two metal spheres on insulating stands similar to the one shown in Fig. 20-3, and you wish to give them equal and opposite charge using a rod with positive charge. Using sketches, describe how to proceed. How do you give them equal positive charge? How do you give them equal negative charge?

20-10 A conducting sphere suspended from a string is attracted to a positively charged rod. Does the sphere necessarily have a negative charge? Another suspended conducting sphere is repelled by the positively charged rod. Does this sphere necessarily have a positive charge?

20-11 A positively charged conducting sphere suspended from a string is repelled by a positively charged rod at large distances, but attracted at short distances. Using sketches, show how this happens.

20-12 In the discussion of charged rods in Sec. 20-2, we considered insulating rods, not conducting rods. But conducting rods as well as insulating rods can be charged by rubbing. Why did we confine the discussion to insulating rods? What precautions would you need to take in order to perform the charging experiments with a conducting rod?

20-13 Can the following quantities be described as fields? If so, are they scalar fields or vector fields?
(a) Money in the bank
(b) The water velocity in a stream
(c) The mass density of concrete

20-14 To determine **E** due to a positively charged conducting sphere at a point P near the sphere, we measure the force $\mathbf{F}_1$ on a test particle with positive charge q_1 placed at P. However, q_1 is not sufficiently small, and consequently the charge distribution on the sphere is significantly affected by the presence of particle 1. How will F_1/q_1 compare with E? If we measure the force $\mathbf{F}_2$ on test particle 2 with positive charge $q_2 = \frac{1}{2}q_1$, how does $\frac{1}{2}F_1$ compare with F_2? Which is closer to E, F_1/q_1 or F_2/q_2? Reconsider these questions when the test particles have negative charge rather than positive.

20-15 Suppose $E = 100$ N/C at $r = 40$ cm from a point charge. What is E at $r = 20$ cm?

20-16 Consider E in the perpendicular bisector plane of a dipole at points such that $R \gg a$, where R is the distance from the dipole and $2a$ is the charge separation. If $E = 100$ N/C at $R = 40$ cm, what is E at $R = 20$ cm?

20-17 At a distance $R = 40$ cm from a long, straight, uniform line charge, far from its ends, $E = 100$ N/C. What is E at $R = 20$ cm?

20-18 At a distance $|x| = 40$ cm from a large plane sheet of uniform surface charge, far from its edges, $E = 100$ N/C. What is E at $|x| = 20$ cm?

20-19 Figure 20-16 shows a graph of E_x versus x on the axis of a positively charged ring centered at the origin. Suppose a proton, constrained to move along the x axis, is released from rest at $x = 1.0$ m. (a) What sort of motion will the proton undergo? Similarly consider (b) a proton released at $x = -1.0$ m, (c) an electron released at $x = 1.0$ m, (d) an electron released at $x = 0.1$ m.

20-20 Since protons are crowded together in atomic nuclei, there must be another type of force in addition to gravitational and electric. This is evidence for the existence of a nuclear force that acts on protons (and, as we shall see later, neutrons). Do you expect that this nuclear force falls off more strongly with distance than $1/r^2$ or less strongly with distance than $1/r^2$? Explain. (*Hint:* The nuclear force between protons is much weaker than the electric force when the protons are separated by distances much greater than a nuclear diameter.)

20-21 When released from rest in an electric field, a positively charged particle will begin to move along a field line (assuming the electric force is the net force). (a) Will the path of the particle follow the field line if the field line is straight? (b) Will the path of the particle follow the field line if the field line is not straight? If it does not follow the field line, then will its path bend more or less than the field line?

20-22 If we draw 10 field lines directed away from a point charge of $+2.5\ \mu$C, how many lines should we draw directed toward a $-1.5\ \mu$C point charge in the same diagram?

20-23 Explain why lines of the electric field cannot cross. Suppose the lines do cross at some point; what would this say about the electric force on a charged particle at that point?

20-24 Sometimes the term "quantum" is used to denote the smallest value that a quantized quantity can have. For example, the quantum of cash in the monetary system of the United States is the penny. What is the quantum of electric charge? Give some examples of quantities that are quantized, and some examples of quantities that are not quantized. Is there a quantum of mass? Can you ever be sure that a seemingly unquantized quantity is really unquantized?

20-25 Can the electric field contributions due to two point charges of the same sign separated by a distance ℓ cancel each other to give $\mathbf{E} = 0$ at any point? If so, describe the location of this point. If so, and if the charges are of different magnitude, is the point of zero field nearer the large charge or the small one?

20-26 Can the electric field contributions due to two point charges of opposite sign and different magnitude separated by a distance ℓ cancel each other to give $\mathbf{E} = 0$ at any point? If so, describe the location of this point. If so, is the point of zero field nearer the charge of large magnitude or the one of small magnitude?

20-27 Consider a dipole in a uniform field **E**. Is there a net electric force on the dipole? If so, what is the direction of the force relative to **E**? If the dipole moment **p** is oriented perpendicular to **E**, is there a torque on the dipole? If so, does this torque tend to align the moment parallel to **E** or opposite **E**?

20-28 Suppose a dipole is in an electric field and its moment **p** points in the direction of **E**. Further, suppose **E** is nonuniform such that its magnitude increases in the direction of **E**. Is there a net electric force on the dipole? If so, is the net electric force in the direction of **E** or opposite **E**? Reconsider this question for the case where the magnitude of **E** decreases in the direction of **E**.

20-29 Complete the following table:

Symbol	Represents	Type	SI unit
q	Electric charge		
ϵ_0			
e			C
E		Vector	
p			
λ			
σ			

EXERCISES

Section 20-3. Insulators and conductors

20-1 Draw a figure similar to Fig. 20-3 for the case where the rod has a positive charge.

20-2 Two uncharged conducting spheres on insulating stands are brought into contact (so that they touch one another) and then a charged rod is brought nearby (Fig. 20-22). (a) Draw a figure similar to Fig. 20-22 and use positive and negative signs to show where excess charge resides on the spheres. (b) Suppose the spheres are separated while the rod is nearby, and the rod is removed far away. One of the spheres is thereafter found to have a charge of −4 nC. Which sphere has this negative charge? What is the charge on the other sphere? What would the charge on the spheres be if the rod was far removed before they were separated?

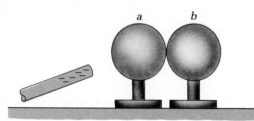
Figure 20-22. Exercise 20-2.

Section 20-4. Coulomb's law

20-3 Two charged particles exert an electric force of magnitude 4.0 μN on each other at a distance of 0.10 m. Construct a table listing r and F for values of r between 0.10 and 0.50 m at intervals of 0.10 m. Plot your data on a graph similar to Fig. 20-6.

20-4 Two charged particles exert a 3.6-μN electric force of attraction on one another at a separation of 120 mm. If one of the particles has a charge of +1.2 nC, what is the charge on the other?

20-5 (a) If an object has a charge of +1.0 nC, how many of its electrons are missing? (b) If an object has a charge of −3.0 nC, how many extra electrons does it contain?

20-6 Estimate the total number of electrons in a 0.5-kg solid block by assuming the material has about the same number of protons and neutrons. If the block has an excess charge of +10 nC, what is the fraction of missing electrons?

20-7 A unit of charge called a *faraday* is the charge on Avogadro's number ($N_0 = 6.02 \times 10^{23}$) of protons. (a) Determine the conversion factor (C/faraday) for changing a charge from faradays to C. (b) Convert a charge of 0.04 faraday to C.

20-8 (a) The two protons in the H_2 molecule are about 10^{-10} m apart. What is the magnitude of the electric force one of them exerts on the other? (b) The two protons in the helium nucleus are about 10^{-15} m apart. What is the magnitude of the electric force one of them exerts on the other? (c) What is the ratio of the force magnitude found in part (b) to that found in part (a)?

20-9 Three particles with charge $q_a = +14$ nC, $q_b = −26$ nC, and $q_c = +21$ nC are arranged along a straight line (Fig. 20-23). Particle b is between a and c, 120 mm from a and 160 mm from c. (a) Determine F_{ab}, F_{cb}, and the magnitude of the net force on b. Is the net force on b toward a or c? (b) Determine F_{ac}, F_{bc}, and the magnitude of the net force on c. Is the net force on c toward or away from b?

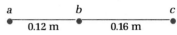
$$a \qquad\qquad b \qquad\qquad\qquad c$$
$$0.12 \text{ m} \qquad\qquad 0.16 \text{ m}$$
Figure 20-23. Exercise 20-9.

20-10 Three particles with charge $q_a = +14$ nC, $q_b = −26$ nC, and $q_c = +21$ nC are arranged on the corners of a right triangle (Fig. 20-24). Particle a is at the 90° corner a distance of 18 cm from b and 24 cm from c. Arrange a coordinate system with a at the origin, b along the x axis, and c along the y axis, and then determine the cartesian components and the magnitude of the net force on c.

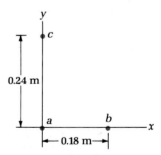
Figure 20-24. Exercise 20-10.

20-11 Three particles with equal charge q are at the corners of an equilateral triangle of side d (Fig. 20-25). What is the force on each of the particles?

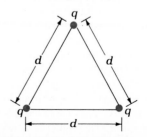
Figure 20-25. Exercise 20-11.

20-12 Three particles with equal positive charge q are at the corners of a square of side d (Fig. 20-26). (a) What is the magnitude of the force on a fourth particle of positive charge q_0 when it is placed at the center of the square? (b) What is the magnitude of the force on the fourth particle when it is placed at the vacant corner of the square?

Figure 20-26. Exercise 20-12.

20-13 Two particles a and b have equal mass of 2.6 g and charge of equal magnitude q but opposite sign. Particle a is suspended from the ceiling on a thread of length 0.35 m and negligible mass (Fig. 20-27). When a and b are separated by a horizontal distance of 0.25 m, a is in static equilibrium, with the string at an angle of 45° with the vertical. Determine q.

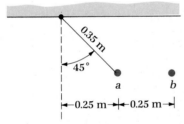

Figure 20-27. Exercise 20-13.

20-14 (a) Two particles a and b are 0.20 m apart and have charge $q_a = +2.0$ nC and $q_b = +1.0$ nC. At what position relative to a and b can we place a third particle with charge q such that the force on it due to a and b is zero? (b) Rework part (a) for the case where $q_b = -1.0$ nC.

Section 20-5. The electric field

20-15 The electric force exerted by a charge distribution on a particle of charge $+2.6$ nC when placed at position P is vertically upward, with $F = 0.58$ μN. (a) At P what is $\mathbf{E}$ due to the distribution? (b) What is the electric force exerted by this field on a particle placed at P with charge -13 nC? (Note: To work this problem with the information given, you must assume the charge on the particles is not large enough to disturb the distribution of charges.)

20-16 The electric force exerted by a distribution of charges on a particle of charge $+1.4$ nC at a particular position is $\mathbf{F} = (-0.24$ μN$)\mathbf{i} + (0.55$ μN$)\mathbf{j}$. (a) What is the electric field due to the distribution at that position?

(b) What is the electric force exerted by this field on a particle with charge -25 nC placed at that position? (See the note at the end of Exercise 20-15.)

20-17 Within the earth's atmosphere there exists an electric field, of average magnitude 150 N/C, that points downward. (a) Determine the charge-to-mass ratio (in C/kg) an object must have in order to be suspended in midair by electric and gravitational forces. (b) Assume that the number of protons and neutrons are equal and determine the fraction of excess electrons within the object. Comment on the feasibility of such an experiment.

20-18 In attempting to evaluate at point P the electric field due to a system of charges, we measure the electric force on particle a ($q_a = +134$ nC) placed at P and find it to be $\mathbf{F}_a = (2.86$ mN$)\mathbf{i} + (3.41$ mN$)\mathbf{j}$. Particle a is then far removed, particle b ($q_b = +66.9$ nC) is placed at P, and the force on b is measured to be $\mathbf{F}_b = (1.46$ mN$)\mathbf{i} + (1.73$ mN$)\mathbf{j}$. (a) Did particle a's presence at point P have a measurable effect on the charge distribution of the system? (b) Estimate the electric field at P when both a and b are far removed.

Section 20-6. Calculating the electric field

20-19 A particle with charge $+5.8$ nC is placed at the origin. (a) Determine the cartesian components of the electric field due to the particle at positions (x, y, z) of (15 cm, 0, 0); (15 cm, 15 cm, 0); (15 cm, 15 cm, 15 cm); (10 cm, 20 cm, 0). (b) Determine E at the positions given in part (a).

20-20 Rework Exercise 20-19 for a particle with charge -5.8 nC at the origin.

20-21 (a) Determine at the position of particle b the electric field that is due to particles a and c ($q_a = +14$ nC and $q_c = +21$ nC) in Fig. 20-23. (b) Determine at the position of particle c the electric field that is due to particles a and b ($q_b = -26$ nC) in Fig. 20-23.

20-22 (a) Determine at the position of particle a the electric field that is due to particles b and c ($q_b = -26$ nC and $q_c = +21$ nC) in Fig. 20-24. (b) Determine at the position of particle c the electric field that is due to particles a and b ($q_a = +14$ nC) in Fig. 20-24.

20-23 Determine the electric field (a) at the center of the square and (b) at the vacant corner in Fig. 20-26.

20-24 A dipole centered at the origin consists of two particles, one with charge $+1.6 \times 10^{-19}$ C at $z = +0.41 \times 10^{-10}$ m and the other with charge -1.6×10^{-19} C at $z = -0.41 \times 10^{-10}$ m. (a) Determine $\mathbf{p}$. (b) Determine the electric field in the xy plane that is due to the dipole at a distance of 1.0 μm from the origin. (c) Rework part (b) when the distance is 2.0 μm.

20-25 A dipole of moment $\mathbf{p} = 2aq\mathbf{k}$ is centered at the origin. Determine $\mathbf{E}$ along the z axis at points far from the dipole, $|z| \gg a$. (Hint: Use the binomial expansion.)

20-26 A uniform line charge with $Q = 24$ nC and length 120 mm($\ell = 60$ mm) is centered at the origin and oriented along the z axis (Fig. 20-14). (a) Determine the linear charge density λ. (b) Determine E at (20 mm, 0, 0), and at (200 mm, 0, 0). (c) E is due to a very long uniform line charge ($\ell \gg 200$ mm) along the z axis, with the same linear charge density as found in part (a). Find E at (20 mm, 0, 0) and at (200 mm, 0, 0) and compare your answers with those found in part (b).

20-27 (a) Show that the integral that gives E_z for the line charge in Example 20-6 is

$$E_z = \frac{-\lambda}{4\pi\epsilon_0} \int_{-\ell}^{+\ell} \frac{z \, dz}{(y^2 + z^2)^{3/2}}$$

(b) Show that $E_z = 0$.

20-28 Determine E due to a very long line charge of linear charge density $\lambda = 300$ nC/m at distances of 0.10 to 0.80 m, using intervals of 0.10 m. Make a graph of E versus r with your data and sketch a continuous curve through the points.

20-29 A uniform ring of charge as shown in Fig. 20-15, with charge $Q = 11.1$ nC and radius $a = 0.50$ m, is centered at the origin and contained in the yz plane. Determine E_x at (1.0 m, 0, 0) and (−0.5 m, 0, 0). Check your answer with Fig. 20-16.

20-30 (a) E is a field due to a point charge, with charge Q located at the origin. Write an expression for E_x at points along the x axis. (b) Determine the ratio of your expression for E_x in part (a) and that due to the charged ring of Example 20-7. (c) Evaluate the ratio found in part (b) at $x = a$, $5a$, and $10a$. (d) Use the binomial expansion to show that E_x due to the charged ring of Example 20-7 approaches that due to a point charge in the limit as $x \gg a$.

20-31 The dipole moment of a water molecule has a magnitude of 6.2×10^{-30} C · m. If we let the water molecule be replaced by a dipole with $p = 2ae$, where e is the magnitude of the electronic charge, what is a?

20-32 A thin, disk-shaped uniform surface charge with $Q = 28$ nC and radius $R_0 = 200$ mm is centered at the origin and contained in the yz plane (Fig. 20-17). (a) Determine the surface charge density σ. (b) Determine E_x along the x axis in both the positive and negative directions between $x = 40$ mm (−40 mm) and $x = 200$ mm (−200 mm) at intervals of 40 mm. (c) Make a graph of E_x versus x with these data and sketch a continuous curve through the points. (d) On the same graph, plot E_x versus x for a disk with the same charge density as found in part (a) but with a very large radius ($R_0 \gg |x|$).

20-33 Use the solution to Example 20-8 to show that for points near a large sheet with uniform surface charge density,

$$E_x = \frac{\sigma}{2\epsilon_0} \frac{x}{\sqrt{x^2}}$$

20-34 Use the binomial expansion to show that the electric field due to a disk-shaped surface charge (Example 20-8) approximates the field due to a point charge at distances large compared with the radius of the disk, $|x| \gg R_0$.

20-35 A rod in the shape of a semicircle with a uniform linear charge density is shown in Fig. 20-28. Develop an equation for the magnitude of the electric field at the center P in terms of the rod's charge Q and radius a.

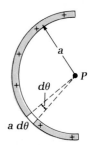

Figure 20-28. Exercise 20-35.

Section 20-7. Lines of the electric field

20-36 The negatively charged particle in Fig. 20-29 has a charge of 62 nC. What is the charge on the positively charged particle?

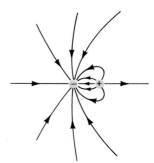

Figure 20-29. Exercise 20-36.

20-37 Draw a figure similar to Fig. 20-25 and sketch the field lines. Each of the three particles has the same positive charge.

20-38 Draw a figure similar to Fig. 20-14 and sketch the field lines in the yz plane. Assume that λ is positive.

Section 20-8. Charged particle in a uniform field

20-39 The particle-dependent quantity that determines the acceleration of a charged particle in an electric field (assuming forces other than electric are negligible) is the particle's charge-to-mass ratio. (a) Determine the charge-to-mass ratio for the electron and for the proton in C/kg. (b) Determine the magnitudes of the acceleration of an electron and of a proton in a field of magnitude 1 N/C. (c) According to your findings in part (b), what is the ratio of the proton's acceleration to the electron's?

20-40 An electron accelerates from rest in a uniform electric field to a speed of 2.9×10^6 m/s in a distance of 14 mm. What is the magnitude of the electric field?

20-41 A charged particle accelerates from rest in a uniform electric field of magnitude $E = 5.6 \times 10^3$ N/C to a speed of 5.7×10^5 m/s after traveling a distance of 0.30 m. (a) What is the particle's charge-to-mass ratio? (b) Is this particle a proton or an electron?

20-42 What is the time interval required for the electron of Example 20-9 to travel the 8.3 mm?

20-43 Show that the angle between the x axis and the electron's subsequent straight-line path as it emerges from the region of the field in Fig. 20-20 is given by $\theta = \tan^{-1}(qE\ell/mv_o^2)$. Evaluate this angle using the numerical values given in Example 20-10.

20-44 An electron enters a region of uniform electric field $\mathbf{E} = -(360 \text{ N/C})\mathbf{j}$ with a velocity $\mathbf{v} = (1.6 \times 10^6 \text{ m/s})\mathbf{i}$. Determine the electron's velocity as it emerges from the region of the field if the field has a horizontal extent of $\ell = 29$ mm (Fig. 20-20).

PROBLEMS

20-1 Four charged particles are arranged at the corners of a square (Fig. 20-30). The particles at opposite corners have equal charge. (a) Find the relationship between Q and q such that the force on each particle with charge Q is zero. (b) With the relationship beween Q and q given by the result of part (a), determine the magnitude of the force on each of the two particles with charge q.

Figure 20-30. Prob. 20-1.

20-2 (a) Show that at a point P in the yz plane the components of $\mathbf{E}$ due to a dipole of moment $\mathbf{p} = 2aq\mathbf{k}$ at the origin (Fig. 20-31) are

$$E_y = \frac{1}{4\pi\epsilon_0} \frac{3pyz}{(y^2 + z^2)^{5/2}}$$

$$E_z = \frac{1}{4\pi\epsilon_0} \frac{p(2z^2 - y^2)}{(y^2 + z^2)^{5/2}}$$

where the distance from the origin to P is much greater than a. (b) Show that this general result agrees with the results of Example 20-5 and Exercise 20-25, which applied to points on the axes only.

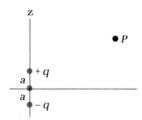

Figure 20-31. Prob. 20-2.

20-3 **A quadrupole.** A quadrupole is an arrangement of charges that, among other characteristics, has zero net charge (monopole moment) and a zero net dipole moment. The charge distribution shown in Fig. 20-32 is an example of a quadrupole; it can be viewed as two dipoles pointing in opposite directions. For this quadrupole show that E varies with distance as r^{-4} at points along the y axis and z axis when $r \gg a$. (Note that E varies with distance as r^{-2} for a monopole, r^{-3} for a dipole, and r^{-4} for a quadrupole at distances far from the charge distribution.)

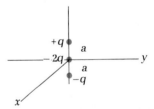

Figure 20-32. Prob. 20-3.

20-4 Show that E_x on the axis of a positively charged ring of radius a has its maximum value at $x = +a/\sqrt{2}$ and its minimum value at $x = -a/\sqrt{2}$. Use Fig. 20-16 to check your answer.

20-5 Show that E_z along the z axis for the line charge in Fig. 20-14 is given by $\lambda/[2\pi\epsilon_0(z^2 - \ell^2)]$, where $z > \ell$. (Hint: Let z' be the coordinate of the infinitesimal charge dq and z be the coordinate of the point P at which the field is determined. The integration variable is z', and z is held fixed during the integration.)

20-6 Determine the cartesian components of $\mathbf{E}$ for the line charge in Fig. 20-14 at a point P in the yz plane. (See the hint in the preceding problem.)

20-7 Two thin, uniformly charged disks are parallel to each other and parallel to the yz plane. The disks have equal radii, and both are centered on the x axis, with disk A at $(+x_0, 0, 0)$ and disk B at $(-x_0, 0, 0)$. Also, the disks are very close together such that x_0 is much less than their radii. If disk A has a surface charge density of $+27$ nC/m^2 and disk B has a surface charge density of -27 nC/m^2, determine the approximate electric field at points along the x axis (a) between the disks and (b) outside the disks but near them ($|x| \ll$ disk radii).

20-8   Determine the approximate electric field at a point near two charge distributions: a long, straight line charge and a large plane surface charge (Fig. 20-33). The surface charge is due to a thin, uniformly charged disk ($\sigma = +42$ nC/m²) with a very large radius. The disk is contained in the yz plane and centered at the origin. The long line charge is uniform ($\lambda = +15$ nC/m) and is parallel to the y axis, with its center on the x axis at the point ($+39$ mm, 0, 0). Estimate the cartesian components of **E** at (55 mm, 0, 62 mm).

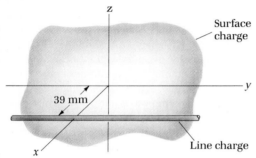

Figure 20-33. Prob. 20-8.

20-9   Determine **E** at points on the axis of a square line charge with side 2ℓ and uniform linear charge density λ (Fig. 20-34). Compare your answer with the results of the charged-ring example (Example 20-7).

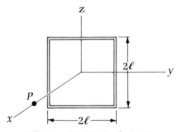

Figure 20-34. Prob. 20-9.

20-10   (a) At points along the y axis find **E** due to a uniform line charge that extends along the z axis from the origin to $z = \ell$. (b) Generalize your answer to part (a) to include points in the xy plane. (c) Use your answer to part (b) to find **E** at points in the xy plane when **E** is due to a semi-infinite line charge that occupies the positive half of the z axis ($z = 0$ to $z = +\infty$).

20-11   Consider the motion of a negatively charged particle (charge q and mass m) that is constrained to move only along the x axis and at the same time experiences an electric force due to the (positively) charged ring discussed in Example 20-7. (a) What sort of motion will the particle execute when released at some point other than the origin? (b) Find an expression for the

period T of the particle's motion if it is released at $x = x_0$, where $x_0 \ll a$.

20-12   ***The Millikan oil-drip experiment.*** In a classic experiment R. A. Millikan (1868–1953) measured the electronic charge. The apparatus he used is shown schematically in Fig. 20-35. Oil drops were formed by an atomizer, and a few fell through a hole and into a region of uniform electric field between charged plates. He could observe a particular drop with the microscope and determine its mass by measuring its terminal speed. He then charged the drop by irradiating it with x-rays and adjusted the electric field so that the drop would be in static equilibrium because of equal and opposite gravitational and electric forces. (a) What is the charge on a drop of mass 2.32×10^{-14} kg that remains suspended in an electric field of 2.03×10^5 N/C? Assume $g = 9.80$ N/kg. (b) How many electronic charges does the answer to part (a) represent?

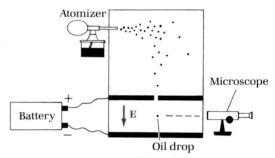

Figure 20-35. Prob. 20-12: The Millikan oil-drop experiment.

20-13   ⬛ Determine the behavior of the electric field on the axis of a square sheet of charge with a uniform surface charge density (Fig. 20-36). Let the square distribution of charge be represented by 10 parallel line charges, with proper spacing to approximate a square. Write a BASIC program that determines the field at about 10 equally spaced points from about 0.2ℓ to 2.0ℓ, where 2ℓ is the length of the sides of the square. Graph your results and compare them with

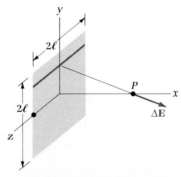

Figure 20-36. Prob. 20-13.

those given for a circular disk with the same charge and with area $(2\ell)^2$. Use numerical values that are both convenient and realistic. You may wish to rework the problem using 20 line charges rather than 10 in order to estimate the accuracy of your answer.

20-14 Two particles, one with positive charge Q_0 and the other with positive charge $3Q_0$, are separated a distance d. Determine the location and charge on a third particle that will result in a net electric force of zero on the first two particles.

20-15 For the uniform line charge shown in Fig. 20-28, determine an expression for $\mathbf{E}$ along an axis that is perpendicular to the plane that contains the semicircle and passes through P. Note that $\mathbf{E}$ has components both parallel and perpendicular to this axis.

CHAPTER 21
GAUSS'S LAW

21-1 INTRODUCTION

The electric field produced by stationary charged objects can be obtained in two equivalent ways: with Coulomb's law or with Gauss's law. The previous chapter described the first way, and this chapter presents the second. Coulomb's law gives a simple and direct way of expressing the electric force. Gauss's law is more subtle, more elegant, and sometimes more useful. Gauss's law requires more mathematical sophistication than Coulomb's law, and the reward is a deeper insight into the electrical interaction.

The genius of Karl Friedrich Gauss (1777–1855) was apparent at a very early age, and his prowess for highly involved mental calculations is legend. His interests were broad and included astronomy and physics, but his most important works were in mathematics. He laid the mathematical foundations for much of the theoretical physics that came in the latter part of the nineteenth and early twentieth centuries, including Einstein's theory of gravitation. *(From Albert Betlex,* The Discovery of Nature, *Simon & Schuster, New York, 1965/Courtesy A.I.P., Niels Bohr Library)*

21-2   FLUX

Gauss's law is expressed in terms of the *flux* of the electric field, or the *electric flux*. Before learning about Gauss's law, you must understand the concept of flux. The word "flux" comes from the Latin *fluere*, which means to flow. The concept originated in the theory of fluids, where flux represents the rate at which a fluid passes through an imaginary surface. As you will see later, flux is perhaps more useful when dealing with magnetic fields than with electric fields.

The flux Φ of a vector field involves (i) the field and (ii) a surface for which the flux is evaluated. To find the flux for a surface, we represent the surface with a *surface vector*. The surface vector $\Delta \mathbf{S}$ for a plane surface has a magnitude ΔS equal to the area of the surface and is directed perpendicular to the surface. Suppose you take a sheet of notebook paper with length a and width b and hold the sheet horizontally, as shown in Fig. 21-1. Then $\Delta \mathbf{S} = \Delta S\mathbf{j} = (ab)\mathbf{j}$. The flux for such a surface is the dot product between the field and the surface vector. For example, the flux Φ_g of the gravitational field $\mathbf{g}$ for this surface is

$$\Phi_g = \mathbf{g} \cdot \Delta \mathbf{S} = (-g\mathbf{j}) \cdot (ab\mathbf{j}) = -gab$$

where we have used $\mathbf{j} \cdot \mathbf{j} = 1$. A typical sheet of notebook paper has dimensions $a = 0.27$ m and $b = 0.22$ m, so that $\Phi_g = -(9.8 \text{ N/kg})(0.27 \text{ m})(0.22 \text{ m}) = -0.58 \text{ N} \cdot \text{m}^2/\text{kg}$.

Now suppose the sheet of notebook paper is held vertically so that it faces toward the x direction. Then $\Delta \mathbf{S} = (ab)\mathbf{i}$, and

$$\Phi_g = \mathbf{g} \cdot \Delta \mathbf{S} = (-g\mathbf{j}) \cdot (ab\mathbf{i}) = 0$$

because $\mathbf{j} \cdot \mathbf{i} = 0$. Suppose the sheet is held at a 45° angle to the vertical so that $\Delta \mathbf{S}$ is parallel to the unit vector $(1/\sqrt{2})\mathbf{i} + (1/\sqrt{2})\mathbf{j}$. What is the flux in this case?

The surface vector's direction has a twofold ambiguity because a plane surface has *two* directions perpendicular to the surface, one opposite the other. We could just as well say that the direction of $\Delta \mathbf{S}$ for the sheet in Fig. 21-1 is $-\mathbf{j}$ rather than $+\mathbf{j}$. This twofold ambiguity can be resolved when the surface is a *closed* surface. By a closed surface, we mean a surface that encloses a volume, like the closed box in Fig. 21-2. In this case, we can define the direction of $\Delta \mathbf{S}$ for each side of the box as either into or out of the enclosed volume. Following custom, we choose the direction of $\Delta \mathbf{S}$ such that it points *out* of the enclosed volume. This means that $\Delta \mathbf{S}$ for the top surface is toward $+\mathbf{j}$, $\Delta \mathbf{S}$ for the right-hand face is toward $+\mathbf{i}$, and so on. What is the direction of $\Delta \mathbf{S}$ for the left-hand face? How about the bottom face?

Similar to the flux for the gravitational field, the flux Φ_E of a uniform electric field $\mathbf{E}$ for a plane surface $\Delta \mathbf{S}$ is

$$\Phi_E = \mathbf{E} \cdot \Delta \mathbf{S} = E \, \Delta S \cos \theta \qquad \text{(plane surface and uniform } \mathbf{E} \text{ only)}$$

The dot product takes into account the orientation of the surface with respect to the field direction. As shown in Fig. 21-3, the factor $\Delta S \cos \theta$ is the area of the projection of the surface onto a plane perpendicular to $\mathbf{E}$ (Fig. 21-3c), and may be viewed as the effective area for the flux. Since it is defined as a dot product, flux is a scalar quantity. The SI unit of electric flux is $(\text{N/C})(\text{m}^2) = \text{N} \cdot \text{m}^2/\text{C}$.

It is often helpful to use field lines to form a mental picture of flux (Fig. 21-3). As we shall discuss in the next section, the number of lines that cross a surface is proportional to the flux for the surface. This field-line characterization pro-

Surface vector $\Delta \mathbf{S}$ for a plane surface

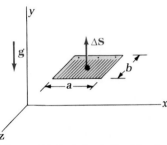

Figure 21-1. A sheet of notebook paper held horizontally. The flux of the gravitational field for the sheet is $\Phi_g = \mathbf{g} \cdot \Delta \mathbf{S} = -g \, \Delta S = -gab$.

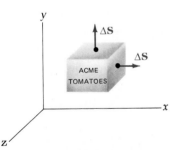

Figure 21-2. When a surface is closed (that is, it encloses a volume), the twofold ambiguity of $\Delta \mathbf{S}$ is resolved by letting $\Delta \mathbf{S}$ point out of the enclosed volume.

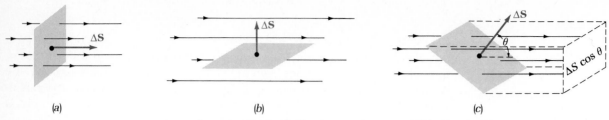

Figure 21-3. Flux Φ_E for plane surfaces with various orientations in a uniform field **E**, shown with field lines. (a) **E** parallel to Δ**S**, $\Phi_E = E\,\Delta S$. (b) **E** perpendicular to Δ**S**, $\Phi_E = 0$. (c) The general case where **E** and Δ**S** are at an angle θ. Note that in the expression $\Phi_E = E\,\Delta S\cos\theta$, the factor $\Delta S\cos\theta$ can be regarded as the surface's effective area.

vides an aid for visualizing flux, but it is not useful for calculations because of the discrete nature of the lines.

EXAMPLE 21-1. The wedge-shaped surface in Fig. 21-4 is in a region of uniform field $\mathbf{E} = (600\text{ N/C})\mathbf{i}$. (a) Determine the electric flux for each of the five surfaces. (b) Find the net flux for the entire closed surface.

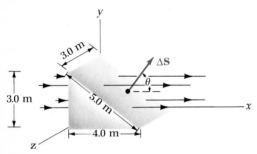

Figure 21-4. Example 21-1: The uniform field **E** is represented by field lines, and the surface vector for the slant surface is shown.

SOLUTION. (a) The flux is zero for the two triangular side surfaces and for the bottom surface because the direction of the surface vector for each of these surfaces is perpendicular to **E** so that $\cos\theta = \cos 90° = 0$. For the square surface on the left-hand side, $\Delta\mathbf{S} = (3.0\text{ m})(3.0\text{ m})(-\mathbf{i}) = -(9.0\text{ m}^2)\mathbf{i}$, and

$$\Phi_E = \mathbf{E}\cdot\Delta\mathbf{S} = [(600\text{ N/C})\mathbf{i}]\cdot[-(9.0\text{ m}^2)\mathbf{i}]$$

$$= -5400\text{ N}\cdot\text{m}^2/\text{C}$$

For the slant surface,

$$\Phi_E = \mathbf{E}\cdot\Delta\mathbf{S} = E\,\Delta S\cos\theta$$

From the figure, $\Delta S = (3.0\text{ m})(5.0\text{ m}) = 15\text{ m}^2$, and $\cos\theta = 3.0\text{ m}/5.0\text{ m} = 0.60$. Therefore, the flux for the slant surface is

$$\Phi_E = (600\text{ N/C})(15\text{ m}^2)(0.60) = 5400\text{ N}\cdot\text{m}^2/\text{C}$$

(b) For three of the five surfaces the flux is 0; for the other two the values are 5400 N · m²/C and -5400 N · m²/C. Thus the net flux for the closed surface is zero. Notice that the contribution to the flux for a closed surface is positive for the portion of the surface where the field is directed out of the enclosed volume and negative for the portion of the surface where the field is directed into the enclosed volume.

The net flux for this closed surface can also be seen to be zero from examination of the field lines. No lines cross the triangular sides or the bottom. Figure 21-4 shows four lines directed into the volume where they cross the square surface and the same four lines directed out of the volume where they cross the slant surface. The net number of lines directed out of the volume where they cross the closed surface is the number out minus the number in. For this case the net number of lines is $4 - 4 = 0$.

The examples of flux discussed above involve only uniform fields and plane surfaces. When the surface is curved, as shown in Fig. 21-5, or when the electric field varies from point to point over the surface, the flux is found by dividing the surface into small surface elements, with each surface element small enough so that it can be considered a plane and so that the electric field variation across the element is negligible. The flux for the entire surface is then the sum of the individual contributions to the flux from each of the small surface elements. In the limit as the size of each element approaches zero and their number approaches infinity, the sum becomes an integral:

$$\Phi_E = \lim_{\Delta S_i \to 0}\sum_i \mathbf{E}_i\cdot\Delta\mathbf{S}_i = \int \mathbf{E}\cdot d\mathbf{S}$$

Or
$$\Phi_E = \int \mathbf{E} \cdot d\mathbf{S} = \int E \cos \theta \, dS \qquad (21\text{-}1)$$

Definition of the flux of an electric field

The integral in Eq. (21-1) is called a *surface integral.* Thus *the flux of the electric field for a surface is the surface integral of* $\mathbf{E}$ *over that surface.*

Mostly we shall be interested in the flux for a closed surface. When the surface of integration is closed, the sign $\oint$ for a closed integral is used:

Electric flux for a closed surface

$$\Phi_E = \oint \mathbf{E} \cdot d\mathbf{S} \qquad (21\text{-}2)$$

A gaussian surface is a hypothetical surface for which the flux is evaluated.

The closed surface for which the flux is calculated is ordinarily an imaginary or hypothetical surface, called a *gaussian surface.* A gaussian surface does not necessarily correspond to the surface of an object. Whenever you use Gauss's law, you may devise a surface of any size and shape to use as your gaussian surface. As you shall see, selecting the proper size and shape for a gaussian surface is one of the key elements in using Gauss's law.

21-3 GAUSS'S LAW

Gauss's law can be stated in this way: *The electric flux for an arbitrary closed surface is equal to the net charge enclosed by the surface divided by* ϵ_0. In equation form,

$$\Phi_E = \frac{\Sigma q}{\epsilon_0} \qquad \text{or} \qquad \oint \mathbf{E} \cdot d\mathbf{S} = \frac{\Sigma q}{\epsilon_0} \qquad (21\text{-}3)$$

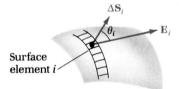

Figure 21-5. To find the flux for a curved surface and/or a nonuniform field, the surface is divided into a large number of small surface elements and the flux for each element is added. In the limit as the size of the elements approaches zero and their number approaches infinity, the sum approaches an integral. Such an integral is called a *surface integral.*

where the closed surface (the gaussian surface) for which the flux is calculated can be of *any shape or size* and the symbol Σq represents the *net* charge contained within the volume enclosed by the surface.

As a first example of Gauss's law, let us suppose we do not know the expression for the field produced by a point charge; we will use Gauss's law to find this field. Figure 21-6 shows a spherical gaussian surface of radius r with a point charge q at its center. In performing the flux integral $\oint \mathbf{E} \cdot d\mathbf{S}$, we assume from symmetry that $\mathbf{E}$ must be radially away from q, which means that $\mathbf{E}$ is parallel to $d\mathbf{S}$ at each point on the sphere's surface, or $\mathbf{E} \cdot d\mathbf{S} = E \, dS$. Also from symmetry we assume that E depends only on distance r from q, so that E is the same at each point on the sphere, or E is constant with respect to the integration. Thus the calculation of the flux for the spherical surface proceeds as follows:

$$\Phi_E = \oint \mathbf{E} \cdot d\mathbf{S} = \oint E \, dS = E \oint dS = E(4\pi r^2)$$

where the integral $\oint dS$ is simply the surface area $4\pi r^2$ of the sphere. Since the total charge contained inside our gaussian sphere is $\Sigma q = q$, Gauss's law gives

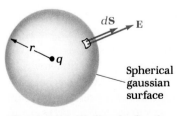

Figure 21-6. Finding the flux due to the field produced by a point charge at the center of a spherical gaussian surface.

$$E(4\pi r^2) = \frac{q}{\epsilon_0} \qquad \text{or} \qquad E = \frac{q}{4\pi\epsilon_0 r^2}$$

This is the same result we obtained with Coulomb's law in the previous chapter. Using symmetry arguments, we have shown that Gauss's law gives the same expression for the field produced by a point charge as does Coulomb's law.

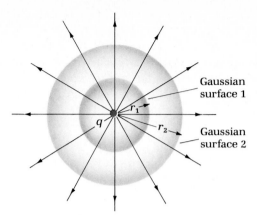

Figure 21-7. Two gaussian spheres with different radii are centered at the same charged particle. Field lines extend continuously from positive to negative charges so that the number of lines crossing each sphere is the same. Also, by Gauss's law the flux for each surface is the same. Therefore, the flux for such a surface is proportional to the number of lines crossing the surface.

In the previous section, we mentioned that the flux for a surface is proportional to the number of field lines that cross the surface. For the case of a spherical surface centered at a point charge, we can now demonstrate this with Gauss's law. Figure 21-7 shows two such surfaces and the field lines around the point charge q. Since the lines emanate from a positive charge, terminate on a negative charge, and are continuous in between, the number of lines that cross each sphere is the same. By Gauss's law, the flux Φ_E for each sphere is the same because the enclosed charge $\Sigma q = q$ is the same. Thus the flux for each surface is proportional to the number of lines that cross the surface. Gauss's law can be used to show this for any charge distribution and any surface, but we shall not pursue the matter further.

When we introduced field lines in Sec. 20-7, we stated that the density of the lines (or their spacing) indicates the field magnitude. Again, this can now be demonstrated for the case of a point charge. In Fig. 21-7, the radius of the larger sphere is twice that of the smaller sphere: $r_2 = 2r_1$. This means that the area of the larger sphere is 4 times that of the smaller sphere: $A_2 = 4\pi r_2^2 = 4\pi(2r_1)^2 = 4(4\pi r_1^2) = 4A_1$. If N is the number of lines crossing a sphere of area A, then the density of lines is N/A. Since the number of lines crossing each sphere is the same, the density of lines at the larger sphere is one-fourth that at the smaller sphere. Also, since the field is an inverse-square field, E at the larger sphere is one-fourth that at the smaller sphere. Thus E is proportional to the density of lines.

When using Gauss's law, you should keep in mind that Σq represents the *net enclosed* charge, that is, the positive charge minus the negative charge inside the surface. We can explore this feature of Gauss's law by considering the flux for the four different gaussian surfaces in the field of a dipole shown in Fig. 21-8. Surface S_1 contains no charge, so that from Gauss's law the flux for surface S_1 is $\Phi_{E1} = 0$. The field lines in Fig. 21-8 substantiate the fact that the flux for S_1 is zero. Three field lines are directed into the volume enclosed by S_1 and three field lines are directed out, so that the net number of lines directed out is zero. Surface S_2 contains charge q so that Gauss's law gives $\Phi_{E2} = q/\epsilon_0$. From the field lines in Fig. 21-8, Φ_{E2} is positive because the lines are directed out of the enclosed volume at each point on S_2. Similarly, the flux for S_3 is $\Phi_{E3} = -q/\epsilon_0$ from Gauss's law, and the field lines show that the flux is negative because they are directed into the enclosed volume at each point on S_3. Surface S_4 contains both particles, so the net charge enclosed is $\Sigma q = q - q = 0$. Consequently, Gauss's law requires $\Phi_{E4} = 0$. As an exercise, count the number of lines directed out of S_4 and the number directed into it. Is your count in agreement with Gauss's law?

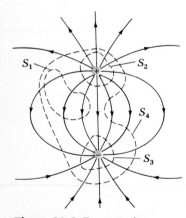

Figure 21-8. Four gaussian surfaces in the field of a dipole. The gaussian surfaces are shown in cross section, and the dashed lines represent the intersection of the surfaces with the plane of the figure. From the field lines, you can verify that $\Phi_{E1} = 0$, $\Phi_{E2} > 0$, $\Phi_{E3} < 0$, and $\Phi_{E4} = 0$.

21-4 DEVELOPING GAUSS'S LAW FROM COULOMB'S LAW

In Chap. 20, we presented Coulomb's law as the result of experiment, and used it to write the field produced by a point charge as

$$\mathbf{E} = \frac{q}{4\pi\epsilon_0 r^2}\,\hat{\mathbf{r}}$$

We now give Gauss's law this same experimental foundation by developing Gauss's law from Coulomb's law and the principle of superposition. The above expression for the field produced by a point charge is the form of Coulomb's law we shall use.

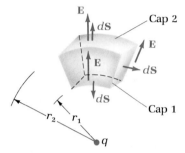

Figure 21-9. Flux of the field due to a charged particle for a rounded-block gaussian surface. The surface is bounded by two spherical caps and four conical sides. The flux for each conical side is zero, and the flux for the two spherical caps is equal and opposite, so the flux for the entire surface is zero.

Flux for an arbitrary surface, charged particle outside. Consider the flux for the rounded-block gaussian surface shown in Fig. 21-9. The field is due to a charged particle, and the surface is bounded by four flat conical sides and two spherical caps. Each conical side is aligned radially with the particle, and each cap is a patch of a sphere centered at the particle. Therefore, the flux for the sides is zero because $\mathbf{E}$ is perpendicular to $d\mathbf{S}$ at each point on the sides. The flux Φ_{E1} for cap 1 is negative (assuming q is positive) because the direction of $\mathbf{E}$ is opposite $d\mathbf{S}$ at each point on cap 1: $\int \mathbf{E} \cdot d\mathbf{S} = -\int E\,dS$. Further, E is the same at each point on the surface and can be factored out of the flux integral: $E = q/4\pi\epsilon_0 r_1^2$. Thus

$$\Phi_{E1} = -\frac{q}{4\pi\epsilon_0 r_1^2}\int dS = -\frac{q}{4\pi\epsilon_0 r_1^2}\,\Delta S_1$$

where ΔS_1 is the area of cap 1. The flux Φ_{E2} for cap 2 is calculated in a similar fashion, except that Φ_{E2} is positive because $\mathbf{E}$ is in the same direction as $d\mathbf{S}$ at each point on cap 2:

$$\Phi_{E2} = \frac{q}{4\pi\epsilon_0 r_2^2}\,\Delta S_2$$

where ΔS_2 is the area of cap 2. Since the two spherical caps are bounded by the same conical sides, the ratio of their areas is equal to the ratio of their radii squared: $\Delta S_2/\Delta S_1 = r_2^2/r_1^2$, or $\Delta S_2 = (r_2^2/r_1^2)\,\Delta S_1$. Substituting this result into the equation for Φ_{E2} gives

$$\Phi_{E2} = \frac{q}{4\pi\epsilon_0 r_2^2}\frac{r_2^2}{r_1^2}\,\Delta S_1 = \frac{q}{4\pi\epsilon_0 r_1^2}\,\Delta S_1 = -\Phi_{E1}$$

The net flux for the closed surface is

$$\Phi_E = \Phi_{E2} + \Phi_{E1} = -\Phi_{E1} + \Phi_{E1} = 0$$

The net flux is zero because the flux for cap 1 is the negative of the flux for cap 2.

Now we introduce another point: *A surface of any shape can be constructed from an infinite number of infinitesimal spherical caps and conical sides.* Figure 21-10a shows a cross section of an arbitrarily shaped, closed surface with a particle of charge q outside the enclosed volume. Figure 21-10b shows this same surface with a superimposed approximation to the surface that consists of a number of spherical caps centered at the particle and conical sides aligned with the particle. You can see that the surface can be viewed as the limit of an infinite number of infinitesimal spherical caps and conical sides. Since the flux for the caps cancels in pairs and the flux for the sides is zero, for the arbitrarily

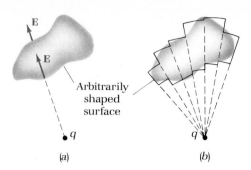

Figure 21-10. (*a*) A charged particle outside the enclosed volume of an arbitrarily shaped gaussian surface shown in cross section. (*b*) Superimposed approximation to the surface in (*a*) consisting of a number of spherical caps and conical sides. The flux for each conical side is zero, and the flux for each pair of spherical caps is equal and opposite: $\Phi_E = 0$.

shaped surface in Fig. 21-10*a*, the flux due to the charged particle outside of the enclosed volume is zero:

$$\Phi_E = 0 \qquad \text{(arbitrarily shaped closed surface, } q \text{ outside)}$$

Flux for an arbitrary surface, charged particle inside. Now consider the flux due to a point charge q at the center of a spherical gaussian surface of radius r (Fig. 21-6). At each point on the surface, **E** is parallel to $d\mathbf{S}$ ($\mathbf{E} \cdot d\mathbf{S} = E\, dS$) and E has the same value and can be factored from the integral ($E = q/4\pi\epsilon_0 r^2$). Thus

$$\Phi_E = \oint \mathbf{E} \cdot d\mathbf{S} = \oint E\, dS = E \oint dS = \frac{q}{4\pi\epsilon_0 r^2}\, 4\pi r^2 = \frac{q}{\epsilon_0}$$

Since Φ_E does not contain r, the flux is the same for a sphere of any radius.

We can use this result to find the flux for the gaussian surface shown in Fig. 21-11. This surface is mostly a sphere centered at the particle, except that a cap of area ΔS_1 is cut out and replaced with a raised cap of area ΔS_2. The volume directly beneath the raised cap is enclosed by conical sides (aligned with the particle) so that the surface is a closed surface. The flux for this surface is the same as for a sphere because the flux for the conical sides is zero and the flux for cap 2 is equal to the flux missing because of the absence of cap 1; the argument is similar to the previous discussion of the rounded block. Thus $\Phi_E = q/\epsilon_0$.

Further, any arbitrarily shaped surface may be regarded as the limit of an infinite number of infinitesimal spherical caps and conical sides. Figure 21-12*a* shows the cross section of an arbitrarily shaped closed surface with a charged particle inside, and Fig. 21-12*b* shows a number of spherical caps and conical sides centered at the particle. As before, the arbitrarily shaped surface can be viewed as the limit of an infinite number of infinitesimal spherical caps and conical sides. Therefore, for a closed surface with any shape, the flux due to a particle of charge q inside the enclosed volume is q/ϵ_0:

$$\Phi_E = \frac{q}{\epsilon_0} \qquad \text{(arbitrarily shaped closed surface, } q \text{ inside)}$$

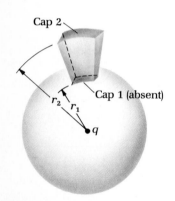

Figure 21-11. Flux of the field produced by a point charge at the center of a gaussian surface that is mostly a sphere except for the raised cap. The flux for cap 2 is equal to the flux missing because of the absence of cap 1, so the flux for the entire surface is the same as that for a sphere: $\Phi_E = q/\epsilon_0$.

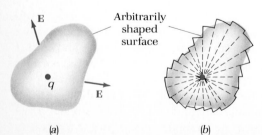

Figure 21-12. (*a*) A charged particle inside the enclosed volume of an arbitrarily shaped gaussian surface shown in cross section. (*b*) Superimposed approximation to the surface in (*a*), consisting of a number of spherical caps and conical sides. The flux for each conical side is zero, and the sum of the fluxes for the spherical caps is the same as for a sphere: $\Phi_E = q/\epsilon_0$.

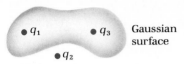

Figure 21-13. Of the three charged particles, particles 1 and 3 are enclosed by the gaussian surface and particle 2 is not. Using the principle of superposition, $\mathbf{E} = \mathbf{E}_1 + \mathbf{E}_2 + \mathbf{E}_3$, we find that the flux for the surface is $\Phi_E = (q_1 + q_3)/\epsilon_0$. That is, particle 2 does not contribute to the flux.

Flux for an arbitrary surface, charged particles inside and outside. So far we have considered the electric flux due to a single charged particle. Suppose there is more than one particle to consider. To be specific, consider the surface in Fig. 21-13, where the flux is due to the three charged particles. From the principle of superposition, the field is the vector sum of the individual contributions to the field: $\mathbf{E} = \mathbf{E}_1 + \mathbf{E}_2 + \mathbf{E}_3$. The flux is

$$\Phi_E = \oint \mathbf{E} \cdot d\mathbf{S} = \oint (\mathbf{E}_1 + \mathbf{E}_2 + \mathbf{E}_3) \cdot d\mathbf{S}$$

Since the integral of a sum is the sum of the integrals, we may write this as

$$\Phi_E = \oint \mathbf{E}_1 \cdot d\mathbf{S} + \oint \mathbf{E}_2 \cdot d\mathbf{S} + \oint \mathbf{E}_3 \cdot d\mathbf{S}$$

Particles 1 and 3 are inside the surface so that their contributions to the flux are q_1/ϵ_0 and q_3/ϵ_0, respectively, and particle 2 is outside the surface so that its contribution to the flux is zero:

$$\Phi_E = \frac{q_1}{\epsilon_0} + 0 + \frac{q_3}{\epsilon_0}$$

Generally, for any number of charged particles, the flux for an arbitrarily shaped closed surface is

$$\Phi_E = \frac{\Sigma q_i}{\epsilon_0} \qquad \text{or} \qquad \oint \mathbf{E} \cdot d\mathbf{S} = \frac{\Sigma q_i}{\epsilon_0}$$

which is Gauss's law. Our development shows clearly that the field $\mathbf{E}$ in the flux integral is the field due to *all charged particles, both inside and outside the enclosed volume,* but the charges included in the sum Σq_i are *only the charges of the particles that are inside the enclosed volume.*

Since Gauss's law can be derived from Coulomb's law [in the form $\mathbf{E} = (q/4\pi\epsilon_0 r^2)\,\hat{\mathbf{r}}$] and the principle of superposition, Gauss's law is the same statement about nature as Coulomb's law (in electrostatics). Each is a consequence of the electric force being an inverse-square force that depends linearly on the charge and is directed along a line between the particles. However, Gauss's law is more general than Coulomb's law. The electric field $\mathbf{E}$ that comes from Coulomb's law is due to stationary charges only. In Chap. 28, we shall find that a time-changing magnetic field produces an electric field. The electric field $\mathbf{E}$ in Gauss's law represents this field as well as the field of stationary charges. Because of its broader validity, Gauss's law is often more useful than Coulomb's law.

EXAMPLE 21-2. Find the flux for (a) gaussian surface A and (b) gaussian surface B that enclose the charged particles shown in Fig. 21-14. The values of the charges are $q_1 = -41$ nC, $q_2 = +73$ nC, and $q_3 = -65$ nC.

SOLUTION. (a) The flux for surface A is

$$\Phi_E = \frac{\Sigma q}{\epsilon_0} = \frac{q_1 + q_2 + q_3}{\epsilon_0}$$

$$= \frac{-41 \text{ nC} + 73 \text{ nC} - 65 \text{ nC}}{8.85 \times 10^{-12} \text{ C}^2/(\text{N} \cdot \text{m}^2)}$$

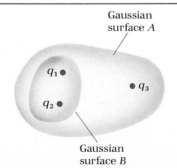

Figure 21-14. Example 21-2: Gaussian surface A encloses all three charged particles. Gaussian surface B encloses only particles 1 and 2.

$$= -3.7 \times 10^3 \text{ N} \cdot \text{m}^2/\text{C}$$

because all three particles are enclosed by A. (b) The flux for surface B is

$$\Phi_E = \frac{\Sigma q}{\epsilon_0} = \frac{q_1 + q_2}{\epsilon_0}$$

$$= \frac{-41 \text{ nC} + 73 \text{ nC}}{8.85 \times 10^{-12} \text{ C}^2/(\text{N} \cdot \text{m}^2)}$$

$$= +3.6 \times 10^3 \text{ N} \cdot \text{m}^2/\text{C}$$

because only q_1 and q_2 are enclosed by B.

21-5 USING GAUSS'S LAW TO FIND E

Gauss's law can be used to find the electric field due to a charge distribution that has a high degree of symmetry. If the charge distribution is highly symmetric, then some features of the field, such as its direction, can be deduced by inspection of the symmetry of the distribution, without need of calculation. You can then (i) select a gaussian surface that capitalizes on the symmetry, (ii) determine the flux for this gaussian surface in terms of E, and (iii) solve Gauss's law for E. The first step is the most crucial. The surface you choose as your gaussian surface should be one for which the flux can be readily determined. The following examples illustrate the technique.

In finding **E**, *you* choose the gaussian surface, and your choice is crucial.

EXAMPLE 21-3. *Field near a long line charge.* Find an approximate expression for E near a long, straight, uniformly charged wire (linear charge density λ) at a point P that is far from either end of the wire.

SOLUTION. The first step in finding E with Gauss's law is the most important; it is the selection of the gaussian surface. To do this we must determine the symmetry of the field by inspection of the charge distribution. In Fig. 21-15, the wire is along the z axis, and P is in the xy plane at a distance R from the z axis ($R = \sqrt{x^2 + y^2}$). Since P is far from either end, we expect from symmetry that **E** will point directly away from the z axis (assuming λ is positive) and be parallel to the xy plane. Also, we expect that E will depend only on distance R

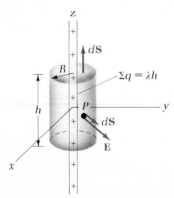

Figure 21-15. Example 21-3: We use a cylinder as a gaussian surface to find the field near a uniform line charge far from its ends. The charge enclosed by the cylinder is $\Sigma q = \lambda h$.

from the wire. That is, we expect that the field has cylindrical symmetry about the z axis. The gaussian surface that takes advantage of these symmetrical features of the field is a right circular cylinder with axis along the z axis (Fig. 21-15). For this gaussian surface we have that (i) the flux for both the top and bottom is zero because **E** is perpendicular to $d\mathbf{S}$ at each point on the top and bottom and (ii) the flux for the cylindrical surface is simply E times the area of the cylindrical surface because **E** is parallel to $d\mathbf{S}$ at each point on the cylindrical surface and its magnitude is the same at each point on the cylindrical surface. Therefore,

$$\Phi_E = \oint \mathbf{E} \cdot d\mathbf{S} = E(2\pi Rh)$$

where $2\pi Rh$ is the surface area of the cylindrical surface of radius R and height h.

From the figure, the charge inside the cylinder is the product of the linear charge density λ and the height h of the cylinder: $\Sigma q = \lambda h$. Thus Gauss's law gives

$$\Phi_E = \frac{\Sigma q}{\epsilon_0} \quad \text{or} \quad E2\pi Rh = \frac{\lambda h}{\epsilon_0}$$

Solving for E, we have

$$E = \frac{\lambda}{2\pi\epsilon_0 R}$$

We should recognize that this is an approximate result for points far from the ends of a very long line charge; it is strictly valid only for an infinitely long line charge. This is the same result we obtained in Chap. 20 [Eq. (20-8)] with Coulomb's law.

EXAMPLE 21-4. *Field near a large plane sheet of charge.* Find an approximate expression for E produced by a large plane sheet of charge with a uniform surface charge density σ at a point near the sheet but far from its edges.

SOLUTION. First we determine the symmetry of the field so that we can select a gaussian surface. In Fig. 21-16, the charged sheet occupies the yz plane and point P is near the x axis. Since P is far from the edges of the sheet, we expect from symmetry that the field must point directly away from the sheet (assuming σ is positive) and along the x axis. Further, if E depends on position at all, then it can only depend on x. We take advantage of this symmetry by using a gaussian surface that is a right circular cylinder, centered at the origin and with axis along the x axis. For this surface we have that (i) the flux for the cylindrical surface is zero because $\mathbf{E}$ is perpendicular to $d\mathbf{S}$ at each point on the cylindrical surface and (ii) the flux for each end is simply E times the area ΔS of that end because $\mathbf{E}$ is uniform and parallel to $d\mathbf{S}$ at each point on either end. Therefore,

$$\Phi_E = \oint \mathbf{E} \cdot d\mathbf{S} = E \, \Delta S + E \, \Delta S = 2E \, \Delta S$$

From the figure, the charge enclosed by the gaussian cylinder is the product of the surface charge density σ and the cross-sectional area of the cylinder, which is the same as the

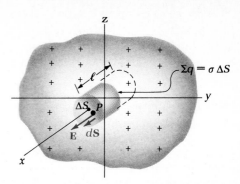

Figure 21-16. Example 21-4: We use a cylinder as a gaussian surface to find the field near a uniform planar sheet of charge far from its edges. The gaussian cylinder extends through the sheet so that it encloses charge $\Sigma q = \sigma \, \Delta S$.

area ΔS of an end. Thus $\Sigma q = \sigma \, \Delta S$. Gauss's law gives

$$\Phi_E = \frac{\Sigma q}{\epsilon_0} \qquad \text{or} \qquad 2E \, \Delta S = \frac{\sigma \, \Delta S}{\epsilon_0}$$

Solving for E, we have

$$E = \frac{\sigma}{2\epsilon_0}$$

Note that this is an approximation for E at points near the charged sheet and far from its edges. This is the same result we obtained in Chap. 20 [Eq. (20-9)] from Coulomb's law.

EXAMPLE 21-5. *A charged spherical shell.* Determine $\mathbf{E}$ at points both inside and outside a thin, uniformly charged spherical shell of radius r_0 and charge Q. The charge distribution is similar to the mass distribution of a ping-pong ball.

SOLUTION. To select a gaussian surface, we determine the symmetry of the field. Since the charge distribution is spherical, we expect that $\mathbf{E}$ has only a radial component and that its magnitude depends only on distance r from the center of the charge distribution. The gaussian surface that capitalizes on this symmetry is a spherical surface with the same center as the spherical shell of charge. First we consider the field at points inside the shell by finding the flux for a spherical gaussian surface whose radius r is less than the radius r_0 of the shell, as shown in Fig. 21-17a. Since $\mathbf{E}$ must be radial and can only depend on r, the flux for the gaussian sphere is

$$\Phi_E = E(4\pi r^2)$$

From Fig. 21-17a the charge inside the gaussian sphere is zero because the gaussian sphere is completely inside the shell of charge. Gauss's law gives

$$\Phi_E = \frac{\Sigma q}{\epsilon_0} \qquad \text{or} \qquad E(4\pi r^2) = 0$$

The field at any point on the gaussian sphere must be zero. This is true for any gaussian sphere as long as its radius is less than the radius of the charged shell. Thus the field is

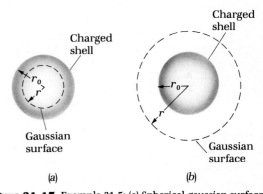

Figure 21-17. Example 21-5: (a) Spherical gaussian surface inside the charged spherical shell: $\Sigma q = 0$. (b) Spherical gaussian surface outside the charged spherical shell: $\Sigma q = Q$.

zero at all points inside the spherical shell of charge:

$$E = 0 \qquad (r < r_0)$$

Now we consider the field at points outside the charged shell by finding the flux for a spherical gaussian surface whose radius r is larger than the radius r_0 of the shell, as shown in Fig. 21-17b. Again, because of the spherical symmetry, the expression for the flux for the gaussian surface is $\Phi_E = E(4\pi r^2)$. This surface encloses the entire charge Q of the shell, $\Sigma q = Q$, so that Gauss's law gives

$$\Phi_E = \frac{\Sigma q}{\epsilon_0} \quad \text{or} \quad E(4\pi r^2) = \frac{Q}{\epsilon_0}$$

Solving for E, we have

$$E = \frac{Q}{4\pi\epsilon_0 r^2} \quad (r > r_0)$$

This expression for E is familiar; it is the same as that due to a point charge Q located at the center of the shell.

Figure 21-18 shows a graph of E for a uniformly charged spherical shell as a function of distance r from its center. Notice the remarkable simplicity of this result. The field at all points inside the charged shell is zero, and the field outside the shell is the same as the field due to a particle with charge Q located at the center of the shell. From field measurements

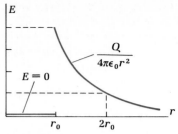

Figure 21-18. Example 21-5: A graph of E versus r for a uniformly charged spherical shell.

outside a uniform spherical shell of charge, one cannot determine whether the field is due to a charged shell or a charged particle with the same charge.

EXAMPLE 21-6. A uniformly charged sphere. Determine **E** at points both inside and outside a uniform spherical distribution of charge of radius r_0 and charge Q. The charge distribution is similar to the mass distribution of a billiard ball; it is continuous and uniform throughout the volume of the sphere.

SOLUTION. As in the previous example, **E** has only a radial component and depends only on distance from the center. Therefore, we use spherical gaussian surfaces with the same center as the charge distribution. To find the field inside the charge distribution, we use a gaussian surface whose radius is less than the radius of the charge distribution, $r < r_0$ (Fig. 21-19a). The expression for the flux for this surface is again $\Phi_E = E(4\pi r^2)$. The charge contained within this gaussian sphere depends on the radius r of the gaussian sphere. We let ρ represent the *volume charge density*:

$$\rho = \frac{Q}{4\pi r_0^3/3}$$

where Q is the total charge on the sphere and $4\pi r_0^3/3$ is the volume of the charged sphere. The amount of charge that is inside the gaussian sphere of radius r is the product of the charge density and the volume of the gaussian sphere:

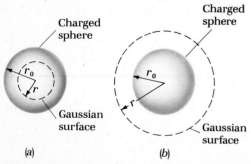

(a)   (b)

Figure 21-19. Example 21-6: (a) A spherical gaussian surface inside a spherical distribution of uniform volume charge density, $\Sigma q = (r^3/r_0^3)Q$. (b) A spherical gaussian surface outside the spherical charge distribution $\Sigma q = Q$.

$$\Sigma q = \rho \frac{4\pi r^3}{3} = \frac{Q}{4\pi r_0^3/3} \frac{4\pi r^3}{3} = Q\frac{r^3}{r_0^3}$$

Gauss's law, $\Phi_E = \Sigma q/\epsilon_0$, for this case is

$$E(4\pi r^2) = \frac{Q(r^3/r_0^3)}{\epsilon_0}$$

Solving for E gives

$$E = \frac{Qr}{4\pi\epsilon_0 r_0^3} \quad (r < r_0)$$

The electric field increases linearly with r at points inside the charged sphere.

Finding the electric field outside the charged sphere is quite similar to the previous example. We use a gaussian sphere with $r > r_0$, as shown in Fig. 21-19b. The expression for the flux is again $E(4\pi r^2)$, and the charge enclosed by the gaussian sphere is the total charge Q on the charged sphere. Gauss's law gives

$$E(4\pi r^2) = \frac{Q}{\epsilon_0}$$

so that

$$E = \frac{Q}{4\pi\epsilon_0 r^2} \quad (r > r_0)$$

The expression for the field at a point outside the sphere is the same as for the spherical shell of charge and for a point charge. A graph of E produced by a uniform spherical charge distribution is shown in Fig. 21-20.

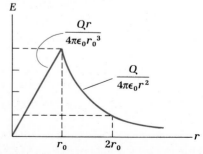

Figure 21-20. Example 21-6: A graph of E versus r for a spherical distribution of uniform volume charge density.

These last two examples, the charged spherical shell and the uniformly charged sphere, exhibit a common feature of spherically symmetric charge distributions: *The field outside a spherically symmetric distribution of charge is directed radially, and its magnitude is*

Field outside a spherically symmetric charge distribution

$$E = \frac{Q}{4\pi\epsilon_0 r^2}$$

where r is the distance from the center of the distribution. This result is independent of how the charge is distributed radially. The field inside a spherical distribution of charge depends on how the charge is distributed radially. The two examples above represent two possibilities.

21-6 ELECTROSTATIC PROPERTIES OF A CONDUCTOR

Some general properties of a conductor in an electric field can be determined with Gauss's law.

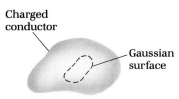

Figure 21-21. Conductor with a gaussian surface completely inside.

Field and charge inside a conductor. In electrostatics, $\mathbf{E} = 0$ inside a conductor because (i) electrostatics is the study of the electrical effects of stationary charges and (ii) a conductor contains charge carriers that move through a material when an electric field exists in that material. When we discuss a conductor in the context of electrostatics, the situation is such that the conductor's charge carriers are not moving, which requires that

$$\mathbf{E} = 0 \qquad \text{(inside a conductor under static conditions)}$$

If $\mathbf{E} \neq 0$ in a conductor, then the charge carriers move and an electric current exists in the conductor. We discuss electric currents in Chap. 24.

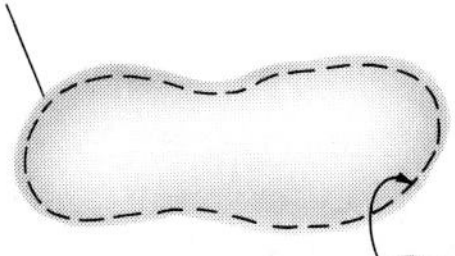

Figure 21-22. Conductor with a gaussian surface just inside its surface.

No excess charge can exist inside a conductor under static conditions.

Given that $\mathbf{E} = 0$ inside a conductor, we can use Gauss's law to determine where a conductor's excess charge resides. Figure 21-21 shows a conductor with a gaussian surface completely inside it. Since $\mathbf{E}$ is zero everywhere inside the conductor, Φ_E is zero for this surface. Therefore, Gauss's law requires that the net enclosed charge be zero. This is true for any closed surface whatsoever, as long as the surface is completely contained within the conductor. This means that no excess charge can exist anywhere inside a conductor—that is, the volume charge density ρ must be zero for a conductor. A net volume charge density can only exist in an insulator.

In electrostatics, excess charge resides on the surface of a conductor.

If none of a conductor's excess charge can reside inside the conductor, then where does the charge reside? It must reside on the conductor's surface. Figure 21-22 shows a charged conductor with a gaussian surface just inside the actual surface of the conductor. The field is zero at each point on the gaussian surface, so that $\Phi_E = 0$ and the charge enclosed by the gaussian surface is zero. Therefore, the conductor's excess charge resides outside the gaussian surface. This means that it must reside on the conductor's actual surface. If a conductor possesses excess charge, then this charge is distributed as a surface charge density σ.

In general, the surface charge density σ on a conductor varies with position on the surface of the conductor. For example, a neutral conductor can have a positive charge density over part of its surface and a negative charge density over another part such that the total charge is zero.

Field just outside a conductor. Gauss's law can be used to determine the

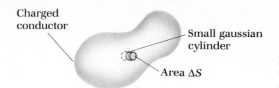

Charged
conductor

Small gaussian
cylinder

Area ΔS

Figure 21-23. Charged conductor
with a small cylindrical gaussian
surface intersecting its surface.

electric field just outside the surface of a conductor. The electric field just outside the surface of a conductor must be directed perpendicular to the surface. If the field were to have a tangential component E_t, then charge carriers would move along the surface in response to the tangential force and static conditions would not exist. Thus $E_t = 0$; the field at the surface of a conductor has only a normal component E_n. We let E_n be positive when the field is directed away from the surface and negative when the field is directed toward the surface.

Since **E** is perpendicular to the conductor's surface, we choose a gaussian surface that is a small cylinder with faces parallel to the conductor's surface, as shown in Fig. 21-23. The cylinder is small enough so that any variation of **E**, or of the curvature of the conductor's surface over its extent, can be neglected. The flux for the cylindrical surface of the cylinder is zero because **E** is perpendicular to $d\mathbf{S}$ at each point on the cylindrical surface. The flux for the planar end of the cylinder inside the conductor is zero because **E** = 0 inside the conductor. The flux for the planar end (of area ΔS) just outside the conductor is $E_n \Delta S$ because **E** is parallel to $d\mathbf{S}$ at each point on the end. For the entire gaussian cylinder, $\Phi_E = E_n \Delta S$. The charge enclosed by the cylinder is $\Sigma q = \sigma \Delta S$, so that Gauss's law gives $E_n \Delta S = \sigma \Delta S / \epsilon_0$, or

Electric field just outside the surface of a conductor

$$E_n = \frac{\sigma}{\epsilon_0} \quad \text{and} \quad E_t = 0 \tag{21-4}$$

At points on the surface where σ is positive, the field just outside the surface points away from the surface (E_n is positive), and at points on the surface where σ is negative, the field just outside the surface points toward the surface (E_n is negative).

EXAMPLE 21-7. Find the magnitude of the field just outside an isolated spherical conductor of radius r_0 and charge Q.

SOLUTION. Since the surface charge density of the sphere is uniform by symmetry, it is simply the charge Q divided by the surface area $4\pi r_0^2$ of the sphere: $\sigma = Q/4\pi r_0^2$. Using Eq. (21-4), the magnitude of the field is

$$E = \frac{|\sigma|}{\epsilon_0} = \frac{|Q|}{4\pi\epsilon_0 r_0^2}$$

Since a conductor carries its charge as a surface charge density, a charged spherical conductor must correspond to a uniform spherical shell of charge. In Example 21-5 we found that a uniformly charged spherical shell has **E** = 0 inside. Therefore, Fig. 21-18 gives the magnitude of the field due to a charged spherical conductor as a function of distance r from the center, and our answer above corresponds to E evaluated at $r = r_0$.

EXAMPLE 21-8. *A parallel-plate capacitor.* A capacitor is a device used in electric circuitry, and a simple capacitor design is two parallel plane sheets of metal whose separation is very small compared with the area of their plane surfaces. During normal operation, the two plates carry

equal and opposite charge. Figure 21-24a shows the plates of a capacitor in cross section. The separation of the plates is greatly exaggerated for purposes of illustration, and the charge distribution and field lines are shown schematically. The charge on each plate is nearly uniformly distributed

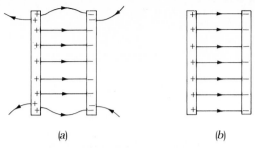

(a)   *(b)*

Figure 21-24. Example 21-8: (*a*) A parallel-plate capacitor showing a fringing field. (*b*) An ideal parallel-plate capacitor with its uniform charge densities and uniform field.

because of the attraction by the charge of opposite sign on the other plate. Also, the field between the plates is nearly uniform except for the "fringing field" near the edges. If we bring the plates closer and closer together, then the two charge distributions and the field become more nearly uniform. For simplicity, assume each plate has a uniform

charge distribution and that the field between the plates is uniform (Fig. 21-24*b*). Find **E** between the plates of a capacitor in which the area A of each plate is 0.19 m² and the magnitude of the charge Q on each plate is 1.3 μC.

SOLUTION. Since the field between the plates is uniform, its magnitude in the entire region is the same as just outside each surface: $|\sigma|/\epsilon_0$ from Eq. (21-4). The magnitude of the uniform surface charge density on each plate is $|\sigma| = Q/A$ so that

$$E = \frac{|\sigma|}{\epsilon_0} = \frac{Q}{A\epsilon_0}$$

$$= \frac{1.3 \; \mu C}{(0.19 \text{ m}^2)[8.85 \times 10^{-12} \text{ C}^2/(\text{N} \cdot \text{m}^2)]}$$

$$= 7.7 \times 10^5 \text{ N/C}$$

The direction of the field is away from the positive plate and toward the negative plate.

The Faraday ice-pail experiment. Neither an electric field nor a volume charge density exists inside a conductor under static conditions. Suppose there is a hollow region inside a charged conductor. Does an electric field exist in this hollow region? Does excess charge reside on the inside surface of the conductor? To answer these questions we consider an operation called the Faraday ice-pail experiment.

    Suppose we hang a charged metal sphere by an insulating thread inside a closed metal can. The can possesses no net charge and is mounted on an insulating stand (Fig. 21-25). An electrometer, a device that measures charge, indicates that the outside of the can becomes charged as the sphere is lowered into the can (Fig. 21-25*a*) and is a maximum when the sphere is completely enclosed (Fig. 21-25*b*). When the can is tilted (Fig. 21-25*c*) so that the sphere and

Figure 21-25. Faraday ice-pail experiment. (*a*) Charged metal sphere is lowered into a neutral metal bucket on an insulating stand. An electrometer shows that the outside of the can becomes charged as the sphere is lowered. (*b*) Bucket completely encloses the sphere. (*c*) Bucket is tilted so that the sphere touches the inside of the can. (*d*) Sphere has zero charge after contact, and the outside of the can has a charge equal to the original charge on the sphere.

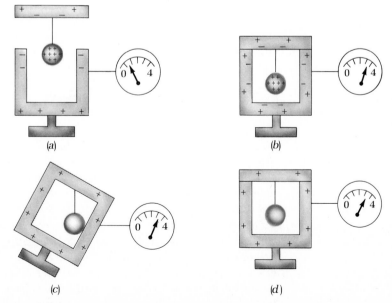

(a)   *(b)*

(c)   *(d)*

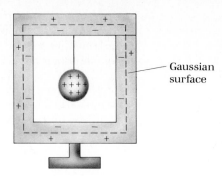

Figure 21-26. For the situation in Fig. 21-25*b*, a gaussian surface is shown within the metal bucket. Since **E** = 0 at each point on the gaussian surface, the charge enclosed is zero. This means that the charge on the inner surface of the bucket is equal and opposite the charge on the sphere. Since the bucket is neutral, the charge on its outer surface is equal to the charge on the sphere.

can make contact, the can and sphere compose a single conductor, but the electrometer reading is unaffected. If the sphere is removed from the can and tested for the presence of charge, it is found to be uncharged.

Gauss's law predicts that the charge induced on the inner surface of the can in Fig. 21-25*b* is the negative of the charge on the sphere. To be specific, suppose the initial charge on the sphere is +26 nC. Figure 21-25*b* is repeated in Fig. 21-26, with the addition of a gaussian surface that is contained inside the conducting material of the metal can. Since **E** = 0 at each point on this gaussian surface, the flux for the gaussian surface is zero. Thus the gaussian surface encloses no net charge. The gaussian surface surrounds the sphere with its charge of +26 nC and the inner surface of the metal can with its induced charge. Therefore, the induced charge on the inner surface of the can must be −26 nC. Since the can was originally neutral and is insulated from ground, its net charge is zero. Therefore, the charge on its outer surface must be +26 nC.

An electric field does exist in the hollow region of the can in Fig. 21-25*b*. You should use Gauss's law to verify this for yourself.

Since the electrometer reading was unaffected by the contact between the sphere and the inner surface of the can in Fig. 21-25*c*, the charge on the outer surface of the can in Fig. 21-25*d* is still +26 nC. Also, since no charge exists on the sphere after contact, we conclude that no net charge exists on the inner surface of the can after contact (Fig. 21-25*d*). As it turns out, not only is the net charge on the inner surface zero, but the surface charge density at every point on the inner surface is also zero, and the field in the hollow region of the can is zero. To prove this requires another property of the electric field—it is a conservative field. This is the subject of the next chapter.

COMMENTARY: MICHAEL FARADAY

Throughout our study of electromagnetism, the name Michael Faraday appears often. The laws of electricity and magnetism owe more to the experimental discoveries of Faraday than to those of any other person. He originated the concept of a field; he discovered electromagnetic induction, which led him to invent the dynamo, the forerunner of the electric generator; and he explained electrolysis in terms of electric forces at the molecular level.

Faraday was born at Newington, Surrey, England, in 1791, the son of a blacksmith. His only formal education was in reading, writing, and arithmetic as a young child. He became an apprentice bookbinder at the age of 14 and developed an insatiable appetite for reading. His lifelong fascination with science began when he happened to read an article on electricity in a copy of the Encyclopaedia Britannica which had been left for rebinding.

Normally, the world of science in the nineteenth century would be closed to a person with Faraday's education, but fortune intervened. Sir Humphry Davy, the famous chemist, was temporarily blinded in a laboratory accident at the Royal Institution in 1812, and Davy hired Faraday as his laboratory assistant. So Faraday began his scientific career as a chemist's assistant, but the assistant soon surpassed the master. During this time Faraday discovered and described benzene and was the first to discover compounds of chlorine and carbon.

Besides Davy, another great scientist played a major role in Faraday's life, the Scottish theoretician James Clerk Maxwell (see the Commentary in Chap. 27). Despite the fact that most of their contemporaries rejected Faraday's idea of electric and magnetic fields, Maxwell seized on it and made it mathematically legitimate. As you will see, the laws of electricity and magnetism, called Maxwell's equations, are normally stated in terms of the electric and magnetic fields. Maxwell showed mathematically that these fields contain energy and momentum, as Faraday had anticipated. Maxwell published these works during the 1860s, but by then Faraday was senile; he was to die a few years later.

Faraday had a great talent for explaining scientific results to the public and for instilling an interest in science. He instigated the Friday Evening Discourses at the Royal Institution, which are still used as a channel of communication between scientist and layperson. He was reknowned for his lectures to the young. His book for children entitled The Chemical History of a Candle *is a classic and is still in print.*

For further reading see Michael Faraday, a Biography, *by L. Pearce Williams (1965).*

Michael Faraday. *(New York Public Library)*

SUMMARY WITH APPLICATIONS

Section 21-2. Flux

The flux of the electric field for a surface is defined as the surface integral of the electric field over the surface. The electric flux for a closed surface is

$$\Phi_E = \oint \mathbf{E} \cdot d\mathbf{S} \qquad (21\text{-}2)$$

The closed surface for which the flux is evaluated is an imaginary or mathematical surface called a gaussian surface. Field lines can be used to visualize the flux for a surface.

Explain the concept of electric flux and define a gaussian surface; determine the flux for cases where it can readily be found.

Section 21-3. Gauss's law

Gauss's law states that the flux for any closed surface is equal to the net charge enclosed by that surface divided by ϵ_0:

$$\Phi_E = \frac{\Sigma q}{\epsilon_0} \qquad \text{or} \qquad \oint \mathbf{E} \cdot d\mathbf{S} = \frac{\Sigma q}{\epsilon_0} \qquad (21\text{-}3)$$

State Gauss's law and describe its meaning.

Section 21-4. Developing Gauss's law from Coulomb's law

In electrostatics Gauss's law is equivalent to Coulomb's law.

Show that Gauss's law follows from Coulomb's law and the principle of superposition.

Section 21-5. Using Gauss's law to find E

Gauss's law can be used to find the electric field produced by some highly symmetric charge distributions. The crucial step in such a calculation is the selection of the gaussian surface. Table 21-1 lists the results we obtained.

Table 21-1. The electric field for various charge distributions

Charge distribution	Field magnitude	
Near a long, straight, uniform line charge, far from the ends	$E \approx \dfrac{\lambda}{2\pi\epsilon_0 R}$	
Near a large planar sheet of uniform surface charge, far from the edges	$E \approx \dfrac{\sigma}{2\epsilon_0}$	
Inside and outside a spherical shell of uniform surface charge density	$E = 0$	$(r < r_0)$
	$E = \dfrac{Q}{4\pi\epsilon_0 r^2}$	$(r > r_0)$
Inside and outside a sphere of uniform volume charge density	$E = \dfrac{Qr}{4\pi\epsilon_0 r_0^3}$	$(r < r_0)$
	$E = \dfrac{Q}{4\pi\epsilon_0 r^2}$	$(r > r_0)$
Inside a conductor	$E = 0$	
Just outside a conductor	$E_n = \dfrac{\sigma}{\epsilon_0}$	$E_t = 0$

Determine the electric field for cases where the charge

distribution is highly symmetric.

Section 21-6. Electrostatic properties of a conductor

Under electrostatic conditions, (i) $\mathbf{E} = 0$ everywhere inside a conductor and (ii) $E_t = 0$ just outside a conductor. With these conditions, Gauss's law requires that (i) no excess charge can exist anywhere inside a conductor and (ii) $E_n = \sigma/\epsilon_0$ just outside a conductor.

Use Gauss's law to find some of the properties of a conductor under electrostatic conditions.

QUESTIONS

21-1 If $\mathbf{E} = 0$ at every point on a surface, is the flux for the surface necessarily zero? Suppose the surface is closed; what can you say about the charge enclosed by the surface?

21-2 If the flux for a surface is zero, is it necessarily true that $\mathbf{E} = 0$ at every point on the surface? Explain.

21-3 If no excess charge exists at any point inside a closed surface, is the field at each point on the surface necessarily zero? Is the flux for the surface necessarily zero?

21-4 If the flux for a closed surface is zero, can excess charge exist at points inside the surface? Explain.

21-5 If the net charge inside a closed surface is zero, can field lines cross the surface? If field lines do cross the surface, what can you say about the number of lines directed into the enclosed volume compared with the number directed out?

21-6 What sort of analogy can you draw between the flow of water and electric flux? What are the similarities and what are the differences?

21-7 In analogy to water flow, positively charged objects are often referred to as "sources" of electric field, and negatively charged objects are referred to as "sinks" of electric field. Explain the usefulness of this terminology in view of electric flux and field lines.

21-8 A Möbius strip (Fig. 21-27) is a one-sided surface that can be constructed by giving a strip of paper a twist and pasting the two ends together. Can you find the flux for a Möbius strip in a uniform field? Explain.

21-9 A Klein bottle (Fig. 21-28) can be considered a closed surface in the sense it has no edges. Can you apply Gauss's law to this "closed surface"? If not, why not?

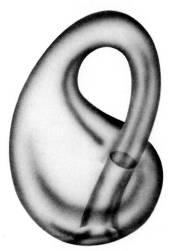

Figure 21-28. Ques. 21-9: A Klein bottle.

21-10 Is the field $\mathbf{E}$ in the flux integral of Gauss's law due (i) only to charges inside the gaussian surface, (ii) only to charges outside the gaussian surface, or (iii) to all charges everywhere?

21-11 Are the charges Σq in Gauss's law (i) only the charges inside the gaussian surface, (ii) only the charges outside the gaussian surface, or (iii) all charges everywhere?

21-12 To find the electric flux for a gaussian surface, do you need any information other than the net charge enclosed by the surface? To find the electric field at points on a gaussian surface, do you need any information other than the net charge enclosed by the surface? Explain.

21-13 What is the flux for a surface that encloses an electric dipole?

21-14 Would Gauss's law be useful in finding the electric field due to a shell shaped as a cube and having uniform surface charge? If so, what sort of gaussian surface would you use? Suppose you use a cube-shaped

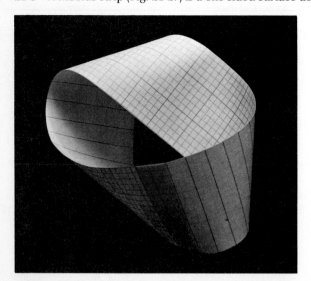

Figure 21-27. Ques. 21-8: A Möbius strip. *(Tom Richard)*

gaussian surface with the same center and orientation as the charged cubical shell. From symmetry, what can you say about the field direction at points on the gaussian cube? From symmetry, what can you say about the variation of E at points on the gaussian cube? Do you think you can find an expression for the flux in terms of E?

21-15 Could a cube-shaped gaussian surface be used to find the approximate electric field at points near the middle of a long, uniformly charged wire (Fig. 21-29)? Explain.

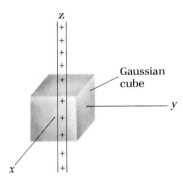

Figure 21-29. Ques. 21-15.

21-16 Could a cube-shaped gaussian surface be used to find the approximate electric field at points near the center of a large, uniformly charged plane disk (Fig. 21-30)? Explain.

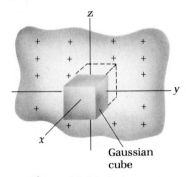

Figure 21-30. Ques. 21-16.

21-17 Suppose two particles with different charge are near one another and are enclosed by a gaussian surface. If the particles exchange positions, does the flux for the surface change? Does the field at points on the surface change?

21-18 A metal sphere with no excess charge is suspended from an insulating string in a region where an electric field exists. Before the sphere is placed in position the field is uniform and pointed vertically upward: $\mathbf{E}_0 = E_0\mathbf{j}$. Will excess charge accumulate anywhere on the sphere? If so, where will it accumulate and what is its sign? If charge does accumulate, what is the contribution, due to this induced charge alone, to the electric field inside the sphere? Would a thin, spherical shell of metal behave differently from a solid metal sphere?

21-19 An irregularly shaped conductor encloses an irregularly shaped hollow region that contains a particle with charge $q = +10$ nC. What is the charge on the inner surface of the conductor? What is the charge on the outer surface of the conductor? Suppose the particle is moved to a different position inside the hollow region. Will the value of the charge on the inner or outer surfaces be affected? Will the surface charge densities at points on the inner or outer surfaces be affected? Will the field inside or outside the conductor be affected?

21-20 Suppose $\mathbf{E}$ is constant in direction but changes in magnitude in a given region. What can you conclude about charge in the region?

21-21 Coulomb's law and Newton's law of universal gravitation are both inverse-square-force laws, with the force directed along the line between the interacting particles. Can we apply Gauss's law to gravitational fields as well as to electric fields? If an object is contained inside a gaussian surface, what property of this object is proportional to the gravitational flux for the surface? Explain.

21-22 Consider using the concept of flux to describe rainfall. What would determine the amount of water collected in a bucket resting on a horizontal surface during a rainfall accompanied by a steady wind? What should be the SI units of rain flux?

21-23 Complete the following table:

Symbol	Represents	Type	SI unit
Φ_E		Scalar	
$d\mathbf{S}$			m²
Σq			
ρ	Volume charge density		
$\oint$		N/A	N/A

EXERCISES

Section 21-2. Flux

21-1 Determine the magnitude of the flux of a uniform field, $E = 660$ N/C directed vertically upward, for a plane rectangular surface (dimensions 1.5 m by 2.1 m) when (a) the surface is horizontal, (b) the surface is vertical, (c) a normal to the surface makes an angle of 32° with respect to the vertical.

21-2   The magnitude of the flux for a plane circular surface of radius 0.54 m in a uniform field is 340 N · m²/C when the surface is oriented with its normal parallel to the field direction. What is E at each point on the surface?

21-3   Determine the magnitude of the flux of a uniform field ($E = 840$ N/C) for an open hemispherical bowl ($r = 0.41$ m) when (a) **E** is parallel to the axis of the bowl and (b) **E** makes an angle of 63° with respect to the axis of the bowl.

21-4   A cubical box of dimension ℓ along each edge has only five sides because one side is missing. Determine the magnitude of the flux of a uniform field of magnitude E_0 for the surface of the box when (a) the field is directed parallel to a normal to the missing side, (b) the field is directed perpendicular to a normal to the missing side, (c) the field makes an angle θ with respect to a normal to the missing side.

21-5   What are the cartesian components of $\Delta \mathbf{S}$ for the slant surface in Fig. 21-4?

21-6   What is the magnitude of the flux of a vertical field $\mathbf{E}_0$ for the surface of a cuspidor (Fig. 21-31) with opening radius a and neck radius b?

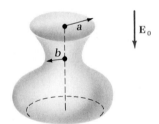

Figure 21-31. Exercise 21-6.

21-7   A plane surface of area 2.8 m² is oriented such that its surface vector is parallel to a uniform field and 98 field lines cross the surface. What is the angle between the field direction and the surface vector when the surface is oriented such that 38 field lines cross the surface?

21-8   (a) What is the flux of a uniform field $\mathbf{E} = (-240$ N/C$)\mathbf{i} + (-160$ N/C$)\mathbf{j} + (390$ N/C$)\mathbf{k}$ for a plane surface $\Delta \mathbf{S} = (-1.1$ m²$)\mathbf{i} + (4.2$ m²$)\mathbf{j} + (2.4$ m²$)\mathbf{k}$? (b) What is the projection of $\Delta \mathbf{S}$ on a plane perpendicular to **E**? (c) What is the angle between $\Delta \mathbf{S}$ and **E**?

Section 21-3. Gauss's law

21-9   A spherical gaussian surface of radius 1.0 m is centered at a particle with charge of 1.0 nC. (a) What is the area of the gaussian sphere? (b) What is E at each point on the gaussian sphere? (c) Determine the flux for the gaussian sphere from your answers to parts (a) and (b). (d) Repeat parts (a), (b), and (c) for a gaussian sphere of radius 2.0 m.

21-10   For an open hemispherical surface, what is the mag-

nitude of the flux due to a particle with charge $q = -26$ nC located at the center of the corresponding sphere?

21-11   A cube-shaped gaussian surface has one corner at the origin of coordinates and the diagonally opposite corner at (ℓ, ℓ, ℓ) such that the edges of the cube are aligned with the coordinate axes. Charged particles and their locations (x, y, z) are $q_1 = 33$ nC at $(\ell/2, 0, 2\ell)$, $q_2 = -54$ nC at $(\ell/3, \ell/4, \ell/3)$, and $q_3 = 28$ nC at $(\ell/4, \ell/2, \ell/3)$. What is the flux for the gaussian surface?

21-12   A particle with charge $q = -72$ nC is at the center of a cubical gaussian surface of dimension ℓ along each edge. (a) What is the flux for the closed gaussian cube? (b) What is the magnitude of the flux for one of the six sides? (c) If the charge were not at the center, would the answer to either part (a) or part (b) be different?

Section 21-4. Developing Gauss's law from Coulomb's law

21-13   A solid angle $\Delta \Omega$ subtended at a point is defined as

$$\Delta \Omega = \frac{\Delta S}{r^2}$$

where ΔS is the area of a spherical cap of radius r centered at the point. A solid angle is dimensionless, and its SI unit is the steradian (sr). Given that $\Delta S_2 / \Delta S_1 = r_2^2 / r_1^2$, show that spherical caps 1 and 2 in Fig. 21-9 subtend the same solid angle at the position of the charged particle.

21-14   Near the surface of the earth there exists an average electric field of about 150 N/C directed downward. Estimate the net charge on the earth. Assuming that this charge is distributed uniformly over the surface of the earth, estimate the surface charge density.

21-15   The downward-directed electric field in the earth's atmosphere is found to decrease in magnitude with increasing altitude above the surface. Suppose E is 100 N/C at 200 m above the surface of the earth and 50 N/C at 300 m above the surface of the earth. Estimate the average volume charge density in the earth's atmosphere in the altitude range from 200 to 300 m.

21-16   Consider a very large slab of plastic that has a thickness of 5.4 mm and a uniform charge density ρ. Just outside the slab and near its center, **E** is directed away from the slab on each side and has a magnitude of 940 N/C. Determine ρ.

21-17   A uniformly charged spherical shell with total charge $Q = -34$ nC is centered at the origin (Fig. 21-32). Find the flux for a gaussian cube with edges aligned with the axes and one corner at the origin. The length of the cube edges is larger than the sphere's radius. What is the flux for each face of the cube?

21-18   Make a cross-sectional sketch of the rounded-block gaussian surface in Fig. 21-9 with the point charge

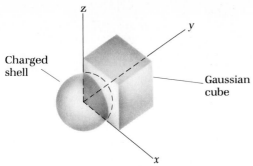

Figure 21-32. Exercise 21-17.

and its field lines in the plane of the drawing. Use your sketch to show that the field-line representation of the field is consistent with $\Phi_E = 0$ for the surface.

21-19 Make a cross-sectional sketch of the gaussian surface in Fig. 21-11 such that the raised cap is shown. Also show the point charge and its field lines in the plane of the drawing. Use your sketch to show that the field-line representation of the field is consistent with $\Phi_E = q/\epsilon_0$ for this surface.

21-20 Show that Gauss's law for gravitation

$$\Phi_G = \oint \mathbf{g} \cdot d\mathbf{S} = -4\pi G \, \Sigma m_i$$

is consistent with Newton's law of universal gravitation. What is the meaning of Σm_i? Why is the minus sign necessary? Why is the 4π present?

Section 21-5. Using Gauss's law to find E

21-21 A thin, straight rod has a charge of -230 nC uniformly distributed along its 6.3-m length. (a) Determine the linear charge density. (b) Estimate **E** near the middle of the rod at a perpendicular distance of 25 mm.

21-22 The electric field at a point which is a perpendicular distance of 18 mm from the middle of a long, thin, straight, uniformly charged rod is directed toward the rod and has a magnitude of 3.5×10^4 N/C. (a) What is the linear charge density of the rod? (b) What is the magnitude of the field at a point that is a perpendicular distance of 9 mm from the middle of the rod?

21-23 Consider a thin, square planar sheet of uniform charge density, with $Q = +79$ nC and area 1.2 m². (a) Determine the surface charge density. (b) Estimate E near the middle of the sheet at perpendicular distances of 10 and 20 mm.

21-24 The electric field at a point which is a perpendicular distance of 12 mm from the middle of a thin, uniformly charged planar disk is directed toward the disk with magnitude 7.4×10^3 N/C. The radius of the disk is 0.91 m. (a) What is the surface charge density of the disk? (b) What is the charge on the disk? (c) Estimate the field at a perpendicular distance of 24 mm

from the center of the disk.

21-25 A thin, uniformly charged spherical shell has $Q = -87$ nC and $r_0 = 55$ mm. (a) What is the surface charge density σ of the shell? (b) Find E at $r = 25, 50, 75$, and 100 mm from the center of the shell.

21-26 Show that the magnitude of the electric field for a uniform spherical shell of charge can be written in terms of σ rather than Q:

$$E = 0 \qquad (r < r_0)$$

$$E = \frac{\sigma r_0^2}{\epsilon_0 r^2} \qquad (r > r_0)$$

21-27 Consider a spherical uniform volume charge ρ, with $Q = 61$ nC and $r_0 = 48$ mm. (a) Determine ρ. (b) Find E at $r = 24, 48$, and 96 mm from the center of the sphere.

21-28 Show that the magnitude of the electric field for a sphere of uniform volume charge can be written in terms of ρ rather than Q:

$$E = \frac{\rho r}{3\epsilon_0} \qquad (r < r_0)$$

$$E = \frac{\rho r_0^3}{3\epsilon_0 r^2} \qquad (r > r_0)$$

21-29 Suppose you measure the electric field to be 284 kN/C radially outward at a distance $r = 15$ mm from the center of a uniform spherical distribution of volume charge. (a) With this information alone, determine any of the following quantities that you can: the charge Q, the radius r_0, the charge density ρ. (b) With the additional information that $E = 370$ kN/C at $r = 30$ mm, determine any of the remaining quantities from part (a) that you can.

Section 21-6. Electrostatic properties of a conductor

21-30 A solid metal ball of radius 62 mm has a charge of $+46$ nC. (a) How is this charge distributed? (b) Find E at $r = 30, 60$, and 90 mm, where r is the distance from the center of the sphere to the point where E is evaluated. (c) Does the answer to part (a) or part (b) change if the ball is hollow?

21-31 When a thin planar conducting sheet is placed in a uniform electric field that is directed perpendicular to the sheet, the field outside the conductor near its middle is nearly unchanged. Suppose such a sheet is placed in a field of magnitude 940 N/C. What is the magnitude of the surface charge density that is induced on each side of the sheet near its middle?

21-32 An irregularly shaped conductor has a surface charge density of -52 nC/m² at point P on its surface. (a) What are E_t and E_n at a point adjacent to P just inside the conductor surface? (b) What are E_t and E_n at a point adjacent to P just outside the conductor surface?

21-33 The electric field just outside point P on the surface of an irregularly shaped conductor is 620 N/C directed away from the surface. What is the surface charge density at point P?

21-34 The square plates of a parallel-plate capacitor are 260 mm on a side and are separated by 1.2 mm. The magnitude of the electric field midway between the plates is 1.4 kN/C. What are the magnitudes of (a) the charge and (b) the charge density on the plates?

21-35 Use Gauss's law to show that **E** is nearly zero in the region near the middle just outside the plates of a parallel-plate capacitor (see Fig. 21-24).

21-36 The *dielectric strength* of an insulating material is the maximum electric field that can exist in the material without dielectric breakdown. When an insulator breaks down, some of its constituent molecules ionize and the material becomes a conductor. Lightning is an example of the dielectric breakdown of air. The dielectric strength of dry air at room temperature is about 3×10^6 N/C. Estimate the maximum charge that can be placed on a conducting sphere of radius 20 mm without breakdown of the surrounding air.

PROBLEMS

21-1 Consider a very long, straight cylindrical shell of uniform surface charge density σ and with radius R_0. The charge is distributed similar to the way mass is distributed for a long, thin-walled pipe. (a) Show that the approximate magnitude of the electric field at points far from the ends of the shell is given by

$$E = 0 \qquad (R < R_0)$$

$$E = \frac{\sigma R_0}{\epsilon_0 R} \qquad (R > R_0)$$

where R is the perpendicular distance from the axis of the cylindrical shell to the point where the field is evaluated. (b) Show that this result is consistent with Example 21-3 when $R > R_0$. (c) Make a graph of E versus R.

21-2 When a long, straight conducting rod is given excess charge, the charge is distributed approximately as a uniform surface charge density. Suppose a solid, straight metal rod of radius 11 mm and length 5.4 m has a charge of -47 nC. (a) Estimate the surface charge density on the rod. (b) Use the answer to the previous problem to find E in the perpendicular bisector plane at $R = 5$, 15, and 30 mm, where R is the perpendicular distance from the axis of the rod to the point where E is evaluated. (c) Is the answer to part (b) changed if the rod is hollow?

21-3 A straight, thin wire filament 12 m long with $Q = -74$ nC and uniform linear charge density is coaxial with a neutral conducting pipe of the same length; the inner radius is 6.0 mm and outer radius is 9.0 mm (Fig. 21-33). (a) Estimate the induced surface charge densities on the inner and outer surfaces of the pipe. (b) For points in the perpendicular bisector plane, make a graph of E versus R in the range from $R = 1.0$ to 15 mm, where R is the perpendicular distance from the filament.

21-4 Consider a very long cylinder of uniform volume charge ρ with radius R_0. The charge is distributed

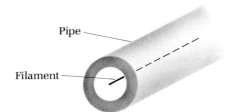

Figure 21-33. Prob. 21-3.

similarly to the mass of a long solid rod with circular cross section, such as a broom handle. (a) Show that the magnitude of the electric field at points far from the ends of the charge distribution is given by

$$E = \frac{R\rho}{2\epsilon_0} \qquad (R < R_0)$$

$$E = \frac{R_0^2 \rho}{2\epsilon_0 R} \qquad (R > R_0)$$

where R is the perpendicular distance from the axis of the cylindrical charge to the point where E is evaluated. (b) Show that this result is consistent with Example 21-3 when $R > R_0$. (c) Make a graph of E versus R.

21-5 Consider two concentric spherical shells of uniform surface charge densities σ_a and σ_b and radii a and b, $b > a$, as shown in cross section in Fig. 21-34. The two spherical shells have equal and opposite charge: $q_a = -Q$ and $q_b = +Q$, where $Q > 0$. (a) Develop ex-

Figure 21-34. Prob. 21-5.

pressions for E in all three regions of space: $r < a$, $a < r < b$, and $r > b$, where r is the distance from the center of the spheres to the point where E is evaluated. (b) Make a graph of E versus r from $r = 0$ to $3a$ for the case in which $b = 2a$.

21-6 Repeat the previous problem, except let $q_b = +2Q$.

21-7 A thick, spherical conducting shell with inner radius $a = 30$ mm, outer radius $b = 50$ mm, and zero net charge has a particle with charge $q = 28$ nC at its center (shown in cross section in Fig. 21-35). (a) Determine the charge densities on the inner and outer surfaces of the conductor. (b) Find E as a function of distance r from the particle and make a graph of E from $r = 20$ to 70 mm.

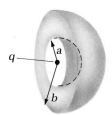

Figure 21-36. Prob. 21-11.

21-8 Consider a thick spherical shell of uniform volume charge density ρ, charge Q, inner radius a, and outer radius b. (a) Show that

$$E = 0 \qquad\qquad (r < a)$$

$$E = \frac{Q}{4\pi\epsilon_0 r^2} \frac{r^3 - a^3}{b^3 - a^3} \qquad (a < r < b)$$

$$E = \frac{Q}{4\pi\epsilon_0 r^2} \qquad\qquad (r > b)$$

where r is the distance from the center of the sphere to the point where E is evaluated. (b) Make a graph of E versus r.

21-9 A spherically symmetric distribution of charge has radius r_0 and charge Q. The volume charge density increases linearly from the center, $\rho = Ar$, where A is constant. Show that

$$A = \frac{Q}{\pi r_0^4}$$

$$E = \frac{Q r^2}{4\pi\epsilon_0 r_0^4} \qquad (r < r_0)$$

$$E = \frac{Q}{4\pi\epsilon_0 r^2} \qquad (r > r_0)$$

(*Hint:* An appropriate volume element for a spherically symmetric charge distribution is a thin spherical shell of thickness dr: $dV = 4\pi r^2\, dr$.)

21-10 A thick spherical shell has a charge Q, an inner radius a, and an outer radius b. The charge distribution between a and b is spherically symmetric but varies with distance from the center: $\rho = A/r$, where A is a constant. A point charge q is placed at the center of the sphere. (a) Determine q in terms of Q, a, and b such that the field between a and b is independent of r. (b) What is the field for $r < a$? (c) What is the field for $r > b$?

21-11 An otherwise uniform spherical distribution of charge has a spherical cavity with no charge completely inside it (Fig. 21-36). The position vector from the center of the sphere to the center of the cavity is $\mathbf{r}_0$. Show that the field inside the cavity is uniform and parallel to $\mathbf{r}_0$: $\mathbf{E} = \rho\mathbf{r}_0/3\epsilon_0$. Notice that this result is independent of the radius of either the sphere or the cavity. (*Hint:* Treat the cavity as a negative uniform charge density superimposed onto the positive uniform charge density of the sphere.)

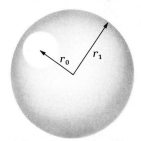

Figure 21-35. Prob. 21-7.

21-12 *A simple atomic model.* Ernest Rutherford, who guided the experiments which established our modern view of atoms, used a simple model of the atom to explain the experimental results. He introduced the concept of a nucleus by representing an atom with atomic number Z as a particle with charge $+Ze$ (the nucleus) at the center of a uniform spherical distribution of charge with charge $-Ze$ and radius r_a (the electrons). Use Gauss's law to show that E at a distance r from the center of this charge distribution is

$$E = 0 \qquad\qquad (r > r_a)$$

$$E = \frac{Ze}{4\pi\epsilon_0}\left(\frac{1}{r^2} - \frac{r}{r_a^3}\right) \qquad (r < r_a)$$

CHAPTER 22
ELECTRIC POTENTIAL

22-1 INTRODUCTION

As we have seen in the previous two chapters, the electrical effect of a charge distribution can be described in terms of the electric field produced by the distribution. In this chapter we introduce another kind of field, called the *electric potential,* or simply the *potential.* The electric field **E** is defined as a *force per unit charge,* and since force is a vector, **E** is a vector field. The potential V is defined as a *potential energy per unit charge,* and since potential energy is a scalar, V is a scalar field. Because V is a scalar, it is often more convenient to use than **E**, but each is derivable from the other. Indeed, the relation between **E** and V is analogous to that between a conservative force and its associated potential energy.

You may be familiar with electric potential by another name; it is often called the *voltage.* This term for potential comes from the common unit that is used in measuring potential, the *volt.* Therefore, referring to potential as voltage is similar to referring to distance as mileage; the name for a concept arises from its unit of measure. The volt is named for Count Alessandro Volta (1745 – 1827), professor of physics at the University of Pavia, Italy. Volta invented the electric cell, or battery, which was the first device to provide steady electric currents.

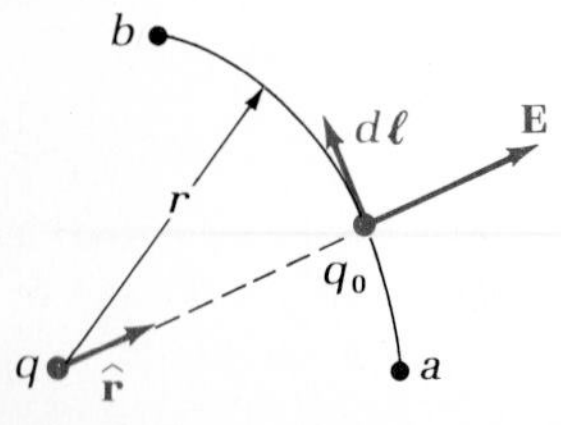

22-2 ELECTRIC POTENTIAL ENERGY

Electric potential is electric potential energy per unit charge. Before presenting a formal definition of potential, we first develop an expression for electric potential energy. The principal ingredients in this discussion are (i) the field due to a point charge and (ii) the principle of superposition.

Potential energy of a test particle in the field of a point charge. Consider the work done by the electric force when a test particle of charge q_0 is moved in the field of a fixed point charge q. In Fig. 22-1, the test particle is

Figure 22-1. A test particle with charge q_0 is moved along a circular arc centered at a fixed point charge q. Since $d\ell$ is perpendicular to **E** at each point on the path, the work done by the electric force is zero.

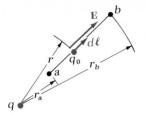

Figure 22-2. The test particle is moved along a radial path, $d\boldsymbol{\ell} = dr\,\hat{\mathbf{r}}$. The work done by the electric force is $(qq_0/4\pi\epsilon_0)(1/r_a - 1/r_b)$.

moved along a circular arc centered at the point charge q. The electric force on the test particle is $\mathbf{F} = q_0\mathbf{E}$, where $\mathbf{E}$ is the field produced by q. Since $\mathbf{E}$ is perpendicular to $d\boldsymbol{\ell}$ at each point along the circular arc path from a to b, the work done by the electric force is zero. That is, $\mathbf{E} \cdot d\boldsymbol{\ell} = E\,d\ell\cos 90° = 0$, so that

$$\int_a^b \mathbf{F} \cdot d\boldsymbol{\ell} = q_0 \int_a^b \mathbf{E} \cdot d\boldsymbol{\ell} = 0$$

As you can see, this is true for any circular arc path centered at the point charge. Indeed, it is true for any path on the surface of a sphere centered at the point charge q.

In Fig. 22-2, the test particle is moved along a radial path from a to b. Because the path is radial, the infinitesimal displacement $d\boldsymbol{\ell}$ can be written as $dr\,\hat{\mathbf{r}}$, where dr is an infinitesimal change in distance between the particles and $\hat{\mathbf{r}}$ is a unit vector that points away from the point charge. The field produced by q is $\mathbf{E} = (q/4\pi\epsilon_0 r^2)\hat{\mathbf{r}}$ so that

$$\int_a^b \mathbf{F} \cdot d\boldsymbol{\ell} = q_0 \int_a^b \mathbf{E} \cdot d\boldsymbol{\ell}$$

$$= q_0 \int_{r_a}^{r_b} \left(\frac{q}{4\pi\epsilon_0 r^2}\,\hat{\mathbf{r}}\right) \cdot (dr\,\hat{\mathbf{r}})$$

$$= \frac{q_0 q}{4\pi\epsilon_0} \int_{r_a}^{r_b} \frac{dr}{r^2} = \frac{q_0 q}{4\pi\epsilon_0}\left[-\frac{1}{r}\right]_{r_a}^{r_b}$$

$$= \frac{q_0 q}{4\pi\epsilon_0}\left(\frac{1}{r_a} - \frac{1}{r_b}\right)$$

Now suppose the test particle is moved along the path $aijb$ in Fig. 22-3. Path a to i is radial, path i to j is a circular arc, and path j to b is radial. The work done by the electric force is

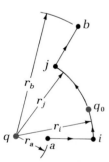

Figure 22-3. The test particle is moved along a radial-arc-radial path. Since the path from i to j is a circular arc, the work done by the electric force is independent of r_i and r_j.

$$\int_a^b \mathbf{F} \cdot d\boldsymbol{\ell} = \int_a^i \mathbf{F} \cdot d\boldsymbol{\ell} + \int_i^j \mathbf{F} \cdot d\boldsymbol{\ell} + \int_j^b \mathbf{F} \cdot d\boldsymbol{\ell}$$

$$= \frac{q_0 q}{4\pi\epsilon_0}\left(\frac{1}{r_a} - \frac{1}{r_i}\right) + 0 + \frac{q_0 q}{4\pi\epsilon_0}\left(\frac{1}{r_j} - \frac{1}{r_b}\right)$$

Since $r_i = r_j$, the two terms containing r_i and r_j, namely $-q_0 q/4\pi\epsilon_0 r_i$ and $q_0 q/4\pi\epsilon_0 r_j$, cancel one another, and

$$\int_a^b \mathbf{F} \cdot d\boldsymbol{\ell} = \frac{q_0 q}{4\pi\epsilon_0}\left(\frac{1}{r_a} - \frac{1}{r_b}\right)$$

For this combination radial-arc-radial path, the work done by the electric force depends only on the separation distance between the particles before the displacement (r_a) and after the displacement (r_b). This is true no matter how many radial and arc segments we wish to use because terms that involve distances other than r_a and r_b always cancel out.

Figure 22-4 shows an arbitrarily shaped path between a and b with a number of small arc paths and radial paths superimposed on it. An arbitrarily shaped path can be viewed as an infinite number of infinitesimal arc paths and radial paths. As a test particle is moved from a to b along the arbitrarily shaped path, the work done for each infinitesimal arc path is zero, so that the work is the sum of the individual contributions from each of the infinitesimal radial paths. When these contributions are added, the terms involving distances other than r_a and r_b cancel out, as shown in the previous paragraph. Thus

$$\int_a^b \mathbf{F} \cdot d\boldsymbol{\ell} = \frac{q_0 q}{4\pi\epsilon_0} \left(\frac{1}{r_a} - \frac{1}{r_b} \right) \tag{22-1}$$

Work done by the electric force on a test particle along any path

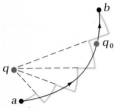

Figure 22-4. An arbitrarily shaped path with a number of small arc paths and radial paths superimposed on it. An arbitrary path may be viewed as an infinite number of infinitesimal arc paths and radial paths. The work done along each arc path is zero, so that the work done along the arbitrarily shaped path is the sum of the individual contributions along each radial path.

for the arbitrarily shaped path between a and b.

The arc paths in Fig. 22-4 are contained in the plane of the page because we are constrained to show figures on a two-dimensional sheet, but they could just as well be out of the plane. Therefore, Eq. (22-1) is valid for any path whatsoever between a and b. That is, the work done by the electric force is independent of the path. If the work done by a force is independent of the path, the force is called a *conservative force* (Chap. 9), and the change in potential energy is the negative of the work done by the conservative force:

$$U_b - U_a = -\int_a^b \mathbf{F} \cdot d\boldsymbol{\ell} \tag{22-2}$$

Substituting from Eq. (22-1), we find that the change in the test particle's potential energy is

$$U_b - U_a = \frac{q_0 q}{4\pi\epsilon_0} \left(\frac{1}{r_b} - \frac{1}{r_a} \right) \tag{22-3}$$

Although only changes in potential energy have physical significance, it is convenient to select a reference position at which we define the potential energy as zero. In this way we can speak of the potential energy of a charged particle at a particular point, always remembering that its value depends on the reference position we have selected. From examination of Eq. (22-3), you can see that a simple choice is to identify the term containing $1/r_b$ with U_b and the term containing $1/r_a$ with U_a. This gives the potential energy $U(r)$ for a separation distance r as

Potential energy in the field E of a point charge q

$$U(r) = \frac{q_0 q}{4\pi\epsilon_0 r} \tag{22-4}$$

By substitution into Eq. (22-4), you can see that this corresponds to setting $U = 0$ at $r = \infty$. That is, the potential energy is chosen to be zero when the two particles are far removed from one another such that the electrical effect they have on one another is negligible. We often indicate this convention by writing $U_\infty = 0$.

We can reinforce our understanding of the test particle's potential energy U by applying our reference-level selection ($U_\infty = 0$) to Eq. (22-2), and then giving the result a physical interpretation. Let the point b in Eq. (22-2) correspond to a separation distance r [$r_b = r$, $U_b = U(r)$], and let the point a correspond to a very large separation ($r_a = \infty$, $U_\infty = 0$). Equation (22-2) then becomes

$$U(r) = -\int_\infty^r \mathbf{F} \cdot d\boldsymbol{\ell}$$

From this expression you can see that $U(r)$ is the negative of the work done by the electric force when the test particle is moved from a distant point to where it is a distance r from the point charge. The negative of the work done *by* a force is the same as the work done *against* that force. Thus we can view $U(r)$ *as the*

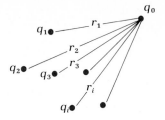

Figure 22-5. The potential energy of the test particle depends on its distance from each of the other particles.

work done against the electric force (by an external agent) when the test particle is moved from a distant point to a separation distance r from the point charge.

Potential energy of a test particle in the field of a number of point charges. Suppose the test particle is in the field of two point charges q_1 and q_2. By the principle of superposition, the electric force $\mathbf{F}$ on the test particle is

$$\mathbf{F} = q_0\mathbf{E} = q_0(\mathbf{E}_1 + \mathbf{E}_2)$$

where $\mathbf{E}_1$ and $\mathbf{E}_2$ are the contributions to the field due to q_1 and q_2. The work done by $\mathbf{F}$ when the test particle is moved from a to b is

$$\int_a^b \mathbf{F} \cdot d\boldsymbol{\ell} = \int_a^b q_0(\mathbf{E}_1 + \mathbf{E}_2) \cdot d\boldsymbol{\ell}$$

$$= q_0\left[\int_a^b \mathbf{E}_1 \cdot d\boldsymbol{\ell} + \int_a^b \mathbf{E}_2 \cdot d\boldsymbol{\ell}\right]$$

We find that the work can be divided into two contributions, each of which is independent of the path from a to b. Thus the sum of the two contributions to the work is also independent of the path, and the force $\mathbf{F}$ is conservative. Following the procedures we used above when the test particle was in the field of a single point charge (with $U_\infty = 0$), we have

$$U = \frac{q_0}{4\pi\epsilon_0}\left(\frac{q_1}{r_1} + \frac{q_2}{r_2}\right)$$

where r_1 and r_2 are the distances between the test particle and point charges 1 and 2, respectively. Extending to a case where the test particle is in the field of a number of point charges, we find

Potential energy of a test particle in the field of a number of point charges

$$U = \frac{q_0}{4\pi\epsilon_0}\sum\frac{q_i}{r_i} \tag{22-5}$$

where r_i is the distance between the test particle and point charge i (Fig. 22-5).

22-3 ELECTRIC POTENTIAL

In Chap. 20, we found that the electric force $\mathbf{F}$ on a test particle of charge q_0 in the proximity of a charge distribution is proportional to q_0. The ratio $\mathbf{F}/q_0$ depends on the charge distribution, but is independent of q_0. We defined this ratio as the electric field $\mathbf{E}$. Equation (22-5) suggests a similar procedure for the electric potential energy U. If we divide U by q_0, then the resulting quantity is independent of q_0. Thus we define the *electric potential V* as

Definition of electric potential

$$V = \frac{U}{q_0} \quad \text{(small } q_0) \tag{22-6}$$

Similar to $\mathbf{E}$, V is a field quantity; it has a value at each point in space. Since U is a scalar, V is a scalar field. From Eq. (22-6), the SI unit of potential is the joule per coulomb (J/C), which is called the volt (V).

The charge q_0 on the test particle that is used to measure the potential must be small, as indicated in Eq. (22-6). If the charge on the test particle is not small, then its presence may alter the charge distribution which produces the potential, and that would change the potential that was to be measured.

Potential due to charged particles. Dividing Eq. (22-5) by q_0 gives, at a point P, the potential produced by a distribution of charged particles:

Potential due to a distribution of charged particles

$$V = \frac{1}{4\pi\epsilon_0} \sum \frac{q_i}{r_i} \tag{22-7}$$

where r_i is the distance between particle i and point P. The simplest application of Eq. (22-7) is in determining the potential V a distance r from a single particle with charge q:

Potential due to a point charge

$$V = \frac{q}{4\pi\epsilon_0 r}$$

Once we know the potential due to a charge distribution, we can determine the potential energy of a charged particle (relative to $U_\infty = 0$). Suppose a particle, say particle 1 with charge q_1, is placed at a point where the potential is V. Then the electric potential energy U_1 of the particle at that point is $U_1 = q_1V$.

In atomic and nuclear physics, the charged particles of interest are protons and electrons, in which case the magnitude of the charge is $e = 1.60 \times 10^{-19}$ C. This makes it convenient to define an energy unit, called the *electron volt* (eV), which is equal to the product of the magnitude of the electronic charge times one volt:

Definition of the electron volt

$$1 \text{ eV} = (1.6 \times 10^{-19} \text{ C})(1 \text{ V}) = 1.6 \times 10^{-19} \text{ J}$$

Thus the conversion factor between J and eV is numerically equal to the magnitude of the electronic charge.

EXAMPLE 22-1. In an atom, a typical distance between an electron and its nucleus is about 1×10^{-10} m. (a) Find the potential due to an oxygen nucleus at a point that is a distance of 1.0×10^{-10} m from the nucleus. Relative to $U_\infty = 0$, find the potential energy of an electron at this point (b) in eV and (c) in J. Neglect any contribution due to the other electrons.

SOLUTION. (a) The atomic number of oxygen is 8; that is, an oxygen nucleus contains eight protons and its charge is $q = 8e = 8(1.6 \times 10^{-19} \text{ C}) = 13 \times 10^{-19}$ C. The potential at a distance of 1.0×10^{-10} m from this charge is

$$V = (9.0 \times 10^9 \text{ N} \cdot \text{m}^2/\text{C}^2) \frac{13 \times 10^{-19} \text{ C}}{1.0 \times 10^{-10} \text{ m}} = 120 \text{ V}$$

(b) In eV, the potential energy of an electron (relative to $U_\infty = 0$) at this point is

$$U = qV = (-e)(120 \text{ V}) = -120 \text{ eV}$$

(c) The potential energy in J is

$$U = qV = (-1.6 \times 10^{-19} \text{ C})(120 \text{ V}) = -1.9 \times 10^{-17} \text{ J}$$

When discussing an electron or proton, it is easier to calculate U in eV than in J, and the size of the numerical value is often more convenient because it is nearer unity.

EXAMPLE 22-2. Find the potential at point P in Fig. 22-6, where $q_1 = 33$ nC, $q_2 = -51$ nC, and $q_3 = 47$ nC.

SOLUTION. From Eq. (22-7),

$$V = \frac{1}{4\pi\epsilon_0} \left(\frac{q_1}{r_1} + \frac{q_2}{r_2} + \frac{q_3}{r_3} \right)$$

$$= (9.0 \times 10^9 \text{ N} \cdot \text{m}^2/\text{C}^2) \left(\frac{33 \text{ nC}}{93 \text{ mm}} + \frac{-51 \text{ nC}}{130 \text{ mm}} + \frac{47 \text{ nC}}{93 \text{ mm}} \right)$$

$$= 4.2 \times 10^3 \text{ V}$$

where we have used $\sqrt{(93 \text{ mm})^2 + (93 \text{ mm})^2} = 130$ mm. No-

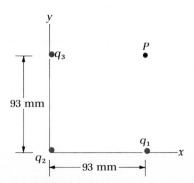

Figure 22-6. Example 22-2.

tice that it is easier to calculate V than **E** because the calcula-

EXAMPLE 22-3. Particle 1 with charge $q_1 = 3q$ is at the origin and particle 2 with charge $q_2 = -q$ is on the x axis at $x = 4d$, where both q and d are positive. (a) Write an equation for $V(x)$ at points along the x axis and (b) make a graph of $V(x)$ between $x = -4d$ and $+8d$. Plot points at intervals of d and sketch the curve between the points.

SOLUTION. (a) From Eq. (22-7),

$$V = \frac{1}{4\pi\epsilon_0}\left(\frac{q_1}{r_1} + \frac{q_2}{r_2}\right).$$

Since we are interested in V along the x axis only, $r_1 = |x|$ and $r_2 = |x - 4d|$, so that

$$V(x) = \frac{1}{4\pi\epsilon_0}\left(\frac{3q}{|x|} - \frac{q}{|x - 4d|}\right)$$

The absolute value is used in each term because the quantity r_i in Eq. (22-7) represents a distance and must be positive, whereas the coordinate x can be negative. (b) The graph is shown in Fig. 22-7. Notice from the figure that the potential near a charged particle is determined mostly by that particle

tion involves a scalar sum rather than a vector sum.

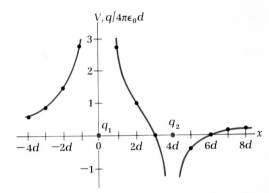

Figure 22-7. Example 22-3: The potential $V(x)$ along the x axis is produced by two point charges, one at the origin and the other on the x axis at $x = 4d$.

alone. The potential is zero at two points on the graph: $x = 3d$ and $x = 6d$. At each of these points the distance to particle 1 ($q_1 = 3q$) is 3 times the distance to particle 2 ($q_2 = -q$), so the two contributions to the potential cancel each other.

EXAMPLE 22-4. *Potential due to a dipole.* Figure 22-8a shows a dipole with moment $\mathbf{p} = (2aq)\mathbf{k}$ located at the origin. Determine the potential produced by the dipole at distances much greater than the separation $2a$ of the charged particles which compose the dipole.

SOLUTION. Letting V_+ and V_- represent the contributions to the potential due to the particles with positive and negative charge respectively, we have

$$V = V_+ + V_- = \frac{q}{4\pi\epsilon_0 r_+} + \frac{-q}{4\pi\epsilon_0 r_-} = \frac{q}{4\pi\epsilon_0}\left(\frac{1}{r_+} - \frac{1}{r_-}\right)$$

$$= \frac{q}{4\pi\epsilon_0}\frac{r_- - r_+}{r_+ r_-}$$

If $r \gg a$, then from Fig. 22-8a $r_+ \approx r_- \approx r$, and from Fig. 22-8b $r_- - r_+ \approx 2a \cos \theta$. Therefore,

$$V \approx \frac{2aq \cos \theta}{4\pi\epsilon_0 r^2} = \frac{p \cos \theta}{4\pi\epsilon_0 r^2}$$

Using a unit vector $\hat{\mathbf{r}}$ that points away from the origin toward point P, we can write this as

$$V \approx \frac{\mathbf{p} \cdot \hat{\mathbf{r}}}{4\pi\epsilon_0 r^2}$$

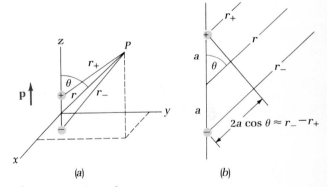

Figure 22-8. Example 22-4:
(a) Potential at point P due to a dipole with moment $\mathbf{p} = (2aq)\mathbf{k}$ located at the origin. (b) When $r \gg a$, $r_- - r_+ \approx 2a \cos \theta$.

The potential due to the dipole is zero at all points in the xy plane ($\theta = 90°$); it is positive at all points above the xy plane ($0 \leqslant \theta < 90°$); and it is negative at all points below the xy plane ($90° < \theta \leqslant 180°$). The potential falls off as $1/r^2$ along any radial line ($r \gg a$). How does the potential due to a point charge depend on r?

Potential due to continuous charge distributions. Equation (22-7) can be transformed into an equation for the potential due to a continuous charge distribution. The continuous charge distribution is divided into an infinite number of infinitesimal charges dq, and in this limit the sum in Eq. (22-7) becomes an integral:

$$V = \frac{1}{4\pi\epsilon_0} \lim_{\substack{N\to\infty \\ q_i\to 0}} \sum_{i=1}^{N} \frac{q_i}{r_i} = \frac{1}{4\pi\epsilon_0} \int \frac{dq}{r}$$

Or

Potential due to a continuous distribution of charge

$$V = \frac{1}{4\pi\epsilon_0} \int \frac{dq}{r} \qquad (22\text{-}8)$$

where the integration is over the extent of the charge distribution and r is the distance from dq to the point P at which the potential is evaluated.

EXAMPLE 22-5. Determine the potential at points along the axis of a uniformly charged circular ring of radius a and total charge Q. The ring is thin enough to be considered a line charge.

SOLUTION. Figure 22-9 shows the ring contained in the yz plane and centered at the origin so that its axis is the x axis. The potential at point P is

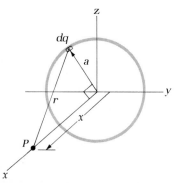

Figure 22-9. Example 22-5: Potential along the axis of a charged ring contained in the yz plane and centered at the origin.

$$V = \frac{1}{4\pi\epsilon_0} \int \frac{dq}{r} = \frac{1}{4\pi\epsilon_0} \int \frac{dq}{\sqrt{x^2 + a^2}}$$

where the integration involves adding the contributions to the potential due to each charge element dq around the ring. Since x and a are constant with respect to this integration.

$$V = \frac{1}{4\pi\epsilon_0 \sqrt{x^2 + a^2}} \int dq = \frac{Q}{4\pi\epsilon_0 \sqrt{x^2 + a^2}}$$

Figure 22-10 shows a graph of V versus x for the case where $a = 0.50$ m and $Q = +11.1$ nC. It is instructive to compare this example with the corresponding calculation of the electric field, Example 20-7.

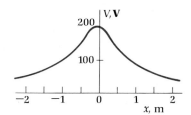

Figure 22-10. Example 22-5: $V(x)$ along the axis of the charged ring in Fig. 22-9; $Q = 11.1$ nC, $a = 0.50$ m.

EXAMPLE 22-6. Determine the potential at points along the axis of a thin, uniformly charged disk of radius R_0 and surface charge density σ.

SOLUTION. As seen in Fig. 22-11, the disk is contained in the yz plane and centered at the origin so that its axis is the x axis. The disk is divided into infinitesimal rings of area $2\pi a\, da$, and the infinitesimal charge of each ring is $dq = \sigma 2\pi a\, da$. Using the result of the previous example, we have

$$dV = \frac{dq}{4\pi\epsilon_0 r} = \frac{\sigma 2\pi a\, da}{4\pi\epsilon_0 \sqrt{x^2 + a^2}}$$

$$V = \int dV = \frac{2\pi\sigma}{4\pi\epsilon_0} \int_0^{R_0} \frac{a\, da}{\sqrt{x^2 + a^2}} = \frac{\sigma}{2\epsilon_0} \left[\sqrt{x^2 + a^2} \right]_0^{R_0}$$

$$V = \frac{\sigma}{2\epsilon_0} \left(\sqrt{x^2 + R_0^2} - \sqrt{x^2} \right)$$

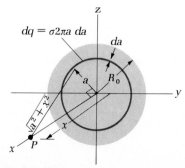

Figure 22-11. Example 22-6: Potential along the axis of a thin disk with uniform surface charge.

22-4 POTENTIAL DIFFERENCE

Our definition of potential is based on the reference position we chose for potential energy: $U = 0$ at $r = \infty$. Therefore, our reference position for potential V is also at $r = \infty$. In other words, V is taken to be zero at points far removed from the charge distribution ($V_\infty = 0$). However, the selection of a reference position is simply a matter of convenience. When dealing with electric circuits (Chap. 25), a convenient reference position is the earth, or "ground." Only a change in potential energy has physical significance, and, correspondingly, only a change in potential, or *potential difference*, has physical significance.

Let $U_b - U_a$ represent the difference in electric potential energy of a test particle with charge q_0 when it is moved from point a to point b. Then, the potential difference $V_b - V_a$ between points a and b is defined as

Definition of potential difference

$$V_b - V_a = \frac{U_b - U_a}{q_0} \quad \text{(small } q_0) \tag{22-9}$$

Sometimes we shall abbreviate the notation by representing $V_b - V_a$ with ΔV.

The potential difference between two points in a region can be determined from the electric field in the region. Since the difference in the electric potential energy of a test particle with charge q_0 is the negative of the work done by the electric force, we have

$$U_b - U_a = -q_0 \int_a^b \mathbf{E} \cdot d\boldsymbol{\ell}$$

Dividing by q_0 gives the potential difference in terms of the electric field:

Potential difference in terms of **E**

$$V_b - V_a = -\int_a^b \mathbf{E} \cdot d\boldsymbol{\ell} \tag{22-10}$$

Since the electric force is conservative, any path connecting points a and b may be used to evaluate the line integral in Eq. (22-10).

A simple application of Eq. (22-10) is to determine the potential difference between points in a uniform electric field. In Fig. 22-12, we let the x axis be along the direction of the field so that $\mathbf{E} = E\mathbf{i}$. Since **E** is perpendicular to the yz plane, the potential is constant in planes parallel to the yz plane. To find the potential difference between different planes parallel to the yz plane, we perform the line integral in Eq. (22-10) along a straight line parallel to the x axis, that is, along a field line. In this case $d\boldsymbol{\ell} = dx\,\mathbf{i}$, so that

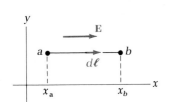

Figure 22-12. Finding $V_b - V_a$ in a uniform field pointing in the $+x$ direction.

$$V_b - V_a = -\int_{x_a}^{x_b} (E\mathbf{i}) \cdot (dx\,\mathbf{i}) = -\int_{x_a}^{x_b} E\,dx$$

Since E is constant, it may be factored out of the integral and we have

$$V_b - V_a = -E(x_b - x_a) \quad \text{or} \quad \Delta V = -E\,\Delta x$$

Suppose we let V_0 represent the potential of points in the yz plane ($x = 0$), and let $V(x)$ be the potential of points in planes parallel to the yz plane with coordinate x. This gives

Potential difference in a uniform field

$$V(x) - V_0 = -Ex \tag{22-11}$$

In a uniform field, the potential difference varies linearly with x and decreases along the field direction.

A gravitational analogy to the uniform electric field is the uniform gravitational field near the surface of the earth. As an object is lifted (moved opposite the field direction), its potential energy relative to some horizontal reference plane (such as the floor of a room) increases linearly with increasing elevation.

EXAMPLE 22-7. *Potential difference between the plates of a parallel-plate capacitor.*

Make a graph of the potential difference $V(x) - V_0$ in the space between the plates of the parallel-plate capacitor shown in cross section in Fig. 22-13, and determine ΔV between the plates. The lateral dimensions of each plate are much larger than the plate separation, which is $d = 0.50$ mm, and the magnitude of the surface charge density on each plate is $|\sigma| = 1.8 \ \mu C/m^2$.

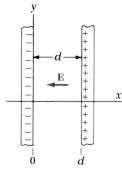

Figure 22-13. Example 22-7: Cross section of a parallel-plate capacitor.

SOLUTION. Since the lateral dimensions of each plate are much larger than the separation between the plates, we may assume that **E** is uniform. In Fig. 22-13 the surface charge of the negative plate occupies the yz plane ($x = 0$)

and the surface charge of the positive plate occupies a parallel plane at $x = d$; the x axis passes through the center of the capacitor. With this arrangement, **E** points in the $-x$ direction. Also, from Example 21-8, $E = |\sigma|/\epsilon_0$. Thus $\mathbf{E} = -E\mathbf{i} = -(|\sigma|/\epsilon_0)\mathbf{i}$, and from Eq. (22.11),

$$V(x) - V_0 = \frac{|\sigma|}{\epsilon_0} x = \frac{1.8 \ \mu C/m^2}{8.85 \times 10^{-12} \ C^2/(N \cdot m^2)} x$$

$$= (2.0 \times 10^5 \ N/C)x$$

A graph of the potential difference is shown in Fig. 22-14. The potential difference ΔV between the plates is

$$\Delta V = V_d - V_0 = Ed = (2.0 \times 10^5 \ N/C)(0.50 \ mm) = 100 \ V$$

What is the potential difference between the negative plate and the plane at $x = 0.25$ mm?

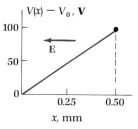

Figure 22-14. Example 22-7: In the space between capacitor plates, $V(x) - V_0$ varies linearly from one plate to the other and increases in the direction opposite **E**.

EXAMPLE 22-8. *Electron gun in a CRT.*

The charged plates of an electron gun in a cathode-ray tube (Fig. 20-21), or CRT, are called the *anode* and the *cathode*. Electrons are emitted from the cathode nearly at rest and are accelerated toward the anode, which is at a positive potential relative to the cathode. By gravitational analogy the electrons are said to "fall through" the potential difference between the cathode and anode. Some of the electrons then emerge from the electron gun through a small hole in the middle of the anode and form the electron beam. Suppose the anode-cathode potential difference is $\Delta V = V_A - V_C = 2500$ V = 2.5 kV. Assuming the electrons start from rest, find (a) the kinetic energy and (b) the speed of an electron as it emerges from the anode.

SOLUTION. (a) The mechanical energy $(K + U)$ of the electrons is conserved as they accelerate from cathode to anode. Letting subscripts C and A refer to quantities evaluated at the cathode and anode, we have $K_A + U_A = K_C + U_C$. Since electrons start from rest at the cathode, $K_C = 0$, and $K_A + U_A = U_C$, or

$$K_A = U_C - U_A$$

The potential energy of an electron (charge $-e$) at the cathode is $U_C = (-e)V_C$, and at the anode is $U_A = (-e)V_A$. The kinetic energy of each electron as it emerges from the hole in the anode is

$$K_A = (-e)V_C - (-e)V_A = e(V_A - V_C) = e \ \Delta V$$

Thus, if an electron starts from rest and accelerates through a potential difference ΔV, then its kinetic energy is $e \ \Delta V$. In this example, $\Delta V = 2.5$ kV, so

$$K_A = e(2.5 \ kV) = 2.5 \times 10^3 \ eV = 2.5 \ keV$$

Often an electron with this kinetic energy is described as a "2.5-keV electron." (b) Since $K_A = \frac{1}{2}mv^2 = e \ \Delta V$, the speed v of an electron as it emerges from the hole in the anode is

$$v = \sqrt{\frac{2e \ \Delta V}{m}}$$

$$= \sqrt{\frac{(2)(1.6 \times 10^{-19} \ C)(2.5 \ kV)}{9.1 \times 10^{-31} \ kg}} = 3.0 \times 10^7 \ m/s$$

EXAMPLE 22-9. Determine the potential energy of a dipole in a uniform electric field.

SOLUTION. Figure 22-15 shows a dipole oriented at an angle θ with respect to a uniform electric field directed along the x axis. The x coordinates of the positive and negative point charges are $x_0 + a \cos \theta$ and $x_0 - a \cos \theta$, respectively. For a uniform field in the x direction [Eq. (22-11)], $V(x) = -Ex + V_0$, where V_0 is the potential at points on the yz plane ($x = 0$). Therefore, the potential energy U_+ of the positive point charge is

$$U_+ = q[-E(x_0 + a \cos \theta) + V_0]$$

and the potential energy U_- of the negative point charge is

$$U_- = -q[-E(x_0 - a \cos \theta) + V_0]$$

We do not include the potential energy of interaction of the two particles because it depends on their separation, which is assumed to be fixed. Thus the potential energy U of the dipole is

$$U = U_+ + U_-$$
$$= q[-E(x_0 + a \cos \theta) + V_0] - q[-E(x_0 - a \cos \theta) + V_0]$$
$$= -2aqE \cos \theta = -pE \cos \theta$$

$$U = -\mathbf{p} \cdot \mathbf{E}$$

where $\mathbf{p}$ is the dipole moment. The potential energy of a dipole in a uniform field is independent of its position x_0. Instead it depends on the orientation of the dipole moment with respect to the field direction. The potential energy is $-pE$ when the dipole is aligned parallel to the field ($\theta = 0$, $\cos \theta = +1$); it is zero when the dipole points perpendicular to the field ($\theta = 90°$, $\cos \theta = 0$); and it is $+pE$ when the dipole is aligned opposite the field ($\theta = 180°$, $\cos \theta = -1$). (See Ques. 22-17 and Exercise 22-19. Problem 22-2 discusses additional features of a dipole in a uniform field.)

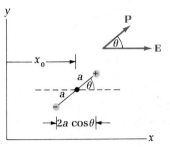

Figure 22-15. Example 22-9: The potential energy of a dipole in a uniform field, $\mathbf{E} = E_x \mathbf{i}$.

EXAMPLE 22-10. *Potential produced by a uniformly charged sphere.* Consider a spherically symmetric volume charge density of radius r_0 and charge Q. The charge distribution is uniform, similar to the mass distribution of a billiard ball. (a) Find the potential difference between two points outside the charge distribution. (b) Find the potential difference between two points inside the charge distribution. (c) Find an expression for the potential $V(r)$ (relative to $V_\infty = 0$) at all points outside the charge distribution ($r \geqslant r_0$). (d) Find an expression for the potential $V(r)$ at all points inside the charge distribution ($r \leqslant r_0$).

SOLUTION. (a) At points outside the charge distribution $\mathbf{E} = (Q/4\pi\epsilon_0 r^2)\hat{\mathbf{r}}$. This field is spherically symmetric, and the field lines are radial. Therefore, when applying Eq. (22-10), the most convenient path of integration is a radial path, as shown in Fig. 22-16a: $d\boldsymbol{\ell} = dr\,\hat{\mathbf{r}}$. Substituting into Eq. (22-10) gives

$$V_b - V_a = -\int_{r_a}^{r_b} \left(\frac{Q}{4\pi\epsilon_0 r^2} \hat{\mathbf{r}} \right) \cdot (dr\,\hat{\mathbf{r}})$$

$$= -\frac{Q}{4\pi\epsilon_0} \int_{r_a}^{r_b} \frac{dr}{r^2} = -\frac{Q}{4\pi\epsilon_0} \left[-\frac{1}{r} \right]_{r_a}^{r_b}$$

$$= \frac{Q}{4\pi\epsilon_0} \left(\frac{1}{r_b} - \frac{1}{r_a} \right) \qquad (A)$$

This is a familiar result. The potential difference between two points outside the spherically symmetric charge distri-

bution is the same as that due to a point charge located at the center of the distribution.

(b) From Example 21-6, the electric field inside the charge distribution is $\mathbf{E} = (Qr/4\pi\epsilon_0 r_0^3)\hat{\mathbf{r}}$. Thus the field inside is also radial so that we find the potential difference by integrating $\mathbf{E}$ along a radial path (Fig. 22-16b). This gives

$$V_b - V_a = -\int_{r_a}^{r_b} \left(\frac{Qr}{4\pi\epsilon_0 r_0^3} \hat{\mathbf{r}} \right) \cdot (dr\,\hat{\mathbf{r}})$$

$$= -\frac{Q}{4\pi\epsilon_0 r_0^3} \int_{r_a}^{r_b} r\,dr = -\frac{Q}{4\pi\epsilon_0 r_0^3} \left[\frac{1}{2} r^2 \right]_{r_a}^{r_b}$$

$$= \frac{Q}{8\pi\epsilon_0 r_0^3} (r_a{}^2 - r_b{}^2) \qquad (B)$$

(c) We can use Eq. (A) to find the potential at points outside

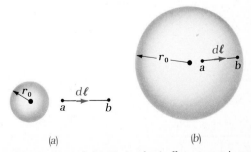

(a) (b)

Figure 22-16. Example 22-10: A spherically symmetric uniform volume charge. Since the field is spherically symmetric, the integration path is made radial: $d\boldsymbol{\ell} = dr\,\hat{\mathbf{r}}$. (a) Outside the charge distribution. (b) Inside the charge distribution.

the sphere by letting point a correspond to a distant point $(r_a = \infty, V_a = V_\infty = 0)$ and point b correspond to the point at which the potential is evaluated $[r_b = r, V_b = V(r)]$. Thus

$$V(r) = \frac{Q}{4\pi\epsilon_0 r} \qquad (r \geq r_0) \qquad (C)$$

The potential outside the spherically symmetric charge distribution is the same as that for a charged particle located at the center of the distribution.

(d) To find the potential inside the charge distribution, we use both Eqs. (B) and (C). From Eq. (C), the potential V_0 evaluated at any point on the surface of the sphere is

$$V_0 = \frac{Q}{4\pi\epsilon_0 r_0} \qquad (D)$$

In Eq. (B), we let r_b correspond to a point inside the sphere $[r_b = r, V_b = V(r)]$, and let r_a correspond to a point on the surface of the sphere $(r_a = r_0, V_a = V_0)$. This gives

$$V(r) - V_0 = \frac{Q}{8\pi\epsilon_0 r_0^3} (r_0^2 - r^2) \qquad (r \leq r_0)$$

Substituting V_0 from Eq. (D) into this expression and solving for $V(r)$, we find

$$V(r) = \frac{Q}{8\pi\epsilon_0 r_0^3} (3r_0^2 - r^2) \qquad (r \leq r_0)$$

Figure 22-17 shows a graph of V versus r for a uniform spherical volume charge. For comparison, it is instructive to reexamine the graph of E versus r for this charge distribution (Fig. 21-20).

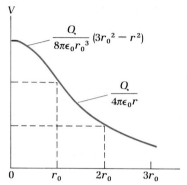

Figure 22-17. Example 22-10: $V(r)$ versus r for the potential due to a spherically symmetric uniform volume charge of radius r_0.

22-5 RELATION BETWEEN E AND V

The potential, with its reference position at a distant point, can be developed from Eq. (22-10) by letting point a correspond to $r = \infty$ $(V_a = V_\infty = 0)$, and by letting point b correspond to the position P at which the potential V is evaluated $(V_b = V)$. This gives

The potential V in terms of the field E

$$V = -\int_\infty^P \mathbf{E} \cdot d\boldsymbol{\ell} \qquad (22\text{-}12)$$

Thus the potential is the negative of the line integral of the electric field from the distant reference position to the point P where the potential is evaluated. If an expression for $\mathbf{E}$ due to a charge distribution is known, then V can be determined, at least in principle, by using Eq. (22-12). As a matter of fact, this was the way we found V for the uniformly charged sphere in Example 22-10.

Now we investigate the reverse operation. We wish to find an expression for $\mathbf{E}$ from a known expression for V. Since V is the negative of the line integral of $\mathbf{E}$, one might expect that $\mathbf{E}$ is related to the negative of some type of derivative of V. As we shall see, this expectation is correct.

Suppose we use Eq. (22-10) to find the potential difference between two nearby points, $a = (x, y, z)$ and $b = (x + \Delta x, y, z)$. Since the two points have the same y and z coordinates, we integrate along a line parallel to the x axis: $d\boldsymbol{\ell} = dx'\,\mathbf{i}$. (We use x' for the variable of integration because x is used in the limits.) Thus

$$\mathbf{E} \cdot d\boldsymbol{\ell} = (E_x\mathbf{i} + E_y\mathbf{j} + E_z\mathbf{k}) \cdot (dx'\,\mathbf{i}) = E_x\,dx'$$

From Eq. (22-10).

$$V(x + \Delta x, y, z) - V(x, y, z) = -\int_x^{x+\Delta x} E_x\,dx'$$

We will presently consider the limit as Δx approaches zero. In anticipation of this, we assume E_x is nearly constant from x to $x + \Delta x$. This means that E_x can be factored out of the integral. With this approximation, the right-hand side of the above expression becomes

$$-E_x \int_x^{x+\Delta x} dx' = -E_x[(x + \Delta x) - (x)] = -E_x\,\Delta x$$

Thus
$$V(x + \Delta x, y, z) - V(x, y, z) \approx -E_x\,\Delta x$$

Dividing by Δx and taking the limit as $\Delta x \to 0$ gives

$$\lim_{\Delta x \to 0}\left[\frac{V(x + \Delta x, y, z) - V(x, y, z)}{\Delta x}\right] = -E_x$$

In the limit as $\Delta x \to 0$, the approximation becomes exact. The quantity on the left-hand side of the above equation is the derivative of V with respect to x, with y and z held constant. That is, only the coordinate x varies during the limiting process; the y and z coordinates are fixed. This quantity is represented by the symbol $\partial V/\partial x$ and is called the *partial derivative of V with respect to x.* * Thus

$$E_x = -\frac{\partial V}{\partial x}$$

Infinitesimal changes of potential in the y and z directions give similar results. Therefore,

The electric field in terms of the potential

$$E_x = -\frac{\partial V}{\partial x} \qquad E_y = -\frac{\partial V}{\partial y} \qquad E_z = -\frac{\partial V}{\partial z} \qquad (22\text{-}13)$$

We find that the components of **E** are given by the negative of the partial derivatives of V. If an expression for V due to a charge distribution is known, then Eqs. (22-13) can be used to find **E**.

Results similar to Eqs. (22-13) can be developed for other types of coordinates besides cartesian. In particular, if a charge distribution has spherical symmetry, then V depends only on the radial coordinate r and **E** has only a radial component E_r. In this case,

$$E_r = -\frac{dV}{dr} \qquad (22\text{-}14)$$

As a brief example, let us use Eq. (22-14) and V due to a point charge to find **E** due to a point charge:

$$E_r = -\frac{d}{dr}\frac{q}{4\pi\epsilon_0 r} = -\frac{q}{4\pi\epsilon_0}\frac{d}{dr}\frac{1}{r} = -\frac{q}{4\pi\epsilon_0}\left(-\frac{1}{r^2}\right) = \frac{q}{4\pi\epsilon_0 r^2}$$

---

* In finding the partial derivative of a function f with respect to one of the coordinates, we treat the other coordinates as constants during the operation. As an example, suppose $f = azx^2/y$, where a is a constant. Then the partial derivative of f with respect to x is

$$\frac{\partial f}{\partial x} = \frac{\partial}{\partial x}\frac{azx^2}{y} = \frac{az}{y}\frac{d}{dx}x^2 = \frac{2azx}{y}$$

Similarly, the partial derivative of f with respect to y is

$$\frac{\partial f}{\partial y} = \frac{\partial}{\partial y}\frac{azx^2}{y} = azx^2\frac{d}{dy}\frac{1}{y} = -\frac{azx^2}{y^2}$$

What is the partial derivative of f with respect to z?

The potential and the electric field are directly related to one another. Either may be determined from the charge distribution, and either may be determined from the other.

Notice that Eqs. (22-13) and (22-14) show that the dimension of electric field is potential divided by distance. Therefore, the SI unit for the electric field may be written as volts per meter (V/m) as well as newtons per coulomb (N/C). Indeed, V/m is probably used more often than N/C.

EXAMPLE 22-11. Use the expression for the potential due to a dipole found in Example 22-4 to determine the electric field due to a dipole at points far from the dipole.

SOLUTION. From Example 22-4, the potential due to a dipole of moment $\mathbf{p} = (2aq)\mathbf{k}$ at points far from the dipole is $V = (p \cos \theta)/4\pi\epsilon_0 r^2$. To use Eqs. (22-13), we express r and $\cos \theta$ in terms of cartesian coordinates. From Fig. 22-8a, $r = (x^2 + y^2 + z^2)^{1/2}$ and $\cos \theta = z/r = z/(x^2 + y^2 + z^2)^{1/2}$ so that

$$V = \frac{p}{4\pi\epsilon_0} \frac{z}{r^3} = \frac{p}{4\pi\epsilon_0} \frac{z}{(x^2 + y^2 + z^2)^{3/2}}$$

Using the first of Eqs. (22-13) gives

$$E_x = -\frac{\partial}{\partial x} \frac{p}{4\pi\epsilon_0} \frac{z}{(x^2 + y^2 + z^2)^{3/2}}$$

$$= -\frac{p}{4\pi\epsilon_0} \frac{(-3/2)(2x)z}{(x^2 + y^2 + z^2)^{5/2}}$$

$$= \frac{p}{4\pi\epsilon_0} \frac{3xz}{(x^2 + y^2 + z^2)^{5/2}}$$

$$= \frac{p}{4\pi\epsilon_0} \frac{3xz}{r^5}$$

Similarly,

$$E_y = \frac{p}{4\pi\epsilon_0} \frac{3yz}{r^5} \quad \text{and} \quad E_z = \frac{p}{4\pi\epsilon_0} \left(\frac{3z^2}{r^5} - \frac{1}{r^3} \right)$$

22-6 EQUIPOTENTIAL SURFACES

An equipotential surface is a surface on which the potential is constant or equal. No work is done by electric forces when a charged particle moves along an equipotential surface. As with field lines for the electric field, equipotential surfaces are useful for visualizing the spatial behavior of the potential.

Figure 22-18 shows equipotential surfaces and field lines outside a uniformly charged sphere. From Example 22-10, $V = Q/4\pi\epsilon_0 r$, so that V is constant if r is constant. Since a surface with constant r is a spherical surface, the equipotential surfaces are spherical, and since r is measured from the charged sphere's center, the equipotential surfaces are concentric with the sphere.

From our discussion in Sec. 22-4, we know that equipotential surfaces in a uniform field are parallel planes that are perpendicular to $\mathbf{E}$. Figure 22-19 shows in cross section a parallel-plate capacitor where $\mathbf{E}$ is uniform, with equipotential surfaces and field lines between the plates.

The field lines in Figs. 22-18 and 22-19 are perpendicular to the equipotential surfaces where they cross. This must be true in all cases because if $\mathbf{E}$ has a component tangent to a surface, then work is done by the electric force when a charged particle moves along the surface. Therefore, $\mathbf{E}$ cannot have a component tangent to an equipotential surface; $\mathbf{E}$ is perpendicular to an equipotential surface at each point on the surface.

In a given drawing in which the potential difference between successive pairs of equipotential surfaces is the same, their spacing indicates the magnitude of $\mathbf{E}$. The surfaces are spaced closer together in a region where E is larger, similar to the way closely spaced contour lines on a map indicate a steep hill. In Fig. 22-18, the spacing increases with increasing r because E decreases with

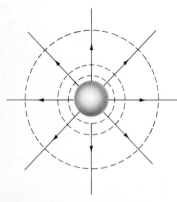

Figure 22-18. Equipotential surfaces outside a uniformly charged sphere. The surfaces are spherical (shown in cross section as dashed circles) and concentric with the charged sphere. Radial field lines are also shown.

Figure 22-19. Equipotential surfaces in the uniform field between capacitor plates are planes (shown in cross section as dashed lines). Field lines are also shown.

increasing r. In Fig. 22-19, the surfaces are equally spaced because E is uniform and V varies linearly along the direction perpendicular to the plates. Since $E_x = -\partial V/\partial x$, the direction of **E** is opposite the direction in which V increases.

22-7 MORE ABOUT ELECTROSTATIC PROPERTIES OF A CONDUCTOR

In Sec. 21-6, we found that $\mathbf{E} = 0$ inside a conductor under static conditions. Also, we showed that because $\mathbf{E} = 0$, no excess charge can exist inside a conductor; a conductor's charge resides on its surface. Further, the field just outside a conductor is perpendicular to the surface and its component is $E_n = \sigma/\epsilon_0$. Using the concept of potential, we now extend our investigation of the electrostatic properties of a conductor.

Since $\mathbf{E} = 0$ inside a conductor, the volume occupied by conducting material must be a region of uniform potential. To prove this, we apply Eq. (22-10) to two points a and b inside a conductor:

$$V_b - V_a = -\int_a^b \mathbf{E} \cdot d\boldsymbol{\ell} \tag{22-10}$$

In electrostatics, all points in a conductor are at the same potential.

In performing the line integral, we choose the path of integration to lie entirely inside the conductor. Then $\mathbf{E} = 0$ at each point along the path, the integral is zero, and $V_b = V_a$. This is true for any two points inside the conductor, so that all points in the conductor are at the same potential. In particular, it is often helpful to remember that the surface of a conductor is an equipotential surface.

Previously we spoke of the potential at a point in space. Since all points in a conductor are at the same potential, we may assign a value of the potential to an entire conductor, as long as electrostatic conditions prevail. It is meaningful to speak of a "150-V metal plate." But an insulator cannot be assigned a particular value of potential because the potential may be different at different points inside and on an insulator.

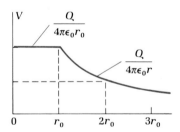

Figure 22-20. $V(r)$ versus r for the potential produced by a charged conducting sphere.

Consider an isolated solid metal sphere of radius r_0 and charge Q. Such a sphere constitutes a spherical shell of uniform surface charge density, and E versus r is shown in Fig. 21-18; E is zero inside the sphere and falls off as $1/r^2$ outside the sphere. Figure 22-20 shows V versus r; V is uniform inside and falls off as $1/r$ outside. At the sphere's surface and within its volume, $V = V(r_0) = Q/4\pi\epsilon_0 r_0$. Suppose $Q = 100$ nC and $r_0 = 0.1$ m, then

$$V = (9 \times 10^9 \text{ N} \cdot \text{m}^2/\text{C}^2)\frac{100 \text{ nC}}{0.10 \text{ m}} = 9000 \text{ V}$$

The potential "of the sphere" is 9 kV.

Not only is the field zero and the potential uniform within a conductor, but this is true as well for a cavity in a conductor (assuming there are no charged objects inside the cavity). In Sec. 21-6 we showed that if there are no charged objects inside a cavity in a conductor, then there is no net charge on the cavity surface. But this does not exclude the possibility that $\sigma > 0$ over part of the cavity surface and $\sigma < 0$ over another part such that the total charge is zero.

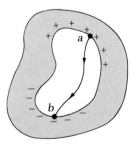

Figure 22-21. Showing that $\mathbf{E} = 0$ inside a cavity in a conductor and that $\sigma = 0$ on the inside surface. The alleged field line drawn between a and b cannot, in fact, exist.

To show that $\sigma = 0$ at each point on the cavity surface, we assume that $\sigma \neq 0$ and see where it leads us. In Fig. 22-21 we show an alleged field line that originates at a positive charge on the cavity surface and terminates at a negative charge on the cavity surface. Suppose we let point a be at the positive charge and point b be at the negative charge and apply Eq. (22-10). If the path for the line integral is taken along the field line, then the line integral cannot be zero because $E > 0$ and $\mathbf{E}$ is parallel to $d\boldsymbol{\ell}$ at each point on the path. This predicts that $V_b \neq V_a$. However, we know that $V_b = V_a$ because both points are on the conductor's surface. The prediction that $V_b \neq V_a$, which is based on the supposition that $\mathbf{E} \neq 0$ inside the cavity and that $\sigma \neq 0$ on the cavity surface, is false. Therefore, we conclude that $\mathbf{E} = 0$ inside the cavity and that $\sigma = 0$ at each point on the cavity surface. A field-free region of space can be maintained by surrounding the region with a conductor. Such a procedure is called *electrostatic screening*.

Electrostatic screening

Suppose we wish to give a spherical conductor a very large charge and potential. What determines the maximum charge and potential the conductor can acquire? To answer this question, we must consider the insulating medium, such as air, that surrounds the conductor. The relevant property of the surrounding medium is its *dielectric strength*. The dielectric strength of an insulating material is the maximum magnitude E_{max} of the electric field that can exist in the material without electrical breakdown. When an insulator breaks down, its constituent molecules ionize and the material begins to conduct. In a gas such as air, visible light is emitted (the gas glows) as the electrons recombine with the ionized molecules, a phenomenon called a *corona discharge*. A corona discharge can sometimes be observed at night around high-voltage transmission lines.

Dielectric strength E_{max} of an insulator

Corona discharge

By symmetry, the charge on an isolated spherical conductor is distributed uniformly on its surface, but what if the conductor is not spherical? Usually $|\sigma|$ on a nonspherical conductor (and E just outside the conductor) tends to be larger where the surface has a small radius of curvature. In particular, $|\sigma|$ can be very large at the pointed end of a spike-shaped metal rod, such as a lightning

Corona discharge around a spike-shaped conductor. (*From Peter E. Viemeister*, The Lightning Book, *The M.I.T. Press, Cambridge, Mass., 1972*)

rod. Often when a highly charged thundercloud is overhead, corona discharge can be observed at the end of a lightning rod. Indeed, this corona discharge serves to extend the effective length of a lightning rod and contributes to the protection the rod affords.

EXAMPLE 22-12. *Van de Graaff generator.* In the physics classroom, a Van de Graaff generator (Fig. 22-22) is used to demonstrate electrical effects. A belt continuously delivers charge to the inside of a metal dome where it is conducted to the outer surface. The ultimate charge and potential of the nearly spherical dome depend on its radius, and on the properties of the surrounding insulators (air, the belt, and the supporting tube). Large Van de Graaff generators are used in research laboratories to accelerate subatomic particles to high kinetic energies in order to study the effects of their collisions. Assume that the maximum magnitudes for the charge (Q_{max}) and potential (V_{max}) of the dome of a Van de Graaff generator are determined by the dielectric strength of the surrounding air ($E_{max} = 3 \times 10^6$ V/m). The radius of the dome is $r_0 = 0.13$ m. Find Q_{max} and V_{max}.

SOLUTION. Treating the dome as an isolated charged spherical conductor, we evaluate the expressions for E and V at the surface of the sphere of radius r_0, and find

$$E = \frac{|Q|}{4\pi\epsilon_0 r_0^2} = \frac{|V|}{r_0}$$

Therefore, the maximum charge Q_{max} and the maximum potential V_{max} for a conducting sphere surrounded by an insulator with dielectric strength E_{max} are

$$Q_{max} = E_{max}\, 4\pi\epsilon_0 r_0^2 \quad \text{and} \quad V_{max} = E_{max} r_0$$

In air a sphere of radius 0.13 m has

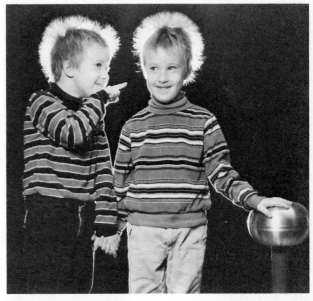

Figure 22-22. Example 22-12: These boys are getting a hair-raising experience from a small Van de Graaff generator. *(Lester V. Bergman and Associates)*

$$Q_{max} = \frac{(3 \times 10^6 \text{ V/m})(0.13 \text{ m})^2}{9 \times 10^9 \text{ N} \cdot \text{m}^2/\text{C}^2} = 6 \ \mu C$$

and

$$V_{max} = (3 \times 10^6 \text{ V/m})(0.13 \text{ m}) = 400 \text{ kV}$$

Notice that a dome with twice this radius could contain four times as much charge and could be at twice the potential.

SUMMARY WITH APPLICATIONS

Section 22-2. Electric potential energy
The electric force is a conservative force. The potential energy of a test particle in the field of a number of fixed particles is

$$U = \frac{q_0}{4\pi\epsilon_0} \sum \frac{q_i}{r_i} \qquad (22\text{-}5)$$

The reference position for U is where the test particle is far removed from the fixed particles ($U_\infty = 0$).

Show that the electric force is a conservative force; define the electric potential energy of a test particle.

Section 22-3. Electric potential
The electric potential is defined as

$$V = \frac{U}{q_0} \qquad \text{(small } q_0) \qquad (22\text{-}6)$$

For a system of charged particles

$$V = \frac{1}{4\pi\epsilon_0} \sum \frac{q_i}{r_i} \qquad (22\text{-}7)$$

For a continuous distribution of charge

$$V = \frac{1}{4\pi\epsilon_0} \int \frac{dq}{r} \qquad (22\text{-}8)$$

Define the electric potential; determine V produced by several charge distributions.

Section 22-4. Potential difference
The definition of the potential difference between points a and b is

$$V_b - V_a = \frac{U_b - U_a}{q_0} \qquad \text{(small } q_0\text{)} \qquad (22\text{-}9)$$

The potential difference in terms of the field $\mathbf{E}$ is

$$V_b - V_a = -\int_a^b \mathbf{E} \cdot d\boldsymbol{\ell} \qquad (22\text{-}10)$$

Define potential difference; determine $V_b - V_a$ due to several charge distributions.

Section 22-5. Relation between E and V
If an expression for $\mathbf{E}$ is known, then V at point P can be found from the line integral of $\mathbf{E}$:

$$V = -\int_\infty^P \mathbf{E} \cdot d\boldsymbol{\ell} \qquad (22\text{-}12)$$

If an expression for V is known, then $\mathbf{E}$ can be found from the partial derivatives of V. In particular, when V is written

in terms of cartesian coordinates,

$$E_x = -\frac{\partial V}{\partial x} \qquad E_y = -\frac{\partial V}{\partial y} \qquad E_z = -\frac{\partial V}{\partial z} \qquad (22\text{-}13)$$

Show that V is given by the line integral of $\mathbf{E}$; show that the components of $\mathbf{E}$ are given by the partial derivatives of V.

Section 22-6. Equipotential surfaces
An equipotential surface is a surface on which the electric potential is constant. As with field lines for the electric field, drawings of equipotential surfaces help one visualize the spatial dependence of V. Field lines are perpendicular to equipotential surfaces at points where they cross.

Use equipotential surfaces to visualize the spatial behavior of V.

Section 22-7. More about electrostatic properties of a conductor
Under static conditions the electric potential is uniform inside a conductor, and consequently the surface of a conductor is an equipotential surface.

Use the concept of potential to investigate some of the electrostatic properties of a conductor.

QUESTIONS

22-1 What property (or properties) causes the electric force to be conservative? That it is an inverse-square force? That it is directed along the line between the particles? That it is proportional to the charge magnitude of each particle?

22-2 If a positively charged particle is moved in the direction of an electric field, does its electric potential energy increase, decrease, or remain the same? How about a negatively charged particle?

22-3 Consider a point at which $\mathbf{E} = E\mathbf{i}$. From that point give a direction (in terms of a unit vector) in which the potential (a) increases, (b) decreases, and (c) remains the same.

22-4 A charged particle is moved in the direction of an electric field and its potential energy increases. What is the sign of the charge of the particle?

22-5 Why is electric potential sometimes called voltage?

22-6 Consider the proper terminology to use when discussing electric potential energy on the one hand and the electric potential on the other. (a) Is it proper to speak of the potential energy of an electron or the potential of an electron? (b) Is it proper to speak of the potential energy of a point in space or the potential of a point in space? (c) Is it proper to speak of the potential energy produced by an electron or the potential produced by an electron?

22-7 Suppose someone tells you that no life can exist on

Mars because the surface of the planet is at a voltage of 20,000 V. Could this person be correct? Explain.

22-8 If the potential difference between two points is zero, is there necessarily a path between those two points on which the field is zero at each point? Give an example that supports your answer.

22-9 If there exists a path on which the field is zero at each point, is the potential difference between two points on this path necessarily zero? Give an example that supports your answer.

22-10 If you know the numerical value of the electric field at a single point in space, can you use that information to find the potential at that point? If so, how?

22-11 If you know an expression for the electric field in terms of coordinates in a region of space, can you use that information to find the potential difference between two points within the region? If so, how?

22-12 If you know the numerical value of the potential at a single point in space, can you use that information to find the electric field at that point? If so, how?

22-13 Suppose you know the numerical value of the potential difference between two nearby points in space. Can you use this to estimate a component of the electric field between the points? Explain. What assumptions must you make?

22-14 If you know an expression for the potential throughout a region of space, can you use that information to find the electric field in that region? If so, how?

22-15 Suppose we interchange the positions of particles 1 and 3 in Fig. 22-6 (Example 22-2). Would the potential V at P be changed? Would the field $\mathbf{E}$ at P be changed?

22-16 Suppose the charge distribution on the ring in Fig. 22-9 is not uniform. Would this change the expression found for the potential at points along the axis in Example 22-5? Would this change the expression found for the electric field at points along the axis (Example 20-7)? Do your answers conform to the relation between $\mathbf{E}$ and V [Eqs. (22-13)]? Explain the apparent discrepancy here.

22-17 Explain why the potential energy of a dipole in a uniform field depends on its orientation with respect to the field, but not on its position. Why is the potential energy a minimum when the dipole is aligned parallel to the field direction and a maximum when aligned opposite the field direction? If a dipole were in a nonuniform field, would you expect its potential energy to depend on its position?

22-18 Figure 22-23 shows graphs of a number of functions versus distance r from the center of a spherically symmetric charge distribution of radius r_0. Which graph best represents (a) E due to a uniform volume charge, (b) V due to a uniform volume charge, (c) E due to a uniform shell of charge, (d) V due to a uniform shell of charge?

22-19 Can equipotential surfaces intersect one another? Explain.

22-20 In electrostatics, why is it meaningful to speak of the potential of a conducting object but not of the potential of an insulating object?

22-21 Suppose the potential difference between the plates in Fig. 22-19 is 100 V. What is the potential difference between the successive pairs of equipotential surfaces shown in the figure?

22-22 Is it possible for a conductor that possesses a net positive charge to be at a negative potential? If so, describe such a situation. If not, why not?

22-23 Your employer instructs you to store a delicate instrument such that it will not be exposed to electric fields. Explain how you can do this.

22-24 Integrated circuit devices are often wrapped in a conducting material when stored or shipped. Why?

22-25 Complete the following table:

Symbol	Represents	Type	SI unit
U			J
V		Scalar	
ΔV	Potential difference		
$d\boldsymbol{\ell}$			
$\partial/\partial x$		N/A	N/A

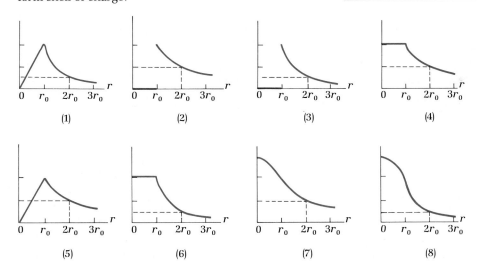

Figure 22-23. Ques. 22-18.

(1) (2) (3) (4)

(5) (6) (7) (8)

EXERCISES

Section 22-2. Electric potential energy

22-1 A test particle with charge $q_0 = 4.0$ nC is moved from position a, where it is 35 mm from a fixed particle with charge $q = 85$ nC, to position b, where it is 76 mm from the fixed particle. (a) What is the potential energy (relative to $U_\infty = 0$) of the test particle at position a and at position b? (b) What is the change in the potential energy of the test particle as a result of the displacement? (c) What is the work done by the electric force on the test particle during the displacement?

22-2 In Fig. 22-24 a test particle with charge $q_0 = 4.0$ nC is shown taken around a closed path in the field of a fixed particle with charge $q = 85$ nC. Path ai is radially aligned with the fixed particle, path ib is a circular arc centered at the fixed particle, and path ba is a circular arc centered at i ($r_a = 45$ mm and $r_i = r_b = 83$ mm). (a) For each of these paths, what is the work done on the test particle by the electric force? (b) For the entire round-trip path $aiba$, what is the work done by the electric force?

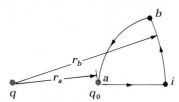

Figure 22-24. Exercise 22-2.

22-3 Suppose a test particle with charge $q_0 = -6.0$ nC and mass $m_0 = 0.22$ kg is released from rest at a distance of 78 mm from a fixed particle with charge $q = 55$ nC. If the electric force is the only force on the test particle, then what is its (a) kinetic energy and (b) speed when it is a distance of 32 mm from the fixed particle?

22-4 Use Eq. (22-4) to make a graph of the potential energy (relative to $U_\infty = 0$) of an electron ($q_0 = -e = -1.6 \times 10^{-19}$ C) versus distance r from an oxygen nucleus [$q = 8e = 8(1.6 \times 10^{-19}$ C$) = 13 \times 10^{-10}$ C]. Make a table of values of $U(r)$ and r for $r = 0.5 \times 10^{-10}$ m to $r = 3.0 \times 10^{-10}$ m at intervals of 0.5×10^{-10} m. Plot the tabulated values and sketch the curve.

22-5 (a) Find the potential energy U (relative to $U_\infty = 0$) of particle 1 in Fig. 22-25 (a) when $q_1 = 2.0$ nC and (b) when $q_1 = 4.0$ nC. The values of the other charges are $q_2 = 25$ nC, $q_3 = 38$ nC, and $q_4 = 32$ nC.

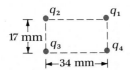

Figure 22-25. Exercise 22-5.

22-6 In a classic experiment that helped establish the structure of atoms, high-energy α particles (helium nuclei) were directed at a thin sheet of gold. (a) What is the closest distance that an α particle (charge $2e$) can come to a gold nucleus (charge $79e$) if the α particle's kinetic energy is 4 MeV at a great distance from the gold nucleus and its direction of travel is straight toward the gold nucleus? Assume that the position of the gold nucleus remains fixed. (b) What must the α particle's initial kinetic energy be in order for it to make contact with the edge of the gold nucleus? Assume that contact is made when the centers of the α

particle and the gold nucleus are about 10×10^{-15} m from each other.

Section 22-3. Electric potential

22-7 (a) Use Eq. (22-6) and the result of Exercise 22-5, part (a), to find the potential due to particles 2, 3, and 4 at the position of particle 1 in Fig. 22-25. (b) Use Eq. (22-6) and the result of Exercise 22-5, part (b), to find the potential due to particles 2, 3, and 4 at the position of particle 1 in Fig. 22-25. (c) Use Eq. (22-7) to find the potential due to particles 2, 3, and 4 at the position of particle 1 in Fig. 22-25.

22-8 What is the potential (relative to $V_\infty = 0$) at the point $(0.4$ m, 0.2 m, -0.5 m) due to a particle with charge $q = 75$ nC and located at the origin?

22-9 A particle with a charge of 27 nC is at a position where the potential (relative to $V_\infty = 0$) is 450 V. What is the particle's potential energy (relative to $U_\infty = 0$)?

22-10 The structure of some types of salt crystals has an ion surrounded by six ions of opposite sign as nearest neighbors. Consider six ions, each with charge e, each a distance of 1.5×10^{-10} m along the cartesian axes as shown in Fig. 22-26. Treat the ions as charged particles. (a) Find the potential at the origin due to these six ions. (b) Find the potential energy (in eV) of an ion with charge $-e$ at the origin.

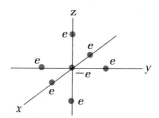

Figure 22-26. Exercise 22-10.

22-11 Consider the potential V due to a dipole with moment $\mathbf{p} = (2aq)\mathbf{k}$ located at the origin, with $q = e$ and $a = 0.4 \times 10^{-10}$ m. Evaluate V along the z axis from $z = -1.2 \times 10^{-10}$ to 1.2×10^{-10} m at intervals of 0.2×10^{-10} m. (The result of Example 22-4 cannot be used here. Why?) Plot your results on graph paper and sketch in $V(z)$. How would a graph of V versus x along the x axis look?

22-12 Consider a particle with charge Q located at $(0, 0, a)$. Find an expression for the potential due to this particle at points along the x axis and compare your answer with the result of Example 22-5.

22-13 Graph the results of Example 22-6. Plot $V/(\sigma/2\epsilon_0)$ versus x/R_0 for $x/R_0 = -2.5$ to 2.5 in intervals of 0.5. Sketch in $V(x)$.

22-14 From Prob. 22-7, the electric potential in the perpendicular bisector plane (xy plane in Fig. 22-27) of a uniform line charge ($\lambda = Q/2\ell$) is

$$V = \frac{\lambda}{2\pi\epsilon_0} \ln \frac{\ell + \sqrt{\ell^2 + R^2}}{R}$$

where $R = \sqrt{x^2 + y^2}$. Make a graph of V (in units of $\lambda/2\pi\epsilon_0$) versus R (in units of ℓ). Plot points for $R = \frac{1}{2}\ell, \ell, \ldots, 5\ell$, and sketch the curve.

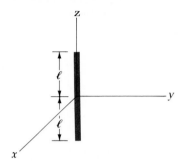

Figure 22-27. Exercise 22-14.

Section 22-4. Potential difference

22-15 Consider a uniform electric field: $\mathbf{E} = -(220 \text{ V/m})\mathbf{i}$. (a) What is the potential difference between the origin and (1.5 m, 0, 0)? (b) What is the potential difference between the origin and (1.5 m, 1.0 m, 0)? (c) What is the potential difference between (1.5 m, 0, 0) and the origin? (d) What is the potential difference between the origin and (3.0 m, 0, 0)? (e) What is the potential difference between (1.5 m, 0, 0) and (3.0 m, 0, 0)?

22-16 The potential difference between point a (1.2 m, -2.6 m, 1.8 m) and point b (2.3 m, 1.4 m, -0.8 m) in a uniform field, $\mathbf{E} = E_x\mathbf{i}$, is 730 V. What is E_x?

22-17 The magnitude of the charge possessed by each plate of a parallel-plate capacitor is 260 nC, the separation of the plates is 0.32 mm, and the lateral area of each plate is 2.2×10^{-2} m². Assuming the plates are close enough together to approximate the field as uniform, (a) find the magnitude E of the field between the plates and (b) find the potential difference ΔV between the plates.

22-18 The plates of a parallel-plate capacitor have a separation of 0.25 mm, and each plate has a lateral area of 4.6×10^{-2} m². The potential difference between the plates is $\Delta V = 540$ V. Assuming that the field between the plates is uniform, find (a) E; (b) $|\sigma|$; (c) $|Q|$.

22-19 Make a graph of the result of Example 22-9. Evaluate the potential energy U of a dipole in a uniform field when the angle between the dipole moment and the field is 0, 30°, . . . 180°. Make a table of your results and plot U in terms of pE versus θ in degrees. Sketch the curve.

22-20 (a) What is the kinetic energy in eV at which an electron emerges from an electron gun with a potential difference between cathode and anode of 970 V? (b) What is the speed of an electron as it emerges from the electron gun?

22-21 A spherically symmetric uniform volume charge distribution with total charge 78 nC and radius 53 mm is centered at the origin. (a) What is the potential (relative to $V_\infty = 0$) at (-12 mm, 17 mm, 22 mm)? (b) What is the potential at (28 mm, -45 mm, -42 mm)?

22-22 Consider a spherically symmetric uniform volume distribution of charge with $Q = 45$ nC and $r_0 = 74$ mm. Determine the potential (relative to $V_\infty = 0$) at the following distances from the center: (a) $r = 0$; (b) $r = 37$ mm; (c) $r = 74$ mm; (d) $r = 148$ mm.

22-23 Make a rough estimate of the potential at points on the surface of the earth (relative to $V_\infty = 0$). Assume that the magnitude of the electric field is 150 V/m at the surface of the earth, that it decreases linearly with height above the surface to zero at a height of 50 km, and that it is zero beyond 50 km. The field is directed toward the center of the earth. (The magnitude of your answer will be about a factor of 10 too large because of the crudeness of our assumptions.)

22-24 Recall that the magnitude of the field far from the ends of a long, uniformly distributed line charge of linear charge density λ is approximately $E \approx \lambda/2\pi\epsilon_0 R$, where R is the perpendicular distance from the line charge. The field is directed away from the line charge (assuming λ is positive). Show that the approximate potential difference between two points a and b far from the ends of the line charge is

$$V_b - V_a \approx \frac{\lambda}{2\pi\epsilon_0} \ln \frac{R_a}{R_b}$$

where R_a and R_b are both much smaller than the length of the line charge.

Section 22-5. Relation between E and V

22-25 From Fig. 22-20, the potential (relative to $V_\infty = 0$) at all points inside a conducting sphere of radius r_0 and charge Q is $V = Q/4\pi\epsilon_0 r_0$. Use this result to find the electric field at points inside the sphere.

22-26 The potential difference between the origin and points with coordinates (x, y, z) is given by $V(x, y, z) - V_0 = (740 \text{ V/m})x + (-230 \text{ V/m})y + (-690 \text{ V/m})z$. What is $\mathbf{E}$?

22-27 In Example 22-10 we showed that the potential (relative to $V_\infty = 0$) inside a uniform spherical distribution of charge is $V(r) = Q(3r_0^2 - r^2)/8\pi\epsilon_0 r_0^3$. Use this result to find the electric field inside the charge distribution.

22-28 In Example 22-5 we showed that the potential (relative to $V_\infty = 0$) along the axis of a charged ring is $V(x) = Q/4\pi\epsilon_0 \sqrt{x^2 + a^2}$. Determine E_x along the axis.

22-29 In Example 22-6 we showed that the potential along the axis of a uniformly charged circular disk is $V(x) = \sigma(\sqrt{x^2 + R^2} - \sqrt{x^2})/2\epsilon_0$. Determine E_x along the axis.

22-30 The potential as a function of x is plotted in Fig. 22-28. Estimate E_x at (a) $x = -2$ m; (b) $x = 1$ m; (c) $x = 4$ m.

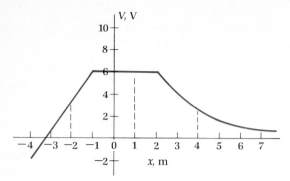

Figure 22-28. Exercise 22-30.

22-31 Complete the calculation in Example 22-11 to show that $E_z = p(3z^2 - r^2)/4\pi\epsilon_0 r^5$ at a point far from a dipole of moment $\mathbf{p} = (2aq)\mathbf{k}$.

22-32 In cartesian coordinates the potential due to a point charge at the origin is $V = q/4\pi\epsilon_0 \sqrt{x^2 + y^2 + z^2}$. Use Eqs. (22-13) to show that this gives $\mathbf{E} = (q/4\pi\epsilon_0 r^2)\hat{\mathbf{r}}$, where the unit vector $\hat{\mathbf{r}}$ in cartesian coordinates is $\hat{\mathbf{r}} = \mathbf{r}/r = (x\mathbf{i} + y\mathbf{j} + z\mathbf{k})/\sqrt{x^2 + y^2 + z^2}$.

Section 22-6. Equipotential surfaces

22-33 The plates of a parallel-plate capacitor are separated by 0.64 mm, have a lateral area of 0.33 m², and carry equal and opposite charges of magnitude 390 nC. If we wish to show six equipotential surfaces between the plates, including the ones at the plate surfaces, what is the potential difference between successive pairs of equipotential surfaces?

22-34 A spherically symmetric charge distribution has a radius of 41 mm and a potential (relative to $V_\infty = 0$) at its surface of 600 V. (a) What is the radius of the 300-V equipotential surface? (b) What is the radius of the 150-V equipotential surface?

22-35 Sketch field lines and equipotential surfaces for a di-

pole. Show five equipotential surfaces: one that is midway between the charges, one surrounding each of the charges, and two others that extend beyond your graph.

22-36 Consider a thin, uniformly charged disk centered at the origin and contained in the yz plane such that its axis is the x axis (Fig. 22-11). Sketch field lines in the xy plane and the intersection of equipotential surfaces with the xy plane. Show four or five equipotential surfaces.

22-37 Consider a long, uniformly charged rod centered at the origin and oriented along the z axis (Fig. 22-27). Sketch field lines in the xy plane and the intersection of equipotential surfaces with the xy plane. Assume that the rod is long enough such that it may be treated as infinitely long. Show four equipotential surfaces and make their radii correspond to the same potential difference between each successive pair of surfaces (see Exercise 22-24).

22-38 Suppose the drawing in Fig. 22-18 corresponds to a charged sphere with $Q = 88.9\ \mu C$ and $r_0 = 0.10$ m. (a) Determine the potential V_0 at the sphere's surface. (b) By making measurements directly from the figure, determine the actual radius of each of the equipotential surfaces shown. (c) Determine the potential of each of the surfaces. What is the potential difference between successive pairs of surfaces?

Section 22-7. More about electrostatic properties of a conductor

22-39 (a) What is the charge on an isolated conducting sphere of radius 76 mm when its potential (relative to $V_\infty = 0$) is 530 V? (b) What is the surface charge density of the sphere? (c) What is the electric field just outside the surface?

22-40 What are the maximum charge and maximum potential in dry air on a metal sphere of radius 45 mm?

PROBLEMS

22-1 Show that the field $\mathbf{E}' = Ay\mathbf{i} + Bx\mathbf{j}$ is *not* conservative if $A \neq B$. (*Hint:* Consider the line integral of $\mathbf{E}'$ from a to b along the two paths shown in Fig. 22-29.)

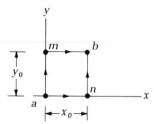

Figure 22-29. Prob. 22-1.

22-2 Consider a dipole in a uniform electric field (Fig.

22-15). (a) Show that the net electric force on the dipole is zero. (b) Show that the torque on the dipole (about an axis perpendicular to the dipole moment and through the center of the dipole) which tends to align it with $\mathbf{E}$ is

$$\tau = \mathbf{p} \times \mathbf{E}$$

(c) Use the result of Example 22-10 to show that the magnitude of the torque may be written

$$\tau = \frac{dU}{d\theta}$$

22-3 The Bohr model of the hydrogen atom has the electron orbiting the proton similar to the way a planet orbits the sun. Assume the electron has a circular orbit and that the much more massive proton remains fixed. (a) Use Newton's second law applied to uniform circular motion ($\Sigma F = mv^2/r$) and Coulomb's law to show that the relation between the kinetic energy K and the potential energy U is $2K = -U$. (Note that $U < 0$.) (b) Show that the mechanical energy ($K + U$) for this bound circular orbit in terms of the electron-proton separation distance r is $-e^2/8\pi\epsilon_0 r$. (c) The ionization energy is the amount of energy required to separate the electron a great distance from the proton. That is, it is the difference in mechanical energy between the bound state of this system [from part (b) above] and the state where the potential energy and the kinetic energy are both zero. Given that the ionization energy of the hydrogen atom is 13.6 eV, determine the radius of the electron's orbit. (d) Find the speed of the electron in its orbit.

22-4　Some of the heaviest nuclei are radioactive and decay by emitting an α particle. These α particles usually have a kinetic energy of about 5 MeV (depending on the type of nucleus) after they are far from the nucleus. Use this information to estimate the size of a nucleus by assuming that the α particle leaves the edge of the nucleus with zero kinetic energy and that the electrostatic potential energy is the only potential energy it has at that position. Because of the error introduced by these assumptions, your answer will be about a factor of 10 too large.

22-5　When a uranium nucleus fissions (splits into two smaller nuclei and other fragments), the combined charge of the two smaller nuclei is the same as the charge of the original uranium nucleus ($92e$) and they have a combined kinetic energy of about 200 MeV when separated a great distance. Assuming these two nuclei have about the same radius r_0 and charge $46e$, make an estimate of r_0.

22-6　In Example 22-6 we found that the potential (relative to $V_\infty = 0$) at points along the axis of a uniformly charged circular disk of radius R_0 is

$$V = \frac{\sigma}{2\epsilon_0}\left(\sqrt{x^2 + R_0{}^2} - \sqrt{x^2}\right)$$

(a) Show that at points on the axis near the center of the disk ($|x| \ll R_0$) the potential is approximately

$$V \approx \frac{\sigma R_0}{2\epsilon_0}\left(1 - \frac{|x|}{R_0}\right)$$

(b) Use the answer to part (a) to find E_x at points on the axis ($|x| \ll R_0$). (Hint: When $x > 0$, $|x| = x$, and when $x < 0$, $|x| = -x$.)

22-7　Consider a uniformly charged rod of length 2ℓ and linear charge density λ (which is $Q/2\ell$) centered at the origin and oriented along the z axis (Fig. 22-27). Show that the potential at points in the perpendicular

bisector plane (the xy plane) is

$$V = \frac{\lambda}{2\pi\epsilon_0} \ln \frac{\ell + \sqrt{\ell^2 + R^2}}{R}$$

where $R = \sqrt{x^2 + y^2}$.

22-8　Use the answer to the previous problem to find E in the perpendicular bisector plane of a uniform line charge. (Hint: When V has cylindrical symmetry about the z axis, $E_R = -\partial V/\partial R$.)

22-9　Figure 22-27 shows a uniform line charge ($\lambda = Q/2\ell$) of length 2ℓ extending along the z axis and centered at the origin. Show that the potential at points along the z axis ($|z| > \ell$) is

$$V(z) = \frac{\lambda}{4\pi\epsilon_0} \ln \frac{|z| + \ell}{|z| - \ell}$$

22-10　Figure 22-30 shows a line charge that extends along the z axis from the origin to $(0, 0, \ell)$. The linear charge density increases with z: $\lambda = cz$, where c is a constant. (a) Find an expression for V along the x axis. (b) Modify your answer to part (a) so that it is valid for all points in the xy plane.

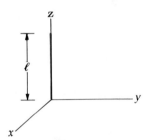

Figure 22-30. Prob. 22-10.

22-11　Show that at point $P(r \gg a)$ the potential due to the linear quadrupole shown in Fig. 22-31 is

$$V \approx \frac{2qa^2 \cos^2 \theta}{4\pi\epsilon_0 r^3}$$

22-12　(a) Express the answer to the previous problem in cartesian coordinates. (b) Use the result of part (a) and Eqs. (22-13) to find E_x, E_y, and E_z due to the linear quadrupole.

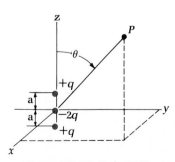

Figure 22-31. Prob. 22-11.

22-13 A thin-walled conducting spherical shell of outer radius r_{bo} and inner radius r_{bi} is concentric with a solid conducting sphere of radius r_a, as shown in Fig. 22-32. Sphere b has a net charge Q_b, sphere a has a net charge Q_a, and both charges are of the same sign. (a) What is the potential of sphere b? (b) What is the potential difference between sphere b and sphere a? (c) What is the potential of sphere a?

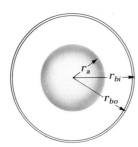

Figure 22-32. Prob. 22-13.

22-14 Reconsider the previous problem for the case where Q_a is positive, Q_b is negative, and $|Q_a| = |Q_b|$.

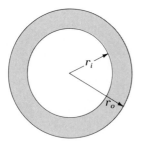

Figure 22-33. Prob. 22-15.

22-15 Consider a uniform spherical distribution of net charge Q between an inner radius r_i and outer radius r_o, as shown in cross section in Fig. 22-33. Find the potential in all three regions of space: $r > r_o$, $r_o > r > r_i$, and $r < r_i$.

22-16 Use the answer to Prob. 22-9 to determine E_z on the z axis in Fig. 22-27 for (a) $z > \ell$ and (b) $z < -\ell$. (Hint: When $z > 0$, $|z| = z$, and when $z < 0$, $|z| = -z$.)

22-17 In Prob. 21-12, we discussed a simple atomic model where the nucleus is treated as a point charge $+Ze$ and the electrons are treated as a uniform spherical distribution of charge $-Ze$ concentric with the nucleus and having radius r_a. (a) Show that the potential produced by this charge distribution is

$$V = \frac{Ze}{4\pi\epsilon_0}\left(\frac{1}{r} - \frac{3}{2r_a} + \frac{r^2}{2r_a^3}\right) \qquad (r < r_a)$$

$$V = 0 \qquad (r > r_a)$$

(b) Use the above answer to find E.

22-18 ⬛ Determine the behavior of the electric potential on the axis of a square sheet of charge with uniform charge density. Let the square distribution of charge be represented by 10 parallel line charges, each of length 2ℓ (see Prob. 22-7), with proper spacing to approximate a square with uniform charge density. Write a program that determines the potential at about 10 equally spaced points from about 0.2ℓ to 2.0ℓ, where 2ℓ is the length of the sides of the square. Graph your results and compare them with those for a circular disk with the same charge and with radius ℓ. Use numerical values that are both convenient and realistic. You may wish to rework the problem using 20 line charges rather than 10 in order to estimate the accuracy of your answer.

CHAPTER 23
CAPACITANCE, ELECTRIC ENERGY, AND PROPERTIES OF INSULATORS

23-1 INTRODUCTION

A *capacitor* is one of several kinds of devices used in the electric circuits of radios, computers, and other such equipment. Capacitors provide temporary storage of energy in circuits; they can be made to store and release electric energy in concert with the functions of the circuit. The property of a capacitor that characterizes its ability to store energy is its *capacitance*.

Capacitors come in a variety of sizes and shapes. *(Dave Riban)*

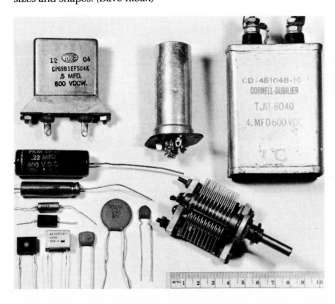

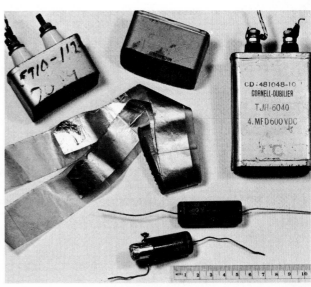

When energy is stored in a capacitor, an electric field exists within the capacitor. This stored energy can be associated with the electric field. Indeed, energy can be associated with the existence of any electric field. The study of capacitors and capacitance leads us to an important aspect of electric fields, *the energy of an electric field.*

The study of capacitors and capacitance also provides the background for learning about some of the properties of insulators. Because of their behavior in electric fields, insulators are often referred to as *dielectrics.*

23-2 CAPACITORS AND CAPACITANCE

Definition of a capacitor

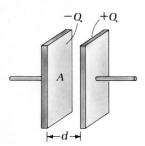

Figure 23-1. A parallel-plate capacitor.

A *capacitor* is a device that consists of two nearby conductors that are insulated from one another. Regardless of their shape, these conductors are referred to as "plates." Figure 23-1 shows a parallel-plate capacitor, which we discussed earlier (Examples 21-8 and 22-7 and Sec. 22-6). The figure also shows conducting wires that are used to connect the plates to other circuit elements. During normal operation the two plates possess charge of equal magnitude but opposite sign. The charge is distributed as a surface charge mostly over the two facing surfaces.

A capacitor can be charged by connecting the wires from the plates to the terminals of a battery, as shown schematically in Fig. 23-2. We shall discuss the behavior of a battery in more detail later (Sec. 25-2). For now we simply note that when a battery is connected to a capacitor, it moves charge carriers from one plate to the other. If the battery remains connected until equilibrium is established (that is, the charge carriers cease to flow), then the potential difference V between the negative plate and the positive plate is the same as that between the terminals of the battery. (We used the symbol ΔV for potential difference in the last chapter. Here we deal only with potential difference, so for brevity we drop the Δ.) The potential difference between the plates is often referred to as the *potential difference* across the capacitor or as the *voltage* across the capacitor.

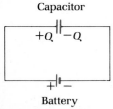

Figure 23-2. A schematic diagram of a capacitor connected to a battery. The longer line at the battery represents its positive terminal and the shorter line its negative terminal. The straight lines represent wires which connect the capacitor to the battery.

At equilibrium, the battery has transferred a positive charge Q to the plate connected to its positive terminal, and the other plate is left with a negative charge $-Q$. Thus the plates possess equal but opposite charge and the net charge on the capacitor is zero. When we speak of the charge Q on a capacitor, we are referring to the magnitude of the charge on each plate and not to the net charge on the entire device.

Consider the relationship between the charge Q on a capacitor and the potential difference V across it. Suppose we charge a capacitor with a 1.5-V battery and find that $Q = 4.5$ nC. If we charge the same capacitor with a 3.0-V battery, then we find that $Q = 9.0$ nC. That is, the ratio Q/V is the same in both cases: $Q/V = 4.5$ nC/1.5 V $= 9.0$ nC/3.0 V $= 3.0$ nC/V. Further investigation shows that the ratio Q/V is characteristic of a given capacitor; when we increase V by some factor, Q increases by the same factor. We call this ratio the *capacitance C* of the capacitor:

Definition of capacitance

$$C = \frac{Q}{V} \tag{23-1}$$

By convention, all quantities in Eq. (23-1) are positive; Q is defined as the magnitude of the charge on each plate, and V is the magnitude of the potential

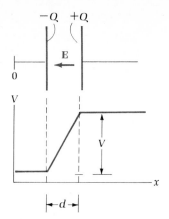

Figure 23-3. Potential difference between the plates of a capacitor.

difference between the plates. Consequently, the capacitance C is always positive.

The term "capacitance" for the quantity C implies that it is a measure of the amount of something that the capacitor can hold or contain. What is it that a capacitor holds? A capacitor holds electric charges, equal but opposite charges on each plate. The capacitance of a capacitor is a measure of its ability to hold these charges. From Eq. (23-1) we see that a larger value of capacitance corresponds to a larger amount of charge for a given potential difference. In Sec. 23-4 we will find that a charged capacitor also holds energy.

From Eq. (23-1), the dimension of capacitance is charge divided by potential and the SI unit of capacitance is coulombs divided by volts (C/V). This SI unit is called a farad (F) in honor of Michael Faraday: 1 F = 1 C/V. One farad is a rather large unit of capacitance; the capacitance of capacitors typically found in electric circuits is in the range from 10^{-12} F, or 1 pF (picofarad), to 10^{-6} F, or 1 μF (microfarad).

We now determine an expression for the capacitance of a parallel-plate capacitor. To find the capacitance, we first calculate the potential difference V across the capacitor for a given charge Q and then divide Q by the expression for V. As we have seen (Examples 21-8 and 22-7), if the lateral dimensions of the plates of a parallel-plate capacitor are much larger than the plate separation, then (i) the surface charge density on the facing surfaces is uniform ($|\sigma| = Q/A$), (ii) the field in the space between the plates is uniform ($E = |\sigma|/\epsilon_0 = Q/\epsilon_0 A$), and (iii) the potential varies linearly with distance from one plate to the other (Fig. 23-3). Thus the potential difference across the capacitor is

$$V = Ed = \frac{Qd}{\epsilon_0 A}$$

As expected, the potential difference is proportional to Q so that Q cancels out of the ratio $C = Q/V$. Therefore,

$$C = \frac{Q}{V} = \frac{Q}{Qd/\epsilon_0 A}$$

Capacitance of a parallel-plate capacitor

or

$$C = \frac{\epsilon_0 A}{d} \qquad (23\text{-}2)$$

The capacitance of a parallel-plate capacitor depends on the plate area and the plate separation. To design a parallel-plate capacitor so that its capacitance is large, we make the area large and the separation small. The expression for C also contains ϵ_0, the permittivity of free space (or vacuum). This implies (correctly) that C depends on the medium between the plates, which we have assumed to be a vacuum. We discuss the effect of insulating material between the plates in Sec. 23-5. Notice that Eq. (23-2) shows that the SI unit for ϵ_0 can be written as F/m as well as $C^2/(N \cdot m^2)$.

EXAMPLE 23-1. (a) What is the capacitance of a parallel-plate capacitor that has square plates with lateral dimensions of 122 mm on a side, a plate separation of 0.24 mm, and a vacuum between the plates? (b) What is the charge on this capacitor if the potential difference across it is 45 V?

SOLUTION. (a) Using Eq. (23-2), we have

$$C = \frac{(8.85 \times 10^{-12} \text{ F/m})(0.122 \text{ m})^2}{2.4 \times 10^{-4} \text{ m}}$$

$$= 5.5 \times 10^{-10} \text{ F} = 0.55 \text{ nF} = 550 \text{ pF}$$

(b) Solving Eq. (23-1) for Q, we obtain

$$Q = CV = (0.55 \text{ nF})(45 \text{ V}) = 25 \text{ nC}$$

EXAMPLE 23-2. *The coaxial cable (cylindrical ca-pacitor).* Coaxial cables are often used to transmit electric signals, and an important property of a coaxial cable is its capacitance. The cable consists of a conducting wire that is encircled by a coaxial conducting cylinder with an insulator in between (Fig. 23-4a). A capacitor of this design is called a cylindrical capacitor. The length of the cable is ordinarily much longer than its radius. Determine the capacitance of a length L of coaxial cable. At this stage, we must assume vacuum is between the wire and the cylinder.

SOLUTION. We treat the wire as the positive plate and the cylinder as the negative plate of a cylindrical capacitor (Fig. 23-4b). To use Eq. (23-1) for the capacitance, we first find the expression for V across the capacitor in terms of Q and then divide Q by V. Since the cable is very long compared with its radius, we can neglect end effects and use the solution to Example 21-3 for E in the space between the plates: $E = \lambda/2\pi\epsilon_0 R$. The linear charge density λ on the positive plate (the wire) is Q/L. The charge on the negative plate (the cylinder) has no effect on the field inside it. (You may wish to use Gauss's law to verify this.) Using Eq. (22-10) and integrating along a field line from the negative plate to the positive plate gives

$$V = -\int_b^a \mathbf{E} \cdot d\boldsymbol{\ell} = \int_{R_a}^{R_b} E\, dR$$

$$= \int_{R_a}^{R_b} \frac{Q/L}{2\pi\epsilon_0 R}\, dR = \frac{Q}{2\pi\epsilon_0 L} \int_{R_a}^{R_b} \frac{dR}{R} = \frac{Q}{2\pi\epsilon_0 L} \left[\ln R \right]_{R_a}^{R_b}$$

$$= \frac{Q}{2\pi\epsilon_0 L} \ln \frac{R_b}{R_a}$$

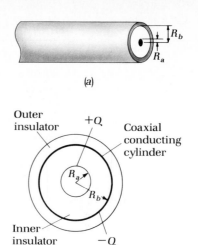

(a)

Outer insulator $+Q$ Coaxial conducting cylinder

Inner insulator $-Q$

(b)

Figure 23-4. Example 23-2: A coaxial cable (cylindrical capacitor).

Since $C = Q/V$,

$$C = \frac{Q}{(Q/2\pi\epsilon_0 L)\ln(R_b/R_a)} = \frac{2\pi\epsilon_0 L}{\ln(R_b/R_a)}$$

Again we see that the charge on the capacitor cancels out. The capacitance of a cylindrical capacitor depends on the length of the cylinders and the ratio of the radii (the ratio of the inner radius of the outer cylinder to the outer radius of the inner cylinder). The capacitance also depends on the properties of the insulator between the two cylinders, but we will learn about that in Sec. 23-5.

23-3   CAPACITORS IN SERIES AND PARALLEL

Circuit elements can be connected in many different ways. Two simple arrangements correspond to the elements being connected in series and in parallel.

Capacitors in series. Figure 23-5 shows two capacitors with capacitances C_1 and C_2 connected in series, one after the other. Also shown is the variation of the potential along the connecting wires and through the capacitors. Under electrostatic conditions, the potential is uniform along the conducting wires. Notice that the potential difference across both capacitors, $V = V_b - V_a$, is equal to the sum of the potential differences across each capacitor: $V = V_1 + V_2$. This is an example of a general rule: *The potential difference across a number of electrical devices connected in series is the sum of the potential differences across the individual devices.*

We assume that the capacitors were initially uncharged before they were connected together and charged by a battery. Thus the section of insulated conductor enclosed by the shaded region in Fig. 23-5 has no net charge, so that $Q_1 = Q_2 = Q$. Indeed, for any number of capacitors in series (initially uncharged), each has the same charge.

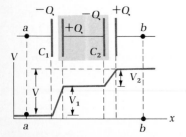

Figure 23-5. Two capacitors connected in series. Since the region inside the shaded area is electrically isolated and initially neutral, the charge on each capacitor is the same.

Equivalent capacitance

We now find the *equivalent capacitance* C_{12} of the series combination of capacitors 1 and 2. *The equivalent capacitance of a combination of capacitors is the capacitance of a single capacitor which, when used in place of the combination, provides the same external effect.* To provide the same external effect as capacitors 1 and 2 in series, this single capacitor must possess charge of magnitude Q on each of its plates when the potential difference across it is V. That is,

$$C_{12} = \frac{Q}{V} \quad \text{or} \quad V = \frac{Q}{C_{12}}$$

Also, $V_1 = Q/C_1$ and $V_2 = Q/C_2$. Substitution into $V = V_1 + V_2$ gives

$$\frac{Q}{C_{12}} = \frac{Q}{C_1} + \frac{Q}{C_2}$$

Thus

$$\frac{1}{C_{12}} = \frac{1}{C_1} + \frac{1}{C_2}$$

In general, the equivalent capacitance C_{eq} of any number of capacitors connected in series is

Equivalent capacitance of
capacitors in series

$$\frac{1}{C_{eq}} = \Sigma \frac{1}{C_i} \tag{23-3}$$

EXAMPLE 23-3. Two capacitors with capacitances of $C_1 = 2.3\ \mu\text{F}$ and $C_2 = 4.6\ \mu\text{F}$ are connected in series, and the potential difference across the combination is 35 V. Determine (a) the equivalent capacitance of the series combination, (b) the charge on each capacitor, and (c) the potential difference across each capacitor.

SOLUTION. (a) For two capacitors in series

$$\frac{1}{C_{12}} = \frac{1}{C_1} + \frac{1}{C_2} = \frac{C_2}{C_1 C_2} + \frac{C_1}{C_1 C_2} = \frac{C_2 + C_1}{C_1 C_2}$$

or

$$C_{12} = \frac{C_1 C_2}{C_2 + C_1} = \frac{(2.3\ \mu\text{F})(4.6\ \mu\text{F})}{2.3\ \mu\text{F} + 4.6\ \mu\text{F}} = 1.5\ \mu\text{F}$$

(b) Each capacitor has the same charge, and this charge is equal to the charge on a capacitor with the equivalent capacitance when the potential difference is V. Thus

$$Q_1 = Q_2 = Q = C_{12}V = (1.5\ \mu\text{F})(35\ \text{V}) = 53\ \mu\text{C}$$

(c) The potential difference across capacitor 1 is

$$V_1 = \frac{Q}{C_1} = \frac{53\ \mu\text{C}}{2.3\ \mu\text{F}} = 23\ \text{V}$$

The potential difference across capacitor 2 is

$$V_2 = \frac{Q}{C_2} = \frac{53\ \mu\text{C}}{4.6\ \mu\text{F}} = 12\ \text{V}$$

Notice that $V_1 + V_2 = 23\ \text{V} + 12\ \text{V} = 35\ \text{V}$.

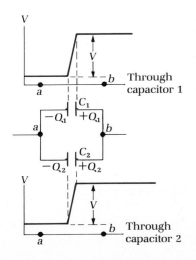

Capacitors in Parallel. Figure 23-6 is a schematic illustration of two capacitors with capacitances C_1 and C_2 connected in parallel, one beside the other. From the figure, you can see that the potential difference across each capacitor is the same: $V_b - V_a = V_1 = V_2 = V$. This is an example of a general rule: *The potential difference across circuit elements arranged in parallel is the same.*

To provide the same external effect as capacitors 1 and 2 in parallel, a single capacitor with capacitance C_{12} must possess charge $Q = Q_1 + Q_2$ when the potential difference across it is V. That is,

$$C_{12} = \frac{Q}{V} = \frac{Q_1 + Q_2}{V} = \frac{Q_1}{V} + \frac{Q_2}{V}$$

Figure 23-6. Two capacitors connected in parallel. Since the potential difference between a and b is independent of the path between a and b, the potential difference across each capacitor is the same.

Since $C_1 = Q_1/V$ and $C_2 = Q_2/V$, we have

$$C_{12} = C_1 + C_2$$

In general, the equivalent capacitance C_{eq} of any number of capacitors connected in parallel is

Equivalent capacitance of capacitors in parallel

$$C_{eq} = \Sigma C_i \qquad (23\text{-}4)$$

EXAMPLE 23-4. Consider the combination of capacitors in Fig. 23-7a, where $C_1 = 2.9 \, \mu F$, $C_2 = 1.8 \, \mu F$, and $C_3 = 2.4 \, \mu F$. The potential difference across the combination is $V_b - V_a = V = 53$ V. Determine (a) the equivalent capacitance C_{123} of the entire combination, (b) the potential difference across each capacitor, and (c) the charge on each capacitor.

SOLUTION. (a) Since capacitors 1 and 2 are in parallel, their equivalent capacitance C_{12} is

$$C_{12} = 2.9 \, \mu F + 1.8 \, \mu F = 4.7 \, \mu F$$

Thus the combination can be represented as shown in Fig. 23-7b. The capacitance C_{12} is in series with C_3 so that

$$C_{123} = \frac{C_{12}C_3}{C_3 + C_{12}} = \frac{(4.7 \, \mu F)(2.4 \, \mu F)}{2.4 \, \mu F + 4.7 \, \mu F} = 1.6 \, \mu F$$

The entire combination is equivalent to the single capacitor shown in Fig. 23-7c. (b) Since capacitors 1 and 2 are in parallel, the potential difference across each of them is the same: $V_1 = V_2$. Also, capacitor 3 is in series with the parallel arrangement of 1 and 2 so that the potential difference V_3 across capacitor 3 plus V_1 (or V_2) gives V:

$$V = V_1 + V_3$$

To find V_1 or V_3 we must first find some of the charges. From the figure you can see that the positive plate of capacitor 3

must possess a charge equal and opposite to the charges on the negative plates of capacitors 1 and 2: $Q_3 = Q_1 + Q_2$. Thus the equivalent capacitance of the entire combination possesses this same charge when the potential difference across it is V:

$$C_{123} = \frac{Q_3}{V} = \frac{Q_1 + Q_2}{V}$$

$$Q_3 = Q_1 + Q_2 = C_{123}V = (1.6 \, \mu F)(53 \text{ V}) = 84 \, \mu C$$

This gives

$$V_3 = \frac{Q_3}{C_3} = \frac{84 \, \mu C}{2.4 \, \mu F} = 35 \text{ V}$$

and

$$V_1 = V_2 = \frac{Q_1 + Q_2}{C_{12}} = \frac{84 \, \mu C}{4.7 \, \mu F} = 18 \text{ V}$$

Notice that $V_1 + V_3 = 18$ V $+ 35$ V $= 53$ V. (c) We already found Q_3 in part (b). The charges on capacitors 1 and 2 are

$$Q_1 = C_1 V_1 = (2.9 \, \mu F)(18 \text{ V}) = 52 \, \mu C$$

and

$$Q_2 = C_2 V_2 = (1.8 \, \mu F)(18 \text{ V}) = 32 \, \mu C$$

Notice that $Q_1 + Q_2 = 52 \, \mu C + 32 \, \mu C = 84 \, \mu C = Q_3$.

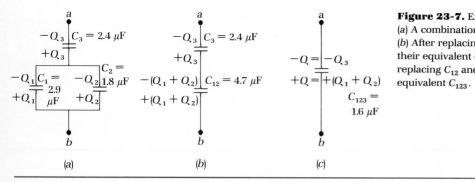

Figure 23-7. Example 23-4: (a) A combination of capacitors. (b) After replacing C_1 and C_2 with their equivalent C_{12}. (c) After replacing C_{12} and C_3 with their equivalent C_{123}.

(a)   (b)   (c)

23-4 ELECTRIC ENERGY AND ENERGY DENSITY

We now develop the concept of electric energy by considering the potential energy of the charges on the plates of a charged capacitor. Once developed, we

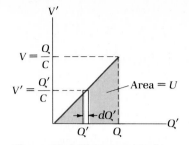

Figure 23-8. The energy U of a capacitor with final charge Q and final potential difference V is given by the area under the graph of the varying potential difference V' versus the varying charge Q'. The area is that of a triangle of height Q/C and base Q; $U = \frac{1}{2}(Q/C)Q = \frac{1}{2}Q^2/C$.

discuss the electric energy in terms of electric fields, and we introduce the concept of electric energy density.

Electric energy stored in a capacitor. When a battery charges a capacitor, the battery does work as it transfers charge carriers from one plate to the other, raising the potential energy of the carriers. This increased potential energy of the charge carriers constitutes the electric energy stored in a capacitor.

Let U represent the energy of a capacitor after it has been charged to a final charge Q and final potential difference V, and let U', Q', and V' represent these quantities as they vary during the charging process. At some instant during the charging, the change dU' in the potential energy of the system of charges when charge dQ' is transferred by the battery is

$$dU' = V' \, dQ'$$

because V' is the potential energy per unit charge. To find U due to the capacitor being charged from zero to Q, we integrate dU':

$$U = \int_0^Q V' \, dQ'$$

The potential difference V' across the capacitor cannot be factored out of the integral because it varies as Q' increases. Indeed, V' (which equals Q'/C) increases linearly with the charge on the capacitor, as shown in Fig. 23-8. Therefore,

$$U = \int_0^Q \frac{Q'}{C} \, dQ' = \frac{1}{C} \int_0^Q Q' \, dQ' = \frac{1}{2} \frac{Q^2}{C}$$

The energy of a capacitor depends on the square of its charge. How this integration leads to this result is shown graphically in Fig. 23-8. The energy, equal to $\int V' dQ'$, is given by the area under the graph of V' versus Q'. Since V' increases linearly with Q', the area is that of a triangle with height Q/C and with base Q, so that the area (the energy of the capacitor) is $\frac{1}{2}(Q/C)(Q) = \frac{1}{2}(Q^2/C)$.

Charging a capacitor is similar to digging a well (or any deep hole in the ground). It is easier to dig the first part of the well than the last part because the soil taken from the well during the first part does not have to be lifted as far as during the last part. Similarly, the increase in potential energy of the first carriers transferred by the battery is less than that of the last carriers because the potential difference across the capacitor is larger when the last carriers are transferred. This accounts for the variation of V' as the charge transfer takes place and is the physical reason V' may not be factored out of the integral.

Using the definition of capacitance, $C = Q/V$, we can express the energy of a charged capacitor in terms of any two of the three quantities Q, C, and V:

Energy of a charged capacitor

$$U = \frac{Q^2}{2C} \qquad U = \frac{CV^2}{2} \qquad U = \frac{QV}{2} \qquad (23\text{-}5)$$

As a brief example, suppose a 5.5-μF capacitor has a potential difference of 42 V across it. The capacitor's energy is $U = \frac{1}{2}CV^2 = \frac{1}{2}(5.5 \ \mu F)(42 \ V)^2 = 4.9$ mJ.

Energy density of an electric field. In the discussion above, we associated the energy of the capacitor with the potential energy of the charges. An alternative view is to attribute this energy to the electric field that exists between the plates. For a parallel-plate capacitor (with small plate separation and large plate area), $C = \epsilon_0 A/d$ and $V = Ed$, so that

$$U = \frac{1}{2}CV^2 = \frac{1}{2}\left(\frac{\epsilon_0 A}{d}\right)(Ed)^2 = \frac{1}{2}\epsilon_0 E^2(Ad)$$

The factor Ad is the volume between the plates, which corresponds to the volume occupied by the electric field (neglecting edge effects). Since the energy is proportional to the volume occupied by the field, we introduce the energy density (or energy per unit volume) u in the space that contains the field:

$$u = \frac{U}{Ad} = \frac{\frac{1}{2}\epsilon_0 E^2(Ad)}{Ad} = \frac{1}{2}\epsilon_0 E^2$$

Energy density of an electric field   Thus $$u = \frac{1}{2}\epsilon_0 E^2 \qquad (23\text{-}6)$$

Equation (23-6) is more than simply another way to express the energy of a charged capacitor. It suggests that we may view the electric energy of a charge distribution as being attributed to the electric field produced by the charge distribution. Although we do not prove it here, Eq. (23-6) is generally valid; it gives at points in space the energy density due to an electric field produced by any charge distribution. The electric energy density is an example of a scalar field.

EXAMPLE 23-5. What is the energy density at a point 0.15 m from the center of a spherically symmetric charge distribution of radius 55 mm and charge 18 nC?

SOLUTION. Since the point in question is outside the charge distribution, the field is the same as the field due to a point charge located at the center of the charge distribution:

$E = Q/4\pi\epsilon_0 r^2$. Equation (23-6) gives

$$u = \frac{1}{2}\epsilon_0 E^2 = \frac{1}{2}\epsilon_0\left(\frac{Q}{4\pi\epsilon_0 r^2}\right)^2 = \frac{Q^2}{32\pi^2\epsilon_0 r^4}$$

$$= \frac{(18 \text{ nC})^2}{32\pi^2(8.85 \times 10^{-12} \text{ F/m})(0.15 \text{ m})^4} = 230 \ \mu\text{J/m}^3$$

EXAMPLE 23-6. Equation (23-6) was developed using the (nearly) uniform field of a parallel-plate capacitor. Show that this equation also gives the energy of a charged cylindrical capacitor, where the field between the plates is not uniform.

SOLUTION. From Example 23-2, E between the plates of a cylindrical capacitor is $E = \lambda/2\pi\epsilon_0 R = Q/2\pi\epsilon_0 RL$, where L is the length of the capacitor. Thus the field is the same at each point in an infinitesimal volume element which is a cylindrical shell of radius R, length L, thickness dR, and volume $2\pi RL \, dR$ (Fig. 23-9). Since this field exists only between the plates, the energy U due to the field is

$$U = \int_{R_a}^{R_b} u(2\pi RL \, dR)$$

The energy density u is

$$u = \frac{1}{2}\epsilon_0 E^2 = \frac{1}{2}\epsilon_0\left(\frac{Q}{2\pi\epsilon_0 RL}\right)^2 = \frac{Q^2}{8\pi^2\epsilon_0 L^2 R^2}$$

Substituting this into the equation for U and factoring constants out of the integral gives

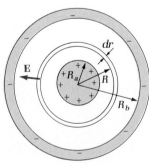

Figure 23-9. Example 23-6: Cross section of a cylindrical capacitor. The field magnitude E is the same at each point in a cylindrical shell of infinitesimal thickness dR and volume $2\pi RL \, dR$.

$$U = \frac{Q^2}{4\pi\epsilon_0 L}\int_{R_a}^{R_b}\frac{dR}{R} = \frac{Q^2}{4\pi\epsilon_0 L}\ln\frac{R_b}{R_a}$$

For a cylindrical capacitor (Example 23-2),

$$C = \frac{2\pi\epsilon_0 L}{\ln(R_b/R_a)}$$

Therefore, the energy of the field between the plates is $U = \frac{1}{2}Q^2/C$, which corresponds to the potential energy of the charges on the plates given by the first of Eqs. (23-5).

EXAMPLE 23-7. (a) Determine an expression for the electric energy of an isolated metal sphere of radius r_0 and charge Q. (b) In Example 22-12, we showed that the dome of a demonstration Van de Graaff generator with $r_0 = 0.13$ m can have a charge $Q = 6$ μC. Evaluate U for such a generator.

SOLUTION. (a) The electric energy of the charged sphere can be attributed to the field produced by the charge. To find the energy, we integrate (sum) the energy density over the volume occupied by the field. The electric energy inside the metal sphere is zero because $E = 0$ inside a conductor. Outside the sphere, $E = Q/4\pi\epsilon_0 r^2$, so that the field occupies all space outside the sphere. Since E is spherically symmetric, it is the same at each point in an element of volume that is a thin spherical shell of radius r, infinitesimal thickness dr, and volume $4\pi r^2\,dr$ (Fig. 23-10). Therefore,

$$U = \int_{r_0}^{\infty} u\,4\pi r^2\,dr = \int_{r_0}^{\infty} \tfrac{1}{2}\epsilon_0 E^2\,4\pi r^2\,dr$$

$$= \tfrac{1}{2}\epsilon_0 \int_{r_0}^{\infty} E^2\,4\pi r^2\,dr$$

$$= \tfrac{1}{2}\epsilon_0 \int_{r_0}^{\infty} \left(\frac{Q}{4\pi\epsilon_0 r^2}\right)^2 4\pi r^2\,dr$$

$$= \frac{Q^2}{8\pi\epsilon_0} \int_{r_0}^{\infty} \frac{dr}{r^2} = \frac{Q^2}{8\pi\epsilon_0}\left[-\frac{1}{r}\right]_{r_0}^{\infty}$$

$$= \frac{Q^2}{8\pi\epsilon_0 r_0}$$

(b) For the Van de Graaff generator dome,

$$U = (9 \times 10^9\ \text{N} \cdot \text{m}^2/\text{C}^2)\frac{(6\ \mu\text{C})^2}{2(0.13\ \text{m})} = 1\ \text{J}$$

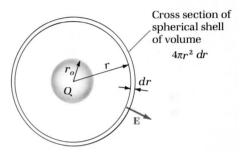

Figure 23-10. Example 23-7. Finding the electric energy of the field produced by a charged metal sphere. The field magnitude E is the same at each point in a spherical shell with infinitesimal thickness dr and volume $4\pi r^2\,dr$.

Cross section of spherical shell of volume $4\pi r^2\,dr$

23-5 ELECTROSTATIC PROPERTIES OF INSULATORS

So far we have only studied cases where no material exists in the space between capacitor plates. Now we consider the effect of filling this space with an insulator. These considerations provide a means for investigating the properties of insulators.

To examine the behavior of an insulating material, such as glass or plastic, we first arrange a parallel-plate capacitor with vacuum between its plates. Next we charge the capacitor by connecting it to a battery, and then we disconnect the charging battery. We measure the potential difference across the plates, as shown in Fig. 23-11a, and refer to this value as V_0. Now we insert the insulating material we wish to study into the space between the plates and again measure the potential difference (Fig. 23-11b). Such experiments reveal that the poten-

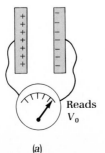

Reads V_0

(a)

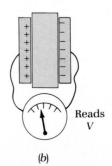

Reads V

(b)

Figure 23-11. (a) With vacuum between the plates of the charged capacitor, the voltmeter reads V_0. (b) With a dielectric between the plates of the charged capacitor, the voltmeter reads V. $V_0 > V$ always.

tial difference changes to a value we call V and that $V < V_0$ in every case.

The reduction of potential difference from V_0 to V due to the insertion of the insulator cannot be attributed to a reduction of charge on the plates, because if the insulator is removed, the value of the potential difference increases from V back to V_0. This would not happen if the charge on the plates had been altered by the insertion of the insulator.

When this experiment is performed with different types of insulating materials, we find that the ratio V_0/V depends on the type of material. An insulator is often called a *dielectric*, and this ratio is the *dielectric constant κ*:

The dielectric constant κ

$$\kappa = \frac{V_0}{V} \tag{23-7}$$

Table 23-1 lists values of κ for some representative materials. (Also listed are values of the dielectric strength E_{max}, which was discussed in Sec. 22-7.) For vacuum, κ is exactly 1 because the dielectric constant is defined relative to vacuum. The dielectric constant of air at room temperature and atmospheric pressure is very nearly the same as that of vacuum; the values differ by only about 0.0006. For most purposes there is no need to distinguish between air and vacuum as far as the dielectric constant is concerned. Since $V < V_0$ in every case, $\kappa > 1$ for all insulating materials.

Now we examine the way some other quantities (E, C, and U) change as an insulator is placed between the plates of a charged capacitor (the battery is disconnected). As we did for V, we let a subscript zero on the symbol designate the quantity when vacuum is between the plates, and use the symbol with no subscript to designate the quantity when the dielectric is inserted. First consider the field between the plates. Since $V = Ed$ and $V_0 = E_0 d$,

$$\kappa = \frac{V_0}{V} = \frac{E_0 d}{Ed} = \frac{E_0}{E}$$

Table 23-1. Properties of some dielectric materials (20°C)

Material	Dielectric constant κ	Dielectric strength E_{max}, 10^6 V/m
Vacuum	1	
Gases		
Dry air (1 atm)	1.00059	3
Carbon dioxide (1 atm)	1.00098	
Helium (1 atm)	1.00007	
Ethanol (100°C, 1 atm)	1.0061	
Liquids		
Benzene	3.1	
Glycerol	43	
Water	80	
Solids		
Teflon	2.1	60
Polystyrene	2.6	25
Nylon	3.4	14
Paper	3.6	15
Fused quartz	3.8	8
Bakelite	4.9	24
Pyrex glass	5	14
Neoprene	6.8	12
Aluminum oxide	10.3	
Strontium titanate	≈ 250	8
Barium strontium titanate	$\approx 10^4$	

or
$$E = \frac{E_0}{\kappa} \qquad (23\text{-}8)$$

As with the potential difference, the field magnitude is reduced by a factor of $1/\kappa$ when a dielectric is inserted.

Next we look at the effect of a dielectric on the capacitance. Since $V = Q/C$ and $V_0 = Q/C_0$,

$$\kappa = \frac{V_0}{V} = \frac{Q/C_0}{Q/C} = \frac{C}{C_0}$$

Therefore,
$$C = \kappa C_0$$

The insertion of the dielectric causes the capacitance to be increased by a factor κ.

In the case of a capacitor's energy, $U = \frac{1}{2}QV$, or $V = 2U/Q$, so that

$$\kappa = \frac{V_0}{V} = \frac{2U_0/Q}{2U/Q} = \frac{U_0}{U}$$

Thus
$$U = \frac{U_0}{\kappa}$$

The energy of the capacitor is reduced by a factor of $1/\kappa$ because of the insertion of the dielectric. Since U is reduced as the dielectric is inserted, there is an electric force that tends to pull the dielectric into the space between the plates (see Prob. 23-11).

Several factors are involved in choosing a dielectric for a practical capacitor (Fig. 23-12). First, since C is proportional to κ, a large dielectric constant is preferred so that C can be made large without making the plate area inordinately large. Second, a large dielectric strength E_{max} allows the capacitor to be subjected to a large field without dielectric breakdown. For a parallel-plate capacitor, $V = Ed$ so that $V_{max} = E_{max}d$. Therefore, a large E_{max} permits d to be small without restricting the maximum operating potential difference, and a smaller value of d means a larger capacitance. Therefore, a dielectric with a large κ is required if V is expected to be large, or if d must be small. Third, a solid insulator provides rigid support between the plates so that the plates cannot make a conducting contact with each other.

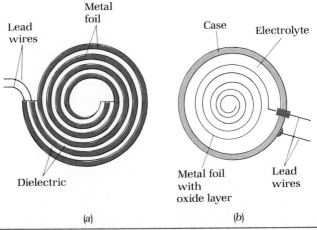

Figure 23-12. Two designs of practical capacitors. (a) Two sheets of dielectric and two sheets of metal foil are sandwiched together and rolled into the shape of a cylinder. (b) An electrolytic capacitor is one that uses an electrolyte (a conducting solution) as one "plate" and a metal foil as the other. The dielectric is a thin oxide layer on the metal foil.

EXAMPLE 23-8. A parallel-plate capacitor is constructed by tightly sandwiching a sheet of paper with thickness 0.14 mm between sheets of aluminum foil. The lateral dimensions of the sheets are 15 mm by 480 mm. Determine

(a) the capacitance of the capacitor and (b) the maximum potential difference that may be placed across it without dielectric breakdown. Neglect edge effects.

SOLUTION. (a) Since $C = \kappa C_0$ and $C_0 = \epsilon_0 A/d$,

$$C = \frac{\kappa \epsilon_0 A}{d}$$

From Table 23-1, $\kappa = 3.6$ for paper so that

$$C = \frac{(3.6)(8.85 \times 10^{-12}\ \text{F/m})(1.5 \times 10^{-2}\ \text{m})(0.48\ \text{m})}{1.4 \times 10^{-4}\ \text{m}}$$

$$= 1.6\ \text{nF}$$

(b) For a parallel-plate capacitor, $V_{max} = E_{max}d$, and from Table 23-1, $E_{max} = 15 \times 10^6$ V/m for paper. Thus

$$V_{max} = (15 \times 10^6\ \text{V/m})(1.4 \times 10^{-4}\ \text{m}) = 2.1\ \text{kV}$$

23-6 ATOMIC DESCRIPTION OF THE PROPERTIES OF INSULATORS

When a dielectric is placed between the plates of a charged capacitor which is disconnected from the charging battery, the field between the plates is reduced even though the charge on the plates remains fixed. What charges are responsible for this reduction in the field and where do they reside? The charges that cause the reduction of the field are called *bound charges,* or *polarization charges,* and they reside on the surface of the dielectric. We now describe the origin of these charges in terms of the molecules that compose the dielectric.

Figure 23-13a shows a simple model of an atom: a nucleus that is effectively a point charge ($+Ze$) surrounded by a spherically symmetric distribution of negative charge ($-Ze$) due to the electrons. Because of the electric attraction between the nucleus and its electrons, the center of negative charge coincides with the position of the nucleus. When the atom is placed in an external electric field $\mathbf{E}_0$ (Fig. 23-13b), the force exerted by the field on the nucleus is in the opposite direction to the force exerted by the field on the electrons. At equilibrium, the position of the nucleus and the center of negative charge are displaced because of two sets of forces: (i) the forces on the nucleus and the electrons due to $\mathbf{E}_0$ (which tend to separate the nucleus from its electrons) and (ii) the forces between the nucleus and its electrons (which tend to superimpose the nucleus and the center of negative charge). As a result of the external field, the atom has an induced dipole moment, and such an atom is said to be *polarized.*

Some molecules possess permanent dipole moments and, as a consequence, are called *polar molecules.* For a polar molecule, the center of positive charge does not coincide with the center of negative charge even when the molecule is in zero electric field. A water molecule is an example of a polar molecule (Fig. 23-14). When no external electric field exists, these molecular dipoles have a random orientation (Fig. 23-15a). If a dipole of moment $\mathbf{p}$ is placed in a field $\mathbf{E}$, the field tends to align $\mathbf{p}$ along the direction of $\mathbf{E}$ (see Prob. 22-2). In the case of molecular dipoles, the alignment is not complete because of thermal agitation

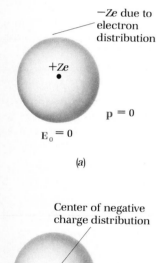

Figure 23-13. A simple model of an atom. The nucleus with charge $+Ze$ is at the center of the spherical distribution of charge $-Ze$ due to the electrons. (a) In zero field the center of negative charge coincides with the positive point charge (the nucleus). (b) In an external electric field $\mathbf{E}_0$, the center of negative charge and the positive point charge are displaced; the atom has an induced dipole moment.

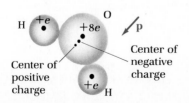

Figure 23-14. The water molecule has a permanent dipole moment.

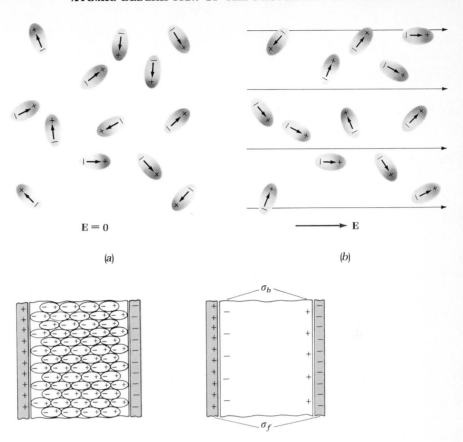

Figure 23-15. (a) Dipole moments of polar molecules are randomly oriented in zero electric field. (b) Molecules tend to align in an external electric field, but the alignment is not complete because of thermal agitation.

$E = 0$

(a)

$\longrightarrow$ E

(b)

Figure 23-16. (a) A dielectric slab is polarized in the uniform field of a parallel-plate capacitor. (b) A surface charge density σ_b is formed on the faces of the dielectric adjacent to the plates.

(a)

(b)

of the molecules (Fig. 23-15b). Thus a characteristic of this type of polarization is its relatively strong temperature dependence; the effect of the polarization decreases with increasing temperature.

Suppose a dielectric slab is placed in the uniform field $\mathbf{E}_0$ between the plates of a parallel-plate capacitor (Fig. 23-16a). The dielectric becomes polarized as dipoles are induced by the field and permanent dipoles, if present, are aligned by the field. Because of this polarization, a surface charge density σ_b (b for bound) forms on the two faces of the dielectric that are adjacent to the plates (Fig. 23-16b), and the sign of this induced charge on each slab face is opposite that of the charge on its adjacent plate. To distinguish it from σ_b, the charge density on the plates is now referred to as σ_f (f for free). Since the charge on the plates was unaffected by the insertion of the dielectric (the battery is disconnected), σ_f is the same charge density we previously designated as σ.

The field $\mathbf{E}$ in the dielectric has two contributions, $\mathbf{E}_f$ due to σ_f ($E_f = |\sigma_f|/\epsilon_0$) and $\mathbf{E}_b$ due to σ_b ($E_b = |\sigma_b|/\epsilon_0$). The two contributions to the field are in opposite directions, as shown in Fig. 23-17. Note that $\mathbf{E}_f$ is the same field that was present before the insertion of the dielectric. That is, $\mathbf{E}_f = \mathbf{E}_0$. Thus

$$\mathbf{E} = \mathbf{E}_0 + \mathbf{E}_b$$

If we place our x axis along $\mathbf{E}$, then

$$E\mathbf{i} = E_0\mathbf{i} + (-E_b)\mathbf{i} = (E_0 - E_b)\mathbf{i}$$

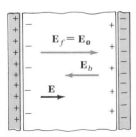

Figure 23-17. The field inside the dielectric has two contributions, $\mathbf{E}_b$ and $\mathbf{E}_f$ (which equals $\mathbf{E}_0$), and they are in opposite directions. In terms of field magnitudes, $E = E_0 - E_b$.

So the relation between the field magnitudes is

$$E = E_0 - E_b$$

E inside the dielectric

In terms of the charge densities, we have

$$E = \frac{|\sigma_f| - |\sigma_b|}{\epsilon_0} \tag{23-9}$$

Next we express $|\sigma_b|$ in terms of $|\sigma_f|$ and κ. From Eq. (23-8), $E = E_0/\kappa = |\sigma_f|/\kappa\epsilon_0$, so that

$$\frac{|\sigma_f|}{\kappa\epsilon_0} = \frac{|\sigma_f| - |\sigma_b|}{\epsilon_0}$$

Solving for $|\sigma_b|$ gives

$$|\sigma_b| = \frac{\kappa - 1}{\kappa} |\sigma_f| \tag{23-10}$$

Since the factor $(\kappa - 1)/\kappa$ is less than 1, $|\sigma_b|$ is always less than $|\sigma_f|$.

Now we can understand why the potential difference decreases when a dielectric is inserted into a capacitor with fixed charge on its plates. The field due to the free charge on the plates induces a bound charge of opposite sign on the adjacent faces of the dielectric. The contribution to the field due to the bound charge (on the dielectric surface) is opposite the contribution to the field due to the free charge (on the plate surface) so that the field (and the potential difference) is reduced because of the presence of the dielectric.

EXAMPLE 23-9. Suppose the potential difference across the parallel-plate capacitor in Example 23-8 is 180 V. Determine (a) E, (b) E_0, (c) E_b, (d) $|\sigma_f|$, and (e) $|\sigma_b|$.

SOLUTION. (a) For the capacitor in Example 23-8, $d = 0.14$ mm so that the field magnitude between the plates is

$$E = \frac{V}{d} = \frac{180 \text{ V}}{0.14 \text{ mm}} = 1.3 \times 10^6 \text{ V/m}$$

(b) Paper ($\kappa = 3.6$) is used between the plates so that the magnitude of the contribution to the field due to the free charge is

$$E_0 = \kappa E = (3.6)(1.3 \times 10^6 \text{ V/m}) = 4.6 \times 10^6 \text{ V/m}$$

(c) Since $E = E_0 - E_b$, the magnitude of the contribution to the field due to the bound charge is

$$E_b = E_0 - E = (4.6 \times 10^6 \text{ V/m}) - (1.3 \times 10^6 \text{ V/m})$$

$$= 3.3 \times 10^6 \text{ V/m}$$

(d) The magnitude of the free charge density is

$$|\sigma_f| = \epsilon_0 E_0 = (8.85 \times 10^{-12} \text{ F/m})(4.6 \times 10^6 \text{ V/m})$$

$$= 4.1 \times 10^{-5} \text{ C/m}^2$$

(e) The magnitude of the bound charge density is

$$|\sigma_b| = \epsilon_0 E_b = (8.85 \times 10^{-12} \text{ F/m})(3.3 \times 10^6 \text{ V/m})$$

$$= 3.0 \times 10^{-5} \text{ C/m}^2$$

We may also find $|\sigma_b|$ from Eq. (23-10):

$$|\sigma_b| = \frac{\kappa - 1}{\kappa} |\sigma_f| = \frac{3.6 - 1}{3.6} (4.1 \times 10^{-5} \text{ C/m}^2)$$

$$= 3.0 \times 10^{-5} \text{ C/m}^2$$

EXAMPLE 23-10. *Model of a dielectric.* Consider a relatively crude model for the polarization of a dielectric (Fig. 23-18). Suppose the dielectric consists of two interpenetrating slabs of uniform charge—one positive (the atomic nuclei) and the other negative (the electrons). Superimposed on one another, the two slabs compose a neutral medium. When placed in a uniform external field $\mathbf{E}_0$, the two slabs are displaced a distance δ at equilibrium. (a) Develop an expression which approximates δ in terms of E and κ. (b) Apply the result of part (a) to estimate δ for the case where paper is the dielectric and $E = E_{\max}$ (see Table 23-1).

SOLUTION. (a) Consider the side of the slab that has a positive bound charge density on its surface (on the right in Fig.

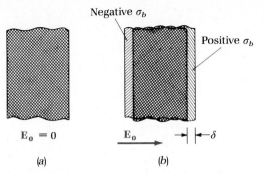

Figure 23-18. Example 23-10: A crude model of a dielectric. (a) A slab of dielectric in zero field. The positive charges (shown as crosshatching sloping downward to the right) are superimposed on the negative charges (shown as crosshatching sloping upward to the right). (b) In an electric field the positive and negative charges are displaced a distance δ.

23-18b). On this surface σ_b is given by the product of the volume charge density ρ_p due to the protons in the nuclei of the dielectric and the distance δ: $\sigma_b = \rho_p \delta$. Using Eq. (23-10), we obtain

$$\rho_p \delta = (\kappa - 1) \frac{|\sigma_f|}{\kappa}$$

Since $E = E_0/\kappa = |\sigma_f|/\kappa\epsilon_0$, we have

$$\delta = \frac{(\kappa - 1)\epsilon_0 E}{\rho_p}$$

To use this relation, we should estimate the charge density ρ_p in terms of quantities that are more readily known. If the slab has cross-sectional area A and thickness d (volume Ad), then

$$\rho_p = \frac{N_p e}{Ad}$$

where N_p is total number of protons in the slab. Note that (i) the mass M of the slab is almost entirely due to the protons

and neutrons, (ii) the mass m_p of a proton is nearly the same as that of a neutron, and (iii) the number of protons and neutrons in a material is nearly the same. Therefore, $M \approx 2N_p m_p$, or $N_p \approx M/2m_p$, and

$$\rho_p \approx \frac{Me}{2Adm_p}$$

Since M/Ad is the mass density ρ_M of the dielectric, we have

$$\rho_p \approx \frac{\rho_M e}{2m_p}$$

Substitution into the equation for δ gives

$$\delta \approx \frac{2(\kappa - 1)\epsilon_0 E m_p}{\rho_M e}$$

The displacement depends on the factor $(\kappa - 1)$. Thus $\delta = 0$ if $\kappa = 1$, which corresponds to vacuum. Our model also predicts that δ is directly proportional to E. (b) The displacement is δ_{max} when $E = E_{max}$, so that

$$\delta_{max} \approx \frac{2(\kappa - 1)\epsilon_0 E_{max} m_p}{\rho_M e}$$

For paper $\rho_M \approx 800 \text{ kg/m}^3$ and $E_{max} = 15 \times 10^6$ V/m, which gives

δ_{max}

$$\approx \frac{2(3.6 - 1)(8.8 \times 10^{-12} \text{ F/m})(15 \times 10^6 \text{ V/m})(1.7 \times 10^{-27} \text{ kg})}{(800 \text{ kg/m}^3)(1.6 \times 10^{-19} \text{ C})}$$

$$\approx 9 \times 10^{-15} \text{ m}$$

The diameter of a typical atom is about 3×10^{-10} m, so that this displacement is only about 3×10^{-5} atomic diameters. As we said at the outset, this model is very crude. But it does serve to show that even at the largest field that the dielectric can bear, the displacement of the charges is very small. However, the effect of the displacement is not small, because a very large number of charges are displaced.

SUMMARY WITH APPLICATIONS

Section 23-2. Capacitors and capacitance
A capacitor is an electrical device used in circuits to store charge and electric energy; it consists of two conducting plates separated by an insulator. The capacitance C of a capacitor is

$$C = \frac{Q}{V} \tag{23-1}$$

The capacitance depends on the geometrical design of the capacitor and the nature of the dielectric between the plates. For a parallel-plate capacitor with vacuum between the plates,

$$C = \frac{\epsilon_0 A}{d} \tag{23-2}$$

Define capacitance and state the properties of a capacitor which determine its capacitance.

Section 23-3. Capacitors in series and parallel
The equivalent capacitance of a combination of capacitors is the capacitance of a single capacitor which, when used in place of the combination, provides the same external effect. The equivalent capacitance of a number of capacitors connected in series is

$$C_{eq} = \frac{1}{\Sigma(1/C_i)} \tag{23-3}$$

For a number of capacitors connected in parallel,

$$C_{eq} = \Sigma C_i \qquad (23.4)$$

Determine the equivalent capacitance of capacitors connected in series and/or parallel; find the charge on and the potential difference across the individual capacitors.

Section 23-4. Electric energy and energy density

The energy of a capacitor is the potential energy of the charges on the capacitor plates:

$$U = \frac{1}{2}\frac{Q^2}{C} = \tfrac{1}{2}CV^2 = \tfrac{1}{2}QV \qquad (23-5)$$

When this energy is associated with the electric field, the energy density u in the space occupied by the field (in vacuum) is

$$u = \tfrac{1}{2}\epsilon_0 E^2 \qquad (23-6)$$

Determine the energy of a charged capacitor; determine, at a point in space, the energy density due to an electric field at that point.

Sections 23-5 and 23-6. Electrostatic properties of insulators; atomic description of the properties of insulators

When an insulator (or dielectric) is placed in an electric field, the atoms and molecules that compose the insulator become polarized and a bound surface charge density is induced. This bound charge produces an electric field directed opposite the external field, so that both V and E are reduced. This polarization of a dielectric is characterized by the dielectric constant κ:

$$\kappa = \frac{V_0}{V} \qquad (23-7)$$

Define the dielectric constant of a dielectric; describe the effect of a dielectric on the properties of a capacitor; describe the origin of the bound charges which produce polarization effects.

QUESTIONS

23-1 Explain the meaning of the phrase "charge Q on a capacitor." Does the capacitor as a whole possess this charge?

23-2 Explain the meaning of the phrase "potential difference V across a capacitor." In terms of the line integral

$$V = V_b - V_a = -\int_a^b \mathbf{E} \cdot d\boldsymbol{\ell}$$

Where is point a and where is point b? Do we have more than one choice for the position a (or b)? Explain.

23-3 Suppose a fellow student tells you that since $C = Q/V$, the capacitance of a capacitor is proportional to the charge on it. How do you respond?

23-4 Suppose the potential difference across a capacitor is doubled. By what factor does the ratio Q/V change?

23-5 The capacity of a bucket to hold a liquid is expressed in terms of its volume. Explain any analogies you can draw between a bucket and a capacitor. Where do your analogies break down?

23-6 Explain any analogies you can draw between the heat capacity of an object and the capacitance of a capacitor. Where do your analogies break down? Do you consider these better analogies than the ones you devised for the previous question? Explain.

23-7 When a battery charges a capacitor, the charges on the plates are of equal magnitude but opposite sign. Why? If the plates have different sizes will they still have charge of the same magnitude?

23.8 Suppose each plate of a capacitor initially has positive charge q on it and then the capacitor is connected to a battery. Will the subsequent charge on the plates be equal and opposite? What is the charge on each plate in terms of q, C, and V?

23-9 Suppose a parallel-plate capacitor is charged and then disconnected from the charging battery. Next the plate separation is doubled. Describe any change in each of the following quantities as a result of the change in plate separation (neglect edge effects): (a) the charge on the plates, (b) the capacitance, (c) the field between the plates, (d) the potential difference across the capacitor, (e) the energy of the capacitor, (f) the energy density between the plates, (g) the energy in the electric field.

23-10 Suppose a parallel-plate capacitor is charged and kept connected to the charging battery. Next the plate separation is doubled. Describe any change in each of the following quantities as a result of the change in plate separation (neglect edge effects): (a) the potential difference across the capacitor, (b) the capacitance, (c) the charge on the plates, (d) the field between the plates, (e) the energy of the capacitor, (f) the energy density between the plates, (g) the energy in the electric field.

23-11 Suppose a thin sheet of metal is placed midway between the plates of a parallel-plate capacitor (Fig.

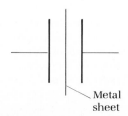

Figure 23-19. Ques. 23-11.

23-19). The metal sheet is insulated from all other objects, and its thickness is negligible compared with the plate separation. By what factor, if any, is the capacitance changed by the insertion of the metal sheet? Does your answer depend on whether the metal sheet is in the middle?

23-12 Suppose a parallel-plate capacitor is charged and then disconnected from the battery. A metal sheet is next inserted between the plates, as shown in Fig. 23-20; the thickness of the sheet is half the plate spacing. Determine the factor by which each of the following is changed: (a) the capacitance, (b) the charge on the plates, (c) the potential difference between the plates, (d) the field between the plates (excluding the volume of the metal sheet), (e) the energy density between the plates (excluding the volume of the metal sheet), (f) the electric energy of the system. (g) Based on energy considerations, do you expect an electric force on the metal sheet as it is being inserted? If so, what is the direction of this force? Explain.

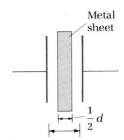

Metal sheet

$\frac{1}{2}d$

Figure 23-20. Ques. 23-12.

23-13 From examination of Fig. 23-5, which capacitance is larger, C_1 or C_2?

23-14 The energy of a capacitor is 3.0 μJ after having been charged by a 1.5-V battery. What is the energy of the capacitor after it is charged by a 3.0-V battery?

23-15 The potential V may be described as the potential energy per unit charge. Why then is the energy of a charged capacitor $\frac{1}{2}QV$ rather than simply QV?

23-16 Since an external electric field exerts forces on nuclei

and electrons in opposite directions, how do atoms hold together in an electric field?

23-17 The dielectric constant of water decreases continuously with increasing temperature: $\kappa = 88$ at $0\,°C$ and $\kappa = 55$ at $100\,°C$. Explain this behavior in terms of the molecules that compose the water.

23-18 Suppose you are asked to construct a capacitor that occupies little space, has a large capacitance, and will operate at a high potential. What properties of the construction materials are important? What compromises will you need to make?

23-19 You can pick up bits of paper with a charged comb even though the paper is neutral. Assuming paper behaves as an ideal insulator (that is, it does not allow charge carriers to move through it), explain how this can happen in terms of the polarization of the atoms in the paper. Will the effect depend on the sign of the charge on the comb? (*Hint:* The electric field due to the charges on the comb falls off with distance from the charged end of the comb.)

23-20 If the bound charge on a dielectric that fills the space between the plates of a parallel-plate capacitor is to be half that of the free charge, what must be the value of the dielectric constant?

23-21 When a dielectric of constant κ fills the space between the plates of a charged capacitor, the magnitude of the field is reduced by a factor of $1/\kappa$ and the energy density is reduced by $1/\kappa$. Given that u is proportional to E^2, how can this be so?

23-22 Complete the following table:

Symbol	Represents	Type	SI unit
C		Scalar	
C_{eq}			F
u	Electric energy density		
σ_b			
E_b			
σ_f			

EXERCISES

Section 23-2. Capacitors and capacitance

23-1 Show that the SI unit for capacitance, the farad (F), is equivalent to $C^2 \cdot s^2/(kg \cdot m^2)$.

23-2 How much charge is transferred from one plate to the other by a 6.0-V battery when it charges a 3.0-nF capacitor?

23-3 If the charge on a capacitor is 14.5 μC when the potential difference across it is 25 V, what is its capacitance?

23-4 A parallel-plate capacitor has circular plates of radius 136 mm that are separated by 1.5 mm in vacuum. What is its capacitance?

23-5 Suppose you wish to build a 1-F parallel-plate capacitor in which the plate separation is 10 mm. If the plates are square and have vacuum between them, what must the length of their sides be?

23-6 What is the capacitance of a cylindrical capacitor of length 220 mm with vacuum between its plates? The outer radius of the inner cylinder is 33 mm, and the inner radius of the outer cylinder is 45 mm.

23-7 Consider a cylindrical capacitor in which the spacing between the plates, $d = R_b - R_a$, is very small compared with the two radii, $R_b \approx R_a \gg d$. Using the result of Example 23-2, show that the expression for the capacitance is nearly the same as for a parallel-plate capacitor with $A = 2\pi R_a L \approx 2\pi R_b L$. (*Hint:* $\ln x \approx x - 1$ when $x \approx 1$.)

23-8 The capacitance of a single isolated conductor is defined as $C = Q/V$, where Q is the charge on the conductor when V is its potential relative to $V_\infty = 0$. Show that the capacitance of an isolated spherical conductor of radius r_0 in vacuum is $C = 4\pi\epsilon_0 r_0$.

23-9 A spherical capacitor consists of a conducting sphere of radius r_a surrounded by a concentric spherical conducting shell of inner radius r_b (Fig. 23-21). The capacitance of a spherical capacitor is $C = 4\pi\epsilon_0 r_b r_a/(r_b - r_a)$. (See Prob. 23-2.) (a) Show that if the spacing between the plates of a spherical capacitor, $d = r_b - r_a$, is much smaller than the two radii, then the capacitance is nearly that of a parallel-plate capacitor of area $A = 4\pi r_a^2 \approx 4\pi r_b^2$. (b) The surface of the earth (radius = 6400 km) and the ionosphere at an altitude of 100 km may be considered to be the plates of a spherical capacitor. Using the result of part (a), determine the capacitance of this capacitor, assuming vacuum between the plates.

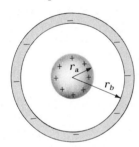

Figure 23-21. Exercise 23-9: Cross section of a spherical capacitor.

Section 23-3. Capacitors in series and parallel

23-10 A 2.4-μF capacitor is connected in series with a 3.1-μF capacitor and then the combination is charged with a 6.1-V battery. (a) What is the equivalent capacitance of the combination? (b) What is the charge on each capacitor? (c) What is the potential difference across each capacitor?

23-11 A 2.4-μF capacitor is connected in parallel with a 3.1-μF capacitor and then the combination is charged with a 6.1-V battery. (a) What is the equivalent capacitance of the combination? (b) What is the potential difference across each capacitor? (c) What is the charge on each capacitor?

23-12 Suppose you need a capacitance of 3.6 μF in a circuit but all you have available is a boxful of capacitors of capacitance 2.4 μF and lower. What is the value of the capacitance of a single capacitor that you can combine with a 2.4-μF capacitor to give an equivalent capacitance of 3.6 μF? How will you connect the two, in series or parallel?

23-13 Suppose you need a capacitance of 1.7 μF in a circuit but all you have available is a boxful of capacitors of capacitance 2.4 μF and higher. What is the value of the capacitance of a single capacitor that you can combine with a 2.4-μF capacitor to give an equivalent capacitance of 1.7 μF? How will you connect the two, in series or parallel?

23-14 A 62-nF capacitor is charged with a 12-V battery and then disconnected from the battery. The capacitor's lead wires are then connected to those of an initially uncharged 38-nF capacitor. (a) What is the final charge on each capacitor after they are connected? (b) What is the final potential difference across each capacitor after they are connected?

23-15 A 62-nF capacitor and a 38-nF capacitor are separately charged with a 12-V battery and then disconnected from the battery. Suppose the two lead wires from the positive plates of the capacitors are connected together, and the two lead wires from the negative plates of the capacitors are connected together. (a) What is the final charge on each capacitor? (b) What is the final potential difference across each capacitor? Now suppose the capacitors' lead wires are reversed such that plates with charge of opposite sign are connected. (c) What is the final charge on each capacitor? (d) What is the final potential difference across each capacitor?

23-16 The equivalent capacitance of a number of capacitors connected in parallel is $C_{eq} = \Sigma C_i$. Thus the equivalent capacitance must be larger than the capacitance of any of the individual capacitors simply because a sum of positive numbers must be larger than any single term in the sum. The equivalent capacitance of a number of capacitors connected in series is $C_{eq} = 1/[\Sigma(1/C_i)]$. Show that the equivalent capacitance must be smaller than the capacitance of any of the individual capacitors.

23-17 In Example 23-3 we showed that the equivalent capacitance of two capacitors connected in series may be written

$$C_{eq} = \frac{C_1 C_2}{C_2 + C_1}$$

(a) Show that the equivalent capacitance of three capacitors connected in series may be written

$$C_{eq} = \frac{C_1 C_2 C_3}{C_2 C_3 + C_1 C_3 + C_1 C_2}$$

(b) Write a similar expression for the equivalent capacitance of four capacitors connected in series.

23-18 For the arrangement in Fig. 23-7, $C_1 = 2.0\ \mu$F, $C_2 = 3.0\ \mu$F, and $C_3 = 5.0\ \mu$F. (a) What is the equivalent capacitance of the combination? Suppose $V_b - V_a = 25$ V. (b) What is the potential difference across each capacitor? (c) What is the charge on each capacitor?

23-19 For the arrangement in Fig. 23-22, $C_1 = 4.0\ \mu F$, $C_2 = 6.0\ \mu F$, and $C_3 = 5.0\ \mu F$. (a) What is the equivalent capacitance of the combination? Suppose $V_b - V_a = 65$ V. (b) What is the potential difference across each capacitor? (c) What is the charge on each capacitor?

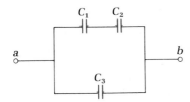

Figure 23-22. Exercise 23-19.

23-20 In Fig. 23-23, capacitor 1 is initially charged to a potential difference of V_0 by throwing switch S to the left. (a) What is the charge on capacitor 1? Suppose the switch is now thrown to the right. (b) What is the final charge on each capacitor and what is the final potential difference across each capacitor? Express your answers in terms of V_0, C_1, C_2, and C_3. (c) Evaluate your answers for the case where $V_0 = 35$ V, $C_1 = 4.0\ \mu F$, $C_2 = 6.0\ \mu F$, and $C_3 = 2.0\ \mu F$.

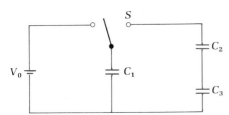

Figure 23-23. Exercise 23-20.

Section 23-4. Electric energy and energy density

23-21 A 1.0-μF capacitor is charged with a 10-V battery. (a) What is the energy of the capacitor? (b) What is the capacitor's energy if it is charged with a 20-V battery?

23-22 A 0.25-μF parallel-plate capacitor is charged with a 96-V battery. (a) What is the energy of the capacitor? (b) If the plates are separated by 0.12 mm, what is the field between the plates? (c) What is the energy density between the plates? (Neglect edge effects and assume vacuum is between the plates.)

23-23 As a rough approximation of the electric field in the earth's atmosphere, assume that it is uniform and of magnitude 100 V/m in the region between the surface and the ionosphere, and then zero above the ionosphere. (a) What is the electric energy density in the atmosphere? (b) Given that the radius of the earth is 6400 km and that the altitude of the ionosphere is about 100 km, estimate the electric energy contained in the earth's atmosphere.

23-24 A typical lead-acid storage battery used in an automobile stores about 1 kW · h (3.6×10^6 J) of electric energy, and the potential difference between its terminals is 12 V. (a) Determine the capacitance of a capacitor that can store this amount of energy when the potential difference across it is 12 V. (b) If this capacitor is a parallel-plate capacitor with square plates separated by 1.0 mm, determine the length of the sides of the plates. Neglect edge effects and assume vacuum between the plates. Do you think capacitors are likely to replace batteries for use in automobiles?

23-25 Determine the electric energy of the system of capacitors discussed in Exercise 23-19 and illustrated in Fig. 23-22.

23-26 (a) Determine the electric energy of the capacitors of Exercise 23-14 before and after their lead wires are connected together. (b) Determine the electric energy of the capacitors of Exercise 23-15 before and after their lead wires are connected together. (As we shall see in the next chapter, the lost electric energy is transferred as heat to the environment.)

23-27 Show that when two capacitors are connected in series the sum of their individual energies $U = U_1 + U_2$ is the same as that of a single capacitor whose capacitance is the equivalent capacitance of the two and whose charge is the same as that for each individual capacitor.

23-28 Show that the equivalent capacitance C_{12} of capacitors 1 and 2 connected in parallel is $C_{12} = C_1 + C_2$ by finding the capacitance of a single capacitor that stores the same energy as capacitors 1 and 2 when it possesses the same charge as 1 and 2 and has the same potential difference across it as is across 1 and 2.

23-29 A spherical capacitor consists of a conducting sphere of radius r_a surrounded by a concentric spherical conducting shell of inner radius r_b (Fig. 23-21). The capacitance of a spherical capacitor is $C = 4\pi\epsilon_0 r_a r_b/(r_b - r_a)$. (See Prob. 23-2.) Show that the energy of the capacitor is $U = \frac{1}{2}Q^2/C$ by integrating the energy density, $u = \frac{1}{2}\epsilon_0 E^2$. (Hint: See Example 23-7. The appropriate volume element is a spherical shell of volume $4\pi r^2\ dr$.)

23-30 The capacitance of a single isolated spherical conductor with radius r_0 is given in Exercise 23-8 as $C = 4\pi\epsilon_0 r_0$, and in Example 23-7 we found that the energy U of an isolated spherical conductor with charge Q is $U = Q^2/8\pi\epsilon_0 r_0$. Show that these two results give the first of Eqs. (23-5): $U = \frac{1}{2}Q^2/C$.

23-31 Assume that the proton can be represented as a charged conducting sphere of radius 1×10^{-15} m. Using this model, estimate the electric energy of a proton in MeV. (Hint: See Example 23-7.)

23-32 For the situation described in Exercise 23-20 (Fig. 23-23), show that the final energy stored in the system of capacitors is reduced by the factor $[C_1(C_2 + C_3)]/(C_1 C_2 + C_1 C_3 + C_2 C_3)$ after the switch is thrown to the right.

23-33 Consider a parallel-plate capacitor in which the plate separation x can be varied while the charge on the plates remains fixed. (a) Show that the force on each plate by the other has magnitude $Q^2/2\epsilon_0 A$. [*Hint:* Recall Eq. (9-9): $F_x = -dU/dx$.] (b) Use the answer to part (a) to find the work done by electric forces when the spacing is changed from d to $3d$. (c) Compare your answer to part (b) with the change in the energy of the capacitor due to the spacing change.

Section 23-5. Electrostatic properties of insulators

23-34 A capacitor is charged with a 9.6-V battery and then the battery is disconnected. A dielectric is fitted snugly between the plates and the potential then measures 3.2 V. What is the dielectric constant of the dielectric material?

23-35 What is the capacitance of a parallel-plate capacitor, with plate area 0.024 m² and plate separation 0.26 mm, that has neoprene (see Table 23-1) in the space between the plates? Neglect edge effects.

23-36 What is the capacitance of a 1-m length of coaxial cable in which the wire radius is 0.91 mm and the inner radius of the coaxial cylinder is 1.22 mm? The insulator between the two is nylon. Neglect end effects.

23-37 A parallel-plate capacitor with plate area 0.087 m² and plate separation 1.8 mm has a capacitance of 2.4 nF when a certain dielectric fills the space between the plates. What is the dielectric constant of this dielectric?

23-38 A parallel-plate capacitor has a plate separation of 0.97 mm and a capacitance of 1.4 nF when vacuum is between the plates. The capacitor is charged with a 9.6-V battery and then disconnected from the battery. (a) What is the field between the plates? (b) What is the charge on the plates? Now, with the battery still disconnected, the space between the plates is filled with a dielectric that has a dielectric constant of 8.2. (c) What is the field between the plates? (d) What is the

charge on the plates?

23-39 What is the maximum potential difference that can be placed across an air-filled parallel-plate capacitor with plate separation 1.0 mm?

23-40 What is the maximum electric energy density that can exist in air at room temperature and atmospheric pressure?

23-41 Suppose you must design a parallel-plate capacitor that has a capacitance of 3.6 nF and a maximum operating potential difference of 4×10^4 V. Further, the dielectric material between the plates must be polystyrene. What is the minimum plate area that you can use?

23-42 Show that the energy density of the electric field between the plates of a parallel-plate capacitor with a dielectric between the plates is $u = \frac{1}{2}\kappa\epsilon_0 E^2$. (*Hint:* Repeat the development presented in Sec. 23-5, except with a dielectric between the plates rather than vacuum.)

Section 23-6. Atomic description of the properties of insulators

23-43 A parallel-plate capacitor with Bakelite between the plates has a plate area of 0.070 m² and a capacitance of 4.0 nF. The capacitor is charged with a 10.0-V battery. (a) What is the free charge density on the plates? (b) What is the bound charge density on the dielectric? (c) What is the magnitude of the electric field? (d) What is the magnitude of the contribution to the electric field due to the free charge? (e) What is the magnitude of the contribution to the electric field due to the bound charge?

23-44 For a charged parallel-plate capacitor with Teflon as the dielectric in the space between the plates, what is the ratio of the bound charge on the Teflon to the free charge on the plates?

23-45 Using the model of a dielectric presented in Example 23-10, determine δ_{max} for fused quartz. The mass density of fused quartz is 2.6×10^3 kg/m³.

PROBLEMS

23-1 Consider a capacitor that consists of a number n of equally spaced, parallel conducting sheets, as shown in Fig. 23-24. Alternate sheets connected together compose the positive plate, and the other alternate sheets compose the negative plate. Show that the capacitance of this arrangement is

$$C = \frac{(n-1)\epsilon_0 A}{d}$$

where A is the area of each sheet and d is the sheet spacing. Assume vacuum is between the sheets and neglect edge effects.

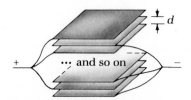

Figure 23-24. Prob. 23-1.

23-2 A spherical capacitor consists of a conducting sphere (radius r_a) as one plate surrounded by a concentric conducting shell (inner radius r_b) as the other plate

(Fig. 23-21). Show that the capacitance of this capacitor with vacuum between the plates is

$$C = 4\pi\epsilon_0 \frac{r_b r_a}{r_b - r_a}$$

23-3 What is the equivalent capacitance of the arrangement shown in Fig. 23-25?

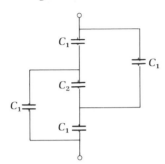

Figure 23-25. Prob. 23-3.

23-4 The section of the circuit that includes the right plate of capacitor a (plate separation d_a) and the left plate of capacitor b (plate separation d_b) in Fig. 23-26 can be rigidly translated back and forth to vary simultaneously the capacitance of both capacitors. During the translation, $d = d_a + d_b$ remains fixed. (a) Show that the equivalent capacitance of the arrangement is

$$C_{eq} = \frac{\epsilon_0 A d}{d_a(d - d_a)}$$

where A is the area of the plates of each capacitor. (b) Make a graph of C_{eq} versus d_a. At what value(s) of d_a is C_{eq} a minimum? Is there a maximum value of C_{eq}? Explain.

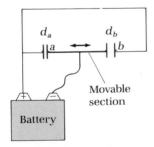

Figure 23-26. Prob. 23-4.

23-5 Consider two conducting spheres a and b, each with a radius (r_a and r_b) that is much smaller than the distance d between their centers. (a) Treating the spheres as capacitor plates, show that the capacitance of the spheres is approximately

$$C \approx \frac{4\pi\epsilon_0}{(1/r_a) + (1/r_b) - (2/d)}$$

(Hint: Since $d \gg r_a$ and $d \gg r_b$, you may assume

that the surface charge density on each sphere is uniform.) (b) Estimate the capacitance of two conducting spheres with $r_a = r_b = 20$ mm that are separated by 1 m.

23-6 *Stray capacitance.* Capacitance is exhibited by systems of conductors in electric circuits, whether the capacitance is purposely included in the circuit or not. The wires used to connect circuit devices together have some capacitance, although quite small in most cases. For example, the two wires in an ordinary lamp cord behave as a capacitor. Capacitance that is inadvertently contained in a circuit is called *stray capacitance*. Consider estimating the capacitance of two long, straight, parallel wires, each of length L and radius R, separated by a perpendicular distance D between their centers. (a) Assuming $L \gg D \gg R$, show that the capacitance of the wires is approximately

$$C \approx \frac{\pi\epsilon_0 L}{\ln(D/R)}$$

(Hint: Since $L \gg D$, you may neglect end effects, and since $D \gg R$, you may assume that the surface charge density on each wire is nearly uniform.) (b) Estimate the capacitance of two such wires with $R = 1$ mm, $D = 10$ mm, and $L = 1$ m.

23-7 A Geiger-Müller tube is a device used to measure ionizing radiation. The tube is essentially a cylindrical capacitor with a wire as one plate, a coaxial conducting cylinder as the other plate, and with a gas ($\kappa \approx 1$) as the dielectric. The tube is operated so that the electric field near the wire is very large. Thus an ionizing particle moving through the gas causes the onset of breakdown, and the particle is detected by a burst of electric current from one plate to the other. (a) Show that the potential difference V between the plates can be written

$$V = ER_a \ln \frac{R_b}{R_a}$$

where E is the magnitude of the electric field just outside the wire, R_a is the radius of the wire, and R_b is the inner radius of the cylinder. Neglect end effects. (b) Determine V for the case where $R_a = 0.30$ mm, $R_b = 20.0$ mm, and $E = 2.0 \times 10^6$ V/m. (c) What is the magnitude of the electric field inside the tube and very close to the cylinder?

23-8 (a) Show that the electric energy of a spherically symmetric uniform volume charge of radius r_0 and charge Q is

$$U = \frac{3Q^2}{20\pi\epsilon_0 r_0}$$

Assume $\kappa = 1$ everywhere. (b) What fraction of the total energy is due to the field inside the charge distribution? (c) Estimate the electric energy of a proton (in MeV), assuming that it can be represented as a spherically symmetric uniform volume charge of radius 1×10^{-15} m. Assume $\kappa = 1$ and compare your answer with that found for Exercise 23-31.

23-9 A single straight wire of length 1.6 m and unknown radius is insulated with neoprene such that the outer radius of the neoprene is 6 mm. A cylindrical capacitor is formed by painting the outside of the neoprene with a conducting layer of silver paint, and the capacitance is measured to be 0.6 nF. What is the radius of the wire? Neglect end effects.

23-10 A parallel-plate capacitor with plate area A and plate separation d is partially filled with a dieletric of thickness x and dielectric constant κ, as shown in Fig. 23-27. Develop an expression for the capacitance. Neglect edge effects.

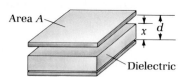

Area A

Figure 23-27. Prob. 23-10.

23-11 A dielectric slab is partially inserted a distance x between the plates of a parallel-plate capacitor of plate separation d and lateral dimensions w_1 and w_2, as shown in Fig. 23-28. (a) Show that the capacitance is $C = \epsilon_0 w_2(\kappa x + w_1 - x)/d$, where κ is the dielectric constant of the dielectric. (b) Suppose the capacitor is charged and then disconnected from the charging battery before the dielectric is inserted. Develop an expression for the electric force on the slab. What is the direction of this force? Neglect edge effects.

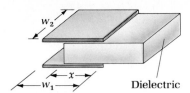

Dielectric

Figure 23-28. Prob. 23-11.

23-12 In Example 23-10 we developed a rough estimate of the displacement of the relative positions of positive and negative charges in a dielectric due to the action of an external electric field. Consider another approach. Assume that the nucleus of an atom can be treated as a point charge with charge Ze and that the electrons can be treated as a uniform volume charge of radius r_0 and charge $-Ze$. (a) Show that the force on the nucleus is zero when it is displaced a distance δ from the center of negative charge with

$$\delta = \frac{4\pi\epsilon_0 r_0^3 E}{Ze}$$

where E is the contribution to the field, at the position of the nucleus, due to charges outside the atom. (Hint: See Example 21-6.) (b) Determine δ when $E = 15 \times 10^6$ V/m, $Z = 10$, and $r_0 = 2 \times 10^{-10}$ m. Compare your answer with that found in Example 23-10.

CHAPTER 24
CURRENT AND
RESISTANCE

24-1 INTRODUCTION

In the last few chapters, we dealt mostly with electrostatics, the effects of stationary charges. Now we begin to consider the motion of charge carriers, or *electric conduction*. In electrostatics, $\mathbf{E} = 0$ inside a conductor. However, if we maintain a nonzero field in a conductor, say by connecting it to a battery, then the conductor's charge carriers will flow, and an *electric current* will exist. In this chapter, we describe the effects of steady currents, and we investigate models that aid in the understanding of electric conduction in matter.

24-2 THE FLOW OF CHARGE

A conductor is a material in which some of the charged particles are free to move; these particles are the conductor's charge carriers. For example, we can regard a metal as an array of positive ions located at fixed lattice sites and interspersed with free electrons. The charge on the free electrons is equal and opposite the charge on the ions to give a neutral medium. The free electrons can move through the lattice; they are the charge carriers in a metal.

Electrons are the charge carriers in a metal.

Electric current. The *electric current* characterizes the flow of charge though a material. Figure 24-1a shows a section of conducting wire, with positive charge carriers moving to the right. Let dQ be the magnitude of the charge that passes through the plane cross-sectional surface labeled S in time dt. The electric current I in the wire is the rate at which charge passes through this surface:

Definition of electric current

$$I = \frac{dQ}{dt} \tag{24-1}$$

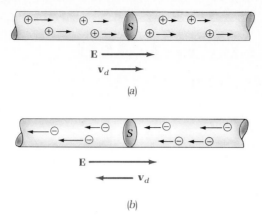

(a)

(b)

Figure 24-1. (a) Current in a wire with positive charge carriers. (b) Current in a wire with negative charge carriers. The sense of the current is to the right in each case.

The SI unit of electric current is the ampere (A), equal to one coulomb per second: 1 A = 1 C/s. The ampere is named for André-Marie Ampère (1775–1836).

Electric current I is a scalar quantity. Even though the electric current is not a vector quantity, it is common practice to speak of the "direction" of the current. This direction corresponds to the direction of flow of positive charge carriers. To emphasize that current is a scalar, we shall refer to the *sense* of the current. The sense of the current in a conductor is given by the direction of motion of positive charge carriers. For example, the current in Fig. 24-1a is to the right.

Consider the effect of the sign of the charge carriers on the sense of the current. For comparison with the positive charge carriers moving to the right in Fig. 24-1a, we show negative charge carriers moving to the left in Fig. 24-1b. In Fig. 24-1a, positive carriers moving to the right tend to cause the region to the right to become more positive and the region to the left to become more negative. In Fig. 24-1b, negative carriers moving to the left also tend to cause the region to the right to become more positive and the region to the left to become more negative. That is, the carrier motion shown in both Fig. 24-1a and 24-1b gives the same result. Thus the sense of the current is the same in Fig. 24-1a as it is in Fig. 24-1b; in each case it is to the right. *This means that we need not concern ourselves with the sign of the carriers when dealing with the external effects of a current; these effects are the same for carriers having either sign.**

Drift velocity. When an externally applied electric field exists in a conductor, it exerts a force on each of the conductor's charge carriers and causes them to move through the material. (Particles other than carriers are displaced slightly, but are confined to their respective lattice sites.) If the charge carriers were free of other forces, then a constant electric field would cause them to have a constant acceleration. However, the charge carriers interact with the other particles of the material. The combined effect of this interaction and the applied electric field causes the charge carriers to move with a constant average velocity called the *drift velocity* $\mathbf{v}_d$.

Now we find the relationship between the current I and the drift speed v_d in a wire with cross-sectional area A. Let n be the number density of charge

> The sense of a current is given by the direction of motion of positive carriers.

> The sense of a current is given by the direction opposite the motion of negative carriers.

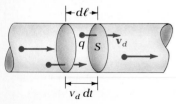

Figure 24-2. Finding the relation between I and v_d. Assuming each carrier has speed v_d, we find that all the carriers in the cylinder of volume $A\,d\ell = Av_d\,dt$ pass through the surface labeled S in time dt. Thus $I = dQ/dt = (nAv_d\,dt|q|)/dt = nAv_d|q|$.

* An exception to this rule is a magnetic phenomenon, called the *Hall effect*, which we discuss in Chap. 26.

carriers in the wire (number of carriers per unit volume), and let q be the charge on each carrier. In Fig. 24-2, we assume that each carrier is traveling with speed v_d so that all carriers in the cylinder of length $d\ell = v_d\,dt$ pass through the surface labeled S in time dt. (For a steady flow, these carriers are replaced by those in a neighboring cylinder on the left so that the net charge in this section of wire is unchanged, as it is for all other sections of the wire.) Since $(nA\,d\ell)$ is the number of charge carriers in the cylinder (all of which pass through the surface labeled S in time dt), the magnitude of the charge dQ that passes through the surface in time dt is

$$dQ = nA\,d\ell\,|q| = nAv_d\,dt\,|q|$$

From Eq. (24-1), $I = dQ/dt$, so that

Current in terms of drift speed
$$I = nAv_d|q| \qquad (24\text{-}2)$$

Thus the current is proportional to the drift speed.

EXAMPLE 24-1. (a) Determine the number density n of carriers in a copper wire assuming there is one carrier (electron) per copper atom. (b) The maximum recommended current in a 14-gauge copper wire (radius = 0.81 mm, $A = 2.1 \times 10^{-6}$ m^2) used in household circuits is 15 A. Use your answer to part (a) to determine the drift speed of the carriers in such a case.

SOLUTION. (a) With one free electron per atom, the number density of carriers is the same as the number density of atoms. Thus, $n = N_A\rho_m/M$ where N_A is Avogadro's number, ρ_m is the mass density of copper ($= 8.95 \times 10^3$ kg/m^3), and M is the molecular weight of copper ($= 63.5$ g/mol).

$$n = \frac{(6.02 \times 10^{23}\ \text{mol}^{-1})(8.95 \times 10^6\ \text{g/m}^3)}{63.5\ \text{g/mol}}$$

$$= 8.48 \times 10^{28}\ \text{carriers/m}^3$$

(b) Solving Eq. (24-2) for v_d and using $|q| = e$, we have

$$v_d = \frac{I}{nAe}$$

$$= \frac{15\ \text{A}}{(8.48 \times 10^{28}\ \text{carriers/m}^3)(2.1 \times 10^{-6}\ \text{m}^2)(1.6 \times 10^{-19}\ \text{C})}$$

$$= 5.3 \times 10^{-4}\ \text{m/s} \approx 2\ \text{m/h}$$

The drift speed is literally slower than a snail's pace.

Electric current density. Electric current I characterizes the flow of charge through the entire cross section of a conductor. To describe the flow of charge at points within a conductor, we use the *current density* $\mathbf{j}$, which is a vector quantity. If the current density is uniform, the magnitude j of the current density is the current I divided by the cross-sectional area A of the wire:

$$j = \frac{I}{A} \qquad (\text{uniform } \mathbf{j}) \qquad (24\text{-}3)$$

Substitution of Eq. (24-2) into Eq. (24-3) gives j in terms of the drift speed v_d:

$$j = \frac{nAv_d|q|}{A} = nv_d|q|$$

This result can be expressed as a vector equation using the drift velocity $\mathbf{v}_d$:

Current density
$$\mathbf{j} = nq\mathbf{v}_d \qquad (24\text{-}4)$$

Notice that the absolute value sign has been taken from $|q|$ in Eq. (24-4). Thus the current density points in the direction of $\mathbf{v}_d$ for positive carriers, and it points opposite $\mathbf{v}_d$ for negative carriers. Consequently, the direction of $\mathbf{j}$ coincides with the sense of the current in a wire.

If the conductor contains more than one type of charge carrier, then there is a contribution to $\mathbf{j}$ from each type of carrier. Suppose there are two types of charge carrier, a and b. Then

$$\mathbf{j} = n_a q_a \mathbf{v}_{da} + n_b q_b \mathbf{v}_{db} \tag{24-5}$$

where the subscripts a and b designate the quantities for each type of charge carrier.

We can use Eq. (24-5) to show that the contributions to $\mathbf{j}$ from charge carriers of opposite sign are in the same direction. Consider the current density in a salt solution in which singly charged ions are the charge carriers. The charges are $+e$ for the positive ions and $-e$ for the negative ions, and for a neutral medium, the number density of each type of ion is the same. If we let the x axis be along the field direction, $\mathbf{E} = E\mathbf{i}$, then the drift velocity of the positive ions is $\mathbf{v}_{d+} = v_{d+}\mathbf{i}$ and the drift velocity of the negative ions is $\mathbf{v}_{d-} = -v_{d-}\mathbf{i}$, where the drift speeds v_{d+} and v_{d-} are positive. That is, the drift velocity of the positive ions is in the direction of the applied field, and the drift velocity of the negative ions is opposite the applied field. The x component of $\mathbf{j}$ is

$$j_x = nev_{d+} + n(-e)(-v_{d-}) = nev_{d+} + nev_{d-}$$

Since each factor is positive, each term provides a positive contribution to the x component of $\mathbf{j}$. Thus the sense of the current I corresponds to the direction of $\mathbf{j}$ for both positive and negative carriers. *Again we see that the external effect of charge carriers of either sign is the same.*

Equations (24-4) and (24-5) are valid for any sort of current distribution, but Eq. (24-3) applies only when the current density is uniform. If the drift velocity of the carriers varies from point to point within a material, as shown in Fig. 24-3, then the current density varies correspondingly. In this case the current I through a surface can be found from the surface integral of the current density $\mathbf{j}$:

$$I = \int \mathbf{j} \cdot d\mathbf{S}$$

Thus the current through a surface is the flux of the current density for that surface. (See Prob. 24-2.)

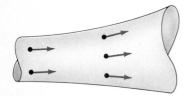

Figure 24-3. The drift velocity is shown as it varies in a conductor with varying cross section. The arrows indicate values of $\mathbf{v}_d$ at a few representative points. If the carriers are positive, these arrows can be used to represent $\mathbf{j}$ also. What if the carriers are negative?

EXAMPLE 24-2. Assuming $\mathbf{j}$ is uniform, determine the current density in the wire in Example 24-1.

SOLUTION. For the wire in Example 24-1, $I = 15$ A and $A = 2.1 \times 10^{-6}$ m². From Eq. (24-3), the magnitude of the current density is

$$j = \frac{I}{A} = \frac{15 \text{ A}}{2.1 \times 10^{-6} \text{ m}^2} = 7.1 \times 10^6 \text{ A/m}^2$$

Since the charge carriers are negative electrons, the direction of $\mathbf{j}$ is opposite the drift velocity.

24-3 RESISTANCE AND OHM'S LAW

If a potential difference V is applied across a section of conductor, such as a metal wire, then a current I will be produced in the conductor. The amount of potential difference required to produce a given current depends on a property of the particular section of conductor, a property called its *resistance*. The resistance R is defined as

Definition of resistance

$$R = \frac{V}{I} \qquad (24\text{-}6)$$

The resistance is appropriately named; for a given section of conductor, it is a measure of that section's opposition to the flow of charge. Since $R = V/I$ (or $I = V/R$), a larger resistance for a section of conductor means that a given potential difference will produce a smaller current. Resistance is often added to circuits to limit or control the current. The circuit element or component used for this purpose is called a *resistor*, and is shown schematically as —∧∧∧— in circuit diagrams.

For many conductors, the current in a section of the conductor is directly proportional to the potential difference across the section, so that the resistance is independent of V (or I). For example, if the potential difference across the section of conductor is doubled, then the current is doubled. For this case we can write

Ohm's law

$$V = IR \qquad (R \text{ independent of } V \text{ or } I) \qquad (24\text{-}7)$$

Equation (24-7) is called *Ohm's law* for Georg Simon Ohm (1787 – 1854), and the SI unit of resistance is the ohm (Ω): $1\ \Omega = 1$ V/A.

The name "Ohm's law" for Eq. (24-7) is possibly misleading because the realm of validity of this equation may be too limited to warrant using the term "law." It is not a fundamental statement about nature as, for example, Coulomb's law is. Rather, the equation is an empirical expression that accurately describes the behavior of many materials over the range of values of V typically encountered in electric circuits. In these important circumstances, Ohm's law is quite useful.

Materials that "obey" Ohm's law are called *ohmic*, and materials that do not obey Ohm's law are called *nonohmic*. An ohmic conductor is characterized by a single value of resistance, as shown in Fig. 24-4a. That is, its graph of V versus I is a straight line, so that the slope at each point on the graph is the same. A nonohmic conductor is not characterized by a single value of resistance, and the graph of V versus I for a nonohmic conductor is not a straight line (Fig. 24-4b). A resistor used as a circuit element will usually have its resistance marked on it (often coded in terms of colored bands or rings). Therefore, such a resistor is assumed to be ohmic.

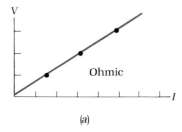

(a)

Resistivity. The resistance of a section of conductor depends on its size, shape, and composition. Consider a section of conductor with length ℓ and uniform cross-sectional area A, as shown in Fig. 24-5. If a potential difference V

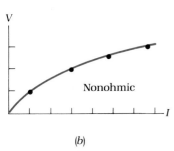

(b)

Figure 24-4. (a) The graph of V versus I for a resistor composed of an ohmic material. The slope of the line gives R. (b) The graph of V versus I for a resistor composed of a nonohmic material. This shows only one of any number of possible relationships.

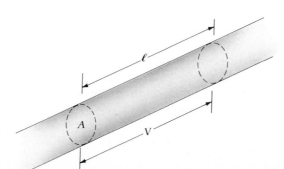

Figure 24-5. The resistance of a section of conductor is directly proportional to ℓ ($R \propto \ell$) and inversely proportional to A ($R \propto 1/A$); $R = \rho\ell/A$.

Table 24-1. Resistivities at 20°C

Substance	$\rho, \Omega \cdot \text{m}$
Metals	
Silver	1.59×10^{-8}
Copper	1.673×10^{-8}
Gold	2.35×10^{-8}
Aluminum	2.655×10^{-8}
Tungsten	5.65×10^{-8}
Nickel	6.84×10^{-8}
Iron	9.71×10^{-8}
Platinum	10.6×10^{-8}
Lead	20.65×10^{-8}
Semiconductors	
Silicon	4.3×10^{3}
Germanium	0.46
Insulators	
Glass	$10^{10} - 10^{14}$
Quartz	7.5×10^{17}
Sulfur	10^{15}
Teflon	10^{13}
Rubber	$10^{13} - 10^{16}$
Wood	$10^{8} - 10^{11}$
Carbon (diamond)	10^{11}

is applied across the section, then a current I exists in it, and the resistance R of the section is $R = V/I$. Suppose we now apply the same potential difference V across a section of conductor that has twice the length of the original one, but is the same in all other respects. We find the current is now half its previous value so that the resistance has doubled. Such measurements indicate that the resistance is directly proportional to the length of a section: $R \propto \ell$. Suppose we now apply the same potential difference across a section of conductor that has twice the cross-sectional area of the original one, but is the same in all other respects. We find that the current is now twice its previous value so that the resistance is halved. Such measurements indicate that the resistance is inversely proportional to the cross-sectional area of a section: $R \propto 1/A$.

In addition to this size dependence, the resistance of a section of conductor depends on the material that composes the section. The material dependence of the resistance is represented by a proportionality factor called the *resistivity*. Thus the resistance of a section of conductor of length ℓ, cross-sectional area A, and resistivity ρ is

$$R = \frac{\rho\ell}{A} \tag{24-8}$$

The resistivities of some representative materials are given in Table 24-1.

EXAMPLE 24-3. The maximum recommended current in a 12-gauge copper wire (radius = 1.03 mm, $A = 3.31 \times 10^{-6}$ m²) used in household circuits is 20 A. (a) What is the resistance of a section of 12-gauge copper wire with length $\ell = 1.00$ m? (b) What is the potential difference across this section when the current is 20 A?

SOLUTION. (a) Using Eq. (24-8) and the resistivity of copper from Table 24-1, we find

$$R = \frac{\rho\ell}{A} = \frac{(1.673 \times 10^{-8}\ \Omega \cdot \text{m})(1.00\ \text{m})}{3.31 \times 10^{-6}\ \text{m}^2}$$

$$= 5.05 \times 10^{-3}\ \Omega = 5.05\ \text{m}\Omega$$

(b) For a current of 20 A,

$$V = IR = (20\ \text{A})(5.05\ \text{m}\Omega) = 100\ \text{mV}$$

The resistance of this 1-m length of wire is small, and the potential difference across the section is correspondingly small, even for this relatively large current. The small resistivity of some metals, such as copper (see Table 24-1), accounts for their extensive use in electric circuits.

Table 24-2. Temperature coefficients of resistivity at 20°C

Substance	α, K^{-1}
Metals	
Silver	3.8×10^{-3}
Copper	3.9×10^{-3}
Gold	3.4×10^{-3}
Aluminum	3.9×10^{-3}
Tungsten	4.5×10^{-3}
Nickel	6×10^{-3}
Iron	5×10^{-3}
Platinum	3.93×10^{-3}
Lead	4.3×10^{-3}
Semiconductors	
Silicon	-7.5×10^{-2}
Germanium	-4.8×10^{-2}

Temperature dependence of the resistivity of metals. The resistivity of many pure metals varies almost linearly with temperature over a wide temperature range, as shown in Fig. 24-6 for copper. Since there is usually only a slight amount of curvature in the graph of ρ versus T for metals, we can write

$$\rho \approx \rho_0[1 + \alpha(T - T_0)] \tag{24-9}$$

where ρ is the resistivity at temperature T, ρ_0 is the resistivity at a reference temperature T_0, and α is called the *temperature coefficient of resistivity*. That is, for a limited temperature range we can approximate the slightly curved graph of ρ versus T with a straight line. Notice that in Fig. 24-6, the straight line given by Eq. (24-9) is hardly discernible from the curved line at temperatures near T_0. The temperature coefficients of resistivity for some representative materials are given in Table 24-2. The values of ρ given in Table 24-1 are for 20°C (293 K), so these values may be used as ρ_0 in Eq. (24-9) if 20°C (or 293 K) is used for T_0. The values of α given in Table 24-2 also correspond to 20°C.

The temperature dependence of the resistivity of metals diverges markedly

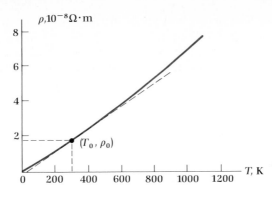

Figure 24-6. Graph of ρ versus T for copper. In the region of the graph near (T_0, ρ_0) the curve is approximately a straight line.

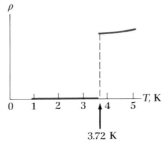

Figure 24-8. The resistivity of tin at low temperatures. The material becomes superconducting below 3.72 K.

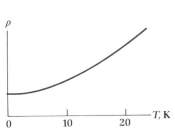

Figure 24-7. Typical low-temperature behavior of the resistivity of a metal.

from linearity at low temperatures, below about 20 K. The typical behavior is shown in Fig. 24-7. At these low temperatures the resistance of a metal depends greatly on trace amounts of impurities. Indeed, measurements of resistivity at low temperatures are often used to estimate the amount of impurity in a metal.

For some metals a remarkable thing happens as they are cooled to very low temperatures. The resistance totally disappears! This behavior is shown in Fig. 24-8. The phenomenon was discovered in 1911 by H. Kamerlingh Onnes (1853–1926) and is called *superconductivity*. Today superconductivity is an active area of research in physics and is increasingly important in engineering.

Superconductivity

EXAMPLE 24-4. *Resistance thermometer.* A metal wire is often used as a thermometer, and the thermometric property that is measured is the wire's resistance. Platinum is commonly used for this purpose. Suppose we measure the resistance of a platinum resistance thermometer to be 107.9 Ω at a temperature of 20°C. Then, when the thermometer is submersed in a boiling liquid, its measured resistance is 139.3 Ω. Estimate the temperature of the boiling liquid.

SOLUTION. Writing Eq. (24-9) in terms of resistance rather than resistivity (see Ques. 24-10), we have

$$R \approx R_0[1 + \alpha(T - T_0)]$$

where R ($= 139.3\ \Omega$) is the resistance at the unknown temperature T, R_0 ($= 107.9\ \Omega$) is the resistance at T_0 ($= 293$ K), and α ($= 3.93 \times 10^{-3}$ K^{-1} from Table 24-2) is the temperature coefficient of resistivity for platinum. Solving for T gives

$$T \approx \frac{R - R_0}{\alpha R_0} + T_0$$

$$\approx \frac{139.3\ \Omega - 107.9\ \Omega}{(3.93 \times 10^{-3}\ \text{K}^{-1})(107.9\ \Omega)} + 293\ \text{K} = 367\ \text{K}$$

Actual resistance thermometers are calibrated at several temperatures, and a regression analysis is used to interpolate between the calibration temperatures.

Ohm's law in terms of j and E. If an electric field E is applied to a conducting material, a current density j is produced in the material. The current density at a point in the material depends on the electric field at that point. That dependence is expressed in terms of a property of the material called the *conductivity* σ:

$$\mathbf{j} = \sigma \mathbf{E} \tag{24-10}$$

(Previously we used the symbol σ to represent a surface charge density. Take care that you do not confuse the two.) From Eq. (24-10), a material that has a larger conductivity than another will have a larger current density for the same electric field. Therefore, the conductivity of a material is a measure of the material's ability to allow charge carriers to flow through it.

If the conductivity of the material is independent of E, then the material is ohmic and Eq. (24-10) is a vectorial expression of Ohm's law. We can show this by considering the section of conductor in Fig. 24-5. We assume $\mathbf{j}$ and $\mathbf{E}$ are uniform within the section so that $I = jA$ and $V = E\ell$. Substituting for V and I in Eq. (24-7), $V = IR$ gives

$$E\ell = jAR$$

Solving for j gives

$$j = \frac{E\ell}{AR} = \frac{\ell}{AR} E$$

Since $j = \sigma E$,

$$\sigma = \frac{\ell}{AR} \tag{24-11}$$

For a material in which R is independent of V, we must have that σ is independent of $\mathbf{E}$ because V and $\mathbf{E}$ are directly related ($V = El$). Thus when σ is independent of $\mathbf{E}$, Eq. (24-10) is a form of Ohm's law. Equation (24-10) expresses Ohm's law at a point within the material, whereas Eq. (24-7), $V = IR$, expresses Ohm's law for a section of material.

From Eq. (24-8) $\rho = RA/\ell$, and from Eq. (24-11) $\sigma = \ell/RA$. Thus

$$\rho = \frac{1}{\sigma}$$

The relation between $\mathbf{E}$ and $\mathbf{j}$ can be written in terms of the resistivity:

$$\mathbf{E} = \rho\mathbf{j} \tag{24-12}$$

EXAMPLE 24-5. (a) Assuming $\mathbf{j}$ is uniform, find E inside the copper wire of Examples 24-1 and 24-2. (b) What is the conductivity of copper at 20°C?

SOLUTION. (a) Assuming a uniform $\mathbf{j}$ in Example 24-2, we found that $j = 7.1 \times 10^6$ A/m². From Table 24-1, $\rho = 1.673 \times 10^{-8}$ $\Omega \cdot$ m for copper:

$E = \rho j = (1.673 \times 10^{-8}\ \Omega \cdot \text{m})(7.1 \times 10^6\ \text{A/m}^2) = 0.12$ V/m

Notice that this electric field is much smaller than the fields typically found between capacitor plates. (b) Since $\rho = 1.72 \times 10^{-8}$ $\Omega \cdot$ m for copper,

$$\sigma = \frac{1}{\rho} = \frac{1}{1.673 \times 10^{-8}\ \Omega \cdot \text{m}} = 5.98 \times 10^7\ \Omega^{-1} \cdot \text{m}^{-1}$$

24-4   DRUDE MODEL OF A METAL

A model proposed by P. K. Drude (1863–1906) in 1900 provides some insight into the nature of electric conduction in metals. The principal characteristic of conduction in metals that a successful microscopic model must yield is Ohm's law. We now show that when Newton's second law is used to describe the average motion of the charge carriers in Drude's model of a metal, the metal obeys Ohm's law.

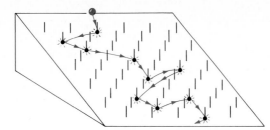

Figure 24-9. A marble rolling down a pegboard. Over a long time interval the motion is characterized by a constant drift velocity down the board.

First, consider an important implication of our discussion so far. From Eq. (24-4), $\mathbf{j} = nq\mathbf{v}_d$, and Eq. (24-10), $\mathbf{j} = \sigma\mathbf{E}$, we see that $\mathbf{v}_d$ and $\mathbf{E}$ are proportional. That is, an applied field causes the carriers to move with a constant average velocity $\mathbf{v}_d$. But if the field were to furnish the only force on a carrier, then the carrier's acceleration would be constant, not its velocity. This means that when a carrier moves through the metal, there must be other forces on it. Indeed, since the average velocity is constant, the sum of all forces on a carrier must be zero on the average.

The situation is analogous to a marble rolling down a pegboard (Fig. 24-9). When first released, a marble will accelerate down the board because of the unbalanced component of the gravitational force down the board. As it collides with the pegs, we notice that its motion, averaged over many collisions, is characterized by a constant average velocity down the board. Averaged over many collisions, the force on a marble due to the pegs is equal and opposite the component of the gravitational force down the board. In Drude's model, a free electron is similar to a marble, the lattice ions are similar to the pegs, and the applied field is similar to the component of the gravitational field down the board.

Drude assumed that the free electrons in metals are the valence electrons that are weakly bound to the atoms when the atoms are isolated (not part of a metal). When the atoms are side by side in a solid, these electrons are free to move through the material. Thus the number density n of carriers is the product of a small integer and the number density of atoms in the material.

The average velocity $\langle \mathbf{v} \rangle$ of the free electrons is the carrier drift velocity $\mathbf{v}_d$: $\langle \mathbf{v} \rangle = \mathbf{v}_d$. Since $\mathbf{E} \propto \mathbf{v}_d$, the average velocity is zero when there is no applied field. That is, if $\mathbf{E} = 0$, then $\langle v_x \rangle = \langle v_y \rangle = \langle v_z \rangle = 0$. The behavior of the free electrons is similar to the behavior of the molecules of a gas in that their velocities are randomly directed.

The force by the applied field $\mathbf{E}$ on an electron is $\mathbf{F} = -e\mathbf{E}$. Since this is the only force on a free electron between collisions, Newton's second law, $\Sigma\mathbf{F} = m\mathbf{a}$, gives the acceleration between collisions as $\mathbf{a} = -e\mathbf{E}/m$. If we align our x axis along $\mathbf{E}$, then the x component of a free electron's velocity at a time t after a collision is

$$v_x = v_{x0} + a_x t = v_{x0} - \left(\frac{eE}{m}\right)t$$

where v_{x0} is the x component of the electron's velocity immediately after the collision. On the average, we have

$$\langle v_x \rangle = \langle v_{x0} \rangle - \left(\frac{eE}{m}\right)\tau$$

where τ characterizes the time interval between collisions. This time interval is often called the *mean free time,* or the *relaxation time.*

For a rather sizable current, the drift speed v_d is only about 10^{-4} m/s (Example 24-1), whereas the average speed $\langle v \rangle$ of the free electrons is about 10^6 m/s. Since $\langle v \rangle$ is a factor of about 10^{10} larger than v_d, the contribution to the motion of the free electrons due to the applied field is negligible at the microscopic level. Therefore, it is valid to assume that the velocity of an electron immediately after each collision is randomly directed relative to $\mathbf{E}$, or $\langle v_{x0} \rangle = 0$. Thus

$$\langle v_x \rangle = \frac{-eE\tau}{m}$$

The drift velocity is $\mathbf{v}_d = \langle \mathbf{v} \rangle = \langle v_x \rangle \mathbf{i}$, so that

$$\mathbf{v}_d = \frac{-eE\tau}{m}\,\mathbf{i}$$

Using Eq. (24-4), $\mathbf{j} = nq\mathbf{v}_d$, we obtain

$$\mathbf{j} = n(-e)\left(\frac{-eE\tau}{m}\,\mathbf{i}\right) = \frac{ne^2\tau}{m}\,E\mathbf{i} = \frac{ne^2\tau}{m}\,\mathbf{E}$$

Comparing this with Eq. (24-10), $\mathbf{j} = \sigma\mathbf{E}$, gives

$$\sigma = \frac{ne^2\tau}{m} \qquad (24\text{-}13)$$

Since $\rho = 1/\sigma$, we also have

$$\rho = \frac{m}{ne^2\tau} \qquad (24\text{-}14)$$

If $\sigma = ne^2\tau/m$ is independent of $\mathbf{E}$, then the model yields Ohm's law. The factors n, e, and m are plainly independent of $\mathbf{E}$, but what about τ? We expect τ to depend on $\langle v \rangle$, and $\mathbf{E}$ may change $\langle v \rangle$ by no more than v_d. But we noted earlier that $\langle v \rangle \approx 10^6$ m/s and $v_d \approx 10^{-4}$ m/s. Because of this vast difference, we expect τ to be essentially independent of $\mathbf{E}$, so Drude's model does give Ohm's law.

Eureka! The model gives Ohm's law.

We can express σ and ρ in terms of the average speed $\langle v \rangle$ by introducing the average distance an electron travels between collisions, the *mean free path* λ:

$$\lambda = \langle v \rangle \tau$$

Substitution for τ into Eqs. (24-13) and (24-14) gives

$$\sigma = \frac{ne^2\lambda}{m\langle v \rangle} \qquad \text{and} \qquad \rho = \frac{m\langle v \rangle}{ne^2\lambda}$$

The Drude model is obviously rather crude. For example, the interaction between an electron and an ion involves the long-range Coulomb force, and in the model we treat this interaction as an abrupt collision. Then, during the time interval between the collisions, we neglect the force on an electron due to the ions. It may seem tempting to try to improve the model by making it more realistic, but there is little to be gained from such an improvement for a very fundamental reason. *It is inappropriate to apply Newton's second law to the motion of an electron in a metal.* An electron in a metal must be described according to *quantum mechanics*. We must learn more about the fundamental laws of physics before we can significantly improve our understanding of conduction in metals.

EXAMPLE 24-6. (a) Estimate the mean free time in copper at 20°C (= 293 K), assuming one free electron per copper atom. (b) Assuming that the average speed of the free electrons is about 10^6 m/s, estimate the mean free path in copper.

SOLUTION. (a) Solving Eq. (24-14) for τ gives

$$\tau = \frac{m}{ne^2\rho}$$

From Example 24-1, $n = 8.48 \times 10^{28}$ carriers/m³, so that

$$\tau = \frac{9.11 \times 10^{-31} \text{ kg}}{\left(\dfrac{8.48 \times 10^{28} \text{ carriers}}{\text{m}^3}\right)(1.60 \times 10^{-19} \text{ C})^2 (1.673 \times 10^{-8} \text{ }\Omega \cdot \text{m})}$$

$$= 2.51 \times 10^{-14} \text{ s}$$

(b) The mean free path is

$$\lambda = \langle v \rangle \tau = (10^6 \text{ m/s})(2.51 \times 10^{-14} \text{ s}) = 10^{-8} \text{ m}$$

This is roughly 100 times the distance between nearest-neighbor atoms in copper.

24-5 CONDUCTION IN SEMICONDUCTORS

We have divided materials into two classes according to their electric conductivity: conductors and insulators. There is a third class, one called *semiconductors,* whose conductivity is intermediate between conductors and insulators. Semiconductors play a central role in modern technology. These are the materials that are used in such devices as diodes, transistors, and integrated circuits. The Drude model showed that σ is directly proportional to the number density n of carriers: $\sigma = (e^2\tau/m)n$. The carrier density n is the key factor in controlling the conductivity of a semiconductor.

Conduction in pure semiconductors. Semiconductors consist of some of the elements in the middle columns in the periodic table, and an element often used is silicon. To be specific, we discuss silicon as our representative semiconductor.

Silicon ($Z = 14$) has a valence of 4, and when the atoms are together in the form of a solid, each has four nearest-neighbors. In Fig. 24-10, we show a two-dimensional portrayal of the three-dimensional silicon lattice; each atom is shown as an ion core of charge $+4e$ accompanied by four valence electrons. In pure silicon at room temperature, almost all of these valence electrons are bound to their respective ion cores, but thermal fluctuations in energy cause some of them to be free. That is, a small fraction of the silicon atoms are *thermally ionized.* (At room temperature, about one silicon atom out of every 5×10^{12} is ionized, a very small fraction indeed.) The electrons that are released by this thermal ionization become negative charge carriers.

In addition to free electrons, semiconductors possess positive charge car-

A free electron is a negative charge carrier in a semiconductor.

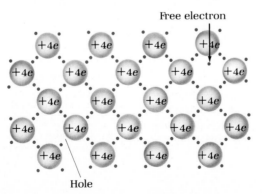

Free electron

Hole

Figure 24-10. A two-dimensional representation of the three-dimensional silicon lattice showing a free electron and a hole.

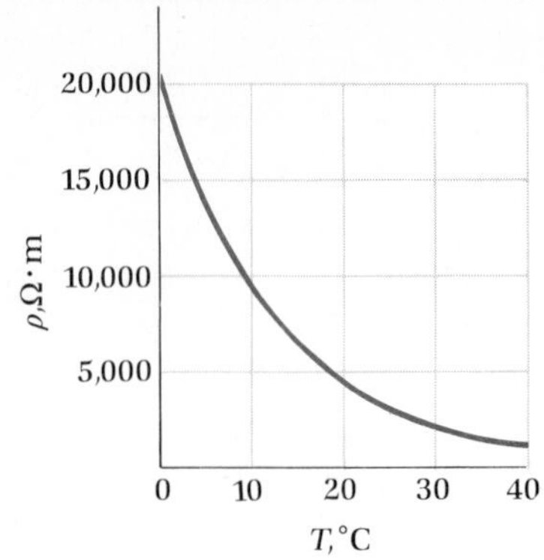

Figure 24-11. Temperature dependence of the resistivity of pure silicon near room temperature.

riers. Figure 24-10 shows that if an electron is released from its site in a solid, it leaves behind a position at which an electron is missing. This "lack-of-an-electron" is called a *hole*, and an applied electric field can cause a hole to move through the solid in the direction of the field. Thus a hole is a positive charge carrier.

A hole moving through a semiconductor because of an applied electric field is similar to a bubble moving upward from the bottom of a swimming pool because of the gravitational field of the earth; the bubble rises through the water, but water is actually falling as the bubble rises. Instead of describing the water as falling, we find it more convenient to describe the bubble as rising. Our attention is fixed on the lack-of-water (the bubble) rather than on the water.

The Drude model can be used to describe qualitatively the resistivity of semiconductors. Consider the temperature dependence of the resistivity of silicon shown in Fig. 24-11. From Eq. (24-14), the Drude model predicts that the resistivity ρ is inversely proportional to the number density n of carriers: $\rho \propto 1/n$. Since the existence of the carriers is a consequence of thermal ionization, n increases sharply with temperature. Thus ρ decreases with temperature, in qualitative agreement with Fig. 24-11.

A hole is a positive charge carrier in a semiconductor.

EXAMPLE 24-7. (a) Using the Drude model and the rough assumption that the mean free time τ for the carriers in silicon is the same as we found for those in copper in Example 24-6 ($\tau = 2.44 \times 10^{-14}$ s), estimate the number density of free electrons in silicon at room temperature from the resistivity given in Table 24-1. (b) From the answer to part (a), estimate the fraction of ionized silicon atoms.

SOLUTION. (a) Solving Eq. (24-13) for n gives

$$n = \frac{m}{\tau e^2 \rho}$$

These carriers consist of both holes and electrons. Thus $n = n_e + n_h$, where the subscripts e and h refer to electrons and holes, respectively. Let us assume that $n_e = n_h = \frac{1}{2}n$. Using the resistivity of silicon from Table 24-1, we have

$$n_e = \frac{\frac{1}{2}(9.11 \times 10^{-31} \text{ kg})}{(2.44 \times 10^{-14} \text{ s})(1.60 \times 10^{-19} \text{ C})^2(4.3 \times 10^3 \ \Omega \cdot \text{m})}$$

$$= 1.7 \times 10^{17} \text{ m}^{-3}$$

(b) To find the fraction of ionized silicon atoms, we must first find the number density n_{Si} of silicon atoms in solid silicon:

$$n_{\text{Si}} = \frac{N_A \rho_m}{M}$$

where N_A is Avogadro's number, ρ_m is the mass density of silicon (= 2.33×10^3 kg/m³), and M is the atomic weight of silicon (= 28.1 g/mol). This gives $n_{\text{Si}} = 4.99 \times 10^{28}$ m⁻³. The fraction of ionized silicon atoms is

$$\frac{n_e}{n_{\text{Si}}} = \frac{1.7 \times 10^{17} \text{ m}^{-3}}{4.99 \times 10^{28} \text{ m}^{-3}} = 3.4 \times 10^{-12}$$

As we stated earlier, there is about one free electron for every 5×10^{12} silicon atoms, so that the fraction of ionized atoms is actually about 2×10^{-13}. Our calculation gives an answer that is too large by a factor of about 20. In view of our crude approximations, this is about the accuracy we should expect.

n-type and p-type semiconductors. From the previous example, the number density of carriers is very low in silicon compared with that of metals. There is about one carrier per atom in a metal, but only about one carrier for every 10^{12} atoms in silicon at room temperature. Consequently, the room temperature resistivity of silicon is about a factor of 10^{11} higher than most metals. However, the number density of carriers in a semiconductor can be increased greatly by the introduction of certain impurities.

Consider the effect of incorporating phosphorus into silicon. Phosphorus ($Z = 15$) has five valence electrons, one more than silicon. If a small amount of phosphorus is introduced into solid silicon, then here and there a site normally occupied by a silicon ion core (charge $+4e$) will be occupied by a phosphorus ion core (charge $+5e$), as shown in Fig. 24-12a. Four of the five valence electrons of the phosphorus atom are bound to the phosphorus ion core (in the arrangement normally occupied by electrons around a silicon ion core), and, at room temperature, the one remaining electron is nearly always free. Thus essentially every phosphorus impurity atom contributes (or donates) a negative charge carrier to the material in the form of a free electron. An impurity atom which donates a free electron to the host material, as phosphorus does in silicon, is called a *donor*.

> A donor atom

Now consider the effect of aluminum in silicon. Aluminum ($Z = 13$) has three valence electrons, one fewer than silicon. If a small amount of aluminum is introduced into solid silicon, then here and there a site normally occupied by a silicon ion core will be occupied by an aluminum ion core (charge $+3e$), as shown in Fig. 24-12b. At room temperature, the hole formed by the one fewer valence electron from aluminum is nearly always free, so that nearly all the aluminum ions have four electrons around them, as do almost all the silicon ions. The aluminum atom "accepts" an electron from the host material and the material now contains a charge carrier in the form of a hole. Essentially every aluminum impurity atom contributes a hole to the material. An impurity atom which accepts an electron from the host material, as aluminum does in silicon, is called an *acceptor*.

> An acceptor atom

When an impurity is purposely incorporated into an otherwise pure material, we say that the material is *doped*. For example, when phosphorus is introduced into silicon, the resulting material is phosphorus-doped silicon. As we have seen, phosphorus-doped silicon contains extra negative charge carriers. Such a material is called an *n-type semiconductor*; the "n" refers to the *n*egative charge of the carriers (electrons). Aluminum-doped silicon is a *p*-type

> An *n*-type semiconductor contains negative electrons as carriers, and a *p*-type semiconductor contains positive holes as carriers.

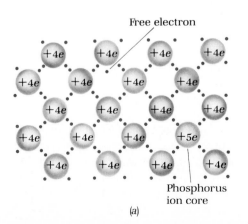

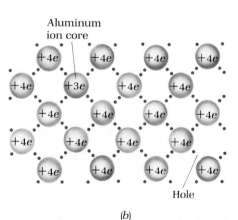

Figure 24-12. (*a*) Phosphorus-doped silicon. The material contains free electrons as carriers; it is *n*-type. (*b*) Aluminum-doped silicon. The material contains holes as charge carriers; it is *p*-type.

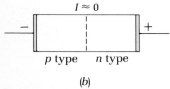

p type | n type
Junction

(a)

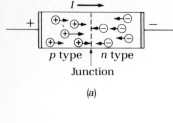

$I \approx 0$

p type n type

(b)

Figure 24-13. (a) A forward-biased pn-junction diode. (b) A reverse-biased pn-junction diode. Practically no carriers are available to maintain a current from right to left.

semiconductor; the "p" refers to the *positive* charge of the carriers (holes).

To qualify as an n-type semiconductor (or a p-type), the donor (or acceptor) concentration should be high enough so that the number density of free electrons (or holes) introduced by the donor (or acceptor) is much higher than the number density of carriers in the pure material. We previously saw that the carrier concentration in pure silicon at room temperature corresponds to a fraction of about 2×10^{-13} ionized silicon atoms. Therefore, to be an n-type (or p-type) semiconductor, the fractional concentration of donor (or acceptor) atoms in silicon has only to be much greater than 2×10^{-13}. Typical doping levels in silicon run around 10^{-10} to 10^{-6}. Consequently, the number density of carriers in a doped semiconductor depends on the impurity concentration, and the sign of the charge carriers depends on the type of the impurity; both are controlled by the manufacturer during the production of the material.

The pn-junction diode. Many of the electronic devices that are so useful in circuits are junction devices. These have one or more junctions, which abruptly separate n-type material from p-type material. The simplest of these devices is the pn-junction diode. A *diode* is a circuit element that readily allows charge carriers to flow in one direction, but not in the other.

The operation of a pn-junction diode can be understood from the following simplified discussion. Suppose a potential difference is applied to a diode in the sense shown in Fig. 24-13a. The contact on the p side of the diode is at a higher potential than the contact on the n side. This tends to produce a current from left to right. For such a current to exist in the p region, holes must flow from left to right, and for such a current to exist in the n region, electrons must flow from right to left. This readily occurs because the electrons can combine with the holes at the junction, mutually eliminating one another, which allows the carriers to flow continuously.

Now suppose a potential difference is applied to a diode in the sense shown in Fig. 24-13b. The contact on the p side of the diode is at a lower potential than the contact on the n side, which tends to produce a current from right to left. For such a current to exist in the p region, holes must flow from right to left, and for such a current to exist in the n region, electrons must flow from left to right. For this to occur continuously, some mechanism for producing free electrons and holes at the junction is required. No such mechanism exists in an ordinary diode. (In photodiodes such a mechanism does exist, but that is a different case altogether.)

Another way a current from right to left could exist in the diode is for holes in the n region to flow from right to left and electrons in the p region to flow from left to right. Then the electrons and holes could combine at the junction. However, there are practically no holes in the n region and practically no electrons in the p region. Therefore, there are practically no carriers available to maintain a current from right to left, so only a negligible current exists in this case.

When a potential difference is applied across a circuit element, we often refer to the potential difference as a *bias*. If the element has directional properties, as a diode does, then it may be *forward-biased* or *reverse-biased* (sometimes called *back-biased*). The diode in Fig. 24-13a is forward-biased, and the diode in Fig. 24-13b is reverse-biased. Current readily flows in a diode that is forward-biased, and practically no current flows in a diode that is reverse-biased.

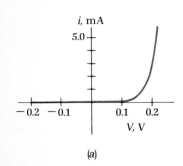

i, mA

5.0

-0.2 -0.1 0.1   0.2
                      V, V

(a)

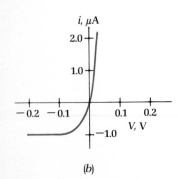

i, μA

2.0

1.0

-0.2 -0.1 0.1   0.2
                      V, V
              -1.0

(b)

Figure 24-14. *I*-*V* curve for a typical pn-junction diode. (a) Current axis marked in mA (10^{-3} A). (b) Same data as in (a), with current axis marked in μA (10^{-6} A).

Figure 24-14 shows an *IV* curve (current versus potential difference) for a typical *pn*-junction diode (see Exercises 24-26 and 24-27). Potential difference *V* is positive for forward biasing and negative for reverse biasing. Notice the large differences in the scale on the current axes of Fig. 24-14*a* and *b*.

24-6 RESISTORS IN SERIES AND PARALLEL

Electric circuits usually contain combinations of resistors. The concept of the equivalent resistance of a combination of resistors is useful in finding the current in the various branches of a circuit. *The equivalent resistance of a combination of resistors is the resistance of a single resistor which, if used in place of the combination, would produce the same external effect.* To produce the same external effect as a combination of resistors, this single resistor must carry the same current as the combination when the potential difference across it is the same as that across the combination. That is, $R_{eq} = V/I$, where R_{eq} is the equivalent resistance of the combination, *V* is the potential difference across the combination, and *I* is the current which enters (and leaves) the combination.

Equivalent resistance

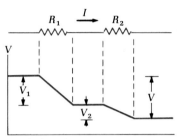

Resistors in series. Figure 24-15 shows two resistors with resistances R_1 and R_2 connected in series. The straight connecting lines indicate wires of negligible resistance. Also shown is the variation of potential along the direction which corresponds to the sense of the current. Notice that the potential difference *V* across the combination of resistors is equal to the sum of the potential differences across each resistor: $V = V_1 + V_2$. Because they are in series, the same current *I* exists in each resistor so that $V_1 = IR_1$ and $V_2 = IR_2$. Therefore,

$$V = IR_1 + IR_2 = I(R_1 + R_2)$$

Thus the equivalent resistance R_{12} is

$$R_{12} = \frac{V}{I} = R_1 + R_2$$

A single resistor with resistance R_{12} can replace these two and maintain the same external effect. For example, if two series resistors of resistances 4.0 and 2.0 Ω are replaced in a circuit by a single resistor of resistance 6.0 Ω, then the rest of the circuit will be unaffected.

Similarly, for a number of resistors connected in series,

$$R_{eq} = \Sigma R_i \qquad (24\text{-}15)$$

Figure 24-15. Two resistors in series. The potential difference *V* across both resistors is equal to the sum of the potential differences across each resistor; $V = V_1 + V_2$. The current *I* in each resistor is the same.

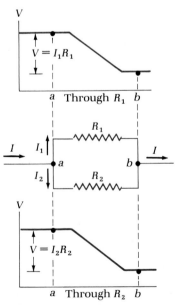

Figure 24-16. Two resistors in parallel. The potential difference *V* across each resistor is the same. The current *I* entering the combination is equal to the sum of the currents in each resistor: $I = I_1 + I_2$.

Resistors in parallel. Figure 24-16 shows two resistors with resistances R_1 and R_2 connected in parallel. Notice that the potential difference *V* must be the same for each path, $V_1 = V_2 = V$. Since no charge accumulates at the points *a* or *b*, called *branch points*, the current *I* in the main branch is equal to the sum of the currents I_1 and I_2 in resistors 1 and 2. Or

$$I = I_1 + I_2$$

Since $V = I_1 R_1$ and $V = I_2 R_2$, we have $I_1 = V/R_1$ and $I_2 = V/R_2$. Therefore,

$$I = \frac{V}{R_1} + \frac{V}{R_2} = V\left(\frac{1}{R_1} + \frac{1}{R_2}\right)$$

The equivalent resistance R_{12} of resistors 1 and 2 in parallel is given by

$$\frac{1}{R_{12}} = \frac{I}{V} = \frac{1}{R_1} + \frac{1}{R_2}$$

Similarly, for a number of resistors connected in parallel,

$$\frac{1}{R_{eq}} = \Sigma \frac{1}{R_i} \qquad (24\text{-}16)$$

Returning to the case of two resistors in parallel and solving for R_{12} gives

$$R_{12} = \frac{R_1 R_2}{R_1 + R_2} \qquad (24\text{-}17)$$

For example, the equivalent resistance of two parallel resistors of resistances 3.0 and 6.0 Ω is

$$\frac{(3.0\ \Omega)(6.0\ \Omega)}{3.0\ \Omega + 6.0\ \Omega} = \frac{18.0\ \Omega^2}{9.0\ \Omega} = 2.0\ \Omega$$

If these two resistors are replaced by a single resistor of resistance 2.0 Ω, then the rest of the circuit will be unaffected.

Consider the way the current in the main branch is divided into I_1 and I_2 at the branch point a in Fig. 24-16. Since $I_1 = V/R_1$ and $I_2 = V/R_2$, the current in each resistor is inversely proportional to its resistance. Suppose a current of 3.0 A is in the main branch in Fig. 24-16 and $R_1 = 3.0\ \Omega$ and $R_2 = 6.0\ \Omega$. Then $R_{12} = 2.0\ \Omega$ and $V = IR_{12} = (3.0\ \text{A})(2.0\ \Omega) = 6.0\ \text{V}$. Thus $I_1 = 6.0\ \text{V}/3.0\ \Omega = 2.0$ A, and $I_2 = 6.0\ \text{V}/6.0\ \Omega = 1.0$ A. The larger current is in the resistor with the smaller resistance.

EXAMPLE 24-8. (a) Determine the equivalent resistance of the combination of resistors shown in Fig. 24-17a. (b) Given that the potential difference across the combination is 36 V, determine the potential difference across each resistor, the total current in the combination, and the current in each resistor.

SOLUTION. (a) Using Eq. (24-17), the equivalent resistance R_{12} of the parallel combination of resistors 1 and 2 (Fig. 24-17b) is

$$R_{12} = \frac{(4.0\ \Omega)(12.0\ \Omega)}{4.0\ \Omega + 12.0\ \Omega} = 3.0\ \Omega$$

This resistance is in series with R_3 so that the equivalent resistance R_{123} of the entire combination is

$$R_{123} = R_{12} + R_3 = 6.0\ \Omega + 3.0\ \Omega = 9.0\ \Omega$$

(b) The current in the equivalent resistance R_{123} is

$$I = \frac{V}{R_{123}} = \frac{36\ \text{V}}{9.0\ \Omega} = 4.0\ \text{A}$$

This is the current in the main branch of the combination, and it is also the current in resistor 3. Therefore, the potential difference V_3 across resistor 3 is

$$V_3 = IR_3 = (4.0\ \text{A})(6.0\ \Omega) = 24\ \text{V}$$

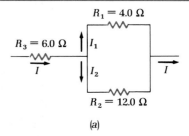

(a)

(b)

(c)

Figure 24-17. Example 24-8: (a) A combination of resistors. (b) After replacing R_1 and R_2 with their equivalent R_{12}. (c) After replacing R_{12} and R_3 with their equivalent R_{123}.

Since $V = V_{12} + V_3$, where V_{12} is the potential difference across the parallel resistors 1 and 2, we have

$$V_{12} = V - V_3 = 36 \text{ V} - 24 \text{ V} = 12 \text{ V} \qquad \text{and}$$

[Alternatively, $V_{12} = IR_{12} = (4.0 \text{ A})(3.0 \text{ }\Omega) = 12 \text{ V}$.] The currents I_1 and I_2 in resistors 1 and 2 are

$$I_2 = \frac{V_{12}}{R_2} = \frac{12 \text{ V}}{12.0 \text{ }\Omega} = 1.0 \text{ A}$$

$$I_1 = \frac{V_{12}}{R_1} = \frac{12 \text{ V}}{4.0 \text{ }\Omega} = 3.0 \text{ A}$$

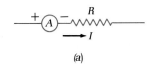

(a)

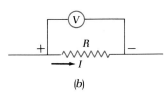

(b)

Figure 24-18. (a) To measure the current in a circuit element (a resistor in this case), an ammeter is placed in series with the element. (b) To measure the potential difference across an element, a voltmeter is placed in parallel with (across) the element.

24-7 AMMETERS AND VOLTMETERS

For an element in an electric circuit, such as a resistor, the two quantities of continuing interest are the current I in the element and the potential difference V across it. It is instructive to consider the way that each of these two quantities is measured. As the names imply, current is measured with an ammeter and potential difference is measured with a voltmeter.

An ammeter measures the current in itself. To measure the current in a circuit element, an ammeter must be placed in series with the element so that the current in the element is the same as the current in the ammeter (Fig. 24-18a).

The principal component of an ammeter is some type of current-detecting device, such as a *galvanometer* (described in Example 26-6). In addition to a current-detecting device, which includes a dial or digital display, an ammeter usually contains several resistors that are used to change the scale of the meter. The scale of the ammeter is selected with a switch which places one of these resistors in parallel with the current-detecting device. Problem 24-10 gives further details about the operation of an ammeter.

A voltmeter measures the potential difference across itself. To measure the potential difference across an element, a voltmeter is placed in parallel with the element (that is, *across* the element) so that the potential difference across the element is the same as the potential difference across the voltmeter (Fig. 24-18b).

As with an ammeter, the principal component of a voltmeter is some type of current-detecting device. Again, as with an ammeter, a voltmeter usually contains several resistors that are used to set the scale of the meter. The scale of the voltmeter is selected with a switch which places one of these resistors in series with the current-detecting device. Thus a distinction between an ammeter and a voltmeter is that an ammeter has a resistor (usually with a small resistance) in parallel with its current-detecting device, and a voltmeter has a resistor (usually with a large resistance) in series with its current-detecting device. Indeed, an ammeter and a voltmeter are often incorporated in the same instrument so that the same current-detecting device is used for both. Problem 24-11 gives further details about the operation of a voltmeter.

An important feature of any measuring device is that its interjection into a system should not significantly alter the quantity to be measured. For an ammeter to have a negligible effect on the current it measures, the resistance of the ammeter must be insignificant compared with the rest of the resistance of the branch into which it is placed. In this way its presence will not significantly alter the current in the branch (see Exercise 24-36). An ideal ammeter is one whose resistance is zero.

For a voltmeter to have a negligible effect on the potential difference it is used to measure, its resistance must be much greater than the resistance of the element it is placed across. If the resistance of the voltmeter in Fig. 24-18b is much greater than R, then a very small current will exist in the voltmeter and the voltmeter will have a negligible effect on the potential difference across the resistor (see Exercise 24-37). An ideal voltmeter is one whose resistance is infinite.

SUMMARY WITH APPLICATIONS

Section 24-2. The flow of charge
Charge flow through a circuit element is characterized by the electric current:

$$I = \frac{dQ}{dt} \qquad (24\text{-}1)$$

The sense of the current corresponds to the direction of the drift velocity $\mathbf{v}_d$ of positive charge carriers. The current density $\mathbf{j}$ describes the flow of charge at a point within a conducting medium:

$$\mathbf{j} = nq\mathbf{v}_d \qquad (24\text{-}4)$$

If $\mathbf{j}$ is uniform, then its magnitude is

$$j = \frac{I}{A} \qquad \text{(uniform } \mathbf{j}) \qquad (24\text{-}3)$$

Describe the concepts of current and current density; estimate the drift speed of carriers in a wire.

Section 24-3. Resistance and Ohm's law
Ohm's law is

$$V = IR \qquad (24\text{-}7)$$

where the resistance R is independent of V (or I). When this is the case, the conductor is called ohmic. For a conductor of length ℓ and cross-sectional area A,

$$R = \frac{\rho\ell}{A} \qquad (24\text{-}8)$$

where ρ is the resistivity of the material. The relation between $\mathbf{E}$ and $\mathbf{j}$ is

$$\mathbf{j} = \sigma\mathbf{E} \qquad (24\text{-}10)$$

where $\sigma = 1/\rho$.

Explain the meaning of Ohm's law; determine the resistivity of a material; describe the temperature dependence of the resistivity of metals.

Section 24-4. Drude model of a metal
The Drude model of a conductor yields Ohm's law with

$$\sigma = \frac{ne^2\tau}{m} \qquad (24\text{-}13)$$

where τ is the mean time between collisions.

Describe the Drude model and explain its results.

Section 24-5. Conduction in semiconductors
For a pure semiconductor, σ is much smaller than for metals because n is much lower than in metals. Doping a semiconductor with certain impurities can greatly increase n and σ. A semiconductor doped with a donor impurity is n-type (carriers are free electons), and a semiconductor doped with an acceptor impurity is p-type (carriers are holes).

Explain how impurities are used to affect the resistivity of semiconductors; explain the operation of a pn-junction diode.

Section 24-6. Resistors in series and parallel
For resistors connected in series,

$$R_{\text{eq}} = \Sigma R_i \qquad (24\text{-}15)$$

and for resistors connected in parallel,

$$\frac{1}{R_{\text{eq}}} = \Sigma \frac{1}{R_i} \qquad (24\text{-}16)$$

Determine R_{eq}, V, and I for combinations of resistors.

Section 24-7. Ammeters and voltmeters
To measure the current in a circuit element, an ammeter is placed in series with the element. To measure the potential difference across a circuit element, a voltmeter is placed in parallel with the element.

Describe the components of an ammeter and a voltmeter and explain how they are used in making measurements.

QUESTIONS

24-1 Wires a and b are made of the same materials and carry the same current, but the radius of wire a is half that of b. What is the ratio of the carrier drift speeds in the wires? What is the ratio of the current densities in the wires?

24-2 When you turn on a light switch, the light comes on almost instantaneously, even though the drift speed of the carriers in the wire is only about 10^{-4} m/s. Draw an analogy between this effect and the prompt flow of water from the open end of a long garden hose (initially full of water) after the water flow is turned on at the valve.

24-3 In developing Eq. (24-2), $I = nAv_d|q|$, we considered only one type of charge carrier. Write a similar equation for the case where there are two types of carriers, a and b. Is your equation valid if the carriers have opposite sign?

24-4 Is $\mathbf{j}$ parallel to $\mathbf{v}_d$ for positive carriers? Is $\mathbf{j}$ parallel to $\mathbf{v}_d$

for negative carriers?

24-5 Is the expression $V = IR$ for a conductor inconsistent with our requirement in electrostatics that $\mathbf{E} = 0$ inside a conductor?

24-6 Suppose you measure the current I in a resistor when the potential difference across it is V, and you determine that $R = V/I = 100 \ \Omega$. If the resistor is known to be nonohmic, is it proper to speak of it as a 100-Ω resistor? Explain.

24-7 Can you apply the expression $V = IR$ to circuit elements that are not ohmic? If so, what can be said of R?

24-8 Discuss the distinction between resistance and resistivity. Which is proper, to speak of the resistance of a penny or the resistivity of a penny? Which is proper, to speak of the resistance of copper or the resistivity of copper?

24-9 If the resistance of a copper wire is 3 Ω at a temperature of 300 K, then what is a reasonable estimate of its resistance at 100 K?

24-10 Justify the equation used for the resistance as a function of temperature in Example 24-4. What assumption(s) must you make?

24-11 Explain the difficulty in determining whether a conductor that is well insulated thermally (such as the filament of a light bulb) is ohmic.

24-12 In the analogy between marbles on a pegboard and charge carriers in a conductor, increasing the tilt of the board corresponds to changing what physical quantity for the conductor? To what does adding more marbles correspond?

24-13 In some crystalline solids, $\mathbf{j}$ is not parallel to $\mathbf{E}$ except when $\mathbf{E}$ is along particular crystalline directions, called the *principal axes*. In this case, the conductivity σ in the expression $\mathbf{j} = \sigma\mathbf{E}$ is no longer a scalar; σ is then a *tensor* quantity. Discuss a marble-and-pegboard analogy to conduction in such a solid. Let the pegs have an elliptical cross section, as shown in Fig. 24-19. Suppose the down-slope direction makes an angle of, say 30°, with respect to the major axes of the elliptical cross sections. Will the direction of the average velocity of the marbles be parallel to the unbalanced component of the gravitational force on them? Find two directions along the pegboard which corre-

spond to principal axes. Which of these principal-axis directions offers the larger resistance to the flow of marbles?

24-14 In the Drude model, how do we know that $\langle v_{x0}\rangle = 0$ when the applied electric field is zero? How do we justify assuming $\langle v_{x0}\rangle = 0$ when there is an applied electric field $\mathbf{E} = E\mathbf{i}$? Is $\langle v_0\rangle = 0$ in either case? (Recall that the subscript 0 refers to the instant immediately following a collision.)

24-15 In applying the Drude-model expression for conductivity ($\sigma = ne^2\tau/m$), which factor mainly accounts for the fact that conductivity in a pure semiconductor is much less than it is in typical metals?

24-16 A potential difference exists across three series resistors of resistances R_1, R_2, and R_3. If $R_1 < R_2 < R_3$, then which resistor has the largest potential difference across it? Which resistor has the smallest potential difference across it?

24-17 A current exists in three parallel resistors of resistances R_1, R_2, and R_3. If $R_1 < R_2 < R_3$, then which resistor carries the largest current? Which carries the smallest current?

24-18 Compare the expressions for the equivalent resistance of resistors in series and parallel with the equivalent capacitance of capacitors in series and parallel. Explain why the expressions do not compare directly, series to series and parallel to parallel.

24-19 Why is it preferable to have an ammeter whose resistance is low? Low compared with what? Why is it preferable to have a voltmeter whose resistance is high? High compared with what?

24-20 It is often difficult to measure a very large resistance by directly measuring the current in it with an ammeter and the potential difference across it with a voltmeter. Why?

24-21 In an integrated circuit, all the elements—diodes, resistors, capacitors, and others—are made of silicon and the insulator is silicon dioxide (SiO_2). Explain how each element might be constructed from these materials.

24-22 Complete the following table:

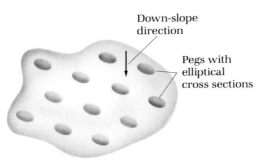

Figure 24-19. Ques. 24-13: Top view of a section of pegboard that has pegs with elliptical cross sections.

Symbol	Represents	Type	SI unit
I			
$\mathbf{j}$			
$\mathbf{v}_d$		Vector	
R			Ω
ρ			
σ			
α			
n	Carrier number density		
τ			
$\langle v\rangle$			m/s
λ			

Down-slope direction

Pegs with elliptical cross sections

EXERCISES

Section 24-2. The flow of charge

24-1 A steady current of 2.5 A exists in a metal wire. (a) What amount of charge passes through a cross section of the wire in 5.0 min? (b) How many electrons pass through this surface in 5.0 min?

24-2 Suppose an electron beam in a television picture tube has a flow of 8.1×10^{15} electrons per second. What is the beam current in A?

24-3 The amount of charge that passes through a cross section of a wire is given by $Q(t) = (6.5 \text{ C/s}^2)t^2 + 3.5 \text{ C}$ for t varying between 0.0 and 8.0 s. (a) What expression gives the current $I(t)$ in this time interval? (b) What is the current at the instant $t = 3.4$ s?

24-4 A 10-gauge aluminum wire (radius 1.30 mm) carries a current of 20 A. Assuming three free electrons per aluminum atom ($\rho_m = 2.7 \times 10^3$ kg/m³, $M = 27.0$ g/mol), determine the drift speed of the electrons.

24-5 Consider a salt solution that carries, in a long insulating tube of inner radius 12 mm, a current of 0.86 A along the tube axis. The carriers in the solution are singly charged positive ions and negative ions with equal number densities: $n_+ = n_- = 5.7 \times 10^{25}$ ions per cubic meter. Assume that the drift speed of the positive ions is 3 times that of the negative ions. (a) Determine the contribution to the current from each type of ion. (b) Assuming **j** is uniform, determine the contribution to j from each type of ion. (c) Determine the drift speed of each type of ion.

24-6 A 16-gauge copper wire (radius 0.65 mm) is connected in series with an 18-gauge copper wire (radius 0.51 mm) so that they both carry the same current of 2.4 A. Assuming a uniform current density, (a) what is the current density in each wire and (b) what is the carrier drift speed in each wire?

Section 24-3. Resistance and Ohm's law

24-7 Show the ohm can be written kg · m²/(s³ · A²).

24-8 A potential difference of 12 V produces a current of 16 mA in a resistor. (a) What is the resistance of the resistor? (b) Assuming the resistor is ohmic, what is the current when the potential difference is 24 V?

24-9 A 1.0-m length of wire has a resistance of 14 Ω, and the potential difference between its ends is 4.1 V. (a) What is the current in the wire? (b) Assuming **E** is uniform, determine E inside the wire.

24-10 Consider the following data taken on two wires:

Wire *a*		Wire *b*	
I, A	**V, V**	**I, A**	**V, V**
0.0	0.0	0.0	0.0
1.0	1.8	1.0	0.6
2.0	2.9	2.0	1.2
3.0	3.7	3.0	1.8
4.0	4.2	4.0	2.4

(a) Make graphs of the data and determine if either wire is ohmic. (b) If either wire is ohmic, what is its resistance? (c) If either wire is nonohmic, make for it a graph of R versus I. (Notice that we cannot speak of *the* resistance of a nonohmic conductor.)

24-11 (a) What is the resistance of a 1.0-m length of 10-gauge (radius 1.3 mm) copper wire at 20°C? (See Table 24-1.) (b) What is the resistance of a 1.0-m length of 10-gauge aluminum wire at 20°C?

24-12 A 1.3-m length of 8-gauge (radius 1.64 mm) metal wire has a resistance of 8.6 mΩ at 20°C. The metal is one of those in Table 24-1. Which one is it?

24-13 A very thin layer of metal can be formed by vaporizing the metal that deposits by condensation on a cool substrate of glass. The thickness of the layer can be determined by a resistance measurement. Suppose the resistance of a rectangular deposit of aluminum (31 mm by 5.6 mm) at 20°C is 19 Ω when the potential difference is applied along the layer's larger dimension. (a) What is the thickness of this layer? (b) What is the resistance of a layer of the same material with the same thickness but with its two rectangular dimensions each twice the value of the previous layer? Can you make a general statement about the resistance of a layer of material of given thickness with rectangular dimensions of a given ratio?

24-14 A tungsten wire with a circular cross section has a length of 58 mm and a resistance of 6.2 mΩ at 20°C. What is the radius of the wire?

24-15 The current-carrying rail of an electric train has a cross section of 5.3×10^{-3} m² and is made of steel with a resistivity of about 3×10^{-7} Ω · m. What is the resistance of 1 km of track?

24-16 A 12-gauge copper wire is inside the wall of a house so that its length cannot be directly measured. If the wire has a resistance of 23 mΩ at 20°C, what is its length?

24-17 A metal wire has a room-temperature resistance of 40 mΩ. The wire is melted and all the metal is used to reform it into a wire 3 times its original length. What is the room-temperature resistance of the new wire?

24-18 Suppose we wish to compare aluminum and copper as materials for a cable that will carry 100 A and have a resistance per unit length of 80×10^{-6} Ω/m. For the two materials compare (a) the cross-sectional areas, (b) the current densities, (c) the mass per unit length of cable. The mass densities of aluminum and copper are 2.7×10^3 kg/m³ and 8.9×10^3 kg/m³, respectively. (d) What is the potential difference across a 1-km length of such a cable?

24-19 What is the resistivity of iron at 40°C? (See Tables 24-1 and 24-2.)

24-20 The resistance of a silver wire is 46 mΩ at 20°C. What is its resistance at 45°C?

24-21 The resistance of a copper wire at 20°C is 130 mΩ. At what temperature is its resistance 110 mΩ?

24-22 At 20°C the resistance of a copper wire is 8.2 mΩ and the resistance of a gold wire is 7.8 mΩ. Determine the temperature at which the wires have the same resistance.

24-23 A 1.8-m length of metal wire with cross-sectional area 2.3×10^{-6} m² carries a current of 65 mA when the potential difference between its ends is 11 mV. (a) Assuming **E** is uniform, what is E in the wire? (b) What is j in the wire? (c) What is σ for the metal? (d) What is ρ for the metal?

Section 24-4. Drude model of a metal

24-24 (a) Estimate the mean free time in aluminum at 20°C, assuming three free electrons per aluminum atom. (b) Using $\langle v \rangle \approx 10^6$ m/s, estimate the mean free path λ in aluminum.

Section 24-5. Conduction in semiconductors

24-25 The number density of free electrons n_e and the number density of holes n_h in pure germanium (a semiconductor) at 20°C is about 2×10^{19} carriers per cubic meter for each type of carrier. Assuming free electrons and holes have the same mass and mean free time, estimate the mean free time for these carriers in germanium.

24-26 Using the data of Fig. 24-14, find the resistance of that *pn*-junction diode for (a) a forward-bias potential difference of 0.2 V and (b) a reverse-bias potential difference of 0.2 V. (c) What is the ratio of the reverse-bias resistance to the forward-bias resistance at 0.2 V?

24-27 The theoretical expression that quite accurately gives the current i in a *pn*-junction diode in terms of the potential difference V across it is

$$i = I_0(e^{eV/kT} - 1)$$

where I_0 is a parameter that depends on the particular diode, k is the Boltzmann constant, T is the temperature (in kelvins), and e is the magnitude of the electronic charge. [We use i rather than I for this current because it may be negative. Indeed, the current *is* negative for negative V (reverse bias).] Using $I_0 = 1.0 \times 10^{-6}$ A, evaluate i at 20°C (293 K) for (a) $V = 0.20$ V and (b) $V = -0.20$ V. (c) Determine the forward-bias and reverse-bias resistances at 0.20 V and find the ratio of the reverse-bias resistance to the forward-bias resistance.

Section 24-6. Resistors in series and parallel

24-28 Three resistors of resistances 23, 45, and 31 Ω are connected in series. (a) What is their equivalent resistance? (b) If the potential difference across the combination is 36 V, what is the current in each resistor and

what is the potential difference across each resistor?

24-29 Three resistors of resistances 16, 25, and 31 Ω are connected in parallel. (a) What is their equivalent resistance? (b) If the potential difference across the combination is 14 V, what is the current in each resistor and what is the potential difference across each resistor?

24-30 (a) If $R_1 = 12$ Ω, $R_2 = 21$ Ω, and $R_3 = 28$ Ω in Fig. 24-20, what is the equivalent resistance of the combination? (b) If a 32-V potential difference is applied across the combination, what is the potential difference across each resistor and what is the current in each resistor?

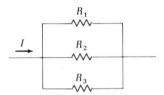

Figure 24-20. Exercise 24-30.

24-31 Show that when a number of resistors are connected in parallel, the equivalent resistance of the combination is always less than the resistance of the resistor with the smallest resistance.

24-32 In Fig. 24-21, $I = 10.0$ A, $R_1 = R_2 = 4.0$ Ω, and $R_3 = 8.0$ Ω. What is the current in each resistor?

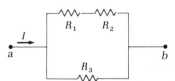

Figure 24-21. Exercise 24-32.

24-33 In the arrangement shown in Fig. 24-22, $R_1 = 5.0$ Ω, $R_2 = 3.0$ Ω, and $R_3 = 4.0$ Ω. (a) What is the potential difference between points c and d? (b) What is the equivalent resistance from a to b? (c) If the potential difference between a and b is 8.0 V, what is the potential difference across each resistor and what is the current in each resistor?

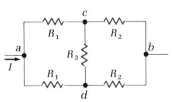

Figure 24-22. Exercise 24-33.

24-34 The equivalent resistance of two resistors in parallel may be written

$$R_{eq} = \frac{R_1 R_2}{R_2 + R_1}$$

(a) Show that the equivalent resistance of three resistors connected in parallel may be written

$$R_{eq} = \frac{R_1 R_2 R_3}{R_2 R_3 + R_1 R_3 + R_1 R_2}$$

(b) Write a similar expression for the equivalent resistance of four resistors connected in parallel.

24-35 For some purposes it is useful to define the *conductance S* of a resistor, $S = 1/R$. (a) Show that the equivalent conductance S_{eq} of a series combination of resistors is

$$\frac{1}{S_{eq}} = \Sigma \frac{1}{S_i}$$

(b) Show that the equivalent conductance of a parallel combination of resistors is

$$S_{eq} = \Sigma S_i$$

[Note: The SI unit of conductance is called the siemens (S); $1\ S = 1\ \Omega^{-1}$. The unit is named for E. W. von Siemens (1816–1892).]

Section 24-7. Ammeters and voltmeters

24-36 To measure the resistance R of a resistor, an ammeter of resistance R_A is placed in series with the resistor and a voltmeter is placed across the series combination, as shown in Fig. 24-23. (a) Show that the resistance R in terms of the measured readings on the ammeter I_{meas} and voltmeter V_{meas} is given by

$$R = \frac{V_{meas}}{I_{meas}} - R_A$$

Notice that if $V_{meas}/I_{meas} \gg R_A$, then $R \approx V_{meas}/I_{meas}$. (b) Given that $V_{meas} = 23$ V, $I_{meas} = 62$ mA, and $R_A = 14\ \Omega$, determine R.

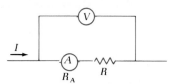

Figure 24-23. Exercise 24-36.

24-37 To measure the resistance R of a resistor, a voltmeter of resistance R_V is placed across the resistor and an ammeter is placed in series with the combination, as shown in Fig. 24-24. (a) Show that the resistance R in terms of the measured readings on the ammeter I_{meas} and voltmeter V_{meas} is given by

$$R = \frac{V_{meas}}{I_{meas} - (V_{meas}/R_V)}$$

(b) Show that if $R_V \gg V_{meas}/I_{meas}$, then $R \approx V_{meas}/I_{meas}$. (c) Given that $I_{meas} = 16$ mA, $V_{meas} = 43$ V, and $R_V = 62$ MΩ, determine R.

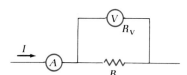

Figure 24-24. Exercise 24-37.

PROBLEMS

24-1 (a) Show that the length dependence in the expression $R = \rho\ell/A$ is consistent with the expression for the equivalent resistance of two resistors in series, $R_{eq} = R_1 + R_2$, by considering a wire of length ℓ and cross-sectional area A as two wires, each with cross-sectional area A and of lengths ℓ_1 and ℓ_2, connected in series: $\ell = \ell_1 + \ell_2$. (b) Show that the area dependence in the expression $R = \rho\ell/A$ is consistent with the expression for the equivalent resistance of two resistors in parallel, $1/R_{eq} = 1/R_1 + 1/R_2$, by considering a wire of length ℓ and cross-sectional area A as two wires of length ℓ and cross-sectional areas A_1 and A_2 connected in parallel: $A = A_1 + A_2$.

24-2 Figure 24-25 shows a thin-walled metal tube (inner radius b and outer radius c), with a thin metal disk (thickness d) covering its end. A thin metal wire (radius a) coaxial with the tube is connected to the center of the disk and a steady current I_0 exists in the wire, disk, and tube as shown. (a) In the region of the disk well away from the connection to the wire and the tube, find an expression for the magnitude j of the current density as a function of the perpendicular distance r from the axis. (b) In this same region of the disk, find an expression for the current density **j** in terms of $\hat{i}$ and $\hat{j}$ unit vectors. Use a coordinate system with origin on the axis and xy plane parallel to the plane sides of the disk.

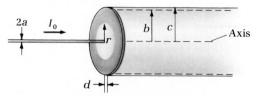

Figure 24-25. Prob. 24-2.

24-3 An expression, based on theory, that accurately gives the temperature dependence of the resistivity ρ of a

pure semiconductor is

$$\rho = \rho_1 e^{E_g/(2kT)}$$

where ρ_1 is a parameter that depends weakly on the temperature T (compared with the exponential), E_g is the so-called energy gap of the material, and k is the Boltzmann constant. For pure silicon near room temperature, $\rho_1 = 1.4 \times 10^{-6}\ \Omega \cdot m$ and $E_g = 1.1$ eV. (a) Using the above expression, evaluate ρ at 5° intervals between 0 and 40°C for silicon and make a graph of resistivity versus temperature. Sketch a curve through the data points and compare your graph with Fig. 24-11. (b) Develop an expression for α to be used in Eq. (24-9). Evaluate your expression for α for silicon at 20°C and compare your result with the value in Table 24-2. (c) Using the linear approximation of Eq. (24-9) with your values of α and ρ_0 for silicon at 20°C, evaluate ρ at 5° intervals from 0 to 40°C and plot the data on the graph you constructed in part (a). Sketch the straight line through the points.

24-4 Suppose we wish to construct a composite resistor whose resistance is nearly temperature-independent by connecting two resistors a and b in series. The two resistors have the same cross-sectional area and are assumed to have the same temperature. Show that the effective temperature coefficient of resistivity of the composite resistor is zero at temperature T_0 if the ratio of the lengths of the resistors is $\ell_a/\ell_b = -\rho_{0b}\alpha_b/\rho_{0a}\alpha_a$, where the subscripts a and b refer to the quantities for each resistor. (Why must α_a and α_b be of opposite sign?)

24-5 The radius of the section of conductor shown in Fig. 24-26 varies linearly from a to b along its axis. Show that the resistance of the section for current along the axis is $R = \rho\ell/\pi ab$, where ρ is the resistivity of the material. (The taper is small, $b - a \ll \ell$, so that you may assume **j** is uniform across any cross section.)

Figure 24-26. Prob. 24-5.

24-6 A concept that is sometimes useful when dealing with nonohmic circuit elements is the *dynamic resistance*, $R_{dyn} = dV/di$. Determine the expression for the dynamic resistance of a pn-junction diode from the relation for $i(V)$ given in Exercise 24-27.

24-7 Show that the equivalent resistance of the infinite network of resistors shown in Fig. 24-27 is $R_{eq} = (1 + \sqrt{3})R$.

24-8 Twelve resistors of equal resistance R are arranged along the edges of a cube, as shown in Fig. 24-28. (a) Show that the equivalent resistance R_{ab} between corner a and corner b is $5R/6$. (b) Show that the equiv-

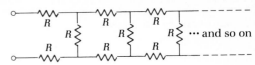

Figure 24-27. Prob. 24-7.

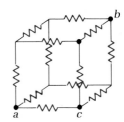

Figure 24-28. Prob. 24-8.

alent resistance R_{ac} between corner a and corner c is $7R/12$. (Hint: Use symmetry considerations to reduce the array to resistors in series and parallel.)

24-9 (a) Show that the resistance R_c of a parallel-plate capacitor of capacitance C is $R_c = \rho\epsilon_0\kappa/C$, where ρ and κ are the resistivity and dielectric constant of the insulator between the plates. (b) Determine R_c for the case where $\rho = 2 \times 10^{13}\ \Omega \cdot m$, $\kappa = 5$, and $C = 1\ \mu F$.

24-10 Suppose we wish to construct an ammeter which reads a current I_m when the pointer on the current-detecting device is at its full-scale position (Fig. 24-29). We do this by placing a resistor (called a *shunt resistor*) of resistance R_{para} in parallel with the current-detecting device so that part of the current in the ammeter is "shunted" through the parallel resistor. The current-detecting device has a resistance R_d, and a current I_{fs} in the device causes a full-scale deflection of its pointer. (a) Show that the resistance of the shunt resistor must be

$$R_{para} = \frac{R_d I_{fs}}{I_m - I_{fs}}$$

Notice that we must have $I_m > I_{fs}$. (b) Evaluate R_{para} for the case where $I_m = 10$ mA, $R_d = 23\ \Omega$, and $I_{fs} = 63\ \mu A$. What is the resistance of the ammeter for this case?

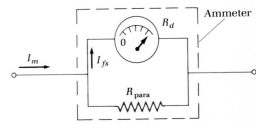

Figure 24-29. Prob. 24-10.

24-11 Suppose we wish to construct a voltmeter which reads a potential difference V_m when the pointer on

566   **CURRENT AND RESISTANCE**

the current-detecting device is at its full-scale position (Fig. 24-30). We do this by placing a resistor of resistance R_{series} in series with the current-detecting device so that part of the potential difference across the voltmeter is across the series resistor. The current-detecting device has a resistance R_d, and a current I_{fs} in the device causes a full-scale deflection of its pointer. (a) Show that the resistance of the series resistor must be

$$R_{series} = \frac{V_m}{I_{fs}} - R_d$$

Notice that we must have $(V_m/I_{fs}) > R_d$. (b) Evaluate R_{series} for the case where $V_m = 10$ V, $R_d = 23$ Ω, and

$I_{fs} = 63$ μA. What is the resistance of the voltmeter for this case?

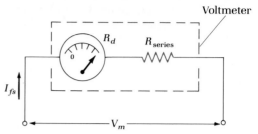

Figure 24-30. Prob. 24-11.

CHAPTER 25
ENERGY AND CURRENT
IN DC CIRCUITS

25-1 INTRODUCTION

Electric circuits are the bloodstreams in the equipment of the scientist and engineer. In this chapter we meet the simplest of circuits and learn the procedures for analyzing circuits. We limit our discussion to cases where the sense of the current is continuous along one direction, *direct-current (dc) circuits.* Circuits in which the sense of the current oscillates back and forth are called *alternating-current (ac) circuits.* We consider ac circuits in Chap. 31.

The design of an electric circuit may be complex, but the principles you will learn in this chapter can be used to analyze any circuit. *(Photo by Tom Richard)*

25-2 EMF AND INTERNAL RESISTANCE OF A BATTERY

For a steady current in a circuit, the circuit must contain a source of emf.

For an electric circuit to have a continuous current, the circuit must contain an element which is a source of electric energy. Such an element is called a *source of emf.* (The term "emf," pronounced ee-em-ef, is a contraction of an older

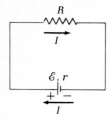

Figure 25-1. A resistor is connected to a battery. The sense of the current outside the battery, through the resistor, is from the positive terminal toward the negative terminal. The sense of the current inside the battery is from the negative terminal toward the positive terminal.

A battery maintains a potential difference across its terminals.

Relation between terminal potential difference, emf, and internal resistance

Definition of emf

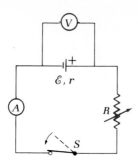

Figure 25-2. Arrangement for finding $\mathscr{E}$ and r. The voltmeter reads the battery's terminal potential difference V, and the ammeter reads the current I. The current is varied by changing the value of the resistance R of the variable resistor.

expression, the *electromotive force*.) A source of emf provides electric energy to the charge carriers in their trip around a circuit.

A battery is a familiar source of emf. In Chap. 23, we saw that when a battery is connected to the plates of a capacitor, the battery transfers charge carriers from one plate to the other. The motion of these carriers constitutes an electric current. When the terminals of a battery are connected to a resistor, as shown in Fig. 25-1, the battery establishes a current in the circuit. As you know from experience with a flashlight, this current tends to be quite steady for some time. The battery produces this steady current by maintaining a nearly constant potential difference across its terminals. The terminal that is at the higher potential is called the *positive terminal* and the terminal that is at the lower potential is called the *negative terminal*. Thus the sense of the current outside the battery (through the resistor) is from the positive terminal toward the negative terminal, and the sense of the current inside the battery is from the negative terminal toward the positive terminal.

Two important characteristics of a battery are its emf $\mathscr{E}$ and its internal resistance r. The emf characterizes the energy that the battery provides the charge carriers, and the internal resistance is the battery's own resistance. In Fig. 25-2, we show how the emf and internal resistance can be determined. A voltmeter placed across the battery measures the battery's *terminal potential difference* V and an ammeter measures the current I. The current can be changed by changing the resistance of the *variable resistor* (shown as —$\Lambda\!\Lambda$—). Figure 25-3 shows a graph of V versus I that is typical for such measurements. The equation which gives this graph is

$$V = \mathscr{E} - Ir \tag{25-1}$$

Equation (25-1) shows that for an open circuit (switch S is open so that $I = 0$), the terminal potential difference equals the emf: $V = \mathscr{E}$. We use this as the definition of the emf of a source:

$$\mathscr{E} = V \quad \text{(source on open circuit)} \tag{25-2}$$

The emf of a battery can be measured by placing a high-resistance voltmeter

Figure 25-3. A graph of V versus I from measurements made for the circuit in Fig. 25-2.

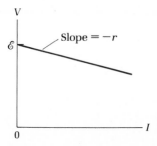

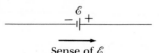

Figure 25-4. The sense of the emf of a battery is from its negative terminal toward its positive terminal.

across its terminals while the terminals are not connected to anything else. In this way the current is so small that the Ir term in Eq. (25-1) is negligible compared with $\mathscr{E}$.

The emf is a scalar quantity. However, a battery does have *polarity;* its terminals are distinguishable. We account for a battery's polarity by assigning a sense to its emf. The sense of a battery's emf is from its negative terminal toward its positive terminal (Fig. 25-4).

From Eqs. (25-1) and (25-2), you can see that emf has the same dimension as electric potential, namely, energy per unit charge. The dimension energy per unit charge indicates the physical nature of emf. If we consider a small current so that we can neglect the Ir term in Eq. (25-1), then we can describe the emf of a battery as the electric potential energy per unit charge given to the charge carriers by nonelectrostatic forces in the battery as the carriers pass from one terminal to the other. These forces are a result of the chemical action of the battery.

In Fig. 25-5, we show the internal resistance separate from the emf, even though they cannot be physically separated. Traversing the battery along the sense of the current, we find that the potential increases by the amount $\mathscr{E}$ because of the chemical action of the battery and decreases by Ir because of the resistance of the battery, which illustrates the relation $V = \mathscr{E} - Ir$.

Often a battery is designated by the approximate value of its emf (Fig. 25-6). For example, the emf of an automobile battery is about 12 V and we speak of a 12-V automobile battery; the emf of a flashlight battery is about 1.5 V and we speak of a 1.5-V flashlight battery. Under ordinary operating conditions, the emf of a battery is nearly independent of its condition or its "state of charge." However, the internal resistance of a battery tends to increase with battery usage (unless the battery is recharged). A worn-out flashlight battery may have essentially the same emf as a fresh flashlight battery, but the worn-out battery will have a significantly larger internal resistance. This means that the terminal potential difference of a battery depends on the battery's condition through the Ir term.

The internal resistance of an automobile battery in good condition is around $0.005\ \Omega$ and the internal resistance of a fresh flashlight battery is about $0.1\ \Omega$. In many cases, the internal resistance is quite low compared with the rest of the resistance in a circuit, and the internal resistance can be neglected.

If the sense of the current in a battery is the same as the sense of its emf, as seen in Figs. 25-1, 25-2 and 25-5, then the battery is said to be "discharging," and Eq. (25-1) is valid for this case. On the other hand, if the sense of the current is opposite the emf, as shown in Fig. 25-7, then the battery is said to be "charg-

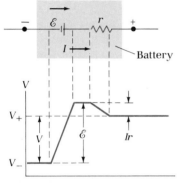

Figure 25-5. A battery with current I in it. The sense of I is the same as the sense of $\mathscr{E}$. The terminal potential difference is $V = V_+ - V_-$.

Figure 25-6. A battery is often designated by its emf. As a battery wears out, its internal resistance tends to increase. *(Photo by Tom Richard)*

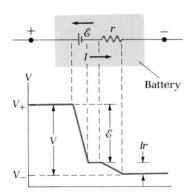

Figure 25-7. A battery being charged. The sense of I is opposite the sense of $\mathscr{E}$. The terminal potential difference is $V = V_+ - V_-$.

ing'' or is ''being charged.'' From the figure we see that if we traverse a charging battery along the sense of the current, then the potential *decreases* by the amount $\mathscr{E}$ because of chemical reactions in the battery. As with a discharging battery, the potential decreases by Ir because of the battery's resistance. Thus the terminal potential difference V across a battery that is being charged is

Terminal potential difference across a charging battery

$$V = \mathscr{E} + Ir$$

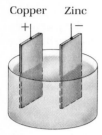

Copper   Zinc

Figure 25-8. A voltaic cell. For these metals a water solution of $CuSO_4$ and $ZnSO_4$ is used as the electrolyte.

What is a battery and how is one constructed? A battery is a number of *voltaic cells* connected in series, even though we often refer to a single voltaic cell as a battery. A voltaic cell can be made from two plates of different metals that are immersed in an electrolyte (Fig. 25-8). The plate with the higher potential is called the *anode*, and a connection to it is the positive terminal. The plate with the lower potential is called the *cathode*, and a connection to it is the negative terminal. For a battery having several cells, the cells are connected in series, with the sense of each cell along the same direction. Then the battery's emf is the sum of the emf's of its cells, and its internal resistance is the sum of the internal resistances of its cells.

A battery is but one example of a source of emf. Other examples are generators (described in Sec. 28-4), thermocouples, and solar cells. These devices transform energy from some other form to electric energy. For example, a battery transforms chemical energy to electric energy, a generator transforms mechanical energy to electric energy, and a solar cell transforms the energy of light (electromagnetic radiation) to electric energy.

EXAMPLE 25-1. In Fig. 25-2 the high-resistance voltmeter reads 1.53 V when switch S is open. When switch S is closed, the voltmeter reads 1.41 V and the ammeter reads 0.59 A. What is the battery's (a) emf and (b) internal resistance? (c) What does the voltmeter read when the resistance of the variable resistor is changed so that the ammeter reads 0.86 A?

SOLUTION. (a) With switch S open, there is no current in the variable resistor. Since the voltmeter has a high resistance, the current in the battery is negligibly small. Thus the

voltmeter reads the battery's emf: $\mathscr{E} = 1.53$ V. (b) Solving Eq. (25-1) for r gives

$$r = \frac{\mathscr{E} - V}{I} = \frac{1.53 \text{ V} - 1.41 \text{ V}}{0.59 \text{ A}} = 0.20 \ \Omega$$

(c) When $I = 0.86$ A, we have

$$V = \mathscr{E} - Ir = 1.53 \text{ V} - (0.86 \text{ A})(0.20 \ \Omega) = 1.36 \text{ V}$$

Note that the terminal potential difference is smaller for larger currents because the Ir term is larger for larger currents.

EXAMPLE 25-2. Two 9-V calculator batteries 1 and 2 have the same emf ($\mathscr{E}_1 = \mathscr{E}_2 = 9.2$ V), but different internal resistances ($r_1 = 2.8 \ \Omega$, $r_2 = 1.2 \ \Omega$). What is the terminal potential difference across each battery when it is required to produce a current of 1.0 A? Which battery is in better condition?

SOLUTION. With a current of 1.0 A, the terminal potential difference across battery 1 is

$$V_1 = \mathscr{E}_1 - Ir_1 = 9.2 \text{ V} - (1.0 \text{ A})(2.8 \ \Omega) = 6.4 \text{ V}$$

With a current of 1.0 A, the terminal potential difference across battery 2 is

$$V_2 = \mathscr{E}_2 - Ir_2 = 9.2 \text{ V} - (1.0 \text{ A})(1.2 \ \Omega) = 8.0 \text{ V}$$

Battery 2 is in better condition than battery 1.

25-3 ELECTRIC ENERGY AND POWER

When a current exists in a circuit element, energy is transformed. We now investigate energy transformations due to currents in circuit elements.

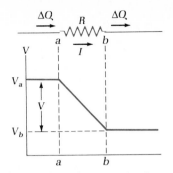

Figure 25-9. Charge carriers lose electric potential energy when they pass through a resistor.

Energy dissipated in a resistor. Consider the energy transformed when a resistor of resistance R carries a current I, as shown in Fig. 25-9. The potential difference across the resistor is $V = V_a - V_b$ and the sense of the current is from a to b. In a time interval Δt, a number of carriers with total charge ΔQ enter the resistor at point a where the potential is V_a, and a number of carriers with an equal total charge ΔQ leave the resistor at point b where the potential is V_b ($V_a > V_b$). The change in the electric potential energy ΔU of the carriers is

$$\Delta U = V_b \, \Delta Q - V_a \, \Delta Q = -(V_a - V_b) \, \Delta Q = -V \, \Delta Q$$

The quantity ΔU is negative because the potential decreases along the sense of the current. The rate at which the carriers lose electric potential energy is $-\Delta U/\Delta t$, and we call this rate the *power P_R dissipated* in the resistor. Thus

$$P_R = \frac{\Delta U}{\Delta t} = -\frac{-V \, \Delta Q}{\Delta t} = V \frac{\Delta Q}{\Delta t}$$

Since $I = \Delta Q/\Delta t$,

$$P_R = VI \tag{25-3}$$

Equation (25-3) can be quickly brought to mind from the dimensions of V and I; the dimension of V is energy per unit charge and the dimension of I is charge per unit time. Their product has the dimension of energy per unit time, or power:

$$\frac{\text{Energy}}{\text{Charge}} \frac{\text{charge}}{\text{time}} = \frac{\text{energy}}{\text{time}} = \text{power}$$

We can write P_R in terms of the resistance R of the resistor by using $V = IR$. We have $P_R = IV = I(IR)$, or

$$P_R = I^2 R \tag{25-4}$$

Alternatively, $P_R = VI = V(V/R)$, or

$$P_R = \frac{V^2}{R} \tag{25-5}$$

Equations (25-3), (25-4), and (25-5) are equivalent, and Eq. (25-4) is called *Joule's law*.

What happens to the lost electric potential energy of the carriers in a resistor? The carriers lose energy in the collisions that are responsible for the resistance of the resistor. When a resistor carries a current, the temperature of the resistor tends to increase as a result of these collisions. If the temperature of the resistor rises above that of its surroundings, then the resistor transfers heat to its surroundings. (Recall that heat is the transfer of energy due to a temperature difference.) Under steady conditions the energy is continuously transferred as heat to the surroundings. We tersely describe this chain of events by saying that the electric energy is *dissipated* as heat. These effects are sometimes called $I^2 R$ (read as "I-squared-R") *heating*, sometimes called *Joule heating*, or sometimes called *ohmic heating*.

EXAMPLE 25-3. Household electric light bulbs are rated according to the power P_R dissipated in the filament of the bulb when the potential difference across the bulb is 120 V. (Part of this dissipated energy is in the form of visible light.) (a) What is the current in a 75-W light bulb when it is operated at a potential difference of 120 V? (b) What is the resistance of the filament of the bulb when it is operated at 120 V? (c) If the bulb is operated continuously for 24 h, how much energy is dissipated in the bulb in kW · h?

SOLUTION. (a) Solving Eq. (25-3) for I, we have

$$I = \frac{P_R}{V} = \frac{75 \text{ W}}{120 \text{ V}} = 0.62 \text{ A}$$

(b) Solving Eq. (25-5) for R, we have

$$R = \frac{V^2}{P_R} = \frac{(120 \text{ V})^2}{75 \text{ W}} = 190 \text{ } \Omega$$

(c) Since the power P_R is constant in time, the energy dissipated in a time interval Δt is $P_R \Delta t$:

$$P_R \Delta t = (75 \text{ W})(24 \text{ h}) = (0.075 \text{ kW})(24 \text{ h}) = 1.8 \text{ kW} \cdot \text{h}$$

Energy to or from a battery. Now consider the transformation of energy when a current exists in a battery. If charge carriers pass through a battery in the direction such that the sense of the current is the same as the sense of the emf (the battery is discharging as in Figs. 25-2 and 25-5), then their electric potential energy increases. Let ΔQ be the amount of charge that passes through the battery in time Δt. The change in the electric potential energy of the carriers is $\Delta U = V \Delta Q$, where V is the terminal potential difference across the battery. In this case, ΔU is positive because the electric potential increases through the battery along the sense of the current (see Fig. 25-5). The rate at which the carriers gain electric potential energy is $\Delta U/\Delta t$, and we call this rate the *power output P_o* from the battery:

$$P_o = \frac{\Delta U}{\Delta t} = V \frac{\Delta Q}{\Delta t} = VI$$

Power output from a discharging battery

Using the expression for the terminal potential difference across a discharging battery, $V = \mathcal{E} - Ir$, we have $P_o = IV = I(\mathcal{E} - Ir)$, or

$$P_o = \mathcal{E}I - I^2 r \tag{25-6}$$

The term $\mathcal{E}I$ in Eq. (25-6) represents the rate at which the electric potential energy of the carriers is increased by chemical reactions in the battery. We shall call this the *power $P_{\mathcal{E}}$ expended by the emf* of the battery: $P_{\mathcal{E}} = \mathcal{E}I$. We recognize the $I^2 r$ term as the power P_r dissipated in the battery due to its resistance r. (The temperature of the battery tends to increase.) This term represents a rate of loss of electric potential energy for the carriers and properly enters the expression with a minus sign. Thus Eq. (25-6) states that the power output P_o of a battery is equal to the power $P_{\mathcal{E}}$ expended by the emf minus the power P_r dissipated as heat: $P_o = P_{\mathcal{E}} - P_r$.

Equation (25-6) is valid for a discharging battery. How is energy transformed in a charging battery? If a battery is being charged, then the sense of the current is opposite the sense of the battery's emf. In this case the potential *decreases* along the sense of the current (see Fig. 25-7), and the electric potential energy of the carriers decreases as they pass through the battery. The power input P_i to the battery is equal to the rate at which the carriers lose electric potential energy in passing through the battery: $P_i = IV$. Since the terminal potential difference across a charging battery is $V = \mathcal{E} + Ir$, we have $P_i = IV = I(\mathcal{E} + Ir)$, or

Power input to a charging battery

$$P_i = \mathcal{E}I + I^2 r$$

In this case the product $\mathcal{E}I$ represents the power delivered to the emf of the battery by the charge carriers.

EXAMPLE 25-4. Suppose a flashlight battery of emf 1.5 V and internal resistance 0.61 Ω carries a current of 1.4 A while delivering power to a flashlight bulb. (a) Determine the power expended by the battery's emf. (b) Determine the power dissipated in the battery. (*c*) Determine the power output of the battery.

SOLUTION. (*a*) The power expended by the battery's emf is

$$P_{\mathscr{E}} = \mathscr{E}I = (1.5 \text{ V})(1.4 \text{ A}) = 2.1 \text{ W}$$

(*b*) The power dissipated in the battery is

$$P_r = I^2 r = (1.4 \text{ A})^2 (0.61 \text{ }\Omega) = 1.2 \text{ W}$$

(*c*) The power output of the battery is

$$P_o = P_{\mathscr{E}} - P_r = 2.1 \text{ W} - 1.2 \text{ W} = 0.9 \text{ W}$$

Energy to or from any circuit element. Now consider the rate of energy transformation *P* in any type of circuit element. If *V* is the potential difference across the element and *I* is the current in the element, then

$$P = IV \tag{25-7}$$

Rate at which energy is transformed in a circuit element

because *V* is the change in the potential energy per unit charge for carriers that pass through the element and *I* is rate at which charge passes through the element. The product *IV* gives the rate at which the electric potential energy of the carriers changes as they pass through the element. If the sense of *I* is along the direction the potential decreases (as in a resistor or a charging battery), then *P* gives the rate at which the carriers lose electric potential energy. If the sense of *I* is along the direction the potential increases (as in a discharging battery), then *P* gives the rate at which the carriers gain electric potential energy. Equations (25-3), (25-4), (25-5), and (25-6) were specific applications of the general relation given by Eq. (25-7).

25-4 KIRCHHOFF'S RULES

In designing a circuit to perform some task, one ordinarily has batteries (or other sources) of known emf and resistors of known resistance. Often the problem is to determine how a given current can be produced in a particular circuit element. Two rules, called *Kirchhoff's rules* and named for G. R. Kirchhoff (1824–1887), guide us in finding the currents. We refer to these rules as the loop rule and the point rule.

The loop rule comes from conservation of energy.

The loop rule. The loop rule states that *the sum of the potential differences encountered in a round-trip around any closed loop in a circuit is zero.* Since the potential is directly related to the potential energy of the carriers, the loop rule is a statement of conservation of energy. We can write the loop rule as

The loop rule

$$\Sigma V = 0 \tag{25-8}$$

As we consider the potential in going around a loop in a circuit, the potential increases as we pass through some elements and decreases as we pass through others; the sum of the potential differences for a complete round-trip is zero.

Before using the loop rule to find the current in a circuit, let us introduce a new symbol for the current, small *i* in place of capital *I*. The symbol *I* was defined such that it is always positive. But in dealing with circuits, it is convenient to let the current be negative in some cases. Therefore, we let the symbol *i* represent a current that may be negative and *I* is simply the magnitude of *i*. *By convention, i is positive when the sense of the current corresponds to the direction of motion of positive carriers.*

Sign convention for current *i*

Consider using the loop rule to find the current in the circuit of Fig. 25-10. The sense of the current *i* is shown in the figure. We begin at point *a* and

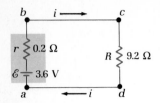

Figure 25-10. Using the loop rule.

traverse the loop in the clockwise sense. The loop rule gives

$$(V_b - V_a) + (V_c - V_b) + (V_d - V_c) + (V_a - V_d) = 0$$

The potential difference across the section from a to b is the terminal potential difference across the battery: $V_b - V_a = \mathcal{E} - ir$. The connecting wires have negligible resistance, so the potential differences $V_c - V_b$ and $V_a - V_d$ are each zero. The current through R is from c to d so that $V_c > V_d$. Therefore, $V_d - V_c = -iR$. Substitution into the loop rule gives

$$(\mathcal{E} - ir) + (0) + (-iR) + (0) = 0$$

Solving for i, we have

$$i = \frac{\mathcal{E}}{r + R}$$

With the numerical values given in Fig. 25-10, the current is $i = 3.6 \text{ V}/(0.2\ \Omega + 9.2\ \Omega) = 0.38$ A.

In the above analysis we chose to traverse the loop clockwise, but that choice is arbitrary. Suppose we traverse the loop counterclockwise, beginning at point a. The loop rule gives

$$(V_d - V_a) + (V_c - V_d) + (V_b - V_c) + (V_a - V_b) = 0$$

The potential difference $(V_c - V_d)$ is $+iR$ because $V_c > V_d$. Also, $V_a - V_b = -(V_b - V_a) = -(\mathcal{E} - ir) = -\mathcal{E} + ir$. This gives

$$iR - \mathcal{E} + ir = 0$$

Solving for i, we have

$$i = \frac{\mathcal{E}}{r + R}$$

This is the same result as before. The answer is independent of which way we go around the loop.

Our analysis of the circuit in Fig. 25-10 shows that there are two rules we can use to give the algebraic sign of terms we enter into the loop-rule equation:

1. In traversing a resistance R along the sense of the current i, the potential difference across the resistance is entered as $-iR$. In traversing a resistance R opposite the sense of the current i, the potential difference is entered as $+iR$.

2. In traversing a source of emf along the sense of the emf, the potential difference across the source is entered as $+\mathcal{E}$. In traversing a source of emf opposite the sense of the emf, the potential difference across the source is entered as $-\mathcal{E}$.

In using these rules, we treat the internal resistance of the source as a separate resistance.

Now consider applying the loop rule to the single-loop circuit shown in Fig. 25-11. Since the senses of the emf's of the two batteries are opposite one another, we are not certain about the sense of i. Let us assume that the sense of i is counterclockwise, as shown in the figure. Starting at point a and going counterclockwise around the loop, we write the sum of the potential differences as

$$(-iR_1) + (+\mathcal{E}_1) + (-ir_1) + (-iR_2) + (-ir_2) + (-\mathcal{E}_2) = 0$$

Solving for the current i, we have

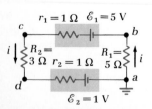

Figure 25-11. In this circuit, $\mathcal{E}_1 > \mathcal{E}_2$ so that the sense of the current is counterclockwise.

$$i = \frac{\mathscr{E}_1 - \mathscr{E}_2}{R_1 + R_2 + r_1 + r_2} \tag{25-9}$$

From the figure, $R_1 + R_2 + r_1 + r_2 = 10 \ \Omega$, $\mathscr{E}_1 - \mathscr{E}_2 = 5 \ V - 1 \ V = 4 \ V$, so that $i = 4 \ V/10 \ \Omega = 0.4 \ A$.

Notice that Eq. (25-9) yields a positive value for i if $\mathscr{E}_1 > \mathscr{E}_2$ and a negative value for i if $\mathscr{E}_2 > \mathscr{E}_1$. If $\mathscr{E}_2 > \mathscr{E}_1$, then the sense of the current is clockwise, opposite our assumed sense for i in Fig. 25-11. Therefore, if we assume a particular sense for the current at the outset of a problem and the value of the current turns out to be negative, then this means that the actual sense of the current is opposite our assumed sense. That is, the equation automatically tells us the sense of the current. We shall find this feature of our equations quite useful when we deal with more complex circuits. In more complex circuits we often cannot predict the sense of the current with certainty at the outset of the analysis. This uncertainty is of no consequence because we can assume the current has a particular sense and if this assumption turns out to be wrong, then i has a negative value. In the case of Fig. 25-11, the actual sense of the current is counterclockwise, the same as our assumed sense.

Figure 25-12 shows a graph of the loop rule for the circuit in Fig. 25-11. In our mind's eye, we break the circuit at point a and string it along a straight line. Then we show the variation of the potential along the sense of the current. The potential of point a has been arbitrarily set to zero (that is, point a is "grounded").

The point rule. In analyzing circuits with two or more loops, we use the point rule in combination with the loop rule. The point rule states that *the sum of the currents toward a branch point is equal to the sum of the currents away from the same branch point.* (Points a and b in Fig. 25-13 are examples of branch points.) Since charge does not accumulate at any point along the connecting wires, the point rule is simply a statement of the conservation of charge. We can write the point rule as

> The point rule comes from conservation of charge.

> The point rule

$$\Sigma i_{\text{toward}} = \Sigma i_{\text{away}} \tag{25-10}$$

For example, the point rule applied to point a in the circuit in Fig. 25-13 gives

$$i_1 = i_2 + i_3 \tag{25-11}$$

because current i_1 is toward a and currents i_2 and i_3 are away from a.

We now use the loop rule and the point rule to find the currents i_1, i_2, and i_3

Figure 25-12. Showing the loop rule, $\Sigma V = 0$, for the circuit in Fig. 25-11.

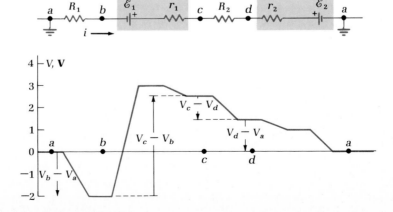

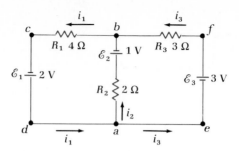

Figure 25-13. A two-loop circuit.

in the circuit of Fig. 25-13. Let loop *abcda* be loop 1 and let loop *aefba* be loop 2. From the figure, our assumed sense for i_1 is chosen to be from *b* to *c* to *d* to *a* (counterclockwise); our assumed sense for i_2 is chosen to be from *a* to *b*; and our assumed sense for i_3 is chosen to be from *a* to *e* to *f* to *b*. Also, for simplicity we include the internal resistance of each battery in the resistance that is in series with that battery. For example, the internal resistance of battery 1 is included in R_1.

The loop rule applied to loop 1 beginning at point *a* and going around counterclockwise gives

$$(-i_2 R_2) + (-\mathcal{E}_2) + (-i_1 R_1) + (\mathcal{E}_1) = 0$$

Rearranging, we have

$$\mathcal{E}_1 - \mathcal{E}_2 = i_1 R_1 + i_2 R_2 \tag{25-12}$$

The loop rule applied to loop 2 beginning at point *a* and going around counterclockwise gives

$$(\mathcal{E}_3) + (-i_3 R_3) + (\mathcal{E}_2) + (i_2 R_2) = 0$$

Rearranging, we have

$$\mathcal{E}_3 + \mathcal{E}_2 = i_3 R_3 - i_2 R_2 \tag{25-13}$$

We have three equations in three unknowns. The three equations are the point-rule equation [Eq. (25-11)] and the loop-rule equations [Eqs. (25-12) and (25-13)]. The three unknowns are the currents i_1, i_2, and i_3. The point-rule equation is simpler than the other two because each of the coefficients is 1. Using the point-rule equation to eliminate i_1 in Eq. (25-12) gives

$$\mathcal{E}_1 - \mathcal{E}_2 = i_2(R_1 + R_2) + i_3 R_1 \tag{25-14}$$

Equations (25-13) and (25-14) represent two equations in two unknowns. Substitution of the numerical values from Fig. 25-13 into these equations gives

$$4 \text{ V} = (3 \ \Omega)i_3 - (2 \ \Omega)i_2$$

and

$$1 \text{ V} = (6 \ \Omega)i_2 + (4 \ \Omega)i_3$$

If we multiply the first of these equations by 3 and add the resulting equation to the second equation, then i_2 is eliminated and we have an equation that contains only i_3. This gives $i_3 = 1$ A. If we now substitute this value of i_3 into either of the above equations, then we find $i_2 = -0.5$ A. Substitution of these value of i_2 and i_3 into Eq. (25-11) gives $i_1 = 0.5$ A. From the signs of our answers we see that the actual senses for i_1 and i_3 are the same as their assumed senses, but the actual sense of i_2 is opposite its assumed sense.

EXAMPLE 25-5. (a) In the circuit of Fig. 25-14a, determine the value of $\mathscr{E}$ such that a current of 0.5 A exists in the 8-Ω resistor with sense from a to b. (b) What is the potential difference across the section from a to b, $V_a - V_b$?

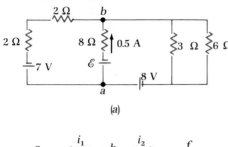

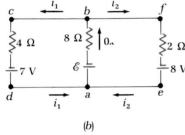

(a)

(b)

Figure 25-14. Example 25-5: (a) Circuit. (b) Circuit reduced.

SOLUTION. (a) First, we notice that the two 2-Ω resistors are in series, so they can be replaced by a single 4-Ω resistor. Also, the 3-Ω resistor is in parallel with the 6-Ω resistor, so they can be replaced by a single 2-Ω resistor. That is, $[(3\ \Omega)(6\ \Omega)]/(3\ \Omega + 6\ \Omega) = 2\ \Omega$. This reduction gives the circuit shown in Fig. 25-14b, where we have shown our as-

sumed senses for currents i_1 and i_2. Let loop $abcda$ be loop 1 and let loop $abfea$ be loop 2. Starting at point a and adding potential differences going counterclockwise around loop 1, we have

$$(-\mathscr{E}) + [-(0.5\ \text{A})(8\ \Omega)] + [-i_1(4\ \Omega)] + (7\ \text{V}) = 0$$

or

$$\mathscr{E} = 3\ \text{V} - i_1(4\ \Omega) \qquad \text{(loop 1 equation)}$$

Starting at point a and adding potential differences going clockwise around loop 2, we have

$$(-\mathscr{E}) + [-(0.5\ \text{A})(8\ \Omega)] + [-i_2(2\ \Omega)] + (8\ \text{V}) = 0$$

or

$$\mathscr{E} = 4\ \text{V} - i_2(2\ \Omega) \qquad \text{(loop 2 equation)}$$

The point rule applied at point a gives

$$i_1 + i_2 = 0.5\ \text{A} \qquad \text{(point-rule equation)}$$

We have three equations in three unknowns; the unknowns are $\mathscr{E}$, i_1, and i_2. We can eliminate i_2 by solving the point-rule equation for i_2 and substituting the result into the loop 2 equation. This gives

$$\mathscr{E} = 3\ \text{V} + i_1(2\ \Omega)$$

If we multiply this equation by 2 and add the resulting equation to the loop 1 equation, then i_1 is eliminated and we find $\mathscr{E} = 3\ \text{V}$.

(b) From the figure we see that

$$V_a - V_b = \mathscr{E} + (0.5\ \text{A})(8\ \Omega) = 3\ \text{V} + 4\ \text{V} = 7\ \text{V}$$

We have shown the procedures for solving one-loop and two-loop circuit problems. Useful circuits often contain many more loops than this. The solution to these problems can be quite complex, but the fundamental principles governing the solutions are the same as for two-loop circuits: conservation of energy (Kirchhoff's loop rule) and conservation of charge (Kirchhoff's point rule).

25-5 RC CIRCUITS

Our circuits so far have contained only two types of elements: resistors and batteries. Now we add a third type, a capacitor. From Chap. 23, a capacitor is a device which can hold or contain charge on its plates, charge $+Q$ on one plate and $-Q$ on the other. The potential difference across a charged capacitor is $V = Q/C$, where C is the capacitance of the capacitor.

We examine two specific cases: (i) An uncharged capacitor is charged by connecting its terminals to a battery in series with a resistor, and (ii) a charged capacitor is discharged by connecting its terminals to a resistor. Our previous discussions have been about steady currents, but now the current varies with time. Indeed, it is the time dependence of the current (and charge) that is our major interest.

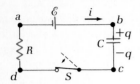

Figure 25-15. A battery charging a capacitor.

Charging a capacitor. Consider a capacitor of capacitance C placed in series with a switch S, resistor of resistance R, and battery of emf $\mathcal{E}$, as shown in Fig. 25-15. (We include the internal resistance of the battery in R.) Initially the capacitor is uncharged and the switch S is open so that no current exists. When S is closed, the battery begins transferring charge carriers from one capacitor plate to the other, and a current exists in the circuit. If i is the current in the circuit and its sense is clockwise (from the negative plate toward the positive plate), then

$$i = \frac{dq}{dt} \tag{25-15}$$

where q is the instantaneous charge on the positive plate of the capacitor. That is, the current in the circuit corresponds to the rate at which charge is transferred from one plate to the other. Consequently, the current is equal to the rate at which the capacitor is charged.

The sum of the potential differences in going clockwise around the loop, beginning at point a, is

$$(V_b - V_a) + (V_c - V_b) + (V_d - V_c) + (V_a - V_d) = 0$$

$$(\mathcal{E}) + \left(\frac{-q}{C}\right) + (0) + (-iR) = 0 \tag{25-16}$$

Notice that the potential difference $V_c - V_b$ across the capacitor is $-q/C$ because the positive plate is on the side with point b and the negative plate is on the side with point c. Thus $V_b > V_c$. Substitution of Eq. (25-15) into Eq. (25-16) gives $\mathcal{E} - q/C - R(dq/dt) = 0$. Rearranging, we find

$$\frac{-dq}{\mathcal{E}C - q} = -\frac{1}{RC} dt$$

where $\mathcal{E}$, C, and R are constant and q depends on t. To solve this differential equation, it is convenient to let $u = \mathcal{E}C - q$, which gives $du = -dq$. The equation then becomes $du/u = -(1/RC) dt$. The indefinite integral is $\ln u = -(t/RC) + \text{constant}$. Replacing u with $\mathcal{E}C - q$, we have

$$\ln(\mathcal{E}C - q) = -\frac{t}{RC} + \text{constant}$$

We evaluate the integration constant by using the initial conditions; when $t = 0$, $q = 0$, so that $\ln \mathcal{E}C = \text{constant}$. Substitution of the integration constant gives $\ln(\mathcal{E}C - q) = -(t/RC) + \ln \mathcal{E}C$. Note that $\ln(\mathcal{E}C - q) - \ln \mathcal{E}C = \ln[(\mathcal{E}C - q)/\mathcal{E}C]$. Thus

$$\ln \frac{\mathcal{E}C - q}{\mathcal{E}C} = -\frac{t}{RC}$$

or

$$\frac{\mathcal{E}C - q}{\mathcal{E}C} = e^{-t/RC}$$

Solving for q gives

Charge on a charging capacitor

$$q(t) = \mathcal{E}C(1 - e^{-t/RC}) \tag{25-17}$$

Figure 25-16 shows a graph of q versus t. We note a few representative points

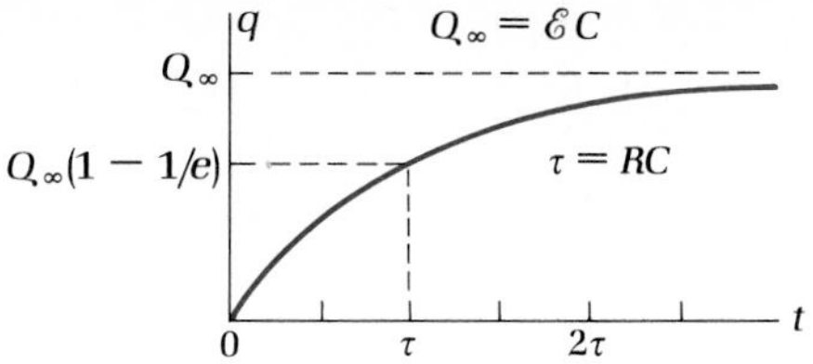

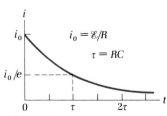

Figure 25-16. Charge on a charging capacitor versus time.

of interest: When $t = 0$, $q = \mathscr{E}C(1 - e^{-0}) = 0$; when $t = RC$, $q = \mathscr{E}C(1 - e^{-1}) = (0.63)\mathscr{E}C$; and as $t \to \infty$, $q \to \mathscr{E}C(1 - e^{-\infty}) = \mathscr{E}C$. The charge asymptotically approaches $\mathscr{E}C$. We let Q_∞ represent the final charge on the capacitor: $Q_\infty = \mathscr{E}C$.

Notice that the product RC characterizes the rate at which the capacitor is charged. From Eq. (25-17), the quantity RC must have the dimension of time because the argument of an exponential must be dimensionless (also see Exercise 25-30). The SI unit for the product RC is the second ($1\,\Omega \cdot \mathrm{F} = 1\,\mathrm{s}$). This product is called the *RC time constant* of the circuit and is given the symbol τ: $\tau = RC$. If τ is large, the capacitor charges slowly, whereas if τ is small, the capacitor charges rapidly. The time required for the capacitor to reach a given fraction of its final charge is determined solely by τ (or RC).

The RC time constant

The current is found by taking the time derivative of Eq. (25-17):

$$i = \frac{dq}{dt} = \frac{d}{dt}\,[\mathscr{E}C(1 - e^{-t/RC})] = \mathscr{E}C\left(-\frac{1}{RC}\right)(-e^{-t/RC})$$

Current in the circuit of a charging capacitor

or

$$i = \frac{\mathscr{E}}{R}\,e^{-t/RC} = i_0 e^{-t/\tau} \qquad (25\text{-}18)$$

where $i_0 = \mathscr{E}/R$ is the initial current. Notice that i_0 is the same as the steady current that would exist if the capacitor were replaced by a connecting wire. Figure 25-17 shows a graph of i versus t. We note a few representative points of interest: When $t = 0$, $i = i_0 e^{-0} = i_0$; when $t = \tau$, $i = i_0 e^{-1} = (0.37)i_0$; when $t = 2\tau$, $i = i_0 e^{-2} = (0.37)^2 i_0 = (0.14)i_0$; and as $t \to \infty$, $i \to i_0 e^{-\infty} = 0$. The current decreases exponentially with time and asymptotically approaches zero as time goes on. Notice that in each time interval equal to one RC time constant, the current is reduced by a factor $e^{-1} = 1/e \approx 0.37$.

Now consider the way energy is exchanged during the charging of a capacitor. The energy transferred to the charge carriers of the circuit by the emf of the battery during the entire charging process (as $t \to \infty$) is $\mathscr{E}Q_\infty = \mathscr{E}(\mathscr{E}C) = \mathscr{E}^2 C$ because $\mathscr{E}$ is the energy per unit charge transferred by the emf of the battery and a charge $Q_\infty = \mathscr{E}C$ passes through the battery during the entire charging process. Recall from Sec. 23-4 that $\frac{1}{2}Q^2/C$ is the energy stored in a capacitor with charge Q. The energy stored in the capacitor after the charging is completed is $\frac{1}{2}Q_\infty^2/C = \frac{1}{2}(\mathscr{E}C)^2/C = \frac{1}{2}\mathscr{E}^2 C$. Thus half of the energy expended by the emf of the battery is stored in the capacitor. What happened to the other half of this energy? It is dissipated as heat in the resistor. The rate at which energy is dissipated in the resistor is $P = -(dU/dt) = i^2 R$, where U is the electric potential energy of the carriers. The energy $-\Delta U$ dissipated in the resistor during the charging is

$$-\Delta U = -\int dU = \int_0^\infty (i^2 R)\, dt$$

Figure 25-17. Current versus time in the circuit of a charging capacitor.

$$= \int_0^\infty \left(\frac{\mathscr{E}}{R} e^{-t/RC} \right)^2 R \, dt = \left(\frac{\mathscr{E}}{R} \right)^2 \left(\frac{RC}{2} \right) R \int_0^\infty e^{-x} \, dx$$

where $x = (2/RC)t$ and $dx = (2/RC) \, dt$. Since

$$\int_0^\infty e^{-x} \, dx = 1$$

we have

$$-\Delta U = \tfrac{1}{2} \mathscr{E}^2 C$$

Half of the energy expended by the battery's emf is stored in the capacitor and half is dissipated as heat in the resistor.

EXAMPLE 25-6. A 5.6-μF capacitor is charged by a 4.2-V battery through a 380-Ω resistor. (a) Write expressions for the charge on the capacitor and the current in the circuit as functions of time. (b) If the sensitivity of our current measurements is 1 percent of i_0, then how long must we wait to assume the current is effectively zero? (c) Evaluate the energy expended by the emf of the battery, stored in the capacitor, and dissipated as heat in the resistor after the charging is complete.

SOLUTION. (a) The RC time constant of the circuit is $\tau = (380 \, \Omega)(5.6 \, \mu F) = 2.1$ ms. (Recall that $1 \, \Omega \cdot F = 1$ s.) The final charge is $Q_\infty = \mathscr{E}C = (4.2 \, V)(5.6 \, \mu F) = 24 \, \mu C$, and the initial current is $i_0 = \mathscr{E}/R = 4.2 \, V/380 \, \Omega = 11$ mA. The expressions for the charge and current are

$$q(t) = (24 \, \mu C)(1 - e^{-t/(2.1 \, ms)})$$

and

$$i(t) = (11 \, mA)e^{-t/(2.1 \, ms)}$$

(b) To find the time required for the current to fall from i_0 to some value $i(t)$, we solve Eq. (25-18) for t:

$$t = \tau \ln \frac{i_0}{i(t)}$$

Since the sensitivity of our current measurements is 1 percent of i_0, the current is effectively zero when $i(t) < (0.01)i_0$. The time required for the current to become 1 percent of i_0 is $t = \tau \ln [i_0/(0.01)i_0] = \tau \ln 100 = 4.6\tau$. A safe rule of thumb is that for 1 percent sensitivity the charging is complete after about 5τ, or about 10 ms (5×2.1 ms) in this example. Suppose we increase our sensitivity by a factor of 100, to 0.01 percent of i_0. Then how long would we need to wait for the current to be effectively zero? (The answer is twice as long, or about 20 ms, not 100 times as long.) (c) The energy expended by the emf of the battery in charging the capacitor is $\mathscr{E}^2C = (4.2 \, V)^2(5.6 \, \mu F) = 10 \, \mu J$. The capacitor stores 5 μJ, and 5 μJ is dissipated as heat in the resistor.

Discharging a capacitor. Consider a capacitor of capacitance C placed in series with a switch S and resistor of resistance R, as shown in Fig. 25-18. Initially the capacitor has charge Q_0 and the switch S is open so that no current exists. At the instant S is closed, charge carriers begin to flow through the circuit to neutralize the charge on the plates. The flow of these carriers constitutes a current in the circuit. Let $q(t)$ be the charge on the capacitor at time t, where $t = 0$ corresponds to the instant S is closed. If i is the current with counterclockwise as its sense (from the positive plate toward the negative plate), then

$$i = -\frac{dq}{dt} \tag{25-19}$$

The minus sign must be included because i is positive and dq/dt is negative. Our assumed sense for i has made i positive, and dq/dt is negative because the charge on the plates is decreasing.

Starting at point a, we add potential differences in going counterclockwise around the loop. The loop rule gives

$$-iR + \frac{q}{C} = 0$$

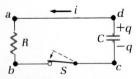

Figure 25-18. A capacitor is discharged through a resistor.

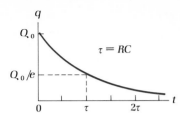

Figure 25-19. Charge versus time on a discharging capacitor.

or

$$iR = \frac{q}{C} \qquad (25\text{-}20)$$

Substituting Eq. (25-19) into Eq. (25-20), we have

$$-\frac{dq}{dt} R = \frac{q}{C} \qquad \text{or} \qquad \frac{dq}{q} = -\frac{1}{RC} dt$$

Since R and C are constant, the indefinite integral gives

$$\ln q = -\frac{t}{RC} + \text{constant}$$

The integration constant can be evaluated by noting that when $t = 0$, $q = Q_0$. Therefore, $\ln Q_0 = \text{constant}$. Since $\ln q - \ln Q_0 = \ln (q/Q_0)$, we have $\ln (q/Q_0) = -(t/RC)$, or

Charge on a discharging capacitor

$$q(t) = Q_0 e^{-t/RC} = Q_0 e^{-t/\tau} \qquad (25\text{-}21)$$

Figure 25-19 shows a graph of q versus t. Notice the similarity between this graph and the one in Fig. 25-17. The charge on the capacitor decreases exponentially with time and asymptotically approaches zero as time goes on. The time required for the charge to decrease by any given fraction of Q_0 is determined by the product $\tau = RC$.

Now consider the current in the circuit. Since $i = -dq/dt$

$$i = -\frac{d}{dt} (Q_0 e^{-t/RC}) = \frac{Q_0}{RC} e^{-t/RC}$$

The initial potential difference V_0 across the capacitor is $V_0 = Q_0/C$, so

Current in the circuit of a discharging capacitor

$$i(t) = \frac{V_0}{R} e^{-t/RC} = i_0 e^{-t/\tau} \qquad (25\text{-}22)$$

where $i_0 = V_0/R$ is the initial current. Similar to the charge on the capacitor plates, the current decreases exponentially with time, and the RC time constant $\tau = RC$ characterizes the decay of the current.

SUMMARY WITH APPLICATIONS

Section 25-2. EMF and internal resistance of a battery

The important electrical properties of a battery are its emf $\mathscr{E}$ and its internal resistance r. The terminal potential difference across a discharging battery is

$$V = \mathscr{E} - Ir \qquad (25\text{-}1)$$

where the sense of the current I in the battery is the same as the battery's emf. For a charging battery,

$$V = \mathscr{E} + Ir$$

where the sense of the current in the battery is opposite the battery's emf.

Define the emf and internal resistance of a battery; describe the properties of a battery.

Section 25-3. Electric energy and power

The power dissipated as heat in a resistor is

$$P_R = IV = I^2 R = \frac{V^2}{R}$$

The power output from a discharging battery is

$$P_o = \mathscr{E}I - I^2 r \qquad (25\text{-}6)$$

The power input to a charging battery is

$$P_i = \mathscr{E}I + I^2 r$$

The rate at which energy is transformed in any circuit element is

$$P = IV \qquad (25\text{-}7)$$

Determine the electric power to or away from a circuit element.

Section 25-4. Kirchhoff's rules

Kirchhoff's rules are the loop rule:

$$\Sigma V = 0 \qquad (25\text{-}8)$$

and the point rule:

$$\Sigma i_{\text{toward}} = \Sigma i_{\text{away}} \qquad (25\text{-}10)$$

These rules are expressions of conservation of energy and conservation of charge, respectively. The rules facilitate the analysis of electric circuits.

Use Kirchhoff's rules to find currents and other circuit quantities.

Section 25-5. *RC* circuits

The charge on a capacitor that is being charged by a battery with emf $\mathscr{E}$ is

$$q(t) = \mathscr{E}C(1 - e^{-t/\tau}) \qquad (25\text{-}17)$$

where $\tau = RC$ is the RC time constant. The current in the circuit is

$$i(t) = \left(\frac{\mathscr{E}}{R}\right) e^{-t/\tau} \qquad (25\text{-}18)$$

The charge on a discharging capacitor is

$$q(t) = Q_0 e^{-t/\tau} \qquad (25\text{-}21)$$

and the current in the circuit is

$$i(t) = i_0 e^{-t/\tau} \qquad (25\text{-}22)$$

Describe the time dependence of the charge on a charging or discharging capacitor; describe the time dependence of the current in the circuit of a charging or discharging capacitor.

QUESTIONS

25-1 Suppose the resistance R in Fig. 25-2 is increased. Will the terminal potential difference across the battery increase or decrease?

25-2 Explain how you would measure the emf and internal resistance of a battery. What apparatus would you need? If you require the use of a resistor, what must the approximate value of its resistance be? What about the internal resistance of any meters you use?

25-3 Explain the distinction between emf and potential difference. What can you say about the nature of the forces involved with these two quantities?

25-4 When we refer to a 6-V battery, are we characterizing the battery by its terminal potential difference or by its emf?

25-5 A battery has two important characteristics, its emf and its internal resistance. Why do we not refer to a battery as a 6-V, 0.5-Ω battery rather than just as a 6-V battery?

25-6 Can the sense of the current in a battery ever be opposite the sense of its emf? If so, explain how this could happen. If this is the case, which terminal is at the higher potential, the positive terminal or the negative terminal?

25-7 Can the terminal potential difference across a battery be larger than the emf of the battery? Explain.

25-8 Explain how a "worn-out" battery can have about the same emf as a fresh battery, but still not produce enough current to be useful. Can a battery that is too worn-out to be used in one circuit still be useful in another circuit?

25-9 A battery can be rated according to ampere-hours (A · h). For example, an automobile battery might be rated as a 12-V, 90-A · h battery. What are the dimensions of the product (12 V) (90 A · h)? From these dimensions, can you guess the meaning of this product?

25-10 Two batteries with the same emf $\mathscr{E}$ and internal resistance r are connected in series such that the sense of their emf's is the same. That is, the positive terminal of one is connected to the negative terminal of the other, and the two remaining terminals are the terminals of their combination. What are the emf and internal resistance of this combination?

25-11 Two batteries with the same emf $\mathscr{E}$ and internal resistance r are connected in parallel. That is, the two positive terminals are connected together and the two negative terminals are connected together, and lead wires from these connections form the terminals of their combination. What are the emf and internal resistance of this combination? Why should such connections only be made with sources which have nearly the same emf? (This is what is done when a car with a worn-out battery is "jump-started" with the battery of another car.)

25-12 Consider the contrasting properties of the metal used as a heating element wire on the one hand and the metal used in a fuse wire on the other. What physical property (or properties) should be greatly different for the two?

25-13 Which household light bulb has the larger resistance, a 75-W, 120-V bulb or a 40-W, 120-V bulb?

25-14 A group of small batteries is connected in series so that the combination has an emf of 120 V. When this source is connected to a 25-W, 120-V light bulb, the bulb glows at its normal brightness. However, when this source is connected to a 300-W, 120-V bulb, the bulb glows much more dimly than it ordinarily does. Explain.

25-15 Two resistors with resistances R_1 and R_2 are connected in parallel and a current is in the combination. If $R_1 < R_2$, which resistor dissipates the larger amount of energy? Which expression, $P = I^2R$ or $P = V^2/R$, is more useful in answering this question?

25-16 Two resistors with resistances R_1 and R_2 are connected in series and a current is in the combination. If $R_1 < R_2$, which resistor dissipates the larger amount of energy? Which expression, $P = I^2R$ or $P = V^2/R$, is more useful in answering this question?

25-17 Which battery in Fig. 25-11 is discharging and which is being charged?

25-18 If the current in a discharging battery is small (so that $\mathscr{E}I \gg I^2r$), then the product $\mathscr{E}I$ is interpreted as the rate at which chemical energy in the battery is being transformed into electric potential energy of the charge carriers. If the current in a charging battery is small, then what is the interpretation of the product $\mathscr{E}I$?

25-19 In Fig. 25-20, is $V_b - V_a$ equal to $+iR$ or $-iR$? What is $V_a - V_b$?

Figure 25-20. Ques. 25-19.

25-20 In Fig. 25-21, is $V_b - V_a$ equal to $+Q/C$ or $-Q/C$? What is $V_a - V_b$?

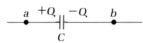

Figure 25-21. Ques. 25-20.

25-21 In Fig. 25-22, is $V_b - V_a$ equal to $+(\mathscr{E} - ir)$, $-(\mathscr{E} - ir)$, $+(\mathscr{E} + ir)$, or $-(\mathscr{E} + ir)$? What is $V_a - V_b$?

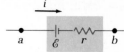

Figure 25-22. Ques. 25-21.   **Figure 25-23.** Ques. 25-22.

25-22 In Fig. 25-23, is $V_b - V_a$ equal to $+(\mathscr{E} - ir)$, $-(\mathscr{E} - ir)$, $+(\mathscr{E} + ir)$, or $-(\mathscr{E} + ir)$? What is $V_a - V_b$?

25-23 Consider the discharge of the capacitor in Fig. 25-18. Note that, because the charges on the plates are equal in magnitude but opposite in sign, the net charge on the plates of the capacitor is zero before it is discharged, during the time it is being discharged, and after the discharge is complete. In view of this, does the capacitor lose net charge? If it does not lose net charge, are there any quantities associated with the capacitor that do have a net decrease? Explain.

25-24 Explain how you would use an RC circuit with an ammeter, a battery, a capacitor of known capacitance, and a stopwatch to measure a large resistance. If the unknown resistance is in the range of $10^6 \ \Omega$, what would be a convenient value for the capacitance of the capacitor?

25-25 Complete the following table:

Symbol	Represents	Type	SI unit
$\mathscr{E}$			V
r	Internal resistance		
i		Scalar	
P			
τ			

EXERCISES

Section 25-2. Emf and internal resistance of a battery

25-1 A battery with an emf of 1.5 V and an internal resistance of 0.4 Ω has a current of 230 mA in it. The sense of the current is the same as the sense of the battery's emf. What is the battery's terminal potential difference?

25-2 The terminal potential difference across a 12.5-V battery is 11.9 V when the current in it is 7.8 A. What is meant by the term "12.5-V battery"? Is the battery charging or discharging? What is the internal resistance of this battery?

25-3 When a high-resistance voltmeter is placed across the terminals of a battery, the voltmeter reads 6.3 V. With the voltmeter leads still in place across the terminals of the battery, the terminals are connected to a resistor in series with an ammeter. The ammeter reads 150 mA and the voltmeter reads 5.9 V. Determine the emf and internal resistance of the battery.

25-4 When a battery with a high-resistance voltmeter across its terminals is connected in series with an ammeter (the ammeter resistance is 3 Ω) and a 19-Ω resistor, the voltmeter reads 33 V and the ammeter reads 1.50 A. Next the 19-Ω resistor is replaced by a 41-Ω resistor, and the meter readings are 37 V and 0.84 A. What are the emf and the internal resistance of the battery?

25-5 Suppose the terminal potential difference across a particular battery is 6.5 V when it is charging with a current of 1.9 A (the sense of the current is opposite the sense of the emf), and the terminal potential difference is 5.8 V when it is discharging with a current of 1.2 A (the sense of the current is the same as the sense of the emf). What are the emf and internal resistance of the battery?

Section 25-3. Electric energy and power

25-6 The potential difference across a resistor is 22 V, and a steady current of 65 mA exists in the resistor. (a) What is the power dissipated in the resistor? (b) How much electric potential energy is lost by the carriers that pass through the element in a time interval of 12 h? Express your answer both in kW · h and in J.

25-7 The current in a 450-Ω resistor is 32 mA. (a) What is the power dissipated in the resistor? (b) If this current persists for 60 min, how much energy is dissipated as heat in the resistor? Express your answer both in kW · h and in J.

25-8 The potential difference across an 880-Ω resistor is 31 V. (a) What is the power dissipated in the resistor? (b) If this potential difference remains steady for 30 min, how much energy is dissipated as heat in the resistor during that period? (c) If the carriers are electrons, how much electric potential energy is lost by each carrier as it passes through the resistor? Express your answer both in J and in eV.

25-9 (a) What is the resistance of a 60-W, 120-V household light bulb when the potential difference across it is 120 V? (b) What is the current in a 60-W, 120-V bulb when the potential difference across it is 120 V? (c) What is the power dissipated in a 60-W bulb when the potential difference across it is 110 V? (Assume the resistance of the filament when operated at 110 V is only negligibly different from when it is operated 120 V. Do you expect the resistance to be higher when the bulb is operated at 110 V or at 120 V?)

25-10 Suppose you intend to heat a room with several 800-W electric heaters designed for 120 V. The heaters will be connected to a single circuit (in parallel) which has a circuit breaker that is designed to trip if the current exceeds 15 A. How many heaters can you operate simultaneously without tripping the breaker?

25-11 Resistors used in electronic circuits have maximum recommended power ratings. (a) What is the maximum current you should allow in a 1000-Ω, 0.25-W resistor? (b) What is the maximum potential difference you should allow across a 500-Ω, 0.50-W resistor?

25-12 Resistors used in electronic circuits have maximum recommended power ratings. Suppose a 200-Ω, 0.50-W resistor is placed in series with a 400-Ω, 0.50-W resistor. What is the maximum allowable current in and potential difference across this combination? Under these conditions, what is the power dissipated in each resistor?

25-13 Resistors used in electronic circuits have maximum recommended power ratings. Suppose a 200-Ω, 0.50-W resistor is placed in parallel with a 400-Ω, 0.50-W resistor. What is the maximum allowable current in and potential difference across this combination? Under these conditions, what is the power dissipated in each resistor? Compare your answers with those found in Exercise 25-12.

25-14 A 6.8-mA current in a battery has the same sense as the battery's emf. The terminal potential difference across the battery is 3.1 V. (a) What is the power output of the battery? (b) If the charge carriers are electrons, what is the increase in the electric potential energy of each carrier as it passes through the battery? Express your answer both in J and in eV.

25-15 In the description of a 12-V automobile battery in a sales catalog, the battery is rated at 90 A · h. (a) Find the charge in coulombs that corresponds to 90 A · h. (b) Estimate the total electric energy (in J) you might expect this battery to provide (without recharging) before it is discharged.

25-16 A battery with an emf of 9.0 V and an internal resistance 1.2 Ω carries a current of 260 mA. The sense of the current is the same as the sense of the battery's emf. (a) What is the power output of the battery? (b) What is power expended by the emf of the battery? (c) What is the power dissipated as heat in the battery?

25-17 A 12-V battery with an internal resistance of 0.011 Ω is being charged with a current of 7.3 A. (a) What is the power input to the battery? (b) What is the power delivered to the emf of the battery? (c) What is the power dissipated as heat in the battery?

25-18 A circuit element with a potential difference of 4.8 V across it carries a steady current of 78 mA. The sense of the current is along the direction that the potential decreases. What is the rate at which the electric potential energy of the carriers changes as they pass through the element? Does the electric potential energy of the carriers increase or decrease?

Section 25-4. Kirchhoff's rules

25-19 Calculate the potential difference across each element in Fig. 25-11 and check your answers with Fig. 25-12.

25-20 For the circuit in Fig. 25-24, determine the value of R such that the current in the circuit is 0.5 A.

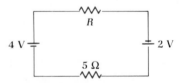

Figure 25-24. Exercise 25-20.

25-21 For the circuit in Fig. 25-25, (a) determine the value of $\mathscr{E}$ such that the current in the circuit is 2 A, with a counterclockwise sense. (b) Determine the value of $\mathscr{E}$ such that the current in the circuit is 2 A, with a

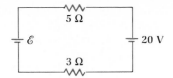

Figure 25-25. Exercise 25-21.

clockwise sense.

25-22 A voltmeter with an internal resistance of 43,000 Ω is connected in series (rather than in parallel) with a resistor of resistance R and a battery of emf 92 V and negligible internal resistance. The voltmeter reads 4.1 V. What is R? (This is a useful procedure for measuring large resistances.)

25-23 For the circuit shown in Fig. 25-13, we found that $4\text{ V} = (3\ \Omega)i_3 - (2\ \Omega)i_2$ and $1\text{ V} = (6\ \Omega)i_2 + (4\ \Omega)i_3$. Solve these equations for i_2 and i_3.

25-24 For each of the two loops in Fig. 25-13 (as defined in Sec. 25-4), construct graphs similar to Fig. 25-12 to illustrate the loop rule. Let point a be grounded.

25-25 Determine (a) current i_1 and (b) current i_2 in the circuit of Fig. 25-14 (Example 25-5). (c) What is the current in the 3-Ω resistor in Fig. 25-14a? (d) What is the current in the 6-Ω resistor in Fig. 25-14a?

25-26 (a) Determine the current in each of the resistors in Fig. 25-26. (b) Determine the potential difference across each of the resistors. (c) Determine the power dissipated in each of the resistors.

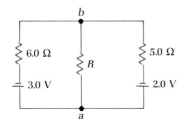

Figure 25-26. Exercise 25-26.

25-27 In Fig. 25-27, determine the value of the resistance R such that the current in R is 0.50 A, with sense from a to b.

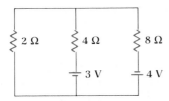

Figure 25-27. Exercise 25-27.

25-28 In Fig. 25-28, determine the emf and the sense of the emf of a battery which can be placed at the empty box such that the current in the 6-Ω resistor is 1 A, with sense from a to b.

25-29 Determine the current in and the potential difference

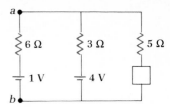

Figure 25-28. Exercise 25-28.

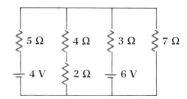

Figure 25-29. Exercise 25-29.

across each of the resistors in Fig. 25-29.

Section 25-5. *RC* circuits

25-30 From Exercise 23-1, the SI unit for capacitance C can be written $\text{s}^2 \cdot \text{C}^2/(\text{kg} \cdot \text{m}^2)$, and from Exercise 24-7, the SI unit of resistance R can be written $\text{kg} \cdot \text{m}^2/(\text{s}^3 \cdot \text{A}^2)$. Show that the SI unit of the product RC is the second.

25-31 In the circuit shown in Fig. 25-15, let $\mathscr{E} = 14$ V, $R = 75$ kΩ, and $C = 0.84\ \mu\text{F}$. (a) What is the RC time constant of the circuit? (b) What is the charge on the capacitor 50 ms after the switch is closed? (c) What is the initial current in the circuit? (d) What is the current in the circuit 50 ms after the switch is closed? (e) What is the final charge on the capacitor?

25-32 In the circuit shown in Fig. 25-18, let $Q_0 = 61\ \mu\text{C}$, $R = 58$ kΩ, and $C = 1.9\ \mu\text{F}$. (a) What is the RC time constant of the circuit? (b) What is the initial potential difference across the capacitor? (c) What is the initial current in the circuit? (d) What is the initial potential difference across the resistor (immediately after the switch is closed)? (e) What is the charge on the capacitor 50 ms after the switch is closed? (f) What is the current in the circuit 50 ms after the switch is closed?

25-33 In the circuit shown in Fig. 25-15, $\mathscr{E} = 21$ V, $R = 33$ kΩ, and $C = 2.7\ \mu\text{F}$. Let $t = 0$ correspond to the instant the switch is closed and assume the internal resistance of the battery is negligible. (a) What is the charge on the capacitor at $t = 60$ ms? (b) What is the energy stored in the capacitor at $t = 60$ ms? (c) What is the energy transferred from the battery to the charge carriers during the time from $t = 0$ to $t = 60$ ms? (d) What is the energy dissipated in the resistor during the time from $t = 0$ to $t = 60$ ms?

25-34 For the circuit shown in Fig. 25-18, let $Q_0 = 45\ \mu\text{C}$, $R = 58$ kΩ, $C = 1.6\ \mu\text{F}$ and let $t = 0$ correspond to the instant the switch is closed. (a) What is the charge on the capacitor at $t = 60$ ms? (b) What is the energy stored in the capacitor at $t = 0$. (c) What is the energy stored in the capacitor at $t = 60$ ms? (d) What is the energy dissipated in the resistor between $t = 0$ and $t = 60$ ms?

25-35 For the circuit shown in Fig. 25-15, let $\mathscr{E} = 35$ V, $R = 64$ kΩ, $C = 1.7$ μF and let $t = 0$ correspond to the instant the switch is closed. The internal resistance of the battery is negligible. (a) What is the current in the circuit at $t = 60$ ms? (b) What is the rate at which the battery is transferring energy to the carriers at $t = 60$ ms? (c) What is the rate at which the resistor is dissipating energy at $t = 60$ ms? (d) What is the rate at which energy is being stored in the capacitor at $t = 60$ ms?

25-36 For the circuit shown in Fig. 25-15, let $\mathscr{E} = 100$ V, $R = 2.0$ kΩ, and $C = 1.0$ μF. On a graph plot the potential difference across the resistor V_R and on the same graph plot the potential difference across the capacitor V_C versus the time t from $t = 0$ to $t = 5.0$ ms. Evalu-

ate V_R and V_C at each 1.0 ms between $t = 0$ and $t = 5.0$ ms; plot the points and sketch the curves. Show the asymptotic value of V_C as a horizontal dashed line. At what instant is $V_R = V_C$?

25-37 For the circuit shown in Fig. 25-18, let $R = 2.0$ kΩ, $C = 1.0$ μF, and the initial potential difference across the capacitor $V_0 = 20$ V. Make a graph of the current in the circuit versus time t from $t = 0$ to $t = 5.0$ ms. Evaluate i at each 1.0 ms between $t = 0$ and $t = 5.0$ ms; plot the points and sketch the curve.

25-38 Show that the energy initially stored in a capacitor is dissipated as heat in a resistor when the capacitor is discharged through the resistor. Do this by evaluating the time integral of the power dissipated in the resistor, $\int_0^\infty (i^2 R)\,dt$, where i is given by Eq. (25-22).

25-39 A capacitor is charged by a 26-V battery through a 6.2-kΩ resistor. At 3.1 ms after the switch is closed, the potential difference across the capacitor is 13 V. What is the capacitance of the capacitor?

PROBLEMS

25-1 Consider the energy transfers in the circuit shown in Fig. 25-2. (a) Show that the power $P_{\mathscr{E}}$ expended by the emf of the battery is given by $P_{\mathscr{E}} = \mathscr{E}^2/(r + R)$. (b) Show that the power P_R dissipated in the resistor is given by $P_R = \mathscr{E}^2 R/(r + R)^2$. (c) Show that the power P_r dissipated in the battery is given by $P_r = \mathscr{E}^2 r/(r + R)^2$. (d) Use your answers to parts (a), (b), and (c) to show that $P_{\mathscr{E}} = P_R + P_r$. (e) Consider maximizing P_R by varying R while $\mathscr{E}$ and r are held constant. Show that P_R has a maximum value of $\mathscr{E}^2/4r$ when $R = r$. (f) On the same graph, plot $P_{\mathscr{E}}$, P_R, and P_r versus R. Evaluate each power expression between $R = 0$ and $R = 3r$ at intervals of $\frac{1}{2}r$. Plot the points and sketch the curves through them. Note that when $R \gg r$, $P_{\mathscr{E}} \approx P_R \gg P_r$.

25-2 Two batteries 1 and 2 with emf's $\mathscr{E}_1$ and $\mathscr{E}_2$ and internal resistances r_1 and r_2 are connected in parallel. That is, the two positive terminals are connected together and the two negative terminals are connected together, and the lead wires from these connections form the terminals of their combination. Show that the effective emf $\mathscr{E}_{12}$ of this combination is

$$\mathscr{E}_{12} = \frac{r_1 \mathscr{E}_2 + r_2 \mathscr{E}_1}{r_1 + r_2}$$

25-3 The turbogenerators of a hydroelectric power plant produce a steady current of 9.8 kA for 4.3 h, with a potential difference of 14 kV across the terminals. During this time the level of the lake above the turbogenerators falls from 41.32 to 40.91 m. A negligible amount of water enters the lake from streams, and a

negligible amount of water is lost by evaporation and transpiration. The area of the lake is 14×10^6 m^2. Estimate the efficiency of the turbogenerators.

25-4 The heating element in an electric coffeepot is designed to carry a current of 5 A when operated at 120 V. (a) What is the power dissipated by the pot's heater when it is operated at 120 V? (b) The pot increases the temperature of 0.63 L of water from 20°C to the boiling point in 45 s. What is the net heat transferred to the water in this time interval? (c) What fraction of the energy dissipated by the heater contributes to the increased internal energy of the water during the 45-s time interval? (d) Account for the remainder of the dissipated energy.

25-5 Consider a solution to the two-loop circuit problem discussed in Sec. 25-4 with the particular current assignments shown in Fig. 25-30. Show that the currents are given by

$$i_1 = \frac{\mathscr{E}_1(R_2 + R_3) - \mathscr{E}_3 R_2 - \mathscr{E}_2 R_3}{R_1 R_2 + R_1 R_3 + R_2 R_3}$$

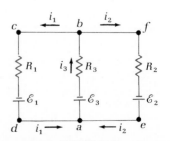

Figure 25-30. Prob. 25-5.

$$i_2 = \frac{\mathscr{E}_2(R_1 + R_3) - \mathscr{E}_3 R_1 - \mathscr{E}_1 R_3}{R_1 R_2 + R_1 R_3 + R_2 R_3}$$

$$i_3 = i_1 + i_2$$

25-6 The contribution, due to an electric current, to the total kinetic energy of the carriers in a section of conductor can be written as $\Sigma K = \frac{1}{2}\Sigma m v_d^2$, where m is the mass of each carrier, v_d is the carrier drift speed associated with the current, and the sum is over all the carriers in the section of the conductor. (a) Using the Drude model of conduction (Sec. 24-4), show that for a section of conductor, $\Sigma K = \frac{1}{2}\tau I V$, where I is the current in the section, V is the potential difference across the section, and τ is the mean time between collisions. (b) Assuming $\tau \approx 10^{-14}$ s (Example 24-6), estimate ΣK for a 1000-Ω resistor carrying a current of 1 A. What is the power dissipated in this resistor? What is the time interval required for the energy dissipated in the resistor to equal ΣK?

25-7 **The Wheatstone bridge.** A Wheatstone bridge, shown in Fig. 25-31, is a circuit used to measure resistance. In the figure, R_x is the unknown resistance we wish to measure, R_1 is an accurately known variable resistance, R_2 and R_4 are accurately known fixed resistances, and G is a sensitive current-detecting device such as a galvanometer. The bridge is balanced by varying R_1 until the current in the galvanometer is zero. Show that when the bridge is balanced, $R_x = R_1 R_4 / R_2$.

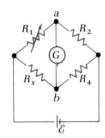

Figure 25-31. Prob. 25-7. A Wheatstone bridge.

25-8 **The potentiometer.** A potentiometer, shown in Fig. 25-32, is a circuit used to measure emf. In the figure, $\mathscr{E}_x$ is the unknown emf we wish to measure, $\mathscr{E}_s$ is an

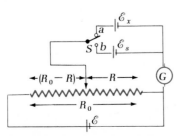

Figure 25-32. Prob. 25-8. A potentiometer.

accurately known standard emf, and G is a current-detecting device such as a galvanometer. The resistance R_0 has a variable center tap (shown with an arrow) which divides it into two sections, one with resistance R and the other with resistance $R_0 - R$. The switch S is used to connect either $\mathscr{E}_x$ or $\mathscr{E}_s$ into the circuit. The bridge is balanced by adjusting the center tap until the current in the galvanometer is zero. Let R_x be the value of R when the bridge is balanced with the switch in position a, and let R_s be the value of R when the bridge is balanced with the switch in position b. Show that $\mathscr{E}_x = \mathscr{E}_s R_x / R_s$.

25-9 Determine the six currents shown in Fig. 25-33.

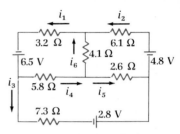

Figure 25-33. Prob. 25-9.

25-10 The resistance of the insulating material between the plates of a parallel-plate capacitor is $R_C = \rho \epsilon_0 \kappa / C$ where ρ is the resistivity of the material, κ is the dielectric constant of the material, and C is the capacitance of the capacitor (see Prob. 24-9). Since this resistance is not infinite, a charged capacitor on open circuit discharges slowly because of charge leaking through the insulator. Suppose a capacitor is charged by a battery and then its leads are disconnected from the battery and left open. (a) Show that the time dependence of the charge on the capacitor is given by

$$Q(t) = Q_0 e^{-t/\rho \epsilon_0 \kappa}$$

where Q_0 is the charge on the capacitor at time $t = 0$. (b) Show that the expression for the time required for half the charge on a capacitor to leak through the insulator is

$$t = \rho \epsilon_0 \kappa \ln 2$$

(c) Suppose the insulating material between the plates of a capacitor has $\rho \approx 10^{13} \Omega \cdot$ m and $\kappa = 5$. How long does it take for half the charge to leak through the insulator? Discuss a procedure for finding the resistivity of insulators.

25-11 Consider the circuit in Fig. 25-34. (a) What is the RC time constant of this circuit? (b) Plot the potential difference across each capacitor, and on the same graph, plot the potential difference across the resistor versus time t. Evaluate these potential differences at each 1 ms between $t = 0$ and $t = 5$ ms. Plot the points and sketch the curves.

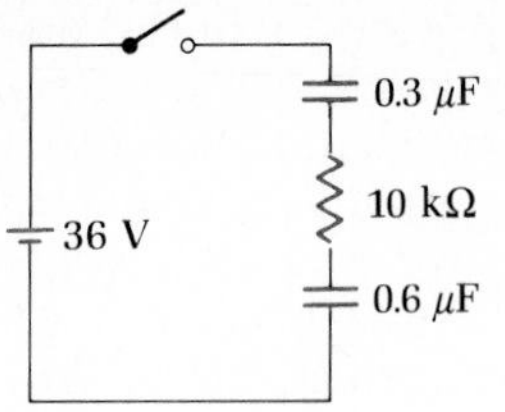

Figure 25-34. Prob. 25-11.

25-12 Consider the energy transfers in the circuit in Fig. 25-15. (a) Show that the power $P_\mathscr{E}$ expended by the emf of the battery is given by $P_\mathscr{E} = (\mathscr{E}^2/R)e^{-t/\tau}$. (b) Show that the power P_R dissipated in the resistor is $P_R = (\mathscr{E}^2/R)e^{-2t/\tau}$. (c) Show that the rate at which electric energy is stored in the capacitor is $P_C = (\mathscr{E}^2/R)e^{-t/\tau}(1 - e^{-t/\tau})$. (d) Use your answers to parts (a), (b), and (c) to show that $P_\mathscr{E} = P_R + P_C$. (e) Show that P_C maximizes at $\mathscr{E}^2/4R$ when $t = \tau \ln 2$. (f) Plot $P_\mathscr{E}$, P_R, and P_C versus t on the same graph. Evaluate each power expression between $t = 0$ and $t = 3\tau$ at intervals of $\frac{1}{2}\tau$. Plot the points and sketch the curves through them.

CHAPTER 26
THE MAGNETIC
FIELD

26-1 INTRODUCTION

Observations of the magnetic properties of the mineral magnetite (Fe_3O_4), or lodestone, probably began several thousand years ago when the early Greeks found that these naturally occurring magnets attracted small pieces of iron.* The use of a magnet (as a compass needle) in navigation began about 1000 A.D., although the Chinese may have known of the north-south alignment effect of a magnet much earlier.

Despite these ancient origins, magnetism has become well understood only in the last two centuries. In 1819 Hans Christian Oersted (1777–1851) discovered that an electric current is a source of magnetism. The experiments of Faraday in England and of Joseph Henry (1797–1878) in the United States led to the synthesis of electricity and magnetism by James Clerk Maxwell in the 1860s. A microscopic theory of magnetic materials came with the development of quantum theory in this century, and magnetism in matter is still an area of intensive research.

We consider in this chapter the effect of a *magnetic field* on electric charges and currents. The sources or causes of magnetic fields are discussed in the next chapter.

26-2 THE MAGNETIC FIELD

Our treatment of electrostatics in Chaps. 20 and 21 made extensive use of the electric field $\mathbf{E}$. The field exists everywhere in a region of space and exerts a force $\mathbf{F}$ on a charge q placed at some point in the region:

$$\mathbf{F} = q\mathbf{E}$$

* Magnetite was found near the city of Magnesia, hence its name.

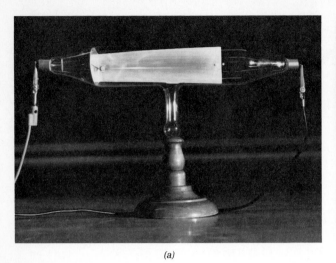

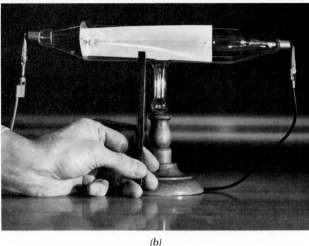

(a)

(b)

Figure 26-1. (a) The path of electrons, moving from left to right in a tube, appears on a fluorescent screen. (b) The magnetic field of a magnet deflects the moving electrons in the tube. *(Tom Richard)*

Magnetic phenomena can be treated similarly by introducing a *magnetic field* **B**. This vector field exerts a force on a *moving* charge. For example, the magnetic field due to a small magnet can deflect the electron beam in a cathode-ray tube, as shown in Fig. 26-1. The deflecting force is observed to be always perpendicular to the velocity of the moving charge. Consider a particle of charge q with a velocity **v** at a point. The magnetic field at the point is defined as the vector field **B** which exerts a force **F** on the charged particle given by

Definition of the magnetic field **B**

$$\mathbf{F} = q\mathbf{v} \times \mathbf{B} \qquad (26\text{-}1)$$

That is, **B** is the vector that gives the magnetic force from Eq. (26-1) on a charged particle moving with any velocity **v** through that point. Recall from Chap. 11 that the direction of the cross product $\mathbf{v} \times \mathbf{B}$ is perpendicular to the plane containing **v** and **B**, with a right-hand sense. Thus the direction of the force on a charge q is perpendicular both to the velocity of the charge and to the magnetic field at that point. If q is positive, then the force is in the direction of $\mathbf{v} \times \mathbf{B}$, as shown in Fig. 26-2a. The magnetic force on a negative charge is opposite the direction of $\mathbf{v} \times \mathbf{B}$, as shown in Fig. 26-2b. For either sign of the charge, the magnitude of the force is given by

The magnetic force **F** is perpendicular to **v** and **B**.

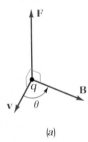

(a)

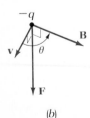

(b)

Figure 26-2. The magnetic force on a charged particle is perpendicular to **v** and **B** for (a) a positive charge and (b) a negative charge.

$$F = |qvB \sin \theta| \qquad (26\text{-}2)$$

where θ is the angle between **v** and **B**. (See Fig. 26-2.) Note that the magnetic force is zero if the charge is stationary ($v = 0$) or if **v** and **B** are either parallel or opposite ($\theta = 0$ or $\theta = \pi$).

The SI unit of magnetic field is, from Eq. (26-2), (N/C)/(m/s) or $(\text{N})(\text{A}^{-1})(\text{m}^{-1})$, which is called the *tesla* (T). Another unit of magnetic field which is used is the *gauss* (G); the conversion is $1\text{ G} = 10^{-4}\text{ T}$. The tesla is a fairly large unit of magnetic field. For example, the magnitude of the magnetic field of the earth at points near its surface varies, but is around 3×10^{-5} T, or 0.3 G. The largest steady magnetic fields that have been produced in the laboratory are in the range of 30 T.

Since the force exerted by a magnetic field on a moving charged particle is always perpendicular to the velocity, the work done by this force is zero. Consider an infinitesimal displacement $d\boldsymbol{\ell}$ of the charge as it moves with velocity **v**. The work done is $dW = \mathbf{F} \cdot d\boldsymbol{\ell} = \mathbf{F} \cdot \mathbf{v}\, dt$, where $\mathbf{v}\, dt$ is the dis-

North geographic pole

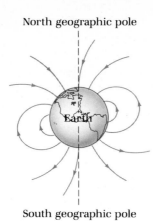

South geographic pole

(a)

(b)

Figure 26-3. (a) A portion of the lines of magnetic field are shown outside the earth's surface. (b) Iron filings align with the field of a bar magnet. *(Fundamental Photographs)*

placement $d\boldsymbol{\ell}$ for a time interval dt. But the dot product of perpendicular vectors is zero ($\mathbf{F} \cdot \mathbf{v} = 0$) and $dW = 0$. A static magnetic field does no work on a charge. An electric field, of course, *can* do work on a charge.

The spatial distribution of the magnetic field in a region can be represented by lines of magnetic field in the same way that lines of electric field were used. As with the electric field, the lines for a magnetic field are drawn such that the direction of **B** is tangent to the line at a point, and the spacing of the lines indicates the magnitude of the field. That is, B is proportional to the number of lines per unit area crossing a surface perpendicular to the lines. As an example of the use of magnetic field lines, Fig. 26-3a shows schematically a portion of the lines for the earth's magnetic field outside its surface. The lines are shown in a plane containing the earth's axis of rotation. Although some of the lines are cut off at the edge of the figure, each line from near the south pole curves around continuously to intersect the surface near the north pole.

Field patterns for a magnetic field can be displayed, as shown in Fig. 26-3b, with the use of iron filings which align with the field. Notice the similarity of the patterns in Fig. 26-3a and b. The earth's magnetic field pattern is similar to that for a bar magnet.

Lines of magnetic field represent **B**.

EXAMPLE 26-1. A proton has a velocity of magnitude 4.4×10^6 m/s at an angle of $62°$, with a magnetic field of magnitude 18 mT. Determine (a) the magnitude and (b) the direction of the magnetic force on the proton. (c) If this is the only force, what is the proton's acceleration? (d) At what rate does the kinetic energy of the proton change?

SOLUTION. (a) The magnitude of the force is given by Eq. (26-2):

$$F = |(1.6 \times 10^{-19} \text{ C})(4.4 \times 10^6 \text{ m/s})(0.018 \text{ T}) \sin 62°|$$

$$= 1.1 \times 10^{-14} \text{ N}$$

(b) The direction of the force on the (positively charged) proton is perpendicular to the plane of **v** and **B**, with a

right-hand sense. The relative directions would be as shown in Fig. 26-2a.

(c) From Newton's second law, the acceleration of the proton has the same direction as the net force. Its magnitude is

$$a = \frac{F}{m} = \frac{1.1 \times 10^{-14} \text{ N}}{1.7 \times 10^{-27} \text{ kg}}$$

$$= 6.5 \times 10^{12} \text{ m/s}^2$$

(d) The work done by the magnetic force (which is the only force in this case) is zero because the magnetic force is perpendicular to the velocity. The kinetic energy of the proton does not change.

How would these questions be answered for an electron ($q = -1.6 \times 10^{-19}$ C, $m = 9.1 \times 10^{-31}$ kg) with the same velocity?

26-3 FORCE ON A CURRENT-CARRYING CONDUCTOR

The magnetic field is defined in Eq. (26-1) in terms of the force on a moving charged particle. If the magnetic field is known in a region, that equation can also be used to determine the magnetic force on a moving charged particle. Since a current in a conductor consists of a collection of moving charge carriers, we can use Eq. (26-1) to determine the magnetic force on a current-carrying conductor.

Consider for simplicity a section of length ℓ of a thin, straight wire of cross-sectional area A, with current I in a uniform magnetic field **B**, as shown in Fig. 26-4. We evaluate the sum of the magnetic forces on the charge carriers by using their average, or drift, velocity $\mathbf{v}_d$ (see Sec. 24-2). The number of charge carriers in the length ℓ is $N = nA\ell$, where n is the number of charge carriers per unit volume and $A\ell$ is the volume of the length of conductor. If q represents the charge of each carrier, then the total magnetic force on the total charge of Nq is

$$\mathbf{F} = Nq\mathbf{v}_d \times \mathbf{B} = nA\ell q\mathbf{v}_d \times \mathbf{B}$$

It is more convenient to express this result in terms of the current I and a displacement $\boldsymbol{\ell}$, a vector whose direction is the same as the drift velocity of positive charge carriers. (We are assuming that the charge carriers are positively charged. You should be able to show that the force **F** is the same if the charge carriers are negatively charged.) The current density has magnitude $j = nqv$ and the current $I = jA = nqv_dA$ [from Eq. (24-2)]. And since $\boldsymbol{\ell}$ has the same direction as $\mathbf{v}_d$, we can write $\boldsymbol{\ell}\mathbf{v}_d = \boldsymbol{\ell}v_d$. Making these substitutions in the expression for the total magnetic force, we have

$$\mathbf{F} = nqA\boldsymbol{\ell}\mathbf{v}_d \times \mathbf{B} = nqv_dA\boldsymbol{\ell} \times \mathbf{B}$$

or

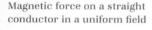

$$\mathbf{F} = I\boldsymbol{\ell} \times \mathbf{B} \qquad (26\text{-}3)$$

The magnetic force on this section of the conductor has the direction of $\boldsymbol{\ell} \times \mathbf{B}$ and thus is perpendicular to the plane of $\boldsymbol{\ell}$ and **B**. In Fig. 26-4 $\boldsymbol{\ell}$ and **B** lie in the plane of the paper, and the direction of the force is perpendicularly out of the plane of the paper. Notice that the direction of the displacement $\boldsymbol{\ell}$ is in accord with the conventional sense of the current: in the direction of motion of positive charge carriers. The magnitude of the force is

$$F = I\ell B \sin \theta$$

where θ is the angle between the directions of $\boldsymbol{\ell}$ and **B**, as shown in Fig. 26-4. The magnitude of the force on the length ℓ of the conductor is proportional to the length as well as to the current in the conductor and to the magnitude of the magnetic field.

Equation (26-3) applies to a straight section of a thin wire in a uniform magnetic field. We must also deal with conducting wires that are not straight

Figure 26-4. A section of a current-carrying wire is in a uniform magnetic field.

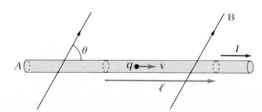

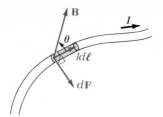

Figure 26-5. A magnetic field exerts an infinitesimal force on a current element. The force is perpendicular to the plane containing $I\, d\ell$ and **B**.

and magnetic fields that are not uniform. We first apply Eq. (26-3) to an infinitesimal length $d\ell$ of a current-carrying conductor. It is convenient to define an infinitesimal *current element I dℓ* as the product of the current I and a displacement $d\ell$ whose direction has the sense of the current for that element. (See Fig. 26-5.) The section of wire containing the current element can be considered as straight, and **B** does not vary significantly along the small length $d\ell$. From Eq. (26-3) the magnetic force $d\mathbf{F}$ on the current element is

The current element $I\, d\ell$ has the same sense as the current.

Force on a current element

$$d\mathbf{F} = I\, d\ell \times \mathbf{B} \qquad (26\text{-}4)$$

The direction of the force is shown in Fig. 26-5, and the magnitude depends on the angle θ between $I\, d\ell$ and **B**:

$$dF = I\, d\ell\, B \sin\theta$$

The magnetic force on a longer section of a current-carrying conductor is determined by adding the force on each element of the conductor; that is, Eq. (26-4) is integrated along the conductor:

General expression for the magnetic force on a conductor

$$\mathbf{F} = \int I\, d\ell \times \mathbf{B} \qquad (26\text{-}5)$$

In applying Eq. (26-5), remember that a vector is being integrated and that a cross product is involved.

EXAMPLE 26-2. A horizontal, straight wire carrying a 16-A current from west to east is in the earth's magnetic field at a place where **B** is parallel to the surface and points north with a magnitude of 0.04 mT. (a) Determine the magnetic force on a 1-m length of the wire. (b) If the mass of the wire is 50 g, then what current will allow the wire to be magnetically supported (that is, magnetic force balances the weight)?

SOLUTION. (a) The magnitude of the force is

$$F = I\ell B \sin\theta = (16\ \text{A})(1\ \text{m})(4 \times 10^{-5}\ \text{T}) \sin 90°$$

$$= 0.6\ \text{mN}$$

The direction of the force is given by $\ell \times \mathbf{B}$. Since ℓ is directed east and **B** is directed north, the force is up, perpendicular to the earth's surface. What is the force if the wire is

oriented so that the sense of the current is from north to south?

(b) With the sense of the current I from west to east, the magnetic force is up, opposite the weight of the wire. To balance the weight with the magnetic force, we equate their magnitudes, $I\ell B = mg$, or

$$I = \frac{mg}{\ell B} = \frac{(0.05\ \text{kg})(9.8\ \text{m/s}^2)}{(1\ \text{m})(4 \times 10^{-5}\ \text{T})}$$

$$= 10\ \text{kA}$$

While it is not feasible for an ordinary thin wire to carry such a large current, this value indicates that the magnitude of a typical magnetic force on a current-carrying wire is small.

EXAMPLE 26-3. Apply Eq. (26-5) to a straight section of a conductor of length ℓ with current I in a uniform magnetic field and show that Eq. (26-3) results.

SOLUTION. The current I is constant along the conductor and can be factored from the integral. Since the conductor is straight and the field is uniform, **B** can be factored from the integral—but only to the right because the cross product is not commutative. Equation (26-5) becomes

$$F = I \left(\int d\boldsymbol{\ell} \right) \times \mathbf{B}$$

and the integral $\int d\boldsymbol{\ell}$ is just $\boldsymbol{\ell}$, the displacement from one end to the other of that section of the conductor. Thus

$$\mathbf{F} = I\boldsymbol{\ell} \times \mathbf{B}$$

which is Eq. (26-3). See Exercise 26-13 also.

EXAMPLE 26-4. A U-shaped conductor carrying current I has its plane perpendicular to a uniform magnetic field, as shown in Fig. 26-6. The curved portion is a semicircle of radius R. Determine the magnetic force on this semicircular portion.

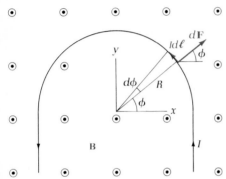

Figure 26-6. Example 26-4: The plane of a U-shaped, current-carrying conductor is perpendicular to a uniform magnetic field.

SOLUTION. In Fig. 26-6, the magnetic field is out of the plane of the figure, perpendicular to each current element, and Eq. (26-4) gives the force on a typical current element as shown. The direction of $d\mathbf{F}$ is radially outward, and its magnitude is

$$dF = I \, d\ell \, B \sin 90° = IB \, d\ell$$

We resolve $d\mathbf{F}$ into its x and y components and separately integrate these components of Eq. (26-5):

$$dF_x = dF \cos \phi = IB \, d\ell \cos \phi$$

$$dF_y = dF \sin \phi = IB \, d\ell \sin \phi$$

and

$$F_x = \int IB \cos \phi \, d\ell \qquad F_y = \int IB \sin \phi \, d\ell$$

where the integrals are around the semicircle, with ϕ ranging from 0 to π. The length $d\ell$ subtends an angle $d\phi$ at the center and $d\ell = R \, d\phi$. Making this substitution in the integrals and factoring out the constants I, R, and B gives

$$F_x = IRB \int_0^\pi \cos \phi \, d\phi = IRB (\sin \pi - \sin 0) = 0$$

$$F_y = IRB \int_0^\pi \sin \phi \, d\phi = -IRB (\cos \pi - \cos 0) = 2IRB$$

Since $F_x = 0$, the force on the semicircular portion of the conductor is in the positive y direction, and its magnitude is $F = 2IRB$. See Prob. 26-1 for another approach to this calculation.

26-4 TORQUE ON A CURRENT LOOP

Since a magnetic field exerts a force on a current-carrying wire, it can also produce a torque. Of particular interest is the torque on a loop of wire pivoted on an axis and carrying a current. The rotational motion caused by such a torque is the basis for an electric motor.

Consider the rectangular current loop shown in two views in Fig. 26-7. The loop carries current I and is in a uniform magnetic field $\mathbf{B}$. The rectangular dimensions of the loop are ℓ and w, so that the area of the plane of the loop is $S = \ell w$. It is convenient to use the vector area $\mathbf{S}$ to specify the loop's orientation, as illustrated in Fig. 26-7b. The direction of $\mathbf{S}$ is perpendicular to the plane of the loop, with a right-hand sense. To determine the sense, curl the fingers of your right hand to follow the sense of the current around the circuit. Then the extended thumb gives the direction of the area.

The magnetic force on each straight segment of the loop can be determined from Eq. (26-3). The force $\mathbf{F}_1$ on the upper element in Fig. 26-7a is directed upward and has magnitude

$$F_1 = I\ell B$$

The right-hand rule for the area of a current loop

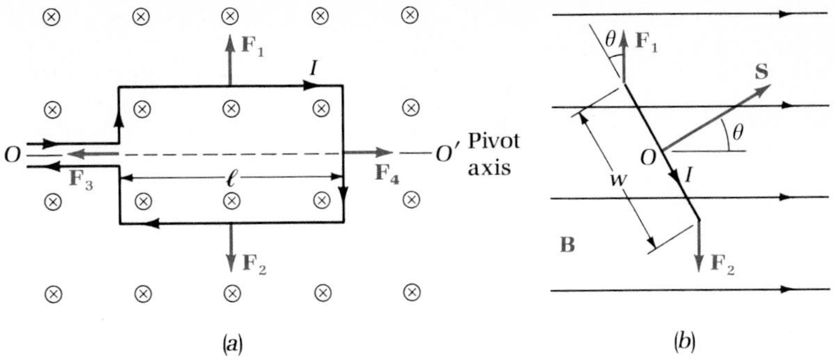

Figure 26-7. A rectangular current loop is in a uniform magnetic field. The area vector **S** is perpendicular to the plane of the loop and has a right-hand sense with respect to the current in the loop.

The force $\mathbf{F}_2$ on the lower element has the same magnitude but the opposite direction. These two forces add to zero. Similarly, the forces $\mathbf{F}_3$ and $\mathbf{F}_4$ on the other two segments of length w are equal in magnitude and opposite in direction. Thus the net magnetic force on the current loop is zero. (What is the net magnetic force on the pair of lead wires that feed current to the loop?)

Although the net magnetic force on this loop is zero, the forces do have some effects. The outward-directed forces shown in Fig. 26-7a tend to change the shape of the current loop. We assume either that the wires are stiff enough or that mechanical constraints exist so that no appreciable distortion of the loop occurs. Another effect is that these forces produce a torque on the current loop about an axis. (See Chap. 11 for a discussion of torque.) A convenient choice for an axis is one in the plane of the loop and perpendicular to **B**, such as the axis labeled OO' in Fig. 26-7. Notice that if the loop is pivoted about that axis, the torque tends to cause the loop to rotate about the axis.

From Fig. 26-7a, we can see that forces $\mathbf{F}_3$ and $\mathbf{F}_4$, acting parallel to axis OO', produce no torque about that axis. The torque produced by $\mathbf{F}_1$ about axis OO' can be determined using Fig. 26-7b. The perpendicular distance from the axis to the line of action of this force is $r_\perp = \frac{1}{2}w \sin\theta$, and the magnitude of the torque is, from Eq. (11-3),

$$\tau_1 = \tfrac{1}{2}wF_1 \sin\theta = \tfrac{1}{2}wI\ell B \sin\theta$$

This torque has a clockwise sense in Fig. 26-7b which corresponds to the direction into the page. Force $\mathbf{F}_2$ also produces a torque with the same sense about this axis, and its magnitude is the same as that produced by $\mathbf{F}_1$. Specifically, $\tau_2 = \tau_1$. Therefore, the net magnetic torque has magnitude

$$\tau = \tau_1 + \tau_2 = wI\ell B \sin\theta = ISB \sin\theta$$

where the area of the loop $S = w\ell$ has been used.

The sense of the net torque is clockwise for the arrangement shown in Fig. 26-7b. That is the same as the sense of rotation that would carry the direction of the area vector **S** through angle θ into the direction of **B**. This clockwise sense, from a right-hand rule, corresponds to the direction of the torque vector τ, which is perpendicularly into the plane of the paper in Fig. 26-7b. (Curl the fingers of your right hand in the sense of the rotation that carries **S** into **B**; the extended thumb then gives the direction into the plane of the figure.) This is the direction of the cross product $\mathbf{S} \times \mathbf{B}$ whose magnitude is $SB \sin\theta$. Thus the torque vector produced on the current loop by a uniform magnetic field is

The right-hand rule gives the direction of $\mathbf{S} \times \mathbf{B}$.

Torque on a current loop

$$\tau = I\mathbf{S} \times \mathbf{B} \tag{26-6}$$

You should apply this equation to configurations similar to that seen in Fig.

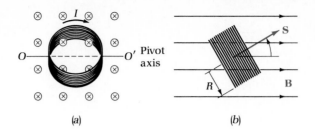

Figure 26-8. A circular coil of radius R is in a uniform magnetic field.

(a)   (b)

26-7b but with the loop rotated about the axis OO' so that the angle θ is in each of the other three quadrants. In each case the cross product gives the correct direction for the torque on the loop.

Equation (26-6) gives the torque on a single current loop with a rectangular shape. The result also is valid for a plane current loop with any shape in a uniform magnetic field. (See Prob. 26-2.) Instead of a single loop or turn of wire, we can consider a coil with N turns, as seen in Fig. 26-8. If the coil is closely wound, then each turn lies essentially in a plane. These planes containing the turns are parallel and have the same area $\mathbf{S}$, so that the torque on each turn is $\boldsymbol{\tau} = I\mathbf{S} \times \mathbf{B}$. The torque on a coil with N turns carrying current I is just N times the torque on a single current loop. Thus the magnetic torque on the coil in a uniform magnetic field is

Magnetic torque on a coil

$$\boldsymbol{\tau} = NI\mathbf{S} \times \mathbf{B} \qquad (26\text{-}7)$$

EXAMPLE 26-5. A simple electric motor has a 100-turn circular coil of radius 15 mm that carries a 65-mA current in a uniform magnetic field of magnitude $B = 23$ mT. At one instant the coil is oriented so that the direction of the area is at $\theta = 25°$ to the field, as shown in Fig. 26-8. The coil is pivoted about an axis through its center perpendicular to $\mathbf{S}$ and to $\mathbf{B}$. (a) Determine the magnitude and direction of the magnetic torque on the coil. (b) What are your findings if the current sense is reversed? (c) For what orientations of the coil is the magnitude of the torque largest and what is this largest value?

SOLUTION. (a) The torque is given by Eq. (26-7). The magnitude is

$$\tau = |NI\mathbf{S} \times \mathbf{B}| = NISB \sin \theta$$

The circular coil has face area $S = \pi r^2 = 7.1 \times 10^{-4}$ m^2, so

$$\tau = (100)(0.065 \text{ A})(7.1 \times 10^{-4} \text{ m}^2)(23 \times 10^{-3} \text{ T}) \sin 25°$$

$$= 4.5 \times 10^{-5} \text{ N} \cdot \text{m}$$

The direction of the torque is given by the direction of $\mathbf{S} \times \mathbf{B}$, which is into the plane of the paper in Fig. 26-8b. The torque tends to produce a clockwise rotation of the coil in that figure.

(b) If the sense of the current is reversed, then $\mathbf{S}$ is reversed and so is the direction of $\mathbf{S} \times \mathbf{B}$. The angle between the directions of $\mathbf{S}$ and $\mathbf{B}$ becomes $180° - 25° = 155°$. The magnitude of the torque is the same as calculated above [$\sin (180° - \theta) = \sin \theta$], but the direction of the torque is reversed.

(c) The maximum value of the magnitude of the torque corresponds to $\sin \theta = \pm 1$, or $\theta = \pm 90°$ in Fig. 26-8b. This maximum value is

$$\tau = NISB = 1.1 \times 10^{-4} \text{ N} \cdot \text{m}$$

What is the direction of the torque for each of these two orientations?

Magnetic dipole moment. If a current-carrying coil is oriented in a uniform magnetic field such that $\mathbf{S}$ and $\mathbf{B}$ are parallel ($\theta = 0$), then the magnetic torque is zero. In the absence of torques due to other forces, the coil is in rotational equilibrium with this orientation. However, for any other orientation (except $\theta = \pi$), there is a magnetic torque that tends to align the coil so that $\mathbf{S}$ and $\mathbf{B}$ are parallel again. In Fig. 26-9a a coil is suspended in a horizontal magnetic field by a vertical fiber. The coil tends to rotate toward alignment with the field ($\mathbf{S}$ parallel with $\mathbf{B}$) because of the magnetic torque. This same kind of behavior is

The coil tends to alignment with the magnetic field.

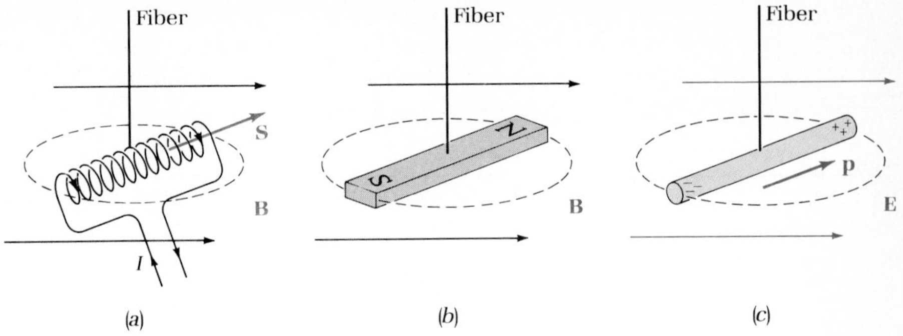

Figure 26-9. Three objects are suspended by vertical fibers in a horizontal field. (*a*) A current-carrying coil in a magnetic field. (*b*) A bar magnet in a magnetic field. (*c*) An insulating rod charged as a dipole in an electric field.

shown by a bar magnet in a uniform magnetic field (Fig. 26-9*b*) and by an electric dipole in a uniform electric field (Fig. 26-9*c*).

The orientation of an electric dipole in a uniform electric field was considered in Chap. 22. The equilibrium orientation — the electric dipole moment **p** aligned with electric field **E** — corresponds to the minimum value of the electric potential energy U of the electric dipole in an external field. This potential energy depends on the relative orientations of the electric dipole moment and the field:

$$U = -\mathbf{p} \cdot \mathbf{E} = -pE \cos \theta$$

where θ is the angle between the directions of **p** and **E**. The torque which tends to align the electric dipole with the electric field is given by the cross product

$$\tau = \mathbf{p} \times \mathbf{E}$$

This expression for the torque on an electric dipole has the same mathematical form as Eq. (26-7), the torque on a current-carrying coil in a uniform *magnetic* field. In analogy with the electric dipole moment **p**, we can define a *magnetic dipole moment* **m** of a coil carrying a current. Equation (26-7) can be written as

$$\tau = \mathbf{m} \times \mathbf{B} \tag{26-8}$$

Torque on a magnetic dipole and the magnetic dipole moment of a coil

where

$$\mathbf{m} = NI\mathbf{S} \tag{26-9}$$

is the magnetic dipole moment of a coil of face area **S** and with N turns and current I. Equation (26-9) shows that magnetic dipole moment has dimensions of current times area, and the SI unit of magnetic dipole moment is A · m².

Also in analogy with the electric dipole, there is a potential energy for a magnetic dipole in a magnetic field. That potential energy is (see Prob. 26-9)

$$U = -\mathbf{m} \cdot \mathbf{B} = -mB \cos \theta \tag{26-10}$$

where θ is the angle between **m** and **B**. The potential energy is a minimum when **m** and **B** are aligned ($\theta = 0$).

Another look at Fig. 26-9*a* and *b* suggests a connection between a current-carrying coil and a bar magnet. The magnet is also characterized by a magnetic dipole moment. We shall explore the connection in Chap. 30 (but see Prob. 26-3).

The magnetic torque on a coil, given by Eq. (26-7), can be interpreted by combining Eqs. (26-8) and (26-9). A coil with a current has a magnetic dipole moment $\mathbf{m} = NI\mathbf{S}$, and a uniform magnetic field produces a torque $\tau = \mathbf{m} \times \mathbf{B}$

on a magnetic dipole. Since rotational motion results from a net torque on a coil, many practical applications follow from the effect. It is the basis of operation of electric motors, for example. And since the torque depends on the current, a galvanometer, a meter that measures current, uses the effect.

EXAMPLE 26-6. *The moving-coil galvanometer.* The essential features of a galvanometer are sketched in Fig. 26-10. A permanent magnet and a soft iron core cause the

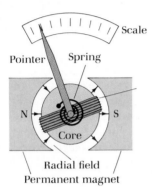

Figure 26-10. Example 26-6: A galvanometer is shown schematically. In the space between the poles of a magnet and the soft iron core, the magnetic field is approximately radial and uniform in magnitude. As a result, the magnetic torque on the current-carrying coil is independent of the orientation of the coil.

magnetic field to be approximately radial and uniform in magnitude in the space between each pole and the core. In this space, the wires of a rectangular coil are always perpendicular to the field, so that the effective angle between the directions of **S** and **B** is always 90°. The coil, pivoted about

an axis through its center, has an attached pointer, and the scale is calibrated to give current values. A spring exerts a restoring torque on the coil that is proportional to the angular displacement ϕ from the equilibrium orientation at zero current. The magnitude of the restoring torque τ_r depends on the torsional constant κ of the spring: $\tau_r = \kappa\phi$. Show that if a current I exists in the galvanometer, then the coil is in rotational equilibrium with an angular displacement ϕ, which is proportional to the current.

SOLUTION. With a current I in the coil, the magnitude of the magnetic torque from Eq. (26-7) is $\tau = NISB$. The coil will rotate from the equilibrium position with no current ($\phi = 0$) to a new equilibrium position where the restoring torque balances the magnetic torque:

$$\kappa\phi = NISB$$

or

$$I = \frac{\kappa}{NSB}\phi$$

Thus the current in the galvanometer is directly proportional to the angular deflection of the pointer. The mechanical galvanometer with a moving coil has been largely replaced by the electronic meter, which has no macroscopic moving parts.

26-5 MOTION OF CHARGES IN ELECTROMAGNETIC FIELDS

To understand the operation of many modern devices and instruments, we must consider the motion of electrons, protons, and other ions in electric and magnetic (electromagnetic) fields. Electromagnetic forces dominate the motion of charged particles at the atomic level. If an electric field **E** and a magnetic field **B** exist in a region, then the combined force **F** on a particle with charge q and velocity **v** is given by

The Lorentz force

$$\mathbf{F} = q\mathbf{E} + q\mathbf{v} \times \mathbf{B} \tag{26-11}$$

This force is often called the *Lorentz force* after H. A. Lorentz (1853–1928), who made many contributions to the understanding of electromagnetic phenomena.

We first consider the motion of a charged particle in a uniform magnetic field with no electric field present. Suppose that the magnitude of the field is B and that the direction is out of the plane of the page, as shown in Fig. 26-11. For simplicity, take the initial velocity to be perpendicular to **B** (but see Prob. 26-4). From the cross product in Eq. (26-11), the magnetic force is perpendicular to **B**

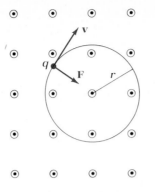

Figure 26-11. A positively charged particle moves in a circular path perpendicular to a uniform magnetic field.

and to the velocity, as shown in Fig. 26-11 for a positive charge. That is, the force and the velocity are perpendicular to each other and lie in a plane which is perpendicular to **B**. If the magnetic force is the only force acting on the particle, then, from Newton's second law, the acceleration of the particle is perpendicular to the velocity and also lies in the plane perpendicular to **B**. Since the acceleration is perpendicular to the velocity, only the direction of the velocity changes, and the path of the particle is in the plane perpendicular to **B**. The charged particle moves in a circular path of radius r with constant speed v, and the acceleration is the centripetal acceleration of magnitude $a = v^2/r$. The centripetal force is provided by the magnetic force of magnitude $|q\mathbf{v} \times \mathbf{B}|$ so that Newton's second law gives

A charged particle moves in a circular path perpendicular to a uniform magnetic field.

$$\frac{mv^2}{r} = |q\mathbf{v} \times \mathbf{B}| = |q|vB \sin 90° = qvB$$

where m is the mass of the particle and we have assumed that q has a positive value ($|q| = q$). We can simplify this expression and solve for one of the quantities, say the radius of the circular path, in terms of the others:

$$r = \frac{mv}{qB} \qquad (26\text{-}12)$$

Equation (26-12) shows that the radius of the circular path and the speed are proportional for a charged particle in a uniform magnetic field. Thus for a given type of particle, those with higher speeds have larger radii of curvature. Notice from Eq. (26-12), however, that the angular speed ω is the same for all such particles:

$$\omega = \frac{v}{r} = \frac{q}{m} B \qquad (26\text{-}13)$$

The cyclotron frequency depends on the charge-to-mass ratio of the particle.

In a uniform magnetic field, the angular speed, or the *angular frequency*, of the circular motion depends only on the field B and on the charge-to-mass ratio q/m for that type of particle. Since the operation of one of the early particle accelerators, the *cyclotron*, is based on this property, the angular frequency is often called the *cyclotron frequency*, $\omega_c = qB/m$.

EXAMPLE 26-7. The bubble chamber. As a charged particle moves through a liquid-hydrogen bubble chamber, it ionizes some of the molecules along its path. Small bubbles that form at the ionized sites make the track of the particle visible. A magnetic field in the region causes the path to be curved, and the momentum of the particle can be determined from the radius of curvature of the path. (See Fig. 26-12.) Determine the magnitude of the momentum and the

speed of a proton ($q = e = 1.60 \times 10^{-19}$ C, $m = 1.67 \times 10^{-27}$ kg) at a point where the radius of curvature of the path is 2.67 m and the magnitude of the magnetic field is 0.140 T.

SOLUTION. The magnitude of the momentum is, from Eq. (26-12),

$$p = mv = qBr = (1.60 \times 10^{-19} \text{ C})(0.140 \text{ T})(2.67 \text{ m})$$

$$= 5.98 \times 10^{-20} \text{ kg} \cdot \text{m/s}$$

The speed of the proton is

$$v = \frac{p}{m} = \frac{5.98 \times 10^{-20} \text{ kg m/s}}{1.67 \times 10^{-27} \text{ kg}}$$

$$= 3.58 \times 10^7 \text{ m/s}$$

This speed is about $0.1c$, where c is the speed of light. Relativistic effects (Chap. 38) become increasingly important for speeds approaching the speed of light.

EXAMPLE 26-8. *The cyclotron.* Charged particles are accelerated repeatedly in a cyclotron by an alternating potential difference applied across the gap between two hollowed, D-shaped conductors, or "dees," as shown in Fig. 26-13. A uniform magnetic field is perpendicular to the

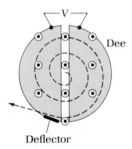

Figure 26-13. Example 26-8: An alternating potential difference accelerates positively charged particles in a beam across the gap between the dees in a cyclotron. The magnetic field is out of the plane of the figure and is uniform in the region of the dees.

plane of the figure and out of the page. A positive charge with speed v in a dee moves in a circular arc of radius $r = mv/qB$. The particle is only accelerated as it crosses the gap between the dees because the electric field is zero within each dee. The speed and radius increase each time the particle is accelerated in the gap, but the angular frequency ω_c remains the same. The key to having the speed increased each time is to have the accelerating potential difference applied in phase with the circulating charge. Thus the potential difference is applied with an oscillator

tuned to the cyclotron frequency. As the beam (a group of charges) reaches the outer edge of the cyclotron, a deflector plate directs the beam out to a target area. Suppose the magnetic field has magnitude 1.4 T in a cyclotron of radius 0.50 m. (a) What frequency oscillator must be used to accelerate deuterons? (A *deuteron*, with $q = e$ and $m = 3.3 \times 10^{-27}$ kg, is the nucleus of heavy hydrogen, or deuterium.) (b) Determine the speed and kinetic energy of deuterons emerging from the cyclotron.

SOLUTION. (a) The angular frequency of the oscillator must match the cyclotron frequency of a deuteron in this magnetic field. From Eq. (26-13),

$$\omega_c = \frac{qB}{m} = \frac{1.6 \times 10^{-19} \text{ C})(1.4 \text{ T})}{3.3 \times 10^{-27} \text{ kg}}$$

$$= 6.8 \times 10^7 \text{ rad/s}$$

Ordinarily, the frequency ν in hertz (Hz; cycles per second) is specified, and

$$\nu = \frac{\omega_c}{2\pi} = 11 \text{ MHz}$$

Electronic oscillators with this frequency are readily available.

(b) The speed of a deuteron at the outer edge of the dee is

$$v = \omega r = (68 \times 10^6 \text{ rad/s})(0.50 \text{ m}) = 3.4 \times 10^7 \text{ m/s}$$

and the kinetic energy is

$$K = \tfrac{1}{2}mv^2 = \tfrac{1}{2}(3.3 \times 10^{-27} \text{ kg})(3.4 \times 10^7 \text{ m/s})^2$$

$$= 1.9 \times 10^{-12} \text{ J} = 12 \text{ MeV}$$

You should be able to show that the kinetic energy of a charged particle emerging from a cyclotron of radius R is given by

$$K = \frac{(qBR)^2}{2m}$$

The maximum kinetic energy is limited for a cyclotron because of relativistic effects, which make the frequency of the circular motion depend on speed for speeds approaching that of light. In the *synchrocyclotron*, the frequency is changed to synchronize with the speed-dependent frequency of the charges. See the Commentary for a description of a *synchrotron*, which is a different kind of accelerator.

A velocity selector. We now consider a configuration of electric and magnetic fields which serves as a *velocity selector* for charged particles. Suppose that uniform electric and magnetic fields exist in a region of space and that these fields are perpendicular, as shown in Fig. 26-14. The force on a charged particle moving in that region is given by Eq. (26-11). For the case illustrated in the figure for a positively charged particle, there is a particular velocity for which the net force is zero. The upward electric force balances the downward magnetic force, so that the net force is zero. For negatively charged particles with this velocity, the directions of the forces would be reversed, and the net force is still zero. Charges with this velocity will pass through the region undeviated. Since the magnetic force depends on the velocity of the particle but the electric force does not, the net force will not be zero for a particle with a different velocity. For a charge with a larger speed, the magnetic force will have a magnitude larger than that of the electric force. Such positively charged particles with a larger speed will be deflected downward. Similarly, slower positively charged particles will be deflected upward.

A velocity selector selects charged particles with speed $v = E/B$.

The value of the "selected" velocity is obtained by requiring that the combined force in Eq. (26-11) be zero:

$$\mathbf{F} = 0 = q(\mathbf{E} + \mathbf{v} \times \mathbf{B})$$

Taking the magnitude of this expression, we determine the speed of the charged particles passing undeviated through the selector:

$$v = \frac{E}{B}$$

A velocity (or speed) selector is used in devices such as the *mass spectrometer* (Prob. 26-5) and in experiments such as the Thomson experiment (Prob. 26-6). A type of "natural" velocity selector is at work in an important effect in conductors called the *Hall effect*.

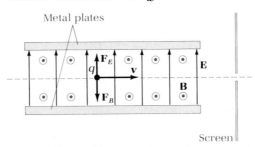

Figure 26-14. A positively charged particle moves in crossed electric and magnetic fields.

EXAMPLE 26-9. *The Hall effect.* Consider a section of a current-carrying conductor in a uniform magnetic field, as shown in Fig. 26-15a. With the sense of the current in the positive x direction, positive charge carriers would move in that direction and negative charge carriers in the opposite direction. Each type of charge would be deflected by the magnetic field to the lower surface. We suppose now that only positive charge carriers are present; then the lower surface would become positively charged, leaving the top surface with a negative charge, a deficiency of positive

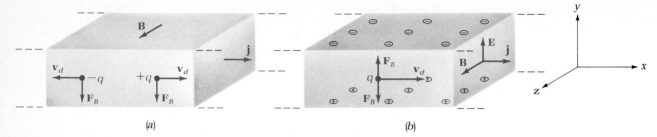

Figure 26-15. Example 26-9: (*a*) A magnetic field is perpendicular to the current density **j** in a conductor. The magnetic force is downward on both positive and negative charge carriers. (*b*) The electric and magnetic forces balance for a positive charge carrier moving with the drift velocity.

charge. This charge separation produces an electric field in the conductor, as seen in Fig. 26-15*b*. In the steady-state case, the electric field component E_y, called the *Hall field*, exerts an electric force on the moving charge carriers which tends to balance the magnetic force due to the magnetic field component B_z. These crossed electric and magnetic fields act, in an average sense, as a velocity selector for the drift velocity $\mathbf{v}_d$. Show that the Hall field E_y is proportional to $j_x B_z$ and that the *Hall coefficient* $R_H = E_y/j_x B_z$ is given by

$$R_H = \frac{1}{nq}$$

where n is the density of carriers, each with charge q.

SOLUTION. Consider a particle of charge q moving with the drift velocity $\mathbf{v}_d = v_{dx}\mathbf{i}$, where $\mathbf{i}$ is a unit vector along the x axis. The current density **j** in the conductor is

$$\mathbf{j} = j_x\mathbf{i} = nqv_{dx}\mathbf{i}$$

Using Eq. (26-11), we require that the y component of the

force be zero: $F_y = q(E_y - v_{dx}B_z) = 0$, or

$$E_y = v_{dx}B_z$$

Multiplying by the density of charge carriers n and using $j_x = nqv_{dx}$ gives

$$nqE_y = nqv_{dx}B_z = j_x B_z$$

or

$$E_y = \frac{j_x B_z}{nq}$$

Thus E_y is proportional to $j_x B_z$, and the Hall coefficient is the constant of proportionality,

$$R_H = \frac{E_y}{j_x B_z} = \frac{1}{nq}$$

Notice that the Hall coefficient has a positive value, corresponding to our assumption that all the charge carriers were positive. You should be able to show that the Hall coefficient reverses sign if you assume that all the charge carriers are negative. The Hall coefficient gives, in this way, information about the signs of charge carriers in conductors. Since E_y depends on B_z, notice also that the Hall effect can be used to determine the magnetic field in a region by measuring the Hall field E_y in a previously calibrated conductor. (How?)

COMMENTARY: MAGNETIC FIELDS AND PARTICLE ACCELERATORS

There seems to be a general rule in physics that the smaller the object of study, the larger the instruments must be. Nowhere is this rule more evident than in particle physics, the study of the fundamental structure of matter. This structure is revealed in collisions of particles, say of a proton with an antiproton (a particle with the same mass but opposite electric charge of a proton). If the energies of the colliding particles are large enough, a multitude of particles can be produced in these collisions. The properties of these particles give clues about the structure of matter on the smallest scale, which is currently expressed in terms of a model that involves fundamental particles called quarks.*

---

* In the "extended" edition of this text, quarks are discussed in Chap. 43.

Now a higher energy of collision produces a richer variety of particles, and there has been a continued push toward developing accelerators capable of providing yet more energy for the colliding particles. As new accelerators have been designed to provide the higher energy needed to probe matter at a smaller scale, the size of these accelerators has become dramatically larger, from those that fit in a laboratory room to a newly proposed accelerator whose size is expressed in tens of kilometers.

Magnetic fields are essential for the operation of particle accelerators. In an accelerator, the charged particles in a beam are accelerated (given energy) in an evacuated tube or region by an electric field, as described for the cyclotron in Sec. 26-5. A magnetic field is often used to deflect the beam or to cause it to move in a curved path. In the cyclotron, which is a relatively small accelerator, the magnetic field is essentially uniform over the cross section. As the particles in the beam gain energy, the radius of the path increases, $r = mv/qB$, from a very small initial radius to a final radius at the edge of the device. Thus the size of the region of the magnetic field limits the energy gained by a particle in this type of accelerator.

The much larger synchrotron type of accelerator is designed to have the particle beam travel along a fixed path in a ringlike tube. Since magnetic fields are needed only at the tube to deflect and guide the beam, it is feasible to have accelerator rings of large diameter. As particles move around the ring, the position of a group of particles in the beam is synchronized with the accelerating stages that increase the particle energy. The currents that produce the magnetic fields are also synchronized with the group, so that the magnetic force on the charged particles bends the beam and causes the group to remain aligned near the center of the tube.

Among the large synchrotrons is one at Fermilab at Batavia, Illinois, which has a 1.9-km ring diameter. In the Tevatron ring at Fermilab, protons are accelerated to a kinetic energy of 1 TeV (10^{12} eV) and a speed that is close to the speed of light. Antiprotons are accelerated to the same energy, but, since they have negative charge, they circulate in the opposite direction. When the proton and

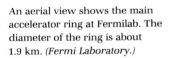

An aerial view shows the main accelerator ring at Fermilab. The diameter of the ring is about 1.9 km. *(Fermi Laboratory.)*

antiproton paths are caused to cross, they collide with 2 TeV of energy. This is the great advantage of a collider: Since none of the energy is associated with the motion of the center of mass, all of the energy is available for processes that occur in the collision.

A much larger synchrotron is presently being planned. The Superconducting SuperCollider (SSC) is designed as a proton-proton collider. It will use superconducting coils on magnets placed around a ring that measures about 80 km around. Two groups of protons will be accelerated to about 20 TeV and caused to collide, so that 40 TeV will be available for collision processes. With the much higher energy provided by this accelerator, it is hoped that some fundamental questions about the structure of matter will be answered. No one will be surprised if the experiments also raise some new questions that call for still higher energies.

SUMMARY WITH APPLICATIONS

Section 26-2. The magnetic field
The magnetic field **B** at a point in space is defined in terms of the force exerted by the field on a particle with charge q and velocity **v** at that point:

$$\mathbf{F} = q\mathbf{v} \times \mathbf{B} \qquad (26\text{-}1)$$

Define the magnetic field; determine the force exerted by a magnetic field on a charged particle.

Section 26-3. Force on a current-carrying conductor
The magnetic force on a straight section of a current-carrying conductor in a uniform field is given by

$$\mathbf{F} = I\boldsymbol{\ell} \times \mathbf{B} \qquad (26\text{-}3)$$

Generally the magnetic force on a section of a current-carrying conductor is

$$\mathbf{F} = \int I \, d\boldsymbol{\ell} \times \mathbf{B} \qquad (26\text{-}5)$$

Determine the force exerted by a magnetic field on a current-carrying conductor.

Section 26-4. Torque on a current loop
If a coil with N turns and current I is in a uniform magnetic field, then the torque exerted by the field on the coil is

$$\boldsymbol{\tau} = NI\mathbf{S} \times \mathbf{B} \qquad (26\text{-}7)$$

where **S** is the area vector of the plane of a loop of the coil. The direction of **S** is perpendicular to the plane of the area, with a sense given by a right-hand rule.

The magnetic dipole moment **m** of a coil with current I is

$$\mathbf{m} = NI\mathbf{S} \qquad (26\text{-}9)$$

and the torque on a magnetic dipole in a uniform magnetic field is

$$\boldsymbol{\tau} = \mathbf{m} \times \mathbf{B} \qquad (26\text{-}8)$$

The potential energy of the dipole is

$$U = -\mathbf{m} \cdot \mathbf{B} \qquad (26\text{-}10)$$

Determine the torque due to a magnetic field on a current-carrying coil; determine the magnetic dipole moment of a coil; determine the torque on and the potential energy of a magnetic dipole in a uniform magnetic field.

Section 26-5. Motion of charges in electromagnetic fields
Electric and magnetic fields each exert a force on a particle of charge q. The combined force is given by

$$\mathbf{F} = q(\mathbf{E} + \mathbf{v} \times \mathbf{B}) \qquad (26\text{-}11)$$

If the velocity is perpendicular to a uniform magnetic field and no other forces are acting, then the charged particle moves in a circular path. The speed of a particle of mass m and the radius of its circular path are connected by

$$r = \frac{mv}{qB} \qquad (26\text{-}12)$$

The cyclotron frequency ω_c is independent of the values of v and r:

$$\omega_c = \frac{v}{r} = \frac{qB}{m} \qquad (26\text{-}13)$$

Crossed electric and magnetic fields act as a velocity selector for charged particles entering the region with velocities perpendicular to the crossed fields. Only those with speed

$$v = \frac{E}{B}$$

pass through the region undeviated.

Determine the force on a charged particle in electric and magnetic fields; determine the motion of a charged particle in a uniform magnetic field; explain how a velocity selector works and determine the speed of charged particles that pass undeviated through a selector.

QUESTIONS

26-1 Is it possible for the magnetic force on a moving charge in a magnetic field to be zero? Explain.

26-2 Is it possible for the electric force on a moving charge in an electric field to be zero? Explain.

26-3 Is it possible for the electromagnetic force on a moving charge in an electromagnetic field to be zero? Explain.

26-4 Is the magnetic force on a moving charge, $F = q\mathbf{v} \times B$, always perpendicular to $\mathbf{v}$? To B? Is $\mathbf{v}$ always perpendicular to F? To B? Explain.

26-5 Suppose the magnetic field were defined so that the field is parallel to the force on a moving positive charge. Explain why such a definition would be unsatisfactory.

26-6 You are given the following information: (i) The force on a charge $q = 2.4 \times 10^{-14}$ C at rest at a point is 3.7×10^{-12} N in the positive z direction; (ii) the force on the charge at that point when moving in the positive x direction with speed 2.2×10^3 m/s is 3.1×10^{-12} N in the positive z direction; (iii) only electric and magnetic forces are significant. Can you completely determine the electric field at that point? Can you completely determine the magnetic field at that point? If you cannot completely determine either field, what additional information is necessary?

26-7 The electric field is defined in terms of the electric force F on a small test charge q: $E = F/q$. Can Eq. (26-1) be similarly solved for B? Explain.

26-8 The charge carriers (electrons) in a metal wire at temperature T are in random thermal motion although the current is zero. The wire is in a magnetic field. Is there a magnetic force on each charge carrier? Is there a magnetic force on the wire? Explain.

26-9 In a current-carrying conductor, a magnetic field exerts a force on the moving electrons in the conductor. What exerts the force on the conductor?

26-10 A simple electric motor consists of a current-carrying coil turning in a static magnetic field which exerts a torque on the coil. Explain how the motor can deliver mechanical energy if a static magnetic field can do no work on a moving charge.

26-11 Explain how you can use a battery, a coil of wire, and a thread as a compass.

26-12 Equation (26-10) gives the potential energy of a magnetic dipole in a uniform magnetic field. What orientation of the dipole corresponds to the lowest energy? The highest energy? For what orientation is the potential energy zero?

26-13 For what orientation(s) of a current-carrying coil in a uniform magnetic field is the magnitude of the magnetic torque a maximum? A minimum?

26-14 The torque on a magnetic dipole in a uniform field, $\tau = \mathbf{m} \times B$, is zero if $\mathbf{m}$ and B are parallel or if they have opposite directions. Does either of these orientations correspond to stable equilibrium? Explain.

26-15 An electron in a cyclotron has a cyclotron frequency of $\omega_c = eB/m$. Can an electron have a cyclotron frequency if it is in a magnetic field but not in a cyclotron? Explain.

26-16 Show that the motion of a charged particle in electric and magnetic fields depends on the charge and mass of the particle only through their ratio q/m. Thus neither q nor m, only their ratio, can be independently determined by observations of the particle's motion in only electromagnetic fields.

26-17 Does a velocity selector pass both protons and alpha (α) particles ($q_\alpha = 2e$, $m_\alpha = 4m_p$) with the same velocity? What about protons and electrons? Explain.

26-18 Can a magnetic field be used to separate protons and electrons with the same velocity? What about protons and alpha particles? Explain.

26-19 Suppose that two charged particles move in circular paths of the same radius in a uniform magnetic field. Must these particles have the same speed? The same charge? The same mass? What can you say about these two particles if they have the same cyclotron frequency? Explain.

26-20 A proton is released from rest in a region with electric and magnetic fields which are parallel and uniform. How does the proton move? Would an electron behave differently? Explain.

26-21 If a conductor had both positive and negative charge carriers, could the Hall coefficient be positive? Negative? Zero? Explain.

26-22 Complete the following table:

Symbol	Represents	Type	SI unit
B			
$I\,d\ell$		Vector	
τ	Torque		
$\mathbf{m}$			
ω_c			rad/s

EXERCISES

Section 26-2. The magnetic field

26-1 A proton has a velocity of magnitude 2.45×10^6 m/s at a point where $B = 0.117$ T. The direction of the velocity is at $134°$ from the direction of the magnetic field. (a) Show in a diagram the directions of $\mathbf{v}$, B, and the magnetic force **F** on the proton. (*b*) Determine the magnitude of the force. (*c*) Repeat for an electron with the same velocity.

26-2 Show that the tesla, the SI unit of magnetic field, can be expressed as kg · A^{-1} · s^{-2}.

26-3 (*a*) Determine the magnetic force on an electron with velocity components $v_x = 4.4 \times 10^6$ m/s, $v_y = -3.2 \times 10^6$ m/s, $v_z = 0$ at a point where the magnetic field has components $B_x = 0$, $B_y = -12$ mT, $B_z = 12$ mT. (*b*) Show the directions of these vectors in a diagram.

26-4 The magnetic field at a point is determined by projecting protons of speed $v = 3.0 \times 10^7$ m/s through the point from several directions and measuring the force, assumed to be magnetic. It is noticed that if the velocity is parallel to the z direction, the force is zero. But if the velocity is parallel to the y direction, the force is in the negative x direction and has magnitude $F = 1.8 \times 10^{-13}$ N. (*a*) Determine the magnitude and direction of the magnetic field at that point. (*b*) What force (magnitude and direction) is exerted on a proton with that speed if the direction of the velocity is parallel to the x direction?

26-5 Compare the magnitudes near the earth's surface of the weight of an electron and a typical magnetic force exerted by the earth's magnetic field ($B = 10^{-5}$ T) on an electron with speed 10^6 m/s.

26-6 Compare the magnitudes near the earth's surface of a typical magnetic force exerted by the earth's magnetic field ($B = 10^{-5}$ T) on an electron with speed 10^6 m/s and the electric force exerted on an electron by an atmospheric electric field ($E = 100$ N/C).

26-7 A 2-g hailstone with charge -7×10^{-12} C falls vertically downward with speed 80 m/s. In this region there are gravitational, electric, and magnetic fields whose magnitudes are $g = 9.8$ m/s², $E = 120$ N/C, and $B = 40$ μT, respectively. The fields **g** and **E** are directed vertically downward, while the direction of **B** is horizontal and to the north. (*a*) Determine the magnitude and direction of the force exerted on the hailstone by each of these fields. (*b*) Are any of these forces negligible? (*c*) List any other significant forces acting on the hailstone.

Section 26-3. Force on a current-carrying conductor

26-8 A section of straight wire of length 0.40 m and with current $I = 7.0$ A is oriented at angle $\theta = 27°$ to a uniform magnetic field of magnitude $B = 1.2$ T, as shown in Fig. 26-16. (*a*) Determine the magnitude and direction of the magnetic force on the section of wire. (*b*) How would the answers to part (*a*) change if I is doubled? If B is doubled? If θ is doubled?

26-9 A force of 2.2 mN is found to act on a 250-mm length of current-carrying wire that is perpendicular to a mag-

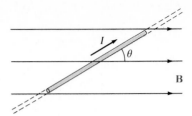

Figure 26-16. Exercise 26-8.

netic field of magnitude 340 mT. (*a*) What current exists in the wire? (*b*) Show the sense of the current and the directions of the force and the field in a diagram.

26-10 Consider a horizontal conducting rod of density ρ and cross-sectional area A that is perpendicular to a horizontal magnetic field **B**, as shown in Fig. 26-17. Flexible lead wires are connected to the ends of the rod, which carries a current I such that the magnetic force balances the weight of the rod. (*a*) Determine the current I in terms of ρ, A, g, and B. (*b*) What is the sense of the current? (*c*) Evaluate the current for $\rho = 2.7 \times 10^3$ kg/m³, $A = 100$ mm², $B = 200$ mT, $g = 9.8$ m/s².

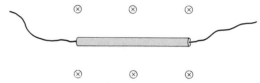

Figure 26-17. Exercise 26-10.

26-11 A wire of length ℓ forms a section of a circuit with current I. The section lies along the x axis, as shown in Fig. 26-18. At points along this axis, the magnetic field has only a y component, which varies as $B_y = A/x$, where A is a positive constant. Determine (*a*) the direction and (*b*) the magnitude of the magnetic force on the wire in terms of I, A, and ℓ.

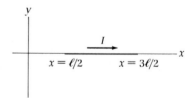

Figure 26-18. Exercise 26-11.

26-12 Consider a current-carrying wire of arbitrary shape lying in a plane perpendicular to a uniform magnetic field. Choose a coordinate system so that the magnetic field is in the z direction and the endpoints of the wire lie on the y axis, as shown in Fig. 26-19. A current element can be expressed as

$$I\, d\boldsymbol{\ell} = I\, dx\, \mathbf{i} + I\, dy\, \mathbf{j}$$

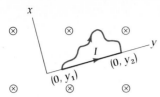

Figure 26-19. Exercise 26-12.

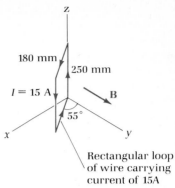

Figure 26-20. Exercise 26-16.

Prove that the net magnetic force on this wire is the same as would be exerted on a straight section of wire connecting the two endpoints. See the next exercise for a generalization.

26-13 (a) Review the discussion in Example 26-3 and prove that the net magnetic force on a current-carrying wire of arbitrary shape in a uniform magnetic field is given by

$$\mathbf{F} = I\boldsymbol{\ell} \times \mathbf{B}$$

where $\boldsymbol{\ell}$ is the displacement from one endpoint of the wire to the other endpoint, with the same sense as the current in the wire. Why must the field be uniform? (b) What is the net magnetic force on a current *loop* of arbitrary shape in a uniform magnetic field?

Section 26-4. Torque on a current loop

26-14 A rectangular current loop of dimensions 20 mm by 30 mm is oriented so that the plane of the loop is at 40° to the direction of a uniform magnetic field of magnitude 380 mT. (a) Show the arrangement on a diagram and assign a sense to the current. (b) What angle does the (vector) area of the loop make with the field? (c) Determine the magnetic torque on the loop about an axis perpendicular to **B**, as seen in Fig. 26-7, if the current is 1.5 A.

26-15 A circular coil has 100 turns, each of radius 15 mm. The coil carries 250-mA current and is pivoted, as shown in Fig. 26-8, to rotate about an axis perpendicular to a uniform magnetic field of magnitude 0.40 T. Determine the magnetic torque on the coil if the direction of the area makes an angle with the field of (a) 60°, (b) 90°, (c) 120°.

26-16 The rectangular loop shown in Fig. 26-20 is pivoted to rotate about the z axis. A uniform magnetic field of magnitude 300 mT is in the y direction. (a) Determine the magnitude and direction of the force on each side of the loop. (b) Determine the torque about the z axis. (c) Determine the torque about an axis parallel to the z axis but through the center of the loop. (d) For what orientation(s) of the loop is the magnitude of the magnetic torque a maximum?

26-17 The rotating coil in the galvanometer in Example 26-6 has 12 turns and face area 4.0×10^{-4} m². The magnitude of the radial magnetic field is 140 mT, and the spring has a torsional constant of $6.7 \times$ 10^{-7} N · m · rad^{-1}. What current causes a deflection of one division on the scale if these divisions are separated by 0.10 rad?

26-18 One of the coils in a direct-current (dc) motor has 78 turns and face area 1.1×10^{-2} m². If the design of the motor specifies the maximum value of the magnitude of the torque to be 4.2 N · m in a field of magnitude 0.34 T, what current must the motor coil draw?

26-19 A 1200-turn coil has a square cross section of edge 12 mm. It carries a 150-mA current in a uniform magnetic field of magnitude 1.2 T. (a) Determine the magnetic dipole moment of the coil. (b) Determine the maximum magnitude of the magnetic torque on the dipole. (c) For what orientation of the dipole does the torque have one-half of the maximum magnitude?

26-20 Show that the SI unit of magnetic dipole moment can be expressed as J/T.

26-21 A compass needle has a magnetic dipole moment of magnitude 0.1 A · m². It points north at a place where the earth's magnetic field points north with a magnitude 5×10^{-5} T. (a) How much work must be done to change the orientation of the needle from north to east in this field? (b) What is the magnetic torque on the needle when it points east? (c) Determine the torque and potential energy if the needle points south.

26-22 Consider the compass needle in the previous exercise. Given 40 m of wire, design a circular coil that can have the same magnetic dipole moment as the needle, subject to the restriction that the current does not exceed 0.5 A. Specify the radius of the circular coil, the number of turns, and the current.

26-23 The torque on a small, 400-turn coil carrying 150 mA has a maximum magnitude of 1.6×10^{-3} N · m in a uniform field of magnitude 400 mT. (a) Determine the magnetic dipole moment of the coil. (b) Determine the face area of the coil. (c) If the dipole moment is at 40° to the field direction, what is the potential energy of the dipole? (d) How much work must an external agent perform to rotate the dipole moment through

180° from alignment with the field to opposite the field?

26-24 The electron has an intrinsic magnetic dipole moment of magnitude 9.3×10^{-24} A · m². (a) Express the value in units of eV/T. (b) An electron is in a uniform magnetic field of magnitude 1.5 T. What change in potential energy (in eV) occurs if the orientation of the magnetic dipole changes from alignment with the field to opposite the field? (c) What are the answers to parts (a) and (b) for a proton ($m = 1.4 \times 10^{-26}$ A · m²)?

Section 26-5. Motion of charges in electromagnetic fields

26-25 An α particle ($q = 2e$, $m = 6.7 \times 10^{-27}$ kg) moves in a plane perpendicular to a magnetic field of magnitude 0.55 T. (a) Determine the magnitude of the momentum of the α particle if the radius of its path is 0.27 m. (b) Determine the speed and (c) the kinetic energy in eV of the α particle.

26-26 Protons with kinetic energy of 7 MeV are injected into a region perpendicular to a uniform magnetic field of magnitude 0.60 T. (a) Determine the radius of the path of a proton. (b) By what factor would the radius change if the kinetic energy were doubled? (c) Determine the cyclotron frequency for both cases.

26-27 Deuterons ($q = e$, $m = 3.3 \times 10^{-27}$ kg) with kinetic energy of 12 keV are injected near the center of a cyclotron with $B = 1.7$ T and a 1.1-m diameter. (a) What should be the angular frequency of the oscillator used to accelerate the deuterons? (b) Determine the initial radius of curvature of the path. (c) Determine the final kinetic energy of a deuteron in eV. (d) How many revolutions are required if the accelerating potential difference across the dees is 500 V?

26-28 The Hall coefficient for Cu is $R_H = -6 \times 10^{-11}$ V · m · A⁻¹ · T⁻¹. (a) Estimate the density of charge carriers (electrons) in Cu. (b) The mass density of Cu is 8.9×10^3 kg/m³, and the mass of a Cu atom is 1.06×10^{-25} kg. How many free or mobile electrons does each atom contribute on the average? (c) What fraction is this of the 29 electrons in the neutral atom?

26-29 Figure 26-21 shows the trace of the path of a charged particle in a bubble chamber. Assume that the magnetic field is into the plane of the paper, with magni-

Figure 26-21. Exercise 26-29.

tude 0.4 T. The smooth spiral path occurs because the particle loses energy in ionizing molecules along the path. (a) Which part of the path corresponds to higher kinetic energy for the particle? (b) Is the charge positive or negative? (c) The radius of curvature ranges from 70 to 10 mm. What is the range of values of the magnitude of momentum if the magnitude of the charge is e?

26-30 For a particle whose speed v is comparable to the speed of light, $c = 3.00 \times 10^8$ m/s, Eq. (26-12) must be rewritten as

$$\frac{mv}{\sqrt{1 - v^2/c^2}} = qBr$$

where m is the rest mass of the particle (to be discussed in Chap. 38). (a) Determine the speed of a proton (rest mass $m = 1.67 \times 10^{-27}$ kg) in a path with radius of curvature 6.43 m in a magnetic field of magnitude 800 mT. (b) Determine the angular frequency of this circular motion and compare with the cyclotron frequency $\omega_c = qB/m$. This relativistic effect limits the cyclotron to accelerating particles to speeds small compared with the speed of light.

26-31 An electron beam is deflected by an electric field of magnitude $E = 4$ kN/C in the region between charged conducting plates, as shown in Fig. 26-22. The kinetic energy of an electron in the beam is 7 keV. (a) What is the direction of the electric field? (b) What uniform magnetic field (magnitude and direction) applied in this region would allow the beam to pass undeviated through the region? (c) Determine the speed and kinetic energy of a proton that this arrangement of fields would pass.

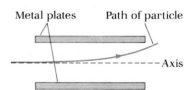

Figure 26-22. Exercise 26-31.

26-32 A velocity selector with fields **E** and **B** passes charged particles with velocity **v**. (a) Prove that the vectors satisfy the relation

$$\mathbf{E} = \mathbf{B} \times \mathbf{v}$$

(b) Which pairs of vectors *must* be perpendicular?

26-33 Very large magnetic fields exist in the vicinity of neutron stars. (a) Determine the cyclotron frequency of a proton in a region where $B = 10^5$ T. (b) Determine the speed of a proton moving in a circular path of radius 1 μm in this field. (c) Determine the speed if $r = 1$ m. (See Exercise 26-30.)

PROBLEMS

26-1 Determine the magnetic force on the semicircular wire in Example 26-4 by evaluating the infinitesimal force $d\mathbf{F} = I\,d\boldsymbol{\ell} \times \mathbf{B}$ in component form. Note that $\mathbf{B} = B\mathbf{k}$ and that $d\boldsymbol{\ell} = dx\,\mathbf{i} + dy\,\mathbf{j}$. The integrals extend from the point $(R, 0)$ to the point $(-R, 0)$.

26-2 Consider a plane loop of arbitrary shape carrying current I in a uniform magnetic field. The actual loop can be approximated by a number of small rectangular loops, each with current I, as shown in Fig. 26-23. Along the edges where two loops join with currents in opposite senses, the net current is zero, as is the force on these imagined conductors. Use this construction to show that the magnetic dipole moment of the plane current loop is given by $\mathbf{m} = I\mathbf{S}$, where $\mathbf{S} = \int d\mathbf{S}$ is the area of the plane of the loop.

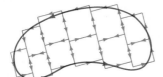

Figure 26-23. Prob. 26-2.

26-3 Suppose that a bar magnet (or a coil) of magnetic dipole moment $\mathbf{m}$ is suspended, as shown in Fig. 26-9, by a vertical fiber whose torsional constant is negligible. The magnet is in rotational equilibrium when aligned with a uniform magnetic field. If the magnet is rotated in a horizontal plane through a small angle θ, the field produces a torque on the magnet. (a) Show that the period of small oscillations of the magnet is given by

$$T = 2\pi\sqrt{\frac{I_0}{mB}}$$

where I_0 is the moment of inertia of the magnet about the axis of rotation. This method can be used in a known magnetic field to measure m for a magnet or a coil — or to measure B if m is known ($m = NIS$ for a coil). (b) A long, thin coil (or solenoid) of mass 24 g, with 450 turns of wire in a 85-mm length, has cross-sectional area 0.75 mm^2 and carries current 140 mA. Determine the magnitude of the magnetic field if the solenoid oscillates as described above with a period of 5.4 s.

26-4 A particle of mass m and charge q moves in a uniform magnetic field $\mathbf{B} = B\mathbf{k}$. Suppose that its initial velocity is $\mathbf{v}_0 = v_{0x}\mathbf{i} + v_{0z}\mathbf{k}$. The path of the particle is a helix (like the windings of a bedspring) whose axis is along the magnetic field direction. Show that the helix has a radius given by

$$r = \frac{mv_{0x}}{qB}$$

and that the pitch of the helix corresponds to a distance

$$d = \frac{2\pi m v_{0z}}{qB}$$

traveled parallel to the axis for each revolution.

26-5 *The mass spectrometer.* One type of mass spectrometer, used for the precise determination of atomic masses, is diagrammed in Fig. 26-24. Ions with velocity $\mathbf{v}$ from a source pass through a velocity selector, with fields $\mathbf{E}_0$ and $\mathbf{B}_0$, into a region of uniform magnetic field $\mathbf{B}$ and zero electric field. The radius of curvature of the path depends on the charge-to-mass ratio q/m of the ion. (a) Show that

$$m = \frac{qBB_0D}{2E_0}$$

where D is the diameter of the path for a particular ion species. Masses are customarily expressed on a scale such that the ^{12}C atom (carbon 12 is the isotope of carbon with six protons and six neutrons) has a mass of exactly 12 atomic mass units (12 u). (b) If the diameter of the circular path for ^{12}C is 732.4 mm and the diameter is 671.9 mm for an isotope of boron, determine the mass of the boron ion in u. Assume the ions have the same positive charge. (c) Is it necessary to account for the mass of the missing electron(s) of the ions? Explain.

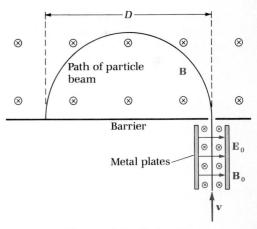

Figure 26-24. Prob. 26-5.

26-6 *The Thomson experiment.* By measuring the charge-to-mass ratio e/m for electrons, J. J. Thomson in 1897 established quantitatively the nature of cathode rays — rays coming from the cathode of a tube similar to a television picture tube. (Refer to Fig. 20-21.) Figure 26-25 shows that, with an electric field $\mathbf{E}$ but no magnetic field in the region between deflecting plates, the electron beam is deflected by an

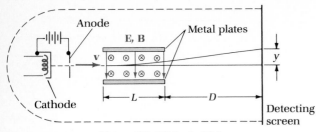

Figure 26-25. Prob. 26-6.

amount y on the detecting screen. (a) Show that the deflection is given by

$$y = \frac{eE}{mv^2}(DL + \tfrac{1}{2}L^2)$$

where v is the speed of electrons entering the plate region. Thomson then adjusted the applied magnetic field **B** until the beam was undeviated in this velocity selector. (b) Show that the charge-to-mass ratio is given in terms of measurable quantities by

$$\frac{e}{m} = \frac{yE}{B^2(DL + \tfrac{1}{2}L^2)}$$

26-7   A coil with N turns and current I is wound on a thin tube of diameter D and length L, as shown in Fig. 26-26. Light strings are wound around the circumference and tied to a rigid support which is not shown. Assume that the tube-and-coil system is in static equilibrium. (a) Show that the strings must be vertical. (b) Determine the *minimum* current I_0 for which the tube-and-coil system (of combined mass m) can be in static equilibrium in a uniform magnetic field **B** directed vertically upward. (c) What is the angle θ in this case? (d) For what angle θ is the system in equilibrium if $I = 2I_0$? (e) Is this second configuration one of stable or unstable equilibrium? Explain.

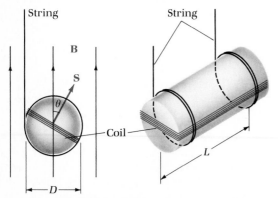

Figure 26-26. Prob. 26-7.

26-8   A rectangular current loop with dimensions a and b carries current I in a *nonuniform* magnetic field. The loop is in the xy plane, as shown in Fig. 26-27, perpendicular to a magnetic field which is out of the plane of the figure. At points in the plane, the field is given by $B_x = B_y = 0$ and $B_z = B_0 a/x$, where B_0 is a constant. Thus the magnetic field is in the z direction and it depends on the coordinate x. Determine the magnetic force (a) on each section of the current loop and (b) on the entire loop. (c) Determine the magnetic torque on the current loop about an axis through the center of the loop parallel to the y axis. Note that Eq. (26-7) applies only for a uniform field.

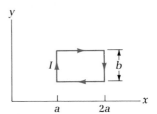

Figure 26-27. Prob. 26-8.

26-9   Show that Eq. (26-10) correctly gives the potential energy of a magnetic dipole in a uniform magnetic field. Begin by considering the work done by the magnetic force on a moving segment of a rectangular current loop as it rotates about an axis, as shown in Fig. 26-7. Then show that for a rotation through an infinitesimal angle $d\theta$, the work done by the magnetic force is $dW = -\tau d\theta$, where $\tau = |\mathbf{m} \times \mathbf{B}|$ is the magnitude of the magnetic torque on the current loop. Express the change in potential energy as the negative of the work done. $U_f - U_i = -\int dW$, and let $U = 0$ if $\mathbf{m}$ is perpendicular to **B**.

26-10   A uniform electric field **E** in the y direction and a uniform magnetic field **B** in the z direction exist in a region of space. A charged particle starts from rest at the origin of a coordinate system. Show that the motion of the particle is determined by the following equations of motion:

$$a_x = \omega_c v_y$$

$$a_y = \frac{qE}{M} - \omega_c v_x$$

$$a_z = 0$$

where $\omega_c = qB/m$ is the cyclotron frequency.

26-11   ✇ Write or adapt a program to integrate the equations of motion in the previous problem. Let the charged particle be a proton and take $E = 2.0 \times 10^5$ N/C, $B = 0.50$ T. The motion takes place in the xy plane. (Why?) Note that the cyclotron frequency sets a time scale for the numerical integration. That is, Δt should be small compared with the period $T = 2\pi/\omega_c$. Graph the path of the particle for a time which is at least twice the period. (This problem can also be solved analytically.)

CHAPTER 27
SOURCES OF THE MAGNETIC FIELD

27-1 INTRODUCTION

The last chapter dealt mainly with the force exerted by a magnetic field on a moving charge or on a current-carrying conductor. We now consider the source or cause of a magnetic field. Most of us have experience with the forces that magnets exert on each other. A magnet can also exert a magnetic force on a current-carrying conductor and on a moving charge. For example, the electron beam in a TV picture tube can be deflected by bringing a magnet close to the screen. (But don't try this with a strong magnet!) The magnet is the source of the magnetic field which deflects the electron beam.

In this chapter the emphasis is on an electric current as the source of a magnetic field. Oersted discovered in 1819 that a compass needle near a conducting wire was deflected when the wire carried a current. The current was the source of the magnetic field that exerted a torque on the compass needle.

Oersted's observation was the first that indicated a connection between electricity and magnetism. Prior to that time, electricity and magnetism were considered to be unrelated. Further connections between these fields will be revealed in the chapters which follow. We begin with the magnetic field produced by a steady distribution of electric current.

27-2 THE BIOT-SAVART LAW

Immediately following Oersted's discovery that an electric current is a source of a magnetic field, experiments by A. M. Ampère (1775–1836) and by J. B. Biot (1774–1862) and F. Savart (1791–1841) led to what we now call the *Biot-Savart*

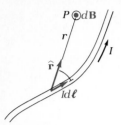

Figure 27-1. A current element $I\,d\boldsymbol{\ell}$ produces a contribution $d\mathbf{B}$ to the magnetic field at point P. If $I\,d\boldsymbol{\ell}$ and $\hat{\mathbf{r}}$ lie in the plane of the figure, then $d\mathbf{B}$ is directed perpendicularly out of the plane for this case.

law. It determines, at a point in space, the magnetic field due to a distribution of electric currents.

The Biot-Savart law is analogous to Coulomb's law for electrostatics. One way of expressing Coulomb's law is to give the electric field produced by a distribution of charge. If dq is a differential or infinitesimal element of charge, then the electric field $d\mathbf{E}$ produced at a point P by that charge is given by Eq. (20-6):

$$dE = \frac{1}{4\pi\epsilon_0}\frac{dq}{r^2}\hat{\mathbf{r}}$$

where r is the distance from the element of charge to the point P and $\hat{\mathbf{r}}$ is the unit vector directed from the charge to the point P. Integrating over the charge distribution gives the electric field at the point P, $\mathbf{E} = \int d\mathbf{E}$.

Now consider a current distribution such as that shown in Fig. 27-1. A current element $I\,d\boldsymbol{\ell}$ produces a contribution $d\mathbf{B}$ to the magnetic field at a point P. Let r represent the distance from the current element to the point P, with the unit vector $\hat{\mathbf{r}}$ pointing from the current element to point P. Then the Biot-Savart law for an infinitesimal current element is

The Biot-Savart law for a current element

$$d\mathbf{B} = \frac{\mu_0}{4\pi}\frac{I\,d\boldsymbol{\ell}\times\hat{\mathbf{r}}}{r^2} \tag{27-1}$$

The direction of $d\mathbf{B}$ is given by the direction of the cross product $I\,d\boldsymbol{\ell}\times\hat{\mathbf{r}}$ and is perpendicular to the current element $I\,d\boldsymbol{\ell}$ and to the unit vector $\hat{\mathbf{r}}$, with a sense given by a right-hand rule. That is, the extended thumb of the right hand gives the direction of $d\mathbf{B}$ if the fingers curl in the sense of the rotation that carries the direction of $I\,d\boldsymbol{\ell}$ into the direction of $\hat{\mathbf{r}}$. The magnitude of dB is

$$dB = \frac{\mu_0}{4\pi}\frac{I\,d\ell\sin\theta}{r^2} \tag{27-2}$$

where θ is the angle between the directions of $I\,d\boldsymbol{\ell}$ and $\hat{\mathbf{r}}$. The constant μ_0 is called the *permeability constant* for vacuum and is analogous to ϵ_0, the permittivity constant for vacuum in electrostatics. Because of the connections between electricity and magnetism, the values of ϵ_0 and μ_0 are not independent. The value of μ_0 in SI units is determined from the definition of the ampere (A) to be exactly $\mu_0 = 4\pi\times10^{-7}\,\mathrm{T\cdot m\cdot A^{-1}}$ (see Sec. 27-5), or since the combination $\mu_0/4\pi$ often occurs,

The permeability constant for vacuum, μ_0

$$\frac{\mu_0}{4\pi} = 1\times10^{-7}\,\mathrm{T\cdot m\cdot A^{-1}} \qquad \text{(exactly)}$$

The magnetic properties of air are so nearly the same as for vacuum that the permeability constant μ_0 for vacuum may be used when air is present.

There are some similarities between the Biot-Savart law for the magnetic field and the corresponding Coulomb's law for the electric field:

Similarities of Coulomb's law and the Biot-Savart law

1. Each contains the inverse-square dependence $1/r^2$ on the distance from the point source, with $I\,d\boldsymbol{\ell}$ as the source for $d\mathbf{B}$ and dq as the source for $d\mathbf{E}$.

2. The constant $1/4\pi\epsilon_0$ gives the strength of the electrical interaction, and the constant $\mu_0/4\pi$ gives the strength of the magnetic interaction.

But there are also some significant differences between the two laws:

Differences between Coulomb's law and the Biot-Savart law

1. The direction of $d\mathbf{E}$ is radial with respect to the charge dq, while the direction of $d\mathbf{B}$ is perpendicular to the plane containing $I\,d\boldsymbol{\ell}$ and $\hat{\mathbf{r}}$.

2. Although the simplest distribution of charge is a single isolated point charge, the single isolated current element does not exist for a steady current. Instead, charge must flow into the element from one end and out of the element at the other end, and Eq. (27-1) must always be integrated along the line(s) of the current distribution. Thus at a point P, the magnetic field due to a current distribution is given by the integral form of the Biot-Savart law:

Integral form of the Biot-Savart law

$$\mathbf{B} = \int \frac{\mu_0}{4\pi} \frac{I \, d\boldsymbol{\ell} \times \hat{\mathbf{r}}}{r^2} \tag{27-3}$$

where the line integral extends along the entire current distribution. That is, the magnetic field at a point is the linear superposition of the vector contributions due to each of the infinitesimal current elements.

Magnetic field due to a current in a long, straight wire. To illustrate the use of Eqs. (27-1) and (27-3), we determine the magnetic field produced by a steady current I in a long, straight wire. Unless otherwise stated, we shall assume that current-carrying wires have negligible thickness so that they can be represented by lines. A typical current element $I \, d\boldsymbol{\ell}$ is shown in Fig. 27-2, where the point P is at a perpendicular distance R from the wire. The contribution $d\mathbf{B}$ to the magnetic field at that point is given by Eq. (27-1). Applying the right-hand rule to the cross product shows that the direction of $d\mathbf{B}$ is perpendicularly out of the plane of the figure. The magnitude dB is given by Eq. (27-2), with $r^2 = x^2 + R^2$ and $I \, d\boldsymbol{\ell} = I \, dx$. Thus

$$dB = \frac{\mu_0}{4\pi} \frac{I \, dx \sin \theta}{x^2 + R^2}$$

$$= \frac{\mu_0}{4\pi} \frac{IR \, dx}{(x^2 + R^2)^{3/2}}$$

where we have used (see Fig. 27-2) $\sin \theta = \sin (\pi - \theta) = R/(x^2 + R^2)^{1/2}$.

The integral Biot-Savart law in Eq. (27-3) contains the integral of a vector. Particular care must be exercised in handling the direction when integrating a vector. For this case the integral involves the sum of contributions $d\mathbf{B}$ for each current element along the x axis. For any position, such as the one shown in Fig. 27-2, the direction of $d\mathbf{B}$ is perpendicularly out of the plane of the page. The integral represents the sum of these infinitesimal contributions, all with the same direction. Therefore, the sum or integral also has that direction, and its magnitude is the sum or integral of the magnitude dB of the contributions. Thus the direction of $\mathbf{B}$ at point P is perpendicularly out of the plane of the figure, and the magnitude is given by

$$B = \int dB = \frac{\mu_0}{4\pi} \int_{-\infty}^{\infty} \frac{IR}{(x^2 + R^2)^{3/2}} \, dx$$

Notice from the limits on the integral that we are considering the ideal case of an infinitely long wire. This integral can be found in tables or evaluated by

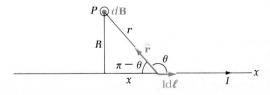

Figure 27-2. A long, straight wire carries a current I. The current element $I \, d\boldsymbol{\ell}$ makes a contribution $d\mathbf{B}$ to the magnetic field at point P. The direction of $d\mathbf{B}$ is out of the plane of the figure.

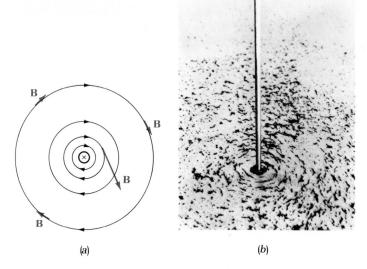

Figure 27-3. (a) Continuous lines represent the magnetic field due to a long, straight wire carrying a current into the page. The magnitude of the field decreases with increasing distance from the wire. (b) Iron filings form a pattern due to the magnetic field of a current in a wire. *(Fundamental Photographs)*

(a)   (b)

using the substitution $x = R \cot (\pi - \theta)$, as suggested by Fig. 27-2. The result is

$$B = \frac{\mu_0 IR}{4\pi} \left[\frac{x}{R^2 (x^2 + R^2)^{1/2}} \right]_{-\infty}^{+\infty} = \frac{\mu_0 IR}{4\pi} \frac{2}{R^2}$$

Magnetic field due to a current in a long, straight wire

Simplifying, we obtain the magnitude of the magnetic field at a perpendicular distance R from a long, straight wire carrying a current I:

$$B = \frac{\mu_0 I}{2\pi R} \qquad (27\text{-}4)$$

The direction of the field at a point is perpendicular to the plane containing the wire and the point in accord with a *right-hand rule:*

The direction of B is given by a right-hand rule.

> Grasp the wire with the right hand such that the extended thumb points in the sense of the current; then the curled fingers give the sense of the field.

The lines representing the magnetic field are shown in Fig. 27-3a in a plane perpendicular to the wire. These lines are circular and close on themselves. Compare with the pattern of iron filings near a current-carrying wire in Fig. 27-3b.

EXAMPLE 27-1. A long, straight wire carries a 20-A current. Determine the magnitude of the magnetic field at points 10, 20, and 50 mm from the wire and construct a graph of the dependence of B on distance r from the wire.

SOLUTION. The magnitude of the field is given by Eq. (27-4). For $R = 10$ mm, the field has magnitude (notice that $\mu_0/2\pi = 2 \times 10^{-7}$ T · m · A^{-1})

$$B = \frac{(2 \times 10^{-7} \text{ T·m·A}^{-1})(20 \text{ A})}{0.01 \text{ m}} = 4 \times 10^{-4} \text{ T}$$

Since B varies inversely with R, the magnitude of the field at 20 mm from the wire is 1/2 its value at 10 mm from the wire, or $B = 2 \times 10^{-4}$ T. Similarly, $B = 0.8 \times 10^{-4}$ T at 50 mm from the wire. These values are shown on the graph in Fig.

27-4, which illustrates the dependence of B on R.

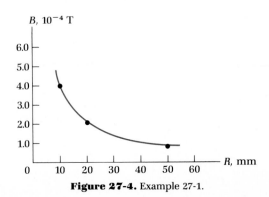

Figure 27-4. Example 27-1.

EXAMPLE 27-2. Two long, straight, parallel wires 240 mm apart carry currents of $I_1 = 20.0$ A and $I_2 = 30.0$ A. The currents have the same sense as shown in Fig. 27-5. The Biot-Savart law implies and experiment shows that the magnetic field due to several currents is the sum of the fields that would be produced by each current separately. Determine the magnetic field in the plane of the two wires at a point P halfway between them.

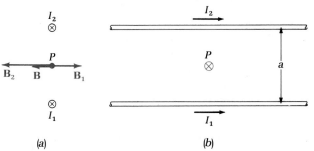

(a)   (b)

Figure 27-5. Example 27-2: The magnetic field at point P is the sum of contributions due to each current. (a) End view. (b) Side view.

SOLUTION. The magnetic field at a point is the vector sum of the fields $\mathbf{B}_1$ due to the current I_1 and $\mathbf{B}_2$ due to the current I_2. The magnitude of each field is given by Eq. (27-4):

$$B_1 = \frac{\mu_0 I_1}{2\pi R_1} \qquad B_2 = \frac{\mu_0 I_2}{2\pi R_2}$$

The direction of each, shown in Fig. 27-5a, is determined from the right-hand rule. At point P the two field contributions have opposite directions. The vector sum $\mathbf{B} = \mathbf{B}_1 + \mathbf{B}_2$ has the direction of $\mathbf{B}_2$, the larger of the two contributions, and the magnitude of the sum is given by

$$B = B_2 - B_1 = \frac{\mu_0}{2\pi}\left(\frac{I_2}{R_2} - \frac{I_1}{R_1}\right)$$

$$= (2 \times 10^{-7}\ \text{T} \cdot \text{m} \cdot \text{A}^{-1})\left(\frac{30.0\ \text{A}}{0.12\ \text{m}} - \frac{20.0\ \text{A}}{0.12\ \text{m}}\right)$$

$$= 1.7 \times 10^{-5}\ \text{T}$$

Suppose the sense of I_2 were opposite the sense of I_1. Show that $B = 8.3 \times 10^{-4}$ T at point P.

Magnetic field of a current loop. As another application of the Biot-Savart law, consider the magnetic field produced by a circular loop of radius a carrying a current I. We confine our calculation to points along the axis of the loop. Such points are equidistant from points on the loop. A typical current element $I\ d\boldsymbol{\ell}$ is shown in Fig. 27-6, where the x axis has been chosen along the axis of the loop. The contribution $d\mathbf{B}$ to the field at a point on the axis is given by Eq. (27-1) and is shown in the figure. For any point on the loop, the current element $I\ d\boldsymbol{\ell}$ and the unit vector $\hat{\mathbf{r}}$ are perpendicular. The magnitude of the field contribution is ($\theta = 90°$ and $\sin\theta = 1$ in Eq. 27-2)

$$dB = \frac{\mu_0 I\ d\ell}{4\pi r^2}$$

For each current element around the loop, the magnitude of $d\mathbf{B}$ remains the same but the direction changes. We resolve $d\mathbf{B}$ into components $dB_x = dB\cos\phi$ along the axis of the loop, and $dB_\perp = dB\sin\phi$ perpendicular to the axis. From the symmetry of the problem, the perpendicular component $dB_\perp$ adds or integrates to zero for the loop. We only need to integrate the component along the axis, dB_x. Thus the magnetic field at a point on the axis of the loop points along the axis, and its component is

$$B_x = \int dB_x = \int \frac{\mu_0 I\ d\ell\ \cos\phi}{4\pi(x^2 + a^2)}$$

where we have used $r^2 = x^2 + a^2$.

As we integrate $d\ell$ around the loop, each factor in the integral remains the same and can be taken out of the integral, leaving $\int d\ell = \ell = 2\pi a$, which is just the circumference of the loop. From the geometry in Fig. 27-6, we can express $\cos\phi$ in terms of a and x:

$$\cos\phi = \frac{a}{r} = \frac{a}{(x^2 + a^2)^{1/2}}$$

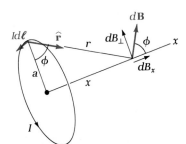

Figure 27-6. A current element of a circular loop produces a magnetic field contribution $d\mathbf{B}$ at a point on the axis of the loop. The vectors $I\ d\boldsymbol{\ell}$ and $\hat{\mathbf{r}}$ are perpendicular.

Making these substitutions in the equation for B_x gives

$$B_x = \frac{\mu_0 I}{4\pi} \frac{2\pi a^2}{(x^2 + a^2)^{3/2}}$$

This result can be expressed more simply in terms of the magnetic dipole moment, $\mathbf{m} = I\mathbf{S}$ from Eq. (26-9). Notice that the factor πa^2 in the numerator is the magnitude S of the area of the loop and that the product $I\pi a^2$ is the magnitude, $m = IS$, of the magnetic dipole moment of the current loop. Notice also that the directions of $\mathbf{B}$ and of $\mathbf{m}$ are the same, along the positive x direction. We have

Magnetic field on the axis of a current loop

$$\mathbf{B} = \frac{\mu_0}{2\pi} \frac{\mathbf{m}}{(x^2 + a^2)^{3/2}} \tag{27-5}$$

For points along the axis of the loop, the magnitude of the magnetic field is a maximum at $x = 0$, the center of the loop. The magnitude of the field decreases with distance along the axis. At points far from the loop, where $|x| \gg a$ so that $(x^2 + a^2)^{3/2} \approx (x^2)^{3/2} = |x|^3$, the magnitude of the field is given approximately by

$$B \approx \frac{\mu_0 m}{2\pi |x|^3}$$

The dependence of B on the inverse cube of the distance from the current loop (far from the loop) is characteristic of a dipole field. (See Exercise 20-25 for the corresponding form of the electric dipole field.)

A current loop behaves as a magnetic dipole in two ways.

We saw in Chap. 26 that a loop with current I and (vector) area $\mathbf{S}$ behaves as a magnetic dipole with dipole moment $\mathbf{m} = I\mathbf{S}$. That is, the torque exerted on such a current loop by an *external* magnetic field $\mathbf{B}_{ext}$ is given by Eq. (26-8), $\boldsymbol{\tau} = \mathbf{m} \times \mathbf{B}_{ext}$. Now we see that a current loop behaves as a magnetic dipole in another respect: The magnetic field *produced* by a current loop is a magnetic dipole field at points far from the loop.

EXAMPLE 27-3. A circular current loop has radius 25 mm and current 750 mA, with a sense as shown in Fig. 27-6. Determine the magnetic field produced by the current loop at $x = 0$, $x = 25$ mm, and $x = -2.0$ m, where the origin of the coordinate is at the center of the loop.

SOLUTION. The magnetic field at any point on the axis of the current loop in Fig. 27-6 is in the positive x direction. This can be seen from the figure for the case of a positive value of x. Sketch similar diagrams to verify this result for a negative value and a zero value of x. The magnitude of the field at a point on the axis is given by Eq. (27-5). The magnetic dipole moment of the current loop has magnitude

$$m = IS = I\pi a^2 = (0.750 \text{ A})\pi(0.025 \text{ m})^2$$

$$= 1.5 \times 10^{-3} \text{ A} \cdot \text{m}^2$$

At $x = 0$, the magnitude of the field is

$$B = (2 \times 10^{-7} \text{ T} \cdot \text{m} \cdot \text{A}^{-1}) \frac{1.5 \times 10^{-3} \text{ A} \cdot \text{m}^2}{[(0)^2 + (0.025 \text{ m})^2]^{3/2}}$$

$$= 1.9 \times 10^{-5} \text{ T}$$

Similar calculations give $B = 6.7 \times 10^{-6}$ T at $x = 0.020$ m and $B = 3.7 \times 10^{-11}$ T at $x = -2.0$ m.

27-3 AMPERE'S LAW

The magnitude of the magnetic field produced at a point by a current I in a long, straight wire is given by Eq. (27-4):

$$B = \frac{\mu_0 I}{2\pi R}$$

where R is the perpendicular distance from the wire to the point. The direction of the magnetic field is tangent to a line of magnetic field, as shown in Fig. 27-7, where the sense of the current is out of the page. Although the magnetic field produced by a steady current is static and the lines representing the magnetic field distribution do not move, each line closes on itself and encircles the current-carrying conductor. This encircling feature of the magnetic field due to a current can be expressed in geometric terms. Consider a circular path of radius R seen in Fig. 27-7. The circle is in a plane perpendicular to the long, straight, current-carrying wire and centered at the axis of the wire. As a simple closed path, this circle forms the boundary of a surface which the current crosses or pierces. The current piercing such a surface is said to *thread* or to *link* the closed path, just as a filament threads the eye of a needle or as one loop in a chain links another.

A current threads or links a closed path.

The encircling relation between a magnetic field and the current linking a closed path can also be expressed quantitatively in a general result known as *Ampere's law*. To obtain the result for the simple case of the circular path illustrated in Fig. 27-7, let $d\mathbf{r}$ represent an infinitesimal displacement along the closed path. Form the dot product of the displacement $d\mathbf{r}$ and the magnetic field $\mathbf{B}$ at a point on the path. Add or integrate these contributions $\mathbf{B} \cdot d\mathbf{r}$ around the circle to form the line integral of $\mathbf{B}$ around a closed path:

$$\oint \mathbf{B} \cdot d\mathbf{r}$$

where the circle on the integral sign denotes a closed path.

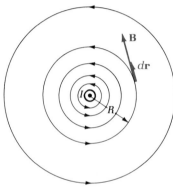

For the case illustrated in Fig. 27-7, we see that $\mathbf{B}$ and $d\mathbf{r}$ are parallel at each point on the circular path. Thus the dot product is just the product of the magnitudes, $\mathbf{B} \cdot d\mathbf{r} = B\, dr \cos 0 = B\, dr$. Further, the magnitude of the magnetic field has the same value at every point on the circle, and B can be factored out of the integral. We have

$$\oint \mathbf{B} \cdot d\mathbf{r} = \oint B\, dr = B \oint dr = B(2\pi R)$$

Figure 27-7. The lines of magnetic field for a long, straight, current-carrying wire encircle the wire. At each point on the circular path, $\mathbf{B}$ and $d\mathbf{r}$ are parallel.

where the integral of dr around the circle is just the circumference $2\pi R$. From Eq. (27-4) we see that $B(2\pi R) = \mu_0 I$. Thus, for the circular path shown in Fig. 27-7, the line integral of $\mathbf{B}$ around the closed path depends only on the current I that links the path and the permeability constant μ_0:

$$\oint \mathbf{B} \cdot d\mathbf{r} = \mu_0 I \tag{27-6}$$

Notice that the result in this equation is independent of the radius R of the circular path.

The result expressed in Eq. (27-6) is even more generally applicable. Consider some other closed paths that are linked by the current in a long, straight wire and that lie in a plane perpendicular to the axis of the wire. The closed path shown in Fig. 27-8 consists of two circular arcs centered on the axis of the wire and two radial lines that connect the arcs. The line integral of $\mathbf{B}$ around this closed path is the sum of four line integrals — a line integral along each of the two circular arcs and a line integral along each of the two radial lines. Along a radial line, such as NP, the magnetic field $\mathbf{B}$ is perpendicular to the displacement $d\mathbf{r}$, as shown in Fig. 27-8, and the dot product is zero, $\mathbf{B} \cdot d\mathbf{r} = 0$. Thus there is no contribution to $\oint \mathbf{B} \cdot d\mathbf{r}$ from the radial lines NP and QM. Along the

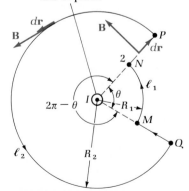

Cross section of wire with current I coming out of plane

Figure 27-8. A closed path consists of two circular arcs PQ and MN and two radial lines QM and NP.

arc MN of radius R_1, the line integral is easily evaluated following the procedure used above for the full circle:

$$\int_M^N \mathbf{B}_1 \cdot d\mathbf{r} = \int_M^N B_1 \, dr = B_1 \int_M^N dr = B_1 \ell_1$$

where ℓ_1 is the arc length subtending the angle $\theta = \ell_1/R_1$. Inserting the value of $B_1 = \mu_0 I/2\pi R_1$ at a distance R_1 from the wire gives for this contribution to the closed path integral,

$$B_1 \ell_1 = \frac{\mu_0 I}{2\pi} \frac{\ell_1}{R_1} = \frac{\mu_0 I}{2\pi} \theta$$

Similarly, a calculation of the contribution from the circular arc PQ of radius R_2 gives

$$B_2 \ell_2 = \frac{\mu_0 I}{2\pi} (2\pi - \theta)$$

Adding the four contributions, we have

$$\oint \mathbf{B} \cdot d\mathbf{r} = \int_M^N \mathbf{B} \cdot d\mathbf{r} + \int_N^P \mathbf{B} \cdot d\mathbf{r} + \int_P^Q \mathbf{B} \cdot d\mathbf{r} + \int_Q^M \mathbf{B} \cdot d\mathbf{r}$$

$$= \frac{\mu_0 I}{2\pi} \theta + 0 + \frac{\mu_0 I}{2\pi} (2\pi - \theta) + 0 = \mu_0 I$$

Therefore, the line integral of $\mathbf{B}$ around this closed path depends only on the current linking the path: $\oint \mathbf{B} \cdot d\mathbf{r} = \mu_0 I$.

Another, more general closed path in a plane perpendicular to the wire and linked by the current I is shown in Fig. 27-9a. This closed path is approximated in Fig. 27-9b by a set of circular arcs and radial lines, and the approximation becomes exact in the limit of an infinite number of infinitesimal circular arcs and radial lines. The procedure used in evaluating the line integral of $\mathbf{B}$ around the closed path in Fig. 27-8 can be used for the path in Fig. 27-9b. The contribution along each radial line is zero, and the sum of the contributions for the circular arcs gives Eq. (27-6) again. This equation is also valid even if the closed path linked by the current I does not lie in a plane. (See Prob. 27-1.)

Now we consider a closed path that is not linked by the current in the long, straight wire. The closed path in Fig. 27-10a has two circular arcs, which subtend the same angle θ at their common center, and two radial lines. Again, the contribution to $\int \mathbf{B} \cdot d\mathbf{r}$ is zero along a radial line. Along the arc of radius R_2, the contribution is $B_2 \ell_2$, where $\ell_2 = R_2 \theta$ and $B_2 = \mu_0 I/2\pi R_2$. But along the arc of radius R_1, $\mathbf{B}_1$ and $d\mathbf{r}$ have opposite directions, so that $\mathbf{B}_1 \cdot d\mathbf{r} = B_1 \, dr \cos 180° = -B_1 \, dr$. The contribution of this part of the path is then $-B_1 \ell_1$, where $\ell_1 = R_1 \theta$ and $B_1 = \mu_0/2\pi R_1$. The line integral of $\mathbf{B}$ around this closed path is the sum of the two contributions $B_2 \ell_2$ and $-B_1 \ell_1$ from the two circular arcs:

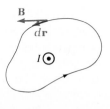

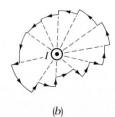

(a)

(b)

Figure 27-9. (a) A closed path. (b) The path is approximated by a set of circular arcs and radial lines.

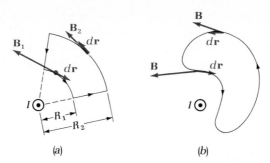

Figure 27-10. Two closed paths that are not linked by the current in a wire.

$$B_2\ell_2 - B_1\ell_1 = \frac{\mu_0 I}{2\pi R_2} R_2\theta - \frac{\mu_0 I}{2\pi R_1} R_1\theta = 0$$

Thus, for the path that is not linked by the current,

$$\oint \mathbf{B} \cdot d\mathbf{r} = 0 \tag{27-7}$$

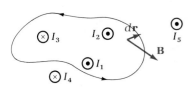

Figure 27-11. Currents I_1, I_2, and I_3 link the closed path, and currents I_4 and I_5 do not link the closed path.

Equation (27-7) is also valid for a more general path such as that shown in Fig. 27-10b. That is, the line integral of **B** around a closed path is zero for a path that is not linked by the current I. (See Exercise 27-20.)

Having calculated the line integral of **B** around a closed path for several cases, we now state the general result. Consider an arbitrary closed path such as that shown in Fig. 27-11. Some of the currents link the closed path and others do not. In addition, these currents may have a general form, not necessarily that of long, straight wires. Let Σi represent the sum of the currents which *link* the closed path. Then

$$\oint \mathbf{B} \cdot d\mathbf{r} = \mu_0 \Sigma i \tag{27-8}$$

which is Ampere's law.

Notice that only the currents that link the closed path are to be included in the sum Σi. For the case illustrated in Fig. 27-11, the currents labeled I_4 and I_5 do not link the closed path and are not included in the sum. The currents labeled I_1, I_2, and I_3 link the path and are added algebraically to give, for this case,

$$\Sigma i = I_1 + I_2 - I_3 \tag{27-9}$$

The sign for each current is determined by a *right-hand rule:*

> Curl the fingers of the right hand to follow the direction of integration around the closed path; the extended thumb gives the sense of a positive current contribution.

Thus in Fig. 27-11, the currents I_1 and I_2 have the sense of the extended right thumb and are entered with a positive sign in Eq. (27-9). The current I_3 has the opposite sense and is entered with a negative sign in the sum. Currents I_4 and I_5, while contributing to the magnetic field at every point in space, do not contribute to the value of the line integral in Ampere's law. That is, the magnetic field **B** at a point depends on all the currents, but the line integral of **B** around a closed path depends only on the currents that link that path.

A given closed path can form the boundary for an infinite number of surfaces. If the closed path in Fig. 27-11 lies in the plane of the figure, then one choice of a surface is the portion of the plane within the path. But you can also imagine a surface bounded by the closed path which bulges out from the plane of the figure. Any choice of a surface bounded by a simple closed path is valid. (See Ques. 27-22 for an example of a closed path that is not simple.) The sum of the currents Σi piercing each surface is the same if we consider only steady current distributions. We shall consider the case of nonsteady currents in Sec. 27-7.

Ampere's law for magnetic fields can be viewed in analogy with Gauss's law for electric fields. Ampere's law is a general statement about the fields that are produced by steady currents. Any such magnetic field must obey Ampere's law. A more advanced mathematical analysis shows that any magnetic field obtained from the Biot-Savart law must also satisfy Ampere's law. The Biot-Savart law and Ampere's law are equivalent in the same sense that Coulomb's law and Gauss's law are equivalent.

Ampere's law is equivalent to the Biot-Savart law.

Gauss's law was used to determine the electric field due to certain types of charge distributions having a high degree of symmetry. Ampere's law can be similarly used to determine the magnetic field due to a current distribution having appropriate symmetry. We shall consider some examples of this procedure in the next section.

Static magnetic fields are different from static electric fields.

The analogy between Gauss's law and Ampere's law is not complete. It is essential to note that Ampere's law involves a *line integral around a closed path*, while Gauss's law involves a very different kind of integral, a surface integral over a closed surface. Static magnetic fields are therefore quite unlike static electric fields. For example, there is no distribution of electric charge that can produce an electrostatic field that is similar to the magnetic field illustrated by the lines in Fig. 27-7.

EXAMPLE 27-4. Determine the value of the line integral of **B** around the closed path in Fig. 27-11, given the current values $I_1 = 1.6$ A, $I_2 = 1.4$ A, $I_3 = 1.7$ A, $I_4 = 4.0$ A, $I_5 = 0.8$ A.

SOLUTION. The value of the line integral is determined from Ampere's law, Eq. (27-8). The currents linking the path

are I_1 and I_2 in a positive sense and I_3 in a negative sense. Therefore

$$\oint \mathbf{B} \cdot d\mathbf{r} = \mu_0 \Sigma i = \mu_0 (1.6 \text{ A} + 1.4 \text{ A} - 1.7 \text{ A})$$

$$= \mu_0 (1.3 \text{ A}) = 1.6 \times 10^{-6} \text{ T} \cdot \text{m}$$

27-4 APPLICATIONS OF AMPERE'S LAW

Ampere's law, $\oint \mathbf{B} \cdot d\mathbf{r} = \mu_0 \Sigma i$, can be used to determine the magnetic field produced by certain current distributions with a high degree of symmetry. As a simple first example of the procedure, we determine the magnitude of the field produced by a long, straight wire carrying a current I. The answer is already known from the Biot-Savart law for a point outside the wire and is given by Eq. (27-4). In addition to reproducing this equation by using Ampere's law, we shall obtain a new result, the magnetic field at a point inside the wire.

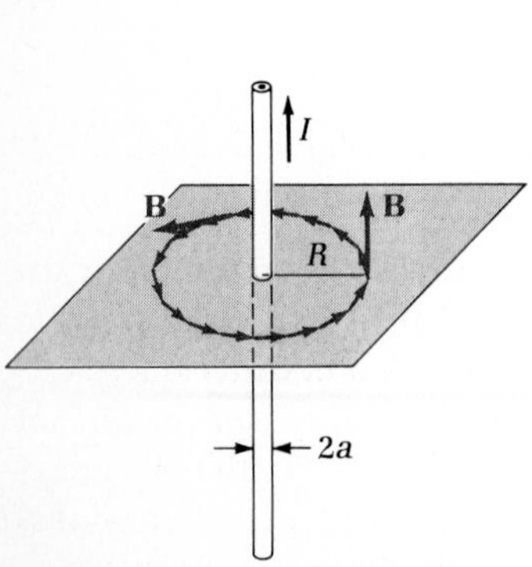

A long, straight wire of radius a carries a current I, as shown in Fig. 27-12. Since Ampere's law applies to any closed path, we choose a path which takes advantage of the symmetry. Thus we select a circular path of radius R lying in a plane perpendicular to the axis of the wire and centered on the axis. We apply Ampere's law to this path. From the symmetry of the problem, we observe that (i) the magnetic field **B** is parallel to the displacement $d\mathbf{r}$ so that $\mathbf{B} \cdot d\mathbf{r} = B \, dr$ and (ii) the magnitude B of the field has the same value at each point on the circular path. Then Eq. (27-8) becomes

Figure 27-12. B and $d\mathbf{r}$ are parallel, and B is constant at each point on the circular path in a plane perpendicular to the axis of the wire.

$$\oint \mathbf{B} \cdot d\mathbf{r} = \oint B \, dr = B \oint dr = B \, 2\pi R = \mu_0 \Sigma i$$

where the integral of dr around the closed circular path equals the circumference $2\pi R$, and, since $R > a$, the single current I links the path, or $\Sigma i = I$. Solving for B, we obtain

$$B = \frac{\mu_0 I}{2\pi R} \qquad (R > a) \qquad (27\text{-}4)$$

which is Eq. (27-4), valid for any point outside the long, straight wire. Notice that in the procedure above, we are able to factor the symbol B, which is constant along the circular path, out of the integral in Ampere's law and then solve for B.

Now we consider a point inside the wire a perpendicular distance R from the axis of the wire, with $R < a$ (see Fig. 27-13). Again we choose a circular path of radius R in a plane perpendicular to the wire and centered on the axis. Making the same symmetry arguments as above, we note that $\mathbf{B} \cdot d\mathbf{r} = B \, dr$ and that B is constant along the path and can be factored out of the integral. Thus

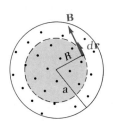

Figure 27-13. Only part of the current links the circular path of radius R, where $R < a$. The current is distributed uniformly over the cross section of the wire, and its sense is out of the plane of the figure.

and

$$\oint \mathbf{B} \cdot d\mathbf{r} = \oint B \, dr = B \oint dr = B \, 2\pi R = \mu_0 \Sigma i$$

$$B = \frac{\mu_0 \Sigma i}{2\pi R}$$

To determine Σi, note that only part of the current I links this circular path. If the current is distributed uniformly over the cross section of the wire, then the current density has magnitude $j = I/\pi a^2$. Since the cross section of the wire within the circle has area πR^2, the current linking the closed circular path is

$$\Sigma i = j\pi R^2 = \frac{I}{\pi a^2} \pi R^2 = I \frac{R^2}{a^2}$$

Substituting this result into the above equation for B gives

$$B = \frac{\mu_0 I R}{2\pi a^2} \qquad (R < a) \qquad (27\text{-}10)$$

According to Eq. (27-10), the magnetic field is zero at a point on the axis of the wire ($R = 0$). The magnitude of the field increases linearly with distance R from the axis, and at the surface of the wire, the value is $B = \mu_0 I / 2\pi a$. This value is obtained from each of Eqs. (27-4) and (27-10) at $R = a$. Outside the wire the magnitude of the magnetic field is given by Eq. (27-4) and decreases inversely with the distance R. These features are summarized graphically in Fig. 27-14.

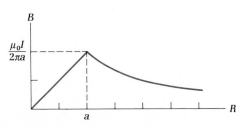

Figure 27-14. The magnitude of the magnetic field due to a current in a long, straight wire of radius a is shown for points inside the wire ($R < a$) and points outside the wire ($R > a$).

EXAMPLE 27-5. A long, straight wire of radius 3.0 mm carries a 25-A current. (a) Determine the magnitude of the magnetic field at the surface of the wire. (b) At what distances from the axis of the wire is the magnitude of the field equal to one-half its value at the surface?

SOLUTION. (a) At the surface of the wire, $R = a$, both Eq. (27-4) and Eq. (27-10) give the same value for B:

$$B = \frac{\mu_0 I}{2\pi a} = \frac{(4\pi \times 10^{-7} \text{ T} \cdot \text{m} \cdot \text{A}^{-1})(25 \text{ A})}{2\pi(3.0 \times 10^{-3} \text{ m})} = 1.7 \text{ mT}$$

(b) Outside the wire the magnitude of the magnetic field falls off inversely with distance according to Eq. (27-4). The field is reduced from its value at the surface by one-half at $R = 2a = 6.0$ mm. Inside the wire, Eq. (27-10) holds, and the field has one-half the surface value at $R = \frac{1}{2}a = 1.5$ mm. These results are apparent in Fig. 27-14.

The magnetic field in a solenoid. A solenoid is formed by winding a very long wire onto a cylinder, usually a circular cylinder. The windings, or turns of wire, form a helical coil whose length, measured along the axis of the solenoid, is typically somewhat larger than the diameter. An important characteristic of a solenoid is the number of turns per unit length n. For a solenoid of length L_0 with N turns, the number of turns per unit length is $n = N/L_0$.

Number of turns per unit length characterizes a solenoid

To understand the magnetic field produced by the current in a solenoid, we first look qualitatively at the magnetic field produced by a single circular current loop. Magnetic field lines are sketched in a plane perpendicular to the plane of the loop in Fig. 27-15a. The magnetic field lines for a loosely wound solenoid are sketched in Fig. 27-15b. For a more tightly wound solenoid, the pitch of the helical windings is less and each turn is approximately a current loop. Then each turn will produce a contribution to the magnetic field similar to that of a current loop. Inside the solenoid the contributions to the field from each turn tend to reinforce each other. The resultant field is approximately uniform and parallel to the axis of the solenoid. Outside the solenoid, the contributions to the field from each turn tend to cancel out, and the resultant field is relatively small.

These tendencies—toward a uniform field inside the solenoid and a zero field outside the solenoid at points far from either end—become more pro-

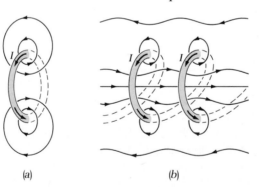

(a)   (b)

Figure 27-15. Some field lines are shown in a plane for (a) a circular current loop and (b) a loosely wound solenoid.

Figure 27-16. The current distribution for an ideal solenoid is equivalent to a cylindrical current sheath.

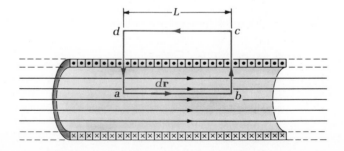

nounced for a very long and tightly wound solenoid. In the ideal case of Fig. 27-16, the current distribution in the windings is equivalent to a cylindrical current sheath, and the solenoid has an effectively infinite length. The magnetic field inside the ideal solenoid is parallel to the axis, and the field outside the solenoid is zero.

We can determine the magnetic field inside the ideal solenoid by applying Ampere's law to the closed path shown in Fig. 27-16. The integral around the closed path is the sum of integrals along each of the four straight-line segments:

$$\oint \mathbf{B} \cdot d\mathbf{r} = \int_a^b \mathbf{B} \cdot d\mathbf{r} + \int_b^c \mathbf{B} \cdot d\mathbf{r} + \int_c^d \mathbf{B} \cdot d\mathbf{r} + \int_d^a \mathbf{B} \cdot d\mathbf{r}$$

The integral along the segment bc is zero because $\mathbf{B}$ and $d\mathbf{r}$ are perpendicular at each point on that segment, making $\mathbf{B} \cdot d\mathbf{r} = 0$. For the same reason, the integral along segment da is also zero. Along segment cd, which is outside the ideal solenoid, $\mathbf{B} = 0$ so that the integral is zero for that segment. The only nonzero contribution to the closed path integral is from segment ab. On this segment, $\mathbf{B}$ and $d\mathbf{r}$ are parallel so that $\mathbf{B} \cdot d\mathbf{r} = B\,dr$, and B has the same value at each point. Thus

$$\oint \mathbf{B} \cdot d\mathbf{r} = \int_a^b B\,dr = B\int_a^b dr = BL$$

where L is the length of segment ab. For a solenoid with n turns per unit length, the number of turns within the closed path is nL. Since each of these turns carries current I, the net current linking this closed path is

$$\Sigma i = nLI$$

Using the above results in Ampere's law, we have

$$\oint \mathbf{B} \cdot d\mathbf{r} = BL = \mu_0 nLI$$

Magnetic field inside a solenoid   or

$$B = \mu_0 nI \qquad (27\text{-}11)$$

While Eq. (27-11) was obtained for the ideal solenoid, it gives a good approximation to the field inside a tightly wound solenoid at points near the axis and far from the ends. The magnetic field is uniform in this region and is determined by the number of turns per unit length n and the current I in the solenoid. A solenoid is often used in the laboratory to provide a region of nearly uniform magnetic field. A *toroid*, which can be viewed as a long solenoid bent to form a doughnut-shaped coil, is also used in the laboratory. (See Prob. 27-2.)

EXAMPLE 27-6. A solenoid has 250 turns on a cylinder of diameter 15.0 mm and length 125 mm. If the current in the solenoid is 0.320 A, determine the magnitude of the magnetic field inside the solenoid.

SOLUTION. Since the length of the solenoid is fairly large compared with its diameter, the field inside the solenoid at points near the axis and far from the ends is approximately given by Eq. (27-11). The number of turns per unit length is

(the unit "turn" is dimensionless)

$$n = \frac{250 \text{ turns}}{0.125 \text{ m}} = 2.00 \times 10^3 \text{ turns} \cdot \text{m}^{-1}$$

and the magnitude of the field is

$$B = \mu_0 nI = (4\pi \times 10^{-7} \text{ T} \cdot \text{m} \cdot \text{A}^{-1})(2.00 \times 10^3 \text{ m}^{-1})(0.320 \text{ A})$$

$$= 8.04 \times 10^{-4} \text{ T}$$

27-5 FORCE BETWEEN CURRENTS

In the last chapter, we determined the force exerted on a straight section of a current-carrying wire by a magnetic field [Eq. (26-3)]. In this chapter, we determined the magnetic field due to the current in a long, straight wire [Eq. (27-4)]. By combining these two results, we can determine the magnetic force that one current-carrying wire exerts on another.

Consider the arrangement of two long, parallel wires carrying currents I_1 and I_2 and separated by a distance R, as shown in Fig. 27-17. We assume that the separation distance R is small compared with the length of the wires so that the length is effectively infinite. The magnetic force on a segment of one of the wires, say the wire with current I_1 and segment length ℓ, can be viewed as due to the magnetic field produced by the current I_2 in the other wire. Let $\mathbf{B}_2$ represent the magnetic field produced by the current I_2 at the position of the wire with current I_1. The direction of this field is as indicated in Fig. 27-17, and the magnitude is given by Eq. (27-4):

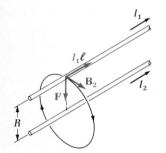

Figure 27-17. The magnetic field of a current I_2 exerts a force on a length of wire with current I_1.

$$B_2 = \frac{\mu_0 I_2}{2\pi R}$$

The force $\mathbf{F}$ exerted by this field on the current element $I_1\ell$ is obtained from Eq. (26-3), $\mathbf{F} = I_1\ell \times \mathbf{B}_2$. The direction of the force is shown in the figure, and the magnitude is

$$F = I_1\ell B_2$$

Substituting for the value of B_2 in terms of the current I_2, we obtain the magnitude of the force exerted by the current I_2 in a long, straight wire on a length ℓ of a parallel wire with current I_1:

Force between parallel currents

$$F = \frac{\mu_0 I_1 I_2}{2\pi R} \ell \tag{27-12}$$

In arriving at Eq. (27-12), we considered the force on a segment of the wire with current I_1 exerted by the magnetic field of the current I_2. Suppose that the roles of the two currents are interchanged. That is, consider the force on a section of the wire with current I_2 exerted by the magnetic field of the current I_1. A similar analysis shows that the magnitude of the force on a length ℓ of wire 2 with current I_2 is also given by Eq. (27-12) and that the direction of the force on wire 2 is opposite the direction of the force on wire 1. Thus Eq. (27-12) gives the magnitude of the force on a length ℓ of either current-carrying wire due to the current in the other wire. This result for the magnitude of the force is also valid if the two currents have opposite senses instead of the same sense. (What is the direction of the force on each wire if the currents have opposite senses?)

Suppose that both current values were 1 A in Eq. (27-12) and that the wires were 1 m apart. Then the magnitude of the force on a 1-m length of each wire would be

$$F = \frac{\mu_0(1\text{ A})(1\text{ A})}{2\pi(1\text{ m})} 1\text{ m}$$

$$= 2 \times 10^{-7}\text{ N}$$

This type of calculation is used to define the ampere (A), the unit of electric current, in terms of the mechanical quantities force and length. [We have been

Definition of the ampere

waiting for Eq. (27-12) to give this definition.] *The ampere is that current which, existing in each of two long (infinite), straight, parallel wires separated by exactly 1 m, corresponds to a force per unit length between the wires of exactly 2 × 10⁻⁷ N/m.*

The coulomb is defined in terms of the ampere.

We note a consequence of this definition of the unit of current. *The unit of charge, the coulomb (C), is defined as the amount of charge that flows past a point in one second in a circuit with a steady current of one ampere: 1 C = 1 (A)(s).* This procedure of defining the unit of current and then defining the unit of charge comes about because the magnetic force between steady currents can be more conveniently measured in practice than can the electric force between known charges.

EXAMPLE 27-7. In a current balance, the force per unit length exerted by one wire on another is measured by balancing, on a section of one of the wires, this magnetic force with a mechanical force. Suppose that the two long, straight wires are separated by 15.0 mm and that the balancing force per unit length on a segment of the wire is 7.11×10^{-6} N/m when the same current I exists in both wires. Determine the value of the current.

SOLUTION. Since $I_1 = I_2 = I$, we have $I_1 I_2 = I^2$ in Eq. (27-12). Solving for I^2,

$$I^2 = \frac{2\pi R}{\mu_0} \frac{F}{l} = \frac{2\pi(0.0150 \text{ m})}{4\pi \times 10^{-7} \text{ T} \cdot \text{m} \cdot \text{A}^{-1}} \, 7.11 \times 10^{-6} \text{ N/m}$$

$$= 0.533 \text{ A}^2$$

Taking the square root gives the current: $I = 0.730$ A.

Although the ampere is defined in terms of a configuration of two long, straight, parallel wires, a modern current balance, such as that used at the National Bureau of Standards, achieves greater precision by measuring the magnetic force between current-carrying coils.

27-6 MAGNETIC FLUX AND GAUSS'S LAW FOR MAGNETIC FIELDS

In analogy with the electric flux Φ_E, introduced in Chap. 21, we define a *magnetic flux* Φ_B of the magnetic field for a surface. Imagine dividing a mathematical surface into infinitesimal area elements. The direction of an area element $d\mathbf{S}$ at a point on the surface is perpendicular to the surface at that point, and a typical element for a surface is shown in Fig. 27-18a, along with the magnetic field $\mathbf{B}$ at a point. The magnetic flux $d\Phi_B$ for the area element $d\mathbf{S}$ is

The area element $d\mathbf{S}$ is perpendicular to the surface.

$$d\Phi_B = \mathbf{B} \cdot d\mathbf{S}$$

The magnetic flux for a general surface is obtained by integrating (summing) the contributions $d\Phi_B$ as the area element $d\mathbf{S}$ ranges over the surface. Thus

Definition of magnetic flux for a surface

$$\Phi_B = \int \mathbf{B} \cdot d\mathbf{S} \tag{27-13}$$

The SI unit of magnetic flux is the *weber* (Wb), with 1 Wb = 1 T · m².

The magnetic flux for a surface can be interpreted in terms of the magnetic lines that represent the spatial distribution of the magnetic field. In analogy

Figure 27-18. (a) The magnetic flux for an infinitesimal area $d\mathbf{S}$ is given by $d\Phi_B = \mathbf{B} \cdot d\mathbf{S}$. (b) The magnetic flux for a surface is proportional to the number of lines intersecting the surface.

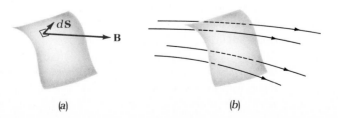

(a)   (b)

with electric lines and as suggested in Fig. 27-18*b*, the number of magnetic lines intersecting a surface is proportional to the magnetic flux for the surface.

EXAMPLE 27-8. Determine the magnetic flux for a circular cross section of the ideal solenoid shown in Fig. 27-16. Let the inside radius of the solenoid be 7.5 mm, the number of turns per unit length be 2.00×10^3 m^{-1}, and the current in the solenoid be 320 mA.

SOLUTION. The magnetic field in the solenoid is parallel to the axis, and its magnitude (see Example 27-6) is given by Eq. (27-11):

$$B = \mu_0 nI = 8.0 \times 10^{-4} \text{ T}$$

Each area element $d\mathbf{S}$ on a circular cross section of radius R

of the solenoid is parallel to the axis and to $\mathbf{B}$ so that $\mathbf{B} \cdot d\mathbf{S} = B \, dS$, and B is uniform inside the solenoid. Applying these results in Eq. (27-13), we have

$$\Phi_B = \int \mathbf{B} \cdot d\mathbf{S} = \int B \, dS = B \int dS = B(\pi R^2)$$

$$= (8.0 \times 10^{-4} \text{ T}) \, \pi \, (7.5 \times 10^{-3} \text{ m})^2 = 1.4 \times 10^{-7} \text{ Wb}$$

Suppose a circle with this area is oriented with a diameter *along* the axis of the solenoid. What is the flux for the plane surface of this circle?

Gauss's law for the electric field involves the electric flux for a *closed* surface. The direction of the area element for a closed surface is conventionally chosen to be directed outward from the enclosed volume. Gauss's law states that the electric flux for a closed surface depends only on the charge inside that surface. Thus

$$\Phi_E = \oint \mathbf{E} \cdot d\mathbf{S} = \frac{\Sigma q}{\epsilon_0} \tag{21-3}$$

where Σq is the algebraic sum of the charge within the volume enclosed by the surface. The form of Gauss's law reminds us that, in electrostatics, electric charge is the source of the electric field. Indeed, the simplest source of an electric field is a single point charge.

What is the corresponding Gauss's law for magnetic fields? What interpretation will it give for the source of a magnetic field? Consider an arbitrary *closed* surface and the magnetic flux for that surface:

$$\Phi_B = \oint \mathbf{B} \cdot d\mathbf{S}$$

Imagine this closed surface drawn anywhere in Fig. 27-3, 27-15, or 27-16. The magnetic flux for any closed surface is zero for any of these magnetic fields. Each magnetic line that pierces into a closed surface at one point also pierces out of the closed surface at some other point. The net number of lines crossing the closed surface is zero. This observation is in accord with the statement of Gauss's law for magnetic fields: *For any closed surface, the magnetic flux is zero.* In equation form this is

Gauss's law for magnetic fields

$$\oint \mathbf{B} \cdot d\mathbf{S} = 0 \tag{27-14}$$

for any closed surface whatsoever. Note that this result does not apply to an open surface, one that does not enclose a volume. The magnetic flux for an open surface may have any value.

According to Gauss's law for electric fields, the electric flux for a closed surface depends on the electric charge inside, and $\oint \mathbf{E} \cdot d\mathbf{S} = \Sigma q/\epsilon_0$ is not zero if the surface encloses a net charge. In contrast, from Gauss's law for magnetic fields, the magnetic flux is zero for any closed surface, $\oint \mathbf{B} \cdot d\mathbf{S} = 0$. That is,

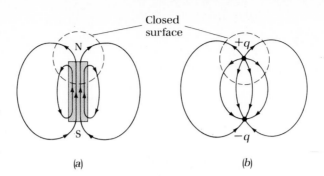

Figure 27-19. (a) The lines representing **B** for a bar magnet have no beginning and no end. The magnetic flux for the closed surface is $\oint \mathbf{B} \cdot d\mathbf{S} = 0$. (b) The lines representing **E** for an electric dipole begin on the positive charge and end on the negative charge. The electric flux for the closed surface is $\oint \mathbf{E} \cdot d\mathbf{S} = q/\epsilon_0$.

(a)

(b)

A magnetic monopole has not been observed.

there seems to be no magnetic counterpart to the electric charge. If the so-called magnetic charge did exist, it would correspond to a *magnetic monopole*, an isolated magnetic pole (an isolated north pole, for example). There has not yet been a confirmed observation of a magnetic monopole. In the absence of a magnetic monopole, the simplest source of a magnetic field is a magnetic dipole.

The nonexistence of the magnetic charge can also be illustrated by the magnetic field lines. A line representing the magnetic field **B** always closes on itself, having no beginning and no end. A bar magnet, which possesses a magnetic dipole moment, has a north pole at one end and a south pole at the other end. The lines representing the field both inside and outside the magnet are sketched in Fig. 27-19a. Each line closes on itself so that the magnetic flux is zero for any closed surface. Notice the essential difference between the magnetic dipole field in Fig. 27-19a and the electric dipole field in Fig. 27-19b. The electric flux for the closed surface in Fig. 27-19b is not zero, but the magnetic flux for the corresponding surface in Fig. 27-19a is zero. This comparison illustrates the fundamental difference between static electric and magnetic fields, a difference in Gauss's law for electric fields and for magnetic fields. For any closed surface,

$$\oint \mathbf{E} \cdot d\mathbf{S} = \frac{\Sigma q}{\epsilon_0}$$

$$\oint \mathbf{B} \cdot d\mathbf{S} = 0$$

27-7 THE DISPLACEMENT CURRENT AND AMPERE'S LAW

Our use of Ampere's law, Eq. (27-8), has been limited so far to magnetic fields produced by currents of the sort that exist in continuous conducting wires. More general distributions of current exist, however, and Ampere's law must be modified. This generalization, discovered by Maxwell, represented a major advance in developing a deeper understanding of electromagnetism, including an understanding of the nature of light. It is a tribute to Maxwell's genius that, at that time, no experiment pointed to the necessity of modifying of Ampere's law. To see why a modification is necessary, we return to the idea of a current linking a closed path.

Consider the closed path that encircles the wire which carries a steady current I in Fig. 27-20. Recall that the current linking a closed path is the current that pierces a surface that has the closed path as its boundary. Two such surfaces S_1 and S_2 are shown in the figure. Each surface is bounded by the

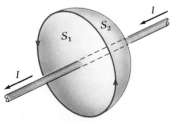

Figure 27-20. The closed path forms the boundary of two surfaces S_1 and S_2. Each surface is pierced by the current I.

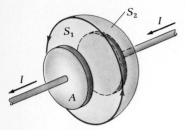

Figure 27-21. Surface S_1 lies in the space between the plates where there is no current. The current I pierces only surface S_2.

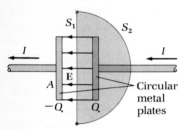

Figure 27-22. The electric flux for the plane surface S_1 is $\Phi_E = EA$, where A is the area of a plate of the capacitor. Edge effects have been neglected.

Displacement current

given closed path. If the current piercing S_1 were different from the current piercing S_2, then there would be an accumulation of charge in the wire between the two surfaces. Since there is no accumulation of charge in this situation, each surface is pierced by the same current I. Either surface may be used in determining the current linking the closed path. That is, Ampere's law is valid for any surface bounded by the closed path.

A fundamentally different situation is shown in Fig. 27-21. There a parallel-plate capacitor is being charged, and I is the instantaneous value of the current in the connecting wires. The surface S_2 is pierced by the current I as before. The surface S_1, however, is not pierced by this current because this surface is in the space between the capacitor plates. There is an accumulation of charge on the plate between S_1 and S_2 as the capacitor is being charged. The rate dQ/dt at which charge accumulates on the plate is just equal (by conservation of charge) to the current piercing the surface S_2. Thus

$$I = \frac{dQ}{dt}$$

where Q is the instantaneous value of the charge on the capacitor. Since the current linking the closed path seems to depend on which surface we select, there is an inconsistency in Ampere's law for this case.

Maxwell's modification of Ampere's law, applied to the situation in Fig. 27-21, consists of considering a mathematically equivalent current to pierce surface S_1. Then the current linking the closed path will be the same for any surface bounded by that path. Figure 27-22 shows a cross section of the capacitor and the electric field in the region between plates. For simplicity we neglect fringing effects near the edges of the plates and assume vacuum between the plates. The magnitude of the electric field is, from Eq. (21-4),

$$E = \frac{|\sigma|}{\epsilon_0} = \frac{Q}{\epsilon_0 A}$$

where $|\sigma| = Q/A$ is the magnitude of the surface charge density on the capacitor plate whose area is A. The magnitude Q of the charge on the plate can be expressed in terms of the electric flux, $\Phi_E = \int \mathbf{E} \cdot d\mathbf{S}$, for the surface S_1. The flux is $\Phi_E = EA$ since the field exists only in the region between plates. Solving the above equation for Q gives

$$Q = \epsilon_0 EA = \epsilon_0 \Phi_E$$

Taking the time derivative of Q, we find that the current I is related to the time derivative of the electric flux for surface S_1:

$$I = \frac{dQ}{dt} = \epsilon_0 \frac{d\Phi_E}{dt}$$

The right-hand side of the above equation contains the derivative of the electric flux piercing surface S_1, while I is the current piercing surface S_2. That is, $\epsilon_0 d\Phi_E/dt$ is mathematically equivalent for surface S_1 to the current I which pierces surface S_2. We define this effective current, called the *displacement current I_d*, to be

$$I_d = \epsilon_0 \frac{d\Phi_E}{dt} \tag{27-15}$$

We emphasize that the current I pierces surface S_2 in Fig. 27-22, that the displacement current I_d pierces surface S_1, and that $I_d = I$.

The general form of Ampere's law, as modified by Maxwell, can now be stated. To the term for true currents Σi linking a closed path, we add the displacement current I_d linking the path; Ampere's law is

Ampere's law including the displacement current

$$\oint \mathbf{B} \cdot d\mathbf{r} = \mu_0(\Sigma i + I_d)$$

or

$$\oint \mathbf{B} \cdot d\mathbf{r} = \mu_0\left(\Sigma i + \epsilon_0\frac{d\Phi_E}{dt}\right) \qquad (27\text{-}16)$$

By including the displacement current—treating the displacement current as a true current—the total current linking the closed path is the same for any surface bounded by the closed path.

The displacement current and the modified form of Ampere's law will be an essential part of our study of electromagnetic waves in Chap. 34. Except for situations similar to that described in the following example, the effect of the displacement current is negligible in circuits with slowly varying currents and fields.

EXAMPLE 27-9. A parallel-plate capacitor with circular plates of radius a is being charged. Determine the magnetic field at a point in the space between plates a distance R from the axis of the capacitor with $R \leqslant a$. (See Fig. 27-23.) Express the result in terms of the instantaneous value of the current I in the charging circuit.

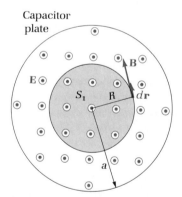

Capacitor plate

Figure 27-23. Example 27-9: One plate of a capacitor is shown, and the electric field is out of the plane of the figure. The electric flux for the surface S_1 is $\Phi_E = E\pi R^2$.

SOLUTION. Select a closed circular path of radius R centered on the axis of the capacitor, with the plane of the circle parallel to the plates. The electric flux for the plane surface S_1 of area πR^2 is

$$\Phi_E = E\pi R^2$$

The magnitude of the electric field is given by

$$E = \frac{|\sigma|}{\epsilon_0} = \frac{Q}{\epsilon_0\pi a^2}$$

where πa^2 is the area of a plate of the capacitor and Q is the

instantaneous charge on the capacitor. The electric flux is then

$$\Phi_E = \frac{Q}{\epsilon_0\pi a^2}\,\pi R^2 = \frac{QR^2}{\epsilon_0 a^2}$$

The displacement current linking the circular path of radius R is given by

$$I_d = \epsilon_0\frac{d\Phi_E}{dt} = \frac{d}{dt}\left(Q\frac{R^2}{a^2}\right) = \frac{R^2}{a^2}\frac{dQ}{dt} = I\frac{R^2}{a^2}$$

because $I = dQ/dt$.

Now we apply Ampere's law to the closed path. From symmetry considerations, note that $\mathbf{B}$ and $d\mathbf{r}$ are parallel at each point on the circular path so that $\mathbf{B} \cdot d\mathbf{r} = B\,dr$. Further, the magnitude of the magnetic field is the same at each point on the path and

$$\oint \mathbf{B} \cdot d\mathbf{r} = \oint B\,dr = B\oint dr = B2\pi R$$

Since the plane surface lies in the space between capacitor plates, only the displacement current pierces this surface. The right-hand side of Ampere's law becomes

$$\mu_0(\Sigma i + I_d) = \mu_0(0 + I_d) = \frac{\mu_0IR^2}{a^2}$$

Thus, $B2\pi R = \mu_0IR^2/a^2$, or

$$B = \frac{\mu_0IR}{2\pi a^2}$$

The magnitude of the magnetic field is zero on the axis of the capacitor ($R = 0$) and increases linearly with distance from the axis (for $R \leqslant a$). What is the magnetic field in this plane for $R > a$?

COMMENTARY: JAMES CLERK MAXWELL

James Clerk Maxwell *(New York Public Library Picture Collection)*

The Scottish physicist, James Clerk Maxwell, was born on June 13, 1831. His father, who was originally named John Clerk, added the Maxwell surname after inheriting some property which had come into the family through marriage to a Maxwell. Young James showed scholastic promise while still in his early teens. By age 14, he had completed work on generalizations of the ellipse. This work was presented to the Royal Society of Edinburgh and was published afterward under the title "Oval Curves."

In 1847, Maxwell attended the University of Edinburgh where, under the tutelage of a physics professor, he received permission to use some of the apparatus after hours. He spent many evenings experimenting and learning. Even his vacations were used for experimenting. He set up a makeshift laboratory "above the wash-house," and, for a lab table, he used "an old door set on two barrels, and two chairs, of which one is safe. . . ." By 1849 he had finished two more papers, one titled "Rolling Curves" and the other, "The Equilibrium of Elastic Solids."

Maxwell was largely responsible for developing the mathematical description of electric and magnetic fields. The use of field lines, as conceived by Faraday, to understand electric and magnetic phenomena was mainly qualitative until 1855 when Maxwell provided a useful mathematical model. In his paper "On Faraday's Lines of Force," Maxwell developed the mathematical analogy between the lines representing a field and the flow of an incompressible fluid. The field strength, say of an electric field $\mathbf{E}$, corresponded in the analogy to the velocity $\mathbf{v}$ of a fluid. This analogy, while imperfect, is still reflected in the language that we use to describe fields. Thus we speak of the flux Φ_E of an electric field as if it were related to the flow of a fluid.

Maxwell's use of a fluid analogy continued in his famous four-part paper, "On Physical Lines of Force," published in 1861. Here the fluid model contained vortices; the magnetic field lines were represented by the axes of the vortices, and the magnetic force was related to the pressure of the vortices. The model was rather complex since neighboring vortices had to revolve with the same sense. Thus Maxwell had to introduce rolling contact particles between these vortices. He obtained the mathematical relationships between currents and magnetic fields by considering the motion of the contact particles in the model fluid. This model also led Maxwell to regard light as an electromagnetic phenomenon: "Light consists in the transverse undulations of the same medium which is the cause of electric and magnetic phenomena."

The mathematical relations between the electric and magnetic fields that Maxwell developed (known as Maxwell's equations and discussed in Chap. 34) provide a complete theoretical basis for all electromagnetic phenomena. These equations were considered by Boltzmann to be so beautiful in their simplicity and elegance that he asked, quoting Goethe, "Was it a god who wrote these lines. . . ?"

In 1871 Maxwell was named the first professor of experimental physics at Cambridge University and was appointed as director of the Cavendish Laboratory, which was then under construction. There he provided, until his death in 1879, the early guidance that allowed the Cavendish Laboratory to become one of the premier centers of basic research in physics.

Maxwell's work in electricity and magnetism merged those two seemingly separate disciplines into a unified theory that encompassed all of electromagne-

tism. In addition to his synthesis of electricity and magnetism, Maxwell also made essential contributions to thermodynamics and statistical mechanics (see the Commentary, Chap. 19). For all of these contributions, he is generally put in the company of Galileo, Newton, and Einstein — as one on whose shoulders we stand to see nature's more distant horizons.

For further reading, see James Clerk Maxwell — A Biography *by Ivan Tolstoy (University of Chicago Press, Chicago, 1981).*

SUMMARY WITH APPLICATIONS

Section 27-2. The Biot-Savart law

At a point in space the contribution $d\mathbf{B}$ to the magnetic field due to an infinitesimal current element $I\,d\boldsymbol{\ell}$ is given by the Biot-Savart law:

$$d\mathbf{B} = \frac{\mu_0}{4\pi}\frac{I\,d\boldsymbol{\ell}\times\hat{\mathbf{r}}}{r^2} \qquad (27\text{-}1)$$

The resultant magnetic field at a point is obtained from the integrated form of the Biot-Savart law:

$$\mathbf{B} = \int\frac{\mu_0}{4\pi}\frac{I\,d\boldsymbol{\ell}\times\hat{\mathbf{r}}}{r^2} \qquad (27\text{-}3)$$

A current in a long, straight wire produces a magnetic field. At a distance R from the axis of the wire, the magnetic field has magnitude

$$B = \frac{\mu_0 I}{2\pi R} \qquad (27\text{-}4)$$

The direction of the magnetic field is given by a right-hand rule. The Biot-Savart law can be used to determine the magnetic field due to other simple current distributions, such as a circular current loop.

Determine the contribution to the magnetic field due to an infinitesimal current element; determine the resultant magnetic field due to simple current distributions; determine the magnetic field due to a current in a long, straight wire.

Section 27-3. Ampere's law

According to Ampere's law, the line integral of the magnetic field for any closed path depends only on the sum of the steady currents Σi piercing a surface bounded by the closed path:

$$\oint\mathbf{B}\cdot d\mathbf{r} = \mu_0\Sigma i \qquad (27\text{-}8)$$

State Ampere's law: apply a right-hand rule to determine the sum of currents piercing a surface bounded by a closed path.

Section 27-4. Applications of Ampere's law

Ampere's law can be used to determine the magnetic field due to certain highly symmetric current distributions. The field inside a long, tightly wound solenoid with current I

and n turns per unit length is given approximately by

$$B = \mu_0 n I \qquad (27\text{-}11)$$

Apply Ampere's law to determine expressions for the magnetic field due to highly symmetric current distributions; determine the magnetic field inside a solenoid.

Section 27-5. Force between currents

The magnitude of the force on a length ℓ between two long, straight, parallel wires a distance R apart and carrying currents I_1 and I_2 is given by

$$F = \frac{\mu_0 I_1 I_2}{2\pi R}\ell \qquad (27\text{-}12)$$

The ampere, the unit of electric current, is defined in terms of the force per unit length between the wires.

Determine the magnetic force between parallel wires with currents; explain how the ampere is defined.

Section 27-6. Magnetic flux and Gauss's law for magnetic fields

Gauss's law for magnetic fields is

$$\oint\mathbf{B}\cdot d\mathbf{S} = 0 \qquad (27\text{-}14)$$

The magnetic flux for any closed surface is zero, corresponding to the absence of magnetic monopoles. A line representing $\mathbf{B}$ closes on itself.

State Gauss's law for magnetic fields; give its interpretation in terms of sources of magnetic fields and in terms of representing $\mathbf{B}$ by lines.

Section 27-7. The displacement current and Ampere's law

The modified form of Ampere's law is given by

$$\oint\mathbf{B}\cdot d\mathbf{r} = \mu_0\left(\Sigma i + \epsilon_0\frac{d\Phi_E}{dt}\right) \qquad (27\text{-}16)$$

where $I_d = \epsilon_0 d\Phi_E/dt$ is the displacement current.

Determine the displacement current in the space between plates of a capacitor; state the modified form of Ampere's law.

QUESTIONS

27-1 Discuss similarities and differences between the electric field $d\mathbf{E}$ due to an element of charge dq and the magnetic field $d\mathbf{B}$ due to a current element $I\,d\boldsymbol{\ell}$.

27-2 Discuss the meaning of the following statement: "The Biot-Savart law, Eq. (27-1), shows that the magnetic field is an inverse-square field."

27-3 Discuss similarities and differences for the electric field due to a long line of charge [see Eq. (20-8)] and the magnetic field due to the current in a long, straight wire [see Eq. (27-4)].

27-4 Reconcile the statement in Ques. 27-2 with the expression for the magnitude of the magnetic field due to the current in a long, straight wire, Eq. (27-4).

27-5 To have a steady current in a wire, the wire must be part of a closed circuit. How can we speak of the magnetic field due to the current in a long, straight wire without considering the rest of the circuit?

27-6 Draw an analogy between a steady current linking a closed path and two links of a chain.

27-7 Suppose that the sense of each of the currents is reversed in Fig. 27-11. Would the magnetic field **B** change at a given point? How would the value of the line integral change in Example 27-4?

27-8 What would the answers in Ques. 27-7 be if the senses of I_4 and I_5 only were reversed?

27-9 Often the two lead wires to an electrical device are twisted together (forming a double helix). Use Ampere's law to describe qualitatively the features of the magnetic field due to a twisted pair of wires carrying equal currents with opposite senses.

27-10 Use the Biot-Savart law qualitatively and the right-hand rule to convince yourself that the lines sketched in Fig. 27-15a and b are representative of the magnetic field distribution.

27-11 Using only words and planar sketches, could you explain the distinction between right- and left-handedness to an intelligent extraterrestrial being? Could you explain how to find the cross product of two vectors? How? (It's not as easy as you may think. Can you explain this to a college student?)

27-12 Figure 27-14 shows the dependence on distance R of the magnetic field inside and outside a long, straight wire carrying a current. Does the magnetic field inside the wire exert a net force on that wire? Explain.

27-13 Equation (27-4) was obtained from the Biot-Savart law by assuming that the long, straight wire had negligible thickness. The same equation was also obtained by using Ampere's law. What assumptions were made about the current distribution in the latter calculation?

27-14 Consider the magnetic field at points in between two current-carrying, long, straight wires. Is the magnitude of the field greater for currents with the same sense or with opposite senses in the wires? Explain. Where is the magnitude of the field largest in the two cases? Where is it smallest?

27-15 A circular loop of fine wire carries a current. At which point in the plane of the loop do you expect the magnetic field to be stronger, at the center of the loop or at a point close to the wire? Does your answer depend on the thickness of the wire? Explain.

27-16 What is the direction of the magnetic force that a long, straight wire exerts on a parallel wire if the currents in the wires have the same sense? What if they have opposite senses?

27-17 How can a solenoid whose length is 100 mm have 2000 turns per meter?

27-18 A solenoid is mistakenly wound in the following way: One layer of windings forms a right-handed helix, which is then covered with a returning second layer. If the solenoid carries current I, the magnetic field at points inside and near the axis of the solenoid is virtually zero. Explain this result.

27-19 Compare the two sketches in Fig. 27-19. How is a north magnetic pole similar to a positive electric charge? How is it different?

27-20 How can the magnetic flux for an open surface be nonzero if the magnetic flux for any closed surface is zero?

27-21 For the situation shown in Fig. 27-22, explain why the displacement current I_d piercing the surface S_1 must equal the current I in the lead wires.

27-22 A simple closed path forms the boundary of a smooth surface which is *orientable*. That is, if you imagine traversing the path so that the surface always is on your left, then that procedure defines a particular side of the surface. There are nonsimple paths for which the above procedure fails. Try applying it to (a) an ellipse, (b) a polygon, (c) a figure eight, (d) the Möbius strip in Fig. 21-27.

27-23 Complete the following table:

Symbol	Represents	Type	SI unit
$\hat{\mathbf{r}}$			—
μ_0		Scalar	
$\oint \mathbf{B} \cdot d\mathbf{r}$			
Σi			
Φ_B			
I_d			A
$\oint \mathbf{B} \cdot d\mathbf{S}$	Magnetic flux for a closed surface		

EXERCISES

Section 27-2. The Biot-Savart law

27-1 Using Eq. (27-2), show that the permeability constant μ_0 has SI units of $T \cdot m \cdot A^{-1}$.

27-2 The magnitude of the magnetic field of the earth averages around 2×10^{-5} T. What current must exist in a long, straight wire in order that its magnetic field at a point 10 mm from the axis of the wire have a magnitude comparable to the earth's magnetic field?

27-3 A long, straight wire carries a 15-A current. (a) Determine the magnitude of the magnetic field at a point 35 mm from the wire. (b) On a diagram show the direction of **B** at that point and the sense of the current in the wire.

27-4 Two long, straight, parallel wires carry currents out of the plane of Fig. 27-24. Determine the magnitude and direction of the magnetic field at (a) point P and (b) point Q. Express the magnitude in terms of μ_0, I, and a. (c) Evaluate B at points P and Q for $I = 12$ A and $a = 250$ mm.

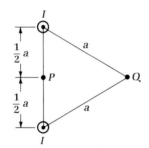

Figure 27-24. Exercise 27-4.

27-5 Rework the previous exercise with the sense of the current in the lower wire reversed.

27-6 Use the Biot-Savart law to determine the magnetic field at the center of a circular current loop. Indicate on a diagram the sense of the current I in the loop and the direction of the magnetic field at the center.

27-7 Two long, straight, parallel wires separated by a distance D carry currents I_1 and $I_2 = 2I_1$ with the same sense. (a) At what distance from the wire with current I_1 is the magnetic field zero between the two wires? (b) Locate other points, if any, at which $B = 0$.

27-8 Suppose the two currents in the previous exercise have opposite senses. Locate those points, if any, at which $B = 0$.

27-9 Consider the contribution to the magnetic field due to a current in a straight length of wire at a point P lying on the axis of the wire. See Fig. 27-25. (a) Show that this contribution is zero. (b) Is your argument valid

Figure 27-25. Exercise 27-9.

even if the point P is inside the wire rather than outside? Explain.

27-10 A 5.0-A current exists in two long, straight, parallel wires joined by a semicircular wire of radius 75 mm, as shown in Fig. 27-26. Determine the magnetic field at the center of the semicircle.

Figure 27-26. Exercise 27-10.

27-11 A current loop consists of two concentric circular arcs and two perpendicular radial lines, as shown in Fig. 27-27. (a) Determine the magnetic field at the center. (b) Evaluate the magnitude of the magnetic field for $I = 20$ A, $a = 30$ mm, $b = 50$ mm.

Figure 27-27. Exercise 27-11.

27-12 A straight section of conductor of length L carries a current I. (a) Show that at point P in Fig. 27-28 the contribution to the magnetic field due to this current has magnitude

$$B = \frac{\mu_0 I}{4\pi R} \frac{L}{\sqrt{R^2 + L^2/4}}$$

[*Hint:* See the discussion leading to Eq. (27-4).] (b) Show that this expression gives $B \approx \mu_0 I/2\pi R$ if $L \gg R$.

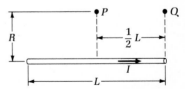

Figure 27-28. Exercise 27-12.

27-13 (a) Determine the contribution to the magnetic field at point Q in Fig. 27-28 due to the current in the straight conductor. (b) By taking an appropriate limit, determine the magnetic field at a point a perpendicular distance R from one end of a long (semi-infinite), straight, current-carrying wire. (*Hint:* See the previous exercise.) (c) Two long, straight wires carrying current I intersect as shown in Fig. 27-29. Show that the magnetic field at point P is directed perpendicu-

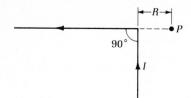

Figure 27-29. Exercise 27-13.

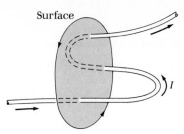

Figure 27-30. Exercise 27-19: Kinky wire punches through the surface three times.

larly into the plane of the page and has magnitude $B = \mu_0 I/4\pi R$.

27-14 (a) Determine the expression for the magnitude of the magnetic field at the center of a square loop of edge a with current I. (See Exercise 27-12.) (b) Evaluate numerically for $a = 150$ mm, $I = 6.0$ A. (c) Show the sense of the current and the direction of **B** at the center on a diagram.

27-15 A circular current loop of radius 2.5 mm carries a 7.4-mA current. (a) Determine the magnitude of the magnetic dipole moment of the current loop. (b) Determine the magnitude of the magnetic field at a point along the axis of the loop 1.0 m from the center. (c) Determine the magnitude of the magnetic field at the center of the loop.

27-16 The magnitude of the magnetic field due to a current loop is 13 μT at a point on the axis of the loop 250 mm from the center. The circular loop has a 15-mm radius. Determine (a) the magnitude of the magnetic dipole moment of the loop and (b) the current in the loop. (c) Show on a diagram the sense of the current, the direction of the dipole moment, and the direction of **B** at a point on the axis.

27-17 The electric field at a point on the perpendicular bisector plane of an electric dipole is given approximately (far from the dipole) by

$$E = \frac{-\mathbf{p}}{4\pi\epsilon_0 r^3}$$

where **p** is the electric dipole moment and r is the distance from the dipole. By analogy, write down the expression for the magnetic field **B** at a point in the plane of and far from a current loop with magnetic dipole moment **m**.

Section 27-3. Ampere's law

27-18 (a) Determine Σi in Ampere's law for the case illustrated in Fig. 27-11. Take $I_1 = 1.0$ A, $I_2 = 2.0$ A, $I_3 = 3.0$ A, $I_4 = 4.0$ A, $I_5 = 5.0$ A. (b) Explain how you determine the sign of each term in the sum.

27-19 Consider the surface bounded by the closed path shown in Fig. 27-30, with $I = 10.0$ A. (a) Determine the sum ΣI for this case. (b) What is the value of $\oint \mathbf{B} \cdot d\mathbf{r}$ for this closed path?

27-20 Show that Eq. (27-7) is satisfied for any simple closed path that is not linked by the current in a long,

straight wire. The path can be approximated by sets of radial lines and circular arcs in planes perpendicular to the axis of the wire and line segments parallel to the axis.

Section 27-4. Applications of Ampere's law

27-21 A long, straight wire of diameter 2.5 mm carries a uniformly distributed 12-A current. (a) At what distance from the axis of the wire is the magnitude of the magnetic field a maximum? (b) Construct a graph of the magnitude of the magnetic field B versus the radial distance R from the axis of the wire for the region $0 \leq R \leq 3.0$ mm.

27-22 Determine the magnetic field due to a 320-mA current at a point 2.50 mm from the axis of a long, straight wire of radius (a) 4.00 mm, (b) 2.50 mm, (c) 2.00 mm.

27-23 Idealized sketches of magnetic lines often show a region of uniform magnetic field ending abruptly; that is, a uniform field region is adjacent to a field-free region. Use Ampere's law and paths such as that shown in Fig. 27-31 to show that the magnetic field must change gradually in regions where there are no currents.

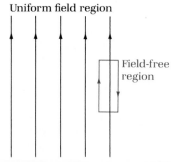

Figure 27-31. Exercise 27-23.

27-24 A long, straight wire carries a current I_0, which is uniformly distributed over the cross section of the wire of radius a. (a) For the closed path shown in Fig. 27-32, explicitly evaluate $\oint \mathbf{B} \cdot d\mathbf{r}$ using one or both of Eqs. (27-4) and (27-10). (b) Show that the current linking this closed path is given by $\Sigma i = I_0 \theta/2\pi$.

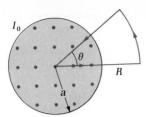

Figure 27-32. Exercise 27-24.

27-25 A long hollow conducting cylinder carries a current I_0, which is uniformly distributed over the cross section, as shown in Fig. 27-33. Determine the magnitude of the magnetic field at a point a distance R from the axis of the cylinder for (a) $R \leq b$; (b) $b \leq R \leq c$; (c) $c \leq R$.

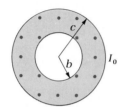

Figure 27-33. Exercise 27-25.

27-26 A cross section of a long *coaxial cable* is shown in Fig. 27-34. Equal currents I have opposite senses in the inner and outer conductors. Assume that the current density **j** is uniform in each conductor. Determine the magnitude of the magnetic field at a point a distance R from the axis of the cable for (a) $R \leq a$; (b) $a \leq R \leq b$; (c) $b \leq R \leq c$; (d) $c \leq R$.

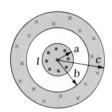

Figure 27-34. Exercise 27-26.

27-27 A long solenoid with 850 turns per meter has a 2.4-A current. (a) Determine the magnitude of the magnetic field near the center of the solenoid. (b) How many turns of wire are on the solenoid if its length is 200 mm? (c) Estimate the diameter of the wire.

27-28 By applying Ampere's law and symmetry arguments

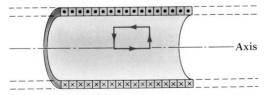

Figure 27-35. Exercise 27-28.

to the closed path shown in Fig. 27-35 for an ideal solenoid, show that the magnetic field is uniform inside the solenoid.

27-29 A circular solenoid is designed with a 260-mm² cross-sectional area and a 150-mm length. (a) How many turns are required if the magnetic field near the center of the solenoid is to have a maximum field magnitude of 1.8 mT and a maximum current of 0.75 A? (b) What length of wire is required? (c) If the solenoid is tightly wound with a single layer of copper wire of resistivity $1.7 \times 10^{-8} \, \Omega \cdot \mathrm{m}$, what is the resistance of the solenoid? Neglect the thickness of the insulation. (d) What potential difference must be applied across the leads to produce a steady magnetic field of magnitude 1.8 mT?

27-30 Two long, straight, parallel wires are shown in cross section in Fig. 27-36. Each wire carries the same current I with a sense out of the plane of the page. Let x locate a point in the plane containing the axes of the wires. Determine the magnetic field as a function of x for (a) $0 \leq x \leq a$; (b) $a \leq x \leq D - a$; (c) $D - a \leq x \leq D$.

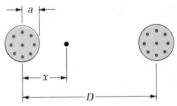

Figure 27-36. Exercise 27-30.

27-31 Rework the previous exercise with the current in the wire on the right reversed.

Section 27-5. Force between currents

27-32 Two long, straight, parallel wires 30 mm apart carry currents of 12 and 15 A with opposite senses. (a) Show on a diagram the direction of the force each wire exerts on the other. (b) Determine the magnitude of the force per unit length between the wires. (c) How do the answers to parts (a) and (b) change if the currents have the same sense?

27-33 Equal currents exist in two long, straight, parallel sections of wire separated by 15 mm. (a) If the magnetic force on a 250-mm length of one of the wires is measured to be 0.93 mN, what current exists in the wires? (b) By what factor does the force between the wires change if the currents are halved?

27-34 With the definition of the ampere as the SI unit of current, the four basic units are conventionally taken to be kilogram, meter, second, and ampere. Units for all other quantities in mechanics and electromagnetism are defined in terms of these four. (a) Express the unit of magnetic field, the tesla (T), in terms of the four basic units. (b) Express μ_0 in these units.

Section 27-6. Magnetic flux and Gauss's law for magnetic fields

27-35 The plane surface within a circle of radius 250 mm is in a uniform magnetic field of magnitude 320 mT such that the axis of the circle is at 28° to the field direction. Determine the magnetic flux for this surface.

27-36 Two surfaces form a closed surface, as shown in Fig. 27-37. Surface S_1 is the plane within a circle of radius a, and surface S_2 is a hemisphere of radius a. Suppose that a uniform magnetic field is at angle θ relative to the axis of the hemisphere. (a) Determine the magnetic flux for the plane surface. (b) Determine the magnetic flux for the hemispherical surface.

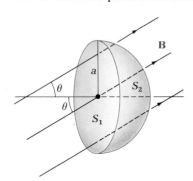

Figure 27-37. Exercise 27-36.

27-37 A long, straight wire carries current I. (a) Evaluate the magnetic flux for the plane surface bounded by the rectangle shown in Fig. 27-38. (b) Evaluate the magnetic flux for a bubblelike surface bulging out of the plane of the figure but having the rectangle as its boundary.

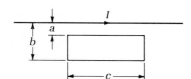

Figure 27-38. Exercise 27-37.

PROBLEMS

27-1 A general closed path, not necessarily in a plane, forms the boundary of a surface that is pierced by a current in a long, straight wire. The closed path can be approximated by a large number of lines of three types: circular arcs centered on the axis of the wire, radial lines, and lines parallel to the axis. Show that Eq. (27-6) is satisfied for this type of path.

27-2 *The toroid.* A toroid is a doughnut-shaped coil with N turns of wire wound about the doughnut, or *torus*. A typical toroid is illustrated in Fig. 27-39. For an ideal

Section 27-7. The displacement current and Ampere's law

27-38 A capacitor is being charged as shown in Fig. 27-22. At a certain instant the current in the lead wires is 1.45 A. (a) What is the displacement current for the surface S_1 at the same instant? (b) After the capacitor is fully charged, there is no current in the wires. What is the displacement current for surface S_1 in this case? (c) Suppose the capacitor is being discharged and the current in the wires is 2.33 A, with a sense opposite that shown in the figure. Now what is the displacement current for surface S_1?

27-39 A current I is uniformly distributed over the circular cross section S_1 of a long, straight wire. The current density has magnitude $j = I/A$, where A is the area of the surface S_1. An electric field exists at points in the wire whose resistivity is ρ. (Review the discussion connecting $\mathbf{j}$, $\mathbf{E}$, and ρ in Chap. 24.) (a) Determine the electric flux for the surface S_1 in terms of the current I piercing that surface. (b) Under what conditions is there a displacement current piercing this surface? (c) Evaluate the displacement current for a copper wire ($\rho = 1.7 \times 10^{-8}\ \Omega \cdot \text{m}$) in which the current changes from 320 to 340 mA in 5.0 μs. (d) What fraction of the total current is this displacement current in the wire?

27-40 A 30-nF capacitor in an RC circuit (see Chap. 25) is charged with a 12-V battery through a 10-kΩ resistor, beginning at $t = 0$. Consider the displacement current piercing a surface such as S_1 in Fig. 27-22. (a) At what value of t is the displacement current a maximum? (b) Evaluate the displacement current at $t = 1.0$ ms and (c) at $t = 15$ ms.

27-41 A capacitor is being charged as shown in Fig. 27-22. At a certain instant the current in the lead wires is 500 μA, and the current leaking from one plate to the other is 40 μA. (This is a "leaky" capacitor. The current would be zero in an ideal capacitor.) (a) Determine the displacement current piercing the surface S_1. (b) If each plate has area 240 mm², at what rate is the electric field changing at that instant? (Neglect edge effects.)

toroid the magnetic field exists only inside the torus, but the field is not uniform over the cross section. (a) Apply Ampere's law to the circular path in the figure to show that the magnitude of the magnetic field is given by

$$B = \frac{\mu_0 NI}{2\pi R}$$

where I is the current in the toroid and R is the radial distance from the axis. (b) Find the maximum and

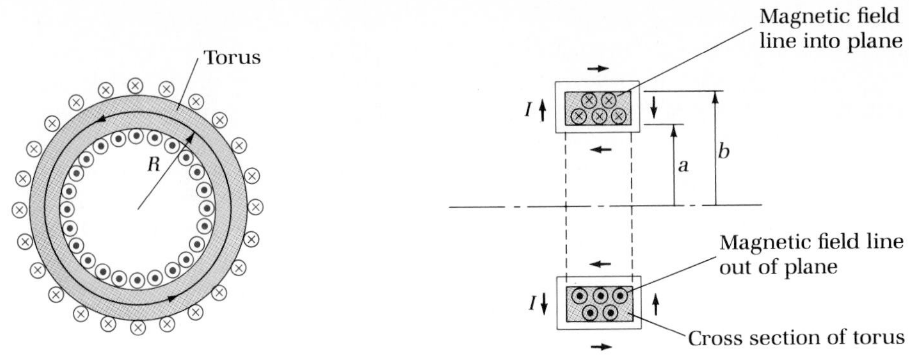

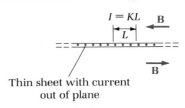

Figure 27-39. Prob. 27-2.

minimum values of the magnitude of the field for a 500-turn toroid with current 300 mA and with $a = 75$ mm and $b = 90$ mm. (c) Compare the values above with the magnitude of the magnetic field in a solenoid with N turns in a length $2\pi R_{av}$, where $R_{av} = \frac{1}{2}(R_1 + R_2)$.

27-3 An ideal solenoid with n turns per unit length can be considered as a continuous set of current loops, as illustrated in Fig. 27-40. For a current loop of width dx, the current is $dI = nI\,dx$. The magnitude dB of the magnetic field of a circular current loop for a point on the axis of the loop is given by Eq. (27-5), with $m = \pi a^2\,dI = \pi a^2 nI\,dx$. Use these results and the principle of superposition to determine the magnetic field at a point on the axis of an ideal solenoid.

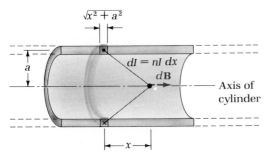

Figure 27-40. Prob. 27-3.

27-4 Use the method outlined in the previous problem to determine the magnetic field on the axis at the mouth of a semi-infinite solenoid. Let the open end of the solenoid be at $x = 0$, with the solenoid extending along the negative x axis.

27-5 Use the method of the previous two problems to determine the magnetic field at the center of a solenoid of length L and radius a. Let $x = 0$ be at the center of the solenoid, with the ends at $x = \pm\frac{1}{2}L$. Show that the result agrees with the field at the center of a current loop if $a \gg L$ and with the field inside an ideal solenoid if $a \ll L$.

27-6 Consider the idealized *sheet current* shown in Fig. 27-41. The current exists everywhere in the plane perpendicular to the plane of the page and is described by a *surface current density K*. The current I within a length L is $I = KL$, so that K is the current per unit length on the sheet. Use symmetry arguments and Ampere's law to show that the magnetic field is directed as shown, with a magnitude $B = \frac{1}{2}\mu_0 K$ on each side of the sheet.

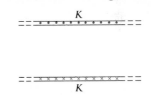

Figure 27-41. Prob. 27-6.

27-7 Using the result of the previous problem, determine the magnetic field above, below, and in between the two sheet currents shown in Fig. 27-42.

Figure 27-42. Prob. 27-7.

27-8 Use the Biot-Savart law to verify the result in Prob. 27-6 by considering the sheet current as a collection of long, straight wires of width dx and carrying current $dI = K\,dx$.

27-9 A particle of charge q moves with constant velocity $\mathbf{v}$. (a) Justify the interpretation of the product $q\mathbf{v}$ as a current element $I\,d\boldsymbol{\ell}$ located at the instantaneous position of the charged particle. (b) If the unit vector $\hat{\mathbf{r}}$ gives the direction from the particle to a point a distance r from the charge, then show that the magnetic field at that point due to the moving charge is given by

$$\mathbf{B} = \frac{\mu_0 q\mathbf{v} \times \hat{\mathbf{r}}}{4\pi r^2}$$

27-10 🔋 Consider a solenoid approximated by 101 parallel

current loops of radius $a = 10.0$ mm and spaced $d = 0.50$ mm apart. Each loop carries a 1.00-A current and the loop centers lie on the axis of the solenoid. The field at a point on the axis of a current loop has a magnitude given by Eq. (27-5). Choose the x axis to lie along the axis with the origin in the plane of the fifty-first loop. Then the end loops are at $\pm 50d$. Write a program to evaluate the magnetic field at (a) $x = 0$; (b) $x = 50d$; (c) $x = 100d$. (d) Compare the answers for parts (a) and (b) with the values for an ideal solenoid and a semi-infinite solenoid.

27-11 Modify the program in the previous problem to consider 201 loops, but with the same number of turns per unit length. Evaluate the field at (a) $x = 0$; (b) $x = 50d$; (c) $x = 100d$; (d) $x = 200d$. (e) Compare with the values for the previous problem.

CHAPTER 28
FARADAY'S LAW

28-1 INTRODUCTION

If a current I exists in a circuit with resistance R, then energy is dissipated through Joule heating at a rate given by $P = I^2R$. What is the source of this energy? In the simple circuits considered so far, a battery has usually supplied the energy. The emf $\mathscr{E}$ of the battery, interpreted as the energy per unit charge transferred to a charge carrier through chemical processes, provides energy to the charge carriers in the circuit at the rate $P = I\mathscr{E}$.

There are also other types of emf, other ways to transfer energy to and from the charge carriers in a circuit. The energy transfer need not occur through chemical reactions. The conversion of mechanical energy (from a rotating steam turbine) to electric energy at a generating station involves a different type of emf, one in which a magnetic field plays an essential role. The development of this important process is based on principles discovered more than 150 years ago. The independent and almost simultaneous observations of magnetically induced currents by Michael Faraday in England and Joseph Henry in the United States led to what is now called *Faraday's law of induction*.

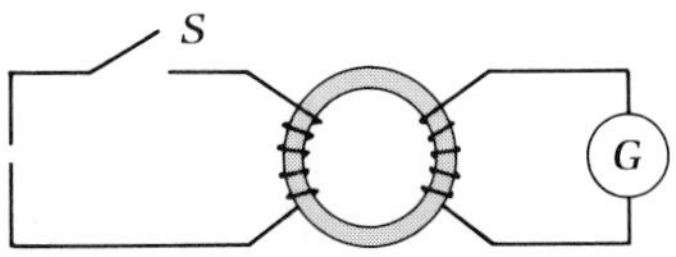

Figure 28-1. Two coils are wrapped around an iron ring. The galvanometer G deflects momentarily when the switch is opened or closed.

A current is induced in the coil when the magnetic field changes.

28-2 FARADAY'S LAW

Since a steady current in a wire produces a steady magnetic field, Faraday initially (and mistakenly) thought that a steady magnetic field could produce a current. Some of Faraday's investigations of magnetically induced currents utilized an arrangement similar to that shown in Fig. 28-1. A current in the coil on the left produces a magnetic field which is concentrated in the iron ring. The coil on the right is connected to a galvanometer G which indicates the presence of any induced current in that circuit. There is no induced current for a steady magnetic field. But an induced current does appear momentarily in the circuit on the right when switch S is closed in the circuit on the left. When switch S is opened, an induced current with the opposite sense appears momentarily. Thus the induced current exists only when the magnetic field, due to the current in the circuit on the left, is *changing*.

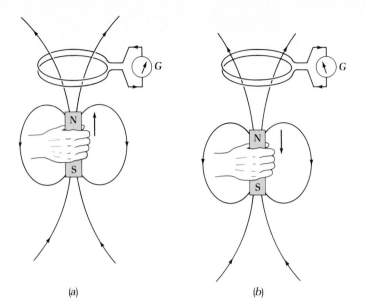

Figure 28-2. (a) A current is induced in the coil if the magnet moves toward the coil. (b) The induced current has the opposite sense if the magnet moves away from the coil.

(a)   (b)

A current is induced in the coil if the magnet and coil are in relative motion.

The importance of a change is also demonstrated by the arrangement shown in Fig. 28-2. If the magnet is at rest relative to the coil, then no induced current exists. But if the magnet is moved toward the coil, then a current is induced with a sense as indicated in Fig. 28-2a. If the magnet is moved away from the coil, then a current is induced with the opposite sense, as shown in Fig. 28-2b. Notice that in either case the magnetic field is changing in the vicinity of the coil. An induced current also exists in the coil if it is moved relative to the magnet.

An induced current is caused by an induced emf.

The presence of such currents in a circuit implies the existence of an *induced emf* $\mathscr{E}$. That is, energy must be supplied to the charge carriers which constitute the current, and emf is the energy per unit charge given to a charge carrier that traverses the circuit. This induced emf is present when the magnetic field is changing, as described above.

The quantitative connection between the changing magnetic field and the induced emf is expressed in terms of the magnetic flux Φ_B for a surface. (Magnetic flux was introduced in Sec. 27-6.) For simplicity, consider a fine loop of conducting wire and an open, mathematical surface bounded by the loop such as the one shown in Fig. 28-3. The magnetic flux for a surface bounded by the loop is given by the surface integral

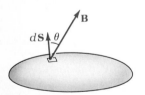

Figure 28-3. A conducting loop forms the boundary of a surface. The magnetic flux for the surface is $\Phi_B = \int \mathbf{B} \cdot d\mathbf{S}$.

$$\Phi_B = \int \mathbf{B} \cdot d\mathbf{S}$$

Magnetic flux links a loop.

where $d\Phi_B = \mathbf{B} \cdot d\mathbf{S} = B \, dS \cos\theta$ is the flux for the surface element $d\mathbf{S}$. The magnetic flux Φ_B is said to *link* the loop. Notice that if the magnetic field in the vicinity of the loop changes with time, then the magnetic flux linking the loop also changes with time.

A changing magnetic flux linking a loop and the induced emf in the loop are related by *Faraday's law:*

Faraday's law

$$\mathscr{E} = -\frac{d\Phi_B}{dt} \tag{28-1}$$

The emf $\mathscr{E}$ depends on the rate of change of the magnetic flux. The negative sign in this form of Faraday's law relates to the sense of the induced emf in the circuit. (See Lenz's law below.) From Faraday's law, we obtain the relation between the weber (Wb), the unit of magnetic flux, and the volt (V), the unit of emf: 1 V = 1 Wb/s.

Often we shall consider the induced emf in a closely wound coil. Each turn in such a coil behaves approximately as a loop, and we can apply Faraday's law to determine the emf induced in each turn. Since the turns are in series, the total induced emf $\mathscr{E}_T$ in a coil is the sum of the emf's induced in each turn. We suppose that the coil is so closely wound that the magnetic flux linking a turn of the coil at a given instant has the same value for each turn. Then the same emf $\mathscr{E}$ is induced in each turn, and the total induced emf for a coil with N turns is given by

Induced emf in an N-turn coil

$$\mathscr{E}_T = N\mathscr{E} = N\left(-\frac{d\Phi_B}{dt}\right) = -N\frac{d\Phi_B}{dt} \qquad (28\text{-}2)$$

where Φ_B is the magnetic flux linking each of the turns.

The magnetic flux linking a loop or a turn of a coil in Eq. (28-1) is the flux of the *total* magnetic field for a surface bounded by the loop. There is a contribution to the magnetic flux for a loop due to the loop's own current in addition to the contribution due to an external source such as a magnet or the current in another circuit. In this chapter, we shall always assume that loops or coils are part of a circuit with a large resistance so that the induced current is small. Then the flux contribution due to the small induced current is assumed to be negligible compared with the flux due to the other sources. Thus we shall neglect the effect of the induced current in determining the magnitude of the induced emf (but see Lenz's law below). The next chapter will concentrate on the effect that an induced current has on itself.

EXAMPLE 28-1. A 75-turn circular coil of radius 35 mm has its axis parallel to a spatially uniform magnetic field. The magnitude of the field changes at a constant rate from 18 to 43 mT in 240 ms. Determine the magnitude of the induced emf in the coil during this time interval.

SOLUTION. Since the magnetic field is spatially uniform and parallel to the axis of the coil, the flux linking each turn is given by

$$\Phi_B = B\pi R^2$$

where R is the radius of a turn. From Eq. (28-2) the induced emf in the coil is

$$\mathscr{E}_T = -N\frac{d\Phi_B}{dt} = -N\frac{d(B\pi R^2)}{dt} = -N\pi R^2\frac{dB}{dt}$$

The magnitude of the magnetic field changes at a constant rate given by

$$\frac{dB}{dt} = \frac{0.043\ \text{T} - 0.018\ \text{T}}{0.24\ \text{s}} = 0.10\ \text{T/s}$$

The magnitude of the emf induced in the coil is then

$$\mathscr{E}_T = 75\pi(0.035\ \text{m})^2(0.10\ \text{T/s}) = 0.030\ \text{V} = 30\ \text{mV}$$

Lenz's law gives the sense of the induced current.

Lenz's law. The negative sign which appears in Faraday's law, Eq. (28-1), refers to the sense of the induced current. In determining the *magnitude* of an induced emf from Faraday's law, we shall ignore the negative sign in the calculation. The sense of the induced emf is determined by applying *Lenz's law*, a principle attributed to Heinrich Friedrich Lenz (1804–1865). One way to state Lenz's law is in terms of the contribution of the induced current to the magnetic field: *The sense of the induced current is such that its contribution to the magnetic field opposes the change in magnetic flux which produces the induced current.*

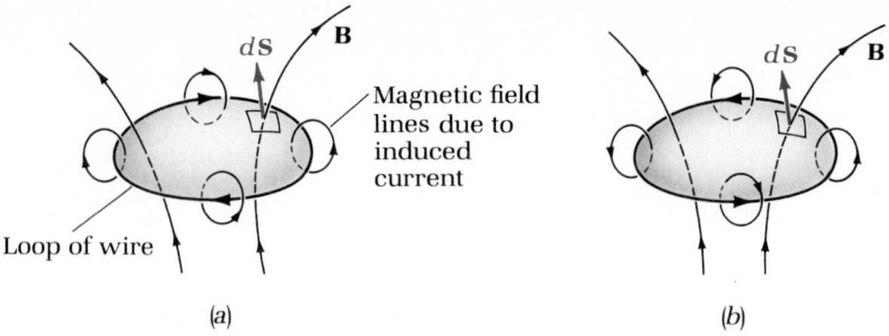

Figure 28-4. The magnetic field contribution due to the induced current opposes the change in flux. The magnetic flux for the surface is (a) increasing and (b) decreasing.

dS **B**

Magnetic field lines due to induced current

Loop of wire

(a)

dS **B**

(b)

An understanding of Lenz's law and its application can best be obtained by considering examples. Suppose that the magnetic field, and therefore the flux for the surface in Fig. 28-4a, is increasing. The sense of the induced current must be shown in the figure in order to oppose the increasing flux. That is, the contribution to the magnetic field due to the induced current tends to reduce the increasing value of B at points on the surface. In contrast, if the induced current had the opposite sense, its field contribution would further increase the flux for the surface, in violation of Lenz's law.

In Fig. 28-4b, the magnetic field is assumed to be decreasing at points on the surface. Thus the magnetic flux linking the loop is decreasing, and the field contribution of the induced current must tend to increase the decreasing value of B. The induced current has the sense shown in Fig. 28-4b. Notice that if the current had the opposite sense, then the induced current contribution would further decrease the decreasing flux for the surface, again a violation of Lenz's law.

Figure 28-5 shows another interpretation of Lenz's law applied to the situation of Fig. 28-4a. The flux linking the loop due to the field of the magnet is increasing as the magnet is moved toward the loop. The induced current in the loop produces a magnetic field similar to the field of a bar magnet (as outlined in Fig. 28-5). The north pole of the equivalent bar magnet repels the real magnet. That is, the magnetic field of the induced current exerts a force on the moving magnet which is opposite the motion of the magnet. In this way the induced current opposes the change in flux which produces it.

Since the induced current always opposes the change in flux which produces it, Lenz's law prohibits runaway situations. Suppose that the magnetic flux linking a loop is increasing. If the induced current had a sense which tended to increase the increasing flux (violating Lenz's law), then the flux could increase at a greater rate, which in turn could induce a larger current to increase the flux at a still greater rate. . . . There is no source of energy for

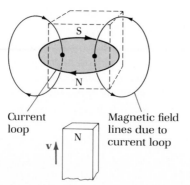

Figure 28-5. The induced current in the loop produces a magnetic field contribution similar to the field of a bar magnet. The two north poles repel.

Current loop

Magnetic field lines due to current loop

such an unstable growth of current, and the runaway effect does not occur.

In applying Lenz's law to a loop or a coil, you assume the sense of the current to be either one way or the other. One of those senses will be such as to oppose the change in flux which produces the induced current. That is the correct sense. The other sense of the current would aid the change in flux and represents the incorrect choice. Thus you make an initial guess for the sense of the current and then apply Lenz's law to determine if the choice is correct. We shall be applying Lenz's law to a variety of examples in the following sections.

28-3 MOTIONAL EMF'S

An emf is induced in a stationary loop or coil if the magnetic flux linking it changes. The magnetic flux, $\Phi_B = \int \mathbf{B} \cdot d\mathbf{S}$, linking a loop involves three things: the field, the area, and the orientation. A change in any one of these can change the flux and lead to an induced emf. One way to change the flux is to change the magnetic field in the region. An emf can also be induced in a conducting circuit if part or all of the circuit moves in a region of magnetic field. These motionally induced emf's have great practical importance. This type of emf occurs in an electric generator, a device which converts mechanical energy to electric energy.

Motionally induced emf's

As an example, consider the sliding-wire circuit shown in Fig. 28-6. A U-shaped conductor is at rest in a region of uniform magnetic field perpendicular to the plane of the U. The circuit is completed by a conducting wire of length ℓ that slides on the rails of the U with a velocity $\mathbf{v}$ that is perpendicular to $\mathbf{B}$. For simplicity we assume that the wire is caused to slide with constant velocity. Because the sliding wire moves, the charge carriers in the wire also move. Consequently, the magnetic field exerts a force on each carrier, $\mathbf{F} = q\mathbf{v} \times \mathbf{B}$. The direction of the magnetic force on a positive charge carrier is from the top to the bottom of the sliding wire in the figure.

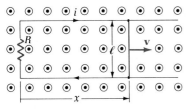

Figure 28-6. A uniform magnetic field is out of the plane of the figure, and an emf is induced in the sliding-wire circuit.

The magnetic force acting on the charge carriers in the sliding wire tends to make them move around the circuit, thus giving an induced current with the sense indicated in the figure. There are, of course, other forces acting on the charge carriers. (For example, there is a Hall field in the sliding wire; see Example 26-9.) Experiment shows that the net effect of these forces can be expressed in terms of an induced emf determined by applying Faraday's law to the circuit. Since the magnetic field is perpendicular to the plane of the circuit, the magnetic flux for that plane is given by

$$\Phi_B = \int \mathbf{B} \cdot d\mathbf{S} = B\ell x$$

where $S = \ell x$ is the instantaneous area of the circuit loop. The sliding wire is moving with speed v, $v = |dx/dt|$, so that the area and therefore the magnetic flux linking the circuit are changing. The magnitude of the change in flux linking the circuit is

$$\left| \frac{d\Phi_B}{dt} \right| = \left| \frac{d(B\ell x)}{dt} \right| = B\ell \left| \frac{dx}{dt} \right| = B\ell v$$

Induced emf for a sliding-wire circuit

From Faraday's law, the induced emf in the sliding-wire circuit is

$$\mathcal{E} = B\ell v \tag{28-3}$$

This result applies for **B** perpendicular to a plane circuit, with the velocity of the sliding wire perpendicular to the wire's length. See Exercises 28-11 and 28-12 for extensions to other cases.

The sense of the induced current, for the case shown in the figure, is in accord with Lenz's law. The flux $\Phi_B = B\ell x$ is increasing, and the contribution of the induced current to the magnetic field over the plane surface is opposite the applied magnetic field. Thus the sense of the induced current is such as to oppose the increasing flux. What is the sense of the induced current in the circuit of Fig. 28-6 if the sliding wire moves in the opposite direction?

The expression for the induced emf given in Eq. (28-3) for the sliding-wire circuit can also be obtained from energy considerations. Let i represent the instantaneous current in the circuit and $\mathscr{E}$ the induced emf. The rate at which electric energy is supplied to the circuit is given by $P = i\mathscr{E}$ (Sec. 25-3). The source of this energy can be identified as follows: There is a magnetic force acting on the current-carrying sliding wire in the uniform magnetic field. From Eq. (26-3) this force has magnitude $F = i\ell B$ and its direction, from Fig. 28-6, is to the left, opposite the velocity of the sliding wire. Since the wire moves with constant velocity, the net force acting on it must be zero. To balance the magnetic force (we neglect friction), an applied force of magnitude $F_a = i\ell B$ must act to the right in the figure. This applied force, parallel to the velocity, does work on the wire at the rate [see Eq. (8-15)] $P = \mathbf{F}_a \cdot \mathbf{v} = F_a v = i\ell B v$. Equating the rate at which this mechanical work is done to the rate at which it is transformed to electric energy, we obtain

$$i\mathscr{E} = i\ell B v$$

or, on dividing by the current i,

$$\mathscr{E} = B\ell v$$

in agreement with Eq. (28-3). Notice that the source of the electric energy associated with this induced emf is the work done by the applied force. Problem 28-4 considers a case in which no applied force is present.

Induced emf's occur in circuits in a variety of situations involving the motion of a conductor in a static, uniform magnetic field. One example is illustrated in Fig. 28-7. A circular loop whose plane is perpendicular to a uniform magnetic field is distorted by applied forces pushing in the sides. The area of the plane of the loop decreases as a result and an induced emf exists. The magnetic flux linking the loop is $\Phi_B = \int \mathbf{B} \cdot d\mathbf{S} = BS$, where S is the instantaneous area of the plane of the loop. Applying Faraday's law gives

$$\mathscr{E} = \left|\frac{d\Phi_B}{dt}\right| = \left|\frac{d(BS)}{dt}\right| = B\left|\frac{dS}{dt}\right|$$

The emf depends on the rate dS/dt at which the area of the loop changes. What is the sense of the induced current in Fig. 28-7? What supplies the electric energy?

The magnetic flux linking a loop or a coil also changes if the loop or coil rotates in a static uniform field. We shall consider this important case in the next section.

In a more general case, an induced emf exists in a circuit if the flux linking it is changing. That change in flux can be due to a combination of a changing magnetic field and the motion of the circuit in a magnetic field. Further, the magnetic field need not be spatially uniform. Faraday's law gives the emf

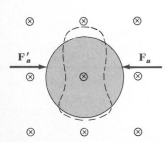

Figure 28-7. A loop in a magnetic field is distorted by applied forces that reduce the area so that the flux changes.

whether the flux changes because of each process alone or because of a combination of processes.

EXAMPLE 28-2. Determine (a) the induced emf and (b) the induced current in the sliding-wire circuit of Fig. 28-6 if $\ell = 450$ mm, $B = 0.50$ T, and $v = 1.6$ m/s. The 250-Ω resistance R of the circuit is assumed to be concentrated in the base of the U; the rails and sliding wire having negligible resistance. Thus there is a negligible change in the resistance of the circuit as the wire slides along the rails.

SOLUTION. (a) The magnitude of the emf is given by Eq. (28-3):

$$\mathscr{E} = B\ell v = (0.50 \text{ T})(0.450 \text{ m})(1.6 \text{ m/s}) = 0.36 \text{ V}$$

(b) Since R represents the total resistance in the circuit, the current is

$$i = \frac{\mathscr{E}}{R} = \frac{0.36 \text{ V}}{250 \ \Omega} = 1.4 \text{ mA}$$

Would either of these answers change if the velocity of the wire were reversed? Would the sense of the induced current change?

28-4 GENERATORS AND ALTERNATORS

Faraday's law provides the basis, or principle, for the conversion of mechanical energy into electric energy. The practical importance of this energy conversion in a technological society is evident. For example, it occurs in an electric generator or dynamo at a commercial generating plant and in the alternator of an automobile. These devices are the result of extensive engineering development; however, the basic principles of their operation can be understood by considering a conducting loop rotating in a magnetic field.

Generators. A conducting loop is in a region of magnetic field, as shown in Fig. 28-8. For simplicity we assume that the magnetic field is uniform and that the loop is caused to rotate by some external agent about an axis O. The axis is in the plane of the loop and perpendicular to the field. The plane loop may have any shape (not necessarily rectangular as in the figure). Let θ represent the angle between the magnetic field and the area vector $\mathbf{S}$, which is perpendicular to the plane of the loop. The flux linking this loop is

$$\Phi_B = \int \mathbf{B} \cdot d\mathbf{S} = \mathbf{B} \cdot \mathbf{S} = BS \cos \theta$$

Since the loop is rotating, the angle θ is changing, which leads to a changing flux and, therefore, to an induced emf. Suppose that the loop rotates with a constant angular speed ω about the axis. Then $\theta = \omega t$ and the flux linking the loop is

Figure 28-8. A rectangular loop rotates in a uniform magnetic field. Electrical contact is made with brushes sliding on rotating rings.

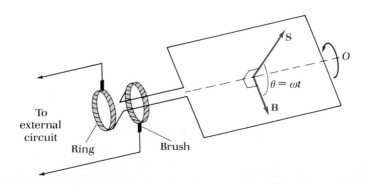

$$\Phi_B = BS \cos \omega t$$

The induced emf from Faraday's law, $\mathscr{E} = -d\Phi_B/dt$, is given in this case by

Induced emf in a rotating loop

$$\mathscr{E} = BS\omega \sin \omega t \tag{28-4}$$

For a coil with N loops or turns, an induced emf exists in each turn (in series), and the induced emf in the rotating coil is just N times the emf in one loop:

Induced emf in a rotating coil

$$\mathscr{E} = NBS\omega \sin \omega t \tag{28-5}$$

An emf given by Eq. (28-4) or (28-5) oscillates sinusoidally with angular frequency ω or with frequency $\nu = \omega/2\pi$. The maximum, or peak, value of the emf is $\mathscr{E}_{max} = NBS\omega$, which occurs when $\sin \omega t = 1$. Thus the emf oscillates between $+\mathscr{E}_{max}$ and $-\mathscr{E}_{max}$ as the sine function ranges between $+1$ and -1.

Alternating current (ac) and the ac generator

The associated current also oscillates, or *alternates,* at this frequency and is called an *alternating current* (abbreviated ac). A generator giving an emf of the form of Eq. (28-5) is called an ac generator. Notice that the angular frequency ω appears twice in Eq. (28-5). It is contained in the oscillatory term $\sin \omega t$, and the maximum emf is proportional to ω: $\mathscr{E}_{max} = NBS\omega$.

To act as a generator for an external circuit, a rotating coil must be connected to the circuit through lead wires. One connecting arrangement is shown schematically in Fig. 28-8. The wires from the loop are joined to rings which rotate with the loop on a shaft (the shaft is not shown). Electrical contact with the external circuit is through conducting *brushes* which slide on the rotating rings. The emf produced across the brushes is the output voltage V, which is essentially the induced emf. For the ac generator described above, the output voltage is oscillatory, with a time dependence shown in Fig. 28-9.

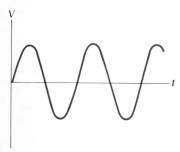

Figure 28-9. The output voltage (or emf) from an ac generator oscillates.

A different type of connection with a rotating loop is shown schematically in Fig. 28-10. The two brushes contact the halves of a *split-ring commutator.* During one part of the rotation, the output voltage from the coil corresponds to the positive part of the cycle in Fig. 28-9. But when the negative part of the cycle begins, the brushes contact the opposite halves of the commutator. By switching in this way, the commutator causes the sense of the output voltage to remain the same, as shown in Fig. 28-11, rather than alternating. The use of such a commutator leads to a *direct current* (dc), in which the current maintains the same sense in the circuit. (Often the symbol "dc" implies a constant value, as well as a constant sense, of the current.) A generator with a commutator to maintain the sense of the output current is called a *dc generator.*

Direct current (dc) and the dc generator

Lenz's law gives the sense of the induced current in a generating loop. For example, the sense of the induced current i in the loop in Fig. 28-10 is shown at an instant when θ is increasing between 0 and 90°. The flux $\Phi_B = BS \cos \theta$ is

Figure 28-10. Brushes make electrical contact with a rotating split-ring commutator.

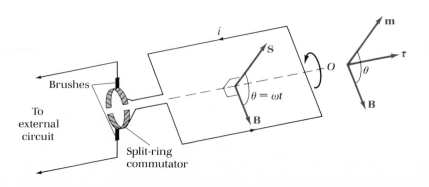

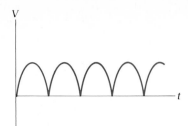

Figure 28-11. The output voltage from a dc generator maintains the same sense.

decreasing, and the induced current opposes that decrease. This result can also be expressed in terms of the torque produced by the magnetic field on the loop which has the induced current i. In a uniform field the torque on a current loop of area $\mathbf{S}$ with magnetic dipole moment $\mathbf{m} = i\mathbf{S}$ is given by Eq. (26-8): $\boldsymbol{\tau} = \mathbf{m} \times \mathbf{B}$. Notice from Fig. 28-10 that this torque tends to cause a rotation that is opposite the sense of rotation of the loop. This torque would tend to bring the rotating loop to rest. That is, the magnetic torque opposes the externally applied torque that causes the loop to rotate. The mechanical work done by this external agent in maintaining the constant angular speed of the loop is the source of the electric energy "generated" in this generator.

EXAMPLE 28-3. A 25-turn circular coil of radius $a = 140$ mm rotates at frequency $\nu = 60$ Hz about an axis that is perpendicular to a uniform magnetic field of magnitude 420 mT. The coil is connected to an external circuit with brushes and rings, as shown in Fig. 28-8. (a) Write an expression for the output voltage of this generator as a function of time. (b) Determine the maximum value of the induced emf in the coil. (c) Determine the maximum current in the circuit whose total resistance is 35 kΩ. (d) What is the orientation of the coil with respect to the field when the current is maximum? (e) Estimate the magnitude of the external torque that must be provided to keep the coil rotating.

SOLUTION. (a) The brushes-and-rings connection of Fig. 28-8 corresponds to an ac generator, and the output voltage is essentially given by the induced emf in Eq. (28-5):

$$\mathscr{E} = NBS\omega \sin \omega t$$

(b) The maximum value of the induced emf in the coil occurs when $\sin \omega t = 1$ and is $\mathscr{E}_{max} = NBS\omega = NBS(2\pi\nu)$, where $\omega = 2\pi\nu$. The area of each turn is $S = \pi a^2$ and

$$\mathscr{E}_{max} = (25)(420 \text{ mT})(\pi)(0.14 \text{ m})^2(2\pi)(60 \text{ Hz}) = 240 \text{ V}$$

(c) With no other emf's in the circuit, the maximum current is

$$i_{max} = \frac{\mathscr{E}_{max}}{R} = \frac{240 \text{ V}}{35 \text{ k}\Omega} = 7.0 \text{ mA}$$

(d) The maximum current and maximum emf occur when the flux is changing most rapidly. From part (a) above, the emf is maximum when $|\sin \omega t| = 1$, corresponding to $\omega t = \theta = \pm 90°$. Since θ is the angle between the field and the area vector, this orientation corresponds to the plane of the coil being parallel to the field. (e) From Eq. (26-8), the torque, $\boldsymbol{\tau} = Ni\mathbf{S} \times \mathbf{B}$, produced by the magnetic field on the coil has a maximum magnitude when the current is a maximum: $\tau_{max} = Ni_{max}SB$, or

$$\tau_{max} = (25)(7.0 \text{ mA})(\pi)(0.14 \text{ m})^2(420 \text{ mT})$$

$$= 4.5 \times 10^{-3} \text{ N} \cdot \text{m}$$

To keep the coil rotating uniformly, the external torque must have a maximum magnitude of at least this value. There will also be frictional torques to counter. Can you estimate the minimum mechanical energy that must be provided to operate this generator for an hour?

Alternators. The value of the current in the example above was small (7 mA maximum) because of the large resistance of the circuit. In the lighting circuits of an automobile, currents are typically 10 A or greater. If a generator with brushes is used to provide large currents and emf's, arcing often occurs at the commutator, which leads to deterioration of the electrical contacts. An alternator avoids this problem because the emf is induced in a nonrotating coil (or coils). Thus there are no sliding contacts or brushes in the coil carrying a large current. Instead the brushes are used to supply a smaller current to a rotating

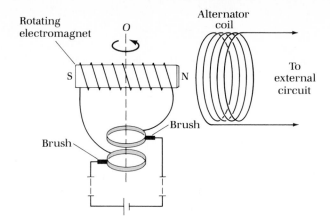

Figure 28-12. A rotating electromagnet induces an emf in a stationary coil of an alternator.

electromagnet, as shown schematically in Fig. 28-12. (Some alternators use a rotating permanent magnet.) An emf is induced in the stationary coil as the flux linking the coil changes because of the rotation of the electromagnet. The energy required to keep the electromagnet rotating is supplied by the automobile engine. Although the output current from the coil is ac (can you explain why?), a direct current (dc) is then obtained with the use of diodes of the type described in Sec. 24-5.

28-5 INDUCED ELECTRIC FIELDS

When a conductor moves in a uniform magnetic field, the charge carriers — moving along with the conductor with average velocity $\mathbf{v}$ — experience a magnetic force ($q\mathbf{v} \times \mathbf{B}$). It is this force on the charge carriers in the moving conductor that leads to induced currents in circuits such as those described in Sec. 28-3. Consider, however, a coil or loop which is stationary and which has a fixed shape and orientation in a region of magnetic field. That is, no part of the conducting circuit is moving. The flux linking the circuit can change if the magnetic field changes. The induced emf is given by Faraday's law, and Sec. 28-2 dealt with this induced emf. What force leads to the induced current in this case? It cannot be the magnetic force $q\mathbf{v} \times \mathbf{B}$ because the average velocity $\mathbf{v}$ of the charge carriers is zero before the current is induced. Equation (26-11) gives the electromagnetic force on a charged particle: $\mathbf{F} = q(\mathbf{E} + \mathbf{v} \times \mathbf{B})$. If an electric field is present, then an electric force acts on a charge carrier, even if it is initially at rest. We conclude that an electric force acts on the charge carrier and that an electric field is present when the magnetic field changes.

To investigate the nature of the electric field, we consider a configuration with cylindrical symmetry. A fine wire loop of radius a lies inside an ideal solenoid. The axes of the loop and the solenoid coincide so that the plane of the loop is perpendicular to a spatially uniform magnetic field, as shown in Fig. 28-13. Suppose that the magnitude $B(t)$ of the magnetic field is time-dependent. The flux linking the loop is $\Phi_B = B(t)S$, where $S = \pi a^2$ is the area of the loop. The induced emf is then $\mathscr{E} = -S\,dB/dt$. The sense of the induced current is obtained from Lenz's law and is as shown in the figure for the case of $B(t)$ increasing. From the symmetry of the system, we can see that there must be a force $\mathbf{F}$ acting on each charge carrier, with a component of the force tangent to the loop to cause the induced current. A force with a tangential component

An electric field causes an induced current.

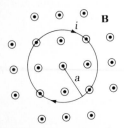

Figure 28-13. A magnetic field with increasing magnitude induces a current in a circular loop. A tangential electric field drives charge carriers around the loop.

must be an electric force, not a magnetic force. (What is the direction of the magnetic force on a charge carrier moving around the loop?) Symmetry also shows that the force has the same magnitude at each point around the conducting wire. Further experiments confirm that an electric field $\mathbf{E}$ exists in this region and exerts a force $\mathbf{F} = q\mathbf{E}$ on any charge q in the region.

The induced emf is interpreted as the work per unit charge done by this electric force on a charge carrier as it completes a circuit around the loop; thus

$$\mathscr{E} = \frac{W}{q} = \oint \frac{\mathbf{F} \cdot d\boldsymbol{\ell}}{q} = \oint \mathbf{E} \cdot d\boldsymbol{\ell}$$

Induced emf and induced electric field

where the electric field $\mathbf{E} = \mathbf{F}/q$ is the force per unit charge. We think of the induced emf in the circuit as a direct consequence of this electric field, which is an *induced electric field*. The relation between them is

$$\mathscr{E} = \oint \mathbf{E} \cdot d\boldsymbol{\ell} \tag{28-6}$$

where the closed path is around the conducting circuit.

The induced electric field in Eq. (28-6) is different from the electrostatic field introduced in Chap. 20 via Coulomb's law. The electric field due to a static distribution of charge is conservative. Electrostatic fields are conservative in that the work per unit charge done by the electrostatic field is independent of the path connecting two points. One way of expressing the conservative nature of the electrostatic field is in terms of the line integral for any closed path:

$$\oint \mathbf{E} \cdot d\boldsymbol{\ell} = 0 \qquad \text{(for an electrostatic field)}$$

An induced electric field is nonconservative.

But from Eq. (28-6), we see that the induced electric field has a nonzero closed-path integral. An induced electric field is a *nonconservative* electric field, a field that cannot be produced by a static distribution of charge. *The nonconservative electric field is produced by a changing magnetic field.*

Using Eq. (28-6), we can express Faraday's law in terms of the nonconservative induced electric field. Substituting the closed-path integral (around the conducting circuit) in Eq. (28-6) for the emf in Faraday's law gives

$$\oint \mathbf{E} \cdot d\boldsymbol{\ell} = -\frac{d\Phi_B}{dt}$$

and $\Phi_B = \int \mathbf{B} \cdot d\mathbf{S}$ is the flux for any surface bounded by the closed path.

This form of Faraday's law was obtained for the closed path that coincided with the conducting loop. Experiment shows that the relation is more general. An induced electric field also exists outside the wire in Fig. 28-13. In fact, the above form of Faraday's law is valid even if no conductor is present in the region.

A form of Faraday's law expressed in terms of the fields is customarily taken to be the fundamental form. It is valid whether conductors are present or absent. (Emf is not a useful concept in the absence of conductors.) The general form, or *integral form*, of Faraday's law is stated as

Integral form of Faraday's law

$$\oint \mathbf{E} \cdot d\boldsymbol{\ell} = -\frac{d}{dt} \int \mathbf{B} \cdot d\mathbf{S} \tag{28-7}$$

where the line integral is for any closed path and the magnetic flux $\Phi_B =$

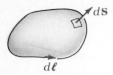

Figure 28-14. The closed path forms the boundary of the oriented surface.

Eddy currents are induced in conductors.

Laminated fabrication reduces eddy currents.

Changing electric and magnetic fields are sources of each other.

$\int \mathbf{B} \cdot d\mathbf{S}$ is for any surface bounded by the closed path. The sense of the closed path (given by the direction of $d\boldsymbol{\ell}$) and the orientation of the surface (given by the direction of the area element $d\mathbf{S}$) are connected by a right-hand rule: Orient the right hand so that the fingers curl in the sense of $d\boldsymbol{\ell}$. The extended thumb gives the orientation of the area element, as shown in Fig. 28-14. This connection between the sense of the closed path for $\mathbf{E}$ and the orientation of the surface for $\mathbf{B}$ is consistent with Lenz's law.

Eddy currents. Suppose that a changing magnetic field is perpendicular to a face of an extended conductor such as a plate. The induced electric field causes circulating currents called *eddy currents* in the plate. Such eddy currents are also produced if a conductor moves through a region of magnetic field. These currents dissipate energy through Joule heating (at a rate $P = i^2R$). A conducting material can be "heated" by the eddy currents induced by changing the magnetic field in the substance, a process called *induction heating.*

In other cases, the dissipation of energy that accompanies eddy currents may be undesirable. To reduce the eddy currents in the iron core of a transformer (see Sec. 29-6), the core is laminated. That is, thin layers of conducting iron are separated by insulating layers. The insulating layers effectively increase the resistance of the path for circulating charges so that the current is reduced.

Faraday's law and Ampere's law. There are some similarities between Faraday's law and Ampere's law with the displacement current included [Eq. (27-16)]. These two laws are

$$\oint \mathbf{B} \cdot d\boldsymbol{\ell} = \mu_0 \left(\Sigma i + \epsilon_0 \frac{d\Phi_E}{dt} \right) \qquad \text{(Ampere's law)}$$

$$\oint \mathbf{E} \cdot d\boldsymbol{\ell} = -\frac{d\Phi_B}{dt} \qquad \text{(Faraday's law)}$$

The equations are most similar if $\Sigma i = 0$. We can interpret Ampere's law by regarding a changing electric field as a cause or source of a magnetic field. And we can interpret Faraday's law by regarding a changing magnetic field as a cause or source of an electric field. These laws, along with Gauss's law for electric fields and for magnetic fields, are obeyed everywhere, even in regions far from charges and currents. The possibility that these laws allow electric and magnetic fields that can sustain each other is explored in Chap. 34. There we shall see that light is an electromagnetic wave.

EXAMPLE 28-4. The magnitude of the spatially uniform magnetic field in a long solenoid increases at a constant rate dB/dt. Determine the distribution of the induced electric field in this region.

SOLUTION. The electric field must be symmetric with respect to the axis of the solenoid. (See Exercise 28-29.) To apply Faraday's law, Eq. (28-7), we use a circle of radius R centered on the axis, with its plane perpendicular to the axis. This path forms the boundary for the plane surface within the circle. We choose the sense of the path integral to

be as shown by the direction of $d\boldsymbol{\ell}$ in Fig. 28-15a. With this choice, the area element $d\mathbf{S}$ is out of the plane of the figure, opposite to $\mathbf{B}$. Since $\mathbf{B} \cdot d\mathbf{S} = B \, dS \cos 180° = -B \, dS$, the flux $\Phi_B = -BS = -B\pi R^2$. From symmetry the electric field is tangent to the path ($\mathbf{E} \cdot d\boldsymbol{\ell} = E \, d\ell$) and has the same magnitude E at each point on the path. Thus

$$\oint \mathbf{E} \cdot d\boldsymbol{\ell} = \oint E \, d\ell = E \oint d\ell = E(2\pi R)$$

where $2\pi R$ is the distance around the circular path. Substituting these results in Eq. (28-7) gives

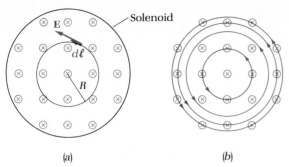

Figure 28-15. Example 28-4: (a) The closed path integral $\oint \mathbf{E} \cdot d\boldsymbol{\ell}$ is evaluated for a circle of radius R. (b) The lines representing **E** are circular. The field **E** also exists outside the solenoid (see Exercise 28-26).

$$E(2\pi R) = -\frac{d}{dt}(-B\pi R^2) = \pi R^2 \frac{dB}{dt}$$

or

$$E = \frac{1}{2} R \frac{dB}{dt}$$

The electric field is zero on the axis ($R = 0$), and its magnitude increases linearly with distance R from the axis. (Note that dB/dt is independent of R inside the solenoid.) The electric field distribution is shown schematically in Fig. 28-15b. See Exercise 28-26 for the electric field outside the solenoid.

SUMMARY WITH APPLICATIONS

Section 28-2. Faraday's law
A current is induced in a conducting loop if the magnetic flux linking the loop changes. The induced emf in a single loop is given by Faraday's law:

$$\mathscr{E} = -\frac{d\Phi_B}{dt} \qquad (28\text{-}1)$$

According to Lenz's law, the sense of the induced current is such as to oppose the change in flux which produces it. A small coil with N turns may be treated as N single loops, and the total emf induced is given by

$$\mathscr{E}_T = -N\frac{d\Phi_B}{dt} \qquad (28\text{-}2)$$

Describe situations for which changes in flux cause an induced current in a loop or coil; use Faraday's law to determine the induced emf; use Lenz's law to determine the sense of the induced current.

Section 28-3. Motional emf's
A motional emf is induced if part or all of a circuit moves through a region of magnetic field. In a sliding-wire circuit, the emf is

$$\mathscr{E} = B\ell v \qquad (28\text{-}3)$$

Determine the induced emf and the sense of the induced current in circuits that have conductors moving in a magnetic field.

Section 28-4. Generators and alternators
From Faraday's law, the emf induced in a rotating coil generator is

$$\mathscr{E} = NBS\omega \sin \omega t \qquad (28\text{-}5)$$

In an alternator, an emf is induced in stationary coils by a rotating magnet.

Describe the basic principle of operation of generators and alternators; determine the emf induced in a rotating-coil generator.

Section 28-5. Induced electric fields
If a magnetic field is changing, then an induced electric field exists. The electric field is nonconservative. The induced emf due the induced electric field is

$$\mathscr{E} = \oint \mathbf{E} \cdot d\boldsymbol{\ell} \qquad (28\text{-}6)$$

Faraday's law can be expressed in terms of the fields as

$$\oint \mathbf{E} \cdot d\boldsymbol{\ell} = -\frac{d}{dt}\int \mathbf{B} \cdot d\mathbf{S} \qquad (28\text{-}7)$$

Explain the difference between conservative and nonconservative electric fields; for high symmetry cases, use the integral form of Faraday's law to determine the electric field distribution due to a changing magnetic field.

QUESTIONS

28-1 What are some similarities and some differences between an emf induced by a changing magnetic field and the emf of a battery?

28-2 Suppose that an emf is induced in a conducting loop by a changing magnetic field. Is there an internal resistance similar to that in a battery? Explain.

28-3 Can you think of any way to distinguish between a current induced magnetically in a conducting loop and a current in a loop produced by a battery? Explain.

28-4 Under what circumstances is the induced emf in a coil with N turns equal to N times the emf induced in one turn of the coil?

28-5 Which would cause the larger induced emf in a loop perpendicular to a spatially uniform magnetic field: the magnitude of the field changes linearly from 200 mT to 0 in 1.0 ms or from 1.20 to 1.30 T in 1.0 ms? Explain.

28-6 Suppose that in Fig. 28-2a the coil moves toward the magnet, which is held stationary. In what direction does the pointer deflect on the galvanometer? What if the coil moves away from the stationary magnet? Explain, using Lenz's law.

28-7 The bar magnet in Fig. 28-16 moves to the right. What is the sense of the induced current in the stationary loop A? In loop B?

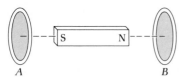

Figure 28-16. Ques. 28-7.

28-8 Suppose that (negatively charged) electrons are the charge carriers in the circuit in Fig. 28-6. What is the direction of the magnetic force on a typical electron in the sliding wire? What is the sense of the current in this case?

28-9 Determine the sense of the induced current in Fig. 28-6 if the wire slides to the left at constant speed v. What is the magnitude of the induced emf in this case?

28-10 Suppose that the wire of length ℓ in Fig. 28-6 is at rest, but that the U-shaped wire moves to the left with speed v. Is there an induced current in the circuit? If so, give its sense. If not, explain why not.

28-11 If the wire of length ℓ and the U-shaped conductor in Fig. 28-6 move together with speed v in the uniform magnetic field, is there an induced current? If so, give its sense. If not, explain why not.

28-12 What is the sense of the induced current in Fig. 28-8 at an instant when $0 < \theta < 90°$? Explain.

28-13 Compare the simple generator in Fig. 28-8 with the simple motor in Fig. 26-7. Is there any distinction in principle between a generator and an electric motor? Explain.

28-14 Imagine measuring the force on a small stationary test charge placed at a point in the changing magnetic field shown in Fig. 28-15. Explain why the force must be exerted by an electric field and not by the magnetic field.

28-15 What are some similarities and some differences between Faraday's law [Eq. (28-7)] and Ampere's law [Eq. (27-16)]?

28-16 A cross section of an ideal solenoid is shown in Fig. 28-17. The magnitude of the spatially uniform field is increasing inside the solenoid and $B = 0$ outside the solenoid. In which of the conducting loops is there an induced current? What is the sense of each current?

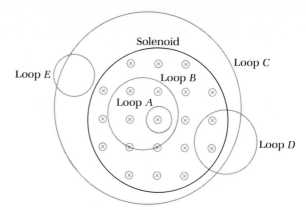

Figure 28-17. Ques. 28-16.

28-17 Suppose that the magnetic field in Fig. 28-17 is not changing. Loop D fits through a slot in the wall of the solenoid. If this loop is pulled out of the solenoid, what is the sense of the induced current? In what direction must you exert a force to pull the loop steadily out of the solenoid?

28-18 Suppose that loop C in Fig. 28-17 is moved in the plane of the figure, but each point on the loop remains outside the solenoid. If the magnetic field in the solenoid is not changing, is there an induced current in the loop? Explain. Must you exert a force to move this loop about very slowly? Explain. What would the answers to the above questions be if B is increasing in the solenoid as the loop is moved?

28-19 A bar magnet, aligned with its axis along the axis of a copper ring, is moved along its length toward the ring. Is there an induced current in the ring? Is there an induced electric field in the ring? Is there a magnetic force on the bar magnet? Explain.

28-20 The bar magnet in the previous question is moved toward a glass (insulating) ring. Is there an induced current in the ring? Is there an induced electric field in the ring? Is there a magnetic force on the bar magnet? Explain.

28-21 Is it possible to have an induced emf in a conducting loop (loop C in Fig. 28-17) even though the magnetic field is zero at each point on the loop? Explain.

28-22 Complete the following table:

Symbol	Represents	Type	SI unit
$d\Phi_B/dt$		Scalar	
$\mathcal{E}$	emf		
$d\mathbf{S}$			
$d\boldsymbol{\ell}$			
$\oint \mathbf{E} \cdot d\boldsymbol{\ell}$			
ω			rad/s

EXERCISES

Section 28-2. Faraday's law

28-1 A circular loop of wire of radius 45 mm is perpendicular to a spatially uniform magnetic field. During a 120-ms time interval, the magnitude of the field changes steadily from 240 to 360 mT. (a) Determine the magnetic flux linking the loop at the beginning and at the end of the time interval. (b) Determine the induced emf in the loop. (c) Construct a diagram with the direction of **B** out of the plane of the paper. Show the sense of the induced current.

28-2 The perpendicular to the plane of a conducting loop makes a fixed angle θ with a spatially uniform magnetic field. If the loop has area S and the magnitude of the field changes at a rate dB/dt, show that the magnitude of the induced emf in the loop is given by $\mathscr{E} = |(dB/dt)S \cos \theta|$. For what orientation(s) of the loop is $\mathscr{E}$ a maximum? A minimum?

28-3 A 25-turn coil with face area 78 mm² is placed inside a long solenoid, near its center. The axes of the coil and of the solenoid coincide. The current in the solenoid is changed so that the magnetic field in the solenoid changes at a constant rate from 150 mT in one direction to 150 mT in the opposite direction in 75 ms. (a) Evaluate the change in flux $\Delta\Phi_B$ linking each turn of the coil for this time interval. (b) Determine the induced emf in the coil. (c) Rework parts (a) and (b), with the axis of the coil making an angle of 70° with the axis of the solenoid.

28-4 The magnetic flux linking each loop of a 250-turn coil is given by the expression $\Phi_B(t) = A + Dt^2$, where $A = 3.0$ mWb and $D = 15$ mWb/s² are constants. (a) Show that the magnitude of the induced emf in the coil is given by $\mathscr{E} = (2ND)t$. (b) Evaluate the flux linking each turn at $t = 0.0$, 1.0, 2.0, and 3.0 s. (c) Evaluate the induced emf in the coil at each of these instants.

28-5 Each loop in a 250-turn coil has face area $S = 9.0 \times 10^{-2}$ m². (a) What is the rate of change of the flux linking each turn of the coil if the induced emf in the coil is 7.5 V? (b) If the flux is due to a uniform magnetic field at 45° from the axis of the coil, what must be the

rate of change of the field to induce that emf?

28-6 The plane of a conducting ring is placed perpendicular to a spatially uniform magnetic field (**B** and **S** parallel, with $S = 10^{-3}$ m²), as shown in Fig. 28-18a. The magnitude of the field has a time dependence shown graphically in Fig. 28-18b. (a) For each 10-ms time interval on the graph, determine the magnitude of the induced emf in the ring and give the sense of the induced current. (b) For which 10-ms time interval is the induced current largest? (c) Is there any interval for which the emf is obviously not constant? Ignore the behavior near the endpoints of each interval. (d) Construct a graph of $\mathscr{E}$ versus t.

28-7 If the magnetic flux linking a loop changes by $\Delta\Phi_B$ in a *finite* time interval Δt, then the average emf $\overline{\mathscr{E}}$ induced in the loop is $\overline{\mathscr{E}} = \Delta\Phi_B/\Delta t$. (a) Determine the average emf induced in the coil of Exercise 28-4 for the time interval between 0.0 and 3.0 s. (b) At what time is the instantaneous emf equal to this average value? (c) What is the current in the coil at this time if the coil's resistance is 15 kΩ?

28-8 Suppose that the magnetic flux linking a loop changes by $\Delta\Phi_B = \Phi_B(t_2) - \Phi_B(t_1)$ during the time interval between t_1 and t_2. (a) Show that the amount of charge that flows past a point in the loop during this time interval is given by $\Delta Q = \Delta\Phi_B/R$, where R is the resistance of the loop. (b) The coil in Exercise 28-4 has resistance 15 kΩ. What charge flows past a point in the coil during the 3.0-s time interval beginning at $t_1 = 0.0$ s?

Section 28-3. Motional emf's

28-9 (a) What emf is induced in the sliding-wire circuit of Fig. 28-6, given that $B = 430$ mT, $\ell = 150$ mm, and $v = 2.6$ m/s? (b) Assume that the sliding wire and the rails of the U have negligible resistance and that the 750-Ω resistance of the circuit is concentrated at the left in the figure. What current exists in the circuit? (c) Determine the magnitude and direction of the magnetic force acting on the sliding wire.

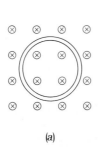

(a)

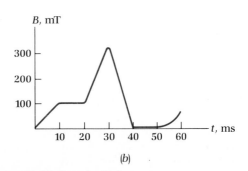

(b)

Figure 28-18. Exercise 28-6.

28-10 The rolling wheels and axles of railroad cars maintain electrical contact with the rails and form a circuit similar to that shown in Fig. 28-6. (Imagine that a resistor connects the rails at a distant point along the track.) Estimate the emf induced in such a circuit by a typical moving freight train in a region where the vertical component of the earth's magnetic field has magnitude 0.1 mT.

28-11 Suppose that the direction of **B** in the sliding-wire circuit of Fig. 28-6 is not perpendicular to the plane of the loop. Determine the emf and construct a diagram for each of the following cases: (*a*) **B** is parallel to **v**. (*b*) **B** is perpendicular to **v** but parallel to the plane of the loop. (*c*) **B** is at angle θ with the area **S** of the loop.

28-12 In the circuit of Fig. 28-19, the velocity of the sliding wire is parallel to the rails so that the wire maintains contact with the rails as it slides. Assume that **B** is uniform and perpendicular to the plane of the circuit and determine the expression for the induced emf in terms of B, ℓ, v, and θ.

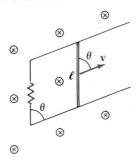

Figure 28-19. Exercise 28-12.

28-13 One conducting U-tube slides inside another, as shown in Fig. 28-20. The arrangement is similar to the slide on a trombone. Assume that electrical contact is maintained between the tubes and that a uniform magnetic field is perpendicularly into the plane of the figure. (*a*) If each tube moves toward the other at constant speed, determine the emf induced in the circuit in terms of B, ℓ, and v. (*b*) What is the sense of the induced current?

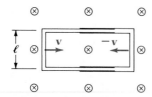

Figure 28-20. Exercise 28-13.

28-14 Two thin, flexible tubes, similar to those in the previous exercise, slide together in a plane perpendicular to a magnetic field **B**. In the case illustrated in Fig. 28-21, the tubes constitute an expanding conducting circle. (*a*) If the radius R of the circle increases at a constant rate $v_R = dR/dt$, determine the emf induced in the circuit in terms of B, R, and v_R. (*b*) What is the sense of the induced current?

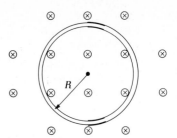

Figure 28-21. Exercise 28-14.

28-15 The rectangular conducting loop shown in Fig. 28-22, of dimensions $w = 0.40$ m and $\ell = 0.20$ m, moves perpendicularly into a region of uniform field with constant speed $v = 5.6$ m/s. The leading edge of the loop enters the field region at $t = 0$ and $B = 0.15$ T. (*a*) At what time t_1 does the trailing edge enter the field region? (*b*) Evaluate the induced emf in the loop for $0 < t < t_1$. (*c*) What is the sense of the induced current? (*d*) Determine the net magnetic force acting on the loop during this time interval if the loop's resistance is 1200 Ω (*e*) Can the magnetic field have an abrupt spatial variation, as assumed in this exercise? See Exercise 27-23.

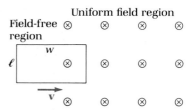

Figure 28-22. Exercise 28-15.

28-16 A rectangular current loop moves with constant velocity from a field-free region into a region of uniform magnetic field, as shown in Fig. 28-22. Determine an expression for the induced emf in the moving loop when (*a*) the entire loop is in the field-free region, (*b*) part of the loop is in the region of uniform field, and (*c*) the entire loop is the region of uniform field. (*d*) In each case give the sense of the induced current if one exists in the loop.

28-17 A conducting rod of length $\ell = 120$ mm is pivoted at one end as the other end slides on a circular conductor perpendicular to a uniform magnetic field $B = 400$ mT, as shown in Fig. 28-23. The rod rotates counterclockwise with constant angular speed $\omega = 370$ rad/s. Assume that all of the $R = 1200$-Ω resistance of the circuit is contained in the resistance symbol in the figure. (*a*) Determine an expression for the induced current in the circuit in terms of ℓ, B, ω, and R. (*b*) Evaluate the current using the values above. (*c*) What is the sense of the induced current? (*d*) Evaluate the magnitude of the magnetic torque on the rotating rod about an axis parallel to **B** and through the pivot point. How can the rod rotate with constant angular speed?

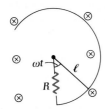

Figure 28-23. Exercise 28-17.

28-18 Suppose that the sliding wire in Fig. 28-6 starts from rest at $t = 0$ and is caused to move with a constant acceleration to the right with magnitude a. (a) Show that the induced emf is given by $\mathscr{E} = B\ell at$. (b) What is the sense of the induced current?

Section 28-4. Generators and alternators

28-19 Show that the SI units for each side of Eq. (28-5) are consistent. That is, show that the SI unit of the product $NBS\omega \sin \omega t$ equals the volt.

28-20 A plane conducting loop has face area of 5×10^{-2} m^2 and rotates about an axis perpendicular to a uniform magnetic field of magnitude $B = 0.4$ T, as shown in Fig. 28-8. The loop rotates with a constant frequency $\nu = 60$ Hz. (a) Determine the angular frequency ω of rotation of the loop. (b) What maximum emf is induced in the loop?

28-21 For the rotating loop in the previous exercise, determine (a) the maximum value of the flux linking the loop and (b) the maximum value of the current in the loop if the total resistance of the circuit is 1500 Ω. (c) If the flux linking the loop has a maximum at $t = 0$, at what times is the induced current a maximum?

28-22 A generator coil rotates at 480 Hz about an axis perpendicular to a uniform magnetic field such as shown in Fig. 28-8. (a) If the coil has face area 2.5×10^{-3} m^2 and $B = 37$ mT, then what maximum emf is induced in each turn of the coil? (b) How many turns must this coil have if the maximum emf in the coil is to be 170 V?

28-23 The 25-turn coil of a generator rotates with angular frequency $\omega = 377$ rad/s in a *nonuniform* but constant magnetic field. The magnetic flux linking each turn of the coil is given by $\Phi_B(t) = C_1 \cos \omega t + C_3 \cos 3\omega t$, where $C_1 = 2.4 \times 10^{-4}$ Wb and $C_3 = 7.1 \times 10^{-6}$ Wb are constants. (a) Determine an expression for the induced emf in each turn of the coil. (b) What is the maximum value of the output voltage of this generator? (c) Evaluate the output voltage of the generator at $t = 2.1$ ms.

28-24 A generator has six coils spaced symmetrically at 60° around a rotating armature. A multiple commutator connects each coil in turn to an external circuit so that a given coil is connected for only 1/6 of a revolution of the armature. The flux linking the connected coil has a time dependence that is shown graphically in Fig. 28-24. Disregard the abrupt changes in flux that correspond to one coil being disconnected from the circuit at the commutator while the next coil is being connected. (a) Construct a graph showing qualitatively the time dependence of the emf of this generator. (b) Estimate the maximum emf. (c) Is this generator ac or dc?

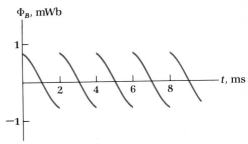

Figure 28-24. Exercise 28-24.

28-25 The flux linking each turn of a 300-turn alternator coil is approximately given by $\Phi_B \approx C \cos \omega_1 t$, where $C = 3 \times 10^{-4}$ Wb and $\omega_1 = 2\pi\nu_1$ is the angular frequency of rotation of the alternator shaft. The alternator shaft is connected by a drive belt to an automobile engine and makes three revolutions for each revolution of the engine. (a) Determine an expression for the induced emf in the alternator. Determine the maximum emf if the engine speed is (b) $\nu_0 = 600$ rev/min and (c) $\nu_0 = 4000$ rev/min.

Section 28-5. Induced electric fields

28-26 Assume that the wall of the ideal solenoid in Fig. 28-15a is very thin and has radius a, so that **B** is spatially uniform for $R < a$ and $B = 0$ for $R > a$. (a) Extend Example 28-4 to show that the induced electric field at a point outside the solenoid has magnitude

$$E = \frac{a^2}{2R} \frac{dB}{dt} \qquad (R > a)$$

(b) Construct a graph showing the dependence of E on R for $0 \leqslant R \leqslant 2a$.

28-27 The magnitude of the magnetic field inside an ideal solenoid, as seen in Fig. 28-15a, changes steadily from 0 at $t = 0$ to 0.40 T at $t = 1.4$ s. The solenoid is thin-walled, with a diameter of 15 mm. Determine the magnitude of the electric field at $t = 0.8$ s at a point (a) on the axis of the solenoid, (b) 5.0 mm from the axis, and (c) outside the solenoid 10.0 mm from the axis. (d) What are the answers to parts (a), (b), and (c) at $t = 1.2$ s?

28-28 A circular loop of wire is placed with its plane perpendicular to the axis of the solenoid described in the previous exercise. The center of the loop is on the solenoid axis. Evaluate $\oint \mathbf{E} \cdot d\boldsymbol{\ell}$ at $t = 0.8$ s around a circular path coinciding with the loop if the loop has radius (a) 5.0 mm and (b) 10 mm. (c) In each case determine the induced emf in the loop. (d) What is the answer to part (a) if the center of the loop is 1.0 mm off the solenoid axis?

28-29 Gauss's law for electric fields [Eq. (21-3)] holds generally, even if the magnetic field is changing. Give an argument, based on symmetry and Gauss's law for electric fields, to support the assertion that the induced electric field shown in Fig. 28-15 has only a tangential component. That is, the electric field has no component directed toward or away from the axis of the solenoid. Assume that there is no excess charge

inside the solenoid and that the electric field is perpendicular to the axis of the solenoid.

28-30 The axis of a bar magnet, which produces an axially symmetric magnetic field, coincides with the axis of a circular conducting loop of radius 0.25 m. The magnet moves along this axis toward the loop. At a certain instant the induced emf in the loop is 0.17 V. (a) Determine the magnitude of the induced electric field in the loop. Assume that $\mathbf{E}$ is tangent to the loop at each point (see the previous exercise). (b) At what rate is the magnetic flux linking the loop changing at this instant? (c) Can you determine how $\mathbf{B}$ is changing at any given point? Explain.

PROBLEMS

28-1 Consider the sliding-wire circuit shown in Fig. 28-25. The wire slides at constant speed and the plane of the circuit is perpendicular to a uniform magnetic field. Show that the induced emf is given by $\mathscr{E} = B\ell v^2 t/D$ for $0 < t < D/v$. What is the expression for the emf for $t > D/v$?

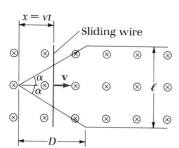

Figure 28-25. Prob. 28-1.

28-2 A rectangular conducting loop lies in a plane which contains the axis of a long, straight wire carrying a current $i(t)$, as shown in Fig. 28-26. Determine expressions for (a) the flux linking the loop and (b) the induced emf in the loop in terms of the current in the wire.

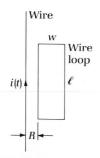

Figure 28-26. Prob. 28-2.

28-3 A rectangular conducting loop moves at constant velocity from a field-free region into a region with a

time-dependent but spatially uniform magnetic field, as shown in Fig. 28-22. The leading edge enters the uniform field region at $t = 0$, and the trailing edge enters that region at $t_1 = w/v$. During this time interval, the magnetic field changes at a constant rate from B_0 to $2B_0$. Determine expressions, valid for $0 < t < t_1$, for (a) the magnetic flux linking the loop and (b) the induced emf in the loop. (c) Evaluate the emf at $t = 0.10$ s for the case $B_0 = 0.30$ T, $w = 0.50$ m, $\ell = 0.20$ m, $v = 4.0$ m/s.

28-4 Suppose that the sliding-wire circuit in Fig. 28-6 lies in a horizontal plane, and the wire of mass m slides with negligible friction on the rails. The rails and the sliding wire have negligible resistance, and the resistance R of the circuit is concentrated in the symbol to the left in the figure. The magnetic field is uniform and constant, but the speed $v(t)$ of the wire is not constant. (a) Show that the emf in the circuit is given by $\mathscr{E}(t) = B\ell v(t)$. (b) If $i(t)$ represents the current in the circuit, determine the magnetic force acting on the wire. (c) Suppose that no other horizontal force acts on the wire, which has speed v_0 at $t = 0$. By applying Newton's second law, show that the speed of the sliding wire is given by $v(t) = v_0 e^{-t/\tau}$, where $\tau = mR/B^2\ell^2$ is a damping time for the motion. (d) How far does the wire slide in coming to rest?

28-5 Suppose that the sliding wire in Fig. 28-6 and in the previous problem is initially at rest at $x = x_0 > 0$. Further, the magnetic field is not constant, but its magnitude increases from B_0 at $t = 0$ at a constant rate $dB/dt = C$ (with $C > 0$). An induced current will exist in the wire, and the wire will move in response to the magnetic force acting on it. (a) Show that the induced emf is given by $\mathscr{E} = \ell [B(t)v_x(t) + Cx(t)]$, where $v_x(t)$ is the x component of the velocity of the wire. (b) What is the sense of the induced current at $t = 0$? (c) In what direction does the wire begin to move at $t = 0$? (d) What are the answers to parts (b) and (c) if B decreases $(C < 0)$?

28-6 A sliding-wire circuit is mounted on a board whose plane is vertical, as shown in Fig. 28-27. Assume that all of the resistance R in the circuit is concentrated at the bottom and that the wire slides with negligible friction on the rails. A uniform magnetic field **B** is perpendicular to the plane of the circuit. (*a*) Show that the speed of the sliding wire will approach a terminal speed given by $v_T = mgR/B^2 \ell^2$, where m is the mass of the wire. (*b*) What is the expression for the terminal speed if the top of the board is tilted back so that the plane of the circuit makes an angle θ with the horizontal magnetic field?

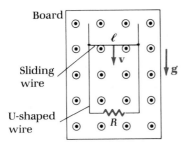

Figure 28-27. Prob. 28-6.

28-7 Suppose that the rectangular loop in Fig. 28-26 is moving to the right at constant speed v so that $R = R_0 + vt$. If a steady current I exists in the long, straight wire, determine expressions for (*a*) the magnetic flux linking the loop and (*b*) the induced emf. (*c*) What is the sense of the induced current in the loop?

28-8 A magnetic field directed along the z axis has axial symmetry about the axis. If R represents the perpendicular distance from the axis, then at points in the xy plane, the z component of the magnetic field at time t is given by

$$B_z(t) = \frac{Ct/\tau}{a^2 + R^2}$$

where $C = 15$ mWb, $a = 64$ mm, and $\tau = 2.0$ s are constants. (*a*) Determine an expression for the magnitude of the electric field E at a point in the xy plane. (*b*) At what distance from the axis is E a maximum? (*c*) Construct a graph showing the dependence of E on R for $0 \leqslant R \leqslant 2a$. Assume that $E = 0$ for $R = 0$.

28-9 A *search coil* (also called a *flip coil*) is sometimes used to measure the magnitude of the magnetic field B in a region. Such a coil has N turns, each with face area S. The coil is small so that the magnetic field is essentially uniform over the dimensions of the coil. The search coil is initially placed with its axis parallel to the field to be measured. It is then rotated, or "flipped," through 180° so that the axis is again parallel to the field but with the opposite sense. During this time, the coil is connected to a *ballistic galvanometer*, a device that measures the total charge $\Delta Q = \int i(t) \, dt$

passing through it. Show that B is given by

$$B = \frac{R \, \Delta Q}{2NS}$$

where R is the resistance of the circuit.

28-10 The *betatron* uses a changing magnetic field in accelerating electrons (beta particles) to energies around 100 MeV. The electrons circulate in a tube of mean radius R, as shown schematically in Fig. 28-28. They are accelerated by an induced electric field which is tangent to the circular path. (*a*) Show that the magnitude of the tangential force on an electron is given by

$$F = eE = \frac{e}{2\pi R} \frac{d}{dt} \int B_z(t) \, dS$$

where $B_z(t)$ is the axial component of the magnetic field and the flux is evaluated over the plane bounded by the circular path. (*b*) The magnetic field at the position of an electron in the beam exerts a force directed toward the center. Show that the magnitude of the momentum of an electron in the tube is given by $p = eRB_{0z}(t)$, where $B_{0z}(t)$ is the magnetic field component at the position of the electron beam. (*c*) Parts (*a*) and (*b*) show that the induced electric field provides the tangential force and the magnetic field provides the centripetal force on an electron in a stable orbit. Show that for such an orbit, the magnetic field component B_{0z} at the beam position must be one-half the average field component over the circle; that is,

$$B_{0z}(t) = \frac{1}{2\pi R^2} \int B_z(t) \, dS$$

(*d*) Explain how this result shows the necessity of a nonuniform magnetic field in the betatron.

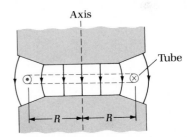

Figure 28-28. Prob. 28-10: Cross section of a betatron.

28-11 The nonuniform magnetic field in the betatron in the previous problem is obtained by using the beveled pole pieces shown schematically in Fig. 28-28. The time dependence of the field is due to an alternating current in the coils (not shown) of the magnet. Suppose that the magnetic field varies sinusoidally, with a frequency $\nu = 60$ Hz, $B_z(t) = B_z(0) \sin 2\pi\nu t$, and the magnetic flux for the circle of radius $R = 0.80$ m has a maximum value of 1.6 Wb. (*a*) What is the sense of the accelerating electron beam if the magnitude of the magnetic field in the figure is increasing? (*b*) Explain why the entire acceleration process must take place over one-fourth of a cycle ($\frac{1}{240}$ s). (*c*) Estimate the kinetic energy gained by an electron in one revolution.

(*d*) An electron accelerated in this betatron may have a final kinetic energy of 100 MeV. Estimate the number of revolutions of an electron during the $\frac{1}{240}$-s time interval.

CHAPTER 29
INDUCTANCE

29-1 INTRODUCTION

The last chapter introduced Faraday's law, a fundamental law of electromagnetism. The emphasis was on induced emf's and induced electric fields. We discussed generators and alternators as examples of practical devices based on Faraday's law. In this chapter the emphasis is on the application of Faraday's law to determine the behavior of simple circuit elements in circuits with currents that change. An induced emf can appear in a circuit element called an *inductor*, and the circuit is then said to contain *inductance*. We shall also encounter an important principle of electromagnetism — that energy is associated with (or stored in) a magnetic field.

29-2 SELF-INDUCED EMF'S AND SELF-INDUCTANCE

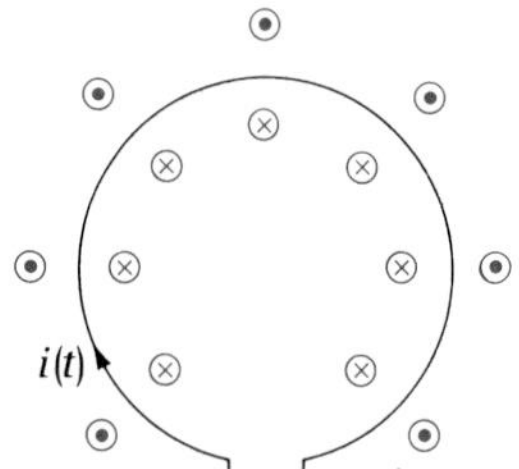

If the magnetic flux linking a circuit loop changes, then an induced emf exists in the circuit and is given by Faraday's law, $\mathcal{E} = -d\Phi_B/dt$ [Eq. (28-1)]. In the last chapter we assumed that the flux linking a loop was due to an external magnetic field — one produced by a magnet, for example. We now consider a case for which the magnetic field is due to the current in the loop itself.

A circuit with a single plane loop is shown in Fig. 29-1. When the switch S is closed (say at $t = 0$), the battery causes charge carriers to begin moving. That is, a nonzero current $i(t)$ exists at any time after the switch is closed. The current in the loop produces a magnetic field in the vicinity of the loop, as shown schematically in the plane of the figure. Thus there is a magnetic flux linking the loop, and the flux is due to the loop's own current. Since this current is changing, the magnetic flux is also changing, and from Faraday's law an induced emf, a *self-induced emf*, exists in the loop. Faraday's law and Lenz's law apply generally to a magnetically induced emf. A self-induced emf is a special case: The self-induced emf in a circuit is due to the changes that occur in that circuit; in a sense, the changing current acts back on itself.

Figure 29-1. A changing current in a loop produces a changing flux linking the loop and a self-induced emf.

A self-induced emf is due to a change in the current in a circuit.

To see how the self-induced emf in the circuit of Fig. 29-1 depends on the changing current, note that at a point the magnetic field due to the current is proportional to the current. This result can be seen from the linear relationship between $\mathbf{B}$ and i in the Biot-Savart law, Eq. (27-3), or in Ampere's law, Eq. (27-8). Since the magnetic flux linking the loop is $\Phi_B = \int \mathbf{B} \cdot d\mathbf{S}$, we see that the flux is also proportional to the current in the loop, or

$$\Phi_B = Li \qquad (29\text{-}1)$$

Self-inductance L and self-induced emf $\mathcal{E}_L$

where the constant of proportionality L is defined as the *self-inductance* of the loop. Applying Faraday's law, $\mathcal{E} = -d\Phi_B/dt$, we obtain the self-induced emf $\mathcal{E}_L$ in the loop,

$$\mathcal{E}_L = -L\frac{di}{dt} \qquad (29\text{-}2)$$

Notice that the self-induced emf depends on the rate of change of the current. The negative sign in Eq. (29-2) determines the sense of the induced emf in accord with Lenz's law. For example, suppose that the current in the loop in Fig. 29-1 is increasing. Then the magnetic flux is also increasing, and the sense of the self-induced emf is opposite the sense of the increasing current.

Although Eq. (29-2) was obtained for a simple loop circuit in a plane, experiments on more complicated circuits and circuit elements show that the result is more generally valid. A circuit element is characterized by a self-inductance (or inductance) L, and the self-induced emf in the element is given by Eq. (29-2). In the absence of magnetic materials such as iron, the inductance of a circuit element such as a coil depends only on the geometry of the element. The SI unit of inductance is the henry (H), named after Joseph Henry (see the Commentary in this chapter). From Eq. (29-2), we have $1 \text{ H} = 1 \text{ V} \cdot \text{s} \cdot \text{A}^{-1}$. The henry is a fairly large unit of inductance. In electronic circuits, values of self-inductance of coils are typically in the $1\text{-}\mu\text{H}$ to 1-mH range.

The self-inductance L can be calculated for a few simple circuit elements from an expression similar to Eq. (29-1). That equation shows how the flux (due to the magnetic field of the current) linking the loop depends linearly on the current in the loop. For a coil such as a long solenoid that has essentially the same flux Φ_B linking each turn, the self-induced emf is the same in each of the turns. The emf induced in an N-turn coil is $\mathcal{E}_L = -N\,d\Phi_B/dt = -L\,di/dt$, where L is the self-inductance of the coil. For such a coil we write, in analogy with Eq. (29-1),

$$N\Phi_B = Li \qquad (29\text{-}3)$$

If the flux Φ_B linking each turn of the coil can be calculated in terms of the current in the coil, then the inductance can be determined from Eq. (29-3).

To illustrate the calculation of inductance, suppose that a long, tightly wound solenoid has length ℓ, cross-sectional area S, and n turns per unit length. Inside the solenoid the magnetic field due to the current i is approximately uniform and parallel to the axis of the solenoid. The magnitude of the field is given by Eq. (27-11), $B = \mu_0 ni$, and we neglect end effects. Each turn is approximately a loop with plane area S, and the flux linking a loop is $\Phi_B = \int \mathbf{B} \cdot d\mathbf{S} = \int B\,dS = BS = \mu_0 niS$. For a solenoid of length ℓ, there are $N = n\ell$ turns, so that $N\Phi_B = (n\ell)(\mu_0 niS) = \mu_0 n^2 S\ell i$. Using Eq. (29-3), we obtain the self-inductance of a long, tightly wound solenoid:

Inductance of a long solenoid

$$L = \mu_0 n^2 S\ell \qquad (29\text{-}4)$$

Notice that the inductance depends, apart from the constant μ_0, only on the length, area, and number of turns per unit length — that is, only on geometrical quantities. We emphasize that Eq. (29-4) is an approximate result, based on the field inside an ideal (infinitely long) solenoid; end effects have been neglected.

Calculating the inductance of a circuit element is feasible for only a few configurations (see Prob. 29-1). Generally, the inductance can be measured by observing its effect on a circuit containing the element. In the next section we consider a simple circuit with inductance.

EXAMPLE 29-1. A coil with self-inductance $L = 23\ \mu$H is in a circuit. Determine the self-induced emf in the coil if the current changes steadily from 1.7 to 2.9 mA in a 50-μs time interval.

SOLUTION. Since the current changes steadily in the time interval,

$$\frac{di}{dt} = \frac{2.9\ \text{mA} - 1.7\ \text{mA}}{0.050\ \text{ms}} = 24\ \text{A/s}$$

From Eq. (29-2), the value of the self-induced emf is

$$\mathcal{E}_L = (23\ \mu\text{H})(24\ \text{A/s}) = 550\ \mu\text{V}$$

The sense of the induced emf, from Lenz's law, is opposite the sense of the increasing current in the coil.

EXAMPLE 29-2. A solenoid is constructed by winding fine wire on a cylindrical frame of radius 25 mm and length 120 mm. How many turns must be wound on the frame if the inductance is to be 0.67 mH? Neglect effects at the ends of the solenoid.

SOLUTION. The number of turns per unit length can be obtained from Eq. (29-4). Solving for n^2,

$$n^2 = \frac{L}{\mu_0 S \ell}$$

$$= \frac{0.67\ \text{mH}}{(4\pi \times 10^{-7}\ \text{T} \cdot \text{m} \cdot \text{A}^{-1})[\pi(0.025\ \text{m})^2](0.12\ \text{m})}$$

$$= 2.3 \times 10^6\ \text{m}^{-2}$$

Taking a square root gives $n = 1500\ \text{m}^{-1}$. The number of turns in the 120-mm length is then

$$N = n\ell = (1500\ \text{m}^{-1})(0.12\ \text{m}) = 180\ \text{turns}$$

29-3 *LR* CIRCUITS

Suppose that a solenoid is connected to a battery through a switch. Beginning at $t = 0$, when the switch is closed, the battery causes charge to move in the circuit. A solenoid, such as the one in Example 29-1, has inductance L and resistance R, and each of these influences the current in the circuit. The inductive and resistive effects of a solenoid are shown schematically in Fig. 29-2. The symbol for inductance ($-\!\!\infty\!\!-$) is shown in series with the resistance symbol. For simplicity we assume that all of the resistance in the circuit, including the internal resistance of the battery, is represented by R. Similarly, L includes the self-inductance of the connecting wires. A circuit, such as that seen in Fig. 29-2, containing resistance and inductance in series is called an *LR circuit*.

The role of the inductance in determining the current in the circuit can be understood qualitatively: As the current $i(t)$ in the circuit increases (from $i = 0$ at $t = 0$), there is a self-induced emf $\mathcal{E}_L = -L\ di/dt$ in the inductance whose sense is opposite the sense of the increasing current. That is, since the current is increasing, the sense of the induced emf opposes that increase. This opposition to the increase in current prevents the current from rising abruptly (prevents di/dt from becoming very large). On the other hand, if the current changed negligibly (that is, di/dt is very small), there would be little opposition

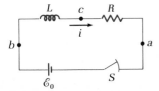

Figure 29-2. An inductance L and resistance R are in series with a battery of emf $\mathcal{E}_0$. Switch S is closed at $t = 0$.

to a change in the current. The net effect of the inductance is to moderate between these extremes so that the current changes, but not too abruptly. The instantaneous value of the current depends on the values of L, R, and the emf of the battery, $\mathcal{E}_0$.

The time dependence of the current in the LR circuit of Fig. 29-2 can be determined by applying the loop rule (Sec. 25-4). Beginning at point a in the figure and proceeding clockwise, we sum the voltage changes encountered and equate the sum to zero:

$$(V_b - V_a) + (V_c - V_b) + (V_a - V_c) = 0$$

$$\mathcal{E}_0 - L\frac{di}{dt} - Ri = 0$$

Notice that the emf across the inductance, $V_c - V_b = -L\,di/dt$, is negative in accord with Lenz's law if i is increasing $(di/dt > 0)$. Rearranging the above equation, we see that the time dependence of the current in the LR circuit is governed by the differential equation

LR circuit equation

$$L\frac{di}{dt} + Ri = \mathcal{E}_0 \tag{29-5}$$

This LR circuit equation is mathematically equivalent to the equation for the RC circuit in Chap. 25 where we solved it by separating variables. That is, Eq. (29-5) can be rearranged to give

$$\frac{di}{i - \mathcal{E}_0/R} = -\frac{R}{L}\,dt$$

Integrating each side of the equation, we obtain

$$\ln\left(i - \frac{\mathcal{E}_0}{R}\right) = -\left(\frac{R}{L}\right)t + \ln K$$

Inductive time constant

where $\ln K$ is a constant of integration. The exponential form of this result is $i - \mathcal{E}_0/R = Ke^{-(R/L)t}$. The constant of integration K is evaluated by applying the initial condition, $i(0) = 0$. Thus $K = -\mathcal{E}_0/R$. We introduce a characteristic time parameter, $\tau_L = L/R$, called the *inductive time constant*, so that the exponential function is written e^{-t/τ_L}. Then the current in the circuit at time t is given by

Current in an LR circuit with a battery

$$i(t) = \frac{\mathcal{E}_0}{R}\left(1 - e^{-t/\tau_L}\right) \tag{29-6}$$

Notice that as $t \to \infty$, the current approaches the asymptotic value $I = \mathcal{E}_0/R$, which is the value we would obtain by neglecting inductance altogether.

The inductive time constant τ_L in the exponential e^{-t/τ_L} sets the time scale for the LR circuit. That is, the current cannot change significantly over a time interval much smaller than τ_L. For example, the current changes from zero at $t = 0$ to $(\mathcal{E}_0/R)(1 - e^{-1}) \approx 0.63\mathcal{E}_0/R$ at $t = \tau_L$. The exponential function e^{-t/τ_L} decreases with time and approaches zero. At $t = 5\tau_L$, for instance, $e^{-5} \approx 6.7 \times 10^{-3}$ and $i \approx 0.993\mathcal{E}_0/R$. In this way the current asymptotically approaches the steady value $I = \mathcal{E}_0/R$. These features of the time dependence of the current in an LR circuit are shown graphically in Fig. 29-3.

The inductance in the LR circuit of Fig. 29-2 opposed the increasing current in the circuit. The sense of the self-induced emf was opposite the sense of the increasing current. There is also an LR circuit in which the current decreases,

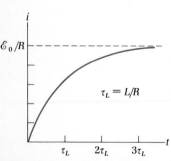

Figure 29-3. The current in the LR circuit increases from zero to the asymptotic value $\mathcal{E}_0/R$. The inductive time constant τ_L sets the time scale for changes in current.

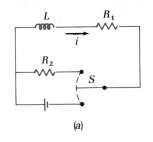

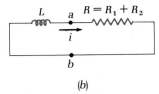

(a)

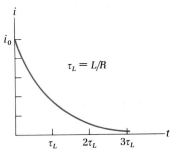

(b)

Figure 29-4. (a) A switch S removes the battery from the circuit and forms a new circuit containing L, R_1, and R_2. (b) The equivalent circuit has $R = R_1 + R_2$.

Current in an LR circuit without a battery

Figure 29-5. The current decreases exponentially from i_0 initially to zero asymptotically.

and the self-induced emf in the inductor then has the same sense as the decreasing current. The induced emf again opposes the change that produces it.

Figure 29-4a shows a circuit with a switching arrangement that removes the battery from the original circuit and forms a new circuit. We suppose that the current in the new circuit, shown as an equivalent circuit in Fig. 29-4b, with $R = R_1 + R_2$, has an initial value i_0 when the switching occurs at $t = 0$. The current will decrease from this initial value, and the sense of the self-induced emf, $\mathscr{E}_L = -L\,di/dt$, is the same as the sense of the decreasing current ($di/dt < 0$). Application of the loop rule (Exercise 29-15) gives $-L\,di/dt - iR = 0$, or

$$L\frac{di}{dt} + Ri = 0 \tag{29-7}$$

which is the same as the LR circuit equation of Eq. (29-5) with no battery in the circuit ($\mathscr{E}_0 = 0$).

Equation (29-7) can be solved with the approach used for the LR circuit with a battery (see Exercise 29-16). The solution is

$$i(t) = Ke^{-t/\tau_L}$$

where K is a constant of integration. We apply the initial condition, $i = i_0$ at $t = 0$, to evaluate the constant K. Since $e^0 = 1$, we have $K = i_0$, and the current in the circuit at time t is given by

$$i(t) = i_0 e^{-t/\tau_L} \tag{29-8}$$

The current decreases exponentially from the initial value i_0 to zero. At $t = \tau_L$ the current has dropped to $i_0 e^{-1} \approx 0.37 i_0$, and at $5\tau_L$ the current has dropped to about $6.7 \times 10^{-3} i_0$. Once again the inductive time constant, $\tau_L = L/R$, sets the time scale for substantial current changes in the LR circuit. The time dependence of the current is shown graphically in Fig. 29-5.

In some circuits an external emf, such as a battery, is periodically switched in and out of an LR circuit. The time dependence of the current alternates between increasing, as in Fig. 29-3, and decreasing, as in Fig. 29-5. The behavior of the current is shown graphically in Fig. 29-6 for a switching period $T = 6\tau_L$.

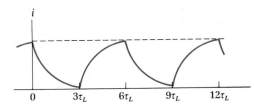

Figure 29-6. The current in an LR circuit is alternately increasing and decreasing as a battery is switched in and out of the circuit. This switching is periodic, with period $T = 6\tau_L$.

EXAMPLE 29-3. A 1.2-mH coil is removed from the ignition circuit of an automobile for testing. The coil is connected in series with a 13.6-V storage battery and a switch that is closed at $t = 0$. After several seconds the current in the circuit has a steady value of 1.6 A. Determine (a) the resistance in the circuit, (b) the inductive time constant, and (c) the time at which the current is 0.80 A.

SOLUTION. (a) From Eq. (29-6), we note that the steady, asymptotic value of the current in an LR circuit is $I = \mathscr{E}_0/R$.

Thus

$$R = \frac{\mathscr{E}_0}{I} = \frac{13.6 \text{ V}}{1.6 \text{ A}} = 8.5 \ \Omega$$

(b) The inductive time constant is

$$\tau_L = \frac{L}{R} = \frac{1.2 \text{ mH}}{8.5 \ \Omega} = 0.14 \text{ ms}$$

(c) Let t_1 represent the time when $i = 0.80$ A. Substituting into Eq. (29-6) gives

$$0.80 \text{ A} = (1.6 \text{ A})(1 - e^{-t_1/\tau_L})$$

Solving for the exponential, we have $e^{-t_1/\tau_L} = 0.50$. Taking the logarithm gives

$$\ln e^{-t_1/\tau_L} = \frac{-t_1}{\tau_L} = \ln 0.50 = -\ln 2.0$$

or $t_1 = \tau_L \ln 2.0 = 0.69 \, \tau_L$. Thus the current reaches 0.80 A, half its asymptotic value, at

$$t_1 = (0.69)(0.14 \text{ ms}) = 0.098 \text{ ms}$$

EXAMPLE 29-4. The coil in Example 29-3 is in a different circuit with total series resistance $R = 24 \, \Omega$ and no battery. (a) Determine the inductive time constant for this circuit. (b) What is the initial current value i_0 at $t = 0$ if $i = 38$ mA at $t = 0.075$ ms?

SOLUTION. (a) The inductive time constant is

$$\tau_L = \frac{L}{R} = \frac{1.2 \text{ mH}}{24 \, \Omega} = 0.050 \text{ ms}$$

(b) Substituting into Eq. (29-8), we have

$$38 \text{ mA} = i_0 e^{-(0.075 \text{ ms})/(0.050 \text{ ms})} = 0.22 i_0$$

This gives, for the initial current value,

$$i_0 = \frac{38 \text{ mA}}{0.22} = 170 \text{ mA}$$

29-4   ENERGY TRANSFERS IN *LR* CIRCUITS

The electric potential energy of charge carriers changes as carriers move through a potential difference in a circuit element. The power, or rate of energy transformation, in a circuit element with current i and potential difference V is given by Eq. (25-7): $P = iV$. What energy transformations occur in an inductor? Joule heating occurs at the rate $P = iV = i(iR) = i^2R$ because of the ohmic resistance of an inductor. An additional energy transformation takes place while the current is changing in an inductor. That is, across the inductor there is a self-induced emf $V = L \, di/dt$ and the power for this transformation is $P = iV = i(L \, di/dt)$, or

Power in an inductance

$$P = Li \frac{di}{dt} \tag{29-9}$$

Whether the charge carriers gain or lose electric potential energy depends on how the current changes. If the current is increasing in the inductor, the sense of the self-induced emf is opposite the current, and the carriers lose potential energy. If the current is decreasing, the sense of the self-induced emf is the same as the sense of the current, and the carriers gain potential energy. Since the charge carriers can either gain or lose potential energy because of the inductance, the potential energy is transformed to and from a *stored energy* in the inductance. That is, this energy is stored as the carriers lose potential energy when the current is increasing in the inductor (as in the circuit in Fig. 29-2). The energy is *recovered* as the carriers gain potential energy when the current is decreasing in the inductor (as in the circuit in Fig. 29-4b). We shall call this energy the *energy stored in the inductor,* and later we shall associate this stored energy with the magnetic field of the inductor. Notice that energy is not stored (is not recoverable) in the resistance of a circuit. Charge carriers can only lose potential energy through Joule heating at the rate $P = i^2R$ in the resistance.

Energy stored in an inductor is recoverable.

The amount of energy stored in an inductor with current i depends on the current. To determine the amount, consider the circuit in Fig. 29-2. At some time t, the current in the circuit is $i(t)$ and it is changing (increasing in this case) at the rate di/dt. From Eq. (29-9), the stored energy U in the inductor is increasing at the rate $dU/dt = P = Li\,di/dt$. Equivalently, the infinitesimal change dU in the stored energy corresponding to a change di in current is $dU = P\,dt = Li(di/dt)\,dt$, or

$$dU = Li\,di$$

Integrating this expression, we obtain the energy stored in the inductor:

Energy stored in an inductor
$$U = \tfrac{1}{2}Li^2 \qquad\qquad (29\text{-}10)$$

The constant of integration has been chosen so that the stored energy in an inductor with no current is zero. For an inductor with current i, the stored energy is positive and independent of the sense of the current.

EXAMPLE 29-5. (a) Determine the energy stored in a 23-mH coil carrying a 2.5-A current. (b) By what factor must the current be increased to have twice that stored energy?

SOLUTION. (a) Applying Eq. (29-10) gives

$$U = \tfrac{1}{2}Li^2 = \tfrac{1}{2}(23\text{ mH})(2.5\text{ A})^2 = 72\text{ mJ}$$

(b) Since the stored energy is proportional to the square of the current, the energy is doubled if i^2 is doubled: $i'^2 = 2i^2$. Thus the current i' must be larger by a factor of $\sqrt{2}$, or $i' = \sqrt{2}(2.5\text{ A}) = 3.5\text{ A}$.

Magnetic energy and energy density. The stored energy in an inductor carrying a current, $U = \tfrac{1}{2}Li^2$, is analogous to the energy stored in a charged capacitor, $U = \tfrac{1}{2}Q^2/C$ [Eq. (23-5)]. In Chap. 23 we saw that the stored energy in a capacitor could be considered as energy stored in the electric field. The general expression for the electric energy density u_E (energy per unit volume stored in the electric field E) is given by $u_E = \tfrac{1}{2}\epsilon_0 E^2$ [Eq. (23-6)]. There is a similar interpretation of the energy stored in an inductor as a special case of energy stored in the magnetic field.

To see how the energy stored in an inductor is related to a magnetic field, consider a long, tightly wound solenoid carrying a current i. The solenoid has length ℓ, cross-sectional area S, and n turns per unit length. We treat it as an ideal solenoid, so that the self-inductance is given by Eq. (29-4), $L = \mu_0 n^2 S\ell$. In obtaining this result we took **B** to be parallel to the axis and uniform inside the solenoid, with $B = \mu_0 ni$. Outside the solenoid, B is assumed to be negligibly small. Substituting the above expression for L into Eq. (29-10) gives for the stored energy

$$U = \tfrac{1}{2}Li^2 = \tfrac{1}{2}\mu_0 n^2 S\ell i^2$$

Since $B = \mu_0 ni$, the current $i = B/\mu_0 n$ can be eliminated from the expression above; this gives, after simplifying,

$$U = \frac{B^2}{2\mu_0}\,S\ell \qquad\qquad (29\text{-}11)$$

The energy stored in this solenoid depends on the square of the magnetic field in the solenoid and a geometrical factor $S\ell$, which is the volume of the space inside the solenoid where the magnetic field exists. Dividing the energy U stored in the inductor by the volume $S\ell$ gives the energy per unit volume u_B:

Energy density of the magnetic field
$$u_B = \frac{B^2}{2\mu_0} \qquad\qquad (29\text{-}12)$$

We associate this energy density with *energy stored in the magnetic field.* Experiment shows that the expression applies to any magnetic field. That is, the energy per unit volume stored in the magnetic field **B** at a point in space is given by Eq. (29-12).

Returning to the simple case of the solenoid, we can interpret the energy stored in the inductor, $U = \frac{1}{2}Li^2$, as energy stored in the magnetic field, $U = u_B(S\ell)$. In this instance u_B is uniform; it has the same value at each point inside the solenoid, a region of volume $S\ell$. Notice that if there is no current in the solenoid initially ($i = 0$), then $B = 0$, $u_B = 0$, and $U = 0$. As the current increases to a value i, an increasing magnetic field is produced in the solenoid, and energy is stored in the magnetic field. If the current decreases, then the magnetic field decreases, and the energy is recovered from the magnetic field by the charge carriers in the circuit. This energy may be dissipated in Joule heating in the resistance. Exercise 29-23 explores this process quantitatively.

EXAMPLE 29-6. A long coaxial cable with a circular cross section is shown in Fig. 29-7. The inner and outer conductors carry current i with opposite senses. (a) Determine the energy stored in the magnetic field in the space between conductors for a length ℓ of the cable. (b) Estimate the self-inductance per unit length of this coaxial cable.

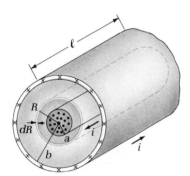

Figure 29-7. Example 29-6: A magnetic field exists in the space between conductors of a long coaxial cable.

SOLUTION. (a) Ampere's law can be used as in Sec. 27-4 (also see Exercise 27-26) to determine the magnetic field at a point between the conductors at a perpendicular distance R from the axis. The magnitude is $B = \mu_0 i/(2\pi R)$. From Eq. (29-12), the magnetic energy density at this point is

$$u_B = \frac{B^2}{2\mu_0} = \frac{\mu_0 i^2}{8\pi^2 R^2}$$

Since the energy density depends on the distance R, we must set up an integral to determine the energy in this space. An appropriate volume element is a cylindrical shell of radius R, thickness dR, and length ℓ, as shown in the figure. Its volume is $dV = (2\pi R)(\ell)(dR)$, and the energy stored in this volume element is $dU = u_B \, dV = u_B(2\pi R\ell \, dR)$. We integrate this expression from the inner radius a to the outer radius b to obtain

$$U = \int_a^b \frac{\mu_0 i^2}{8\pi^2 R^2} \, 2\pi R\ell \, dR = \frac{\mu_0 i^2 \ell}{4\pi} \int_a^b \frac{1}{R} \, dR = \frac{\mu_0 i^2 \ell}{4\pi} \ln \frac{b}{a}$$

The energy stored in this space is proportional to the square of the current. A magnetic field also exists inside the inner conductor and in the outer conductor. The magnetic energy stored in these regions is small for the case shown in the figure. There the volume of the conductors is small compared with the volume of the space between them. Notice that the magnetic field is zero outside the cable.

(b) If we consider a section of length ℓ of the cable as an inductor of self-inductance L, then the energy stored in the inductor is given by Eq. (29-10), $U = \frac{1}{2}Li^2$. Neglecting the energy stored in the magnetic field inside the conductors (see Prob. 29-2), we equate $\frac{1}{2}Li^2$ to the expression above for the stored energy and solve for the inductance per unit length L/ℓ. We obtain

$$\frac{L}{\ell} = \frac{\mu_0}{2\pi} \ln \frac{b}{a}$$

The inductance per unit length is an important property of a cable used to transmit electromagnetic signals, such as a TV cable.

29-5 MUTUAL INDUCTANCE

When the current changes in a coil in a circuit, there is a self-induced emf in the coil, $\mathscr{E}_L = -L \, di/dt$. As we have seen, the magnetic flux linking each turn of the coil is due to the magnetic field of the current in that circuit — hence the use of

Figure 29-8. A changing current in each coil induces an emf in the other coil.

the term "self-induced." The magnetic field also extends outside the coil and may influence another nearby circuit.

Figure 29-8 shows stationary coils belonging to separate circuits. Each coil carries a current, and these currents and the magnetic field they produce can be changing. Thus the flux linking each turn of coil 2 changes because of the changing current in coil 1. Similarly, the flux linking each turn of coil 1 changes because of the changing current in coil 2. These contributions to the flux changes and the corresponding induced emf's are in addition to the self-induced contributions. Since induced emf's appear in each coil because of a change in the other coil, the interaction is mutual between the coils, and the effect is called *mutual induction*.

Mutual induction

Consider the induced emf in one of the coils, say coil 2, due to a change in the current i_1 in coil 1. The flux linking each turn of coil 2 has a contribution due to the magnetic-field contribution B_1 of coil 1. We let the symbol Φ_{21} represent the contribution of the magnetic field of coil 1 to the magnetic flux linking a turn in coil 2. It is this flux that changes when the current i_1 changes. We assume that the flux linking each of the N_2 turns is the same. The product $N_2\Phi_{21}$ is called the *number of flux linkages* for the coil. If no magnetic materials such as iron are around, the field contribution B_1 is proportional to the current i_1 which produces it (from the Biot-Savart law). Then both Φ_{21} and $N_2\Phi_{21}$ are proportional to i_1. We write the linear relation between $N_2\Phi_{21}$ and i_1 by introducing a constant M_{21}, a *coefficient of mutual inductance*:

Number of flux linkages

$$N_2\Phi_{21} = M_{21}i_1 \tag{29-13}$$

We now apply Faraday's law to determine the induced emf due to coil 1 in a turn of coil 2. The induced emf in each turn is $\mathcal{E} = -d(\Phi_{21})/dt$, and the total emf $\mathcal{E}_{21}$ induced in coil 2 is $N_2\mathcal{E}$:

$$\mathcal{E}_{21} = -N_2\frac{d}{dt}\Phi_{21} = -\frac{d}{dt}(N_2\Phi_{21}) = -\frac{d}{dt}(M_{21}i_1) = -M_{21}\frac{di_1}{dt}$$

Thus the induced emf $\mathcal{E}_{21}$ in coil 2 is proportional to the rate of change of the current di_1/dt in coil 1. The coefficient M_{21} depends on geometrical factors such as the shapes of the coils, the way they are wound, and their relative separation and orientation. The minus sign is used to determine the sense of the induced emf from Lenz's law.

By reversing the roles of the two coils, we can consider the emf $\mathcal{E}_{12}$ induced in coil 1 by the changing current i_2 in coil 2. The number of flux linkages for coil 1 is proportional to the current i_2, $N_1\Phi_{12} = M_{12}i_2$, where M_{12} is a coefficient determined by the geometry. The induced emf in coil 1 is given by

$$\mathcal{E}_{12} = -M_{12}\frac{di_2}{dt}$$

The coefficients M_{12} and M_{21} can be calculated easily for only a few simple

Mutual inductance *M*

arrangements. The values can be generally determined from measurements on the circuits. It turns out that the dependence on geometry of M_{12} and M_{21} is also mutual. That is, $M_{12} = M_{21}$ and we shall drop the subscripts and let M represent the *mutual inductance* of the pair. Thus the emf's induced in each coil by the changing current in the other are given by

$$\mathscr{E}_{12} = -M\frac{di_2}{dt} \qquad \mathscr{E}_{21} = -M\frac{di_1}{dt} \tag{29-14}$$

This result applies generally to any pair of circuit elements. A changing current in each element induces an emf in the other element. The mutual inductance depends only on the geometry if no magnetic materials such as iron are nearby. The SI unit of mutual inductance is the henry (H), the same as the unit of self-inductance.

EXAMPLE 29-7. A coil in one circuit is close to another coil in a separate circuit. The mutual inductance of the combination is 340 mH. During a 15-ms time interval, the current in coil 1 changes steadily from 23 to 57 mA, and the current in coil 2 changes steadily from 36 to 16 mA. Determine the emf induced in each coil by the changing current in the other coil.

SOLUTION. During the 15-ms time interval, the currents in the coils change at the constant rates of

$$\frac{di_1}{dt} = \frac{57\text{ mA} - 23\text{ mA}}{15\text{ ms}} = 2.3\text{ A/s}$$

$$\frac{di_2}{dt} = \frac{16\text{ mA} - 36\text{ mA}}{15\text{ ms}} = -1.3\text{ A/s}$$

From Eqs. (29-14), the magnitudes of the induced emfs are

$$\mathscr{E}_{21} = (340\text{ mH})(2.3\text{ A/s}) = 0.77\text{ V}$$

$$\mathscr{E}_{12} = (340\text{ mH})(1.3\text{ A/s}) = 0.45\text{ V}$$

Remember that the minus signs in Eqs. (29-14) refer to the sense of each induced emf.

EXAMPLE 29-8. A circular loop of wire of radius *a* is inside and near the center of a long, tightly wound solenoid with *n* turns per unit length. The axis of the loop is parallel to the axis of the solenoid. (*a*) Determine an expression for the mutual inductance of the loop and solenoid in terms of geometrical quantities. (*b*) Evaluate the mutual inductance for $n = 2200$ turns per meter and $a = 12$ mm. (*c*) What emf is induced in the loop if the solenoid current changes at a rate of 1.4 A/s? (*d*) What is the sense of the induced current in the loop for the arrangement shown in Fig. 29-9?

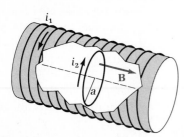

Figure 29-9. Example 29-8: A current is induced in the loop by a changing current in the solenoid.

SOLUTION. (*a*) The magnetic field inside the solenoid due to its current i_1 is given approximately by Eq. (27-11): $B = \mu_0 n i_1$. Since this field is perpendicular to the plane of the loop with area πa^2, the flux linking the loop is $\Phi_{21} = B(\pi a^2) = \pi\mu_0 na^2 i_1$. There is only one loop or turn so that $N_2 = 1$ in Eq. (29-13). Thus $Mi_1 = N_2\Phi_{21} = \pi\mu_0 na^2 i_1$, or $M = \pi\mu_0 na^2$, is the mutual inductance for the loop and solenoid.
(*b*) The value of the mutual inductance is

$$M = \pi(4\pi \times 10^{-7}\text{ T}\cdot\text{m}\cdot\text{A}^{-1})(2200\text{ m}^{-1})(0.012\text{ m})^2$$

$$= 1.3\ \mu\text{H}$$

(*c*) The induced emf in the loop is

$$\mathscr{E}_{21} = M\frac{di_1}{dt} = (1.3\ \mu\text{H})(1.4\text{ A/s}) = 1.8\ \mu\text{V}$$

(*d*) Since the current i_1 is increasing ($di_1/dt > 0$), the flux linking the loop is increasing. From Lenz's law, the induced current must oppose the increase of the flux for a surface bounded by the loop. Thus the sense of the induced current is as shown in the figure.

29-6 TRANSFORMERS

Mutual induction, an emf induced in one circuit by a changing current in another, is a process that can sometimes be a problem. For example, unwanted emf's may be induced in a sensitive electronic circuit by other nearby circuits. In other cases mutual induction can be put to useful purposes. Some pacemakers operate with an emf induced by a changing current in a circuit external to the patient's body. This technique avoids the use of an internal power supply which would require surgery for replacement or maintenance. (But can you think of a disadvantage of using mutual induction to power a pacemaker?)

Primary and secondary coils of a transformer

Of great practical importance is the *transformer*, which uses mutual induction to change (or transform) the voltage from one circuit to another. A simple type of transformer consists of two coils wrapped around an iron core or ring, as shown in Fig. 29-10a. The magnetic field produced by the currents in the coils is largely concentrated in the iron. Another arrangement has the turns of one coil wound directly on top of the other coil, as shown in Fig. 29-10b. In each case the magnetic flux linking each turn in each coil is virtually the same. One of the coils of the transformer, is designated as the *primary coil*; it has N_p turns. The other coil is the *secondary coil* with N_s turns. Often we consider the primary as the input coil to the transformer and the secondary as the output coil. However, the reference to input and output is not always useful.

The iron core causes the flux Φ_B to be essentially the same for each turn in both the primary and the secondary, and the same emf $\mathscr{E} = -d\Phi_B/dt$ will be induced in each turn if the flux changes. Thus the induced emf, or voltage V_s, in the secondary with N_s turns is

$$V_s = N_s \mathscr{E} = -N_s \frac{d\Phi_B}{dt}$$

The induced emf, or voltage V_p, in the primary with N_p turns is

$$V_p = N_p \mathscr{E} = -N_p \frac{d\Phi_B}{dt}$$

Taking the ratio of the voltages gives

$$\frac{V_s}{V_p} = \frac{N_s}{N_p} \tag{29-15}$$

Step-up and step-down transformers

For example, if the secondary has $N_s = 5N_p$, then $V_s = 5V_p$. Such a trans-

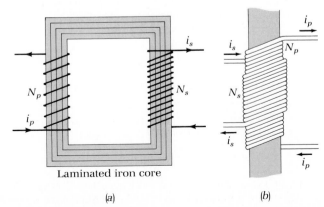

Figure 29-10. Two arrangements are shown for the primary and secondary coils of a transformer. (a) The magnetic field is mainly confined to the laminated iron core. (b) The secondary coil is wrapped around the primary.

Laminated iron core

(a)

(b)

former is called a *step-up transformer*. That is, the secondary voltage is greater than, or "stepped up" from, the primary voltage. The secondary of a *step-down* transformer has fewer turns than the primary, and the secondary voltage is less than the primary voltage.

The detailed operation of a transformer depends on the properties of the other elements in the two circuits. We shall discuss a simple case in which a sinusoidally changing emf is applied to the primary coil and the primary circuit has negligible resistance. We also assume that the secondary circuit has a large resistance. Further, we neglect eddy currents and other losses in the (laminated) iron core. Under these conditions the transformer acts to transfer energy from the primary circuit to the secondary circuit. The power for the primary is $P_p = i_p V_p$, where i_p is the current in the primary. Similarly, $P_s = i_s V_s$ is the power in the secondary, where the current is i_s. For the ideal case of no losses (typical transformers have high efficiencies, up to 99 percent), we equate the power in the secondary to that in the primary, by conservation of energy, to get $i_s V_s = i_p V_p$ or $i_s/i_p = V_p/V_s$. Using Eq. (29-15), we express the ratio of currents in terms of the number of turns on the coils:

By energy conservation, $i_s V_s = i_p V_p$.

$$\frac{i_s}{i_p} = \frac{N_p}{N_s} \qquad (29\text{-}16)$$

Comparing Eqs. (29-15) and (29-16), we see that the voltage ratio V_s/V_p and the current ratio i_s/i_p behave inversely in a transformer. For example, in a step-up transformer with $N_s > N_p$, the secondary voltage is larger than the primary voltage, but the secondary current is smaller than the primary current.

Transformers are used by electric utilities to reduce Joule heating losses in the distribution of electric energy over long distances. At a generating station, a generator is on the primary side of a step-up transformer. The transmission lines leading to distant points are on the secondary side of the transformer. A relatively large current i_p can exist in the primary circuit, with a moderate voltage V_p determined by the generator. The voltage is stepped up in the secondary (V_s may be in the range of 500,000 V), and the secondary current is correspondingly smaller. Reducing the current i_s in the transmission lines reduces the $i_s^2 R$ Joule heating loss in the lines. Step-down transformers are used at the other end to reduce the voltage (and increase the current) to safe and convenient levels. Without the use of transformers, the large-scale transmission and distribution of electric energy would not be feasible.

EXAMPLE 29-9. A transformer is used to convert 120-V voltage from a wall receptacle to the 9.0-V voltage required for a radio. (*a*) Is a step-up or a step-down transformer used? (*b*) If the primary has 480 turns, how many turns are on the secondary? (*c*) Determine the current in the primary coil if the radio operates with 400 mA.

SOLUTION. (*a*) We regard the primary side of the transformer as the side that supplies energy. In this case it is the 120-V side. A step-down transformer is used to reduce the

voltage to 9.0 V.

(*b*) From Eq. (29-15),

$$N_s = N_p \frac{V_s}{V_p} = 480 \, \frac{9.0 \text{ V}}{120 \text{ V}} = 36 \text{ (turns)}$$

(*c*) The primary current is determined from Eq. (29-16):

$$i_p = i_s \frac{N_s}{N_p} = 400 \text{ mA} \, \frac{36}{480} = 30 \text{ mA}$$

EXAMPLE 29-10. A generator at a hydroelectric station operates at 14 kV and 12 A. (These are root-mean-square

values; see Chap. 31.) A step-up transformer is used to step up the transmission-line voltage to 140 kV. (*a*) Determine the current in the transmission line. (*b*) If the resistance of the transmission line is 170 Ω, determine the rate of Joule heating in the line. (*c*) What would be the Joule heating rate if the line voltage were 14 kV?

SOLUTION. (*a*) Since $i_s V_s \approx i_p V_p$, we have

$$i_s = \frac{(12\ A)(14\ kV)}{140\ kV} = 1.2\ A$$

(*b*) The rate of Joule heating in the line is

$$P = i_s^2 R = (1.2\ A)^2(170\ \Omega) = 240\ W$$

(*c*) If the line voltage were 14 kV, the current would be 12 A and the heating loss rate would be

$$P = (12\ A)^2(170\ \Omega) = 24\ kW$$

COMMENTARY: JOSEPH HENRY

Joseph Henry. *(Culver Pictures)*

Joseph Henry, born in Albany, New York, in 1797, is often considered the independent codiscoverer, along with Michael Faraday, of electromagnetic induction. Henry began his study of magnetism as a teacher at the Albany Academy, where he had earlier been a student. Trying to keep abreast of research being done in Europe, he refined an electromagnet described by William Sturgeon of London. Sturgeon's magnet was a soft iron horseshoe wrapped with only a few turns of bare copper wire. These turns were spaced apart so as to prevent a short circuit. Because of the small number of turns, the electromagnet was relatively weak. Henry used silk threads from his wife's petticoat to insulate copper wire. He was able to wrap a horseshoe with 400 overlapping turns, thereby obtaining a much stronger electromagnet.

In 1831, Henry described a primitive electric motor, powered "by magnetic attraction and repulsion." A bar electromagnet was pivoted about a horizontal axis through its center of gravity, with the north pole of a permanent magnet placed under each end of the electromagnet. To reverse the current in the electromagnet and cause it to oscillate, Henry devised a mechanism for dipping the ends of the connecting wires from the electromagnet in and out of the acid of the voltaic cells with each cycle. Of this motor, Henry remarked that "not much importance, however, is attached to the invention, since the article in its present state can only be considered a philosophical toy; although . . . some modification of it on a more extended scale may hereafter be applied to some useful purpose." Henry refused to patent any of his inventions because he "did not consider it compatible with the dignity of science to confine the benefits which might be derived from it to the exclusive use of any individual."

As to the discovery of induction, Faraday in England had "established the general fact, that when a piece of metal is moved in any direction . . . between the poles of a horseshoe magnet, electrical currents are developed in the metal. . . . " This note by a Peter M. Roget was dated December 12, 1831, and appeared in an issue of the Library of Useful Knowledge. *Henry's account of his own work on induction appeared shortly thereafter (July 1832) in Gilliman's* Journal. *It is possible that Henry's discovery may have predated Faraday's, but it is not clear who had discovered what nor exactly when it had been discovered in the period prior to publication.*

Henry later wrote, "Before having any knowledge of the method given in the above account [Faraday's], I had succeeded in producing electrical effects in the following manner, which differs from that employed by Mr. Faraday. . . ." He then described his experiments on self-induction and concluded, "we have . . . electricity converted into magnetism and this magnetism again into electricity. . . ." In any event, the law of induction is known as Faraday's law, and the unit of inductance is the henry.

Henry had a long and productive career in science. He taught at Princeton and was an advisor to the United States government. He served for 32 years as the first secretary (director) of the Smithsonian Institution. During this period of service, he refused to accept an increase in his salary. He is often described as the father of meteorology for his work in that field. Joseph Henry remained active until his death at age 82 in 1878.

For further reading, see "Joseph Henry" in Famous American Men of Science *by J. G. Crowther (Books for Libraries Press, Freeport, N.Y., 1937) and* Joseph Henry — His Life and Work *by Thomas Coulson (Princeton University Press, Princeton, N.J., 1950).*

SUMMARY WITH APPLICATIONS

Section 29-2. Self-induced emf's and self-inductance

If the current changes in a circuit element such as a coil, a self-induced emf exists and is given by

$$\mathscr{E} = -L\frac{di}{dt} \qquad (29\text{-}2)$$

The self-inductance L depends on the geometry of the element. For a coil,

$$Li = N\Phi_B \qquad (29\text{-}3)$$

where Φ_B is the flux linking each of the N turns in the coil. The self-inductance of a long, tightly wound solenoid is

$$L = \mu_0 n^2 S\ell \qquad (29\text{-}4)$$

Determine the self-induced emf due to a changing current in an inductor; determine the self-inductance for an element with a simple geometry; evaluate the inductance of a long solenoid.

Section 29-3. *LR* circuits

In an *LR* circuit the time scale for appreciable changes in the current is set by the inductive time constant $\tau_L = L/R$. For an *LR* circuit with a battery, the current is

$$i(t) = \frac{\mathscr{E}_0}{R}\left(1 - e^{-t/\tau_L}\right) \qquad (29\text{-}6)$$

For a circuit without a battery, the current decreases according to

$$i(t) = i_0 e^{-t/\tau_L} \qquad (29\text{-}8)$$

Evaluate the *LR* time constant for an *LR* circuit; evaluate and describe the time dependence of the current in *LR* circuits.

Section 29-4. Energy transfers in *LR* circuits

The energy stored in an inductor with current i is

$$U = \tfrac{1}{2}Li^2 \qquad (29\text{-}10)$$

This energy is stored in the magnetic field due to the current. The energy density of magnetic field energy is

$$u_B = \frac{B^2}{2\mu_0} \qquad (29\text{-}12)$$

Evaluate the energy stored in an inductor; determine the magnetic energy density at a point and evaluate the magnetic energy stored in a region.

Section 29-5. Mutual inductance

The changing currents in two nearby coils mutually induce emf's in each other:

$$\mathscr{E}_{12} = -M\frac{di_2}{dt}$$
$$\qquad (29\text{-}14)$$
$$\mathscr{E}_{21} = -M\frac{di_1}{dt}$$

where M is the mutual inductance of the pair.

Calculate mutually induced emf's and determine the mutual inductance for a simple geometry.

Section 29-6. Transformers

In a transformer the voltages and currents in the primary and secondary coils depend on the number of turns in each:

$$\frac{V_s}{V_p} = \frac{N_s}{N_p}$$
$$\qquad (29\text{-}15)$$
$$\frac{i_s}{i_p} = \frac{N_p}{N_s}$$

Describe step-up and step-down transformers; determine currents and voltages in transformer coils.

QUESTIONS

29-1   Why is the term "self" used for a self-induced emf?

29-2   Suppose the current in a circuit element is increasing. Can the self-induced emf cause the current to increase further? Explain.

29-3 Which would you expect to have the larger self-inductance — a length of wire forming a single loop or the same length wound to form a small coil? Explain.

29-4 Does the earth's magnetic field affect the value of the self-inductance of a solenoid? Explain.

29-5 Suppose that two solenoids carry the same current and are identical except that one solenoid has a laminated iron core. The magnetic field in the iron core is proportional to the current in the solenoid but has a much larger magnitude than in the solenoid without the iron core. Which solenoid has the larger inductance? Explain.

29-6 A resistor in the form of a solenoid is wound with two layers of wire. The first layer is wound from one end to the other, and the second layer returns so that the currents have opposite senses in the two layers. The manufacturer of the resistor claims it to have a negligible self-inductance. Why?

29-7 If end effects were included, would the self-inductance of a solenoid be larger or smaller than the approximate value given by Eq. (29-4)? Explain.

29-8 How would the value of τ_L for an LR circuit change if $\mathscr{E}_0$ were doubled? If L were doubled? If R were doubled? If L and R were doubled?

29-9 How long after the switch in Fig. 29-2 is closed does the current equal $\mathscr{E}_0/R$? Explain.

29-10 Suppose the current in Fig. 29-2 is increasing. Which point is at the higher potential, b or c? What about points a and c? Explain.

29-11 The current in Fig. 29-4b is decreasing. Which point is at the higher potential, a or b? Explain.

29-12 Compare and contrast the expressions $\frac{1}{2}q^2/C$ and $\frac{1}{2}Li^2$ for the energy stored in a capacitor and in an inductor.

29-13 In what sense can we speak of the energy stored in an inductor? Where is the energy? Could part of the energy be outside the inductor (outside a solenoid for example)? Explain.

29-14 What provides the magnetic energy stored in an inductor in a circuit such as that shown in Fig. 29-2?

29-15 Why is the term "mutual" used for mutual induction?

29-16 Two dissimilar coils are close together, with changing currents in each. Must the currents change at the same rate? Must the mutually induced emf's be the

same? Can there be a self-induced emf in either coil? Explain.

29-17 Suppose that one of the coils in Fig. 29-8 is rotated so that the axes of the coils are perpendicular rather than parallel. Would the mutual inductance increase, decrease, or remain the same? Explain.

29-18 Some residential areas are served by electric distribution lines at 22 kV. A step-down transformer is used to provide 220-V service to each residence. Why not have the distribution lines at 220 V and eliminate the costly transformers? Why not have household appliances operate at 22 kV and eliminate the transformers?

29-19 The primary coil for an automobile ignition system is connected to the 12-V automobile battery. The secondary coil provides several kV to give a spark. If you disassembled an ignition-system unit, how could you determine which coil was the primary and which was the secondary?

29-20 A hand calculator operates with a 9-V battery. Alternatively it can be used with an adapter that plugs into a 120-V wall outlet. What is inside the adapter? Explain.

29-21 Step-up transformers are used to reduce the i^2R (Joule heating) losses in electric distribution lines serving distant points. (Recall that a step-up transformer has a smaller current in the secondary.) Why not reduce the resistance R of the lines instead?

29-22 Transformers are used to change voltages in ac circuits. Can you think of a way to step up a voltage in dc (constant-current) circuits? Explain.

29-23 Complete the following table:

Symbol	Represents	Type	SI unit
L			
τ_L		Scalar	
U			J
u_B	Magnetic energy density		
M			
N_p			—
N_s			—

EXERCISES

Section 29-2. Self-induced emf's and self-inductance

29-1 Show that the unit of inductance, the henry (H), can be expressed as $1\ \text{H} = 1\ \text{kg} \cdot \text{m}^2 \cdot \text{s}^{-2} \cdot \text{A}^{-2}$.

29-2 The current in a 17-μH coil changes at the constant rate of 82 mA/s. Determine the self-induced emf in the coil.

29-3 A solenoid has inductance $L = 23$ mH. Determine the self-induced emf in the solenoid when (a) the current is 125 mA and increasing at the rate 37 mA/s, (b) the current is zero and increasing at the rate 37 mA/s, (c) the current is 125 mA and decreasing at the rate 37 mA/s, (d) the current is 125 mA and not changing.

29-4 A graph of the time dependence of the current in a

100-mH coil is shown in Fig. 29-11. Construct the corresponding graph of the self-induced emf in the coil. Make estimates of the maximum and minimum values of the emf and explain any change in the sense of the emf.

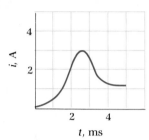

Figure 29-11. Exercise 29-4.

29-5 (a) At what rate must the current change in a 65-mH coil to have a 1.0-V self-induced emf? (b) Should the current be increasing, decreasing, or either? Explain.

29-6 A solenoid with 1200 turns per meter has length 150 mm and radius 16 mm. (a) Determine the self-inductance of the solenoid. (b) If the solenoid current increases at a constant rate from 0 to 20 μA in 50 ms, what is the self-induced emf?

29-7 Show that the SI unit for the permeability constant μ_0 can be expressed as H/m.

29-8 A 250-turn coil has self-inductance $L = 65$ μH. (a) At an instant when $i = 24$ mA, what is the magnetic flux linking each turn on the coil? (b) If the current changes at a rate of 96 mA/s, what emf is induced in the coil?

29-9 Two long, straight, parallel wires carry a current i, as shown in Fig. 29-12. Each wire has radius a and the axes are separated by distance D. (a) Use Ampere's law to show that, at a point between the wires in the plane containing the axes, the magnitude of the magnetic field is (see Chap. 27)

$$B = \frac{\mu_0 i}{2\pi}\left(\frac{1}{R} + \frac{1}{D-R}\right)$$

(b) In this plane consider a surface of length ℓ and width $D - 2a$ between the wires and determine the magnetic flux for the area $\ell(D - 2a)$. Note that the flux for a strip of area $\ell\,dR$ is $B\ell\,dR$. (c) Show that the

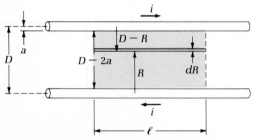

Figure 29-12. Exercise 29-9.

inductance per unit length for this two-conductor line is

$$\frac{L}{\ell} = \frac{\mu_0}{\pi}\ln\frac{D-a}{a}$$

This calculation neglects the effect of the magnetic field inside the wires and is valid for $D \gg a$.

Section 29-3. *LR* circuits

29-10 Show that the SI unit of L/R is the second (s).

29-11 The circuit in Fig. 29-13 has $\mathscr{E}_0 = 12$ V, $R = 25$ Ω, $L = 0.48$ H. The switch is closed at $t = 0$. Determine (a) the inductive time constant, (b) the current at $t = 25$ ms, (c) the current at 1.0 s. (d) What is the asymptotic value of the current?

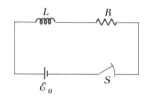

Figure 29-13. Exercise 29-11.

29-12 Switch S in the circuit of Fig. 29-14 is closed at $t = 0$. Determine the currents i_1 and i_2 (a) immediately after the switch is closed, (b) after the switch has been left closed for several minutes, (c) immediately after the switch is opened. (*Hint:* The current in the inductor cannot change discontinuously.)

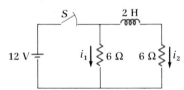

Figure 29-14. Exercise 29-12.

29-13 You are given a 23-mH coil with resistance 0.15 Ω and a wide choice of batteries and resistors. Design an *LR* circuit (specify values of R and $\mathscr{E}_0$) with an asymptotic current of 0.80 A that can be reached within about 10 ms.

29-14 The *LR* circuit in Fig. 29-13 has $R = 2.3$ Ω and $\mathscr{E}_0 = 12$ V; the switch is closed at $t = 0$. At $t = 33$ ms the current is 3.6 A. (a) What is the asymptotic current? (b) What is the time constant for this circuit? (c) At what time is the current 5.0 A? (d) What is the value of L?

29-15 Apply the loop rule to the *LR* circuit without a battery in Fig. 29-4b to obtain Eq. (29-7).

29-16 Solve Eq. (29-7) by direct integration. Use the initial condition $i = i_0$ at $t = 0$ to obtain Eq. (29-8).

29-17 An *LR* circuit has $\mathscr{E}_0 = 9.2$ V, $R = 72$ Ω, $L = 250$ μH. If the switch is closed at $t = 0$, determine (a) the current in the circuit, (b) the potential difference across the resistor, and (c) the potential difference across the inductance at $t = 0$, $t = 3.0$ μs, $t = 7.5$ μs, and $t = 35$ μs.

29-18 (a) Show that if two inductors L_1 and L_2 are in series in a circuit, as shown in Fig. 29-15a, the combination is equivalent to an inductance $L = L_1 + L_2$. Assume that no flux from either inductor links the other inductor. (b) What is the equivalent inductance if the two are in parallel, as shown in Fig. 29-15b?

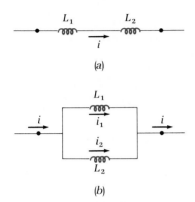

(a)

(b)

Figure 29-15. Exercise 29-18: (a) Inductors in series. (b) Inductors in parallel.

29-19 Suppose that the initial value of the current is 3.0 A in the circuit shown in Fig. 29-4b. The current drops to 1.5 A in 65 ms. (a) Determine the inductive time constant for the circuit. (b) If $R = 0.50$ Ω, what is the inductance L? (c) Construct a graph of i versus t for $0 \leq t \leq 200$ ms.

Section 29-4. Energy transfers in LR circuits

29-20 A 45-mH solenoid can carry a maximum current of 6.0 A without overheating. (a) What maximum energy can be stored in the solenoid? (b) For what current is the stored energy half the maximum value?

29-21 (a) For the LR circuit in Fig. 29-4b, obtain an expression for the stored energy $U(t)$ in the inductor as a function of time. The expression should be in terms of L, i_0, τ_L, and t. (b) Let $L = 1.0$ H, $i_0 = 1.0$ A, $\tau_L = 1.0$ s and prepare graphs of $i(t)$ versus t and $U(t)$ versus t. Use the same time scale for both graphs and discuss similarities and differences between the two graphs.

29-22 Consider the circuit described in Exercise 29-11. (a) How much energy is ultimately stored in the inductor? (b) How long after the switch is closed is the stored energy half the ultimate value?

29-23 At $t = 0$ an initial energy $U_0 = \frac{1}{2}Li_0^2$ is stored in the inductor in the circuit in Fig. 29-4b. (a) Determine the explicit time dependence of the instantaneous rate $P(t)$ of Joule heating in the resistor. (b) Compare the total energy dissipated in the resistor, $\int_0^\infty P(t)\,dt$, with the initial energy stored in the inductor.

29-24 At a point inside a long solenoid, far from either end, the magnetic field has magnitude $B = \mu_0 ni$. (a) Deter-

mine the energy per unit volume stored in the magnetic field at such a point if $n = 2000$ turns per meter, $i = 0.50$ A. (b) Assuming that the energy density is the same throughout the solenoid, which has length 0.25 m and area 800 mm², determine the energy stored in the solenoid. (c) Evaluate the self-inductance of the solenoid using Eq. (29-4).

29-25 A typical solenoid has 1000 turns per meter and a 1-A current. A typical parallel-plate capacitor has a plate separation of 0.1 mm and a potential difference of 10 V. Compare the magnetic energy density in a typical solenoid with the electric energy density in a typical capacitor.

Section 29-5. Mutual inductance

29-26 Two coils are arranged such that the mutual inductance is 75 mH. Coil 1 is in a circuit whose current is changing at a rate of 12 A/s. Coil 2 is in an open circuit (no current). Determine the mutually induced emf in (a) coil 1 and (b) coil 2.

29-27 A small N-turn coil of area S is placed inside a long solenoid with n turns per unit length. The coil is far from either end of the solenoid and its axis coincides with the solenoid axis. (a) Show that the mutual inductance of the pair is $M = \mu_0 nNS$. (b) Evaluate the mutual inductance for $N = 75$, $n = 2000$ m^{-1}, and $S = 300$ mm².

29-28 Solenoid 1 with n_1 turns per unit length, cross-sectional area S_1, and length ℓ_1 lies inside solenoid 2, which is characterized by n_2, S_2, and ℓ_2. The two solenoids have the same axis. (a) Determine an expression for the mutual inductance of the pair in terms of the above quantities. (b) Determine an expression for the mutual inductance if the axis of the inner solenoid makes an angle θ with the axis of the outer solenoid.

29-29 Two coils are wrapped around insulating cylinders with senses as shown in Fig. 29-16. (a) Just after the switch is closed in circuit 1, what is the sense of the current in resistor R_2? (b) If coil 2 were wound with the opposite sense, what would be the answer to part (a)? (c) What if both coils were wrapped with senses opposite those in the figure?

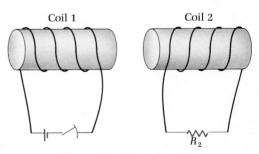

Coil 1   Coil 2

R_2

Figure 29-16. Exercise 29-29.

29-30 Two circular loops are separated by a distance D that is large compared with their radii R_1 and R_2. The center of one loop lies on the axis of the other and θ represents the angle between their axes, as shown in Fig. 29-17. Show that the mutual inductance of the loops is given approximately by

$$M = \frac{\mu_0 \pi R_1{}^2 R_2{}^2}{2D^3} \cos \theta$$

(*Hint:* The field at a point on the axis of a current loop is considered in Sec. 27-2.)

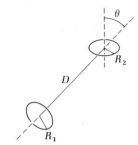

Figure 29-17. Exercise 29-30.

Section 29-6. Transformers

29-31 A transformer is used to supply up to 100 A at 240 V to a residence in a neighborhood. The distribution-line voltage is 22 kV. (*a*) What is the ratio of turns in the secondary to turns in the primary? (*b*) If the residence is "drawing" 100 A, what is the minimum primary current? (*c*) At what rate is the transformer supplying energy to the residence?

29-32 An old vacuum-tube radio plugs into a 115-V wall outlet. For proper operation, the filament in each tube requires 6.3 V, which is supplied by a transformer. (*a*) If the secondary has 28 turns, how many turns are on the primary? (*b*) If the primary current is 60 mA and the secondary provides current for five tube filaments wired in parallel, what is the average current in each filament?

29-33 The 13-kV output of a 2.0-MW generator is stepped up to 140 kV for transmission to an industrial user 40 km away. (*a*) Determine the transmission-line current. (*b*) Determine the Joule heating loss rate if the transmission line has resistance 20 Ω. (*c*) What percentage is this loss rate of the transmitted power? (*d*) Estimate the diameter of the aluminum transmission line.

29-34 A variable transformer has a sliding contact that changes the number of turns in the secondary coil. The primary has 600 turns and operates at 120 V. The secondary voltage ranges from near zero to 9.0 V, depending on how many turns are engaged. (*a*) How many turns are used for a 9.0-V output? (*b*) What is the lowest nonzero secondary voltage available from this transformer?

29-35 An oil furnace uses a transformer to provide an arc for igniting the fuel. The secondary voltage must be around 6 kV, while the primary operates at 120 V and 4.6 A. (*a*) What are reasonable values for N_s and N_p for such a transformer? (*b*) What is the secondary current? (*c*) Estimate the resistance of the secondary coil. (Assume that the coil has all of the resistance in the secondary circuit.)

PROBLEMS

29-1 In an N-turn toroid with current i and rectangular cross section, the magnetic field varies with distance R from the axis (Prob. 27-2):

$$B = \frac{\mu_0 N i}{2\pi R}$$

(*a*) For the toroid shown in Fig. 29-18, evaluate the magnetic flux for the rectangular cross section of area ab. (*b*) Determine the self-inductance of the toroid.

29-2 A long, straight wire of radius a carries a current i uniformly distributed over its cross section. (*a*) Determine the energy in a length ℓ stored in the magnetic field inside the wire [see Eq. (27-10)]. (*b*) Apply this result to the coaxial cable of Example 29-6 and determine the inductance per unit length of the cable. Assume that the outer conductor has negligible thickness.

29-3 Consider the plane of length ℓ between the conduc-

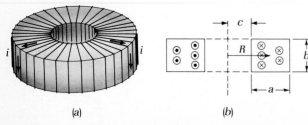

(*a*)   (*b*)

Figure 29-18. Prob. 29-1: (*a*) Toroid in perspective. (*b*) In cross section.

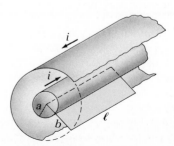

Figure 29-19. Prob. 29-3.

tors of the coaxial cable in Fig. 29-19. The outer conductor has negligible thickness. (a) Evaluate the magnetic flux for this plane. (b) Apply Eq. (29-1) to the loop that forms the boundary of this plane to estimate the self-inductance per unit length. (c) Compare with the result given by Example 29-6.

29-4 A rectangular loop has an edge parallel to a long, straight wire, as shown in Fig. 29-20. (a) Determine the mutual inductance of the system. (b) What is the sense of the mutually induced emf in the loop if i_1 is decreasing and i_2 is increasing?

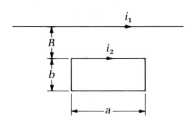

Figure 29-20. Prob. 29-4.

29-5 The linear extent of the loop shown in Fig. 29-21 is small compared with its mean distance R from the long, straight wire. (a) Show that the mutual inductance is approximately given by $M = \mu_0 S/(2\pi R)$, where S is the area of the loop whose plane lies in the plane of the figure. (b) Use the approximation $\ln(1+x) \approx x$, valid for $|x| \ll 1$, to show that the answer to part (a) is consistent with the answer to the previous problem for the case $b \ll R$. (c) How would the expression in part (a) change if the plane of the loop made angle θ with the plane of the figure?

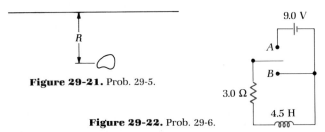

Figure 29-21. Prob. 29-5.

Figure 29-22. Prob. 29-6.

29-6 The current in the LR circuit of Fig. 29-22 is zero at $t = 0$ when the switch first closes at position A. The switch remains at position A for 5.0 s and then is quickly changed to position B for the next 5.0 s. (a) Determine the current in the circuit at $t = 5.0$ s just before the switch is changed to B. (b) Determine the current at $t = 10$ s. (c) If the switch is changed back to A at this instant, determine the current at $t = 15$ s and explain why this answer is different from the answer to part (a).

29-7 A solenoid is constructed by winding 200 turns of 1.0-mm-diameter copper $(\rho = 1.7 \times 10^{-8}\ \Omega \cdot \mathrm{m})$ wire in a single layer on a 25-mm-diameter cylinder. The wire has a very thin insulating coat so that the consecutive turns, which touch, are insulated from each

other. (a) What is the length of the solenoid? (b) What length of wire is required? Determine (c) the resistance and (d) the self-inductance of the solenoid.

29-8 A long, straight wire of radius a carries a current i uniformly distributed over its cross section. Consider a region of space, a cylinder of length ℓ and radius R whose axis coincides with the axis of the wire and which is far from the ends of the wire. (a) Determine an expression for the magnetic energy stored in this region in terms of μ_0, i, a, ℓ, and R. Separately consider the cases $R < a$ and $R > a$. (b) Explain why you should not allow R to be arbitrarily large.

29-9 The two circuits shown in Fig. 29-23 interact through their mutual inductance M. (a) Show that the loop rule applied to each circuit gives

$$L_1 \frac{di_1}{dt} + M \frac{di_2}{dt} + R_1 i_1 = \mathcal{E}_0$$

$$L_2 \frac{di_2}{dt} + M \frac{di_1}{dt} + R_2 i_2 = 0$$

(b) If L_1, L_2, and M are all comparable and $R_2 \gg R_1$, then di_2/dt may be neglected in comparison with di_1/dt. Solve the equations in this approximation. Use the initial conditions $i_1(0) = i_2(0) = 0$. (c) Construct graphs of $i_1(t)$ and $i_2(t)$ versus t for $0 \le t \le 1.0$ s. Use the values $L_1 = 1.2$ H, $R_1 = 6.0\ \Omega$, $M = 0.80$ H, $L_2 = 1.4$ H, $R_2 = 600\ \Omega$, $\mathcal{E}_0 = 48$ V. (d) Compare the values of the maximum potential difference across R_1 and across R_2.

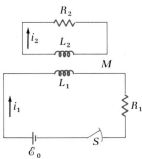

Figure 29-23. Prob. 29-9.

29-10 ⬛ Write or adapt a program to solve the coupled equations in the previous problem numerically. The equations can be solved for the derivatives:

$$\frac{di_1}{dt} = \frac{L_2 \mathcal{E}_0 - L_2 R_1 i_1 + M R_2 i_2}{L_1 L_2 - M^2}$$

$$\frac{di_2}{dt} = -\frac{R_2}{L_2} i_2 - \frac{M}{L_2} \frac{di_1}{dt}$$

and these can be numerically integrated in turn for i_1 and i_2. Compare graphically the numerical solution for i_1 and i_2 with the solution of the approximate equations from the previous problem. The coupled equations can also be solved exactly, by using Laplace transforms, for example.

CHAPTER 30
MAGNETIC FIELDS
IN MATTER

30-1 INTRODUCTION

Small bits (filings) of iron scattered in the vicinity of an ordinary bar magnet are strongly attracted to the magnet. Sawdust particles, on the other hand, have a much weaker interaction with the magnetic field of the magnet. If the magnet is passed over a mixture of sawdust and iron filings, the filings are pulled from the mixture, leaving the sawdust behind. Why do wood and iron have such different magnetic properties? And what causes the magnetic field of the permanent magnet?

We have approached our study of magnetism chiefly in terms of electric currents—currents as sources of magnetic fields, current-carrying conductors on which the magnetic field exerts forces and torques, currents induced by a changing magnetic flux. The magnetic properties of matter are also described in terms of currents. In many materials these currents are due to the motion of electrons at the atomic level. The effect of these microscopic currents in various materials can range from the almost insignificant interaction of wood with the magnet to the strong attraction of iron filings to the magnet. Such currents are also responsible for the magnetic field of the magnet. In this way the description of magnetic phenomena is ultimately expressed in terms of currents.

30-2 ATOMIC CURRENTS, MAGNETIC DIPOLES, AND MAGNETIZATION

In earlier chapters we pointed out the similarity between a permanent bar magnet and a localized current distribution such as in a loop or a coil. Each has features that depend on its magnetic dipole moment **m**. The similar magnetic fields produced by a current loop (Chap. 27) and by a bar magnet are sketched

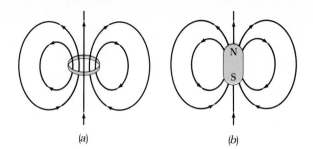

Figure 30-1. A magnetic dipole field exists at points distant from (a) a current loop and (b) a bar magnet.

(a)

(b)

in Fig. 30-1. Further, the torque τ on a magnetic dipole placed in a uniform field **B** (see Fig. 26-9) is given by Eq. (26-8): $\tau = \mathbf{m} \times \mathbf{B}$. The similarity in magnetic behavior for localized currents and magnets is not coincidental. Indeed, our description of magnetism in matter is based on a picture of currents (and hence magnetic dipole moments) at the molecular level.

Currents and moments. In a classical model of an atom, one imagines the negatively charged electrons circulating in orbits about the nucleus. Such circulating charges constitute a localized current distribution which contributes to the atom's magnetic dipole moment. Of course, we do not claim validity for any classical model of an atom. The electronic structure of an atom must be described using quantum theory.* But some of the results from a simple classical theory are the same as those obtained from the quantum theory. One such result is the connection between the orbital contribution to the magnetic moment and the orbital angular momentum **L** of an electron in an atom.

Consider an electron of charge $-e$ and mass m_e in a circular orbit with speed v and radius r about a fixed nucleus, as seen in Fig. 30-2. The orbital period T is the time interval for the electron to travel a distance $2\pi r = vT$ for each revolution. The average electric current for the orbital motion corresponds to the electronic charge passing a section (such as PP' in the figure) in a time interval T, that is, $i = e/T = e/(2\pi r/v) = ev/(2\pi r)$. Notice that the sense of this current is opposite the sense of the orbital motion because the electron bears a negative charge. The magnetic moment of a loop or a coil is given by Eq. (26-9): $\mathbf{m} = i\mathbf{S}$. For a circular current loop with area $S = \pi r^2$ and current i, the magnitude of the magnetic moment is $m = i\pi r^2$. Substituting $i = ev/(2\pi r)$ from above, we obtain

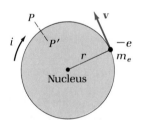

Figure 30-2. An electron orbiting counterclockwise gives a clockwise current. The orbital angular momentum **L** is out of the plane of the figure. The magnetic dipole moment **m** is into the plane of the figure, opposite **L**.

$$m = \tfrac{1}{2}evr$$

The direction of **m** is perpendicular to the plane of the loop. Applying the right-hand rule relative to the sense of the current in Fig. 30-2, we see that **m** is directed into the plane of the figure.

The orbital angular momentum of the electron, $\mathbf{L} = \mathbf{r} \times \mathbf{p} = \mathbf{r} \times (m_e\mathbf{v})$, has magnitude

$$L = m_evr$$

Its direction in Fig. 30-2 is perpendicularly out of the plane of the figure, opposite the direction of the magnetic moment **m**. Since the expressions for both m and L contain the product vr, we can eliminate this factor. Thus $m = \tfrac{1}{2}evr = \tfrac{1}{2}e(L/m_e)$. Noting that **m** and **L** have opposite directions, we write the relation between these two vectors as

---

* In the "extended" edition of this text, electronic structure of atoms is discussed in Chap. 41.

Magnetic moment and orbital
angular momentum

$$\mathbf{m} = -\frac{e}{2m_e}\mathbf{L} \tag{30-1}$$

This result is valid in general, not just for circular orbits. That is, the orbital contribution of an electron to the magnetic moment is proportional to the orbital angular momentum of the electron. The constant of proportionality $e/2m_e$ depends only on the electronic charge and mass. The two vectors have opposite directions because of the negative charge on the electron.

In addition to an orbital contribution to the magnetic moment, there is a contribution to the magnetic moment of each electron due to its *intrinsic*, or *spin*, angular momentum $\mathbf{S}$.* The spin contribution to $\mathbf{m}$ is proportional to $\mathbf{S}$, with a proportionality constant that is approximately twice that for the orbital case. It is given by an expression similar to Eq. (30-1), with $e/2m_e$ and $\mathbf{L}$ replaced by $2(e/2m_e)$ and $\mathbf{S}$:

Magnetic moment and spin
angular momentum

$$\mathbf{m} = -\frac{e}{m_e}\mathbf{S} \tag{30-2}$$

Together, Eqs. (30-1) and (30-2) give the contribution of an electron to the magnetic moment of an atom. The magnetic moment for an atom (or a molecule) is obtained by adding the contributions of all the electrons. (Some nuclei have magnetic moments, but the values are negligible compared with the electronic contribution.) Many types of molecules have zero magnetic moment if no external field is imposed. We can think of the electronic contributions as canceling because of the different directions of the angular momentum vectors of individual electrons. In the case of the spin angular momentum, most electrons in a molecule pair off with opposite spins, so that the pair gives no net spin contribution to the magnetic moment. For molecules in which the pairing

Permanent magnetic moment due
to unpaired electrons

is incomplete, the magnetic moment is due to the few (usually only one) unpaired electrons. These molecules have permanent magnetic moments.

Magnetization. So far we have restricted our discussion to isolated atoms or molecules and their magnetic dipole moments. Now consider a large collection of molecules that composes a macroscopic object. At the macroscopic level we deal with quantities that involve averages over many molecules. A useful quantity that is related to an average magnetic dipole moment for many molecules is the *magnetization* $\mathbf{M}$.

Consider a volume element ΔV in a material. We assume that ΔV is small on a macroscopic scale but is large enough to contain a large number of molecules. If $\mathbf{m}_i$ represents the magnetic moment of a molecule labeled by i in the volume element, then the net average magnetic moment for this volume is $\langle \Sigma\,\mathbf{m}_i \rangle$, where the vector sum is over all molecules in the element. *The magnetization is defined as the magnetic dipole moment per unit volume in the medium:*

Magnetization defined

$$\mathbf{M} = \frac{\langle \Sigma\,\mathbf{m}_i \rangle}{\Delta V} \tag{30-3}$$

Thus if the magnetization is known at points in a medium, then the magnetic moment $\mathbf{m}$ of a region in the medium with volume ΔV is $\mathbf{m} = \mathbf{M}\,\Delta V$. Notice that the magnetization is a vector quantity. The SI unit of magnetization is ampere/meter (A/m).

---

* In the "extended" edition of this text, electronic structure of atoms is discussed in Chap. 41.

The magnetization describes the magnetic state of a medium or a material. For example, if $\mathbf{M} = 0$ everywhere in a medium, then no part of the medium has a magnetic dipole moment. In a magnetized piece of steel on the other hand, the magnitude of the magnetization is large throughout the sample. On what does the magnetization of a material depend? It is observed to change, for example, if an external magnetic field is imposed or if the temperature is changed. Various materials respond in different ways to changes in their surroundings. Most materials fall into one of three categories of magnetic behavior. We shall discuss *diamagnetism*, *paramagnetism*, and *ferromagnetism* in the following sections.

EXAMPLE 30-1. A typical molecule with one unpaired electron has a permanent magnetic moment with a magnitude of around $m_i = 1 \times 10^{-23}$ A $\cdot$ m². Suppose that an external magnetic field is applied to a gas of these molecules at temperature $T = 273$ K and pressure $p = 1.01 \times 10^5$ Pa. Assume that the component of $\mathbf{m}_i$ along the direction of the magnetic field averages to 1 percent of m for a molecule. (a) Determine the magnetization at a point in this gas, assumed to be ideal. (b) Determine the magnetic dipole moment for a 1-mm³ region in the gas.

SOLUTION. (a) Since all molecules are the same, the sum over molecules in Eq. (30-3) is $\Delta N \langle \mathbf{m}_i \rangle$, where ΔN is the number of molecules in a volume ΔV. The ideal gas equation of state, $p \, \Delta V = \Delta N \, kT$, where k is the Boltzmann

constant, connects ΔN and ΔV. Taking the z axis along the external field direction, we have $\langle m_{iz} \rangle = 0.01 m_i = 1 \times 10^{-25}$ A $\cdot$ m², and for the z component of Eq. (30-3),

$$M_z = \frac{\Delta N \langle m_{iz} \rangle}{\Delta V} = \frac{p \langle m_{iz} \rangle}{kT}$$

$$= \frac{(1.01 \times 10^5 \text{ Pa})(1 \times 10^{-25} \text{ A} \cdot \text{m}^2)}{(1.38 \times 10^{-23} \text{ J} \cdot \text{K}^{-1})(273 \text{ K})} = 3 \text{ A/m}$$

That is, $\mathbf{M}$ is along the z axis, with magnitude $M = 3$ A/m.

(b) Since the magnetization is the magnetic moment per unit volume, the magnetic moment of the 1-mm³ region is $\mathbf{m} = \mathbf{M} \, \Delta V$. The magnetic moment has only a z component, which is

$$m_z = M_z \, \Delta V = (3 \text{ A/m})(10^{-9} \text{ m}^3) = 3 \times 10^{-9} \text{ A} \cdot \text{m}^2$$

30-3 DIAMAGNETISM

There are many materials whose individual molecules have no magnetic moment because of their electronic structure. Even if the molecules form a relatively dense liquid or solid, the magnetization $\mathbf{M}$ of most materials is zero if no external magnetic field is present. That is, even if the molecules are close together, the electrons remain paired so that the substance has no net magnetic moment. However, in the presence of an external magnetic field, molecules do have a small magnetic moment. These molecular magnetic moments are *induced* by the external field. The direction of the induced magnetic moment is opposite the magnetic field direction so that the magnetization of the material is also opposite the magnetic field direction. Such materials are called *diamagnetic*.

M and B are opposite in diamagnetic materials.

A diamagnetic material can be distinguished from a paramagnetic material (discussed in the next section) by its behavior in a *nonuniform* magnetic field. To understand the effect, consider a magnetic dipole in a nonuniform magnetic field. Recall that $\mathbf{m}$ for a bar magnet is directed from its south pole to its north pole. The nonuniform field exerts forces of different magnitudes on the two poles. (See Prob. 30-3.) Thus the dipole experiences a net force in the nonuniform field. Figure 30-3 shows a magnetic dipole in a nonuniform field near the end of a current-carrying solenoid. The direction of the dipole moment in Fig. 30-3a is parallel to the magnetic field at points on the axis of the solenoid. In this case the nonuniform field attracts the dipole toward the strong

A nonuniform magnetic field exerts a net force on a magnetic dipole.

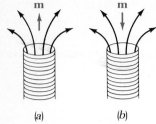

Figure 30-3. (a) The magnetic dipole moment **m** of a small magnet is parallel to **B** near the mouth of a solenoid. The nonuniform field attracts the dipole to the stronger field region because the attractive force on the south pole of the magnet has a larger magnitude than the repulsive force on the north pole. (b) The magnetic dipole moment **m** is opposite **B**. The nonuniform field repels the dipole from the stronger field region.

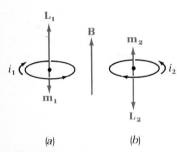

Figure 30-4. If a magnetic field is applied, the magnetic moments of paired electrons do not cancel. Since $m_1 > m_2$ for the case shown, a diamagnetic effect results.

field region, that is, toward the solenoid. With the direction of the dipole moment opposite the direction of the field, as shown in Fig. 30-3b, the dipole is repelled from the strong field region, away from the solenoid. Thus the direction of the force depends on the direction of the dipole moment.

Suppose a small, needle-shaped sample of diamagnetic material is placed in a nonuniform magnetic field. The direction of the magnetization in a diamagnetic sample is opposite the magnetic field, and the arrangement is that of Fig. 30-3b. The diamagnetic sample is repelled (but very weakly) from the strong field region. (This effect was discovered by Faraday in 1845, and he termed the behavior "diamagnetic.") The magnitude of the repelling force is so small that the interaction of a diamagnetic material with a magnetic field is difficult to observe. You have probably never seen the effect.

The relation between the magnetization **M** in a diamagnetic material and the field **B** can be determined by quantitative measurement. Such measurements usually show that the magnitude of the magnetization is proportional to the magnitude of the magnetic field. That is, the magnetization induced by the magnetic field depends linearly on that field and, for this reason, the material is said to be *linear*.

In isotropic diamagnetic materials, **M** and **B** have opposite directions because the induced magnetic dipole moment is directed opposite **B**, even at the atomic level. While quantum theory must be used to treat the electronic structure of atoms and molecules, the diamagnetic behavior of an atom in an external magnetic field is suggested by applying Faraday's law and Lenz's law to a simple classical model:

Consider an electron orbiting a nucleus, as shown in Fig. 30-4. The orbital contribution to the magnetic moment is opposite the orbital angular momentum and is given by Eq. (30-1): $\mathbf{m}_1 = -e\mathbf{L}_1/2m_e$. An orbit with the opposite orientation is shown in Fig. 30-4b: $\mathbf{m}_2 = -e\mathbf{L}_2/2m_e$. These two parts of the figure are shown separately for clarity. You should picture these orbits as having the same center. Before a magnetic field is applied, these orbits are paired if $\mathbf{L}_2 = -\mathbf{L}_1$ so that $\mathbf{m}_1 + \mathbf{m}_2 = 0$.

As a uniform magnetic field is applied in the direction indicated in the figure, an induced electric field [see Faraday's law in Eq. (28-7)] changes the orbital speed or frequency differently for the two orbits. To apply Lenz's law, remember that the sense of the current is opposite the sense of the motion of an electron because the charge is negative. In Fig. 30-4a, the current increases to oppose the changing magnetic flux. Therefore, the angular frequency increases for this orbit. As a consequence, the magnitudes of both $\mathbf{L}_1$ and $\mathbf{m}_1$ increase. Note that $\mathbf{m}_1$ and **B** have opposite directions. The same reasoning applied to the orbit in Fig. 30-4b shows that the magnitudes of $\mathbf{L}_2$ and $\mathbf{m}_2$ decrease. Now we see that $\mathbf{m}_1$ and $\mathbf{m}_2$ do not completely cancel if a magnetic field is applied. Since $\mathbf{m}_1$ has the larger magnitude, the vector sum $\mathbf{m}_1 + \mathbf{m}_2$ is directed opposite the magnetic field. Thus the direction of the induced magnetic moment is opposite **B**, and this is the diamagnetic effect.

The model used above to illustrate diamagnetic behavior is exceedingly simplistic. A more realistic treatment shows that (i) the induced magnetic moment of such an atom is directed opposite the applied field, (ii) the magnetic moment is usually proportional to the field (leading to a linear material), (iii) the effect is very small, and (iv) diamagnetic properties of materials are essentially independent of temperature.

We have associated diamagnetism with the response of atoms or molecules

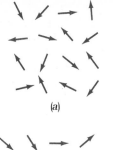

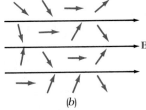

Figure 30-5. (a) Magnetic moments of molecules are randomly oriented, and the magnetization **M** = 0. (b) Magnetic moments tend to align with the applied field so that **M** is parallel to **B**.

M and B are parallel in paramagnetic materials.

with paired electrons to an applied magnetic field. (In a substance such as a metal, the free electrons also contribute to the magnetic properties.) It turns out that all molecules possess diamagnetic behavior. However, diamagnetism is completely masked in materials that exhibit paramagnetism or ferromagnetism.

30-4 PARAMAGNETISM

Molecules with one or more unpaired electrons — Al, O_2, and Fe are examples — possess a permanent magnetic moment. In many materials containing such molecules, the molecular magnetic moments are oriented randomly if no magnetic field is applied. The magnetization, the magnetic moment per unit volume, is zero in this situation because it involves a sum over many molecules. See Fig. 30-5a.

When a magnetic field is applied to the material, the potential energy of a magnetic dipole is lowered if it can change its orientation and align with the field. To see this, recall that the potential energy of a magnetic dipole in a uniform magnetic field is given by Eq. (26-10): $U = -\mathbf{m} \cdot \mathbf{B}$. This energy is lowest ($U = -mB$) if **m** and **B** are aligned and highest ($U = +mB$) if **m** and **B** are oppositely directed. Thus the potential energy is lowered if the dipole tends toward alignment with the field. (Notice that we are discussing the orientation of the *permanent* magnetic moment of a molecule and not the induced magnetic moment considered in the previous section.)

Opposing the tendency to alignment with the magnetic field are the randomizing thermal motions of the molecules. The average, or overall, alignment is a balance between these influences, as shown schematically in Fig. 30-5b. There is a partial alignment of the molecular magnetic moments with the field, and, as a consequence, for isotropic materials the magnetization of the material is parallel to the field. If the applied field is removed, the randomness in orientation returns and the magnetization is again zero. Materials with these properties are called *paramagnetic*.

Diamagnetic and paramagnetic materials behave differently in a nonuniform magnetic field, as stated in the last section. If a needle-shaped sample of a paramagnetic substance is oriented along the axis of a solenoid near one end, the magnetization is parallel to the magnetic field. This configuration is shown in Fig. 30-3a, and the paramagnetic needle is weakly attracted to the stronger field region. This behavior is just opposite that of a diamagnetic needle, which is repelled from the strong field region.

Paramagnetism is due to the partial alignment of the permanent magnetic moments with the applied magnetic field. The aligning tendency should increase with an increase in the magnitude of the magnetic field. On the other hand, the randomizing effect of thermal motions should increase with an increase in temperature. These dependencies were first observed by Pierre Curie (1859–1906) and are summarized in *Curie's law*, which relates the magnetization **M** of an isotropic paramagnetic substance with the applied magnetic field **B** and the Kelvin temperature T:

$$\mathbf{M} = \frac{C\mathbf{B}}{\mu_0 T} \tag{30-4}$$

The constant C, called *Curie's constant*, is characteristic of the material and

Paramagnetic materials are linear.

depends on the molecular magnetic moment. The permeability constant μ_0 appears in Eq. (30-4), so Curie's constant has dimensions of temperature. Curie's law is valid except for high fields and/or low temperatures. It shows that, at a given temperature, **M** and **B** are proportional and the paramagnetic material is linear. Further, the magnetization decreases with increasing temperature. For very high fields or very low temperatures, the magnetization *saturates* (approaches an ultimate limit) as all molecular magnetic moments approach alignment with the field. Paramagnetic materials are not linear under these extreme circumstances.

Some materials, notably the metals, have free electrons which are not bound to any particular atom or molecule. These electrons also contribute to the magnetization of the substance through the magnetic moment associated with their angular momentum. This contribution is typically small and has essentially no dependence on temperature. No classical model can describe the effect adequately, and we shall not discuss it further.

EXAMPLE 30-2. A small amount of doubly ionized manganese (Mn^{++}) is distributed uniformly throughout a crystal of NaCl so that the sample is isotropic and paramagnetic. The magnitude of the magnetization is 6.1 A/m at 310 K in a magnetic field of magnitude 0.87 T. Determine Curie's constant for this sample.

SOLUTION. Since **M** and **B** are parallel in the isotropic

paramagnetic material, we take the magnitude of Eq. (30-4) and solve for Curie's constant C:

$$C = \frac{\mu_0 M T}{B}$$

$$= \frac{(4\pi \times 10^{-7} \text{ T} \cdot \text{m} \cdot \text{A}^{-1})(6.1 \text{ A/m})(310 \text{ K})}{0.87 \text{ T}}$$

$$= 2.7 \times 10^{-3} \text{ K}$$

30-5 FERROMAGNETISM

Magnetic moments align spontaneously in a ferromagnetic material.

For both diamagnetic and paramagnetic materials, the magnetization is nonzero only if an applied magnetic field is present. If the applied field is reduced to zero, the magnetization also becomes zero. There are some substances for which the magnetization persists after the applied field is removed. In *ferromagnetic materials* all of the molecular magnetic moments tend to align spontaneously in the same direction. Iron (Fe) is a prime example of a ferromagnetic substance, as the prefix "ferro" suggests. Other elemental solids such as Co, Ni, Gd, and Dy, as well as alloys and compounds containing some of these elements, exhibit ferromagnetic behavior.

A permanent magnet is made of ferromagnetic material. Even in the absence of an applied magnetic field, the magnetization is nonzero inside the magnet. There is, of course, a magnetic field produced by the magnet itself. The magnetization and the magnetic field of the permanent magnet are due to the alignment of magnetic dipoles.

In paramagnetic materials, an applied magnetic field provides the dominant influence toward partially aligning the magnetic dipoles. A different mechanism is responsible for ferromagnetic behavior. This mechanism involves a quantum phenomenon called *exchange coupling* between neighboring atoms or molecules that cannot be described in classical terms. The effect, however, is quite simple: Large numbers of magnetic dipoles cooperate by having their magnetic moments aligned together. That is, the interaction energy of a partic-

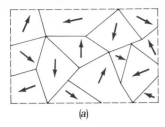

(a)

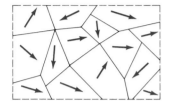

Applied field direction

(b)

Figure 30-6. Magnetic domains are shown schematically. (a) The domains are randomly oriented in unmagnetized material. (b) After a magnetic field is applied, the domains are preferentially oriented.

Magnetic domains are separated by domain walls.

Soft and hard ferromagnetic materials

ular magnetic moment with its nearby neighbors is lower if they all have the same orientation. The alignment is typically much more complete than is achievable in a paramagnetic substance. Consequently, the magnetization in a ferromagnetic material can be large. In an isolated, needle-shaped carbon-steel magnet for example, the magnitude of the magnetization can be around $M = 8 \times 10^5$ A/m.

Countering the cooperative alignment of the dipole moments in a ferromagnetic substance is the tendency toward random orientations that increases with increasing temperature. At temperatures above a critical temperature characteristic of the material, the ferromagnetic state is unstable. The critical temperature for iron is 1043 K. At higher temperatures, the magnetic dipole moments are not spontaneously aligned, and iron is not ferromagnetic but is paramagnetic.

Magnetic domains. Although we think of a magnet as having a permanent magnetization, the magnetization can be changed. For example, a common sewing needle will typically be "unmagnetized." But after being exposed to a strong magnetic field, it will attract small bits of iron. The needle has been "magnetized." There are two essential points to consider in this process: (i) How can the needle be unmagnetized initially if the magnetic dipoles are aligned in ferromagnetic materials? (ii) How did applying a magnetic field magnetize the needle?

To understand these features, we must recognize that all of the magnetic dipoles in a ferromagnetic solid may not be aligned in a single direction. Rather, the sample typically consists of a large number of regions, with the magnetic dipoles aligned differently in each region. These regions are called *magnetic domains.* In a given domain the magnetic dipoles are aligned in a particular direction, which is the direction of the magnetization in this domain. In an adjacent domain the magnetization has a different direction, and the boundary between these domains is called a *domain wall.* The domain structure is shown schematically in Fig. 30-6a for a portion of an unmagnetized sample. In this case the magnetic domains have randomly distributed directions of magnetization. For the whole sample, the average magnetization is nearly zero.

If a magnetic field is applied, then a net magnetization results, as sketched in Fig. 30-6b. The direction of the magnetization in some domains switches toward closer alignment with the applied field. In some materials the size of a domain as well may change because of the motion of domain walls. That is, the direction of the magnetization in some of the domains is close to the applied field direction, and some of these domains can grow at the expense of neighboring domains that are not so closely aligned. These changes are usually irreversible in that some of the domains retain a preferential orientation after the applied field is removed. In this way a net permanent magnetization results; the sample becomes a permanent magnet.

The "permanent" magnetization of typical ferromagnetic substances is not really permanent. The domains tend to relax back toward the unmagnetized state. Materials are classified as magnetically "soft" or "hard" according to the time required for a significant relaxation. For example, a common iron nail is magnetically soft. It can be magnetized in an applied field, but the magnetization becomes small almost immediately after the applied field is removed. On the other hand, many different types of steel and other alloys and compounds are magnetically hard. The magnetization can persist with little change for years. This "permanence" is important for reliability in a magnetic data-storage medium such as a cassette tape or a floppy disk.

The magnetization can be large in a ferromagnetic material if many of the magnetic domains have nearly the same orientation. The magnetic field produced by the oriented domains is correspondingly large. However, the magnetization is not proportional to the magnetic field in ferromagnetic materials. There is an upper limit on the magnetization, which corresponds to all magnetic domains having the same alignment. The magnetization approaches this saturation value as the applied field increases. The magnitude of the saturation magnetization for Fe is around $M = 2 \times 10^6$ A/m, corresponding to $B = 2.2$ T in the material. Figure 30-7 shows the nonlinear saturation effect. Another nonlinearity occurs because of the irreversibility of magnetic domain changes. Thus the magnetization at some instant depends not only on the present value of B but also on the previous treatment of the sample. No linear equation connecting **M** and **B** can describe this relationship.

M and B are not proportional in ferromagnetic materials.

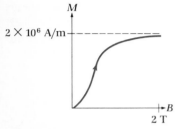

Figure 30-7. In a ferromagnetic material such as Fe, **M** and **B** are not proportional. The magnetization **M** saturates as the magnitude of **B** increases.

30-6 MAGNETIC INTENSITY H

In previous chapters we assumed that **B** was due solely to a known macroscopic current distribution. We neglected the effect of nearby materials in obtaining expressions for the magnetic field due to these currents. In this chapter we have seen that the magnetic field in a material medium can have two types of contributions. One of these is the contribution due to known macroscopic currents, such as in the windings of a solenoid or a toroid. In some cases we think of this field contribution as an applied field. The other contribution to **B** is from the medium. We describe the effect in terms of the magnetization **M** in the substance. The current in a coil can usually be adjusted, but the magnetization in a sample both depends on and contributes to **B**. Therefore, it is not always easy to determine or control **B**, particularly for ferromagnetic materials. In a ferromagnetic substance, **M** and **B** depend on the previous treatment of the sample.

To determine **B** and **M**, it is often convenient to introduce another field. This vector field is represented by the symbol **H** and is called the *magnetic intensity*. It is defined by the expression $\mathbf{H} = \mathbf{B}/\mu_0 - \mathbf{M}$, or equivalently,

Definition of magnetic intensity H

$$\mathbf{B} = \mu_0(\mathbf{H} + \mathbf{M}) \tag{30-5}$$

Notice that **H** and **M** have the same dimensions; the SI unit for **H** is A/m.

According to Eq. (30-5), **H** and **M** (when multiplied by μ_0) are the two contributions to **B**. (We take **B** as the fundamental field that exerts a force on a moving charged particle: $\mathbf{F} = q\mathbf{v} \times \mathbf{B}$.) Consider these contributions for the simple case of the medium inside a long, closely wound solenoid carrying current i. We assume that end effects can be neglected as well as the magnetization of the windings of the solenoid. Suppose first that the core of the solenoid is vacuum. Since **M** = 0 for vacuum (why?), Eq. (30-5) shows that $\mathbf{B} = \mu_0\mathbf{H}$, or $\mathbf{H} = \mathbf{B}/\mu_0$ in this case. Both the magnetic field **B** and the magnetic intensity **H** are uniform inside the solenoid and directed along the axis. From Eq. (27-11), $B = \mu_0 n i$, where n is the number of turns per unit length. Thus the magnitude of the magnetic intensity is $H = B/\mu_0 = ni$. We conclude that **H** inside the solenoid is due to the current distribution in the solenoid windings. Notice that H can be adjusted in an experiment by changing the solenoid current.

Now suppose that the space inside the solenoid is filled with some material, and the solenoid current i is adjusted to have the same value as before. For this geometry, it turns out that **H** in the material is the same as with vacuum in the space. That is, the magnetic intensity **H** inside the ideal solenoid is determined solely by the solenoid current. The magnetic field **B** in the material, however, is different from the vacuum case because of the contribution in Eq. (30-5) from the magnetization **M**.

Since the magnetic intensity **H** can be determined from the solenoid current i, the magnetic field, $\mathbf{B} = \mu_0(\mathbf{H} + \mathbf{M})$ can be calculated if **M** is known. In a typical linear diamagnetic or paramagnetic material, **M** and **B** are proportional. Then from Eq. (30-5), **H** and **B** are also proportional in such materials. The linear relation between **H** and **B** is expressed as

$$\mathbf{B} = \mu\mathbf{H} \qquad\qquad (30\text{-}6)$$

where μ is called the *permeability constant* of the linear material. For vacuum, $\mathbf{M} = 0$, so that $\mathbf{B} = \mu_0(\mathbf{H} + 0)$ and $\mu = \mu_0$.

Suppose the material in the solenoid is diamagnetic. Then the directions of **M** and **B** are opposite, so that, from Eq. (30-5), **H** and **B** are parallel. Eliminating **B** from Eqs. (30-5) and (30-6), we obtain $\mu\mathbf{H} = \mu_0(\mathbf{H} + \mathbf{M})$, or $(\mu - \mu_0)\mathbf{H} = \mu_0\mathbf{M}$.

Since **H** and **M** have opposite directions, we see that $\mu - \mu_0$ is negative; $\mu < \mu_0$ for a diamagnetic material. The permeability constant μ for normal diamagnetic materials is only *slightly* less than μ_0. Bismuth, one of the "most diamagnetic" substances, has a permeability constant $\mu = 0.99983\mu_0$. For most practical purposes, diamagnetic effects can be neglected.

For a typical paramagnetic substance, **M**, **H**, and **B** are all parallel so that $\mu > \mu_0$. Since the magnetization **M** of a paramagnetic substance is temperature-dependent, the permeability constant μ likewise changes with temperature. For many paramagnetic substances over a wide range of temperatures, μ is slightly greater than μ_0. For example, $\mu = 1.00026\mu_0$ for Pt at 293 K. Since $\mu \approx \mu_0$ under such conditions, paramagnetic effects can often be neglected in determining **B**; that is, $\mathbf{B} = \mu\mathbf{H} \approx \mu_0\mathbf{H}$. Under other circumstances, particularly at low temperatures, paramagnetic effects are important.

In a ferromagnetic material, there is no linearity among **M**, **H**, and **B**. Although Eq. (30-6) can be used to connect **H** and **B**, the value of μ is not characteristic of the material but depends on the previous treatment of the sample. The detailed relationship between the magnetic field **B** and the magnetic intensity **H** can be measured by using the ferromagnetic material as the core of a toroid called a *Rowland ring*. The arrangement is shown in Fig. 30-8. The toroid is like a long solenoid that has been bent, with its ends joined to form a doughnut shape. If the toroid has N_T turns and a mean ring radius R, the number of turns per unit length is $n = N_T/2\pi R$. With this geometry, both **H** and **B** are essentially confined to the ferromagnetic core of the toroid. The magnetic intensity has magnitude $H = ni$ and can be controlled by adjusting the current i. A secondary or search coil is used to monitor a change in B, which causes an induced emf, $\mathscr{E} = NS\,dB/dt$, in the N-turn search coil.

Suppose that initially the core is unmagnetized and that there is no current in the toroid; thus $\mathbf{M} = 0$, $\mathbf{H} = 0$, and $\mathbf{B} = 0$. The current is increased to some value i so that H increases to ni. During this process, B and the flux $\Phi_B = BS$ linking each turn of the search coil change, and an emf is induced in the coil. The coil is connected to a device, such as a ballistic galvanometer, which measures the net charge ΔQ passing through it. (See Prob. 28-9.) This charge $\Delta Q = \int i_s\,dt$ corresponds to the induced current i_s in the search coil. Since i_s is

Figure 30-8. A Rowland ring is used to measure B in a ferromagnetic core. *(Tom Richard)*

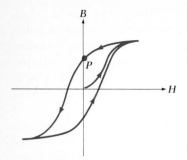

Figure 30-9. A ferromagnetic material exhibits hysteresis. The relation between **H** and **B** depends on the previous treatment of the sample.

proportional to the induced emf $\mathcal{E} = NS\,dB/dt$, the integral $\Delta Q = \int i_s\,dt$ is proportional to the integral $NS \int (dB/dt)dt = NS\,\Delta B$. In this way, the change ΔB in the magnitude of the magnetic field is determined by measuring the charge passing through the search coil.

By changing the toroid current in steps, one obtains pairs of values of components of **H** and **B**. Figure 30-9 shows a curve, typical of a hard ferromagnetic core, obtained by plotting such points on a graph. Conventionally, H is taken as the independent variable, since it is changed by adjusting the current in the toroid. The irreversibility of changes in the magnetic domain structure, called *hysteresis,* is evident in the figure. The magnetic intensity component H is changed such that the curve is traversed with the sense of the arrows. (Since H and B represent toroidal components of the fields in this discussion, negative values correspond to a reversal of direction. The sign of H is changed by reversing the sense of the current in the toroidal windings.) Note that $H = 0$, $B \neq 0$ at point P on the curve; the ferromagnetic core has a permanent magnetization in this state. You can also see that a value of B is not uniquely determined by a value of H. The state of the sample is determined by the history of its treatment.

30-7 THE MAGNETIC FIELD OF THE EARTH

North geographic pole

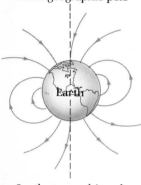

South geographic pole

Figure 30-10. Outside the earth the magnetic field is approximately a dipole field. The region near the north geographic pole (toward the star Polaris) has lines similar to those near a south magnetic pole. The magnetic lines are continuous and close on themselves, although the behavior deep inside the earth is not known in detail.

A simple compass consists of a magnetized needle that can rotate freely in a plane. When used for navigation or direction finding at the earth's surface, the compass is usually held with its plane horizontal, and the compass needle aligns with an approximately north-south orientation. The end of the needle that points north is identified as the north (north-seeking) pole of the needle. In the absence of other sources of magnetic field, the torque which orients a compass needle is provided by the magnetic field of the earth. The needle aligns with the magnetic field, and the direction of the field is from the south to the north pole of the needle.

The earth's magnetic field distribution outside its surface is shown schematically in Fig. 30-10. Note that the field has a component perpendicular to the earth's surface at most places. A compass can be used to map out the magnetic field of the earth. The direction of the needle when the plane of the compass is horizontal corresponds to the horizontal component of the field. If the plane of the compass is rotated about that direction until the plane is vertical, then the needle will give the direction of **B** at that point. (Try it using a small compass.) Notice from Fig. 30-10 that the lines representing **B** generally emerge from the earth's surface in the southern hemisphere and reenter in the northern hemisphere. These lines are suggestive of a magnetic dipole field. That is, outside the earth's surface, the magnetic field is essentially the same as that due to a magnetic dipole located at the center of the earth. Notice in the figure that lines entering the region near the north *geographic* pole correspond roughly to a *magnetic* south pole centered there. Likewise, the *magnetic* north pole is centered near the south *geographic* pole in Antarctica.

At points several earth radii outside the surface, the earth's magnetic field is distorted by a contribution from the solar wind, a stream of charged particles from the sun. Some of the particles are trapped by the magnetic field around the earth. Light emitted by these particles in the upper atmosphere is responsible for the *auroras* that are sometimes visible in the higher latitudes.

The magnetic field distribution in the earth's interior is not known. This inaccessible region contains the source or cause of the earth's magnetic field. The mechanism by which the magnetic field is maintained is not understood. A successful theory of geomagnetism must account for features that are characterized by very different time scales. On a time scale measured in days or years, the earth's magnetic field seems static and, therefore, useful for navigation. But on a geologic time scale, the earth's magnetism is dynamically active. There are variations in the local magnetic field that occur over hundreds or thousands of years. And there is evidence from the direction of the magnetization in dated rocks that the direction of the earth's magnetic field undergoes abrupt reversals with intervals of up to a million years. The most recent reversal seems to have occurred somewhat over 10,000 years ago.

SUMMARY WITH APPLICATIONS

Section 30-2. Atomic currents, magnetic dipoles, and magnetization

In a simple model, an orbiting electron has a magnetic moment proportional to its orbital angular momentum,

$$\mathbf{m} = -\frac{e}{2m_e}\mathbf{L} \tag{30-1}$$

and a similar contribution due to the spin angular momentum,

$$\mathbf{m} = -\frac{e}{m_e}\mathbf{S} \tag{30-2}$$

The magnetization in a material is the magnetic moment per unit volume:

$$\mathbf{M} = \frac{\langle \Sigma\, \mathbf{m}_i \rangle}{\Delta V} \tag{30-3}$$

Evaluate the contributions of the orbital and spin angular momenta to the electron magnetic moment; define the magnetization and evaluate the magnetic moment of a volume element in a material.

Section 30-3. Diamagnetism

In diamagnetic materials, magnetic dipole moments are induced in molecules by the magnetic field, and the vectors **M** and **B** have opposite directions.

Describe the relation between **M** and **B** in a linear diamagnetic material.

Section 30-4. Paramagnetism

The permanent magnetic moment of an unpaired electron in a paramagnetic substance tends to become aligned with the magnetic field. The vectors **M** and **B** are parallel and are related by Curie's law

$$\mathbf{M} = \frac{C\mathbf{B}}{\mu_0 T} \tag{30-4}$$

valid except at low temperatures and high fields.

Describe the relation between **M** and **B** in a linear paramagnetic material; apply Curie's law to a paramagnetic material.

Section 30-5. Ferromagnetism

Molecular magnetic dipoles in a magnetic domain tend to be aligned in a ferromagnetic material. If the domains are oriented preferentially by applying a magnetic field, the sample has a large magnetization. The magnetization can persist in hard magnetic materials to form a permanent magnet.

Describe the domain structure of ferromagnetic materials; explain how a hard magnetic material can have a permanent magnetization.

Section 30-6. Magnetic intensity H

The magnetic intensity **H** is defined by the relation

$$\mathbf{B} = \mu_0(\mathbf{H} + \mathbf{M}) \tag{30-6}$$

For a linear medium with permeability μ, the relation can be expressed as $\mathbf{B} = \mu\mathbf{H}$. For a Rowland ring, **H** is due to the macroscopic current in the windings. The relation between **B** and **H** for ferromagnetic materials is nonlinear, and hysteresis effects are present.

State the relation between the fields **M**, **B**, and **H** and use it to determine one of them; define the permeability of a linear material and classify paramagnetic and diamagnetic substances by the values of μ; describe hysteresis in ferromagnetic materials and sketch a typical hysteresis curve.

Section 30-7. The magnetic field of the earth

Outside its surface, the earth's magnetic field is approximately a dipole field. Large changes in the field occur over geological time intervals.

Describe the earth's magnetic field and determine its horizontal and vertical components at the surface.

QUESTIONS

30-1 What is the direction of the orbital contribution to the magnetic moment **m** of an electron relative to the direction of its orbital angular momentum **L**?

30-2 A free electron at rest has a magnetic moment **m** due to its spin angular momentum **S**. What are the relative directions of these two vectors? A proton also has an intrinsic angular momentum and a magnetic moment. What are the relative directions of **m** and **S** for a free proton?

30-3 The electrons in an isolated He atom are paired so that the total angular momentum of the electrons is zero. Explain why you should expect that the net magnetic moment is also zero. Do you expect liquid helium to be diamagnetic or paramagnetic? Explain.

30-4 When isolated, a neutral Na atom and a neutral Cl atom are expected to have permanent magnetic moments. In table salt (NaCl), the *ions* Na^+ and Cl^- form an ionic crystal which is diamagnetic. Give a possible explanation of the diamagnetic behavior of NaCl.

30-5 An iron filing, released from rest near a stationary permanent magnet, accelerates toward the magnet. (a) What is the source of the increased kinetic energy of the filing as it moves toward the magnet? (b) What becomes of this kinetic energy as the filing strikes the magnet and sticks to it?

30-6 Why does a typical transformer have an iron core?

30-7 In a paramagnetic material, **M** and **B** are parallel and the permeability μ is positive. In a diamagnetic material, **M** and **B** have opposite directions. Why is the permeability μ not negative? From the value of μ, how can you distinguish a diamagnetic material from a paramagnetic one?

30-8 The core of a long solenoid can be filled with any of a variety of materials. A current in the windings causes a magnetic intensity **H** inside the solenoid parallel to the axis. Relative to the direction of **H**, what are the directions of **M** and **B** inside the solenoid if the core is (a) diamagnetic and (b) paramagnetic? (c) Explain why the question cannot be answered in general for a ferromagnetic core.

30-9 One property of a *superconductor* is that the magnetic field **B** is excluded from its interior. If the core of the solenoid in the previous question is a superconductor, then the magnetic field **B** = 0 in the core. But

H is not zero in the core if a current exists in the solenoid windings. (a) What is the direction of **M** in the core relative to the direction of **H**? (b) Explain why a superconductor is sometimes called "perfectly diamagnetic."

30-10 What is the magnetization **M** for vacuum? Explain.

30-11 A small nonferromagnetic sample is brought near the north pole of a strong magnet where the field is highly nonuniform. The sample is very weakly repelled by the north pole. (a) Is the sample diamagnetic or paramagnetic? (b) What happens to the sample if it is brought close to the south pole of the magnet?

30-12 What are the answers to the two parts of the previous question if the sample is weakly attracted to the north pole?

30-13 Consider the magnetic field **B** inside a long solenoid carrying current i (a) with and (b) without a soft iron core. In which case is B larger? Explain.

30-14 For the two cases in the previous question, which has the larger self-inductance? Explain.

30-15 You are given a small piece of wood, a glass of water, and a magnetized needle. Explain how a compass can be formed from these items.

30-16 Suppose that you have the compass from the previous question in an otherwise empty room. The magnetized needle is unmarked, and the room has no windows or other openings. Is it possible under these circumstances to determine which way is north? Explain.

30-17 A compass needle points north when the plane of the compass is horizontal. If the plane is rotated through $90°$ about a north-south axis, the north-pole end of the needle points above the horizon. Are you more likely to be in Austria or in Australia? Explain.

30-18 Complete the following table:

Symbol	Represents	Type	SI unit
M			
L	Orbital angular momentum		
S			$kg \cdot m^2 \cdot s^{-1}$
H			
μ		Scalar	

EXERCISES

Section 30-2. Atomic currents, magnetic dipoles, and magnetization

30-1 Suppose that the z component of the orbital angular momentum of an electron in an atom is $L_z = 1.06 \times 10^{-34} \ kg \cdot m^2 \cdot s^{-1}$. Determine the z component of

the orbital contribution to the magnetic dipole moment.

30-2 Verify, using Eq. (30-1), that the SI unit of magnetic moment is $A \cdot m^2$ and, using Eq. (30-3), that the SI unit of magnetization is A/m.

30-3 A free electron at rest has a magnetic moment component $m_z = 9.3 \times 10^{-24}$ A · m². Determine the corresponding component S_z of the electron's spin angular momentum.

30-4 ***The Bohr magneton.*** Experiment shows that a component of angular momentum is *quantized.* That is, only certain discrete values occur, and for orbital angular momentum these are integer multiples of $h/2\pi$, where $h = 6.63 \times 10^{-34}$ kg · m² · s⁻¹ is *Planck's constant.* (See Chap. 39.) (a) Show that the corresponding component of magnetic moment for an electron is also quantized in integer multiples of $m_B = eh/4\pi m_e$. This value, called the *Bohr magneton,* is a convenient unit of magnetic moment at the atomic level. (b) Determine the value of the Bohr magneton to three significant figures.

30-5 ***The nuclear magneton.*** Some species of atomic nuclei have magnetic moments, and a convenient unit of nuclear magnetic moment is the *nuclear magneton* $m_N = eh/4\pi m_p$, where m_p is the proton mass. (See the previous exercise.) (a) Determine the value of the nuclear magneton to three significant figures. (b) Compare the values of the nuclear magneton and the Bohr magneton and explain why the nucleus of an atom usually contributes negligibly to the magnetic properties of materials.

30-6 Bismuth is one of the most diamagnetic of substances. If a 1-T magnetic field is applied parallel to the axis of a long Bi rod, the magnetization in the rod has magnitude $M = 1.7$ A/m. (a) What is the direction of **M** relative to the direction of **B**? (b) Determine the average magnetic moment per Bi atom. The density of Bi is 9.8×10^3 kg/m³, and the mass of a Bi atom is 3.5×10^{-25} kg. (c) What fraction of a Bohr magneton (see Exercise 30-4) is the average magnetic moment per atom?

30-7 In a strong permanent magnet, the average magnitude of the magnetic moment per atom is around 1×10^{-23} A · m². Estimate the magnitude of the magnetization in such a magnet.

30-8 A permanently magnetized sphere of radius 25 mm has a uniform magnetization of magnitude 8400 A/m. (a) Determine the magnitude of the magnetic moment of the sphere. (b) Sketch the lines representing **B** inside and outside of the sphere. Recall that a line representing **B** must close on itself and assume that **B** is uniform inside the sphere and parallel to **M**.

Section 30-3. Diamagnetism

30-9 No dissipation occurs for electronic currents in molecules, so they are resistanceless. To see how diamagnetism is related to Faraday's law, consider a *resistanceless* circular conducting filament. Initially there is no magnetic field and no current in the loop. A magnetic field is then applied perpendicular to the plane of the loop, and a current is induced in the loop.

This current will persist even after the magnetic field stops changing. (Why?) (a) Construct a diagram showing the direction of the applied magnetic field and the sense of the induced current. (b) Determine the direction of the magnetic moment of the current loop and explain how this model is suggestive of diamagnetic behavior.

30-10 In an applied magnetic field of 1 T, the magnitude of the magnetization of water is about 8 A/m. What is the magnetization of water if (a) $B = 0$; (b) $B = 0.5$ T?

Section 30-4. Paramagnetism

30-11 Curie's constant for a paramagnetic salt is 1.8×10^{-3} K. (a) Determine the magnetization of this salt at room temperature ($T = 293$ K) in a 0.35-T magnetic field. (b) At what temperature would the magnetization have the same magnitude in a 0.25-T field?

30-12 Curie's constant for an ideal ($pV = nRT$) paramagnetic gas is proportional to the density of the gas. For O_2 at a density corresponding to 293 K and atmospheric pressure, the Curie constant is 5.5×10^{-4} K. (a) Determine the magnetization of O_2 with this density at 293 K in a 0.50-T magnetic field. (b) Determine the magnetization of the gas in the same field at 200 K at atmospheric pressure. (Notice that the density has changed.)

30-13 Curie's law is valid except for low temperatures or high fields. One way to express this is in terms of the ratio of two energies: $m_0 B/kT$. For a system at temperature T, the typical energy change due to random thermal processes is about kT, where $k = 1.38 \times 10^{-23}$ J/K is the Boltzmann constant. (See Chap. 18.) (a) Consider a dipole, with a permanent dipole moment of magnitude m_0, that is aligned either parallel to or opposite the applied field **B**. Show that the difference in energy for these two orientations is $2m_0 B$. (b) A typical molecular magnetic moment has $m_0 \approx 1 \times 10^{-23}$ A · m². Evaluate $m_0 B$ for such a molecule in a 1-T field. (c) Curie's law is valid if $m_0 B/kT \ll 1$. Estimate a temperature range for the validity of Curie's law for the conditions in part (b).

Section 30-5. Ferromagnetism

30-14 The magnetic moment per atom in Ni is about 6×10^{-24} A · m², and there are about 9×10^{28} atoms per cubic meter in the solid. (a) Determine the magnetization for a sample that has a single domain with virtually all of the magnetic moments aligned. (b) Determine the magnetization for a sample averaged over many domains oriented randomly. (c) What is the effective fraction of the many domains in a sample that are aligned with the average magnetization to give a magnitude $M = 2000$ A/m?

30-15 The magnetic moments per atom for Ni, Co, and Fe are 0.6×10^{-23} A · m², 1.6×10^{-23} A · m², and $2.1 \times$

10^{-23} A · m², respectively. Estimate the maximum (or saturation) magnetization that can exist in each of these solids.

Section 30-6. Magnetic intensity H

30-16 A long solenoid has 2500 turns per meter and carries a 4.8-A current. Neglect end effects and determine B, M, and H inside the solenoid for (a) vacuum in the space, (b) a Pb core ($\mu = 0.999984\mu_0$), (c) air in the space ($\mu = 1.0000004\mu_0$).

30-17 For most practical purposes, the permeability of air is the same as for vacuum, $\mu \approx \mu_0$. Determine the magnitude H of the magnetic intensity at a point just above the earth's surface where $B = 42\ \mu$T.

30-18 If the relation $\mathbf{B} = \mu\mathbf{H}$ is used for a ferromagnetic material, then μ does not have a single value. A hysteresis curve for a ferromagnetic substance is shown in Fig. 30-11. For a point on the curve, the value of $\mu = B/H$ is the slope of the straight line from the origin to the point on the curve. Identify those portions (if any) for which μ is (a) positive, (b) negative, (c) zero, (d) infinite.

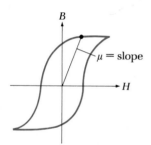

Figure 30-11. Exercise 30-18.

30-19 A soft iron rod forms the core of a long solenoid. Inside the rod the fields have magnitude $B = 1.10$ T, $H = 345$ A/m. (a) Determine a value of μ for this state. (b) Determine the magnetization in the iron rod, given that $\mathbf{H}$ and $\mathbf{B}$ are parallel to each other and to the solenoid axis. (c) Determine the percent error in evaluating B in this case from the approximate expression

$B \approx \mu_0 M$.

30-20 Ferromagnetic iron forms the core of a Rowland ring. Measurements of H and B for the ring are shown in the following table:

H, A/m	B, mT	H, A/m	B, mT
0.0	0.0	32	16
0.8	0.2	48	30
4.0	1.5	64	150
8.0	2.6	80	540
16	6.3	160	1100
24	11	800	1600

Construct graphs of B versus H for (a) $0 \leqslant H \leqslant 24$ A/m and (b) $0 \leqslant H \leqslant 800$ A/m. (c) Estimate minimum and maximum values of $\mu = B/H$ from the two graphs. (d) Determine the magnitude of the magnetization when $H = 800$ A/m.

Section 30-7. The magnetic field of the earth

30-21 Over much of the surface of the United States, the magnitude of the earth's magnetic field is around 6×10^{-5} T. The inclination (the angle between the direction of $\mathbf{B}$ and a horizontal plane tangent to the surface) averages around 70°. Estimate the vertical and horizontal components of $\mathbf{B}$ at a point in this region.

30-22 At points a large distance from a magnetic dipole in the perpendicular bisector plane of the dipole moment, the magnitude of the magnetic field is given by $B = \mu_0 m/4\pi r^3$, where m is the magnitude of the magnetic moment. The magnetic field outside the earth can be approximated by the field due to a magnetic dipole located at the earth's center. (a) Estimate the magnitude of this equivalent magnetic moment, given that $B = 3 \times 10^{-5}$ T at a point on the equator near the southern tip of India. (b) If the earth had a uniform magnetization, what magnitude M would correspond to the magnetic moment calculated above? (c) What direction should each of the vectors $\mathbf{m}$ and $\mathbf{M}$ have relative to the geographic poles?

PROBLEMS

30-1 Ampere's law for steady current distributions, Eq. (27-8), is often written in terms of the magnetic intensity: $\oint \mathbf{H} \cdot d\boldsymbol{\ell} = \Sigma i$. Apply this form of Ampere's law and symmetry arguments to determine the magnetic intensity inside an ideal solenoid with n turns per unit length and current I. Note that the result is independent of the material in the core.

30-2 A long solenoid has 2500 turns per meter and carries a steady 120-mA current. The core of the solenoid is ferromagnetic. (a) Determine $\mathbf{H}$ inside the solenoid core. (b) The core is in a state such that $\mu = 150\mu_0$.

Determine $\mathbf{B}$ inside the solenoid core. (c) Determine $\mathbf{M}$ inside the solenoid core.

30-3 A square current loop, shown in perspective in Fig. 30-12, lies in the xy plane perpendicular to a *nonuniform* magnetic field in the z direction. The z component of the field depends only on the y coordinate and ranges from B_{1z} to B_{2z} (with $B_{1z} < B_{2z}$) over a distance $\Delta y = a$. (a) Give the direction of the magnetic moment $\mathbf{m}$ of the loop relative to the direction of $\mathbf{B}$. (b) Determine the direction of the net magnetic force on the current loop and explain why this result is suggestive of the force on a paramagnetic sample in a nonuniform magnetic field. (c) Reconsider parts (a) and (b) if the sense of the current is opposite that in the figure.

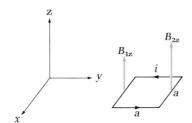

Figure 30-12. Prob. 30-3.

30-4   ***The Larmor frequency.*** Consider an electron with speed v in a circular orbit of radius r about a nucleus. It is convenient to consider the angular speed, or angular frequency $\omega_0 = v/r$. The magnitude of the orbital angular momentum is $L = m_e v r = m_e r^2 \omega_0$. The centripetal force on the electron in this circular orbit, $m_e v^2/r$ or $m_e r \omega_0^2$, is provided by the electrostatic attraction F_E toward the nucleus, $m_e r \omega_0^2 = F_E$. Now suppose that an external magnetic field **B** is applied perpendicular to the plane of the orbit. For the orientation shown in Fig. 30-4a, the magnetic field exerts an additional force $-e\mathbf{v} \times \mathbf{B}$ on the electron. The force is directed radially inward and the electron increases its speed. Let $\omega_1 = \omega_0 + \omega_L$ represent the angular frequency for this case; the quantity ω_L is the small change in angular frequency due to the external magnetic field. (a) Assume that the radius of the orbit changes negligibly and show that $\omega_L = eB/2m_e$. This small change in frequency due to the magnetic field is called the *Larmor frequency*. (b) Show that the orbital angular momentum of the electron has changed by $\Delta L = \frac{1}{2} e r^2 B$.

30-5   Apply the ideas of the previous problem to a pair of electrons in orbits such as shown in Fig. 30-4. Show that this simplistic model leads to a net magnetic moment $\mathbf{m} = \mathbf{m}_1 + \mathbf{m}_2 = -e^2 r^2 \mathbf{B}/2m_e$. Why is this model suggestive of diamagnetic behavior?

30-6   A permanently magnetized steel sphere of radius 8.5 mm has a uniform magnetization of magnitude 2500 A/m. At points inside the sphere, the magnetic field is given by $\mathbf{B} = 2\mu_0\mathbf{M}/3$. Outside the sphere, **B** is a magnetic dipole field due to the dipole moment of the sphere. (a) Determine the magnitude and direction of **H** inside the sphere. (b) Determine the magnetic moment of the sphere. (c) What is **H** outside the sphere?

30-7   Very strong magnetic fields exist in a *neutron star,* the last stage in the evolution of stars somewhat more massive than our sun. In a model of a neutron star, the interior consists of a small sphere (radius $a \approx 20$ km) of an extremely dense fluid of neutrons (density $\rho \approx 10^{17}$ kg/m^3). The neutron, although neutral, has a magnetic moment of magnitude $m_N \approx 10^{-26}$ A · m^2. Suppose that the neutron star has a uniform magnetization similar to the sphere in the previous problem and that the magnetic field inside has magnitude $B \approx 10^8$ T. (a) Determine the magnitude of the magnetization inside the star. (b) Estimate the saturation magnetization which would correspond to the alignment of all the neutron magnetic moments. The neutron mass is $M_N = 1.67 \times 10^{-27}$ kg.

30-8   Consider the material in the core of a long solenoid of cross-sectional area S, with N turns on a length ℓ. If the magnetic field **B** is changed by changing the current i in the windings, then an emf $\mathscr{E} = S \, dB/dt$ is induced in each turn. An external agent must supply energy at a rate $dW/dt = Ni\mathscr{E}$ to counter the induced emf in the N turns. (a) Show that the infinitesimal work can be expressed in terms of the fields and the volume of the region: $dW = \ell SH \, dB$. (b) The work per unit volume for a hysteresis loop can be expressed as $\oint H \, dB$. Explain how this integral can be interpreted as the area enclosed by a hysteresis loop such as that graphed in Fig. 30-11. This work corresponds to the dissipation of energy, called *hysteresis loss,* due to the irreversible changes in domain structure for such ferromagnetic materials.

CHAPTER 31
ELECTROMAGNETIC OSCILLATIONS AND AC CIRCUITS

31-1 INTRODUCTION

Practically every day of our lives we use electrical devices that operate with alternating current (ac). Such devices include radios, television sets, computers, telephones, refrigerators, and on and on. The feature which makes ac electricity often more useful than dc is that ac can be more readily controlled. In this chapter we shall see how resistance, capacitance, and inductance in a circuit play a crucial role in the behavior of alternating currents and potential differences.

31-2 *LC* OSCILLATIONS

In Sec. 25-5, we discussed the behavior of a circuit which contains a resistor and a capacitor, an *RC* circuit. When a capacitor is discharged through a resistor, the current in the circuit decreases exponentially to zero. The electric energy U_E stored in a capacitor is dissipated as heat in the resistor during the discharge. Similarly, in Sec. 29-3, we discussed the behavior of a circuit which contains a resistor and an inductor, an *LR* circuit, and we found the magnetic energy U_B produced by the current. In an *LR* circuit the current decreases exponentially to zero while energy U_B is dissipated as heat in the resistor. Capacitors and inductors are energy-storage devices; a capacitor can store electric energy and an inductor can store magnetic energy. Resistance in a circuit causes energy to be dissipated as heat.

We now examine the behavior of a circuit which contains only a capacitance C and an inductance L, an *LC* circuit (Fig. 31-1). Ordinary circuits contain

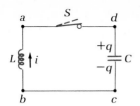

Figure 31-1. Applying the loop rule to an *LC* circuit.

resistance, but for simplicity we begin by discussing an idealized circuit with negligible resistance. Suppose the capacitor in the circuit of Fig. 31-1 is charged by an external battery and then the battery is taken away. When the switch is closed, the capacitor will begin to discharge through the inductor so that at time t there will be a current i in the circuit and a charge q on the capacitor. The charge and the current are related because the current gives the rate at which charge is transferred from one plate to the other: $i = \pm dq/dt$. The choice of plus or minus depends on our sign convention for i and q. Suppose we let i be positive when the current is clockwise and let q be positive when the charge on the upper plate is positive. With this choice, q increases when i is positive: $i = dq/dt$.

From Kirchhoff's loop rule, the sum of the potential differences around the loop is zero:

$$(V_b - V_a) + (V_c - V_b) + (V_d - V_c) + (V_a - V_d) = 0$$

The potential difference across the inductor is $(V_b - V_a) = L(di/dt)$, where the algebraic sign is determined by Lenz's law. The induced emf opposes the change that causes it. Therefore, when $di/dt > 0$, $V_b > V_a$. With our sign convention for q, the potential difference across the capacitor is $V_d - V_c = q/C$. Thus

$$L\frac{di}{dt} + \frac{q}{C} = 0$$

Since $i = dq/dt$, we have $di/dt = d^2q/dt^2$. Making this substitution and rearranging, we have

Differential equation for *LC* oscillations

$$\frac{d^2q}{dt^2} = -\frac{1}{LC}q \tag{31-1}$$

This equation has the same mathematical form as the differential equation which describes a simple harmonic oscillator (Chap. 14). An example of a simple harmonic oscillator is the one-dimensional mass-spring system where frictional forces are negligible. For the mass-spring system, Newton's second law gives

$$\frac{d^2x}{dt^2} = -\frac{k}{m}x \tag{14-11}$$

where x is the coordinate of an object of mass m connected to a spring of force constant k. The mass-spring harmonic oscillator provides a mechanical analog to the *LC* circuit. Table 31-1 lists some of the analogous quantities. From our experience with the motion of a simple harmonic oscillator, we expect that the charge on the capacitor in the *LC* circuit varies sinusoidally with time:

Oscillating charge

$$q = Q_m \cos(\omega_0 t + \phi) \tag{31-2}$$

Table 31-1. Analogy between the mechanical block-spring harmonic oscillator and the electromagnetic *LC* circuit

Mechanical system	Electromagnetic system
Mass m	Inductance L
Force constant k	Reciprocal capacitance $1/C$
Coordinate x	Charge q
Velocity component $v_x = dx/dt$	Current $i = dq/dt$
Mechanical energy	Electromagnetic energy
$E = \frac{1}{2}kx^2 + \frac{1}{2}mv_x^2$	$U = \frac{1}{2}q^2/C + \frac{1}{2}Li^2$

where Q_m is the maximum charge on the capacitor, ω_0 is the angular frequency of the oscillation, ϕ is the phase constant, and $(\omega_0 t + \phi)$ is the phase. The current is

$$i = \frac{dq}{dt} = \frac{d}{dt}[Q_m \cos(\omega_0 t + \phi)] = -\omega_0 Q_m \sin(\omega_0 t + \phi)$$

or

$$i = -I_m \sin(\omega_0 t + \phi) \qquad (31\text{-}3)$$

where $I_m = \omega_0 Q_m$ is the maximum current.

We now verify that Eq. (31-2) is a solution to Eq. (31-1). As a by-product of this exercise, we shall find an expression for ω_0. To make this verification, we first determine d^2q/dt^2:

$$\frac{d^2q}{dt^2} = \frac{di}{dt} = \frac{d}{dt}[-\omega_0 Q_m \sin(\omega_0 t + \phi)] = -\omega_0{}^2 Q_m \cos(\omega_0 t + \phi)$$

Substituting this expression for d^2q/dt^2 and q from Eq. (31-2) into Eq. (31-1), we have

$$-\omega_0{}^2 Q_m \cos(\omega_0 t + \phi) = -\frac{1}{LC} Q_m \cos(\omega_0 t + \phi)$$

or

$$\omega_0{}^2 \cos(\omega_0 t + \phi) = \frac{1}{LC} \cos(\omega_0 t + \phi)$$

This equation is satisfied only if $\omega_0{}^2 = 1/LC$, or

Angular frequency of oscillation

$$\omega_0 = \frac{1}{\sqrt{LC}} \qquad (31\text{-}4)$$

Therefore, if $\omega_0 = 1/\sqrt{LC}$, then Eqs. (31-2) and (31-3) describe the oscillating charge and current. The frequency ν_0 of the oscillation is $\nu_0 = \omega_0/2\pi = 1/(2\pi\sqrt{LC})$.

The constants Q_m and ϕ in Eq. (31-2) are determined from the initial conditions. Suppose the capacitor was given a charge Q_0 while the switch was open, and the switch was closed at $t = 0$. Then the initial conditions are $q = Q_0$ and $i = 0$ at $t = 0$. Substituting $i = 0$ and $t = 0$ into Eq. (31-3), we have $0 = -I_m \sin\phi$. This condition can be satisfied by setting $\phi = 0$. Then we find Q_m by substituting $q = Q_0$ and $t = 0$ into Eq. (31-2): $Q_0 = Q_m \cos 0 = Q_m$. With these initial conditions, Eqs. (31-2) and (31-3) become

$$q = Q_0 \cos(\omega_0 t) \qquad \text{and} \qquad i = -I_m \sin(\omega_0 t)$$

where $I_m = \omega_0 Q_0$. Figure 31-2 shows graphs of the oscillating charge and current versus time for the case with these initial conditions.

Now consider the energy of the LC circuit. From Sec. 23-4 the electric energy stored in a charged capacitor is $U_E = \frac{1}{2}q^2/C$, and from Sec. 29-4 the magnetic energy stored in a current-carrying inductor is $U_B = \frac{1}{2}Li^2$. The electromagnetic energy U of the LC circuit is

Definition of electromagnetic energy

$$U = U_E + U_B$$

Using Eqs. (31-2) and (31-3), we find that the electric and magnetic energies at time t are

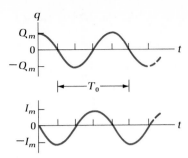

Figure 31-2. Oscillating charge and current versus time.

$$U_E = \frac{\frac{1}{2}q^2}{C} = \frac{\frac{1}{2}Q_m^2}{C} \cos^2(\omega_0 t + \phi)$$

and

$$U_B = \frac{1}{2}Li^2 = \frac{1}{2}LI_m^2 \sin^2(\omega_0 t + \phi)$$

We can use $I_m = \omega_0 Q_m$ and $\omega_0^2 = 1/LC$ to show that the factors which multiply $\cos^2(\omega_0 t + \phi)$ and $\sin^2(\omega_0 t + \phi)$ in the two expressions above are equal:

$$\frac{1}{2}LI_m^2 = \frac{1}{2}L(Q_m\omega_0)^2 = \frac{1}{2}LQ_m^2 \frac{1}{LC} = \frac{\frac{1}{2}Q_m^2}{C}$$

This means that the electromagnetic energy remains constant in an *LC* circuit:

$$U = U_E + U_B$$

$$= \frac{\frac{1}{2}Q_m^2}{C} \cos^2(\omega_0 t + \phi) + \frac{1}{2}LI_m^2 \sin^2(\omega_0 t + \phi)$$

$$= \frac{\frac{1}{2}Q_m^2}{C} [\cos^2(\omega_0 t + \phi) + \sin^2(\omega_0 t + \phi)]$$

Since $\cos^2(\omega_0 t + \phi) + \sin^2(\omega_0 t + \phi) = 1$ for all t,

$$U = \frac{\frac{1}{2}Q_m^2}{C} = \frac{1}{2}LI_m^2$$

Thus the electromagnetic energy remains constant, continually changing back and forth between electric energy in the capacitor and magnetic energy in the inductor, as shown schematically in Fig. 31-3. Figure 31-4 shows graphs of the energies versus time for the same initial conditions as discussed above: $q = Q_0$

Figure 31-3. Electromagnetic energy is passed back and forth between the capacitor and the inductor in an *LC* circuit.

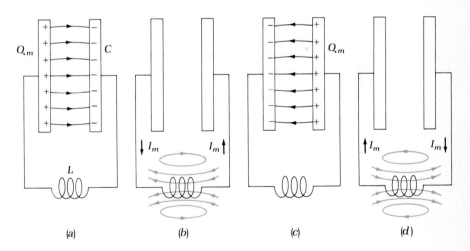

(a)   (b)   (c)   (d)

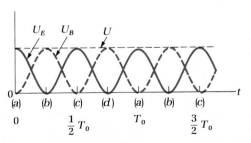

Figure 31-4. Energy in an *LC* circuit. The letters *a*, *b*, *c*, and *d* along the time axis correspond to the situations shown in Fig. 31-3.

and $i = 0$ at $t = 0$ so that $Q_m = Q_0$, $I_m = \omega_0 Q_0$, and $\phi = 0$. The correlation with Fig. 31-3 is shown along the time axis in Fig. 31-4.

EXAMPLE 31-1. With the switch open in Fig. 31-1, a 12-V battery is used to charge the capacitor and then the battery is removed. Given that $C = 3.7~\mu F$ and $L = 96$ mH, determine (a) ω_0, (b) Q_m, (c) I_m, and (d) U for the oscillations that occur after the switch is closed.

SOLUTION. (a) The angular frequency of the oscillations is

$$\omega_0 = \frac{1}{\sqrt{LC}} = \frac{1}{\sqrt{(96~\text{mH})(3.7~\mu F)}} = 1.7~\text{krad/s}$$

(b) The charge on the capacitor due to the battery is $Q_m =$

$C\mathscr{E}$, where $\mathscr{E}$ is the emf of the battery (Sec. 25-5). Thus the amplitude of the oscillating charge is

$$Q_m = (3.7~\mu F)(12~V) = 44~\mu C$$

(c) The amplitude of the oscillating current is

$$I_m = \omega_0 Q_m = (1.7~\text{krad/s})(44~\mu C) = 74~\text{mA}$$

(d) The electromagnetic energy of the circuit is

$$U = \frac{\frac{1}{2}Q_m{}^2}{C} = \frac{\frac{1}{2}(44~\mu C)^2}{3.7~\mu F} = 0.27~\text{mJ}$$

31-3 SERIES *RLC* CIRCUIT

In the previous section we made the simplifying assumption that the resistance in the circuit was negligible. In that case we found that the electromagnetic energy of the circuit was constant. We now consider a circuit in which the resistance R is significant: an *RLC* circuit. When a significant resistance is present in the circuit, the electromagnetic energy of the circuit decreases with time because energy is dissipated as heat from the resistor. Thus in an *RLC* circuit we expect that the charge on the capacitor and the current in the circuit will tend to approach zero as time goes by, but that oscillations in the charge and current may occur while they are dying out.

Figure 31-5 shows an *RLC* circuit. As before, the capacitor is charged by a battery, the battery is taken away, and then the switch is closed. We let i be positive when the current is clockwise and we let q be positive when the charge on the upper plate is positive so that $i = dq/dt$. Applying the loop rule, we have

$$(V_b - V_a) + (V_c - V_b) + (V_d - V_c) + (V_a - V_d) = 0$$

With our chosen sign convention for q and i, the loop rule gives

$$L\frac{di}{dt} + iR + \frac{q}{C} = 0$$

Rearranging and substituting dq/dt for i and d^2q/dt^2 for di/dt, we have

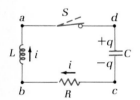

Figure 31-5. Applying the loop rule to an *RLC* circuit.

Differential equation for an *RLC* circuit

$$\frac{d^2q}{dt^2} + \frac{R}{L}\frac{dq}{dt} + \frac{1}{LC}q = 0 \tag{31-5}$$

This equation has the same mathematical form as the differential equation which describes the damped harmonic oscillator. The one-dimensional mass-spring system with a frictional force that is proportional to the object's speed is an example of a damped harmonic oscillator (Sec. 14-7). Newton's second law applied to the mass-spring system with friction gives

$$\frac{d^2x}{dt^2} + \frac{\gamma}{m}\frac{dx}{dt} + \frac{k}{m}x = 0$$

where γ is the proportionality factor between the magnitude of the frictional force and the speed. If the damping factor γ is not too large, then the object oscillates and the amplitude of the oscillation decreases exponentially to zero. For example, the amplitude of a pendulum swinging in air gradually dies out. This is called the *under*damped case. On the other hand, if the damping factor is larger than a certain critical amount, the object does not oscillate, and its displacement monotonically approaches zero. For example, suppose a pendulum is immersed in a viscous fluid, such as molasses, and the bob is displaced from its central position and released. The bob tends to return to its central position without overshooting. This is the *over*damped case. Because these two differential equations have the same form, we expect the *RLC* circuit to exhibit a behavior similar to the damped harmonic oscillator. From our discussion above and from a comparison of the two equations, you can see that the resistance R plays a role analogous to the damping factor γ. To remind yourself of some of the other analogous quantities, reexamine Table 31-1.

From this mechanical analogy to the *RLC* circuit, we expect that a solution to Eq. (31-5) is

Oscillating charge with damping

$$q = Q_m e^{-t/\tau} \cos(\omega_d t + \phi) \tag{31-6}$$

The factor $e^{-t/\tau}$ provides the exponentially decreasing amplitude, and the factor $\cos(\omega_d t + \phi)$ provides the oscillations. (The subscript "*d*" on ω_d stands for *d*amped.) You can show that Eq. (31-6) is a solution by using it to substitute q, dq/dt, and d^2q/dt^2 into Eq. (31-5). (See Prob. 31-3.) Further, this substitution will allow you to find values for τ and ω_d. The results are

$$\tau = \frac{2L}{R}$$

and

$$\omega_d = \sqrt{\frac{1}{LC} - \left(\frac{R}{2L}\right)^2} = \sqrt{\omega_0{}^2 - \frac{1}{\tau^2}}$$

Note that when $\omega_0 \gg 1/\tau$, $\omega_d \approx \omega_0$. In terms of R, L, and C this occurs when $(1/LC) \gg (R/2L)^2$ or $R \ll \sqrt{4L/C}$. This corresponds to the negligible-resistance case discussed in the previous section. Thus the criterion for the amount of damping caused by the resistance is the comparison between R and $\sqrt{4L/C}$. If $R > \sqrt{4L/C}$, then the circuit is overdamped. (Recall the pendulum in molasses.) Problem 31-2 provides further investigation of this case. For the particular case where $R = R_{\text{crit}} = \sqrt{4L/C}$, the circuit is said to be *critically damped*. Figure 31-6 shows a graph of q versus t for an underdamped circuit in which $R = 2.00 \times 10^2\ \Omega$, $L = 1.00$ mH, and $C = 1.00$ nF. The initial conditions are such that $Q_m = Q_0$ and $\phi = 0$ in Eq. (31-6).

Critical damping

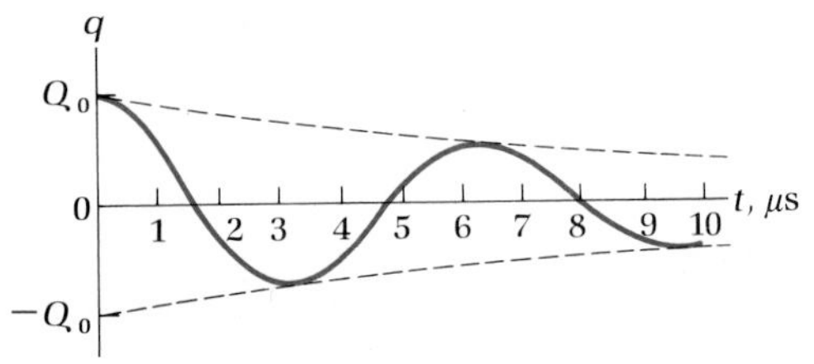

Figure 31-6. Charge on the capacitor in an underdamped *RLC* circuit.

EXAMPLE 31-2. Using the values of R, L, and C given above for the graph in Fig. 31-6, find the expression for q.

SOLUTION. To find the expression for q, we must determine τ and ω_d:

$$\tau = \frac{2L}{R} = \frac{2(1.00 \text{ mH})}{2.00 \times 10^2 \ \Omega} = 10.0 \ \mu s$$

$$\omega_d = \sqrt{\frac{1}{LC} - \left(\frac{R}{2L}\right)^2}$$

$$= \sqrt{\frac{1}{(1.00 \text{ mH})(1.00 \text{ nF})} - \left[\frac{2.00 \times 10^2 \ \Omega}{2(1.00 \text{ mH})}\right]^2}$$

$$= 9.95 \times 10^5 \text{ rad/s} = 995 \text{ krad/s}$$

Since the initial conditions are such that $Q_m = Q_0$ and $\phi = 0$, we have

$$q = Q_0 e^{-t/10.0 \, \mu s} \cos{[(995 \text{ krad/s})t]}$$

31-4 AC SOURCE CONNECTED TO A RESISTOR

The circuits we considered in earlier chapters had a source of emf, such as a battery, that was constant in time. We now investigate ac circuits. An ac circuit is a circuit that has an alternating current. An ac current is sustained by an *ac source.* An ac source is a source of emf which produces an oscillating potential difference across its terminals; examples are the generator and the alternator discussed in Sec. 28-4. An electric outlet in your home is an ac source. The symbol for an ac source in a circuit diagram is Ⓥ. The potential difference V across the terminals of an ac source oscillates. For simplicity, we consider a sinusoidally varying potential difference across the source:

$$V = V_m \sin{(\omega t)} \qquad (31\text{-}7)$$

where V_m is the amplitude of the oscillating potential difference and ω is its angular frequency. This oscillating potential difference is called an *ac voltage.* The frequency ν of the ac voltage across the two connections to an electric outlet in your room is 60.0 Hz, so that $\omega = 2\pi\nu = 2\pi(60.0 \text{ Hz}) = 377 \text{ rad/s}$.

In this section we consider a circuit which contains only a source and a resistor, a purely resistive ac circuit. Applying the loop rule to the circuit shown in Fig. 31-7, we find that the potential difference across the source is equal to the potential difference across the resistor:

$$V_m \sin{(\omega t)} = iR$$

Solving for i, we have

$$i = \frac{V_m}{R} \sin{(\omega t)}$$

If the resistor is ohmic (R is independent of V or i), then the time dependence of i is

$$i = I_m \sin{(\omega t)} \qquad (31\text{-}8)$$

where the current amplitude I_m is constant:

$$I_m = \frac{V_m}{R} \qquad (31\text{-}9)$$

The analysis of an ac circuit is facilitated by the use of a *phasor diagram.* The phasor diagram for the circuit in Fig. 31-7 is shown in Fig. 31-8. A *phasor* is a vector which rotates about the origin with angular speed ω, as shown in the figure. The vertical components of phasors **V** and **I** represent the sinusoidally varying quantities V and i. The magnitudes of phasors **V** and **I** represent the amplitudes V_m and I_m of these oscillating quantities. The figure shows the

AC source

AC voltage across a source

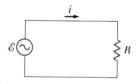

Figure 31-7. An ac source connected to a resistor.

AC current in a resistive circuit

Phasor diagram

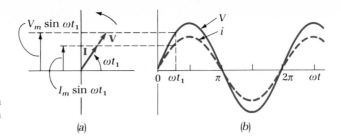

Figure 31-8. (a) A phasor diagram for the circuit in Fig. 31-7. (b) Graph of V and i versus ωt.

relationship between a phasor diagram and a graph of the oscillating quantities versus ωt.

Voltage and current are in phase in a purely resistive circuit.

Figure 31-8 shows that for a purely resistive ac circuit, the voltage and current are in phase. Or, stated another way, the phase angle difference between the voltage and the current is zero. The phasor diagram shows this phase relationship with the phasors **V** and **I** being parallel.

31-5 AC SOURCE CONNECTED TO A CAPACITOR

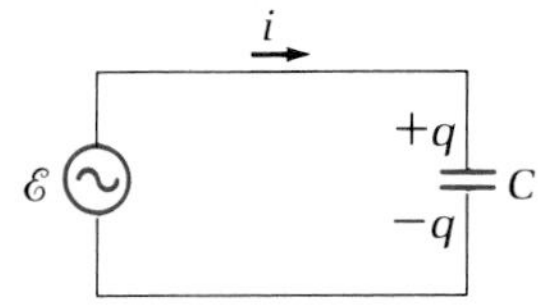

Figure 31-9. An ac source connected to a capacitor.

Figure 31-9 shows an ac source connected to a capacitor only, a purely capacitive ac circuit. We let i be positive when the current is clockwise and we let q be positive when the charge on the upper plate is positive so that $i = dq/dt$. We let Eq. (31-7) describe the voltage across the source: $V = V_m \sin(\omega t)$. From the loop rule, the voltages across the source and the capacitor are equal:

$$V_m \sin(\omega t) = \frac{q}{C}$$

To find the current, we solve for q and take its time derivative: $q = CV_m \sin(\omega t)$, so that

$$i = \frac{dq}{dt} = \omega C V_m \cos(\omega t)$$

Using $\cos(\omega t) = \sin(\omega t + \frac{1}{2}\pi)$, we have

AC current in a capacitive circuit

$$i = I_m \sin(\omega t + \tfrac{1}{2}\pi) \tag{31-10}$$

where the amplitude of the oscillating current is $I_m = \omega C V_m = V_m/(1/\omega C)$. In the previous section where we had a purely resistive circuit, the amplitude of the oscillating current was $I_m = V_m/R$. By analogy to the resistance, we introduce the *capacitive reactance* X_C:

Capacitive reactance

$$X_C = \frac{1}{\omega C} \tag{31-11}$$

so that the amplitude of the current is

$$I_m = \frac{V_m}{X_C} \tag{31-12}$$

Thus the current amplitude is inversely proportional to the capacitive reactance. Note that the dimension of capacitive reactance is the same as resistance and its SI unit is the ohm (Ω).

The capacitive reactance limits the amplitude of the current in a purely

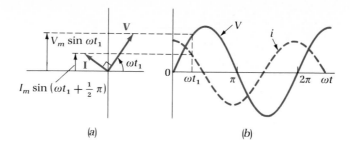

Figure 31-10. (a) A phasor diagram for the circuit in Fig. 31-9. (b) Graph of V and i versus ωt.

capacitive circuit similar to the way resistance limits the amplitude of the current in a purely resistive circuit. But unlike resistance, capacitive reactance is frequency-dependent; it is inversely proportional to the frequency. The capacitive reactance of a capacitor is also inversely proportional to its capacitance. At a given frequency, a capacitor with a smaller capacitance impedes the current more than a capacitor with a larger capacitance.

A comparison between the expressions for V and i shows that these oscillating quantities are out of phase by $\frac{1}{2}\pi$ rad. From Eq. (31-7), $V = V_m \sin(\omega t)$, and from Eq. (31-10), $i = I_m \sin(\omega t + \frac{1}{2}\pi)$. This phase difference has been incorporated into Fig. 31-10, which shows the phasor diagram and graphs of V and i versus ωt for the purely capacitive circuit. In the phasor diagram, phasor **V** is $\frac{1}{2}\pi$ rad behind phasor **I** as they rotate counterclockwise. In the graphs of V and i versus ωt, the maxima in V are shifted $\frac{1}{2}\pi$ rad (or 90°) to the right of the maxima in i. This means that the voltage reaches its maximum value later than the current by one-fourth of a period $[T/4 = (\frac{1}{2}\pi)/\omega]$. To describe this, we say, "The voltage lags the current by 90°," or "The current leads the voltage by 90°."

Voltage lags the current in a capacitive circuit.

EXAMPLE 31-3. The terminals of a 650-nF capacitor are connected to an ac source with $V_m = 158$ V. (a) If the frequency of the source is 20 kHz, determine the capacitive reactance of the capacitor and find the amplitude of the current. (b) If the frequency of the source is 20 Hz, determine the capacitive reactance of the capacitor and find the amplitude of the current.

SOLUTION. (a) Using $\omega = 2\pi\nu$, we find that when $\nu = 20$ kHz, the capacitive reactance is

$$X_C = \frac{1}{\omega C} = \frac{1}{2\pi\nu C} = \frac{1}{(2\pi)(20 \text{ kHz})(650 \text{ nF})} = 12 \ \Omega$$

The amplitude of the current in this case is

$$I_m = \frac{V_m}{X_C} = \frac{158 \text{ V}}{12 \ \Omega} = 13 \text{ A}$$

(b) When $\nu = 20$ Hz, the capacitive reactance is

$$X_C = \frac{1}{(2\pi)(20 \text{ Hz})(650 \text{ nF})} = 12 \text{ k}\Omega$$

The amplitude of the current in this case is

$$I_m = \frac{158 \text{ V}}{12 \text{ k}\Omega} = 13 \text{ mA}$$

The capacitive reactance is larger and the current amplitude is smaller for the case with the smaller frequency. The current-limiting ability of a capacitor increases with decreasing frequency. For a steady current, the frequency is zero, and a capacitor (ideally) stops all current.

31-6 AC SOURCE CONNECTED TO AN INDUCTOR

Figure 31-11 shows an ac source connected to an inductor only, a purely inductive ac circuit. (Many inductors have appreciable resistance in their windings, but we make the simplifying assumption that this inductor has a negligibly small resistance.) We again let Eq. (31-7), $V = V_m \sin(\omega t)$, describe the voltage across the source. From the loop rule, the voltage across the source

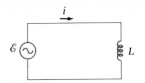

Figure 31-11. An ac source connected to an inductor.

and the inductor are equal: $V_m \sin(\omega t) = L \dfrac{di}{dt}$

To find the current, we integrate di/dt with respect to time:

$$\int \frac{di}{dt}\, dt = \frac{V_m}{L} \int \sin(\omega t)\, dt$$

Integration gives $\qquad i = -\dfrac{V_m}{\omega L} \cos(\omega t) + \text{constant}$

The integration constant represents a component of the current which is steady. Since the source produces an emf which oscillates symmetrically about zero, the current it sustains also oscillates symmetrically about zero, so that no steady component of the current exists. Consequently, we set the integration constant equal to zero. Using $-\cos(\omega t) = \sin(\omega t - \tfrac{1}{2}\pi)$, we have

AC current in an inductive circuit

$$i = I_m \sin(\omega t - \tfrac{1}{2}\pi) \tag{31-13}$$

where the amplitude of the current is $I_m = V_m/(\omega L)$.

By analogy to the resistance and the capacitive reactance, we introduce the *inductive reactance X_L*:

Inductive reactance

$$X_L = \omega L \tag{31-14}$$

so that the amplitude of the current is

$$I_m = \frac{V_m}{X_L} \tag{31-15}$$

The current amplitude is inversely proportional to the inductive reactance; the dimension of inductive reactance is the same as resistance and the same as capacitive reactance; and its SI unit is the ohm (Ω). The inductive reactance limits the current in a purely inductive circuit similar to the way the resistance limits the current in a purely resistive circuit or the way the capacitive reactance limits the current in a purely capacitive circuit. The inductive reactance of an inductor is directly proportional to its inductance and to the frequency of the current. That is, contrary to capacitive reactance, inductive reactance increases with increasing frequency. An inductor which weakly impedes a slowly varying current will strongly impede a rapidly varying current.

As with the capacitive circuit, a comparison between the expressions for V and i shows that these oscillating quantities are out of phase by $\tfrac{1}{2}\pi$ rad. But the phase difference has the opposite sign from the capacitive circuit. From Eq. (31-7), $V = V_m \sin(\omega t)$; and from Eq. (31-13), $i = I_m \sin(\omega t - \tfrac{1}{2}\pi)$. This phase difference has been incorporated into Fig. 31-12, which shows the phasor diagram and graphs of V and i versus ωt for the purely inductive circuit. In the phasor diagram, phasor **V** is $\tfrac{1}{2}\pi$ rad ahead of phasor **I** as they rotate counter-

Figure 31-12. (a) A phasor diagram for the circuit in Fig. 31-11. (b) Graph of V and i versus ωt.

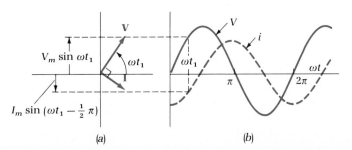

clockwise. In the graphs of V and i versus ωt, the maxima in V are shifted $\frac{1}{2}\pi$ rad (or 90°) to the left of the maxima in i. This means that the voltage reaches its maximum value earlier than the current by one-fourth of a period [$T/4 = (\frac{1}{2}\pi)/\omega$]. To describe this, we say, "The voltage leads the current by 90°," or "The current lags the voltage by 90°."

Voltage leads the current in an inductive circuit.

EXAMPLE 31-4. A 14-mH inductor is connected to an ac source whose voltage amplitude is 6.3 V and whose frequency is variable. (a) Determine the reactance of the inductor and the current amplitude in the circuit when $\omega = 340$ rad/s. (b) Determine the reactance of the inductor and the current amplitude in the circuit when $\omega = 340$ krad/s.

SOLUTION. (a) When $\omega = 340$ rad/s,

$$X_L = \omega L = (340 \text{ rad/s})(14 \text{ mH}) = 4.8 \ \Omega$$

and

$$I_m = \frac{V_m}{X_L} = \frac{6.3 \text{ V}}{4.8 \ \Omega} = 1.3 \text{ A}$$

(b) When $\omega = 340$ krad/s,

$$X_L = 340 \text{ krad/s})(14 \text{ mH}) = 4.8 \text{ k}\Omega$$

and

$$I_m = \frac{6.3 \text{ V}}{4.8 \text{ k}\Omega} = 1.3 \text{ mA}$$

31-7 SERIES *RLC* CIRCUIT DRIVEN BY AN AC SOURCE

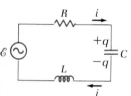

Figure 31-13. A series *RLC* circuit driven by an ac source.

A series *RLC* circuit driven by an ac source exhibits many properties that are common to ac circuits in general. The study of this circuit brings together the features of the previous three sections. Figure 31-13 shows the series combination of a resistor, inductor, capacitor, and source. From the loop rule, the sum of the voltages across the inductor, the resistor, and the capacitor is equal to the voltage across the source:

$$L\frac{di}{dt} + iR + \frac{q}{C} = V \tag{31-16}$$

where the voltage across the source is

$$V = V_m \sin(\omega t)$$

Five parameters characterize this circuit: L, R, C, V_m, and ω. The values of these parameters determine the current in the circuit.

Equation (31-16) is analogous to the equation of motion for the forced, damped, harmonic oscillator discussed in Sec. 14-8. However, we shall not use that analogy to help solve this circuit problem. Because of their extensive use in solving more complicated ac circuit problems, we shall use phasor diagrams.

Phasor-diagram solutions. Since the four elements in our circuit (inductor, resistor, capacitor, and source) are in series, the current in each element is the same. From the results of the past three sections, we expect that the oscillating voltage V across the source will sustain an oscillating current i with the same frequency ω, but that the voltage and the current may be out of phase. Therefore, we write

$$i = I_m \sin(\omega t + \phi) \tag{31-17}$$

where ϕ is the phase difference between the voltage across the source and the current in the circuit. We wish to construct a phasor diagram that will allow us to determine ϕ and the current amplitude I_m. In this diagram, a single phasor **I**,

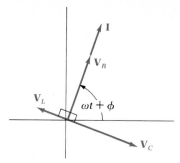

Figure 31-14. Relation between phasors $\mathbf{V}_L$, $\mathbf{V}_R$, $\mathbf{V}_C$, and $\mathbf{I}$ for the circuit in Fig. 31-13.

whose vertical component gives Eq. (31-17), represents the current in each element.

The voltage across each element is different in general, so we shall require four phasors — $\mathbf{V}_L$, $\mathbf{V}_R$, $\mathbf{V}_C$, and $\mathbf{V}$ — to represent the voltage across the inductor, the resistor, the capacitor, and the source, respectively. Figure 31-14 shows a diagram with phasors $\mathbf{V}_L$, $\mathbf{V}_R$, $\mathbf{V}_C$, and $\mathbf{I}$. In constructing this diagram, we are guided by our experience with the three previous sections. Phasor $\mathbf{V}_R$ corresponds to the voltage phasor discussed in Sec. 31-4; $\mathbf{V}_C$ corresponds to the voltage phasor discussed in Sec. 31-5; $\mathbf{V}_L$ corresponds to the voltage phasor discussed in Sec. 31-6. This means that as these phasors rotate counterclockwise:

1 $\mathbf{V}_R$ is parallel to $\mathbf{I}$ because the voltage across a resistive element is in phase with the current.
2 $\mathbf{V}_C$ is $\frac{1}{2}\pi$ rad behind $\mathbf{I}$ because the voltage across a capacitive element lags the current by $\frac{1}{2}\pi$ rad.
3 $\mathbf{V}_L$ is $\frac{1}{2}\pi$ rad ahead of $\mathbf{I}$ because the voltage across an inductive element leads the current by $\frac{1}{2}\pi$ rad.

From Eqs. (31-9), (31-12), and (31-15), the lengths of these phasors are

$$V_{Rm} = I_m R \qquad V_{Cm} = I_m X_C \qquad V_{Lm} = I_m X_L \tag{31-18}$$

Now we use Eq. (31-16) to find the relation between phasors $\mathbf{V}_L$, $\mathbf{V}_R$, $\mathbf{V}_C$, and $\mathbf{V}$. Rewriting Eq. (31-16), we have

$$V_L + V_R + V_C = V \tag{31-19}$$

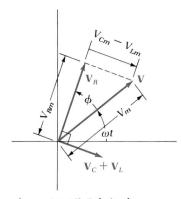

Figure 31-15. Relation between phasors $\mathbf{V}$, $\mathbf{V}_R$, and $(\mathbf{V}_C + \mathbf{V}_L)$ for the circuit in Fig. 31-13.

where V_L, V_R, V_C, and V are the instantaneous voltages across the inductor, the resistor, the capacitor, and the source, respectively. The phasor relation whose vertical component gives Eq. (31-19) is

$$\mathbf{V}_L + \mathbf{V}_R + \mathbf{V}_C = \mathbf{V} \tag{31-20}$$

Figure 31-15 shows the phasor relation which represents Eq. (31-20). Since $\mathbf{V}_C$ and $\mathbf{V}_L$ are always along the same line and in opposite directions, we combine them into a single phasor $(\mathbf{V}_C + \mathbf{V}_L)$ which has magnitude $|V_{Cm} - V_{Lm}|$. Since $\mathbf{V}$ is represented as the hypotenuse of a right triangle whose sides are $\mathbf{V}_R$ and $(\mathbf{V}_C + \mathbf{V}_L)$, the pythagorean theorem gives

$$V_m{}^2 = V_{Rm}{}^2 + (V_{Cm} - V_{Lm})^2$$

Using Eqs. (31-18) to substitute for V_{Rm}, V_{Cm}, and V_{Lm}, we have

$$V_m{}^2 = (I_m R)^2 + (I_m X_C - I_m X_L)^2 = I_m{}^2[R^2 + (X_C - X_L)^2]$$

Solving for I_m, we have

Current amplitude

$$I_m = \frac{V_m}{\sqrt{R^2 + (X_C - X_L)^2}} \tag{31-21}$$

By analogy to the resistance in a circuit, we introduce the *impedance Z* in an ac circuit:

Impedance of an ac circuit

$$V_m = I_m Z \qquad \text{or} \qquad Z = \frac{V_m}{I_m}$$

From Eq. (31-21), we see that the impedance of a series *RLC* circuit is

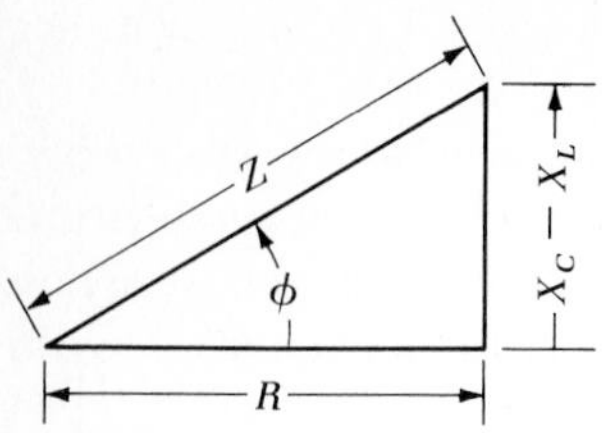

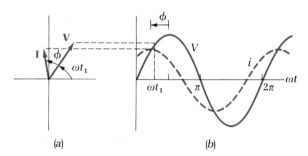

Figure 31-16. Impedance diagram.

$$Z = \sqrt{R^2 + (X_C - X_L)^2} \tag{31-22}$$

Since phasor **I** is parallel to phasor $\mathbf{V}_R$, the phase difference ϕ between i and V can be determined from Fig. 31-15: $\tan \phi = (V_{Cm} - V_{Lm})/V_{Rm}$. Using Eqs. (31-18), we can write this as

$$\tan \phi = \frac{X_C - X_L}{R} \tag{31-23}$$

Equations (31-22) and (31-23) are shown graphically in Fig. 31-16. This is an *impedance diagram*, a right triangle with Z as its hypotenuse. Note that if $X_C > X_L$, then ϕ is positive. In this case the circuit is predominantly capacitive, and the voltage across the source lags the current. Figure 31-17 shows this case. On the other hand, if $X_C < X_L$, then ϕ is negative. In this case the circuit is predominantly inductive, and the voltage across the source leads the current.

Using phasor diagrams to solve our circuit problem is instructive, but causes us to bypass a feature that is sometimes significant. Notice that there is no mention of the initial conditions in our phasor-diagram discussion. The solution we obtained is called the *steady-state solution*. There is also a *transient solution* whose form is similar to that of the *RLC* circuit without a source (Sec. 31-3). The *general solution* is the sum of the transient and the steady-state solutions. After a sufficiently long time interval, the effects of the transient solution become insignificant, and the behavior of the circuit is described by the steady-state solution. (Recall Sec. 14-8.)

Figure 31-17. (*a*) Phasor diagram of **V** and **I**. (*b*) Graphs of V and i versus ωt for a predominantly capacitive *RLC* series circuit driven by an ac source.

(a)

(b)

EXAMPLE 31-5. A series *RLC* circuit with $R = 580\ \Omega$, $L = 31$ mH, and $C = 47$ nF is driven by an ac source. The amplitude and angular frequency of the source are 65 V and 33 krad/s. Determine (*a*) the reactance of the capacitor, (*b*) the reactance of the inductor, (*c*) the impedance of the circuit, (*d*) the phase difference between the voltage across the source and the current, and (*e*) the current amplitude. (*f*) Does the current lead or lag the voltage across the source?

SOLUTION

(*a*) $X_C = \dfrac{1}{\omega C} = \dfrac{1}{(33\ \text{krad/s})(47\ \text{nF})} = 640\ \Omega$

(*b*) $X_L = \omega L = (33\ \text{krad/s})(31\ \text{mH}) = 1.0\ \text{k}\Omega$

(*c*) $Z = \sqrt{R^2 + (X_C - X_L)^2}$

    $= \sqrt{(580\ \Omega)^2 + (640\ \Omega - 1.0\ \text{k}\Omega)^2} = 690\ \Omega$

(*d*) $\phi = \tan^{-1} \dfrac{X_C - X_L}{R}$

    $= \tan^{-1} \dfrac{640\ \Omega - 1.0\ \text{k}\Omega}{580\ \Omega} = -0.58\ \text{rad}$

(*e*) $I_m = \dfrac{V_m}{Z} = \dfrac{65\text{V}}{690\ \Omega} = 94\ \text{mA}$

(*f*) Since ϕ is negative, the voltage across the source leads the current.

Resonance. An interesting and useful characteristic of the series *RLC* circuit driven by an ac source is the phenomenon of *resonance*. Resonance is a feature which is common among systems that have a tendency to oscillate at a particular frequency. This oscillation frequency is called the system's *natural frequency*. If such a system is driven by an energy source at a frequency that is near the natural frequency, then the amplitude of the oscillation is large. An example is a child on a playground swing. The child seated on the swing has a natural frequency for swinging back and forth. If the child pulls on the ropes at regular intervals and the frequency of the pulls is almost the same as the natural frequency of swinging, then the amplitude of the swinging will be large.

Suppose we have a series *RLC* circuit driven by an ac source whose frequency can be varied. Consider the current amplitude I_m as we change the frequency while keeping other quantities (R, L, C, and V_m) fixed. Equation (31-20) shows that the current amplitude is limited by the impedance of the circuit: $I_m = V_m/Z$, where $Z = \sqrt{R^2 + (X_C - X_L)^2}$. Since $X_C = 1/\omega C$ and $X_L = \omega L$, there is a particular frequency at which $X_C = X_L$ so that the impedance is minimum at $Z = \sqrt{R^2 + (0)^2} = R$. This angular frequency is represented by the symbol ω_0 and is called the *resonant angular frequency*. Using $X_C = X_L$ at $\omega = \omega_0$, we have $1/\omega_0 C = \omega_0 L$, or

Resonant angular frequency

$$\omega_0 = \frac{1}{\sqrt{LC}} \tag{31-24}$$

When $\omega = \omega_0$, the current amplitude is maximum at $I_m = V_m/R$. Notice that ω_0 is given by the same expression as the angular frequency of oscillation for the *LC* circuit with no resistor or source [Eq. (31-4) in Sec. 31-2]. It is often called the circuit's *natural* angular frequency.

Figure 31-18 shows graphs of I_m versus ω for two cases; in the upper curve, $R = 100\ \Omega$, and in the lower curve, $R = 200\ \Omega$. The other quantities are the same for each curve: $V_m = 100$ V, $L = 1.00$ mH, $C = 1.00$ nF. Each curve exhibits a maximum current at a resonant frequency. Since the product *LC* is the same for each case, the resonant frequency is also the same: $\omega_0 = 1/\sqrt{LC} = 1/\sqrt{(1.00\ \text{mH})(1.00\ \text{nF})} = 1.00$ Mrad/s. At resonance, $I_m = V_m/R$. Thus the current amplitude at resonance is twice as great for the circuit with $R = 100\ \Omega$ compared with the circuit with $R = 200\ \Omega$. At frequencies much less than ω_0, a circuit is predominantly capacitive and the current is limited mainly by its capacitive reactance. At frequencies much greater than ω_0, a circuit is predominantly inductive, and the current is limited mainly by its inductive reactance.

The tuning circuit of a radio or television set is an example of a circuit with a

Figure 31-18. Current amplitude I_m versus ω for two cases: (*i*) $R = 100\ \Omega$ and (*ii*) $R = 200\ \Omega$. Other quantities are $V_m = 100$ V, $L = 1.00$ mH, and $C = 1.00$ nF.

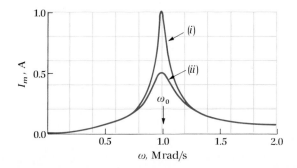

resonant frequency. The antenna of a radio accepts signals from many nearby stations. The antenna is the source in the tuning circuit, so the circuit is driven at many frequencies. However, the only component of the current which is large is the component that oscillates near the circuit's resonant frequency. The circuit discriminates against signals that are not near its resonant frequency. When you tune a radio, you vary the capacitance of a capacitor in the tuning circuit. This varies the resonant frequency of the circuit so that it matches the transmitting frequency of the station you wish to hear.

31-8 POWER FOR AN *RLC* CIRCUIT DRIVEN BY AN AC SOURCE

We now consider the rate at which energy is exchanged among the circuit elements of an *RLC* circuit driven by an ac source. That is, we examine the rate at which energy enters and leaves each of the elements. Ordinarily, the source frequency is too high for the time dependence of these energy exchanges to be of interest. Thus we are concerned chiefly with the average power $\overline{P}$, and this average is taken over an integral number of cycles. For simplicity, we continue to assume that the circuit's entire resistance is contained in the resistor, its entire capacitance is contained in the capacitor, and its entire inductance is contained in the inductor.

Consider the exchange of energy between the four elements of our circuit:

1. The source delivers electromagnetic energy to the circuit; it converts energy from some other form to electromagnetic energy.

2. The resistor dissipates electromagnetic energy as heat; energy leaves the circuit through i^2R heating in the resistor (Sec. 25-3).

3. At any instant, electromagnetic energy may be entering or leaving the capacitor, depending on whether it is charging or discharging. Since the current oscillates sinusoidally, the energy which enters during the charging part of the cycle is equal to the energy which leaves during the discharging part of the cycle (Sec. 31-2). Consequently, the average power for the capacitor is zero.

4. As with the capacitor, the inductor is an energy-storage device. The average power for the inductor is zero.

For the circuit as a whole, energy enters at the source and leaves at the resistor. We shall refer to the average rate of this energy transfer as the *average power $\overline{P}$* for the circuit.

The average power involves the average of the product of two sinusoidally varying quantities—for example, the square of the current. Therefore, it is convenient to introduce the *root-mean-square (rms) values* of the current and voltage. Because a sine function oscillates symmetrically about zero, the average value of a sinusoidally varying quantity, such as the current or voltage, is zero. For any instant that the function has a particular positive value, there is a corresponding instant in which its value has the same magnitude but is negative (Fig. 31-19a). However, the average value of the *square* of a sinusoidally varying quantity is *not* zero. The square of a sine function is always positive and oscillates symmetrically about +1/2 (Fig. 31-19b). For any instant that $\sin^2(\omega t)$ has a value greater than +1/2, there is a corresponding instant in which its value is the same amount smaller than +1/2. Thus the average value of $\sin^2(\omega t)$ is +1/2.

The root-mean-square value of a quantity is the square root of the average

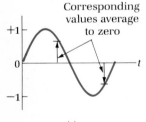

(a)

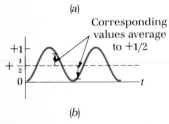

(b)

Figure 31-19. (a) The average value of $\sin(\omega t)$ over an integral number of periods is zero. (b) The average value of $\sin^2(\omega t)$ over an integral number of periods is 1/2.

value of the square of the quantity. For example, the rms voltage is

$$V_{\text{rms}} = \left(\overline{V^2}\right)^{1/2} = \left\{\overline{[V_m \sin{(\omega t)}]^2}\right\}^{1/2} = V_m\left[\overline{\sin^2{(\omega t)}}\right]^{1/2} = V_m(1/2)^{1/2}$$

or

RMS voltage

$$V_{\text{rms}} = \frac{V_m}{\sqrt{2}}$$

Similarly,

RMS current

$$I_{\text{rms}} = \frac{I_m}{\sqrt{2}}$$

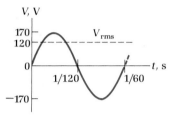

Figure 31-20. The voltage across the terminals of an electric outlet in your room.

When a value is given for an ac voltage or current, it is ordinarily the rms value. AC voltmeters and ammeters are calibrated to measure rms values. The voltage across the terminals of an outlet in your room is nominally 120 V. As shown in Fig. 31-20, this refers to the rms value of the voltage. The amplitude of this voltage is $V_m = \sqrt{2}\, V_{\text{rms}} = \sqrt{2}(120\text{ V}) = 170$ V.

Now we evaluate the average power $\overline{P}$ for an *RLC* circuit driven by an ac source. The instantaneous power P dissipated in the resistor is $P = i^2R$. Using Eq. (31-17), we have

$$P = [I_m \sin{(\omega t + \phi)}]^2 R$$

The average power $\overline{P}$ dissipated in the resistor is $\overline{P} = I_m{}^2R\,\overline{\sin^2{(\omega t + \phi)}} = \frac{1}{2}I_m{}^2R$, or

Average power

$$\overline{P} = (I_{\text{rms}})^2 R \tag{31-25}$$

This expression for the average power dissipated in the resistor resembles the expression for the power dissipated in a resistor in a dc circuit; the dc current is replaced by the rms current.

Another useful way to express $\overline{P}$ is in terms of the product of V_{rms} and I_{rms}, where V_{rms} refers to the rms value of the voltage across the source. If we divide both sides of the equation $V_m = I_m Z$ by $\sqrt{2}$, then we have

$$V_{\text{rms}} = I_{\text{rms}}Z \qquad \text{or} \qquad I_{\text{rms}} = \frac{V_{\text{rms}}}{Z}$$

Substitution into Eq. (31-25) gives

$$\overline{P} = \frac{V_{\text{rms}}}{Z} I_{\text{rms}} R = V_{\text{rms}} I_{\text{rms}} \frac{R}{Z}$$

From the impedance diagram, Fig. 31-16, we have

Power factor

$$\cos\phi = \frac{R}{Z} = \frac{R}{\sqrt{R^2 + (X_C - X_L)^2}}$$

where $\cos\phi$ is called the *power factor*. In terms of the power factor, the average power is

Average power in terms of the power factor

$$\overline{P} = V_{\text{rms}} I_{\text{rms}} \cos\phi \tag{31-26}$$

If the circuit is driven by the source at the resonant frequency, then $X_C = X_L$, $Z = R$, and $\cos\phi = 1$. At resonance, the average power is $V_{\text{rms}}I_{\text{rms}}$.

Figure 31-21 shows graphs of $\overline{P}$ versus ω for the same two cases that were used in Fig. 31-18: (i) $R = 100\ \Omega$ and (ii) $R = 200\ \Omega$. For each case, $V_m = 100$ V, $L = 1.00$ mH, and $C = 1.00$ nF.

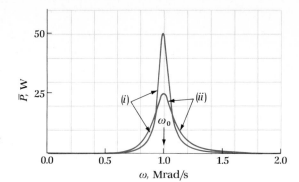

Figure 31-21. Average power $\bar{P}$ versus ω for two cases: (i) $R = 100\ \Omega$ and (ii) $R = 200\ \Omega$. Other quantities are $V_m = 100$ V, $L = 1.00$ mH, and $C = 1.00$ nF.

EXAMPLE 31-6. The five parameters which describe the series RLC circuit driven by an ac source are R, L, C, V_m, and ω. Develop an expression for $\bar{P}$ in terms of these parameters.

SOLUTION. Using $I_{rms} = V_{rms}/Z$ to substitute for $(I_{rms})^2$ in Eq. (31-25), we have

$$\bar{P} = \frac{(V_{rms})^2 R}{Z^2} = \frac{(V_{rms})^2 R}{R^2 + (X_C - X_L)^2}$$

Substituting for V_{rms}, X_C, and X_L, we have

$$\bar{P} = \frac{\frac{1}{2}V_m^2 R}{R^2 + [(1/\omega C) - \omega L]^2}$$

Note that if the circuit is driven by the source at the resonant frequency, then $1/\omega C = \omega L$, and the average power is $\frac{1}{2}V_m^2/R$.

SUMMARY WITH APPLICATIONS

Section 31-2. *LC* oscillations

In an LC circuit, the charge on the capacitor and the current in the circuit oscillate sinusoidally with the same angular frequency ω_0:

$$\omega_0 = \frac{1}{\sqrt{LC}} \tag{31-4}$$

The electromagnetic energy U, which is the sum of the electric energy U_E of the capacitor and the magnetic energy U_B of the inductor, remains constant. This energy is passed back and forth between the capacitor and the inductor.

Determine the time dependence of the charge on the capacitor and the current in an LC circuit.

Section 31-3. Series *RLC* circuit

In an RLC circuit, if $R < \sqrt{4L/C}$, then the charge on the capacitor and the current in the circuit oscillate, and the circuit is said to be underdamped. These oscillations tend to die out as electromagnetic energy is dissipated in the resistor. If $R > \sqrt{4L/C}$, then no oscillations occur, and the circuit is said to be overdamped. A circuit is critically damped if $R = R_{crit} = \sqrt{4L/C}$.

Describe the time dependence of the charge on the capacitor in an RLC circuit for both the underdamped and overdamped cases.

Sections 31-4 through 31-7. AC sources connected

to a resistor, to a capacitor, to an inductor; series *RLC* circuit driven by an AC source

We considered circuits with an ac source in which the voltage across the source is given by

$$V = V_m \sin(\omega t) \tag{31-7}$$

The current sustained by this source is

$$i = I_m \sin(\omega t + \phi) \tag{31-17}$$

In a purely resistive circuit, $\phi = 0$ and $I_m = V_m/R$. In a purely capacitive circuit, $\phi = \frac{1}{2}\pi$ and $I_m = V_m/X_C$, where X_C is the capacitive reactance:

$$X_C = \frac{1}{\omega C} \tag{31-11}$$

In a purely inductive circuit, $\phi = -\frac{1}{2}\pi$ and $I_m = V_m/X_L$, where X_L is the inductive reactance:

$$X_L = \omega L \tag{31-14}$$

In a series RLC circuit driven by an ac source,

$$\tan \phi = \frac{X_C - X_L}{R} \tag{31-23}$$

and

$$I_m = \frac{V_m}{\sqrt{R^2 + (X_C - X_L)^2}} \tag{31-21}$$

The impedance of the circuit is

$$Z = \sqrt{R^2 + (X_C - X_L)^2} \tag{31-22}$$

If the angular frequency of the source is the same as the circuit's resonant angular frequency, $\omega = \omega_0 = 1/\sqrt{LC}$, then $X_C = X_L$, $\phi = 0$, the impedance has a minimum value $Z = R$, and the current amplitude has a maximum value $I_m = V_m/R$.

Determine the phase relationships between the current and the voltage; determine the current amplitude for purely resistive, purely capacitive, and purely inductive elements in an ac circuit; determine the impedance, the current amplitude, and the phase difference for a series *RLC* circuit driven by an ac source; describe resonance and determine the resonant angular frequency of a series *RLC* circuit.

Section 31-8. Power for an *RLC* circuit driven by ac source

The rms values of the current and resistance are

$$V_{\mathrm{rms}} = \frac{V_m}{\sqrt{2}} \quad \text{and} \quad I_{\mathrm{rms}} = \frac{I_m}{\sqrt{2}}$$

Two useful expressions for the average power are

$$\bar{P} = (I_{\mathrm{rms}})^2 R \qquad (31\text{-}25)$$

and

$$\bar{P} = V_{\mathrm{rms}} I_{\mathrm{rms}} \cos \phi \qquad (31\text{-}26)$$

where $\cos \phi$ is the power factor.

Explain the use of rms values of the current and voltage; describe the average power for each of the elements in a series *RLC* circuit driven by an ac source; determine the average power for the circuit.

QUESTIONS

31-1 Once a current is started in an *LC* circuit (assumed to be resistanceless), why does it continue to oscillate despite the fact that no source is in the circuit?

31-2 By what factor will the frequency of the oscillations of an *LC* circuit change if the inductance is doubled while the capacitance is kept fixed? What is this factor if the capacitance is doubled while the inductance is kept fixed? What is this factor if both the capacitance and the inductance are doubled?

31-3 Using Lenz's law, explain why $V_b - V_a$ in Fig. 31-1 is given by $L(di/dt)$ rather than by $-L(di/dt)$.

31-4 In the analogy between the *LC* circuit and the harmonic oscillator, which energy — the electric or the magnetic — is analogous to the kinetic energy? Which is analogous to the potential energy?

31-5 What analogous quantities should be added to Table 31-1 to make a comparison between the *RLC* circuit and the damped harmonic oscillator?

31-6 In an *LC* circuit (resistance is negligible), the frequency depends on the product *LC*. Does the frequency of an underdamped *RLC* circuit depend only on the product *LC*? Suppose that for an underdamped *RLC* circuit you increase *L* and decrease *C* while keeping the product *LC* fixed. Will the frequency increase, remain the same, or decrease?

31-7 The current in a circuit is effectively stopped by an "open" and is not limited at all by a "short." At high frequencies, is a capacitor a short or an open? How about low frequencies? Consider whether an inductor is an open or a short at low frequencies and at high frequencies.

31-8 An inductor called a "ballast" is often used to limit the current in fluorescent lights. Why is an inductor preferable to a resistor for this purpose?

31-9 A solenoid with a resistance of 1.2 Ω is connected across the terminals of an electric outlet in your room ($V_{\mathrm{rms}} = 120$ V). Despite the fact that a circuit breaker in the circuit will trip if I_{rms} in the circuit exceeds 15 A, the breaker does not trip. Explain why.

31-10 In some textbooks the oscillating current or voltage is taken to be the horizontal component of a phasor rather than the vertical component. How would such a convention affect the results we have given here? Find an equation in this chapter that would be different if we adopted this convention.

31-11 In some textbooks the expressions for the voltage and current are taken as $V = V_m \sin(\omega t)$ and $i = I_m \sin(\omega t - \phi)$. How would such a convention affect the results we have given here? Find an equation in this chapter that would be different if we adopted this convention.

31-12 In an *RLC* circuit driven by an ac source, the net energy delivered by the source during one cycle is 25 mJ. During one cycle, (a) what is the net energy which enters the inductor, (b) what is the net energy which enters the capacitor, (c) what is the energy dissipated as heat in the resistor?

31-13 The power rating of an element used in ac circuits refers to the element's average power rating. What is the maximum instantaneous power to a 60-W light bulb?

31-14 Consider the net power delivered by the source in an *RLC* circuit. Is the instantaneous power always positive? Does your answer depend on the frequency of the source relative to the resonant frequency? Explain.

31-15 The average current in the power line to your house is zero. Despite this fact, electric power is delivered to your house. Explain.

31-16 A resistor and an ac source are each inside unmarked boxes so that you cannot tell which is which by visual inspection. Two wires carry an alternating current between the two. Can you determine the direction of energy flow and so determine which box contains the resistor and which contains the source by measuring rms current and voltage values? By measuring instantaneous current and voltage values?

31-17 Capacitors have a maximum voltage rating. If this rating is exceeded, the dielectric between the plates may break down. In a series RLC circuit, it is possible to exceed the voltage rating of the capacitor (and damage the capacitor) even though this rating is higher than the amplitude of the voltage across the source. Explain. With a variable frequency source, is this more likely to happen at the resonant frequency, or when the circuit is predominantly capacitive?

31-18 Consider the "resonance curves" for the current amplitude (Fig. 31-18) and average power (Fig. 31-21). Discuss the appearance of these curves as R approaches zero while L and C are fixed.

31-19 Is the impedance diagram (Fig. 31-16) always a right triangle? Explain.

31-20 Is the circuit in Example 31-5 predominantly capacitive or predominantly inductive?

31-21 An RLC circuit with a resonant angular frequency in the range of 1 krad/s to 1 Mrad/s can be readily constructed. What practical problems make it difficult to construct a circuit with a resonant angular frequency of 1 rad/s?

31-22 What is a common characteristic between a radio playing the station you selected and a child swinging on a swing? What are some other systems that exhibit this characteristic?

31-23 Suppose an RLC series circuit is driven by an ac source at a particular frequency. If you know the power factor, can you determine whether the circuit is predominantly capacitive or predominantly inductive? Explain.

31-24 Electric power companies prefer to have the value of the power factor for their "load" be as nearly 1 as possible. Explain why this is so. (*Hint:* Take into account the i^2R losses on the transmission lines.)

31-25 In the latter part of the nineteenth century, prior to the advent of electric power transmission, George Westinghouse (1846–1914) and Thomas A. Edison (1847–1931) entered into a disagreement about whether ac or dc should be used to transmit electric energy. Westinghouse favored ac and Edison favored dc. Which system do you think is preferable? Explain. (*Hint:* Reexamine Sec. 29-6.)

31-26 Complete the following table:

Symbol	Represents	Type	SI unit
ω_0			
I_m			
U	Electromagnetic energy		
V			
X_C			
X_L			
Z			Ω
ϕ			
I_{rms}		Scalar	
$\bar{P}$			
$\cos \phi$			

EXERCISES

Section 31-2. *LC* oscillations

31-1 Show that $\sqrt{LC}$ has the dimension of time.

31-2 (a) What is the angular frequency of oscillation of the charge and current in an LC circuit with $L = 25$ mH and $C = 41$ nF? (b) What is the frequency of the oscillations? (c) What is the period of the oscillations?

31-3 In an LC circuit with $C = 58$ nF, the angular frequency of oscillation of the charge and current is 58 krad/s. What is the inductance of the inductor?

31-4 In an LC circuit with $L = 94$ mH, the frequency of oscillation of the charge and current is 130 kHz. What is the capacitance of the capacitor?

31-5 Consider an LC circuit in which $L = 5.3$ mH, $C = 17$ nF, the initial charge of the capacitor is 2.2 μC, and the initial current in the circuit is zero. Write expressions for q, i, U, U_E, and U_B as functions of t.

31-6 Consider an LC circuit in which $L = 71$ mH, $C = 130$ nF, the initial current in the circuit is 44 mA, and the initial charge on the capacitor is zero. Write expressions for q, i, U, U_E, and U_B as functions of t.

31-7 Consider an LC circuit in which $L = 31.4$ mH and $C = 159$ nF. At $t = 0$, the current in the circuit is 265 mA and the charge on the capacitor is 7.18 μC. Write expressions for q, i, U, U_E, and U_B as functions of t.

31-8 The current in an LC circuit is given by the expression $i = (27$ mA$) \cos [(280$ krad/s$)t]$. (a) Write an expression for the charge on the capacitor. (b) Determine L if $C = 140$ nF. (c) Write expressions for U, U_E, and U_B.

31-9 The charge on the capacitor in an LC circuit is given by the expression $q = (71 \mu$C$) \cos [(54$ krad/s$)t - \pi/4]$. (a) Write an expression for the current in the circuit. (b) Determine C if $L = 17$ mH. (c) Write expressions for U, U_E, and U_B.

31-10 The potential difference across the capacitor in an LC circuit is given by the expression $V_C = (32$ V$) \sin [(42$ krad/s$)t]$, and the inductance of the inductor is $L = 22$ mH. Write expressions for (a) the charge on the capacitor, (b) the current in the circuit, (c) the potential difference across the inductor, (d) U, (e) U_E, (f) U_B.

31-11 The potential difference across the inductor in an LC circuit is given by the expression $V_L = $ (4.8 V) cos [(16 krad/s)t], and the capacitance of the capacitor is $C = 54$ nF. Write expressions for (a) the charge on the capacitor, (b) the current in the circuit, (c) the potential difference across the capacitor, (d) U, (e) U_E, (f) U_B.

31-12 Suppose switch S_2 in the circuit in Fig. 31-22 has been closed for a long enough time so that the potential difference across the capacitor is steady. At $t = 0$, switch S_1 is closed and switch S_2 is opened. Write expressions for the charge on the capacitor and the current in the inductor as functions of t.

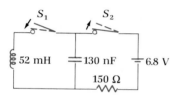

Figure 31-22. Exercise 31-12.

31-13 Suppose switch S_2 in the circuit of Fig. 31-23 has been closed for a long enough time so that the current in the inductor is steady. At $t = 0$, switch S_1 is closed and switch S_2 is opened. Write expressions for the charge on the capacitor and the current in the inductor as functions of t.

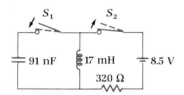

Figure 31-23. Exercise 31-13.

31-14 Consider an LC circuit at the instant the electric energy in the capacitor is equal to the magnetic energy in the inductor. (a) What is the charge on the capacitor in terms of its maximum charge? (b) What is the current in the circuit in terms of its maximum current?

31-15 Consider an LC circuit at an instant when 25 percent of the electromagnetic energy is stored in the capacitor and 75 percent is stored in the inductor. At this time, (a) what is the charge on the capacitor in terms of its maximum charge, and (b) what is the current in the circuit in terms of its maximum current?

31-16 Suppose you are given an inductor with $L = 38$ mH and two capacitors with $C_1 = 230$ nF and $C_2 = 510$ nF. What are the LC oscillation frequencies that you can produce with these elements?

31-17 Suppose you have a variable capacitor whose capacitance can be continuously varied in the range 0.14 to 3.2 nF. To produce a circuit whose oscillation frequency can be made to vary from 0.10 MHz to higher values, what value of inductance would you use in the circuit? What is the upper limit of the frequency for this circuit?

Section 31-4. Series *RLC* circuit

31-18 Show that the SI unit of $\sqrt{4L/C}$ (or R_{crit}) is the ohm.

31-19 An RLC circuit has $R = 350$ Ω, $L = 16$ mH, and $C = 390$ nF. (a) Is this circuit underdamped or overdamped? If the circuit is underdamped, determine (b) ω_d and (c) τ.

31-20 Suppose you have an inductor with inductance 16 mH and a capacitor with capacitance 840 nF. Determine the value of the resistance you need in order to construct a critically damped RLC circuit.

31-21 The charge as a function of time for an RLC circuit is given by

$$q = (710 \text{ nC})e^{-t/(380 \text{ } \mu s)} \cos [(12.6 \text{ krad/s})t - 0.206]$$

The inductance of the inductor is 52 mH. (a) What is the resistance of the resistor? (b) What is the capacitance of the capacitor? (c) Determine the charge on the capacitor at $t = 230$ μs.

31-22 (a) Show that if the charge on the capacitor in an RLC circuit is given by Eq. (31-6), then the current in the circuit is

$$i = -Q_m e^{-t/\tau}\left[\frac{1}{\tau}\cos(\omega_d t + \phi) + \omega_d \sin(\omega_d t + \phi)\right]$$

(b) Use the answer to part (a) to write an expression for the current in the circuit of the previous exercise. (c) Determine the value of the current at $t = 230$ μs.

31-23 In an underdamped RLC circuit, the resistance is such that $\omega_d = \frac{1}{2}\omega_0$. Find this resistance in terms of L and C.

31-24 In an underdamped RLC circuit, the resistance is such that the time τ equals the period $2\pi/\omega_d$. Find this resistance in terms of L and C.

31-25 Consider an RLC circuit in which L and C are fixed, but the resistance can be varied in the range $0 < R < R_{crit}$, where R_{crit} is the resistance which produces critical damping: $R_{crit} = \sqrt{4L/C}$. (a) Show that the angular frequency of oscillation can be written $\omega_d = \omega_0\sqrt{1 - (R/R_{crit})^2}$. Make a graph of ω_d versus R for $R/R_{crit} = 0.01, 0.10, 0.20, 0.30, \ldots, 0.80, 0.90, 0.99$.

Section 31-4. AC source connected to a resistor

31-26 An ac source with amplitude $V_m = 170$ V and frequency 60 Hz is connected to a resistor with resistance 1.4 kΩ. (a) Determine the amplitude of the oscillating current i. Use Eqs. (31-7) and (31-8) to write expressions for (b) the voltage V across the resistor and (c) the current i in the circuit.

31-27 Consider the oscillating voltage and current calculated in the previous exercise. (a) What is the period of the oscillations? Determine V at (b) $t = \frac{1}{240}$ s and (c) $t = \frac{1}{120}$ s. Determine i at (d) $t = \frac{1}{240}$ s and (e) $t = \frac{1}{120}$ s.

Section 31-5. AC source connected to a capacitor

31-28 Show that the SI unit for the capacitive reactance, $X_C = 1/\omega C$, is the Ω.

31-29 Determine the capacitive reactance of a 1.0-nF capacitor when the source frequency is (a) 100 Hz, (b) 100 kHz, (c) 100 MHz.

31-30 With a source frequency of 100 kHz, determine the capacitive reactance of a capacitor whose capacitance is (a) 1.0 pF, (b) 1.0 nF, (c) 1.0 μF.

31-31 What is the capacitance of a capacitor whose capacitive reactance is 2.5 kΩ when the source frequency is 3.8 krad/s?

31-32 Make a graph of X_C versus ω for a 1.0-nF capacitor. Plot points for $\omega = 1.0, 2.0, 3.0, 5.0, 7.0,$ and 10.0 krad/s, and sketch a curve through the points. It is instructive to make this plot and that of Exercise 31-40 on the same graph.

31-33 A 2.6-nF capacitor is connected to a source in which $V_m = 71$ V and $\omega = 360$ rad/s. What is the current amplitude?

31-34 The voltage across the terminals of a 230-pF capacitor is given by $V = (27 \text{ V}) \sin [(5.8 \text{ krad/s})t]$. (a) Write an expression for the current. (b) Determine the current at $t = 0.43$ ms.

31-35 A 2.1-μF capacitor is connected to a source whose voltage amplitude is 49 V and whose frequency can be varied. What value of the source angular frequency yields a current amplitude of 310 mA?

Section 31-6. AC source connected to an inductor

31-36 Show that the SI unit for the inductive reactance, $X_L = \omega L$, is the Ω.

31-37 Determine the inductive reactance of a 1.0-mH inductor when the source frequency is (a) 100 Hz, (b) 100 kHz, (c) 100 MHz.

31-38 Determine the inductive reactance of an inductor with a source frequency of 100 kHz and with an inductance of (a) 1.0 μH, (b) 1.0 mH, (c) 1.0 H.

31-39 What is the inductance of an inductor whose inductive reactance is 420 Ω when the frequency of the source is 89 krad/s?

31-40 Make a graph of X_L versus ω for a 1.0-mH inductor. Plot points for $\omega = 0.0, 2.0, 4.0, 6.0, 8.0,$ and 10.0 krad/s, and sketch a curve through the points. It is instructive to make this plot and that of Exercise 31-32 on the same graph.

31-41 A 65-mH inductor is connected to a source in which $V_m = 130$ V and $\omega = 410$ rad/s. What is the current amplitude?

31-42 The voltage across the terminals of a 0.45-mH inductor is given by $V = (8.1 \text{ V}) \sin [(13 \text{ krad/s})t]$. (a) Write an expression for the current. (b) Determine the current at $t = 160$ μs.

31-43 A 16-mH inductor is connected across a source whose voltage amplitude is 9.8 V and whose frequency can be varied. What value of the source angular frequency yields a current amplitude of 740 mA?

Section 31-7. Series *RLC* circuit driven by an ac source

31-44 A series RLC circuit with $R = 510$ Ω, $L = 25$ mH, and $C = 240$ nF has an ac source with $V_m = 17$ V and $\omega = 6.3$ krad/s. Determine the (a) capacitive reactance, (b) inductive reactance, (c) impedance, (d) current amplitude, (e) phase difference between V and i.

31-45 The voltage across an ac source is given by $V = (5.4 \text{ V}) \sin [(830 \text{ rad/s})t]$. The source is in a series RLC circuit with $R = 37$ Ω, $L = 85$ mH, and $C = 25$ μF. (a) Write an expression for the current in the circuit. (b) On the same graph, plot V and i versus t from $t = 0$ to $t = 7.6$ ms.

31-46 Suppose the frequency of the source in the previous exercise can be varied. (a) What is the resonant frequency of the circuit? (b) What is the current amplitude at resonance?

31-47 Construct a graph similar to that of Fig. 31-17, except make it applicable to a predominantly inductive circuit.

31-48 Verify some of the values for each of the resonance curves shown in Fig. 31-18. For the values of the parameters given in the caption, find I_m when $\omega = 0.5, 0.9, 1.0, 1.1,$ and 1.5 Mrad/s. Use the figure to check your answers.

31-49 On the same graph, make plots of the phase difference ϕ versus ω for the two cases used in Fig. 31-18.

31-50 In a series RLC circuit driven by an ac source, $R = 140$ Ω, $L = 150$ mH, $C = 5.1$ μF, and $V = (14 \text{ V}) \sin [(530 \text{ rad/s})t]$. Write expressions for the voltage across the (a) resistor, (b) capacitor, (c) inductor. (d) Draw a phasor diagram which includes $\mathbf{V}$, $\mathbf{V}_R$, $\mathbf{V}_C$, and $\mathbf{V}_L$.

31-51 Write Eq. (31-16) as a differential equation for the charge q on the capacitor. Compare your equation with Eq. (14-30) and make a table of analogous quantities.

31-52 By changing the capacitance of a capacitor, you can vary the resonant frequency of the tuning circuit in a radio from 500 to 1700 kHz. If you are to vary the resonant frequency of a series RLC circuit in this way, and the inductor has an inductance of 25 mH, what is the range of capacitance for the capacitor?

31-53 (a) Show that the current amplitude in a series RLC circuit driven by an ac source can be written

$$I_m = \frac{V_m \omega}{\sqrt{\omega^2 R^2 + L^2(\omega_0^2 - \omega^2)^2}}$$

(b) Show that the phase angle difference can be written

$$\phi = \tan^{-1} \frac{L(\omega_0^2 - \omega^2)}{\omega R}$$

Section 31-8. Power for an *RLC* circuit driven by an ac source

31-54 The current amplitude in an *RLC* series circuit driven by an ac source is $I_m = 260$ mA. (a) What is the rms current? (b) If the resistance in the circuit is 140 Ω, what is the average power delivered by the source?

31-55 In a series *RLC* circuit driven by an ac source, the voltage across the source is given by $V = (17 \text{ V}) \sin [(230 \text{ rad/s})t]$ and the current in the circuit is given by $i = (97 \text{ mA}) \sin [(230 \text{ rad/s})t + 0.82 \text{ rad}]$. What is the average power for the circuit?

31-56 The rms value of a time-dependent quantity $f(t)$ over the time interval T is

$$f_{\text{rms}} = \left\{ \frac{1}{T} \int_0^T [f(t)]^2 \, dt \right\}^{1/2}$$

Show that if $V = V_m \sin (\omega t)$, then $V_{\text{rms}} = V_m / \sqrt{2}$,

where $T = 2\pi/\omega$. [*Hint:* Use the trigonometric identity $\sin^2 \theta = \frac{1}{2} - \frac{1}{2} \cos (2\theta)$.]

31-57 A series *RLC* circuit is driven by an ac source at a frequency such that the circuit's impedance is 97 Ω. If the resistance in the circuit is 36 Ω and the rms voltage across the source is 6.2 V, what is average power for the circuit?

31-58 Suppose an ac source with a variable frequency drives a series *RLC* circuit in which $R = 1.5$ kΩ, $C = 10$ nF, and $L = 10$ mH. Determine the power factor when the source frequency is (a) 50 krad/s, (b) 100 krad/s, (c) 200 krad/s.

31-59 Verify some of the values for each of the resonance curves shown in Fig. 31-21. For the values of the parameters given in the caption, find $\bar{P}$ when $\omega = 0.5$, 0.9, 1.0, 1.1, and 1.5 Mrad/s. Use the figure to check your answers.

31-60 In a series *RLC* circuit driven by an ac source, the rms voltages across the source and the resistor are 9.4 and 2.7 V, respectively. Determine the power factor for the circuit.

31-61 Show that the average power for an *RLC* series circuit driven by an ac source can be written

$$\bar{P} = \frac{(V_{\text{rms}})^2 R \omega^2}{R^2 \omega^2 + L^2(\omega_0^2 - \omega^2)^2}$$

PROBLEMS

31-1 By direct substitution, show that Eq. (31-6) is a solution to Eq. (31-5) if

$$\tau = \frac{2L}{R} \quad \text{and} \quad \omega_d = \sqrt{\frac{1}{LC} - \left(\frac{R}{2L}\right)^2}$$

[*Hint:* If the equation $A \sin (\omega t) + B \cos (\omega t) = 0$ is satisfied for all time t, then $A = 0$ and $B = 0$.]

31-2 When $R > \sqrt{4L/C}$, ω_d in Eq. (31-6) becomes imaginary:

$$\omega_d = j\sqrt{\left(\frac{R}{2L}\right)^2 - \frac{1}{LC}} = j\alpha$$

where $j = \sqrt{-1}$ and α is real. This corresponds to the overdamped circuit. (a) Show that

$$q = e^{-t/\tau}(C_1 e^{\alpha t} + C_2 e^{-\alpha t})$$

is a solution to Eq. (31-5), where C_1 and C_2 are constants that depend on the initial conditions. (b) Using typical values for the parameters, make a graph of the solution you found in part (a).

31-3 In Fig. 31-24, capacitor C_2 is initially uncharged; C_1 is charged with a 12-V battery and then the battery is removed. Switches S_1 and S_2 are electronically controlled and can be opened and closed virtually instantaneously. (a) Describe a switching procedure which leaves C_1 with zero potential difference across it and

C_2 with a potential difference of 36 V across it. (b) Determine the time interval between each change in switch settings. (*Hint:* Use energy considerations.)

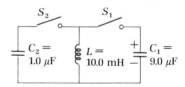

Figure 31-24. Prob. 31-3.

31-4 **Q value.** Circuits that exhibit resonance are often characterized by their Q value. The Q value of a circuit is defined as $Q = L\omega_0/R$ and is related to the sharpness of the resonance peak in a graph of $\bar{P}$ versus ω (Fig. 31-21). (a) For a series *RLC* circuit driven by an ac source, show that $Q \approx \omega_0/\Delta\omega$, where $\Delta\omega$ is the width of the curve at half its maximum value. Assume that the resonance curve is sharply peaked ($\omega_0 \gg \Delta\omega$). (b) Using its definition, evaluate Q for each of the cases shown in Fig. 31-21. (c) Using a ruler to find $\Delta\omega$ for the curves in Fig. 31-21, determine Q for each case and compare your answers with those you found for part (b).

31-5 Equation (31-16) can be converted to an equation in

which each term represents a power. (*a*) Multiply the equation by *i* and show that the resulting equation can be written

$$\frac{d}{dt}\left(\frac{1}{2}Li^2\right) + i^2R + \frac{d}{dt}\left(\frac{q^2}{2C}\right) = iV$$

(*b*) Give a physical interpretation of each term in this expression.

31-6   Figure 31-25 shows an *RC* low-pass filter. Assume that the voltage across the input is a variable-frequency ac source in which $V = V_m \sin(\omega t)$. (*a*) Show that the amplitude of the output voltage is $V_{Cm} = V_m/\sqrt{(RC\omega)^2 + 1}$. (*b*) Make a graph of V_{Cm} versus ω. Plot points corresponding to $\omega = 0.0, 0.5, 1.0, \ldots, 3.5, 4.0$ in units of $1/RC$. (*c*) Explain the significance of the name of this circuit.

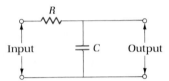

Figure 31-25. Prob. 31-6: An *RC* low-pass filter.

31-7   Figure 31-26 shows an *RC* high-pass filter. Assume that the voltage across the input is a variable-frequency ac source in which $V = V_m \sin(\omega t)$. (*a*) Show that the amplitude of the output voltage is $V_{Rm} = V_m/\sqrt{(1/RC\omega)^2 + 1}$. (*b*) Make a graph of V_{Rm} versus ω. Plot points corresponding to $\omega = 0.0, 0.5, 1.0, \ldots, 3.5, 4.0$ in units of $1/RC$. (*c*) Explain the significance of the name of this circuit.

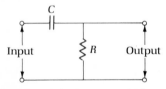

Figure 31-26. Prob. 31-7: An *RC* high-pass filter.

31-8   The circuit in Fig. 31-26 can be used as a phase shifter. Suppose $C = 14 \ \mu F$ and the input voltage is $V_i = (8.8 \ V) \sin[(716 \ rad/s)t]$. (*a*) Determine R such that the output voltage leads the input voltage by 0.56 rad. (*b*) Find the amplitude of the output voltage.

31-9   The circuit in Fig. 31-27 can be used as a phase shifter. Suppose $L = 86 \ mH$ and the input voltage is $V_i =$

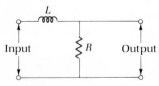

Figure 31-27. Prob. 31-9.

(9.3 V) sin [(530 rad/s)*t*]. (*a*) Determine *R* such that the output voltage lags the input voltage by 0.70 rad. (*b*) Find the amplitude of the output voltage.

31-10   The instantaneous power for the capacitor in a series *RLC* circuit driven by an ac source is $P_C = iV_C$, where $i = I_m \sin(\omega t + \phi)$ and $V_C = X_C I_m \sin(\omega t + \phi - \frac{1}{2}\pi)$. Show that the average power for the capacitor is zero.

31-11   The instantaneous power for the inductor in a series *RLC* circuit driven by an ac source is $P_L = iV_L$, where $i = I_m \sin(\omega t + \phi)$ and $V_L = X_L I_m \sin(\omega t + \phi + \frac{1}{2}\pi)$. Show that the average power for the inductor is zero.

31-12   Consider the nonsinusoidal alternating current shown in Fig. 31-28. Show that the rms value of the current is $I_{rms} = I_m/\sqrt{3}$. Refer to Exercise 31-56 for the definition of the rms value of a quantity.

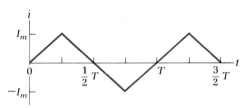

Figure 31-28. Prob. 31-12.

31-13   Figure 31-29*a* shows a parallel *RLC* circuit driven by an ac source. Since the elements are in parallel, the voltage across each element is the same as the voltage across the source: $V = V_m \sin(\omega t)$. On the other hand, the current in each element is different. Figure 31-29*b* shows the phasor diagram for this circuit. (*a*) Explain the relative orientation of these phasors. (*b*) Show that the current in the source is $i = I_m \sin(\omega t + \phi)$, where

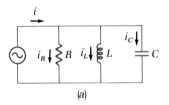

(*a*)

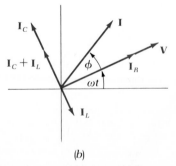

(*b*)

Figure 31-29. Prob. 31-13; (*a*) Schematic diagram of a parallel *RLC* circuit driven by an ac source. (*b*) Phasor diagram for this circuit.

$$I_m = V_m \sqrt{\left(\frac{1}{R}\right)^2 + \left(\frac{1}{X_C} - \frac{1}{X_L}\right)^2}$$

and

$$\phi = \tan^{-1}\left[R\left(\frac{1}{X_C} - \frac{1}{X_L}\right)\right]$$

(c) Discuss the frequency dependence of I_m.

31-14 The instantaneous power produced by the source in a series RLC circuit driven by an ac source is $P = Vi$, where V is the voltage across the source and i is the current in the circuit. Use Eqs. (31-7) and (31-17) to show that this power averaged over a period is

$$\bar{P} = V_{\text{rms}}I_{\text{rms}} \cos \phi$$

[*Hint:* Use the identity $\sin(\alpha + \beta) = \sin \alpha \cos \beta + \cos \alpha \sin \beta$. Also note that the product $\sin(\omega t) \cos(\omega t)$ averaged over a cycle is zero.]

CHAPTER 32
WAVES

32-1 INTRODUCTION

As you read these words, the information comes to you in the form of light waves reflected from the page. When you go to class, the professor's lecture comes to you in the form of sound waves. Waves are important because a great deal of the contact we have with our environment comes to us as waves. But there is an additional reason to study waves. Matter in the size range of atoms and smaller exhibits an intrinsic wave behavior. For you to understand the nature of atoms, molecules, and nuclei, you must first learn about waves.

So that we may begin on familiar ground, this chapter is mostly about waves on a stretched rope, string, or spring. Waves on a rope are easy to visualize, and they exhibit many features that are common to all waves.

32-2 CHARACTERISTICS OF WAVES

Waves on a lake. *(Werner H. Müller/ Peter Arnold)*

A traveling wave

A standing wave

We can separate waves into two categories. (i) *traveling waves* and (ii) *standing waves*. A wave propagating across the surface of water is an example of a traveling wave. *A traveling wave can be defined as the propagation of energy without the propagation of matter.* By contrast, a standing wave is confined to a specific region of space by boundaries. For example, when you pluck a guitar string, you produce standing waves between the fixed ends of the string. For a standing wave, the energy associated with the wave remains between the boundaries. We begin by discussing traveling waves, and then we examine standing waves in Sec. 32-7.

Sound waves, waves on ropes and strings, and water waves are examples of mechanical waves. Mechanical waves exist in a *medium* and can be described with Newton's laws. In Sec. 32-5, we shall find that there are two properties of a medium that govern the behavior of a mechanical wave: a restoring force and an inertial mass. In a water wave, for example, gravity provides a force that

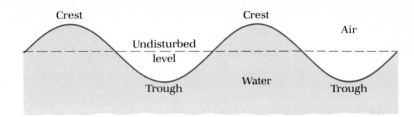

Figure 32-1. A water wave. Gravity (and surface tension) tends to restore the water surface to the equilibrium condition (flat).

tends to restore the water to its equilibrium (flat) condition. That is, gravity pushes the wave crests down and the wave troughs are "filled in" (Fig. 32-1). Because the water has inertial mass, it overshoots the equilibrium condition; the disturbance persists and the wave propagates.

When a wave propagates through a medium, the particles of the medium do not move along with the wave. Suppose you tie one end of a rope to a post, stretch the rope out horizontally, and then wiggle the other end so that a wave moves along the rope. The wave moves along the length of the rope, but a particle of the rope oscillates about a central point. When we describe the motion associated with a wave, we must distinguish between two aspects of the motion: (i) the motion of the wave through the medium and (ii) the oscillatory motion of the particles of the medium.

Waves involve two motions: that of the wave through the medium and that of the particles in the medium.

One way to classify waves is according to the direction of the displacement of the particles relative to the propagation direction of the wave. A *transverse wave* is one in which the particles oscillate perpendicular to the propagation direction (Fig. 32-2a). A *longitudinal wave* is one in which the particles oscillate parallel to the propagation direction (Fig. 32-2b). A light wave is an example of a transverse wave. Rather than consisting of oscillating particles in a medium, a light wave consists of oscillating electric and magnetic fields. In Chap. 34, we show that the directions of these wave fields are perpendicular to the wave velocity. In the next chapter, we find that sound in air (or any fluid) is an example of a longitudinal wave. Some waves have both transverse and longitudinal components. For example, in a water wave the particles of the water follow elliptical paths, so that the displacement of a particle can be resolved into components parallel and perpendicular to the wave velocity (Fig. 32-3).

A transverse wave

A longitudinal wave

Figure 32-2. Waves on a spring. (a) A transverse wave. (b) A longitudinal wave.

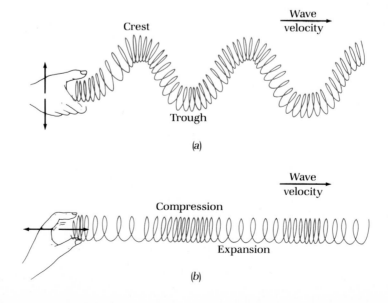

Figure 32-3. Particle motion in a water wave. As the wave goes by, the displacement of a particle of the water has a component parallel to and a component perpendicular to the wave velocity. A water wave is a combination transverse and longitudinal wave.

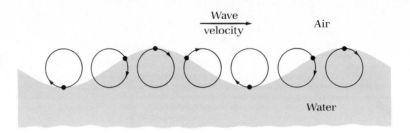

32-3 WAVE PULSES

A wave pulse is a wave of relatively short extent. Because of this compactness, photographs of wave pulses can be used to demonstrate some important properties of waves. In this section, we use these photographs to discover the mathematical form for a traveling wave and to demonstrate the meanings of some of the terms used to describe waves.

Mathematical expression for a traveling wave. In Fig. 32-4 we show a sequence of photographs of a wave pulse propagating toward the left along a stretched spring. The time interval between each photograph is the same. These photographs indicate that (i) the speed of a pulse is constant and (ii) the shape of the pulse remains nearly the same as the pulse moves along. Closer examination shows that the pulse gradually spreads out as it moves along; the pulse height decreases and the pulse width increases. This spreading out of the pulse is a result of *dispersion*. Dispersive effects are complex and depend on the properties of the medium. Also, dispersion is not of primary interest in the waves we wish to consider. Therefore, we neglect dispersion.

Figure 32-5 shows sketches of a pulse on a rope at two different times as the pulse moves to the right with speed v. A coordinate frame is shown as a backdrop, with the x axis along the undisturbed rope. Suppose the shape of the rope at $t = 0$ is given by the expression $y = f(x)$ (Fig. 32-5a). At a later time t, the pulse has moved to the right a distance vt (Fig. 32-5b). Recall that a function $f(x - a)$ has the same shape as the function $f(x)$, but $f(x - a)$ is displaced a

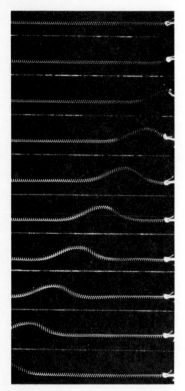

Figure 32-4. A wave pulse is generated by rapidly flipping the end of a long, stretched spring. The time interval between each subsequent photograph is the same. The pulse moves toward the left and, as far as we can tell from the photographs, travels at constant speed while maintaining its shape. (Physics, *2nd ed., Physical Science Study Committee, 1965. Reprinted by permission of D. C. Heath and Co. and Educational Development Center.*)

Figure 32-5. A pulse on a rope propagating in the $+x$ direction is shown at (a) time $t = 0$ and (b) time t. If $f(x)$ gives the pulse shape at $t = 0$ and the pulse maintains its shape as it moves with speed v, then the shape of the pulse at time t is given by $f(x - vt)$.

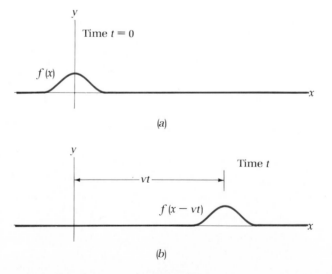

distance a in the $+x$ direction. If we assume that the pulse maintains its shape as it moves, then the shape of the pulse at time t is given by

A wave traveling in the $+x$ direction

$$y(x, t) = f(x - vt) \tag{32-1}$$

A similar description with the pulse moving to the left at speed v gives

A wave traveling in the $-x$ direction

$$y(x, t) = f(x + vt) \tag{32-2}$$

To be specific, we usually discuss waves traveling in the $+x$ direction, Eq. (32-1).

Wave function

A function $y(x, t)$ which describes a wave is called a *wave function*. In the case of a wave on a rope, the wave function is the coordinate y of an element of the rope. Thus the wave function gives the displacement $y\mathbf{j}$ of the element from its equilibrium position at $y = 0$. A wave function depends on both x and t. This means that the displacement of an element of the rope depends on (i) the coordinate x of that element and (ii) the time t of the observation. Neglecting dispersion and leaving the shape of the wave unspecified, we have found that a wave function for a traveling wave has the form $f(x - vt)$ or $f(x + vt)$. That is, x and t must enter $y(x, t)$ in the combination $x - vt$ or $x + vt$. To specify the wave function, we must write it in terms of a particular function. For example, a specific wave function which we discuss in the next section is $y(x, t) = A \sin [k(x - vt)]$. Another specific wave function is given in the following example.

EXAMPLE 32-1. Consider a wave pulse given by the wave function

$$y(x, t) = \frac{y_0}{[(x - vt)/x_0]^2 + 1}$$

where $y_0 = 10.0$ mm, $x_0 = 1.00$ m, and $v = 2.00$ m/s. (a) Make graphs of the pulse at times $t = 0.00$ s and $t = 2.50$ s. (b) The pulse is characterized by its height and width. The pulse height h is the magnitude of the maximum displacement due to the pulse, and the pulse width w is the distance between the two points on the pulse where the magnitude of the displacement is half the pulse height. Determine h and w for this pulse.

SOLUTION. (a) Substituting the numerical values given for the parameters and $t = 0.00$ s into the expression for the pulse, we obtain

$$y(x, 0) = \frac{10.0 \text{ mm}}{[x/(1.00 \text{ m})]^2 + 1}$$

This function is shown as the solid curve in Fig. 32-6. To find y at $t = 2.50$ s, we set $vt = (2.00 \text{ m/s})(2.50 \text{ s}) = 5.00$ m:

$$y(x, 2.50 \text{ s}) = \frac{10.0 \text{ mm}}{[(x - 5.00 \text{ m})/(1.00 \text{ m})]^2 + 1}$$

This function is shown as the dashed curve in Fig. 32-6.

(b) By inspection of the graphs, you can see that the pulse height is $h = y_0 = 10.0$ mm and that the pulse width is $w = 2x_0 = 2.00$ m.

Figure 32-6. Example 32-1: A pulse traveling in the $+x$ direction at $t = 0.00$ s (solid line) and $t = 2.50$ s (dashed line). The pulse height is 10.0 mm and the pulse width is 2.00 m. Note the difference in scale between the x axis and the y axis.

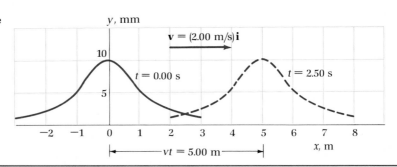

Interference of waves. When two or more waves encounter each other, we say that they *interfere*. Figure 32-7 shows the interference of two pulses with

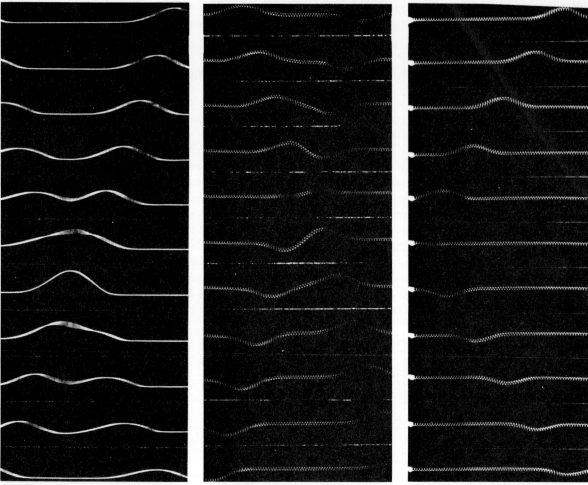

Figure 32-7. Two pulses traveling in opposite directions encounter each other. When the pulses are superposed (seventh photograph of the sequence), the maximum displacement of the rope is the sum of the maximum displacements due to each pulse acting alone.

Figure 32-8. An ''up'' pulse moving to the right encounters a ''down'' pulse moving to the left. In accordance with the principle of superposition, the pulses nearly cancel when they are superposed (fifth photograph of the sequence).

Figure 32-9. A pulse is reflected from a boundary where the end of the spring is fixed. The reflected pulse is inverted relative to the incident pulse.

(Credit for Figures 32-7 through 32-11: Physics, 2nd ed., Physical Science Study Committee, 1965. Reprinted by permission of D. C. Heath and Co. and Education Development Center.)

nearly the same size and shape. When the pulses come together, so that they occupy the same region of the spring, we say that they are *superposed*. From the figure you can see that when the pulses are superposed, the maximum displacement due to both pulses is the sum of the maximum displacements due to each pulse acting alone. To describe this result mathematically, let $f_1(x - vt)$ represent the pulse traveling to the right, $f_2(x + vt)$ represent the pulse traveling to the left, and $y(x, t)$ represent the shape of the rope due to both pulses. The photographs in Fig. 32-7 demonstrate that

$$y(x, t) = f_1(x - vt) + f_2(x + vt) \tag{32-3}$$

Principle of superposition

This result is an example of the *principle of superposition*. The principle of superposition states that *the resultant wave function due to two or more individual wave functions is the sum of the individual wave functions.* According to the principle of superposition, the individual pulses act independently of each other. After the encounter, the size, shape, and speed of each pulse is the same as if there had been no encounter.

Figure 32-8 shows two pulses, one up and one down, encountering each other. As you can see from the photographs, when the pulses are superposed, they nearly cancel each other, giving a displacement of almost zero. This result is in accord with the principle of superposition. In this case y_1 is positive over the extent of pulse 1, and y_2 is negative over the extent of pulse 2. At the instant when both pulses occupy the same region of the spring, the sum of their displacements is nearly zero.

Reflection and transmission. Waves can be reflected from boundaries and transmitted from one medium to another. Figure 32-9 shows a pulse on a spring traveling to the left and encountering a boundary where the end of the spring is fixed. The pulse, as it approaches the boundary, is referred to as an *incident pulse.* Note that the pulse is reflected from the boundary and that the *reflected pulse* is inverted relative to the incident pulse.

Figure 32-10 shows an incident pulse traveling to the left on a relatively light spring and encountering another spring that is relatively heavy. After the encounter, we see a reflected pulse on the light spring and a *transmitted pulse* on the heavy spring. The reflected pulse is inverted relative to the incident

Figure 32-10. A pulse on a light spring is incident on a light-spring–heavy-spring boundary. The reflected pulse is inverted relative to the incident pulse, but the transmitted pulse is not inverted. Note that the pulse speed on the light spring is greater than it is on the heavy spring.

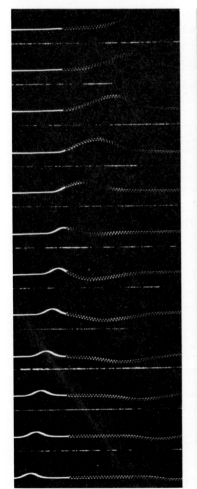

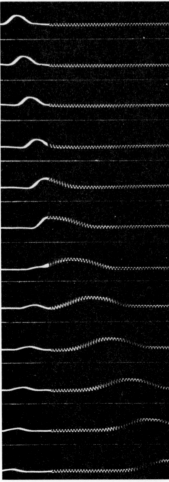

Figure 32-11. A pulse on a heavy spring incident on a light-spring–heavy-spring boundary. Neither the reflected pulse nor the transmitted pulse is inverted relative to the incident pulse. Note that the pulse speed on the light spring is greater than it is on the heavy spring.

pulse but the transmitted pulse is not. Also, the speed of the pulse on the heavy spring is significantly less than on the light spring. The speed of a wave depends on the medium in which it travels.

Figure 32-11 shows an incident pulse traveling to the right on a heavy spring and encountering another spring that is light. In this case, when the incident pulse is on the heavy spring, the reflected pulse is not inverted. Again, note that the speed of the pulse on the heavy spring is less than the speed of the pulse on the light spring.

32-4 HARMONIC WAVES

The mathematical description of waves is based primarily on the wave function for a *harmonic wave*. For a harmonic wave on a string, the string is shaped as a sine function at any particular instant. Figure 32-12 shows a "snapshot" of such a wave at two different instants — the solid curve shows the string at $t = 0$, and the dashed curve shows it a short time Δt later. At $t = 0$,

$$y = A \sin\left(\frac{2\pi}{\lambda}x\right)$$

Amplitude A and wavelength λ

The *amplitude A* is the maximum displacement of any element of the string from its equilibrium position at $y = 0$, and the *wavelength λ* is the wave's repeat distance, or the distance between successive crests or successive troughs. In the previous section we found that, for a wave moving to the right with speed v, the wave's time dependence can be developed from the expression for the wave's shape by simply replacing x with $x - vt$. Thus the wave function for a harmonic wave is

Wave function for a harmonic wave

$$y(x, t) = A \sin\left[\frac{2\pi}{\lambda}(x - vt)\right] \tag{32-4}$$

The argument of the sine function, $(2\pi/\lambda)(x - vt)$, is the *phase* of the wave.

Consider the motion of an element of the string as a harmonic wave moves along. For the element at $x = 0$, we have $y = A \sin[(-2\pi v/\lambda)t] = -A \sin[(2\pi v/\lambda)t]$. From Chap. 14, we know that simple harmonic motion (SHM) with period T is described by $y \propto \sin[(2\pi/T)t]$. Therefore, the element executes SHM with period

$$T = \frac{\lambda}{v}$$

as shown in Fig. 32-13. Each element of the string executes SHM with this same period.

Figure 32-12. A graph of y versus x for a harmonic wave of amplitude A and wavelength λ. The solid curve shows the wave at $t = 0$, and the dashed curve shows the wave at a short time Δt later. Displacements along the y axis in this figure, and in others in this chapter, are exaggerated for purposes of illustration. Ordinarily, $\lambda \gg A$ for real waves.

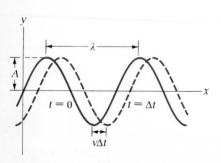

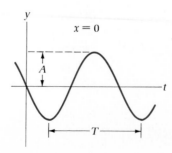

Figure 32-13. A graph of y versus t for a harmonic wave of amplitude A and period T. The motion of a particular element of the string is simple harmonic motion (SHM).

The above relation between T, λ, and v can be obtained another way. The period T is the time for a particular element to complete one oscillation, and it is also the time for a particular wave displacement (say a crest) to move a distance of one wavelength λ. This means that the wave moves a distance λ in a time T, so its speed v is

Speed of a harmonic wave

$$v = \frac{\lambda}{T} \qquad (32\text{-}5)$$

Frequency $\nu = 1/T$

Angular frequency $\omega = 2\pi/T$

Wave number $k = 2\pi/\lambda$

Traditionally, a number of parameters are used to describe a harmonic wave. The frequency ν of the wave is $\nu = 1/T$, and the angular frequency ω is $\omega = 2\pi/T = 2\pi\nu$. The *wave number* k is $k = 2\pi/\lambda$. A wave function can be written many different ways by using different combinations of these parameters, but a convenient way, because of its conciseness, is in terms of k and ω:

$$y = A \sin (kx - \omega t)$$

The wave speed v can also be expressed a number of ways with these parameters. Two useful expressions are

$$v = \lambda\nu \qquad \text{and} \qquad v = \frac{\omega}{k}$$

The wave functions we have presented so far are not completely general because they require that $y = 0$ when $x = 0$ and $t = 0$. A more general expression includes a *phase constant* ϕ:

$$y = A \sin (kx - \omega t + \phi)$$

Often it is convenient to choose $x = 0$ and $t = 0$ such that $\phi = 0$, as we did in the discussion above.

A real wave cannot be perfectly harmonic because a harmonic wave extends to infinity in each direction along the x axis and has no beginning or ending time. A real wave must begin and end somewhere in space and in time. A wave that exists in nature, such as a sound wave or a light wave, often can be approximated as a harmonic wave because its extent in space is much larger than its wavelength, and the time interval for it to pass a point is much longer than its period. Such a wave is called a *wave train*. A harmonic wave is an idealized representation of a wave train.

Wave train

EXAMPLE 32-2. A harmonic wave on a string has an amplitude of 15 mm, a wavelength of 2.4 m, and a speed of 3.5 m/s. (a) Determine the period, the frequency, the angular frequency, and the wave number for the wave. (b) Write the wave function for this wave with the $+x$ direction as the direction of wave travel.

SOLUTION. (a) Since the speed of a harmonic wave is given by $v = \lambda/T$, the period is

$$T = \frac{\lambda}{v} = \frac{2.4 \text{ m}}{3.5 \text{ m/s}} = 0.69 \text{ s}$$

The frequency is $\nu = 1/T = 1/0.69 \text{ s} = 1.5$ Hz, and the angular frequency is $\omega = 2\pi/T = 9.2$ rad/s. The wave number is $k = 2\pi/\lambda = 2\pi/2.4 \text{ m} = 2.6$ rad/m. (b) Using the concise form $y = A \sin (kx - \omega t)$, we have

$$y = 15 \text{ mm} \sin [(2.6 \text{ rad/m})x - (9.2 \text{ rad/s})t]$$

Since the factor which involves x enters the expression with the opposite sign of the factor which involves t, the $+x$ direction is the direction of wave travel.

The wave equation. By investigating the derivatives of the wave function for a harmonic wave, we now introduce a differential equation that is called the *wave equation.* Later we shall find systems where the application of physical

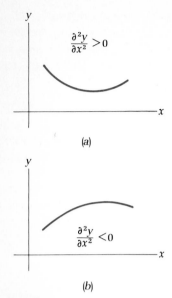

Figure 32-14. (a) A section of a curve with $\partial^2 y/\partial x^2 > 0$. The curve bends upward with increasing x. (b) A section of a curve with $\partial^2 y/\partial x^2 < 0$. The curve bends downward with increasing x. For a straight section, $\partial^2 y/\partial x^2 = 0$.

laws, such as Newton's second law, produces the wave equation. Such a finding constitutes a theoretical prediction that waves exist in the system.

First consider the derivative of y with respect to t, holding x constant — the partial derivative, $\partial y/\partial t$. This derivative gives the y component of the velocity of an element. Using $y(x, t) = A \sin (kx - \omega t)$, we have

$$\frac{\partial y}{\partial t} = \frac{\partial}{\partial t} [A \sin (kx - \omega t)] = -\omega A \cos (kx - \omega t)$$

A second time derivative of y, holding x constant, is the y component of the acceleration of the element:

$$\frac{\partial^2 y}{\partial t^2} = \frac{\partial}{\partial t} \frac{\partial y}{\partial t} = \frac{\partial}{\partial t} [-\omega A \cos (kx - \omega t)] = -\omega^2 A \sin (kx - \omega t)$$

Using $v = \omega/k$ in the form $\omega^2 = v^2 k^2$, we can write the acceleration component as

$$\frac{\partial^2 y}{\partial t^2} = -v^2 k^2 A \sin (kx - \omega t)$$

Since $y(x, t) = A \sin (kx - \omega t)$,

$$\frac{\partial^2 y}{\partial t^2} = -v^2 k^2 y(x, t) \tag{32-6}$$

Next consider the derivative of y with respect to x, holding t constant — $\partial y/\partial x$:

$$\frac{\partial y}{\partial x} = \frac{\partial}{\partial x} [A \sin (kx - \omega t)] = kA \cos (kx - \omega t)$$

This derivative gives the slope of the string at a point x and time t. For example, it gives the slope at a point x for one of the graphs of y versus x shown in Fig. 32-12. The second derivative of y with respect to x, holding t constant is the change of the slope with x:

$$\frac{\partial^2 y}{\partial x^2} = \frac{\partial}{\partial x} \frac{\partial y}{\partial x}$$

This quantity gives a measure of the amount of bending in the string. The larger $|\partial^2 y/\partial x^2|$, the tighter the bend in the string. If $\partial^2 y/\partial x^2$ is positive, then the slope of the string increases with increasing x. We describe this case by saying that the string bends upward (Fig. 32-14a). If $\partial^2 y/\partial x^2$ is negative, then the slope of the string decreases with increasing x and we say that the string bends downward (Fig. 32-14b). If $\partial^2 y/\partial x^2 = 0$ at a point, then the string is straight at that point. For a harmonic wave,

$$\frac{\partial^2 y}{\partial x^2} = \frac{\partial}{\partial x} \frac{\partial y}{\partial x} = \frac{\partial}{\partial x} [kA \cos (kx - \omega t)] = -k^2 A \sin (kx - \omega t)$$

Since $y(x, t) = A \sin (kx - \omega t)$,

$$\frac{\partial^2 y}{\partial x^2} = -k^2 y(x, t) \tag{32-7}$$

Combining Eqs. (32-6) and (32-7), we have

The wave equation

$$\frac{\partial^2 y}{\partial x^2} = \frac{1}{v^2} \frac{\partial^2 y}{\partial t^2} \tag{32-8}$$

This differential equation is the wave equation. Because derivatives of a harmonic wave function produce this equation, we know that the wave function for a harmonic wave satisfies the wave equation, or is a solution to the wave equation. Indeed, the general traveling wave function $y(x, t) = f(x - vt)$ [or $y(x, t) = f(x + vt)$] is also a solution to the wave equation. (See Prob. 32-3.)

The wave equation expresses the result that the acceleration of an element of the string is related to the amount of bending of the string at that element. At points along the string where the bending is large ($|\partial^2 y/\partial x^2|$ is large), the acceleration magnitude is large ($|\partial^2 y/\partial t^2|$ is large). At points where the string is straight ($\partial^2 y/\partial x^2 = 0$), the acceleration is zero ($\partial^2 y/\partial t^2 = 0$). If $\partial^2 y/\partial x^2$ is positive at a point (the string bends upward), the acceleration is directed upward; if $\partial^2 y/\partial x^2$ is negative (the string bends downward), the acceleration is directed downward. Why should the acceleration of an element depend on the bending of the string at that element? The answer comes from dynamics, the application of Newton's second law to each element of the string.

32-5 THE WAVE EQUATION FROM NEWTON'S SECOND LAW

Newton's second law predicts that waves can occur in a medium with a linear elastic restoring force. As an example, consider an element of a uniform string. In equilibrium, the string is held taut along the x axis. Figure 32-15 shows an element of the string which is displaced from equilibrium by a wave. Forces $\mathbf{F}_1$ and $\mathbf{F}_2$ are exerted on ends 1 and 2 of the element by its neighboring elements. We assume that the effect of the wave is small enough such that the tension F in the string is essentially uniform. This means that $|\mathbf{F}_1| = |\mathbf{F}_2| = F$. Also, we assume that the tension is large so that the weight of the element can be neglected. With these approximations, the y component of the net force on the element is

$$\Sigma F_y = F_{y1} + F_{y2} = -F \sin \theta_1 + F \sin \theta_2 = F(\sin \theta_2 - \sin \theta_1)$$

Note that if the string is straight, then $\theta_1 = \theta_2$ and the net force on the element is zero. If the string is bent, $\theta_1 \neq \theta_2$ and there is a nonzero net force on the element.

Next we assume that the angles θ_1 and θ_2 are small so that $\sin \theta_1 \approx \tan \theta_1$ and $\sin \theta_2 \approx \tan \theta_2$. This approximation is useful because the slope of the string at a point equals the tangent of the angle between the string and the x axis at that point: $\tan \theta = \partial y/\partial x$. Accordingly, $\sin \theta \approx \partial y/\partial x$ and we can write the net force as

$$\Sigma F_y = F \left[\left(\frac{\partial y}{\partial x} \right)_2 - \left(\frac{\partial y}{\partial x} \right)_1 \right]$$

The quantity $[(\partial y/\partial x)_2 - (\partial y/\partial x)_1]$ is the change in the slope between ends 1 and 2. If the element is small, then

$$\left(\frac{\partial y}{\partial x} \right)_2 - \left(\frac{\partial y}{\partial x} \right)_1 = \Delta \frac{\partial y}{\partial x} = \frac{\Delta(\partial y/\partial x)}{\Delta x} \Delta x \approx \frac{\partial}{\partial x} \left(\frac{\partial y}{\partial x} \right) \Delta x = \frac{\partial^2 y}{\partial x^2} \Delta x$$

where the approximation becomes exact as the size of the element approaches zero. The y component of the net force on a small element is

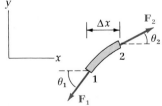

Figure 32-15. Forces $\mathbf{F}_1$ and $\mathbf{F}_2$ exerted on ends 1 and 2 of an element of a string by its neighboring elements. The y component of the net force is $F(\sin \theta_2 - \sin \theta_1)$, where F is the tension in the rope.

$$\Sigma F_y = F \frac{\partial^2 y}{\partial x^2} \Delta x$$

Let M and L represent the mass and length of the string, respectively. For a uniform string, the mass per unit length, or *linear mass density* μ, of the string is $\mu = M/L$. Using μ, we can write the mass m of the element in terms of Δx: $m = \mu \Delta x$. Applying the y component of Newton's second law, $\Sigma F_y = ma_y$, to the element gives

$$F \frac{\partial^2 y}{\partial x^2} \Delta x = \mu \Delta x \frac{\partial^2 y}{\partial t^2}$$

where we have used $a_y = \partial^2 y / \partial t^2$. Dividing by Δx and rearranging, we obtain

Wave equation for waves on a string

$$\frac{\partial^2 y}{\partial x^2} = \frac{\mu}{F} \frac{\partial^2 y}{\partial t^2} \tag{32-9}$$

which is the wave equation. Thus Newton's second law predicts the existence of waves on a string.

Comparing Eq. (32-8) with Eq. (32-9), we see that $1/v^2 = \mu/F$, or

Speed of a wave on a string

$$v = \sqrt{\frac{F}{\mu}} \tag{32-10}$$

In addition to producing the wave equation, Newton's second law gives the speed of the waves in terms of the tension F in the string and the linear mass density μ of the string. For example, if a string of length 10 m and mass 1 kg ($\mu = M/L = 1 \text{ kg}/10 \text{ m} = 0.1 \text{ kg/m}$) is under a tension of 90 N, then the speed of a wave on this string is $v = \sqrt{F/\mu} = \sqrt{(90 \text{ N})/(0.1 \text{ kg/m})} = 30 \text{ m/s}$. Experiment shows that Eq. (32-10) gives the correct value for the speed of waves on a string.

In the above derivation of the wave equation, we assumed that the angle between an element of the string and the x axis is small. For a harmonic wave, this corresponds to the wavelength being much larger than the amplitude, $\lambda \gg A$. The wave equation that is a result of this assumption, Eq. (32-9), is called a *linear* wave equation. A differential equation is linear if its terms involve y and derivatives of y to the first power. For example, a differential equation is linear if its terms involve y, or $\partial y/\partial x$, or $\partial^2 y/\partial t^2$, but it is not linear if its terms involve $y(\partial y/\partial t)$, or $(\partial^2 y/\partial x^2)^2$, or y^2. An important feature of a linear wave equation is that the sum of individual wave functions is also a wave function. Suppose $y_1(x, t)$ and $y_2(x, t)$ are individual wave functions which satisfy a linear wave equation. Then

The principle of superposition is obeyed by waves that satisfy a linear wave equation.

$$y(x, t) = y_1(x, t) + y_2(x, t) \tag{32-11}$$

is also a wave function which satisfies the same linear wave equation. (See Exercise 32-25.) In other words, the principle of superposition is obeyed by waves that satisfy a linear wave equation.

In the next chapter we shall see another example in which Newton's second law yields a wave equation, a wave equation for sound in a fluid. For sound waves, the wave function represents the longitudinal displacement of the fluid caused by the wave. In Chap. 34 we shall find that the equations of electricity and magnetism predict the existence of electromagnetic waves, an example of which is visible light. For electromagnetic waves, the wave function represents the oscillating electric and magnetic fields. In general, we can write the wave equation as

Wave equation for a physical
quantity ψ

$$\frac{\partial^2 \psi}{\partial x^2} = \frac{1}{v^2} \frac{\partial^2 \psi}{\partial t^2} \qquad (32\text{-}12)$$

where $\psi(x, t)$ represents the physical quantity which oscillates or "waves" as the wave goes by. In the case of a wave on a string, ψ gives the transverse displacement of the string; in the case of a sound wave in a fluid, ψ gives the longitudinal displacement of the fluid; in the case of electromagnetic waves, ψ gives the electric or magnetic field.

When the wave equation is developed for a physical system, an expression for the wave speed v in terms of the properties of the medium is forthcoming. In the case of the string, we found that $v = \sqrt{F/\mu}$. For mechanical waves in a medium, the important characteristics of the medium are (i) a factor which characterizes the restoring force in the medium and (ii) a factor which characterizes the inertial mass of the medium. The expression for the wave speed has the form

The speed of a wave depends on
the medium.

$$v = \sqrt{\frac{\text{restoring force factor}}{\text{inertial mass factor}}}$$

which shows how the speed of a wave depends on the properties of the medium through which the wave travels.

32-6 POWER OF A WAVE

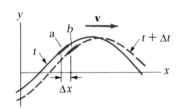

Figure 32-16. With a wave traveling in the $+x$ direction, the string is shown at time t and at time $t + \Delta t$. The energy of element a at t is equal to the energy of element b at $t + \Delta t$. Thus energy propagates along the string with speed $\Delta x/\Delta t = v$.

As a wave moves along, it carries energy in the direction of wave travel. To determine the rate at which energy is propagated by a wave, or the power of a wave, we first find the wave's energy density. As we shall see, the power of a wave is given by the product of its energy density and its speed.

Consider element a of the string in Fig. 32-16 at some instant t as a wave moves along the string. Because of the wave, element a has both a kinetic energy due to its motion, and a potential energy due to the amount it is stretched. The kinetic energy of the element is one-half its mass times its speed squared:

$$\Delta K = \frac{1}{2} (\mu \, \Delta x) \left(\frac{\partial y}{\partial t} \right)^2$$

Therefore, the kinetic energy per unit length, or the kinetic energy density of the wave, is

$$\frac{\Delta K}{\Delta x} = \frac{1}{2} \mu \left(\frac{\partial y}{\partial t} \right)^2$$

By solving Prob. 32-7, you can show that the potential energy density is

$$\frac{\Delta U}{\Delta x} = \frac{1}{2} F \left(\frac{\partial y}{\partial x} \right)^2$$

The *energy density* of the wave is the sum of the kinetic and potential energy densities:

Energy density of a wave

$$\frac{\Delta E}{\Delta x} = \frac{1}{2} \mu \left(\frac{\partial y}{\partial t} \right)^2 + \frac{1}{2} F \left(\frac{\partial y}{\partial x} \right)^2$$

In Fig. 32-16, we show that the condition of element a at time t (its motion and the amount it is stretched) is the same as that of element b at time $t + \Delta t$. That is, the energy possessed by a is passed along to b in the time interval Δt, so that energy is propagating along the string with speed $\Delta x/\Delta t$, which is the same as the wave speed v. Thus the rate at which energy is propagating along the string, or the power of the wave, is $P = (\Delta E/\Delta x)(\Delta x/\Delta t)$, or

$$P = \left[\frac{1}{2}\mu\left(\frac{\partial y}{\partial t}\right)^2 + \frac{1}{2}F\left(\frac{\partial y}{\partial x}\right)^2\right]v \qquad (32\text{-}13)$$

For a harmonic wave, $y = A \sin (kx - \omega t)$,

$$\frac{\partial y}{\partial t} = -\omega A \cos (kx - \omega t)$$

and

$$\frac{\partial y}{\partial x} = kA \cos (kx - \omega t)$$

Also, $v^2 = F/\mu = \omega^2/k^2$. With these expressions, we can write the power of a harmonic wave as

Power of a harmonic wave

$$P = \mu\omega^2 A^2 v \cos^2 (kx - \omega t)$$

Figure 32-17 shows a graph of the power of a harmonic wave versus time at a fixed point on the string. Note that the power remains positive at all times, indicating a continuous transfer of energy in the direction of wave travel.

Since the power of a harmonic wave oscillates between zero and a maximum value, a quantity of interest is the average power $\overline{P}$, and the average is taken over a whole number of cycles at a fixed point. The time dependence of P at a fixed point, say $x = 0$, is $\cos^2(\omega t)$ [or equivalently, $\sin^2(\omega t)$]. As we have seen previously, (Sec. 31-8), the average of $\cos^2(\omega t)$ over a whole number of cycles is 1/2. Thus

Average power of a harmonic wave

$$\overline{P} = \tfrac{1}{2}\mu\omega^2 A^2 v \qquad (32\text{-}14)$$

The dependence of the average power (and the power) on the amplitude squared, $P \propto A^2$, is a feature common to harmonic waves, be they sound waves, electromagnetic waves, or waves on a string.

According to Eq. (32-14), the average power of a wave is the same at each point along the string. That is, no energy is lost by the wave as it propagates along the string. When energy is lost by a wave as it propagates through a medium, we say that the wave is *attenuated.* Since our harmonic wave has a fixed amplitude, it describes an unattenuated wave. Real mechanical waves passing through a medium always exhibit some attenuation, but often the attenuation is small enough to be neglected. In our discussions, we neglect attenuation.

Attenuation

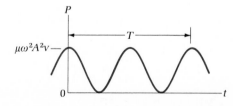

Figure 32-17. Power of a harmonic wave at a fixed point versus time. The time dependence of the power is $\cos^2(\omega t)$.

EXAMPLE 32-3. A string with a linear mass density of 47 g/m is held taut so that the tension in the string is 75 N. A harmonic wave of amplitude $A = 13$ mm and frequency $\nu = 32$ Hz propagates along the string. What is the average power of the wave?

SOLUTION. To use the expression for the average power given in Eq. (32-14), we must determine values for v and ω:

$$v = \sqrt{\frac{F}{\mu}} = \sqrt{\frac{75 \text{ N}}{47 \text{ g/m}}} = 40 \text{ m/s}$$

$$\omega = 2\pi\nu = 2\pi(32 \text{ Hz}) = 200 \text{ rad/s}$$

From Eq. (32-14),

$$\bar{P} = \tfrac{1}{2}\mu\omega^2 A^2 v = \tfrac{1}{2}(47 \text{ g/m})(200 \text{ rad/s})^2(13 \text{ mm})^2(40 \text{ m/s})$$
$$= 6.4 \text{ W}$$

Waves in three dimensions: wave intensity. If you wiggle your finger up and down on the surface of water, waves propagate radially outward from the point of the disturbance. Each wave crest forms a circle whose radius continually increases as the wave propagates, and each of these expanding circles is called a *wavefront*. In Fig. 32-18 the wavefronts appear as a series of concentric circles with a separation of one wavelength. Waves on the surface of water are an example of waves propagating in two dimensions. You can use these two-dimensional waves to help visualize waves in three dimensions.

For a wave in three dimensions, such as a sound wave or a light wave, the wavefronts form surfaces. In Fig. 32-19a we show sections of concentric spherical surfaces. These spherical sections represent parts of the wavefronts of waves emanating from a point source located at the center of the spheres. In a uniform medium, each wavefront forms a complete spherical surface. Waves emanating from a point source in a uniform medium are often called *spherical waves*. The lines shown in the figure that are directed radially outward from

Wavefront

Spherical waves

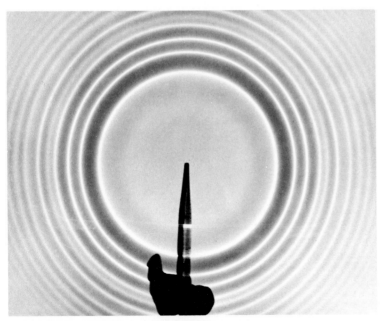

Figure 32-18. Circular wavefronts of water. The waves are caused by a periodic disturbance of the water surface; the disturbance behaves as a point source. *(Bernice Abbott/Photo Researchers)*

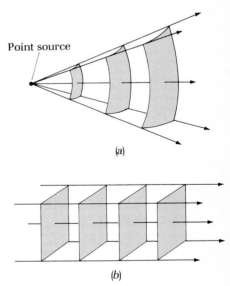

(a)

(b)

Figure 32-19. (a) Spherical sections used to represent part of the spherical wavefronts of waves emanating from a point source. (b) Planar sections used to represent part of the planar wavefronts of waves far from their source.

Rays

the source are called *rays*. Rays are drawn perpendicular to wavefronts and are used to indicate the direction of propagation of a wave.

At a large distance from a point source, the wavefronts become nearly planar. Then a section of a plane can be used to represent part of a wavefront, as shown in Fig. 32-19*b*. Such waves are referred to as *plane waves*. In the case of plane waves, the rays are straight lines that are parallel and equally spaced.

Plane waves

When sunlight comes through your window and into your room, the power to the room due to these electromagnetic waves depends on the area of the window — the larger the window area, the more power to the room. The effective area of the window is the projection of the window's area onto a plane perpendicular to the rays of the sunlight. The quantity which characterizes the energy flow due to the sunlight is the *wave intensity*. The intensity I of a wave is the power P propagated per unit area of a surface which is normal to the propagation direction. Since power is the rate of energy transfer, $P = \Delta E/\Delta t$, we have

Definition of wave intensity

$$I = \frac{P}{\Delta S} = \frac{\Delta E}{\Delta t \, \Delta S} \tag{32-15}$$

where ΔS is the area of a surface which is normal to the propagation direction and ΔE is the energy that passes through the surface in the time Δt. Since the dimension of power is energy divided by time, the dimension of intensity is (energy)/[(time)(area)]. The SI unit of intensity is the watt per square meter (W/m^2).

Consider the way the intensity decreases with distance from a point source of waves. Let P_o represent the steady power output of the source, and assume that (i) the medium does not attenuate the waves and (ii) the waves emitted by the source travel uniformly in all directions. Since the intensity I is the power per unit area, the rate at which energy passes through a spherical surface of radius r (area $4\pi r^2$) centered at the source is $I(4\pi r^2)$. By conservation of energy, the power output of the source is equal to the rate at which energy passes through this spherical surface. That is, $P_o = 4\pi r^2 I$, or

Intensity of waves from a point source

$$I = \frac{P_o}{4\pi r^2} \tag{32-16}$$

Because the energy spreads out uniformly in three-dimensional space as it propagates from the point source, the intensity decreases as the inverse square of the distance r from the source.

EXAMPLE 32-4. Determine the intensity of visible light waves at a distance of 1.5 m from a 60-W light bulb. Assume that 5 percent of the power to the bulb is emitted in the form of visible light and treat the bulb as a point source that emits waves uniformly in all directions through a uniform medium.

SOLUTION. The power output of the bulb in the form of

visible light waves is $P_o = (0.05)(60 \text{ W}) = 3 \text{ W}$. Using Eq. (32-16), we find that the wave intensity at a distance of 1.5 m from the source is

$$I = \frac{P_o}{4\pi r^2} = \frac{3 \text{ W}}{4\pi(1.5 \text{ m})^2} = 0.1 \text{ W/m}^2$$

What is the intensity at a point 15 m from the source?

32-7 INTERFERENCE OF HARMONIC WAVES

If two or more waves exist in the same region, then the waves interfere. That is, when individual waves are superposed, they combine to produce a resultant wave. We examine two special cases of the interference of two harmonic waves. In one of these cases we discover phenomena called *constructive* and *destructive interference*. In the other case we discover a phenomenon called *standing waves*.

Constructive and destructive interference. Consider the interference of two harmonic waves, waves 1 and 2:

$$y_1 = A \sin (kx - \omega t + \phi_1)$$

and

$$y_2 = A \sin (kx - \omega t + \phi_2)$$

Each wave is traveling in the same direction and has the same amplitude A, wave number k, and angular frequency ω, but their phase constants ϕ_1 and ϕ_2 may be different. The *phase difference* $\Delta\phi$ between these waves is

$$\Delta\phi = (kx - \omega t + \phi_2) - (kx - \omega t + \phi_1) = \phi_2 - \phi_1$$

In Fig. 32-20, each wave is plotted on a separate graph and the phase difference is shown. If $\phi_2 = \phi_1$ (or $\Delta\phi = 0$), we say that the waves are in phase, and if $\phi_2 \neq \phi_1$ (or $\Delta\phi \neq 0$), we say that the waves are out of phase by the phase difference $\Delta\phi$.

To find the resultant wave y due to the interference of y_1 and y_2, we use the principle of superposition:

$$y = y_1 + y_2 = A [\sin (kx - \omega t + \phi_1) + \sin (kx - \omega t + \phi_2)]$$

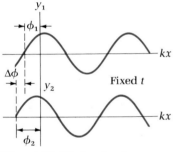

We can see the effect of the interference more clearly by using the trigonometric identity

$$\sin \alpha + \sin \beta = 2 \sin [\tfrac{1}{2}(\alpha + \beta)] \cos [\tfrac{1}{2}(\alpha - \beta)] \qquad (32\text{-}17)$$

Figure 32-20. Graphs of y versus kx at fixed t for harmonic waves 1 and 2. The phase difference between the waves is $\Delta\phi$.

Letting $\alpha = kx - \omega t + \phi_2$ and $\beta = kx - \omega t + \phi_1$, we find $\tfrac{1}{2}(\alpha + \beta) = kx - \omega t + \tfrac{1}{2}\Delta\phi$ and $\tfrac{1}{2}(\alpha - \beta) = \tfrac{1}{2}\Delta\phi$, so that

$$y = [2A \cos (\tfrac{1}{2}\Delta\phi)] \sin (kx - \omega t + \tfrac{1}{2}\Delta\phi) \qquad (32\text{-}18)$$

Two features of the resultant wave are apparent from Eq. (32-18):

1. The resultant wave y is a harmonic wave with the same wave number k (or the same wavelength λ), the same angular frequency ω (or the same period T), and the same propagation direction $(+x)$ that each individual wave (y_1 or y_2) would have if one of them were present alone.

2. The amplitude of y, which is $2A \cos (\tfrac{1}{2} \Delta\phi)$, depends on the phase difference $\Delta\phi$ between y_1 and y_2. Thus the phase difference plays an important role in the interference of these harmonic waves.

Suppose the phase difference between y_1 and y_2 is zero; the waves are in phase. Since $\Delta\phi = 0$, $\cos (\tfrac{1}{2}\Delta\phi) = \cos 0 = 1$, and the amplitude of y is

$2A \cos 0 = 2A$. This type of interference is called *constructive interference*. When y_1 and y_2 constructively interfere, the resultant wave has twice the amplitude that either y_1 or y_2 would have if one of them were acting alone. In this case, y_1 and y_2 superpose crest on crest and trough on trough, as shown in Fig. 32-21a.

Suppose y_1 and y_2 are out of phase such that their phase difference is 180°, or π rad. Then $\cos(\frac{1}{2}\Delta\phi) = \cos(\frac{1}{2}\pi) = 0$, and the amplitude of y is $2A\cos(\frac{1}{2}\pi) = 0$. This type of interference is called *destructive interference*. The resultant wave is nonexistent because y_1 and y_2 superpose crest on trough and trough on crest, as shown in Fig. 32-21b. When harmonic waves are out of phase by 180°, or π rad, we say that the waves are completely out of phase.

For other values of the phase difference $\Delta\phi$, the resultant wave has an amplitude intermediate between $2A$ and zero. A graph of the case where $\Delta\phi = \pi/2$ rad $= 90°$ is shown in Fig. 32-22. In this case the amplitude of y is $2A\cos(\pi/4) = 1.41A$.

These interference phenomena are peculiar to waves, and when we are investigating an effect, they can be used as evidence that waves are responsible for the effect. As we shall see in Chap. 36, the first convincing proof that light behaves as a wave was made with experiments in which light exhibited constructive and destructive interference.

Standing waves. If a wave train encounters a boundary, the reflected part of the wave train interferes with the incident part of the wave train. This interference can create a stationary wave pattern called a *standing wave*. When waves are confined to a region of space by boundaries, waves reflected back and forth from the boundaries can establish standing waves. Standing waves are important in many aspects of science and engineering (see the Commentary). They are also important in the design of buildings, bridges, and musical instruments.

Figure 32-23 shows photographs of standing waves produced on a long rubber tube by wiggling one end of the tube. As we shall see, to establish a particular standing-wave pattern, like one of those shown in the figure, the end must be wiggled at a specific frequency.

To see how standing waves are formed, consider the interference of two harmonic waves that have the same amplitude, wave number, and angular frequency, but travel in opposite directions:

$$y_1 = A \sin(kx - \omega t) \qquad \text{and} \qquad y_2 = A \sin(kx + \omega t)$$

Wave 1 is traveling toward $+x$, wave 2 is traveling toward $-x$, and each has speed $v = \omega/k$. We can let y_1 represent the incident wave and y_2 represent the reflected wave. Using the principle of superposition, we find that the resultant wave y is

$$y = y_1 + y_2 = A \sin(kx - \omega t) + A \sin(kx + \omega t)$$

The resultant wave can be expressed more simply by using the trigonometric identity given in Eq. (32-17). Letting $\alpha = kx + \omega t$ and $\beta = kx - \omega t$, we obtain

$$y(x, t) = 2A \cos(\omega t) \sin(kx) \qquad (32\text{-}19)$$

This is the wave function for a standing wave.

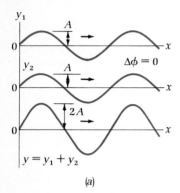

$\Delta\phi = 0$

$y = y_1 + y_2$

(a)

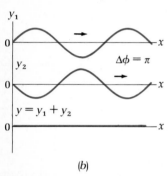

$\Delta\phi = \pi$

$y = y_1 + y_2$

(b)

Figure 32-21. Interference of two harmonic waves. Each wave has the same A, k, ω, and propagation direction. (a) Constructive interference ($\Delta\phi = 0$). (b) Destructive interference ($\Delta\phi = \pi$).

A standing wave

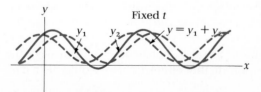

Fixed t

Figure 32-22. The interference of waves 1 and 2 on the same rope produce a resultant wave. In the case shown, waves 1 and 2 are out of phase by 90°.

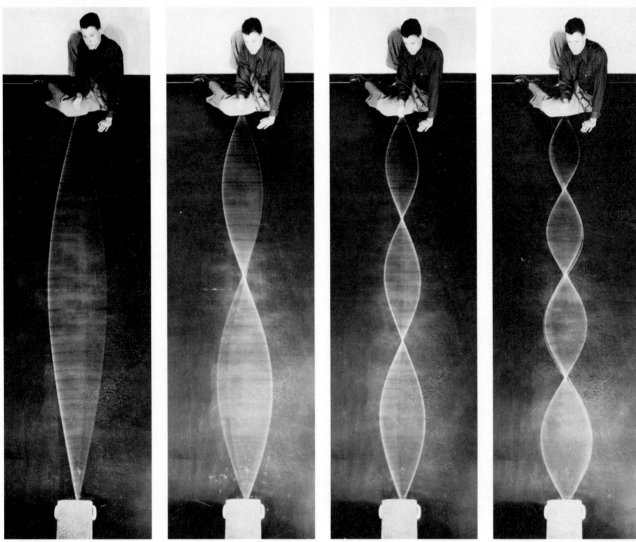

Figure 32-23. Standing waves on a long rubber tube. In each case the end of the tube is wiggled gently at a frequency given by Eq. (32-23). The tube is moving so rapidly that it appears blurred over the extent of its motion. (Physics, *2nd ed., Physical Science Study Committee, 1965. Reprinted by permission of D. C. Heath and Co. and Educational Development Center*.)

In a standing wave, the wave pattern does not move, but the elements of the rope do move. The motion is illustrated by the time sequence shown in Fig. 32-24. Writing the standing wave as $y = [2A \sin (kx)] \cos (\omega t)$, we can see that a particular element of the rope executes SHM with an amplitude equal to $2A \sin (kx)$. The amplitude of the SHM has its maximum value of $2A$ at positions where $\sin (kx) = 1$, or $kx = \pi/2, 3\pi/2, 5\pi/2$, and so on. These positions of maximum amplitude are called *antinodes*. Since $k = 2\pi/\lambda$, the antinodal positions are

Antinodes

$$x_n = \left(n + \frac{1}{2} \right) \frac{1}{2} \lambda \qquad (n = 0, 1, 2, \ldots) \qquad (32\text{-}20)$$

The antinodes are spaced one-half wavelength apart and are indicated by the letter A in Fig. 32-24.

Since $\sin (kx) = 0$ at values of x such that $kx = 0, \pi, 2\pi$, and so on, elements located at these positions do not move. The positions of these elements are called *nodes*. The nodal positions are

$$x_{n'} = n' \frac{1}{2} \lambda \qquad (n' = 0, 1, 2, \ldots) \qquad (32\text{-}21)$$

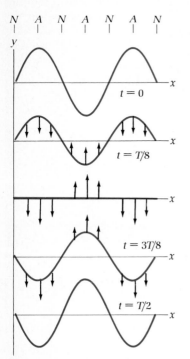

Nodes

The nodes are spaced one-half wavelength apart and are indicated by the letter *N* in Fig. 32-24.

To produce standing waves of a single wavelength, like those shown in Fig. 32-23, the experimenter must wiggle the tube at a specific frequency. A node exists at each end of the tube, one at the experimenter's hand and the other at the fixed end.* If we let the ends of the tube be at $x = 0$ and $x = L$, then this requirement can be stated in terms of *boundary conditions* on the wave function:

$$y(0, t) = 0 \qquad \text{and} \qquad y(L, t) = 0$$

Since a node is at each end of the tube and since nodes are a distance $\frac{1}{2}\lambda$ apart, an integral number of half-wavelengths must fit along the length *L* of the tube, or

$$n\left(\frac{1}{2}\lambda_n\right) = L \qquad (n = 1, 2, 3, \ldots) \qquad (32\text{-}22)$$

where *n* is an integer and λ_n represents the specific wavelengths that satisfy the boundary conditions. Solving for λ_n, we have

$$\lambda_n = \frac{2L}{n}$$

Figure 32-24. A standing wave at five instants of time. The arrows indicate the velocities of some representative elements. Note that at $t = 0$ and $t = T/2$, the entire rope is instantaneously at rest. The amplitude is exaggerated for purposes of illustration.

The allowed wavelengths for standing waves are $\lambda_1 = 2L$, $\lambda_2 = L$, $\lambda_3 = 2L/3$, and so on.

A standing wave cannot have just any wavelength whatsoever; it can only have one of the specific wavelengths λ_n that fit the boundary conditions. Since the frequency of a wave is related to its wavelength by the expression $v = \lambda \nu$, the frequency of a standing wave is similarly restricted to certain specific values ν_n. Using Eq. (32-22), we find that these values are

$$\nu_n = \frac{v}{\lambda_n} = n\left(\frac{v}{2L}\right)$$

These frequencies are called the *natural frequencies*. The lowest natural frequency, $\nu_1 = v/2L$, is called the *fundamental frequency*. Since $v = \sqrt{F/\mu}$, the fundamental frequency can be written

Fundamental frequency

$$\nu_1 = \frac{\sqrt{F/\mu}}{2L}$$

In terms of the fundamental frequency, the natural frequencies are

Natural frequencies for standing waves

$$\nu_n = n\nu_1 \qquad (n = 1, 2, 3, \ldots) \qquad (32\text{-}23)$$

Harmonics

Thus the natural frequencies are whole multiples of the fundamental frequency. These natural frequencies are called *harmonics*; the fundamental frequency ν_1 is called the first harmonic, $\nu_2 = 2\nu_1$ is called the second har-

---

* Actually, the experimenter must continuously wiggle the end of the tube slightly to compensate for attenuation. Thus the end held by the experimenter is only approximately a node.

monic, $\nu_3 = 3\nu_1$ is called the third harmonic, and so on. If the experimenter in Fig. 32-23 wiggles the end of the tube with SHM at one of the harmonic frequencies, then the standing wave corresponding to that frequency will exist on the tube.

Consider the fundamental frequency of a string in a musical instrument such as a guitar. Since $\nu_1 = \sqrt{F/\mu}(1/2L)$, the frequency depends on (i) the tension F in the string, (ii) the linear mass density μ of the string, and (iii) the length L of the string between fixed ends. In the playing of a guitar, all three factors are taken into account. A guitar is tuned by changing F. Different strings have different values of μ. The length L between fixed ends of a string is changed by pushing the string against a fret.

EXAMPLE 32-5. For the tube in Fig. 32-23, suppose $F = 72$ N, $M = 0.84$ kg, and $L = 3.8$ m. (a) What is the fundamental frequency? (b) At what frequency should the experimenter wiggle the end of the tube in order to produce a standing wave with two antinodes?

SOLUTION. (a) Since $\mu = M/L$, the fundamental frequency is

$$\nu_1 = \frac{\sqrt{F/\mu}}{2L} = \frac{\sqrt{FL/M}}{2L} = \frac{1}{2}\sqrt{\frac{F}{LM}}$$

$$= \frac{1}{2}\sqrt{\frac{72 \text{ N}}{[(3.8 \text{ m})(0.84 \text{ kg})]}} = 2.4 \text{ Hz}$$

(b) A standing wave with two antinodes is the second harmonic, $n = 2$. The frequency of the second harmonic is $\nu_2 = 2\nu_1 = 2(2.4 \text{ Hz}) = 4.8 \text{ Hz}$.

COMMENTARY: ATOMS, STANDING WAVES, AND QUANTIZATION

Suppose you have an account with a bank, and the bank has a rather strange rule. The rule is that your account is allowed to have only certain values, say $0.00, $17.40, $34.02, $52.87, and so on. If the account is at $17.40, then you can deposit $16.62 because $16.62 + $17.40 = $34.02. This deposit puts your account at an allowed value. But you cannot deposit $16.61 or $16.63 or any other amount that would give the account a forbidden value. If your account is at $34.02, then you can withdraw $16.62 or $34.02, but you cannot withdraw any other amount. We describe this strange rule by saying that your bank balance is quantized. (Of course, bank accounts really are quantized in units of one penny, but our strange rule provides a better analogy.)

Curiously, the energy of atoms is quantized. When an atom releases energy or accepts energy, it can release or accept only an amount that takes it from one allowed energy value to another. These allowed energy values are called energy levels.

What property of atoms is responsible for the quantization of atomic energies? The characteristics of standing waves provide a clue to the answer. In the previous section we found that when waves are confined to a region, standing waves can be established and the frequencies of these standing waves are quantized. On a string fixed at each end, the standing wave frequencies are $\nu_n = n\nu_1$, where ν_1 is the fundamental frequency and n is an integer. For example, if $\nu_1 = 2.1$ Hz, then the allowed frequencies are 2.1, 4.2, 6.3 Hz, and so on. A frequency of 4.1 Hz is forbidden; no standing wave with this frequency can exist on this string. These quantized frequencies are a result of boundary conditions placed on the wave function of the wave.

What do waves have to do with atoms? Atoms contain electrons, and electrons manifest a wave behavior. *Indeed, an electron can be described by a wave function. Since the electrons in an atom are confined to that atom, the wave functions of atomic electrons must conform to boundary conditions. These boundary conditions cause the wave functions of atomic electrons to exhibit nodes and antinodes similar to those of standing waves on a string. Different atomic energy levels are associated with different standing wave patterns for the electron wave functions. The quantization of atomic energies is a result of the boundary conditions placed on the wave functions of atomic electrons.*

SUMMARY WITH APPLICATIONS

Section 32-2. Characteristics of waves

A traveling wave is a disturbance that propagates from one position to another. In a transverse wave, the particles of the medium are displaced perpendicular to the propagation direction, and in a longitudinal wave, the particles of the medium are displaced parallel to the propagation direction.

Describe transverse and longitudinal waves and give examples of each.

Section 32-3. Wave pulses

A wave is described by a wave function $y(x, t)$. In the case of a wave on a rope or string, the wave function gives the displacement $y\mathbf{j}$ of the string from equilibrium. For a wave traveling with speed v toward $+x$,

$$y(x, t) = f(x - vt) \tag{32-1}$$

and toward $-x$,

$$y(x, t) = f(x + vt) \tag{32-2}$$

When two or more waves interfere, the resultant wave function can be found with the principle of superposition.

Give the meaning of a wave function and explain why a traveling wave depends on x and t as $x - vt$ or $x + vt$; state the principle of superposition.

Section 32-4. Harmonic waves

A harmonic wave can be expressed as

$$y(x, t) = A \sin (kx - \omega t)$$

where $k = 2\pi\lambda$ and $\omega = 2\pi\nu = 2\pi/T$. The speed of a harmonic wave is $v = \lambda/T = \omega/k$. Harmonic waves satisfy the wave equation:

$$\frac{\partial^2 y}{\partial x^2} = \frac{1}{v^2} \frac{\partial^2 y}{\partial t^2} \tag{32-8}$$

Define the parameters used to describe a harmonic wave; show that a harmonic wave function is a solution to the wave equation.

Section 32-5. The wave equation from Newton's second law

Newton's second law applied to an element of a rope or

string yields the wave equation and gives the speed of the wave as $v = \sqrt{F/\mu}$. In general, the wave equation for a physical quantity ψ is

$$\frac{\partial^2 \psi}{\partial x^2} = \frac{1}{v^2} \frac{\partial^2 \psi}{\partial t^2} \tag{32-12}$$

This wave equation is a linear differential equation, which means that waves that satisfy this equation obey the principle of superposition.

Show that Newton's second law predicts the existence of waves on a string; describe the way the properties of a medium determine the speed of a wave in that medium.

Section 32-6. Power of a wave

A wave's power is the product of its energy density and speed:

$$P = \left[\frac{1}{2} \mu \left(\frac{\partial y}{\partial t} \right)^2 + \frac{1}{2} F \left(\frac{\partial y}{\partial x} \right)^2 \right] v \tag{32-13}$$

For a harmonic wave,

$$P = \mu\omega^2 A^2 v \cos^2 (kx - \omega t)$$

The average power of a harmonic wave at a particular point is

$$\bar{P} = \tfrac{1}{2}\mu\omega^2 A^2 v \tag{32-14}$$

In three dimensions, the intensity of a wave is the incident power per unit area for a surface normal to the propagation direction:

$$I = \frac{P}{\Delta S} \tag{32-15}$$

The intensity at a distance r from a point source is

$$I = \frac{P_o}{4\pi r^2} \tag{32-16}$$

Define the power of a wave; determine the power of a harmonic wave; define the intensity of a wave.

Section 32-7. Interference of harmonic waves

When two harmonic waves with the same amplitude, wave

number, and angular frequency interfere, the resultant wave is

$$y = [2A \cos (\tfrac{1}{2} \Delta\phi)] \sin (kx - \omega t + \tfrac{1}{2} \Delta\phi) \quad (32\text{-}18)$$

If the phase difference $\Delta\phi$ is 0, the interference is constructive. If $\Delta\phi$ is π rad, the interference is destructive. When waves are confined to a region, a standing wave can be

formed:

$$y = 2A \cos (\omega t) \sin (kx) \quad (32\text{-}19)$$

Because of the boundary conditions, only waves of certain wavelengths λ_n and frequencies ν_n can exist.

Describe constructive and destructive interference; determine the allowed wavelengths and frequencies for standing waves on a string.

QUESTIONS

32-1 Discuss the similarities between the physical waves in this chapter and the waves in each of the following sentences:
  (a) If your boss treats you unfairly, do not make waves by reporting it to the head of the company because you might be the one that gets hurt.
  (b) Gene has wavy hair.
  (c) Elda waved goodbye to Frank.
  (d) The enemy attacked by sending forth waves of infantry.

32-2 List five different examples of mechanical waves. What is the medium in each case?

32-3 If you twirl one end of a horizontally stretched rope in a circle in a plane perpendicular to the rope, a wave will propagate along the rope. Is this wave transverse, longitudinal, some combination of the two, or none of these?

32-4 Suppose two wave pulses traveling in opposite directions interfere with each other. After they are no longer superposed, have their shapes been changed by the encounter? Have their speeds been changed by the encounter? If your answer to either question is yes, describe these changes.

32-5 When two wave pulses traveling in opposite directions encounter each other, do they bounce off one another like billiard balls in a head-on collision, or does each pulse pass through the other like a ghost in a cartoon? Which figure in this chapter best supports your answer?

32-6 When a wave pulse is reflected from a fixed barrier, as shown in Fig. 32-9, we say that the phase of the wave is reversed on reflection. When a pulse on a light spring is reflected from the light-spring–heavy-spring boundary, is the phase of the wave reversed on reflection? When a pulse on a heavy spring is reflected from a heavy-spring–light-spring boundary, is the phase of the pulse reversed on reflection?

32-7 Consider a harmonic wave of amplitude A on a horizontal string. What is y for an element with maximum upward acceleration? What is y for an element with maximum downward acceleration? What is y for an element with zero acceleration? What is y for an element that is instantaneously at rest? What is y for an element with maximum speed?

32-8 For a harmonic wave, what part of the wave has a positive $\partial^2 y/\partial x^2$? What part of the wave has a negative $\partial^2 y/\partial x^2$? What is y for an element that is straight?

32-9 Two harmonic waves are on different ropes and each rope has the same density and tension. The waves have the same frequency, but wave 1 has twice the amplitude of wave 2. Which wave has the larger speed? Which wave causes the larger maximum speed for the elements of the rope on which it travels?

32-10 A graph of part of a wave pulse on a string at a particular instant is shown in Fig. 32-25, with the direction of propagation as indicated. Which, if any, of the elements marked with letters is instantaneously at rest? What is the sign of the velocity component of the elements that are moving? Do any of your answers depend on the direction of propagation?

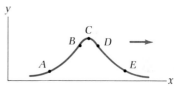

Figure 32-25. Ques. 32-10.

32-11 A graph of part of a wave pulse on a string at a particular instant is shown in Fig. 32-25, with the direction of propagation as indicated. The elements at B and D are inflection points—that is, $\partial^2 y/\partial x^2 = 0$ at these points. Which, if any, of the lettered elements has a zero acceleration? What is the sign of the acceleration component of those elements that have a nonzero acceleration? Do any of your answers depend on the propagation direction?

32-12 If the speed of a wave on a string is v_0 when the tension in the string is F_0, what is the speed of a wave when the tension is $2F_0$?

32-13 Two strings are under the same tension. The mass per unit length of string 1 is μ_0, and the mass per unit length of string 2 is $2\mu_0$. If the speed of a wave on string 1 is v_0, what is the speed of a wave on string 2?

32-14 If the amplitude of a harmonic wave is doubled, with other factors held fixed, how does the power of the wave change?

32-15 If the frequency of a harmonic wave on a rope is doubled and other factors are held fixed, how does the power of the wave change?

32-16 How does the amplitude of a harmonic wave depend on distance from a point source which emits waves uniformly in all directions in three-dimensional space?

32-17 The wavefronts of waves emitted uniformly from along the length of a long line source in a homogeneous medium are in the form of cylinders concentric with the line source, as shown in Fig. 32-26. If there is no attenuation, then the intensity of such waves falls off as $1/R$, where R is the perpendicular distance from the line source to the point where the intensity is measured. Explain this dependence on R.

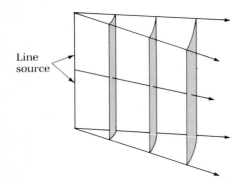

Line source

Figure 32-26. Ques. 32-17: Cylindrical sections used to represent cylindrical wavefronts emanating from a line source. Waves whose wavefronts have this shape are called *cylindrical waves*.

How does the amplitude of a harmonic wave depend on distance from a line source?

32-18 A wave propagates down a long rope which hangs freely from a support. As it propagates, what happens to the speed of the wave?

32-19 The distance from the sun to Mars is about 3/2 that from the sun to the earth. Compare the intensity of sunlight at Mars with the intensity of sunlight at the earth.

32-20 Why do the strings on a guitar have different diameters? Which strings produce the lower notes?

32-21 Sometimes when an airplane flies near a house, the television signal received at the house fades periodically. Why?

32-22 Complete the following table:

Symbol	Represents	Type	SI unit
$y(x, t)$		Component	
v			m/s
A			
λ	Wavelength		
k			
ν			
$\partial y/\partial t$			
$\Delta\phi$			
F			
μ			
P			
I			

EXERCISES

Section 32-3. Wave pulses

32-1 Figure 32-27 shows a wave pulse on a string at two different times: (i) $t = 0.0$ s and (ii) $t = 2.3$ s. Use the figure to estimate (a) the speed of the pulse, (b) the height of the pulse, (c) the width of the pulse. Note that the vertical and horizontal scales in the figure are different.

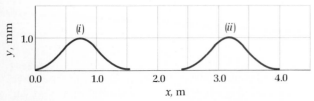

Figure 32-27. Exercise 32-1: $t = 0.0$ s at (i) and 2.3 s at (ii).

32-2 A wave pulse is given by the expression $y(x, t) = y_0 e^{-[(x-vt)/x_0]^2}$, where $y_0 = 4.1$ mm and $x_0 = 1.28$ m.

The speed of the pulse is $v = 7.4$ m/s. (a) On the same graph, plot y versus x for the pulse at $t = 0.00$ s and $t = 0.50$ s. Exaggerate the vertical scale relative to the horizontal scale for purposes of illustration. (b) Determine the pulse height h and the pulse width w.

32-3 A wave pulse is given by the expression $y(x, t) = y_0(2.00)^{-[(x-vt)/x_0]^4}$, where $y_0 = 10.0$ mm and $x_0 = 1.00$ m. The speed of the pulse is $v = 2.00$ m/s. (a) On the same graph, plot y versus x for the pulse at $t = 0.00$ s and $t = 1.00$ s. Exaggerate the vertical scale relative to the horizontal scale for purposes of illustration. (b) Determine the pulse height h and the pulse width w.

32-4 Plot y versus t at $x = 0$ for the pulse in Exercise 32-2.

32-5 Plot y versus t at $x = 0$ for the pulse in Exercise 32-2.

32-6 Longitudinal and transverse waves produced by an earthquake travel at different speeds in the earth's crust, about 8 km/s for longitudinal and 5 km/s for transverse. If these two types of waves from an earthquake are initially received 250 s apart, what is the distance from the receiving site to the earthquake?

32-7 State which of the following functions have the form $y = f(x - vt)$ or $y = f(x + vt)$:

1 $y = y_0[(x + vt)/x_0]^{1/2}$

2 $y = y_0[(x^2 - 2vtx + v^2t^2)/x_0^2]$

3 $y = y_0[(x^2 - v^2t^2)/x_0^2]$

4 $y = y_0 \ln x/vt$

Could any of these functions be used to represent a traveling wave on a string? If not, why not?

Section 32-4. Harmonic waves

32-8 A harmonic wave on a rope is given by the expression

$$y(x, t) = (4.3 \text{ mm}) \sin \left\{ \frac{2\pi}{0.82 \text{ m}} [x + (12 \text{ m/s})t] \right\}$$

What are the wave's (a) amplitude, (b) wavelength, (c) speed, (d) period, (e) wave number, (f) frequency, (g) angular frequency, (h) direction of propagation? (i) Determine y for the element located at $x = 0.58$ m at the instant $t = 0.41$ s.

32-9 A harmonic wave on a rope is given by the expression

$$y(x, t) = (6.8 \text{ mm}) \sin [(1.47 \text{ rad/m})x - (4.18 \text{ rad/s})t]$$

What are the wave's (a) amplitude, (b) wave number, (c) angular frequency, (d) speed, (e) wavelength, (f) frequency, (g) period, (h) direction of propagation? (i) Determine y for the element located at $x = 0.22$ m at the instant $t = 0.75$ s.

32-10 For the wave in Exercise 32-8, determine expressions for (a) the velocity component and (b) the acceleration component of each element of the rope. What are the (c) maximum speed and (d) maximum acceleration magnitude for each element of the rope? Determine (e) the velocity component and (f) the acceleration component of the element located at $x = 0.58$ m at the instant $t = 0.41$ s. (g) From your answer to part (f), is the rope bending upward or downward at that element and at that instant?

32-11 For the wave in Exercise 32-9, determine expressions for (a) the velocity component and (b) the acceleration component of each element of the rope. What are (c) the maximum speed and (d) the maximum acceleration magnitude for each element of the rope? Determine (e) the velocity component and (f) the acceleration component of the element located at $x = 0.22$ m at the instant $t = 0.75$ s. (g) From your answer to part (f), is the rope bending upward or downward at that element and at that instant?

32-12 For the wave in Exercise 32-8, determine expressions for (a) the slope of the rope and (b) $\partial^2 y/\partial x^2$ as functions of x and t. Determine (c) the slope and (d) $\partial^2 y/\partial x^2$ at the element located at $x = 0.58$ m at the instant $t = 0.41$ s. (e) From your answer to part (d), is the rope accelerat-

ing upward or downward at that element and at that instant?

32-13 For the wave in Exercise 32-9, determine expressions for (a) the slope of the rope and (b) $\partial^2 y/\partial x^2$ as functions of x and t. Determine (c) the slope and (d) $\partial^2 y/\partial x^2$ at the element located at $x = 0.22$ m at the instant $t = 0.75$ s. (e) From your answer to part (d), is the rope accelerating upward or downward at that element and at that instant?

32-14 Starting with the expression for the speed of a harmonic wave, $v = \lambda/T$ and using the relations between λ and k and between T, ν, and ω, show that (a) $v = \lambda\nu$ and (b) $v = \omega/k$.

32-15 The speed of electromagnetic waves in vacuum (or in air) is 3.0×10^8 m/s. The wavelengths of visible electromagnetic waves extend from about 750 nm (red light) to about 400 nm (violet light). Determine the frequency range of visible light.

32-16 The frequency range of the electromagnetic waves which correspond to commercial broadcasts (radio and television) extend from about 10^4 to 10^9 Hz. The speed of electromagnetic waves in vacuum (or air) is 3.0×10^8 m/s. What is the wavelength range of commercial broadcasts?

32-17 The frequency range of audible sound is from about 20 Hz to 20 kHz. The speed of sound in air is about 330 m/s. What is the wavelength range of audible sound in air?

32-18 (a) Write an expression for a wave on a string in which the amplitude is 25 mm, the wavelength is 0.72 m, and the frequency is 4.1 Hz. The propagation direction is toward $+x$. (b) What is the speed of the wave? What is the maximum (c) speed and (d) acceleration magnitude for an element of the string? What is the maximum (e) slope and (f) $\partial^2 y/\partial x^2$ at each element of the string?

32-19 (a) Write an expression for a wave on a string in which the amplitude is 17 mm, the wave number is 5.3 rad/m, and the angular frequency is 19 rad/s. The propagation direction is toward $-x$. (b) What is the speed of the wave? What is the maximum (c) speed and (d) acceleration magnitude at each element of the string? What is the maximum (e) slope and (f) $\partial^2 y/\partial x^2$ at each element of the string?

32-20 Show that the dimensions are the same for each side of the wave equation

$$\frac{\partial^2 y}{\partial x^2} = \frac{1}{v^2} \frac{\partial^2 y}{\partial t^2}$$

32-21 The harmonic wave on a string shown in Fig. 32-28 has an amplitude of 25 mm, a speed of 46 m/s, an angular frequency of 160 rad/s and propagates toward $+x$. Determine (a) the velocity components and (b) the acceleration components of the lettered elements. Determine (c) the slope of the string and

(d) $\partial^2 y/\partial x^2$ at the lettered elements.

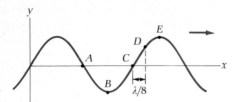

Figure 32-28. Exercise 32-21.

Section 32-5. The wave equation from Newton's second law

32-22 Show that the SI unit of $\sqrt{F/\mu}$ is m/s.

32-23 A 5.5-m length of string has a mass of 0.34 kg. If the tension in the string is 77 N, what is the speed of a wave on the string?

32-24 The speed of a wave on a rope is 21 m/s when the tension in the rope is 92 N. What is the mass per unit length of the rope?

32-25 Suppose that $y_1(x, t)$ and $y_2(x, t)$ are solutions to the wave equation, $\partial^2 y/\partial x^2 = (1/v^2)(\partial^2 y/\partial t^2)$. Show that $y(x, t) = y_1(x, t) + y_2(x, t)$ is a solution to the wave equation. Thus solutions to the wave equation obey the principle of superposition.

32-26 The speed of a sound wave in a solid is given by $v = \sqrt{Y/\rho}$, where Y is Young's modulus (Chap. 15), and ρ is the mass density. Show that the SI unit of Y is N/m².

32-27 When the tension in a guitar string is 25 N, the speed of a wave on the string is 15 m/s. What tension would make the wave speed 30 m/s?

Section 32-6. Power of a wave

32-28 A string with a mass per unit length of 0.15 kg/m is under a tension of 59 N. What is the average power of a wave of amplitude 42 mm and angular frequency of 130 rad/s that is propagated along the string?

32-29 The harmonic wave on a string shown in Fig. 32-28 has an amplitude of 25 mm, a speed of 46 m/s, and an angular frequency of 160 rad/s and propagates in the $+x$ direction. What is the power of the wave at each of the lettered elements? Let $\mu = 0.029$ kg/m.

32-30 (a) Explain why the power of a wave traveling in the $-x$ direction is

$$P = -\left[\frac{1}{2}\mu\left(\frac{\partial y}{\partial t}\right)^2 + \frac{1}{2}F\left(\frac{\partial y}{\partial x}\right)^2\right]v$$

(b) Show that the power of a harmonic wave traveling in the $-x$ direction is

$$P = -\mu\omega^2 A^2 v \cos^2(kx + \omega t)$$

(c) Explain the physical significance of the fact that this power is negative at all times and at any point.

32-31 A harmonic wave on a string has an amplitude of 32 mm, an angular frequency of 110 rad/s, and a speed of 28 m/s and propagates in the $+x$ direction. The mass per unit length of the string is 0.12 kg/m. At a particular element, plot the power of the wave versus time over an interval of 1.5T.

32-32 (a) Show that for a harmonic wave, the kinetic energy density is equal to the potential energy density at any instant t and at any point x. (b) Use this result to show that the power of a harmonic wave $y = A \sin(kx - \omega t)$ is

$$P = \mu\omega^2 A^2 v \cos^2(kx - \omega t)$$

32-33 The intensity of the sunlight transmitted by a window of area 0.94 m² is 850 W/m². If the angle between the sun's rays and a normal to the window is 41°, what is the power to the room?

32-34 The intensity of sunlight just outside the earth's atmosphere is called the *solar constant* and has an average value of about 1.35 kW/m². What is the power incident on the earth due to sunlight?

32-35 A loudspeaker resting on the floor directs the sound upward such that the wave intensity is uniform over the surface of an imaginary hemisphere. If the power of the waves emitted from the loudspeaker is 12 W, what is the wave intensity at a distance of 1.4 m from this source?

Section 32-7. Interference of harmonic waves

32-36 Two waves with the same amplitude, wave number, angular frequency, and propagation direction are present on a rope. The phase difference between the waves is 0.65 rad, and the amplitude of each wave is 51 mm. What is the amplitude of the resultant wave?

32-37 Two waves 1 and 2 are present on a rope at the same time and are given by the expressions

$$y_1 = (14 \text{ mm}) \sin[(4.8 \text{ rad/m})x - (29 \text{ rad/s})t - 0.21 \text{ rad}]$$

$$y_2 = (14 \text{ mm}) \sin[(4.8 \text{ rad/m})x - (29 \text{ rad/s})t + 0.35 \text{ rad}]$$

(a) What is the phase difference between the waves? (b) What is the amplitude of the resultant wave $y = y_1 + y_2$. (c) Write an expression for the resultant wave.

32-38 A wave on a string is given by the expression

$$y_1 = (22 \text{ mm}) \sin[(3.4 \text{ rad/m})x + (36 \text{ rad/s})t + 0.16 \text{ rad}]$$

(a) Write an expression for a wave y_2 with the same amplitude as y_1 that constructively interferes with y_1. (b) Write an expression for a wave y_2 that destructively interferes with y_1.

32-39 Two waves 1 and 2 have the same amplitude ($A_1 = A_2 = 46$ mm), angular frequency, and propagation direction, but they are out of phase with each other. Waves 1 and 2 are both present on a string, and the amplitude of the resultant wave is 31 mm. What is the phase difference between waves 1 and 2?

32-40 Two waves 1 and 2 are present on a string:

$$y_1 = (35 \text{ mm}) \sin [(8.4 \text{ rad/m})x - (15.7 \text{ rad/s})t]$$

$$y_2 = (35 \text{ mm}) \sin [(8.4 \text{ rad/m})x + (15.7 \text{ rad/s})t]$$

(a) Write the expression for the resultant wave $y = y_1 + y_2$ in the form of a wave function for a standing wave. (b) Give the x coordinates of the first two antinodes, starting at the origin and progressing toward $+x$. (c) What is the x coordinate of the node that is between the antinodes of part (b)? What is the distance between the antinodes of part (b)?

32-41 The ends of a string are fixed such that the string is held taut with a tension of 122 N. The string is 2.4 m long and has a mass of 0.19 kg. What is the frequency of a standing wave with three antinodes?

32-42 On the same graph, plot the standing wave of Exercise 32-40 from $x = 0.00$ to 1.50 m at three different times: $t = 0.00$ s, $t = 0.10$ s, and $t = 0.20$ s.

32-43 A length L of string with mass per unit length μ is held taut with a tension F. Show that the frequency ν_n of a standing wave with n antinodes on the string is given by

$$\nu_n = \frac{n}{2L} \sqrt{\frac{F}{\mu}}$$

32-44 A standing wave with two antinodes exists on a 1.6-m-long string that is held fixed at each end. The string vibrates at a frequency of 7.2 Hz. (a) Write an expression for the wave function of this standing wave. (b) At what point on the string is the origin of the coordinates y and x? (c) Does $t = 0$ in your expression correspond to the string being straight, or to each element being at its maximum displacement magnitude, or to some other configuration?

32-45 A particular guitar string is in tune when the $n = 1$ standing wave has a frequency of 247 Hz. If the string has a mass per unit length of 1.3 g/m and the distance between its fixed ends is 0.58 m, what should the tension be?

32-46 The fundamental frequency for a standing wave on the rope in Fig. 32-29 is 16 Hz, and the linear mass density of the rope is 0.18 kg/m. What is the mass of the suspended block?

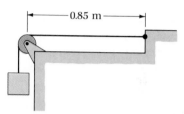

Figure 32-29. Exercise 32-46.

32-47 A beam of light with wavelength $\lambda = 630$ nm is normally incident on a mirror. The reflected light interferes with the incident light to form a standing wave that has a node at the mirror surface. (a) How far from the mirror is the nearest antinode. (b) How many nodes are within 1.0 mm of the mirror?

PROBLEMS

32-1 A pulse on a rope travels with a speed of 18 m/s in the $+x$ direction. The following data were taken from a photograph of the pulse at the time $t = 0$:

x, m	-2.0	-1.0	0.0	1.0	2.0	3.0	4.0
y, mm	2.0		7.8	10.0	8.2	4.1	2.0	1.0

There was no measurable displacement of the string for $x < -3.0$ m or $x > 5.0$ m. (a) Make a graph of y versus x by plotting the above data and sketching a smooth curve between the points. For purposes of illustration, exaggerate the scale along the y axis relative to the x axis. (b) Make a similar graph of y versus t at the coordinate $x = 0$. Compare the shapes of these two graphs.

32-2 A procedure for finding the approximate distance to a thunderstorm is to measure the time interval between when a lightning flash is seen and when the subsequent thunderclap is heard. The time interval in s divided by 3 gives the distance in km. (a) Justify this procedure and (b) estimate the percent error you might expect. Take the speed of light to be 3.0×10^8 m/s and the speed of sound to be 350 m/s. (c) Would you need to modify the procedure if the speed of sound were twice its given value? If the speed of light were twice its given value?

32-3 (a) Show that the expression for a traveling wave, $y(x, t) = f(x - vt)$, is a solution to the wave equation,

$$\frac{\partial^2 y}{\partial x^2} = \frac{1}{v^2} \frac{\partial^2 y}{\partial t^2}$$

(Hint: Let $\xi = x - vt$ and note that

$$\frac{\partial f}{\partial x} = f' \frac{\partial \xi}{\partial x} \qquad \text{and} \qquad \frac{\partial f}{\partial t} = f' \frac{\partial \xi}{\partial t}$$

where $f' = df/d\xi$.) (b) Similarly show that the expression $y(x, t) = f(x + vt)$ is a solution to the wave equation.

32-4 (a) Show that the speed of transverse waves on a stretched spring is $v = \sqrt{kL(L - \ell)/M}$, where k is the spring constant, ℓ is the unstretched length of the spring, L is the stretched length of the spring, and M is the spring's mass. (b) For the case where $L \gg \ell$, show that the time Δt required for a wave to travel from one end of the spring to the other is $\Delta t \approx \sqrt{M/k}$. The interesting feature of this result is that Δt is independent of the length L of the spring. The more the spring is stretched, the faster the wave travels, so the travel time remains nearly the same.

32-5   A rope of length L and mass M hangs freely from the ceiling. Show that the time Δt required for a transverse wave to travel the length of the rope is $\Delta t = 2\sqrt{L/g}$. (*Hint:* The wave speed varies with coordinate x measured from the rope's free end because the tension in the rope at a point is due to the weight of the rope below that point.)

32-6   Consider a wave pulse described by $y(x, t) = y_0 e^{-[(x-vt)/x_0]^2}$. Show explicitly that this wave function is a solution to the wave equation.

32-7   ***Potential energy density.*** Because a wave distorts the medium in which it travels, potential energy is associated with the wave. In Fig. 32-30, we show an element of a string that is stretched from its original length of Δx to a new length $\sqrt{(\Delta x)^2 + (\Delta y)^2}$ by a wave. The distance $\Delta \ell$ that the element is stretched by the wave is $\Delta \ell = \sqrt{(\Delta x)^2 + (\Delta y)^2} - \Delta x$. (a) Assuming that the element is small, show that

$$\Delta \ell = \left[\sqrt{1 + \left(\frac{\partial y}{\partial x}\right)^2} - 1 \right] \Delta x$$

(b) Use the binomial expansion (App. M) and the assumption that $(\partial y/\partial x)^2 \ll 1$ to show that

$$\Delta \ell = \frac{1}{2} \left(\frac{\partial y}{\partial x}\right)^2 \Delta x$$

(c) The potential energy ΔU of the element due to the wave is the work done by the tension F in stretching the element: $\Delta U = F \Delta \ell$. Show that the potential energy per unit length $\Delta U/\Delta x$ of the wave is

$$\frac{\Delta U}{\Delta x} = \frac{1}{2} F \left(\frac{\partial y}{\partial x}\right)^2$$

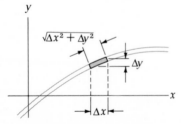

Figure 32-30. Prob. 32-7.

32-8   The wave function for an arbitrarily shaped wave traveling in the $+x$ direction is $y = f(x - vt)$. Show that such a wave's kinetic energy density is equal to

its potential energy density, so that

$$\frac{\Delta E}{\Delta x} = 2 \frac{\Delta K}{\Delta x} = 2 \frac{\Delta U}{\Delta x} = \mu \left(\frac{\partial y}{\partial t}\right)^2 = F \left(\frac{\partial y}{\partial x}\right)^2$$

(*Hint:* See Prob. 32-3.)

32-9   ***Energy of a standing wave.*** Consider a standing wave with n antinodes on a string of length L:

$$y = 2A \cos(\omega t) \sin(kx)$$

where $k = \pi n/L$. Show that the wave's average energy $\bar{E}$ (averaged over a whole number of cycles) is

$$\bar{E} = \frac{\pi^2 F A^2}{L} n^2$$

Thus, for standing waves of a given amplitude, the energy of the wave increases with the square of the number of antinodes. This result is analogous to an important problem in quantum mechanics called the "particle-in-a-box."

32-10   Strings a and b are tied together at one end of each string and then held taut such that they compose two media for waves. Waves can then encounter the boundary where the strings are joined. Three harmonic waves exist on the strings: an incident wave (wave 1), a reflected wave (wave 2), and a transmitted wave (wave 3). Let the boundary be at $x = 0$ and assume that these waves can be written

$$y_1 = A_1 \sin(k_a x - \omega t)$$
$$y_2 = A_2 \sin(k_a x + \omega t)$$
$$y_3 = A_3 \sin(k_b x - \omega t)$$

Note that since the frequency of a wave depends on the wave source, each wave has the same angular frequency ω. However, the wave number is different for waves on different strings (k_a for string a and k_b for string b) because the wave speed is different. We have chosen the $+x$ direction as the direction of travel for the incident wave, which means that the reflected wave travels in the $-x$ direction and the transmitted wave in the $+x$ direction. Show that the amplitudes of the reflected and transmitted waves are

$$A_2 = \frac{k_b - k_a}{k_b + k_a} A_1 \qquad A_3 = \frac{2k_a}{k_b + k_a} A_1$$

(*Hint:* Since the strings are smoothly joined at $x = 0$, we must have $y_1 + y_2 = y_3$ at $x = 0$ and $\partial y_1/\partial x + \partial y_2/\partial x = \partial y_3/\partial x$ at $x = 0$. That is, the strings and the slope of the strings are continuous at the point where they are joined.)

32-11   (a) Show that the power of the wave pulse $y(x, t) = y_0 e^{-[(x-vt)/x_0]^2}$ is

$$P = 4\mu v^3 \left(\frac{y_0}{x_0}\right)^2 \left(\frac{x - vt}{x_0}\right)^2 e^{-2[(x-vt)/x_0]^2}$$

(b) What is the value of the power at the point of maximum displacement due to the pulse?

32-12 Two harmonic waves

$$y_1 = A \sin (kx - \omega t + \phi_1)$$

and

$$y_2 = A \sin (kx + \omega t + \phi_2)$$

combine to form a standing wave. Show that, if we adjust the coordinate origin and beginning time, the standing wave can be written

$$y = 2A \cos (\omega t') \sin (kx')$$

Determine the values of x' and t'.

CHAPTER 33
SOUND

33-1 INTRODUCTION

Mechanical waves with frequencies between about 20 Hz and 20 kHz are particularly important to us because these *sound waves* cause the sensation of hearing in our ears. Most of the sound that we hear is transmitted through air, but sound may also travel in liquids and solids. The wall of your room transmits the sound of your neighbor's radio, for example. Similar waves at higher frequencies, called *ultrasound,* have other uses — in medical diagnosis, for instance, and in detecting flaws in metal castings. For bats, dolphins, and submarines, these high-frequency waves are their means of finding their way about in the dark.

33-2 SOUND WAVES

A sound wave can be produced in a fluid, such as water or air, with the arrangement shown in Fig. 33-1. A long tube with a uniform cross section contains a fluid. If the piston remains at rest, as shown in Fig. 33-1a, the fluid is in equilibrium and has uniform density and pressure. The other end of the tube is assumed to be far away.

Suppose that the piston at one end of the tube moves back and forth, say in simple harmonic motion as sin (ωt). As the piston moves to the right, the layer of fluid next to it will also move in that direction. This element, or layer, of fluid exerts a force on the neighboring element of fluid, and a moving region of *compression* forms. In this region the density and pressure of the fluid are higher than the equilibrium values. The region of compression will continue to travel down the tube, even after the piston begins moving back to the left. During this return motion of the piston, a region of *rarefaction* of the fluid forms, where the density and pressure are lower than for equilibrium. This region of rarefaction will likewise move down the tube, sandwiched between

A sound wave has compressions and rarefactions.

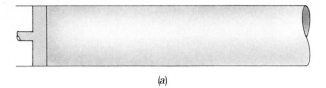

(a)

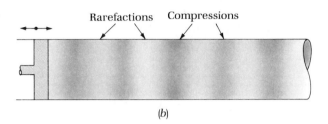

Rarefactions   Compressions

(b)

Figure 33-1. (a) No wave exists in the fluid. (b) The piston moves back and forth, causing regions of compression and of rarefaction to move along the tube.

one compression and the next compression formed as the piston moves again to the right. Thus a pattern of compressions and rarefactions of the fluid moves along the tube, and this is a traveling sound wave.

Although compressions and rarefactions move long distances along the tube, the fluid itself does not move very far. As the wave propagates along the tube, an element of the fluid moves back and forth along the tube. This motion is illustrated in Fig. 33-2, which shows velocities for elements of the fluid at an instant in a region containing two rarefactions and two compressions. Notice that the motion of the elements repeats for this wave, and the distance between consecutive compressions (or between consecutive rarefactions) is a wavelength λ. Figure 33-2 also indicates that the sound wave in a fluid is a longitudinal wave. The motion of the fluid is back and forth along the direction of propagation of the wave.

The sound wave in a fluid is longitudinal.

Consider an element of the fluid that is at x if no wave exists in the fluid. When a wave is propagating in the x direction, this element is displaced in the x direction by $\psi(x, t)$ at time t. (We use ψ instead of y to represent the longitudinal x component of the displacement of an element of the fluid.) A positive value of ψ corresponds to a displacement in the positive x direction.

A harmonic sound wave propagating in the positive x direction is described by

$$\psi(x, t) = A \cos (kx - \omega t) \tag{33-1}$$

where the amplitude A represents the maximum magnitude of the displacement, $k = 2\pi/\lambda$ is the wave number, and ω is the angular frequency. If v is the wave speed, then $\omega = kv$ (from Sec. 32-4).

If a sound wave exists in a fluid, the pressure of the fluid also varies. Let $p(x, t)$ represent the pressure of the fluid at position x at time t. If p_e is the equilibrium

Figure 33-2. The arrows represent velocities of elements of the fluid. Regions of compression C and rarefaction R are indicated.

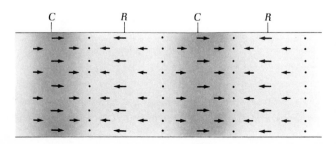

pressure when no wave exists, then $\Delta p(x, t) = p(x, t) - p_e$ is the pressure change due to the wave. For a harmonic wave, the pressure change Δp also varies sinusoidally:

$$\Delta p(x, t) = \Delta p_{max} \sin (kx - \omega t) \tag{33-2}$$

where Δp_{max} is the maximum pressure change and occurs at a compression. At a rarefaction, $\Delta p = -\Delta p_{max}$; that is, $p(x, t)$ is less than the equilibrium value p_e. We now have two descriptions of a (harmonic) sound wave in a fluid, Eq. (33-1) for the longitudinal displacement and Eq. (33-2) for the pressure change. The connection between these descriptions is developed in Sec. 33-8.

Speed and intensity of sound waves. We saw in Chap. 32 that the speed of a wave on a string (or a rope), $v = \sqrt{F_s/\mu}$, depends on the square root of the string tension divided by the mass per unit length. There is a similar expression for the speed of a sound wave in a fluid. The forcelike factor is related to the response of a fluid to a pressure change: If the pressure increases, the volume decreases. For a given fluid, this response is expressed by the bulk modulus B. As defined in Chap. 15, the adiabatic bulk modulus is $B_s = -V(dp/dV)$, where dV is the small volume change that accompanies a small pressure change dp and V is the original volume. The adiabatic bulk modulus is used because, for a typical sound wave, the pressure changes (and temperature changes) in the fluid occur so rapidly that heat flow between neighboring elements of the fluid is negligible. See Sec. 17-6 for a discussion of an adiabatic process.

The adiabatic bulk modulus has the dimension of pressure, force per unit area. If we divide B_s by the equilibrium density ρ (the inertialike term) of the fluid, the ratio B_s/ρ has the dimension of speed squared. Thus the square root has the dimension of speed, and this dimensional analysis suggests that the wave speed v is proportional to $\sqrt{B_s/\rho}$. This result is confirmed in Sec. 33-8 where Newton's laws are applied to the fluid. The speed of sound in a fluid is given by

$$v = \sqrt{\frac{B_s}{\rho}} \tag{33-3}$$

For sound waves in many gases, including air, the gas may be treated as an ideal gas, and we can determine the adiabatic bulk modulus. (See Prob. 33-3 for Newton's calculation of the speed of sound in air.) If an ideal gas undergoes an adiabatic process, the pressure and volume changes occur such that

$$pV^\gamma = \text{constant}$$

where $\gamma = C_p/C_V$ is the ratio of specific heats. Since the derivative of $pV^\gamma = $ constant is zero, we have

$$\frac{d}{dV} pV^\gamma = p\gamma V^{\gamma-1} + V^\gamma \frac{dp}{dV} = 0$$

Rearranging and solving for $-V(dp/dV)$, we obtain

$$B_s = -V \frac{dp}{dV} = \gamma p$$

The density of the ideal gas can be expressed as $\rho = m/V = nM/V$, where V is the volume occupied by n mol and M is the mass of 1 mol, the molecular weight. Then

$$\frac{B_s}{\rho} = \frac{\gamma p}{nM/V} = \frac{\gamma p V}{nM}$$

Since $pV = nRT$ for an ideal gas [Eq. (17-1)], this becomes

$$\frac{B_s}{\rho} = \frac{\gamma RT}{M}$$

Speed of sound in an ideal gas

Taking the square root, as in Eq. (33-3), gives the speed of sound in an ideal gas:

$$v = \sqrt{\frac{\gamma RT}{M}} \qquad (33\text{-}4)$$

Notice that the speed depends only on the absolute temperature T and the molar mass (or molecular weight) M. For air, which is about 80 percent N_2 and 20 percent O_2, the molecular weight is about 29 g/mol = 0.029 kg/mol and $\gamma = 1.4$. The speed of sound in air at $T = 273$ K (0°C) is $v = 330$ m/s. (See Exercise 33-3.)

Just as for the other types of waves that we have considered, the energy carried by a sound wave is proportional to the square of the wave amplitude. For sound waves, it is often convenient to use the intensity I, the energy per unit area per unit time, to describe the propagation of energy. For the harmonic wave described by Eq. (33-1), the average intensity $\bar{I}$ (averaged over a cycle of the wave) is given by

$$\bar{I} = \tfrac{1}{2} B_s \omega k A^2 \qquad (33\text{-}5)$$

Average intensity of a harmonic sound wave

Alternatively, if the wave is described by the pressure change Δp in Eq. (33-2), the intensity is proportional to the square of the pressure amplitude Δp_{max}:

$$\bar{I} = \frac{(\Delta p_{\text{max}})^2}{2 v \rho} \qquad (33\text{-}6)$$

where ρ is the equilibrium density of the fluid. The two expressions above are obtained in Sec. 33-8.

Sound waves also exist in solids as well as in fluids. The displacement of an element of a solid can have a component perpendicular to, as well as along, the direction of propagation. Thus both longitudinal and transverse sound waves occur in solids. In the simple case of a longitudinal wave propagating along a thin elastic rod, the speed of sound is given by (Prob. 33-1)

Speed of a longitudinal sound wave in a thin rod

$$v = \sqrt{\frac{Y}{\rho}} \qquad (33\text{-}7)$$

where ρ is the density and Y is the Young's modulus for the substance. (See Tables 15-1 and 15-2.)

EXAMPLE 33-1. A sound wave travels in He. The equilibrium pressure of the gas is $p_e = 1.2 \times 10^5$ Pa and its temperature is 310 K. (a) Determine the speed of sound. (b) The wave is harmonic with a pressure amplitude $\Delta p_{\text{max}} = 0.75$ Pa; determine the average intensity.

SOLUTION. (a) The molecular weight of He is $M = 0.0040$ kg/mol and, from Table 18-1, $\gamma = C_p/C_V = 1.63$ for

this monatomic ideal gas. From Eq. (33-4), the speed of sound is

$$v = \sqrt{\frac{1.63(8.31 \text{ J} \cdot \text{mol}^{-1} \cdot \text{K}^{-1})(310 \text{ K})}{0.0040 \text{ kg/mol}}}$$

$$= 1.0 \text{ km/s}$$

(b) The density of the gas can be determined from the ideal

gas equation of state:

$$\rho = \frac{nM}{V} = \frac{p_e}{RT} M$$

$$= \frac{(1.2 \times 10^5 \text{ Pa})(0.0040 \text{ kg/mol})}{(8.31 \text{ J} \cdot \text{mol}^{-1} \cdot \text{K}^{-1})(310 \text{ K})}$$

$$= 0.19 \text{ kg/m}^3$$

The average intensity is given by Eq. (33-6):

$$\bar{I} = \frac{(0.75 \text{ Pa})^2}{2(1.0 \times 10^3 \text{ m/s})(0.19 \text{ kg/m}^3)} = 1.5 \times 10^{-3} \text{ W/m}^2$$

Suppose the temperature were doubled to 620 K, but the equilibrium pressure and the pressure amplitude remained the same. How would the above answers change?

33-3 HEARING

When a sound wave arrives at a human ear, the ear converts the pressure changes due to the sound wave into nerve impulses that are processed and interpreted by the brain as something heard. Although this process is complex and not completely understood, we shall discuss several important features of hearing.

Musicians describe what they hear by terms such as pitch, loudness, and quality. There are correlations between this subjective description of a sound and the physical description of the same sound wave, but the correlations are complex. Pitch has to do with the frequency of the sound wave, loudness with its intensity, and quality with the waveform.

Frequency and pitch. Figure 33-3 gives a schematic picture of the human ear. The outer ear collects the wave and transmits it to the middle ear through the eardrum. The bones in the middle ear control the amplitude of the vibrations transmitted to the inner ear. Nerves in the cochlea of the inner ear respond to the sound wave, and there is a correlation between the position of the nerve cells along the basilar membrane, which extends along the coiled length of the cochlea, and the frequency of the sound to which the nerves respond. Frequencies near 20 kHz are detected near the base, and lower frequencies are detected further along the basilar membrane. For about every 3.5 mm along the basilar membrane the frequency to which the nerves respond is reduced by half. Since the basilar membrane is about 35 mm long, the average healthy young person can hear frequencies which differ by a factor of 2^{10}, or about 1000—a range from 20 Hz to 20 kHz.

For a harmonic sound wave, the higher the frequency, the higher the perceived pitch. Perhaps because of the spacing of sensitive regions of the basilar membrane, two frequencies which differ by a factor of 2 are particularly

Figure 33-3. The basic parts of the human ear are shown. The basilar membrane (not shown) extends along the coiled length of the cochlea and responds strongly to different frequencies at different positions.

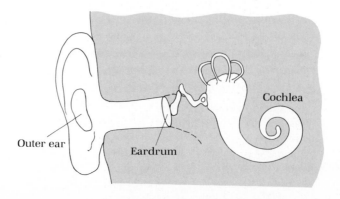

Outer ear   Eardrum   Cochlea

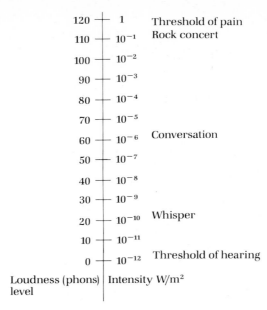

Loudness (phons) level	Intensity W/m²	
120	1	Threshold of pain
110	10^{-1}	Rock concert
100	10^{-2}	
90	10^{-3}	
80	10^{-4}	
70	10^{-5}	
60	10^{-6}	Conversation
50	10^{-7}	
40	10^{-8}	
30	10^{-9}	
20	10^{-10}	Whisper
10	10^{-11}	
0	10^{-12}	Threshold of hearing

Figure 33-4. Equal steps in perceived loudness level at 1 kHz correspond to equal ratios of the sound intensity.

pleasing when sounded together and are said to differ by an octave. Subjective judgments of equal steps in pitch level correspond roughly to equal multiples in the frequency of harmonic waves. Because of this, succeeding notes in music are not equally spaced in frequency. Rather, the succeeding notes are equal multiples of each other. For historical reasons, the octave is divided into 12 "half-steps." (Two adjacent keys on a piano, say a black and a white, produce notes that are a half-step apart.) In the equal-tempered scale used on most modern instruments, the ratio of the frequency of two notes a half-step apart is $2^{1/12}$ since there are 12 half-steps in an octave.

Intensity and loudness. The correlation between the perceived loudness and the physical intensity of a harmonic sound wave is also such that equal steps (in loudness) correspond roughly to equal multiples (in intensity). This is shown in Fig. 33-4 for a harmonic wave of 1-kHz frequency. The subjective loudness level at a given frequency is expressed in *phons,* and is the average of the perceptions of many listeners. The threshold of hearing is the lowest intensity that can be heard at a given frequency. At the threshold of hearing, the subjective loudness level is taken to be 0 phons. For a 1-kHz harmonic wave, the threshold of hearing corresponds to an intensity of about 10^{-12} W/m². This marks the ear as a very sensitive receiver, able to respond to a power input of about 10^{-16} W. The ear has a large range of intensities to which it is sensitive at 1 kHz, a factor of 10^{12} in intensity.

Logarithms have two properties that are useful in describing sound: (i) numbers that cover a large range have logarithms that cover a smaller range and (ii) numbers that have the same ratio have logarithms that differ by equal steps. Human hearing covers a large range of intensities, and we judge sounds which have equal ratios of intensity to have nearly equal steps in loudness. Thus sound intensity is conveniently measured by the *sound-intensity level β* defined by

Threshold of hearing

Sound-intensity level β and the decibel

$$\beta = 10 \log_{10} \frac{I}{I_0} \tag{33-8}$$

where $I_0 = 10^{-12}$ W/m². The reference level I_0 is set so that the sound-intensity level β is zero when the intensity I equals 10^{-12} W/m², the threshold of hearing at 1 kHz. Although β is dimensionless, it is given units of decibels (dB), the name stemming from Alexander Graham Bell (1847–1922).

The sound-intensity level β is defined so that change in intensity I by a factor of 10^n corresponds to a change in β of $10 \cdot n$. For example, if $I/I_0 = 10^7$, then $\beta = 10 \log_{10}(10^7) = 10 \cdot 7 = 70$ dB. Although $n = 7$ is an integer in this case,

Figure 33-5. Each curve shows the intensities at various frequencies that are perceived to have the same loudness level by the average listener.

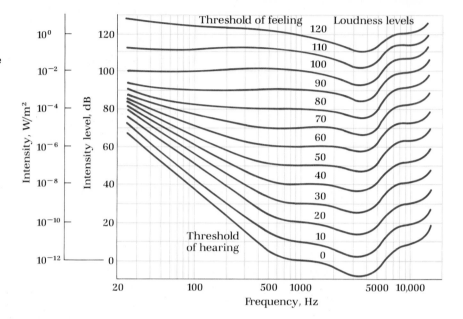

Figure 33-6. (a) Waveforms are shown for a flute and a bassoon playing the same note. Each waveform has a period that corresponds to a fundamental frequency of 440 Hz. (b) The amplitudes of the first few harmonics are shown for each waveform. (*Adapted from Robert M. Eisberg and Lawrence S. Lerner*, Physics, Foundations and Applications, *McGraw-Hill, New York, 1981.*)

Flute

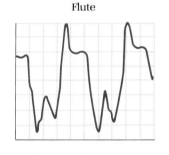

Bassoon

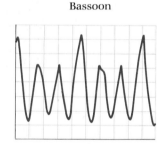

(a)

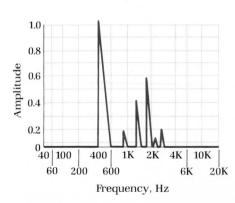

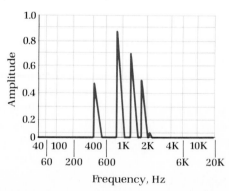

(b)

noninteger factors are also valid. Thus, if $I/I_0 = 2.0 \times 10^7$, then $\beta = 10 \log_{10}(2.0 \times 10^7) = 73$ dB.

The ear is not equally sensitive to all frequencies. Figure 33-5 shows an average listener's subjective judgments of the loudness level of harmonic waves of differing frequency. Each curve represents sounds of differing frequencies that are perceived to have the same loudness level in phons. The loudness level in phons at 1 kHz is set equal to the sound-intensity level in dB. The relation between loudness level and sound-intensity level at other frequencies is not simple.

EXAMPLE 33-2. For the safety and comfort of the workers, the sound-intensity level in a certain factory must remain below 85 dB. What is the maximum sound intensity allowed in this factory?

SOLUTION. Since $\beta = 10 \log_{10}(I/I_0) = 85$,

$$\frac{I}{I_0} = 10^{8.5} = 3.2 \times 10^8$$

(Use the *inverse* $\log_{10}$, or the 10^x, operation on your calculator.) Thus

$$I = (3.2 \times 10^8)(10^{-12} \text{ W/m}^2) = 3.2 \times 10^{-4} \text{ W/m}^2$$

Waveform and quality. The perceived property of sound called *quality* has to do with the waveform, rather than with the frequency or amplitude. The physical description of the form of a wave that is not a harmonic wave is the subject of the next section, where the concept of quality will also be discussed.

33-4 FOURIER ANALYSIS OF PERIODIC WAVES

Although harmonic (sinusoidal) waves are common, most sounds of interest have periodic structures which are more complicated. Figure 33-6 shows the time dependence of the waveforms of two sounds which have the same period. These sounds have waveforms that are anharmonic (periodic but not sinusoidal). Both sounds are perceived subjectively to have the same pitch, but different quality. It appears that the pitch of these sounds has to do with the period of the waveform, which is the same for both sounds, and the quality has to do with the details of the waveform, which is different for each of these sounds.

Jean Baptiste Joseph Fourier (1768–1830) showed that complex periodic waveforms can be regarded as a sum of harmonic waves. Let $y(t)$ represent the periodic displacement of a wave at a certain position. If $y(t)$ and its derivative are continuous, then it can be shown that $y(t)$ can be represented by a sum of the form,

$$y(t) \approx \sum_{n=1}^{N} A_n \sin(n\omega t + \phi_n) \tag{33-9}$$

where $\omega = 2\pi/T$ and T is the period of the waveform. How large N must be to obtain a good representation depends on the waveform. The representations of some waveforms are shown in Fig. 33-7. As illustrated there, the use of just a few terms gives a reasonable facsimile of the desired waveform.

Fourier analysis of a waveform

The process of determining mathematically the coefficients A_n and phase constants ϕ_n for a given waveform is called *Fourier analysis* and is covered in more advanced texts. It is also possible to find the A_n's and ϕ_n's electronically. The waveforms of a flute and of a bassoon, both sounding the same pitch, are

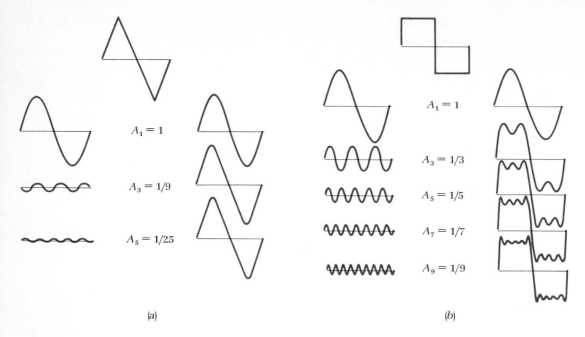

(a)

(b)

Figure 33-7. One cycle of a waveform is shown at the top of each diagram. Each sinusoidal wave that is added is shown on the left. On the right is the cumulative sum of the terms. (*Adapted from Richard E. Berg and David G. Stork,* The Physics of Sound, *© 1982, pp. 92, 93. Prentice Hall, Inc., Englewood Cliffs, NJ.*)

shown in Fig. 33-6a. The measured amplitudes A_n for the first few terms in the Fourier analysis of each waveform are indicated in Fig. 33-6b. In the analysis, the lowest frequency present is called the *fundamental frequency* and the multiples of this frequency are called *higher harmonics,* or *overtones.* The difference in the quality of the sounds produced by a bassoon and a flute playing the same note is due to the differences in the overtones.

Just as a periodic waveform may be analyzed in terms of a Fourier series to give the relative amounts of the fundamental frequency and the higher harmonics present in the waveform, new periodic waveforms can be formed electronically by adding to a fundamental various amounts of its higher harmonics. This process is called *Fourier synthesis.* Some modern music is performed on a synthesizer rather than on a musical instrument that makes its sounds mechanically.

33-5 SOURCES OF SOUND

Musical instruments are common sources of sound waves in air. A tuning fork is a particularly simple "musical instrument." When a tuning fork is struck, it will vibrate in very nearly simple harmonic motion and generate a harmonic sound wave in the surrounding air. The intensity of the sound wave in the air will depend on how much air the tuning fork is able to move — that is, on how well the tuning fork couples to the air.

A vibrating tuning fork is usually difficult to hear from a distance of a few meters or more. The area of the vibrating tines of the fork is small. Thus the tuning fork does not move much air, and the fork cannot deliver much power to the air. However, if the fork is held with its base in contact with a tabletop, it can be heard many meters away. The whole tabletop will vibrate with the tuning fork, so that much more air is moved and a sound wave with a larger intensity is generated.

If the tuning fork is put in a holder on top of a hollow wooden box of a

A sounding box enhances the
coupling of a vibration and a
sound wave.

suitable size, with one end of the box open, the coupling to the air that results is
even better, and the sound can be heard at the back of a large lecture room. The
hollow box is called a *sounding box*. The tuning fork is able to put much more
power into the sound wave if its frequency of vibration is the same as the
frequency of a standing wave of sound in the sounding box. This enhanced
matching or coupling of a vibrating body with a sound wave is an example of
resonance that was discussed in Sec. 14-8.

Many musical instruments use such standing waves in a container of some
sort to generate sound waves of sufficient intensity. The standing wave in the
column of air in such a container is similar to the standing wave on a stretched
string discussed in the previous chapter.

Consider a standing wave in a column of air in a container such as a tube or a
pipe that is closed at both ends. Since the ends are closed, the displacement of
the air must be zero at both ends. The standing wave has a node at each closed
end. This condition is the same as for the transverse displacement at the ends of
a string for standing waves on the string. Thus the frequencies of the standing
waves which can be set up in a closed column of length ℓ are the same as the
frequencies of standing waves on a string of length ℓ. These frequencies correspond to fitting a whole number n of half-wavelengths in the distance ℓ:
$\frac{1}{2}\lambda n = \ell$, or $\lambda_n = 2\ell/n$. Using $\nu_n = v/\lambda_n$, we have

Standing wave frequencies for a
closed-closed air column

$$\nu_n = n\,\frac{v}{2\ell} \qquad (n = 1, 2, 3, \ldots) \qquad (33\text{-}10)$$

where v is the speed of sound waves in the air. Patterns of nodes N and
antinodes A for several standing waves are shown in Fig. 33-8a for a closed-
closed column.

Some musical instruments contain a column of air open to the atmosphere at
one end and closed at the other, similar to the wooden box mentioned above
that enabled the tuning fork to be heard at the back of a lecture room. It turns

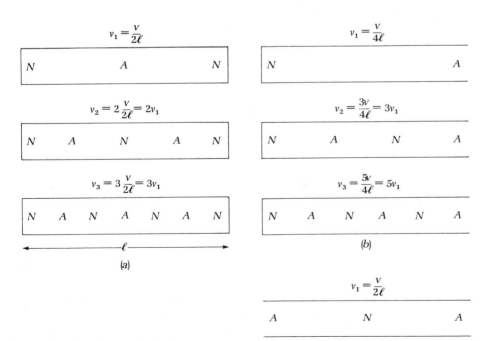

Figure 33-8. Standing wave
patterns in air columns show the
positions of displacement nodes N
and antinodes A for (a) closed-
closed, (b) closed-open, and (c)
open-open ends.

out that a standing sound wave in an open column has a node at the closed end and an antinode near the open end. Exactly where the antinode occurs depends on the details of the opening, such as whether the opening is in the side of the tube or in the end, and how the opening is shaped.

The patterns for several standing waves in a closed-open column are shown in Fig. 33-8b. In such a column, a standing wave can be regarded as being the sum of two traveling waves going in opposite directions. Each of these waves has the same wavelength, and their relative phase gives a node at the closed end and an antinode at the open end. For the lowest or fundamental frequency ν_1, the standing wave has a single node and a single antinode. This corresponds to fitting one-fourth of a wavelength in the length ℓ: $\frac{1}{4}\lambda_1 = \ell$, or $\lambda_1 = 4\ell$. Thus the frequency of this standing wave is $\nu_1 = v/\lambda_1 = v/4\ell$. The next-higher frequency occurs with an additional node and an additional antinode between the ends, as shown in the second case of Fig. 33-8b. This pattern corresponds to fitting three-fourths of a wavelength into the length ℓ. Thus the frequency is $\nu_2 = 3v/4\ell$. The general relation for the frequency of standing waves in a column open at one end and closed at the other is

Standing wave frequencies for a closed-open air column

$$\nu_{n'} = (2n' - 1)\,\frac{v}{4\ell} \qquad (n' = 1, 2, \ldots) \qquad (33\text{-}11)$$

Notice that only the odd harmonics (ν_1, $3\nu_1$, $5\nu_1$, . . .) occur for the closed-open column. Examples of musical instruments that use columns of air open at one end and closed at the other are the clarinet and the xylophone.

Open-open and closed-closed columns have the same frequencies.

As you can see from Fig. 33-8c, the standing-wave pattern in a column open at both ends is similar to that in a column closed at both ends. The positions of the nodes and antinodes are just interchanged. Thus the standing-wave frequencies for open-open columns are the same as those for closed-closed columns and are given by Eq. (33-10). Examples of musical instruments that act as if they have open-open columns are the oboe, flute, and trombone.

The quality of the sound coming from an organ pipe closed at one end is different from the quality of the sound coming from an organ pipe open at both ends, even though the pitch of the two sounds is the same. This is due to the difference in the harmonics produced when the organ pipes are sounded. In a column open at both ends, both even and odd harmonics of the fundamental are present, but only the odd harmonics are present in the sound when the pipe is "stopped" to form a closed-open column. The absence of the even harmonics is readily apparent to the listener.

The quality of the sounds made by the human voice similarly depends on the various resonant cavities (see Fig. 33-9) which are opened and closed to make the consonants and vowels of language. Figure 33-10 shows the difference between the waveforms of the vowels "e" and "o" said at the same pitch by one of the authors. It has been proposed that among the differences between early and late forms of *Homo sapiens* is the presence of more of these cavities in late forms that enable more sounds to be made and hence more information to be transmitted in a given time by speech.

A common feature of modern life is the electrical reproduction of sound. Figure 33-11 is a diagram of a simple speaker in which sound is generated with essentially the same waveform as the electric current in the coil. The field of a permanent magnet surrounds the coil so that, when a current passes through the coil, a force is exerted that moves the coil back and forth. The coil is connected to a paper cone which moves in and out, pushing the air and generating a sound wave.

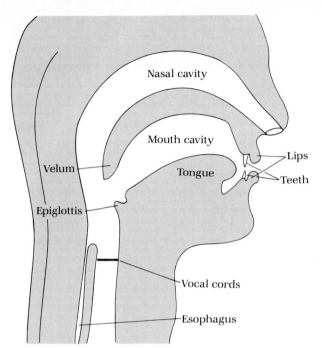

Nasal cavity

Mouth cavity

Velum   Tongue

Lips

Teeth

Epiglottis

Vocal cords

Esophagus

Figure 33-9. Some of the resonant chambers used in vocalization are shown schematically.

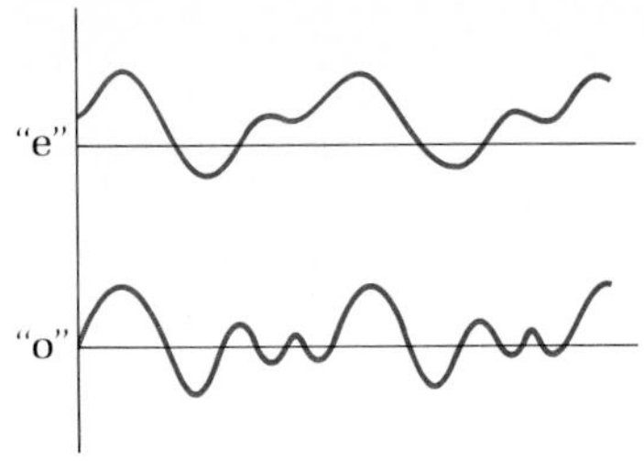

"e"

"o"

Figure 33-10. Waveforms are shown for the long vowel sounds "e" and "o" as voiced by one of the authors.

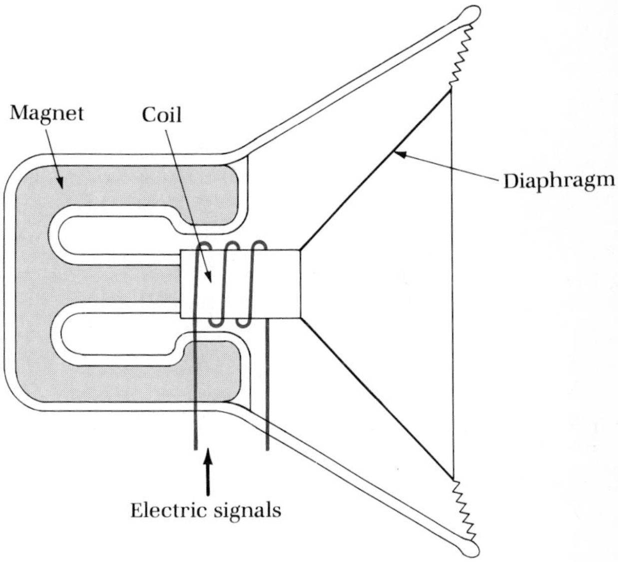

Magnet   Coil

Diaphragm

Electric signals

Figure 33-11. A simple speaker is shown schematically. Current in the voice coil causes a magnetic force that moves the paper diaphragm in and out.

33-6 INTERFERENCE OF SOUND WAVES AND BEATS

When sound waves from two sources combine at a point, their displacements add, in accord with the principle of superposition. If the two waves are harmonic waves with the same frequency, then the resultant wave at a point where they combine will depend on the phase difference between them, as discussed in Sec. 32-7. Constructive interference occurs if the waves meet in phase, crest for crest, and the resultant amplitude is a maximum. Since the intensity is proportional to the square of the amplitude, the intensity is also a maximum if the waves are in phase. If the waves are out of phase by π rad, meeting crest for trough, then the resulting amplitude and intensity are at minimum.

It is important to consider interference effects when designing an auditorium, a recording studio, or audio components such as speakers and speaker cabinets. When the cone of a speaker moves, it not only creates sound waves in front of it, but also moves the air behind it and creates a backward-moving sound wave. That wave can reflect from a wall behind the speaker and lead to interference between the waves moving forward and backward from the speaker, as shown in Fig. 33-12. For simplicity we consider the speaker to emit a harmonic wave. Suppose the listener is at a position such that the path for the backward wave is longer than the path for the forward wave by half a wavelength. Then the waves will be out of phase by π rad and will destructively

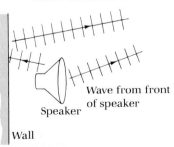

Wave reflected from wall

Wave from front of speaker

Speaker

Wall

Figure 33-12. Sound waves coming from the front and back of a speaker interfere where they combine.

interfere. If one of these waves is not suppressed, then sound of this frequency will not be heard at such a position.

To avoid such effects, speakers are put into enclosures of some kind. The enclosure is not just for decoration, but prevents the backward wave from interfering with the forward wave. Some enclosures, called *ducted-port enclosures,* have a means of reflecting the backward wave so that it will be in phase with the forward wave for the low frequencies (long wavelengths). This enables the speaker plus enclosure to reproduce low-frequency sounds more effectively, as if the speaker were larger. One such design is shown in Fig. 33-13.

Another effect of the interference of sound waves must be considered in the design of speaker arrays; it is illustrated in Fig. 33-14. The sound waves coming from an array of speakers interfere with each other. Consider the sound arriving at a point P that is not directly in front of the array. If the path difference between speaker 1 and speaker 5 is half a wavelength, the sound from these two speakers will interfere destructively because these two waves are out of phase by π rad. If the listener is far away compared with the separation of the speakers, then the waves from the pairs $2-6$, $3-7$, and $4-8$ also interfere destructively. Thus no sound of this wavelength will be heard at position P. Effects of this type concentrate the sound in the forward direction, and make such arrays useful in projecting sound to a large audience.

Beats. Suppose two harmonic waves have slightly different frequencies. At a point where they combine, the phase difference will change with time, and the interference of the waves alternates between constructive and destructive. This behavior is illustrated graphically in Fig. 33-15 for waves of the same amplitude. At times when the waves are in phase, the resultant amplitude is large. At other times, the waves are out of phase, and the resultant amplitude is small. Since the intensity is proportional to the square of the amplitude, the intensity alternates between maxima and minima (loud and soft) over a time interval that is large compared with the period of either wave. These alternations of intensity are called *beats,* and a wave of one frequency is said to *beat* against a wave of a slightly different frequency. The *beat frequency* ν_b is the reciprocal of the period of the beats, which is the time interval between successive intensity maxima.

To see how the beat frequency is related to the frequencies of the two waves, we consider the time dependence of each wave at the point in space where they combine. Let $y_1 = A \sin(\omega_1 t)$ and $y_2 = A \sin(\omega_2 t)$ represent these combining waves, where $\omega_1 = 2\pi\nu_1$ and $\omega_2 = 2\pi\nu_2$ are the angular frequencies. To

Interference effects and speaker design

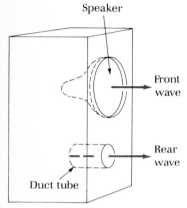

Figure 33-13. A ducted-tube speaker enclosure is built so that the rear wave interferes constructively with the front wave for low frequencies.

Beats and the beat frequency ν_b

Figure 33-14. Sound waves emitted in phase by an array of small speakers can interfere destructively at a point that is not directly in front of the array.

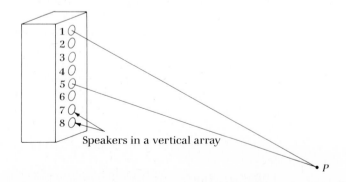

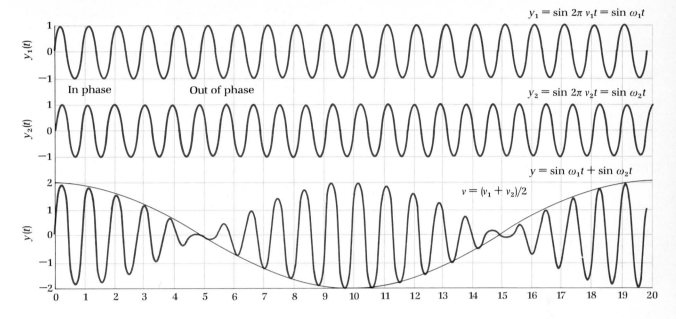

$$y_1 = \sin 2\pi \nu_1 t = \sin \omega_1 t$$

$$y_2 = \sin 2\pi \nu_2 t = \sin \omega_2 t$$

$$y = \sin \omega_1 t + \sin \omega_2 t$$

$$\nu = (\nu_1 + \nu_2)/2$$

In phase   Out of phase

Figure 33-15. The time dependence is shown for two sinusoidal waves of slightly differing frequencies, ν_1 and $\nu_2 = 1.1\nu_1$. The resultant wave, $y = y_1 + y_2$, at a point oscillates with the average frequency and is modulated at the beat frequency, $\nu_b = |\nu_2 - \nu_1|$, which determines the envelope of the resultant wave.

obtain beats, we have $\omega_1 \approx \omega_2$ and, to be definite, we take $\omega_1 < \omega_2$. The resultant wave $y = y_1 + y_2$ at the point has a time dependence,

$$y = A \left[\sin (\omega_1 t) + \sin (\omega_2 t) \right] \tag{33-12}$$

It is convenient here to introduce the average angular frequency $\overline{\omega}$ and the angular frequency difference $\Delta\omega$ given by

$$\overline{\omega} = \tfrac{1}{2}(\omega_1 + \omega_2) \qquad \Delta\omega = \omega_2 - \omega_1$$

These equations can be solved for ω_1 and ω_2 in terms of $\overline{\omega}$ and $\Delta\omega$:

$$\omega_2 = \overline{\omega} + \tfrac{1}{2}\Delta\omega \qquad \omega_1 = \overline{\omega} - \tfrac{1}{2}\Delta\omega \tag{33-13}$$

Substituting Eqs. (33-13) into Eq. (33-12), we obtain

$$y = A \left\{ \sin \left[(\overline{\omega} - \tfrac{1}{2}\Delta\omega)t \right] + \sin \left[(\overline{\omega} + \tfrac{1}{2}\Delta\omega)t \right] \right\}$$

This expression can be simplified by using the trigonometric identity, $\sin (\alpha \pm \beta) = \sin \alpha \cos \beta \pm \sin \beta \cos \alpha$. The result is

$$y = 2A \cos \left(\tfrac{1}{2}\Delta\omega\, t \right) \sin \left(\overline{\omega} t \right) \tag{33-14}$$

We interpret Eq. (33-14) as a sinusoidal term, $\sin (\overline{\omega} t)$ with frequency $\overline{\nu} = \overline{\omega}/2\pi$, the average frequency. This gives the pitch of the sound. It is multiplied or *modulated* by an overall amplitude factor, $2A \cos (\tfrac{1}{2}\Delta\omega\, t)$, which varies more slowly in time. This second factor is responsible for the envelope of the resultant wave in Fig. 33-15, which corresponds to beats. The beats that we hear are beats in intensity, and the intensity is proportional to the square of the amplitude factor, or to $[\cos (\tfrac{1}{2}\Delta\omega\, t)]^2$. The time interval Δt between successive intensity maxima corresponds to the cosine ranging from $+1$ to 0 to -1, so that the (cosine)^2 factor ranges from $+1$ to 0 back to $+1$. Thus $\tfrac{1}{2}\Delta\omega \cdot \Delta t = \pi$, or $\Delta t = 2\pi/\Delta\omega$ is the period for beats. Since the beat frequency ν_b is the reciprocal of the beat period, we have

$$\nu_b = \frac{1}{\Delta t} = \frac{\Delta\omega}{2\pi} = \frac{\omega_2 - \omega_1}{2\pi} = \nu_2 - \nu_1$$

We took $\omega_1 < \omega_2$, or $\nu_1 < \nu_2$, in obtaining $\nu_b = \nu_2 - \nu_1$. We prefer to deal with a positive beat-frequency value regardless of whether ν_1 or ν_2 is larger. Therefore we write the beat frequency for waves of frequencies ν_1 and ν_2 as the absolute value of the frequency difference

The beat frequency is the absolute difference in frequencies.

$$\nu_b = |\nu_2 - \nu_1| \tag{33-15}$$

If the two frequencies are almost equal, then the beat frequency ν_b is small and the time Δt between beats is correspondingly large. If the two frequencies are exactly equal, then the beat frequency is zero, and beats do not occur.

Beats are used in tuning stringed instruments such as pianos and guitars. If the frequency from the fundamental of a string is different from the frequency of a standard such as a tuning fork, then beats are heard when the two are sounded together. If the tension in the string is adjusted so that no beats are heard, then the string has the same fundamental frequency as the standard. In tuning an equally tempered piano, beats between higher harmonics are used. Between the notes C_4 (261.63 Hz) and G_4 (392 Hz), for example, beats between the third harmonic of C_4 ($3 \cdot 261.63$ Hz = 784.89 Hz) and the second harmonic of G_4 (784 Hz) have a beat frequency of 0.89 Hz.

Beat frequencies are also used in radios, where "heterodyning" adds the frequency of the electromagnetic signal that is received to a signal produced in the radio by a "local oscillator." The beat frequency caused by this addition is much lower than the received frequency. Since lower-frequency signals are easier to amplify, the radio is made simpler and more effective by amplifying this beat frequency than by further amplifying the received radio frequency.

EXAMPLE 33-3. Two cellos bowed on their C_2 strings at the same time give rise to beats that have a minimum of intensity every $\frac{3}{4}$ s and thus a beat frequency of $\frac{4}{3}$ Hz. (a) If one cello is known to be properly tuned (65.406 Hz), by how much is the other out of tune? (b) By what fraction will the tension in the out-of-tune cello have to be changed to bring it into tune? (c) How can you tell if the tension in the out-of-tune cello needs to be increased or decreased?

SOLUTION. (a) The difference in frequencies is the beat frequency:

$$|\nu_1 - \nu_2| = \nu_b = \tfrac{4}{3} \text{ Hz}$$

Thus the out-of-tune cello is off by $\frac{4}{3}$ Hz. (b) The fundamental frequency of standing waves on a string fixed at each end, as on a cello, is the same as that of standing waves in a closed-closed air column. We use Eq. (33-10), but with $v = \sqrt{F_s/\mu}$ from Chap. 32. Thus

$$\nu_1 = \frac{v}{2\ell} = \frac{\sqrt{F_s/\mu}}{2\ell} = C\sqrt{F_s}$$

where C is a constant for small changes in F_s. The change in the frequency can be obtained by differentiation. Thus

$$\Delta\nu = \frac{d\nu}{dF_s}\Delta F_s = \frac{\frac{1}{2}C}{\sqrt{F_s}}\Delta F_s$$

The *fractional* changes are obtained by dividing both sides by $\nu = C\sqrt{F_s}$:

$$\frac{\Delta\nu}{\nu} = \frac{\frac{1}{2}\Delta F_s}{F_s}$$

or

$$\frac{\Delta F_s}{F_s} = \frac{2\,\Delta\nu}{\nu} = \frac{2(\frac{4}{3} \text{ Hz})}{65.406 \text{ Hz}} = 0.04 = 4 \text{ percent}$$

(c) We cannot determine from the beats whether the out-of-tune cello string is above or below the frequency of the correctly tuned one. If the beat frequency increases with a small increase in tension, then the frequency was too high and the tension should be reduced to bring the string into tune. If the beat frequency decreases with a small increase in tension, then the frequency was too low and the tension should be increased.

33-7 THE DOPPLER EFFECT

If you listen to the sound of an automobile horn as it passes by, you will hear a characteristic lowering in pitch of the sound. Such a shift in frequency, called

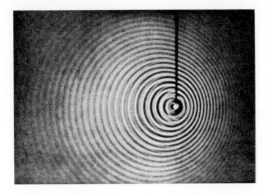

Figure 33-16. Water waves are generated by a vibrating tip moving to the right in the water. (Physics, 2nd ed., Physical Science Study Committee, 1965. Reprinted by permission of D. C. Heath and Co. and Educational Development Center.)

The Doppler effect, or Doppler shift in frequency, is due to the motion of the source and the observer.

the *Doppler effect* or *Doppler shift,* is due to a difference in the number of oscillations per second reaching your ear because of the motion of the source. The Doppler shift was first discussed by Christian Doppler (1803 – 1853) in 1842 in connection with similar shifts in the frequency of light emitted by the stars revolving about each other in double-star systems. It is interesting to note that the speeds of travel in 1842 were such that observations of this shift in the frequency of sound were not common (but see Exercise 33-37). The effect was first discussed in connection with light.

The Doppler shift occurs in other types of waves. Figure 33-16 shows the water waves produced by a vibrating tip that is moving to the right with respect to the water. The wavelength in front of the moving source is compressed, and the wavelength in back of the moving source is expanded. The speed v of the waves is the same in all directions relative to points fixed in the water. Since $\nu = v/\lambda$, the frequency of the waves reaching a point in front of the source will be greater than the frequency of waves reaching a point behind the source.

When the source of a wave and an observer are in relative motion, there is a difference between the frequency ν_s emitted by a source and the frequency ν_o received by an observer. We now determine the relation between these frequencies. For simplicity, we consider the case when the directions of the velocities of the observer and source lie along the line joining them, as seen in Fig. 33-17a. We work in an inertial reference frame in which the medium is at

Figure 33-17. (a) Successive crests are emitted by the source as it moves a distance $v_s T_s$ toward an observer O. The wavelength in the forward direction is $\lambda = (v - v_s)T_s$. (b) A wave crest moves a distance vT_O from A to A' as the observer moves to the right a distance $v_O T_O$.

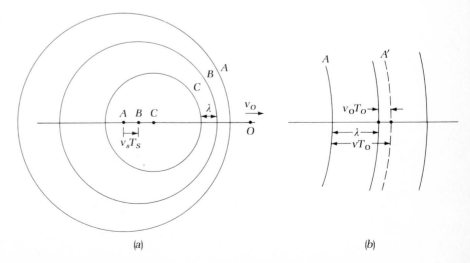

(a)

(b)

rest, and the speed of the wave in this medium is v. In Fig. 33-17 we take the positive x direction to be from the source to the observer.

First we find the wavelength λ in the medium for the portion of the wave that will be received by the observer. Since the source emits a wave crest every period T_s of the source vibration, each wave crest moves a distance vT_s along the x axis before the source emits another wave crest. But the source is also moving through the medium, along the positive x axis, with speed v_s, so that the next wave crest is emitted a distance $vT_s - v_sT_s$ behind the one in front of it. Thus the wavelength λ of the wave in the medium is the distance moved by the wave in one period of the source vT_s minus the distance moved by the source in one period v_sT_s:

$$\lambda = vT_s - v_sT_s \tag{33-16}$$

Now we take the motion of the observer into account. Suppose the observer moves in the positive x direction (away from the source) with speed v_o, as seen in Fig. 33-17b. Then the time T_o for two successive wave crests to reach the observer is greater, because the observer is "running away" from the waves. In a time interval T_o, the observer moves a distance v_oT_o. In order for the wave crest labeled A in Fig. 33-17b to move to the position labeled A', the wave must travel a distance vT_o. This distance is a wavelength λ plus the distance moved by the observer, $vT_o = \lambda + v_oT_o$. Thus

$$\lambda = (v - v_o)T_o \tag{33-17}$$

Eliminating λ from Eqs. (33-16) and (33-17), we obtain

$$(v - v_s)T_s = (v - v_o)T_o$$

which relates the period of waves emitted by the source T_s to the period of waves received by the observer T_o. Since the frequency is the reciprocal of the period, we have

Doppler shift for sound

$$\nu_o = \nu_s \frac{v - v_o}{v - v_s} \tag{33-18}$$

which gives the Doppler shift for sound.

The Doppler shift expression in Eq. (33-18) was obtained for the case of all velocities along the positive x axis. It holds more generally, however, if v_o and v_s represent the x components of the velocities. Thus the components v_o and v_s could be negative. In Fig. 33-17a, for example, the velocity component v_o would be negative if the observer moved to the left toward the source, and the velocity component v_s would be negative if the source moved to the left away from the observer. If we set $v_s = v_o$ in Eq. (33-18), we find $\nu_s = \nu_o$. As expected, there is no frequency shift if source and observer move with the same velocity through the medium, or if neither source nor observer move: $v_s = v_o = 0$.

EXAMPLE 33-4. A foghorn on a ship vibrates at 69.3 Hz. The wind speed is zero, you are standing on the shore, the ship is approaching you at 30.3 knots (15.6 m/s), and the speed of sound is 345 m/s. (a) What is the wavelength of the sound in the air in front of the ship? (b) What frequency do you hear?

SOLUTION. (a) Using Eq. (33-16) with $v_s = +15.6$ m/s, we have

$$\lambda = (v - v_s)T_s = \frac{v - v_s}{\nu_s} = \frac{345 \text{ m/s} - 15.6 \text{ m/s}}{69.3 \text{ Hz}}$$

$$= 4.75 \text{ m}$$

Note that if the ship were not moving, the wavelength would be $v/\nu_s = (345 \text{ m/s})/(69.3 \text{ Hz}) = 4.98$ m. (b) Using Eq. (33-18), we have

$$\nu_o = \frac{(69.3 \text{ Hz})(345 \text{ m/s} - 0)}{345 \text{ m/s} - 15.6 \text{ m/s}}$$

= 72.6 Hz

This raises the pitch from C_2 sharp to almost D_2, a difference barely discernible by the human ear.

EXAMPLE 33-5. A warning foghorn on land vibrates at 69.3 Hz in still air. You approach the foghorn in a ship with a speed of 30.3 knots, and the speed of sound is 345 m/s. (a) What is the wavelength of the sound in the air? (b) What frequency do you hear?

SOLUTION. (a) The wavelength of the sound is just v/ν_s, because the source is stationary with respect to the air. Thus $\lambda = (345 \text{ m/s})/(69.3 \text{ Hz}) = 4.98$ m. (b) In this case the velocity of the source is zero, but the velocity component v_o of the observer is -15.6 m/s rather than zero as in the previous example. The sign of v_o is negative because the ship's velocity has a direction opposite to the direction from the source to the observer. Using Eq. (33-18), we have

$$\nu_o = 69.3 \text{ Hz} \frac{345 \text{ m/s} - (-15.6 \text{ m/s})}{345 \text{ m/s}}$$

$$= 72.4 \text{ Hz}$$

The relative speeds in the two examples above were the same, $|v_o| = |v_s|$, and the frequency shifts were almost the same. There is little difference in the frequency shift of sound if the source approaches the observer or the observer approaches the source with the same speed. It does make *some* difference, however. This difference makes it possible to determine whether the observer or the source is moving with respect to the medium in the foghorn examples above. As we will see in Chaps. 34 and 38, light does not have to have a medium in which to propagate, and only relative motions of source and observer affect measurements of the frequencies of light. There is a different expression for the Doppler shift for light, which we now quote. If c is the speed of light in vacuum and v_R is the relative velocity component, positive if the source and observer approach each other and negative if they recede from each other, then

Doppler shift for light

$$\nu_o = \nu_s \left(\frac{c - v_R}{c + v_R} \right)^{1/2} \tag{33-19}$$

Exercise 33-43 asks you to show that the difference between using Eq. (33-18) and using Eq. (33-19) for light is immeasurably small for relative speeds small compared with that of light. Thus Doppler could not have known that his formula was correct when applied to sound, but incorrect when applied to the light waves in which he was interested.

There are further limitations on the Doppler shift for sound in Eq. (33-18). If the observer moves away from the source with a speed greater than the speed of sound, then the wave can never "catch up" with the observer, and the formula should not be applied. Another problem occurs if v_s exceeds v; the formula then predicts a negative frequency. Since this does not appear to make physical sense, we must look at the derivation and see where it goes wrong when $v_s \geq v$.

The problem comes in the calculation of λ. If $v_s \geq v$, then $\lambda \leq 0$. But a zero or negative wavelength does not make sense physically. Thus the Doppler formula for sound does not apply when the source moves toward the observer with a speed greater than the speed of sound.

A shock wave is formed if $v_s > v$.

What does happen when $v_s \geq v$? What happens, among other things, is that a *shock wave* is formed. Figure 33-18 shows the conical envelope formed by the waves emitted by an object moving faster than the speed of the wave. On this envelope the wave crests pile up, so that the wave amplitude becomes large. In air the resulting shock wave can increase the local pressure by enough to hurt an eardrum or break a window. A shock wave is responsible for the "sonic

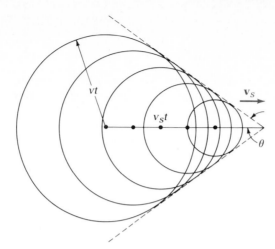

Figure 33-18. Wavefronts pile up on a cone and form a shock wave if the speed of the source exceeds the speed of sound in a medium.

boom'' that is heard when an aircraft passes by at a supersonic speed ($v_s > v$). Similar to the envelope for a shock wave in air is the bow wave produced by a boat or a ship that moves in the water with a speed greater than the speed of the water waves. Another like effect is Cerenkov radiation, light that is produced when a charged particle moves in a medium such as water with a speed v_s greater than the speed of light v in that medium. In each case, the half-angle θ of the envelope in Fig. 33-18 is given by $\sin \theta = v/v_s$. (See Exercise 33-42.)

33-8 THE WAVE EQUATION FOR SOUND

The wave equation for a wave on a string or a rope was obtained in Sec. 32-5 by considering the motion of an element due to the force exerted by the elements on either side. In a similar way, we develop the wave equation for a sound wave in a fluid by determining how an element of the fluid moves.

First we need the connection between the displacement $\psi(x, t)$ of an element of the fluid and the pressure change $\Delta p(x, t) = p(x, t) - p_e$. As discussed in Sec. 33-2, the adiabatic bulk modulus B_s relates a small pressure change Δp to a change in volume ΔV of an element of fluid, $B_s = -V(\Delta p/\Delta V)$, or

$$\Delta p = -B_s \frac{\Delta V}{V} \tag{33-20}$$

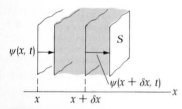

Figure 33-19. The volume $S\,\delta x$ between x and $x + \delta x$ changes to the volume $S[\delta x + \psi(x + \delta x, t) - \psi(x, t)]$ if a wave is present in the fluid.

Consider an element of fluid in the shape of a slab of area S that lies between faces at x and $x + \delta x$ when the fluid is in equilibrium. If a longitudinal wave is present, these faces are displaced by $\psi(x, t)$ and $\psi(x + \delta x, t)$, as shown in Fig. 33-19. Thus, because of the presence of the wave, the volume changes from $V = S\,\delta x$ to $V + \Delta V = S[\delta x + \psi(x + \delta x, t) - \psi(x, t)]$. The change in volume is $\Delta V = S[\psi(x + \delta x, t) - \psi(x, t)]$, and the fractional change in volume, $\Delta V/V$ that appears in Eq. (33-20), is given by

$$\frac{\Delta V}{V} = \frac{S[\psi(x + \delta x, t) - \psi(x, t)]}{S\,\delta x} = \frac{\psi(x + \delta x, t) - \psi(x, t)}{\delta x}$$

Pressure change and the derivative $\partial\psi/\partial x$

In the limit as $\delta x \to 0$, this ratio approaches $\partial\psi/\partial x$. Thus Eq. (33-20) becomes

$$\Delta p(x, t) = -B_s \frac{\partial\psi}{\partial x} \tag{33-21}$$

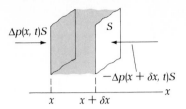

Figure 33-20. The x component of the net force on the element of fluid is $\delta F_x = S[\Delta p(x, t) - \Delta p(x + \delta x, t)]$.

We now consider the net force on the element shown in Fig. 33-20. The x component of the force exerted on the face at x due to the pressure change there is $\Delta p(x, t)S$. Similarly, the x component of the force exerted on the face at $x + \delta x$ is $-\Delta p(x + \delta x, t)S$. The x component of the net force on this element is

$$\delta F_x = S[\Delta p(x, t) - \Delta p(x + \delta x, t)]$$

Using Eq. (33-21), we express this force component in terms of the derivatives of ψ,

$$\delta F_x = B_s S \left(\left. \frac{\partial \psi}{\partial x} \right|_{x+\delta x} - \left. \frac{\partial \psi}{\partial x} \right|_x \right)$$

where the derivatives are evaluated at $x + \delta x$ and at x as indicated. The acceleration of this element is $a_x = \partial^2 \psi / \partial t^2$, and the mass of the element is $\delta m = \rho S \, \delta x$, where ρ is the density of the fluid and $S \, \delta x$ is the volume of the element. Newton's second law gives $\delta m \, a_x = \delta F_x$, or

$$\rho S \, \delta x \, \frac{\partial^2 \psi}{\partial t^2} = B_s S \left(\left. \frac{\partial \psi}{\partial x} \right|_{x+\delta x} - \left. \frac{\partial \psi}{\partial x} \right|_x \right)$$

The area S divides out of the equation. Next we divide both sides of the equation by δx. The difference of first derivatives divided by δx becomes the second derivative $\partial^2 \psi / \partial x^2$ as $\delta x \to 0$. Thus we obtain

$$\rho \frac{\partial^2 \psi}{\partial t^2} = B_s \frac{\partial^2 \psi}{\partial x^2} \tag{33-22}$$

Comparing this result with the form of the wave equation, Eq. (32-8), we see that sound waves in a fluid obey the wave equation and that the speed of sound in the fluid is given by

$$v = \sqrt{\frac{B_s}{\rho}}$$

which is Eq. (33-3).

Intensity of a sound wave in a fluid. The intensity of a sound wave in a fluid can be obtained by considering the rate at which work is done on a part of the fluid by the surrounding fluid when a wave is present. For simplicity we consider a wave traveling in one dimension, say in the positive x direction. Figure 33-21 shows a plane surface in the fluid of area S that is perpendicular to the direction of propagation of the wave. The pressure change due to the wave at this surface is $\Delta p(x, t)$, and the x component of the force exerted by the fluid on the surface is given by $F_x = \Delta p \, S$. The rate at which work is done is the power P, the rate at which energy passes in the x direction. Since $\partial \psi / \partial t$ is the x component of the velocity of the fluid at this surface, the power is $P = F_x \, \partial \psi / \partial t$. Substituting $\Delta p \, S$ for F_x, we obtain

$$P = \Delta p \, S \, \frac{\partial \psi}{\partial t}$$

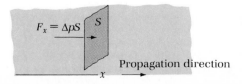

Figure 33-21. Work is done by the fluid to the left of the surface S as the surface moves when a wave is present.

The intensity I is the power per unit area and is obtained by dividing P by S:

$$I = \frac{P}{S} = \Delta p \, \frac{\partial \psi}{\partial t}$$

The intensity can be expressed in terms of the bulk modulus B_s and the derivatives of the displacement ψ by using Eq. (33-21), $\Delta p = -B_s(\partial \psi/\partial x)$. Thus

Intensity of a sound wave in a fluid

$$I = -B_s \, \frac{\partial \psi}{\partial x} \, \frac{\partial \psi}{\partial t} \qquad (33\text{-}23)$$

In Sec. 33-2, we displayed expressions for the average intensity of a harmonic wave, Eqs. (33-5) and (33-6). We now show how Eq. (33-23) leads to these expressions for a harmonic wave, say the wave given by Eq. (33-1), $\psi(x, t) = A \cos (kx - \omega t)$. The derivatives are

$$\frac{\partial \psi}{\partial x} = -kA \sin (kx - \omega t)$$

$$\frac{\partial \psi}{\partial t} = \omega A \sin (kx - \omega t)$$

and the intensity is $\qquad I = B_s \omega k A^2 \sin^2 (kx - \omega t)$

Usually we are interested in the intensity averaged over a cycle of the wave. Since the average over a cycle of a sine squared is one-half, the average intensity is

$$\bar{I} = \tfrac{1}{2} B_s \omega k A^2$$

which is Eq. (33-5).

If the pressure change Δp is used to describe the harmonic wave, then the average intensity can be expressed in terms of Δp_{max}. Using $\psi = A \cos (kx - \omega t)$ and Eq. (33-21), we have

$$\Delta p = -B_s \, \frac{\partial \psi}{\partial x} = B_s kA \sin (kx - \omega t)$$

so that the maximum pressure change is

$$\Delta p_{max} = B_s kA \qquad (33\text{-}24)$$

Solving Eq. (33-24) for the displacement amplitude A and substituting into $\bar{I} = \tfrac{1}{2} B_s \omega k A^2$, we have

$$\bar{I} = \frac{(\Delta p_{max})^2 \omega}{2 B_s k}$$

Substituting $\omega/k = v$ and $B_s = \rho v^2$ from Eq. (33-3) gives

$$\bar{I} = \frac{(\Delta p_{max})^2}{2v\rho}$$

which is Eq. (33-6).

Our treatment of the intensity of a harmonic wave was developed for a wave propagating in one dimension. Often we deal with sound waves propagating in two and three dimensions. A spherical sound wave propagating outward in all directions from a small source, sometimes called a *point source*, is an example of a sound wave in three dimensions.

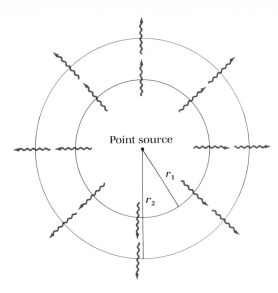

Figure 33-22. A point source produces a steady spherical wave. By conservation of energy, the energy per second, or power, passing through the inner sphere equals the energy per second passing through the outer sphere.

Consider a steady spherical wave passing through each of two spheres of radii r_1 and r_2 centered on the source, as shown in Fig. 33-22. By conservation of energy, the energy per second passing through an inner sphere of radius r_1 must equal the energy per second passing through an outer sphere of radius r_2. That is, the power at a distance r from the small source must be independent of r, $\bar{P} = \bar{I}4\pi r^2$, where $4\pi r^2$ is the surface area of the sphere. Thus the average intensity falls off as the inverse square of the distance from the point source:

Intensity for a spherical wave decreases as $1/r^2$.

$$\bar{I} = \frac{\bar{P}}{4\pi r^2} \tag{33-25}$$

We can still use Eqs. (33-5) and (33-6) for the average intensity of a harmonic spherical wave, but the amplitude A and the maximum pressure change Δp_{max} are then proportional to $1/r$. For example, if the amplitude is A_1 at a distance r_1 from a point source, then the amplitude at a distance r_2 from the source is $A_2 = A_1(r_1/r_2)$.

Amplitude for a spherical wave decreases as $1/r$.

SUMMARY WITH APPLICATIONS

Section 33-2. Sound waves

A longitudinal sound wave in a fluid may be described by the displacement $\psi(x, t)$ of an element in the direction of propagation of the wave or by the pressure change from the equilibrium pressure, $\Delta p(x, t) = p(x, t) - p_e$. A harmonic wave is given by

$$\psi(x, t) = A \cos (kx - \omega t) \tag{33-1}$$

$$\Delta p(x, t) = \Delta p_{max} \sin (kx - \omega t) \tag{33-2}$$

The wave speed depends on the density and the adiabatic bulk modulus,

$$v = \sqrt{\frac{B_s}{\rho}} \tag{33-3}$$

The speed of sound in an ideal gas is given by

$$v = \sqrt{\frac{\gamma RT}{M}} \tag{33-4}$$

The average intensity of a harmonic wave is given by either

$$\bar{I} = \tfrac{1}{2}B_s\omega kA^2 \tag{33-5}$$

or

$$\bar{I} = \frac{(\Delta p_{max})^2}{2v\rho} \tag{33-6}$$

Equations (33-3), (33-5), and (33-6) are derived in Sec. 33-8.

Using the displacement ψ and the pressure change Δp, describe a longitudinal sound wave in a fluid; determine the wave speed in a fluid and in an ideal gas; determine the average intensity of a harmonic wave.

Section 33-3. Hearing

Subjective judgments of equal steps in pitch correspond to equal multiples of frequency. Subjective judgments of equal steps in loudness level correspond to equal multiples of intensity. The intensity level is defined as

$$\beta = 10 \log_{10} \frac{I}{I_0} \qquad (33\text{-}8)$$

where $I_0 = 10^{-12} \text{ W/m}^2$.

Describe the relationships between pitch and frequency and between loudness level and intensity; convert between intensity and intensity level.

Section 33-4. Fourier analysis of periodic waves

A periodic wave can be represented by a Fourier series, a linear combination of harmonic terms.

Describe the Fourier analysis of a periodic wave and its connection with the subjective quality of a sound.

Section 33-5. Sources of sound

Many musical instruments excite standing waves in an air column. The fundamental and higher harmonics depend on the length of the air column and the conditions at the ends of the column.

Determine the fundamental and higher harmonics of air columns with various end conditions.

Section 33-6. Interference of sound waves and beats

Sound waves exhibit interference, and the effect is important for acoustic design. Sounds with nearly equal frequen-

cies produce beats with a beat frequency

$$\nu_b = |\nu_2 - \nu_1| \qquad (33\text{-}15)$$

Show how constructive and destructive interference can occur for sound; determine the beat frequency for two sounds.

Section 33-7. The Doppler effect

The frequency of sound received by a moving observer is Doppler-shifted from the frequency emitted by a moving source:

$$\nu_0 = \nu_s \frac{v - v_o}{v - v_s} \qquad (33\text{-}18)$$

The Doppler shift for light depends only on the relative-velocity component of source and receiver:

$$\nu_o = \nu_s \left(\frac{c - v_R}{c + v_R} \right)^{1/2} \qquad (33\text{-}19)$$

Determine the Doppler shift for sound and for light.

Section 33-8. The wave equation for sound

The pressure change in a fluid is related to the fluid displacement by

$$\Delta p = -B_s \left(\frac{\partial \psi}{\partial x} \right) \qquad (33\text{-}21)$$

Newton's second law applied to a fluid leads to the wave equation for $\psi(x, t)$. The wave speed is given by Eq. (33-3).

Determine the pressure change in a fluid from the displacement wave function $\psi(x, t)$; show how the wave equation for sound is obtained from Newton's second law.

QUESTIONS

33-1   Water is denser than air, but the speed of sound in water is about 4 times faster than in air. Why?

33-2   When a sound wave goes from air to water, the frequency, which is determined by the source, is unchanged. Does the wave speed increase, decrease, or stay the same? Does the wavelength increase, decrease, or stay the same?

33-3   The average molecular mass of air is 29 g/mol. Would you expect the speed of air to be higher in humid air or in dry air at the same temperature? Explain.

33-4   Would you expect the speed of sound in air to vary with altitude? Why? Where would it be greater?

33-5   If you see a lightning bolt and count seconds until you hear the thunder, you can then divide by 5 to determine the distance to the bolt in miles (dividing by 3 gives the distance in kilometers). Explain how this works.

33-6   By what fraction does the speed of sound in a dilute gas change when (a) the pressure p is increased by a factor of 2 at constant temperature T, (b) T is increased by a factor of 2 at constant p, (c) the gas changes from

monatomic to diatomic while p and T are kept constant?

33-7   What is your answer to the old riddle, "If a tree falls in the forest with nobody around, is there any sound?" Explain.

33-8   Propose a mechanism whereby you can tell from which direction a sound wave comes.

33-9   Explain why you must be able to hear sounds of frequency higher than 1000 Hz if you are to distinguish between the vowel sounds "a" and "o" sung at 1000 Hz.

33-10 A tripling of the intensity of a sound increases the sound-intensity level from 70 to 75 dB. If the intensity is tripled yet again, what will the sound-intensity level be?

33-11 If doubling the intensity of a sound wave increases the sound-intensity level by about 3 dB, what does quadrupling the intensity do to the sound-intensity level?

33-12 The tubes below the bars of a xylophone or marimba (see Fig. 33-23) are sometimes called *resonant chambers.* The term "resonant" implies that an oscillator is in resonance with a driving frequency. What oscillator is in resonance with what driving frequency in these instruments? Why are the tubes of differing lengths?

Figure 33-23. Ques. 33-12: The vertical tubes of the xylophone are resonant air columns.

33-13 How does an increase in room temperature affect the pitch of an organ pipe?

33-14 The highest note played by a piano has a fundamental frequency of about 4 kHz. Why is it necessary that sounds with frequencies above 10 kHz be reproduced by the audio equipment in order to "capture" the sound of the piano on a recording?

33-15 Why does your voice sound different when you have a cold?

33-16 A loudspeaker giving off a constant-frequency sound is moved toward a wall at the front of a class. The class hears the sound coming directly from the speaker and the sound reflecting from the wall. The class re-

ports that beats are heard. Explain how this result can be described either as a moving interference pattern or as beats between two Doppler-shifted waves.

33-17 Under what circumstances might you be able to hear beats from the sound waves given off by two tuning forks, both of which vibrate at 440 Hz?

33-18 Explain the V-shaped waves that a motorboat makes when moving fast on the water.

33-19 Two sound waves have the same amplitude, but one has twice the frequency of the other. Which has the greater intensity? How much greater?

33-20 A train blows its whistle as it approaches a tunnel cut into a sheer cliff, and the sound is reflected back toward the train. Compare the frequencies of the original sound and the reflected sound heard by (a) the engineer on the train, (b) a bystander near the tracks in front of the train, and (c) a bystander near the tracks in back of the train. Which listener hears the highest and which hears the lowest frequency? Does any listener hear the same frequency for the two sounds? Explain.

33-21 Complete the following table:

Symbol	Represents	Type	SI unit
$\psi(x, t)$	Longitudinal displacement		
Δp_{max}			
B_s			Pa
M			
β			
ν_n			
ν_b		Scalar	
ν_s			

EXERCISES

Section 33-2. Sound waves*

33-1 A harmonic sound wave propagates in He in the positive x direction, with wave speed 950 m/s and wavelength 750 mm. Determine the (a) frequency, (b) angular frequency, (c) wave number for this wave. (d) Write an expression for the longitudinal displacement $\psi(x, t)$ if the wave amplitude is 5.0 μm.

33-2 A 1200-Hz sound wave travels in air at 348 m/s in the negative x direction. If the displacement amplitude is 3.0 μm, write expressions for (a) the longitudinal displacement, (b) the velocity component, (c) the acceleration component of an element of the air for this harmonic wave.

33-3 Determine the speed of sound in air at 0°C.

* Useful data for some of the exercises in this set can be found in Tables 15-1 and 15-2.

33-4 (a) Show that the bulk modulus has the dimension of pressure. (b) What is the percent change in pressure if the volume of a given mass of water is increased by 1 percent? (The bulk modulus of water is given in Table 15-1.) Repeat part (b) for air for which the volume change is (c) adiabatic and (d) isothermal.

33-5 Estimate the speed of sound in (a) ethyl alcohol and (b) glycerine.

33-6 What is the speed of sound at room temperature in (a) oxygen (O_2), (b) carbon monoxide (CO), (c) carbon dioxide (CO_2)? Assume γ is 7/5 for diatomic gases and 1.25 for CO_2.

33-7 A 100-m-long tube is filled with He gas at atmospheric pressure. If you shout at one end of the tube, how much sooner will your voice arrive at the other end through the tube than it will through the air outside the tube? Assume a uniform temperature of 300 K.

33-8 A ship emits a pulse of sound in water. The pulse is reflected off a submarine and returned to the ship in 5.2 s. How far away is the submarine?

33-9 Determine the speed of compressional sound waves in a rod of (a) Al, (b) Cu, (c) steel.

33-10 The sound of a train wheel hitting a pebble carries through the air and through the steel rails. How much sooner will the sound arrive through the rails at a position 3 km down the track than through the air?

33-11 Find the speed of compressional waves (a) in a rod of ice at $0°C$ and (b) in water at $0°C$.

33-12 (a) Determine the average intensity of the wave of Exercise 33-2. Assume the wave travels in air of density 0.029 kg/m^3. (b) What is the maximum pressure change for this wave?

33-13 A 1.0-kHz sound wave of intensity 8.8 nW/m^2 travels in water. Determine (a) the maximum pressure change and (b) the amplitude of the longitudinal displacement. (c) Repeat the calculations for a wave of the same frequency and intensity traveling in air at atmospheric pressure and 300 K.

33-14 Using Eqs. (33-5) and (33-6), show that $\Delta p_{max} = B_s k A$ for a harmonic wave.

Section 33-3. Hearing

33-15 The note A_4 ("middle A") is defined in modern music to be 440 Hz and corresponds to a white key on a piano. (a) What is the fundamental frequency of the next note, one half-step higher ($A_4^{\#}$, the next black key)? (b) What is the fundamental frequency of A_5, the note an octave higher than A_4?

33-16 What is the fundamental frequency of the sound five half-steps higher than A_4 (440 Hz)?

33-17 Sound B is louder than sound A. Sound C is perceived to be just as much louder than B as B is louder than A. If A has an intensity of 3.1 nW/m^2 and B has an intensity of 15 nW/m^2, what is the intensity of sound C? All sounds have a frequency of 1 kHz.

33-18 (a) A sound has an intensity of $9.2\ \mu$W/m^2. What is the sound-intensity level of this sound? (b) A sound has a sound-intensity level of 65.3 dB. What is the intensity of this sound?

33-19 Determine the change in sound-intensity level if the intensity changes by a factor of (a) 2, (b) 4, (c) 10, (d) 20, (e) 50, (f) 100, (g) 10^6.

Section 33-4. Fourier analysis of periodic waves

33-20 Sum the first few terms in Eq. (33-9) graphically for $\omega = 1000$ rad/s. Take $A_n = (100$ mm$)/n^2$, $\phi_n = 0$, and graph $A_n \sin(n\omega t)$ for $0 \le t \le 2\pi/\omega$. Choose a scale for $y(t)$ on your graph so that you can add the graphs for $n = 1$, 2, and 3.

33-21 Repeat the previous exercise with $A_n = 100$ mm$/n$, $\phi_n = 0$ for $n = 1$, 3, 5, . . . , and $A_n = 0$ for $n = 2$, 4, 6, ... Include terms through $n = 6$.

Section 33-5. Sources of sound*

33-22 Determine the frequencies of the standing sound waves that can be set up in a 2.97-m organ pipe open at both ends.

33-23 Determine the frequencies of standing sound waves that can be set up in a 2.97-m organ pipe open at one end and closed at the other.

33-24 An organ pipe open at both ends and "tuned" to have a 440-Hz fundamental has its second harmonic ($n = 2$) with the same frequency as the third harmonic ($n' = 3$) of an organ pipe closed at one end and open at the other. How long is each pipe?

33-25 The finger holes on a flute effectively move the antinode from near the end to near the position of the first open hole. In the flutelike tube shown in Fig. 33-24, how far would the hole be from the open end for (a) "middle C" (262 Hz) and (b) the note that is a half-step lower than middle C?

Finger holes

Figure 33-24. Exercise 33-25: Primitive flute.

33-26 How many of the harmonics of a 1.5-m-long organ pipe are within the hearing range of an average human if the pipe is (a) open at both ends and (b) open at one end and closed at the other?

33-27 A tuning fork is heard to resonate with a column of air in a soda bottle when the liquid level in the bottle is such that the air column is 50 mm long and again when it is 70 mm long. What is the frequency of vibration of the tuning fork? Assume the soda bottle is a straight tube like an organ pipe.

33-28 If you normally speak with a fundamental frequency of 280 Hz, what will be your fundamental frequency if you are breathing He gas?

33-29 By what fraction will the fundamental frequency of an open-open steel organ pipe change if the room temperature increases from 20 to $25°C$? Take into account changes in both the steel (see Table 16-1) and the air. How would your answer change if the tube were open-closed?

Section 33-6. Interference of sound waves and beats

33-30 Sound of frequency 1.16 kHz enters the arrangement of Fig. 33-25. For what values of x will the sound heard at the exit be (a) loudest and (b) faintest? Take $v = 348$ m/s.

33-31 Three loudspeakers a, b, and c emit sound waves of the same frequency. When the sound waves arrive at point P, far from the loudspeakers, the sounds from

* Take the speed of sound in air to be 348 m/s in this set of exercises.

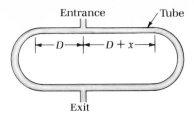

Figure 33-25. Exercise 33-30.

the speakers have the same amplitude but different phases:

$$\psi_a = A \sin (\omega t - 2\pi/3)$$

$$\psi_b = A \sin (\omega t)$$

$$\psi_c = A \sin (\omega t + 2\pi/3)$$

Show that the sound intensity at point P is zero at all times.

33-32 Two loudspeakers emit sounds, one at 432.5 Hz and the other at 431.9 Hz. What is the frequency of beats heard where the two sounds combine?

33-33 Standing waves are set up in two open-ended tubes. One tube is 1.000 m long and the other is identical except that it is 1.002 m long. What is the frequency of beats heard when sound from both tubes is present? Take $v = 348$ m/s.

33-34 Standing waves are set up on two violin strings of the same length and density. The tensions are adjusted until the fundamental frequency of each string is 440 Hz. The tension in the string of one violin is then changed until the beat frequency heard between the violins is 5 Hz. By what fraction was the tension changed?

33-35 Two tuning forks are struck, and the sound coming from the two is found to have six beats per second. The first fork is labeled 880 Hz. The beat frequency decreases when the second tuning fork has putty stuck to one of its tines. What is the frequency of the second fork (but without the putty)?

Section 33-7. The Doppler effect*

33-36 A sound source with a frequency of 8.46 kHz moves in the positive x direction with a speed of 34.8 m/s relative to an observer in still air. (a) What is the wavelength of the sound wave in front of the source along the x axis? (b) What frequency will be heard by the observer in front of the source along the x axis? (c) What frequency would be heard if the observer were in front of the source and moving in the negative x direction at 5.2 m/s relative to still air?

* Take the speed of sound in air to be 348 m/s in this set of exercises.

33-37 The first experimental confirmation of the effect Doppler predicted in 1842 was made by C. H. D. Buys Ballot in 1845. He compared the sound of stationary trumpeters and trumpeters approaching and receding on the Utrecht railway. How fast would the trains have to travel to have a difference of one half-step (a factor of $2^{1/12}$) for observers standing between the approaching and receding trumpeters?

33-38 An ambulance siren has a fundamental frequency of 261 Hz. If the ambulance travels at 100 km/h (27.8 m/s), what frequency is heard in still air by bystanders (a) in front of the ambulance? (b) In back of the ambulance?

33-39 Two police officers in separate cars head for the same wreck for which the ambulance of the previous exercise was called. One follows the ambulance at 90 km/h and the other approaches the wreck from the other direction at 90 km/h. What frequency does the ambulance siren have for each of the officers?

33-40 A bat chasing a moth emits a 55-kHz ultrasound. The bat is traveling at 13 m/s and the moth at 2.4 m/s in still air. (a) What frequency does the moth receive? (b) The ultrasound reflects from the moth and returns to the bat. What frequency does the bat hear from the reflected signal?

33-41 A train chases Wiley Coyote (*Famishus permanentus*) down a track toward a tunnel cut into a sheer cliff. The train's speed is 40 m/s and Wiley's is 30 m/s. The train blows its whistle, which has a fundamental frequency of 440 Hz. (a) What frequency does Wiley hear for the sound coming directly from the train? (b) What frequency does he hear for the sound reflected from the cliff?

33-42 Show that the half-angle of the cone for a shock wave is given by $\sin \theta = v/v_s$.

33-43 The binomial expansion $(1 + x)^p = 1 + px + \cdots$ is valid for $|x| \ll 1$. Show that the Doppler shift given by Eq. (33-18), with v replaced by c and both v_s and v_o replaced by v_R, is essentially the same as that given by Eq. (33-19) if $v_R \ll c$ so that terms involving $(v_R/c)^2$ can be neglected. [*Hint*: $(c - v_R)^p (c + v_R)^{-p} = (1 - v_R/c)^p (1 + v_R/c)^{-p}.$]

33-44 An experimental police radar used to measure automobile speeds operates at 140 MHz. Suppose that the signal sent out from a police car traveling behind a suspect gives 5.5 beats per second when added to the signal reflected from the suspect car. How much faster is the suspect going than the police car? The speed of light is 3.00×10^8 m/s.

Section 33-8. The wave equation for sound

33-45 A harmonic sound wave of amplitude A travels in the positive x direction in a fluid. (a) Show that the maximum pressure change is $\Delta p = B_s A k$. (b) Write an expression for the pressure change $\Delta p(x, t)$ for such a wave of frequency 880 Hz and amplitude 25 nm in water.

33-46 A baby cries, putting 1 mW of power into a piercing wail at 1 kHz. The sound spreads out in all directions with equal intensity. The baby's mother can detect sound intensities of 10 pW/m² or greater. How far can the mother be from the baby and still hear its cry? Assume that there are no reflections and no absorption of the sound wave.

33-47 The intensity of the sound generated by a rock band at an open-air concert is 0.1 W/m² at a position 10 m from the band. Estimate the intensity of the sound 100 m from the band.

33-48 In 1 ms a volcanic eruption puts 10^{12} J of energy into a sound wave. Estimate the intensity of the wave when it reaches a point 1 km from the eruption.

PROBLEMS

33-1 Two marks are made on a solid bar of cross-sectional area S at positions x and $x + \Delta x$. Suppose a compressional wave travels in the bar. (a) Show that the distance between marks is then $\Delta x + \psi(x + \Delta x) - \psi(x)$, where ψ is the displacement of the solid due to the wave. (b) Using Young's modulus $Y = (F/S)/(\Delta\ell/\ell)$, let $\Delta x \to 0$ and show that the stress F/S in the bar due to the wave is $-Y\,\partial\psi/\partial x$. (c) Show that the x component of the force on a small section of the bar δx long is $YS(\partial\psi/\partial x|_{x+\delta x} - \partial\psi/\partial x|_x)$. (d) Use Newton's second law for this small section of the bar to show that $Y\,\partial^2\psi/\partial x^2 = \rho\,\partial^2\psi/\partial t^2$, so that the speed of compressional waves in the solid is $\sqrt{Y/\rho}$.

33-2 Suppose the gas in the tube of Fig. 33-1 is He at a pressure of 0.11 MPa and a temperature of 297 K. If the piston has an area of 400 mm² and is moved sinusoidally with a frequency of 60 Hz, creating a wave with amplitude of 3.8 mm, what power goes into the sound waves formed?

33-3 Newton first obtained the result $v = \sqrt{B/\rho}$ for the speed of sound in a fluid. He calculated the speed of sound in air by using Boyle's measurement of the *isothermal* bulk modulus B_T instead of the *adiabatic* bulk modulus B_s. Consequently, his value for v was too small. This error was not resolved until 1816 when Laplace noted that the changes in volume were adiabatic instead of isothermal. (a) Treat air as an ideal gas and show that $B_T = p$, the pressure. (b) Determine the percent error in the calculated speed of sound at 300 K if B_T is used instead of B_s.

33-4 (a) If one student yelling at a football game gives a sound-intensity level on the field of 35 dB, how many students must yell to give a sound-intensity level of 55 dB? Assume that the yells have random phases so that the net intensity is the sum of the intensities from each student. (b) If one loudspeaker gives a sound-intensity level of 35 dB on the field, how many loudspeakers producing identical sounds that arrive in phase at a point on the field would be necessary to give a sound-intensity level of 55 dB at that point?

33-5 Two loudspeakers are set up facing each other 20 m apart. They produce sounds with identical frequency, amplitude, and phase and of wavelength $\frac{1}{2}$ m. Quantitatively describe the minima and maxima of intensity you would hear as you walk with speed v_o from one speaker to the other in terms of (a) an interference phenomenon that leads to standing waves and (b) beats between Doppler-shifted frequencies received from the speakers.

33-6 Suppose that a source of sound with frequency v_s moves with a velocity $\mathbf{v}_s$ with respect to a distant observer at rest in the medium. However, $\mathbf{v}_s$ does not lie along the line joining the source and observer. (See Fig. 33-26.) (a) Show that the wavelength according to the observer is $\lambda = (v - v_s \cos \alpha)/v_s$, where v is the speed of sound in the medium and α is the angle between $\mathbf{v}_s$ and the line directed from the source to the observer. (b) Show that the Doppler-shifted frequency received by the observer is

$$v_o = \frac{v_s}{1 - (v_s/v)\cos\alpha}$$

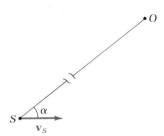

Figure 33-26. Prob. 33-6.

33-7 Two small loudspeakers 3.00 m apart emit sound waves of frequency 1.04 kHz with the same phase. Loudspeaker 1 produces 4.00 W of sound power, and loudspeaker 2 produces 2.56 W of sound power. Assume that there are no reflections from nearby surfaces and that the speed of sound is 348 m/s. (a) Show that the phase difference between the spherical waves arriving at a point is given by $2\pi d/\lambda$, where d is the difference in the distances from the speakers to the point. (b) Determine the average sound intensity at position P in Fig. 33-27. (c) Determine the average intensity at position Q in the figure. (d) Suppose speaker 2 is wired backwards so that its speaker cone moves out when that of speaker 1 moves in and vice versa. What are the intensities at points P and Q in this case?

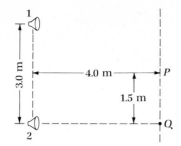

Figure 33-27. Prob. 33-7.

33-8 Write a program or use a calculator to sum the first few terms of the right-hand side of Eq. (33-9), with $A_n = [\sin (n\pi/2)]/n$, $\phi_n = 0$, and $\omega = 400$ rad/s. Include enough terms, n from 1 to 10 perhaps, and enough values of t to sketch the form of $y(t)$ for a period.

33-9 Modify the procedure in the previous problem to sum the first few terms of the right-hand side of Eq. (33-9), with $A_n = e^{-2n^2}$, $\phi_n = 0$, and $\omega = 400$ rad/s. Include enough terms and enough values of t to sketch the form of $\psi(t)$ for a period. Was it necessary to include as many terms as in the previous problem? Explain.

CHAPTER 34
MAXWELL'S EQUATIONS AND ELECTROMAGNETIC WAVES

The aurora borealis (northern lights). The aurora is light emitted from atoms in the upper atmosphere that are bombarded by charged particles from the sun. *(Steve McCutcheon/Photo Researchers)*

34-1   INTRODUCTION

In 1864 Maxwell published a paper entitled "Dynamical Theory of the Electromagnetic Field." In this paper, Maxwell presented his celebrated equations which unified the electric and magnetic fields. In addition, he showed that these equations predict the existence of waves in the electric and magnetic fields—*electromagnetic waves*. Maxwell identified these electromagnetic waves as light. Therefore, Maxwell's equations not only unified electric and magnetic phenomena, but optical phenomena as well. We now know that visible light is but one form of an electromagnetic wave; some other forms are radio waves, microwaves, and x-rays.

It is doubtful that Maxwell could have guessed the full impact of his findings on later human endeavors. However, the following quote from a letter to C. H. Hay on January 5, 1865, indicates that he believed his discoveries were quite significant: "I have also a paper afloat, with an electromagnetic theory of light, which, till I am convinced to the contrary, I hold to be great guns." In this chapter, we present a brief description of those "great guns."

34-2   MAXWELL'S EQUATIONS

You have already been introduced to Maxwell's equations in Chaps. 21, 27, and 28. The equations are

Gauss's law
$$\oint \mathbf{E} \cdot d\mathbf{S} = \frac{\Sigma q}{\epsilon_0} \tag{34-1}$$

Gauss's law for the magnetic field
$$\oint \mathbf{B} \cdot d\mathbf{S} = 0 \tag{34-2}$$

Faraday's law
$$\oint \mathbf{E} \cdot d\boldsymbol{\ell} = -\frac{d}{dt} \int \mathbf{B} \cdot d\mathbf{S} \tag{34-3}$$

Ampere's law (modified form)
$$\oint \mathbf{B} \cdot d\boldsymbol{\ell} = \mu_0 \Sigma I + \epsilon_0 \mu_0 \frac{d}{dt} \int \mathbf{E} \cdot d\mathbf{S} \tag{34-4}$$

Let us briefly review each of these equations. Equation (34-1) is Gauss's law. For static fields it is equivalent to Coulomb's law. It states that the flux of the electric field for a *closed* surface is proportional to the net charge contained in the volume enclosed by the surface. (See Sec. 21-4.)

Equation (34-2) is Gauss's law for the magnetic field. It states that the flux of the magnetic field for a *closed* surface is zero. Since this flux is zero, a magnetic counterpart to the electric charge does not exist. (See Sec. 27-6.)

Equation (34-3) is Faraday's law. It states that the line integral of the electric field around a *closed* path is proportional to the time rate of change of the magnetic flux for the surface bounded by that path. Thus a changing magnetic field is accompanied by an electric field. (See Sec. 28-5.)

Equation (34-4) is the modified form of Ampere's law. Maxwell modified the equation by adding the second term on the right-hand side, the displacement-current term which involves the flux of the electric field. The modified form of Ampere's law states that the line integral of the magnetic field around a *closed* path is proportional to the sum of two terms. The first term contains the net current which flows through a surface bounded by the closed path. The second term (Maxwell's modification) contains the time rate of change of the flux of the electric field for a surface bounded by the path. Because of Maxwell's modification, the equation states that a changing electric field is accompanied by a magnetic field. (See Sec. 27-7.)

Maxwell's equations represent a complete and concise description of the electric and magnetic fields. Although these equations appear formidable, we shall use them in a simple way. For the surface integrals we shall choose flat surfaces with straight boundaries, and for the line integrals we shall choose straight-line paths. These simple applications will provide the result we seek —namely, to demonstrate that these equations predict the existence of an electromagnetic wave.

34-3 THE WAVE EQUATION FOR E AND B

In Chap. 32 we showed that Newton's second law applied to an element of a rope yields the wave equation:

$$\frac{\partial^2 y}{\partial x^2} = \frac{\mu}{F} \frac{\partial^2 y}{\partial t^2}$$

The wave equation predicts the existence of waves in a system.

Thus Newton's second law predicts that a disturbance on a rope propagates as a wave. Even if we never had the opportunity to observe such waves, we would expect that they exist because of our confidence in Newton's second law and because we know that the wave equation is the theoretical harbinger of the existence of waves. That is, if we find some system that obeys the wave equation, then we expect waves to occur in that system. From Chap. 32, the wave equation is

The wave equation

$$\frac{\partial^2 \psi}{\partial x^2} = \frac{1}{v^2} \frac{\partial^2 \psi}{\partial t^2} \tag{34-5}$$

where ψ is the physical quantity that "waves" and v is the wave speed.

We now show that Maxwell's equations can be combined to produce two wave equations, one for the electric field and one for the magnetic field. Along the way, we discover some of the properties of these waves, and we determine the numerical value of their speed.

Plane-wave approximation. We simplify our discussion by anticipating the result. That is, we consider electric and magnetic fields that vary in a wavelike manner only. Any contribution to the fields that is uniform in space or constant in time is of no present interest. The space and time dependence of a wave field is oscillatory. For example, a harmonic wave in the electric field traveling in the $+x$ direction has the form $\mathbf{E} = \mathbf{E}_0 \sin (kx - \omega t)$.

Wave fields are oscillatory in space and time.

Also, we consider the fields in a region of free space, or vacuum, far from the source of the waves (point P in Fig. 34-1). The distance D from the source to P is much greater than the largest linear dimension d of the source. (We investigate the nature of the source in Sec. 34-7.) When $D \gg d$, the spatial variation of the wave fields depends only on a coordinate measured along the line from the source to the point P, and is independent of a coordinate measured perpendicular to this line. That is, a wave traveling along the x axis depends only on x, not on y or z. Therefore, we orient our coordinate axes so that the x axis is along the direction of propagation (unit vector $\mathbf{i}$ points away from the source). With this

Far from the source, the wave fields depend only on x and t.

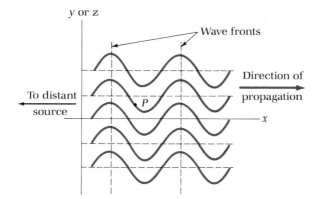

Figure 34-1. A wavelike field plotted along lines parallel to the x axis in a region far from the source. The field depends only on x; it is independent of y or z.

orientation, the wave fields can be written

$$\mathbf{E} = \mathbf{E}(x, t) \qquad \text{and} \qquad \mathbf{B} = \mathbf{B}(x, t)$$

Later in this section, we show that such fields have planar wavefronts, so that this assumption ($D \gg d$) is called the *plane-wave approximation*.

Wave fields E and B are transverse. We now find the direction of the electric field wave by applying Gauss's law, $\oint \mathbf{E} \cdot d\mathbf{S} = (\Sigma q)/\epsilon_0$, to the cube shown in Fig. 34-2. The surface of the cube is our gaussian surface. Since free space has no charge, the net charge Σq enclosed by the gaussian surface is zero, so that $\oint \mathbf{E} \cdot d\mathbf{S} = 0$. Using the labeling of the cube sides shown in the figure, we have

$$\int \mathbf{E}(1) \cdot d\mathbf{S}_1 + \int \mathbf{E}(2) \cdot d\mathbf{S}_2 + \int \mathbf{E}(3) \cdot d\mathbf{S}_3$$

$$+ \int \mathbf{E}(4) \cdot d\mathbf{S}_4 + \int \mathbf{E}(5) \cdot d\mathbf{S}_5 + \int \mathbf{E}(6) \cdot d\mathbf{S}_6 = 0$$

where $\mathbf{E}(n)$ is the electric field evaluated on the surface of side n and $d\mathbf{S}_n$ is the differential surface vector of side n. Recall that the surface vector for a closed surface points out of the enclosed volume, as shown by $d\mathbf{S}_2$ in the figure. The differential surface vectors are written: $d\mathbf{S}_1 = -(dy\,dz)\mathbf{i}$, $d\mathbf{S}_2 = +(dy\,dz)\mathbf{i}$, $d\mathbf{S}_3 = -(dx\,dz)\mathbf{j}$, $d\mathbf{S}_4 = +(dx\,dz)\mathbf{j}$, $d\mathbf{S}_5 = -(dx\,dy)\mathbf{k}$, and $d\mathbf{S}_6 = +(dx\,dy)\mathbf{k}$. Substituting into Gauss's law and performing the dot product, we obtain

$$-\int E_x(1)\,dy\,dz + \int E_x(2)\,dy\,dz - \int E_y(3)\,dx\,dz$$

$$+ \int E_y(4)\,dx\,dz - \int E_z(5)\,dx\,dy + \int E_z(6)\,dx\,dz = 0$$

Figure 34-2. Gauss's law applied to a cube. The cube sides are numbered 1 through 6. An expanded view of side 2 shows that $d\mathbf{S}_2 = (dy\,dz)\mathbf{i}$. Can you write the expression for $d\mathbf{S}_4$ from examination of the figure?

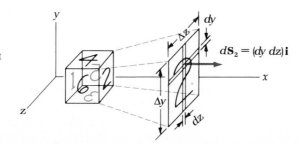

Since **E** does not depend on y, $E_y(3) = E_y(4)$. Consequently, terms 3 and 4 cancel each other; the flux for side 3 is equal and opposite the flux for side 4. Similarly, **E** does not depend on z, so that $E_z(5) = E_z(6)$, and terms 5 and 6 cancel each other; the flux for side 5 is equal and opposite the flux for side 6. Gauss's law applied to the cube now becomes

$$-\int E_x(1)\,dy\,dz + \int E_x(2)\,dy\,dz = 0$$

Since **E** is independent of y and z, E_x can be factored out of each integral and we have

$$E_x(1)\int dy\,dz = E_x(2)\int dy\,dz \qquad \text{or} \qquad E_x(1)\,\Delta y\,\Delta z = E_x(2)\,\Delta y\,\Delta z$$

where $\Delta y\,\Delta z = \int dy\,dz$ is the area of a cube side. Dividing by the area $\Delta y\,\Delta z$, we see that Gauss's law requires $E_x(1) = E_x(2)$. This means that E_x does not depend on x. However, the wave field *does* depend on x; otherwise no wave exists. We must conclude that $E_x = 0$ for the wave field. Thus the electric field wave is transverse; it has no component along the direction of propagation. With a similar analysis using Eq. (34-2), you can show that the magnetic field wave is also transverse (Prob. 34-1).

Wave fields E and B are mutually perpendicular. We have oriented the x axis of our coordinate frame along the direction of propagation, but we are still free to choose a direction for the y (or z) axis. Since **E** is perpendicular to the x axis, it is customary to let the y axis be parallel to the oscillating **E** field so that **E** has neither an x nor a z component: $\mathbf{E} = E_y(x, t)\,\mathbf{j}$.

Now, with the y axis along **E**, what is the direction of **B**? We can find out by applying Faraday's law, $\oint \mathbf{E} \cdot d\boldsymbol{\ell} = -d/dt \int \mathbf{B} \cdot d\mathbf{S}$, to the small square path shown in Fig. 34-3. Since each differential displacement $d\boldsymbol{\ell}$ along this path is perpendicular to **E**, we have $\oint \mathbf{E} \cdot d\boldsymbol{\ell} = 0$, and Faraday's law gives $d/dt \int \mathbf{B} \cdot d\mathbf{S} = 0$, where the surface of integration is bounded by the square path. For this surface, $d\mathbf{S} = (dx\,dz)\mathbf{j}$ so that $\int \mathbf{B} \cdot d\mathbf{S} \approx B_y(\Delta x\,\Delta z)$, where B_y is evaluated at point P. Therefore,

$$0 \approx \frac{d}{dt}[B_y(\Delta x\,\Delta z)] = (\Delta x\,\Delta z)\frac{\partial}{\partial t}B_y$$

The equation becomes exact as the sides of the square converge on P. A partial derivative is indicated because **B** is a function of x as well as of t, and the point at which the derivative of B_y is evaluated is held fixed at P. Thus Faraday's law requires $\partial B_y/\partial t = 0$. That is, the y component of any time-varying magnetic field is zero. But a wave field *does* depend on time. Therefore, $B_y = 0$ for the wave field. Since Gauss's law for the magnetic field requires that $B_x = 0$ for the wave field, the magnetic wave field can have a z component only: $\mathbf{B} = B_z(x, t)\mathbf{k}$. Since $\mathbf{E} = E_y(x, t)\mathbf{j}$, this means that the electric and magnetic fields are mutually perpendicular.

We are now in a position to construct a schematic picture of the waves far from the source. Figure 34-4 shows some of the lines of **E** in the xy plane at a particular instant. The pattern moves to the right as the wave propagates. The lines of **B** in the xz plane have a similar appearance. From the figure you can see that the oscillating **E** field and the direction of propagation are contained in

Wave fields **E** and **B** are transverse to the direction of propagation.

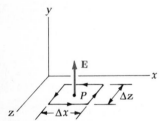

Figure 34-3. Faraday's law applied to a small square path contained in a plane parallel to the xz plane. Since **E** is along the y axis, each path element is perpendicular to **E**, so that $\oint \mathbf{E} \cdot d\boldsymbol{\ell} = 0$. Consequently, $d/dt \int \mathbf{B} \cdot d\mathbf{S} = 0$.

Wave fields **E** and **B** are mutually perpendicular.

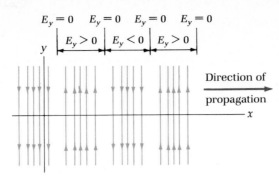

$E_y = 0$ $E_y = 0$ $E_y = 0$ $E_y = 0$

$E_y > 0$ | $E_y < 0$ | $E_y > 0$

Direction of propagation

Figure 34-4. Lines of the **E** wave field in the xy plane at a particular instant. The pattern moves to the right as the wave propagates. Lines of the **B** wave field in the xz plane are similar in appearance.

planes parallel to the xy plane. Similarly, the oscillating **B** field and the direction of propagation are contained in planes parallel to the xz plane. Such a wave is called a *plane-polarized wave,* and the *plane of polarization* is defined as the plane that contains **E** and the direction of propagation. For the case shown in Fig. 34-4, the xy plane is the plane of polarization.

Definition of the plane of polarization

The wave equation. Keeping in mind that **E** is along the y axis and **B** is along the z axis, we now apply Faraday's law, $\oint \mathbf{E} \cdot d\boldsymbol{\ell} = -d/dt \int \mathbf{B} \cdot d\mathbf{S}$, to the square path in Fig. 34-5. Again, point P is at the center of the square, and we consider the limit as the sides converge on P. With each side of the square path labeled as shown in the figure, the left-hand side of Faraday's law is

$$\oint \mathbf{E} \cdot d\boldsymbol{\ell} = \int \mathbf{E}(1) \cdot d\boldsymbol{\ell}_1 + \int \mathbf{E}(2) \cdot d\boldsymbol{\ell}_2 + \int \mathbf{E}(3) \cdot d\boldsymbol{\ell}_3 + \int \mathbf{E}(4) \cdot d\boldsymbol{\ell}_4$$

From the figure, $d\boldsymbol{\ell}_1 = dy\,\mathbf{j}$, $d\boldsymbol{\ell}_2 = -dx\,\mathbf{i}$, $d\boldsymbol{\ell}_3 = -dy\,\mathbf{j}$ and $d\boldsymbol{\ell}_4 = dx\,\mathbf{i}$. Since **E** has only a y component, **E** is perpendicular to $d\boldsymbol{\ell}_2$ and $d\boldsymbol{\ell}_4$ so that $\int \mathbf{E}(2) \cdot d\boldsymbol{\ell}_2 = 0$ and $\int \mathbf{E}(4) \cdot d\boldsymbol{\ell}_4 = 0$. This gives

$$\oint \mathbf{E} \cdot d\boldsymbol{\ell} = \int E_y(1)\,dy - \int E_y(3)\,dy = [E_y(1) - E_y(3)]\,\Delta y$$

where we have factored E_y out of each integral because it is independent of y. Assuming Δx is small, we can write

$$E_y(1) - E_y(3) = \frac{E_y(1) - E_y(3)}{\Delta x}\,\Delta x \approx \frac{\partial E_y}{\partial x}\,\Delta x$$

which gives

$$\oint \mathbf{E} \cdot d\boldsymbol{\ell} \approx \frac{\partial E_y}{\partial x}\,\Delta x\,\Delta y$$

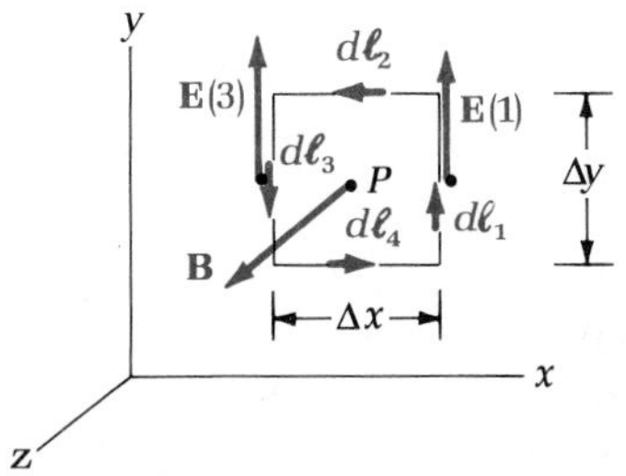

Now consider the right-hand side of Faraday's law. From the right-hand rule applied to the sense of the path of the line integral around the square, the differential surface vector for the plane surface bounded by this path is directed toward $+z$, so that $d\mathbf{S} = (dx\,dy)\mathbf{k}$. Therefore, the approximate flux of the magnetic field for this surface is

$$\int \mathbf{B} \cdot d\mathbf{S} \approx B_z(\Delta x\,\Delta y)$$

where B_z is evaluated at P. Substituting our results into Faraday's law, we have

$$\frac{\partial E_y}{\partial x}\,\Delta x\,\Delta y \approx -\frac{\partial B_z}{\partial t}\,\Delta x\,\Delta y$$

Figure 34-5. Faraday's law applied to a small square path contained in a plane parallel to the xy plane. The **E** wave field has a y component only, so that it is perpendicular to paths 2 and 4. The **B** wave field has a z component only, so that it is along a surface element $d\mathbf{S}$ on the flat surface enclosed by the square path. Apply the right-hand rule to the path shown, and determine whether $d\mathbf{S}$ is directed toward $+\mathbf{k}$ or $-\mathbf{k}$.

In the limit, the equation becomes exact so that

$$\frac{\partial E_y}{\partial x} = -\frac{\partial B_z}{\partial t} \tag{34-6}$$

With a similar analysis using Ampere's law, Eq. (34-4), you can show that (Prob. 34-2)

$$\frac{\partial B_z}{\partial x} = -\mu_0 \epsilon_0 \frac{\partial E_y}{\partial t} \tag{34-7}$$

We obtain the wave equations for E_y and B_z by combining Eqs. (34-6) and (34-7). Differentiating Eq. (34-6) with respect to x and Eq. (34-7) with respect to t, we find

$$\frac{\partial^2 E_y}{\partial x^2} = -\frac{\partial}{\partial x}\frac{\partial B_z}{\partial t} \quad \text{and} \quad \frac{\partial}{\partial t}\frac{\partial B_z}{\partial x} = -\mu_0 \epsilon_0 \frac{\partial^2 E_y}{\partial t^2}$$

If we assume that the order of the x and t differentiation of B_z does not affect the result (see Exercises 34-6 and 34-7), then we can combine these two equations and obtain

The wave equation for E_y

$$\frac{\partial^2 E_y}{\partial x^2} = \mu_0 \epsilon_0 \frac{\partial^2 E_y}{\partial t^2} \tag{34-8}$$

Similarly, if we differentiate Eq. (34-6) with respect to t and Eq. (34-7) with respect to x, we find

The wave equation for B_z

$$\frac{\partial^2 B_z}{\partial x^2} = \mu_0 \epsilon_0 \frac{\partial^2 B_z}{\partial t^2} \tag{34-9}$$

Equations (34-8) and (34-9) are the wave equations for E_y and B_z. Comparison with Eq. (34-5) shows that $1/v^2 = \mu_0 \epsilon_0$, so that the wave speed is $v = 1/\sqrt{\mu_0 \epsilon_0}$. Inserting the numerical values of μ_0 and ϵ_0, we have

$$v = \frac{1}{\sqrt{(4\pi \times 10^{-7}\ \text{kg} \cdot \text{m/s}^2 \cdot \text{A}^2)(8.85 \times 10^{-12}\ \text{s}^4 \cdot \text{A}^2/\text{kg} \cdot \text{m}^3)}}$$
$$= 3.00 \times 10^8\ \text{m/s}$$

This speed has the same value as the speed c of light in vacuum or free space. (The traditional symbol for the speed of light in vacuum is c.)

As was Maxwell, we are led to the next logical leap. We proclaim that we now know what light is. Light is a wave in the electric and magnetic fields, and its speed in vacuum depends on the electric and magnetic properties of vacuum:

Speed of light in vacuum

$$c = \frac{1}{\sqrt{\mu_0 \epsilon_0}} \tag{34-10}$$

In other words, light is a propagating wrinkle in the electric and magnetic fields.

EXAMPLE 34-1. For electromagnetic waves traveling in a transparent dielectric, such as air or glass, the speed v of the wave is given by $v = 1/\sqrt{\mu_0 \kappa \epsilon_0}$, where κ is the dielectric constant of the material. That is, we replace ϵ_0 with $\kappa \epsilon_0$ in the formula which gives the speed. The value of κ depends on the wave frequency. The magnetic properties of transpar-

ent materials are usually such that a similar adjustment to μ_0 is too small to be significant. (a) For air at optical frequencies, $\kappa = 1.006$. Determine the speed of visible light in air. (b) Given that the speed of visible light in a particular type of glass is 2.0×10^8 m/s, determine κ at optical frequencies for this type of glass.

SOLUTION. (a) Since $v = 1/\sqrt{\mu_0 \kappa \epsilon_0}$ and $c = 1/\sqrt{\mu_0 \epsilon_0}$ the speed of light in air is

$$v = \frac{c}{\sqrt{\kappa}} = \frac{3.00 \times 10^8 \text{ m/s}}{\sqrt{1.006}} = 2.99 \times 10^8 \text{ m/s}$$

The speed of visible light in air is nearly the same as in vacuum. (b) Solving for κ from $v = c/\sqrt{\kappa}$, we have

$$\kappa = \frac{c^2}{v^2}$$

The dielectric constant of this type of glass at optical frequencies is

$$\kappa = \frac{(3.0 \times 10^8 \text{ m/s})^2}{(2.0 \times 10^8 \text{ m/s})^2} = 2.2$$

34-4 ELECTROMAGNETIC WAVES

In Chap. 32 we studied solutions to the wave equation in one dimension, especially the harmonic or sinusoidal solution. The harmonic solutions to Eqs. (34-8) and (34-9) are

$$E_y = E_0 \sin (k_e x - \omega_e t) \tag{34-11}$$

and

$$B_z = B_0 \sin (k_b x - \omega_b t + \phi) \tag{34-12}$$

By placing subscripts on the wave numbers k_e and k_b, and on the angular frequencies ω_e and ω_b, we have allowed for the possibility that they may be different. Also, we allow for the possibility that the waves may be out of phase by inserting a phase constant ϕ in the expression for **B**. At this point in our investigation, we do know that both the electric field waves and the magnetic field waves have the same speed because the proportionality factor in both wave equations is the same: $c = 1/\sqrt{\mu_0 \epsilon_0}$. Thus $c = \omega_e/k_e = \omega_b/k_b$.

Using Eq. (34-6), we can determine ϕ and find relations between k_e and k_b, between ω_e and ω_b, and between E_0 and B_0. Differentiating Eqs. (34-11) and (34-12), we find

$$\frac{\partial E_y}{\partial x} = k_e E_0 \cos (k_e x - \omega_e t)$$

and

$$\frac{\partial B_z}{\partial t} = -\omega_b B_0 \cos (k_b x - \omega_b t + \phi) = -k_b c B_0 \cos (k_b x - \omega_b t + \phi)$$

Substitution into Eq. (34-6) gives

$$k_e E_0 \cos (k_e x - \omega_e t) = k_b c B_0 \cos (k_b x - \omega_b t + \phi) \tag{34-13}$$

For this equation to be valid for all x and t requires that $k_e = k_b$, $\omega_e = \omega_b$, and $\phi = 2\pi n$ ($n = 0$ or an integer). Thus we let $k = k_e = k_b$, $\omega = \omega_e = \omega_b$, and $\phi = 0$. This means that the electric field waves and the magnetic field waves have the same wavelength λ ($\lambda = 2\pi/k$) and the same frequency ν ($\nu = \omega/2\pi$) and that they are in phase. Dividing Eq. (34-13) by k, we have

$$E_0 \cos (kx - \omega t) = c B_0 \cos (kx - \omega t)$$

For this equation to hold requires

$$E_0 = c B_0 \tag{34-14}$$

Consolidating these results, we now rewrite Eqs. (34-11) and (34-12):

Field components E_y and B_z for a harmonic electromagnetic wave

$$E_y = E_0 \sin (kx - \omega t) \tag{34-15}$$

and

$$B_z = B_0 \sin (kx - \omega t) \tag{34-16}$$

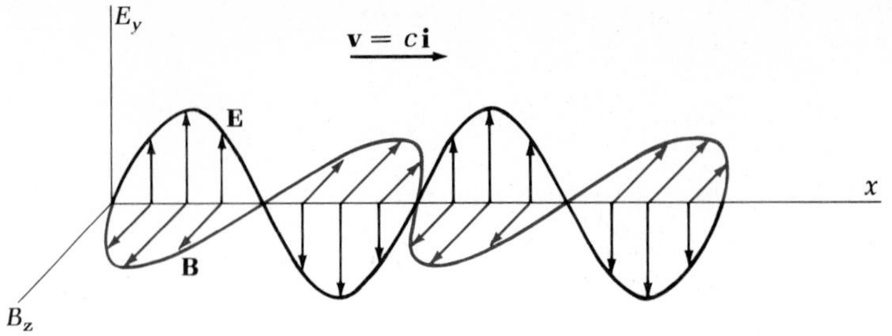

Figure 34-6. A schematic representation of a plane-polarized electromagnetic wave at a particular instant. The wave is propagating toward $+x$.

Also, as you can show (Exercise 34-17),

$$E_y = cB_z \tag{34-17}$$

We have found that the speed, wavelength, frequency, and phase of the electric field waves and magnetic field waves are the same, that their amplitudes are directly proportional (the proportionality constant is c), and that the fields are mutually perpendicular. Thus the electric field waves and magnetic field waves are not independent entities; the existence of one requires the existence of the other. There is but one wave, an *electromagnetic* wave. These features are shown in Fig. 34-6, which is a schematic representation of a plane-polarized electromagnetic wave at a particular instant.

There is but one wave, an electromagnetic wave.

EXAMPLE 34-2. Suppose that the electric field amplitude of the wave shown in Fig. 34-6 is $E_0 = 120$ N/C and that its frequency is $\nu = 50.0$ MHz. (a) Determine B_0, ω, k, and λ. (b) Find expressions for **E** and **B**.

SOLUTION. (a) From Eq. (34-14)

$$B_0 = \frac{E_0}{c} = \frac{120 \text{ N/C}}{3.00 \times 10^8 \text{ m/s}} = 400 \text{ nT}$$

Using $\omega = 2\pi\nu$, we have

$$\omega = 2\pi(50.0 \text{ MHz}) = 3.14 \times 10^8 \text{ rad/s}$$

Since $k = \omega/c$,

$$k = \frac{3.14 \times 10^8 \text{ rad/s}}{3.00 \times 10^8 \text{ m/s}} = 1.05 \text{ rad/m}$$

Also, $\lambda = 2\pi/k$, so that

$$\lambda = \frac{2\pi}{1.05 \text{ rad/m}} = 6.00 \text{ m}$$

(b) Using the results from part (a), we have

$$\mathbf{E} = \{(120 \text{ N/C}) \sin [(1.05 \text{ rad/m})x - (3.14 \times 10^8 \text{ rad/s})t]\}\,\mathbf{j}$$

$$\mathbf{B} = \{(400 \text{ nT}) \sin [(1.05 \text{ rad/m})x - (3.14 \times 10^8 \text{ rad/s})t]\}\,\mathbf{k}$$

Electromagnetic waves in this frequency range are used in television broadcasts.

34-5   ELECTROMAGNETIC WAVE INTENSITY

Electromagnetic waves transport energy. For example, the sun emits electromagnetic radiation, and after traveling to the earth, a tiny fraction of this radiant energy is absorbed by green plants. By the process of photosynthesis, part of this absorbed energy is stored in the form of sugar molecules. This is how energy enters the life cycle of which we humans are a part. You used some of this energy when you picked up this book.

The energy transported by an electromagnetic wave consists of both electric energy and magnetic energy. In Sec. 23-4 we found that the energy density u_E associated with an electric field is $u_E = \frac{1}{2}\epsilon_0 E^2$, and in Sec. 29-4 we found that the energy density u_B associated with a magnetic field is $u_B = \frac{1}{2}B^2/\mu_0$. We now show that these energy densities are equal for plane electromagnetic waves. Using the relation $E_y = cB_z$ from the previous section and $c = 1/\sqrt{\mu_0\epsilon_0}$ or $\epsilon_0 = 1/\mu_0 c^2$, we have

$$u_E = \frac{1}{2}\epsilon_0 E^2 = \frac{1}{2}\epsilon_0 E_y^2 = \frac{1}{2}\left(\frac{1}{\mu_0 c^2}\right)(cB_z)^2 = \frac{\frac{1}{2}B^2}{\mu_0} = u_B$$

The sum of u_E and u_B is the electromagnetic energy density u:

Electromagnetic energy density

$$u = u_E + u_B$$

Since $u_E = u_B$, we have that $u = 2u_E = 2u_B$. By using $E_y = cB_z$ and $\epsilon_0\mu_0 = 1/c^2$, we can express u in several forms. A customary form is

$$u = \epsilon_0 E^2 \qquad (34\text{-}18)$$

In Fig. 34-7 a plane electromagnetic wave is shown passing through a slab-shaped region of space of thickness Δx and cross-sectional area $A = L^2$. We choose Δx to be much smaller than the wavelength so that the fields (and the energy density) in the volume are essentially uniform. Thus the electromagnetic energy ΔU within this volume is the product of the energy density and the volume:

$$\Delta U = u(A\,\Delta x)$$

Since the wave travels at speed c, the time Δt required for this energy to leave the slab-shaped volume and fill the adjoining volume on the right is $\Delta t = \Delta x/c$. Dividing ΔU by Δt gives the rate at which energy passes through a surface of area A perpendicular to the propagation direction:

$$\frac{\Delta U}{\Delta t} = uA\frac{\Delta x}{\Delta t} = uAc \qquad (34\text{-}19)$$

From Sec. 32-6, the wave *intensity* S is the rate at which energy passes through this area divided by the area:

Wave intensity

$$S = \frac{1}{A}\frac{\Delta U}{\Delta t} \qquad (34\text{-}20)$$

Inserting $\Delta U/\Delta t$ from Eq. (34-19) into Eq. (34-20), we have

$$S = uc \qquad (34\text{-}21)$$

The intensity is equal to the product of the energy density and the wave speed.

Figure 34-7. A plane electromagnetic wave passing through a slab-shaped volume element of area $A = L^2$ and thickness Δx. Because the wave speed is c, the time required for the energy $\Delta U = u(A\,\Delta x)$ contained in the slab to pass through the slab face is $\Delta t = \Delta x/c$.

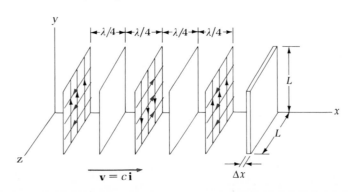

We can express the intensity in terms of the magnitude of the electric field by substituting for u from Eq. (34-18):

$$S = \epsilon_0 E^2 c \tag{34-22}$$

Suppose we construct an intensity vector $\mathbf{S}$ which points in the direction of propagation: $\mathbf{S} = S\mathbf{i}$. Note that the cross product $\mathbf{E} \times \mathbf{B}$ points in the propagation direction:

$$\mathbf{E} \times \mathbf{B} = (E_y\mathbf{j}) \times (B_z\mathbf{k}) = E_y B_z\mathbf{i}$$

You can show that S can be expressed in terms of the product $E_y B_z$ (see Exercise 34-22): $S = E_y B_z/\mu_0$. Therefore, $\mathbf{S} = (E_y B_z/\mu_0)\mathbf{i}$, or, more generally

Poynting vector

$$\mathbf{S} = \frac{1}{\mu_0} \mathbf{E} \times \mathbf{B} \tag{34-23}$$

The vector $\mathbf{S}$ is called the *Poynting vector,* named for its originator, J. H. Poynting (1852–1914). The magnitude of $\mathbf{S}$ is the wave intensity, and its direction is the direction in which energy is propagated by the wave. (Be careful to avoid confusing the Poynting vector $\mathbf{S}$ with the differential surface vector $d\mathbf{S}$.)

For the case of a harmonic plane wave,

$$S = \frac{1}{\mu_0} E_0 B_0 \sin^2 (kx - \omega t) \tag{34-24}$$

Figure 34-8 shows graphs of E_y, B_z, and S versus the time at a particular point in space. The field components E_y and B_z depend on time as $\sin (\omega t)$, whereas S depends on time as $\sin^2 (\omega t)$. Therefore, the direction of $\mathbf{S}$ does not oscillate, but its magnitude varies between zero and a maximum ($S_{max} = E_0 B_0/\mu_0$) each quarter of a period.

The time interval over which the intensity of an electromagnetic wave is measured or detected is usually much longer than the period of the wave. Therefore, a quantity of more interest than the time-dependent value of S is its average value $\overline{S}$ over an integral number of half-periods. Since the average value of $\sin^2 (\omega t)$ over an integral number of half-periods is 1/2, we have

$$\overline{S} = \frac{1}{2\mu_0} E_0 B_0 \tag{34-25}$$

Two alternative forms of $\overline{S}$ are

$$\overline{S} = \tfrac{1}{2}\epsilon_0 E_0^2 c \quad \text{and} \quad \overline{S} = \frac{cB_0^2}{2\mu_0}$$

The average intensity is proportional to the square of the wave amplitude.

The average intensity of a wave is proportional to the wave amplitude squared. Ordinarily when one speaks of the intensity of a wave, one is referring to the average intensity.

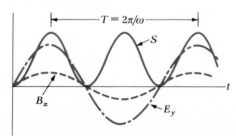

Figure 34-8. Graphs of E_y, B_z, and S versus time t. Each of these quantities has a different unit, so the scales shown here are arbitrary.

EXAMPLE 34-3. (*a*) Determine the average intensity of the wave discussed in Example 34-2. (*b*) Write an expression for the Poynting vector of this wave.

SOLUTION. (*a*) From Example 34-2, $E_0 = 120$ N/C. Using $\bar{S} = \frac{1}{2}\epsilon_0 E_0^2 c$, we have

$$\bar{S} = \frac{1}{2}(8.85) \times 10^{-12} \text{ C}^2/\text{N} \cdot \text{m}^2)(120 \text{ N/C})^2(3.00 \times 10^8 \text{ m/s})$$

$$= 19.1 \text{ W/m}^2$$

(*b*) From Eq. (34-25), we see that $E_0 B_0/\mu_0 = 2\bar{S}$. Substitution into Eq. (34-24) gives

$$S = 2\bar{S} \sin^2{(kx - \omega t)}$$

Using the values of k and ω from Example 34-2 and $\bar{S}$ from part (*a*), we have

$$\mathbf{S} = \{(38.2 \text{ W/m}^2) \sin^2{[(1.05 \text{ rad/m})x - (3.14 \times 10^8 \text{ rad/s})t]}\}\boldsymbol{i}$$

34-6 RADIATION PRESSURE

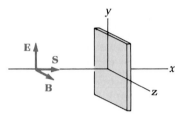

Figure 34-9. An electromagnetic wave is incident normally on a completely absorbing dielectric slab.

We have discussed electromagnetic waves passing through free space. What happens when such a wave encounters a material object? For example, what happens when electromagnetic radiation is absorbed at the surface of an object? In Prob. 34-3, we present a model that is helpful in visualizing the absorption of radiation by matter. This model introduces the concept of *radiation pressure* and provides the relation between absorbed intensity and radiation pressure. In this section, we give a qualitative discussion of the results you will get when you solve the problem.

When an electromagnetic wave is absorbed by an object, the wave's energy is transferred to some of the charged particles which compose the object. Consider the absorption of radiation by an opaque insulator (Fig. 34-9). Recall that the charged particles of an insulator are bound and are not free to move through the material. Although an electric field can displace the particles, the displacement is temporary and the particles will return to their original sites after the field is reduced to zero. Therefore, in our model of absorption, each charged particle is bound to a center and executes an oscillatory motion in response to the oscillating fields of the wave. We assume that the resulting velocity of a particle is parallel to the direction of the force due to the electric field, so the electric field does work on each of the particles. This work constitutes the energy transfer from the wave to the object. This electric force averaged over an integral number of cycles is zero because its direction changes every half-cycle. Thus the electric field does work on the charges but does not tend to displace the entire object.

In contrast, the magnetic field of the wave does no work on the particles because the magnetic force on a particle is directed perpendicular to its velocity ($\mathbf{F}_m = q\mathbf{v} \times \mathbf{B}$). Even though the oscillating magnetic field changes direction every half-cycle, the magnetic force on a particle averaged over an integral number of cycles is not zero. This average magnetic force is in the direction of propagation so that it tends to displace the entire object in that direction. In this model of absorption, the electric field part of the wave is responsible for energy being transferred to the object, and the magnetic field part of the wave is responsible for a force being exerted on the object in the direction of the propagation of the wave.

The solution to Prob. 34-3 shows that the relation between the pressure p exerted on a surface and the intensity S absorbed by the surface is

$$p = \frac{S}{c} \qquad \text{(total absorption)} \qquad (34\text{-}26)$$

where **S** is normal to the surface. The force on the object due to this radiation pressure changes the momentum of the object. By conservation of momentum, the momentum transferred to the object must have come from the wave. Thus electromagnetic waves transport momentum as well as energy. When the waves encounter a material object, the waves transfer this momentum to the object.

Suppose the radiation incident on an object is reflected instead of absorbed. Recall the analogous case of a ball of mass m and speed v thrown against a wall such that the ball's initial velocity is normal to the wall's surface. The magnitude of the momentum Δp_w imparted to the wall is equal to the magnitude of the change in momentum of the ball by conservation of momentum. If the ball sticks to the wall, then $\Delta p_w = mv$ because the ball's initial momentum has magnitude mv and its final momentum is virtually zero. If the ball has an elastic collision with the wall, then $\Delta p_w = 2mv$ because the ball's final momentum is equal in magnitude but opposite in direction to its initial momentum.

Similarly, we can apply the principle of conservation of momentum to the interaction of radiation with a surface. The pressure exerted on a surface by a normally incident wave that is totally absorbed is $p = S/c$ from Eq. (34-26). The initial momentum of the wave was directed toward the surface and the wave was absorbed. Now suppose a normally incident wave is totally reflected by a surface. In this case the final momentum of the reflected wave is equal in magnitude but opposite in direction to the initial momentum of the incident wave. Thus the momentum imparted to the surface is double what it is for absorption, so the resulting pressure is doubled. In this case,

$$p = \frac{2S}{c} \quad \text{(total reflection)} \tag{34-27}$$

where S is the incident intensity of the wave.

The two expressions for radiation pressure, Eqs. (34-26) and (34-27), are valid for the two extreme cases of total absorption and total reflection. A real object partially reflects and partially absorbs radiation incident on its surface. The radiation pressure depends on the fraction of light that is reflected. Its value is in the range $S/c < p < 2S/c$.

Radiation pressure is difficult to detect. An ordinary beam of light that is readily observed because of its intensity will exert a radiation pressure that is miniscule. The first measurements of radiation pressure were made just after the turn of the century (1901–1903), about 30 years after the effect was predicted by Maxwell.

Comet Mrkos. Comets have two tails. One tail is dust being blown from the comet by the radiation of sunlight, and the other is the ion tail which is caused by solar wind, a flow of charged particles (mostly protons and electrons) from the sun. *(Photo Researchers)*

EXAMPLE 34-4. When the sun is directly overhead on a clear day, the incident intensity on a horizontal surface at sea level is about 1 kW/m². (a) Assuming that 50 percent of this intensity is reflected and 50 percent is absorbed, determine the radiation pressure on this horizontal surface. (b) Find the ratio of this pressure to atmospheric pressure p_0 (about 1×10^5 Pa) at sea level.

SOLUTION. (a) The half of the light that is absorbed exerts a radiation pressure of $\frac{1}{2}(S/c)$ and the half that is reflected exerts a pressure $\frac{1}{2}(2S/c)$. The total radiation pressure on the

surface is

$$p_{\text{rad}} = \frac{\frac{3}{2}S}{c} = \frac{(1.5)(1 \text{ kW/m}^2)}{3 \times 10^8 \text{ m/s}} = 5 \times 10^{-6} \text{ Pa}$$

(b)

$$\frac{p_{\text{rad}}}{p_0} = \frac{5 \times 10^{-6} \text{ Pa}}{1 \times 10^5 \text{ Pa}} = 5 \times 10^{-11}$$

The radiation pressure due to sunlight at the earth's surface is negligibly small compared with the atmospheric pressure.

34-7 EMISSION OF ELECTROMAGNETIC WAVES

As electromagnetic waves propagate through space, the time-varying magnetic field induces an electric field and the time-varying electric field induces a magnetic field. According to Maxwell's equations, the existence of one of these time-varying fields requires the existence of the other. What is the source of these wave fields? We know that a stationary object with a static charge distribution produces a static electric field. Also, a wire carrying a steady current (the charge carriers have a constant average velocity) produces a static magnetic field. Therefore, stationary charges or charges moving with constant velocity do not produce time-dependent wave fields. To produce a wave field, a charge must accelerate. An accelerating charge (or system of charges) is a source of electromagnetic waves.

An accelerating charge produces electromagnetic waves.

To visualize how accelerated charges can lead to the generation of electromagnetic waves, consider the electric field of a dipole with point charges $+q$ at $(0, \frac{1}{2}\ell, 0)$ and $-q$ at $(0, -\frac{1}{2}\ell, 0)$ shown in Fig. 34-10. In Fig. 34-10a you are reminded that the field **E** is the vector sum of the individual fields due to each charge, so that at point O on the x axis the field is directed in the $-y$ direction. Now suppose the positions of the two charges are quickly interchanged around the time $t = 0$. Maxwell's equations show that the effect of this interchange propagates outward from the charges at speed c. Figure 34-10b shows the field at time t at points along the x axis in the vicinity of point O, far from the dipole. Since O is a distance ct from the dipole, the field at points farther from the dipole than point O is still directed toward $-y$, characteristic of the positions of the charges at times earlier than $t = 0$. At points closer to the dipole than O, the field is directed toward $+y$, which is characteristic of the positions

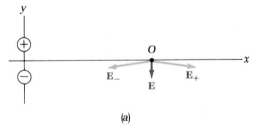

(a)

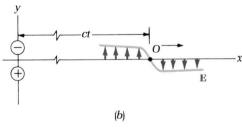

(b)

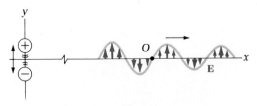

(c)

Figure 34-10. (*a*) A stationary electric dipole. (*b*) The charges exchange positions at time $t = 0$, which causes a wave pulse to propagate at speed c and pass point O at time t. (*c*) The charges continually exchange positions, producing an oscillating electric field at point O.

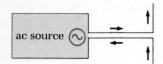

Figure 34-11. A transmitting electric-dipole antenna.

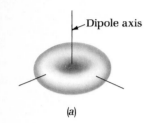

(a)

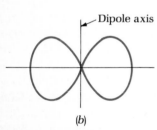

(b)

Figure 34-12. Intensity distribution for a transmitting electric-dipole antenna located at the origin. (a) Shown in three dimensions. (b) Shown in cross section.

of the charges at times later than $t = 0$. A wave pulse in the electric field propagates outward at speed c. If the two charges oscillate back and forth between the two positions, then an oscillating electric field propagates outward, as suggested in Fig. 34-10c.

This simple picture is useful to illustrate the emission of electromagnetic waves, but we cannot extend it further. We based this picture on the static field of a dipole, but at large distances r from the charges this field falls off with distance as $1/r^3$ (Sec. 20-6). From Sec. 32-6, the intensity of a wave decreases with distance from a distant source as $1/r^2$. Also, the intensity of an electromagnetic wave depends on E^2. For the intensity to fall off as $1/r^2$, E^2 must fall off as $1/r^2$. Thus the wave fields which transport significant energy from the source must fall off as $1/r$.

The oscillating charges of Fig. 34-10 are similar to a common arrangement used to emit electromagnetic waves, an electric-dipole antenna. Figure 34-11 schematically shows an electric-dipole antenna used to emit electromagnetic waves, a transmitting antenna. The source of alternating current alternately places charges of first one sign and then the other on each half of the antenna. An electromagnetic wave is emitted whose frequency ν is the same as the frequency of the ac source.

The distribution of the radiated intensity from a transmitting electric-dipole antenna located at the origin is shown in Fig. 34-12. On the scale of this figure, the antenna is too small to be seen. The (nearly) doughnut-shaped surface in Fig. 34-12a depicts the intensity pattern. The distance from the antenna to a point on the surface along a particular direction corresponds to the intensity emitted in that direction. The figure indicates that the intensity emitted in the perpendicular bisector plane of the antenna is maximum and that no energy is radiated along the axis of the antenna.

During the period from 1887 to 1890, H. R. Hertz (1857–1894) conducted a series of experiments in which he generated and detected electromagnetic waves. He used an ac source which drove a transmitting antenna at a frequency of about 1 GHz. The receiving antenna was connected to a circuit tuned to the same frequency. The distances over which he transmitted and

Heinrich Hertz (1857–1894) was born in Hamburg, Germany, and graduated from the University of Berlin. In addition to his famous experiments on electromagnetic waves, he discovered the photoelectric effect (Chap. 39). (*A.I.P., Niels Bohr Library*)

detected waves were as great as 20 m.* Hertz showed that, similar to light, these waves could be polarized, reflected, and refracted, and he measured their speed to be the same as the speed of light. This direct verification of Maxwell's theory was performed about a decade after Maxwell's death.

34-8 THE ELECTROMAGNETIC SPECTRUM

The wavelength λ and the frequency ν of electromagnetic waves in vacuum are related by the expression

$$c = \lambda\nu$$

where $c = 3.00 \times 10^8$ m/s. All frequency and wavelength values which satisfy $c = \lambda\nu$ are allowed. There are no intrinsic upper or lower limits to the wavelengths or frequencies. The *electromagnetic spectrum*, shown in Fig. 34-13, is the range of wavelengths or frequencies that are of most interest to us. To display conveniently the vast range of values of wavelength and frequency, scaling about 24 orders of magnitude, we use a logarithmic scale. Various intervals of the spectrum are given names which correspond to the origin or use of the waves — for instance, radio waves.

Figure 34-14 shows the range of wavelengths that can be readily detected by the human eye, the visible spectrum. Not only does the eye detect this radiation, but it also can distinguish different wavelengths by the sensation of color. The colors associated with various wavelength intervals are shown in the figure. A harmonic electromagnetic wave with its wavelength (or frequency) in the visible spectrum corresponds to a specific color. For this reason, visible

> Monochromatic light consists of a harmonic electromagnetic wave.

light which consists of a harmonic wave is sometimes called *monochromatic* (meaning one color) light. The term "monochromatic" is often used to refer to any single-frequency or harmonic electromagnetic wave. For example, we might refer to harmonic x-rays as monochromatic x-rays. In addition to his many other contributions, Maxwell was an expert on color vision and made several important discoveries in this field.

---

* By 1901 Guglielmo Marconi (1874–1937) had detected electromagnetic waves that were transmitted from the other side of the Atlantic Ocean.

Figure 34-13. The electromagnetic spectrum.

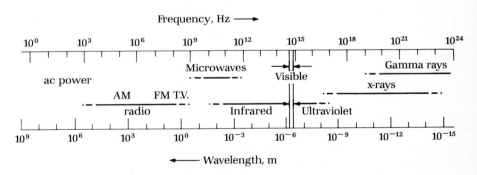

Figure 34-14. The wavelengths of the visible spectrum.

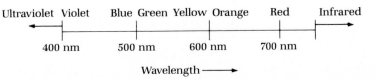

White light, such as sunlight, is a mixture of many wavelengths, or colors. Several phenomena can separate white light into its constituent colors; a rainbow is a beautiful example. The entire electromagnetic spectrum shown in Fig. 34-13 has been called "Maxwell's rainbow."

COMMENTARY: THE SPEED OF LIGHT

The speed of light in vacuum is a fundamental property of nature. As such, an accurate and precise measurement of c has been of great importance to the development of physics.

In 1638 Galileo published a description of his attempts at measuring the speed of light. He reportedly stationed himself on a hilltop with a lamp and an assistant on a neighboring hilltop with another lamp (initially covered). The assistant was instructed to remove the cover from his lamp at the instant he saw a flash from Galileo's lamp. Galileo intended to determine the speed of light from the round-trip distance between the two hills and the time interval between when the flash was sent out and his observation of light from the assistant's lamp. The time interval was so small that Galileo correctly concluded that the human reaction time was longer than the time required for light to complete the round-trip. But he was unable to state whether the speed was simply very large or, indeed, infinite.

During the seventeenth century a great debate raged over the issue of whether light traveled at a finite speed. In 1676 Ole Roemer (1644–1710) reported that he had discovered a variation in the times at which the moon Io, in its orbit around Jupiter, was eclipsed by Jupiter. Roemer correlated this variation to the relative positions of the earth and Jupiter in their orbits around the sun. He attributed the variation of the observed eclipse times to the different time intervals required for light to travel from Io to the earth. He found that light required 22 min to traverse the diameter of the earth's orbit. (From modern measurements, we now know that this time interval is about 17 min.)

Despite Roemer's evidence, the debate continued well into the next century. In 1729 James Bradley (1693–1762) effectively ended the controversy when he published his discovery of the aberration of light from stars due to the earth's orbital motion. The value of the speed of light determined by Bradley was in close agreement with values found using Roemer's method.

The definition of the meter is now based on the speed of light in vacuum (Sec. 1-2). A meter is the distance traveled by light in vacuum in a time interval of (1/299,792,458) s. Thus, from the definition of the meter, the speed of light in vacuum is exactly 299,792,458 m/s.

SUMMARY WITH APPLICATIONS

Sections 34-2 through 34-4. Maxwell's equations; the wave equation for E and B; electromagnetic waves

Maxwell's equations can be used to show that the **E** and **B** fields for a plane wave in vacuum (i) are perpendicular to the propagation direction, (ii) are perpendicular to each other, (iii) obey the wave equations with the speed $c = 1/\sqrt{\mu_0\epsilon_0}$, (iv) are in phase and have the same wavelength and frequency,

and (v) have amplitudes related by $E_0 = cB_0$. Equations for a harmonic, plane-polarized electromagnetic wave are

$$E_y = E_0 \sin (kx - \omega t) \qquad (34\text{-}15)$$

$$B_z = B_0 \sin (kx - \omega t) \qquad (34\text{-}16)$$

where the wave propagates in the $+x$ direction with speed $c = \omega/k$ and the xy plane is the plane of polarization.

Show that Maxwell's equations require the wave fields to be transverse and mutually perpendicular; show that Maxwell's equations lead to wave equations for **E** and **B** and describe the harmonic solutions to these equations; use Maxwell's equations to develop the connection between the electric and magnetic fields for a plane wave.

Section 34-5. Electromagnetic wave intensity

The Poynting vector **S** points in the direction of propagation and its magnitude is the wave intensity:

$$\mathbf{S} = \frac{1}{\mu_0}\mathbf{E} \times \mathbf{B} \qquad (34\text{-}23)$$

The average intensity $\bar{S}$ is proportional to the square of the wave amplitude:

$$\bar{S} = \tfrac{1}{2}\epsilon_0 E_0^2 c = \left(\frac{B_0{}^2}{2\mu_0}\right) c$$

Describe the meaning of the Poynting vector and determine the intensity of electromagnetic waves.

Section 34-6. Radiation pressure

Electromagnetic waves transport momentum as well as energy. If an electromagnetic wave with intensity S is incident normally on a surface and is totally absorbed by the surface, then the radiation pressure on the surface is $p = S/c$. If the wave is completely reflected by the surface, then $p = 2S/c$.

Describe how an electromagnetic wave can exert a force on an object whose charged particles interact with the wave.

Section 34-7. Emission of electromagnetic waves

The source of electromagnetic waves is an accelerating charge or system of charges. If a charge oscillates with frequency ν, then it generates waves of the same frequency.

Describe the way an oscillating charge is a source of electromagnetic waves.

Section 34-8. The electromagnetic spectrum

The frequencies (or wavelengths) of electromagnetic waves span many orders of magnitude. Visible light corresponds to a small slice of the electromagnetic spectrum.

State the range of frequencies and wavelengths which correspond to some of the important types of electromagnetic waves.

QUESTIONS

34-1   What is it that waves when an electromagnetic wave goes by?

34-2   Can an electric or magnetic field that is static in a region of free space have an effect on an electromagnetic wave passing through the region? Explain. Now reconsider this question for a transparent medium, assuming that κ depends on **E**.

34-3   When electric and magnetic fields were first introduced in this text (Chaps. 20 and 26), we could have regarded them as no more than computational tools for the calculation of electric and magnetic forces. In view of the electromagnetic waves described in this chapter, do you think that these fields are simply mathematical artifacts or do you think they really exist? Use experimental facts to support your contention that the fields do or do not exist.

34-4   When we discovered that the wavelike **E** and **B** fields far from their source were transverse (Sec. 34-3), we oriented the y axis of our coordinate system along **E** and later found that Faraday's law requires **B** to be along the z axis. Now suppose we let the y axis be along **B**, and proceed to find the direction of **E**. Which one of Maxwell's equations do we use? Describe the integration path that we should use.

34-5   Suppose an electromagnetic wave passes through a region that contains a volume charge density. Must the wavelike electric field be perpendicular to the direction of propagation? Explain.

34-6   If Ampere's law did not contain the term added by Maxwell, could Maxwell's equations still be combined to give wave equations for **E** and **B**? Suppose this added term is entered into Ampere's law with a minus sign instead of a plus sign. Could Maxwell's equations still be combined to give wave equations?

34-7   In developing the wave equations for **E** and **B**, we assumed that the order of the x and t differentiation of B_z did not affect the result. Make up a function of x and t and take its derivative with respect to x and then its derivative with respect to t. Now take these derivatives of your function in reverse order—first t, then x. Are the derivatives equal? Attempt to find a function of x and t in which changing the order of differentiation changes the result.

34-8   Consider a comparison between sound waves and light waves. What are some similarities and what are some differences?

34-9   Can light waves travel through a perfect vacuum? Does vacuum have any physical properties? If so, name some of the properties of vacuum.

34-10 Recall that a wave in an elastic medium, such as a sound wave in air, has a speed given by the square root of the ratio of an elastic-force factor to an inertial-mass factor. Both of these factors are characteristic of the medium. If we regard vacuum as an elastic "medium" which supports light waves, then what can be said about this ratio for vacuum?

34-11 In a letter to William Thomson (Lord Kelvin) in 1861, Maxwell wrote: "I made out the equations in the country before I had any suspicion of the nearness of the two values of the velocity of propagation of magnetic effects and that of light, so that I think I have reason to believe that the magnetic and luminiferous media are identical.'' What did Maxwell mean by the magnetic medium? What did he mean by the luminiferous medium?

34-12 Consider a plane-polarized electromagnetic wave traveling horizontally toward the north. The plane of polarization is vertical. Determine which of the quantities, **E**, **B**, or **S**, is described by each of the following statements:

(a) It points continually northward with a magnitude that oscillates between zero and a maximum.

(b) Its direction oscillates along the vertical, pointing upward for half a cycle and then downward the other half.

(c) Its direction oscillates along the horizontal, pointing eastward for half a cycle and then westward for the other half.

34-13 In each part of Fig. 34-15, two of the three quantities **E**, **B**, and **S** which describe a plane electromagnetic wave are shown at a point in space. (The waves are different in each case.) In terms of the cartesian unit vectors, (a) what is the direction of **S** in Fig. 34-15a? (b) What is the direction of **B** in Fig. 34-15b? (c) What is the direction of **E** in Fig. 34-15c?

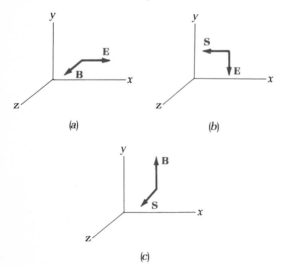

(a)   (b)

(c)

Figure 34-15. Ques. 34-13.

34-14 A number of parameters are associated with the description of a harmonic, plane-polarized electromagnetic wave: E_0, B_0, $\bar{S}$, k, λ, ω, and ν. To write an equation for a particular wave traveling in vacuum, what is the minimum number of these parameters that must be given? Of this minimum number, will any of the above suffice or do we need specific ones? For example, if you are given ν, do you also need k? If you are given $\bar{S}$, do you also need E_0?

34-15 If the amplitude of the electric field part of a wave is tripled, by what factor is the average intensity

changed? By what factor is the amplitude of the magnetic field changed?

34-16 Consider the flux of the Poynting vector for a surface: $\int \mathbf{S} \cdot d\mathbf{A}$, where $d\mathbf{A}$ is the differential surface vector for an element of area. What is the dimension of this flux? What is its SI unit? Explain the physical meaning of this flux.

34-17 When you turn on a flashlight, does the flashlight tend to recoil in your hand. If so, will you feel this recoil? Explain.

34-18 Would it be possible in principle to use a ''sailing'' spaceship to travel to Jupiter? To Venus? Should your sails be good reflectors or good absorbers?

34-19 In principle, is it possible for an electromagnetic wave to transfer momentum to an object but not transfer energy? Explain. Is it possible to transfer energy but not momentum? Explain.

34-20 A magnetic-dipole antenna is shown in Fig. 34-16. An ac source drives a current around the circular loop of wire first in one sense and then in the other. Sketch a representation of the magnetic field along the x axis in the vicinity of point P which is far from the loop compared with the loop size or the wavelength of the waves. Explain why this antenna is called a magnetic-dipole antenna.

Figure 34-16. Ques. 34-20.

34-21 Consider the electromagnetic spectrum shown in Fig. 34-13. What type of waves have wavelengths about the length of a football field? The length of a finger? The width of a hair? The size of an atom? The size of a nucleus?

34-22 Figure 34-12 indicates that no intensity is emitted from an electric-dipole transmitting antenna along the direction in which the antenna is aligned. Give a plausible argument why this is so by using the transverse nature of electromagnetic waves.

34-23 In a comparison of infrared and ultraviolet light, which has the larger wavelength? Which has the larger frequency?

34-24 Describe how you could determine the speed of light by making electric and magnetic measurements. List the apparatus you would need. Is a clock necessary?

34-25 Complete the following table:

Symbol	Represents	Type	SI unit
c	Speed of light in vacuum		
u			J/m³
S		Vector	
p			

EXERCISES

Section 34-3. The wave equation for E and B

34-1   (a) Show that the dimension of $1/\sqrt{\epsilon_0\mu_0}$ is length/time. (b) Show by substitution that the SI unit for $1/\sqrt{\epsilon_0\mu_0}$ is m/s.

34-2   (a) Show that $E_y = E_0 \sin[k(x-ct)]$ is a solution to Eq. (34-8) if $c = 1/\sqrt{\mu_0\epsilon_0}$. What is the direction of propagation of this wave? (b) Show that $E_y = E_0 \sin[k(x+ct)]$ is a solution to Eq. (34-8) if $c = 1/\sqrt{\mu_0\epsilon_0}$. What is the direction of propagation of this wave?

34-3   (a) Show that if the dependence of E_y on x and t is in the form $x - ct$, then E_y is a solution to the wave equation. That is, show that $E_y = f(x - ct)$ is a solution to Eq. (34-8), with $c = 1/\sqrt{\mu_0\epsilon_0}$. [Hint: Let $\xi = x - ct$. Note that $\partial E_y/\partial x = df/d\xi$ and $\partial E_y/\partial t = -c(df/d\xi)$.] What is the direction of propagation of this wave? (b) Show that $E_y = g(x + ct)$ is a solution to Eq. (34-8). What is the direction of propagation of this wave?

34-4   The speed of visible light in water is 2.25×10^8 m/s. What is the dielectric constant of water at optical frequencies?

34-5   The dielectric constant of ice at optical frequencies is 1.71. What is the speed of visible light in ice?

34-6   Suppose $B_z = B_0 \sin[k(x - ct)]$. Show that

$$\frac{\partial}{\partial x}\frac{\partial B_z}{\partial t} = \frac{\partial}{\partial t}\frac{\partial B_z}{\partial x}$$

34-7   Suppose the x and t dependence of B_z can be expressed $B_z = f(x - ct)$, where f and its first and second derivatives are continuous. Show that

$$\frac{\partial}{\partial x}\frac{\partial B_z}{\partial t} = \frac{\partial}{\partial t}\frac{\partial B_z}{\partial x}$$

(You may wish to use the hint from Exercise 34-3.)

34-8   To show that the wavelike **E** and **B** fields are mutually perpendicular, we oriented our y axis along the oscillating **E** field and used Faraday's law to show that the oscillating **B** field is along the z axis. Instead, let the y axis be along **B** and use the modified form of Ampere's law to find the direction of **E**. Note that the term involving ΣI is zero in vacuum.

34-9   To develop Eq. (34-6), we integrated around the square path in Fig. 34-5 in the counterclockwise sense. Develop Eq. (34-6) by integrating around this path in the clockwise sense.

34-10   Use Eqs. (34-6) and (34-7) to develop the wave equation for B_z, Eq. (34-9).

Section 34-4. Electromagnetic waves

34-11   (a) What is the wavelength of the waves from an FM radio station with a frequency of 100 MHz? (b) What is the wavelength of the waves from an AM radio station with a frequency of 1000 kHz?

34-12   A harmonic electromagnetic wave passes by a foot-ball field. At an instant the spatial variation of the electric field part of the wave can be represented as shown in Fig. 34-17. (a) Estimate the frequency of this wave. (b) Use Fig. 34-13 to categorize this wave.

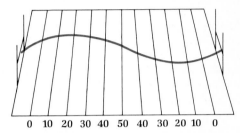

Figure 34-17. Exercise 34-12.

34-13   The amplitude of the magnetic field part of a harmonic electromagnetic wave in vacuum is $B_0 = 510$ nT. What is the amplitude of the electric field part of the wave? Would your answer be different if the wave were in air?

34-14   The angular frequency of a harmonic electromagnetic wave in vacuum is $\omega = 8.2 \times 10^{12}$ rad/s. Determine the wave number, wavelength, frequency, and period of this wave. Would any of your answers be different if the wave were in air? From Fig. 34-13, what type of wave is this?

34-15   Suppose the electric field part of an electromagnetic wave in vacuum is

$$\mathbf{E} = \{(31\text{ N/C}) \cos[(1.8\text{ rad/m})y + (5.4 \times 10^8\text{ rad/s})t]\}\,\mathbf{i}$$

(a) What is the direction of propagation? (b) What is the wavelength λ? (c) What is the frequency ν? (d) What is the amplitude of the magnetic field part of the wave? (e) Write an expression for the magnetic field part of the wave.

34-16   Write expressions for the **E** and **B** fields of an electromagnetic wave which propagates in vacuum toward the $+z$ direction and has its plane of polarization parallel to the xz plane. The amplitude of the magnetic field part of the wave is $B_0 = 350$ nT and the frequency of the wave is $\nu = 9.8$ GHz. Would your expressions be different if the wave were traveling in air? From Fig. 34-13, what type of wave is this?

34-17   Using Eqs. (34-14) (34-15), and (34-16), develop Eq. (34-17).

Section 34-5. Electromagnetic wave intensity

34-18   Equation (34-21) connects intensity with energy density, $S = uc$. Show that the dimension of intensity is the same as the dimension of the product of energy density and speed.

34-19   Suppose the electromagnetic wave intensity at a particular instant and at a point in vacuum is 1 kW/m².

What is the energy density at that point and instant? Would your answer be different if the wave were in air?

34-20 The magnitude of the electric field due to an electromagnetic wave at a particular instant at a point in free space is 97 N/C. What is the energy density at that point and instant? Would your answer be different if the wave were in air?

34-21 (a) Show that the energy density due to an electromagnetic wave at a particular instant at a point in free space can be written $u = B^2/\mu_0$. (b) Show that the intensity can be written $S = B^2c/\mu_0$. (c) Determine u and S at a point and instant at which $B = 530$ nT.

34-22 Show that the intensity due to a plane-polarized electromagnetic wave in which the plane of polarization is parallel to the xy plane and the direction of propagation is toward $+x$ can be written $S = E_yB_z/\mu_0$.

34-23 Show that the average intensity of a harmonic wave can be written as (a) $\bar{S} = \frac{1}{2}\epsilon_0 E_0^2 c$ and (b) $\bar{S} = (B_0^2/2\mu_0)c$.

34-24 Suppose the average intensity $\bar{S}$ of a harmonic electromagnetic wave in vacuum or free space is 553 W/m². (a) What is the amplitude of the electric field due to the wave? (b) What is the amplitude of the magnetic field due to the wave? (c) Determine these amplitudes when a wave of this average intensity travels in air.

34-25 The Poynting vector of an electromagnetic wave in vacuum is

$$\mathbf{S} = -\{(220 \text{ W/m}^2) \cos^2 [(12 \text{ rad/m})z$$
$$+ (3.6 \times 10^9 \text{ rad/s})t]\}\mathbf{k}$$

(a) What is the direction of propagation? (b) What is the wavelength λ? (c) What is the frequency ν? (d) Write expressions for the $\mathbf{E}$ and $\mathbf{B}$ fields.

34-26 An electromagnetic wave in vacuum is traveling in the $+z$ direction, and its plane of polarization is parallel to the xz plane. The frequency of the wave is $\nu = 50$ MHz and its average intensity is $\bar{S} = 480$ W/m². Write expressions for $\mathbf{E}$, $\mathbf{B}$, and $\mathbf{S}$ as functions of z and t. Would these expressions be different if the wave were in air?

34-27 A light wave (in vacuum) with its plane of polarization parallel to the xy plane propagates in the $+x$ direction. The wavelength of the wave is 580 nm, and its oscillating magnetic field has an amplitude of 86 nT. Write expressions for $\mathbf{E}$, $\mathbf{B}$, and $\mathbf{S}$.

34-28 The average intensity of sunlight at the top of the earth's atmosphere is 1.35 kW/m². This radiation is unpolarized and consists of many frequencies, but, for purposes of this calculation, regard it as plane-polarized and harmonic or monochromatic. (a) What is the amplitude of the electric field part of the wave? (b) What is the amplitude of the magnetic field part of the wave? (c) What is the average electromagnetic energy density of the wave?

34-29 A helium-neon laser sends a beam of collimated, plane-polarized, monochromatic light into the air of a room. The beam has a circular cross section with a radius of 1.0 mm, and the intensity is essentially uniform within the beam. The average power of the beam is 3.5 mW and the wavelength of the light is 633 nm. (a) Determine $\bar{S}$ for the beam. (b) Determine the electromagnetic energy contained in a 1.0-m length of the beam. (c) Determine the amplitude of the electric field part of the wave. (d) Determine the amplitude of the magnetic field part of the wave. (e) If the beam direction is horizontal toward the north and the electric field oscillates along the horizontal east-west, what is the direction of the oscillating magnetic field? (f) Determine the frequency of the wave.

Section 34-6. Radiation pressure

34-30 From Eq. (34-26), the radiation pressure is $p = S/c$. Show that the dimension of pressure is the same as the dimension of the ratio of intensity to speed.

34-31 The average power in a laser beam is 4.3 mW, and the beam has an essentially uniform intensity within the 1.2-mm radius of the beam. Suppose the beam is normally incident on a completely absorbing surface. (a) What is the pressure exerted by the beam on the part of the surface it strikes? (b) What is the force exerted on the surface by the beam?

34-32 The reflectivity r of a surface is the fraction of light intensity incident on the surface that is reflected. Show that the radiation pressure exerted on a surface of reflectivity r by a normally incident beam of intensity S is $p = (r + 1)S/c$.

34-33 The average intensity of sunlight at the top of the earth's atmosphere is 1.35 W/m². Consider the force exerted on the earth by the absorption of the sun's radiation. (a) Explain why, for purposes of calculating this force, the earth may be regarded as a flat disk facing the sun. (b) Estimate this radiation force by assuming complete absorption. (c) Find the ratio of the radiation force to the gravitational force on the earth by the sun.

34-34 A 10,000-kg spaceship is drifting in interstellar space where all external forces on it are negligible. To propel the spaceship, a 30,000-W laser is turned on and directed into space. (a) What is the acceleration of the spaceship? (b) How many years will it take for the spaceship to change its speed by 1 m/s?

Section 34-7. Emission of electromagnetic waves

34-35 About 5 percent of the power of a 100-W light bulb is converted to visible radiation. (a) What is the average intensity of visible radiation at a distance of 1 m from the bulb? (b) At a distance of 10 m? Assume that the radiation is emitted isotropically and neglect reflections.

34-36 The average intensity of sunlight at the top of the earth's atmosphere is 1.35 kW/m². What is the radiative power of the sun?

34-37 Consider a long array of fluorescent tubes lined up end to end. Each 40-W tube is 1.22 m long and 20 percent of its power is emitted in the visible spectrum. (a) What is the average intensity in the visible spectrum at a perpendicular distance of 1 m from the tubes? (b) At a perpendicular distance of 10 m?

Section 34-8. The electromagnetic spectrum

34-38 What is the wavelength of the radiation from the 60-Hz alternating current in electric power lines?

34-39 Sodium arc lamps are often used in street lights and can be distinguished by their yellow light. The wavelength of this light is 590 nm. What is its frequency?

34-40 It is believed that the two hills used by Galileo in his speed-of-light experiment (see the Commentary) were about 1.5 km apart. What is the time required for light to traverse this round-trip distance?

34-41 The average earth-sun distance is 1.496×10^{11} m. What is the average time required for sunlight to reach the earth?

34-42 One light-year (ly) is the distance light travels in one year. (a) What is the conversion factor that changes meters to light years? (b) What is the conversion factor that changes light years to meters?

PROBLEMS

34-1 Use Gauss's law for the magnetic field to show that the magnetic field for a plane wave is transverse.

34-2 Use the modified form of Ampere's law to develop Eq. (34-7). Note that the term which contains ΣI is zero in vacuum.

34-3 **Radiation pressure.** Consider the following model for the absorption of an electromagnetic wave. A plane-polarized electromagnetic wave propagating in the $+x$ direction is incident normally on the surface of an insulator and is completely absorbed by interacting with the charged particles of the material. These particles are bound to their lattice sites, but they oscillate parallel to the y axis because of the driving electric force $\mathbf{F}_e = (qE_y)\mathbf{j}$ resulting from the oscillating electric field of the wave (Fig. 34-18). Recall from Sec. 14-8 that the power absorbed by an oscillator from the driving force is maximum when the driving force is in phase with the particle's velocity $\mathbf{v}$ (at resonance). Therefore, assume that $\mathbf{F}_e$ is in phase with $\mathbf{v}$. (a) Show that the magnetic force on the particle is $\mathbf{F}_m = (F_e v/c)\mathbf{i}$. (Assume that $v \ll c$ so that $F_m \ll F_e$ and the magnetic force has a negligible effect on the oscillations.) Explain why the magnetic force does *not* alternate in direction along the x axis, but varies between zero and a maximum while being directed toward $+x$ for charges of either sign. (b) Since $\mathbf{F}_e$ and $\mathbf{v}$ have the same direction, the power delivered to a particle by the wave is $F_e v$, and the power delivered to all such particles in the slab is $\Sigma(F_e v)$. Further, the pressure p on the slab of area A due to the magnetic forces on all such particles in the slab is $p = \Sigma(F_m)/A$. Use these results to show that $p = S/c$, where S is the absorbed intensity.

34-4 Consider placing a space station of mass m in the solar system without putting it in orbit around the sun. The station has a large reflecting surface which faces the sun so that it is in equilibrium; the force $\mathbf{F}_{rad}$ due to radiation pressure from the sun's radiated power P is equal and opposite the gravitational force $\mathbf{F}_G$ due to the sun's mass M_S. (Neglect forces due to the planets.) (a) Show that the area A of the station's reflecting surface is

$$A = \frac{2\pi G M_S mc}{P}$$

where G is the gravitational constant. Why is this equilibrium condition independent of the distance between the sun and the station? (b) Suppose the reflecting area is a square of side L and the mass of the station is 10^6 kg. Determine L. The power radiated by the sun is 3.77×10^{26} W.

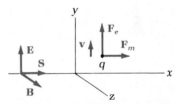

Figure 34-18. Prob. 34-3: An electromagnetic wave interacting with a charged particle. The particle is bound to a central position by a linear restoring force, and we assume that its oscillation frequency is the same as the frequency of the wave. Thus the wave provides a driving force $\mathbf{F}_e = q\mathbf{E}$ in resonance with the particle so that $\mathbf{v}$ is parallel to $\mathbf{F}_e$. The magnetic force $\mathbf{F}_m$ exerted on the particle by the wave is in the direction of propagation.

34-5 Consider a section of wire of length ℓ, resistance R, and radius a carrying a current i (Fig. 34-19). (a) Show that the magnitude of the Poynting vector at the surface of the wire is $S = (i^2 R)/(2\pi a \ell)$. (b) Show that the direction of the Poynting vector at each point on the surface of the wire is normal to the surface and inward (toward the axis of the wire). (c) What is the flux of the Poynting vector for the surface of the wire? (d) Give a physical interpretation of these results.

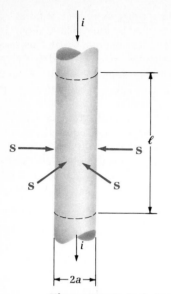

Figure 34-19. Prob. 34-5.

34-6 A plane wave is normally incident on a surface. Show that the energy density just outside the surface is equal to the radiation pressure on the surface.

34-7 **Comet tails.** Consider a spherical object of radius a and uniform mass density ρ that is in equilibrium in the solar system under the action of the attractive gravitational force and the repulsive radiation force due to the sun. (Neglect forces due to the planets.) (a) Show that a completely absorbing object is in equilibrium if

$$a = \frac{3P}{16\pi cGM_s\rho}$$

where M_s is the sun's mass, P is the sun's radiated power, and G is the gravitational constant. (b) Why is this equilibrium condition independent of the distance between the object and the sun? (c) Determine a for a particle whose mass density is about the same as ice $(\rho \approx 10^3 \text{ kg/m}^3)$. The sun's radiated power is 3.77×10^{26} W. (d) What is the fate of particles of this density with radius smaller than a?

34-8 The distance from the earth to the sun in early Jan-uary is 1.446×10^{11} m, and in early July this distance is 1.543×10^{11} m. The power radiated by the sun is 3.77×10^{26} W. Determine the intensity at the top of the earth's atmosphere in (a) early January and (b) early July. (c) With this result, how do you account for the cold weather during January and the hot weather during July?

34-9 Suppose we use the torsion balance shown in Fig. 34-20 to measure radiation pressure. Two coin-shaped mirrors, each of area A and centered a per-pendicular distance ℓ from the axis are connected by a horizontal bar which is suspended by a fiber. The restoring torque τ when the fiber is twisted through an angle $\Delta\theta$ is $\tau = \kappa \, \Delta\theta$, where κ is the torque con-stant of the fiber. Light of known intensity $\bar{S}$ is nor-mally incident on mirror 1 while mirror 2 is shaded, and the suspension comes to equilibrium after turn-ing through an angle $\Delta\theta$. (a) Show that $\Delta\theta$ is given by

$$\Delta\theta = \frac{2\bar{S}A\ell}{c\kappa}$$

(b) Estimate the value required for κ in an experiment in which $\Delta\theta \approx 0.01$ rad, $A \approx 10^{-4}$ m^2, $\ell \approx 0.1$ m, and $\bar{S} \approx 10^5$ W/m^2.

34-10 Estimate the area required to produce electricity, using solar cells, for a typical family of four. Assume the cells have an efficiency of 10 percent for convert-ing solar energy into electric energy. Will the area of a typical rooftop suffice?

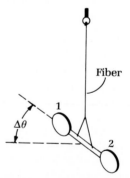

Figure 34-20. Prob. 34-9: A torsion balance for measuring radiation pressure.

CHAPTER 35
GEOMETRICAL OPTICS

35-1 INTRODUCTION

The propagation of light waves is described by Maxwell's equations. The solution of these equations for the conditions of a given physical situation will determine **E** and **B** at every point — and thus the amplitude, polarization, and phase of the light wave at every point. Solving Maxwell's equations may be difficult, and often the detailed information they give is not needed. The information usually required is obtainable by a simpler method called *geometrical optics,* which was devised before light was known to be an electromagnetic wave. It has since been shown to approximate the results of Maxwell's equations when the wavelength of the light is much smaller than the objects that the light wave encounters.

35-2 GEOMETRICAL OPTICS

The crests of an electromagnetic wave progressing outward from a source are shown in Fig. 35-1. Two useful ways to represent the propagating wave are wavefronts and light rays. *Wavefronts* are surfaces of constant phase of the light wave, and can be likened to the crests of a water wave. The wavefronts of a spherical light wave are shown as concentric circles in the two dimensions of Fig. 35-1. A *light ray* is a line pointing in the direction of wave propagation. If the speed of propagation is the same in all directions, the light rays are perpendicular to the wavefronts.

The path followed by a laser beam is a good example of the path of a ray of light. The beam can be observed by the light scattered off small particles in the path of the beam. When a laser beam hits a surface that bounds two different materials, several things can happen. The beam can be absorbed, as happens when a laser beam hits a black piece of paper. If the surface the laser beam hits is rough on a scale comparable to or greater than the wavelength of the light,

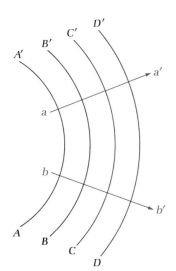

Figure 35-1. Wavefronts in an optical wave. *AA′* is a wavefront and represents positions that have the same phase at a given time, such as the positions of a certain crest of the wave. *BB′, CC′,* and *DD′* are other wavefronts. Lines *aa′* and *bb′* show the direction of propagation of the wave and are called *light rays.*

then the light will be reflected in many directions, as happens when a laser beam hits a white piece of paper. If the laser beam hits a polished metal surface it will be reflected in a single direction, a process called *specular reflection*. If a laser beam in air hits a glass surface it will be both reflected back into the air and transmitted, or *refracted*, into the glass. In this chapter we will be concerned with specular reflection, which we will just call reflection, and refraction.

When the wavelength of the light is much smaller than the dimensions of the physical system through which the light propagates, then the following three laws of *geometrical optics* apply:

Law of rectilinear propagation

1. The law of rectilinear propagation. Light rays in homogeneous media propagate in straight lines.

Law of reflection

2. The law of reflection. At an interface between two media, an incident wave is (partially) reflected. The incident ray and the normal to the surface determine the plane of incidence, as seen in Fig. 35-2. If the incident ray makes an angle θ_1 with the normal, then the reflected ray lies in the plane of incidence on the other side of the normal and makes the same angle with it: $\theta_1 = \theta_{1r}$. In words, the angle of incidence equals the angle of reflection.

3. The law of refraction. The refracted ray is transmitted into the second medium, as shown in Fig. 35-3 (where the reflected ray has been omitted for clarity). The refracted ray also lies in the plane of incidence. It makes an angle θ_2 with the normal given by *Snell's law:*

Snell's law

$$n_1 \sin \theta_1 = n_2 \sin \theta_2 \tag{35-1}$$

where n_1 and n_2 are properties of the two media. The ratio n_1/n_2 is called the *relative index of refraction* and is related to the speed of light rays in the media.

The first two of these laws were known to the ancient Greeks. The law of refraction was assiduously searched for in the early 1600s. Johannes Kepler, for example, found some 27 empirical rules to use in the design of lenses, but

Figure 35-2. The geometry of reflection. The plane of incidence is the plane defined by the normal to the interface between the two media and the incident light ray. The reflected ray lies in this plane on the side of the normal opposite to the incident beam, such that $\theta_{1r} = \theta_1$.

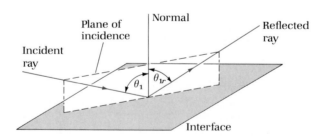

Figure 35-3. The geometry of refraction. The refracted ray lies in the incident plane in the second medium and makes an angle θ_2 with the normal to the interface.

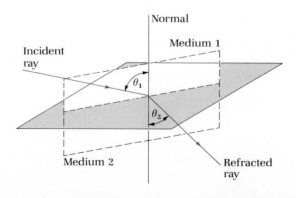

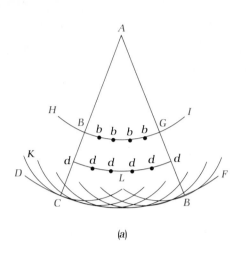

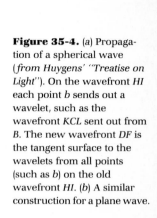

Figure 35-4. (a) Propagation of a spherical wave (*from Huygens' "Treatise on Light"*). On the wavefront *HI* each point *b* sends out a wavelet, such as the wavefront *KCL* sent out from *B*. The new wavefront *DF* is the tangent surface to the wavelets from all points (such as *b*) on the old wavefront *HI*. (b) A similar construction for a plane wave.

(a)   (b)

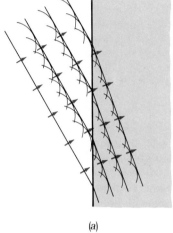

(a)

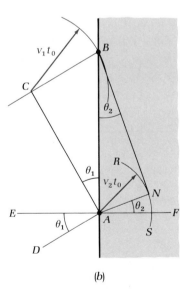

(b)

Figure 35-5. Refraction at a surface. (a) Huygens' construction for refraction at a surface between media with differing speeds for light. Successive positions of the wavefronts as they are refracted. (b) An enlargement of a portion of part (a).

could not formulate a general rule. The law of refraction was probably first formulated by Willebrod Snell about 1620, and was first published by Descartes in 1637 (without mentioning Snell's name).

Pierre de Fermat (1601–1665) and Christian Huygens (1629–1695) formulated principles which led to the laws of ray optics. These principles have been shown to follow from Maxwell's equations in the approximation of ray optics — namely, that the wavelength of light is small compared with the dimensions of all of the parts of the optical system. We now discuss the theory of Huygens. Fermat's principle is illustrated in Probs. 34-1 and 34-2.

Huygens' principle. Huygens, a contemporary of Newton, advocated a wave theory of light in contrast to Newton's corpuscular theory. Huygens' principle states that the propagation of a light wave can be determined by assuming that at every point on a wavefront there arises a spherical wavelet centered on that point. The next wavefront is the outward surface that is tangent to these wavelets. Figure 35-4a, from Huygens, shows that this predicts spherical waves from a point source. Similarly, a plane wavefront generates further plane waves, as shown in Fig. 35-4b. From this, the law of rectilinear propagation follows.

In Fig. 35-5 a plane wavefront is incident on a boundary. Following Huygens' principle, wavelets are constructed from the wavefront AC. The wavelet spreading from C will reach the boundary in a time $t_0 = CB/v_1$, where v_1 is the speed of light in medium 1. The wavelet spreading from A into the second medium travels at a speed v_2, so that it goes a distance $v_2 t_0$ during this time t_0. This wavelet is represented by SNR in the figure. At the same time the other parts of the wave will have sent out wavelets whose radii have as a common tangent the wavefront BN.

To establish Snell's law, note that the angle of incidence $\theta_1 = \angle EAD$ is equal to $\angle CAB$ between the wavefront in medium 1 and the interface, since the sides of these angles are perpendicular. Similarly, θ_2 is equal to the angle between the wavefront in medium 2 and the interface: $\angle FAN = \angle ABN$. From the figure, $\sin \theta_1 = BC/BA$ and $\sin \theta_2 = AN/BA$. Forming the ratio of these gives

$$\frac{\sin \theta_1}{\sin \theta_2} = \frac{BC}{AN} = \frac{v_1 t_0}{v_2 t_0}$$

or

$$v_1^{-1} \sin \theta_1 = v_2^{-1} \sin \theta_2$$

This is same as Snell's law if $n_1/n_2 = v_2/v_1$. Thus not only does Snell's law follow from Huygens' principle, but Huygens' principle predicts that light travels slower in media of higher index. J. B. L. Foucault in 1850 showed that this was true by a direct measurement of the speed of light in water and in air.

Since only the ratio of speeds is involved in Snell's law, only the ratio n_1/n_2 is determined by measurements of refraction. The definition of the index of refraction of a single medium requires a convention. The convention used is that the index of refraction of a vacuum is exactly 1. Since the speed of light in vacuum is the constant c, the index of refraction n for a substance is given by $n/1 = c/v$, or

Definition of index of refraction

$$n = \frac{c}{v}$$

where v is the speed of light in the substance. The indices of several substances are given in Table 35-1.

The index of refraction of a substance depends somewhat on the wavelength of the light being used. If a ray composed of many wavelengths of light is refracted, it will be dispersed into rays whose directions depend on the index of refraction for the various wavelengths. The property whereby n varies with wavelength is called *dispersion*. For many substances at optical wavelengths, the index of refraction decreases as the wavelength increases. Figure 35-6 shows the index of refraction as a function of wavelength for a few substances.

At a boundary where the wave is reflected, Huygens' principle leads to the law of reflection, as shown in Fig. 35-7 and discussed in Exercise 35-3.

Table 35-1. The approximate index of refraction for several substances

Substance	n^*
Gases (at 0°C)	
Air	1.000293
Ammonia	1.000376
Carbon dioxide	1.000451
Chlorine	1.000773
Hydrogen	1.000132
Methane	1.000444
Sulfur dioxide	1.000686
Liquids	
Benzene	1.501
Carbon disulfide	1.625
Ethyl alcohol	1.362
Methyl alcohol	1.329
Methlyene iodide	1.726
Water	1.333
Solids	
Sapphire, ruby (Al_2O_3)	1.767
Diamond	2.417
Glasses: Fused quartz	1.458
Soda lime	1.512
Pyrex	1.474
Dense flint	1.655
Ice (0°C)	1.310
Lucite plastic	1.491
Rutile, E (470 nm)	3.095
Salt (NaCl)	1.544

*Values are at room temperature and atmospheric pressure for light of wavelength 589 nm unless otherwise indicated.

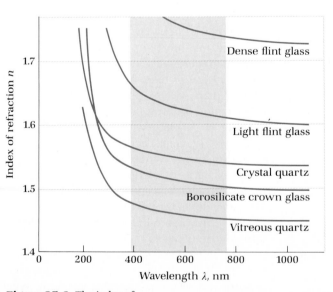

Figure 35-6. The index of refraction of some optical materials as a function of wavelength.

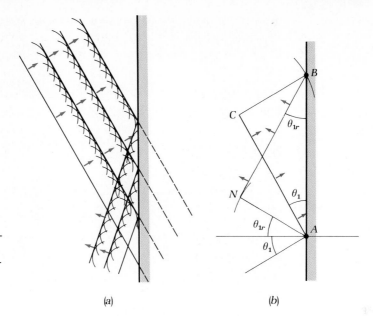

Figure 35-7. (a) Huygens' constuction for reflection. (b) An enlargement of a portion of part (a). The incident wavefronts are parallel to AC, and the reflected wavefronts are parallel to NB.

(a)   (b)

EXAMPLE 35-1. (a) Measurements show that the speed of light in water is 225,000 km/s and in air 299,706 km/s. What are the indices of refraction of the two media? (b) A ray of light is incident from air onto a flat surface of water, as shown in Fig. 35-8. What is the angle of refraction, θ_2?

SOLUTION. (a) The index of refraction for air is $n = (299,792 \text{ km/s})/(299,706 \text{ km/s}) = 1.00029$, and for water $n = (299,792 \text{ km/s})/(225,000 \text{ km/s}) = 1.33$.

(b) From the drawing, the angle of incidence is 28°. From Snell's law, $n_1 \sin \theta_1 = n_2 \sin \theta_2$; thus

$$\theta_2 = \sin^{-1}\left(\frac{n_1}{n_2} \sin \theta_1\right) = 21°$$

Notice that the path of the ray is bent toward the normal to the surface. When a ray goes from a medium of lower index to a medium of higher index, it is always bent toward the normal. What would the angle of refraction be for a ray going from water to air with an angle of incidence of 21°?

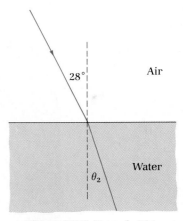

Figure 35-8. Example 35-1.

Total internal reflection. A ray of light proceeding from water to air cannot always get into air. Suppose a light ray comes up to the surface of water at an angle of incidence $\theta_1 = 50°$. Using Snell's law to solve for the angle θ_2 between the ray and the normal on the air side of the interface, we get

$$\theta_2 = \sin^{-1}\left(\frac{n_1}{n_2} \sin \theta_1\right) = \sin^{-1}\left(\frac{1.333}{1.000} 0.766\right)$$

$$= \sin^{-1} 1.021$$

But there is no angle whose sine is greater than 1, so there is no solution to Snell's law for this situation! Why is there no solution? It is because no refracted ray exists for this angle of incidence. The only ray that leaves the interface is the reflected ray.

Figure 35-9. Refraction at an interface between plastic and air. On the top of the plastic semicircle, the light ray is perpendicular to the interface and the angles of incidence and refraction are both 90°. On the bottom, the angle of refraction varies with the angle of incidence. In (c), the refracted ray makes an angle near 90° with the normal to the interface, so that the ray incident on the surface from the plastic hits the surface at nearly the critical angle. In (d), the incident ray makes an angle greater than the critical angle with the normal to the interface, and there is no refracted ray. Notice how the intensity of the reflected and refracted rays vary with the angle of incidence. *(Tom Richard)*

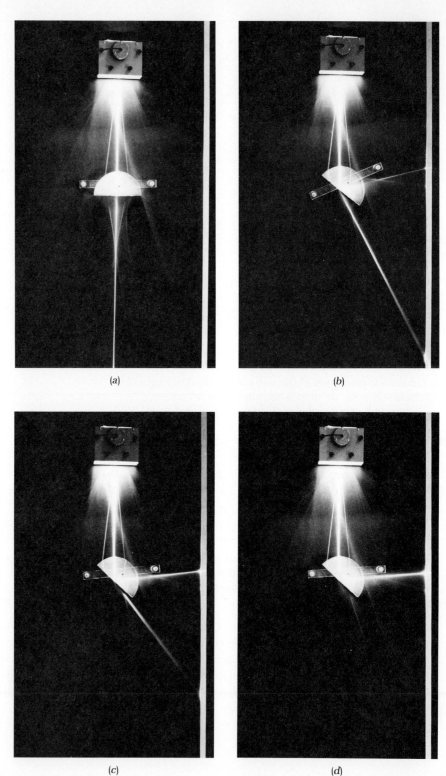

(a)

(b)

(c)

(d)

Figure 35-9 shows what happens to rays approaching such an interface at various angles. Since the rays are going from a medium of higher n to a medium of lower n, each ray is bent away from the normal. The angle of incidence that produces an angle of refraction equal to $90°$ is called the *critical angle* θ_c. Suppose $n_2 < n_1$. Then from Snell's law

$$n_1 \sin \theta_c = n_2 \sin 90° = n_2$$

Critical angle

or
$$\sin \theta_c = \frac{n_2}{n_1} \qquad (35\text{-}2)$$

Rays that approach an interface from the higher-index side with an angle of incidence less than the critical angle are partially reflected and partially refracted. A reflected ray and a refracted ray leave the interface, as seen in Fig. 35-9a, b, and c. Rays that approach the interface from the higher-index side at an angle of incidence greater than the critical angle are totally reflected, as shown in Fig. 35-9d. No refracted ray exists in this case. This phenomenon is

Total internal reflection

called *total internal reflection*. Note that there is no critical angle for light proceeding from a medium of lower index to a medium of higher index. In that case there is always a refracted beam.

Solving the same problem using Maxwell's equations shows that there is an *evanescent wave* in the medium of lower index. The evanescent wave is so called because it decays exponentially to a negligible amplitude a few wavelengths into the lower-index medium. Since ray optics is only valid for geometries in which all dimensions are much larger than a wavelength, ray optics cannot deal with this phenomenon. This evanescent wave can be detected by placing a third medium of index n_1 close to the interface, as shown in Fig. 35-10. If the third medium is very close (several wavelengths of light) to the interface, a ray will be found in the third medium, and the reflection will no longer be total. This phenomenon is called *frustrated total internal reflection*. (See Ques. 35-24.) There is a close relation between this phenomenon and the behavior of electrons at a similar barrier in tunnel diodes.

35-3 IMAGES FORMED BY REFLECTION

When you look into a plane mirror, you see a world very much like your own. Your mind projects the diverging rays that are incident on your eye backwards to the point of convergence, as shown in Fig. 35-11. In other words, the rays diverge from what you perceive to be the object. When you look at a candle at

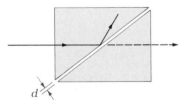

Figure 35-10. Schematic drawing of two prisms placed close together. A ray having an incident angle greater than the critical angle is shown approaching the boundary between the prisms. An evanescent wave is present several wavelengths into the medium of lower index between the prisms. If the prism to the right is pushed within several wavelengths of the prism to the left, a ray will propagate across the interface and into the second prism.

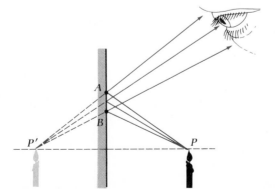

Figure 35-11. Formation of an image by a plane mirror. The backwards projection of the light rays converges at P', the location of the image.

point P in a mirror, you perceive there to be a candle flame at the intersection of the rays, point P'. This is called an *image* of the candle flame. The law of reflection shows that the line PP' is normal to the plane of the mirror and that P and P' are the same distance from the mirror. The image seen in a plane mirror is always the same distance behind the mirror as the object is in front of the mirror. (See Exercise 35-16.)

Curved mirror surfaces also form images. For example, the curved surfaces in fun-house mirrors make images of you that appear elongated or shortened or otherwise distorted. The easiest curved surface to construct and analyze is a spherical surface. Further, spherical or nearly spherical mirrors are used in optical systems such as telescopes and solar collectors. We now discuss the images they form.

Consider the rays which leave a point object P and travel toward the concave mirror of Fig. 35-12. The line joining the object and the center C of the spherical mirror is called the *optic axis*. Rays close to the optic axis, called *paraxial rays,* are all reflected close to the same point P', forming an image of P. The rays that are not paraxial blur this image, an effect called *spherical aberration*. Practical instruments using spherical mirrors minimize this blurring by allowing only rays that are nearly paraxial to be seen.

If we use the law of reflection and geometry with Fig. 35-13, the position of the image formed by paraxial rays can be found in terms of the position of the object and the radius of curvature R of the mirror. The distances s, s', and R are measured from the *vertex V* of the mirror, the point where the optic axis intersects the mirror. From plane geometry, the exterior angle of a triangle is the sum of the two opposite interior angles. For triangles PAC and PAP', this gives $\beta = \alpha + \theta$ and $\gamma = \alpha + 2\theta$. Notice that the radius CA is normal to the mirror surface at A, and thus the incident and reflected rays make the same angle θ with the radius. Eliminating θ between the two equations gives:

$$\alpha + \gamma = 2\beta \qquad (35\text{-}3)$$

For paraxial rays, all these angles are small, so that the radian measures of the angles are $\alpha \approx \ell/s$, $\beta = \ell/R$, and $\gamma \approx \ell/s'$. Substituting the radian measures into

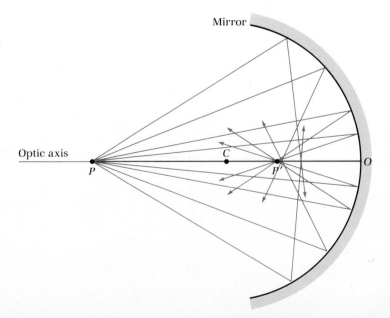

Figure 35-12. Reflection of rays from a concave spherical mirror. Rays from point P are reflected to P' if they are near the optic axis PCO.

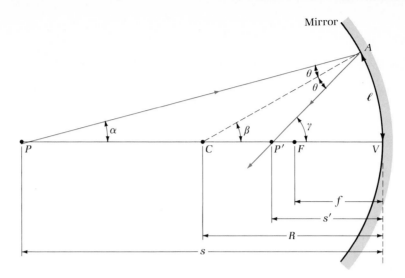

Figure 35-13. The geometry of reflection of paraxial rays by a spherical mirror. A ray leaving the object point P is reflected through the image point P'.

Eq. (35-3) gives

$$\frac{1}{s} + \frac{1}{s'} = \frac{2}{R} \tag{35-4}$$

If $s \to \infty$, then according to the mirror equation the image distance $s' \to R/2$. Thus a source of light far away from the mirror is imaged at point F, a distance $R/2$ from the mirror. This point is called the *focal point F* of the mirror, and the distance $R/2$ is called the *focal length f* of the mirror. In terms of the focal length, the mirror equation is

Focal point and focal length of a mirror

Mirror equation

$$\frac{1}{s} + \frac{1}{s'} = \frac{1}{f} \tag{35-5}$$

When $s \to R/2 = f$, then the image distance $s' \to \infty$. This is like a time-reversed picture of the last case. In this case, rays leave f and on reflection from the mirror propagate to the left, parallel to the optic axis. This is a particular case of the principle of *optical reversibility*, which states that if the direction of a ray is reversed, then it will trace back the path on which it came. The answer to the question at the end of Example 35-1 shows that reversibility works for refraction also.

Optical reversibility

An illustration of the case $s \to f$ involves the concave mirror used to form a beam of parallel rays from a flashlight bulb located at the focal point of the mirror. An illustration of the other case ($s \to \infty$) is a spherical mirror that brings the sun's rays to the focal point of a solar heater such as that shown in Fig. 35-14. Actually, a paraboloid of revolution is a better collector of light for rays

Figure 35-14. A solar heater.

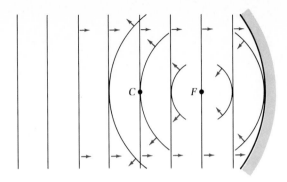

Figure 35-15. Plane wavefronts approaching a spherical mirror are reflected into sperical waves which converge to the focal point *F* of the mirror and then expand in spherical waves like those that would be given off by a point source at *F*.

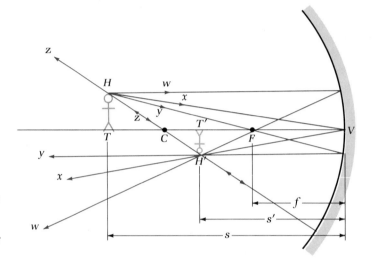

Figure 35-16. The principal rays for a mirror. Ray *w* is parallel to the optic axis *CV*, ray *x* hits the vertex *V*, ray *y* passes through the focus *F*, and ray *z* passes through the center of curvature of the mirror *C*.

Principal rays

which are parallel to the optic axis, bringing all such rays to the same focus, not just the paraxial rays. Such a parabolic shape is not as easy to form as a spherical surface is and does not work well for rays which are not parallel to the optic axis. The geometry of reflection for a parabolic mirror is discussed further in Prob. 35-6.

Another way of picturing the path of light incident on a mirror from a distant point is shown in Fig. 35-15. The wavefronts are from a distant object and are thus essentially plane wavefronts. After striking the mirror, they are reflected so that they form spherical wavefronts that converge on the focal point *F*. After passing through the focal point, the wavefronts expand in spherical waves as they would if there were a point source at *P*. Here we have again assumed paraxial rays that are all focused to *F*.

The image of an extended object can be located using a graphical construction. Consider the stick person as an object in Fig. 35-16. The rays from the toes will be focused to point *T'* a distance *s'* from the mirror, where *s'* is given by the mirror equation. For paraxial rays, the rays from the head will also be focused at a distance *s'* from the vertex of the mirror. The position of the head of the image can be found by using any two of the *principal rays* whose paths are particularly easy to trace. These principal rays are illustrated in Fig. 35-16. Ray *w* is parallel to the optic axis and is reflected toward the focal point. Ray *x* strikes the vertex of the mirror. The law of reflection shows that this ray makes equal angles with the optic axis. Ray *y* passes through the focal point and upon reflection follows a path parallel to the optic axis. Ray z passes through the center of the sphere and is reflected back on itself.

The image formed by a plane mirror, as seen in Fig. 35-11, is right side up, or *erect.* Notice that the image in Fig. 35-17 is upside down, or *inverted,* and smaller than the object. The *magnification m* of an optical system is defined as the ratio of the image size to the object size, with the magnification positive for an erect image and negative for an inverted image. Since triangles *HTV* and *H'T'V* in Fig. 35-17 are similar, the magnification of the mirror is $m = -H'T'/HT = -s'/s.$

Magnification

You can see that in Fig. 35-17 the image is formed by rays that actually pass through the position of the image. Such an image is called a *real image.* A real image can be projected onto a screen. A *virtual image* is formed by tracing back along the paths of rays, as in the plane mirror of Fig. 35-11. A virtual image cannot be shown on a screen since no rays pass through a virtual image. The virtual image formed by a plane mirror is right side up, or erect.

Real images and virtual images

Figure 35-18 shows that, when the object distance s is less than f, the rays from the object diverge as they leave the mirror, and the image is virtual. To take care of this situation, and of other cases with mirrors, refracting surfaces, and lenses, we adopt the following sign convention, parts of which will only be clear later as you study refracting surfaces and lenses:

1. An object distance s is positive if the object is on the same side of the surface as the incoming light. Otherwise the object distance is negative.

2. An image distances s' is positive if the image is on the same side of the surface as the outgoing light. Otherwise the image distance is negative. If s' is negative the image is virtual.

3. A radii R is positive if the center of curvature is on the same side of the surface as the outgoing light. Otherwise the radius is negative. The sign of the

Figure 35-17. Geometry of image formation by a concave spherical mirror. Since triangles *HTV* and *H'T'V* are similar, $m = -H'T'/HT = -VT'/VT = -s'/s$, where the negative sign indicates that the image is inverted.

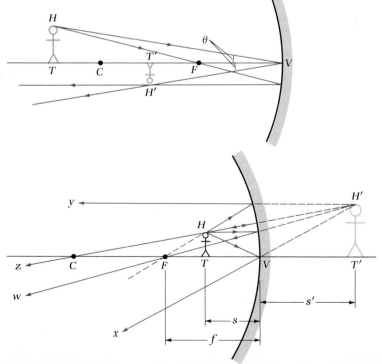

Figure 35-18. Reflection from a spherical mirror when the object is between the focal point and the mirror. Projecting the rays backward shows that they appear to be diverging from a virtual image located behind the mirror. By similar triangles, $FV/HT = (FV + VT')/H'T'$ and $VT/HT = VT'/H'T'$. After some algebra one gets $1/FV = (1/VT) - (1/VT')$ or $1/f = (1/s) + (1/s').$

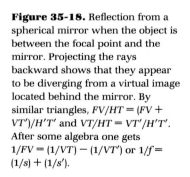

Figure 35-19. Reflection from a convex spherical mirror. Two principal rays define the image position. Ray w is parallel to the optic axis before reflection and diverges from F after reflection. Ray z is aimed at the center of the sphere and reflects back on itself. The image is found at the intersection of these rays. Problem 35-3 asks you to show that the mirror equation $1/f = 1/s + 1/s$ works for this case if f is taken to be negative, in agreement with our convention.

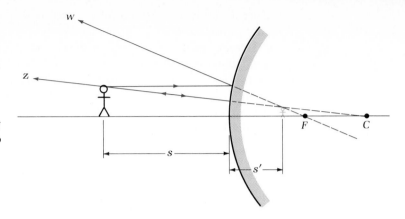

focal length f is determined by the sign of the radii.

4. The magnification m is positive for an erect image and negative for an inverted image.

Problem 35-3 asks you to show that Eq. (35-5) is valid using this sign convention when any of s, s', or R is negative.

A spherical mirror whose reflecting face is convex to the incoming light has a negative radius by this convention. Our illustrations so far have been of concave mirrors. Figure 35-19 shows a ray diagram for a convex mirror.

EXAMPLE 35-2. A concave shaving mirror has a 240-mm radius. If you look into it from a distance of 60 mm, (a) where will your face appear to be and (b) how big will a 5-mm feature on your face appear to be?

SOLUTION. Figure 35-20 shows a ray diagram of this example. (You are advised to sketch the ray diagram for each exercise you do.) Dimensions can be measured from a well-constructed sketch or, for more precision, calculated from the mirror equation:

(a)
$$f = \frac{R}{2} = 120 \text{ mm}$$

and
$$\frac{1}{s} + \frac{1}{s'} = \frac{1}{f}$$

$$s' = \frac{sf}{s-f} = \frac{(60 \text{ mm})(120 \text{ mm})}{60 \text{ mm} - 120 \text{ mm}} = -120 \text{ mm}$$

The negative sign indicates that the image is 120 mm behind the mirror, and thus virtual.

(b)
$$m = -\frac{s'}{s} = 2$$

Since m is positive, the image is erect. This means you see yourself right side up. The feature will appear to be twice as large as it is on your face, or 10 mm.

Figure 35-20. Example 35-2: Principal rays that pass through the focus and through the center locate the image.

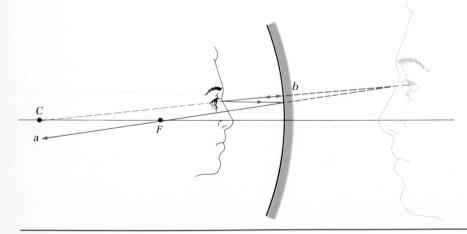

35-4 IMAGES FORMED BY REFRACTION

In preparation for the study of thin lenses, we first look at refraction at a single spherical interface. Consider the two rays shown leaving point P in Fig. 35-21. The ray propagating toward A will be refracted at the surface and meet the ray propagating along the optic axis at point P'. The ray propagating along the optic axis hits the interface normally and hence is not bent. An object at point P thus has its image at P'. If the rays are paraxial, then the angles $\alpha, \beta, \gamma, \theta_1$, and θ_2 are all small. From Snell's law, $n_1 \sin \theta_1 = n_2 \sin \theta_2$, or since the angles are small,

$$n_1 \theta_1 = n_2 \theta_2 \tag{35-6}$$

From plane geometry, the exterior angle of a triangle is equal to the sum of the two opposite angles. Thus in triangle PAC,

$$\theta_1 = \alpha + \beta \tag{35-7}$$

and in triangle $P'AC$,

$$\beta = \theta_2 + \gamma \tag{35-8}$$

The angles θ_1 and θ_2 can now be eliminated between these equations. Substituting for θ_2 from Eq. (35-6) into Eq. (35-8) gives

$$\beta = \frac{n_1}{n_2} \theta_1 + \gamma \tag{35-9}$$

Substituting for θ_1 from Eq. (35-7) into Eq. (35-9) gives

$$\beta = \frac{n_1}{n_2} (\alpha + \beta) + \gamma$$

Simplifying, we get

$$n_1 \alpha + n_2 \gamma = \beta(n_2 - n_1)$$

But $\beta = \ell/R$, $\alpha \approx \ell/s$, and $\gamma \approx \ell/s'$. Thus

$$\frac{n_1}{s} + \frac{n_2}{s'} = \frac{n_2 - n_1}{R} \tag{35-10}$$

Our sign convention is applicable to refracting surfaces as well as to mirrors. Note that in the last section the incoming and outgoing rays were on the same side of the mirror, whereas in this section we deal with incoming and outgoing rays that are on opposite sides of the refracting surfaces. With our sign conven-

Figure 35-21. Refraction at a spherical surface.

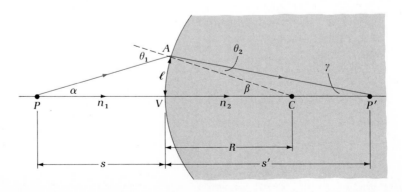

tion, Eq. (35-10) is valid for both concave and convex spherical refracting surfaces. (See Prob. 35-4.)

EXAMPLE 35-3. A fish viewed from directly above appears to be 1.5 m deep in the water. The index of refraction of air is 1.000 and of water is 1.333. What is the actual depth of the fish?

SOLUTION. First draw Fig. 35-22. Notice that the image is on the incoming side of the surface. This means that the image distance is negative, so $s' = -1.5$ m. Since the surface is flat, the radius of curvature is infinite. Thus Eq. 35-10 becomes

$$\frac{1.333}{s} + \frac{1.000}{-1.5\text{ m}} = \frac{1.000 - 1.333}{\infty} = 0$$

or $s = 2.0$ m, so that the fish is deeper than it appears to be. Note that the image of the fish is formed by an extrapolation of the light rays; it is a virtual image.

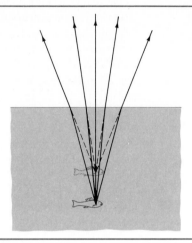

Figure 35-22.
Example 35-3.

35-5 LENSES

A piece of glass can be ground and polished to a smooth surface by rubbing it with a series of grits which have smaller and smaller particles. The nature of the polishing process makes spherical surfaces particularly easy to grind. When a slab of glass has a spherical surface ground on one or both sides, it forms a *lens*. "Burning glasses" were known to the Greeks and Romans, and lenses reappeared in Europe by the 1300s. The use of these lenses in spectacles became common after the invention of printing, although an understanding of how they worked came much later.

Figure 35-23 shows the path of rays through a lens. If the lens is thin, Eq. (35-10) can be applied at each surface to develop an equation to describe the formation of images by a lens. At the first surface, application of Eq. (35-10) gives

$$\frac{n_1}{s_a} + \frac{n_2}{s_a'} = \frac{n_2 - n_1}{R_a} \tag{35-11}$$

Here the subscripts "a" on s_a, s_a', and R_a refer to the first surface of the lens. For the second surface we will use subscript "b." The image formed by the first surface acts as the object for the second surface of the lens: $s_b = -s_a' + t$, where t is the lens thickness. The negative sign comes from the convention we have

Figure 35-23. Path of light rays from an object at A through a lens to the image at A'.

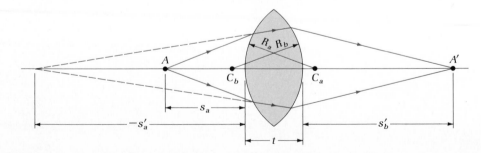

adopted, in which (virtual) objects on the outgoing-light side of a surface have negative object distances.

In the thin-lens approximation, the thickness t of the lens is small compared with the object and image distances. In this approximation, $s_b = -s_a'$. Applying Eq. (35-10) at this surface gives

$$\frac{n_2}{s_b} + \frac{n_1}{s_b'} = \frac{n_2}{-s_a'} + \frac{n_1}{s_b'} = \frac{n_1 - n_2}{R_b} = \frac{n_2 - n_1}{-R_b}$$

Using Eq. (35-11) and rearranging, we get

$$\frac{n_1}{s_a} + \frac{n_1}{s_b'} = (n_2 - n_1)\left(\frac{1}{R_a} - \frac{1}{R_b}\right) \tag{35-12}$$

At this point, it is convenient to rename things. Considering the lens as a single entity, (i) let the object distance for the lens as a whole be $s = s_a$, (ii) let the image distance for the lens as a whole be $s' = s_b$, and (iii) let the focal length of the lens as a whole be f. The focal length f of the lens is defined to be equal to s' as $s \to \infty$. Substitution in Eq. (35-12) gives

Lens-makers' equation

$$\frac{n_1}{f} = (n_2 - n_1)\left(\frac{1}{R_a} - \frac{1}{R_b}\right) \tag{35-13}$$

Equation (35-13) is known as the *lens-makers' equation*. It gives a prescription for making a lens with a given focal length. With these notation changes, Eq. (35-12) becomes

Lens equation

$$\frac{1}{s} + \frac{1}{s'} = \frac{1}{f} \tag{35-14}$$

Since the derivation of Eq. (35-14) used Eq. (35-10) for refraction at each surface, it is valid for objects and images on either side of the lens if the convention stated at the end of Sec. 35-3 is adopted.

A mirror has one focal point, whereas a lens has two, as shown in Fig. 35-24. The second focal point F_2 is the position where parallel light incident on the lens is focused. The first focal point F_1 is the position where an object produces an image at infinity. The focal points of a thin lens lie on opposite sides of the lens, each a distance f from the center of the lens. The focal points lie on the *optic axis* of the lens, which is the line that passes through the centers of curvature of the two surfaces of the lens.

Optic axis of lens

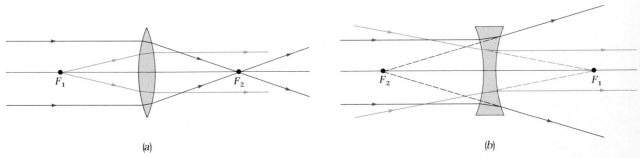

(a) (b)

Figure 35-24. (a) Focal point of a converging lens. Rays diverging from the first focal point F_1 leave the lens as parallel rays. Parallel rays incident on the lens converge toward the second focal point F_2. (b) Focal point of a diverging lens. Rays converging toward the first focal point F_1 leave the lens as parallel rays. Parallel rays incident on the lens diverge from the second focal point F_2.

Note that in Eq. (35-13), as stated in the sign convention, R_a will be negative if the first surface is concave toward the object, and R_b will be negative if the second surface is concave toward the object. Using this sign convention gives the proper sign to f.

For an ordinary glass lens in air $n_2 > n_1$. A double convex lens (Fig. 35-24a) bends the rays toward the optic axis at each surface, so that the rays tend to converge. Equation (35-13) shows that the focal length f of a double convex glass lens in air is positive because R_a is positive, R_b is negative, and $n_2 > n_1$. A lens with a positive focal length is called a *converging*, or *positive*, *lens*.

Figure 35-24b shows the path of rays through a double concave lens. Both surfaces of the lens bend the rays away from the optic axis, so that the rays tend to diverge. The focal length of a double concave glass lens in air is negative because R_a is negative, R_b is positive, and $n_2 > n_1$. A lens with a negative focal length is called a *diverging*, or *negative*, *lens*.

EXAMPLE 35-4. (a) Find the focal length of the planoconvex lens shown in Fig. 35-25. The spherical surface has a radius of curvature of 57.1 mm, and the index of refraction of the glass is 1.523. The lens is in air. An object is placed on the optic axis 50 mm in front of this lens. (b) Where does the lens form an image of this object? (c) Is the image real or virtual?

SOLUTION. (a) The focal length is given by the lens-makers' equation:

$$\frac{1}{f} = (1.523 - 1)\left(0 - \frac{1}{-57.1 \text{ mm}}\right)$$

$$f = 109 \text{ mm}$$

Since the center of curvature of the second surface of the lens is not on the outgoing-light side of the interface, R_b is negative.

(b) The image distance is given by Eq. (35-14):

$$\frac{1}{50 \text{ mm}} + \frac{1}{s'} = \frac{1}{109 \text{ mm}}$$

$$s' = -150 \text{ mm}$$

(c) The negative sign indicates that the image is on the incoming-light side of the lens, and is thus a virtual image.

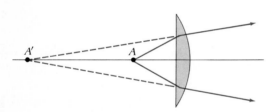

Figure 35-25. Example 35-4.

You can measure f for a converging lens by standing in a darkened room near a wall opposite a window. Hold the lens near the wall and vary the distance until you can see a clear image projected on the wall. This is an image of the scene outside the window. Because the object is far from the lens, the distance from the lens to the wall is f.

Images formed by thin lenses can be found by tracing principal rays through

Figure 35-26. The principal rays of a lens. Ray a passes through the first focal point F_1 of the lens and is refracted by the lens parallel to the axis. Ray b passes through the center of the lens and is undeviated. Ray c enters the lens parallel to the optic axis and is refracted through the second focal point F_2.

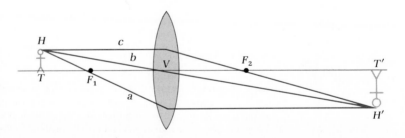

Ray tracing and principal rays

the lens. The three principal rays of a lens are those that (a) pass through a focus of the lens, (b) pass through the center of the lens, or (c) are parallel to the optic axis of the lens. Figure 35-26 shows the simple paths these rays take for a positive lens. Tracing the paths of these rays will locate the image position of an extended object and show whether the image is erect or inverted.

The magnification m can be determined using the principal ray that passes through the center of the lens, as shown in Fig. 35-26. The similar triangles HTV and $H'T'V$ show that $m = -H'T'/HT = T'V/TV$. But TV is the object distance s and $T'V$ is the image distance s'. Thus

Magnification of a lens

$$m = -\frac{s'}{s} \qquad (35\text{-}15)$$

EXAMPLE 35-5. Use the ray-tracing method to find the image of a 7.5-mm-high object 35 mm in front of a lens of focal length (a) 20 mm and (b) −20 mm.

SOLUTION. (a) The drawing is shown in Fig. 35-27a. Ray a passes through the first focal point of the lens and comes out on the other side parallel to the optic axis. Ray b passes through the center of the lens and is undeviated. Ray c is parallel to the optic axis and comes out on the other side along a line through the second focal point of the lens. Since light passes through the position of the image, the image is

real. By a scaled measurement on the diagram, $s' =$ 46.5 mm and the image is 10 mm high. For more precision, the algebraic solutions can be used.

(b) The drawing is shown in Fig. 35-27b. Ray a is aimed at F_1 and leaves the lens parallel to the optic axis. Ray b goes straight through the vertex of the lens. Ray c is parallel to the optic axis so that its path on the other side of the lens is directly away from F_2. The image is 12.7 mm in front of the lens and 2.8 mm high. Since all but one of the light rays do not pass through the position of the image, the image is virtual.

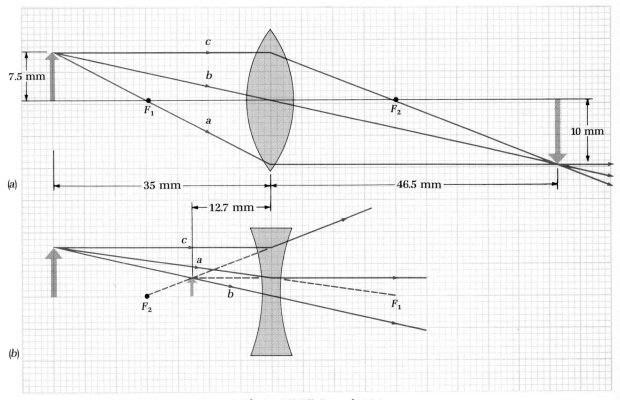

Figure 35-27. Example 35-5.

35-6   OPTICAL DEVICES

We have developed the theory of geometric optics to the point where it is possible to discuss the principles of some practical optical systems. These systems have extended the range of our senses to the very small and the very far away, making possible the sciences of microbiology and astronomy.

There are details in the design of optical instruments that we do not have space to discuss. In particular, we will not discuss the blurring of the image that occurs in finite-size lenses, the difficulties in forming an image of three-dimensional objects, or the techniques for minimizing the variation of the focal length with wavelength in lenses. The imperfections in the image caused by these effects are called *aberrations*. The design of lens combinations which minimize aberrations is a difficult procedure, one that does not need to be considered in the principles of these optical devices. One can build a serviceable telescope using the paraxial theory.

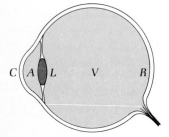

Figure 35-28. Schematic diagram of the eye. *C* is the cornea, *L* the lens, *A* the aqueous humor, *V* the vitreous humor, and *R* the retina.

The eye. Many optical instruments are aids to the eye. Since the eye is part of the process, as well as an optical instrument itself, we discuss it first. The parts of the eye essential for our discussion are shown in Fig. 35-28. At the front of the eye is the sharply curved *cornea C.* Behind the cornea is a space filled with a liquid called the *aqueous humor A* ($n = 1.336$). Most of the refraction of incoming light occurs as light passes from air into this liquid. Next comes the lens *L*, which is made of material of average index $n = 1.396$. (The index is different at the center than at the edges.) The curvature of the lens can be adjusted by muscles attached to it in order to form images of objects at different distances. Behind the lens is a fluid similar to the aqueous humor called the *vitreous humor V*, and then the *retina R*. The retina contains photosensitive cells, which produce nerve signals when light hits them, and nerve cells, which process these signals and send them to the rest of the brain for interpretation.

How can you best distinguish the details of a small object? The detail that you can distinguish in an object depends on the size of the image of that object on your retina. In the unaided eye, this is determined by the angle subtended by the object at your eye. To enlarge the apparent size of the object, you bring it closer to your eye, making the angle that it subtends larger. Eventually you will reach a point where your eye can no longer comfortably focus the image on your retina. The closest distance at which you can comfortably bring an object into focus is called the *near point.* You can find your near point by bringing this text as close to your eyes as you can while still seeing a sharp image of the print.

When the muscles attached to the lens are relaxed, the normal eye is focused at infinity. If you tighten the muscles attached to the lens, in a process called *accommodation*, your eye can focus on objects at different distances. An infant can form clear images of objects as close as 70 mm. The lens of the average college student can accommodate objects as close as 100 mm. A 60-year-old professor may be able to accommodate only to 2 m, and be forced to wear glasses to focus on objects closer than 2 m. We will use an accommodation distance of 250 mm as an average near point.

The simple magnifier. If you place a converging lens in front of your eye, as shown in Fig. 35-29, it effectively increases the accommodation of your eye and decreases your near point. Your eye looks at a virtual object (not shown in figure) somewhere between the near point and infinity. The virtual object subtends a larger angle at your eye than the object would subtend at the near point. Thus the lens is called a *simple magnifier.*

Near point

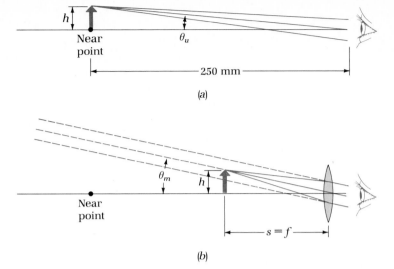

Figure 35-29. The simple magnifier. (a) An object of height h subtends an angle $\theta_u = h/250$ mm when seen by the eye at the near point of 250 mm. (b) The virtual image of this object when seen through a converging lens of focal length f subtends an angle $\theta_m = h/f$. Here the image is at infinity, so that $s = f$ and $s' = -\infty$.

To calculate the magnification, assume that you place the converging lens so that your eye is focused at infinity. You can then clearly see the object when it is placed just inside the focal point of the lens, a distance f from the lens. As shown in Fig. 35-29, the object subtends an angle θ_u when you see it with your unaided eye, but a larger angle θ_m when you see it through a simple magnifier. The *angular magnification M* is defined as the ratio of the angles subtended with and without the magnifier. Thus $M \equiv \theta_m/\theta_u = (h/250 \text{ mm})/(h/f)$, or

Magnification of a simple magnifier

$$M = \frac{250 \text{ mm}}{f} \tag{35-16}$$

Because of this relation, the *power P* of a lens is defined to be the inverse of its focal length f: $P = 1/f$. The power of a lens is measured in *diopters* (abbreviated D) with 1 D equal to 1 m^{-1}.

As the object is moved closer to the lens, the virtual image becomes closer to your eye. Exercise 35-42 asks you to show that if the lens is placed so that the virtual image is at 250 mm ($s' = -250$ mm, the average near point) then the angular magnification is

$$M = 1 + \frac{250 \text{ mm}}{f}$$

Simple magnifiers are generally used with the image at infinity because the normal eye is most comfortable when focused at infinity.

Notice that large magnifications M require small focal lengths f. Small focal lengths in turn require small radii of curvature of the lens. The small radius of curvature makes the lens thick and causes aberrations that blur the image. Simple single-lens magnifiers are limited by these aberrations to a magnification M of about 2.5, conventionally denoted as 2.5X. Simple magnifiers using more than one lens can decrease aberrations enough to reach a useful magnification of 15X.

The compound microscope. When higher angular magnifications are necessary, a compound microscope can be used. Invented around 1600 in Holland, it consists, in elemental form, of two lenses. The *objective lens* is placed so that the object to be examined is just beyond its first focal point, as shown in Fig.

35-30. An enlarged, real image I_o is formed beyond the second focal point of the objective lens. This image is viewed by a second lens, the *eyepiece*. The eyepiece acts as a simple magnifier, producing a virtual image I_e of its object I_o.

The magnification m of the objective lens is given by Eq. 35-15: $m_o = -s'_o/s_o$. In this case the object is approximately at the focal point F_o of the objective lens so that $s_o \approx f_o$. The distance from the objective lens to its image is called the *tube length T* and is often set to 160 mm. In this case $m_o = -160$ mm/f_o. The angular magnification M_e of the eyepiece using the simple magnifier relation is 250 mm/f_e, where f_e is the focal length of the eyepiece. The overall magnification M is thus

$$M = |M_e m_o| = \frac{(250 \text{ mm})(160 \text{ mm})}{f_e f_o} \tag{35-17}$$

Limitations due to the wave nature of light limit useful magnification to about 1000X when using visible light. These limitations will be discussed in Chap. 37.

Telescopes. A telescope whose primary element is a lens is called a *refracting telescope*. A simple refracting telescope is shown in Fig. 35-31. The objective lens has a long focal length f_o and the eyepiece a short focal length f_e. When the eyepiece is placed so that its first focal point F_{e1} coincides with the second focal point F_{o2} of the objective lens, parallel light rays entering the telescope emerge as parallel light rays from the eyepiece. The angle that the rays make with the axis of the telescope is changed, however. Using the triangles $F_{o1}CD$ and $F_{e2}EG$, where $CD = AB = EG$ and θ and θ' are small so that the angles are approximately equal to their sines,

$$\theta = \frac{-AB}{f_o} \qquad \theta' = \frac{AB}{f_e}$$

Figure 35-30. The compound microscope. An object just beyond the focal point F_{o1} of the objective lens is imaged by the objective lens at I_o. This real image forms the object of the eyepiece, which in turn forms an image at I_e.

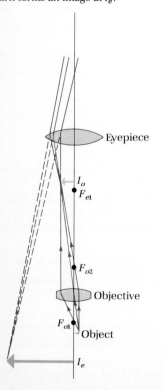

Figure 35-31. A simple keplerian refracting telescope. Parallel light rays from an object at infinity are focused by the objective lens to form an image at F_{o2}. When the eyepiece is adjusted so that its focal point F_{e2} coincides with F_{o2}, a virtual image is formed at infinity by the eyepiece.

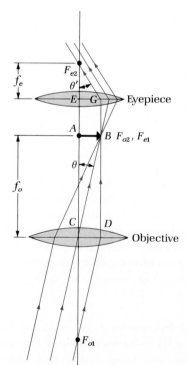

Figure 35-32. A newtonian reflecting telescope.

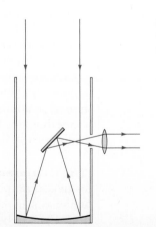

The angular magnification M of the telescope is the ratio θ'/θ, or

$$M = \frac{f_o}{f_e} \qquad (35\text{-}18)$$

Magnification of a simple refracting telescope

Galileo constructed a telescope with $M = 3$ as soon as he heard that someone had built a telescope using two lenses. His later telescopes had magnifications of around 30X. It is interesting to note that the Dutch government tried to keep the knowledge of the design of telescopes secret, but Galileo built a working model a very short time after he heard of the existence of the telescope. Historically it has often proved futile to keep the details of militarily and commercially important devices secret after the mere existence of the device is known.

The difficulties in making a large lens with acceptable aberrations limit the size of refracting telescopes. Large mirrors that are sufficiently free of aberrations are easier to make. A *reflecting telescope* has a mirror as its primary element. Figure 35-32 illustrates the path of the rays in a newtonian reflecting telescope.

SUMMARY WITH APPLICATIONS

Section 35-2. Geometrical optics
Geometrical optics is an approximation to the results of Maxwell's equations that is valid when the dimensions of the system are much greater than the wavelength of the light used. The laws of geometrical optics are

1 Light travels in straight lines in a homogeneous medium.
2 The angle of reflection is equal to the angle of incidence.
3 Snell's law gives the angle of refraction:

$$n_1 \sin \theta_1 = n_2 \sin \theta_2 \qquad (35\text{-}1)$$

When a light ray propagates from a medium of higher index n_1 to a medium of lower index n_2, there is a critical value of the angle of incidence $\theta_c = \sin^{-1}(n_2/n_1)$ above which a ray suffers total internal reflection.

Find the reflected and refracted rays formed when a ray of light hits a boundary.

Section 35-3. Images formed by reflection
The object distance s and the image distance s' of a spherical mirror are related by

$$\frac{1}{s} + \frac{1}{s'} = \frac{1}{f} \qquad (35\text{-}5)$$

If the image has light rays that pass through it, it is called a real image. If the image is formed by the backward projection of light rays, it is called a virtual image. The magnification of a mirror (or lens) is given by $m = -s'/s$.

Relate the image and object distances for mirrors.

Section 35-4. Images formed by refraction
The image and object distances s and s' for a refracting surface of radius R between media of index n_1 and n_2 are related by

$$\frac{n_1}{s} + \frac{n_2}{s'} = \frac{n_2 - n_1}{R} \qquad (35\text{-}10)$$

Section 35-5. Lenses
The focal length of a lens is given by the lens-makers' equation:

$$\frac{n_1}{f} = (n_2 - n_1)\left(\frac{1}{R_a} - \frac{1}{R_b}\right) \qquad (35\text{-}13)$$

The image distance s' and object distance s of a lens of focal length f are related by

$$\frac{1}{s} + \frac{1}{s'} = \frac{1}{f} \qquad (35\text{-}14)$$

All of the relations above assume paraxial rays and use the sign convention given in Sec. 35-3.

Relate the image and object distances for lenses.

Section 35-6. Optical devices
Expressions for the angular magnification of the simple magnifier, the compound microscope, and the telescope are

$$M = \frac{250 \text{ mm}}{f}$$

$$M = \frac{(250 \text{ mm})(160 \text{ mm})}{f_o f_e}$$

$$M = \frac{f_o}{f_e}.$$

Determine the magnification of simple magnifiers, microscopes, and telescopes; describe their construction.

QUESTIONS

35-1 Suppose that light did not travel in straight lines. How would you tell whether a line was straight or not?

35-2 Are sound waves both reflected and refracted? Is it possible to make a lens or a mirror that focuses sound waves? If such a lens or mirror existed, about how large would it have to be so that the conditions of geometrical optics were satisfied for speech sounds, which have a wavelength around 1 m?

35-3 In Fig. 35-33, is Venus admiring herself in the mirror? Explain.

Figure 35-33. Ques. 35-3: *The Rokeby Venus* by Velásquez. *(London National Gallery/Art Resources)*

35-4 Huygens discussed the path of a light ray in a medium in which the index of refraction *n* varies with position. Will a light ray in such a medium be bent toward increasing or decreasing *n*? Explain.

35-5 At noon on a clear day, the air near the surface of a road is warmer than the air higher up. The index of refraction of air decreases with increasing temperature. Use these facts to explain the mirage one sees on such a road, in which the blue sky, when seen a long way ahead on the road, appears to be water.

35-6 Can a one-eyed fish see out of an aquarium in all directions? Does it have to look in all directions to see all the room around it? Explain.

35-7 Light has a wavelength, a frequency, and a speed. Which, if any, of these change when light goes from air to glass? Explain.

35-8 Does a mirror reverse left to right? Does a mirror reverse up to down? How about east to west?

35-9 What is the focal length of a plane mirror? What is the magnification of a plane mirror (including sign)?

35-10 Is the wide-angle rearview mirror used on many trucks and buses convex or concave? Estimate the radius of curvature of such mirrors.

35-11 Estimate the focal length of the mirror of Fig. 35-34. Is the image of the man's face virtual or real? Why is the image distorted at the edges of the sphere? What is the actual shape of the room reflected in the sphere?

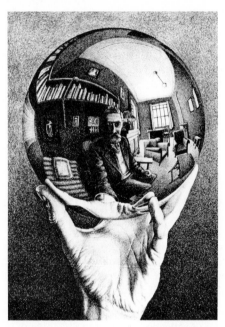

Figure 35-34. Ques. 35-11: *Hand with Reflecting Globe* by Escher. *(Cordon Art, Baarn, Holland)*

35-12 Suppose you have trouble seeing things far away when the muscles that control the shape of the lens in your eye are relaxed. Should you use eyeglasses which have diverging or converging lenses? What if you have trouble seeing close objects when your muscles have made the lens in your eye as converging as possible?

35-13 Would a double convex lens of index $n = 1.250$ be a converging or a diverging lens in air? In water ($n = 1.333$)? Explain why many people have difficulty seeing under water. Why do goggles help?

35-14 During a thunderstorm, the speed of sound in air is generally faster near the earth than above it. Consider the path of sound "rays" and concoct an explanation as to why thunder is usually not heard more than about 15 mi from a storm.

35-15 Is the image location changed when a planoconvex lens is turned around so that it is a "convexplano" lens? Explain.

35-16 Consider what happens to a light ray in a medium in which the index of refraction fluctuates with time. How can this explain "twinkle, twinkle, little star"?

35-17 Nonparaxial rays in a parallel beam of light reflected by a spherical concave mirror do not cross the optical axis at the focal point where paraxial rays do. Do the nonparaxial rays cross it between the mirror and its focus or beyond the focus? Use a diagram to check your answer.

35-18 As the object of a thin lens is moved from infinity to the first focal point of the lens, the image moves from the second focal point of the lens to infinity. What happens to the image as the object is moved closer to the lens?

35-19 Consider a two-lens system. Show that it is possible for the second lens to have a "virtual object" — that is, an object through which no rays pass and for which the object distance for the second lens is negative.

35-20 Can the magnification of a thin lens be infinite? Is this a practical possibility or a mathematical one?

35-21 A positive lens made of material of index $n = 2$ and a mirror have the same focal length in air. Which has the smaller focal length in water?

35-22* The invisible man in H. G. Wells's novel of that name made himself invisible by changing the index of refraction of his body to that of air (Fig. 35-35). Could the invisible man see anything?

Figure 35-35. Ques. 35-22: The invisible man.

35-23* Can you explain why the shadow of a partially submerged pencil looks as it does in Fig. 35-36?

Figure 35-36. Ques. 35-23: Shadow of a partially submerged pencil. (*Photo by D. R. Overcash*)

35-24* If you place a coin in a glass of water and look down at the proper angle, you will see the coin's image

* Adapted from Jearl Walker, The Flying Circus of Physics, Wiley, New York, 1975.

near the surface of the water (Fig. 35-37). Putting your hand on the opposite side of the glass has no effect on the image unless your hand is wet. Then the image of the coin disappears. Why?

Figure 35-37. Ques. 35-24: Image of a coin inside a glass of water. (*Photo by D. R. Overcash*)

35-25 How could you make a double convex lens that is diverging?

35-26 Is the image formed on the back of your retina right side up or upside down? (Experiments have been done with people wearing inverting prisms. After a relatively short time they were able to get around — and had trouble again when they took the inverting prisms off!)

35-27 The index of refraction of substances usually decreases with increasing wavelength. Will red or blue light bend more as a ray enters water from air? If the image of a star formed by a simple refracting telescope is a blue image on the retina of the eye, is the red image in front of the retina or behind it?

35-28 Can you use a lens to focus the rays of the sun to a point so that the point is at a higher temperature than the surface of the sun? (Consider the second law of thermodynamics.) Explain.

35-29 Where can a small length scale, etched in glass, be placed in a simple microscope so that the observer sees it coincident with the object of the microscope?

35-30 Some simple refracting telescopes have cross hairs. Where in the telescope are the hairs?

35-31 Complete the following table:

Symbol	Represents	Type	SI units
n			
s			m
s'			
f		Scalar	
m			
M	Angular magnification		

EXERCISES

Section 35-2. Geometrical optics

35-1 Two plane mirrors are joined so that their normals make an angle of 60°, as shown in Fig. 35-38. If an incoming ray makes an angle of 22° with one normal, by how much is the ray deviated by the mirrors; that is, what angle does the outgoing ray make with the incoming ray?

Figure 35-38. Exercise 35-1.

35-2 What angle must two mirrors make with each other if a ray in the plane formed by the normals to the mirrors is reflected by both mirrors so that it leaves on a path parallel to the path on which it entered?

35-3 *Huygens' construction for reflection.* Consider the reflection process shown in Fig. 35-7. Using Huygens' principle, show (a) that the length of *AN* is equal to the length of *BC*, (b) that the triangles *ABN* and *ABC* are congruent, (c) that $\theta_1 = \theta_{1r}$.

35-4 Parallel rays from the sun strike a window 3.0 m high by 2.0 m wide in a vertical wall of a building and are reflected onto the ground. If the normal to the window surface is north-south and the sun is due south 50° above the horizon, what is the size of the bright spot made by the parallel reflected rays on the flat ground?

35-5 Parallel light rays are incident on a glass prism as shown in Fig. 35-39. Show that the angle between the two reflected rays is twice the prism angle α.

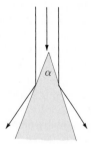

Figure 35-39. Exercise 35-5.

35-6 A ray of light hits a mirror and is reflected. If the mirror is rotated by an angle α about an axis perpendicular to the plane of incidence, through what angle is the reflected ray rotated?

35-7 What is the speed of light in methylene iodide? See Table 35-1.

35-8 A ray of sunlight in air hits a water surface, making an angle of 40° with the normal to the water surface. What angle does the refracted ray make with the normal?

35-9 A ray of light in air makes an angle of 25° with the surface of a glass plate of index of refraction 1.525. (a) What angle does the incident ray make with the normal to the surface? (b) What angle does the refracted ray make with the surface of the glass?

35-10 A Pyrex glass prism has two faces which join at an angle $\alpha = 42°$. A ray of light hits one of these faces, making an angle $\theta = 18°$ with the normal to the surface, as shown in Fig. 35-40. A ray leaves the vertical surface. What angle does it make with the normal of that face? See Table 35-1 for indices of refraction.

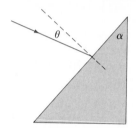

Figure 35-40. Exercise 35-10.

35-11 A light ray is refracted at an air-glass surface, making an angle of 75.00° with the normal on the air side and an angle of 39.71° with the normal on the glass side. Using Table 35-1, guess from which glass the prism is made.

35-12 When a ray of light passes through a plane-parallel sheet of material, it is displaced from its original path by an amount d, as shown in Fig. 35-41. A ray of light in air is incident on a plane-parallel sheet of index n' and thickness t oriented so that the normal to the surface makes an angle ϕ with the ray in the air and an angle ϕ' in the medium. Show that the displacement d of the ray is

$$d = t \sin \phi \left(1 - \frac{\cos \phi}{n' \cos \phi'} \right)$$

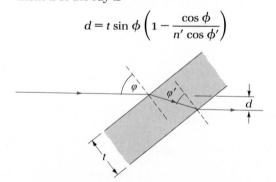

Figure 35-41. Exercise 35-12.

35-13 What is the critical angle for a ray leaving a diamond and entering air?

35-14 At what angle with respect to the vertical must a fish beneath water look to see the setting sun? Assume the fish is in a calm freshwater lake.

35-15 In Fig. 35-40, if $\alpha = 45°$ and the index of refraction of the prism is 1.655, what must θ be if the ray is to hit the right side of the prism at the critical angle?

Section 35-3. Images formed by reflection

35-16 (a) Use the law of reflection in Fig. 35-11 to show that triangle ABP is congruent to triangle ABP'. (b) Show that the distance from the plane of the mirror to the object is equal to the distance from the plane of the mirror to the image. (c) Show that this result is consistent with Eq. (35-4).

35-17 A student is 1.65 m tall, and her eyes are 120 mm below the top of her hair. She wishes to see her whole self in a vertical plane mirror. (a) How far above the floor can the bottom of the mirror be? (b) At least how far above the floor must the top of the mirror be? (c) Does it make any difference how close she stands to the mirror?

35-18 Two large plane mirrors are vertical, with an angle of 90° between them. (a) If you stand 1 m in front of their intersection on the bisector of the angle, how many images of yourself can you see? (b) How far from you is each one?

35-19 A 5-mm-high object is placed 250 mm in front of a convex mirror of radius of curvature $R = 400$ mm. (a) How far from the mirror will the image be? (b) Is the image erect or inverted? (c) What is the size of the image?

35-20 A concave shaving mirror has a radius of 335 mm. (a) What is the focal length of the mirror? (b) If your face is 105 mm from the mirror, how far from you is your image? (c) By what fraction is your image larger than you? (d) Is your image erect or inverted? (e) Is your image real or virtual?

35-21 In a convex spherical portion of a truck rearview mirror, the back of the truck, 20 m away, has a virtual image one-twentieth its real size. (a) What is the radius of curvature of the mirror? (b) Where is the image?

35-22 Complete the table below for spherical mirrors with paraxial rays. All distances are in mm.

Type	Radius	Focal length	Object distance	Image distance	Real image?	Inverted image?	m^*
Convex	−90	−45	+15	−11	No	No	+0.75
Plane			+300				
Concave	120		+400				
	−480			−120			
		96		−36			
Convex			+160				0.5
	∞			−48			
Concave				+50	Yes		1.5

* Provide sign (+ or −) for all m values.

35-23 A *Cassegrain telescope* uses two mirrors, as shown in Fig. 35-42. Such a telescope is built with the mirrors 20 mm apart. If the radius of curvature of the large mirror is 220 mm and of the small mirror 140 mm, where will the final image of an object at infinity be?

Figure 35-42. Exercise 35-23: A Cassegrain telescope.

Section 35-4. Images formed by refraction

35-24 On its back surface, a 200-mm-diameter transparent sphere in air forms an image of paraxial rays from an object 1000 mm away. What is the index of refraction of the sphere?

35-25 A jar is filled with glycerine to a depth of 100.0 mm. The bottom appears to an observer to be raised 32.5 mm. Find the index of refraction of glycerine.

35-26 Complete the table for spherical refracting surfaces below. All distances are in mm. Let $n_1 = 1$ and $n_2 = 1.333$. Assume all rays are paraxial.

Type	Radius	Object distance	Image distance	Real image?	Inverted image?
Convex	−90	+15	−19	No	No
Plane		+300			
	+120		+480		
	−480	+120			
		+96	−96		

Section 35-5. Lenses

35-27 Complete the following table for thin lenses. All distances are in mm. Assume paraxial rays.

35-28 The *newtonian* form of the lens equation is given in terms of the distance of the object and image from the first and second focal points. (The form we have used, $1/s + 1/s' = 1/f$, is called the *gaussian* form.) Let $x = s - f$ and $x' = s' - f$ and derive the newtonian form of the lens equation: $xx' = f^2$.

Type of lens	Focal length	Object distance	Image distance	Real image?	Inverted image?	m^*
Converging	+96	+144	+288	Yes	Yes	−2.0
Diverging		+300	−150			
	−120		−60			
Positive	+480	+120				
Negative		+96	36 (sign?)			
		−240		Yes		3.0
		+∞	+180		—	—
			−170			+2.5

* Provide sign (+ or −) for all m values.

35-29 A double concave lens made of Lucite has both radii of curvature of magnitude 63 mm. What is its focal length? (See Table 35-1.)

35-30 An equiconcave lens is to have a focal length of −330 mm and be made of dense flint glass. (See Table 35-1.) What radii of curvature should it have?

35-31 A planoconvex lens is to have a focal length of 240 mm and be made of glass of index 1.675. What radius of curvature should it have?

35-32 A polar explorer, out of matches, fashions a lens of ice to focus the sun's rays to start a fire. If he makes a planoconvex lens with the radius of curvature of $\frac{1}{4}$ m, how far from the tinder should he hold the lens?

35-33 A candle flame is 1.8 m from the side of a tent wall. A lens forms an image of the flame on the wall such that the image is inverted with a magnification of −6.0. What is the focal length of the lens?

35-34 An object on a 35-mm photographic slide is 20 mm high. The slide is 4.0 m from a screen. A lens of what focal length will be required to project an image of the slide that is 0.5 m high?

35-35 An object 15.7 mm high is 175 mm in front of a lens of focal length 85 mm. Fifty millimeters behind that lens is another lens of focal length −300 mm. (a) Where would the image of the first lens be if there were no second lens? (b) The image of the first lens acts as the (virtual) object for the second lens. Where does the second lens form its image? Is that image real or virtual?

35-36 Two thin lenses of focal length f_1 and f_2 are placed close together. Show that the combination of lenses acts like a single lens of focal length $f = f_1 f_2/(f_1 + f_2)$.

35-37 Prove that a diverging lens cannot form a real image of a real object. Note that real images have $s' > 0$.

35-38 (a) Prove that a positive lens forms a real image of a real object if and only if the object distance is greater than the focal length of the lens. (b) Show that if the object is virtual, the image formed by a positive lens is always real.

Section 35-6. Optical devices

35-39 A certain glass has $n = 1.66650$ for light of wavelength 656.3 nm and $n = 1.68882$ for light of wavelength 434.0 nm. An equiconvex lens made of this glass has radii of magnitude 125.5 mm. For this lens, what is the difference between the focal lengths for light of these two wavelengths? Assume the lens is in air.

35-40 If the lens of the eye is treated as having an index $n_2 = 1.396$ in a medium of $n_1 = 1.336$ and as having radii of 10.0 mm and −6.0 mm, what is its focal length?

35-41 A quartz lens has a power of 4.5 D. What is its focal length?

35-42 Figure 35-43 shows a simple magnifier of focal length f, with the eye focused at a point corresponding to $s' = 250$ mm. (a) Show that the angle subtended at the eye by the object at the near point without the lens is $\theta_u \approx h/250$ mm and that the angle subtended by the image when the lens is in place is $\theta_m \approx h/s$, where $1/s - 1/s' = 1/f$. (b) Show that $M = \theta_m/\theta_u$ is given by

$$M = 1 + \frac{250 \text{ mm}}{f}$$

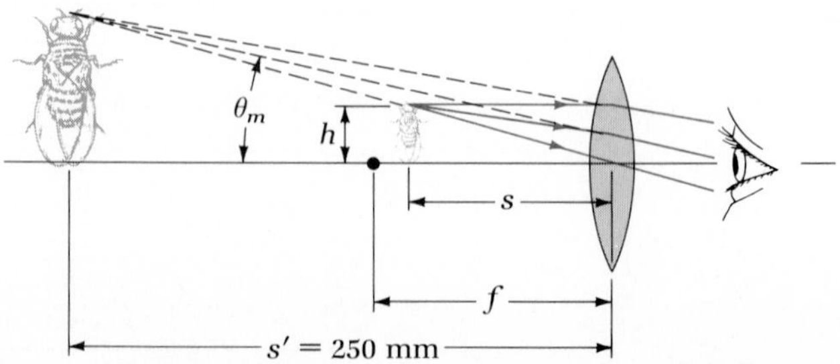

Figure 35-43. Exercise 35-42: A simple magnifier.

35-43 (a) What is the focal length of a 3X simple magnifier, where the 3X is measured with the eye focused at infinity? (b) What is the maximum magnification that a young child with an accommodation distance of 70 mm could obtain from this magnifier?

35-44 (a) If you use a 2X simple magnifier, with the magnification measured with your eye relaxed, how far from the magnifier is the object? (b) What is the magnification if you accommodate to a distance of 150 mm? (c) How far from the magnifier is the object in this case?

35-45 The objective and the eyepiece of a microscope have focal lengths of $+4.9$ and $+8.3$ mm, respectively. The tube length is 160 mm. Find (a) the distance from the objective to the object, (b) the linear magnification of the objective, (c) the overall magnification if the final (virtual) image is formed at infinity.

35-46 A microscope has an eyepiece marked 10X and an objective with a focal length of $+4.0$ mm. What is the overall magnification if the tube length is 160 mm?

35-47 A galilean telescope is shown in Fig. 35-44. Use a ray diagram to show that its image is virtual and erect.

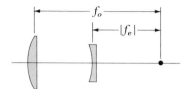

Figure 35-44. Exercise 35-47: A galilean telescope.

35-48 A simple refracting telescope of the keplerian design (Fig. 35-31) has an objective of focal length 850 mm and an eyepiece of focal length 25 mm. What is its angular magnification?

PROBLEMS

35-1 ***Fermat's principle for reflection.*** Fermat's principle states that the path of a light ray between two points is such that the time for light to travel between the points is a minimum with respect to nearby paths (actually, that the time is stationary with respect to such variations). In Fig. 35-45 the path that a light ray might follow from point P to point P' is shown for rays reflected from a surface. Let the path length from P to P' be Δ and the position where the ray hits the mirror be x. According to Fermat's principle, the actual path will be the one for which the derivative $d\Delta/dx$ is zero, and the time taken for the light to go from P to P' is a minimum compared with that for neighboring paths. Show that the path length is $\Delta = (d^2 + x^2)^{1/2} + [d^2 + (\ell - x)^2]^{1/2}$ and that this path length (and therefore the time interval) is a minimum when $x = \ell/2$, so that $\theta = \theta_r$.

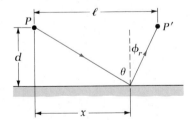

Figure 35-45. Prob. 35-1.

35-2 ***Fermat's principle for refraction.*** In Fig. 35-46, the path a light ray might follow from P to P' is shown for rays refracted at a surface. Suppose the speed of light in the lower medium is n_2/n_1 times that in the upper medium. Show that the time for the light to go from P to P' is a minimum if $n_1 \sin \theta_1 = n_2 \sin \theta_2$, and thus that Fermat's principle (see Prob. 35-1) leads to Snell's law.

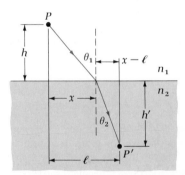

Figure 35-46. Prob. 35-2.

35-3 ***Sign convention for mirrors.*** (a) Show that the mirror equation $1/f = 1/s + 1/s'$ is valid for a convex spherical mirror if f and s' are taken to be negative as the sign convention demands. (b) A negative object distance s implies that the object is on the other side of the mirror from the incoming rays and is thus virtual. This can be accomplished by using the image of one mirror as the object of a second mirror, as seen in Fig. 35-42. The rays from the first mirror can be extrapolated beyond the second mirror, with the point where the extrapolated rays meet being the (virtual) object of a second mirror. Note that the virtual object of the second mirror is behind it. (See Fig. 35-42.) Show that $1/f = 1/s + 1/s'$ for the second mirror, providing $|-s|$ is the distance from the vertex of the second mirror to the point where the image of the first mirror would be formed if the second mirror were not there.

35-4 ***Sign convention for refraction at a surface.*** Using Fig. 35-47, show that Eq. (35-10) holds for paraxial rays if the radius R of the surface and the image distance s' are taken to be negative in accordance with the sign convention.

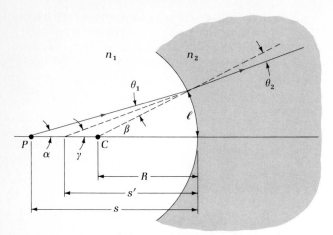

Figure 35-47. Prob. 35-4.

35-5 The index of refraction of a liquid can be determined by the following method. A double convex lens of measured focal length f and radii of curvature $\pm R$ is brought near a flat glass plate, and a drop of liquid put between the lens and the plate. The liquid thus forms a planoconcave lens of radius $-R$. If the focal length of the combination of these two lenses is found to be f', show that

$$n = R\left(\frac{1}{f} - \frac{1}{f'}\right) + 1$$

35-6 **_Reflections from a parabolic mirror._** A parabola can be defined as the locus of all points such that the distance from a point called the *focus* is equal to the distance $2p$ from a line called the *directrix*. (a) For the

parabola $y^2 = 4p(x - p)$, show that the directrix is the y axis and the focus is at the point $(2p, 0)$. (b) Show that the tangent to the parabola is $dy/dx = 2p/y$, and that the tangent of the angle α in Fig. 35-48 is $y/(x - 2p)$ where x and y give the position where the ray hits the parabola. (c) Using the trigonometric formula for the tangent of the difference of angles, show that $\tan \gamma = \tan(\alpha - \beta) = \tan \beta$. Thus show that all rays perpendicular to the directrix are reflected to the focus of the parabola.

35-7 Four thin lenses are placed along a common optic axis and spaced a distance d apart. Their focal lengths have identical magnitude f but alternating signs, with the first lens that the light encounters being positive. Show that if $f < d$, parallel light rays will all be brought to a focal point on the axis by the combination.

35-8 Show that the minimum real-object-to-real-image distance for a converging lens is $4f$.

35-9 **_Geometric construction for refraction._** The path of the refracted ray at a surface between media of indices n_1 and n_2 can be found with a geometric construction. Two arcs of circles centered at O, with radii of length proportional to n_1 and n_2, are drawn as

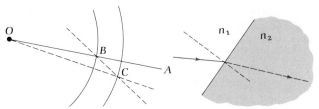

Figure 35-49. Prob. 35-9.

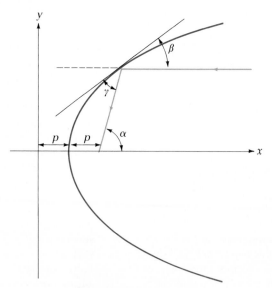

Figure 35-48. Prob. 35-6.

shown in Fig. 35-49. Line *OA* is drawn parallel to the incident ray, and a line parallel to the normal to the surface is drawn through point *B*, where *OA* intersects the arc of radius n_1. This line intersects the arc of radius n_2 at *C*. Show that line *OC* is parallel to the refracted ray.

35-10 A double convex lens of focal length *f* is sliced in half with a cut perpendicular to its optic axis. The plane surface of the cut is polished and silvered so that it forms a mirror. Show that an object 2*f* in front of this lens-mirror will be coincident with its own image. See Fig. 35-50.

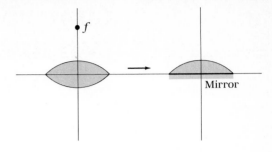

Figure 35-50. Prob. 35-10.

CHAPTER 36
INTERFERENCE AND
DIFFRACTION

36-1 INTRODUCTION

What is light? This question has occupied the minds of many great scientists. Newton thought that light is a stream of particles, though he acknowleged some uncertainty. He was able to explain many optical effects using a particle, or corpuscular, theory of light. Christian Huygens (1629–1695), a contemporary of Newton's, believed that light is composed of waves. He initiated a wave theory of light, but his theory was partially unsuccessful because he assumed that light waves were longitudinal. We saw in Chap. 34 that in 1864 Maxwell provided compelling theoretical evidence that light is a transverse wave in the

Circular waves on the surface of a pond. Notice how waves interfere when they occupy the same region. *(Randy Matusow)*

electric and magnetic fields. However, the wave behavior of light had already been established experimentally in 1800 by Thomas Young (1773–1829). Young's experiments with light demonstrated effects that can only be explained in terms of destructive and constructive interference, effects that are exhibited only by waves.

In this chapter we discuss Young's famous double-slit experiment and several other important effects of the interference of light waves.

36-2 YOUNG'S DOUBLE-SLIT EXPERIMENT

Young's double-slit experiment provides a simple demonstration of the wave nature of light. Before discussing the double-slit experiment, we first consider an experiment where light passes through a single slit. The result may surprise you.

Suppose the light from an incandescent bulb passes through a narrow slit in a barrier and then impinges on a screen, as shown in Fig. 36-1. A color filter, such as a sheet of red cellophane, is placed over the bulb so that monochromatic light is incident on the slit. (Monochromatic light means light of one color or frequency or wavelength.) We are interested in the distribution of light intensity along the screen in the direction perpendicular to the slit, along the x direction in Fig. 36-1. If the slit is very narrow, then we observe that the light near the center of the screen (near $x = 0$) is almost uniform, gradually decreasing in intensity toward each side of the center. (In the next chapter we will see just how narrow we must make the slit.)

The surprising feature about this experiment is that we do not see a narrow band of light on the screen. Instead, the light bends around the edges of the slit and illuminates part of the screen that is in the geometric shadow of the barrier. This phenomenon, whereby light spreads around the edge of a barrier, is called *diffraction.* We shall discuss diffraction and the single-slit experiment in more detail in the next chapter. For now we simply use the knowledge that when light passes through a very narrow slit, the light spreads out and is nearly uniformly distributed in the region close to $x = 0$ in Fig. 36-1. The narrow slit behaves as a line source of waves, sending out cylindrical wavefronts (Sec. 32-6).

Diffraction is a characteristic feature of wave behavior. As another example of diffraction, Fig. 36-2 shows a photograph of water waves spreading out as they pass through a small opening in a barrier.

Diffraction, the spreading of light around the edge of a barrier

Figure 36-1. Monochromatic light from a bulb with a color filter passes through a slit and impinges on a screen.

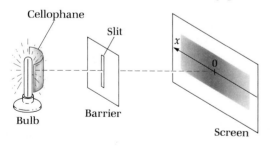

Cellophane

Slit

x

0

Bulb

Barrier

Screen

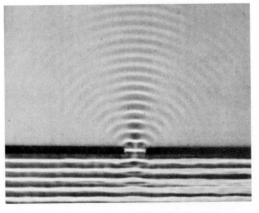

Figure 36-2. Water waves in a ripple tank. As the waves pass through the opening, they bend around the edge of the barrier. This is an example of diffraction. (Physics, *2nd ed., Physical Science Study Committee, 1965. Reprinted by permission of D. C. Heath and Co. and Educational Development Center.)*

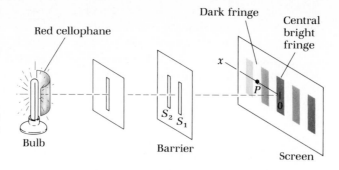

Figure 36-3. Young's double-slit experiment. Light from a bulb is made monochromatic by passing through a color filter. The light then passes through a collimating slit and parallel slits S_1 and S_2. The slit size and separation and the size of the double-slit interference pattern are exaggerated for clarity.

Figure 36-4. The double-slit interference pattern. *(Photo Researchers)*

Dark fringes are a consequence of destructive wave interference.

The double-slit experiment. In Fig. 36-3, monochromatic light passes through a collimating slit and then through two parallel slits S_1 and S_2 before impinging on a screen. The pattern of light seen on the screen consists of a series of brighter regions separated by darker regions, as shown in Fig. 36-4. These alternating bright and dark regions are called *fringes*, and this pattern of fringes is called the *double-slit interference pattern*.

Suppose we cover one of the slits, say S_1, so that only light passing through S_2 illuminates the screen. Then we find that the fringes have disappeared and the light near the center of the screen is nearly uniform, as described previously (Fig. 36-1). Consider a specific point on the screen that corresponds to the center of a dark fringe when both slits are open, point P in Fig. 36-3. The light intensity at that point on the screen is essentially zero when both slits are open. However, if one of the slits is covered so that light from it cannot reach the screen, then the intensity at P is *not* zero.

How is it possible for light to arrive at a point on the screen when only one slit is open, but when both slits are open, so that twice as much light passes through, no light arrives at that point? We can understand this result by assuming that light consists of waves. At the positions of the dark fringes, light waves from S_1 arrive out of phase with light waves from S_2. When two waves of equal intensity arrive out of phase at a point, they destructively interfere and the resultant wave is zero (Sec. 32-7). Thus the dark fringes are a consequence of the destructive interference between light waves from S_1 and light waves from S_2.

Figure 36-5 shows a demonstration of interference effects from two sources

Figure 36-5. Water waves in a ripple tank give a two-dimensional analog of the double-slit experiment. Two small spheres, vibrating up and down together, create waves of the same wavelength. Curved lines along which the waves destructively interfere are called *nodal lines*. The top edge of the photograph is analogous to the screen in the double-slit experiment. A point where a nodal line intersects the top edge is analogous to a dark fringe. *(Bernice Abbott/ Photo Researchers)*

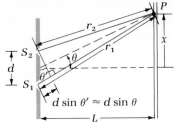

Figure 36-6. Light waves from S_1 and S_2 travel different distances to reach point P on the screen. In the actual experiment $L \gg d$, so the lines from each slit to P are essentially parallel and $\theta' \approx \theta$. Therefore, $d \sin \theta' \approx d \sin \theta$ and $r_1 - r_2 \approx d \sin \theta$.

of water waves. The interference of these waves can be used to visualize the way the double-slit interference pattern is formed.

We can use the principle of superposition to determine the positions of the fringes in the double-slit pattern. In Fig. 36-6 we show slits S_1 and S_2 a perpendicular distance L from the screen. A point P on the screen can be located by the angle θ measured relative to the center line. From the figure you can see that the waves from slits S_1 and S_2 travel different distances to reach point P; a wave from S_1 travels a distance r_1, and a wave from S_2 travels a distance r_2. For clarity in the figure, the separation d between the slits is greatly exaggerated compared with the distance L to the screen. In the experiment, d is much less than L, so the path difference $\Delta r = r_1 - r_2$ is approximately

$$r_1 - r_2 = d \sin \theta$$

The interference of waves arriving at a point on the screen depends on this path difference. In Fig. 36-7a we show waves that produce the central bright fringe located at $\theta = 0$. The waves emerge from the slits in phase and arrive at the screen still in phase because they have the same wavelength and each wave travels the same distance to arrive at the screen: $r_1 - r_2 = 0$. Since the light waves arrive at the screen in phase, they constructively interfere and a bright fringe is produced.

Figure 36-7. Light waves emerge from S_1 and S_2 in phase. (a) Waves from each slit arrive at P_0 in phase (crest on crest and trough on trough) so that they constructively interfere at the screen to produce the central bright fringe. (b) Waves arrive at P_0' out of phase (crest on trough and trough on crest) so that they destructively interfere to produce the $m' = 0$ dark fringe. (c) Waves arrive at P_1 in phase so that they constructively interfere to produce the $m = 1$ bright fringe.

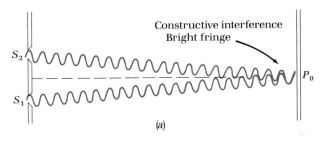

(a)

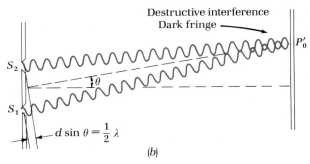

(b)

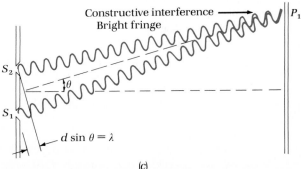

(c)

In Fig. 36-7b we show light waves that produce the first dark fringe to one side of the central bright fringe. To reach the screen, the waves from S_1 travel half a wavelength farther than the waves from S_2: $r_1 - r_2 = \frac{1}{2}\lambda$. The waves emerge from the slits in phase, but, in traveling different distances, they arrive at the screen π rad (180°) out of phase. Thus the waves destructively interfere and a dark fringe is produced. Similarly, a dark fringe is centered at any point where the path difference is given by an odd integer times $\frac{1}{2}\lambda$. That is, path differences given by $r_1 - r_2 = \pm(m' + \frac{1}{2})\lambda$, where $m' = 0, 1, 2, \ldots$, correspond to the centers of the dark fringes. Positive and negative values of $\pm(m' + \frac{1}{2})\lambda$ refer to positions on either side of the central bright fringe. The angles $\theta_{m'}$ that locate the centers of the dark fringes are given by

Angles $\theta_{m'}$ that locate dark fringes

$$d \sin \theta_{m'} = \pm(m' + \frac{1}{2})\lambda \qquad (m' = 0, 1, 2, \ldots) \qquad (36\text{-}1)$$

Figure 36-7c shows how the first bright fringe to one side of the central bright fringe is produced. The light waves emerge from the slits in phase and arrive at the screen in phase because the waves from S_1 travel a full wavelength farther than the waves from S_2: $r_1 - r_2 = \lambda$. Thus the waves constructively interfere and a bright fringe is produced. Similarly, a bright fringe is centered at any point where the path difference is an integral number of wavelengths. That is, if $r_1 - r_2 = \pm m\lambda$, where $m = 0, 1, 2, \ldots$, then a bright fringe is produced. The angles θ_m that locate the centers of the bright fringes are given by

Angles θ_m that locate bright fringes

$$d \sin \theta_m = \pm m\lambda \qquad (m = 0, 1, 2, \ldots) \qquad (36\text{-}2)$$

The bright fringes in the pattern are referred to according to their *order*, and the integer m in Eq. (36-2) labels the order of the fringe. The central bright fringe located at $\theta = 0$ corresponds to $m = 0$ and is called the *zeroth-order maximum*; the two bright fringes on either side of the central bright fringe correspond to $m = 1$ and are called the *first-order maxima*; and so on.

EXAMPLE 36-1. (a) Find an expression for the spacing Δx between the centers of adjacent bright fringes for light of wavelength λ. Assume that $L \gg x_m$, where L is the distance from the slits to the screen and x_m is the coordinate of the center of a bright fringe relative to the center of the central bright fringe. (See Fig. 36-6.) (b) When red light is used in a double-slit experiment in which $L = 1.3$ m and $d = 0.12$ mm, we find that $\Delta x = 7.3$ mm. Determine the wavelength of this red light.

SOLUTION. (a) Equation (36-2) gives the angles which locate the centers of the bright fringes. From Fig. 36-6, we see that $\sin \theta = x/\sqrt{x^2 + L^2}$. Since $L \gg x_m$, θ is small and $\sin \theta \approx \tan \theta = x/L$. Therefore, $d \sin \theta_m \approx d(x_m/L) \approx \pm m\lambda$. Thus

$$x_m \approx \pm m \frac{L\lambda}{d}$$

The spacing between two adjacent bright fringes, say be-

tween the mth and the $(m + 1)$th for positive x_m, is

$$\Delta x \approx (m + 1)\left(\frac{L\lambda}{d}\right) - m\left(\frac{L\lambda}{d}\right) = \frac{L\lambda}{d}$$

Thus, in an experiment where L and d are fixed, the spacing is greater (the pattern is more spread out) for light waves with longer wavelengths.

(b) Solving the above expression for λ gives

$$\lambda \approx \frac{d \, \Delta x}{L} = \frac{(1.2 \times 10^{-4} \text{ m})(7.3 \times 10^{-3} \text{ m})}{1.3 \text{ m}}$$

$$\approx 6.7 \times 10^{-7} \text{ m} = 670 \text{ nm}$$

This result shows that the wavelength of visible light is very small. To produce an easily observable interference pattern with visible light, we must make the slit separation correspondingly small.

Coherence. To understand how the double-slit interference pattern is produced, we used the fact that the light waves have the same phase as they emerge from S_1 and S_2. The pattern is then produced because the waves have a specific phase relation as they arrive at a particular point on the screen. They arrive at P_0 in phase (bright), they arrive at P_0' out of phase (dark), they arrive at P_1 in phase (bright), and so on.

Suppose we arrange to have the waves emerge from S_1 out of phase by π rad with the waves emerging from S_2. (See Ques. 36-8.) Then, by a similar analysis, the waves arrive at P_0 out of phase (dark), they arrive at P_0' in phase (bright), they arrive at P_1 out of phase (dark), and so on. If the waves emerge from the slits π rad out of phase, then an interference pattern is still produced, but the positions of the bright and dark fringes are shifted from their positions when the waves emerge with a zero phase difference. Extending this argument to other phase differences, we can see that a pattern is produced for any particular phase difference between the waves emerging from the slits. Changing the phase difference of the emerging waves simply shifts the positions of the fringes. To produce the double-slit interference pattern, there is no need for the phase difference between the waves emerging from the two slits to be zero, but there is a need for this phase difference, whatever it is, to remain constant.

Now suppose that the phase difference of the emerging waves varies randomly. If the time of this variation in phase difference is short compared with the time of observation, then we would observe the average of many overlapping patterns. That is, *we would observe no double-slit interference pattern at all!* The fact that we do observe a stable pattern shows that the waves emerging from S_1 maintain a constant phase difference with the waves emerging from S_2.

If waves emerging from two sources maintain a constant phase difference, then the two sources are *coherent*. Only coherent sources can produce a stable interference pattern. The two vibrating spheres that produced the water waves in Fig. 36-5 are coherent sources because the spheres vibrate up and down together. The two slits in Young's double-slit experiment are coherent sources because the light from these sources originates from the same primary source, the collimating slit in Fig. 36-3.

In an ordinary light source, such as a light-bulb filament, the light is emitted from many individual atoms radiating independently. Consequently, the phase relation among these emissions is totally random. Thus two separate light-bulb filaments are incoherent sources, and they do not produce a stable interference pattern. In the double-slit experiment, the slits behave as two identical images of the same source. Any phase relation that exists for light emerging from one of the slits also exists for the other. Therefore, the slits are coherent sources.

Coherent sources maintain a constant phase difference.

36-3 INTENSITY DISTRIBUTION IN THE DOUBLE-SLIT INTERFERENCE PATTERN

To find an expression for the distribution of light intensity in the double-slit interference pattern, we use the principle of superposition. That is, we add vectorially the electric fields due to the light waves from each slit. This addition is performed at each point P along the screen (Fig. 36-6). Then we find the intensity I at P by taking the square of the resultant electric field amplitude. (From Sec. 34-5, $I = \overline{S} = \frac{1}{2}\epsilon_0 E_0^2 c$.)

Let E_1 and E_2 be the electric field components of the light waves from S_1 and

S_2 at point P on the screen. (For brevity, we drop the coordinate subscript on the symbols for the field components.) We assume that the slits are very narrow, so they may be treated as line sources of light. This means that the intensity distribution due to each slit acting alone is nearly uniform around the center of the screen, and the field components may be written as

$$E_1 = E_0 \sin (\omega t + \phi) \qquad \text{and} \qquad E_2 = E_0 \sin (\omega t)$$

Because the monochromatic light originates from the same source, each expression contains the same frequency ω. Also, since each slit has the same width and is nearly the same distance from P, we assume that the amplitude E_0 of each wave is the same. The crucial feature in the expressions for E_1 and E_2, as far as the interference pattern is concerned, is that the waves have a phase difference at P. The phase difference ϕ is due to the path difference $d \sin \theta$. In Fig. 36-7b the path difference is $d \sin \theta = \frac{1}{2}\lambda$, and the waves arrive at the screen with a phase difference $\phi = \pi$ rad. In Fig. 36-7c the path difference is $d \sin \theta = \lambda$, and the waves arrive at the screen with a phase difference $\phi = 2\pi$ rad. Thus the phase difference and the path difference are directly proportional:

$$\frac{\text{Phase difference}}{2\pi} = \frac{\text{path difference}}{\lambda} \qquad \text{or} \qquad \frac{\phi}{2\pi} = \frac{d \sin \theta}{\lambda}$$

Therefore
$$\phi = \frac{2\pi d \sin \theta}{\lambda} \tag{36-3}$$

To find the component E_{12} of the resultant electric field at P, we add E_1 and E_2:

$$E_{12} = E_1 + E_2 = E_0 \sin (\omega t + \phi) + E_0 \sin (\omega t)$$

Using the trigonometric identity

$$\sin \alpha + \sin \beta = 2 \cos [\tfrac{1}{2}(\alpha - \beta)] \sin [\tfrac{1}{2}(\alpha + \beta)]$$

with $\alpha = \omega t + \phi$ and $\beta = \omega t$, we obtain

$$E_{12} = [2E_0 \cos (\tfrac{1}{2}\phi)] \sin (\omega t + \tfrac{1}{2}\phi) \tag{36-4}$$

Thus E_{12} oscillates with an amplitude of $2E_0 \cos (\tfrac{1}{2}\phi)$.

Intensity is proportional to amplitude squared, so that if we let I_0 represent the intensity at P due to light from one of the slits acting alone (the other slit covered), then $I_0 \propto E_0^2$. From Eq. (36-4), the amplitude of the resultant wave is $2E_0 \cos (\tfrac{1}{2}\phi)$, so the intensity I_{12} due to light from both slits is

$$I_{12} \propto 4E_0^2 \cos^2 (\tfrac{1}{2}\phi)$$

Since the proportionality factor between intensity and amplitude squared is the same for both slits open as it is for each slit acting alone, we have

Double-slit intensity in terms of ϕ
$$I_{12} = 4I_0 \cos^2 (\tfrac{1}{2}\phi) \tag{36-5}$$

Using Eq. (36-3), $\phi = (2\pi d \sin \theta)/\lambda$, we can express this result in terms of the angle θ that locates the point P on the screen in Fig. 36-6:

Double-slit intensity in terms of θ
$$I_{12} = 4I_0 \cos^2 \left(\frac{\pi d \sin \theta}{\lambda} \right) \tag{36-6}$$

Let us check the agreement of this expression with Eqs. (36-1) and (36-2). From

Eq. (36-1), dark fringes are located at angles $\theta_{m'}$ given by $d \sin \theta_{m'} = \pm(m' + \frac{1}{2})\lambda$. Substitution into Eq. (36-6) gives $I_{12} = 4I_0 \cos^2 [\pm(m' + \frac{1}{2})\pi]$. Since $\cos [\pm(m' + \frac{1}{2})\pi] = 0$ for $m' = 0$ or any integer, $I_{12} = 0$ at these angles. From Eq. (36-2), bright fringes are located at angles θ_m given by $d \sin \theta_m = \pm m\lambda$. Substitution into Eq. (36-6) gives $I_{12} = 4I_0 \cos^2 (\pm m\pi)$. Since $\cos^2 (\pm m\pi) = 1$ for $m = 0$ or any integer, $I_{12} = 4I_0$ at these angles. Thus Eq. (36-6) gives positions of dark fringes and bright fringes that are in agreement with Eqs. (36-1) and (36-2).

Often the experiment is performed such that the separation Δx of the fringes is much smaller than the distance L from the slits to the screen. In this case we are only interested in the intensity at points with $x \ll L$ in Fig. 36-6, and the approximation $\sin \theta \approx x/L$ is valid. Equation (36-6) then becomes

Double-slit intensity in terms of x

$$I_{12} \approx 4I_0 \cos^2 \left[\left(\frac{\pi d}{\lambda L}\right) x\right] \qquad (36\text{-}7)$$

In Fig. 36-8, we show a graph of Eq. (36-7). With our assumption that the slits are very narrow, the intensity varies from zero to $4I_0$ as a cosine-squared function across the middle of the screen ($x \ll L$).

More about coherence. To emphasize the distinction between coherent and incoherent sources, we recast Eq. (36-5) by using the trigonometric identity $2 \cos^2 (\frac{1}{2}\phi) = 1 + \cos \phi$:

$$I_{12} = 2I_0 + 2I_0 \cos \phi \qquad \text{(coherent sources)}$$

The phase difference ϕ corresponds to a particular point on the screen so that the average value of the second term over any integral number of fringes across the screen is zero. If the light from the slits originated from different sources, then the slits would be incoherent sources and the phase difference ϕ would vary rapidly and randomly with time. In this case the second term would have a time average of zero at each point on the screen and the intensity would be

$$I_{12} = 2I_0 \qquad \text{(incoherent sources)}$$

That is, the intensity would be simply the sum of the intensities of two sources acting alone. The horizontal dashed line in Fig. 36-8 shows the intensity from two incoherent sources where I_0 is the intensity from each source acting alone.

When finding the intensity due to combined waves from coherent sources, we add the electric field components and then square the resultant field. A stable interference pattern is a consequence of the combination of waves from coherent sources. When finding the intensity due to the combined waves from incoherent sources, we first square the field components to determine the intensity of each source acting alone and then add the intensities. No stable interference pattern is produced by the combined effects of waves from incoherent sources.

Figure 36-8. Intensity distribution of the double-slit interference pattern versus coordinate x in units of $\lambda L/\pi d$. The slits are very narrow and $x \ll L$.

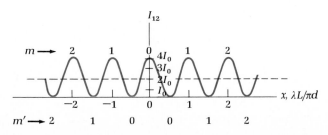

36-4 DIFFRACTION GRATINGS

A *diffraction grating* is a device that can separate a beam of light into its constituent wavelengths or colors. A grating is an important tool for a scientist or engineer who performs research in optics. There are two types of gratings: *reflection gratings* and *transmission gratings*. A grating is constructed by forming parallel, evenly spaced grooves or scratches on a flat surface of a metal (reflection grating) or glass (transmission grating) plate. The action of a grating can be described in terms of a regular array of parallel slits. The grooves scatter the light and are effectively opaque, and the space between the grooves behaves as a slit. Typically the grating plate is rectangular, with dimensions of several centimeters on a side. The spacing d between the slits is very small, about 2 μm, and the number N of slits is usually large, about 10,000. A great deal of precision is required to assure that the closely spaced slits are parallel and of equal size and spacing.

Consider a beam of monochromatic light incident normally on a diffraction grating. (For nonnormal incidence see Prob. 36-6.) The light waves are in phase as they emerge from each of the slits, as shown in Fig. 36-9. To reach point P on the screen, the waves from adjacent slits travel a different distance by the amount $d \sin \theta$. For the particular case in the figure, the waves are shown directed such that $d \sin \theta = \lambda$. These waves arrive at the screen in phase and interfere constructively at P to form a first-order interference maximum. Waves will interfere constructively at the screen when the path difference $d \sin \theta$ is an integral number of wavelengths. That is, interference maxima are located at angles θ_m given by

Angles θ_m that locate interference maxima

$$d \sin \theta_m = \pm m\lambda \qquad (m = 0, 1, 2, \ldots) \qquad (36\text{-}8)$$

where the integer m labels the order of the interference maximum. Note that this is the same equation as Eq. (36-2) for the bright fringes in the double-slit interference pattern.

The angle θ_m of an interference maximum for light of a given wavelength depends only on the spacing d. For example, consider light at each end of the visible spectrum passing through a grating with $d = 2.0$ μm. The angles which locate the two first-order maxima ($m = 1$) for violet light ($\lambda \approx 400$ nm) are given by $\sin \theta_1 = \pm(1)(400 \text{ nm})/2.0 \ \mu\text{m} = \pm 0.20$, so that $\theta_1 = \sin^{-1}(\pm 0.20) = \pm 12°$. Similarly, the first-order maxima for red light ($\lambda \approx 750$ nm) occurs at $\theta_1 = \pm 22°$.

Figure 36-9. Waves from adjacent slits travel different distances by the amount $d \sin \theta$ to reach point P on the screen. In this particular case, $d \sin \theta = \lambda$, so an interference maximum is produced at P.

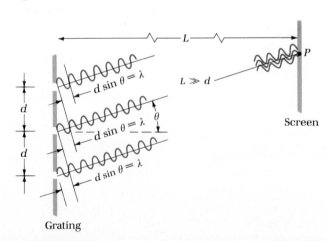

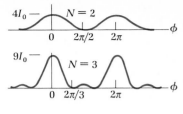

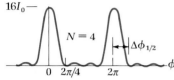

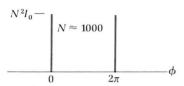

$N^2 I_0$ —

$N \approx 1000$

0   2π ϕ

Figure 36-10. Progression of the intensity distribution with increasing N (d is fixed). The light is monochromatic and the slits are very narrow: $\phi = (2\pi d \sin \theta)/\lambda$.

Now let us examine the effect of adding slits to a grating, beginning with a double slit. From Eq. (36-4), the intensity distribution of the double-slit interference pattern is $I = 4I_0 \cos^2 (\tfrac{1}{2}\phi)$. Using the trigonometric identity $2\cos \alpha = \sin (2\alpha)/\sin \alpha$, with $\alpha = \tfrac{1}{2}\phi$, we can write the double-slit ($N = 2$) intensity distribution as

$$I = I_0 \frac{\sin^2 [2(\tfrac{1}{2}\phi)]}{\sin^2 (\tfrac{1}{2}\phi)}$$

You can show (see Prob. 36-4) that for the case of three slits ($N = 3$),

$$I = I_0 \frac{\sin^2 [3(\tfrac{1}{2}\phi)]}{\sin^2 (\tfrac{1}{2}\phi)}$$

The general relation for the intensity distribution from a monochromatic source due to a grating with N slits (Prob. 36-13) is

$$I = I_0 \frac{\sin^2 [N(\tfrac{1}{2}\phi)]}{\sin^2 (\tfrac{1}{2}\phi)} \tag{36-9}$$

In each of these expressions, I_0 is the intensity at the screen due to one of the slits acting alone, and ϕ is the phase difference at the screen between waves from adjacent slits.

Figure 36-10 shows the progression of the intensity distribution from a double slit to a diffraction grating. The important feature of the interference pattern from a grating is that when N is large the waves combine to give nearly complete cancellation at all angles except those which correspond to the interference maxima. The light is very intense at angles where $d \sin \theta_m = \pm m\lambda$, and much less intense at all other angles (Prob. 36-7).

Figure 36-10 shows two effects that result from adding more slits. First, the intensity of each interference maximum increases with N as N^2. That is, if we double the number of slits, keeping the slit size fixed, then the intensity of a maximum increases by a factor of 4. Second, the width of each interference maximum decreases with increasing N. We define the angular half-width $\Delta\theta_{1/2}$ of an interference maximum as the angle between the center of the maximum and its adjacent minimum. The change $\Delta\phi$ in phase difference between the center of an interference maximum and its adjacent minimum is $\Delta\phi_{1/2} = 2\pi/N$. This result is suggested by the progression in Fig. 36-10. Also, see Exercise 36-21. If we differentiate the expression $\phi = (2\pi d \sin \theta)/\lambda$, with ϕ and θ as variables, then we find $d\phi = [(2\pi d \cos \theta)/\lambda]d\theta$. Thus a small change $\Delta\phi$ in phase difference corresponds to a small change $\Delta\theta$ in angle: $\Delta\theta = [\lambda/(2\pi d \cos \theta)]\Delta\phi$. Using $\Delta\theta = \Delta\theta_{1/2}$ and $\Delta\phi = \Delta\phi_{1/2} = 2\pi/N$, we find that the angular half-width of an interference maximum is

Half-width of an interference maximum

$$\Delta\theta_{1/2} = \frac{\lambda}{Nd \cos \theta_m} \tag{36-10}$$

The angular half-width of an interference maximum is proportional to $1/N$.

Suppose we have a source that emits light of two discrete wavelengths (or colors), $\lambda_v = 400$ nm (v for violet) and $\lambda_r = 750$ nm (r for red). For simplicity, we suppose each color is emitted with the same intensity. Figure 36-11 shows the $m = 0$ and $m = 1$ interference maxima in a graph of intensity versus θ for a grating with $d = 1.7$ μm. The light at the center ($\theta = 0$), which corresponds to the zeroth-order maximum, is a mixture of red and violet light, the same as the

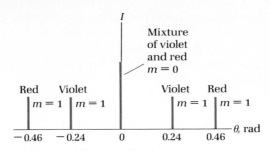

Figure 36-11. First-order interference maxima for light from a source that emits light with two discrete wavelengths of the same intensity.

incident light. The first-order maxima on each side of $\theta = 0$ are spatially separated into violet and red. When the emission from a source is in the form of discrete wavelengths, as in this case, the spectrum is called a *line spectrum* because the interference maxima appear as colored lines on the screen.

Discrete wavelengths give a line spectrum.

Some light sources, such as the sun or an incandescent light bulb, emit light which contains a continuous distribution of wavelengths over a limited range. A grating will separate this light into a *continuous spectrum* for each order. When we view, say, a first-order spectrum from such a source, we see all the colors in the visible range of wavelengths spread out across the screen. For the grating in Fig. 36-11, we would see a "rainbow of colors" between $\theta = 0.24$ and 0.46 rad.

Continuous distribution of wavelengths gives a continuous spectrum.

A quantity which characterizes the capability of a grating to spatially spread a light beam according to wavelength is called the grating's *dispersion D*. The dispersion of a grating is defined as

Definition of the dispersion of a grating

$$D = \frac{\Delta\theta_m}{\Delta\lambda}$$

where $\Delta\theta_m$ is the angular spacing between the interference maxima (of the same order) of waves with wavelengths that differ by an amount $\Delta\lambda$. If we differentiate the expression $d \sin\theta_m = m\lambda$, with θ_m and λ as variables, then we have $(d \cos\theta_m)\, d\theta_m = m\, d\lambda$. Thus two waves of nearly the same wavelength have their interference maxima separated by an amount $\Delta\theta_m = [m/(d \cos\theta_m)]\Delta\lambda$. Using $D = \Delta\theta_m/\Delta\lambda$, we have

Dispersion of a grating

$$D = \frac{m}{d \cos\theta_m} \qquad (36\text{-}11)$$

Since d is in the denominator, Eq. (36-11) shows that the dispersion is larger for gratings with a smaller slit spacing d.

EXAMPLE 36-2. (a) Determine an expression for $\Delta\theta_{1/2}$ for an interference maximum in terms of its order m. (b) What is the angular half-width of the first-order interference maximum when monochromatic light of wavelength 500 nm illuminates 1700 slits of a grating with $d = 1.8 \ \mu$m?

SOLUTION. (a) For the mth-order interference maximum, $\sin\theta_m = \pm m\lambda/d$. Using the identity $\sin^2\theta + \cos^2\theta = 1$, we have

$$\cos\theta_m = \sqrt{1 - \sin^2\theta_m} = \sqrt{1 - \left(\frac{m\lambda}{d}\right)^2}$$

(We keep only the positive square root. Why?) Substitution

into Eq. (36-10) gives

$$\Delta\theta_{1/2} = \frac{\lambda}{Nd\sqrt{1 - (m\lambda/d)^2}} = \frac{1}{N\sqrt{(d/\lambda)^2 - m^2}}$$

(b) Using the above expression, we have

$$\Delta\theta_{1/2} = \frac{1}{1700\sqrt{(1.8 \ \mu\text{m}/500 \ \text{nm})^2 - 1^2}}$$

$$= 1.7 \times 10^{-4} \ \text{rad} = 0.0097°$$

The width of an interference maximum is very narrow for typical gratings because N is very large.

EXAMPLE 36-3. In a sodium vapor lamp, the sodium atoms are excited by an electric arc and emit radiation. A prominent part of the spectrum from this emission consists of two yellow lines with wavelengths 589.00 and 589.59 nm. Suppose a beam of light from a sodium lamp is incident normally on a grating with 12,000 slits and a spacing of 2.1 μm. The beam is narrow so that it illuminates a width of 1.7 mm of the grating. Determine whether the lines in the first-order spectra of these two wavelengths are resolved by the grating.

SOLUTION. We use the *Rayleigh criterion* to decide whether the lines are resolved. According to this criterion, the lines are resolved if their angular separation $\Delta\theta_m$ is greater than the angular half-width $\Delta\theta_{1/2}$ of either line. (See Fig. 36-12.) From our discussion of dispersion, the angular separation $\Delta\theta_m$ of two lines with wavelengths that differ by $\Delta\lambda$ is

$$\Delta\theta_m = \frac{m}{d\cos\theta_m}\Delta\lambda$$

The Rayleigh criterion requires that $\Delta\theta_m > \Delta\theta_{1/2}$. Using $\Delta\theta_{1/2}$ from Eq. (36-11), we have that the lines are resolved when

$$\frac{m}{d\cos\theta_m}\Delta\lambda > \frac{\lambda}{Nd\cos\theta_m}$$

or
$$\Delta\lambda > \frac{\lambda}{Nm}$$

If the wavelengths of the two lines differ by more than λ/Nm, then the lines are separated enough so that they can be distinguished as two lines rather than one. In this expression, λ is the wavelength of either of the lines (they are nearly equal), N is the number of slits illuminated by the beam, and m is the order of the spectrum. For the beam of light in this example, the width w of the beam is too narrow to illuminate all the slits. The number of slits illuminated is $N = w/d = 1.7$ mm/2.1 μm $= 810$. For the first-order spectrum of the yellow lines from sodium, $\lambda/Nm = 589$ nm/$[(810)(1)] = 0.73$ nm. Since the wavelength difference for these lines is $\Delta\lambda = 589.59$ nm $- 589.00$ nm $= 0.59$ nm, they are not resolved; they appear as one line. The lines could be resolved by either illuminating more slits, or by observing a higher-order spectrum.

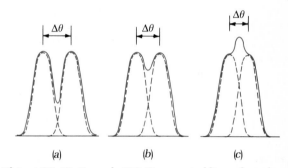

(a)   (b)   (c)

Figure 36-12. Example 36-3: Two spectral lines of equal intensity (shown dashed) separated by an angle $\Delta\theta$. (a) $\Delta\theta > \Delta\theta_{1/2}$. (b) $\Delta\theta = \Delta\theta_{1/2}$. (c) $\Delta\theta < \Delta\theta_{1/2}$. The Rayleigh criterion for resolution is $\Delta\theta > \Delta\theta_{1/2}$.

36-5   X-RAY DIFFRACTION BY CRYSTALS

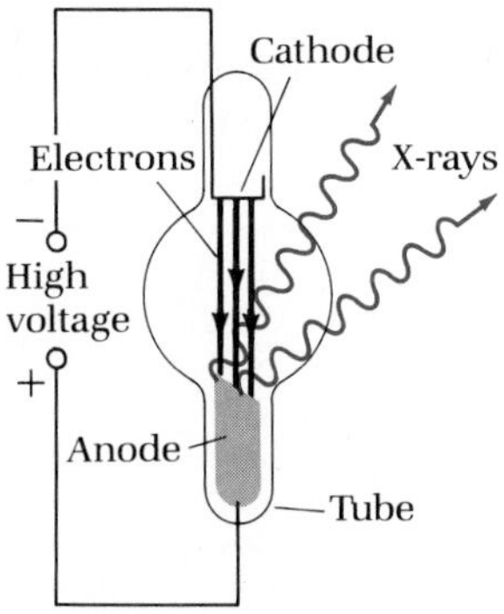

X-rays were discovered in 1895 by Wilhelm Roentgen (1845–1923). They can be produced by accelerating electrons to high speeds through a large potential difference, 10 to 100 kV, and then causing these electrons to strike a metal target. X-rays are then emitted from the target. (See Fig. 36-13.) The identity of x-rays remained a mystery for some years after their discovery; that is why they were called "x." It was known that these rays were very penetrating, could darken photographic film, and could cause minerals to fluoresce. Since the deflection of a beam of x-rays by an electric or magnetic field could not be detected, it was assumed that the beam did not consist of charged particles. These properties led to the conclusion that x-rays consist of short-wavelength electromagnetic radiation — that is, light with wavelengths much smaller than visible light.

In 1912 Max von Laue (1879–1960) suggested an experiment which verified the wave nature of x-rays. Von Laue pointed out that if x-rays have wavelengths λ that are about the same as the spacing d between planes of atoms in crystals, then x-ray waves impinging on crystals would exhibit interference effects. Recall that a transmission grating, because it consists of a regular array of slits, causes light waves to exhibit strong constructive interference at a few particular angles and almost complete cancellation at all other angles. To ob-

Figure 36-13. An x-ray tube. Electrons are emitted from the cathode and are accelerated to high speeds before striking the anode target. Rapid slowing (deceleration) of the electrons in the anode causes the emission of the x-rays.

Cathode

Electrons   X-rays

High voltage

Anode

Tube

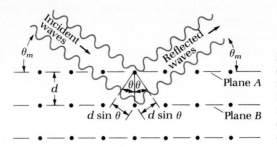

Figure 36-14. To reach the detector, x-ray waves reflected from plane B must travel a distance $2(d \sin \theta)$ farther than those reflected from plane A. The waves constructively interfere at the detector when $2d \sin \theta = m\lambda$.

serve these interference effects, the slit spacing must be almost as small as the wavelength. Similarly, a crystalline solid consists of a regular array of atoms. When a beam of x-rays impinges on a crystal, strong constructive interference effects can be observed readily if the wavelength λ is somewhat smaller than the interplanar spacing d in the crystal.

Figure 36-14 shows a two-dimensional representation of a three-dimensional crystal; the rows of dots portray planes of atoms. X-rays of a single wavelength are in phase before being scattered from the atoms in plane A and the atoms in plane B. For constructive interference of the x-rays scattered from each plane of atoms, the angle of incidence turns out to be equal to the angle of reflection. To reach the detector, the waves scattered from the atoms in plane B travel a greater distance than those scattered from the atoms in plane A by the amount $2(d \sin \theta)$. If the angle θ_m is given by the relation

Bragg's law

$$2d \sin \theta_m = m\lambda \qquad (m = 1, 2, \ldots) \qquad (36\text{-}12)$$

then the waves scattered from the atoms in plane A will arrive at the detector in phase with the waves scattered from the atoms in plane B. Thus the waves will constructively interfere and produce an interference maximum. Similarly, constructive interference will occur for waves scattered from the atoms of each of the many planes that are parallel to planes A and B. This relation was first developed by W. L. Bragg (1890–1971) and is called *Bragg's law*.

Bragg's law gives the angles which locate the maxima produced by the constructive interference of x-rays. The interference is caused by the scattering from the atoms in parallel sets of planes. Figure 36-15 shows the two-dimensional analog of three such sets of planes. Thus the distance d in Bragg's law refers to any of the many interplanar spacings that exist in a crystal. However, the intensity of the interference maxima for a set of planes depends on the density of atoms in those planes.

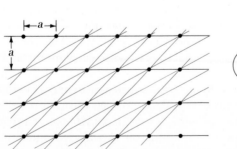

Figure 36-15. Two-dimensional analog of crystalline planes with closely packed atoms. Three such sets of planes are shown.

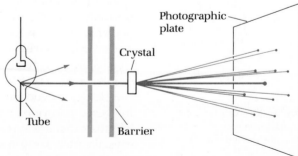

Figure 36-16. Experimental arrangement for x-ray diffraction.

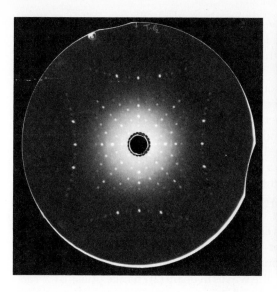

Figure 36-17. Photograph of the Laue pattern from a crystal. The symmetry of the crystal is indicated by the symmetry of the spots. *(Photo Researchers)*

Figure 36-18. Interference of reflected light from the front and back surfaces of a soap film. The film is very thin at the top, where it appears dark, and increases in thickness toward the bottom so that interference fringes are produced.

Figure 36-16 shows one experimental arrangement for x-ray diffraction. A collimated beam of x-rays which contains a continuous distribution of wavelengths strikes the crystal. Interference maxima are produced at angles which satisfy Bragg's law. These maxima form a pattern of spots on the film called a *Laue pattern.* (See Fig. 36-17.) Properties of the crystal can be determined from the positions and intensities of the spots. Indeed, x-ray diffraction is one of the most powerful tools we have for studying the structure of solids.

36-6 INTERFERENCE FROM THIN FILMS

An easily observed interference effect is that due to reflections from thin transparent films such as soap bubbles or oil films. The brilliant colors you often see reflected from such films are caused by interference.

Figure 36-18 shows a photograph of a soap film in a circular wire loop, the sort of arrangement used by children to blow bubbles. The loop is oriented vertically so that the film is slightly wedge-shaped because of its own weight; it is very thin at the top and becomes thicker toward the bottom. A source of monochromatic light was positioned behind the camera in taking the photograph in Fig. 36-18, and the incident light beam is directed nearly normal to the film surface. The light from the soap film arrived at the camera after reflection from the film's front and back surfaces. Two features of this reflected light are apparent from Fig. 36-18: (i) There is no reflected light from the top region of the film, which appears dark; and (ii) horizontal interference fringes occur below the dark region.

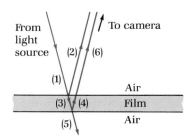

Figure 36-19. Reflections from the front and back surfaces of a film. Beams (2) and (6) have nearly the same intensity and are coherent.

Consider the reflections that occur at the two surfaces of the soap film. Figure 36-19 shows a light beam at nearly normal incidence on a transparent film with air on each side. (The angle between the beam direction and the normal is exaggerated for clarity.) The incident beam (1) is split into two beams at the film's front surface: a reflected beam (2) and a transmitted beam (3). The transmitted beam (3) is then split into two beams at the film's back surface: a reflected beam (4) and a transmitted beam (5). The reflected beam (4) is further split into a transmitted beam (6) and a reflected beam (not shown) at the film's front surface, and so on. The superposition of beams (2) and (6) is observed at

Reflection from a surface where
the index changes from low to
high causes a phase reversal.

the camera. These beams are coherent because they originate from the same source. Also, their waves usually have about the same amplitude. (See Prob. 36-11.) It is interference between the waves in these two beams that causes the effects shown in Fig. 36-18.

There is an additional point to consider before we attempt to understand the effects shown in Fig. 36-18. Under certain conditions light waves undergo a phase change of π rad upon reflection; that is, they undergo a *phase reversal*. Suppose light is incident on a boundary between transparent media. If the light is incident on the boundary from the medium with lower index of refraction, then the reflected waves undergo a phase reversal. If the light is incident on the boundary from the medium with higher index, then the reflected waves do not undergo a phase reversal. (A verse which may help you remember this is "low to high, phase change by π.") These phase relationships are predicted from the application of Maxwell's equations to the electric and magnetic fields at the boundary. Waves incident on the boundary between two stretched springs show similar phase relations (Sec. 32-3). Since the film in Fig. 36-19 has a larger index of refraction than air, the waves in beam (2) change phase by π rad when they are reflected, but the waves in beam (6) do not change phase when they are reflected.

Suppose the film in Fig. 36-19 has a thickness τ that is much less than the wavelength λ_n of the light. In this case, the waves in beams (2) and (6) will travel nearly the same distance to reach P; they will not become out of phase because of traveling different distances. However, because of the phase reversal of the waves in beam (2), the waves in beams (2) and (6) emerge from the film nearly π rad out of phase and interfere destructively. Therefore, the top of the film appears dark. The dark appearance of the film in this region is verification of the phase reversal discussed above.

The film is thicker at positions farther down. Consider a position where the thickness is a quarter of a wavelength: $\tau = \lambda_n/4$. The waves in beam (6) travel farther than the waves in beam (2) by the amount $2\tau = 2(\lambda_n/4) = \frac{1}{2}\lambda_n$. This path difference for the two beams causes a phase difference of π rad. Since the phase reversal of beam (2) causes an additional phase difference of π rad, the waves emerge in phase. A bright fringe appears along the region of the film that has a thickness of $\lambda_n/4$. The relation between film thickness and wavelength that corresponds to constructive interference is

$$2\tau = (m + \tfrac{1}{2})\lambda_n \qquad (m = 0, 1, 2, \ldots) \tag{36-13}$$

Similarly, the relation which corresponds to destructive interference is

$$2\tau = m'\lambda_n \qquad (m' = 0, 1, 2, \ldots) \tag{36-14}$$

Thus, as the film in Fig. 36-18 becomes progressively thicker toward the bottom, interference fringes are produced in accordance with Eqs. (36-13) and (36-14).

We should note that λ_n in Eqs. (36-13) and (36-14) refers to the wavelength in the film. If the film has an index of refraction n, then the wavelength in the film is

$$\lambda_n = \frac{\lambda}{n}$$

where λ is the wavelength in vacuum (or, to a good approximation, in air).

Now we can understand the origin of the full spectrum of colors we often see

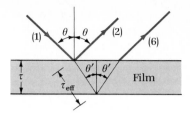

Figure 36-20. A beam of light incident at an angle θ to a normal to a film. Beam (6) must travel an extra distance $2\tau_{eff}$ compared with beam (2).

reflected from a soap bubble or a film of oil. As you can see in Fig. 36-20, when light is reflected from a film at various angles of incidence, the extra distance $2\tau_{eff}$ that beam (6) must travel compared with beam (2) depends on the angle of incidence. (See Exercise 36-39.) This gives an angular dependence in the equations that describe interference maxima (and minima). When white light is incident on a film at a particular angle, the color corresponding to the wavelength that satisfies the relation describing constructive interference will be reflected with greater intensity than other colors. As we view different places on the film, we see light that is reflected at different angles. At each angle a given color is reflected with greater intensity than the other colors. This property, where the color of an object depends on the angle from which the object is viewed, is called *iridescence*. Thus the film appears as a rainbow as the incident white light is dispersed into its constituent colors.

EXAMPLE 36-4. *Nonreflecting coatings.* To reduce reflection from an optical surface, such as the surface of a lens, the surface is often coated with a thin film. Suppose a glass lens ($n = 1.50$) is coated with a thin film of MgF_2 ($n = 1.38$). Determine the minimum thickness for a coating which will minimize reflection for normal incidence of light near the middle of the visible spectrum, say $\lambda = 550$ nm.

SOLUTION. Equation (36-14) describes minimum reflection from a thin film (destructive interference between reflected beams), but it is not valid in this case. That equation was developed for the case where one of the beams had a phase reversal upon reflection and the other did not. For the case of a MgF_2 film on glass, the light reflected from the front surface of the film is incident from the medium of lower index (from air with $n = 1.00$ to MgF_2), so the reflected waves undergo a phase reversal. The light reflected from the back surface is also incident from the medium of lower index (from MgF_2 to glass), so these reflected waves also undergo a phase reversal. Since the effect of these two phase reversals cancels, the phase difference between waves re-

flected from the two surfaces is due to the path difference 2τ; the phase difference is π rad if 2τ equals an odd half-integral number of wavelengths. Thus Eq. (36-13) describes destructive interference (minimum reflection) in this case. Solving for τ, we have

$$\tau = \tfrac{1}{2}(m + \tfrac{1}{2})\lambda_n = \frac{\tfrac{1}{2}(m + \tfrac{1}{2})\lambda}{n}$$

Since we wish to find a minimum thickness for the film, we set $m = 0$. The extra distance that provides the phase difference is in the MgF_2 film, so $n = 1.38$. Thus

$$\tau = \frac{1}{2}\frac{1}{2}\frac{550 \text{ nm}}{1.38} = 100 \text{ nm}$$

This film thickness will minimize reflection of light with wavelengths near the middle of the visible spectrum. Lenses often have a purplish tint because the reflection contains only a small amount of light from the middle of the visible spectrum; most of the reflected light is from the red and violet ends of the spectrum. Thin films can also be used to maximize reflection. (See Exercise 36-38.)

36-7 THE MICHELSON INTERFEROMETER

A device which uses wave-interference effects to make measurements is called an *interferometer*. Because the wavelength of visible light is very small, optical interferometers can be used to measure distance with great precision. The Michelson interferometer (named for A. A. Michelson, 1852–1931) is one of simple design and of historical importance.

Figure 36-21 shows the principal features of a Michelson interferometer. A beam of monochromatic light from the source impinges on mirror $M_{1/2}$ which is mounted at a 45° angle to the beam direction. The silver coating on this mirror is just the right thickness so that it reflects half of the incident beam and transmits the other half. Thus half of the incident beam is directed toward a movable mirror M_m [beam (1)], and the other half is directed toward a fixed mirror M_f [beam (2)]. Mirrors M_m and M_f then reflect the beams back to $M_{1/2}$,

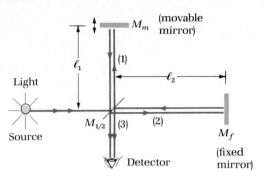

Figure 36-21. A schematic diagram of the Michelson interferometer.

where half of each beam is again reflected and transmitted. We are interested in the parts of each beam which combine to form beam (3) and then propagate to the detector.

Beam (3) consists of waves which have traversed different distances. Beam (1) traversed a distance of $2\ell_1$ and beam (2) traversed a distance of $2\ell_2$. The difference in distance traversed by the beams is $|2\ell_2 - 2\ell_1|$. Since beams (1) and (2) are of equal intensity and are coherent (why?), they will constructively interfere if $2|\ell_2 - \ell_1|$ is an integral number of wavelengths, and they will destructively interfere if $2|\ell_2 - \ell_1|$ is an odd half-integral number of wavelengths. (For simplicity we ignore the thickness of $M_{1/2}$.) Therefore, the intensity of the light measured at the detector depends on this distance difference.

Mirror M_m can be smoothly displaced small distances along the direction of beam (1) by turning a finely threaded screw. The light intensity measured by the detector can be caused to change from a maximum to a minimum by moving M_m a distance of $\lambda/4$. With a sensitive detector, distances as small as 1 percent of a wavelength (about 5 nm) can be readily detected.

At the time Michelson developed his interferometer, the standard of length, the meter, was defined as the distance between two fine scratches in a particular platinum-iridium bar kept at Sèvres, France. Using his interferometer, Michelson was able to measure the wavelength of an emission line from a cadmium light source with an accuracy of one part in 10^8. This capability utimately led to a definition of the meter in terms of the wavelength of a certain spectral line from the element krypton.

COMMENTARY: THOMAS YOUNG

Thomas Young. (*New York Public Library*)

Thomas Young was born at Milverton, Somerset, England, in 1773. Blessed with a remarkable memory and extraordinary mechanical ability, Young applied his talents to physics, medicine, physiology, and languages. By the age of 14, he was familiar with Latin, Greek, Hebrew, Arabic, Persian, French, and Italian, and by the time he was 17, he had mastered Newton's Principia and Opticks.

Young's great-uncle, who was a prominent physician, persuaded him to study medicine so he could eventually acquire his practice. Young's studies of vision and hearing seem to have led to his more fundamental investigations of light and sound. He reported his definitive experiments on the interference of light in a paper entitled "Outlines of Experiments and Enquiries Respecting Sound and Light" (1800). There he compared the corpuscular theory of Newton with the wave theory of Huygens and showed that the experimental results could be explained with a wave theory, thus favoring Huygens. The suggestion that New-

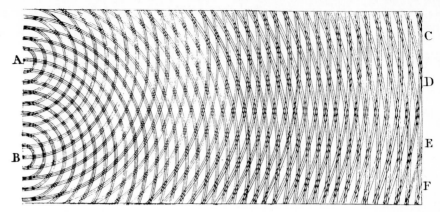

Young's original drawing illustrating the interference of light from two coherent sources. Compare this figure with Fig. 36-5. (*Thomas Young, A Course of Lectures on Natural Philosophy on the Mechanical Arts, Taylor and Walton, London, 1845/courtesy A.I.P. Niels Bohr Library*)

ton could be wrong was not greeted with enthusiasm, especially in England, and it angered some scientists. Young showed how the wave theory correctly describes reflection and refraction, and he later explained the dispersive effects of gratings and the iridescence of thin films. Despite the fact that Young is generally credited with establishing the wave theory of light, he remained skeptical of his own theory.

Young published many important papers in physiology. He originated concepts that later developed into the three-color theory of vision. He investigated the functions of the heart and arteries and published a paper on capillarity and cohesion of fluids. He used his linguistic abilities to decipher Egyptian hieroglyphic inscriptions, and is especially remembered for his work on the famous Rosetta Stone.

SUMMARY WITH APPLICATIONS

Section 36-2. Young's double-slit experiment

The double-slit experiment demonstrates the wave nature of light because the pattern on the screen can be explained in terms of the interference of waves. Constructive interference gives bright fringes at angles θ_m:

$$d \sin \theta_m = \pm m\lambda \qquad (m = 0, 1, 2, \ldots) \qquad (36\text{-}2)$$

and destructive interference gives dark fringes at angles $\theta_{m'}$:

$$d \sin \theta_{m'} = \pm(m' + \tfrac{1}{2})\lambda \qquad (m' = 0, 1, 2, \ldots) \qquad (36\text{-}1)$$

Two coherent sources can produce a stable interference pattern. The two slits in the double-slit experiment are coherent sources because the light originates from a single source.

Describe how the double-slit interference pattern is produced and determine the positions of the maxima and minima; distinguish between coherent and incoherent sources of waves.

Section 36-3. Intensity distribution in the double-slit interference pattern

The principle of superposition gives the intensity distribution for the double-slit interference pattern as

$$I_{12} = 4I_0 \cos^2\left(\frac{\pi d \sin \theta}{\lambda}\right) \qquad (36\text{-}6)$$

where I_0 is the intensity at the screen due to one of the slits acting alone.

Calculate, at a point on the screen, the intensity due to the double-slit interference pattern.

Section 36-4. Diffraction gratings

A diffraction grating is a device used to disperse light according to its wavelength. Angles which locate the interference maxima for light of a specific wavelength are given by

$$d \sin \theta_m = \pm m\lambda \qquad (m = 0, 1, 2, \ldots) \qquad (36\text{-}8)$$

where m is the order of the maximum.

Find the wavelength(s) of light from measurements with a diffraction grating; determine the dispersion of a grating and determine the half-width of spectral lines.

Section 36-5. X-ray diffraction by crystals

X-rays reflected from parallel sets of atomic planes exhibit interference effects. This demonstrates the wave nature of x-rays and provides a powerful tool for studying crystalline solids. Bragg's law gives the condition for constructive interference:

$$2d \sin \theta_m = m\lambda \qquad (m = 1, 2, \ldots) \qquad (36\text{-}12)$$

Use Bragg's law to find the angular positions of interference maxima from x-rays reflected from crystalline planes.

Section 36-6. Interference from thin films
Interference effects can be easily observed when light is reflected from thin transparent films. With these effects, we are able to use thin films on optical surfaces to either enhance or inhibit reflection.

Describe interference effects of thin films.

Section 36-7. The Michelson interferometer
A Michelson interferometer splits a beam of light into two beams which travel different distances and then are rejoined. The observation of interference of the waves in these beams provides a technique for precisely measuring length.

Describe the important features of the operation of a Michelson interferometer.

QUESTIONS

36-1   What is meant by interference? What is the phase relationship between two waves that interfere constructively? What is the phase relationship between two waves that interfere destructively?

36-2   What is meant by diffraction? Do sound waves diffract? Would high frequencies or low frequencies be easier to hear around corners?

36-3   Why did we specify the use of monochromatic light in the double-slit experiment? Describe the appearance of the pattern if we used white light.

36-4   With the assumption that light consists of a beam of particles or corpuscles, develop a theory which describes the double-slit experiment. How do you account for the dark fringes in the pattern? Recall that these dark fringes occur at points on the screen that are not dark when one of the slits is covered. What property of the particles corresponds to different colors? From this property, how do you account for red light giving a pattern that is more spread out than violet light? Give up?

36-5   Explain how the double-slit experiment shows that different colors correspond to different wavelengths.

36-6   The intensity at the interference maxima in the double-slit pattern is $4I_0$, where I_0 is the intensity at that point due to one of the slits acting alone. Does this violate conservation of energy? If not, explain why not.

36-7   Suppose we perform the double-slit experiment under water. How would the pattern be affected?

36-8   Suppose the double-slit experiment is performed with a glass plate with index of refraction n covering the entrance to one of the slits (Fig. 36-22). Describe the effect of this plate on the resulting pattern on the screen.

36-9   Why are interference effects not more commonly observed? For example, why do we not observe interference from the light from two automobile headlamps?

36-10 In the arrangement shown in Fig. 36-3, suppose we let white light from the bulb fall on slits 1 and 2 and put a red color filter over slit 1 and a blue color filter over slit 2. Describe the resulting intensity pattern on the screen.

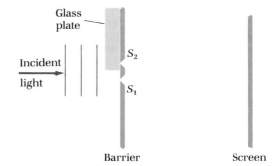

Figure 36-22. Ques. 36-8: A glass plate with index of refraction n covers the entrance to one of the slits.

36-11 Consider water waves from two spheres vibrating in phase as seen in Fig. 36-5. If the separation between the spheres is 4λ, how many nodal lines will exist?

36-12 In his original experiment, Young used pinholes rather than slits and illuminated them with sunlight. Describe the pattern he saw on the screen. Why do you think we chose to discuss an experiment with slits and monochromatic light?

36-13 In developing the double-slit intensity distribution, we write the vector components of the electric field of light waves from slits 1 and 2 as $E_1 = E_0 \sin (\omega t + \phi)$ and $E_2 = E_0 \sin (\omega t)$. On what basis do we set the amplitude E_0 the same in these expressions? On what basis do we set the frequency ω the same in these expressions? Does ϕ represent the phase difference as the waves emerge from the slits or as they arrive at the screen? How does this phase difference arise?

36-14 Imagine observing the double-slit pattern for light of a given wavelength and gradually reducing the slit spacing d. What happens to the pattern? Is there a minimum spacing for observing a pattern? If so, what is this spacing?

36-15 What is the purpose of a diffraction grating? Why does a grating have a large number of slits? Why are the slits of a grating spaced very close together?

36-16 Figure 36-23 shows the interference maxima of the same two spectral lines as they appear in first-order

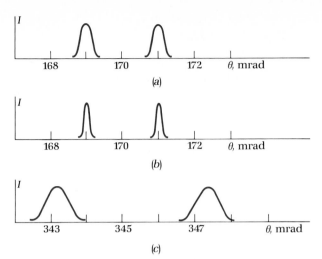

Figure 36-23. Ques. 36-16 and Exercise 36-26: First-order interference maxima of the same two spectral lines with (a) grating A, (b) grating B, and (c) grating C.

diffraction by three different gratings: A, B, and C. (For simplicity we do not show the secondary maxima.) Which grating has the largest number of slits illuminated? Which grating has the smallest slit spacing? Which grating has the largest dispersion?

36-17 Bragg's law, $2d \sin \theta_m = m\lambda$, is closely related to the equation for the interference maxima due to a grating: $d \sin \theta_m = m\lambda$. Explain the origin of the factor 2 in Bragg's law.

36-18 If a beam of highly monochromatic (one wavelength) x-rays impinges on a single crystal with a random orientation, then, in general, no interference maxima will be observed. However, if the beam contains a continuous distribution of wavelengths (polychromatic, or "white," x-rays), then a Laue pattern is observed. Explain.

36-19 When light waves in air encounter the surface of water, is their phase reversed upon reflection?

36-20 Why must a film be thin to cause observable interference effects? Is it really important for the film to be thin, or is it only important that the film's opposite surfaces be very nearly parallel?

36-21 State which of the following objects are iridescent: a quartz crystal, a peacock's tail feather, the inside of an oyster shell, a TV screen, a soap bubble.

36-22 As a light wave passes from one transparent medium to another, say from air to glass, which, if any, of the wave's following characteristics change: speed, wavelength, frequency? Describe any change.

36-23 The index of refraction of air is very nearly 1, the value for vacuum. Explain how the Michelson interferometer could be used to accurately measure the index of refraction of air.

36-24 Complete the following table:

Symbol	Represents	Type	SI unit
m, m'			
ϕ			rad
I_0			
N	Number of slits		
$\Delta\theta_{1/2}$			
D		Scalar	

EXERCISES

Section 36-2. Young's double-slit experiment

36-1 Monochromatic light with a wavelength of 563 nm is used in a double-slit experiment in which the slit spacing is 0.18 mm. (a) What are the angles of the $m = 1$ and $m = 2$ maxima? (b) What are the angles of the $m' = 1$ and $m' = 2$ minima?

36-2 Monochromatic light with a wavelength of 713 nm is used in a double-slit experiment in which the slit spacing is 0.14 mm and the distance between the slits and the screen is 0.96 m. (a) What is the distance on the screen between the center of the zeroth-order maximum and one of the first-order maxima? (b) What is the distance between the center of the zeroth-order maximum and one of the $m' = 3$ minima?

36-3 Suppose you wish to project a double-slit pattern on a screen that is about 1 m from the slits. Your light source is a sodium lamp that has a bright yellow emission at about 590 nm. (a) If you make your slits with a spacing of about 2 mm, do you expect to have any trouble seeing a pattern? (b) Using $\lambda \approx 600$ nm and $L \approx 1$ m, develop a rough criterion for the maximum slit spacing that produces a pattern discernible with the naked eye.

36-4 In a double-slit experiment, $\lambda = 488$ nm, $L = 1.14$ m, and the spacing between dark fringes is $\Delta x = 6.1$ mm. What is the slit spacing?

36-5 Suppose you have a double slit with a spacing of 0.15 mm and a sodium lamp (which produces a bright yellow emission at 589 nm). How far from the slits should you place the screen to observe bright fringes that are 10 mm apart?

36-6 Monochromatic light of wavelength 730 nm is used in a double-slit experiment. Consider the distances the waves from each slit must travel to arrive at point P on the screen in Fig. 36-6. Waves from slit 1 travel a distance r_1, and waves from slit 2 travel a distance r_2. What is the distance difference, $r_1 - r_2$, when (a) point P is at the center of a second-order bright fringe, (b) point P is at the center of an $m' = 3$ dark fringe, (c) point P is halfway between a second-order bright fringe and an $m' = 2$ dark fringe?

36-7 Consider the acoustical equivalent of the double-slit experiment. Suppose you use two loudspeakers that emit sound of frequency 660 Hz. (The speed of sound in air is 330 m/s.) (a) To produce an easily measurable pattern, about how far apart should you place the loudspeakers? (b) At least how far away should you be with your microphone? (c) If the loudspeakers are 2.0 m apart, how many nodal lines will exist?

Section 36-3. Intensity distribution in the double-slit interference pattern

36-8 In a double-slit experiment, the intensity at a particular point on the screen due to each slit acting alone is I_0. What is the intensity due to both slits when the waves have a phase difference of (a) zero, (b) $\pi/2$ rad, (c) π rad, (d) $3\pi/2$ rad, (e) 2π rad, (f) $5\pi/2$ rad?

36-9 Make a graph of Eq. (36-5). Plot I_{12} (in units of I_0) versus ϕ (in units of rad) from zero to 4π rad, with points every $\pi/4$ rad. Sketch a continuous curve through the points.

36-10 In a double-slit experiment, the intensity at the screen due to each of the slits acting alone is I_0, the slit spacing is 0.150 mm, and the wavelength of the light is 500 nm. What is the intensity due to both slits at points on the screen which correspond to angles θ of (a) zero, (b) 0.833 mrad, (c) 1.67 mrad, (d) 2.50 mrad, (e) 3.33 mrad, (f) 4.17 mrad? (g) What is the intensity at each of the above angles if the slits are replaced by two incoherent sources which each produce an intensity of I_0 when acting alone?

36-11 Make a graph of Eq. (36-6). Let $d = 0.150$ mm and $\lambda = 500$ nm. Plot I_{12} in units of I_0 versus θ in units of rad from zero to 5.00 mrad, with points every 0.833 mrad. Sketch a continuous curve through the points.

36-12 In a double-slit experiment, the intensity at the screen due to each of the slits acting alone is I_0, the slit spacing is 0.150 mm, the wavelength of the light is 500 nm, and the perpendicular distance from the slits to the screen is 1.00 m. What is the intensity due to both slits at positions x (see Fig. 36-6) of (a) zero, (b) 0.83 mm, (c) 1.7 mm, (d) 2.5 mm, (e) 3.3 mm, (f) 4.2 mm? (g) What is the intensity at each of the above points if the slits are replaced by incoherent sources, each of which produces intensity I_0 when acting alone?

36-13 Using the same data as Exercise 36-11, make a graph of Eq. (36-7). Plot I_{12} in units of I_0 versus x (see Fig. 36-6) in units of millimeters from zero to 4.2 mm, with points every 0.83 mm. Sketch a continuous curve through the points.

36-14 For a double-slit interference pattern, find the relationship similar to Eqs. (36-1) and (36-2) which gives the angles θ at which $I_{12} = 2I_0$.

36-15 Consider the first bright fringe on the positive x side of the zeroth bright fringe in a double-slit pattern. Let $d = 0.16$ mm, $\lambda = 550$ nm, and $L = 1.24$ m. Find the coordinate x of each of the two positions on each side of the fringe at which I_{12} is 75 percent its maximum.

Section 36-4. Diffraction gratings

36-16 A hydrogen discharge tube emits light in the visible spectrum at four discrete wavelengths: the H_α line at $\lambda_\alpha = 656.3$ nm, the H_β line at $\lambda_\beta = 486.1$ nm, the H_γ line at $\lambda_\gamma = 434.1$ nm, and the H_δ line at $\lambda_\delta = 410.2$ nm. If a collimated beam of light from a hydrogen discharge tube is incident normally on a diffraction grating with a slit spacing of 1.9 μm, what are the angles which locate the first- and second-order maxima for these hydrogen lines?

36-17 A first-order maximum of the H_α line ($\lambda_\alpha = 656.3$ nm) from a hydrogen discharge tube is at $\theta = 18.3°$ for a particular grating. (a) What is the slit spacing of the grating? (b) A discrete line from another source has a maximum at $\theta = 15.7°$. What is the wavelength of this emission?

36-18 Suppose we are in possession of two gratings A and B. We know that the slit spacing of grating A is 1.86 μm, but we do not know the slit spacing of grating B. A monochromatic source gives a first-order line at $\theta = 19.4°$ when the light is incident normally on A, and the same source gives a first-order line at 22.1° when the same light is incident on B. What is the slit spacing of grating B?

36-19 Verify the angular positions of the lines in Fig. 36-11. The slit spacing is $d = 1.7$ μm, the wavelength of the red emission is $\lambda_r = 750$ nm, and the wavelength of the violet emission is $\lambda_v = 400$ nm.

36-20 Make a graph of Eq. (36-9), $I = I_0 \sin^2 [N(\frac{1}{2}\phi)]/\sin^2 (\frac{1}{2}\phi)$, between $\phi = 0.0001$ rad and $\phi = (2\pi - 0.0001)$ rad for the case where $N = 5$. (Note that I is indeterminate at $\phi = 0$ and 2π. See Prob. 36-5.) Plot points for $\phi = 0.0001$, $\pi/10$, $2\pi/10$, ..., $19\pi/10$, and $(2\pi - 0.0001)$ rad. Sketch a continuous curve through the points. Compare your graph with Fig. 36-10.

36-21 Consider a minimum adjacent to a primary maximum in Eq. (36-9). To be specific, consider the minimum on the positive ϕ side of the central primary maximum ($m = 0$). (a) By direct substitution show that $I = 0$ when $\phi = 2\pi/N$. (b) Show that I is nonzero in the range $0 < \phi < 2\pi/N$. (Note that I is indeterminate at $\phi = 0$. See Prob. 36-5.)

36-22 (a) Write Eq. (36-9) in terms of the angular position θ. (b) When N is odd, a secondary maximum occurs midway between primary maxima. (See Fig. 36-10.) Find the angular position of the secondary maximum that is midway between the zeroth-order and first-order primary maxima for the case where $N = 9$, $d = 40.0$ μm, and $\lambda = 600$ nm. (c) Substitute your answer from part (b) into the expression you found in part (a) to find the intensity at this secondary maximum. (d) What is the ratio of this intensity to the intensity at a primary maximum?

36-23 A beam of monochromatic light with $\lambda = 532.8$ nm is incident normally on a grating with $d = 2.16\ \mu m$. (a) What are the angular positions of the first- and second-order interference maxima? (b) If 758 of the grating slits are illuminated by the beam, what is the angular half-width of each of these maxima?

36-24 Suppose the beam of light from the hydrogen discharge tube in Exercise 36-16 illuminates 844 slits of the grating. (a) What is the half-width of the first-order interference maxima of the H_α ($\lambda_\alpha = 656.3$ nm) and the H_δ ($\lambda_\delta = 410.2$ nm) lines? (b) What is the value of m such that the mth maximum of the H_α line has a larger angle than the $(m + 1)$th maximum of the H_δ line.

36-25 (a) By using Eq. (36-8), show that the angular half-width of a bright fringe or interference maximum in the double-slit pattern is $\Delta\theta_{1/2} \approx \lambda/2d$. [Note that Eq. (36-8) is valid only if $x \ll L$.] (b) Show that the result in part (a) is consistent with Eq. (36-10).

36-26 The two emission lines which gave the intensity distributions shown in Fig. 36-23 have wavelengths $\lambda_1 = 504.6$ nm and $\lambda_2 = 510.5$ nm. (a) From information given in the figure, determine the slit spacing for each of the gratings. (b) From information given in the figure, estimate the number of slits illuminated by the beam for each of the gratings.

36-27 Consider monochromatic light with $\lambda = 550$ nm incident normally on a grating with slit spacing $d = 2.11\ \mu m$. (a) What are the angular positions of the first-order interference maxima? (b) What is the dispersion of this grating at the angular positions of the maxima found in part (a)?

36-28 (a) Show that the expression for the dispersion of a grating can be written as

$$D = \frac{m}{\sqrt{d^2 - (m\lambda)^2}}$$

(b) Use the expression in part (a) to find the dispersion for the case where $m = 1$, $d = 2.11\ \mu m$, and $\lambda = 550$ nm. Compare your answer with that from the previous exercise.

36-29 Show that the expression for the dispersion of a grating can be written as $D = (\tan \theta_m)/\lambda$.

36-30 A beam of light from a source whose emission contains two lines of wavelengths 462.74 and 463.35 nm is incident normally on a grating, and the beam illuminates 1000 slits. According to the Rayleigh criterion, are the first-order interference maxima for these lines resolved?

36-31 For the grating in Example 36-3, determine the minimum number of slits that must be illuminated in order to satisfy the Rayleigh criterion.

36-32 In Fig. 36-12b, the spacing $\Delta\theta$ between two spectral lines of equal intensity is the same as their half-width $\Delta\theta_{1/2}$. Show that the ratio of the intensity at the point midway between the maxima and the intensity at the maxima is $2(2/\pi)^2 = 0.81$. [Hint: $\sin(\pi/2N) \approx \pi/2N$ for large N.]

36-33 **Resolving power R.** The resolving power of an optical device whose purpose is to disperse light according to wavelength is defined as

$$R = \frac{\lambda}{\Delta\lambda}$$

where $\Delta\lambda$ is the difference in wavelength of two spectral lines which can barely be resolved and λ is the wavelength of either line (they have nearly the same wavelength). Show that the resolving power of a grating for the mth-order spectrum is Nm.

Section 36-5. X-ray diffraction by crystals

36-34 An interference maximum for the scattering of a beam of x-rays of wavelength 0.156 nm occurs when the angle between the beam and the surface of the crystal face is $12.8°$. This maximum is due to scattering from the atoms in planes parallel to the crystal face. Assuming that this is a first-order maximum, determine the interplanar spacing for this set of planes of atoms?

36-35 A beam of x-rays gives a second-order interference maximum when it makes an angle of $24.1°$ with crystalline planes that have an interplanar spacing of 0.314 nm. What is the wavelength of these x-rays?

36-36 X-rays of wavelength 0.114 nm are scattered from the atoms in sets of crystalline planes with a spacing of 0.278 nm. At what angle will a first-order interference maximum occur?

Section 36-6. Interference from thin films

36-37 A thin film of a transparent material with $n = 1.29$ is to be placed on a glass ($n = 1.50$) surface. What is the minimum thickness for the film such that the reflection of normally incident light with $\lambda = 600$ nm is minimized?

36-38 A thin film of transparent material ($n = 1.27$) with air on each side is exposed to a normally incident beam of light that contains the full visible spectrum of colors. If the thickness of the film is 112 nm, what wavelength(s) of light will exhibit maximum reflection?

36-39 For nonnormal incidence of light on a thin film as shown in Fig. 36-20, show that

$$\tau_{eff} = \frac{\tau}{\cos\{\sin^{-1}[(\sin\theta)/n]\}}$$

where n is the index of refraction of the film.

36-40 A thin film of water ($n = 1.33$) on a flat glass ($n = 1.50$) surface is illuminated by a beam of light incident normally. The light in the beam is monochromatic but its wavelength can be varied. As the wavelength is varied continuously, the reflected intensity changes from a minimum at $\lambda = 530$ nm to a maximum at $\lambda = 790$ nm. What is the thickness of the film?

Section 36-7. The Michelson interferometer

36-41 When the movable mirror of a Michelson interferometer is moved a distance Δl, 140.0 full fringes pass by the detector. (A full fringe consists of a maximum and a minimum in intensity.) The light used has a wavelength of 526.31 nm. Determine Δl.

36-42 Suppose we use a Michelson interferometer to measure the wavelength of a discrete emission from an arc lamp. When the movable mirror is moved a dis-

tance of 0.1724 mm, 628.00 fringes pass by the detector. What is the wavelength of the emission?

36-43 How many fringes move by the detector when the movable arm of a Michelson interferometer is moved a distance of 0.1152 mm? The light used has a wavelength of 754.1 nm.

36-44 Because it is nearly 1, the index of refraction of air is difficult to measure with a refraction experiment. Consider measuring n for air with a Michelson interferometer. A tube with glass end plates is aligned with its axis along one of the arms of an interferometer, say along ℓ_2 in Fig. 36-21. As the air in the tube is evacuated with a pump, 47.2 fringes of light with wavelength $\lambda = 589$ nm are observed to pass by the position of the detector. The length of the column of air that is evacuated is 47.9 mm. Determine the index of refraction of air.

PROBLEMS

36-1 *Lloyd's mirror.* A pattern similar to the double-slit pattern can be produced using Lloyd's mirror, which is shown in Fig. 36-24. At grazing angles almost 100 percent of the light that falls on the glass is reflected so that the reflected beam has nearly the same amplitude at P as the beam which passes directly from slit S to P. Slit S and its virtual image S' behave as coherent sources. Develop expressions similar to Eqs. (36-1) and (36-2) to give the positions of bright and dark fringes on the screen.

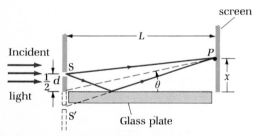

Figure 36-24. Prob. 36-1: Lloyd's mirror. Slit S and its virtual image S' behave as coherent sources, and a pattern similar to the double-slit pattern is seen on the screen. Distance d is exaggerated for clarity.

36-2 Suppose the slit openings in the double-slit experiment are different sizes so that the vector components of the electric field due to the waves must be written with different amplitudes. Thus

$$E_1 = E_{10} \sin(\omega t + \phi) \quad \text{and} \quad E_2 = E_{20} \sin(\omega t)$$

The intensities due to the slits acting alone are $I_1 \propto E_{10}^2$ and $I_2 \propto E_{20}^2$. (a) Use Fig. 36-25 to show that the component E_{12} of the resultant electric field is

$$E_{12} = E_a \sin(\omega t + \delta)$$

where E_a is the amplitude of the resultant wave and δ is a phase constant. (b) Use the law of cosines to find E_a and show that

$$I_{12} = I_1 + I_2 + 2\sqrt{I_1 I_2} \cos \phi$$

(c) Show that your answer reduces to Eq. (36-5) when $E_{10} = E_{20} = E_0$.

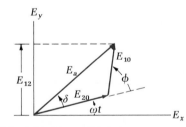

Figure 36-25. Prob. 36-2: A phasor diagram, similar to those used in Chap. 31, can be used to find resultant wave amplitudes. The vector triangle rotates around the origin in the $E_x E_y$ plane. The square of the resultant amplitude, E_a^2, is proportional to the resultant intensity I_{12}.

36-3 In Fig. 36-26, two coherent point sources of waves, S_1 and S_2, are separated by a distance d along the x axis. Show that the nodal lines are hyperbolas. That is, show that the coordinates of nodal lines satisfy the equation $(x/a)^2 - (y/b)^2 = 1$. (*Hint:* Recall that $|r_1 - r_2|$ is a constant on a nodal line.)

36-4 Consider finding the intensity distribution due to light passing through three slits. The component E_c of the resultant electric field is $E_c = E_1 + E_2 + E_3$, where

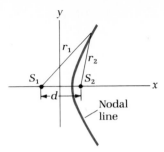

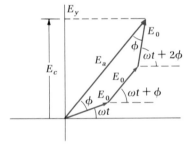

Figure 36-26. Prob. 36-3: A nodal line due to two coherent sources of waves is a hyperbola.

$$E_1 = E_0 \sin (\omega t)$$

$$E_2 = E_0 \sin (\omega t + \phi)$$

$$E_3 = E_0 \sin (\omega t + 2\phi)$$

(a) Use Fig. 36-27 to show that

$$E_c = E_a \sin (\omega t + \phi)$$

where the amplitude E_a of the resultant wave is

$$E_a = E_0[2 \cos (\phi) + 1]$$

Figure 36-27. Prob. 36-4: A phasor diagram, similar to those introduced in Chap. 31, can be used to find resultant wave amplitudes. The square of the resultant amplitude, E_a^2, is proportional to the resultant intensity.

(b) Use trigonometric identities to show that

$$E_a = E_0 \frac{\sin [3(\tfrac{1}{2}\phi)]}{\sin (\tfrac{1}{2}\phi)}$$

(c) Show that your result in part (b) agrees with the general result given by Eq. (36-9) for the case where $N = 3$. (d) Draw the diagram similar to Fig. 36-27 that extends this argument to the case of four slits.

36-5   Show that the expression for the intensity distribution due to N slits, $I = I_0 \sin^2 [N(\tfrac{1}{2}\phi)]/\sin^2 (\tfrac{1}{2}\phi)$, is indeterminate for $\phi = \pm 2\pi m, m = 0, 1, 2, \ldots$. Note that these values of ϕ correspond to the interference maxima. (b) Use l'Hospital's rule to show that $I = N^2 I_0$ when $\phi = \pm 2\pi m, m = 0, 1, 2, \ldots$.

36-6   Consider a beam of light incident on a grating at an angle γ with respect to the normal, as shown in Fig. 36-28. Show that the interference maxima satisfy the

relation

$$d(\sin \gamma + \sin \theta) = \pm m\lambda \qquad (m = 0, 1, 2, \ldots)$$

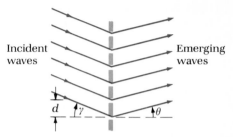

Figure 36-28. Prob. 36-6: A light beam incident on a grating at an angle γ with respect to a normal to the grating face.

36-7   Consider the secondary maxima between two primary maxima in the intensity distribution due to a diffraction grating with a large number of slits. (a) Show that the intensity of the secondary maxima that are in the region midway between primary maxima is approximately I_0, the intensity due to one slit acting alone. (b) Show that the intensity of a secondary maximum adjacent to a primary maximum is approximately 4.5 percent of the intensity of the primary maximum. To be specific, consider the secondary maximum on the positive θ side of the $m = 0$ primary maximum. It is a valid approximation to assume that this secondary maximum occurs at $\phi = 3\pi/N$. Recall that the intensity of a primary maximum is $N^2 I_0$.

36-8   In Fig. 36-29, a flat glass plate is resting on a similar (horizontal) glass plate. The plates are in contact along one edge and are separated a distance d along the other edge by a thin wire: $d \ll L$. A thin wedge of air exists between the plates. Monochromatic light is incident from above and is nearly normal to the surface of both plates. Develop expressions for the positions x of (a) dark fringes and (b) bright fringes in the reflected light. (c) What is the spacing Δx between dark fringes for the case where $d = 31$ μm, $L = 0.27$ m, $\lambda = 724$ nm?

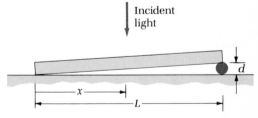

Figure 36-29. Prob. 36-8: An air wedge is formed between two flat glass plates by placing a thin wire along one edge.

36-9   **Newton's rings.** A planoconvex lens is shown with its spherical face down on a flat, horizontal glass plate in Fig. 36-30a. The planar side of the lens is horizontal and the spherical side has a radius of curvature R. A beam of monochromatic light of wavelength λ is directed vertically downward. When viewed from above, circular interference fringes of radius r, called *Newton's rings*, can be seen in the reflected light (Fig. 36-30b). Show that the radius of a bright fringe near the center of the pattern ($r \ll R$) is given by

$$r = \sqrt{(m + \tfrac{1}{2})\lambda R} \qquad (m = 0, 1, 2, \ldots)$$

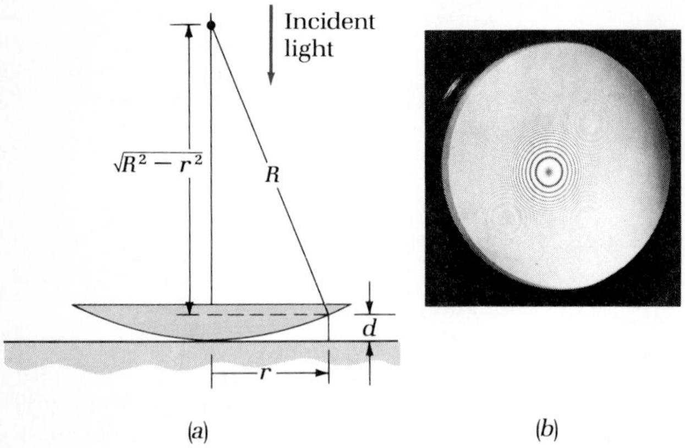

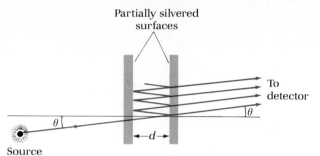

Figure 36-30. Prob. 36-9: Newton's rings. (a) Light incident from above on a planoconvex lens. (b) Newton's rings. *(Bausch & Lomb)*

36-10 Show that the intensity at the detector in the Michelson interferometer (Fig. 36-21) varies with position x of the movable mirror as

$$I = 4I_0 \cos^2 \frac{2\pi x}{\lambda}$$

What are the interpretations of I_0 and of $x = 0$?

36-11 When light is reflected normally from the surface of a transparent material in air, the ratio of the intensities of the reflected and incident beams is $[(n-1)/(n+1)]^2$, where n is the index of refraction of the material. In Fig. 36-19, let I_i represent the intensity of beam (1) acting alone and suppose that the film is water ($n = 1.33$). (a) Determine I_2 in terms of I_1. (b) Using your result from part (a), estimate I_6 in terms of I_1. The comparison of the answers to parts (a) and (b) justifies our assumption that beams (2) and (6) acting alone would have about the same intensity.

36-12 **The Fabry-Perot interferometer.** A useful interferometer design is the Fabry-Perot interferometer. The essential elements of this design are shown in Fig. 36-31. Show that the condition for constructive inter-

Figure 36-31. Prob. 36-12: The Fabry-Perot interferometer. Multiple reflections from partially silvered mirrors set up the conditions for interference fringes in the light that reaches the detector.

ference of the waves which reach the detector is

$$2d/\cos\theta = m\lambda$$

where $m =$ an integer and d is the distance between the parallel mirrors.

36-13 Consider using complex variables to develop the expression for the intensity due to a diffraction grating, Eq. (36-9). The resultant amplitude E_r may be written

$$E_r = E_0 \sum_{j=0}^{N-1} \cos(\omega t + j\phi)$$

where j is an index for summing the electric field components due to the slits. Since $e^{i\alpha} = \cos\alpha + i\sin\alpha$, we can write this as

$$E_r = E_0 \, \mathbf{Re} \sum_{j=0}^{N-1} e^{i(\omega t + j\phi)}$$

where **Re** means "the real part of." (a) Use the sum of the geometric progression

$$a + ax + ax^2 + \cdots + ax^{N-1} = \frac{a(x^N - 1)}{x - 1}$$

to show that

$$E_r = E_0 \, \mathbf{Re} \, e^{i\omega t} \frac{e^{iN\phi} - 1}{e^{i\phi} - 1}$$

(b) Use the relation $\sin\alpha = (e^{i\alpha} - e^{-i\alpha})/2i$ to show that

$$E_r = E_0 \cos[\omega t + \tfrac{1}{2}(N-1)\phi] \frac{\sin[N(\tfrac{1}{2}\phi)]}{\sin(\tfrac{1}{2}\phi)}$$

[*Hint:* Note that $e^{i\alpha} - 1 = e^{i\alpha/2}(e^{i\alpha/2} - e^{-i\alpha/2})$.] (c) Use your answer from part (b) to develop Eq. (36-9).

CHAPTER 37
DIFFRACTION AND POLARIZATION

37-1 INTRODUCTION

We are accustomed to the notion that light travels in a straight line. But light is a wave, and waves do not always propagate in a straight line. In particular, when waves pass near a barrier, they tend to bend around the barrier and spread into the region of the geometrical shadow. This phenomenon is called *diffraction*. In this chapter we consider a particularly simple example of diffraction, the diffraction of light as it passes through a slit.

From electromagnetic theory, light is a transverse wave in the electric and magnetic fields. In Chap. 34, we introduced the polarization of a light wave, which characterizes the directions of the oscillations of **E** and **B**. Here we describe how light can be polarized and how polarization can be measured.

Figure 37-1. The shadow of a gear. The gear was illuminated with monochromatic light from a small (nearly a point) source. *(Photo Researchers)*

37-2 DIFFRACTION

In the study of geometrical optics, light traveling in a homogeneous medium is assumed to follow a straight-line path. According to this assumption, the shadow cast by an object illuminated by a point source of light would have sharp edges. Figure 37-1 shows the shadow of a gear illuminated by a point source, and, as you can see, the edges of the shadow are not sharp; fringes occur around the shadow edges. This is evidence of *diffraction*—the bending of light around the edge of a barrier. The amount of diffraction depends on wavelength; the longer the wavelength the more noticeable the bending. The assumption that light follows a straight-line path is often valid because light has a very small wavelength. If we do not look too closely, diffraction may be neglected.

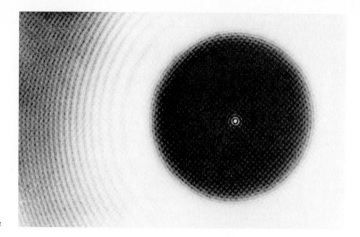

Figure 37-2. The shadow of a penny. The penny was illuminated with monochromatic light from a small (nearly a point) source. The distance from the source to the penny was 20 m, and the distance from the penny to the screen was 20 m. *(Philip M. Rinaro, Los Alamos National Laboratory)*

A curious phenomenon, called the *Arago spot* (sometimes called the *Poisson spot*), provides a startling example of diffraction. If a disk-shaped object, such as a penny, is illuminated with monochromatic light from a point source, then a bright spot appears in the center of the shadow (Fig. 37-2). The Arago spot played an interesting role in the development of wave optics. In 1819, A. J. Fresnel (1788–1827) presented a wave theory of light which explained diffraction. Skeptical of this theory, S. D. Poisson (1781–1840) showed that it predicted a bright spot at the center of the shadow of a disk, a result so incredible that Poisson asserted that it discounted the wave theory. But the subsequent discovery of the spot by D. F. J. Arago (1786–1853) provided a striking confirmation of the wave nature of light.

The study of diffraction is divided into two regimes: Fresnel diffraction and Fraunhofer diffraction. In Fresnel diffraction, the waves impinging on the barrier and the observing screen are not necessarily plane waves. In Fraunhofer diffraction, the source and the screen are effectively an infinite distance from the diffracting barrier so that the waves impinging on the barrier and on the screen are plane waves. Fraunhofer diffraction is a special case which is simpler to discuss than Fresnel diffraction. Fraunhofer diffraction can be achieved experimentally with the use of lenses or, to a good approximation, by placing the source and the viewing screen a large distance from the diffracting object.

37-3   DESCRIPTION OF THE SINGLE-SLIT DIFFRACTION PATTERN

In this section, we describe the diffraction pattern due to light passing through a narrow slit, and then we present a qualitative explanation of how the pattern is formed. For simplicity, we consider Fraunhofer diffraction; the source and the screen are far from the slit compared with the slit width.

In Fig. 37-3 we show a beam of monochromatic light of wavelength λ incident on a slit of width a. The light which passes through the slit and impinges on the screen produces the *single-slit diffraction pattern* shown in Fig. 37-4a. Figure 37-4b shows the intensity distribution as a function of $\sin \theta$, where θ is the angle which locates a point on the screen. The pattern consists of a bright central maximum which is flanked by secondary maxima, and the intensity of

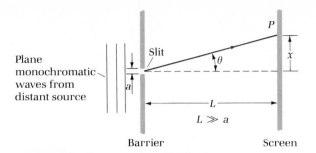

Figure 37-3. The arrangement used for the single-slit experiment (Fraunhofer diffraction).

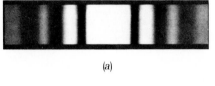

(a)

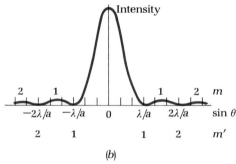

(b)

Figure 37-4. The single-slit diffraction pattern. (a) Photograph of the pattern. (*Cagnet, Francon, Phrierr,* Atlas of Optical Phenomena, *Springer Verlag, Berlin, 1962*) (b) The intensity distribution.

each succeeding secondary maximum decreases with distance from the center. Between successive maxima, intensity minima occur at angles $\theta_{m'}$ given by

Intensity minima at angles $\theta_{m'}$

$$a \sin \theta_{m'} = \pm m'\lambda \qquad (m' = 1, 2, \ldots) \qquad (37\text{-}1)$$

Note that $m' = 0$ is *not* included among the values of m' that give intensity minima. Indeed, $m' = 0$ corresponds to the center of the pattern, or the middle of the central maximum. This means that the width of the central maximum is twice that of the secondary maxima, as you can see in Fig. 37-4.

In Fig. 37-4, the secondary maxima are approximately midway between their adjacent minima. Thus the angles θ_m which locate the secondary maxima are given by

Secondary maxima at angles θ_m

$$a \sin \theta_m = \pm(m + \tfrac{1}{2})\lambda \qquad (m \approx 1, 2, \ldots) \qquad (37\text{-}2)$$

Note that the value of m which designates a pair of secondary maxima is only approximately an integer, because the secondary maxima are only approximately midway between their adjacent minima. (More accurate estimates of the two lowest values of m are $m = 0.93$ and $m = 1.96$. See Prob. 37-3.)

We can understand how the single-slit pattern is formed by replacing, in our mind's eye, the slit of width a with a number of parallel elementary slits, each of width Δy (Fig. 37-5). The more elementary slits we use, the smaller will be their width, and the more precise will be our conclusions. In the figure, we show 12 elementary slits so that $\Delta y = a/12$. Because the waves incident on the slit are plane waves (Fraunhofer approximation), they emerge from each elementary slit in phase. Figure 37-5a shows schematically those waves which

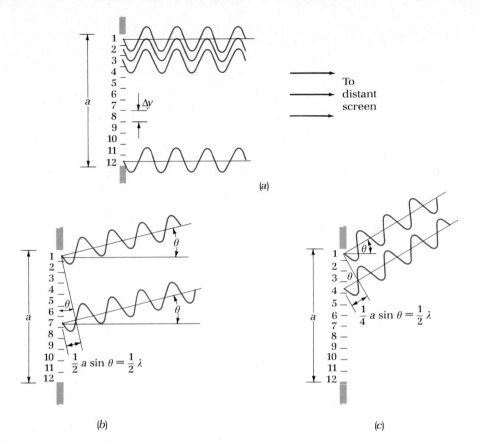

Figure 37-5. Waves emerging in phase from a single slit. The slit is shown divided into 12 elementary slits. (a) Waves which form the central maximum. (b) Waves which form one of the $m' = 1$ minima. (c) Waves which form one of the $m' = 2$ minima.

form the central maximum. Since $L \gg a$, the lines along the propagation direction of these waves are essentially parallel (Fraunhofer approximation), and each wave traverses approximately the same distance. Therefore, they arrive at the center of the screen in phase, interfere constructively, and form an intensity maximum.

Figure 37-5b shows the waves which form one of the two minima adjacent to the central maximum. To arrive at the screen, the waves from elementary slit 7 travel half a wavelength farther than the waves from elementary slit 1; this pair of waves arrives at the screen with a phase difference $\phi = \pi$ rad and interferes destructively. Similarly, wave pairs from elementary slits 8 and 2, 9 and 3, 10 and 4, 11 and 5, and 12 and 6 arrive at the screen with $\phi = \pi$ rad and interfere destructively. This accounts for all 12 elementary slits. Thus the intensity is a minimum at this point on the screen. From Fig. 37-5b we see that the angle θ which locates this position on the screen is given by $\frac{1}{2}\lambda = \frac{1}{2}(a \sin \theta)$ or $a \sin \theta = +(1)\lambda$. This corresponds to $m' = 1$ in Eq. (37-1).

Figure 37-5c shows the waves which form one of the $m' = 2$ minima. To arrive at the screen, waves from elementary slit 4 travel half a wavelength farther than waves from elementary slit 1, so that this pair arrives with a phase difference $\phi = \pi$ rad and interferes destructively. Similarly, wave pairs from elementary slits 5 and 2, 6 and 3, 10 and 7, 11 and 8, and 12 and 9 arrive with $\phi = \pi$ rad and interfere destructively. From Fig. 37-5c we see that the angle θ which locates this point on the screen is given by $(a/4) \sin \theta = \frac{1}{2}\lambda$ or $a \sin \theta = +(2)\lambda$. This result corresponds to $m' = 2$ in Eq. (37-1).

If we consider an angle θ between the $m' = 1$ and $m' = 2$ minima, we find that this cancellation from pairs of elementary slits cannot account for the waves emerging from all the elementary slits. (See Ques. 37-10.) These remaining waves give rise to the light around an $m \approx 1$ secondary maximum.

We characterize the width of the single-slit pattern by the distance between the two $m' = 1$ minima. From Fig. 37-4, you can see that this width depends on the ratio λ/a. For a given slit width, light of longer wavelength undergoes a larger amount of diffraction. For a given wavelength, a narrower slit causes more diffraction than a wider slit. This means that if we try to confine a beam of light so that it illuminates a tiny region of the screen, then the narrower we make the slit, the more the light spreads into the region of the geometrical shadow of the barrier. This may contradict your expectations, but it is a characteristic feature of wave behavior.

A light beam cannot be confined by making the slit narrower and narrower.

EXAMPLE 37-1. (a) Develop an expression for the width Δx of the central maximum (distance between the $m' = 1$ minima). (b) Use the answer from part (a) to find the width of the central maximum when light from a sodium lamp ($\lambda = 590$ nm) is diffracted by a slit of width $a = 0.30$ mm. The distance from the slit to the screen is $L = 0.87$ m.

SOLUTION. (a) From Eq. (37-1), the angles which locate the $m' = 1$ minima are given by

$$\sin \theta_1 = \frac{\pm(1)\lambda}{a}$$

From Fig. 37-3, $\sin \theta = x/\sqrt{x^2 + L^2}$. Since Δx is the distance between the two $m' = 1$ minima, the values of x which correspond to the $m' = 1$ minima are $x = \pm\frac{1}{2}\Delta x$. Therefore,

$$\frac{\frac{1}{2}\Delta x}{\sqrt{(\frac{1}{2}\Delta x)^2 + L^2}} = \frac{\lambda}{a}$$

Solving for Δx, we find

$$\Delta x = \frac{2L\lambda}{\sqrt{a^2 - \lambda^2}}$$

Notice that if we make the slit width a smaller and smaller, then the width Δx of the central maximum becomes larger and larger, approaching infinity as the slit width becomes as small as the wavelength. (b) For the value given in this example, $a \gg \lambda$, so we can use the approximation $\sqrt{a^2 - \lambda^2} \approx a$. Thus

$$\Delta x \approx \frac{2L\lambda}{a} = \frac{2(0.87 \text{ m})(590 \text{ nm})}{0.30 \text{ mm}} = 3.4 \text{ mm}$$

37-4 THE SINGLE-SLIT INTENSITY DISTRIBUTION

In the previous section, we gave a qualitative explanation of the formation of the single-slit diffraction pattern by dividing the slit into 12 elementary slits. Now we develop an expression for the intensity distribution by dividing the slit into an infinite number of elementary slits, each with infinitesimal width. First we add vectorially the electric field contribution from each elementary slit to find the resultant field at a point on the screen. Then the intensity is determined by squaring the resultant field amplitude.

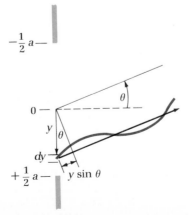

Figure 37-6. Developing an expression for the single-slit intensity distribution. The slit is divided into an infinite number of infinitesimal elementary slits.

Figure 37-6 shows a wave emerging from an elementary slit of infinitesimal width dy. The coordinate y of the elementary slit is measured from the center of the actual slit. (By letting y be positive downward, we encounter fewer minus signs in the calculation.) At the screen the component dE of the electric field* due to the wave emerging from this elementary slit may be written

$$dE = \left(E_c \frac{dy}{a}\right) \sin(\omega t + \phi) \tag{37-3}$$

The amplitude $E_c(dy/a)$ is proportional to the fraction dy/a of the slit occupied by the elementary slit because, as the wave emerges from the slit, it is uniformly distributed along y. It turns out that E_c is the amplitude of the wave at the center of the screen (Prob. 37-2). Consistent with the Fraunhofer approximation, we neglect any θ dependence in the amplitude. The phase difference ϕ arises because waves emerging from different elementary slits arrive at the screen with different phases. The waves are in phase as they emerge from the slit, but become out of phase while traveling different distances to the screen. Thus ϕ is the phase difference at the screen between a wave that emerges at y and a wave that emerges at $y = 0$. To reach a point on the screen located by the angle θ (Fig. 37-6), a wave that emerges from the slit at y travels a distance $y \sin \theta$ farther than a wave that emerges at $y = 0$. Since a path difference of one wavelength causes a phase difference of 2π rad, we have

$$\frac{\text{Phase difference}}{2\pi} = \frac{\text{path difference}}{\lambda} \quad \text{or} \quad \frac{\phi}{2\pi} = \frac{y \sin \theta}{\lambda}$$

The relation between ϕ and y is

$$\phi = \left(\frac{2\pi}{\lambda} \sin \theta\right) y \tag{37-4}$$

To find the resultant electric field component E, we must add the contributions due to each elementary slit from $y = -\frac{1}{2}a$ to $y = +\frac{1}{2}a$. That is, we must integrate Eq. (37-3) with respect to y between these limits. The integration is performed at a specific instant (t fixed) and for a specific point on the screen (θ fixed). The value of E at a point on the screen is

$$E = \frac{E_c}{a} \int_{-\frac{1}{2}a}^{+\frac{1}{2}a} \sin(\omega t + \phi) \, dy \tag{37-5}$$

As we have seen, ϕ depends on y. To evaluate the integral we must either substitute for ϕ in terms of y or substitute for dy in terms of $d\phi$. We choose the latter. Solving Eq. (37-4) for y and differentiating (θ fixed), we obtain

$$dy = \frac{\lambda}{2\pi \sin \theta} \, d\phi$$

This substitution into Eq. (37-5) changes the variable of integration; so we must change the limits accordingly. Equation (37-4) shows that, when $y = \pm\frac{1}{2}a$, $\phi = \pm(\pi a/\lambda) \sin \theta$. For brevity we let $\beta = (\pi a/\lambda) \sin \theta$, so that the limits on ϕ are from $-\beta$ to $+\beta$. [Note that β is the phase difference at the screen between a wave emerging from the center of the slit ($y = 0$) and a wave emerging from one edge

---

* As in the last chapter, for brevity we drop the coordinate subscript on the symbol for the field component.

of the slit ($y = \frac{1}{2}a$).] Now $\qquad E = \dfrac{E_c}{2\beta} \displaystyle\int_{-\beta}^{+\beta} \sin (\omega t + \phi)\, d\phi$

Time t is constant with respect to this integration, so we factor constants out of the integral with the trigonometric identity

$$\sin (\alpha + \gamma) = \sin \alpha \cos \gamma + \cos \alpha \sin \gamma$$

where we let $\alpha = \omega t$ and $\gamma = \phi$. This gives

$$E = \dfrac{E_c}{2\beta} \left[\sin (\omega t) \int_{-\beta}^{+\beta} \cos \phi\, d\phi + \cos (\omega t) \int_{-\beta}^{+\beta} \sin \phi\, d\phi \right]$$

The second term is zero because it involves the integral of an odd function between symmetric limits. (See Ques. 37-15 or Exercise 37-15.) After integration the first term becomes

$$E = \dfrac{E_c}{2\beta} \sin (\omega t)[\sin \phi]_{-\beta}^{+\beta} = \dfrac{E_c}{2\beta} \sin (\omega t)[\sin \beta - \sin (-\beta)]$$

$$= \dfrac{E_c \sin \beta}{\beta} \sin (\omega t)$$

The resultant amplitude at a point on the screen is $(E_c \sin \beta)/\beta$.

Light intensity is proportional to the square of the amplitude of the electric field component: $I \propto [(E_c \sin \beta)/\beta]^2$. Letting I_c be the intensity at the center of the screen (see Prob. 37-2), we obtain

Single-slit intensity distribution

$$I = I_c \dfrac{\sin^2 \beta}{\beta^2} \tag{37-6}$$

This is the *single-slit diffraction formula*. The dependence of the intensity on angular position θ is contained in β: $\beta = (\pi a/\lambda) \sin \theta$. A graph of I versus $\sin \theta$ is shown in Fig. 37-4b and was discussed in the previous section. Since $\sin \beta = 0$ when $\beta = \pm m'\pi$ ($m' = 1, 2, \dots$), Eq. (37-6) gives $I = 0$ when $(\pi a/\lambda) \sin \theta = \pm m'\pi$. This corresponds to the angles which locate minima given in Eq. (37-1), $a \sin \theta_{m'} = \pm m'\lambda$.

Figure 37-7 shows a comparison of I versus θ for two cases where the slit width is different by a factor of 2, but the wavelength and intensity of the incident beam are the same. When the slit width is reduced by a factor of 2, the amplitude of the wave at the center of the screen is reduced by a factor of 2, so the intensity at the center is reduced by a factor of 4.

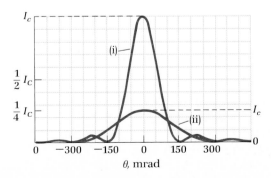

Figure 37-7. Comparison of intensity distributions for slits of widths different by a factor of 2. (i) Wide slit and (ii) narrow slit.

EXAMPLE 37-2. Suppose the width of the wider slit for the intensity distribution shown in Fig. 37-7 is 4.0 μm. Determine the wavelength of the light.

SOLUTION. The $m' = 1$ minima in the pattern for the wider slit are at $\theta = \pm 150$ mrad. Solving Eq. (37-1) for λ, with $m' = 1$, we have

$$\lambda = a \sin \theta = (4.0 \ \mu\text{m}) \sin (0.15 \ \text{rad}) = 600 \ \text{nm}$$

EXAMPLE 37-3. (a) Develop an expression for the intensity of the secondary maxima in terms of I_c. Employ the approximation that integers can be used for the values of m in Eq. (37-2). (b) Use your answer from part (a) to find the relative intensities of the $m \approx 1$ and $m \approx 2$ secondary maxima.

SOLUTION. (a) From Eq. (37-2), angles θ_m which locate secondary maxima are given by $a \sin \theta_m = \pm (m + \frac{1}{2})\lambda$. Values of β which correspond to secondary maxima are

$$\beta_m = \frac{\pi a}{\lambda} \sin \theta_m = \pm (m + \tfrac{1}{2})\pi$$

Substitution into Eq. (37-6) gives the intensity I_m of a secondary maximum:

$$I_m = I_c \frac{\sin^2 [\pm (m + \frac{1}{2})\pi]}{[\pm (m + \frac{1}{2})\pi]^2}$$

If we use the approximation that the secondary maxima correspond to integral values of m, then we have $\sin^2 [\pm (m + \frac{1}{2})\pi] \approx 1$ for all m. Thus

$$I_m \approx \frac{I_c}{[(m + \frac{1}{2})\pi]^2}$$

where $m \approx 1, 2, \ldots$.
(b) For the $m \approx 1$ maxima,

$$I_1 \approx \frac{I_c}{[(1 + \frac{1}{2})\pi]^2} = 0.045 I_c$$

For the $m \approx 2$ maxima,

$$I_2 \approx \frac{I_c}{[(2 + \frac{1}{2})\pi]^2} = 0.016 I_c$$

The $m \approx 1$ maxima have an intensity of about 4.5 percent that of the central maximum, and the $m \approx 2$ maxima have an intensity of about 1.6 percent that of the central maximum.

The double-slit experiment revisited. In discussing the double-slit pattern in the previous chapter, we made the simplifying assumption that the intensity distribution due to one slit acting alone is uniform across the screen. We now see, from Eq. (37-6), that this assumption is valid when the width of each slit is much less than the wavelength, $a \ll \lambda$. Then the central maximum would be spread across the screen. This situation is rarely achieved in an experiment because such narrow slits are difficult to make and would allow an exceedingly small amount of light to reach the screen. Using this assumption, we developed an expression for the intensity in the double-slit interference pattern [Eq. (36-5)]: $I_{12} = 4I_0 \cos^2 (\frac{1}{2}\phi)$, where $\phi = (2\pi d/\lambda) \sin \theta$.

We can now relax the condition that $a \ll \lambda$, and write a more general expression for the double-slit intensity distribution. Now the intensity due to one slit acting alone is not uniform; it is given by the single-slit diffraction formula. The expression for the double-slit pattern is found by replacing I_0 in Eq. (36-5) with $I_c \sin^2 \beta / \beta^2$:

Double-slit intensity distribution

$$I_{12} = 4I_c \left(\frac{\sin^2 \beta}{\beta^2} \right) \cos^2 (\tfrac{1}{2}\phi) \tag{37-7}$$

where $\beta = (\pi a/\lambda) \sin \theta$ and $\phi = (2\pi d/\lambda) \sin \theta$. The factor $\sin^2 \beta / \beta^2$ depends on the slit width a and is usually called the *diffraction factor*. The factor $\cos^2 (\frac{1}{2}\phi)$ depends on the slit separation d and is usually called the *interference factor*. The intensity I_c is the intensity at the center of the single-slit pattern due to one of the slits acting alone. Figure 37-8 shows how the diffraction factor and the interference factor combine to give the double-slit pattern.

Figure 37-8. The double-slit intensity distribution. (a) A graph of the interference factor, $\cos^2(\tfrac{1}{2}\phi)$. (b) A graph of the diffraction factor, $\sin^2\beta/\beta^2$. (c) A graph of the double-slit intensity distribution, which is proportional to the product of parts (a) and (b). (d) Photograph of a double-slit pattern. (Atlas of Optical Phenomena, *Cagnet, Francon, Phriess,* Springer-Verlag, Berlin, 1962.)

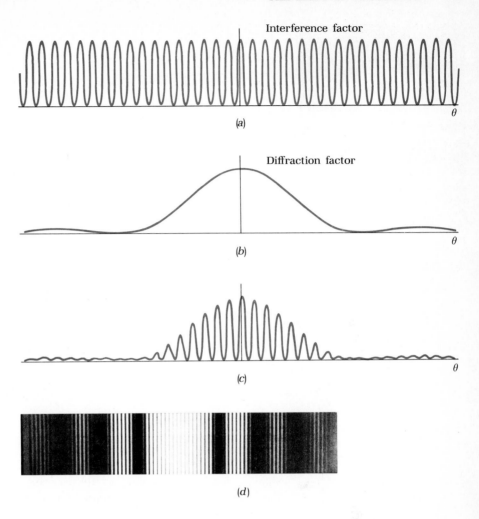

Resolving power is limited because light is a wave.

37-5 THE LIMIT OF RESOLUTION

An important property of any optical instrument, such as a telescope, a camera, or an eye, is its resolving power. The *resolving power* of an optical instrument is a measure of the instrument's ability to produce separate images of two adjacent point objects. Often the measured resolving power of a particular instrument depends on imperfections in the lenses and/or mirrors, and sometimes on the properties of the surrounding medium. However, because of the wave nature of light there is an *ultimate limit* to the resolving power of all optical instruments. It is this ultimate limit we now discuss.

In the last section we described the diffraction of light by a slit. A slit is a rectangular aperture, very long and very narrow. Optical instruments, for example the pupil of an eye, usually have circular apertures. As you can see from Fig. 37-9, a circular aperture produces a diffraction pattern similar to that of a slit, except that it has circular symmetry. A mathematical analysis similar to

Figure 37-9. Fraunhofer diffraction by a circular aperture, the circular analogy to Fig. 37-4a. The central maximum is called the *Airy disk,* named for Sir George Airy (1801–1892). *(Photo Researchers)*

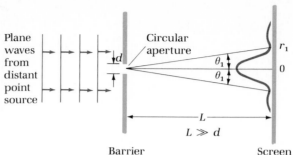

Figure 37-10. The angle θ_1 which locates the first dark ring in the Fraunhofer diffraction by a circular aperture is the half-angle of a cone. The base of the cone is bounded by the first dark ring, and the apex of the cone is at the center of the aperture.

the one we used in discussing a slit gives the expression for the angular position θ_1 of the first dark ring surrounding the bright central maximum in Fig. 37-9:

$$\sin \theta_1 = 1.22 \frac{\lambda}{d} \tag{37-8}$$

In this equation, d is the diameter of the circular aperture and θ_1 is the half-angle of a cone. As shown in Fig. 37-10, the cone has a circular base (of radius r_1) which is bounded by the first dark ring, and its apex is at the center of the aperture.

Ordinarily the angle θ_1 is small so that the approximations $\sin \theta_1 \approx \tan \theta_1 \approx \theta_1$ are valid and we can use

$$\theta_1 \approx 1.22 \frac{\lambda}{d} \tag{37-9}$$

Or, since $\tan \theta_1 = r_1/L$ (Fig. 37-10),

$$r_1 \approx 1.22 \frac{\lambda L}{d} \tag{37-10}$$

Notice from Eqs. (37-9) and (37-10) that the size of the central maximum is directly proportional to λ/d. That is, the central maximum is more spread out for longer wavelengths and for smaller apertures.

Suppose we observe two distant stars with a telescope; the angular separation of the stars is very small and each star produces about the same intensity at the earth. In this case the circular aperture is the entrance mirror (or lens) of the telescope, and instead of a screen we have a solid-state detector. Each star is a point source, and its image on the film is the diffraction pattern due to the circular aperture. Since there are two stars, there will be two such diffraction patterns. No stable interference pattern will be produced by the interference of light from these sources because they are incoherent; the resultant intensity is the sum of the intensity from each diffraction pattern.

What must be the angular separation of the two stars for us to be able to tell that there are two and not one? To answer, we need a criterion for resolution. Figure 37-11 shows the images (diffraction patterns) of two point sources when they are unresolved, just resolved, and clearly resolved. The accepted criterion for resolution is the *Rayleigh criterion.* According to this criterion, two images are just resolved if the center of the central maximum of one pattern falls on the first dark ring of the other, the case shown in Fig. 37-11b. Therefore, two point objects separated by an angle $\Delta\theta$ are resolved when $\Delta\theta > \Delta\theta_R$, where

Rayleigh criterion

Limiting angle of resolution

$$\Delta\theta_R \approx 1.22 \frac{\lambda}{d} \tag{37-11}$$

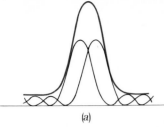

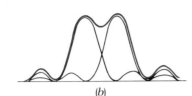

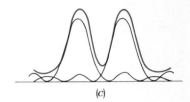

(a)   (b)   (c)

Figure 37-11. Showing the Rayleigh criterion. The diffraction patterns of two point sources by a circular aperture are (a) unresolved, (b) just resolved, with the maximum of one pattern at the minimum of the other, and (c) clearly resolved.

The angle $\Delta\theta_R$ is the limiting angle of resolution for an optical instrument with aperture diameter d. For the Rayleigh criterion to be useful, the intensity of the light which reaches the instrument from each object should be nearly the same. Regardless of the criterion we choose, the ultimate resolving power of an optical instrument depends on the wavelength of the light and the diameter of the instrument's aperture.

EXAMPLE 37-4. In an astronomical research telescope, the aperture diameter is usually large, and consequently, the telescope's limiting angle of resolution is small. The Mount Palomar telescope has a diameter of 5.1 m. Determine the limiting angle of resolution for this telescope when light of wavelength 550 nm is used.

SOLUTION. From Eq. (37-11), the limiting angle is

$$\Delta\theta_R = 1.22 \frac{550 \text{ nm}}{5.1 \text{ m}} \approx 0.1 \ \mu\text{rad}$$

This is about the same angle that is subtended by a dime at a distance of 14 km! This angle is smaller than the limiting angle due to "atmospheric blurring," which is from about 5 μrad to about 0.5 μrad., depending on conditions. Atmospheric problems can be avoided by placing a research telescope in earth orbit. However, even if we have a perfect telescope and ideal surroundings, the limit on resolution given by Eq. (37-11) cannot be avoided, since the limit is due to the wave nature of light.

37-6 POLARIZATION

The polarization of a wave characterizes the direction of the wave oscillations. As we saw in Chap. 34, light is an electromagnetic wave in which the oscillating quantities are the electric and magnetic fields. In a plane wave, the directions of **E** and **B** are perpendicular to each other and perpendicular to the direction of propagation of the wave. Light is a transverse wave, and consequently, it can be polarized in different ways.

The simplest type of polarization to discuss is linear or plane polarization, shown schematically in Fig. 37-12. Recall from Chap. 34 that the propagation

Figure 37-12. A plane-polarized light wave. The propagation direction is toward $+x$, and the plane of polarization is the xy plane.

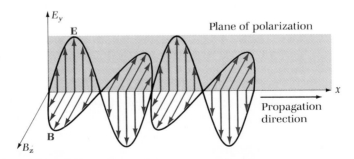

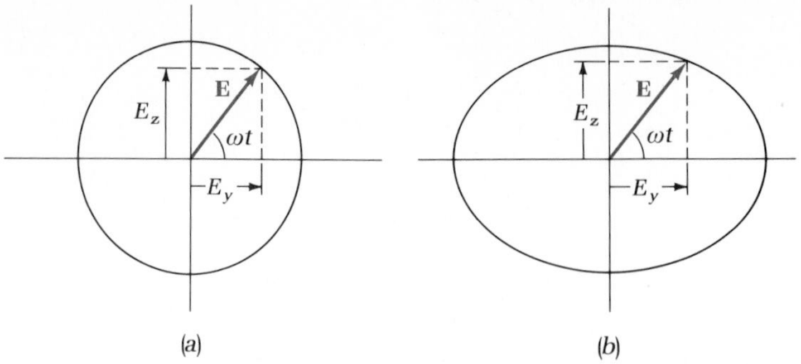

Figure 37-13. (*a*) The **E** vector of a circularly polarized wave at a particular point. The propagation direction is out of the page (toward $+x$). (*b*) An elliptically polarized wave.

direction (the direction of the Poynting vector **S**) is given by the direction of **E** $\times$ **B**. In the figure, **E** is directed toward $+y$ at the same position and time that **B** is directed toward $+z$. Since $\mathbf{j} \times \mathbf{k} = \mathbf{i}$, the direction of propagation is toward $+x$. It is customary to let the polarization direction be defined as along **E** rather than **B**. In Fig. 37-12, the wave is polarized parallel to the y axis because **E** oscillates along the $\pm y$ directions. A plane which contains **E** and the propagation direction is called the *plane of polarization* (the xy plane for the case shown in the figure).

At any point along a plane-polarized wave, **E** oscillates along a fixed line. Waves may also be *circularly* or *elliptically polarized*. At any point along a circularly polarized wave, **E** maintains a fixed magnitude, but its direction rotates in space with a constant angular frequency. Figure 37-13*a* shows the time dependence of **E** at a particular point due to a circularly polarized wave that is propagating along the $+x$ direction (out of the page). The variation of **E** may be represented by a vector of fixed magnitude that rotates about the x axis with a constant angular frequency ω. In this picture, the tip of the **E** vector traces out a circle, and the components of $\mathbf{E}$—E_y and E_z—oscillate with the same amplitude and have a phase difference of $\frac{1}{2}\pi$ rad. If the tip of the **E** vector in Fig. 37-13*a* rotates in the clockwise sense, then the light is *right*-circularly polarized, whereas if the tip rotates in the counterclockwise sense, then the light is *left*-circularly polarized.

An elliptically polarized wave (Fig. 37-13*b*) is similar to a circularly polarized wave except that, at a particular point, E_y and E_z have different amplitudes. In this case the tip of the **E** vector traces out an ellipse.

Ordinarily when one speaks of polarized light without qualifying it as plane, circular, or elliptical, one means *plane*-polarized light. Henceforth, we shall confine our attention to plane-polarized light.

Light emitted from an ordinary source, such as the filament of a light bulb, is *unpolarized*. Acting independently, the atoms and molecules emit wave trains of light and the polarizations of these wave trains are unrelated. The resulting light consists of a random mixture of polarizations; it is unpolarized.

Plane-polarized light

Circularly polarized light

Elliptically polarized light

Unpolarized light

37-7 MEASUREMENT OF POLARIZATION

Light can be polarized by passing it through a *polarizer*. A familiar polarizer is the Polaroid film that is often used in sunglasses. A polarizer is an optical device that selectively transmits light having its plane of polarization parallel to the polarizer's *transmission axis*. Light having its plane of polarization perpendicular to the transmission axis is blocked out by absorbtion or reflection. Figure

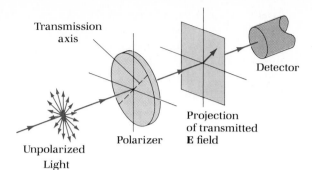

Figure 37-14. A polarizer transmits light with its plane of polarization parallel to the polarizer's transmission axis.

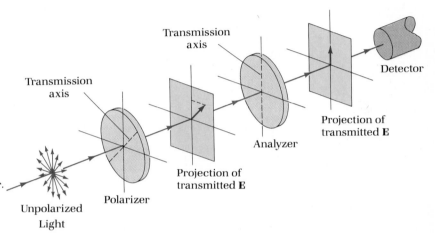

Figure 37-15. Plane-polarized light is transmitted by the polarizer. The analyzer transmits only the component of **E** parallel to its transmission axis.

37-14 shows a beam of unpolarized light incident on a polarizer. The electric field of the transmitted wave at a particular point and time is parallel to the polarizer's transmission axis.

Malus's law. Suppose we pass the polarized light from a polarizer through a second polarizer, as shown in Fig. 37-15. The second polarizer is often called the *analyzer* to distinguish it from the first polarizer. The azimuthal angle θ is a measure of the orientation of the polarizer's transmission axis relative to the analyzer's transmission axis. Let I_0 represent the intensity transmitted by the polarizer and incident on the analyzer. Notice that the detector can measure I_0 if the analyzer is removed temporarily. What light intensity I is transmitted by the analyzer and measured by the detector? In Fig. 37-16 we show the projection of the field components of the light as it emerges from the polarizer with amplitude E_0 and from the analyzer with amplitude $E_0 \cos \theta$. That is, the analyzer transmits only the component of the wave that is parallel to its transmission axis. Since the intensity is proportional to the square of the wave amplitude, we have that $I_0 \propto (E_0)^2$ and $I \propto (E_0 \cos \theta)^2$. The proportionality constant is the same in each case so that

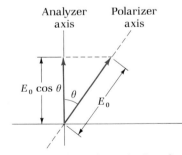

Figure 37-16. The projection of the field $\mathbf{E}_0$ transmitted by the polarizer onto the transmission axis of the analyzer is $E_0 \cos \theta$.

Malus's law

$$I = I_0 \cos^2 \theta \tag{37-12}$$

This is Malus's law (named for E. L. Malus, 1775–1812). When $\theta = 0$ is substituted into Malus's law, we have $I = I_0 \cos^2 0 = I_0$. That is, the intensity transmitted by the analyzer is maximum when the transmission axes of the polarizer and analyzer are parallel. Further, when $\theta = \frac{1}{2}\pi$ rad, $I = I_0 \cos^2 (\frac{1}{2}\pi) = 0$.

That is, the intensity transmitted by the analyzer is minimum when the transmission axes are perpendicular. Because there is no positive sense associated with a transmission axis, all possible intensity values, $0 < I < I_0$, are realized in the interval from $\theta = 0$ to $\theta = \frac{1}{2}\pi$ rad.

Suppose a beam of unpolarized light is incident on a polarizer, as shown in Fig. 37-14. The unpolarized light consists of wave trains with a random mixture of polarizations. The polarizer transmits only the component of **E** from each wave train that is parallel to the polarizer's transmission axis. Since they are emitted from independent atoms and molecules, the wave trains are incoherent. To find the resultant intensity due to incoherent waves, we add their intensities (not their amplitudes). The intensity transmitted by the polarizer is the sum of the intensities due to each wave train. This sum is equivalent to averaging over the random mixture of polarizations. We can use Malus's law to express the transmitted intensity due to a wave train, where θ is then the angle between the plane of polarization of the wave train and the polarizer's transmission axis. Since the average value of $\cos^2 \theta$ over the interval from $\theta = 0$ to $\theta = \frac{1}{2}\pi$ rad is 1/2, the transmitted intensity is one-half the incident intensity. This intensity is independent of the orientation of the polarizer because of the random polarizations of the incident wave trains.

An unpolarized light beam consists of incoherent wave trains with randomly oriented planes of polarization. We can determine the contribution to the intensity due to a single wave train by resolving the field due to the wave train along two mutually perpendicular axes. This can be done for each wave train in the beam. Thus an unpolarized beam may be considered as two incoherent plane-polarized beams with perpendicular planes of polarization.

Degree of polarization. In our development of Malus's law, we tacitly assumed that both the polarizer and the analyzer were ideal. That is, all light polarized parallel to the transmission axis was transmitted, and no light polarized perpendicular to the transmission axis was transmitted. Although polarizers that are nearly ideal can be constructed, real polarizers do not polarize light completely. The quantity used to characterize the polarization of light is the *degree of polarization P.*

Suppose the polarizer in Fig. 37-15 is not ideal, but the analyzer is effectively ideal. Let $I_\parallel$ represent the intensity measured by the detector when the transmission axes are parallel ($\theta = 0$), and let $I_\perp$ represent the intensity when the axes are perpendicular ($\theta = \frac{1}{2}\pi$ rad). The degree of polarization P of the light transmitted by the polarizer is defined as

Degree of polarization

$$P = \frac{I_\parallel - I_\perp}{I_\parallel + I_\perp} \tag{37-13}$$

As an example, suppose the light incident on the analyzer is not polarized at all. Then $I_\parallel = I_\perp$ and substitution into Eq. (37-13) gives $P = 0$. As another example, suppose the light incident on the analyzer is completely polarized. Then $I_\perp = 0$ and substitution into Eq. (37-13) gives $P = 1$. Thus the degree of polarization ranges from a minimum of zero for unpolarized light to a maximum of 1 for completely polarized light.

EXAMPLE 37-5. Suppose the degree of polarization of the light transmitted by a polarizer is checked by using the arrangement shown in Fig. 37-15. The intensity measured by the detector when the axes are parallel is I_m, and the intensity measured when the axes are perpendicular is $0.127I_m$. Assuming the analyzer is ideal, determine the degree of polarization due to the polarizer.

SOLUTION. Using Eq. (37-13), we have

$$P = \frac{I_m - 0.127I_m}{I_m + 0.127I_m}$$

$$= \frac{0.873}{1.127} = 0.775$$

Often this result is stated as a percentage, and we say that the light is 77.5 percent polarized.

37-8 METHODS FOR POLARIZING LIGHT

When light undergoes some process such as reflection or scattering, it tends to become polarized. These processes can be utilized to produce polarized light. The particular processes which we shall discuss are (i) selective absorbtion, (ii) reflection and transmission, (iii) double refraction, and (iv) scattering.

Selective absorbtion, or dichroism. A common method of polarizing light is with a sheet of Polaroid, the material often used in sunglasses. Polaroid is an example of a *dichroic material.* A dichroic material transmits light that has its plane of polarization parallel to a particular alignment in the material and strongly absorbs light that has its plane of polarization perpendicular to this alignment. These alignments correspond to certain molecular or crystalline orientations. Figure 37-17 indicates the action of a dichroic material. A number of naturally occurring crystals are dichroic; an important example is tourmaline.

Polaroid is produced by stretching plastic sheets that contain long-chain molecules and thereby aligning these molecules. When the plastic is stained with an ink that contains iodine, the material becomes dichroic. Polaroid is a convenient and inexpensive polarizer, but the transmitted light is colored because the absorbtion depends on wavelength as well as polarization. Also,

Figure 37-17. A dichroic material selectively transmits light with its plane of polarization parallel to a crystalline or molecular orientation and absorbs light perpendicular to this orientation.

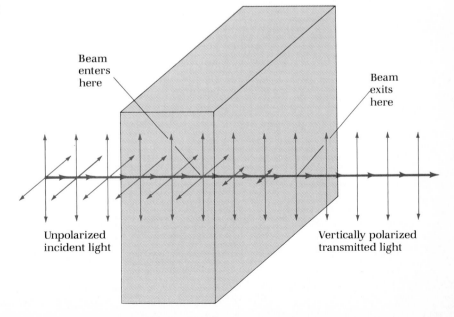

Beam enters here

Beam exits here

Unpolarized incident light

Vertically polarized transmitted light

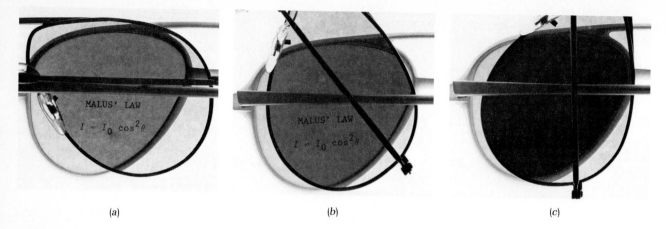

(a)   (b)   (c)

Figure 37-18. Using Polaroid sunglasses to demonstrate Malus's law. (a) Transmission axes parallel. (b) Transmission axes at $\frac{1}{4}\pi$ rad (45°). (c) Transmission axes perpendicular. *(Tom Richard)*

the transmitted light is not completely polarized, and its degree of polarization depends somewhat on the wavelength. We have used Polaroid sunglasses to demonstrate Malus's law in Fig. 37-18.

Reflection and transmission. Using a pair of Polaroid sunglasses as an analyzer, you can observe the polarization of light by reflection. The next time you are wearing a pair of these glasses, tilt your head to one side and notice the greatly increased light intensity reflected from horizontal surfaces. Since the source of the light is the sun above, most of the light reaching your eyes is reflected from horizontal surfaces. When the light is reflected, it is also polarized, and the orientation of the plane of polarization depends on the orientation of the reflecting surface. The transmission axis of the Polaroid film in the glasses is aligned so that light that has been polarized by reflection from a horizontal surface is absorbed. With this alignment, these glasses reduce the bright glare from horizontal surfaces.

Consider an unpolarized light beam in air that is incident on a glass surface (Fig. 37-19). Except for a few particular angles, both the reflected and the refracted beams are partially polarized. If the beam is normally incident on the surface ($\theta = 0$), or if the beam grazes the surface ($\theta = \frac{1}{2}\pi$ rad), then the reflected light is not polarized. In the discussion that follows, we consider angles of incidence between these two extremes, where the refracted beam is partially polarized at all angles. The reflected beam is also partially polarized at all angles except for one particular angle. At this angle, called the *polarizing angle* θ_p, the reflected beam is totally polarized.

When $\theta = \theta_p$, the reflected beam is completely polarized, with its plane of polarization perpendicular to the plane of incidence. Recall from Sec. 35-3 that

The reflected beam is totally polarized at $\theta = \theta_p$.

Figure 37-19. An unpolarized beam is incident at the polarizing angle. The plane of the page is the plane of incidence. Field oscillations in the plane of the page are marked $\updownarrow$, and field oscillations perpendicular to the page are marked.

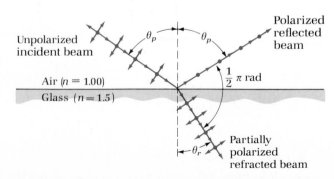

the plane of incidence contains the incident beam, the reflected beam, and the normal to the surface. Thus the electric field of the reflected beam oscillates parallel to the reflecting surface (Fig. 37-19). For angles other than θ_p, the reflected beam is partially polarized perpendicular to the plane of incidence.

In 1812 Sir David Brewster (1781–1868) experimentally discovered that when the angle of incidence θ_i is set at the polarizing angle θ_p, the reflected beam and the refracted beam are perpendicular, as shown in Fig. 37-19. Since $\theta_i = \theta_p$ in this case and since the angle of reflection equals the angle of incidence, Brewster's discovery may be written as $\theta_p + \theta_r = \frac{1}{2}\pi$ rad. We can use this result and Snell's law to find θ_p in terms of the relative index of refraction of the media. Let n_1 be the index of refraction of the medium which contains the incident and reflected beams, and let n_2 be the index of refraction of the medium which contains the refracted beam. Using Snell's law, $n_1 \sin \theta_i = n_2 \sin \theta_r$, with $\theta_i = \theta_p$ and $\theta_r = \frac{1}{2}\pi$ rad $- \theta_p$, we have

$$n_1 \sin \theta_p = n_2 \sin (\tfrac{1}{2}\pi - \theta_p)$$

Since $\sin (\frac{1}{2}\pi - \theta_p) = \cos \theta_p$,

$$\frac{n_2}{n_1} = \frac{\sin \theta_p}{\cos \theta_p} = \tan \theta_p$$

The ratio n_2/n_1 is the relative index of refraction n_{21}. Therefore,

Brewster's law

$$\tan \theta_p = n_{21} \tag{37-14}$$

This equation is called *Brewster's law*, and sometimes the polarizing angle θ_p is called *Brewster's angle*. Brewster's law gives the value of the angle of incidence for which the reflected beam is completely polarized. Suppose medium 1 is air ($n_1 = 1.00$) and medium 2 is glass ($n_2 = 1.5$). Brewster's law gives $\tan \theta_p = 1.5$, or $\theta_p = \tan^{-1} 1.5 = 0.98$ rad $= 56°$. Unpolarized light incident from air and reflected from this glass surface will be totally polarized if the angle of incidence is about 1 rad.

When unpolarized light is incident on the surface of a dielectric, the reflected beam is polarized. What about the refracted beam? The light in the reflected and refracted beams originated in the unpolarized incident beam. With the reflected beam polarized perpendicular to the plane of incidence, the refracted beam is left with light that is polarized parallel to the plane of incidence. This polarization is partial at all angles, even at $\theta = \theta_p$.

The refracted beam is partially polarized.

EXAMPLE 37-6. For an unpolarized light beam incident from air onto glass ($n = 1.50$) at the polarizing angle, 7.4 percent of the incident intensity is reflected and 92.6 percent is refracted. Determine the degree of polarization of (a) the reflected beam and (b) the refracted beam.

SOLUTION. (a) Since the light is incident at the polarizing angle, all the reflected light is polarized perpendicular to the plane of incidence: $P = 1$. (b) We may treat the unpolarized incident beam (of intensity I_i) as if half its intensity is polarized parallel to the plane of incidence and the other half perpendicular to the plane of incidence. All of the incident beam which is polarized parallel to the plane of incidence is refracted, because none of it is reflected. Therefore if we let

$I_\parallel$ be the refracted beam intensity polarized parallel to the plane of incidence, then $I_\parallel = 0.500I_i$. Now let $I_\perp$ be the refracted beam intensity polarized perpendicular to the plane of incidence. Since all the reflected light (7.4 percent) is polarized perpendicular to the plane of incidence, $I_\perp = (0.500 - 0.074)I_i = 0.426I_i$. Using Eq. (37-13), we have

$$P = \frac{0.500I_i - 0.426I_i}{0.500I_i + 0.426I_i} = \frac{0.074}{0.926} = 0.080$$

The refracted beam is 8.0 percent polarized. Despite the 100 percent polarization of the reflected beam, the refracted beam has a rather small degree of polarization. The reason is that very little light is reflected; almost all of it is refracted.

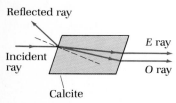

Figure 37-20. An unpolarized ray is incident on a birefringent crystal (say, calcite). The O ray and E ray are polarized, with mutually perpendicular planes of polarization.

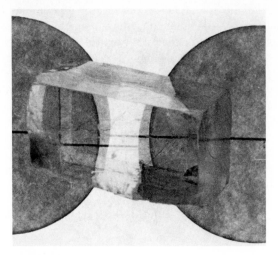

Figure 37-21. Demonstration of the polarization of the O and E rays. A straight horizontal line on a sheet of paper is viewed normally through circular Polaroid disks and through a calcite crystal. Since the light path is normal to the crystal faces, the O ray is unrefracted but the E ray is refracted. The transmission axis of the Polaroid disk on the left is horizontal and that of the disk on the right is vertical. You can see that the O ray and E ray are both polarized, and their planes of polarization are perpendicular.

Double refraction, or birefringence. Certain crystalline materials exhibit double refraction, or birefringence. Two important examples are calcite ($CaCO_3$) and crystalline quartz (SiO_2). In Fig. 37-20, we show a beam of unpolarized light incident on a calcite crystal. Within the crystal there are two refracted beams or rays, the *ordinary ray*, or O ray and the *extraordinary ray*, or E ray. These two rays take divergent paths within the medium and are polarized with mutually perpendicular planes of polarization. If the angles of refraction are measured for a number of angles of incidence, one finds that Snell's law holds for the O ray but not for the E ray. (There is a special axis in birefringent crystals called the *optic axis*. If the plane of incidence is perpendicular to the optic axis, then Snell's law holds for the E ray as well as the O ray.) Birefringent materials are quite useful in optics, especially as polarizers.

Figure 37-21 shows a demonstration of the polarization of the O and E rays. For the normal incidence in the photograph, the light from the O ray is unrefracted, whereas the E ray is refracted. The transmission axes of the polariod sheets are given in the figure caption. Can you determine the plane of polarization of each ray?

Scattering. You can verify that scattered light is polarized by viewing the sky with a pair of Polaroid sunglasses on a clear day. Light comes to us from the sky because sunlight is scattered by the gas molecules in the atmosphere. If there were no atmosphere, the sky would be black and we could see stars during the day. The amount of scattering depends strongly on the wavelength; shorter wavelengths are scattered more than longer wavelengths. Thus the sky appears blue because the scattered light has a larger mixture of shorter wavelengths (violet and blue) than of longer wavelengths (yellow and red). Sunsets are red because this light comes to our eyes after passing through a large amount of atmosphere and the short wavelengths have been selectively depleted from the light we see.

When you observe polarized skylight with your sunglasses, notice that the degree of polarization is maximum for light coming from the direction perpendicular to the sun's direction. Figure 37-22 shows the reason for this. A beam of unpolarized light propagating toward $+x$ is scattered by molecules in the vicinity of the origin. The direction of the scattered light which reaches an

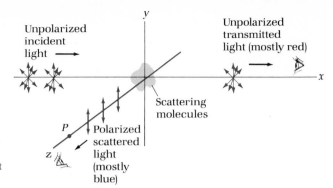

Figure 37-22. Molecules located near the origin scatter polarized light to point P on the z axis.

observer at point P on the z axis is at right angles to the incident beam direction. Since light is a transverse wave, the oscillating electric field of the waves incident on the scattering molecules has no component along the x axis. As a result, the oscillations in the beam scattered to the observer at P can have no component along the x axis. The light detected at P is plane-polarized in the yz plane.

Some bees and ants can distinguish polarized skylight, and they use it as a compass to navigate from their nest to a food source and back.

COMMENTARY: HOLOGRAPHY

Holography is a technique for producing three-dimensional photographs by using the interference of light waves. A hologram of a scene gives a truly three-dimensional replica of the scene. Suppose we have a hologram of a saltshaker, a pepper shaker, and a bottle. When viewed from a particular angle, the saltshaker is seen beside the bottle, but the pepper shaker cannot be seen because it is behind the bottle. Then the viewer may change the angle of observation such that the saltshaker disappears behind the bottle and the pepper shaker is seen on the other side.

One way in which the film is exposed in taking a hologram of an object is shown in Fig. 37-23a. A collimated beam of coherent, monochromatic light from a laser is incident on a mirror and on the object. The photographic film is exposed simultaneously to light reflected from the mirror and light scattered from the object. The light incident on the film from the mirror is called the reference beam *and the light incident on the film from the object is called the* modified beam. *The incident light must be sufficiently coherent so that these two beams can produce a stable interference pattern on the surface of the film during exposure. The hologram is the photographic record of this interference pattern.*

The viewing of a hologram is shown in Fig. 37-23b. The incident laser light is diffracted by the interference pattern of the hologram, which causes images of the object to be produced — a virtual image on the laser side of the hologram and a real image on the side opposite the laser.

We can get some understanding of how a hologram image is recorded and then viewed by simplifying the arrangement. In Fig. 37-24a we show a plane wave incident on a sheet of photographic film. (The wavelength is greatly exaggerated for purposes of illustration.) Waves scattered from the point object O are spherical waves centered at O's position. The incident plane waves and the

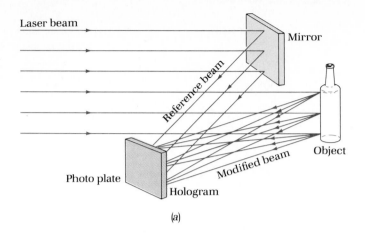

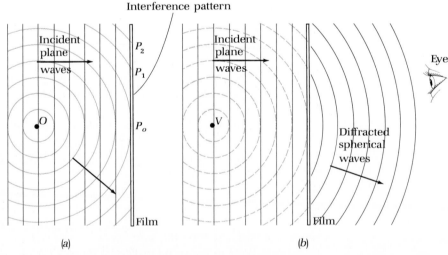

Figure 37-23. (a) A hologram is produced by exposing the film to a reference beam reflected from a mirror and a modified beam scattered from the object. *(Adapted from* Fundamentals of Optics, *4th ed., F. A. Jenkins and H. E. White, 1976, McGraw-Hill, p 662.)* (b) A hologram is viewed by observing the light which is diffracted by the hologram. The same type of laser light that was used in the exposure is also used in the viewing.

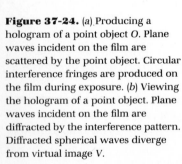

Figure 37-24. (a) Producing a hologram of a point object O. Plane waves incident on the film are scattered by the point object. Circular interference fringes are produced on the film during exposure. (b) Viewing the hologram of a point object. Plane waves incident on the film are diffracted by the interference pattern. Diffracted spherical waves diverge from virtual image V.

scattered spherical waves produce a stable interference pattern on the film because they are coherent. At points where these waves arrive in phase they constructively interfere to produce interference maxima, and at points where they arrive out of phase they destructively interfere to produce minima. For the *case shown in the figure, O is an integral number of wavelengths from the center of the screen at P_0. In this case interference maxima occur at P_0, P_1, and P_2. Thus interference fringes are formed and recorded on the film, and this exposed film is a hologram of a point object.*

In the case of an extended object, there is interference between light scattered from each point on the object (within the modified beam in Fig. 37-23a) and the incident plane wave (the reference beam in Fig. 37-23a). The interference pattern produced on the film is due to the superposition of the interference of waves scattered from each point on the object and waves in the reference beam. Thus the hologram of an extended object consists of a very complex interference pattern, which is characteristic of the phases of waves scattered from the three-dimensional object.

The viewing of the hologram of the point object O is shown in Fig. 37-24b. Plane waves are incident on the hologram from the left. Although it is beyond the scope of this text to show it, the circular fringes recorded on the film diffract the light into spherical waves diverging from point V, which is the virtual image of point object O. (In addition, the diffracted waves consist of spherical waves that converge to a point, and plane waves are transmitted. For simplicity these waves are not shown.) In the case of an extended object, the viewer sees diffracted light which produces a complete three-dimensional image.

SUMMARY WITH APPLICATIONS

Section 37-2. Diffraction

Diffraction is the spreading of a wave around the edges of a barrier and into the region shaded by the barrier. In Fraunhofer diffraction the waves impinging on the barrier and the screen are plane waves, and in Fresnel diffraction the waves are not necessarily plane waves.

Define and compare Fresnel diffraction and Fraunhofer diffraction.

Section 37-3. Description of the single-slit diffraction pattern

The single-slit diffraction pattern is cast on a screen by monochromatic light passing through a narrow slit. The pattern is composed of fringes with a central maximum flanked by secondary maxima.

Describe the single-slit diffraction pattern and qualitatively explain how it is formed.

Section 37-4. The single-slit intensity distribution

The single-slit diffraction formula is

$$I = I_c \frac{\sin^2 \beta}{\beta^2} \qquad (37\text{-}6)$$

where $\beta = (\pi a/\lambda) \sin \theta$.

Develop and use the single-slit diffraction formula.

Section 37-5. The limit of resolution

The resolving power of optical instruments has an ultimate limit because of the wave nature of light. Using the Rayleigh criterion, we find that the limiting angle of resolution is

$$\Delta \theta_R \approx 1.22 \left(\frac{\lambda}{d} \right) \qquad (37\text{-}10)$$

where d is the aperture diameter of the instrument.

Determine the limiting angle of resolution for an optical instrument.

Section 37-6. Polarization

For a plane-polarized wave, the plane of polarization contains the oscillating electric field and the direction of propagation. Light may also be circularly or elliptically polarized.

Describe plane, circular, and elliptical polarization.

Section 37-7. Measurement of polarization

If plane-polarized light of intensity I_0 is incident on a polarizer, then the transmitted intensity I is given by Malus's law:

$$I = I_0 \cos^2 \theta \qquad (37\text{-}12)$$

where θ is the angle between the plane of polarization of the incident light and the polarizer's transmission axis.

Describe how the polarization of light can be measured.

Section 37-8. Methods for polarizing light

Light can be polarized by selective absorbtion, reflection and transmission, double refraction, and scattering. Light reflected from a surface is 100 percent polarized perpendicular to the plane of incidence if the angle of incidence is equal to the polarizing angle θ_p:

$$\tan \theta_p = n_{21} \qquad (37\text{-}14)$$

where n_{21} is the relative index of refraction.

Explain the ways in which light can become polarized.

QUESTIONS

37-1   Explain the distinction between Fresnel diffraction and Fraunhofer diffraction.

37-2   We have discussed three processes by which the propagation direction of waves may be altered: reflection, refraction, and diffraction. Which, if any, of these processes may be described by wave interference? Explain.

37-3   Use Fig. 37-25 to give a qualitative explanation for the formation of the Arago spot. Two rays are shown which pass the edge of the disk and impinge on the screen. What can you say about the path difference between these rays? What can you say about the phase difference between the light waves traveling along these rays? Extend your conclusions to include all light waves that similarly pass the edge of the disk.

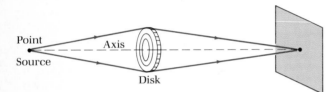

Figure 37-25. Ques. 37-3: A disk casts a shadow on a screen when illuminated by a point source of monochromatic light. The Arago spot is formed on the screen at the center of the shadow.

37-4   Suppose two astronauts are space-walking outside their spacecraft and each has a flashlight and walkie-talkie radio. When the spacecraft is between them, neither astronaut can see the other's flashlight, but they can communicate with their walkie-talkies. Explain this result. Assume that neither the radio waves nor the light waves can reach the other astronaut by reflection.

37-5   Consider the single-slit diffraction pattern. What is the effect on the width of the pattern, say the distance between the $m' = 1$ minima, when (a) the wavelength is doubled, (b) the slit width is doubled, (c) the incident intensity is doubled?

37-6   Consider the single-slit diffraction pattern. What is the effect on the intensity at the center of the central maximum when (a) the wavelength is doubled, (b) the slit width is doubled, (c) the incident intensity is doubled?

37-7   Consider the single-slit diffraction pattern. What is the effect on the ratio of the intensity at the first secondary maximum to the intensity at the central maximum when (a) the wavelength is doubled, (b) the slit width is doubled, (c) the incident intensity is doubled?

37-8   Suppose the single-slit diffraction experiment is performed in air and then the entire apparatus is immersed in water and the experiment is performed again. Describe any differences in the patterns for the two cases.

37-9   Suppose the single-slit diffraction experiment is performed with sunlight rather than monochromatic light. Describe the appearance of the pattern.

37-10 Use Fig. 37-26 to give a qualitative description of the formation of the $m \approx 1$ secondary maxima. (*Hint:* Recall the discussion of Fig. 37-5.) Extend your discussion to account for the $m \approx 2$ secondary maxima.

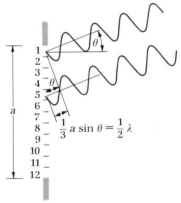

Figure 37-26. Ques. 37-10: Waves emerging in phase from a single slit. The slit is divided (in our mind's eye) into 12 elementary slits, and the waves shown arrive at the screen very near one of the $m \approx 1$ secondary maxima.

37-11 In our discussions of single-slit diffraction, we assumed that the length of the slit was much larger than its width, so we considered only the variation of light intensity in a direction perpendicular to the length of the slit. Suppose the slit's length is twice its width. Describe the way you think the pattern will appear.

37-12 In Figs. 37-5 and 37-6, we assumed that the waves emerged from each elementary slit in phase, and, to reach the same point on the screen, their directions of propagation were parallel. Explain the connection between these approximations and the assumption of Fraunhofer diffraction.

37-13 In Eq. (37-5), which of the factors inside the integral, ω, t, and/or ϕ, depends on the variable of integration y?

37-14 Note that the angle β entered the expression for the single-slit diffraction pattern as the limits to the variation of the phase difference ϕ. Give a physical interpretation of β.

37-15 A mathematical function $f(x)$ is an odd function of x if $f(-x) = -f(x)$. An example of an odd function is $f(x) = \sin x$. Use Fig. 37-27 to explain why the integral of an odd function between symmetric limits, say from $-a$ to $+a$, is always zero. (Also, see Exercise 37-15.)

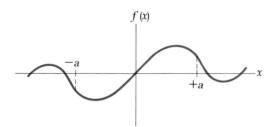

Figure 37-27. Ques. 37-15: Graph of an odd function. The area under the curve from $-a$ to $+a$ is zero.

37-16 If the width of a single slit is doubled, the power through the slit is doubled but the intensity at the center of the pattern is quadrupled. Does this violate energy conservation? Explain.

37-17 Consider the double-slit intensity distribution, Eq. (37-7). Is it possible to have the $m' = 1$ minima in the interference term [see Eq. (36-1)] to appear at the same point on the screen as the $m' = 1$ minima in the diffraction term [see Eq. (37-1)]? Explain.

37-18 Suppose you are using a high-quality microscope whose resolution is determined solely by diffraction effects. Would higher resolution be attained with red light or blue light?

37-19 We have noted that a telescope with a larger aperture will have a better resolving power. Can you think of any other advantages to a large aperture? Are there disadvantages in having a large aperture? Explain.

37-20 In their dark and murky environment, sperm whales find their prey (squid) with echolocation. They emit high-frequency sound waves and then detect the reflected waves. Why do they use high- rather than low-frequency sound? Discuss the advantages of widely spaced ears for a whale.

37-21 How do Polaroid sunglasses "reduce glare"? Is the transmission axis in these glasses horizontal or vertical?

37-22 Fishers usually prefer Polaroid sunglasses because it helps them "see into the water." Explain why this is so.

37-23 Some photographers use a polarizing filter over their camera lenses. Explain how such a filter could be useful in photography.

37-24 A light beam directed along the horizontal may be polarized in a variety of ways. For example, it might be plane-polarized in a horizontal plane or in a vertical plane. Can a similar thing be done to sound waves in air? Explain.

37-25 The polarization of light is considered as evidence that light is a transverse wave. But could it also have a longitudinal component? To answer, consider explaining Malus's law taking a longitudinal component into account.

37-26 Consider a double-slit experiment in which we polarize the light from the slits. Describe the pattern when the planes of polarization of the light from the two slits are (a) parallel and (b) perpendicular.

37-27 An unpolarized light beam of intensity I may be considered as two incoherent plane-polarized beams, each with intensity $\frac{1}{2}I$ and with perpendicular planes of polarization. Why must these two beams be incoherent? Consider two coherent beams that are in phase, of equal amplitude, and with perpendicular planes of polarization. Describe the polarization of a single beam which is equivalent to these two.

37-28 Suppose you are given a piece of plastic and asked to determine whether it is Polaroid. You do not have a polarizer at your disposal. Explain how you would make this determination. If it does turn out to be Polaroid, how would you determine the axis of transmission?

37-29 Viewed from the surface of the moon, the moon's sky is black. Explain.

37-30 Complete the following table:

Symbol	Represents	Type	SI unit
β		Scalar	
$\Delta\theta_R$			rad
P	Degree of polarization		
$I_\perp$			
θ_p			

EXERCISES

Section 37-3. Description of the single-slit diffraction pattern

37-1 Monochromatic light is used in a single-slit diffraction experiment. The slit width is $a = 0.14$ mm, the distance to the screen is $L = 1.16$ m, and the width of the central maximum (distance between the $m' = 1$ minima) is 4.6 mm. What is the wavelength of the light?

37-2 A single-slit diffraction pattern is produced with the H_α line from a hydrogen source ($\lambda_\alpha = 656.3$ nm) onto a slit of width 0.041 mm. (a) What are the angles which locate the $m' = 1$ and $m' = 2$ minima? (b) What are the approximate angles which locate the $m \approx 1$ and $m \approx 2$ secondary maxima?

37-3 The width Δx of the central maximum (distance between the $m' = 1$ minima) in a single-slit pattern is 5.4 mm. The light has a wavelength $\lambda = 584$ nm, and the screen is 1.31 m from the slit. What is the width of the slit?

37-4 Determine the positions x_1 and x_2 (relative to the central maximum) of the $m' = 1$ and $m' = 2$ minima in the single-slit diffraction pattern of light of wavelength 450 nm. The slit width is 0.36 mm, and the screen is 1.03 m from the slit.

37-5 In the single-slit diffraction pattern of infrared light with wavelength 945 nm, the angular positions of the $m' = 1$ minima are $\theta_1 = \pm\pi/4$ rad. What is the width of the slit?

37-6 Consider the single-slit diffraction pattern due to a rather narrow slit: $a = 2.0$ μm. Let $\lambda = 550$ nm. (a) Determine the angular width $2\theta_1$ of the central maximum (θ_1 represents the angular position of an $m' = 1$ minimum). (b) Determine the width Δx of the central maximum (distance between the $m' = 1$ minima) on a screen which is 1.00 m from the slit. Note that the approximation $\sin\theta \approx x/L$ is not valid in this case.

37-7 Consider the graph of the single-slit diffraction intensity, I versus $\sin\theta$, shown in Fig. 37-4b. What is the percent error in the values of $\sin\theta$ for the secondary maxima if you use $m = 1$ and $m = 2$ rather than the more accurate values—$m = 0.93$ and $m = 1.96$?

37-8 Suppose microwaves of wavelength 32 mm are incident normally on a slit in a metal barrier of width 25 mm. Is there a diffraction angle at which the intensity is zero? If so, what is this angle? If not, explain why not.

Section 37-4. The single-slit intensity distribution

37-9 Using Eq. (37-6), make a graph of I versus β. Plot points corresponding to $\beta = \pm\pi/4$, $\pm\pi/2$, $\pm3\pi/4$, . . . , $\pm3\pi$, and use $I = I_c$ at $\beta = 0$. (See Prob. 37-2.) Sketch a smooth curve through the points.

37-10 Determine the intensity at a point midway between the center of the central maximum and an $m' = 1$ minimum on a graph of the single-slit diffraction formula, I versus β.

37-11 Divide the single-slit diffraction formula into two factors, $\sin^2\beta$ and $(1/\beta)^2$, and plot each factor on the same graph. Plot points corresponding to $\beta = 0$, $\pi/4$, $\pi/2$, $3\pi/4$, . . . , 2π, and sketch smooth curves for the two functions. Keep in mind that the single-slit pattern depends on the product of these two factors. From these curves, can you explain why the secondary maxima are not midway between their adjacent minima? Which do you expect to be closer to an integer,

larger values of the index m or smaller values? The product of these factors is 1 at $\beta = 0$. (See Prob. 37-2.)

37-12 Using the approximation that the positions of secondary maxima correspond to integral values of m (see Example 37-3), determine the intensity of the $m \approx 3$ and $m \approx 4$ secondary maxima in terms of I_c.

37-13 Use the more accurate values of the two lowest indices of m, $m = 0.93$ and $m = 1.96$, in Eq. (37-6) to determine the intensity at these secondary maxima. From your answers, determine the percent error in the values of the intensity found in Example 37-3.

37-14 In developing the expression for the single-slit intensity distribution, Eq. (37-5) was integrated after replacing the variable y in terms of the variable ϕ. Accomplish the reverse procedure. Replace ϕ in terms of y in Eq. (37-5) and perform the integral using y as the variable of integration.

37-15 Many mathematical functions can be classified as either even functions or odd functions. For an odd function, $f(-x) = -f(x)$, and for an even function, $f(-x) = f(x)$. An example of an odd function is $f(x) = \sin x$, and an example of an even function is $f(x) = \cos x$. Show that the integral of an odd function between symmetric limits, say from $-a$ to $+a$, is zero.

37-16 In Eq. (37-7), we wrote the double-slit intensity distribution for the more general case where the slit width is not necessarily much smaller than the wavelength. Make a similar modification to the intensity distribution due to a grating, Eq. (36-9).

37-17 Consider the double-slit intensity distribution [Eq. (37-7)]. What must be the ratio of the slit separation to the slit width, d/a, in order to have the $m = 2$ maxima in the interference term [see Eq. (36-2)] occur at the same points on the screen as the $m' = 1$ minima in the diffraction term [Eq. (37-1)]?

37-18 Consider the double-slit intensity distribution [Eq. (37-7)]. (a) What must be the ratio of the slit separation to the slit width, d/a, in order to have the $m' = 2$ minima in the interference term [see Eq. (36-1)] occur at the same points on the screen as the $m' = 1$ minima in the diffraction term [Eq. (37-1)]? (b) How many maxima in the interference term will occur "inside" the central maximum of the diffraction term (that is, between $\beta = -\pi$ and $\beta = +\pi$)? (c) How many interference maxima will occur "inside" one of the fringes corresponding to the $m \approx 1$ diffraction maxima (for positive θ, this is between $\beta = +\pi$ and $\beta = +2\pi$). (d) Make a sketch of I versus $\sin\theta$ for this case.

37-19 Determine the ratio of the slit separation to the slit width d/a for the double-slit intensity distribution shown in Fig. 37-8.

Section 37-5. The limit of resolution

37-20 Monochromatic light ($\lambda = 610$ nm) from a distant source impinges normally on a barrier that has a circular hole of diameter 0.50 mm. The light which passes through the hole forms a diffraction pattern on a screen. The screen is 1.0 m from the hole. What is the radius of the first dark ring in the pattern?

37-21 What is the limiting angle of resolution of a telescope that has an aperture diameter of 75 mm? The light from the objects being viewed has a wavelength of 500 nm.

37-22 Estimate the maximum distance a car can be from a person with perfect vision such that the person, viewing without the aid of a telescope, can tell whether both headlights are on. It is nighttime and the car is facing the person. (*Hint:* The diameter of the pupil of the human eye is several mm.)

37-23 Two stars, each of which produce about the same intensity at the earth, have an angular separation of 7 μrad. If the light from the stars has an average wavelength of 600 nm, what is the minimum aperture diameter needed to resolve them?

Section 37-7. Measurement of polarization

37-24 A polarizer and analyzer (both ideal) are arranged as shown in Fig. 37-15. Suppose the intensity at the detector is 0.65 W/m² when the azimuthal angle θ between the transmission axes is 0. (a) What is the intensity when $\theta = \pi/4$ rad? (b) What is the intensity when $\theta = 3\pi/4$ rad?

37-25 A polarizer and analyzer (both ideal) are arranged as shown in Fig. 37-15. The intensity at the detector is I_0 when the azimuthal angle θ between the transmission axes is zero. What is θ when $I = 0.25I_0$?

37-26 **Rotating the plane of polarization.** Using two or more polarizers, one can rotate the plane of polarization of a light beam. Suppose three polarizers are placed in a beam of unpolarized light of intensity I_0 as shown in Fig. 37-28. Polarizer 1 polarizes the beam and polarizers 2 and 3 rotate the plane of polarization. Let θ be the azimuthal angle between the transmission axes of polarizers 1 and 2, and let α be the azimuthal angle between the axes of polarizers 2 and 3. (a) Assuming that all three polarizers are ideal, show that the intensity at the detector is $I = \frac{1}{2}I_0 (\cos \theta)^2 (\cos \alpha)^2$. Note that the emergent beam has had its plane of polarization rotated by the angle $\theta + \alpha$. (b) Determine I when $\theta = \alpha = \pi/4$ rad so that $\theta + \alpha = \pi/2$ rad.

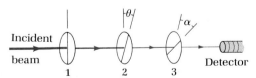

Figure 37-28. Exercise 37-26.

37-27 An effectively ideal polarizer is used to measure the polarization of a beam which is directed horizontally.

As the polarizer is rotated, it transmits a maximum intensity I_m when the transmission axis is aligned with the vertical and a minimum intensity $0.10i_m$ when aligned horizontally. (a) Is the plane of polarization horizontal or vertical? (b) What is the degree of polarization of the beam?

37-28 A partially polarized beam may be regarded as a combination of a completely unpolarized beam with intensity I_u and a completely polarized beam with intensity I_p. If this beam is incident on an ideal analyzer, then the maximum transmitted intensity is $I_\parallel = I_p + \frac{1}{2}I_u$ when the analyzer's axis is parallel to the plane of polarization of the polarized part of the beam. When the analyzer's axis is perpendicular to the plane of polarization of the polarized part of the beam, the transmitted intensity is $I_\perp = \frac{1}{2}I_u$. Show that the degree of polarization of the beam can be written $P = I_p/(I_p + I_u)$.

Section 37-8. Methods for polarizing light

37-29 What is the polarizing angle for a beam incident from air onto the surface of water ($n = 1.33$)?

37-30 A beam of light reflected from the surface of a transparent medium is completely polarized when the angle of reflection is 1.1 rad. What is the angle of refraction?

37-31 A flashlight beam is incident from air onto a sheet of plastic. The reflected light is found to be completely polarized when the angle of incidence is 0.89 rad. What is the index of refraction of the plastic?

37-32 A block of glass ($n = 1.5$) is immersed in water ($n = 1.3$). (a) What is the polarizing angle for a beam of light incident from the glass onto the glass-water surface? (b) What is the polarizing angle for a beam of light incident from the water onto the glass-water surface?

37-33 Brewster's law, $\tan \theta_p = n_2/n_1$, gives the angle of incidence for a beam in medium 1 onto the surface between media 1 and 2 such that the reflected beam is completely polarized. Let θ_{1p} represent this polarizing angle and θ_{2p} represent the angle of the refracted beam. Now suppose that a beam is incident from medium 2 onto the surface between media 1 and 2. Show that the polarizing angle for this beam is θ_{2p}.

37-34 (a) Show that if the incident beam is in the medium with the lower index of refraction, the polarizing angle must be between $\pi/4$ and $\pi/2$ rad. (b) Show that if the incident beam is in the medium with the higher index of refraction, the polarizing angle must be between 0 and $\pi/4$ rad.

37-35 Suppose the critical angle for the total internal reflection of light incident from medium 2 onto the surface between media 1 and 2 is 0.68 rad. (a) What is the polarizing angle for light incident from medium 2? (b) What is the polarizing angle for light incident from medium 1?

37-36 When light is reflected at the polarizing angle from a certain type of transparent plastic, 8.5 percent of the incident beam intensity is reflected. What is the degree of polarization of the refracted beam?

PROBLEMS

37-1 The single-slit diffraction formula can be developed by considering the slit to be a narrow grating of width a that has an infinite number of slits with infinitesimal separation. In Chap. 36 we gave the intensity distribution from a grating: $I = I_0 \sin^2 [N(\frac{1}{2}\phi)]/\sin^2 (\frac{1}{2}\phi)$, where $\phi = (2\pi d/\lambda) \sin \theta$, N is the number of slits, d is the slit separation, and I_0 is the intensity from one slit acting alone. Consider letting d approach zero as N approaches infinity such that the product $Nd = a$ remains fixed. Thus a is initially interpreted as the width of the grating, but in taking the limit this interpretation changes so that a becomes the width of a single slit. Also in this limit, I_0 approaches zero, but the product $N^2 I_0$ approaches I_c. Show that this limiting process leads to Eq. (37-6). Explain why $N^2 I_0 \to I_c$ rather than $N I_0 \to I_c$. [Hint: For large N, $\sin (\beta/N) \approx \beta/N$.]

37-2 Use l'Hospital's rule to show that $[(\sin \beta)/\beta] \to 1$ as $\beta \to 0$. Note that this means E_c in Eq. (37-3) is the field amplitude and I_c in Eq. (37-6) is the intensity at the center of the single-slit diffraction pattern.

37-3 Consider finding accurate values for the secondary maxima in the single-slit diffraction intensity distribution, Eq. (37-6). (a) Show that the relation which gives the values of β for the maxima is $\tan \beta_m = \beta_m$. (Hint: Maxima in the function $\sin^2 \beta/\beta^2$ occur at the same positions as extrema in the function $\sin \beta/\beta$.) (b) Verify that $\beta_m = \pm (m + \frac{1}{2})\pi$, with $m \approx 0.93$ and $m \approx 1.96$, give approximate solutions to the expression in part (a). (c) By a trial-and-error procedure with your pocket calculator, determine the value of the index $m \approx 3$ that is accurate to three significant digits.

37-4 Use a graphical procedure to find the solutions to the expression that gives maxima in the single-slit diffraction formula. From the previous problem, the maxima correspond to values of β given by $\tan \beta_m = \beta_m$. On the same graph plot $y_1 = \beta$ and $y_2 = \tan \beta$ from $\beta = 0$ to $\beta = 3\pi$. Points of intersection give values of β in which $\tan \beta = \beta$ so that they correspond to the values of β_m. Determine the two lowest values of β_m (other than 0).

37-5 Using an iterative procedure with your hand calculator, you can find values of m in Eq. (37-2) to a high degree of accuracy. Since $\beta_m = \tan \beta_m$ (see Prob. 37-3), we also have $\beta_m = \tan^{-1} \beta_m$. To accurately find $m \approx 1$ ($\beta_1 \approx 3\pi/2$), make a guess at β_1 and call the guess β_{1a}. Try $\beta_{1a} = (3\pi/2 - 0.01)$ rad. Now calculate $\tan^{-1} \beta_{1a}$. The calculator finds the angle in the range $-\frac{1}{2}\pi$ to $+\frac{1}{2}\pi$, so you must add π to the value given by the calculator. Designate this angle β_{1b} and then find $\tan^{-1} \beta_{1b}$. Add π to the calculator's answer and call this β_{1c}. Continue this procedure until the calculator's answers no longer change with the next iteration. (a) Determine m for this value of β_m. Use this iterative procedure to find accurate values of m for (b) $m \approx 2$ and (c) $m \approx 3$.

37-6 Consider the values of β in Eq. (37-6) such that $I = \frac{1}{2}I_c$ and call these values $\beta_{1/2}$. Show that $\sin \beta_{1/2} = \beta_{1/2}\sqrt{2}$. To find numerical values of $\beta_{1/2}$, use either a trial-and-error procedure similar to that used in Prob. 37-3 or a graphical procedure similar to that used in Prob. 37-4.

37-7 A beam of unpolarized light with intensity I_i is incident on a boundary between transparent media. The reflected beam has an intensity of $0.060I_i$ and its degree of polarization is 0.90. What is the degree of polarization of the refracted beam?

37-8 A light beam can be polarized by passing it through a "stack of glass plates," as shown in Fig. 37-29. The incident beam encounters the first plate at the polarizing angle. This causes the refracted beam inside the plate to encounter the opposite surface at the polarizing angle. (See Exercise 37-32.) Since the plates are parallel, each beam encounters each surface at the polarizing angle. Determine the degree of polarization of the beam that passes through one of the plates. The fraction of the incident intensity reflected from each surface is 0.074. Neglect multiple reflections inside the plate.

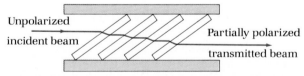

Figure 37-29. Prob. 37-8: Polarization of a beam by passing it through a stack of glass plates. The reflected beams are not shown.

37-9 A partially polarized beam may be regarded as two incoherent beams with different intensities and with perpendicular planes of polarization. Let I_1 represent the intensity of the more intense beam, and let I_2 represent the intensity of the less intense beam. (a) Show that when a partially polarized beam is incident on an ideal polarizer the transmitted intensity is

$$I = (I_1 - I_2) \cos^2 \theta + I_2$$

where θ is the angle between the polarizer's transmission axis and the plane of polarization of the more intense beam. (b) Show that the intensity transmitted by the polarizer may be written

$$I = I_1 \frac{1 + P \cos (2\theta)}{1 + P}$$

where P is the degree of polarization of the beam.

37-10 Suppose the angle between the transmission axes of polarizers 1 and 3 in Fig. 37-28 is held fixed at $\pi/2$ rad while the angle θ between the axes of 1 and 2 is allowed to vary. Show that the intensity at the detector is given by

$$I = I_0 \frac{1 - \cos (4\theta)}{16}$$

where I_0 is the intensity of the unpolarized beam incident on polarizer 1.

37-11 **Optical activity.** Suppose we have N (ideal) polarizers in the beam in Fig. 37-28 instead of three. The beam incident on polarizer 1 is plane-polarized, and polarizer 1 has its transmission axis rotated an angle θ/N to the plane of polarization of the incident beam. Each subsequent polarizer has its axis rotated in the same sense by an angle of θ/N to the one before it, so that the last polarizer has its axis rotated by an angle θ to the plane of polarization of the beam incident on polarizer 1. (a) Show that the intensity transmitted by the last polarizer is

$$I = I_0 \left(\cos \frac{\theta}{N} \right)^{2N}$$

where I_0 is the intensity of the incident beam. Determine I/I_0 for the case where $\theta = \pi/2$ rad and (b) $N = 10$, (c) $N = 100$, (d) $N = 1000$. Some substances, for example sugar dissolved in water, can rotate the plane of polarization of a polarized beam without noticeably reducing the beam intensity. This phenomenon is called *optical activity*.

CHAPTER 38
RELATIVITY

38-1 INTRODUCTION

Commenting on the close relationship between our description of nature and our direct experience, Albert Einstein wrote ". . . this universe of ideas is just as little independent of the nature of our experiences as clothes are of the form of the human body. This is particularly true of our concepts of time and space. . . ." *

Our everyday experience, on which intuition is based, is limited to observations of slowly moving objects of ordinary size. An object is slowly moving in the sense that its speed is very small compared with the speed of light in vacuum. The orbital speed of an earth satellite, for example, is less than 10^4 m/s, much smaller than $c = 3 \times 10^8$ m/s. If an object moves with a speed that is comparable to the speed of light, the object is said to move *relativistically*. Most of us have had no experience with objects moving at such high speeds.

In this chapter we consider the physics of the very fast. As we extrapolate far beyond the realm of our ordinary experience, our intuition will be challenged and the most basic physical concepts must be modified. Be prepared for a profound change in the way you think of time and space.

38-2 TRANSFORMATIONS

The basic process in the observation of phenomena is the cataloging of events. An event such as the collision of two particles is cataloged according to where and when it occurred. The location of the event can be specified by giving its coordinates (x, y, z) relative to a cartesian coordinate system. The time t of the event is assigned to be the simultaneous reading on a nearby clock. In discuss-

---

* From Albert Einstein, *The Meaning of Relativity*, 3d ed., Princeton University Press, Princeton, N.J., 1950.

ing events, we often imagine an observer O noting the four space-time coordinates (x, y, z, t) for each event. The values of these space-time coordinates are relative — relative to that observer's set of coordinate axes and clock. A different observer O' may use a different clock and make a different choice of coordinate axes. Consequently, in this second observer's reference frame, the space-time coordinates for a given event (x', y', z', t') generally differ from the values (x, y, z, t) assigned by observer O to this same event.

A transformation connects observations in different reference frames.

By knowing the relationship between the reference frames of the two observers O and O', we can write the *transformation equations* that connect their observations. First we consider a simple transformation that illustrates the idea. We shall see how this transformation is related to the properties of space and time.

The simplest transformation is the *identity transformation* that connects observations by viewers in the same reference frame. Both viewers use the same set of coordinate axes and the same clock. Thus the space-time coordinates that each assigns to an event are identical. The transformation equations are

$$x' = x$$
$$y' = y$$
$$z' = z$$
$$t' = t$$

Although the transformation equations are trivial in this case, they illustrate the general property: Given the space-time coordinates of an event for one observer, say O, the transformation gives the space-time coordinates of that event for the other observer, O'.

Suppose that two observers use coordinate systems with origins separated by a fixed distance a, as illustrated in Fig. 38-1. For convenience the observers use the same clock (so that $t' = t$). The transformation can be obtained by considering an arbitrary event such as the one shown in the figure. Since the origins of the coordinate systems lie on the xx' axes, we have that $x = x' + a$, $y = y'$, and $z = z'$. Therefore, the transformation is

$$x' = x - a$$
$$y' = y$$
$$z' = z$$
$$t' = t$$

(38-1)

This transformation contains an implicit assumption about the nature of space. It can be illustrated by considering the spatial separation of two events. For simplicity we suppose the events occur on a line parallel to the xx' axes so that y and z coordinates can be ignored. Let one event, according to observer O, have space-time coordinates (x_1, t_1), while the second event occurs at (x_2, t_2). The spatial separation of the two events is $s_{12} = |x_2 - x_1|$ for observer O. The same two events have a spatial separation $s'_{12} = |x'_2 - x'_1|$ for the other observer, O'. How do these distances s_{12} and s'_{12} compare? The transformation in Eqs. (38-1) allow us to translate (or transform) one observer's results into the language of the other. We express the primed distance s'_{12} in terms of the unprimed quantities:

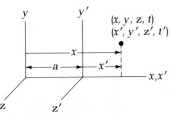

Figure 38-1. The origins of two coordinate systems are separated by a fixed distance a.

$$s'_{12} = |x'_2 - x'_1| = |(x_2 - a) - (x_1 - a)| = |x_2 - x_1| = s_{12}$$

Invariant distance corresponds to
homogeneity of space.

Since the spatial separation of two events has the same value for both observers, it is *invariant* under this transformation. Put another way, the distance between two points in space does not depend on where we place the origin of the coordinate system — space is *homogeneous*. Of course, the homogeneity of space was tacitly assumed in the discussion that led to Eqs. (38-1). This is an example of how transformation equations contain our concepts of space and time.

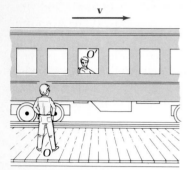

Figure 38-2. Each observer describes the other as moving with constant speed *v*.

The galilean transformation. Of particular interest is the transformation connecting reference frames in relative uniform motion. Figure 38-2 shows observer *O* at rest relative to a train-station platform and observer *O'* at rest relative to a train on a straight track. If the train is moving at constant speed *v* past the station platform, then observer *O'* is moving to the right with speed *v* relative to observer *O*. But according to observer *O'*, observer *O* is moving to the left with speed *v*. That is, each observer argues that the other is moving with relative speed *v*. Which one is *really* moving? Imagine that the argument is settled by an alien space traveler: "Silly humans. Both of them are moving as the earth rotates about its axis and revolves around the sun." The point is, of course, that motion is relative, relative to each observer. As we consider the transformation connecting such reference frames, we must remain flexible, identifying first with one observer, then with the other.

Motion is relative to each observer.

Suppose that the coordinate axes of these two observers are oriented as shown in Fig. 38-1 but with this essential difference: The distance *a* between origins is not fixed. Instead, there is relative motion along the *xx'* axes, with constant speed *v*. Because the observers are in relative motion, they do not use the same clock. Each observer has a clock for noting the time of events. For simplicity suppose that they synchronize their clocks so that $t = t' = 0$ at the instant that the origins of their coordinate systems coincide. This event is shown in Fig. 38-3*a*.

Each observer now classifies an event that occurs later. The situation is shown as interpreted by observer *O* in Fig. 38-3*b*. At the time *t* that the event occurs, the origin of *O'* has moved a distance *vt* to the right along the positive *x* axis. A similar situation is shown in Fig. 38-3*c* as interpreted by observer *O'*. The event occurs at time *t'*, and the origin of *O* has moved a distance *vt'* to the left along the negative *x'* axis.

Transformation contains some
assumptions about space and time.

Writing down the transformation connecting these two reference frames involves some assumptions about the nature of space and time. Using Fig.

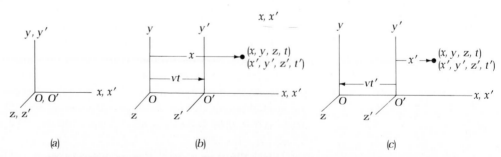

(a)   (b)   (c)

Figure 38-3. (*a*) The coordinate axes of two observers coincide at $t = t' = 0$. (*b*) An event occurs at (*x*, *y*, *z*, *t*) in the reference frame of observer *O*. (*c*) The same event occurs at (*x'*, *y'*, *z'*, *t'*) in the reference frame of observer *O'*.

38-3b, you might think that the difference $x - vt$ should equal the coordinate x' that observer O' assigns to the event. Using Fig. 38-3c in the same way, you would interpret $x' + vt'$ as the coordinate x of the event for observer O. Notice that these two results, $x' = x - vt$ and $x = x' + vt'$, are not quite the same, since t appears in one of them and t' appears in the other. The expressions become the same if we make the further assumption that $t = t'$ for any event. This assumption embodies the newtonian concept of a universal, absolute time. Furthermore, a clock is assumed to run at a rate independent of its motion relative to another identically constructed clock. Similarly, the measurement of lengths (to determine the coordinates of a point) is assumed to be independent of relative motion. With these assumptions, the transformation (solved for the primed quantities) is

Galilean transformation

$$x' = x - vt$$
$$y' = y$$
$$z' = z \qquad (38\text{-}2)$$
$$t' = t$$

This *galilean* transformation, named after Galileo, was commonly (but incorrectly) thought, until near the beginning of this century, to reflect the essence of space and time. Indeed, the transformation provides an adequate interpretation for relative motion at speeds corresponding to trains, airplanes, and earth satellites ($v \ll c$ in these cases). Many of us make daily use of the transformation in walking, running, biking, and driving.

Suppose that each observer measures the velocity of an object. Such a measurement involves two events. The position of the object is determined at each of two instants. For simplicity we consider only the x component of velocity. Let (x_1, t_1) and (x_2, t_2) represent the space-time coordinates of the events for observer O. The x component of the velocity u_x of the object is given by

$$u_x = \frac{x_2 - x_1}{t_2 - t_1}$$

(This gives the average velocity component; the limit as t_2 approaches t_1 can be taken at any stage.) Observer O' similarly evaluates the velocity component:

$$u_x' = \frac{x_2' - x_1'}{t_2' - t_1'}$$

We use the galilean transformation, Eqs. (38-2), to express u_x' in terms of the measurements of observer O. Using $t' = t$, we have $t_2' - t_1' = t_2 - t_1$ and

$$u_x' = \frac{x_2' - x_1'}{t_2' - t_1'} = \frac{(x_2 - vt_2) - (x_1 - vt_1)}{t_2 - t_1}$$

or, since $(x_2 - x_1)/(t_2 - t_1) = u_x$,

$$u_x' = u_x - v \qquad (38\text{-}3)$$

This result from kinematics was first encountered in Chap. 4. It is the galilean velocity-transformation formula.

EXAMPLE 38-1. Observer O, while waiting for a train to pass the station, notices a helicopter traveling parallel to the tracks overtaking the train. She estimates the speed of the helicopter to be 100 km/h and that of the train to be 60 km/h.

(a) What is the speed of the helicopter relative to an observer O' on the train? (b) If these speeds are maintained, how far ahead of the train is the helicopter after a half hour?

SOLUTION. The galilean transformation applies since the speeds are small compared with the speed of light. (a) Selecting the xx' axes along the direction of motion and using Eq. (38-3), with $u_x = 100$ km/h and $v = 60$ km/h, we have

$$u'_x = 100 \text{ km/h} - 60 \text{ km/h} = 40 \text{ km/h}$$

(b) For the time interval $\Delta t' = 0.50$ h, the x' coordinate of the helicopter changes by $\Delta x' = u'_x \Delta t' = (40 \text{ km/h})(0.50 \text{ h}) = 20$ km according to observer O'. That is, the helicopter is 20 km ahead of the train at this time. What is the answer according to observer O?

38-3 THE PRINCIPLE OF RELATIVITY

One of the most fundamental tenets of science is the existence of an objective reality (nature) that can be described in logical terms. Furthermore, a description of nature, if correct, should be conceptually independent of a particular describer or observer. These ideas are contained in a postulatelike statement called the *principle of relativity: The laws of nature have the same mathematical form in all inertial reference frames.* Put another way, the principle of relativity asserts that a valid law of nature cannot refer in any way to a special or particular reference frame. A law must have the same content in every reference frame. Consider as an example the law of conservation of momentum for an isolated system. The total momentum **P** evaluated in one reference frame may be different from the total momentum **P**$'$ evaluated in another reference frame. But the law is stated (and obeyed) in the same way in each frame: $d\mathbf{P}/dt = 0$ in one frame and $d\mathbf{P}'/dt' = 0$ in the other frame. We shall restrict our attention to inertial reference frames except in the Commentary of this chapter. Remember that, in an inertial reference frame, a particle has zero acceleration unless a net force acts on it.

The importance of the principle of relativity was recognized well before Einstein changed our views of space and time. Since the galilean transformation embodies earlier concepts of space-time, the pre-Einstein ideas of relative motion and relativity theory are often referred to as *galilean relativity.* We shall be discussing galilean relativity and problems associated with it in this section.

If we use the galilean transformation to connect inertial reference frames in relative motion, how do the laws of nature (as we have stated them so far) transform? Is Newton's second law, for example, in accord with the principle of relativity? Consider the acceleration component, $a_x = du_x/dt$, of a particle relative to an observer O. In the reference frame of observer O', moving with constant speed v relative to O, the acceleration component of the particle is $a'_x = du'_x/dt'$. Using the galilean transformation and Eq. (38-3), we have (note that $d/dt' = d/dt$ if $t' = t$)

$$a'_x = \frac{du'_x}{dt'} = \frac{d(u_x - v)}{dt} = \frac{du_x}{dt} = a_x$$

where $dv/dt = 0$ since v is the constant relative speed of the two observers. Thus the acceleration of a particle is invariant, $a'_x = a_x$, under a galilean transformation. If we assume that the mass of the particle is invariant, $m' = m$, then the product of mass and acceleration is also invariant: $m'a'_x = ma_x$. Suppose further that the net force component is the same in both frames, $\Sigma F'_x = \Sigma F_x$. (See Exercise 38-9.) Then, on combining the last pair of equalities, we find that if $\Sigma F'_x = m'a'_x$ is satisfied for observer O', then $\Sigma F_x = ma_x$ is satisfied for observer

Principle of relativity

Galilean relativity

O. That is, Newton's second law has the same form in all inertial reference frames connected by galilean transformations and is in accord with the principle of relativity.

A problem arises, however, when we turn to Maxwell's equations, the laws of electromagnetism. As we saw in Chap. 34, Maxwell's equations in vacuum have wave solutions which we interpret as light. The waves travel with speed $c = (\mu_0 \epsilon_0)^{-1/2}$, the speed of light in vacuum. These wave solutions and the value of their speed c come from the equations solved in *any* inertial reference frame. Therein lies a conflict in galilean relativity between electromagnetism and the galilean transformation. In the reference frame of observer O, the velocity component of a light wave in vacuum, propagating in the positive x direction, is $u_x = c$, the value obtained by solving Maxwell's equations in this frame. In the reference frame of observer O', related by the galilean transformation to the frame of O, the velocity component of the light is given by Eq. (38-3), $u_x' = c - v$. In contradiction, the wave solution of Maxwell's equations in this (and any) frame has velocity component $u_x' = c$.

One proposed resolution of the conflict was to regard light waves as propagating in a medium, and the name given to this supposed medium was *ether*, or *aether*. Light waves were assumed to propagate in this ether similar to the way mechanical waves propagate in a mechanical medium. In the wave equation that describes mechanical waves, the wave speed is the speed relative to the medium. So it was thought that Maxwell's equations were valid only in the *rest frame* of the ether, a reference frame in which the ether was at rest. The speed of light in vacuum, $c = (\mu_0 \epsilon_0)^{-1/2}$, was the speed in the rest frame of the ether. (The ether supposedly permeated all of space.) In another reference frame, moving with speed v relative to the ether, the velocity of light was determined by the galilean transformation connecting this frame with the rest frame of the ether.

The Michelson-Morley experiment. The ether concept was widely accepted, in spite of serious objections, until an experiment, performed in 1887 by A. A. Michelson (1852–1931) and E. W. Morley (1838–1923), cast doubt on the whole idea. Michelson and Morley reasoned that, in its orbital motion about the sun, the earth must be moving through the ether. Since the speed of light (measured on the earth) would depend on its direction of propagation relative to the direction of the earth's velocity through the ether, an experiment should determine how the earth moved through the ether.

The experiment utilized Michelson's interferometer (Sec. 36-7) in an attempt to detect phase shifts. These phase shifts were expected because of the dependence on direction of the speed of light in the earth frame. (See Exercise 38-11 and Prob. 38-1 for some details about the experiment.) Under a variety of conditions and during different times in the year, no phase shift was observed. Although this null result was puzzling at the time, we now recognize the implication of the Michelson-Morley experiment: *The speed of light in vacuum is the same in all inertial reference frames. That is, the speed of light in vacuum is an invariant.*

The speed of light in vacuum is invariant.

Our modern interpretation of the Michelson-Morley experiment removes the need for the ether concept. The ether helped to explain how light could have different speeds in different reference frames. But light does not have different speeds; its speed in vacuum is the same in all inertial frames.

This "constancy" of the speed of light in different frames is devastating to galilean relativity. The speed of light is invariant, in contradiction to the galilean velocity-transformation formula of Eq. (38-3). We conclude that the galilean transformation and our ideas of space and time contained in the transformation are incorrect. It is important to note that the galilean transformation, although incorrect, does provide an adequate account of our everyday experience. It is only when high speeds are involved that the unusual or strange features of space and time are noticeable. But when they are noticeable, they can be jarringly so, as the following anecdotal example illustrates.

EXAMPLE 38-2. A spaceship moves on a straight path past the earth at speed $v = 2 \times 10^8$ m/s. An earth-based observer directs a laser beam (light) along a parallel path and measures the speed of the light in the beam to be $u_x = c = 3 \times 10^8$ m/s. What is the speed of this beam of light as measured by an observer on the spaceship?

SOLUTION. Since the speed of light in vacuum is invariant, the observer in the spaceship measures the speed of this same beam of light to be $u'_x = c = 3 \times 10^8$ m/s, the same as the earth-based observer. Notice that if Eq. (38-3) were applied to this case, the result (1×10^8 m/s) would be grossly incorrect.

38-4 THE LORENTZ TRANSFORMATION

In 1905 Albert Einstein proposed a new view of space-time and a new theory of relativity which we now call the *special theory of relativity*. It is special, or restricted, in the sense that it deals only with inertial reference frames and does not deal with gravitation. More general reference frames and the connection with gravity are considered in the *general theory of relativity*, which is described in the Commentary in this chapter.

Einstein developed the special theory from two postulates which we state below. The first postulate is the principle of relativity, which presumably has a place in any meaningful physical theory. The second postulate formally acknowledges the invariance of the speed of light in vacuum. (It is not clear whether Einstein knew of the Michelson-Morley experiment. He likely was led to the second postulate on the basis of his belief in the correctness of Maxwell's equations.)

Postulates of the special theory of relativity

> Postulate I. The laws of nature have the same mathematical form in all inertial reference frames.
> Postulate II. The speed of light in vacuum is the same for all inertial reference frames.

The first task in developing the special theory is to determine the transformation connecting inertial reference frames in relative motion. This transformation replaces the galilean transformation, which is incorrect. We can be guided, however, by some features of the galilean transformation since it is adequate at low speeds. In particular, the correct transformation equations must reduce to the galilean transformation in the limit of low speeds.

We consider for simplicity only the transformation connecting two reference frames in relative motion along the xx' axes with constant speed v. Again we assume that observers O and O' associated with these reference frames set $t = t' = 0$ at the instant that the two coordinate systems coincide. The relationship later is shown in Fig. 38-4 (from the perspective of observer O). Each observer assigns space-time coordinates to events. Observer O assigns the set (x, y, z, t) to an event, and O' similarly assigns the set (x', y', z', t') to the same event. We seek the transformation connecting these sets for any event.

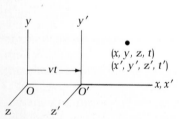

Figure 38-4. Two observers in uniform relative motion observe an event. This view is from the perspective of observer O.

Since we assume that space-time is homogeneous and that there is a one-to-one correspondence of events for the observers, we consider only linear transformations. The origin of O' moves along the positive x axis with speed v relative to O, so that the equation for x' in terms of the unprimed quantities must be proportional to $x - vt$. In this way an event that occurs at $x' = 0$, the origin in the primed frame, occurs at $x = vt$ in the unprimed frame. Thus this transformation equation can be written in the form

$$x' = \gamma(x - vt) \tag{38-4}$$

where γ is independent of the space-time coordinates of the event.

An equation similar to Eq. (38-4) must hold for x expressed in terms of x' and t'. It is

$$x = \gamma(x' + vt') \tag{38-5}$$

The positive sign between x' and vt' corresponds to the origin of O moving along the negative x' axis with speed v relative to O'. The quantity γ must be the same in the two equations above. Consistent with the principle of relativity, we must not be able to single out one observer in favor of the other. All inertial observers have equally valid descriptions of nature. The value of γ does not characterize either observer but relates this pair of observers.

As with the galilean transformation, the primed and unprimed coordinates should be the same for axes perpendicular to the direction of the relative motion of the frames. This corresponds to the homogeneity and isotropy of space. For the case illustrated in Fig. 38-4, we have

$$y' = y$$
$$z' = z \tag{38-6}$$

The remaining ingredient in the transformation involves time. What is the equation connecting t and t' for an event? It *cannot* be the galilean result $t' = t$. That would lead directly back to the galilean transformation. (See Exercise 38-15.) The form of the equation can be obtained by combining Eqs. (38-4) and (38-5). We substitute the expression in Eq. (38-4) for x' in Eq. (38-5) to obtain

$$x = \gamma[\gamma(x - vt) + vt']$$

and solve for t' in terms of t and x. The result is

$$t' = \gamma\left(t - \frac{\gamma^2 - 1}{\gamma^2 v}x\right) \tag{38-7}$$

The set of four equations in Eqs. (38-4), (38-6) and (38-7) gives the form of the transformation connecting the reference frames of observers O and O'. The equations contain the quantity γ which is yet to be determined. Its value must be consistent with postulate II: Both observers agree on the value of c, the speed of light in vacuum. Consider the following pair of events, which constitute a speed-of-light measurement:

1. At $t = t' = 0$ when the coordinate systems coincide, a pulse of light is emitted from a point source at the common origin. [If the space-time coordinates of this event are $(0, 0, 0, 0)$ for observer O, what are they for observer O'?] The light propagates in vacuum.

2. The light pulse enters a detector located on the xx' axes. This event occurs at $(x, 0, 0, t)$ for observer O and at $(x', 0, 0, t')$ for observer O', as shown in Fig.

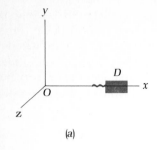

(a)

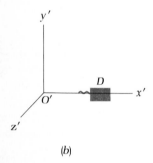

(b)

Figure 38-5. A light pulse enters a detector D, as seen in the reference frame of (a) observer O and (b) observer O'.

Lorentz transformation

38-5. Since the speed of light in vacuum is the same for both observers, we have $x = ct$ and $x' = ct'$.

We substitute these expressions for x and x' in Eqs. (38-4) and (38-7), which results in

$$ct' = \gamma(ct - vt)$$

and

$$t' = \gamma\left(t - \frac{\gamma^2 - 1}{\gamma^2 v}ct\right)$$

Dividing one of these equations by the other eliminates both t and t', and we can solve for γ^2 (Exercise 38-16):

$$\gamma^2 = \frac{1}{1 - v^2/c^2}$$

On taking the positive square root (so that positive x and positive x' correspond to the same direction), we have

$$\gamma = \frac{1}{\sqrt{1 - v^2/c^2}} \tag{38-8}$$

From the above expression for γ^2, we can express the factor that appears in Eq. (38-7) in terms of v and c: $(\gamma^2 - 1)/\gamma^2 v = v/c^2$.

We have now determined the transformation connecting the observers O and O'. The equations, solved for the primed space-time coordinates in terms of the unprimed ones, are

$$x' = \frac{x - vt}{\sqrt{1 - v^2/c^2}}$$

$$y' = y$$

$$z' = z \tag{38-9}$$

$$t' = \frac{t - vx/c^2}{\sqrt{1 - v^2/c^2}}$$

This type of transformation is called a *Lorentz transformation*. The name honors H. A. Lorentz (see the Lorentz force in Sec. 26-5), who tried to explain the null result of the Michelson-Morley experiment in terms of a contraction of lengths by the factor $\sqrt{1 - v^2/c^2}$. But it was Einstein who first obtained this transformation from the postulates of special relativity.

The transformation equations can also be solved the other way, expressing the unprimed quantities in terms of the primed ones. You should do the algebra (Exercise 38-17) to obtain

$$x = \frac{x' + vt'}{\sqrt{1 - v^2/c^2}}$$

$$y = y'$$

$$z = z'$$

$$t = \frac{t' + vx'/c^2}{\sqrt{1 - v^2/c^2}}$$

More simply, the result can be obtained from Eqs. (38-9) by interchanging the primed and unprimed quantities and changing the (−) sign in front of the vt and vx/c^2 terms to a (+). This change of sign corresponds to the observers describing each other as moving in opposite directions.

Since the transformation equations containing x, t, x', and t' are lengthy, we often write them using the factor γ from Eq. (38-8). Thus the first and the last equations in the Lorentz transformation above can be written

$$x' = \gamma(x - vt)$$
$$t' = \gamma\left(t - \frac{vx}{c^2}\right) \quad \text{with} \quad \gamma = \frac{1}{\sqrt{1 - v^2/c^2}}$$

In the last section we arrived at the galilean transformation by using our (incorrect) views of space and time. In this section we obtained the Lorentz transformation by more formal and abstract means, by appealing to Einstein's postulates of special relativity. Equipped with the Lorentz transformation, we are now able to discover the nature of space and time as revealed by special relativity.

38-5 A NEW VIEW OF SPACE AND TIME

It is a remarkable fact that the speed of light in vacuum is independent of the relative motions of inertial reference frames in which the speed is measured. Two observers measuring the speed of light obtain the same value even though they may be moving relative to each other at a high speed. Are there other features of space-time that seem counter to our ordinary experience? What modifications in our everyday view of space and time are required in order to understand these features? To broaden our knowledge of space and time, we shall apply the Lorentz transformation to interpret some simple sets of events.

An inspection of the Lorentz transformation equations

$$x' = \gamma(x - vt)$$
$$y' = y$$
$$z' = z \tag{38-9'}$$
$$t' = \gamma\left(t - \frac{vx}{c^2}\right)$$

shows that we must alter the concept of an absolute or universal time, independent of the concept of space. Notice from the last equation that the value of the time t' assigned to an event by observer O' depends not only on the time t but also on the coordinate x assigned to the event by observer O. Thus we cannot draw a sharp distinction between space and time as separate concepts. Instead of three spatial coordinates (x, y, z) and a separate time (t) characterizing an event, there are four space-time coordinates (x, y, z, t) that are "mixed up" by a Lorentz transformation. In a mathematical way, time can be treated somewhat as if it were a fourth spatial coordinate. For this reason time is sometimes popularly referred to as the "fourth dimension."

Time as a "fourth dimension"

It is important to understand how the factor $\gamma = 1/\sqrt{1 - v^2/c^2}$ in the Lorentz transformation equations depends on v, the relative speed of the two observers. This dependence is shown graphically in Fig. 38-6. If the relative speed v is small, $v/c \ll 1$, then $\gamma \approx 1$. For example, if $v = 0.001c$, then $\gamma =$

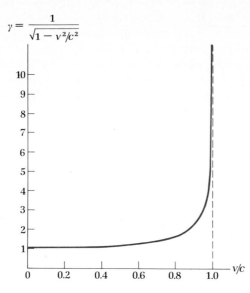

$$\gamma = \frac{1}{\sqrt{1 - v^2/c^2}}$$

Figure 38-6. At low speeds, the factor $\gamma \approx 1$. As $v \to c$, the value of γ increases without bound.

$1/\sqrt{1 - 0.001^2} = 1.0000005$. For increasing values of v, γ also increases. If $v = 0.70c$, then $\gamma = 1.4$; if $v = 0.99c$, then $\gamma = 7.1$. As v approaches c, the value of γ increases without bound.

The mixing of space and time is not apparent for transformations between reference frames with a low relative speed, $v \ll c$. Consider the time interval Δt between two events which are nearby for observer O so that the separation Δx is not large. From the Lorentz transformation, the time interval $\Delta t'$ between the events for observer O' is

$$\Delta t' = \gamma \left(\Delta t - \frac{v \, \Delta x}{c^2} \right)$$

If the relative speed is small compared with the speed of light, then $v/c \ll 1$ and $\gamma \approx 1$. Further, the term $v \, \Delta x/c^2 \ll \Delta t$. In this case the time-interval transformation equation becomes $\Delta t' \approx \Delta t$. That is, the observers agree on the time interval between the events. A similar analysis can be applied to the Lorentz transformation in Eqs. (38-9'). You should be able to show (Exercise 38-20) that the Lorentz transformation connecting reference frames can be approximated by the galilean transformation in the limit of a low relative speed, $v \ll c$.

Lorentz transformation approaches galilean transformation if $v \ll c$.

Simultaneity. In galilean relativity, time was considered to be absolute, the same for all observers ($t' = t$). If two events occurred at the same time, that is, simultaneously, in one reference frame, it was assumed that the two events would be simultaneous in all reference frames. The Lorentz transformation shows that this idea of absolute simultaneity is not valid. (See also Ques. 38-8.) Suppose that two events occur simultaneously in the reference frame of observer O. For example, a radioactive nucleus decays at (x_1, y_1, z_1, t_1) and a pair of molecules collide at (x_2, y_2, z_2, t_2), with $t_2 = t_1$. The time interval $\Delta t = t_2 - t_1$ being zero means that the events are simultaneous in this reference frame.

Are these events simultaneous in the reference frame of observer O', moving with speed v relative to O? We use the Lorentz transformation to determine the time interval $\Delta t' = t'_2 - t'_1$:

$$\Delta t' = \gamma \left[(t_2 - t_1) - \frac{v(x_2 - x_1)}{c^2} \right] = \gamma \left(0 - \frac{v \, \Delta x}{c^2} \right)$$

$$= -\frac{\gamma v \, \Delta x}{c^2}$$

where $\Delta x = x_2 - x_1$ is the separation in x of the events according to observer O. Since $\Delta t'$ is different from zero (because $\Delta x \neq 0$), these two events are not simultaneous for observer O'. We see that events that are simultaneous for one observer O are *not* generally simultaneous for another observer O'. Thus *simultaneity is relative to the observer*. This lack of agreement on events being simultaneous has consequences for the comparisons of lengths and of time intervals by different observers.

Time dilation. Suppose two observers in relative motion compare the periods of the clocks that they use in their measurements. Figure 38-7 shows the essential features of a special type of clock that uses the speed of light in its operation, which makes the analysis simple. The period of the clock is determined by the time for light to travel (in vacuum) from a source S to a detector D next to the source. A light pulse emitted by the source reflects from a mirror M that is a fixed distance L from both S and D. The reception of the light pulse by the detector triggers the emission of another light pulse and the process repeats. Suppose the clock is at rest relative to O', as seen in Fig. 38-7a. The round-trip distance traveled by the light from S to D is $2L = c \, \Delta t'$, or the period of the clock according to O' is

$$\Delta t' = \frac{2L}{c}$$

According to the other observer, the clock is moving with speed v, as seen in Fig. 38-7b. The light travels from S to M along a path of length $c \, (\frac{1}{2}\Delta t) = \sqrt{L^2 + v^2(\frac{1}{2}\Delta t)^2}$, and an equal distance on the return to D. Squaring this expression and solving for Δt, the period of the moving clock according to observer O, we obtain

$$\Delta t = \frac{2L}{\sqrt{c^2 - v^2}}$$

We directly compare the periods $\Delta t'$ and Δt by forming the ratio $\Delta t/\Delta t'$ from the two expressions above. The result is $\Delta t/\Delta t' = c/\sqrt{c^2 - v^2}$, or

$$\Delta t = \frac{\Delta t'}{\sqrt{1 - v^2/c^2}}$$

The two observers disagree on the period of this clock!

The dependence of the period of a clock on its motion relative to an observer is a general feature of space-time; it is not a property of a specific type of clock, such as the one described above. To see this, suppose that the two observers use clocks that are identically constructed and that have the same period when at rest together. How do the periods compare if they are in relative motion?

While the clock mechanism is not important, we suppose that a device is attached to a clock that emits a flash of light at regular intervals, say at each "tick" of the clock. Then the period of the clock is just the time interval between flashes, which is easily measurable. We concentrate on flashes from the clock used by observer O'. This clock is at rest according to O', as illustrated in Fig. 38-8a, and this reference frame is called the *rest frame* of this clock. The period in this frame is denoted by $T'_0 = t'_2 - t'_1$, where the subscript on T'_0 indicates the value measured in the rest frame. In the reference frame of

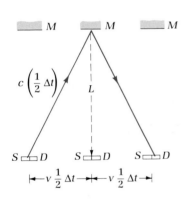

(a)

(b)

Figure 38-7. (a) A light pulse is emitted by source S, reflected by mirror M, and detected by detector D. As viewed in the rest frame of the clock by observer O', the time interval between emission and detection is such that $2L = c \, \Delta t'$. (b) For observer O, the clock is moving with speed v and $\sqrt{L^2 + v^2(\frac{1}{2}\Delta t)^2} = c(\frac{1}{2}\Delta t)$.

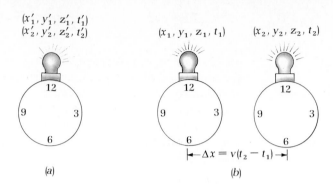

Figure 38-8. A light on clock flashes at each "tick." (a) Observer O' is in the rest frame of the clock. Two ticks occur at the same place, and the period of the clock is $T'_0 = t'_2 - t'_1$. (b) The clock moves with speed v relative to observer O, and the period of the moving clock is $t_2 - t_1$.

observer O, this clock (belonging to O') is moving. The time interval between flashes as measured by O is $T = t_2 - t_1$. The flashes from the moving clock occur at different positions in this reference frame, as shown in Fig. 38-8b. Since the clock is moving in the positive x direction, with speed v, the spatial separation of the events is $\Delta x = x_2 - x_1 = v(t_2 - t_1) = vT$.

We substitute these results into the last equation in the Lorentz transformation of Eqs. (38-9'):

$$T'_0 = t'_2 - t'_1 = \gamma \left[(t_2 - t_1) - \frac{v(x_2 - x_1)}{c^2} \right]$$

$$= \gamma \left[T - \frac{v(vT)}{c^2} \right] = T\gamma \left(1 - \frac{v^2}{c^2} \right)$$

$$= T \sqrt{1 - \frac{v^2}{c^2}}$$

since $\gamma = 1/\sqrt{1 - v^2/c^2}$. Solving for T, we obtain the time interval between flashes from the moving clock:

$$T = \frac{T'_0}{\sqrt{1 - v^2/c^2}} = \gamma T'_0 \tag{38-10}$$

Since the factor γ is greater than 1, the time interval T is greater than the time interval T'_0 in the rest frame of the clock. The interpretation of this result by observer O is that the moving clock is running slow. For example, suppose that T'_0 is 1 s. That is, the clock "ticks" once each second in its rest frame. But according to observer O, the time interval between the "ticks" of this *moving* clock is greater than 1 s. If $v = 0.600c$, then $\gamma = 1.25$ and $T = 1.25$ s. That is, the moving clock runs slow. This effect, the "stretching out" of time for a moving clock, is called *time dilation*.

Time dilation: Moving clocks run slow.

Our analysis of time dilation is independent of the mechanism of the clock. All physical processes in a moving system run at a slower rate. The biological clocks associated with the aging process should be no exception. See Prob. 38-3 for a discussion of the intriguing "twin paradox."

EXAMPLE 38-3. The *muon* is an elementary particle similar to the electron. It is unstable and spontaneously disintegrates or decays, with a characteristic mean lifetime of 2.2 μs in its rest frame. High-speed muons are created by cosmic rays in the upper atmosphere. Determine the mean lifetime of muons with speed $v = 0.99c$.

SOLUTION. Let a muon be at rest relative to observer O'; then $T'_0 = 2.2$ μs. Since $\sqrt{1 - v^2/c^2} = \sqrt{1 - (0.99)^2} = 0.14$, we have $T = (2.2 \ \mu s)/0.14 = 16 \ \mu s$ from Eq. (38-10). The observed increase in the lifetime of high-speed muons produced by cosmic rays was one of the first tests of time dilation.

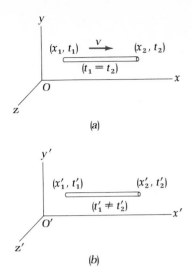

(a)

(b)

Figure 38-9. Events that occur at the ends of a rod are used to measure the length of (a) a moving rod and (b) the rod in its rest frame.

Length contraction. To measure a length, an observer compares the spatial interval between two endpoints with a standard such as a meter stick. It is straightforward to measure the length of an object in its rest frame, the reference frame in which the object is at rest. Suppose an object such as a rod is at rest in the reference frame of O' and that the length of the rod is parallel to the x' axis so that y' and z' are not needed. The position of one end is observed [event 1 at (x_1', t_1')], as is the position of the other end [event 2 at (x_2', t_2')]. Then the length $L_0' = x_2' - x_1'$ is obtained by laying off the distance with the meter stick. The subscript on L_0' indicates the result of a measurement in the rest frame.

Measuring the length of an object that is moving is not so straightforward. Relative to observer O, the rod and the reference frame of O' are moving along the positive x axis with speed v. How does observer O determine the length of the rod? One method, outlined in Exercise 38-26, involves the measurement of a time interval and makes use of time dilation. Another procedure, illustrated in Fig. 38-9, is to determine *simultaneously* (in the reference frame of observer O) the endpoints x_1 and x_2 of the object. The length of the moving rod is the distance between its simultaneously observed endpoints, $L = x_2 - x_1$. How do L and L_0' compare? Using the first equation in the Lorentz transformation, we have

$$L_0' = x_2' - x_1' = \gamma[(x_2 - x_1) - v(t_2 - t_1)]$$

The ends were observed simultaneously by O so that $t_2 - t_1 = 0$. Thus

$$L_0' = \gamma(x_2 - x_1) = \gamma L = \frac{L}{\sqrt{1 - v^2/c^2}}$$

Solving for L, the length of the moving rod in the direction of its velocity, we have

$$L = L_0' \sqrt{1 - \frac{v^2}{c^2}} = \frac{L_0'}{\gamma} \tag{38-11}$$

Length contraction: The length of a moving object is shortened.

The length of a moving object, in the direction of its motion, is obtained by dividing its rest length L_0' by γ. Since $\gamma > 1$, we see that $L < L_0'$. For example, if $v = 0.600c$, then $\gamma = 1.25$ and $L = L_0'/1.25$. There is a shortening, or *contraction*, of the length of an object in the direction of its motion. For a larger speed of the object, the factor γ is also larger, and the more contracted is the length. The analysis applies to the measurement by observer O of the length of any moving object, including the meter stick of observer O'.

Observer O' disagrees with the measurements performed by observer O. Suppose that the roles of the two observers are reversed so that O' measures the length of a moving object, an object at rest relative to observer O. The result (see Exercise 38-25) is that the length L' of the moving object is contracted from its rest length L_0 by the factor $\sqrt{1 - v^2/c^2}$—that is, $L' = L_0\sqrt{1 - v^2/c^2} = L_0/\gamma$. Thus each observer concludes that the length of a moving object is contracted.

EXAMPLE 38-4. A superfast train, of rest length 1200 m, passes through an enclosed station. According to the stationmaster, the length of the station is 900 m and the train just fits into the station as it passes. That is, the stationmaster observes the train's back end just inside the entrance at the same time that its front end is just inside the exit. (See Fig.

38-10.) What is the speed of the train?

SOLUTION. To fit into the 900-m station, the train's moving length L must be 900 m. From Eq. (38-11), we have

$$900 \text{ m} = 1200 \text{ m} \sqrt{1 - \frac{v^2}{c^2}}$$

so that

$$1 - \frac{v^2}{c^2} = \left(\frac{900}{1200}\right)^2$$

Then

$$v = c\sqrt{1 - (\tfrac{9}{12})^2} = 2 \times 10^8 \text{ m/s}$$

What is the length of the station according to the conductor on the train?

Obviously, a train cannot travel at such a high speed relative to the stationmaster. Suppose that the train were almost

supersonic: $v = 300$ m/s. What would be its contracted length?

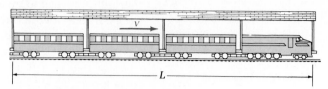

Figure 38-10. Example 38-4: Relative to the stationmaster, a moving train just fits into a station of length L.

38-6 THE ADDITION OF VELOCITIES

Although it is adequate for low speeds, the galilean formula for combining velocities, Eq. (38-3), is not correct for high speeds. Using the Lorentz transformation, we must reconsider the transformation of velocity components. Let events 1 and 2 correspond to observations of the position of a particle. The x component of the velocity of the particle according to observer O is $u_x = \Delta x/\Delta t = (x_2 - x_1)/(t_2 - t_1)$. Similarly, observer O' expresses the x' component of the velocity of the particle as $u'_x = (x'_2 - x'_1)/(t'_2 - t'_1)$. We transform the numerator and denominator using the first and last equations of the Lorentz transformation in Eqs. (38-9'):

$$u'_x = \frac{\gamma[(x_2 - x_1) - v(t_2 - t_1)]}{\gamma[(t_2 - t_1) - v(x_2 - x_1)/c^2]}$$

Dividing numerator and denominator by $t_2 - t_1$ and canceling the common factor γ, we have

$$u'_x = \frac{(x_2 - x_1)/(t_2 - t_1) - v}{1 - (v/c^2)[(x_2 - x_1)/(t_2 - t_1)]}$$

Since $u_x = (x_2 - x_1)/(t_2 - t_1)$, we obtain

Lorentz velocity transformation

$$u'_x = \frac{u_x - v}{1 - vu_x/c^2} \tag{38-12}$$

This *Lorentz velocity transformation* replaces the galilean result. In the limit of low speeds, $|vu_x/c^2| \ll 1$, the denominator in Eq. (38-12) approaches 1, and the galilean formula, $u'_x = u_x - v$, is recovered.

The transformation for the other components of the velocity of a particle can be obtained by a procedure similar to that above (see Exercise 38-29):

$$u'_y = \frac{u_y\sqrt{1 - v^2/c^2}}{1 - vu_x/c^2}$$

$$u'_z = \frac{u_z\sqrt{1 - v^2/c^2}}{1 - vu_x/c^2}$$

The transformation equations can also be solved for the unprimed velocity components. For example, Eq. (38-12) can be rearranged to give

$$u_x = \frac{u'_x + v}{1 + vu'_x/c^2} \tag{38-13}$$

The mathematical structure of these velocity-transformation equations results in an important feature. If one observer, say O', determines the speed of an object to be less than the speed of light c, then the other observer O also determines the speed of that object to be less than c. The two observers do not agree on the value of the object's speed, but each finds the speed to be less than c. This result is one of many indications that the speed of light in vacuum is an upper limit on speeds. There has been no observation of an object with a speed that exceeds c. In this sense the speed of light in vacuum is the ultimate speed.

The speed of light in vacuum is the ultimate speed.

EXAMPLE 38-5. Observers in separate spaceships have relative speed $v = 2.4 \times 10^8$ m/s. Observer O' fires a space torpedo forward, as shown in Fig. 38-11, and measures its speed to be 1.8×10^8 m/s. (a) Determine the speed of the torpedo according to observer O. (b) Suppose O' fires a laser beam (light) forward instead of a torpedo. What is the speed of the light according to observer O?

SOLUTION. (a) We use Eq. (38-13) to determine the velocity component u_x of the torpedo according to observer O (notice that $u'_x = 1.8 \times 10^8$ m/s):

$$u_x = \frac{(1.8 \times 10^8 \text{ m/s}) + (2.4 \times 10^8 \text{ m/s})}{1 + (2.4 \times 10^8 \text{ m/s})(1.8 \times 10^8 \text{ m/s})/c^2}$$

$$= \frac{4.2 \times 10^8 \text{ m/s}}{1 + (4.32 \times 10^{16})/(9.0 \times 10^{16})} = 2.8 \times 10^8 \text{ m/s}$$

The speed of the torpedo according to O is less than c. (The galilean formula would have incorrectly given the speed of the torpedo according to O to be greater than c.)

(b) Since the light has speed c according to O', we have $u'_x = c$. Substituting into Eq. (38-13) gives

$$u_x = \frac{c + v}{1 + vc/c^2} = \frac{c(1 + v/c)}{1 + v/c} = c$$

Observer O also determines the speed of light to be c. We should have expected this result because the Lorentz transformation was designed so that the speed of light in vacuum is invariant.

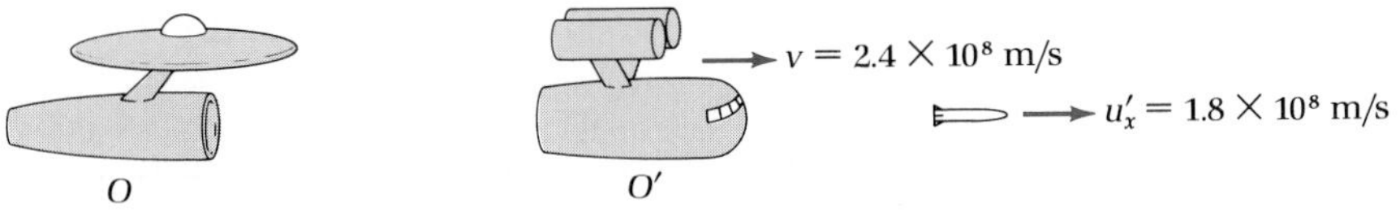

$v = 2.4 \times 10^8$ m/s

$u'_x = 1.8 \times 10^8$ m/s

O

O'

Figure 38-11. Example 38-5: Observer O', moving with speed v relative to observer O, fires a torpedo forward with speed $|u'_x|$.

38-7 MOMENTUM AND ENERGY

In everyday life we do not see relativistic effects such as length contraction or time dilation. The ordinary-sized objects around us do not move rapidly enough for the effects to be observable. Nor have we been in contact with another observer moving relative to us at a speed which is a significant fraction of the speed of light. Objects that do travel at speeds comparable to the speed of light are particles of atomic and subatomic sizes. For example, electrons in a television picture tube are accelerated to speeds of around $\frac{1}{2}c$. In dealing with such particles, our emphasis is usually placed on momentum and energy.

Along with revising our notions of space and time, we must modify the definitions of some dynamical quantities, if these are to be useful. To be useful concepts, momentum and energy should be defined such that they are conserved for an isolated system. In a collision of two particles for example, the momentum gained by one particle should equal the momentum lost by the other particle. Further, the modified definition of momentum should reduce to our original definition, $\mathbf{p} = m\mathbf{v}$, for $v \ll c$.

Consider a particle of mass m with velocity $\mathbf{v}$ in some reference frame. The modified definition of the momentum $\mathbf{p}$ of the particle is

Definition of momentum

$$\mathbf{p} = \frac{m\mathbf{v}}{\sqrt{1 - v^2/c^2}} = \gamma m\mathbf{v} \tag{38-14}$$

With this definition, momentum is conserved, in every inertial reference frame, in collisions between particles. Notice that the speed $v = |\mathbf{v}|$ that appears in the square root is the speed of the particle. If the speed is small compared with the speed of light, then $\gamma = 1/\sqrt{1 - v^2/c^2} \approx 1$, and the old definition of momentum, $\mathbf{p} = m\mathbf{v}$, is obtained. However, as the speed v approaches the speed of light, the square root approaches zero and the magnitude of the momentum increases without bound. This suggests that no particle can be accelerated to the speed of light. Its momentum change would be infinite in magnitude and that is not possible. The mass m of the particle is sometimes called its *rest mass*. It is the particle's mass in the rest frame of the particle —

Rest mass of a particle

that is, in a frame for which the particle is at rest.

We must also reconsider energy and its conservation. In accounting for the conservation of energy, we must include every form of energy that is changing in a system. Einstein showed that there is a form of energy associated with mass and defined the *total energy E* of a particle of mass m and speed v to be

Total energy of a particle

$$E = \frac{mc^2}{\sqrt{1 - v^2/c^2}} = \gamma mc^2 \tag{38-15}$$

This definition of the total energy of a particle results in the conservation of energy for an isolated system. (The term "total energy of a particle" does not include potential energy, which must be added in separately.)

Rest-mass energy, $E = mc^2$

Notice from Eq. (38-15) that the total energy of the particle is not zero if the particle is at rest. Setting $v = 0$ results in $E = mc^2$. This is the energy of a particle when it is at rest, and it is called the *rest-mass energy* of the particle. There are instances when the sum of the rest masses for an isolated system changes. The change Δm may be positive or negative as a result of energy transformations that are occurring in the system. The change in mass energy, $\Delta E = \Delta mc^2$, is balanced by changes in other types of energy so that the total energy of the system is conserved. This inclusion of rest-mass energy into the

Conservation of mass-energy

total energy balance generalizes the law of conservation of energy. Often this generalized form is called the *law of conservation of mass-energy*. The conversion of mass energy to other forms in nuclear fusion and fission processes has had political, economic, and military consequences that are controversial and well publicized.

If a system is not isolated, then its energy changes by the amount ΔE added to or taken from it. If we use the expression $\Delta E = \Delta mc^2$, then $\Delta m = \Delta E/c^2$ is

Equivalence of mass and energy, $\Delta m = \Delta E/c^2$

interpreted as the change in the mass of the system. That is, *energy added to a system is equivalent to increasing the inertial mass of the system*. This result is often expressed as *the equivalence of mass and energy*.

The rest-mass energy mc^2 is the total energy of a particle at rest. When the particle is moving, its total energy is larger. The additional energy that a particle has because it is moving is defined to be the *kinetic energy K* of the particle. Subtracting mc^2 from the total energy of a particle in Eq. (38-15) gives the modified definition of the kinetic energy of a particle, $K = E - mc^2$, or

Definition of kinetic energy

$$K = mc^2 \left(\frac{1}{\sqrt{1 - v^2/c^2}} - 1 \right) = (\gamma - 1)mc^2 \tag{38-16}$$

This same expression for kinetic energy is obtained by calculating the work done on the particle by the net force. (See Prob. 38-9.) At low speeds ($v/c \ll 1$), the term $\gamma = 1/\sqrt{1 - v^2/c^2} \approx 1 + \frac{1}{2}v^2/c^2$ (see App. M) and $K \approx \frac{1}{2}mv^2$. Only at low speeds is the kinetic-energy formula $\frac{1}{2}mv^2$ valid. As the speed of the particle approaches the speed of light, the square root in Eq. (38-16) approaches zero and the kinetic energy increases without bound. Again we see that no particle can have its speed increased to the speed of light. The particle would have gained an infinite kinetic energy and this is not possible.

Often it is useful to have an expression connecting the total energy E of a particle with the magnitude p of its momentum. Exercise 38-36 and Prob. 38-6 suggest different ways to obtain the following result:

$$E = \sqrt{p^2c^2 + m^2c^4} \tag{38-17}$$

Note that if the particle is at rest, $p = 0$ and $E = mc^2$. At the other extreme, for a particle with $p \gg mc$, then $E \approx pc$. The relation $E = pc$ holds exactly for a photon, the quantum of electromagnetic radiation discussed in the next chapter, whose rest mass $m = 0$.

EXAMPLE 38-6. An electron in a dentist's x-ray tube is accelerated from rest through a potential difference of 2.0×10^5 V. (a) Determine the resulting speed of the electron. (b) What is the magnitude of the momentum of an electron with this speed?

SOLUTION. (a) In moving through a potential difference V, the electron gains kinetic energy due to the change in electric potential energy. Thus, $K = eV$ where e is the electronic charge. Solving Eq. (38-16) for the square root factor, we obtain

$$\sqrt{1 - \frac{v^2}{c^2}} = \frac{1}{1 + K/mc^2}$$

Squaring, rearranging, and solving for v gives

$$v = c\sqrt{1 - \frac{1}{(1 + K/mc^2)^2}}$$

The ratio

$$\frac{K}{mc^2} = \frac{eV}{mc^2} = \frac{(1.6 \times 10^{-19}\ \text{C})(2.0 \times 10^5\ \text{V})}{(9.1 \times 10^{-31}\ \text{kg})(3.0 \times 10^8\ \text{m/s})^2} = 0.39$$

Then

$$v = c\sqrt{1 - \frac{1}{(1 + 0.39)^2}} = 0.69c = 2.1 \times 10^8\ \text{m/s}$$

(b) Taking the magnitude of Eq. (38-14), the magnitude of the momentum is $p = mv/\sqrt{1 - v^2/c^2}$. Since $v = 0.69c$, the square root is $\sqrt{1 - v^2/c^2} = \sqrt{1 - 0.69^2} = 0.72$. Thus

$$p = \frac{(9.1 \times 10^{-31}\ \text{kg})(2.1 \times 10^8\ \text{m/s})}{0.72}$$

$$= 2.6 \times 10^{-22}\ \text{kg} \cdot \text{m/s}$$

EXAMPLE 38-7. In a nuclear-fusion reaction, a deuteron (^{2}H) of mass $m_d = 2.01355$ u and a triton (^{3}H) of mass $m_t = 3.01550$ u react to give a neutron (^{1}n) of mass $m_n = 1.00867$ u and an alpha particle (^{4}He) of mass 4.00150 u. Determine the mass-energy released in this fusion reaction. [The mass values are expressed in unified atomic mass units (u) defined so that the mass of ^{12}C is exactly 12.00000 u. For conversion to the SI unit of mass, 1 u = 1.66054×10^{-27} kg.]

SOLUTION. The rest mass of the system decreases

from $m_i = 2.01355$ u $+ 3.01550$ u $= 5.02905$ u to $m_f = 1.00867$ u $+ 4.00150$ u $= 5.01017$ u. The magnitude of the change (in kilograms) is

$$(5.02905\ \text{u} - 5.01017\ \text{u})(1.66054 \times 10^{-27}\ \text{kg/u})$$
$$= 3.135 \times 10^{-29}\ \text{kg}$$

The energy released in the fusion reaction is

$$|\Delta E| = |\Delta m|c^2 = (3.135 \times 10^{-29}\ \text{kg})(2.998 \times 10^8\ \text{m/s})^2$$

$$= 2.818 \times 10^{-12}\ \text{J} = 17.59\ \text{MeV}$$

COMMENTARY: GENERAL RELATIVITY

Einstein's special theory applied the principle of relativity to inertial reference frames. In 1916, about 10 years after the special theory was introduced, Einstein extended the theory to include noninertial reference frames as well. This gener-

In his early life, Albert Einstein, born in Germany in 1879, showed little promise of his later accomplishments. After an undistinguished academic performance, he took his first job in the Swiss patent office, where he developed four profound papers on brownian motion, the photoelectric effect, and the special theory of relativity. While not seeking fame or publicity, Einstein's name and features now have instant recognition. In this photograph, Einstein shows off his athletic prowess. *(California Institute Millikan Library)*

alization is called the general theory of relativity. *Since the mathematical structure of general relativity is too advanced for us to consider here, we shall instead discuss qualitatively some of the interesting aspects of space-time.*

A noninertial reference frame is accelerated relative to an inertial reference frame. As an example of a noninertial reference frame, consider an observer, Aaron, in an enclosed box that has a constant acceleration **a** *relative to an inertial frame. This situation is shown in Fig. 38-12a where, for simplicity, the box is imagined to be in intergalactic space where gravitational forces are negligible. Suppose Aaron drops a coin and watches it fall. He describes the coin as falling to the floor with a constant acceleration* −**a**.

The same kind of experiment is performed by Gloria in a similar box. As indicated in Fig. 38-12b, Gloria is in an inertial reference frame but in the presence of a uniform gravitational field **g**, *with* **g** = −**a**. *She drops a coin and describes it as falling with a constant acceleration* −**a**. *Gloria observes her coin falling in exactly the same way that Aaron observes his coin falling.*

Since the descriptions are identical, how can Gloria be sure that she is in an inertial reference frame with a gravitational field present? How can Aaron be sure that his reference frame is accelerated with no gravitational field present? A generalization of these ideas can be expressed as: No experiment performed locally (inside such a box) can distinguish between a constantly accelerated frame and an inertial frame in a uniform gravitational field. *This is a statement of the* principle of equivalence, *which is a postulate of the general theory of relativity.*

The principle of equivalence is related to the equivalence of inertial and gravitational mass *(Sec. 7-4). The inertial mass of an object, such as the released coin, determines its response to a force in the inertial reference frame, and the gravitational mass of the object determines its response to the uniform gravitational field. Since the motion is indistinguishable from the corresponding motion in the accelerated reference frame, the two types of mass are equivalent.*

The special theory of relativity caused us to merge separate concepts of space and time into a four-dimensional space-time. The general theory requires yet another change in our view of space-time, one in which gravity is reduced to geometry! Instead of a "flat" space-time, it is curved or warped in the vicinity of a mass. The curvature is in the four-dimensional space-time, and it cannot be easily visualized by three-dimensional creatures like us.

The distinction between a flat space and a curved space can be illustrated in two dimensions. The surface of a plane is flat, whereas the surface of a sphere is curved. These two-dimensional surfaces have very different geometries. For example, the shortest path between two points in a plane is a straight line. But on the surface of a sphere, the shortest path between two points is along a great

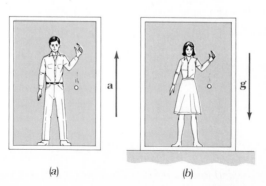

(a)   (b)

Figure 38-12. Measurements made inside the boxes cannot distinguish between (a) a uniformly accelerated reference frame and (b) a uniform gravitational field with **g** = −**a**.

circle. (A great circle *on a sphere has its center at the center of the sphere. Lines of longitude on a globe are great circles.)*

Imagine being a two-dimensional creature constrained to move on the surface of a spherical earth. You know left from right and forward from backward, but you have no concept of up and down. Suppose you take the shortest path connecting two points on the surface (from San Francisco to Hong Kong by ship, for example). Since you are always going forward, bearing neither to the right nor to the left, you may think that you are traveling in a straight line. But viewed in three dimensions, the path is along a great circle; it is curved.

General relativity treats gravitation as a curvature of space-time in four dimensions. The curvature is determined by the presence of mass. Gravity is explained in terms of geometry. Consider the motion of the earth about the sun. Because of its large mass, the sun distorts space-time in its vicinity. The earth moves along the shortest path between two points in the curved space-time, "bearing neither to the right nor to the left," as it were. In this view, no force acts on the earth; the distortion of space-time is gravity. Of course, we can only see things from our three-dimensional, "flat-space" perspective; we see the path taken by the earth as an ellipse.

The effects of the curvature of space-time are important near a large distribution of mass such as a massive star or in cosmological theories. The consequences are dramatic near a black hole, which is thought to be the last stage in the evolution of a massive star. A black hole is very compact, as if the mass of our sun were in a sphere of radius 2 km, 3×10^{-5} of its actual radius. At the surface of a black hole, the space-time is so distorted that light does not emerge from within — hence the name "black hole."

In everyday situations, however, such extreme general relativistic effects are not noticeable. The effect of the earth's gravity on you, for example, is adequately described by Newton's law of universal gravitation, which is a limiting case of the general theory of relativity.

SUMMARY WITH APPLICATIONS

Section 38-2. Transformations

A transformation connects observations in different reference frames. The galilean transformation,

$$x' = x - vt$$
$$y' = y$$
$$z' = z \qquad (38\text{-}2)$$
$$t' = t$$

which connects two inertial frames in relative motion with speed v, is adequate only for $v \ll c$. Velocity components in the direction of relative motion transform according to

$$u_x' = u_x - v \qquad (38\text{-}3)$$

where all speeds are small compared with c.

Transform velocity components using galilean relativity.

Section 38-3. The principle of relativity

The principle of relativity states that the laws of nature have the same form in all inertial reference frames. Maxwell's equations and the galilean transformation cannot both be in accord with the principle of relativity. The Michelson-Morley experiment showed that the speed of light in vacuum is independent of the motion of the earth.

State and discuss the ramifications of the principle of relativity; describe the conflict between the galilean transformation and Maxwell's equations; describe the result of the Michelson-Morley experiment and how it removed the necessity for the ether.

Section 38-4. The Lorentz transformation

Einstein's special theory of relativity is developed from two postulates:

  I. The principle of relativity.
 II. The speed of light in vacuum is the same for all inertial reference frames.

Observers in relative motion with speed v are connected by a Lorentz transformation,

$$x' = \gamma(x - vt)$$
$$y' = y$$
$$z' = z \qquad (38\text{-}9)$$
$$t' = \gamma\left(t - \frac{vx}{c^2}\right)$$

with $\gamma = 1/\sqrt{1 - v^2/c^2}$.

State and discuss the content of the postulates of the special theory of relativity; use a Lorentz transformation to transform space-time coordinates for events.

Section 38-5. A new view of space and time

Simultaneity is relative to the observer. Moving clocks run slow by the factor $\gamma = 1/\sqrt{1 - v^2/c^2}$. The length of a moving object is contracted in the direction of motion by the factor $\sqrt{1 - v^2/c^2}$.

Describe the relative nature of simultaneity; determine the time dilation of a moving clock and the length contraction of a moving object.

Section 38-6. The addition of velocities

Velocity components in the direction of relative motion

transform under Lorentz transformation as

$$u_x' = \frac{u_x - v}{1 - vu_x/c^2} \qquad (38\text{-}12)$$

The speed of light in vacuum is the upper limit on speeds.

Transform velocity components for the case of high speeds; argue that the speed of light in vacuum is the ultimate speed.

Section 38-7. Momentum and energy

The momentum of a particle of rest mass m and velocity $\mathbf{v}$ is defined by

$$\mathbf{p} = \frac{m\mathbf{v}}{\sqrt{1 - v^2/c^2}} \qquad (38\text{-}14)$$

and the kinetic energy is defined by

$$K = mc^2(\gamma - 1) \qquad (38\text{-}16)$$

The rest-mass energy of the particle is mc^2, and the total energy is $E = K + mc^2 = \gamma mc^2$. The rest-mass energy of a system can change and must be included in the overall conservation-of-energy law.

Determine the momentum and kinetic energy of a particle; identify rest-mass energy and include it in the conservation of energy for an isolated system.

QUESTIONS

38-1   What is the highest speed of an object that you have observed directly and visually?

38-2   Suppose that the speed of light were 3×10^3 m/s instead of 3×10^8 m/s. What are some everyday phenomena that would seem different from our present perceptions? See *Mr. Tompkins in Wonderland* by George Gamow (Macmillan, New York, 1940) for some interesting discussions of relativity.

38-3   Do you have any direct evidence to support the claim that the length of an object is independent of its speed? Explain.

38-4   What procedures could two widely separated observers (an earthling and Martian, for example) use to compare the rates at which their clocks run?

38-5   Imagine that a civilization in another galaxy is technologically comparable with our own. Is it reasonable to

expect that their expressions for the laws of nature would be fundamentally different from ours? Explain.

38-6   An astronomer claims to have detected the light from a galaxy that is located 2×10^9 ly from us. When did the light received by the telescope originate? What answer should the astronomer give if asked, "Where is the galaxy now?"

38-7   How could you measure the length of a fire truck as it speeds by at 75 km/h? Describe in detail a procedure for doing so. Assume that you have ample opportunity to set up the necessary apparatus beforehand.

38-8   Einstein described the following situation to illustrate the relativity of simultaneity: A train moves with constant speed past a ground-based observer. Lightning bolts strike the train at each end, as shown in Fig.

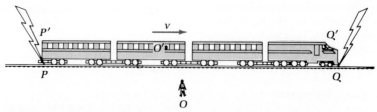

Figure 38-13. Ques. 38-8: Lightning strikes at each end of a train. The illustration shows the perspective of observer O, who stands on the ground beside the tracks.

38-13, leaving marks P', Q' on the train and marks P, Q on the ground. Observer O is positioned midway between the marks P and Q. Likewise, observer O' on the train is positioned midway between the marks P' and Q'. These observers note the light from the two events (the lightning bolts) reaching their eyes. For simplicity, assume that the light travels in vacuum. Observer O claims that the light from each bolt reaches her eyes at the same time. Are the events simultaneous for observer O? For observer O'? Explain.

38-9   Commercial airliners fly at an average speed relative to the ground of around 250 m/s. Should passengers adjust their watches after a flight to correct for time dilation? Explain.

38-10 The density of an object is defined as its rest mass divided by its volume. Will two observers in relative motion agree on the value of the rest mass of an object? Will they agree on the value of the density of the object? Explain.

38-11 Imagine that you speed by the earth toward the moon in a fast spaceship. If you measure the earth-moon separation, how does your measurement compare with the distance quoted in books such as this one? Explain.

38-12 Suppose that you are the earth-based observer of Example 38-2 who measures the speed of light. How can it be that the observer on the spaceship obtains the same value for the speed of the light as you do? Give a qualitative answer based on the length contraction of a measuring stick and time dilation for a moving clock.

38-13 Imagine that you catch the interstellar space shuttle to the nearby star Sirius. Will you find that your average pulse rate during the journey seems slower, faster, or the same as you found it to be on earth? Explain.

38-14 Suppose that you, at age 20, join the Space Cadet Corps. Your five-year training consists of a tour of nearby star systems aboard a fast starship. Explain why, at a celebration of your return to earth, your friends seem so much older than you.

38-15 The speed of a particle doubles, from 1×10^8 m/s to 2×10^8 m/s. Does the magnitude of the particle's momentum double? Does its kinetic energy quadruple? Explain.

38-16 There is an upper limit ($v < c$) on the speed of a particle such as an electron. Are there similar upper limits on its kinetic energy or on the magnitude of its momentum? Explain.

38-17 If you were responsible for programming the launch of a space shuttle into earth orbit, would you use $\mathbf{p} = m\mathbf{v}$ or $\mathbf{p} = \gamma m\mathbf{v}$ for the momentum of the shuttle? Explain.

38-18 Suppose that you add heat to a stationary object, such as a penny, and raise its temperature. Has the rest mass of the penny changed? Has its weight changed? Explain.

38-19 If a spring is compressed, its elastic potential energy increases. Can this increase be interpreted as an increase in rest-mass energy of the spring? Explain.

38-20 In the nuclear-fusion reaction of Example 38-7, why were the masses given with so many significant digits?

38-21 If an electron is moving fast so that Eqs. (38-14) and (38-16) must be used, then the electron is often described as a *relativistic electron*. What is meant by a *relativistic proton?*

38-22 Complete the following table:

Symbol	Represents	Type	SI unit
γ		Scalar	
T_0'			s
L_0	Rest length of an object		
$\mathbf{p}$			
mc^2			
E			

EXERCISES

Section 38-2. Transformations

38-1   Consider two reference frames related by the transformation in Eqs. (38-1). Show that the spatial separation between any two points is invariant. Consider points that have different y and z coordinates as well as different x coordinates.

38-2   The transformation in Eqs. (38-1) connects reference frames that have origins at different points. Suppose that two observers have the same origin but use different clocks. Observer O uses standard time and observer O' uses daylight saving time. (a) Determine the transformation equations connecting these reference frames. (b) Show that the number of daylight hours (the time interval between sunrise and sunset) is invariant.

38-3   Show that the galilean transformation for space-time coordinates $x, x', y, \ldots, t'$ is also obeyed by space-time coordinate differences $\Delta x, \Delta x', \Delta y, \ldots, \Delta t'$.

38-4   Two reference frames are connected by the galilean transformation in Eqs. (38-2), with observer O' in a train traveling with speed $v = 60$ km/h relative to observer O at the station. At $t = 1.2$ min, observer O notices a bus crossing the track at $x = 3.0$ km. Where and when does the crossing occur according to observer O'?

38-5   Equation (38-3) can be generalized and written as a vector equation using the velocity vectors **u**, **u′**, and **v**, where **v** is the relative velocity of observer $O′$ with respect to observer O. (a) Write this vector galilean velocity-transformation formula. (b) What is the velocity of observer O relative to observer $O′$?

38-6   Two observers, $O′$ on a train and O on the station platform, as illustrated in Fig. 38-2, notice a flying goose overtaking and passing the train parallel to the tracks. The goose has a speed of 2 m/s according to $O′$ and a speed of 9 m/s according to O. (a) What is the speed of the train relative to O? (b) What is the relative speed of the two observers if O describes the same goose seen before, but $O′$ describes a goose flying *backwards* at 2 m/s?

38-7   Observers O and $O′$ are connected by a galilean transformation with speed v, and observers $O′$ and $O″$ are connected by the same type of transformation with relative speed $v′$. Show that observers O and $O″$ are also connected by a galilean transformation and determine their relative speed.

38-8   Relative to an observer standing at the roadside, you are traveling south in an automobile at 80 km/h and a truck is traveling north at 60 km/h. You observe a south-bound bus passing you at 10 km/h. Determine the velocity of the bus relative to (a) the bystander and (b) the truck driver.

Section 38-3. The principle of relativity

38-9   Suppose that the force on one particle due to another particle, such as the newtonian gravitational force, depends only on the instantaneous separation of the particles. (a) Show that this type of force is invariant with respect to galilean transformations. (b) List some forces discussed in this text that do *not* depend only on the instantaneous separation of the particles.

38-10   Observer O on a train-station platform tosses a ball straight up to a height of 2.6 m and catches it on its return. Observer $O′$ is on a train passing the station at a constant speed of 12 m/s. Coordinate axes are oriented as shown in Fig. 38-3, with the y axis vertical. Determine for the motion of the ball according to observer $O′$, (a) the path, (b) the time of flight, (c) the maximum height, (d) the velocity components $u′_x$ and $u′_y$ when the ball reaches the maximum height, (e) the acceleration components $a′_x$ and $a′_y$. Neglect air-resistance effects.

38-11   In the ether theory, the earth should move at some time during the year relative to the ether with a speed at least equal to its orbital speed about the sun. (a) Estimate the fraction of the speed of light that the speed of the earth through the ether would be. (b) This fraction indicates the sensitivity required to detect such a speed in the Michelson-Morley experiment. Can you think of a speed larger than the orbital speed that was available or accessible at that time for

this kind of experiment?

38-12   Suppose that the sun were at rest relative to the ether. (a) Using galilean relativity, estimate the expected maximum and minimum values of the speed of light in vacuum, depending on relative directions of the light and the earth's motion. (b) What are the results obtained from actual measurements?

Section 38-4. The Lorentz transformation

38-13   Two events occur at the origin of the coordinate system of observer O at times $t_1 = 1.58$ s and $t_2 = 2.13$ s. Use the Lorentz transformation in Eqs. (38-9) to determine the spatial interval $\Delta x′ = x′_2 - x′_1$ and the time interval $\Delta t′ = t′_2 - t′_1$ between the events according to observer $O′$ if the relative speed of the observers is (a) $0.0010c$, (b) $0.10c$, (c) $0.99c$.

38-14   The origins of the coordinate systems of two observers coincide at $t = t′ = 0$. The observers are in relative motion along the $yy′$ axes, with constant speed v. Write the Lorentz transformation connecting these reference frames.

38-15   Two of the equations used to obtain the Lorentz transformation were $x′ = \gamma(x - vt)$ and $x = \gamma(x′ + vt′)$, where γ was to be determined. Show that if the assumption $t = t′$ is used with the above equations, then $\gamma = 1$ and the galilean transformation results. Since the galilean transformation is adequate only for low speeds, the assumption $t = t′$ is not valid.

38-16   (a) Review the discussion that led from Eq. (38-7) to Eq. (38-8) and show that $\gamma^2 = 1/(1 - v^2/c^2)$. (b) By considering the sign of spatial intervals Δx and $\Delta x′$, explain why the positive square root is taken to give $\gamma = 1/\sqrt{1 - v^2/c^2}$.

38-17   Starting with the Lorentz transformation in Eqs. (38-9), solve for the unprimed space-time coordinates in terms of the primed ones. This results in the *inverse* of the transformation.

38-18   Two intergalactic travelers O and $O′$ are drifting with a relative velocity along their $xx′$ axes of magnitude 2.5×10^8 m/s. Observer O catalogs an exploding star at $x_1 = -1.55 \times 10^{14}$ m, $t_1 = 1.68 \times 10^6$ s and an unrelated eclipse of a binary star system at $x_2 = 0.68 \times 10^{14}$ m, $t_2 = 2.94 \times 10^6$ s. (a) Where and when did these events occur relative to $O′$? (b) Explain how $x′_2 - x′_1$ can be negative.

38-19   The symbol β is often used to represent the ratio v/c, where v is the relative speed of two reference frames. (a) Rewrite the Lorentz transformation in Eqs. (38-9), using β instead of v. (b) If $\beta \ll 1$, show that $\gamma = 1/\sqrt{1 - \beta^2} \approx 1 + \frac{1}{2}\beta^2$. Determine the percent error in using the approximation in part (b) for (c) $\beta = 0.010$, (d) $\beta = 0.20$, (e) $\beta = 0.50$.

Section 38-5. A new view of space and time

38-20   Show that the Lorentz transformation reduces to the

galilean transformation in the limit of low relative speed, $v \ll c$. Justify your treatment of the term vx/c^2 in one of the Lorentz transformation equations.

38-21 An astronomer on earth determines that a volcanic eruption on Jupiter's moon Io, 8×10^{11} m from earth, occurred simultaneously with an eruption of a volcano in Mexico. These two events were also observed by a space traveler moving past the earth toward Jupiter at 2.5×10^8 m/s. According to the space traveler (a) which eruption occurred first and (b) what distance separated these two events? (See the next exercise also.)

38-22 (a) What is the distance between earth and Io according to the space traveler in the previous exercise? (b) Explain why this distance is different from the answer to part (b) of that exercise.

38-23 Two intergalactic observers are connected by the Lorentz transformation in Eqs. (38-9), with $v = 0.95c$. Observer O detects two supernova events at $x_1 = 30$ ly, $t_1 = 2.6$ y and $x_2 = 47$ ly, $t_2 = 5.4$ y. [One light-year (ly) is the distance light travels in one year. It equals cT, where $T = 1$ y.] (a) Where and when does each supernova occur according to observer O'? For which observer were the two events closer (b) in space and (c) in time?

38-24 Reconsider the previous exercise, changing only x_1, t_1 to the following values: $x_1 = 35$ ly, $t_1 = -6.0$ y. How do you account for the difference from the answers you found in the previous exercise?

38-25 Review the discussion around Eq. (38-11) and then consider a measurement by O' of the length L' of a moving object that is at rest relative to observer O. (Thus the rest length of the object is L_0.) Show that $L' = L_0 \sqrt{1 - v^2/c^2}$.

38-26 Observer O measures the length of a stick moving with a known speed v by determining the time interval Δt required for the ends of the stick to pass a particular spatial point. The measured length is then $L = v \, \Delta t$. Use time dilation to show that the length of the moving stick is given by $L = L_0' \sqrt{1 - v^2/c^2}$, where L_0' is the rest length of the stick.

38-27 The mean lifetime of a free neutron is about 1×10^3 s in its rest frame. Estimate the mean lifetime in a reference frame in which the neutron speed (a) is $0.99c$, (b) is $0.80c$, (c) is $0.10c$, (d) corresponds to an average kinetic energy of $\frac{3}{2}kT$ in a nuclear reactor. (Assume $T = 600$ K; k is the Boltzmann constant.)

38-28 The rest length of a Klingon space cruiser is 1800 m and its chronometer (clock) utilizes a mechanism with a period of 4.77×10^{-7} s. The cruiser moves past the planet Xzalb at 2.95×10^8 m/s. Determine (a) the length of the cruiser and (b) the period of its chronometer relative to a Xzalbian observer.

Section 38-6. The addition of velocities

38-29 Consider the transformation of the y and z components of the velocity of an object for observers connected by the Lorentz transformation in Eqs. (38-9). Show that these velocity components transform as given in the equations following Eq. (38-12).

38-30 Two observers O and O' are in relative motion, with speed v. Observer O' moves in the positive x direction according to observer O. Both observers measure the speed of a proton moving along the xx' axes. According to observer O, the velocity component of the proton is $u_x = 2.76 \times 10^8$ m/s. What is the velocity (magnitude and direction) of the proton according to observer O' if the relative speed of the observers is (a) 300 m/s, (b) 1.00×10^8 m/s, (c) 2.76×10^8 m/s, (d) 2.95×10^8 m/s?

38-31 Observer O detects observer O' moving in the positive x direction with speed $v = 0.9990c$. Observer O' measures the velocity component of an electron to be $u_x' = 0.9999c$. What is the electron velocity component u_x according to observer O?

38-32 Use Eq. (38-13) to show that if $0 < u_x' < c$ and $0 < v < c$, then $0 < u_x < c$. That is, if the speed of an object is less than c for one observer, then the speed of the object is less than c for another observer.

Section 38-7. Momentum and energy

38-33 Determine the kinetic energy and the magnitude of the momentum of an electron with speed (a) $0.99c$, (b) $0.50c$, (c) $0.10c$, (d) $0.001c$. (e) For which, if any, of these speeds can the nonrelativistic expressions $\frac{1}{2}mv^2$ and mv be used? Justify your answer.

38-34 For what speed v is the kinetic energy of a particle equal to (a) 10, (b) 1.0, (c) 0.10, (d) 0.01 times its rest-mass energy?

38-35 The nonrelativistic expression $\frac{1}{2}mv^2$ for the kinetic energy of a particle can be used if the speed v is small compared with c. For what speed does the use of this formula correspond to an error in the kinetic energy of (a) 1 percent and (b) 10 percent?

38-36 Eliminate the velocity $\mathbf{v}$ (and speed v) of the particle from Eqs. (38-14) and (38-16) to obtain the following relation between the total energy E of the particle and the magnitude p of its momentum:

$$E = \sqrt{p^2c^2 + m^2c^4}$$

(See Prob. 38-6 for another approach to this equation.)

38-37 In addition to his work on relativity, Einstein proposed a quantum picture of light as consisting of a stream of particles called *photons* (to be discussed in the next chapter). Each photon travels at the speed of light. To be consistent with special relativity, a particle traveling at speed c must have a zero rest mass. (Why?) Show that the energy and momentum of a photon are related by the simple expression $E = pc$.

38-38 An alpha particle (⁴He nucleus with a rest mass of 6.6×10^{-27} kg) is emitted when ^{238}U spontaneously decays. The alpha particle has a kinetic energy of

4.2 MeV. Determine (a) the speed and (b) the magnitude of the momentum of the alpha particle. (c) What fraction of its rest-mass energy is the kinetic energy of the alpha particle?

38-39 (a) Determine the speed of an electron with kinetic energy equal to its rest-mass energy. (b) Repeat for a proton.

38-40 (a) Show that mc^2 has dimensions of energy. (b) The atomic mass unit (1 u = 1.6605×10^{-27} kg) is a convenient mass unit for atomic and nuclear masses. Determine the equivalent rest-mass energy in J for 1 u. (c) What is the equivalent rest-mass energy of 1 u in MeV?

38-41 The ^{8}Be nucleus is unstable and spontaneously decays into two ^{4}He nuclei. (a) If the rest masses of the elements are m_{Be} = 8.005308 u and m_{He} = 4.002603 u, then what rest-mass energy is converted in the decay? (b) In a reference frame in which the Be nucleus is initially at rest, what kinetic energy does each He nucleus have after they are well separated? (c) What is the magnitude of the momentum of each He nucleus? (d) What is the speed of each He nucleus?

38-42 The rest mass M of a bound system such as an atom is less than the sum Σm_i of the rest masses of its constituent particles. The *binding energy B* of the system, the minimum energy required to separate the constituents, is given by the difference in rest-mass energies: $B = \Sigma m_i c^2 - Mc^2$. Determine the mass of (a) the deuteron (which consists of a proton and a neutron), given that $B = 2.23$ MeV, $m_p = 1.00728$ u, $m_n = 1.00867$ u and (b) the hydrogen atom (which consists of an electron and a proton), given that $B = 13.6$ eV, $m_p = 1.672648 \times 10^{-27}$ kg, $m_e = 9.1095 \times 10^{-31}$ kg.

PROBLEMS

38-1 ***Michelson-Morley experiment.*** The design of the Michelson-Morley experiment involved the difference in path length for light traveling in different directions with respect to the velocity of the apparatus through the ether. For simplicity, consider the case where the interferometer (discussed in Chap. 36) moves relative to the ether, as shown in Fig. 38-14. (a) Consider the time $\Delta t_\parallel$ required for light to travel on the parallel path from $M_{1/2}$ to M_a and back to $M_{1/2}$. Show that $\Delta t_\parallel = 2Lc/(c^2 - v^2)$. (b) Similarly show, using Fig. 38-14b, that the time interval along the perpendicular path is $\Delta t_\perp = 2L/\sqrt{c^2 - v^2}$. The interference pattern is determined by these time differences and should change if the apparatus is rotated through 90° in the plane of the figure so as to interchange the parallel and perpendicular paths. No significant shift in the pattern occurred in the experiment, which implied that $v = 0$.

38-2 ***Causality.*** Since simultaneity is a relative concept, what about causality? That is, if event 1 is the cause of event 2, then does the cause precede the effect for all observers? Suppose that these events occur at (x_1, t_1) and (x_2, t_2) in one reference frame, with $t_2 > t_1$. (We suppress the y and z coordinates for simplicity.) Suppose further that the events can be connected by a light signal: $|x_2 - x_1| < c(t_2 - t_1)$. Show that the events are also causal $(t_2' > t_1')$ in a second reference frame, connected to the first by the Lorentz transformation. This result suggests that the influences (forces) that one particle has on another cannot be instantaneous

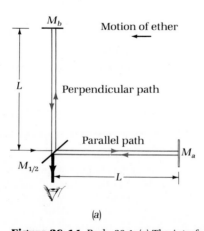

(a)

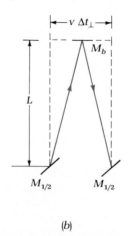

(b)

Figure 38-14. Prob. 38-1: (a) The interferometer is shown in its rest frame. The light rays are assumed to travel from $M_{1/2}$ to M_a at speed $c - v$ and from M_a back to $M_{1/2}$ at speed $c + v$. (b) In the rest frame of the ether, the apparatus moves and the light traverses the perpendicular path with speed c.

but are propagated at a speed no greater than c.

38-3   *The twin paradox.* Consider two identical twins, Orestes and Opie. On their twenty-fifth birthday, Opie leaves earth on a spaceship, which quickly accelerates to a cruising speed of $v = 0.99c$ relative to Orestes. The cruise lasts for 12 years according to Opie, and he returns to celebrate his thirty-seventh birthday. (*a*) How old is Orestes at this celebration? (*b*) The paradox is that Opie could claim that Orestes (along with the solar system) accelerated and cruised at high speed; Orestes should return much younger than he. Suggest some ways to resolve the paradox.

38-4 Suppose that three observers — O, O', and O'' — are related in turn by the Lorentz transformations

$$x' = \gamma(x - vt) \qquad x'' = \gamma'(x' - v't')$$

$$y' = y \qquad\qquad y'' = y'$$

$$z' = z \qquad\qquad z'' = z'$$

$$t' = \gamma\left(t - \frac{vx}{c^2}\right) \qquad t'' = \gamma'\left(t' - \frac{v'x'}{c^2}\right)$$

where $\gamma = 1/\sqrt{1 - v^2/c^2}$, $\gamma' = 1/\sqrt{1 - v'^2/c^2}$, and v and v' are relative speeds of pairs of observers. (*a*) Show that the transformation directly connecting O and O'' is also a Lorentz transformation, with relative speed

$$u = \frac{v + v'}{1 + vv'/c^2}$$

(*b*) Can you explain why, if $v = v'$, then $u \ne 2v$? (*c*) What is the interpretation of these transformations for the case $v' = -v$? (Think of v and v' as velocity components rather than speeds in this instance.)

38-5   *Proper time.* Isotropy and homogeneity of space require that the distance $\Delta s = (\Delta x^2 + \Delta y^2 + \Delta z^2)^{1/2}$ between two points be invariant, independent of the orientation or origin of the three-dimensional coordinate system. There is a corresponding invariant quantity in four-dimensional space-time. It is convenient to express this invariant as a time interval called the *proper time interval* $\Delta\tau$ between two events. It is defined by the expression

$$c^2\,\Delta\tau^2 = c^2\,\Delta t^2 - (\Delta x^2 + \Delta y^2 + \Delta z^2)$$

Another observer (O') would evaluate the proper time interval for the same two events using

$$c^2\,\Delta\tau^2 = c^2\,\Delta t'^2 - (\Delta x'^2 + \Delta y'^2 + \Delta z'^2)$$

Use the Lorentz transformation in Eqs. (38-9) to show that the two expressions above are identically equal. A physical interpretation of the proper time comes from considering two events that occur at the same spatial point in the reference frame of one observer, say O. Then $\Delta\tau = \Delta t$, but notice that $\Delta\tau \ne \Delta t'$ in this case.

38-6 The three momentum components p_x, p_y, and p_z and the total energy E of a particle give four quantities $(p_x,\ p_y,\ p_z,\ E/c^2)$ which transform under Lorentz transformation just as the space-time coordinates do. Thus

$$p_x' = \gamma\left(p_x - \frac{vE}{c^2}\right)$$

$$p_y' = p_y$$

$$p_z' = p_z$$

$$\frac{E'}{c^2} = \gamma\left(\frac{E}{c^2} - \frac{vp_x}{c^2}\right)$$

(*a*) Using the previous problem as a guide, show that the quantity $E^2 - p^2c^2$ is an invariant. Note that $p^2 = p_x^2 + p_y^2 + p_z^2$. (*b*) What is the value of the invariant?

38-7 Observers O and O' are connected by the Lorentz transformation in Eqs. (38-9). (*a*) Observer O detects a light ray traveling in the xy plane at an angle θ from the x axis, as shown in Fig. 38-15. Show that observer O' detects the ray traveling at angle θ' given by

$$\tan\theta' = \frac{\sin\theta}{\gamma(\cos\theta - v/c)}$$

(*b*) Suppose that observer O holds a rigid stick at angle θ from the x axis. Show that observer O' measures the angle θ' given by

$$\tan\theta' = \gamma\tan\theta$$

(*c*) Explain why the expressions in parts (*a*) and (*b*) are different.

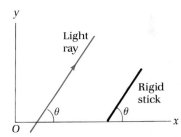

Figure 38-15. Prob. 38-7: A propagating light ray and a stationary rigid stick are at the same angle θ from the x axis in the xy plane of observer O.

38-8 In the relativistic dynamics of a particle, Newton's second law is written in the form $\mathbf{F} = d\mathbf{p}/dt$, where $\mathbf{F}$ is the net force acting on the particle and $\mathbf{p} = \gamma m\mathbf{v}$, with $\gamma = 1/\sqrt{1 - v^2/c^2}$. (*a*) Show that the second law written in terms of the acceleration $\mathbf{a}$ is given in general by

$$\mathbf{F} = \frac{m\mathbf{a}}{\sqrt{1 - v^2/c^2}} + \frac{m\mathbf{v}(\mathbf{v}\cdot\mathbf{a})}{c^2(1 - v^2/c^2)^{3/2}}$$

(*b*) Consider the special case of uniform circular motion of a particle of charge q in a uniform magnetic field. At low speeds the particle circulates at the cyclotron frequency $\omega_0 = qB/m$, which is independent of the radius r of the path. (See Chap. 26.) Show that the angular frequency $\omega = v/r$ of the circular motion, correct for all speeds, is given by $\omega = \omega_0 \sqrt{1 - v^2/c^2}$.

38-9   Consider the one-dimensional motion of a particle of rest mass m along the x axis, with a constant net force $F_x\mathbf{i}$ acting. The work dW for a small displacement $dx\ \mathbf{i}$ is given by $F_x\ dx = F_x v_x\ dt$, where v_x is the velocity component of the particle. (a) Use Newton's second law, $F_x = dp_x/dt$, and integrate to obtain the work done for a finite displacement. [*Hint:* Integrate $(dp_x/dt)v_x\ dt$ by parts, with $p_x = mv_x/\sqrt{1 - v_x^2/c^2}$.] (b) Apply the work-energy theorem to the case of a particle starting from rest and show that the kinetic energy of the particle is given by Eq. (38-16).

38-10   ***The Doppler shift.*** Although the speed of light in vacuum is the same in all inertial reference frames, the frequency of the light can be different for different observers. Suppose that observer O sends a light signal of frequency ν_s along the x axis. Let observer O', connected to O by the Lorentz transformation in Eqs. (38-9), measure the frequency $\nu_{O'} = 1/T_{O'}$ by timing consecutive crests passing a point in that frame. (a) If the time between these events according to observer O is T (T is *not* the period of the wave according to observer O), explain why the time-dilation formula $T = T_{O'}/\sqrt{1 - v^2/c^2}$ can be used. (b) During this time, according to O, the wave travels a distance cT while O' travels a distance vT. Thus the wavelength $\lambda_s = c/\nu_s = cT - vT$, or $T = 1/[\nu_s(1 - v/c)]$. Show that the Doppler-shift formula for this situation (observer and source separating) is given by

$$\nu_{O'} = \nu_s \sqrt{\frac{1 - v/c}{1 + v/c}}$$

(c) What is the Doppler-shift formula if observer and source are approaching each other?

CHAPTER 39
QUANTIZATION OF ELECTROMAGNETIC RADIATION

39-1 INTRODUCTION

Imagine being a young scientist in 1899–1900 and celebrating the turn of the century by reflecting on how well you understood the workings of the universe: Newtonian mechanics dealt with the motion of objects of all sizes — from planetary motions to a falling grain of sand. Thermodynamics had been developed from and had contributed to the improvements in the steam engine. Indeed, the steam locomotive provided fast, economical transportation across a continent. Electricity and magnetism had been unified in Maxwell's equations. Further, since light consists of electromagnetic waves, optics was just a branch of electromagnetism. Of course, there were still some intriguing problems around. Many of these dealt with the structure of atoms and the light emitted and absorbed by them. But given a little more time and effort, these problems would soon be resolved and the body of basic physical science would be complete.

The investigation of these problems led, however, to a revolution of ideas in physics. The basic outlines of what is now called *quantum mechanics* or *quantum physics* developed during a 30-year period beginning around 1900. Although the older, or *classical,* physics remains useful in its range of applicability, quantum physics deals with a whole new range of phenomena at the atomic and subatomic levels. We shall consider some of these phenomena in this chapter.*

---

* In the "extended" edition of this text, the remaining chapters are devoted to discussion of quantum physics.

39-2 INTERACTION OF LIGHT AND MATTER

Our perceptions of the physical world are dominated by the interaction of light and matter. One interaction occurs at the retina of the eye, leading physiologically to the sense of sight. The light that enters the eye, flooding our sight with a rich variety of images, is the result of the interaction of light and the matter of external objects. Although our eyes are sensitive to only a small part of the spectrum, we shall use the term "light" generically to represent electromagnetic radiation of any frequency, not necessarily in the visible spectrum. Thus we include the interaction of matter and ultraviolet light, for example.

Light and matter seem to interact passively in some cases. For a nominally transparent substance such as glass, the main result of the interaction is the behavior at the surface — reflection and refraction (Chap. 35). The absorption of electromagnetic energy is usually negligible, at least in the visible spectrum.

In other cases the interaction of light and matter seems more active, as in the emission of light. Intense light is emitted from matter at high temperatures such as from the surface of the sun or from the flash of a photographer's light.

When light is incident on the surface of an opaque object, part of the light penetrates into the material and is absorbed. The remaining light is reflected from the surface. It is this reflected light that we observe; that is, we "see" the object by the light reflected from it. The fraction of light that is reflected from the surface depends on the wavelength. For example, the surface of an object may reflect most of the light in the blue portion of the spectrum and absorb strongly in the red portion. Thus if white light is incident on the surface, the reflected light contains a greater proportion of blue than red. As a result, the perceived color of the object is a shade of blue or perhaps green. The vast range of hues distinguishable by the human eye is a consequence of the sensitivity of the eye to this selective absorption and reflection for different wavelengths.

Surfaces with darker colors are more strongly absorbing than surfaces with lighter colors. You have probably noticed this effect directly in the absorption of sunlight by your clothing. A dark shirt or blouse absorbs more of the incident sunlight than a light one, so that light clothing is cooler in summer. A white surface is one that reflects a large fraction of all frequencies of the incident light. Another type of surface that is a good reflector (and a poor absorber) is a polished, metallic surface of a substance such as aluminum or untarnished silver. At the other extreme are strongly absorbing (poorly reflecting) surfaces. Examples are tar, lampblack, and printer's ink. (How can you account for the high contrast between the paper and the printed symbols on this page?)

In addition to seeing objects by the light reflected from them, we can see some objects by the light that they emit. A glowing coal, for example, emits a significant fraction of its light in the visible spectrum; it can be seen in an otherwise darkened room. Other objects in the room, at much lower temperatures, do not emit with an appreciable intensity in the visible part of the spectrum. All objects emit electromagnetic radiation, and they do so at a rate that depends on the temperature of the surface. Only for temperatures well above room temperature does the surface emit enough in the visible spectrum to be easily observable.

The radiated power P (rate of emission of electromagnetic energy) from an area A of surface at temperature T is given by the Stefan-Boltzmann law from Chap. 16:

Stefan-Boltzmann law

$$P = e\sigma AT^4$$

(16-12)

where $\sigma = 5.67 \times 10^{-8}$ W $\cdot$ m^{-2} $\cdot$ K^{-4} is the Stefan-Boltzmann constant. Josef Stefan (1835–1893) proposed the T^4 dependence in 1879 from an analysis of experimental data. Five years later Ludwig Boltzmann derived the law theoretically. The emissivity e characterizes the emitting properties of the surface and is material-dependent. It is a dimensionless number with a range of $0 \leqslant e \leqslant 1$. The upper limit, $e = 1$, would correspond to a perfect, or ideal, emitter.

A surface that is a good absorber of light is also a good emitter of light. Using the second law of thermodynamics, you can show (in Prob. 39-1) that the rate of emission of electromagnetic radiation of a given frequency must equal the rate of absorption at that frequency. Thus the ideal emitting surface with $e = 1$ would also be an ideal absorbing surface. That is, all of the radiation incident on the ideal absorbing surface would be absorbed and none would be reflected. Since no incident light would be reflected by the surface of an ideal emitter-absorber, such an object is sometimes called a *blackbody*. The electromagnetic radiation, or light, emitted by the ideal blackbody is often called *blackbody radiation*.

A blackbody is an idealization in that no material has a surface with unit emissivity. Lampblack, with $e \approx 0.99$, closely approximates a blackbody. Only a small fraction of the light incident on such a surface is reflected.

The light that would be emitted by a blackbody can be approximated as closely as desired by the radiation emerging from a small opening in a cavity (at temperatures below the melting point of the material that forms the walls of the cavity). Consider light entering the cavity through the opening shown in Fig. 39-1a. Part of the light is absorbed on each reflection from the interior cavity wall. After many reflections, virtually all of the energy that was incident on the opening has been absorbed. In this way the opening behaves as an ideal absorber, a blackbody. Thus the light emerging from the small opening of a cavity, as seen in Fig. 39-1b, is blackbody radiation. The emissivity $e = 1$ for a blackbody or for the opening of a cavity, and the radiated power is independent of material that forms the inside walls of the cavity.

The power in Eq. (16-12) includes all frequencies. In the next section we shall consider in detail how the radiation is distributed over a range of frequencies. This frequency dependence of blackbody radiation turns out to be universal, the same for all blackbodies. It is a feature of the interaction of light and matter and was one of the unsolved problems in classical physics that led to the development of quantum theory.

A blackbody is an ideal emitter and absorber.

Cavity radiation approximates blackbody radiation.

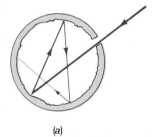

(a)

(b)

Figure 39-1. (a) Light entering a small opening to a cavity is absorbed after many reflections. (b) The light coming from the small opening to a cavity approximates blackbody radiation.

39-3 CAVITY RADIATION

The electromagnetic radiation that exists in a cavity is a mixture of standing waves. In analogy with one-dimensional standing waves that can fit on a string, three-dimensional standing wave modes of various frequencies ν can "fit" into the cavity. The electromagnetic energy is distributed among the standing wave modes such that at temperature T the radiation is in thermal equilibrium with the walls of the cavity. This energy distribution can be determined by sampling the radiation emerging from a small opening in the cavity wall. Since the small opening is equivalent to a blackbody, the power radiated from the opening is $P = \sigma A T^4$, where A is the area of the opening. We use the *radiancy* $R = P/A$ to denote the *radiated* power per unit area from the opening. Similarly, the *spectral radiancy* R_ν is the radiated power per unit area per unit frequency range. That is, $R_\nu \, d\nu$ is the radiated power per unit area with frequencies between ν and $\nu + d\nu$. The spectral radiancy R_ν summed or integrated over all frequencies gives the radiancy:

$$R = \int_0^\infty R_\nu \, d\nu$$

A related spectral radiancy R_λ is often used when wavelengths are measured. For a wavelength range $d\lambda$ between λ and $\lambda + d\lambda$, the radiated power per unit area is $R_\lambda \, d\lambda$. These two spectral radiancies are simply related (see Exercise 39-9) since $\nu\lambda = c$.

The spectral radiancy is measured by analyzing the radiation from the cavity with a spectrometer, as shown schematically in Fig. 39-2. The dependence on frequency or wavelength is shown for two different temperatures in Fig. 39-3. Notice the following general features:

1 At a given temperature, the spectral radiancy has a single peak or maximum.
2 If the temperature is increased, the spectral radiancy increases for every frequency or wavelength.
3 The peak wavelength, the wavelength at which the spectral radiancy is a maximum, shifts to smaller wavelengths (larger frequencies) at higher temperatures. (See Prob. 39-2.)

These features, along with the detailed dependence on frequency, must be explained by any successful theory of the interaction of light and matter.

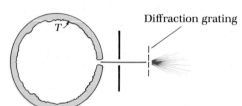

Figure 39-2. Light from a cavity passes through a collimating slit and is separated into its component wavelengths by a diffraction grating.

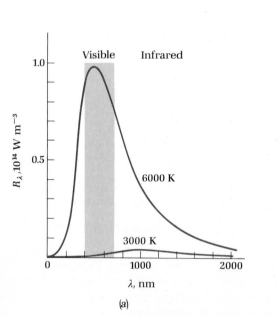

(a)

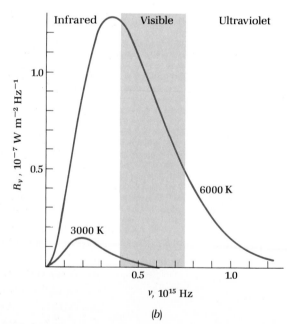

(b)

Figure 39-3. The spectral radiancy for a blackbody, or from an opening to a cavity, is shown for two temperatures. The frequency and wavelength ranges for visible light are indicated by the shaded regions. (a) The dependence of R_λ on λ is shown. (b) The dependence of R_ν on ν is shown.

Classical approaches to the problem of cavity radiation were not successful. The Rayleigh-Jeans theory, due to Lord Rayleigh (1842–1919) and modified by Sir James Jeans (1877–1946), made use of the mathematical equivalence of a standing wave mode in the cavity and a harmonic oscillator. The analogy may be seen by comparing the expressions $\frac{1}{2}\epsilon_0 E^2$ for the electric energy density of the standing wave and $\frac{1}{2}\alpha x^2$ for the potential energy of an oscillator with spring constant α. For a system of classical oscillators at temperature T, the average energy per oscillator is $\langle E \rangle = kT$ from the equipartition-of-energy theorem (Chap. 18), where k is the Boltzmann constant. Classically, a standing-wave mode should similarly have an average energy of $\langle E \rangle = kT$.

The number of standing wave modes per unit volume with frequencies in a range $d\nu$ between ν and $\nu + d\nu$ can be calculated to be $8\pi\nu^2 \, d\nu/c^3$. The radiancy, which is proportional to the energy per unit volume in the cavity, should be proportional to the product of the number of modes per unit volume and the average energy per mode. This reasoning gives the Rayleigh-Jeans formula, $R_\nu = 2\pi\nu^2 kT/c^2$. The Rayleigh-Jeans formula agrees with experiment only at low frequencies; at higher frequencies it is clearly wrong because it increases without bound (as ν^2). This mathematical behavior with increasing frequency of the Rayleigh-Jeans formula was called the "ultraviolet catastrophe."

In 1900 Max Planck (1858–1947) presented a formula that could describe the measured frequency distribution of blackbody radiation. To obtain a physical basis for some constants in the formula, Planck made some proposals which were thought to be unfounded and extremely radical at the time. These proposals can now be stated as follows:

Quantum of energy $h\nu$

1 An oscillator (including a standing wave mode) of frequency ν can change its energy only by a whole multiple of a discrete amount, a *quantum of energy* $\Delta E = h\nu$, where h is a constant described below.

The energy of an oscillator is quantized.

2 The energy of an oscillator is *quantized*; its energy is restricted to one of the values $E_n = n \cdot h\nu$, where the *quantum number n* is an integer.

Planck was able to show, as a consequence of energy quantization, that the average energy per oscillator for a collection of oscillators of frequency ν at temperature T is given by

$$\langle E \rangle = \frac{h\nu}{e^{h\nu/kT} - 1} \tag{39-1}$$

The constant h that connects energy and frequency is called *Planck's constant*. It is considered to be a fundamental constant, ranking with the speed of light c or the electronic charge e. The modern value of Planck's constant in SI units is

Planck's constant

$$h = 6.626076 \times 10^{-34} \text{ J} \cdot \text{s} \approx 6.63 \times 10^{-34} \text{ J} \cdot \text{s}$$

Using Eq. (39-1) for the average energy for a standing wave mode in the cavity and incorporating the number of modes per unit volume from above, we can obtain *Planck's radiation law* (see Exercise 39-10) for the spectral radiancy for blackbody radiation:

Planck's radiation law

$$R_\nu = \frac{2\pi h\nu^3}{c^2(e^{h\nu/kT} - 1)} \tag{39-2}$$

This expression accounts for all of the features of blackbody radiation, including the Stefan-Boltzmann law. (See Prob. 39-3.)

What was the radical element in Planck's proposals? It was the assumption that the energy of an oscillator is quantized, that the energy can have only particular, discrete values and not any value in between. For a classical mechanical or electric oscillator, the energy appears to be a continuously variable quantity. For example, the energy of a harmonic oscillator of mass m and angular frequency $\omega = 2\pi\nu$ can be expressed in terms of the amplitude A of the motion: $E = \frac{1}{2}m\omega^2 A^2$. If the energy is quantized, then the amplitude likewise can have only particular, discrete values. However, no one had yet observed a discreteness in the amplitude of oscillators. The energy (and amplitude) of ordinary-sized oscillators does indeed seem to be continuously variable. The quantized values are closely spaced, as the following example shows, because of the small value of Planck's constant h.

EXAMPLE 39-1. The 0.10-kg tip of a tuning fork vibrates harmonically at 440 Hz with amplitude $A = 1.2$ mm. (a) Determine the quantum number n for this state of the oscillating tip. (b) If the quantum number decreases from n to $n - 1$, determine the change ΔA in amplitude.

SOLUTION. (a) The energy of the oscillator is

$$E = \tfrac{1}{2}m(2\pi\nu)^2 A^2 = \tfrac{1}{2}(0.10 \text{ kg})(2\pi \cdot 440 \text{ Hz})^2(0.0012 \text{ m})^2$$

$$= 0.55 \text{ J}$$

Since $E = nh\nu$, we can solve for the quantum number n:

$$n = \frac{E}{h\nu} = \frac{0.55 \text{ J}}{(6.63 \times 10^{-34} \text{ J} \cdot \text{s})(440 \text{ Hz})}$$

$$= 1.9 \times 10^{30}$$

This large value of n for a typical state of a macroscopic oscillator is due to the small value of the quantum of energy, $h\nu = (6.63 \times 10^{-34} \text{ J} \cdot \text{s})(440 \text{ Hz}) = 2.9 \times 10^{-31} \text{ J}$. (b) Since $E = nh\nu = \frac{1}{2}m(2\pi\nu)^2 A^2$, we have $A^2 = nh/(2\pi^2 m\nu)$. Taking the differential of this expression connects the change ΔA due to a change Δn: $2A \, \Delta A = h \, \Delta n/(2\pi^2 m\nu)$. Dividing by $A^2 = nh/2\pi^2 m\nu$, we obtain $2 \, \Delta A/A = \Delta n/n$. Since $\Delta n = -1$, we have

$$\Delta A = \frac{\tfrac{1}{2}(1.2 \text{ mm})(-1)}{1.9 \times 10^{30}} = -3.2 \times 10^{-34} \text{ m}$$

Such a small change in the amplitude is unobservable, and the amplitude of a macroscopic oscillator seems continuously variable.

39-4   THE PHOTOELECTRIC EFFECT

Planck's assumption, that the energy of an oscillator is quantized, did not at the time represent a new view of light. The oscillators discussed by Planck were thought to be atomic oscillators, which formed the interior walls of the cavity, and not the standing wave modes. In 1905 Einstein extended the idea of quantization to light itself, as it propagated freely and interacted with matter. This new theory of light answered some puzzling questions about the photoelectric effect.

In the *photoelectric effect*, electrons are emitted from a material when light is incident on its surface. Ordinarily an electron is bound to the material and cannot escape from it unless energy is supplied. The light must supply each emitted electron with sufficient energy to escape from the surface. To be emitted from the surface, an electron must receive a minimum amount of energy ϕ, called the *work function* of the surface. The value of the work function depends on the material and is sensitive to the condition of the surface. For example, the work function for aluminum (with a clean, unoxidized surface) is 4.2 eV.

Quantitative studies of the photoelectric effect are made with an arrangement such as that shown in Fig. 39-4. Light is incident on the photosensitive surface, which is the cathode C of the photocell. Electrons emitted from the

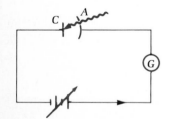

Figure 39-4. Light incident on the cathode C of a photocell causes electrons to be emitted. Electrons collected at the anode A contribute to the current in the circuit as measured by the galvanometer G. The potential difference across the photocell can be adjusted.

cathode are collected at the anode A at a rate that determines the current i in the galvanometer G. The potential difference across the photocell can be varied. If the anode is at a higher potential than the cathode, then the anode attracts the emitted electrons. If the polarity is reversed so that the anode is at a lower potential than the cathode, then the anode repels the electrons.

Suppose that monochromatic light of frequency ν is incident on the photocell. We list below several observed features of the photoelectric effect. These features have no reasonable explanation if we use the classical picture of electrons in the material interacting with the electromagnetic wave of the incident light.

1. There is a *threshold frequency* ν_0 below which no electrons are emitted from the surface. The current in the circuit in Fig. 39-4 is zero if the cathode is illuminated with light whose frequency ν is below the threshold value, $\nu < \nu_0$. The threshold frequency is characteristic of the material and the condition of its surface; it is independent of the intensity of the light. For example, $\nu_0 = 5.6 \times 10^{14}$ Hz for sodium with a clean surface. The classical wave theory provides no mechanism for a lowest, or threshold, frequency for the emission of electrons.

2. When the frequency of the incident light is above the threshold frequency, $\nu > \nu_0$, electrons are emitted with a distribution of kinetic energies. There is a maximum kinetic energy K_{max} for electrons emitted from the surface which is independent of the intensity. The maximum value of the kinetic energy is measured by having the anode at a lower potential than the cathode. When electrons leave the cathode and move to a lower potential, they are slowed as their kinetic energy is transformed into electric potential energy. Electrons that are stopped before reaching the anode do not contribute to the current. An electron moving toward the anode with the maximum kinetic energy will be stopped before reaching the anode if the potential difference is adjusted to V_s, the *stopping potential,* which stops all of the emitted electrons. Its value corresponds to the conversion of the maximum kinetic energy K_{max} into electric potential energy $eV_s = K_{max}$. Contrary to experiment, the wave theory would have the distribution of kinetic energy dependent on intensity.

3. The maximum kinetic energy depends linearly on the frequency of the incident light. This behavior is shown graphically in Fig. 39-5 for two different materials. Notice that the intercept, which is the threshold frequency, is different for the two materials, but each line has the same slope. There is no basis for this kind of behavior in the wave theory.

4. Experiment shows that there is no appreciable time delay between the incidence of light on the surface and the emission of electrons. The wave theory requires that energy be continuously absorbed from the wave by an electron. If the intensity is low, there would be a time lag before the electrons could absorb enough energy to escape from the surface. (See Exercise 39-18.) The wave theory is completely at odds with the observation that electrons are emitted immediately.

The photon. Einstein proposed a *corpuscular,* or particle, theory of light: Monochromatic light of frequency ν propagating in vacuum consists of a stream of particles or *quanta,* which we now call *photons.* Each photon travels at speed c and has a discrete amount or quantum of energy:

$$E = h\nu \tag{39-3}$$

Threshold frequency ν_0

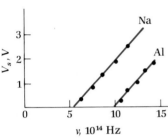

Figure 39-5. The maximum kinetic energy K_{max} of emitted electrons, and the stopping potential V_s $K_{max} = eV_s$, depend linearly on the frequency of the incident light. The two lines have the same slope.

$K_{max} = eV_s$, independent of intensity.

K_{max} depends linearly on frequency.

There is no time delay for emission of electrons.

Energy of a photon

where h is Planck's constant. Further, when a photon interacts "one on one" with an electron, the electron acquires all of the energy of the photon, which then exists no longer.

All of the features of the photoelectric effect can be simply explained by using the photon concept. Consider each of the properties listed above that could not be understood with the wave picture of light.

Threshold frequency and work function, $h\nu_0 = \phi$

1. To escape from the surface of a material, an electron must gain an energy at least equal to the work function ϕ. If the energy acquired by absorbing a photon of energy $h\nu$ is less than the work function, then the electron will not be emitted. Thus there is a threshold frequency ν_0 such that $h\nu_0 = \phi$. Only for a frequency greater than the threshold frequency, $\nu > \nu_0$, can the electron obtain enough energy from a photon to escape from the surface.

2. An electron receives a definite amount of energy $h\nu$ by absorbing a photon. It must give up at least an amount equal to the work function ϕ in escaping from the surface. Therefore, there is a maximum kinetic energy for the emitted electrons.

3. The maximum kinetic energy K_{max} equals, by conservation of energy, the energy $h\nu$ absorbed from the photon, less the minimum energy ϕ required to escape from the surface. Thus

Einstein's photoelectric equation

$$K_{max} = h\nu - \phi \tag{39-4}$$

which is known as *Einstein's photoelectric equation.* In terms of the stopping potential V_s, where $K_{max} = eV_s$, Eq. (39-3) can be expressed as

$$V_s = \frac{h}{e}(\nu - \nu_0)$$

where $\nu_0 = \phi/h$. This result gives the linear dependence of the stopping potential on frequency. Each line in Fig. 39-5 has a threshold frequency ν_0 determined by the work function of the material. The slope of each line is independent of the material; its value is h/e.

4. Since an electron absorbs a photon and acquires the energy all at once, there need be no appreciable time delay between the incidence of light and the emission of electrons. An electron can be emitted immediately.

The experimental features of the photoelectric effect discussed above were not clearly established when Einstein proposed the photon interpretation of light in 1905. The linear dependence of the stopping potential on frequency was confirmed by careful experiments in 1916 by R. A. Millikan (1868–1953). This work helped to gain the general acceptance of the photon picture of light and provided a value for the combination of fundamental constants h/e. Einstein was awarded the Nobel prize in 1921 for his work on the photoelectric effect.

The particlelike photon, the quantum of electromagnetic radiation, carries momentum as well as energy. Since the photon travels at the speed of light, its rest mass is zero. Using Eq. (38-17), $E = \sqrt{p^2c^2 + m^2c^4}$, with $m = 0$, we find that the magnitude of the momentum of the photon is given by $p = E/c$, where $E = h\nu$. Since $E/c = h\nu/c = h/\lambda$, we can write

Momentum of a photon

$$p = \frac{h}{\lambda} \tag{39-5}$$

for the magnitude of the momentum of a photon.

EXAMPLE 39-2. Monochromatic light of wavelength 450 nm is incident on a clean Na surface of work function $\phi = 3.7 \times 10^{-19}$ J = 2.3 eV. Determine (a) the energy of a photon of this light, (b) the maximum kinetic energy of emitted electrons, (c) the threshold frequency for Na, and (d) the magnitude of the momentum of a photon in the incident light.

SOLUTION. (a) From Eq. (39-3), the energy of a photon is $E = h\nu$. Since $\nu = c/\lambda = 6.7 \times 10^{14}$ Hz,

$$E = (6.63 \times 10^{-34} \text{ J} \cdot \text{s})(6.7 \times 10^{14} \text{ Hz})$$

$$= 4.4 \times 10^{-19} \text{ J} = 2.8 \text{ eV}$$

Notice that the photon energy is greater than the work function, so electrons are emitted from the surface.

(b) Einstein's photoelectric equation, Eq. (39-4), expresses conservation of energy for the interaction of an electron and a photon. An electron absorbs a photon and acquires its energy $h\nu$. If the electron gives up the minimum energy ϕ in escaping from the surface, it emerges with a maximum kinetic energy,

$$K_{\max} = h\nu - \phi = 2.8 \text{ eV} - 2.3 \text{ eV} = 0.5 \text{ eV}$$

(c) The threshold frequency is related to the work function by $h\nu_0 = \phi$, or

$$\nu_0 = \frac{\phi}{h} = \frac{3.7 \times 10^{-19} \text{ J}}{6.63 \times 10^{-34} \text{ J} \cdot \text{s}} = 5.6 \times 10^{14} \text{ Hz}$$

(d) The magnitude of the momentum of a photon for the incident light is given by Eq. (39-5):

$$p = \frac{h}{\lambda} = \frac{6.63 \times 10^{-34} \text{ J} \cdot \text{s}}{450 \text{ nm}}$$

$$= 1.5 \times 10^{-27} \text{ kg} \cdot \text{m/s}$$

39-5 PHOTONS AND ELECTRONS

In the photoelectric effect, the interaction of light and matter occurs as electron-photon encounters: A photon is absorbed by an electron, and the electron acquires the energy of the photon. If the photon energy $h\nu$ is greater than the work function of the material, then an electron, after absorbing a photon, has enough energy to escape from the surface. There are other processes which clearly involve the interaction of individual electrons and photons. We shall consider one of these to illustrate further the particle nature of light.

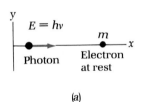

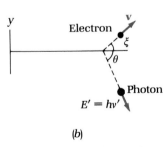

Figure 39-6. (a) A photon of energy $E = h\nu$ and momentum component $p_x = h/\lambda$ is incident on an electron that is initially at rest. (b) The electron recoils with velocity **v**, and the scattered photon has energy $E' = h\nu'$.

The Compton effect. The scattering of an electromagnetic wave by a charged particle, such as an electron in an atom, had been described in classical terms in the following way: The incident plane wave, with electric and magnetic fields oscillating at frequency ν, exerts a sinusoidal driving force on the particle and causes it to oscillate at that same frequency. A charged particle oscillating with frequency ν emits electromagnetic radiation of that frequency, and this outgoing spherical wave is the scattered wave. Thus an incident wave of frequency ν is scattered by the charged particle, and the scattered wave has the same frequency as the incident wave.

In 1923 A. H. Compton (1892–1962) found that the frequency of some of the x-rays scattered by electrons was not the same as the frequency of the incident x-rays. This frequency change on scattering is called the *Compton effect*. Compton showed that the interaction can be interpreted as a collision of two particles, a photon and an electron. The final state is determined by applying the conservation laws for energy and momentum. The initial state is shown schematically in Fig. 39-6a. The initial momentum of the photon is along the x axis of a coordinate system, and the electron is initially at rest. As a result of the collision, the electron recoils with velocity **v** at angle ξ, as shown in Fig. 39-6b, and the photon scatters at angle θ from the incident direction. Since the electron has received kinetic energy in the collision, the energy of the scattered photon $h\nu$ must be less than the energy of the incident photon $h\nu$. Relativistic expressions should be used for the energy [Eq. (38-15)] and momentum [Eq. (38-14)] of the electron because its speed may be comparable to the speed of light.

The initial energy of the system is $h\nu + mc^2$, the sum of the photon energy and the rest-mass energy of the stationary electron. After the collision, the energy is $h\nu' + \gamma mc^2$, where the second term is the total energy of the moving electron from Eq. (38-15) and $\gamma = 1/\sqrt{1 - v^2/c^2}$. Applying conservation of energy gives $h\nu' + \gamma mc^2 = h\nu + mc^2$, or

$$h(\nu - \nu') + mc^2 = \gamma mc^2$$

Conservation of energy for Compton scattering

It is more convenient to express this in terms of wavelengths; since $h(\nu - \nu') = h(c/\lambda - c/\lambda')$, we have

$$hc\left(\frac{1}{\lambda} - \frac{1}{\lambda'}\right) + mc^2 = \gamma mc^2 \tag{39-6}$$

Only the x component of the total momentum of the system is different from zero. Initially, this component is due to the incident photon, so $P_x = h\nu/c = h/\lambda$ from Eq. (39-5). After the collision the x component of the total momentum is $(h/\lambda')\cos\theta + \gamma mv \cos\xi$. The y component of the total momentum is zero before and after the collision, so, from Fig. 39-6b, $0 = -(h/\lambda')\sin\theta + \gamma mv \sin\xi$. Conservation of each component of the total momentum gives

Conservation of x and y components of momentum

$$\frac{h}{\lambda} - \frac{h}{\lambda'}\cos\theta = \gamma mv \cos\xi$$

$$\frac{h}{\lambda'}\sin\theta = \gamma mv \sin\xi \tag{39-7}$$

These two equations, along with Eq. (39-6), connect four quantities that describe the final state of the system: v and ξ for the electron and λ' and θ for the photon. The wavelength λ' of the scattered radiation depends on the angle of scatter θ of the photon. Accordingly, we eliminate v and ξ from the above equations and solve for λ' in terms of θ. We omit the details of solving the equations here (but see Prob. 39-4) and just give the result:

Change in wavelength for Compton scattering

$$\lambda' - \lambda = \frac{h}{mc}(1 - \cos\theta) \tag{39-8}$$

The wavelength λ' of the scattered radiation depends on the scattering angle θ. For the forward or incident direction ($\theta = 0$), the factor $(1 - \cos 0) = 0$, and there is no change in wavelength. At other angles there is a shift $\Delta\lambda = \lambda' - \lambda$ toward longer wavelengths. The maximum shift $\Delta\lambda_{max}$ occurs for backscattering ($\theta = 180°$) and from Eq. (39-8) $\Delta\lambda_{max} = (h/mc)[1 - (-1)] = 2h/mc$. Notice that the quantity h/mc, with dimensions of length, determines the shift in wavelength for scattering at a given angle. This length depends on the mass of the charged particle and is called the *Compton wavelength* for this type of

Compton wavelength

particle. The Compton wavelength for an electron is $h/m_e c = 2.43 \times 10^{-12}$ m. Since this value is small compared with wavelengths in the visible spectrum (around 500 nm), the Compton effect is easily observable only for much shorter wavelengths, such as those in the x-ray region of the spectrum.

EXAMPLE 39-3. X-rays of wavelength 1.14×10^{-11} m scatter from free electrons in a metal. (a) Determine the wavelength of x-rays scattered at $\theta = \pi/2$ from the incident direction. Assume that each electron is at rest initially. (b) What is the recoil kinetic energy of an electron?

SOLUTION. (a) From Eq. (39-8), the change in wavelength is $\Delta\lambda = (h/mc)[1 - \cos(\pi/2)] = h/mc$. For an electron, the Compton wavelength is $h/mc = 2.43 \times 10^{-12}$ m. The wavelength of the scattered x-rays at this angle is

$$\lambda' = \lambda + \Delta\lambda = \lambda + \frac{h}{mc} = 1.14 \times 10^{-11} \text{ m} + 2.43 \times 10^{-12} \text{ m}$$

$$= 1.38 \times 10^{-11} \text{ m}$$

(b) The kinetic energy K received by the electron equals the difference in the energies of the incident and scattered photons. Thus

$$K = h\nu - h\nu' = hc\left(\frac{1}{\lambda} - \frac{1}{\lambda'}\right) = 3.07 \times 10^{-15} \text{ J}$$

$$= 19.2 \text{ keV}$$

39-6 LINE SPECTRA

To see the structure or inner workings of a device such as a mechanical clock or an electric motor, we expose the object to light. With a good microscope we can resolve details of the structure that approach the limit of resolution which is determined (Chap. 37) by the wavelength range of visible light, about 400 to 750 nm. We cannot directly see the structure of an atom because its size, around 0.1 nm, is less than the wavelength of visible light. Nevertheless, the structure of an atom or molecule can be investigated through the interaction of light and matter. That is, atoms emit and absorb light and do so in a way that depends on their structure.

If the light from a cavity is analyzed with a spectrometer, as shown schematically in Fig. 39-2, then the intensity distribution contains all wavelengths in the range dispersed by the spectrometer. The spectrum is a *continuous spectrum*. In contrast, the light emitted from a "neon" sign contains intense light at a discrete set of wavelengths. Each wavelength from this source forms an image on a photographic plate of the narrow entrance slit of the spectrometer, so that the plate contains a sequence of lines (Fig. 39-7). Because of this appearance, a spectrum with a discrete set of wavelengths is called a *line spectrum*.

Continuous and line spectra

A spectrum of the light emitted by a source, whether a continuous or a line spectrum, is called an *emission spectrum*. An *absorption spectrum* can also show abrupt intensity changes for a discrete set of wavelengths, so it is a line spectrum. The absorption spectrum for a substance is obtained by passing light with a continuous spectrum through a substance. The transmitted light is analyzed with a spectrometer. Those wavelengths strongly absorbed by the substance are shown by their reduced intensity. Figure 39-8 shows portions of the absorption and the emission spectra for sodium vapor.

Emission and absorption spectra

Figure 39-7. Light from a source passes through a slit S and is separated into its component wavelengths by a diffraction grating G. The position of each wavelength is recorded on the photographic plate P.

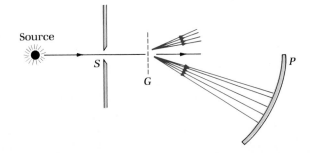

Source

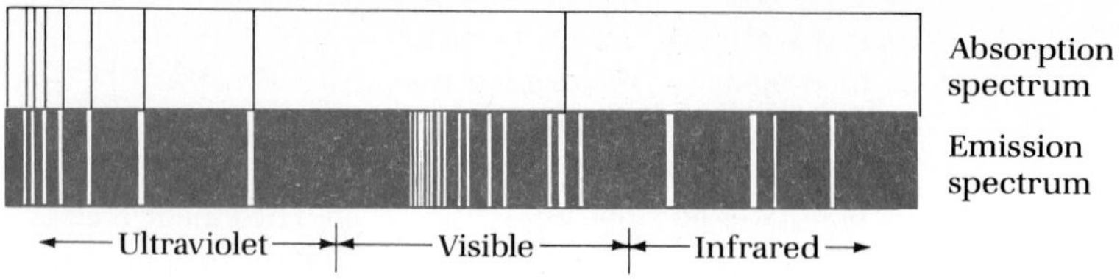

Figure 39-8. The emission and absorption spectra for sodium are shown. Notice the correspondence of lines in the absorption spectrum. (*From Gerald Holton and Duane Roller*, Foundations of Modern Physical Science, *Addison-Wesley, Reading, Mass., 1958.*)

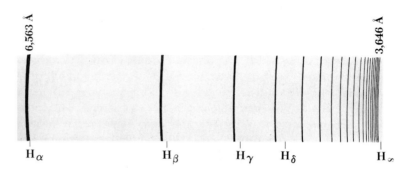

Absorption spectrum

Emission spectrum

←——— Ultraviolet ———→|←——— Visible ———→|←——Infrared——→

Figure 39-9. The Balmer series of spectral lines of hydrogen are shown. The four lines on the right are in the visible portion of the spectrum. The remaining lines are in the ultraviolet. (*From Gerhard Herzberg*, Atomic Spectra and Atomic Structures, *Prentice-Hall, Englewood Cliffs, N.J., 1937.*)

6,563 Å

3,646 Å

H_α H_β H_γ H_δ H_∞

Whether an emission or an absorption spectrum, the line spectrum for a substance is unique. It is analogous to a fingerprint, and can be used for identifying the presence of that substance in a sample. (Notice also the correspondence of certain lines in the emission and absorption spectra in Fig. 39-9.) A spectrum for a substance is characteristic of its atomic or molecular structure and provides information about that structure. A successful model of an atom must account for its characteristic emission and absorption spectra.

The lightest atom, and presumably the simplest, is hydrogen. A portion of its emission spectrum is shown in Fig. 39-9. The four labeled lines — H_α, H_β, H_γ, and H_δ — are in the visible part of the spectrum. The remaining lines shown are in the ultraviolet. Notice the apparent regularity of the spacing of the lines and how the lines come to a wavelength limit at around 364.6 nm. They are members of a series of lines called the *Balmer series.*

Johann Balmer (1825–1898), a Swiss schoolteacher, discovered in 1885 a simple mathematical formula for the wavelengths of the visible lines in the hydrogen spectrum. The Balmer formula had no theoretical basis but was instead an empirical relation that correctly described the regularity in the spectrum. In addition to describing the four visible lines known to Balmer, the formula also gave the wavelengths of lines in the ultraviolet part of the series that were observed thereafter. It is convenient to write the Balmer formula in a form that gives the reciprocal of the wavelength:

Balmer series formula

$$\frac{1}{\lambda} = R_H \left(\frac{1}{2^2} - \frac{1}{n^2} \right) \qquad (n = 3, 4, 5, \ldots) \qquad (39\text{-}9)$$

where $R_H = 1.097 \times 10^7 \text{ m}^{-1}$ is the *Rydberg constant* for hydrogen, named after J. R. Rydberg (1854–1919). If $n = 3$ is inserted into the Balmer formula, the calculated wavelength is $\lambda = 656.3$ nm. This is the wavelength of the first, or longest-wavelength, line H_α in the Balmer series. Using successively larger integers n gives the wavelengths of the corresponding lines in the series. As $n \to \infty$, the Balmer formula gives the series limit, $\lambda = 364.6$ nm.

Series of spectral lines of hydrogen were later discovered in other parts of the spectrum. Each series is described by a formula similar to the Balmer formula. The *Lyman series,* which is entirely in the ultraviolet, has wavelengths given by

Lyman series

$$\frac{1}{\lambda} = R_H \left(\frac{1}{1^2} - \frac{1}{n^2} \right) \qquad (n = 2, 3, 4, \ldots)$$

There are several series that contain lines in the infrared with wavelengths given by

Paschen series

$$\frac{1}{\lambda} = R_H \left(\frac{1}{3^2} - \frac{1}{n^2} \right) \qquad (n = 4, 5, 6, \ldots)$$

Brackett series

$$\frac{1}{\lambda} = R_H \left(\frac{1}{4^2} - \frac{1}{n^2} \right) \qquad (n = 5, 6, 7, \ldots)$$

Pfund series

$$\frac{1}{\lambda} = R_H \left(\frac{1}{5^2} - \frac{1}{n^2} \right) \qquad (n = 6, 7, 8, \ldots)$$

Notice that the Rydberg constant R_H appears in all of these equations. From the common structure of the formulas for these series, it is evident that they can all be expressed by the single, more general expression:

Rydberg formula

$$\frac{1}{\lambda} = R_H \left(\frac{1}{n_f^2} - \frac{1}{n_i^2} \right) \tag{39-10}$$

The integer n_f determines the series: $n_f = 1$ for the Lyman series, $n_f = 2$ for the Balmer series, ... For a given n_f, the values $n_i = n_f + 1$, $n_f + 2$, $n_f + 3$, ... give the wavelengths of successive lines in the series.

It is remarkable that the simple expression in Eq. (39-10) correctly gives the wavelength of each line in the spectrum of hydrogen. It provides a stringent test for a model of the structure of the atom. A successful model must be able to account for the emission of light with wavelengths given by Eq. (39-10) and *only* those wavelengths. That is, there are no observed lines in the spectrum of atomic hydrogen that are not given by Eq. (39-10).

EXAMPLE 39-4. Show that the Paschen series of spectral lines lies entirely in the infrared part of the spectrum.

SOLUTION. The Paschen series corresponds to $n_f = 3$ in Eq. (39-10). Different lines in the series are obtained with $n_i = 4, 5, 6, \ldots$. The longest-wavelength line has $n_i = 4$ and

$$\frac{1}{\lambda_4} = (1.097 \times 10^7 \text{ m}^{-1}) \left(\frac{1}{3^2} - \frac{1}{4^2} \right)$$

$$= 5.333 \times 10^5 \text{ m}^{-1}$$

Inverting gives $\lambda_4 = 1875$ nm, which is a wavelength in the infrared. Other lines in the series have shorter wavelengths and approach the series limit of wavelength λ_∞ given by

$$\frac{1}{\lambda_\infty} = R_H \left(\frac{1}{3^2} - \frac{1}{\infty^2} \right) = \frac{R_H}{9}$$

Inverting gives $\lambda_\infty = 9/R_H = 820.4$ nm, which is also in the infrared. Thus the range of the entire series, 820.4 to 1875 nm, is in the infrared.

39-7 THE BOHR MODEL OF HYDROGEN

In the period 1909–1913, two profound changes occurred in the accepted "picture" of the structure of an atom. It was (and is) widely believed that atoms contain electrons and that the size of an atom is around 0.1 nm. To be neutral, an atom must have, in addition to the negatively charged electrons, an equal amount of positive charge. In the "plum-pudding" model due to J. J. Thomson (1856–1940), a continuous, positively charged medium extended throughout the atom with pointlike electrons arranged inside.

The first change in the picture of the atom concerned the distribution of positive charge and was developed by Ernest Rutherford (1871–1937) as a result of experiments performed under his direction. In these experiments, positively charged α particles (doubly ionized He ions from a naturally occurring radioactive source) were scattered by a thin gold foil. Rutherford was surprised to find that some of the particles were scattered backward from the foil. He later wrote: "It was almost as incredible as if you fired a 15-inch shell at a piece of tissue paper and it came back and hit you." Rutherford argued that the backscattering could occur only if the positive charge of the atom were concentrated in a region very much smaller than the size of that atom. It turns out (see Prob. 39-6) that this region has a linear dimension of less than 10^{-14} m, much smaller than the atom's size of 10^{-10} m.

Rutherford's nuclear, or planetary, model of the atom

Rutherford proposed a *nuclear* model of the atom in which the positive charge, and most of the mass, of an atom is confined to a small *nucleus*. The electric force exerted by the positively charged nucleus on each electron is given by Coulomb's law. Thus the force on an electron is directed toward the nucleus, and its magnitude varies inversely with the square of the electron-nucleus separation. In analogy with the equivalent gravitational problem — planets attracted to a massive sun by the inverse-square gravitational force — the atom was pictured as a miniature solar system with electrons in orbit about the nucleus. The size of the atom was determined by the orbital motion of the electrons about the nucleus.

Consider the planetary model for hydrogen. For simplicity we neglect the motion of the more massive proton (the nucleus of hydrogen with charge $+e$) and suppose that an electron of mass m and charge $-e$ is in a circular orbit of radius r about a stationary proton, as shown in Fig. 39-10. For a circular orbit, the acceleration is v^2/r and, by Newton's second law, the centripetal force is mv^2/r. The centripetal force on the electron is provided by the Coulomb force so that

$$\frac{mv^2}{r} = \frac{e^2}{4\pi\epsilon_0 r^2}$$

By multiplying this equation by $\frac{1}{2}r$, $\frac{1}{2}r(mv^2/r) = \frac{1}{2}mv^2$, we obtain the kinetic energy K of the electron in terms of the radius of the orbit.

$$K = \frac{e^2}{8\pi\epsilon_0 r} \tag{39-11}$$

(We have assumed that $v \ll c$ so that $K = \frac{1}{2}mv^2$.) The electric potential energy U of the pair of charges is given by (see Chap. 22)

$$U = -\frac{e^2}{4\pi\epsilon_0 r} \tag{39-12}$$

Adding Eqs. (39-11) and (39-12), we obtain the mechanical energy, $E = K + U$, for an electron in a circular orbit of radius r about the proton:

$$E = -\frac{e^2}{8\pi\epsilon_0 r} \tag{39-13}$$

Notice that the zero of mechanical energy corresponds to an infinite separation

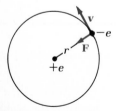

Figure 39-10. In a planetary model of the hydrogen atom, an electron is in a circular orbit about a proton.

$(r \rightarrow \infty)$ of the particles, with both at rest. Thus the negative value of E in Eq. (39-13) corresponds to a *bound* state or orbit. Orbits of smaller radius have energies that are lower or more negative.

Using Eq. (39-13), we can discuss a serious difficulty with the planetary model of an atom. In classical electromagnetism, an accelerated charge emits electromagnetic radiation. Since an electron in orbit is accelerated ($a = v^2/r$), it should radiate electromagnetic energy. From conservation of energy, the atom would lose energy and, according to Eq. (39-13), the radius of the oribit would decrease as the energy decreases. Thus, in a classical planetary model, an electron orbit would be unstable, with the electron spiraling into the nucleus as it radiates electromagnetic energy. Contrary to the classical model, this catastrophic process does not occur: Stable atoms do exist.

The Bohr model. In 1913 Niels Bohr (1885–1962) modified the planetary model for hydrogen. This modified model contained features that conflicted with some of the principles of classical physics. It represented the beginning of a *quantum* theory of matter. To circumvent the classical problem of an electron radiating and spiraling into the nucleus, Bohr postulated the existence of certain *stationary* states of the atom. Such states are stationary in the sense that no radiation is emitted when an electron is in one of these states. That is, even though the electron in a stationary state is moving, it does not emit radiation.

An electron in a stationary state does not emit light.

Guided by the discreteness of the emission spectrum of hydrogen, which is described by Eq. (39-10), Bohr assumed that radiation is emitted by the atom when the electron undergoes a *transition* from one stationary state to another. The energy emitted in a transition from an initial stationary state of energy E_i to a final stationary state of energy E_f is $E_i - E_f$. The radiated energy (the energy of a photon), $h\nu = E_i - E_f$, corresponds to radiation of frequency ν or wavelength $\lambda = c/\nu$. The discrete character of the spectrum of hydrogen suggested a corresponding discreteness in the energy of stationary states or orbits. The word "quantum" refers to this discreteness in a quantity, which classically could have a continuous range of values.

A photon is emitted in a transition between stationary states.

Bohr recognized that discrete orbits result from a new, nonclassical condition—that the orbital angular momentum be discrete or *quantized*. For an electron in a circular orbit or radius r and speed v, the Bohr model requires that the magnitude, $L = mvr$, of the orbital angular momentum be a positive integer multiple of $h/2\pi$:

Angular momentum is quantized.

$$L = \frac{nh}{2\pi} \qquad (n = 1, 2, 3, \ldots) \tag{39-14}$$

The radius of each of these circular orbits can be obtained by applying Coulomb's law and the quantization condition in Eq. (39-14). Since the centripetal force is provided by the Coulomb force exerted on the electron by the proton, we have

$$\frac{mv^2}{r} = \frac{e^2}{4\pi\epsilon_0 r^2}$$

$$\tag{39-15}$$

$$mvr = \frac{nh}{2\pi}$$

where the second relation comes from Eq. (39-14). The two equations above can be solved (see Exercise 39-37) for the radius r and the speed v of the electron in the circular orbit. The radius of the orbit depends on the integer n and is given by

$$r_n = \frac{\epsilon_0 h^2}{\pi m e^2} n^2 \qquad (n = 1, 2, 3, \ldots) \qquad (39\text{-}16)$$

Notice that $n = 1$ corresponds to the orbit with the smallest radius. This distance, denoted by the symbol a_0 and called the *Bohr radius*, is determined by fundamental constants, $a_0 = (\epsilon_0 h^2)/(\pi m e^2)$. Inserting the values of the constants, we obtain $a_0 = 0.053$ nm, which is about the size of an atom. The radii of the other orbits are given by $r_n = a_0 n^2$ from Eq. (39-16). Thus $r_2 = 4a_0$, $r_3 = 9a_0$, $r_4 = 16a_0$, ...

The energy E for an electron in a circular orbit is given in terms of the radius by Eq. (39-13). If r in that equation is replaced by r_n, the discrete, or *quantized*, energy of a stationary state of hydrogen is obtained:

$$E_n = -\frac{e^2}{8\pi\epsilon_0 r_n}$$

Substituting for r_n from Eq. (39-16) and simplifying (see Exercise 39-38), we have

$$E_n = -\frac{m e^4}{8\epsilon_0^2 h^2 n^2} \qquad (n = 1, 2, 3, \ldots) \qquad (39\text{-}17)$$

The stationary state with the lowest, or most negative, energy is called the *ground state* and corresponds to $n = 1$. The ground-state energy is $E_1 = -2.17 \times 10^{-18}$ J $= -13.6$ eV. The energies of the next few states, given by $E_n = E_1/n^2$, in order of increasing energy are $E_2 = E_1/2^2 = -3.4$ eV, $E_3 = -1.5$ eV, $E_4 = -0.9$ eV, ...

The discrete nature of the energy for the stationary states is conveniently displayed on an *energy-level diagram*. A simple energy-level diagram for hydrogen is shown in Fig. 39-11. Each of the horizontal lines represents an allowed value of the energy of a stationary state. The vertical line shows the energy scale, with the zero of energy corresponding to an ionized atom. Notice that the *quantum number n* labels the energy of a stationary state.

According to Bohr, an atom does not radiate when in a stationary state. Radiation is emitted, in the form of a photon, only when an atom undergoes a transition from one stationary state to another one of lower energy. To see how this idea results in the spectrum of hydrogen, consider an atom initially in a state with quantum number n_i. The energy of this state is given by inserting n_i for n in Eq. (39-17). Suppose the atom makes a transition to a state of lower energy with quantum number n_f, so that $n_f < n_i$. If a photon of energy $h\nu$ is emitted in the transition, then by conservation of energy, $E_i = E_f + h\nu$, or

$$h\nu = E_i - E_f \qquad (39\text{-}18)$$

Since $\nu = c/\lambda$, Eq. (39-18) can be solved for $1/\lambda$ and compared with the formula containing the Rydberg constant in Eq. (39-10). If the energies E_i and E_f are expressed in terms of n_i and n_f, then Eq. (39-18) can be rewritten as (Exercise 39-39)

$$\frac{1}{\lambda} = \frac{m e^4}{8\epsilon_0^2 h^3 c} \left(\frac{1}{n_f^2} - \frac{1}{n_i^2} \right) \qquad (39\text{-}19)$$

From Eq. (39-10), the Rydberg constant R_H is identified with the combination of fundamental constants that multiplies the term in parentheses in Eq. (39-19). Thus the Bohr model gives a theoretical basis to the Rydberg constant and

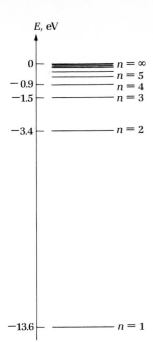

Figure 39-11. An energy-level diagram for hydrogen shows the energy of each of the stationary states.

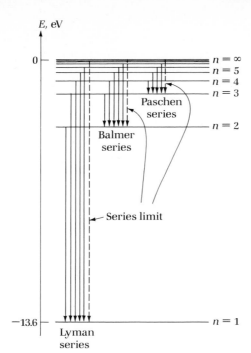

Figure 39-12. Transitions are shown for three of the series in the hydrogen emission spectrum.

$$R_{\text{H}} = \frac{me^4}{8\epsilon_0{}^2 h^3 c} \tag{39-20}$$

Each of the lines in the spectrum of hydrogen can be associated with a transition between two stationary states. These transitions are conveniently displayed on the energy-level diagram in Fig. 39-12. The horizontal lines representing the energy levels have been extended so that a number of transitions can be shown. The transitions are arranged according to series. Notice that each line in the Lyman series is due to a transition to the ground state from a state of higher energy. Similarly, each line in the Balmer series corresponds to a transition to a state with $n = 2$ from a state of higher energy. You can also see from the diagram how a series limit occurs because of the concentration of levels near $E = 0$. If the atom is in the ground state ($n = 1$), there is no state of lower energy to which a downward transition can occur. Thus an atom in the ground state is stable.

The Bohr model of hydrogen represented a beginning step in the development of a quantum theory of atomic structure. It contained a mixture of the older classical physics and the newer quantum ideas that were being sorted out during the early part of this century. Some of the features of the Bohr model, such as a set of discrete circular orbits, are no longer taken seriously. However, many of Bohr's concepts are essential parts of the structure of quantum theory.*

* We shall look at these concepts in the next few chapters in the "extended" edition of this text.

EXAMPLE 39-5. An electron in a hydrogen atom makes a transition between the states with $n_i = 5$ and $n_f = 2$. (a) Determine the energy of the initial state and of the final state. (b) Determine the energy of the photon and the wavelength of the emitted radiation.

SOLUTION. (a) Using Eq. (39-17) with $me^4/(8\epsilon_0{}^2 h^2) = 13.6$ eV, we have

$$E_i = \frac{-13.6 \text{ eV}}{n_i{}^2} = -0.544 \text{ eV}$$

$$E_f = \frac{-13.6 \text{ eV}}{n_f^2} = -3.40 \text{ eV}$$

$$\nu = \frac{(2.86 \text{ eV})(1.60 \times 10^{-19} \text{ J/eV})}{6.63 \times 10^{-34} \text{ J} \cdot \text{s}} = 6.89 \times 10^{14} \text{ Hz}$$

(b) Conservation of energy, as expressed in Eq. (39-18), gives the energy of the photon:

The wavelength, $\lambda = c/\nu$, is

$$h\nu = E_i - E_f = (-0.54 \text{ eV}) - (-3.40 \text{ eV}) = 2.86 \text{ eV}$$

Solving for the frequency of the radiation, we obtain

$$\lambda = \frac{3.00 \times 10^8 \text{ m/s}}{6.89 \times 10^{14} \text{ Hz}} = 435 \text{ nm}$$

COMMENTARY: NIELS BOHR AND HIS MODEL OF THE HYDROGEN ATOM

Niels Bohr in 1917. (A.I.P., Niels Bohr Library/W. F. Meggers Collection)

Niels Bohr, born in Copenhagen, Denmark, on October 7, 1885, began his study of physics in 1903 at the University of Copenhagen. Four years later, he was awarded the gold medal of the Royal Danish Academy for his careful work on the surface tension of liquids. For his graduate work, Bohr considered electric, magnetic, and thermal properties of metals and noted the inadequacy of the existing theory of electrons for understanding these properties.

After receiving the doctoral degree in 1911, Bohr obtained an appointment at Cambridge University and worked in the Cavendish Laboratory under the direction of J. J. Thomson. There was a notable and unresolved language problem. He wrote to his mother, "You have no idea of the confusion reigning in the Cavendish laboratory, and a poor foreigner, who does not even know what the different things he cannot find are called, is in a very awkward position . . . ."

Early in 1912, Bohr left Cambridge and joined the Manchester Laboratory under the leadership of Ernest Rutherford. Only the year before, Rutherford had proposed his nuclear, or planetary, model of the atom. Bohr was interested in the model because of its success in describing alpha-particle scattering, and he wanted to work on the apparent lack of stability in the planetary model.

Although the eventual picture that emerged of the atom is familiar to us and seems obvious, there was no general agreement in 1912 about some of the most elementary features of the atom. For example, it was not at all clear how many electrons were contained in an atom. J. J. Thomson had earlier supposed that each atom contained thousands of electrons arranged in coplanar, revolving rings inside a uniform sphere of positive charge. One of Thomson's major goals was to determine the number of electrons in an atom. His experiments led him to revise the number downward. It was Rutherford's alpha-particle experiments that provided the evidence that the number of electrons was approximately half the mass number of an atom.

Returning to Copenhagen, Bohr attempted to find the final, stable configuration of electrons revolving about a central nucleus. He was not successful, but his calculations did lead to the suggestion that hydrogen should have one electron, helium should have two electrons, lithium should have three electrons, ...

Since he had been concentrating on determining a final, stable electronic configuration, Bohr had not yet attempted to deal with the characteristic spectra emitted by atoms. In February of 1913, a colleague of Bohr's called his attention to Balmer's formula for the spectral lines of hydrogen. Bohr later related, "As soon as I saw Balmer's formula, everything became clear to me." In less than a month, he was able to put together the first of his famous papers on the structure of the atom.

Bohr was still a very young man when he developed his model of atomic hydrogen. He made many important contributions to atomic and nuclear physics. Perhaps even more important was the leadership that he provided as the quantum theory developed over the next 20 years.

For further reading, see Niels Bohr—His Life and Work as Seen by His Friends and Colleagues, *edited by Stefan Rozental (North-Holland, Amsterdam, 1967) and ''Bohr's First Theories of the Atom'' by John L. Heilbron in* Physics Today *(vol. 38, no. 10, 1985, pp. 28–36).*

SUMMARY WITH APPLICATIONS

Section 39-2. Interaction of light and matter
A surface that is a good absorber (poor reflector) is a good emitter of light, and a surface that is a poor absorber (good reflector) is a poor emitter of light. The power radiated by a surface is given by the Stefan-Boltzmann law:

$$P = e\sigma A T^4$$

The ideal absorber, a blackbody with emissivity $e = 1$, is an ideal emitter. Blackbody radiation can be approximated by radiation emerging from a cavity.

Describe the connection between the radiative emitting and absorbing properties of a surface and explain why the radiation from a cavity can be treated as blackbody radiation.

Section 39-3. Cavity radiation
The energy of an oscillator of frequency ν is quantized;

$$E = nh\nu$$

Spectral radiancy for blackbody radiation is given by the Planck expression,

$$R_\nu = \frac{2\pi h\nu^3}{c^2(e^{h\nu/kT} - 1)} \tag{39-2}$$

State Planck's proposals on the energy of an oscillator and explain how this behavior differs from that of a classical oscillator; determine the spectral radiancy for a given frequency or wavelength.

Section 39-4. The photoelectric effect
Einstein proposed that light consists of a stream of photons; each photon has energy

$$E = h\nu \tag{39-3}$$

In the photoelectric effect, an ejected electron has a maximum kinetic energy:

$$K_{\max} = h\nu - \phi \tag{39-4}$$

The work function ϕ for a material is related to the threshold frequency ν_0 by $\phi = h\nu_0$. A photon for light of wavelength λ has momentum of magnitude

$$p = \frac{h}{\lambda} \tag{39-5}$$

Determine the energy and momentum of a photon for radiation of a given frequency; apply the photon picture to explain the photoelectric effect.

Section 39-5. Photons and electrons
In the Compton effect, electrons scatter radiation with a change in the wavelength of the radiation that depends on the scattering angle,

$$\lambda' - \lambda = \frac{h}{mc}(1 - \cos\theta) \tag{39-8}$$

Determine the wavelength shift in the Compton effect.

Section 39-6. Line spectra
The spectrum of hydrogen consists of series of lines described by

$$\frac{1}{\lambda} = R_H\left(\frac{1}{n_f{}^2} - \frac{1}{n_i{}^2}\right) \tag{39-10}$$

Each pair of integers, n_i and n_f with $n_i > n_f$, corresponds to a line in the spectrum.

Determine the wavelength of any line in the spectrum of hydrogen.

Section 39-7. The Bohr model of hydrogen
In the Rutherford-Bohr model of the hydrogen atom, the angular momentum and the energy of stationary states are quantized:

$$L = \frac{nh}{2\pi} \tag{39-14}$$

$$E_n = -\frac{me^4}{8\epsilon_0{}^2 h^2 n^2} \tag{39-17}$$

In a transition between stationary states, a photon is emitted with energy

$$h\nu = E_i - E_f \tag{39-18}$$

Describe the Bohr model of atomic hydrogen; determine the energy of a stationary state of the hydrogen atom and the energy of a photon emitted or absorbed in a transition.

QUESTIONS

39-1 If all objects emit radiation, then why can we not see in the dark? What *is* "the dark"?

39-2 A surface absorbs more strongly in the red than in the blue part of the spectrum. What would you expect the color of the surface to be if illuminated by (*a*) the sun, (*b*) a red incandescent bulb, (*c*) a blue incandescent bulb?

39-3 The fraction of light reflected by a surface can depend on the wavelength of the radiation. When you look at your image in a mirror, are all colors faithfully imaged? How can you be sure?

39-4 Develop an analogy between the quantized energy of an oscillator and the currency of the United States. What is the discrete amount or quantum of money? Is it possible to make change for an item costing $1.50? 1.5¢?

39-5 The light coming from the surface of the sun approximates blackbody radiation for $T = 6000$ K. Would the temperature of the surface of a red giant star be higher or lower than 6000 K? Explain.

39-6 As a result of the "big bang," the universe seems to contain background electromagnetic radiation as if it were a cavity. How can a measurement of this radiation be related to the background temperature (about 3 K) of the universe?

39-7 Use a mirror to look at the pupil (the innermost circle) of your eye, or look at the pupil of a friend's eye. What color is it? Explain.

39-8 Consider electrons ejected from a surface due to monochromatic incident light. How does the maximum kinetic energy of ejected electrons change if (*a*) the frequency is changed, (*b*) the intensity is doubled, (*c*) the exposure time is doubled?

39-9 Explain how a circuit similar to that in Fig. 39-4 could be used in a burglar alarm. What are some other applications of the photoelectric effect?

39-10 A chemical bond can be broken if a sufficient amount of energy is suddenly supplied. It is observed that most plastic storage bags are stable when exposed to ordinary house lights but deteriorate when exposed to sunlight. Explain.

39-11 Photosynthesis proceeds by chemical reactions that are initiated by the absorption of light. Explain why a plant can thrive if exposed to light containing visible and ultraviolet frequencies but cannot if exposed only to infrared radiation.

39-12 A beam of monochromatic x-ray photons is scattered by free electrons in a metal foil. Is the frequency of the scattered radiation greater or less than that of the incident radiation? How do the wavelengths compare? Explain.

39-13 A shift in x-ray wavelength due to Compton scattering by free electrons in a foil can be detected. Would you expect a detectable shift due to Compton scattering by the positively charged ions in the foil? Explain.

39-14 Which series in the emission spectrum of hydrogen has the highest frequencies? In what part of the spectrum are these lines?

39-15 The lines in the Lyman series do not overlap those of the Balmer series. Is there a series that overlaps the Paschen series? If so, what series?

39-16 Which series in the spectrum of hydrogen has lines in the visible part of the spectrum? How many lines are there in the visible spectrum? In what part of the spectrum are the remainder of the lines of this series?

39-17 The masses of the electron, alpha particle, and gold atom are $m_e = 9.1 \times 10^{-31}$ kg, $m_\alpha = 6.4 \times 10^{-27}$ kg, $m_{Au} = 3.3 \times 10^{-25}$ kg. Why could Rutherford neglect the effect on the alpha particle of the electrons in a gold atom while claiming that the positive charge of the atom is confined to a very small region?

39-18 In the Bohr model, is an electron in a stationary state of hydrogen at rest? Explain.

39-19 List and explain some similarities and differences between the Bohr model of hydrogen and the orbital motion of a planet about the sun.

39-20 When an electron undergoes a transition from a state of higher energy to one of lower energy, how is the energy difference accounted for? What is the interpretation if the transition is from lower to higher energy?

39-21 Consider the transitions shown in Fig. 39-12 for the lines of the Balmer series. Is one electron in one atom responsible for all of these transitions, or are these lines formed by electrons making transitions in many different atoms? Explain.

39-22 Complete the following table:

Symbol	Represents	Type	SI unit
R			
R_ν			
R_λ			
h			
V_s	Stopping potential		
K_{max}		Scalar	
R_H			m^{-1}

EXERCISES

Section 39-2. Interaction of light and matter

39-1 A sphere of radius 250 mm has a layer of lampblack on its surface. Determine the radiated power if the surface temperature is (a) $T = 300$ K, (b) $T = 600$ K, (c) $T = 1500$ K.

39-2 Treating the sun as a blackbody at 6000 K, estimate the intensity of solar radiation incident on the earth. The radius of the sun is 7×10^8 m, and the mean radius of the earth's orbit is 1.5×10^{11} m.

39-3 A thin-walled Al sphere of radius $R = 280$ mm has a circular opening in its surface of radius $a = 2.8$ mm. The sphere is kept at 1100 K, and the emissivity of its surface under these conditions is $e = 0.32$. (a) Determine the energy radiated from the opening in an hour. (b) What surface area of the sphere would radiate the same energy in that time interval? (c) What differences do you expect in the visual appearances of the opening and the surface?

Section 39-3. Cavity radiation

39-4 Show that Planck's constant has dimensions of (a) (energy)(time), (b) (momentum)(length), (c) (angular momentum)(angle).

39-5 A quantum oscillator has frequency $\nu = 10^{13}$ Hz. (a) What is the minimum change in energy of the oscillator? (b) For what frequency would the minimum energy change be 1 eV? 1 J?

39-6 Consider a cavity in the form of a cube of edge 200 mm. (a) Using standing waves on a string (Chap. 32) as a guide, estimate the lowest frequency for standing wave modes in the cavity. (b) What is the minimum change in the energy of this mode? (c) Compare the answer for part (b) with the average energy of a classical standing-wave mode at $T = 300$ K.

39-7 Determine the average energy of a quantum oscillator of frequency 2×10^{12} Hz in equilibrium at (a) $T = 0.42$ K, (b) $T = 4.2$ K (liquid helium temperature), (c) $T = 300$ K, (d) $T = 1000$ K.

39-8 (a) For each case in the preceding exercise, compare the average energy of the quantum oscillator with the average energy of a classical oscillator at that temperature. (b) Using Eq. (39-1), show that $\langle E \rangle \approx kT$ if $h\nu \ll kT$. Note that $e^x \approx 1 + x$ if $x \ll 1$.

39-9 The spectral radiancy is often expressed for a differential range $d\lambda$ of wavelength such that $R_\lambda \, d\lambda = -R_\nu \, d\nu$, or $R_\lambda = -R_\nu \, d\nu/d\lambda$, with R_ν given by Eq. (39-2). Determine the expression for R_λ. This is the form used by Planck.

39-10 (a) Obtain Eq. (39-2) by taking 1/4 of the product of Eq. (39-1), the average energy of an oscillator, and $8\pi\nu^2 \, d\nu/c^3$, the number of standing-wave modes per unit volume with frequencies in the range $d\nu$.

(b) Show from Eq. (39-2) that $R_\nu \, d\nu$ has dimensions of (power)/(area).

Section 39-4. The photoelectric effect

39-11 The visible part of the spectrum has wavelengths in the range of 400 to 750 nm. What is the range of energies of photons in this part of the spectrum? Express your answers both in eV and in J.

39-12 One of the intense spectral lines emitted by a mercury vapor light has a wavelength $\lambda = 546.1$ nm. For light of this wavelength, determine (a) the frequency, (b) the energy of a photon, (c) the magnitude of the momentum of a photon. (d) Suppose that a beam of this monochromatic light has intensity 1 W/m². Determine the number of photons per second that pass through a 1-m² area oriented perpendicular to the direction of the beam.

39-13 The work function for a clean surface of Na is 2.5 eV. (a) Determine the photoelectric threshold frequency. (b) The surface is illuminated with monochromatic light of wavelength 550 nm. Will electrons be emitted from the surface? Explain.

39-14 Monochromatic light of frequency 6.77×10^{14} Hz is incident on a Na surface with work function 2.46 eV. (a) Determine the maximum kinetic energy of the photoelectrons. (b) What potential must be applied between cathode and anode to reduce the photocurrent to zero?

39-15 In a photoelectric experiment, the stopping potential is determined for each of a set of frequencies. The data for one run is summarized in the table below. (a) Construct a graph similar to that in Fig. 39-5. (b) Use the graph to determine a value for the work function of the cathode surface and a value for Planck's constant:

ν, 10^{14} Hz	V_s, V
7.8	0.11
7.9	0.16
8.1	0.25
8.6	0.46
8.7	0.49

39-16 For the surface described in the previous exercise, determine the stopping potential for electrons emitted when the surface is illuminated with light of wavelength (a) 200 nm, (b) 400 nm, (c) 600 nm.

39-17 When light of wavelength $\lambda_1 = 620$ nm is incident on a photocell surface, electrons are ejected with a maximum kinetic energy of 0.14 eV. Determine (a) the work function and (b) the threshold frequency for this surface. What is the maximum kinetic energy of ejected electrons if the surface is illuminated with light of wavelength (c) $\lambda_2 = \frac{1}{2}\lambda_1$ and (d) $\lambda_3 = 2\lambda_1$?

39-18 Monochromatic light of intensity 10^{-14} W/m² illuminates at normal incidence a 1-cm² surface with work function 3 eV. Suppose that an electron bound to an atom near the surface can continuously absorb all of the energy from the *classical wave* incident on an area of 1 nm by 1 nm. (a) What is the power absorbed by the electron? (b) Estimate the time necessary for an electron to absorb enough energy from the classical wave to escape from the surface. (c) Using the photon picture, explain how an electron can be ejected from the surface with no noticeable time delay.

39-19 The surface of a metal alloy is illuminated with 280-nm light in the presence of oxygen. As the surface gradually becomes corroded, the stopping potential changes from 1.3 to 0.7 V. Determine the corresponding changes, if any, in (a) the maximum kinetic energy of electrons ejected from the surface, (b) the work function, (c) the threshold frequency, (d) Planck's constant.

39-20 For monochromatic light of wavelength λ and frequency ν, show that (a) the energy of a photon is $E = hc/\lambda$ and (b) the magnitude of the momentum of a photon is $p = h\nu/c$. (c) What is the value of E/p for a photon?

Section 39-5. Photons and electrons

39-21 Show that the meter is the SI unit of the Compton wavelength h/mc for a particle.

39-22 Determine the Compton wavelength for (a) an electron, (b) a proton, (c) an O_2 molecule, (d) a 75-kg student.

39-23 X-rays of wavelength 71 pm are scattered by free electrons in a metal foil. Determine the wavelength of x-rays Compton-scattered through an angle of (a) π rad, (b) $\frac{1}{2}\pi$ rad, (c) 0.1 rad.

39-24 When a beam of x-rays is Compton-scattered through 60° by free electrons, the wavelength is measured to be 12.6 pm. Determine the wavelength of (a) the incident radiation and (b) the radiation scattered through 120°.

39-25 X-ray wavelengths can be measured in a certain spectrometer with a resolution of 1 pm. An incident x-ray beam of wavelength 71 pm is scattered by free electrons. At what minimum angle of scatter can the Compton-scattered wavelength be resolved from the wavelength of the incident beam?

39-26 X-rays of wavelength 0.1542 nm are scattered by free electrons. (a) Determine the energy of a photon in the incident beam. (b) If an electron, initially at rest, scatters a photon through π rad, determine the recoil energy of the electron.

39-27 An 8.3-MeV gamma ray (electromagnetic radiation from a nuclear process) is Compton-scattered through $\frac{1}{2}\pi$ rad by a free electron initially at rest. Determine (a) the energy of the scattered photon and

(b) the magnitude and direction of the recoil momentum of the electron.

Section 39-6. Line spectra

39-28 Calculate (a) the wavelength and (b) the frequency of each of the four lines of hydrogen that are in the visible part of the spectrum.

39-29 (a) Show that the Balmer series formula can be written in the form $\lambda_m = bm^2/(m^2 - n^2)$, where b is a constant, $n = 2$, and $m = 3, 4, 5, \ldots$. This is the form originally proposed by Balmer. (b) Express b in terms of the Rydberg constant R_H. (c) What is the numerical value of b?

39-30 Determine the values of the longest wavelength and the series limit for (a) the Lyman series, (b) the Balmer series, (c) the Paschen series, (d) the Brackett series. (e) Which, if any, of these series has lines in overlapping regions of the spectrum?

39-31 Show that the frequency ν_{31} of the hydrogen line for $n_i = 3, n_f = 1$ equals the sum $\nu_{32} + \nu_{21}$, where ν_{32} corresponds to $n_i = 3$, $n_f = 2$, and ν_{21} corresponds to $n_i = 2$, $n_f = 1$.

39-32 One of the lines in the hydrogen spectrum has a frequency $\nu = 1.6 \times 10^{14}$ Hz. Determine the series to which this line belongs and identify the line by giving the values of n_i and n_f.

Section 39-7. The Bohr model of hydrogen

39-33 (a) Show that the Bohr radius, $a_0 = (\epsilon_0 h^2/\pi m e^2)$, has dimensions of length. (b) Substitute in the values of the constants and determine the value of a_0 to three significant figures.

39-34 A hydrogen atom is in the state $n = 2$. Assume that the electron is in a circular orbit and determine (a) the radius of the orbit, (b) the electric potential energy, (c) the kinetic energy, (d) the total energy of the electron in this orbit.

39-35 An electron in a hydrogen atom makes a transition from an initial state with $n_i = 5$ to a final state with $n_f = 3$. (a) Identify the series and the line for the radiation emitted for this transition. (b) Determine the initial and the final energies of the electron. (c) Determine the frequency and wavelength of the radiation emitted for this transition.

39-36 An electron undergoes successive transitions in a hydrogen atom. Initially the electron is in the state $n_a = 6$. In the first transition, to an intermediate state n_b, a photon of energy 1.13 eV is emitted. After the second transition, the electron is in the ground state $n_c = 1$. (a) Determine the quantum number n_b for the intermediate state. (b) Determine the energy of the photon emitted in the second transition. (c) Show these two transitions on an energy-level diagram for hydrogen.

39-37 Solve Eqs. (39-15) for the radius r_n and speed v_n of an electron in a Bohr orbit.

39-38 The mechanical energy, $E = K + U$, of an electron in a circular orbit in the Bohr model of hydrogen is given by Eq. (39-13). Use the radius of the nth Bohr orbit in Eq. (39-16) to obtain the energy of a stationary state of hydrogen, Eq. (39-17).

39-39 (a) Show that Eqs. (39-17) and (39-18) lead to the Balmer formula and express the Rydberg constant in terms of the fundamental constants. (b) Substitute in the values of the constants and determine the value of R_H to five significant figures.

39-40 (a) Suppose that the orbital angular momentum of the earth about the sun is quantized as in Eq. (39-14). Assume a circular orbit of radius 1.5×10^{11} m and estimate the value of n for this orbit. (b) Develop the counterpart of Eq. (39-16) by replacing the Coulomb force of the proton on the electron by the gravitational force of the sun on the earth. (c) Determine the radius of an orbit with $n = 1$. Is this a physically meaningful value?

39-41 **Absorption spectrum.** Consider an electron in the ground state of a hydrogen atom. It can undergo a transition by absorbing a photon. (a) Develop an expression, similar to the Rydberg formula for emission, for the inverse wavelengths $(1/\lambda)$ *absorbed* by atomic hydrogen. (b) Show these transitions on an energy-level diagram. (c) To which series in the *emission* spectrum of hydrogen does this absorption series correspond? (d) Explain why lines corresponding to the other emission series are not readily observed in the absorption spectrum.

39-42 A large number of hydrogen atoms are initially in the state with $n = 6$. Consider all possible combinations of transitions originating from atoms in this state as the electrons undergo radiative transitions. Be sure to include transitions to and from intermediate states. (a) Show each of these transitions on an energy-level diagram. (b) Identify the series and line in the emission spectrum of hydrogen that corresponds to each transition. (c) What is the total number of distinct transitions in this sequence?

PROBLEMS

39-1 Consider an object in thermal equilibrium with its surroundings at temperature T, as shown in Fig. 39-13. Prove that the rate at which the object emits radiation equals the rate at which it absorbs radiation. The proof consists of assuming that the rates are unequal and showing that this assumption would lead to a violation of the second law of thermodynamics. The space between the object and the surrounding walls is evacuated so that there is no convection or conduction of heat. How can the proof be extended to show that the rates of emission and absorption are the same at each frequency?

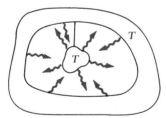

Figure 39-13. Prob. 39-1: A body at temperature T is suspended by an insulating thread and is surrounded by walls at the same temperature.

39-2 **Wien's displacement law.** (a) Obtain, as in Exercise 39-9, the blackbody spectral radiancy R_λ for a differential wavelength range $d\lambda$. (b) Show that the wavelength λ_m at which the spectral radiancy is maximum depends on the temperature such that $\lambda_m T = $ constant and show that the value of this constant is 2.90×10^{-3} K · m. This result is known as *Wien's dis-*placement law. (*Hint:* $e^{hc/\lambda kT} \gg 1$ for $\lambda = \lambda_m$.) (c) Determine λ_m for a blackbody at $T = 6000$ K, the surface temperature of the sun.

39-3 Show that Planck's radiation law leads to (a) the Rayleigh-Jeans result, $R_\nu = 2\pi\nu^2 kT/c^2$, at low frequencies ($h\nu \ll kT$), where $e^{h\nu/kT} - 1 \approx h\nu/kT$, and to (b) the Stefan-Boltzmann law, $R = \sigma T^4$. Determine the constant σ in terms of fundamental constants. (*Hint:* You should encounter an integral which can be put in the form

$$\int_0^\infty \frac{x^3}{e^x - 1}\, dx = \frac{\pi^4}{15}$$

39-4 Apply the conservation laws for energy and momentum to the Compton effect and obtain Eq. (39-8).

39-5 If the incident photon energy is not too high, nonrelativistic expressions for the energy ($\frac{1}{2}mv^2$) and magnitude of momentum (mv) of the electron may be used. (a) Set up the equations similarly to those in Sec. 39-5 and show that

$$\lambda' - \lambda = \frac{h}{2mc}\left(\frac{\lambda'}{\lambda} + \frac{\lambda}{\lambda'} - 2\cos\theta\right)$$

(b) For a low photon energy, $h\nu = hc/\lambda \ll mc^2$ and $\lambda' \approx \lambda$; show that the right-hand side of the above expression then reproduces Eq. (39-8), which is valid for any photon energy.

39-6 Consider a head-on collision between an alpha particle, treated as a point particle of charge $+2e$, and a spherical, positively charged part of an atom of charge $+Ze$, where Z is the atomic number and R is the radius of the sphere. Assume that the massive atom remains essentially at rest and that the alpha particle has initial kinetic energy K, with $K \ll m_\alpha c^2$. If the alpha particle is scattered backward as a result of the Coulomb force, then it must come momentarily to rest at a minimum distance r_0 from the center of the atom. (a) Show that this minimum distance is $r_0 = Ze^2/(2\pi\epsilon_0 K)$ if the alpha particle does not penetrate the sphere of charge—that is, if $r_0 > R$. (b) Use this result to estimate an upper limit on the size of the sphere of charge for gold ($Z = 79$) if $K = 5$ MeV. (c) If the positively charged sphere were larger, so that an alpha particle penetrated the sphere of charge, then explain why the alpha particle would not be expected to backscatter.

39-7   *The correspondence principle.* One of the arguments used by Bohr to obtain Eq. (39-17) involved the *correspondence principle.* In the context of the hydrogen-atom problem, this principle states that the frequency of the radiation emitted in a transition between state n and state $n - 1$, where n is very large, is the same as the classical orbital frequency of an electron in an orbit of radius r_n. (a) Show that the Rydberg formula, coupled with the expression $h\nu = E_{n_i} - E_{n_f}$, implies that $E_n = -hcR_H/n^2 = -e^2/(8\pi\epsilon_0 r_n)$ from Eq. (39-13). Use the last equality to obtain $r_n = n^2 e^2/(8\pi\epsilon_0 hcR_H)$. (b) Use the Rydberg formula to show that the frequency emitted in the transition from state n to state $n - 1$, with $n \gg 1$, is $\nu = 2cR_H/n^3$. (c) Classically, the frequency emitted by a charged particle in a circular orbit is equal to the particle's orbital frequency, $\nu = v_n/2\pi r_n$. Express this frequency in terms

of the radius r_n of the orbit and show that its square is $\nu^2 = e^2/(16\pi^3\epsilon_0 m r_n^3)$. (d) Equate expressions for ν^2 from parts (b) and (c) and solve for r_n^3. (e) Eliminate r_n from parts (a) and (d) to show that $R_H = me^4/(8\epsilon_0^2 h^3 c)$, and that $E_n = -me^4/(8\epsilon_0^2 h^2 n^2)$.

39-8   The mass m that appears in Eqs. (39-16), (39-17), and (39-20) is the electron mass m_e, based on the assumption that the nucleus is at rest. To correct for the motion of the nucleus of mass M, the *reduced mass* $m = m_e M/(m_e + M)$ of the system should be used in those expressions. Determine the values, to five significant figures, of the Rydberg constant and the wavelength of the H_α line for (a) normal hydrogen with a single proton as the nucleus and (b) deuterium, or heavy hydrogen, with the deuteron as the nucleus ($m_d = 3.3441 \times 10^{-27}$ kg). (c) Determine the difference in wavelengths of the H_α line for normal and heavy hydrogen. This difference can be observed in the spectrum and corresponds to the 0.015 percent natural abundance of the heavy-hydrogen isotope.

39-9   Singly ionized He has one remaining electron and a nuclear charge of $2e$. (a) Show that the Rydberg constant for singly ionized He is 4 times the Rydberg constant for H. (b) Identify the quantum numbers for the transitions in singly ionized He that have virtually the same wavelengths as the wavelengths of the Balmer series lines in H. How is this part of the singly ionized He spectrum different from the H spectrum? Bohr's explanation of these spectral lines of singly ionized He was an early success (in 1913) of his model of the atom.

CHAPTER 40
QUANTUM MECHANICS

40-1 INTRODUCTION

The phenomena discussed in the last chapter emphasized the corpuscular or particlelike nature of electromagnetic radiation. Instead of viewing light as a continuous wave, we pictured it as consisting of a stream of photons. Each photon carries discrete energy and momentum, determined by the frequency and wavelength of the light.

Is the preceding sentence paradoxical? Discrete energy and momentum imply localization, as with the energy and momentum of a particle. Frequency and wavelength are properties of a sinusoidal or harmonic wave. How can we think of wavelike properties such as frequency and wavelength if light consists of particlelike photons? We shall see in this chapter that matter also exhibits both wavelike and particlelike behaviors. For example, an electron, which we have regarded as a particle, has wave properties. This paradoxical combination of wave and particle properties is summarized in the phrase *wave-particle duality*, which is an essential feature of the subject of this chapter, quantum mechanics.

40-2 DE BROGLIE WAVES

Consider a beam of monochromatic light of frequency ν and wavelength $\lambda = c/\nu$. The photon, the quantum of electromagnetic radiation, has zero rest mass, travels at speed c, and carries energy and momentum. Each photon in the beam has energy E and momentum of magnitude p given, from the last chapter, by

$$E = h\nu \tag{39-3}$$

$$p = \frac{h}{\lambda} \tag{39-5}$$

These equations connect the particlelike quantities E and p to the wavelike quantities ν and λ.

By thinking of the photon as a particle, carrying its energy and momentum along with it, we form a picture that is often associated with a particle of matter, say a pellet shot from an air gun. Similarly, as an electron moves from one place to another, it carries energy and momentum. Of course, the electron has a nonzero rest mass, and so its speed is less than c. Nevertheless, the feature of energy and momentum carried by and localized on the particle is common to both the photon for radiation and the electron for matter.

What are other common features of radiation and matter? Perhaps it has occurred to you that the two equations above, which connect the wave and particle properties of electromagnetic radiation, could also apply to matter. Louis Victor de Broglie (1892–1987) made just such a proposal in 1924. He suggested that a particle of matter such as an electron also has wavelike properties. A particle with energy E and momentum of magnitude p has frequency ν and wavelength λ that satisfy the equations above. Solving Eq. (39-5) for λ, the *de Broglie wavelength* of the particle, we have

De Broglie wavelength of a particle

$$\lambda = \frac{h}{p} \tag{40-1}$$

For a particle moving with speed v small compared with the speed of light, the momentum has magnitude $p = mv$, and the de Broglie wavelength is $\lambda = h/mv$. If the particle is moving relativistically, then $p = \gamma mv$, where $\gamma = 1/\sqrt{1 - v^2/c^2}$.

EXAMPLE 40-1. Determine the de Broglie wavelength of (*a*) an electron with speed 2×10^6 m/s and (*b*) a 10-μg dust particle with speed 1 mm/s.

SOLUTION. Each particle has a speed small compared with the speed of light, so the expression $p = mv$ can be used and $\lambda = h/mv$. (*a*) For the electron,

$$\lambda = \frac{6.63 \times 10^{-34} \text{ J} \cdot \text{s}}{(9.11 \times 10^{-31} \text{ kg})(2 \times 10^6 \text{ m/s})}$$

$$= 0.4 \text{ nm}$$

This wavelength is comparable to the size of an atom and should be observable. (*b*) For the dust particle (a small but macroscopic object),

$$\lambda = \frac{6.63 \times 10^{-34} \text{ J} \cdot \text{s}}{(1 \times 10^{-8} \text{ kg})(1 \times 10^{-3} \text{ m/s})}$$

$$= 7 \times 10^{-23} \text{ m}$$

There exists no method for measuring a distance this small, so the de Broglie wavelength of a macroscopic dust particle is too small to be observed. For comparison, the size of the nucleus of an atom is about 10^{-14} m.

40-3 ELECTRON DIFFRACTION

The de Broglie wavelength for a macroscopic object, such as the dust particle in Example 40-1, is too small to be observed. The wavelength for the electron in that example is also small, comparable to the size of an atom and to the range of

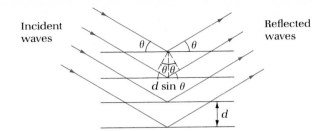

Figure 40-1. The path difference for waves reflected from consecutive atomic planes in a crystal is $2d \sin \theta$. Constructive interference occurs for $2d \sin \theta_m = m\lambda$.

Electron diffraction

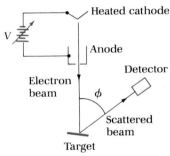

Figure 40-2. Electrons are accelerated through a variable potential difference V. The electron beam strikes the target, and scattered electrons are counted at the detector.

The Davisson-Germer experiment confirmed the wave nature of electrons.

G. P. Thomson observed electron diffraction from a foil.

wavelengths of x-rays in the electromagnetic spectrum. Although small, a wavelength of this size is measurable. For x-rays, the regular array of atoms in a crystal forms a diffracting system, as described in Sec. 36-5. Substituting an electron beam for an x-ray beam in a diffraction experiment provides a test for de Broglie's hypothesis of matter waves. That is, *electron diffraction* for electrons with wavelength λ should satisfy the same conditions as those for x-ray diffraction of x-rays with the same wavelength.

If an x-ray beam or an electron beam, characterized by wavelength λ, is incident on a crystal, then the beam is scattered by the atoms. Constructive interference occurs only for scattered beams in particular directions. The condition for constructive interference is Bragg's law, Eq. (36-12): $2d \sin \theta_m = m\lambda$. This law is interpreted in terms of reflections from sets of planes of atoms. As shown in Fig. 40-1, the incident and reflected waves make an angle θ_m with the planes which are separated by distance d. You should review the discussion in Sec. 36-5 to see that Bragg's law is a consequence of the wave nature of the beam. That is, constructive interference comes from the superposition of waves and is independent of the type of wave. Thus Bragg's law should be satisfied by an electron beam if de Broglie's hypothesis is correct.

Early in 1927, experiments at Bell Labs in the United States by C. J. Davisson (1881–1958) and L. H. Germer (1896–1971) conclusively confirmed the wave nature of electrons. A monoenergetic beam of electrons was incident on a nickel target, as shown schematically in Fig. 40-2. Electrons accelerated through a potential difference V acquire a kinetic energy $\frac{1}{2}mv^2 = eV$ and momentum of magnitude $mv = \sqrt{2meV}$. Electrons scattered in various directions were counted with a movable detector. A number of electron diffraction peaks were observed from a single crystal target. Using Bragg's law, Davisson and Germer subsequently verified the de Broglie wavelength hypothesis, $\lambda = h/p = h/mv$, for 16 diffraction peaks.

The technique used by Davisson and Germer to confirm the wave nature of electrons utilized a single crystal. They were led to the use of a single crystal by accident. Their experiments, begun well before de Broglie's hypothesis, were on polycrystalline nickel; the target consisted of a large number of very small crystals with a variety of orientations that were simultaneously exposed to the electron beam. Distinct diffraction peaks were not observed from the polycrystalline sample under the conditions of their experiment. However, as a result of overheating, the sample developed some larger crystal facets, and they were able to observe a diffraction peak from one of them.

The wave nature of electrons was confirmed independently by G. P. Thomson (1892–1975) in Britain. Thomson demonstrated electron diffraction using a polycrystalline foil, as illustrated in Fig. 40-3. In this method, many small crystals are exposed to the electron beam. Some of the crystallites are oriented with respect to the beam such that Bragg's law is satisfied. Each of these will

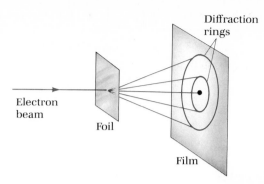

Figure 40-3. An electron beam is incident on a polycrystalline foil. Characteristic rings are formed by diffracted beams of electrons.

Figure 40-4. Diffraction patterns produced by (a) electrons on a silver foil *(Courtesy of Dr. L. H. Germer, Bell Telephone Laboratories)* and (b) x-rays on an aluminum film. *(Courtesy of Mrs. M. H. Read, Bell Telephone Laboratories.)*

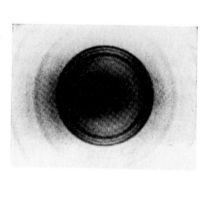

(a)

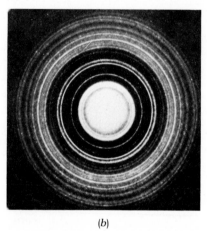

(b)

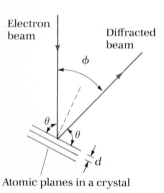

Figure 40-5. Example 40-2.

produce a diffracted beam. Together these beams form circular patterns on the film, and the pattern is characteristic of the atomic spacing in the crystal structure. The electron-diffraction pattern for a silver foil is shown in Fig. 40-4a. For comparison, the x-ray diffraction pattern for an aluminum foil is shown in Fig. 40-4b. Notice that the diffraction pattern for electrons is the same as for photons (x-rays).

It is interesting to note that G. P. Thomson was the son of J. J. Thomson. It was J. J. Thomson's experiment in 1897 (see Prob. 26-6) that identified the electron as a charged particle. He showed that an electron beam is deflected by electric and magnetic fields in a way described by Newton's laws. G. P. Thomson's experiment 30 years later confirmed the wave nature of electrons. These opposing views of the electron by father and son represent quite a generation gap!

EXAMPLE 40-2. One of the diffraction peaks observed by Davisson and Germer occurred for a 65-eV electron beam and a scattering angle $\phi = \pi/4$, as shown in Fig. 40-5. Determine the spacing d of the crystal planes responsible for this peak.

SOLUTION. An electron accelerated from rest through a potential difference V has momentum of magnitude $p = \sqrt{2meV}$. The de Broglie wavelength is $\lambda = h/p = h/\sqrt{2meV}$. If we insert the values of h, m, and e, the last expression can be written (see Exercise 40-10) $\lambda = (1.23 \text{ nm} \cdot V^{1/2})/\sqrt{V}$. For

$V = 65$ V,

$$\lambda = \frac{1.23 \text{ nm}}{\sqrt{65}} = 0.15 \text{ nm}$$

The angle θ in Bragg's law is the angle between the incident beam and the set of planes. From the figure, we have $\theta + \frac{1}{2}\phi = \frac{1}{2}\pi$, or $\theta = \frac{1}{2}\pi - \frac{1}{8}\pi = \frac{3}{8}\pi$. Solving Bragg's law for d gives

$$d = \frac{\lambda}{2 \sin \theta} = \frac{0.15 \text{ nm}}{(2)(\sin 3\pi/8)}$$

$$= 0.083 \text{ nm}$$

40-4 WAVE-PARTICLE DUALITY — A DOUBLE-SLIT EXPERIMENT

The wave nature of light was established by Young's double-slit experiment. In this experiment (described in Sec. 36-2) the intensity distribution of the light on an observing screen is a result of the interference of the waves arriving at the screen from the two slits. However, in other phenomena, such as the photoelectric effect, the particle nature of light is manifest. The energy and momentum are carried by the particlelike photons. This dual nature of light, wavelike and particlelike, is described by the phrase *wave-particle duality*.

Electrons also exhibit a wave-particle duality. Our initial picture of an electron was as a (charged) particle. For example, the electrons that form the beam in a television picture tube obey Newton's laws as they respond to the electric and magnetic fields that deflect the beam. However, in the electron-diffraction experiments of Davisson and Germer and of Thomson, the wave nature of electrons was confirmed. Thus both electromagnetic radiation and microscopic matter (electrons) exhibit wave-particle duality.

In classical physics, there was no wave-particle duality. Instead, there was a clear conceptual distinction between wave motion and particle motion. An entity was classified either as a wave or as a particle. For example, a disturbance on a string was treated as a wave and a bullet was treated as a particle. Wave-particle duality seems puzzling or paradoxical against the background of this classical dichotomy between particles and waves.

To illustrate the paradox further, we consider an experiment that can distinguish an entity that is a classical wave from one that is a classical particle. It is Young's double-slit experiment. First suppose that a wave is incident on the double-slit system, as shown schematically in Fig. 40-6. The intensity distribution on the observing screen S is different, depending on whether (a) only the top slit is open, (b) only the bottom slit is open, or (c) both slits are open simultaneously. Intensity profiles for these three cases are shown in Fig. 40-7. In Fig. 40-7a and b, where only one slit is open, the distribution is a single-slit diffraction pattern. That is, the beam spreads out after passing through the narrow slit. In Fig. 40-7c, both slits are open, and the intensity distribution is the result of the interference of *waves* coming from the two slits.

Wave-particle duality

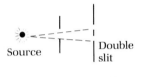

Figure 40-6. A collimated beam from a source is incident on a double slit. The intensity distribution is measured on an observing screen S.

Figure 40-7. Intensity distributions on an observing screen are shown for a wave that is incident on a double-slit system with (a) only the top slit open, (b) only the bottom slit open, (c) both slits open simultaneously.

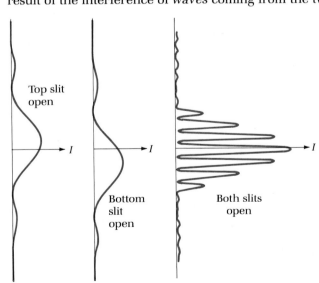

Interference of waves comes from the principle of superposition.

Interference of waves follows from the principle of superposition: The resultant wave at a point is the sum of the individual wave contributions — in this case the waves coming from each slit. Thus at points on the screen where the individual waves have the same phase, the resultant wave has a relatively large amplitude. At points where the individual waves are out of phase, the resultant wave has a relatively small amplitude. Since the intensity is proportional to the square of the amplitude, the interference pattern contains alternating maxima and minima of intensity. Notice that at the position of a minimum on the screen, the intensity would be appreciable if only the top slit were open or if only the bottom slit were open. If both slits are open, the waves interfere destructively at that point, and *the intensity is virtually zero.*

If a broad beam of classical particles is incident on a double-slit system, then the distribution of energy or of intensity [intensity has dimensions of (energy)/(area · time)] is fundamentally different. The arrangement would also be as shown in Fig. 40-6 where now the source is a source of particles. For simplicity we suppose that each particle in the beam has the same energy E. Then each particle that arrives at the screen brings energy E to the screen. The average intensity for some time interval is therefore proportional to the number of particles N that come to a region of the screen. The intensity profile for classical particles is shown in Fig. 40-8 for the case where (a) only the top slit is open, (b) only the bottom slit is open, and (c) both slits are open simultaneously. In Fig. 40-8a and b, where only one slit is open, the spread in the intensity pattern at the screen is due to a slight scattering of the particles by the edges of the slit. Because of the spreading, particles can reach the central portion of the screen by passing through either slit. With both slits open, as in Fig. 40-8c, the intensity is the sum of intensities for particles coming through each of the slits.

There is no interference for classical particles.

There is no interference pattern for classical particles. That is, the number of particles arriving at a place on the screen is the sum of the particles arriving there that passed through the top slit and the particles arriving there that passed through the bottom slit.

The double-slit experiment distinguishes between classical particles and waves.

Comparing Figs. 40-7c and 40-8c, we see that classical waves and classical particles behave quite differently in a double-slit experiment. This type of experiment distinguishes classical particlelike behavior from classical wavelike behavior. (An easily observable interference pattern for the wave requires the spacing between slits to be comparable to the wavelength.) Now the paradox of wave-particle duality for light is apparent: If light consists of a stream of

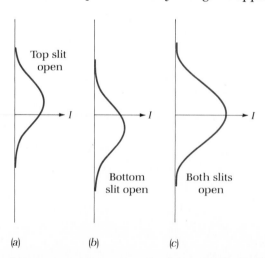

Top slit open

Bottom slit open

Both slits open

(a)   (b)   (c)

Figure 40-8. Intensity distributions on an observing screen are shown for classical particles that are incident on a double-slit system with (a) only the top slit open, (b) only the bottom slit open, (c) both slits open simultaneously.

particles (photons), how can the double-slit experiment show the interference pattern for a wave?

What about electrons? Suppose that a beam of electrons is incident on a double-slit system. What type of pattern results? If the observing screen has a fluorescent coating, then an electron reaching the screen causes the screen to glow briefly at that point; individual electrons can be counted as they reach the screen. An electron hitting the screen is clear evidence of particlelike behavior. Yet after a large number of electrons have been counted, the intensity pattern that emerges exhibits the interference pattern of a wave, as shown in Fig. 40-9. Notice that the interference pattern is not recognizable if only a few electrons have been counted. Thus there is a statistical aspect to the pattern, the basis of which we shall discuss in Sec. 40-6.

The double-slit experiment for electrons yields the same paradox as the double-slit experiment for light. How can individually counted particles passing through a double-slit system form the interference pattern for a wave? The pattern is not the result of electrons in the beam interacting with one another. The same interference pattern emerges even if only one electron at a time passes through the double-slit system. Thus wave-particle duality for electrons is a dualism that applies to each individual electron. The same is true for photons.

You should now be able to appreciate the paradox. Even the language that we use contains it — we speak of the *wavelength of a particle*. Classically, these two concepts are mutually exclusive. The resolution of the paradox, discussed in the following section, requires us to alter our classical concepts of waves and particles.

Electrons exhibit an interference pattern in a double-slit experiment.

An individual electron shows wave behavior.

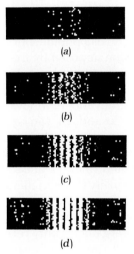

(a)

(b)

(c)

(d)

Figure 40-9. A computer simulation shows a double-slit interference pattern emerging as more particles reach the screen. (a) 38 particles; (b) 181 particles; (c) 361 particles; (d) 594 particles.

40-5 THE HEISENBERG UNCERTAINTY RELATIONS

To describe the motion of a typical macroscopic object — such as a baseball on a playing field — we have no need to resort to ultrahigh precision measurements. For example, determining the coordinate x for a baseball to within an uncertainty $\Delta x = 0.1$ mm is usually sufficient. Knowing the position of a 100-mm-diameter ball to within 0.1 mm justifies our treating it as localized. If we can localize something in this manner, then we can regard it as a particle. This point of view is at the root of our intuitive concept of a particle. In determining the motion of a classical particle subjected to known forces, we assumed that the initial conditions could be ascertained exactly. That is, the initial position of a particle and its initial velocity (or just as well, its initial momentum) could be measured with arbitrarily high precision, and the act of measurement had a negligible effect on the motion. Then the path of the particle is precisely determined from Newton's second law.

If we attempt to apply this concept of a particle to an electron or a photon, we find that the picture is not so clear. Consider an electron in an atom. Thinking of the electron as a classical particle whose motion can be followed implies that we can determine *simultaneously* its momentum and its position for much smaller distances than for a macroscopic object. For example, the uncertainty Δx in a coordinate would have to be around 1 pm or less because the size of an atom is about 100 pm. At the same time we would have to determine a component of momentum, say p_x, to within an uncertainty Δp_x that is a small fraction of p_x.

A fundamentally new aspect of nature emerges if we attempt to minimize the uncertainties Δx and Δp_x in simultaneous measurements of x and p_x for particles at the atomic level. The measurement process itself results in a lower limit on the product $\Delta p_x \Delta x$ of these uncertainties. The limitation was proposed in 1927 by one of the founders of quantum mechanics, Werner Heisenberg (1901–1976), and is one of the *Heisenberg uncertainty relations*. The Heisenberg uncertainty relation for position and momentum components x and p_x is

Heisenberg uncertainty relation for $\Delta x \, \Delta p_x$

$$\Delta x \, \Delta p_x \geq \tfrac{1}{2}\hbar \qquad (40\text{-}2)$$

$\hbar = h/2\pi = 1.05 \times 10^{-34} \, \text{J} \cdot \text{s}$

where $\hbar = h/2\pi$, Planck's constant divided by 2π. (The combination $h/2\pi = 1.05 \times 10^{-34} \, \text{J} \cdot \text{s}$ appears so often in quantum mechanics that the symbol $\hbar$, sounded as "h-bar," is used for convenience.)

The product of uncertainties $\Delta x \, \Delta p_x$ has a lower bound $\tfrac{1}{2}\hbar$. If the position of an electron is determined to within a small distance, so that Δx is small, then the corresponding uncertainty in momentum, $\Delta p_x \geq \tfrac{1}{2}\hbar/\Delta x$, is large. Conversely, if Δp_x is small, then $\Delta x \geq \tfrac{1}{2}\hbar/\Delta p_x$ and there is a large uncertainty in position. Thus it is not possible for both Δx and Δp_x to be arbitrarily small.

Obviously there are some technical difficulties in measuring precisely the position and momentum of a particle such as an electron or a photon. But even if the best instruments available are used, the limitation imposed by the Heisenberg uncertainty relation on $\Delta x \, \Delta p_x$ remains. This limit is independent of the details of any measuring device or procedure. It is a basic property of nature. It cannot be circumvented by any technological advance or innovation.

For a classical particle, we have assumed that both Δx and Δp_x can be zero simultaneously, so that the product $\Delta x \, \Delta p_x$ can also be zero. But the Heisenberg uncertainty relation states that the product must be at least $\tfrac{1}{2}\hbar$ and cannot be zero. Thus the concept of a classical particle has limited validity. Since $\tfrac{1}{2}\hbar$ is small, the Heisenberg uncertainty relation imposes virtually no restrictions for a macroscopic object. (See Example 40-3 below.) At the atomic and subatomic realms, however, the concept of a classical particle must be abandoned.

One way to illustrate the "workings" of the Heisenberg uncertainty relation is to consider the process of measurement. To observe the position of a particle, we must see it by using a probe of some kind. We see a ball, for example, by the light reflected from its surface. Electromagnetic waves, as well as other types of waves, can be used to resolve or distinguish features of dimensions no smaller than about a wavelength λ. Since $\lambda \approx 500$ nm for visible light, the uncertainty Δx in the position of a ball cannot be much less than λ. This precision in determining the position of a ball is usually more than adequate. We should also consider the momentum transferred to the ball by the reflected light. Typically this is a small fraction of the ball's momentum and can be neglected. That is, the measurement has virtually no effect on the motion of the ball.

The situation is very different for an electron, however. Consider one of the electrons in a monoenergetic beam that is incident on a single slit, as shown in Fig. 40-10. This arrangement may be regarded as a way to measure the lateral coordinate y of an electron that passes through the slit. An electron just emerging from the opening has a position that is uncertain by $\Delta y = a$, the width of the slit. Since we don't know beforehand where the electron will hit the screen, the momentum component p_y is uncertain by Δp_y, which we now estimate. Using the wave nature of an electron, we can expect that an electron is likely to hit the screen somewhere between the two minima of the single-slit diffraction pattern as indicated in the figure. The condition for the minimum for a wave of

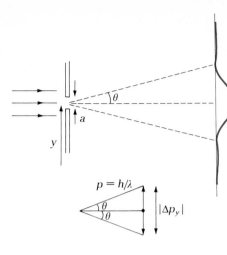

Figure 40-10. An electron beam is incident on a single slit. The y coordinate for an electron just passing through the slit is uncertain by $\Delta y = a$. The uncertainty in momentum corresponds to the central region of the single-slit diffraction pattern, so that $\frac{1}{2}|\Delta p_y| = p \sin \theta$.

The measurement process introduces uncontrolled uncertainties.

wavelength λ is $a \sin \theta = \lambda$ (from Sec. 37-3). The uncertainty in momentum that corresponds to an electron hitting anywhere between these minima is $|\Delta p_y| = 2p \sin \theta = 2(h/\lambda) \sin \theta$, as indicated in the figure. The uncertainty product is

$$\Delta y \, \Delta p_y = a \left[2 \left(\frac{h}{\lambda} \right) \sin \theta \right] = 2h$$

since $a \sin \theta = \lambda$. The measuring process introduces uncertainties consistent with the Heisenberg uncertainty relation. In this example the estimate of the uncertainties Δy, Δp_y in the particlelike quantities are connected with the wave nature of an electron, and that is generally true.

There are several relations of the form of Eq. (40-2) that collectively are called the *Heisenberg uncertainty relations*. For a particle in three dimensions, there is an uncertainty-relation product for each coordinate and momentum-component pair. These pairs are

Heisenberg uncertainty relations for coordinates and momenta

$$\Delta x \, \Delta p_x \geq \tfrac{1}{2}\hbar \qquad \Delta y \, \Delta p_y \geq \tfrac{1}{2}\hbar \qquad \Delta z \, \Delta p_z \geq \tfrac{1}{2}\hbar$$

Notice that in an uncertainty product a coordinate appears only with the corresponding component of momentum, such as Δx with Δp_x. There is no minimum uncertainty product for a coordinate and a perpendicular momentum component. For example, the product $\Delta x \, \Delta p_y$ can be zero.

In addition to the relations above, there are uncertainty relations for other pairs of quantities. One that is of interest involves energy E and time t. Suppose that the energy of a system is measured with an uncertainty ΔE and that the measurement extends over a time interval Δt. Then the Heisenberg uncertainty relation for this pair is

Heisenberg uncertainty relation for time and energy

$$\Delta t \, \Delta E \geq \tfrac{1}{2}\hbar \qquad\qquad (40\text{-}3)$$

If a measurement of energy occurs over a time interval Δt, then the consequent uncertainty in the value of the energy must be at least $\frac{1}{2}\hbar/\Delta t$. Thus an infinite time interval is required to determine exactly ($\Delta E = 0$) the energy of a system.

EXAMPLE 40-3. Show that the Heisenberg uncertainty relation imposes no practical limitations for a macroscopic object such as a marble.

SOLUTION. Consider a 5-g marble moving with a not-un-typical velocity component $v_x = 1$ m/s. The momentum component is $p_x = mv_x = 0.005$ kg · m/s. Suppose that, by careful measurement, we determine this momentum to a precision of 1 part in 10^6: $\Delta p_x = 5 \times 10^{-9}$ kg · m/s. The lower limit on the coordinate uncertainty Δx is given by the Heisenberg uncertainty relation in Eq. (40-2):

$$\Delta x \geqslant \frac{\frac{1}{2}\hbar}{\Delta p_x} = \frac{\frac{1}{2}(1.05 \times 10^{-34} \text{ J} \cdot \text{s})}{5 \times 10^{-9} \text{ kg} \cdot \text{m/s}}$$

$$\geqslant 1 \times 10^{-26} \text{ m}$$

This limitation on Δx from the Heisenberg uncertainty relation has no practical significance because of its small value. For comparison, the size of the nucleus of an atom is about 10^{11} times larger than this Δx.

EXAMPLE 40-4. Use the Heisenberg uncertainty relation to estimate the kinetic energy of an electron in a hydrogen atom.

SOLUTION. The uncertainty in a coordinate of an electron in a hydrogen atom is about the size of the atom. The Bohr radius, $a_0 = 0.053$ nm, provides a reasonable estimate for the uncertainty in position Δx. The uncertainty in momentum has a lower limit given by Eq. (40-2): $\Delta p_x \geqslant \frac{1}{2}\hbar/\Delta x \approx \frac{1}{2}\hbar/a_0$. We use the value $\frac{1}{2}\hbar/a_0$ as an estimate for an average magnitude of momentum p. That is, the magnitude of

the momentum can be at least as large as its uncertainty. The estimate of kinetic energy is $K = \frac{1}{2}mv^2 = p^2/2m \approx (\frac{1}{2}\hbar/a_0)^2/2m$. Thus $K \approx \hbar^2/(8ma_0^2)$, or

$$K \approx \frac{(1.05 \times 10^{-34} \text{ J} \cdot \text{s})^2}{(8)(9.11 \times 10^{-31} \text{ kg})(0.053 \text{ nm})^2}$$

$$\approx 5 \times 10^{-19} \text{ J} = 3 \text{ eV}$$

Using the Bohr model of hydrogen for comparison, recall that an electron in the ground state has kinetic energy $K = 13.6$ eV, so the above estimate is reasonable.

40-6 INTERPRETATION OF THE WAVE FUNCTION

The de Broglie relation, $\lambda = h/p$, gives the wavelength of the wave associated with a particle, such as a photon or an electron, with momentum p. In the case of light, we have already discussed both the wave and the particle descriptions. That is, when we view light as a wave, we view it as an electromagnetic wave with oscillatory electric and magnetic fields. For the particle picture or model of light, we consider individual photons, each having a discrete energy and momentum.

What are the corresponding descriptions for an electron? The particle picture of an electron is suggested by giving its momentum and energy in addition to listing some of its intrinsic properties, such as its charge and its mass. The wave picture for an electron is more elusive. The question is, what is it that is waving for an electron? So far we know how to determine the wavelength of the wave from the momentum of the particle. We also have used the superposition principle for linear waves to explain the interference effects observed for electrons. But we have not displayed a mathematical form for such a wave, nor have we given its physical interpretation.

An important feature of the interference pattern for electrons was mentioned in our discussion of the double-slit experiment in Sec. 40-4. The observed interference pattern gives the distribution of the *many* electrons that have hit the screen. In the early stages of the experiment, as indicated in Fig. 40-9a, there is no obvious pattern formed by the few electrons that have hit the screen. We have no idea at what spot on the screen the next electron will hit. Only after many electron hits have been observed does the characteristic double-slit pattern become well defined.

Suppose that we determine the fraction f of electrons that have hit some small region of the screen. We do not know where the next electron will strike. But we can estimate the chance or the *probability P* that the next electron will hit within the given small region. The best guess is that it is just the fraction of electrons that have already reached that region on the screen; that is, $P = f$. If the region on the screen is near a minimum in the interference pattern, then the probability of an electron hitting there is very small. For a region near a maximum in the interference pattern, the probability is relatively larger. Thus we can think of the double-slit interference pattern as a pattern of probability — the probability that an electron, after passing through the double-slit system, will hit a region of the screen.

The use of probability, which gives the description of an electron a statistical nature, is a key ingredient of quantum mechanics. The physical interpretation of the wave function, due largely to the German physicist Max Born (1882 – 1970), is expressed in terms of probability in the following way:

The wave function for a particle such as an electron is denoted by $\psi(x, y, z)$. Consider a volume element $dV = dx\, dy\, dz$ centered at the point with coordinates (x, y, z). *The (differential) probability dP that the particle is within the volume element dV is given by*

Probability interpretation of the wave function ψ

$$dP = |\psi(x, y, z)|^2\, dV \tag{40-4}$$

Probability density $|\psi|^2$

where $|\psi|^2$ is called the *absolute square** of the wave function ψ. Since $|\psi|^2$ multiplied by a volume element dV gives a probability, the absolute square $|\psi(x, y, z)|^2$ of the wave function is the *probability density* — that is, the probability per unit volume that the particle is at point (x, y, z).

For a finite region of volume V, Eq. (40-4) is integrated to obtain the probability P_V that the particle is in that region:

$$P_V = \int_V |\psi|^2\, dV$$

Normalization of the wave function

Since it is certain that the particle is somewhere in all of space, the probability is unity ($P_\infty = 1$) if the integral extends over all space. That is,

$$1 = \int_\infty |\psi|^2\, dV \tag{40-5}$$

and the wave function is said to be *normalized*.

To see how interference occurs for probability in a double-slit system, we apply the principle of superposition to obtain the wave function for an electron at a point on the observing screen. Let ψ_1 represent the wave function at a point on the screen for an electron from one of the slits alone — say the top one, with the bottom slit closed. As a function of position on the screen, the absolute square $|\psi_1|^2\, dV$ will be proportional to the intensity in Fig. 40-7a for the single-slit diffraction pattern. Similarly, let ψ_2 represent the wave function at a point on the screen for an electron from the bottom slit alone, with the top slit closed. If both slits are open, then we form the wave function $\psi = \psi_1 + \psi_2$. The probability that the electron is at a point on the screen depends on $|\psi|^2$, where

$$|\psi|^2 = |\psi_1 + \psi_2|^2 \tag{40-6}$$

The interference pattern for electrons in the double-slit experiment is the result of the phase difference between the wave functions ψ_1 and ψ_2. Constructive interference occurs at points on the screen where ψ_1 and ψ_2 are in phase so that $\psi_2 = \psi_1$. Destructive interference occurs at points where $\psi_2 = -\psi_1$ and $\psi = \psi_1 + \psi_2 = 0$. Thus $|\psi|^2$ gives a double-slit interference pattern for the prob-

---

* In general, the wave function is *complex*, $\psi = \psi_R + i\psi_I$, with real and imaginary parts ψ_R and ψ_I, where $i = \sqrt{-1}$. Then $|\psi|^2 = \psi_R^2 + \psi_I^2$. (See Prob. 40-6.)

ability on the screen, and this probability pattern is proportional to the intensity pattern in Fig. 40-7c. *Notice that the probability interference pattern results because we first add ψ_1 and ψ_2 and then* take the absolute square.

40-7 THE SCHRÖDINGER EQUATION

In the last section, we gave the physical interpretation of the wave function for a particle. If we know the wave function ψ for an electron, then we can evaluate $|\psi|^2$ at a point, which is the probability density for finding the electron there. But how do we find the wave function? Is there a wave equation to be solved for an electron, analogous to the wave equation for light? In 1926, Erwin Schrödinger (1887 – 1961) proposed such an equation and solved it for several important cases. It is now called the *Schrödinger equation.*

The Schrödinger equation cannot be derived. Like Maxwell's equations in classical electromagnetism, the validity of the Schrödinger equation rests on its ability to predict or describe correctly the outcome of experiments. Similar to the wave equation that was developed in Chaps. 32 through 34, the Schrödinger equation contains derivatives of the wave function ψ.

We can be led to the form of the equation by using the relation $p = h/\lambda$ that describes wave-particle duality. Consider a sinusoidal wave of wavelength λ along the x direction. We use the wave number $k = 2\pi/\lambda$ and the waveform

$$\psi = A \sin (kx) + B \cos (kx) \tag{40-7}$$

where A and B are independent of x. (This type of waveform was used in Chap. 32.) We suppose that it is a wave function for a free particle with constant momentum of magnitude $p = mv$. Since $p = h/\lambda$ and $k = 2\pi/\lambda$, we have $p = (h/2\pi)(2\pi/\lambda)$, or

$$p = \hbar k \tag{40-8}$$

For a free particle with momentum of magnitude $p = mv$, the energy E is entirely kinetic and $E = \frac{1}{2}mv^2 = p^2/2m$. Substituting for p from Eq. (40-8), we obtain

$$E = \frac{\hbar^2 k^2}{2m} \tag{40-9}$$

This expresses the energy E in terms of the wave number k, which is the important parameter in the wave function ψ in Eq. (40-7). Since ψ depends sinusoidally on x, taking a second derivative of ψ results in $d^2\psi/dx^2 = -k^2\psi$, or

$$k^2 = -\frac{1}{\psi} \frac{d^2\psi}{dx^2}$$

Substituting for k^2 in Eq. (40-9) gives

$$E = -\frac{1}{\psi} \frac{\hbar^2}{2m} \frac{d^2\psi}{dx^2}$$

or

$$-\frac{\hbar^2}{2m} \frac{d^2\psi}{dx^2} = E\psi$$

which is the Schrödinger equation for this special case.

Now we make two generalizations: (i) The equation should also contain the other spatial coordinates, y and z, and (ii) the potential energy $U(x, y, z)$ for a particle should be included. These generalizations lead to the *Schrödinger wave equation* for $\psi(x, y, z)$:

$$-\frac{\hbar^2}{2m}\left(\frac{\partial^2\psi}{\partial x^2} + \frac{\partial^2\psi}{\partial y^2} + \frac{\partial^2\psi}{\partial z^2}\right) + U(x, y, z)\psi = E\psi \tag{40-10}$$

Notice the use of partial derivatives because x, y, and z are independent variables.

Once the potential energy $U(x, y, z)$ is specified, the Schrödinger equation is to be solved for ψ, subject to appropriate conditions on ψ at the boundary of the spatial region. A solution ψ of the Schrödinger equation determines a *state* of the particle, because the wave function determines everything we can know in quantum mechanics about the motion of the particle in that state. By solving the Schrödinger equation, we are able to predict, in terms of probabilities, the outcome of an experiment. Of course this is the ultimate test of a theory — that it correctly predicts the results of experiments. We shall consider several specific examples of the Schrödinger equation and its solutions in the following sections.

Equation (40-10), which does not contain the time t, is called the *time-independent Schrödinger equation*. There is also a Schrödinger equation that is *time-dependent*, which is

$$-\frac{\hbar^2}{2m}\left(\frac{\partial^2\Psi}{\partial x^2} + \frac{\partial^2\Psi}{\partial y^2} + \frac{\partial^2\Psi}{\partial z^2}\right) + U(x, y, z)\Psi = i\hbar\,\frac{\partial\Psi}{\partial t} \tag{40-11}$$

where $i = \sqrt{-1}$. This equation governs the evolution of the *time-dependent* wave function $\Psi(x, y, z, t)$ for a particle. In this respect, the Schrödinger equation is similar to Newton's second law, which governs the evolution of the motion of a particle in classical mechanics. We shall concentrate on the time-independent Schrödinger equation, Eq. (40-10). (But see Exercise 40-35 and Prob. 40-6.)

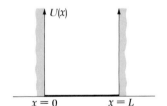

Figure 40-11. A free particle confined to a box of length L has potential energy $U = 0$ for $0 < x < L$, and $U \rightarrow \infty$ for $x < 0$ and $x > L$.

40-8 A PARTICLE IN A BOX

As a simple illustration of solving the Schrödinger equation, we consider a particle of mass m that is confined to a one-dimensional region $0 \le x \le L$. We suppose that the particle can move freely in either direction. The endpoints of the region behave as reflecting barriers so that the particle cannot leave the region. A potential-energy function $U(x)$ for this situation is sketched in Fig. 40-11. The figure is suggestive of a particle in a box. In the region between $x = 0$ and $x = L$, the particle moves freely. This corresponds to a constant potential energy, and since the zero of potential energy can be arbitrarily chosen, we set $U = 0$ for this region. The effect of the reflecting barriers is represented by $U \rightarrow \infty$ for $x < 0$ and for $x > L$. This one-dimensional system serves as a simple but useful model for an electron in some chainlike molecules. (See Example 40-5 below.) In Chap. 42, we consider a particle in a three-dimensional box.

The Schrödinger equation for the particle in a box is obtained from Eq. (40-10) by setting $U = 0$ and noting that only the x coordinate is relevant. Then,

$$-\frac{\hbar^2}{2m}\frac{d^2\psi}{dx^2} = E\psi$$

We simplify the equation by multiplying by $-2m/\hbar^2$ and making the substitution $k^2 = 2mE/\hbar^2$, from Eq. (40-9), to obtain

$$\frac{d^2\psi}{dx^2} = -k^2\psi \qquad (40\text{-}12)$$

To solve this equation, recall from the last section that sine and cosine functions are proportional to their second derivatives. You can show (see Exercise 40-37) that a general solution of Eq. (40-12) is

$$\psi(x) = A \sin(kx) + B \cos(kx)$$

We require the wave function ψ to be zero everywhere outside of the box, since the probability of finding the particle outside is zero. The wave function must also be zero at the endpoints, the "walls" of the box, because the probability density $|\psi(x)|^2$ must be continuous. Thus $\psi(x) = 0$ for $x = 0$ and for $x = L$ are the *boundary conditions* for this problem. For $x = 0$,

Boundary conditions: $\psi(0) = 0 = \psi(L)$

$$\psi(0) = A \sin(k0) + B \cos(k0) = A \cdot 0 + B \cdot 1 = B = 0$$

which means that $\psi(x) = A \sin(kx)$. The requirement that $\psi(L) = A \sin(kL) = 0$ can be satisfied only for certain values of k, which we represent by k_n. Since the sine of an integer times π is zero, $\sin(n\pi) = 0$, we have $k_n L = n\pi$ or

$$k_n = \frac{n\pi}{L} \qquad (n = 1, 2, 3, \ldots) \qquad (40\text{-}13)$$

For each allowed k_n value, there is a wave function $\psi_n(x)$. It is the wave function for the stationary state with energy $E_n = \hbar^2 k_n^2/2m$ or, on using Eq. (40-13),

Energies and wave functions for a particle in a box

$$E_n = \frac{\hbar^2\pi^2}{2mL^2} n^2 \qquad (n = 1, 2, 3, \ldots) \qquad (40\text{-}14)$$

The wave function for a particle in a box with energy E_n is $\psi_n(x) = A \sin(k_n x)$ or

$$\psi_n(x) = \sqrt{\frac{2}{L}} \sin\left(\frac{n\pi x}{L}\right) \qquad (n = 1, 2, 3, \ldots) \qquad (40\text{-}15)$$

The value for the constant $A = \sqrt{2/L}$ gives a normalized wave function $[\int_0^L |\psi_n(x)|^2 \, dx = 1$; see Exercise 40-40]. Our solution shows that the energy of a particle in a box is *quantized;* the energy is restricted to the set of values given by Eq. (40-14). Notice that the quantization of energy resulted from the application of the boundary conditions.

For each value of the energy E_n, there is a wave function ψ_n given by Eq. (40-15). The wave functions for the particle in a box can be viewed in analogy with standing waves on a string (discussed in Sec. 32-6). The wave function for a standing wave that has nodes at the endpoints is of the form $\psi(x) = A \sin(n\pi x/L)$. (Recall that $\psi = 0$ at a node.) The condition for a standing wave can also be expressed in terms of a wavelength, $\lambda_n = 2\pi/k_n = 2\pi/(n\pi/L) = 2L/n$. That is, since $n\lambda_n/2 = L$, a whole number n of half-wavelengths $\lambda_n/2$ can fit into the distance L. Several wave functions are shown graphically in Fig. 40-12a.

The wave function ψ_n is similar to a standing wave on a string.

The absolute square $|\psi(x)|^2$ of a wave function gives the probability density, the probability per unit length of finding the particle at a point x. Graphs of the probability density are shown for several states in Fig. 40-12b. Notice the oscillatory behavior of

$$|\psi_n|^2 = \psi_n^2 = \frac{2}{L} \sin^2\left(\frac{n\pi x}{L}\right)$$

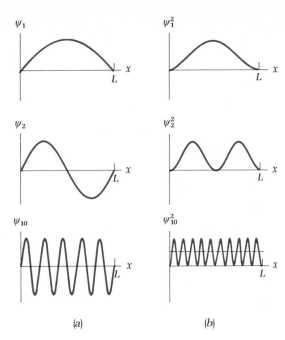

Figure 40-12. (a) The wave function ψ_n and (b) the probability density ψ_n^2 are shown for $n = 1$, $n = 2$, and $n = 10$. For ψ_{10}^2, the average probability density is shown, which is suggestive of the classical probability distribution for a particle in a box.

(a)   (b)

Quantum and classical probability distributions are different.

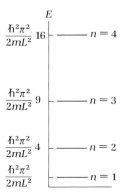

Figure 40-13. The four lowest energy levels for a particle in a box are shown.

Zero-point energy

At some points in the box, ψ^2 is zero, so that the particle can never be found at such a point. For the state labeled by $n = 1$, the probability density ψ_1^2 is largest at the center of the box. These quantum mechanical features contrast with the probability distribution for a *classical* particle in a box. If we knew only the energy of a classical particle moving freely between the walls of a box, the classical probability density would be the same at every point in the box. This classical behavior is suggested by the *quantum* probability density in the limit of large n. For a state with a large quantum number n, the wave function ψ and the probability density ψ^2 vary rapidly with x. If we average the probability density over a length containing a cycle, the resulting distribution mimics the classical case, as indicated in Fig. 40-12b for ψ_{10}^2.

Some of the possible energies for a particle in a box are shown on an energy-level diagram in Fig. 40-13. The energy levels, which are proportional to n^2, have a spacing that increases with increasing n. Notice that the lowest energy E_1 is positive. In contrast, a classical particle in a region with potential energy $U = 0$ could also be at rest so that $E = K + U = 0$. In quantum mechanics, the particle in a box cannot be at rest. Its minimum energy E_1 is positive and is often called the *zero-point energy*.

EXAMPLE 40-5. Some organic dye molecules have a chain of several carbon atoms along a line. An electron participating in the bonding of these atoms behaves somewhat as a particle in a box. In a model of one type of dye molecule, suppose that an electron is confined to a one-dimensional chain of length 0.94 nm. (a) Determine the energies of the four lowest states. (b) Compare the probability density at the midpoint of the region for the $n = 3$ and $n = 4$ states. (c) The color of the dye is due to the transition between these two states. What is that color?

SOLUTION. (a) The energy levels are given by Eq. (40-14):

$$E_n = \frac{\hbar^2 \pi^2}{2mL^2} n^2 = \frac{(1.05 \times 10^{-34} \text{ J} \cdot \text{s})^2 \pi^2}{2(9.11 \times 10^{-31} \text{ kg})(0.94 \text{ nm})^2} n^2$$

$$= (0.43 \text{ eV})n^2$$

For $n = 1, 2, 3, 4$, we have $E_1 = 0.43$ eV, $E_2 = 1.7$ eV, $E_3 = 3.8$ eV, $E_4 = 6.8$ ev.

(b) At $x = \frac{1}{2}L$ these two wave functions are

$$\psi_3 = \sqrt{\frac{2}{L}} \sin\left(\frac{3\pi}{2}\right) = -\sqrt{\frac{2}{0.94 \text{ nm}}}$$

and

$$\psi_4 = \sqrt{\frac{2}{L}} \sin\left(\frac{4\pi}{2}\right) = 0$$

The probability per unit length for finding the electron at this position is the absolute square of the wave function evaluated there. Thus at $x = L/2$, $|\psi_3|^2 = (-\sqrt{2/L})^2 = 2/L =$ 2.1 nm^{-1} and $|\psi_4|^2 = (0)^2 = 0$.

(c) A photon is emitted in the transition of the electron from the $n = 4$ state to the $n = 3$ state. Its energy is $h\nu = E_4 - E_3 = 3.0$ eV. The frequency of the emitted light is $\nu = (3.0 \text{ eV})/h = 7.2 \times 10^{14}$ Hz and its wavelength is $\lambda = c/\nu = 410$ nm, which is in the violet part of the spectrum.

40-9 THE HARMONIC OSCILLATOR

In classical physics, the harmonic oscillator is used as a model for many mechanical and electric oscillations. In quantum mechanics as well, the harmonic oscillator serves as an important idealization of real systems. We consider here some of the quantum-mechanical features of a one-dimensional harmonic oscillator.

The potential energy for a harmonic oscillator is $U = \frac{1}{2}\kappa x^2$, where κ is a stiffness or spring constant. Classically, a particle of mass m moving with this potential energy undergoes oscillations with frequency ν and angular frequency $\omega = \sqrt{\kappa/m} = 2\pi\nu$. The potential energy is conveniently written, using $\kappa = m\omega^2$, as $U = \frac{1}{2}m\omega^2 x^2$. The Schrödinger equation for the harmonic oscillator is obtained by using this potential energy in Eq. (40-10) and specializing to one coordinate x:

$$-\frac{\hbar^2}{2m}\frac{d^2\psi}{dx^2} + \tfrac{1}{2}m\omega^2 x^2\psi = E\psi \tag{40-16}$$

Boundary conditions: $\psi \to 0$ as $x \to \pm\infty$

Since the potential energy increases with x, as $\frac{1}{2}m\omega^2 x^2$, the range of x is limited for the classical harmonic oscillator; it is a bound system. This suggests that the probability of finding the particle at a large distance from the equilibrium position is small. Thus we require ψ to approach zero as $x \to \pm\infty$. The Schrödinger equation has solutions with this behavior only for a *discrete* set of values of the energy E. Obtaining the solution of this problem requires a mathematical level beyond that assumed for this course. The results, however, have some familiar features. Just as with the particle in a box, the energy of a harmonic oscillator is quantized. We label the energy levels with an integer index n:

Energy levels for the harmonic oscillator

$$E_n = (n + \tfrac{1}{2})\hbar\omega = (n + \tfrac{1}{2})h\nu \qquad (n = 0, 1, 2, \ldots) \tag{40-17}$$

Figure 40-14. (a) The energy levels for a harmonic oscillator are evenly spaced. (b) The potential energy, $U = \frac{1}{2}m\omega^2 x^2$, for a harmonic oscillator is shown. The energy scale is the same as for the energy-level diagram.

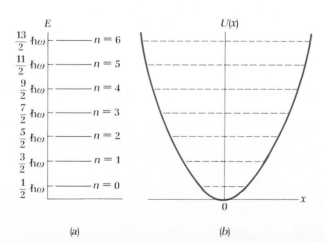

(a)

(b)

The energy-level diagram in Fig. 40-14 shows levels beginning with the ground state, $E_0 = \frac{1}{2}\hbar\omega$, and the next few levels of higher energy. Notice from Eq. (40-17), and from the figure, that the energy levels are evenly spaced. Thus $E_{n+1} - E_n = \hbar\omega = h\nu$, which is essentially Planck's assumption described in Sec. 39-3.

For each energy level E_n, there is a characteristic wave function ψ_n of the form

$$\psi_n(x) = f_n(x)e^{-x^2/2a^2}$$

where $a = \sqrt{\hbar/m\omega}$ is a constant with dimensions of length and $f_n(x)$ is a polynomial of degree n. For the first three wave functions (see Exercise 40-43), we have $f_0 = A_0$, $f_1 = A_1 x$, $f_2 = A_2(2x^2 - a^2)$, where A_0, A_1, and A_2 are constants. This gives

$$\psi_0 = A_0 e^{-x^2/2a^2}$$

$$\psi_1 = A_1 x e^{-x^2/2a^2} \tag{40-18}$$

$$\psi_2 = A_2(2x^2 - a^2)e^{-x^2/2a^2}$$

Each of these wave functions is shown in Fig. 40-15. On the graph for each wave function, the x axis is marked at the positions of the turning points for the corresponding classical harmonic oscillator. That is, a classical oscillator with that energy would oscillate between those two turning points. (Recall that at a turning point, the classical particle is momentarily at rest, and the potential energy is equal to the total energy.) Notice that the wave function extends beyond the classically accessible region. Thus in quantum mechanics, it is possible to find a particle in a region that is classically forbidden. Classically, a particle in this forbidden region would have a total energy E less than the potential energy U.

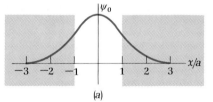

(a)

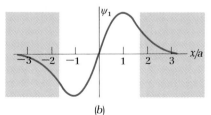

(b)

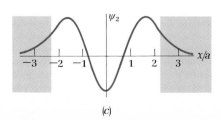

(c)

Figure 40-15. Harmonic oscillator wave functions are shown for (a) $n = 0$, (b) $n = 1$, (c) $n = 2$. Each wave function extends into the classically inaccessible region, which is indicated by shading.

40-10 TUNNELING

The operating characteristics of some important electronic devices are a consequence of the fact that an electron's wave function extends into a classically forbidden region. Examples of such devices are a semiconducting tunnel diode and a superconducting Josephson junction. Each has properties that are similar to the simple one-dimensional model illustrated in Fig. 40-16a. In the figure, a particle with energy E is incident from the left on a barrier represented by a rectangular potential-energy function U_0 in the interval $0 < x < a$. If the total energy E of the particle is less than U_0, then the region $x > 0$ is classically inaccessible. That is, a classical particle would be reflected at the barrier at $x = 0$ and could not enter the region $x > 0$.

In the quantum-mechanical treatment, the wave function extends into and beyond the barrier region, as suggested in Fig. 40-16b. Thus there is a nonzero probability that the particle will be to the right of the barrier, where it could not be classically. If the particle is found to the right of the barrier, then it is described as having "leaked" or "tunneled" through the barrier; hence the name "tunnel" diode for the semiconducting device that utilizes this effect.

The tunneling probability is obtained by solving the Schrödinger equation. The resulting wave function is oscillatory to the left and to the right of the barrier, as shown in the figure. Within the barrier, which is the classically forbidden region for $E < U_0$, the wave function does not oscillate but has a decreasing dependence on x. Because of this decrease, the wave function has a smaller amplitude on the right of the barrier than on the left. This amplitude depends strongly on the height U_0 and the width a of the barrier. The tunneling probability becomes very small for a barrier that is either high or wide. For the earlier case of a particle in a box, the height and the width both approach infinity for the barrier that forms *each* wall of the box. (See Fig. 40-12 and imagine a barrier of infinite height extending infinitely to the right from $x = L$.) Therefore, a particle in this type of box does not tunnel, and the wave function is zero everywhere outside the box.

Tunneling for a particle such as an electron is a quantum phenomenon. There is no classical counterpart of tunneling for a particle. It is a manifestation

A particle tunnels through the barrier.

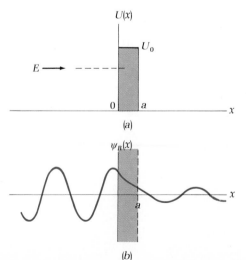

(a)

(b)

Figure 40-16. (a) A barrier type of potential energy has width a and barrier "height" U_0. A particle with energy $E < U_0$ is incident on the barrier from the left. (b) The real part of the wave function $\psi_R(x)$ is shown schematically. The wave function extends into and beyond the barrier region.

of a wave nature, and it does occur for some classical waves. In the optical analogy, the process is a "frustrated" total internal reflection. (See Sec. 35-2.)

COMMENTARY: SCHRÖDINGER'S CAT

Erwin Schrödinger. *(Ullstein courtesy of A.I.P., Niels Bohr Library)*

Where is a particle when it is in a box? In classical physics the answer is obvious, as the classical solution gives the position of the particle as a function of time. The simple question "Where is the particle?" has a complicated answer in quantum theory. Suppose that the wave function is given by ψ_2 in Fig. 40-12. All that can be known is the probability that the particle is at various places in the box, with the probability density given by $\psi_2{}^2$. You might say that surely the particle must be some particular place, but it can be shown that a consistent quantum theory requires that if you know the energy of a particle in a box, then you must give up the idea that the position of the particle exists in a more definite way than the probabilistic description that $\psi_2{}^2$ gives.

This probabilistic nature was brought out in a series of "thought experiments" proposed by Albert Einstein and Niels Bohr, among others, during the development of quantum theory. A thought experiment consists of a description of an experiment that can be done in principle and that brings out the difference between the way the state of a system is given in classical and quantum theory. Einstein did not like the probabilistic nature of quantum theory, saying that "God does not play dice with the universe." Of course, Einstein knew that quantum theory correctly described the results of real experiments, but he hoped for the development of a theory in which the probabilistic nature was absent.

A thought experiment that is known as Schrödinger's cat *was proposed by Erwin Schrödinger in 1935:*[*]

> *A cat is penned in a steel chamber, along with the following diabolical device (which must be secured against direct interference from the cat): In a Geiger counter there is a tiny bit of radioactive substance, so small that perhaps in the course of one hour one of the atoms decays, but with equal probability, perhaps none; if it happens, the counter tube discharges and through a relay releases a hammer which shatters a small flask of hydrocyanic acid. If one has left this entire system by itself for one hour one would say that the cat lives if meanwhile no atom has decayed. The first atomic decay would have poisoned it.*

What is the state of the system after 1 h? In classical theory, Schrödinger's cat is either alive or dead, and when we open the chamber we will find out which is true. In quantum theory the cat is neither alive nor dead before the chamber is opened, but in a state which is a superposition of both states, $\Psi = \Psi_{\text{alive}} + \Psi_{\text{dead}}$. It is not until a measurement is made, in this case by opening the chamber and looking at the cat, that the wave function that describes the cat changes from "half alive – half dead" to either a wave function of a live cat or a wave function of a dead cat. This sudden change in the state of a system when a measurement is performed is often described as the collapse of the wave function.

It is paradoxical, if not distasteful, to think of a cat that is neither alive nor dead, but a 50 percent superposition of the two. What is the resolution of this paradox? To some extent, the paradox has not been resolved. Most physicists believe that these considerations do not affect the measurements or theory they use on atomic-size systems and hope that somewhere between atoms and cats quan-

[*] E. Schrödinger, *Naturwiss*, **23,** 807, 823, 844 (1935).

tum physics "turns into" classical physics. Among the more serious interpretations that have been put forth to resolve the paradox are those that propose:

1   *"Mind over matter," an interpretation which supposes that the wave-function change involves a conscious mind that behaves differently from other objects in the universe.*

2   *"Many worlds," an interpretation which supposes that when the cat is observed, the universe splits into two, one in which the cat is alive and one in which the cat is dead. In this view, there would be countless parallel universes that result from splittings at all of the measurements that have occurred in the course of time.*

These ideas are discussed more fully in several sources that do not require an extensive background in physics: The Ghost in the Atom, *edited by P. C. W. Davies and J. R. Brown (Cambridge University Press, New York, 1986);* Quantum Physics: Illusion or Reality *by Alastair Rae (Cambridge University Press, New York, 1986); A. J. Leggett's "Schrodinger's Cat and Her Laboratory Cousins" in* Contempory Physics *(vol. 25, 1984, pp. 583–98); and N. D. Mermin's "Is the Moon There When Nobody Looks? Reality and the Quantum Theory" in* Physics Today *(April 1985, pp. 38–47).*

SUMMARY WITH APPLICATIONS

Section 40-2. De Broglie waves
The de Broglie wavelength for a particle with momentum of magnitude p is

$$\lambda = \frac{h}{p} \qquad (40-1)$$

Determine the de Broglie wavelength for a particle.

Section 40-3. Electron diffraction
The de Broglie wavelength for an electron can be measured using electron diffraction by a crystal.

Describe the diffraction of electrons by a crystal and explain how the wavelength can be measured.

Section 40-4. Wave-particle duality — a double-slit experiment
Both light and the basic constituents of matter have wavelike and particlelike properties. Interference experiments show that an individual particle such as a photon or an electron has wave properties.

Illustrate wave-particle duality by describing the results of interference experiments.

Section 40-5. The Heisenberg uncertainty relations
The Heisenberg uncertainty relations of the form

$$\Delta x \, \Delta p_x \geqslant \tfrac{1}{2} \hbar \qquad (40-2)$$

$$\Delta t \, \Delta E \geqslant \tfrac{1}{2} \hbar \qquad (40-3)$$

express the limitation imposed by nature on the precision of simultaneous measurements of certain pairs of quantities.

Use the Heisenberg uncertainty relations to describe the limitations of particlelike behavior and to estimate typical values for small systems.

Section 40-6. Interpretation of the wave function
The wave function ψ has a statistical interpretation. The absolute square $|\psi|^2$ of the wave function is the probability density, so that the probability dP that the particle is within a volume element dV is

$$dP = |\psi(x, y, z)|^2 \, dV \qquad (40-4)$$

Use the wave function to provide the statistical description of a particle in quantum mechanics.

Section 40-7. The Schrödinger equation
The wave function for a particle in a stationary state of energy E satisfies the time-independent Schrödinger equation,

$$-\frac{\hbar^2}{2m} \left(\frac{\partial^2 \psi}{\partial x^2} + \frac{\partial^2 \psi}{\partial y^2} + \frac{\partial^2 \psi}{\partial z^2} \right) + U(x, y, z)\psi = E\psi \quad (40\text{-}10)$$

Describe the role of the Schrödinger equation in quantum mechanics.

Section 40-8. A particle in a box
A particle in a one-dimensional box has quantized energy levels and wave functions given by

$$E_n = \frac{\hbar^2 \pi^2}{2mL^2} n^2 \qquad (40\text{-}14)$$

$$\psi_n = \sqrt{\frac{2}{L}} \sin \frac{n\pi x}{L} \qquad (40\text{-}15)$$

Solve the Schrödinger equation for a particle in a box.

Section 40-9. The harmonic oscillator

A harmonic oscillator of angular frequency ω has quantized energy levels given by

$$E_n = (n + \tfrac{1}{2})\hbar\omega = (n + \tfrac{1}{2})h\nu \qquad (n = 0, 1, 2, 3, \ldots) \tag{40-17}$$

Each wave function extends into the region beyond the turning points of a classical oscillator.

Describe features of the solution of the Schrödinger equation for the harmonic oscillator.

Section 40-10. Tunneling

A particle can tunnel through a barrier into a region that is inaccessible to a classical particle.

Describe the relation between the tunneling process and a wave function existing in a barrier region.

QUESTIONS

40-1 What are some similarities and some differences between photons and electrons?

40-2 Consider the de Broglie wavelengths of an electron and of a proton. Which has the smaller wavelength if the two particles have the same (a) speed, (b) kinetic energy, (c) momentum? Explain.

40-3 If a particle's kinetic energy increases, does the de Broglie wavelength of the particle increase or decrease? Explain.

40-4 The de Broglie wavelength for an electron is given by $\lambda = h/p$. Is this expression valid for a proton? A neutron? A photon?

40-5 The Bragg equation $2d \sin \theta = \lambda$ can be used for both x-ray diffraction and electron diffraction. Can it be used for neutron diffraction? Explain.

40-6 What experimental evidence supports the view of an electron as a particle? What experimental evidence supports the view of an electron as a wave?

40-7 If an electron has a wavelength, does it also have a color? Explain.

40-8 What are some examples of things that you have seen that behave as particles? As waves? Explain your classification.

40-9 What is the meaning of the phrase "wavelength of a particle"?

40-10 What mental picture do you first have on hearing or reading the word "electron"? What about the word "light"? Try to justify these pictures.

40-11 It is awkward to call an electron a particle since it has wave properties. The word "wavicle" has been suggested to refer to an entity that exhibits wave-particle duality. What are some advantages to the use of this word? Are there disadvantages?

40-12 When a wave passes the edge of an obstacle, a sharp shadow is not formed. Instead, a diffraction pattern exists in the region behind the edge. Figure 40-17 shows two such patterns, each formed on photographic film by a beam that is partially blocked by the sharp edge of an obstacle. One of the patterns was made with light and the other was made with electrons. Can you tell which was made by electrons?

40-13 Do the Heisenberg uncertainty relations apply to you

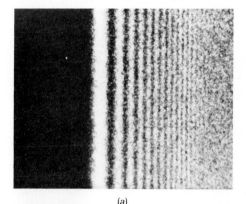

(a)

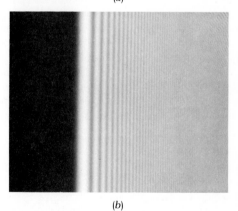

(b)

Figure 40-17. Ques. 40-12: Patterns formed on photographic film by beams partially blocked by the sharp edge of an obstacle. Which pattern was made by electrons? (a) From H. Raether, *Handbuch der Physik* 32 (Springer, Berlin, 1957). (b) From Joseph Valasek, *Introduction to Theoretical and Experimental Optics* (Wiley, New York, 1949).

as a macroscopic object? Explain.

40-14 The position of a marshmallow on a tabletop can be determined from the light reflected from it. How can you determine its position without using light?

40-15 Suppose that you located the marshmallow in the previous question by throwing marbles in its general direction and detecting the marbles that rebounded after colliding with it. Would there be uncertainties in the position and the momentum of the marshmallow? If so, how could you reduce such uncertainties?

40-16 Suppose that you locate the marshmallow in the previous question by aiming a flashlight toward it and detecting photons that reflect from it. Does this approach differ from that in either of the previous two questions? What of the uncertainties in position and momentum for this case?

40-17 The value of a probability is conventionally taken to range between 0 and 1. Do the expressions in Eqs. (40-4) and (40-5) have this property? Explain.

40-18 If the probability is 1/2 for getting a heads on a coin toss, then what is the probability of getting a tails? Is this the same as the probability for getting a "not-heads"? Explain.

40-19 Is it possible for $\psi = 0$ but $|\psi|^2 \neq 0$ at a point? Is it possible for $|\psi| \neq 0$ but $|\psi|^2 = 0$ at a point? Is it possible for $\psi_1 \neq 0$ and $\psi_2 \neq 0$ but $|\psi_1 + \psi_2|^2 = 0$ at a point? Explain.

40-20 Are the following statements reasonable?

    1 A particle in a box is not at rest, even in the ground state.

    2 A particle in a box is not at rest, even at $T = 0$ K.

Does the size of the box have any bearing on your explanations?

40-21 Two wave functions are shown in Fig. 40-18 for a particle in a box. Which state has the higher energy?

40-22 Is it more probable to find a pendulum bob at an endpoint or at the lowest point of its swing? Compare with a harmonic oscillator in the $n = 0$ quantum state.

40-23 Consider the three harmonic-oscillator wave functions shown in Fig. 40-15. Sketch graphs of ψ^2 for each. What is the probability of finding the particle to

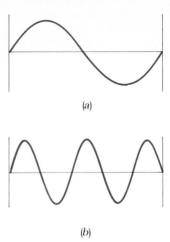

Figure 40-18. Ques. 40-21.

the left of the origin for each state?

40-24 A railway tunnel through a mountain allows a train to pass from one side to the other without changing its elevation. How is the tunneling of a particle through a potential-energy barrier similar to this? How is it different?

40-25 Complete the following table:

Symbol	Represents	Type	SI unit
λ			
Δx			m
Δp_x			
$\hbar$		Scalar	
Δt			
ΔE			
$|\psi|^2$	Probability density		
ψ			

EXERCISES

Section 40-2. De Broglie waves

40-1 Show that h/p, where p is the magnitude of momentum and h is Planck's constant, has dimensions of length.

40-2 An electron, a proton, and a Pb atom have the same speed, $v = 2.0 \times 10^6$ m/s. Determine the de Broglie wavelength for each.

40-3 An electron, a proton, and a Pb atom have the same de Broglie wavelength, $\lambda = 280$ pm. Determine the kinetic energy of each.

40-4 (a) An electron and an x-ray have the same wavelength, 28 pm. Determine the magnitude of the momentum of each. (b) An electron and an x-ray have the same energy, 2 keV. Determine the wavelength of each.

40-5 A "thermal neutron" in a substance at temperature T is a neutron with kinetic energy equal to $\frac{3}{2}kT$, where $k = 1.38 \times 10^{-23}$ J/K is the Boltzmann constant. Determine the wavelength of a thermal neutron in a reactor at (a) 300 K and (b) 800 K.

40-6 Determine the de Broglie wavelength of an electron with (a) speed 2.0×10^7 m/s, (b) speed 2×10^8 m/s, (c) kinetic energy 20 eV, (d) kinetic energy 20 MeV.

40-7 A 10^{-9}-kg dust particle has a de Broglie wavelength of 10^{-6} m. Determine (a) the momentum and (b) the kinetic energy of the dust particle. (c) Compare the kinetic energy with the mean kinetic energy of a gas molecule at $T = 300$ K. (See Exercise 40-5.) (d) Comment on the possibility of measuring the de Broglie wavelength of the dust particle.

40-8 Estimate the kinetic energy of a typical electron in a metal by assuming that its wavelength is about 0.5 nm, twice the typical spacing between atoms in the crystal.

Section 40-3. Electron diffraction

40-9 An electron is accelerated from rest through a potential difference of 250 V. Determine (a) the momentum and (b) the de Broglie wavelength of the electron.

40-10 An electron is accelerated from rest through a potential difference V. (a) Show that the de Broglie wavelength can be calculated from the formula $\lambda = h/\sqrt{2meV}$. Assume that the motion of the electron is nonrelativistic so that the kinetic energy can be written $K = \frac{1}{2}mv^2$. (But see Prob. 40-2.) (b) Using the values of e, m, and h, show that, for an electron, $\lambda = (1.23 \text{ nm} \cdot V^{1/2})/\sqrt{V}$.

40-11 A heated filament emits electrons with virtually zero kinetic energy. It forms the cathode of an electron gun. The anode is at a potential V with respect to the cathode, as shown schematically in Fig. 40-19. What is the range of de Broglie wavelengths for electrons from this gun if the potential difference is varied from 68 to 440 V?

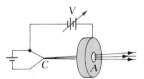

Figure 40-19. Exercise 40-11: Electrons are accelerated through a variable potential difference V from rest at the heated cathode C to the anode A.

40-12 Electrons from the filament in a TV picture tube are accelerated through a potential difference of around 35 kV. What is the wavelength of an electron in the beam?

40-13 Determine the wavelength of (a) an electron, (b) a proton, and (c) an alpha particle (He^{++}), each accelerated from rest through a potential difference of 10 kV.

40-14 A first-order electron diffraction intensity maximum occurs when the 140-V beam makes an angle of 8.5° with a set of crystalline planes in Al. Determine (a) the wavelength of an electron in the beam and (b) the spacing of that set of planes.

40-15 A set of crystalline planes in Ni has a 0.352-nm spacing. A monoenergetic electron beam makes a 30° angle with these planes. Determine the (lowest) kinetic energy of electrons in the beam which will result in a diffraction maximum.

40-16 In an electron diffraction experiment on Ni, a fourth-order diffraction peak occurs for 70-eV electrons from planes of spacing 0.304 nm. (a) Determine the

angle between the incident beam and the set of planes. (b) What is the angle between the incident beam and this diffracted beam? (c) Construct a diagram showing the orientations of the incident beam, the diffracted beam, and the set of planes.

40-17 Crystalline surfaces can be studied by the surface diffraction of neutral atoms in a monoenergetic beam. The surface has a two-dimensional periodic structure with a repeat distance of around 0.2 nm, determined by the distance between surface atoms. (a) What wavelength is appropriate for observing diffraction from such surfaces? (b) Suppose that a monoenergetic neutral atom beam has atoms with energy 20 meV. Determine the de Broglie wavelength for He, Ne, and Ar atom beams. (c) How do the wavelengths in part (b) compare with your answer to part (a)? See Prob. 40-3 for more on atom surface diffraction.

Section 40-4. Wave-particle duality — A double-slit experiment

40-18 A double-slit interference pattern is easily observable for waves whose wavelength λ is somewhat smaller than the spacing d between slits; typically, $\lambda \approx 0.01d$. What is an appropriate slit spacing for a beam of (a) monochromatic visible light, (b) 300-eV photons, (c) 300-eV electrons, (d) 300-eV alpha particles? (e) In each case above, is it feasible to construct a double slit of the appropriate spacing?

40-19 A monoenergetic beam of 25-eV electrons is incident on a double slit of spacing $d = 1.0 \ \mu$m. Determine the separation between an intensity maximum and the adjacent minimum on a observing screen 1.0 m from the slit system.

40-20 A biophysicist proposes a double-slit experiment for a beam of viruses. A double-slit system is available with spacing $d = 100$ nm that is suitable for observing interference for waves of wavelength as small as about 1 nm. If virus particles of mass 10^{-19} kg have this wavelength, determine (a) the magnitude of the momentum of a virus particle and (b) the minimum time required for an experiment if the observing screen is 1 m from the slit system. (c) Is this experiment feasible? Explain.

Section 40-5. The Heisenberg uncertainty relations

40-21 Show that the uncertainty products $\Delta x \, \Delta p_x$ and $\Delta E \, \Delta t$ have the same dimensions as $\hbar$.

40-22 The electron volt is a convenient energy unit for small particles such as electrons. Determine the values of h and $\hbar$ in units of eV $\cdot$ s.

40-23 If the uncertainty in the momentum of an electron is $\Delta p_x = 5 \times 10^{-25}$ kg $\cdot$ m/s, then what is the minimum uncertainty Δx in its position? Is there a maximum uncertainty in its position?

40-24 An electron is confined to a thin metallic film of thickness $d = 200$ nm. Determine its minimum momentum-component uncertainty Δp_x.

40-25 The kinetic energy of an electron can be expressed in terms of its momentum as $K = \frac{1}{2}mv^2 = p^2/2m$. (a) Show that the uncertainty in the kinetic energy is given by $\Delta K = v \Delta p$, where $v = p/m$ is the speed of the electron. (b) An electron has kinetic energy of approximately 500 eV, and its position along a given direction is known to within 1 mm. What is the minimum uncertainty in the kinetic energy? (In practice, the typical uncertainty in kinetic energy is much larger than this minimum value.)

40-26 Suppose that the uncertainty in the position of a particle is equal to its de Broglie wavelength. Show that the minimum momentum uncertainty is $\Delta p_x = p/4\pi$.

40-27 The wave number $k = 2\pi/\lambda$ is often used instead of the wavelength to describe a wave. (a) Show that the momentum of a particle can be written in terms of the wave number as $p = \hbar k$ and so $\Delta p = \hbar \, \Delta k$, where Δk is the spread or uncertainty in wave number for a wave. (b) Show that the uncertainty relation for $\Delta x \, \Delta p_x$ can be written as $\Delta x \, \Delta k_x \geq \frac{1}{2}$. (c) Similarly use $E = h\nu = \hbar\omega$ to show that $\Delta E \, \Delta t \geq \frac{1}{2}\hbar$ becomes $\Delta\omega \, \Delta t \geq \frac{1}{2}$. The relations $\Delta x \, \Delta k_x \geq \frac{1}{2}$ and $\Delta\omega \, \Delta t \geq \frac{1}{2}$ are used in describing beats in sound waves (Chap. 33).

40-28 An electron exists in the $n = 2$ excited state of hydrogen for about 10^{-9} s before making a transition to the $n = 1$ ground state. Determine (a) the energy of the emitted photon (use the Bohr model) and (b) the minimum uncertainty in the energy of the photon. (c) What is the minimum wavelength spread $\Delta\lambda$ in the spectral line for this transition?

40-29 Conservation of energy can be verified only to within the uncertainty ΔE in the measurement of the energy. Thus conservation of energy may be "violated" for a sufficiently short time interval. Over what maximum time interval can the energy of a system be uncertain by (a) twice the electron rest-mass energy mc^2 (corresponding to a photon spontaneously producing an electron-positron pair), (b) twice the proton rest-mass energy, (c) twice your rest-mass energy? (d) What is the feasibility of directly observing such violations within these time intervals?

Section 40-6. Interpretation of the wave function

40-30 Probability is a dimensionless quantity. (a) Use Eq. (40-4) to determine the dimensions of probability density $|\psi|^2$. (b) What are the dimensions of ψ? (c) What are the dimensions of $\psi(x)$, the wave function for a particle in one dimension?

40-31 In a double-slit experiment, individual electrons are counted as they hit an observing screen. Of the 12,000 electrons already counted, 519 have hit the screen within a small region near the center. Estimate the probability (a) that the next electron will hit within this same region and (b) that the next electron will not hit within this region.

40-32 Electrons pass through a double-slit system in which one slit is larger than the other, although both slits are narrow. Let ψ_1 represent the wave function at a point on the observing screen if only one slit is open. Similarly, let ψ_2 represent the wave function if the other slit alone is open. Suppose that $|\psi_1|^2 \approx 4|\psi_2|^2$ throughout a region near the center of the screen. Use the superposition principle to determine the ratio of intensities for maxima and minima in this region of the screen if both slits are open.

Section 40-7. The Schrödinger equation

40-33 Show that the Schrödinger equation in Eq. (40-11) is dimensionally correct; that is, show that each term has the same dimensions.

40-34 Show that the sinusoidal function in Eq. (40-7) has the property,

$$\frac{d^2\psi}{dx^2} = -k^2\psi$$

40-35 Obtain the time-independent Schrödinger equation from the time-dependent Schrödinger equation by using the product form $\Psi(x, y, z, t) = \psi(x, y, z)e^{-i\omega t}$. [*Note*: $(\partial/\partial t)e^{-i\omega t} = -i\omega e^{-i\omega t}$ and $E = \hbar\omega$.]

40-36 Establish the principle of superposition for solutions of the Schrödinger equation: If Ψ_1 and Ψ_2 are each solutions of the Schrödinger equation, then $\Psi = A\Psi_1 + B\Psi_2$ is also a solution, where A and B are arbitrary constants. Is this principle valid for both the time-dependent and the time-independent Schrödinger equations? Explain.

Section 40-8. A particle in a box

40-37 Show that $\psi = A \sin(kx) + B \cos(kx)$, where A and B are arbitrary constants, is a solution of Eq. (40-12).

40-38 (a) Determine the energy of the ground state of an electron confined to a one-dimensional box of length 500 nm. (b) Write down the wave function for this state. (c) What is the energy of the next-lowest state? (d) What are the energies of the two lowest levels in a box of twice that length?

40-39 The energy of the $n = 5$ state of a particle in a box is 7.5 meV. (a) What is the energy of the ground state? (b) If this particle is a proton, then what is the length of the box?

40-40 (a) Show that the wave function $\psi_n = A \sin(n\pi x/L)$ for a particle in a box is normalized if $A = \sqrt{2/L}$. (b) If the particle is in this state, determine the probability that the particle will be found in the interval $0 \leq x \leq L/n$. (*Hint*: Consider a sketch of $|\psi_n|^2$ versus x.)

40-41 Establish the following two properties of the energy levels for a particle in a box: (a) The energies are in the ratio $1:4:9:16:25: \ldots$. (b) The differences

$E_{n+1} - E_n$ in the energies are in the ratio $3:5:7:9:11: \ldots$.

40-42 Consider an electron in the $n = 3$ state of a one-dimensional box that extends from 0.00 to 1.00 nm. (a) Determine the energy of the electron in this state. Construct and use a graph of $\psi_3{}^2$ to estimate the probability that the electron will be found in the range (b) 0.24 nm $\leqslant x \leqslant$ 0.26 nm; (c) 0.32 nm $\leqslant x \leqslant$ 0.34 nm; (d) 0.49 nm $\leqslant x \leqslant$ 0.51 nm.

Section 40-9. The harmonic oscillator

40-43 Show that each of the functions in Eqs. (40-18) is a solution of the Schrödinger equation for a harmonic oscillator in one dimension. Notice that the corresponding value of E_n must be used for each wave function.

40-44 A nitrogen atom in a molecule behaves approximately as a one-dimensional harmonic oscillator of angular frequency 3.4×10^{12} rad/s. (a) Determine the ground-state energy of the oscillator. (b) The oscillator makes a transition from the ground state to the $n = 1$ (first excited) state by absorbing a photon. Determine the photon energy.

40-45 In a model, credited to Einstein, of the specific heat of a solid due to atomic vibrations, each atom was assumed to oscillate with the same frequency ν. Suppose that $\nu = 10^{12}$ Hz. (a) Determine the zero-point energy ($n = 0$) for such an atom. (b) What energy is required to change the oscillator to the $n = 1$ state? (c) Compare this minimum energy change of an oscillator with kT at room temperature. The quantization of the energy of an oscillator has a profound effect on the low-temperature behavior of the specific heat of a solid. This quantization also affects the spectral distribution of cavity radiation, as you should recall from Sec. 39-3.

40-46 Suppose that a classical oscillator of mass m and angular frequency ω had energy equal to the ground-state energy $\tfrac{1}{2}\hbar\omega$ of the quantum oscillator. (a) Determine the amplitude of the motion of the classical oscillator in terms of m, ω, and $\hbar$. Note that the amplitude gives the extent of the classical motion. (b) On the graph of ψ_0 in Fig. 40-15a, locate the positions that would correspond to the amplitude of a classical oscillator with this energy.

PROBLEMS

40-1 De Broglie showed that the expression $\lambda = h/p$ led to the quantization of angular momentum in the Bohr model of hydrogen. Consider an electron moving with speed v in a circular orbit of radius r about the nucleus. Impose the condition that a whole number m_ℓ of wavelengths must fit into the circumference of the orbit. Show that this condition leads to the expression $L = m_\ell \hbar$, where L is the magnitude of the orbital angular momentum and m_ℓ is an integer. Although the quantization of angular momentum turns out to be somewhat different, this result suggests that an electron exhibits wavelike behavior in an atom.

40-2 If an electron is accelerated from rest through a large potential difference V so that its kinetic energy, $K = eV$, is not very small compared with its rest-mass energy mc^2, then relativistic expressions must be used for K and p. (a) Show that the de Broglie wavelength, $\lambda = h/p$, is given by

$$\lambda = \frac{h}{\sqrt{2meV(1 + eV/2mc^2)}}$$

(b) If $eV \ll mc^2$ ($V \ll 510$ kV), then show that the above expression reduces to the form used in Exercise 40-10. (c) For the ultrarelativistic case, $eV \gg mc^2$, show that

$$\lambda = \frac{1.24 \times 10^{-6} \text{ V} \cdot \text{m}}{V} \qquad (V \gg 510 \text{ kV})$$

(d) What is the de Broglie wavelength of an electron if $V = 510$ kV?

40-3 *Surface diffraction.* Consider waves of wavelength λ incident on a surface as seen in Fig. 40-20, which shows a line of atoms on the surface with spacing d. The incident beam makes an angle θ_i with the normal to the surface. (a) For a scattered beam making an angle θ_m with the normal, show that the condition for a surface-diffraction maximum is

$$m\lambda = d(\sin \theta_m - \sin \theta_i) \qquad (m = 0, \pm 1, \pm 2, \ldots)$$

(b) Does this expression also describe specular reflection of the incident beam? Explain. (c) In an experiment, 20-meV He atoms are incident at $\theta_i = 15°$ on a surface containing carbon atoms with spacing $d = 0.14$ nm. At what angles do diffracted beams appear?

40-4 An early model of the nucleus assumed that it con-

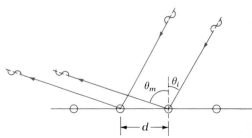

Figure 40-20. Prob. 40-3.

tained protons and electrons confined within a sphere of radius less than 10^{-14} m. (The neutron was discovered in 1932.) The Heisenberg uncertainty relation $\Delta x\,\Delta p_x$ can be used to assess the reasonableness of this model. Suppose that a spherical uranium nucleus of radius 7×10^{-15} m has 238 protons and 146 electrons to account for its mass and its net charge. (a) Estimate the electric potential energy U of an electron in the nucleus by calculating its value at the surface of the sphere of charge. (b) Estimate the kinetic energy K of an electron by using the approach used in Example 40-4. Note that relativistic expressions for K and p must be used in this case. (c) Estimate the total energy $E = K + U$, which must be negative if the electron is to be bound. (d) What do you conclude about the viability of the above model?

40-5 **Dispersion.** The angular frequency $\omega = 2\pi\nu$ and the wave number $k = 2\pi/\lambda$ are proportional (no dispersion) for an electromagnetic wave in vacuum, $\omega = ck$. An equation giving ω as a function of k is called a *dispersion relation*. (a) Multiply the relation $\omega = kc$ by $\hbar$ and obtain the expression $E = pc$ for a photon. (b) Starting with the nonrelativistic expression, $K = p^2/2m$ between the kinetic energy and the momentum of a particle of mass m, determine how ω depends on k for the corresponding wave. (c) Now use the relativistic relation between the total energy and the momentum of a particle of rest mass m and determine how ω depends on k. (d) The wave velocity v of a wave is given by ω/k. Energy and momentum of a wave propagate with the *group velocity*, $v_g = d\omega/dk$. Determine the wave velocity and the group velocity for each of the three cases above. (e) For the cases in parts (b) and (c), show that the group velocity for the wave is the same as the speed of the classical particle.

40-6 A complex number c is expressed as $c = a + ib$, where a and b are real numbers and $i = \sqrt{-1}$. The absolute square, $|c|^2 = a^2 + b^2$, of the complex number is nonnegative. The wave function can be written as $\Psi = \Psi_R + i\Psi_I$, where Ψ_R and Ψ_I are real. Evaluate the probability density $|\Psi|^2$ using the wave function of a free particle, $\Psi = A\cos(kx - \omega t) + B\sin(kx - \omega t)$ with $B = iA$, where A is a real number. How does this probability density depend on x and t?

40-7 **Expectation value.** If $\psi(x)$ is the normalized wave function for a particle in one dimension, then the probability of finding the particle in the interval between x and $x + dx$ is $|\psi|^2\,dx$. Therefore, the average value, or *expectation value* $\langle g \rangle$, of a quantity $g(x)$ is given by $\langle g \rangle = \int g(x)|\psi|^2\,dx$. A particle moves freely between impenetrable barriers at $x = 0$ and $x = L$. For the state with quantum number n, (a) show that $\langle x \rangle = L/2$ and (b) evaluate $\langle x^2 \rangle$.

40-8 A particle of mass m is confined to a one-dimensional box of length $2a$ centered at $x = 0$. (a) Solve the Schrödinger equation and determine the energy levels and the normalized wave function for each level. (b) How do these solutions correspond to those for a particle in a box in Sec. 40-8? (c) Determine the expectation values (see the previous problem) $\langle x \rangle$ and $\langle x^2 \rangle$ for each state of this system.

40-9 Consider the classical turning points for a harmonic oscillator with energy $E_n = (n + \frac{1}{2})\hbar\omega$. (a) Show that these points are given by $x_n = \pm a\sqrt{2n + 1}$, where $a = \sqrt{\hbar/m\omega}$. (b) Show that $d^2\psi/dx^2 = 0$ at $x = x_n$. (c) Is this result apparent in Fig. 40-15? Explain.

40-10 Determine the constants A_0, A_1, and A_2 in the harmonic-oscillator wave functions of Eqs. (40-18) by requiring each wave function to be normalized. [*Hint:*

$$\int_{-\infty}^{\infty} e^{-u^2/2}\,du = \sqrt{2\pi}$$

$$\int_{-\infty}^{\infty} u^{2p}e^{-u^2/2}\,du = 1 \cdot 3 \cdots (2p - 1)\sqrt{2\pi}$$

where p is a positive integer.]

40-11 (a) Show that the expectation value $\langle x \rangle = 0$ for each state of the harmonic oscillator. (See Prob. 40-7.) (b) Evaluate $\langle U \rangle = \frac{1}{2}m\omega^2\langle x^2 \rangle$ for the $n = 0$ and $n = 1$ states of the harmonic oscillator. Use the hint in the previous problem. (c) Determine the expectation value of the kinetic energy of the oscillator for the two states in part (b). Note that $\langle E \rangle = E_n = (n + \frac{1}{2})\hbar\omega$.

CHAPTER 41
THE HYDROGEN ATOM AND THE PERIODIC TABLE

41-1 INTRODUCTION

To understand the periodic table is to go a long way toward understanding atoms. One of the great triumphs of quantum mechanics is its description of the periodic table; it explains why the periodic table is periodic. The key to the periodic table is the first atom listed, the hydrogen atom. The quantum states of hydrogen form a pattern which is followed by the other atoms, and it is this pattern that is displayed in the periodic table.

41-2 QUANTUM MECHANICS AND THE HYDROGEN ATOM

The simplest atom is the hydrogen atom. In the hydrogen atom, a single electron (charge $-e$, mass m_e) is in a bound quantum state about a nucleus (proton with charge $+e$, mass M). The potential energy of interaction is

$$U = \frac{(+e)(-e)}{4\pi\epsilon_0 r} = -\frac{e^2}{4\pi\epsilon_0 r} \tag{41-1}$$

Because the nucleus is much more massive than the electron ($M \approx 2000 m_e$), we neglect the motion of the nucleus and fix the origin of coordinates at its position. Therefore, $r = \sqrt{x^2 + y^2 + z^2}$, where $x, y,$ and z are the coordinates of a point at which the electron's wave function is evaluated. With this approximation, the kinetic energy of the system is entirely due to the motion of the electron, and the Schrödinger equation for the electron's wave function ψ is

$$-\frac{\hbar^2}{2m_e}\left(\frac{\partial^2\psi}{\partial x^2}+\frac{\partial^2\psi}{\partial y^2}+\frac{\partial^2\psi}{\partial z^2}\right)+U\psi=E\psi \tag{41-2}$$

The properties of the hydrogen atom which we seek are contained in the wave functions ψ and in the energies E that correspond to these wave functions. The procedures used in solving Eq. (41-2) are too lengthy to discuss here. In this section, we introduce the quantum numbers that arise from the solution, and in the next section we describe a few of the wave functions.

In three dimensions, three quantum numbers characterize a wave function.

We are interested in the atom, the case where the electron is bound to the nucleus (Fig. 41-1). As we saw in the previous chapter, if a particle is confined to a specific region, then the boundary conditions on the wave functions cause the energy to be quantized and these discrete energy values are called *energy levels.* For the one-dimensional problems of the previous chapter, there was a wave function associated with each energy level, and a single quantum number characterized an energy level and its associated wave function. In a three-dimensional problem, three quantum numbers characterize a wave function. The names and symbols that are used to designate the quantum numbers for the hydrogen-atom wave functions are (i) the *principal quantum number n,* (ii) the *orbital angular-momentum quantum number ℓ,* and (iii) the *orbital magnetic quantum number m_ℓ.*

The principal quantum number n. The energy level E_n of a hydrogen atom depends on the principal quantum number n:

Energy levels for the hydrogen atom

$$E_n=-\frac{m_e}{2}\left(\frac{e^2}{4\pi\epsilon_0\hbar}\right)^2\frac{1}{n^2}=-\frac{13.6\text{ eV}}{n^2} \tag{41-3}$$

where n can take on positive integer values only: $n=1,\,2,\,3,\,\ldots$. This is the same result as that found from the Bohr model [Eq. (39-17)]. The energy-level diagram (the same as that discussed in Sec. 39-7) is shown in Fig. 41-2. In the

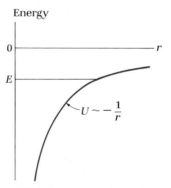

Figure 41-1. In the hydrogen atom, the electron's potential-energy function is $U=-e^2/4\pi\epsilon_0 r$, and the electron is bound to the nucleus so that its total energy E is negative. As we saw in the previous chapter, if a particle is confined to a specific region, then discrete energy levels arise from applying boundary conditions to the particle's wave functions.

Figure 41-2. Quantum mechanics gives the same energy-level diagram for hydrogen as does the Bohr theory. As you know, these levels are well verified by the spectral lines of hydrogen.

case of the Bohr model, the quantization of the energy was the result of Bohr's hypothesis that the electron's orbital angular momentum is quantized. In quantum theory, energy quantization comes from solving the Schrödinger equation and from applying boundary conditions to the wave functions.

The orbital angular-momentum quantum number ℓ. The orbital angular-momentum quantum number ℓ determines the magnitude L of the electron's orbital angular momentum:

Magnitude L of the orbital angular momentum

$$L = \sqrt{\ell(\ell + 1)}\,\hbar \qquad (41\text{-}4)$$

where ℓ can be zero or a positive integer: $\ell = 0, 1, 2, \ldots$. Thus a solution to the Schrödinger equation for the hydrogen atom is characterized by a discrete, or quantized, value of L.

The value of L is limited by the energy because, for a given energy level E_n, L cannot exceed an amount which is consistent with this energy. In terms of the quantum numbers, this means that the value of n puts a limit on the maximum value of ℓ. As it turns out, ℓ can be no larger than $n - 1$. For example, if $n = 3$, then ℓ can take on the values 0, 1, or 2 only. If the principal quantum number is n, then the possible values of ℓ are $0, 1, 2, \ldots, (n - 1)$.

The orbital magnetic quantum number m_ℓ. The orbital magnetic quantum number m_ℓ determines the value of a component of the orbital angular momentum, and the component customarily chosen is the z component. With this choice, we have

The z component of the orbital angular momentum

$$L_z = m_\ell \hbar \qquad (41\text{-}5)$$

where m_ℓ can be zero or a positive or negative integer: $m_\ell = 0, \pm 1, \pm 2, \ldots$. As the name implies, the orbital magnetic quantum number is associated with magnetic effects, and the quantization of L_z becomes observable if the atom is placed in a magnetic field.

Since a component of a vector cannot be larger than the magnitude of the vector, the value of ℓ provides a limit to the possible values of m_ℓ. Suppose $\ell = 2$ so that $L = \sqrt{2(2 + 1)}\,\hbar = \sqrt{6}\,\hbar = 2.45\,\hbar$. From Eq. (41-5), the possible values of L_z are $m_\ell \hbar$. Since $|L_z| \le L = 2.45\,\hbar$, we have $|m_\ell \hbar| \le 2.45\,\hbar$, or $|m_\ell| \le 2.45$. Therefore, when $\ell = 2$, the largest value of m_ℓ is $+2$ and the smallest value is -2. In this case, m_ℓ is limited to the values $-2, -1, 0, +1$, or $+2$. This is shown graphically in Fig. 41-3. In general, for a given value of ℓ, the possible values of m_ℓ are $0, \pm 1, \pm 2, \ldots, \pm \ell$.

A quantum state is defined by a set of quantum numbers. To completely define a quantum state for the hydrogen atom, we need a fourth quantum number. This final quantum number will be introduced in Sec. 41-5. Until then, we let the quantum numbers n, ℓ, and m_ℓ define a quantum state for hydrogen. For example, the state characterized by $n = 2$, $\ell = 1$, and $m_\ell = -1$ is referred to as the 2, 1, -1 state, and the symbol for its wave function is written as ψ_{21-1}.

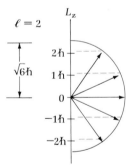

Figure 41-3. The possible values of L_z for the case where $\ell = 2$ and $L = \sqrt{2(2 + 1)}\,\hbar = \sqrt{6}\,\hbar$ are $-2\,\hbar$, $-\hbar, 0, +\hbar, +2\,\hbar$. The possible values of m_ℓ are $-2, -1, 0, +1, +2$.

EXAMPLE 41-1. A hydrogen atom is in the 2, 1, -1 state. Determine (a) the atom's energy, (b) the electron's orbital angular momentum magnitude, and (c) the z component of the electron's orbital angular momentum.

SOLUTION. A hydrogen atom in the 2, 1, -1 state has $n = 2$, $\ell = 1$, and $m_\ell = -1$. From Eqs. (41-3), (41-4), and (41-5), we have

(a) $\qquad E_2 = -\dfrac{13.6\text{ eV}}{2^2} = -3.40\text{ eV}$

(b) $\qquad L = \sqrt{\ell(\ell + 1)}\,\hbar = \sqrt{1(1 + 1)}\,\hbar = \sqrt{2}\,\hbar = 1.41\,\hbar$

(c) $\qquad L_z = m_\ell \hbar = (-1)\hbar = -\hbar$

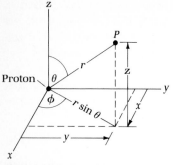

Figure 41-4. Electron wave functions may be expressed in terms of cartesian coordinates x, y, and z or spherical coordinates r, θ, and ϕ. For the hydrogen-atom problem, spherical coordinates are more convenient. Note that $x = r \sin \theta \sin \phi$, $y = r \sin \theta \cos \phi$, and $z = r \cos \theta$.

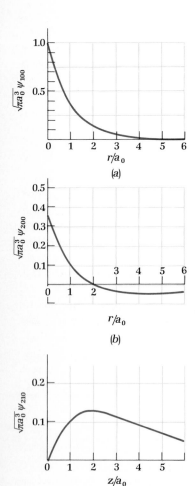

Figure 41-5. Graphs of wave functions. (a) ψ_{100}; (b) ψ_{200}; (c) ψ_{210}.

41-3 THE HYDROGEN-ATOM WAVE FUNCTIONS

The hydrogen-atom wave functions are found by solving the Schrödinger equation [Eq. (41-2)], with U given by Eq. (41-1) and by applying boundary conditions to these wave functions. Because U is spherically symmetric, it is convenient to express these wave functions in terms of spherical coordinates r, θ, and ϕ. The way these coordinates locate a point in space, and their relation to the rectangular coordinates x, y, and z, is shown in Fig. 41-4.

The wave functions for a few of the states are

$$\psi_{100} = \frac{1}{\sqrt{\pi a_0^3}} e^{-r/a_0} \tag{41-6}$$

$$\psi_{200} = \frac{1}{\sqrt{8\pi a_0^3}} \left(1 - \frac{r}{2a_0} \right) e^{-r/2a_0} \tag{41-7}$$

$$\psi_{210} = \frac{1}{\sqrt{32\pi a_0^5}} r e^{-r/2a_0} \cos \theta \tag{41-8}$$

where a_0 is the Bohr radius: $a_0 = 4\pi\epsilon_0 \hbar^2/m_e e^2 = 0.0529$ nm.

As we discuss these functions, keep in mind that $|\psi|^2$ is the electron's probability density. The factor which contains the square root in each of these expressions is called a *normalizing factor*. Its value has been determined by requiring the integral of $|\psi|^2$ over all space to be equal to 1 in each case. This requirement assures that the probability the electron is somewhere is equal to 1. Notice that the dimension of a_0 is length, so that the dimension of $|\psi|^2$ is (length)$^{-3}$ or 1/(volume), as expected for a probability density.

An important feature of $|\psi|^2$ is that it gives the spatial dependence of the charge density due to an electron. Since the electronic charge is $-e$, the charge density due to an electron is given by $-e|\psi|^2$. The spread-out position distribution of the electron results in a spread-out charge distribution.

Figure 41-5 shows graphs of each of the three wave functions: ψ_{100}, ψ_{200}, and ψ_{210}.

1. The function ψ_{100} is the ground-state wave function for hydrogen. This wave function is spherically symmetric (it does not depend on θ or ϕ), so that its graph versus the distance r from the nucleus is the same along any direction. As shown in Fig. 41-5a, ψ_{100} is maximum at the origin and decreases exponentially with r. (Indeed, every hydrogen-atom wave function contains a factor that decreases exponentially with r.) The Bohr radius a_0 in the exponent provides the scale which determines how rapidly the function decreases with distance. Since the wave function decreases monotonically, an electron in a 1, 0, 0 state is more likely to be found near the nucleus than near any other point in space, and the farther a point is from the nucleus, the smaller is the likelihood of finding the electron near that point. Note that $\psi_{100} \rightarrow 0$ as $r \rightarrow \infty$. This asymptotic behavior is a common feature of all wave functions of bound particles.

2. A graph of ψ_{200} is shown in Fig. 41-5b. Similar to ψ_{100}, ψ_{200} is spherically symmetric and maximum at the nucleus. It turns out that every wave function with $\ell = 0$ is spherically symmetric and has a maximum at the nucleus. Unlike ψ_{100}, ψ_{200} passes through zero. The factor $(1 - r/2a_0)$ in ψ_{200} is positive for $r < 2a_0$, zero at $r = 2a_0$, and negative for $r > 2a_0$. Consequently, ψ_{200} has an oscillation along r. For wave functions with different n (but the same ℓ), the number of oscillations along r increases with increasing n. thus the quantum

number n is a measure of the waviness of a wave function along r. As n increases (ℓ fixed), the waviness along r of the wave functions increases. Similar to the particle in a box and the harmonic oscillator in the previous chapter, greater waviness is associated with higher energy.

An important comparison between ψ_{100} and ψ_{200} is that $|\psi_{200}|^2$ is considerably smaller near the nucleus. From the expressions above, you can see that when $r \approx 0, |\psi_{100}|^2 \approx 8|\psi_{200}|^2$. An electron in a 1, 0, 0 state is about 8 times more likely to be near the nucleus than one in a 2, 0, 0 state.

3. The function ψ_{210} is shown in Fig. 41-5c. This wave function is not spherically symmetric; it depends on θ as well as on r. Therefore, a graph of ψ_{210} versus distance from the nucleus depends on the direction chosen. Since $\cos \theta = \cos 0 = 1$ along the positive z axis, we show ψ_{210} along the positive z axis in Fig. 41-5c. The function is zero at the nucleus, reaches a maximum at $z = 2a_0$, and approaches zero as z becomes large.

The factor $\cos \theta$ in ψ_{210} determines its θ dependence; ψ_{210} is positive at all points above the xy plane $(0 < \theta < \frac{1}{2}\pi)$, zero at all points in the xy plane $(\theta = \frac{1}{2}\pi)$, and negative at all points below the xy plane $(\frac{1}{2}\pi < \theta < \pi)$. Thus ψ_{210} oscillates with θ. Wave functions with larger values of ℓ have larger numbers of oscillations with θ.

Since it does not contain ϕ, ψ_{210} has azimuthal symmetry about the z axis. It turns out that every wave function with $m_\ell = 0$ has azimuthal symmetry about the z axis. The quantum number m_ℓ is a measure of the waviness of a wave function with ϕ. The larger the value of $|m_\ell|$ for a wave function, the greater is its waviness with ϕ.

Electron cloud

The probability density $|\psi|^2$ for an electron in a given state can be visualized as an *electron cloud.* The density of the cloud at a point portrays the likelihood that the electron is near that point. Figure 41-6 shows the electron cloud for the 1, 0, 0 and 2, 1, 0 states. This representation is especially useful in revealing the spatial features of the 2, 1, 0 state. The electron cloud which represents this state has lobes that extend along the z axis.

What about the other two $\ell = 1$ states, the 2, 1, -1 state and the 2, 1, $+1$ state? Do these states have lobes that extend along the x and the y axes? As it happens, they do not. However, because the hydrogen-atom potential-energy function is spherically symmetric, the orientation of our axes is arbitrary. This means that we may form two wave functions, which we call ψ_{21x} and ψ_{21y}, from a linear combination of ψ_{21-1} and ψ_{21+1}. These newly formed functions are also solutions to the Schrödinger equation for the hydrogen atom. The electron cloud for the 2, 1, x state (or the 2, 1, y state) appears the same as that for the 2, 1, 0 state, except that the cloud's lobes are along the x axis (or y axis) rather than the z axis. For a consistent notation, we can now refer to ψ_{210} as ψ_{21z}.

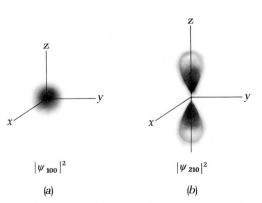

Figure 41-6. Electron cloud for (a) the 1, 0, 0 state and (b) the 2, 1, 0 state.

$|\psi_{100}|^2$

(a)

$|\psi_{210}|^2$

(b)

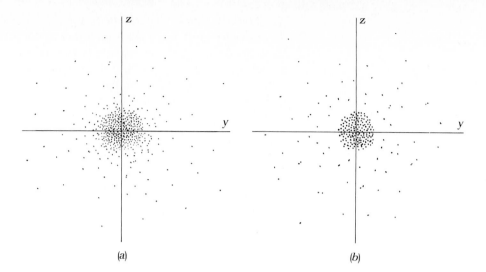

Figure 41-7. Cross section of the electron cloud for (a) the 1, 0, 0 state and (b) the 2, 0, 0 state.

(a)   (b)

Another way to exhibit the probability density for a state is to show a cross section of its electron cloud through the position of the nucleus (Fig. 41-7). This is particularly helpful in displaying the 2, 0, 0 state because it allows us to see inside the outer shell of the electron cloud.

EXAMPLE 41-2. (a) Write the expression for the probability density for the 1, 0, 0 state. (b) Verify that ψ_{100} given in Eq. (41-6) is normalized. (*Hint:*

$$\int_0^\infty x^n e^{-x}\, dx = n!$$

where n is a positive integer.)

SOLUTION. (a) From Eq. (41-6), we find that the probability density $|\psi|^2$ for the 1, 0, 0 state is

$$|\psi_{100}|^2 = [(\pi a_0^{\,3})^{-1/2}\, e^{-r/a_0}]^2 = \frac{1}{\pi a_0^{\,3}}\, e^{-2r/a_0}$$

(b) To verify that ψ_{100} is normalized, we must show that the integral of $|\psi_{100}|^2$ over all space is equal to 1. Since the function is spherically symmetric, we can take a spherical shell of radius r and thickness dr as our element of volume (Fig. 41-8): $dV = 4\pi r^2\, dr$. Using $|\psi_{100}|^2$ from part (a), we have

$$\int_{\substack{\text{all} \\ \text{space}}} |\psi_{100}|^2\, dV = \frac{1}{\pi a_0^{\,3}} \int_0^\infty e^{-2r/a_0}\, 4\pi r^2\, dr$$

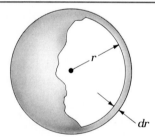

Figure 41-8. Example 41-2: The volume element is the volume of a spherical shell of radius r (surface area $4\pi r^2$) and thickness dr: $dV = 4\pi r^2\, dr$.

If we let $x = 2r/a_0$, then we have

$$\int_{\substack{\text{all} \\ \text{space}}} |\psi_{100}|^2\, dV = \frac{1}{2} \int_0^\infty e^{-x} x^2\, dx = \tfrac{1}{2}(2!) = 1$$

where we have used the hint above to evaluate the integral on the right-hand side. Thus the wave function is normalized.

41-4 QUANTIZATION OF ANGULAR MOMENTUM AND MAGNETIC MOMENT

The distinguishing feature of quantum theory is the quantization of dynamical quantities. In Sec. 41-2, we noted that the solution of the Schrödinger equation

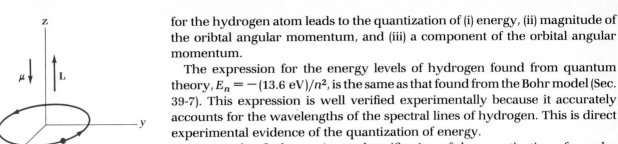

Figure 41-9. For a charged particle in a circular orbit, the magnetic moment μ and angular momentum **L** are proportional in magnitude. In the case of a negative particle, μ and **L** have opposite directions.

The magnetic moment is proportional to the angular momentum.

Bohr magneton

Quantized energy in a magnetic field

for the hydrogen atom leads to the quantization of (i) energy, (ii) magnitude of the oribtal angular momentum, and (iii) a component of the orbital angular momentum.

The expression for the energy levels of hydrogen found from quantum theory, $E_n = -(13.6 \text{ eV})/n^2$, is the same as that found from the Bohr model (Sec. 39-7). This expression is well verified experimentally because it accurately accounts for the wavelengths of the spectral lines of hydrogen. This is direct experimental evidence of the quantization of energy.

Can we also find experimental verification of the quantization of angular momentum? Yes. Briefly, this verification goes as follows: A circulating charged particle produces a magnetic dipole moment μ_ℓ, and μ_ℓ is proportional to the orbital angular momentum **L** of the particle. (The subscript ℓ on μ_ℓ is a reminder that this magnetic moment is due to orbital motion.) If **L** is quantized, then μ_ℓ is also quantized. The effect of the quantization of μ_ℓ can be observed by placing the atom in a magnetic field.

Now consider this verification in more detail. First, we use the Bohr model to guide us to a relation between μ_ℓ and **L**. In Sec. 30-2, we showed that μ_ℓ due to a particle with charge $-e$ and mass m_e traveling in a circular orbit (Fig. 41-9) is

$$\mu_\ell = -\frac{e}{2m_e}\mathbf{L}$$

Thus the particle's magnetic moment is proportional to its orbital angular momentum. (The minus sign in this expression is a consequence of the electron's negative charge. Because of this minus sign, μ_ℓ is directed opposite **L**.) The z component of μ_ℓ is

$$\mu_{\ell,z} = -\frac{e}{2m_e}L_z \tag{41-9}$$

Using the quantized $L_z = m_\ell \hbar$, we find

$$\mu_{\ell,z} = -\frac{e\hbar}{2m_e}m_\ell$$

Since $m_\ell = 0, \pm 1, \ldots, \pm\ell$, the z component of the atom's magnetic dipole moment is quantized in increments of $e\hbar/2m_e$. This quantum of magnetic moment, $e\hbar/2m_e$, is called the *Bohr magneton* and is given the symbol μ_B:

$$\mu_B = \frac{e\hbar}{2m_e} = 5.79 \times 10^{-5} \text{ eV/T}$$

In Chap. 26, we found that the potential energy U_m of an object with magnetic dipole moment μ in a magnetic field **B** is

$$U_m = -\mu \cdot \mathbf{B}$$

If we let the magnetic field be directed along the z axis, $\mathbf{B} = B\mathbf{k}$, then $U_m = -\mu_z B$. Therefore, the potential energy due to the electron's orbital angular momentum is $U_m = -\mu_{\ell,z}B = -(-\mu_B m_\ell)B$, or

$$U_m = (\mu_B B)m_\ell \tag{41-10}$$

We find that an atom in a magnetic field has a contribution to its energy that depends on the orbital magnetic quantum number m_ℓ. Even for very large magnetic fields ($B \approx 1$ to 10 T), this contribution to an atom's energy is small. For example, suppose $B = 1.0 \text{ T}$ and $m_\ell = 1$, then $U_m = (\mu_B B)m_\ell =$

$(5.79 \times 10^{-5} \text{ eV/T})(1.0 \text{ T})(1) = 5.8 \times 10^{-5}$ eV. Compared with the spacing of energy levels which correspond to optical spectra (about 1 eV), this energy is very small. However, because the wavelengths of spectral lines can be measured precisely, this contribution to the energy can be verified experimentally.

Evidence for the quantization given in Eq. (41-10) is found by measuring the wavelengths of the light emitted from atoms in a magnetic field. Before discussing this evidence, we must mention that there can be another contribution to an atom's magnetic moment besides that due to the electron's orbital angular momentum. This additional contribution is due to the electron's *spin angular momentum* and will be introduced in the next section. For now we wish to avoid the added complexity caused by spin. We may do this because in some elements, calcium for example, the effects of spin may cancel out. Thus we confine our discussion to those situations in which the effects of spin cancel.

In 1897 Pieter Zeeman (1865 – 1943) discovered that when atoms are placed in a magnetic field, the spectral lines emitted by the atoms may be split into several lines. Such splitting is now called the *Zeeman effect*. If electron spin is involved in the Zeeman effect, then it is called the *anomalous* Zeeman effect. If electron spin is not involved in the Zeeman effect, then it is called the *normal* Zeeman effect. As stated above, we discuss only the normal Zeeman effect.

Consider measuring the frequency of a particular spectral line. To be specific, suppose the line corresponds to a transition from a level in which $\ell = 1$ to a level in which $\ell = 0$, as shown in Fig. 41-10a. The frequency of the emitted light is $\nu_0 = (E_i - E_f)/h = \Delta E_0/h$. Figure 41-10b shows the effect of the magnetic field. The level with $\ell = 1$ is split into three levels, and the level with $\ell = 0$ is unaffected. Therefore, the spectral line of frequency ν_0 is split into three lines of frequency ν_+, ν_0, and ν_-:

$$\nu_+ = \frac{\Delta E_0 + \mu_B B}{h} \qquad \nu_0 = \frac{\Delta E_0}{h} \qquad \nu_- = \frac{\Delta E_0 - \mu_B B}{h}$$

As the magnetic field is increased from zero, the emission line splits into three lines (corresponding to the three values of m_ℓ), and the spacing $\Delta\nu$ between the lines increases as the field increases: $\Delta\nu = (\mu_B/h)B$.

Interestingly, the normal Zeeman effect can be successfully described using classical mechanics. That is, classical mechanics predicts the same splitting as quantum mechanics. Indeed, the classical description was crucial to the early development of our modern view of atoms. Since the size of the splitting gives a measure of the charge to mass ratio, e/m, for the electron, the Zeeman effect showed that electrons are constituents of atoms and are responsible for the emission of light. Classical mechanics fails to account for the anomalous Zeeman effect; quantum mechanics must be used in this case. It was this failure that prompted the term "anomalous" for the anomalous Zeeman effect.

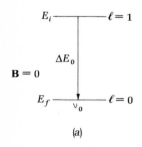

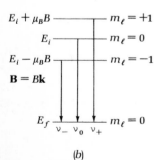

Figure 41-10. Transitions for an element that exhibits the normal Zeeman effect. (a) When the atoms are in a zero magnetic field, a single transition is observed. (b) When the atoms are in a magnetic field, the single line of (a) is split into three lines. The size of the splitting shown is exaggerated for purposes of illustration.

41-5 ELECTRON SPIN

We have seen that three quantum numbers, n, ℓ, and m_ℓ, arise from the solution to the Schrödinger equation for the hydrogen atom. Three quantum numbers are expected from this equation because it describes the electron as a particle with three degrees of freedom (freedom to move in three-dimensional space). In addition to these three external degrees of freedom, experiments show that the electron has still another degree of freedom, an internal degree of freedom which gives rise to an *intrinsic angular momentum*. This intrinsic

Zeeman effect

angular momentum is sometimes viewed in analogy to the angular momentum of a spinning object in classical mechanics. For example, the earth has both an orbital and spin angular momentum. Its orbital angular momentum is due to its annual motion around the sun, and its spin angular momentum is due to its daily rotation about its axis. By analogy, the electron's internal degree of freedom is called *electron spin*, and its associated angular momentum is called the *spin angular momentum*. Other particles besides the electron exhibit spin; examples are the proton and the neutron.

Historically, the concept of spin originated with the explanation of the details of atomic spectra. Many spectral lines that appear to be single lines are found, upon closer examination, to consist of two or more closely spaced lines. This feature of closely spaced lines is called *fine structure*. (See Sec. 41-6.) Fine structure cannot be described adequately with the three spatial quantum numbers n, ℓ, and m_ℓ. In 1925 S. Goudsmit and G. Uhlenbeck, two graduate students at Leiden in the Netherlands, hypothesized the existence of electron spin, and used it to account for fine structure in atomic spectra.

Characteristics of spin. The quantum number associated with electron spin is given the symbol s. A curious feature of this quantum number is that it can take on only one value, $s = 1/2$, so that the magnitude S of the spin angular momentum is quantized with a single value: $S = \sqrt{s(s+1)}\hbar = \sqrt{\frac{1}{2}(\frac{1}{2}+1)}\hbar = \sqrt{\frac{3}{4}}\hbar$. We often express this result by saying that the electron "has a spin of 1/2."

Similar to the orbital angular momentum component L_z, a component of the spin angular momentum is quantized. As before, the axis chosen for this component is usually the z axis. Thus the z component S_z of the spin angular momentum is written

$$S_z = m_s \hbar \tag{41-11}$$

where m_s is the *spin magnetic quantum number*. The quantum number m_s can take on only two values: $m_s = -1/2$ or $m_s = +1/2$. This means that S_z has only two quantized values, $S_z = -\frac{1}{2}\hbar$ or $S_z = +\frac{1}{2}\hbar$. We often refer to these two spin states as "spin down" for $m_s = -1/2$ and "spin up" for $m_s = +1/2$.

The Stern-Gerlach experiment. A famous experiment performed in 1922 by Otto Stern and Walther Gerlach, now called the Stern-Gerlach experiment, demonstrates the bare features of spin without any encumbrance from the orbital angular momentum. Stern and Gerlach used silver atoms, but the experiment was repeated by Phipps and Taylor in 1927 using hydrogen. We discuss the experiment with hydrogen because it is simpler and still contains the salient features of the original experiment.

The Stern-Gerlach experiment involves the force on an atom in a magnetic field. This force is due to the atom's magnetic dipole moment μ. In the previous section, we found that the z component of the magnetic moment due to orbit was given by $\mu_{\ell,z} = -(e/2m_e)L_z$. That is, $\mu_{\ell,z}$ is proportional to $-L_z$. Similarly, for electron spin we have $\mu_{s,z} \propto -S_z$. The proportionality constant is written as $ge/2m_e$, so that

$$\mu_{s,z} = -g\frac{e}{2m_e}S_z \tag{41-12}$$

where g is a dimensionless number and is called the *electron-spin g factor*. The electron-spin g factor is approximately 2. The accepted value is $g = 2.0023193044$, with an uncertainty of 1 in the last digit.

We find the quantized values of $\mu_{s,z}$ by substituting $S_z = m_s\hbar$ into Eq. (41-12):

Quantized component of the magnetic moment due to spin

$$\mu_{s,z} = -g\frac{e\hbar}{2m_e}m_s = -g\mu_B m_s \qquad (41\text{-}13)$$

Thus there are two quantized values for $\mu_{s,z}$. Substituting $g = 2.00$ and $m_s = -1/2$, we find that $\mu_{s,z} = -2.00\ \mu_B(-1/2) = +1.00\mu_B$. Similarly, when $m_s = +1/2$, we have $\mu_{s,z} = -1.00\mu_B$. Keeping in mind that the values are accurate to three significant digits, we can write

$$\mu_{s,z} = \mu_B \qquad \text{(spin down)}$$

and

$$\mu_{s,z} = -\mu_B \qquad \text{(spin up)}$$

Now consider a hydrogen atom in the ground state. Since $n = 1$ in the ground state, $\ell = 0$ and $\mu_\ell = 0$. However, the electron's spin angular momentum is intrinsic and can never be zero. Because of the electron's spin magnetic moment, the atom behaves as a quantized magnetic dipole.

If a magnetic dipole is placed in an *nonuniform* field, then there is a net force on the dipole. In Fig. 41-11 we show two dipoles (bar magnets) suspended in a nonuniform field; **B** is directed generally toward $+z$ (upward) and its magnitude increases with z. The orientation of the dipole on the left is such that its north pole is higher than its south pole so that the net force on this dipole is upward because the upward force on its north pole is larger than the downward force on its south pole. On the other hand, the moment of the dipole on the right is oriented such that its south pole is higher than its north pole, which causes the net force on this dipole to be downward. Thus the direction of the net force on a dipole in a nonuniform field depends on the orientation of the dipole moment. This is the basis of the Stern-Gerlach experiment.

In the Stern-Gerlach experiment, a ribbon-shaped beam of atoms passes through a nonuniform magnetic field and then strikes a collector plate or other detector (Fig. 41-12). We may consider the beam as two subbeams, one with atoms whose electrons have spin up and the other with atoms whose electrons have spin down, and the magnetic force on the atoms in one subbeam is directed opposite to the magnetic force on the atoms in the other subbeam. One subbeam is deflected up and the other subbeam is deflected down. A measurement of the z component of the atom's spin angular momentum always shows that it is quantized, either up or down. This quantization of the orientation of the angular momentum is called *space quantization*.

Space quantization

Figure 41-13a shows the pattern produced at the detector when the magnet is absent. Then there is no field and no magnetic force on the atoms, and we simply see an image of the collimating slit. Figure 41-13b shows the pattern when the beam passes through the nonuniform field. The important point is

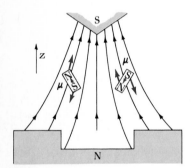

Figure 41-11. There is a net magnetic force on a small magnet (a magnetic dipole) placed in a nonuniform magnetic field. The direction of this force depends on the orientation of the dipole moment.

Figure 41-12. Apparatus used in the Stern-Gerlach experiment. In the original experiment, silver atoms escaping into an evacuated chamber from a hole in an oven were formed into a ribbon-shaped beam. The beam was then passed through a nonuniform magnetic field and detected at the plate.

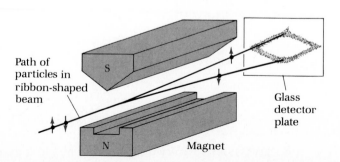

Path of particles in ribbon-shaped beam

Glass detector plate

Magnet

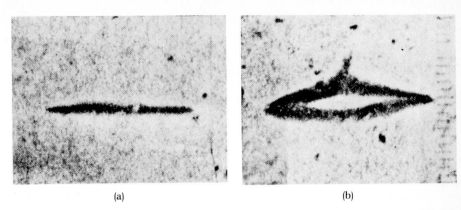

(a)   (b)

Figure 41-13. Silver atoms deposited on the glass detector plates in the Stern-Gerlach experiment. (*a*) Magnetic field absent. (*b*) Magnetic field present. The separation into two quantized subbeams is clearly evident.

that the beam has been separated into two distinct subbeams. If there were no quantization, the magnetic-moment components of atoms in the beam would be continuously distributed and we would have found a continuously distributed smudge on the plate. Thus the Stern-Gerlach experiment clearly shows the two quantized values of $\mu_{s,z}$ (or S_z).

The Dirac theory. You may still be skeptical about the existence of electron spin, even though it explains the results of the Stern-Gerlach experiment. After all, spin does not emerge naturally from the solution to the Schrödinger equation; it was added to quantum mechanics to account for some otherwise inexplicable experimental results. At the stage of the development of quantum theory we have described so far, spin had no firm theoretical foundation. This foundation was laid in 1931 by P. A. M. Dirac (1902–1985). The Schrödinger equation is not relativistically invariant. Dirac discovered a relativistic wave equation for electrons which reduces to the Schrödinger equation in the nonrelativistic limit ($v \ll c$). In addition, Dirac's theory contains some important by-products, one of which is electron spin. Electron spin emerges directly from the theory without any ad hoc assumptions. Thus electron spin is a uniquely relativistic quantity. Unlike many other relativistic effects, the effects of spin do not become negligible when $v \ll c$. Dirac's theory merged relativity with quantum mechanics to yield electron spin, lending support to both theories and revealing the origin of spin.

The origin of electron spin is relativity.

The total angular momentum J. As we have seen, the electron in the hydrogen atom has both an orbital angular momentum **L** and a spin angular momentum **S**. Thus, the electron's total angular momentum **J** is

$$\mathbf{J} = \mathbf{L} + \mathbf{S}$$

The electron's total angular momentum is quantized, similar to the way **L** and **S** are quantized, and this quantization has been verified with a number of experiments. However, since **J** is not essential to a qualitative understanding of the periodic table, we shall not discuss it further.

41-6 QUANTUM STATES OF THE HYDROGEN ATOM

The quantum states of hydrogen are the template for the periodic table. Before investigating multielectron atoms and their arrangement in the periodic table, we must become familiar with the states of hydrogen. A quantum state of hydrogen is identified by a particular set of the four quantum numbers that characterize the state: n, ℓ, m_ℓ, and m_s.

The possible values of n, ℓ, m_ℓ, and m_s

1. The quantum number n is a positive integer. Its value is related to the energy of the atom, and its range of values is unlimited. (See the first row in Table 41-1.)

2. The quantum number ℓ is zero or a positive integer, but ℓ cannot be larger than $n - 1$. (See the second row in Table 41-1.) Suppose $n = 4$. Then ℓ can take on the values 0, 1, 2, or 3 — a total for four values. In general, for a given value of n, ℓ can take on n different values.

3. The quantum number m_ℓ is zero or a positive or negative integer, but $|m_\ell|$ cannot be larger than ℓ. (See the third row in Table 41-1.) Suppose $\ell = 2$. In this case m_ℓ can have the values -2, -1, 0, $+1$, or $+2$ — a total of five possible values. In general, the possible values of m_ℓ are $-\ell, \ldots, -1, 0, +1, \ldots, +\ell$, and the number of possible values of m_ℓ is the sum of (a) ℓ positive values, (b) ℓ negative values, and (c) the value zero. For a particular value of ℓ, there are $2\ell + 1$ possible values of m_ℓ.

4. The quantum number m_s is either $-1/2$ or $+1/2$. (See the fourth row of Table 41-1.) Regardless of the values of the other quantum numbers, there are only two possible values of m_s.

Consider the states which correspond to a few of the energy levels of hydrogen. The lowest energy state for an atom is called its *ground state*. The ground state for hydrogen corresponds to $n = 1$ ($E_1 = -13.6$ eV). Since $n = 1$, we must have $\ell = 0$, and since $\ell = 0$, we must have $m_\ell = 0$. Since m_s can be either $-1/2$ or $+1/2$, the hydrogen-atom ground-state wave functions are designated as $\psi_{100-1/2}$ and $\psi_{100+1/2}$.

The next-higher energy level is the $n = 2$ level ($E_2 = -3.40$ eV). When $n = 2$, ℓ can be 0 or 1, and when $\ell = 1$, m_ℓ can be -1, 0, or $+1$. Therefore, there are eight states with energy E_2: $\psi_{200-1/2}$ and $\psi_{200+1/2}$ for $\ell = 0$; and $\psi_{21-1-1/2}$, $\psi_{210-1/2}$, $\psi_{21+1-1/2}$, $\psi_{21-1+1/2}$, $\psi_{210+1/2}$, and $\psi_{21+1+1/2}$ for $\ell = 1$.

As we consider higher energy levels, the number of states which correspond to a level increases. If an energy level has more than one quantum state, then the level is said to be *degenerate*. The degeneracy of a level is the number of states that correspond to that energy. For example, the $n = 2$ level discussed above has a degeneracy of 8. If a level has only one state, then the level is said to be nondegenerate.

Degeneracy

The result that the energy levels of hydrogen depend only on the principal quantum number n is a unique feature of the $1/r$ potential-energy function. If a potential-energy function has a dependence on r different from $1/r$, then the energy levels depend on ℓ as well as on n. That is, if U does not depend on r as $1/r$, then states with different orbital angular-momentum magnitudes have different energies. This point will be important when we discuss the periodic table in the next section.

Table 41-1. Hydrogen-atom quantum numbers

Quantum number	Quantized physical quantity	Allowed values	Number of allowed values
n	$E_n = -(13.6 \text{ eV})/n^2$	1, 2, 3, . . .	No limit
ℓ	$L = \sqrt{\ell(\ell+1)}\hbar$	0, 1, 2, . . . , $(n-1)$	n
m_ℓ	$L_z = m_\ell \hbar$	$0, \pm 1, \pm 2, \ldots, \pm \ell$	$2\ell + 1$
m_s	$S_z = m_s \hbar$	$\pm 1/2$	2

EXAMPLE 41-3. (a) List the symbols for the wave functions for the $n = 3$ level. (b) What is the degeneracy of this level?

SOLUTION. (a) The wave functions with $m_s = -1/2$ are designated as

$\psi_{300-1/2}$

$\psi_{31-1-1/2}$ $\psi_{310-1/2}$ $\psi_{31+1-1/2}$

$\psi_{32-2-1/2}$ $\psi_{32-1-1/2}$ $\psi_{320-1/2}$ $\psi_{32+1-1/2}$ $\psi_{32+2-1/2}$

There is a similar set of functions with $m_s = +1/2$. (b) The degeneracy of this level is equal to the number of wave

functions described in part (a); it is 18. Notice that the wave functions listed in part (a) were placed in a triangular array. If we list the states for the $n = 4$ level in a similar way, then this list would have an additional row of seven functions across the bottom. Use this device to show that the degeneracy of the $n = 4$ level is 32.

The spin-orbit effect. Many atomic energy levels are split by an effect called the *spin-orbit effect.* The spin-orbit effect is due to an interaction that depends on the electron's spin and orbital angular momenta. The spin-orbit splitting of a level is small compared with the spacing of levels with different n. For example, the spin-orbit splitting of the $n = 2$ level in hydrogen is about 5×10^{-5} eV, and this level is 10.2 eV above the ground-state ($n = 1$) level. Even though the splitting is small, its effect can be measured in emission spectra. This splitting causes the fine structure in atomic spectra which we mentioned in Sec. 41-5. Because of spin-orbit splitting, the 8-fold degeneracy of the $n = 2$ level and the 18-fold degeneracy of the $n = 3$ level discussed above is partially lifted. However, since the splitting is so small, in many cases it can be neglected, and the spin-orbit lifting of the degeneracy can be ignored.

Shell and subshell notation. At this point, we introduce some jargon. States with the same principal quantum number n are said to compose a *shell.* A particular shell is denoted by a shell symbol in the following way:

$$n \qquad 1 \quad 2 \quad 3 \quad 4 \quad \ldots$$

$$\text{Shell symbol} \quad K \quad L \quad M \quad N \quad \ldots$$

For example, a state with $n = 2$ is in the L shell, and an electron in that state is called an *L-shell electron.*

States within a given shell are further subdivided into subshells according to their orbital angular-momentum quantum number ℓ. The letter designation for subshells is

$$\ell \qquad 0 \quad 1 \quad 2 \quad 3 \quad 4 \quad 5 \quad \ldots$$

$$\text{Subshell symbol} \quad s \quad p \quad d \quad f \quad g \quad h \quad \ldots$$

When discussing a specific subshell, the *numerical* designation of the shell is ordinarily used. For example, a state with $n = 3$ and $\ell = 1$ is in the $3p$ subshell, and an electron in that state is called a *3p electron.* Some of the shell and subshell notation is presented in Table 41-2.

A term used to refer to a specific spatial wave function is "orbital." For

Table 41-2. Hydrogen-atom states in terms of shells and subshells

n	ℓ	m_ℓ	m_s	Shell	Number of states in shell	Subshell	Number of states in subshell
1	0	0	$\pm 1/2$	K	2	$1s$	2
2	0	0	$\pm 1/2$	L	8	$2s$	2
2	1	$0, \pm 1$	$\pm 1/2$			$2p$	6
3	0	0	$\pm 1/2$	M	18	$3s$	2
3	1	$0, \pm 1$	$\pm 1/2$			$3p$	6
3	2	$0, \pm 1, \pm 2$	$\pm 1/2$			$3d$	10

Orbitals

example, the electron cloud shown in Fig. 41-6a represents the probability density $|\psi|^2$ for the 1s orbital, and Fig. 41-6b shows the probability density for the 2pz orbital. Note that when a state is described as an orbital, the magnetic spin quantum number m_s for the state is left unspecified.

41-7 THE PERIODIC TABLE OF THE ELEMENTS

In the periodic table, the elements are listed according to increasing atomic number Z, and they are arranged so that elements in the same column have similar chemical properties (App. P). For example, He, Ne Ar, Kr, Xe, and Rn are chemically similar, and they occupy the right-hand column in the table (column VIIIA).

Definition of the ionization energy

In addition, a graph of the *ionization energy I* versus Z reveals the same periodicity (Fig. 41-14). The ionization energy is the energy required to remove an atom's least tightly bound electron when the atom is in the ground state. When an atom is involved in a chemical reaction, it is the outer, or less tightly bound, electrons that are mostly involved. Since the energy of the ground state of hydrogen is $E_1 = -13.6$ eV, we immediately note that the ionization energy for hydrogen is $I_H = 13.6$ eV. Keep in mind that an atom's ionization energy has the same numerical value as the energy of the atom's least tightly bound electron, but it has the opposite sign; the electron's energy is negative, but the ionization energy is positive.

In principle, the properties of an atom can be found by applying the Schrödinger equation to the atom, but the Schrödinger equation cannot be solved in closed form for multielectron atoms. However, we can gain a qualitative understanding of the periodic table by using a two-stage approximation procedure. (i) In the first stage of our approximation we assume that each electron interacts only with the nucleus and not with the other electrons. (ii) In the second stage of the approximation, we use the answers from the first stage to estimate the effects of electron-electron interactions.

First-stage approximation. If we neglect electron-electron interactions, the Schrödinger equation for each electron contains the potential-energy function of an electron interacting with a nucleus of charge Ze [Eq. (41-1) with $+e$ replaced by $+Ze$]. The solution in each case is the same as that for the hydrogen atom, except that the nuclear charge e is replaced by Ze. When this factor Z is included in the calculations, we find that (i) the quantum numbers which

Figure 41-14. Ionization energy I versus Z for the first 36 elements.

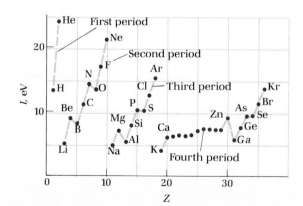

characterize an electron's state are the same as those for the hydrogen atom states, (ii) the wave functions are the same as the hydrogen-atom wave functions except that a_0 is replaced by a_0/Z, and (iii) the energy levels are the same as for the hydrogen atom except for a factor of Z^2:

$$E_n = -\frac{(13.6 \text{ eV})Z^2}{n^2}$$

The chemical properties of an atom are determined mainly by the atom's ground state, or its lowest energy state. Therefore, we consider the electrons to be in those quantum states which minimize the atom's energy. One might expect that the lowest energy state for an atom would correspond to each electron occupying a state with $n = 1$. However, in 1924 Wolfgang Pauli (1900–1958) pointed out that multielectron atoms conform to a rule that is now called the *Pauli exclusion principle*. The exclusion principle states that *no two electrons in the same atom may exist in the same quantum state*. For example, suppose an electron in an atom has $n = 3$, $\ell = 2$, $m_\ell = +2$, and $m_s = -1/2$. No other electron in that atom may have that same set of quantum numbers. This means that an atom's ground state corresponds to the lowest possible energy consistent with allowing each electron a different set of quantum numbers.

Using our first-stage approximation, we find that an element's ionization energy is

$$I = \frac{(13.6 \text{ eV})Z^2}{n_0{}^2} \qquad \text{(neglecting electron-electron interactions)} \quad (41\text{-}14)$$

where n_0 is the principal quantum number of the least tightly bound electron.

Second-stage approximation. In the second stage of our approximation, we assign each electron a set of quantum numbers in accordance with the Pauli exclusion principle, and then we estimate the effects of the electrostatic repulsion of electrons by using the hydrogenlike wave functions from the first stage of our approximation. A given electron is less tightly bound in an atom because of the negative charge distribution due to the other electrons. That is, the electrons tend to screen or shield each other from the full effects of the positive nuclear charge. Taking this effect into account, we write the ionization energy as

$$I = \frac{(13.6 \text{ eV})Z_{\text{eff}}{}^2}{n_0{}^2} \qquad (41\text{-}15)$$

where $Z_{\text{eff}} e$ is the effective positive charge which binds the least tightly bound electron to the atom. For example, if the wave function for the least tightly bound electron extends far beyond the wave functions of the other electrons, then the screening effect is large, $Z_{\text{eff}} \approx 1$, and the ionization energy is small. On the other hand, if the wave function for the least tightly bound electron greatly penetrates the screening of the other electrons, then the screening effect is small, Z_{eff} is relatively large, and the ionization energy is large.

First period: Hydrogen ($Z = 1$) and helium ($Z = 2$). Now we proceed through part of the periodic table beginning with the first row. The set of quantum numbers that characterize the ground state of hydrogen is either 1, 0, 0, $-1/2$ or 1, 0, 0, $+1/2$. Either spin state is appropriate because the ground-state energy does not depend on m_s. As we discuss each element, we

Table 41-3. Electron configuration for the first 36 elements. To avoid repetition, [He] represents $1s^2$, [Ne] represents $1s^2 2s^2 2p^6$, [Ar] represents $1s^2 2s^2 2p^6 3s^2 3p^6$. See App. I for the electron configuration of all the elements.

Z	Element	Electron configuration
1	H	$1s^1$
2	He	$1s^2$
3	Li	[He] $2s^1$
4	Be	$2s^2$
5	B	$2s^2 2p^1$
6	C	$2s^2 2p^2$
7	N	$2s^2 2p^3$
8	O	$2s^2 2p^4$
9	F	$2s^2 2p^5$
10	Ne	$2s^2 2p^6$
11	Na	[Ne] $3s^1$
12	Mg	$3s^2$
13	Al	$3s^2 3p^1$
14	Si	$3s^2 3p^2$
15	P	$3s^2 3p^3$
16	S	$3s^2 3p^4$
17	Cl	$3s^2 3p^5$
18	Ar	$3s^2 3p^6$
19	K	[Ar] $4s^1$
20	Ca	$4s^2$
21	Sc	$3d^1 4s^2$
22	Ti	$3d^2 4s^2$
23	V	$3d^3 4s^2$
24	Cr	$3d^5 4s^1$
25	Mn	$3d^5 4s^2$
26	Fe	$3d^6 4s^2$
27	Co	$3d^7 4s^2$
28	Ni	$3d^8 4s^2$
29	Cu	$3d^{10} 4s^1$
30	Zn	$3d^{10} 4s^2$
31	Ga	$3d^{10} 4s^2 4p^1$
32	Ge	$3d^{10} 4s^2 4p^2$
33	As	$3d^{10} 4s^2 4p^3$
34	Se	$3d^{10} 4s^2 4p^4$
35	Br	$3d^{10} 4s^2 4p^5$
36	Kr	$3d^{10} 4s^2 4p^6$

introduce its *electron configuration*. (See Table 41-3.) The electron configuration is a shorthand notation which gives the quantum numbers n and ℓ for each electron. The electron configuration for hydrogen is $1s^1$. The $1s$ refers to the subshell which the electron occupies ($n = 1$, $\ell = 0$) and the superscript 1 indicates that one electron is in that subshell.

The energy is minimized for helium if we assign $n = 1$ to each of its two electrons. With $n = 1$ we must have $\ell = 0$ and $m_\ell = 0$. Since we can assign different values of m_s to each electron; we see that two sets of quantum numbers which satisfy the exclusion principle and minimize the energy are 1.0, 0, $-1/2$ and 1, 0, 0, $+1/2$. Therefore, helium has two electrons in the $1s$ subshell and its electron configuration is $1s^2$. There are no other sets of quantum numbers with $n = 1$, so the two helium electrons fill the $1s$ subshell.

Second period: Lithium ($Z = 3$) to neon ($Z = 10$). Two of lithium's three electrons fill the $1s$ subshell, so the third must go into the $n = 2$ shell. The $n = 2$ shell has two subshells: $2s$ and $2p$. To determine the electron configuration for lithium, we must determine which of these subshells has the lower energy. For hydrogen these states are degenerate ($E_{2s} = E_{2p}$), but for other atoms they are not. An indication of why this is so can be seen from a comparison of ψ_{200} (or ψ_{2s}) and ψ_{210} (or ψ_{2p}). As shown in Fig. 41-5, ψ_{200} is maximum at the nucleus and ψ_{210} is zero at the nucleus. Consequently, the screening by the two $1s$ electrons has a smaller effect on a $2s$ electron than on a $2p$ electron. This means that Z_{eff} is larger for a $2s$ electron than for a $2p$ electron, so the $2s$ subshell has a lower energy than the $2p$. To minimize the energy, lithium's third electron is $2s$ and its electron configuration is $1s^2 2s^1$. Indeed, this electron-screening effect causes the energy to increase with increasing ℓ for all atoms, as shown schematically in Fig. 41-15.

The fourth electron in beryllium completes the $2s$ subshell, so this element's electron configuration is $1s^2 2s^2$, as shown in Table 41-3. Using the bracket notation introduced in the table, we write the electron configuration for beryllium as [He] $2s^2$.

From boron to neon, each additional electron enters the $2p$ subshell. In Table 41-3, we see that the electron configuration proceeds from [He] $2s^2 2p^1$ for boron to [He] $2s^2 2p^6$ for neon.

Third period: Sodium ($Z = 11$) to argon ($Z = 18$). The filling of the $3s$ and $3p$ subshells mirrors that of the $2s$ and $2p$ (Table 41-3). However, one point needs clarification. Why does this period end after the $3p$ subshell is filled (at $Z = 18$ with argon)? With $n = 3$, ℓ can be 0, 1, or 2. One might expect this period to end after the $3d$ subshell is filled. We mentioned earlier that the screening by the other electrons causes the energy of the least tightly bound electron to increase with ℓ (Fig. 41-15). As we progress to potassium ($Z = 19$), we find that increasing ℓ by 2 (from $\ell = 0$ to $\ell = 2$) raises the energy more than increasing n by 1 (from $n = 3$ to $n = 4$). That is, the $3d$ level is higher than the $4s$, and the fourth period begins with $Z = 19$.

Fourth period: Potassium ($Z = 19$) to krypton ($Z = 36$). After the $3p$ subshell is filled, the energy is minimized by placing the next electron into the $4s$ subshell. Thus potassium's least tightly bound electron is $4s$; its electron configuration is [Ar] $4s^1$. As expected, calcium's least tightly bound electron completes the $4s$ subshell; its electron configuration is [Ar] $4s^2$. From scandium

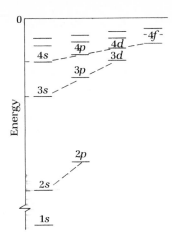

Figure 41-15. Approximate representation of the dependence of atomic energy levels on quantum numbers n and ℓ. The break in the energy scale between the $1s$ and $2s$ levels is for convenience of illustration.

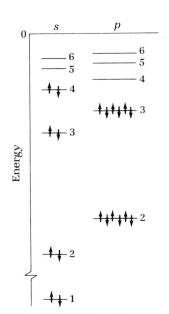

Figure 41-16. Schematic representation of the electron configuration for calcium.

through zinc the ten $3d$ states are backfilled, which indicates that the $4p$ level in Fig. 41-15 is higher than the $3d$. The proximity of the $3d$ and $4s$ levels is indicated by a shifting of these levels between scandium and zinc. Notice that the electron configuration for chromium is [Ar] $3d^5 4s^1$ and not [Ar] $3d^4 4s^2$. A similar shift occurs at copper. In proceeding from gallium to krypton, the $4p$ subshell is filled. The $4d$ and $4f$ levels are higher than the $5s$, so the fourth period ends with krypton ($Z = 36$).

An instructive way to illustrate the electron configuration of an element is shown in Fig. 41-16. Each electron is represented as a small arrow pointing either up, for spin up, or down, for spin down. The placement of the energy levels is taken from Fig. 41-15. Figure 41-16 portrays the electron configuration for calcium.

Variation of the ionization energy with Z. Figure 41-14 is a graph of the ionization energy versus Z for the first 36 elements. Because of the Coulomb attraction between an electron and its nucleus, we expect the ionization energy I to exhibit a general tendency to increase with increasing Z (or increasing nuclear charge). Indeed, I does tend to increase through each period because Z increases while the principal quantum number n_0 of the least tightly bound electron remains the same. In jumping from one period to the next, such as from neon to sodium, I decreases abruptly. This corresponds to n_0 increasing by 1 in Eq. (41-15), $I = (13.6 \text{ eV})Z_{\text{eff}}^2 / n_0^2$. Therefore, the last element of a period has a relatively large ionization energy, and the first element of a period has a relatively small ionization energy.

The trend toward increasing I with increasing Z within a period has two displacements or breaks that can be seen easily in the second and third periods. The first of these breaks, at boron in the second period and at aluminum in the third period, corresponds to beginning the filling of a new subshell, the $2p$ and $3p$ subshells. The reason for the breaks, as discussed previously, is that an outer electron that is described by a p wave function is more effectively screened from its nucleus than one that is described by an s wave function.

The second of these breaks, at oxygen in the second period and at sulfur in the third period, can be seen to arise from the axial form of p wave functions, shown in Fig. 41-6b. Suppose the wave function of the $2p$ electron in boron has its lobes along the z axis. That is, the wave function is ψ_{2pz}. Carbon has two $2p$ electrons. Since electrons repel one another, the energy is minimized by letting the wave functions be, say, ψ_{2pz} and ψ_{2py}. In that way the lobes are along perpendicular axes and as far from each other as possible. In nitrogen the three $2p$ electrons can minimize the energy if the wave functions are ψ_{2pz}, ψ_{2py}, and ψ_{2px}. When we get to oxygen, the fourth $2p$ electron must have a wave function that overlaps those of the previous three $2p$ electrons more than these three overlap each other. Consequently, the trend in increasing ionization energy that is associated with filling the $2p$ subshell has a break, and this break occurs at oxygen. This effect causes a break at other values of Z where a p subshell is being filled. In Fig. 41-14, notice the variation of the ionization energy around sulfur and around selenium.

Chemical properties of some elements. Since the ionization energy of each of the noble gas elements (He, Ne, Ar, and so on) is large, a noble gas atom does not readily share one of its electrons with another atom. Also, if a noble gas atom were to share an electron which came from another atom, then this electron would be forced into a higher energy subshell. Thus a noble gas atom tends neither to donate one of its own electrons to another atom, nor to accept an electron from another atom. Of all the elements, these are the least chemically active.

Since the ionization energy of each of the alkali metal elements (Li, Na, K, and so on) is small, an alkali metal atom readily shares one of its electrons with another atom (or readily donates an electron to another atom). To complete a subshell, an atom of one of the halogen elements (F, Cl, Br, and so on) readily accepts an electron from another atom. An alkali metal atom and a halogen atom can lower their energy by combining with one another. They form a family of tightly bound salts called the *alkali halides*. Similarly, the II-VI compounds represent a family of stable substances; one example is MgO.

In the case of a water molecule (H_2O), two hydrogen atoms share their electrons with an oxygen atom. The energy of the molecule is minimized by having these two shared electrons enter oxygen's two empty $2p$ states. Suppose the outer electron in the oxygen atom is $2pz$. To prevent overlap of the wave functions, we expect the shared electrons from the hydrogen atoms to enter the unoccupied $2py$ and $2px$ states of oxygen. This would cause the positions of the two protons (hydrogen nuclei) to subtend a right angle at the oxygen nucleus. However, after sharing their electrons, the two protons are not screened well from one another, and because of their electrostatic repulsion, the angle turns out to be 105° rather than 90°.

COMMENTARY: LASERS

Quantum theory has led to the development of many useful devices, none more fascinating than the laser. The term "laser" is an acronym coming from light amplification by stimulated emission of radiation. The name refers to a process called stimulated emission, which is crucial to the operation of the device.

Laser light. *Laser light has three characteristics that set it apart from ordinary light: (1) It is highly monochromatic, (2) it is very coherent, and (3) it is well collimated.*

1. Light emitted from atoms in a gas discharge tube (such as an ordinary mercury tube without the fluorescent coating) has highly monochromatic components. This is evident from the narrow lines that are observed when this light is passed through a grating spectrograph. However, laser light is even more monochromatic, usually by a factor of about 1000.

2. The coherence of light from a source can be investigated by separating a beam from the source into two subbeams and finding the distance over which interference effects can be detected. Such measurements show that laser light is highly coherent compared with light from other sources.

3. The angle of divergence of a laser beam is very small. In the case of the helium-neon laser commonly used in classroom demonstrations, it is only about 1 mrad. Scientists used this highly directional property of laser light to measure the earth-moon distance by detecting a beam bounced off reflectors set up on the moon by Apollo astronauts.

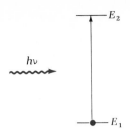

Figure 41-17. Absorption of a photon by an atom. A photon of energy $h\nu = E_2 - E_1$ interacts with an atom in energy level E_1 and causes the atom to undergo a transition to level E_2. After the absorption, the atom is in level E_2 and the photon has disappeared.

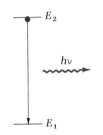

Figure 41-18. Spontaneous emission of a photon by an atom. Without any external stimulus, an atom that is in energy level E_2 undergoes a transition to level E_1 by emitting a photon of energy $h\nu = E_2 - E_1$.

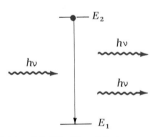

Figure 41-19. Stimulated emission of a photon by an atom. A photon of energy $h\nu = E_2 - E_1$ interacts with an atom in energy level E_2 and stimulates the atom to undergo a transition to level E_1. The transition produces a second photon, which is identical to the incident photon.

Stimulated emission. *To understand stimulated emission, we first discuss the* spontaneous emission *of light, the sort of emission that regularly occurs in familiar light sources such as light bulbs. To get an atom to emit, we must first provide energy to put it into an excited state. Suppose a photon of energy* $h\nu$ *interacts with an atom that is in its ground state, with energy* E_1 *(Fig. 41-17). If the atom has an excited state with energy* E_2 *such that* $E_2 - E_1 = h\nu$*, then the atom may absorb the photon leaving the atom in the excited state with energy* E_2*. Once the atom is in this excited state, it can return to the ground state by the spontaneous emission of a photon with energy* $h\nu = E_2 - E_1$ *(Fig. 41-18). This emission is called spontaneous because it requires no external stimulus, and, for a particular atom, the time interval between absorption and emission is unpredictable. However, for a collection of atoms we can measure a mean time* τ *of a transition. The mean time usually falls into one or the other of two vastly different regimes: For a so-called "allowed" transition,* $\tau \approx 10^{-8}$ s*, and for a "forbidden" transition,* $\tau \approx 10^{-3}$ s*, longer by a factor of* 10^5*.*

Suppose a photon of energy $h\nu = E_2 - E_1$ *interacts with an atom that is already in the excited state* E_2*. Albert Einstein predicted (and experiment confirms) that the incident photon may stimulate the atom to emit a photon; the energy, phase, and direction of travel of this second photon are exactly the same as those of the incident photon (Fig. 41-19). That is, the quantum state of the stimulated photon is identical to that of the incident photon. If these two photons then interact with two more excited-state atoms, two more photons are produced, and so on. Therefore, the stimulation process leads to photon amplification.*

Population inversion. *In an ordinary collection of atoms, say in a gas, almost all the atoms are in the ground state. Consequently, a photon of the proper energy is much more likely to interact with a ground-state atom and be absorbed than it is to interact with an excited-state atom and cause stimulated emission. Even if a photon should happen to beat the odds and interact with an excited-state atom, the two resulting photons will probably be absorbed by ground-state atoms. We see that stimulated emission is in direct competition with absorption. For stimulated emission to dominate, or for* lasing *to occur, we need more atoms in the excited state than in the ground state, a condition called* population inversion.

Helium-neon laser. *Now let us consider how these conditions are established in a particular laser, the common helium-neon laser. This laser contains a mixture of helium and neon at low pressure in a cylindrical tube with mirrors at each end (Fig. 41-20). The energy-level diagram in Fig. 41-21 shows the important energy levels for the helium and neon atoms. A large electric field is estab-*

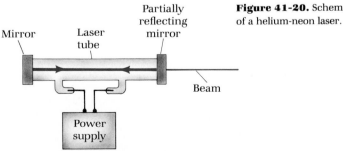

Figure 41-20. Schematic diagram of a helium-neon laser.

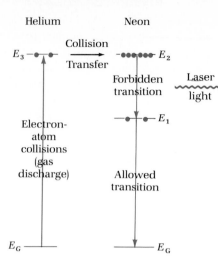

Figure 41-21. Energy-level diagram of the system (helium and neon atoms) in a helium-neon laser. The two-stage process (electron-helium collisions and helium-neon collisions) which populates the E_2 level in neon is called *pumping*, and helium is the pumping medium. During steady-state operation, energy enters this energy-transfer cycle from the electrons accelerated by the high voltage, and then leaves the cycle as laser light (and in other forms). Since the transition from E_2 to E_1 is forbidden and the transition out of E_1 is allowed, the number of atoms in level E_2 can be much greater than in E_1 (population inversion), making stimulated emission occur much more frequently than absorption.

lished in the tube by electrodes connected to a high-voltage power supply. Electrons from ionized atoms are accelerated by the field and collide with atoms. Because of the energy-level structure for helium, collisions often excite helium atoms to the level labeled E_3 in the figure. In a process called collision transfer, energy is transferred from excited helium atoms to neon atoms during collisions, thus producing a population of neon atoms in the E_2 level. The transition from level E_2 to E_1 in neon is forbidden, but the transition out of the E_1 level is allowed. This means that the population of atoms in the E_2 level builds up, and that of the E_1 level is rapidly depleted. A bottleneck exists at the E_2 level, and this creates the population inversion needed for laser action. The laser light consists of photons of energy $h\nu = E_2 - E_1 = 1.96$ eV, which corresponds to $\lambda = 633$ nm (red light).

The mirrors at each end of the tube encourage emissions along the tube axis (at the expense of emissions in other directions) by reflecting the light back and forth inside the tube. The tube is a resonant cavity similar to an organ pipe. The atoms that are stimulated to emit are those that produce light which is in step with light already propagating along the tube. One of the mirrors is slightly leaky, transmitting about 1 percent of the incident light. This transmitted light forms the laser beam which we find so useful.

For further reading, see "Laser Light" by Arthur Schawlow and "Applications of Laser Light" by Donald H. Herriott, both in the September 1968 issue of Scientific American.

SUMMARY WITH APPLICATIONS

Section 41-2. Quantum mechanics and the hydrogen atom

The quantum numbers n, ℓ, and m_ℓ arise from the solution to the Schrödinger equation for the hydrogen atom, and $n = 1, 2, 3, \ldots$; $\ell = 0, 1, 2, \ldots$; $(n-1)$, and $m_\ell = 0, \pm 1, \pm 2, \ldots, \pm \ell$. These quantum numbers are related to the atom's energy and orbital angular momentum:

$$E_n = -\frac{13.6 \text{ eV}}{n^2} \tag{41-3}$$

$$L = \sqrt{\ell(\ell + 1)}\,\hbar \tag{41-4}$$

$$L_z = m_\ell\,\hbar \tag{41-5}$$

A specific set of quantum numbers defines a quantum state.

Describe the hydrogen-atom problem and discuss the quantum numbers; determine E_n, L, and L_z for a given quantum state.

Section 41-3. The hydrogen-atom wave functions

The hydrogen-atom wave functions ψ give the probability density $|\psi|^2$ for the electron's position. At large distances r from the nucleus, all wave functions fall off exponentially with r, and a_0 is the scale factor. Functions with $\ell = 0$ are spherically symmetric, and functions with $m_\ell = 0$ are axially symmetric.

Describe the hydrogen-atom wave functions for the 1, 0, 0; 2, 0, 0; and 2, 1, 0 states.

Section 41-4. Quantization of angular momentum and magnetic moment

The quantization of angular momentum causes the quantization of an atom's magnetic moment. Measurements of spectra from atoms in a magnetic field directly reveal the quantization of angular momentum.

Discuss the effect of the quantized angular momentum on an atom's energy when the atom is in a magnetic field.

Section 41-5. Electron spin

The electron has an internal degree of freedom, called electron spin, which gives rise to a spin angular momentum and

a fourth quantum number: $m_s = \pm\frac{1}{2}$. The Stern-Gerlach experiment demonstrates the existence of spin.

Discuss the experimental and theoretical evidence for electron spin; compare the effects of spin angular momentum with orbital angular momentum.

Section 41-6. Quantum states of the hydrogen atom

The quantum states of hydrogen are described with a shell and subshell terminology. A shell refers to the value of n and the subshell to the values of n and ℓ.

Use the shell and subshell terminology to describe the quantum states of hydrogen.

Section 41-7. The periodic table of the elements

By inserting the quantum-mechanical solution to the hydrogen atom and the Pauli exclusion principle into a two-stage approximation procedure, we can explain many of the details of the periodic table.

Explain the periodicity of the chemical behavior of the elements; determine the electron configuration of any element.

QUESTIONS

41-1   Why do the hydrogen-atom wave functions refer to the electron's position rather than the proton's?

41-2   What are the dimensions of each of the terms in the Schrödinger equation for the hydrogen atom?

41-3   Explain why one expects the value of ℓ to be limited by the value of n. Explain why one expects the value of m_ℓ to be limited by the value of ℓ.

41-4   Why is the quantization of angular momentum not noticed when observing the motion of a macroscopic object such as a gyroscope?

41-5   Quantum theory applied to the hydrogen atom gives the same quantized energy levels as the simpler Bohr model of hydrogen. Why do we regard the quantum theory as more fundamental?

41-6   The magnitude of the orbital angular momentum is quantized in both the Bohr model of hydrogen and in quantum theory. Does each give the same result? If not, how do they differ?

41-7   Why is m_ℓ called the orbital magnetic quantum number?

41-8   What is the distinction between an electron's wave function and its probability density? What is the distinction between an electron's probability density and the charge distribution due to its nonlocalized nature?

41-9   A *nodal surface* for an electron is a surface on which the electron's probability density is zero. Is there a nodal surface for an electron in a 2, 0, 0 state in hydrogen? If so, describe this surface. What about an electron in a 2, 1, 0 state?

41-10   Why does the wave function of any bound electron approach zero at large distances from the nucleus?

41-11   In considering the Zeeman effect, why did we find it useful to restrict our discussion to atoms in which the effects of spin cancel out?

41-12   Why is the degree of freedom associated with an electron's intrinsic angular momentum called "spin"? Is there any reason to believe that this degree of freedom is really due to the electron spinning as a top spins? Is there any reason to believe that it is not?

41-13   Consider a spinning object such as a gyroscope. Suppose parts of the gyroscope are charged, but its net charge is zero. Can the gyroscope have a magnetic dipole moment? Explain.

41-14   Why is the value of the quantum number s not used in defining a quantum state of hydrogen?

41-15   Why is the orbital contribution to an electron's magnetic moment directed opposite the orbital angular momentum?

41-16   Why is a nonuniform magnetic field used in the Stern-Gerlach experiment?

41-17   You might encounter this statement in a quantum mechanics book: "The degeneracy of the ground state of hydrogen is lifted by a magnetic field." Explain the meaning of this statement.

41-18   Is it possible for an electron to be in a $3f$ subshell? Explain.

41-19   Suppose that electron spin could not be directly observed, but that its effect on the periodic table, because of the doubled number of hydrogen-atom states, still occurred. How do you think we would state the Pauli exclusion principle?

41-20 What is the difference between your present age and Pauli's age at the time he discovered the exclusion principle?

41-21 Within a particular period in the periodic table, there is a general trend toward higher ionization energy with increasing Z. Explain.

41-22 In the periodic table, why is there an abrupt change in ionization energy when proceeding from the end of one period to the beginning of the next?

41-23 The ionization energy of In $(Z = 49)$ is less than that of Cd $(Z = 48)$. Use the electron configuration of these elements given in the periodic table in App. P to explain why.

41-24 The ionization energy of Te $(Z = 52)$ is less than that of Sb $(Z = 51)$. Use the electron configuration of these elements given in the periodic table in App. P to explain why.

41-25 Explain why the noble gases are the least chemically active of all the elements.

41-26 The elements in the lanthanide series, $Z = 57$ to 71 (see App. P), have similar chemical properties. Explain.

41-27 The heat of combustion of a substance is a measure of the energy released when the material combines chemically with oxygen. Explain why magnesium has a relatively high heat of combustion.

41-28 Carbon dioxide is more stable than carbon monoxide. Explain.

41-29 In the H_2S molecule, the angle subtended by the protons at the position of the sulfur nucleus is about $95°$. Explain why we expect this angle to be greater than $90°$. Why is it less than the $105°$ found in H_2O?

41-30 Complete the following table:

Symbol	Represents	Type	SI unit
n			
ℓ			
m_ℓ			
m_s	Spin magnetic quantum number		
L			
a_0			
μ_B			J/T

EXERCISES

Section 41-2. Quantum mechanics and the hydrogen atom

41-1 For a hydrogen atom in the 3, 2, +1 state determine (a) the energy in eV, (b) the magnitude of the orbital angular momentum in units of $\hbar$, (c) the z component of the orbital angular momentum in units of $\hbar$.

41-2 (a) If $n = 4$, what is the maximum value of ℓ? (b) If $\ell = 2$, what is the maximum value of m_ℓ? (c) If $\ell = 3$, what is the minimum value of m_ℓ?

41-3 A hydrogen atom is in a 4, 3, -1 state. Determine (a) L^2; (b) L_z^2; (c) $L_x^2 + L_y^2$. (d) Is the sum $L_x^2 + L_y^2$ quantized?

41-4 Construct vector diagrams similar to that of Fig. 41-3 for the cases where (a) $\ell = 1$ and (b) $\ell = 3$.

41-5 Consider a phonograph record of moment of inertia $I = 1.5 \times 10^{-3}$ kg $\cdot$ m² rotating on a turntable at $33\frac{1}{3}$ rev/min. Assume that the magnitude of the angular momentum of the record is quantized: $L = \sqrt{\ell(\ell + 1)}\hbar$, where ℓ is a quantum number that can be zero or a positive integer. Determine ℓ. Do you think this quantization can be observed?

41-6 (a) Find an expression for the quantized rotational kinetic energy of the record in the previous exercise. (b) Construct an energy-level diagram showing the four lowest levels.

Section 41-3. The hydrogen-atom wave functions

41-7 Evaluate ψ_{100} in units of $a_0^{-3/2}$ at the point with cartesian coordinates (x, y, z) of $(0, 0, a_0)$.

41-8 Evaluate ψ_{210} in units of $a_0^{-3/2}$ at the point with cartesian coordinates (x, y, z) of (a) $(0, 0, a_0)$; (b) $(0, a_0/\sqrt{2}, a_0/\sqrt{2})$; (c) $(0, a_0, 0)$.

41-9 (a) Determine the values of r at which ψ_{300} is zero:

$$\psi_{300} = C_3 \left(1 - 2\rho + \frac{2\rho^2}{27}\right) e^{-\rho/3}$$

where $\rho = r/a_0$ and C_3 is the (positive) normalizing factor. Determine the ranges of values of r for which ψ_{300} is (b) positive and (c) negative.

41-10 Make graphs of (a) $|\psi_{100}|^2$ and (b) $|\psi_{200}|^2$ in units of a_0^{-3} from $r = 0$ to $6a_0$, with points plotted every $\frac{1}{2}a_0$.

41-11 Show that ψ_{200} given in Eq. (41-7) is normalized. Use the hint in Example 41-2.

41-12 Consider a sphere of radius $0.1a_0$ centered at the nucleus of a hydrogen atom. Without performing an integral, show that the probability that the electron in the ground state is contained in the sphere is about 1×10^{-3}.

41-13 Note that from Fig. 41-4, $z = r \cos \theta$. Therefore, we may write ψ_{210} as

$$\psi_{210} = \psi_{21z} = (32\pi\, a_0^5)^{-1/2}\, z e^{-r/2a_0}$$

Based on our discussion of the three axial forms of the $n = 2, \ell = 1$ wave functions, write the expressions for (a) ψ_{21y} and (b) ψ_{21x}.

Section 41-4. Quantization of angular momentum and magnetic moment

41-14 The Bohr magneton is given by $\mu_B = e\hbar/2m_e$. Show that $\mu_B = 5.79 \times 10^{-5}$ eV/T.

41-15 Consider an atom in an energy level in which the total spin angular momentum is zero. Thus spin does not contribute to the atom's magnetic moment. Suppose the level corresponds to $\ell = 2$. (a) Into how many levels will this level split when the atom is placed in a magnetic field? (b) If the magnitude of the magnetic field is 0.35 T, then what is the energy spacing of these levels in eV?

41-16 Astronomers use the Zeeman effect to measure the magnetic field on the surface of stars. Suppose an energy splitting of 1.02×10^{-4} eV is observed between levels of atoms on the surface of a star. It is known that the total spin angular momentum of these levels is zero, so spin does not contribute to the angular momentum. What is the magnitude of the magnetic field on the star's surface?

41-17 In measurements of the Zeeman effect, as with many other spectral measurements, the wavelength spacing $\Delta\lambda$ between the lines is measured and then the energy spacing ΔE between the levels is calculated. (a) Using the expression for the photon energy, $E = h\nu = hc/\lambda$, and assuming the spacing ΔE is small, show that $\Delta E \approx -(hc/\lambda^2)\Delta\lambda$. (b) What is the significance of the minus sign in this expression for ΔE? (c) Find the energy spacing in eV between two lines of wavelengths 506.4 and 506.8 nm.

41-18 We mentioned that the splitting of spectral lines in the Zeeman effect can be successfully calculated using classical mechanics. Since h (or $\hbar$) is a purely quantum-mechanical quantity, the frequency (or wavelength) splitting should not depend on h. Show that the frequency splitting of spectral lines in the normal Zeeman effect is independent of h.

Section 41-5. Electron spin

41-19 To three significant digits, what is the z component (in units of eV/T) of the magnetic moment due to spin for an electron whose spin is (a) down and (b) up?

41-20 Similar to the electron, the nucleus of an atom has a spin angular momentum, and a magnetic moment is associated with this nuclear spin. This effect was neglected in the discussions of this chapter because it causes splittings that are very small. The size of the splittings is characterized by the *nuclear magneton*

μ_n: $\mu_n = e\hbar/2m_p$, where m_p is the proton mass. (a) Determine μ_n in units of eV/T. (b) Determine the ratio μ_n/μ_B.

41-21 Silver atoms ($M = 1.8 \times 10^{-25}$ kg) were used in the original Stern-Gerlach experiment. The z component F_z of the force on a magnetic dipole (whose z component is μ_z) is

$$F_z = \mu_z \left(\frac{\partial B_z}{\partial z} \right)$$

where $\partial B_z/\partial z$ is the gradient of the nonuniform magnetic field. (a) Given that μ_z is due to the spin of a single electron, determine F_z for the case where $\partial B_z/\partial z = 1.5$ kT/m. (b) Assuming that this is the only force on the silver atom, determine the z component a_z of an atom's acceleration. (c) Suppose we have a beam of atoms traveling at 1.0 km/s for a distance d of 40 mm through the field. (See Fig. 41-12.) Determine the deflection Δz of each of the two subbeams.

Section 41-6. Quantum states of the hydrogen atom

41-22 (a) List the symbols for the wave functions for each of the states in the $3d$ subshell. (b) Find the energy of a hydrogen-atom electron in this subshell. (c) What is the magnitude of the orbital angular momentum of the electron in this subshell?

41-23 (a) What is the number of states in the $4f$ subshell? Determine (b) the energy and (c) the magnitude of the orbital angular momentum for a hydrogen-atom electron in this subshell.

41-24 What is the number of states in the N shell?

41-25 List the possible values of ℓ for an electron in the $n = 3$ shell.

41-26 List the possible values of m_ℓ for an electron in the $4f$ subshell.

41-27 Extend Table 41-2 to include the N shell.

41-28 From Table 41-2, verify that the number of states in a shell with principal quantum number n is given by $2n^2$.

41-29 What is the degeneracy of the $n = 5$ level in hydrogen? (As in our discussions in the chapter, neglect the spin-orbit effect.)

41-30 An example of the splitting of spectral lines due to the spin-orbit effect that is often cited is the case of the so-called D lines of sodium. These lines have wavelengths of 588.995 and 589.592 nm. (a) Determine the energy splitting ΔE of these lines. (b) Find the ratio of the energy splitting to the average energy of the transitions. (*Hint:* Use the result stated in Exercise 41-17.)

Section 41-7. The periodic table of the elements

41-31 Find the ionization energies for (a) the He$^+$ ion and (b) the Li^{++} ion.

41-32 While paying particular attention to the scaling factor in the exponetial, write the 1, 0, 0 wave functions for (a) the He$^+$ ion and (b) the Li^{++} ion. Consider a sphere of radius $0.5a_0$ centered at the nucleus. (c) In which of the three systems—H, He$^+$, or Li^{++}—is the electron most likely to be found in the volume of the sphere? (d) In which of the three is it least likely to be found in the sphere?

41-33 What are the electron configurations for (a) F ($Z = 9$) and (b) Si ($Z = 14$)? Use Table 41-3 to check your answers.

41-34 What are the electron configurations for (a) Sr ($Z = 38$) and (b) I ($Z = 53$)? Use App. P to check your answers.

41-35 Write the quantum numbers n and ℓ for the least tightly bound electron in (a) Al ($Z = 13$) and (b) Sc

($Z = 21$).

41-36 Determine Z_{eff} for (a) Li and (b) Ne. The ionization energies for these elements are 5.39 and 21.6 eV, respectively.

41-37 Draw schematic representations of the electron configurations, as in Fig. 41-16, for (a) oxygen and (b) sulfur. Based on these representations, do you expect these elements to form similar compounds?

41-38 Draw schematic representations of the electron configurations, as in Fig. 41-16, for (a) calcium, (b) potassium, (c) chlorine. On the basis of these representations, predict the chemical formulas for (d) potassium chloride and (e) calcium chloride.

PROBLEMS

41-1 ***Expectation values.*** Wave functions can be used to find average, or expectation, values of dynamical quantities. For example, the expectation value $\langle r \rangle$ of the electron-nucleus separation distance r is

$$\langle r \rangle = \int_{\substack{\text{all}\\\text{space}}} r|\psi|^2 \, dV$$

(a) Determine $\langle r \rangle$ for the 1, 0, 0 state of hydrogen. (*Hint:* Use the technique shown in Example 41-2.) (b) Similarly, the expectation value of $1/r$ is

$$\langle 1/r \rangle = \int_{\substack{\text{all}\\\text{space}}} \frac{1}{r}|\psi|^2 \, dV$$

Show that $\langle 1/r \rangle = 1/a_0$ for the 1, 0, 0 state of hydrogen.

41-2 (a) Show that the hydrogen energy levels can be written $E_n = -\frac{1}{2}(e^2/4\pi\epsilon_0 a_0)(1/n^2)$. (b) As stated in Prob. 41-1, wave functions can be used to find average, or expectation, values of dynamical quantities. Show that the expectation value $\langle U \rangle$ of the hydrogen-atom potential-energy function [see Eq. (41-1)] is $\langle U \rangle = -(e^2/4\pi\epsilon_0)\langle 1/r \rangle$. (c) Use the result given in part (b) of Prob. 41-1 to show that for the 1, 0, 0 state of hydrogen $\langle U \rangle_1 = -(e^2/4\pi\epsilon_0 a_0)$. (d) Show that $\langle U \rangle_1 = 2E_1$. (e) The expectation value $\langle K \rangle_1$ of the kinetic energy for the 1, 0, 0 state of hydrogen is given by $E_1 = \langle K \rangle_1 + \langle U \rangle_1$. Show that $\langle K \rangle_1 = -E_1$. (f) Determine $\langle U \rangle_1$ and $\langle K \rangle_1$ in eV. Be sure you include the correct algebraic signs to your answers.

41-3 A function that is sometimes useful to consider is the radial probability density $P(r)$:

$$P(r) = 4\pi r^2 |\psi|^2$$

(a) Write the radial probability density P_{100} for the 1, 0, 0 state of hydrogen. (b) Show that P_{100} maximizes at $r = a_0$. (c) Make a graph of P_{100} versus r from $r = 0$

to $4a_0$, with points plotted every $\frac{1}{2}a_0$. (d) Explain why P_{100} is zero at the nucleus despite the fact that $|\psi_{100}|^2$ is maximum at the nucleus.

41-4 (a) Show that ψ_{100} given in Eq. (41-6) is a solution to the Schrödinger equation [Eq. (41-2)] for the hydrogen atom [U given by Eq. (41-1)]. (*Hint:* First show that

$$\frac{\partial r}{\partial x} = \frac{x}{r} \quad \text{and} \quad \frac{\partial^2 r}{\partial x^2} = \frac{r^2 - x^2}{r^3}$$

Similar expressions hold for the y and z derivatives.) (b) Verify that the energy E found in part (a) is the ground-state energy for hydrogen.

41-5 To normalize a wave function that is not spherically symmetric, we use a volume element in spherical coordinates given by $dV = r^2 \, dr \sin \theta \, d\theta \, d\phi$. Further, to integrate over all space, the limits on the θ and ϕ integrals are from 0 to π and from 0 to 2π, respectively. Show that ψ_{210} given in Eq. (41-8) is normalized.

41-6 Consider the system of two particles a and b shown in Fig. 41-22. Each particle is traveling in a circle, they each have the same mass $\frac{1}{2}M$, and they each have the same angular frequency ω. The radii of their orbits are R for particle a and $2R$ for particle b. Let q_a be the charge of a and q_b be the charge of b. (a) Show that the

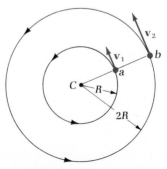

Figure 41-22. Prob. 41-6.

magnitude of the orbital angular momentum of the system about C is $L = 5MR^2\omega/2$. (b) Show that the magnitude of the magnetic dipole moment is $\mu = \omega R^2(q_a + 4q_b)/2$. ($c$) If we define the g factor of the system with the expression $\mu = g(e/2M)L$, then show that $g = 2(q_a + 4q_b)/5e$. (d) Show that if $q_a = q_b = \frac{1}{2}e$, then $g = 1$. (e) Determine q_a and q_b such that $q_a + q_b = e$ and $g = 2$. (f) Determine q_a and q_b such that $q_a + q_b = 0$ and $g = 1.5$. Note that a system with zero net charge can have a nonzero magnetic dipole moment. The neutron is electrically neutral, but has a magnetic dipole moment.

CHAPTER 42
ELECTRONS IN SOLIDS

42-1 INTRODUCTION

Immediately following its introduction, quantum mechanics was applied successfully to a variety of problems that classical physics was unable to explain. Among these problems was that of electric conduction in crystalline solids. The resistivity of these common materials can range over some 30 orders of magnitude—from $10^{-10}\ \Omega \cdot$ m for a good conductor at low temperature to $10^{20}\ \Omega \cdot$ m for a high-quality insulator!

Why do different substances, say aluminum and silicon, have such different resistivities? Silicon has only one more electron than aluminum. They are side by side in the periodic table. They have about the same density. Yet the resistivity at room temperature of pure silicon is about 10^{10} times larger than that of aluminum. In the last chapter we saw how the Pauli exclusion principle was responsible for the periodicity of chemical properties of the elements. In this chapter we develop a description of electric conduction in solids, and we shall see that the Pauli exclusion principle also has a dominating influence on the electrical properties of these substances.

42-2 A FREE-ELECTRON MODEL

If a potential difference is maintained across a length of conductor of resistance R, such as a copper wire, the flow of electrons is described by Ohm's law. That is, the current I in the wire is proportional to the potential difference V between the ends of the wire: $I = V/R$. How can such a complicated system of electrons and copper ions respond in such a simple way to an imposed potential difference? Part of the answer lies in the vast number of electrons involved in the conduction process. The electric current results from averaging over the motion of many electrons.

In the classical Drude model of a conductor, described in Sec. 24-4, electrons were accelerated by the imposed electric field and had collisions with the ions. The electrons were otherwise treated as moving freely, much as if the electrons were a gas in the container formed by the surfaces of the material. The Drude model, which treats electrons as classical particles, provides some insight into the conduction process in a metal. However, it does not give results that agree with experiment, particularly for the temperature dependence of the resistivity. To obtain a better model, we must treat the electrons quantum-mechanically, and we must include effects of the Pauli exclusion principle. As a first step, we consider an electron moving freely in a three-dimensional box.

A free electron in three dimensions. We solved the Schrödinger equation for a particle of mass m in a one-dimensional box of length L in Sec. 40-8. Each state is labeled by a positive integer n. The wave function, given by Eq. (40-15), is

$$\psi_n = \sqrt{\frac{2}{L}} \sin \frac{n\pi x}{L}$$

The energy level for this state is given by Eq. (40-14),

$$E_n = \frac{\hbar^2 \pi^2}{2mL^2} n^2$$

Each state corresponds to a standing wave that can fit into the length L of the one-dimensional box. Fitting such a standing wave into the box corresponds to the boundary condition $\psi = 0$ at $x = 0$ and $x = L$.

Suppose that a particle such as an electron is confined to a three-dimensional box, a cube of edge length L and volume L^3. We require that the wave function $\psi(x, y, z)$ be zero on each of the six walls of the box — that is, at $x = 0$ and $x = L$, $y = 0$ and $y = L$, $z = 0$ and $z = L$. This requirement leads to standing waves in three dimensions. The standing wave for the three-dimensional box is just the product of three one-dimensional waves, one for each dimension. Thus

$$\psi_{n_1 n_2 n_3} = \left(\sqrt{\frac{2}{L}} \sin \frac{n_1 \pi x}{L} \right) \left(\sqrt{\frac{2}{L}} \sin \frac{n_2 \pi y}{L} \right) \left(\sqrt{\frac{2}{L}} \sin \frac{n_3 \pi z}{L} \right)$$

or

Wave functions and energy levels for a particle in a box in three dimensions

$$\psi_{n_1 n_2 n_3} = \sqrt{\frac{8}{L^3}} \left(\sin \frac{n_1 \pi x}{L} \right) \left(\sin \frac{n_2 \pi y}{L} \right) \left(\sin \frac{n_3 \pi z}{L} \right) \qquad (42\text{-}1)$$

where n_1, n_2, and n_3 are positive integers. You should show (Exercise 42-4) that this standing wave is the solution of the Schrödinger equation in three dimensions for a particle in a box [Eq. (40-10) with $U = 0$]. It corresponds to an energy given by

$$E_{n_1 n_2 n_3} = \frac{\hbar^2 \pi^2}{2mL^2} (n_1^2 + n_2^2 + n_3^2) \qquad (42\text{-}2)$$

As with the one-dimensional case, the energy for a particle in a three-dimensional box is quantized. A state is characterized by three quantum numbers n_1, n_2, n_3 that determine the energy of the state. The ground state, which has $n_1 = n_2 = n_3 = 1$, has energy

$$E_{111} = \frac{\hbar^2 \pi^2}{2mL^2}(1^2 + 1^2 + 1^2) = 3\,\frac{\hbar^2 \pi^2}{2mL^2}$$

Although quantized, the energy levels can be quite close together for a box with macroscopic dimensions; see Example 42-1 below.

Density of states for free electrons. Since the energies of electron states are so close together, the quantization of energy is on a much finer scale than we usually resolve. Put another way, there is a large number of states that have energy E within a small range of energy dE. Important properties of a conductor depend on how the electrons populate these many states. We shall need to know how these states are distributed in energy. A quantity which conveniently describes this distribution of states as a function of energy is the *density-of-states* function $g(E)$. It is defined such that the number of states dN with energy in the range dE between E and $E + dE$ is given by

Density of states, $g(E)$

$$dN = g(E)\,dE \qquad (42\text{-}3)$$

Thus *the density of states is the number of states per unit energy with energy between E and $E + dE$.*

To determine the density-of-states function for a value of energy E, we first count the number of states that have energy at or below this value E. This counting is made easier by using the construction in Fig. 42-1 which shows points in a "quantum-number" space. The lattice consists of points with positive integer coordinates (n_1, n_2, n_3) and occupies one octant of the three-dimensional space. (This abstract space is used only to count the states. It is not the real, physical space in which an electron moves.) Since an energy level of an electron is determined by the three positive integers n_1, n_2, n_3, each point in the figure corresponds to one energy level of a particle in a box. Notice that the square of the distance from the origin to a point, $R^2 = n_1^2 + n_2^2 + n_3^2$, is proportional to the energy of the state. From Eq. (42-2), $E_{n_1 n_2 n_3} = (\hbar^2 \pi^2 / 2mL^2)(n_1^2 + n_2^2 + n_3^2)$, or

Each lattice point corresponds to an energy level.

$$E = \frac{\hbar^2 \pi^2}{2mL^2}R^2 \qquad (42\text{-}4)$$

Figure 42-1. A lattice is formed with integer coordinates n_1, n_2, n_3. Only a few points are shown in one octant of the space.

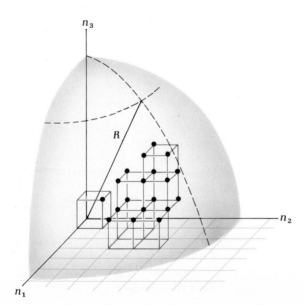

Therefore, all lattice points within the octant of a sphere of radius R correspond to levels with energies less than or equal to this value E. Thus the number of levels with energy at or below E is just the number of lattice points within this octant of the sphere.

Each cubic cell in the figure has an edge of length 1, so that the volume of a cell is $1^3 = 1$. Each cell corresponds to one point of the lattice. Thus there is one point per unit volume in the space, so that the number of points in a region is equal to the volume of that region. Since the volume of a sphere of radius R is $4\pi R^3/3$, the volume of one octant of the sphere is $\frac{1}{8}(4\pi R^3/3) = \pi R^3/6$. This is also the number of lattice points in that octant of the sphere.

Each lattice point represents two states, including spin.

A state for an electron in the box is specified by four quantum numbers. In addition to the numbers n_1, n_2, n_3, the spin quantum number $m_s = \pm 1/2$ must be given. Because m_s has two values, each lattice point in Fig. 42-1 corresponds to two states. Thus the total number of electron states is twice the volume of an octant of the sphere. Let N represent the number of electron states. Then for a radius R in Fig. 42-1, $N = 2 \cdot$ (volume of octant of sphere), or

$$N = \frac{\pi R^3}{3} \tag{42-5}$$

Instead of expressing N in terms of the radius R, we express it in terms of the energy E that corresponds to that R. Using Eq. (40-4), we have

$$R = \sqrt{\frac{2mL^2}{\hbar^2\pi^2} E}$$

so that

$$R^3 = \frac{L^3(2mE)^{3/2}}{\hbar^3\pi^3}$$

$g(E)$

E

Figure 42-2. The free-electron density of states increases with energy, $g(E) \propto E^{1/2}$.

and Eq. (42-5) becomes

$$N = \frac{L^3(2mE)^{3/2}}{3\pi^2\hbar^3} \tag{42-6}$$

Free-electron density of states

Equation (42-6) gives the number of electron states with energy at or below that value E. To get the density of states, we take the derivative of N with respect to E. That is, from Eq. (42-3), $g(E) = dN/dE$ because $dN = g(E)\,dE$. Thus

$$g(E) = \frac{L^3(2m)^{3/2}}{2\pi^2\hbar^3} E^{1/2} \tag{42-7}$$

The density-of-states function for free electrons is proportional to the square root of the energy. This behavior is shown graphically in Fig. 42-2.

It is important to recognize that the density of states determines how the states are distributed in energy. It does not tell how these states are occupied. We think of these states as being *available* for occupancy by electrons, with no more than one electron occupying a state, in accord with the Pauli exclusion principle. It is this feature that we consider in the next section.

EXAMPLE 42-1. Estimate the spacing between the ground-state level and the next-lowest energy level for a free electron in a copper cube of edge 10 mm.

SOLUTION. Assume that a free electron in copper can be treated as a particle in a three-dimensional box. The ground state is specified by $n_1 = n_2 = n_3 = 1$. The state of next-lowest energy corresponds to one of the n's, say n_1, increased to 2. From Eq. (42-2), the energy difference is

$$E_{211} - E_{111} = \frac{\hbar^2\pi^2}{2mL^2}[(2^2 + 1^2 + 1^2) - (1^2 + 1^2 + 1^2)]$$

$$= \frac{(1.05 \times 10^{-34}\ \text{J}\cdot\text{s})^2\pi^2}{2(9.1 \times 10^{-31}\ \text{kg})(10^{-2}\ \text{m})^2}\ 3$$

$$= 2 \times 10^{-33}\ \text{J} \approx 10^{-14}\ \text{eV}$$

To appreciate how small this energy difference is, we compare it with kT, an energy appropriate to a system at temperature T. We shall often use kT as a useful measure of energy exchanges for electrons in a system containing many electrons. At room temperature, $kT = (1.38 \times 10^{-23}\ \text{J/K})(290\ \text{K}) = 25\ \text{meV}$, more than 10^{12} times greater than the energy difference above.

EXAMPLE 42-2. Estimate the number of conduction electron states with energy in a 25-meV energy range at 6.0 eV in a (10 mm)³ sample of copper.

SOLUTION. The density of states is determined from Eq. (42-7):

$$g(6.0\ \text{eV}) = \frac{(10^{-2}\ \text{m})^3(2 \cdot 9.1 \times 10^{-31}\ \text{kg})^{3/2}}{2\pi^2(1.05 \times 10^{-34}\ \text{J}\cdot\text{s})^3}(9.6 \times 10^{-19}\ \text{J})^{1/2}$$

$$= 1.1 \times 10^{41}\ \text{J}^{-1} = 1.7 \times 10^{22}\ \text{eV}^{-1}$$

The number of states ΔN within a 25-meV range of 6.0 eV is, from Eq. (42-3),

$$\Delta N = g(E)\,\Delta E = (1.7 \times 10^{22}\ \text{eV}^{-1})(25\ \text{meV}) = 4.4 \times 10^{20}$$

How many states would there be in this range for a copper cube of edge 100 mm?

42-3   FERMI-DIRAC STATISTICS

The Pauli exclusion principle was essential to our understanding of the periodic table of the elements in Sec. 41-7. We imagined placing electrons in an atom, one by one, so that no two electrons occupied the same site. In the same way, we imagine filling the electron states in a solid, and the Pauli exclusion principle requires that a state is either occupied by one electron or is unoccupied. No state can be occupied by more than one electron.

For electrons in a solid, vast numbers of states are involved, as we saw in Example 42-2. Instead of dealing with these states one at a time, it is more convenient to group states together according to their energies. That is, we consider all states with energy E within a range ΔE. Since there are so many states, we are not concerned with whether a particular state is occupied. We only need to know the average number of states in this group that are occupied. Equivalently, we need to know the probability that an electron state of energy E is occupied. Thus we are treating the occupation of states *statistically*.

There are two different statistical features of our quantum description of electrons in a solid.

1. A single electron is described in terms of probability as outlined in Chaps. 40 and 41. If $\psi(x, y, z)$ is the wave function for the particle, then $|\psi(x, y, z)|^2$ is the probability density for finding the particle at point (x, y, z).

2. A large number of electrons are distributed among a large number of states. Our description of the occupancy of these states by the electrons is in terms of a second probability. It is this second probability that we are dealing with now. We use a statistical approach because of the large number of electrons involved.

The basic statistical question is: For a system at temperature T, what is the probability $p(E)$ that an electron state of energy E is occupied? The answer was provided in 1926 by Enrico Fermi (1901–1954) and is given by

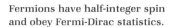

Fermi-Dirac distribution function

$$p(E) = \frac{1}{e^{(E-E_F)/kT} + 1} \tag{42-8}$$

where k is the Boltzmann constant and E_F is a parameter called the *Fermi energy*, which we discuss below. The probability distribution in Eq. (42-8) is known as the *Fermi-Dirac distribution function.** The Fermi-Dirac distribution function also describes other particles that have half-integer spin such as protons, neutrons, neutrinos, and others. For example, neutrons have spin $\frac{1}{2}$ ($m_s = \pm\frac{1}{2}\hbar$) and obey the Pauli exclusion principle. Each species of these particles is said to obey *Fermi-Dirac statistics*, and the particles are often called *fermions*.

Fermions have half-integer spin and obey Fermi-Dirac statistics.

To see how the Fermi-Dirac distribution function depends on the parameter E_F, the Fermi energy, consider a system of free electrons at $T = 0$. In this case electrons fill the available states from the lowest energy up, one electron per state, until all electrons have been accommodated. Then, all states with energy less than a certain value are occupied, and all states with higher energy are unoccupied. In this configuration, the total energy of the system is a minimum, as we expect at $T = 0$. The Fermi energy is the energy value that divides the occupied states and the unoccupied states. Thus the probability of occupation of a state is given by

$$\begin{aligned} p(E) &= 1 \qquad \text{for } E < E_F \\ p(E) &= 0 \qquad \text{for } E > E_F \end{aligned} \qquad (T=0)$$

This result also follows from Eq. (42-8) in the limit of $T \to 0$. The denominator of that expression contains the exponential function $e^{(E-E_F)/kT}$. If $E > E_F$, then $(E - E_F)/kT$ is positive and the exponential approaches infinity as $T \to 0$; this gives $p(E) \to 1/\infty = 0$, $E > E_F$. If $E < E_F$, then $(E - E_F)/kT$ is negative, the exponential approaches zero as $T \to 0$, and $p(E) \to 1/(0 + 1) = 1$, $E < E_F$. The Fermi-Dirac distribution function is discontinuous at $E = E_F$ for $T = 0$. Since $p = 1/2$ is midway between $p(E) = 1$ for $E < E_F$ and $p(E) = 0$ for $E > E_F$, it is convenient to define $p(E_F) = 1/2$. Thus the probability is $1/2$ that a state with energy at the Fermi energy is occupied. This behavior is shown graphically in Fig. 42-3.

At any temperature above absolute zero, the Fermi-Dirac distribution function is continuous. Its behavior, illustrated in Fig. 42-4, is analogous to a "smoothed" version of the discontinuous behavior in Fig. 42-3. At higher temperatures, the Fermi energy has the same interpretation as at $T = 0$. The probability that a state with energy $E = E_F$ is occupied is $p(E_F) = 1/2$. This can be seen from Eq. (42-8). For $E = E_F$, $(E - E_F)/kT = 0$ and $e^0 = 1$. Then $p(E_F) = 1/(1 + 1) = 1/2$.

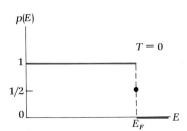

Figure 42-3. The Fermi-Dirac distribution function for $T = 0$ is discontinuous at the Fermi energy E_F.

The value of kT sets a convenient scale for discussing the energy dependence of the Fermi-Dirac distribution function. If E is less than E_F by several units of kT, then the exponential in Eq. (42-8) is small and $p(E)$ is close to 1. If E is several kT greater than E_F, then the exponential is large and $p(E)$ is close to zero. In between, there is an interval of energy, several kT wide, as indicated in Fig. 42-4, in which $p(E)$ changes from nearly 1 to nearly 0. (See Example 42-3 below.)

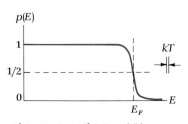

Figure 42-4. The Fermi-Dirac distribution function is continuous for $T > 0$. The occupation probability $p(E)$ changes from nearly 1 to nearly 0 in a range of several kT about E_F.

* P. A. M. Dirac was one of the principal developers of quantum mechanics. Among his contributions is an equation, similar to the Schrödinger equation, that forms a relativistic theory of electrons.

Fermi energy for a free-electron model. The Fermi energy can be determined easily for a system of free electrons at $T = 0$. Equation (42-6) gives the number of electron states with energy less than or equal to a value E:

$$N = \frac{L^3(2mE)^{3/2}}{3\pi^2\hbar^3}$$

If we set $E = E_F$ in this expression, then $N = N_e$, the number of electrons in the box. That is, at $T = 0$, all the states with energy below E_F are filled, so that the number of electrons equals that number of states. It is convenient to express the number of electrons in the box as the number of electrons per unit volume n_e times the volume L^3 of the box. Then

$$N = N_e = n_e L^3 = \frac{L^3(2mE)^{3/2}}{3\pi^2\hbar^3}$$

and we can cancel the factor L^3 in the last equality. Solving for E_F, we find the dependence of the Fermi energy at $T = 0$ on the number density n_e of electrons:

Fermi energy at $T = 0$

$$E_F = \frac{\hbar^2}{2m}(3\pi^2 n_e)^{2/3} \tag{42-9}$$

The Fermi energy at higher temperatures may be different from the value at $T = 0$. For a typical good conductor, such as copper, the temperature dependence of E_F is very slight, and the value determined for $T = 0$ is a good approximation to the Fermi energy for temperatures up to the melting point.

It is important to recognize that the Fermi energy marks the dividing line, in energy, between whether a state is more probably occupied ($E < E_F$) or more probably empty ($E > E_F$). In a free-electron model of a conductor, the Fermi energy depends only on the electron mass and the number density of electrons according to Eq. (42-9). (We neglect the slight temperature dependence of E_F.)

EXAMPLE 42-3. Over what range of energy, expressed in terms of kT, does the Fermi-Dirac distribution function change from 0.90 to 0.10?

SOLUTION. We let E_b represent the energy at which $p(E_b) = 0.1$ in Eq. (42-8). Then solving for the exponential, we have $e^{(E_b - E_F)/kT} = 9.0$ or $(E_b - E_F)/kT = \ln 9.0$. Similarly, let

E_a be such that $p(E_a) = 0.90$. Then $(E_a - E_F)/kT = \ln 0.11$. The difference of these two expressions gives the energy range, $(E_b - E_a)/kT = \ln 9.0 - \ln 0.11 = \ln (9.0/0.11) = 4.4$. Thus the probability that a state is occupied changes from 90 percent to 10 percent over an energy range $E_b - E_a = 4.4\,kT$, which is centered about the Fermi energy.

EXAMPLE 42-4. Assuming one free electron per atom, estimate the Fermi energy for copper.

SOLUTION. The density of Cu is 8.95×10^3 kg/m³ and its atomic weight is 63.5 g/mol. If there is about one free electron for each copper atom, then the free-electron density is about the same as the density of atoms, $n_e = (6.02 \times 10^{23}$ mol$^{-1})(8.95 \times 10^3$ kg/m³)/(0.0635 kg/mol) $= 8.5 \times 10^{28}$

m^{-3}. From Eq. (42-9), the Fermi energy is

$$E_F = \frac{(1.05 \times 10^{-34} \text{ J} \cdot \text{s})^2}{2(9.1 \times 10^{-31} \text{ kg})}[3\pi^2(8.5 \times 10^{28} \text{ m}^{-3})]^{2/3}$$

$$= 1.1 \times 10^{-18} \text{ J} = 7.0 \text{ eV}$$

Notice that this value is large compared with kT, even near the melting point of Cu: $k(1400 \text{ K}) = 0.12$ eV.

42-4 CONDUCTION IN THE FREE-ELECTRON MODEL

The free-electron model provides a simple but useful model for understanding some of the key features of the resistivity of a metal. The expression for the conductivity σ, which is the reciprocal of the resistivity ($\rho = 1/\sigma$), turns out to be the same as in the classical Drude model. Transcribing the result from Eq. (24-14), we write the resistivity as

$$\rho = \frac{m}{n_e e^2 \tau} \qquad (42\text{-}10)$$

where m and e represent the electron mass and charge, n_e is the number density of free electrons, and τ is the relaxation time. The relaxation time characterizes the scattering processes that cause the resistance to the flow of electrons.

Although the expression in Eq. (42-10) appears to be the same as the classical version, we must recognize two important conceptual differences that come from the quantum treatment of resistance in a conductor:

Quantum features of the model for resistivity

1 The electrons are described by wave functions instead of being treated as classical particles.
2 The Pauli exclusion principle limits the scattering to those electrons with energy near the Fermi energy.

We now discuss these features in more detail.

1. In the classical Drude model, the resistance was assumed to be due to the scattering of electrons (behaving as particles) by the ions of the crystalline lattice. Even a perfect lattice, with all the ions at rest, would offer resistance to the classical flow of electrons. However, treating the electron quantum-mechanically, we deal with the wave function for an electron interacting with a perfect lattice. The wave function is determined by this lattice, and there would be no further effect. Scattering from one wave function or state to another can occur if the lattice has imperfections. Thus a conductor with no imperfections would have no resistance! Two important imperfections in metals are vibrations of the ions about the perfect lattice sites and impurities such as Zn ion impurities in a Cu lattice. (In our free-electron model, we have replaced the interaction of an electron with the ion lattice and with the other electrons by a uniform background which forms the "box." We shall look at the effects of a periodic lattice in the next section.)

Electrons are scattered by imperfections.

2. The scattering of electrons by imperfections is quasi-elastic. For example, in the scattering of an electron by a vibrating ion in a conductor at a moderate temperature T, the energy transferred between the electron and the ion is about kT. Consider an electron in a state with energy E_1 well below the Fermi energy, $|E_1 - E_F| \gg kT$. There are many such electrons since the probability that such a state is occupied is essentially 1. (See Fig. 42-4.) Correspondingly, the probability of an *unoccupied* state with energy close to this value E_1 is essentially zero. The Pauli exclusion principle prohibits more than one electron from occupying a state. Thus there is no available state with energy close to E_1 into which an electron with energy E_1 can scatter. These states are already occupied. The Pauli exclusion principle inhibits the scattering of electrons with energy several kT below E_F, because the states into which an electron could scatter are already occupied.

The Pauli exclusion principle limits the scattering to states near the Fermi energy.

There is little scattering for electrons with energy well above the Fermi

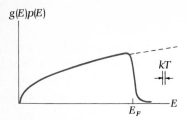

$g(E)p(E)$

kT

E_F E

Figure 42-5. The number of *occupied* states per unit energy range is given by the product $g(E)p(E)$ of the density of states and the occupation probability.

Impurity resistivity is independent of temperature.

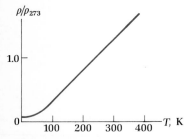

ρ/ρ_{273}

1.0

0

100   200   300   400 T, K

Figure 42-6. The resistivity of a sample of Cu is due to impurities at low temperatures and is approximately linear in T at higher temperatures. The resistivity is scaled to its value at 273 K.

energy, $E - E_F \gg kT$, because there are so few electrons with these higher energies. That is, the probability that an electron occupies such a state is essentially zero. We see then that only those states with energy near the Fermi energy are important in scattering processes. At the Fermi energy, the probability that a state is occupied and the probability that a state is unoccupied are both 1/2. Thus for states within a few kT of the Fermi energy, there are many electrons that can be scattered and there are many unoccupied states available to receive scattered electrons.

Figure 42-5 illustrates the above discussion by showing how the product of the density of states and the Fermi-Dirac distribution function $g(E)p(E)$ depends on energy for $T > 0$. The density of states increases as $E^{1/2}$ and $p(E)$ change from nearly 1 to nearly 0 within a few kT of the Fermi energy. The product gives the number of *occupied* states per unit range of energy. Notice that only near the Fermi energy are there both electrons to be scattered and states available to receive them.

The relaxation time that appears in Eq. (42-10) for the resistivity is characteristic of the scattering of electrons with energies near the Fermi energy. The relaxation time τ_i for scattering due to impurities can be related to the mean free path. Electrons with energy $E \approx E_F = \frac{1}{2}mv_F^2$ have speed v_F, which is called the *Fermi speed*. The mean free path, $\Lambda_i = v_F\tau_i$, is the average distance traveled by electrons between scattering events. It is approximately the average distance between impurities in the conductor and is, therefore, independent of temperature. Since E_F is essentially independent of temperature, so are v_F and $\tau_i = \Lambda_i/v_F$. Thus the resistivity ρ_i for impurity scattering is independent of temperature because each of the quantities in Eq. (42-10) is independent of temperature.

In contrast to impurity scattering, the vibrational contribution to electron scattering does depend on temperature. Higher temperatures correspond to ionic vibrations of greater amplitude, which increases the scattering. More scattering leads to a shorter mean free path and a smaller relaxation time τ_v due to lattice vibrations. It turns out that $1/\tau_v$ is approximately proportional to the absolute temperature T except at very low temperatures. Hence the resistivity ρ_v due to ionic vibrations is essentially proportional to T.

For small impurity concentrations, the resistivity contributions due to impurities and due to vibrations are additive, so that the resistivity of a typical metal is $\rho_i + \rho_v$. At higher temperatures, the vibrational contribution dominates, and ρ is approximately proportional to T, as shown in Fig. 42-6. At low temperatures, the vibrational contribution is negligible, and only the temperature-independent resistivity contribution due to impurities remains.

EXAMPLE 42-5. (a) Use the result of the previous example to estimate the Fermi speed for an electron in Cu. (b) Estimate the relaxation time for impurity scattering in Cu if the average separation of impurities is 30 nm. This corresponds to an atomic-impurity concentration of about 0.1 percent.

SOLUTION. (a) The Fermi energy for Cu was estimated in the previous example to be $E_F = 7.0$ eV $= 1.1 \times 10^{-18}$ J. Since $E_F = \frac{1}{2}mv_F^2$, we have $v_F = \sqrt{2E_F/m}$ and

$$v_F = \sqrt{\frac{2(1.1 \times 10^{-18} \text{ J})}{9.1 \times 10^{-31} \text{ kg}}} = 1.6 \times 10^6 \text{ m/s}$$

(b) Setting the mean free path $\Lambda = v_F\tau_i = 30$ nm, we estimate the relaxation time to be

$$\tau_i = \frac{\Lambda}{v_F} = \frac{30 \text{ nm}}{1.6 \times 10^6 \text{ m/s}} = 2 \times 10^{-15} \text{ s}$$

42-5 ELECTRON ENERGY BANDS

The free-electron model accounts for the general features of the resistivity of conductors such as the metals. It is a simplistic model in that the periodic lattice formed by the ions is completely ignored. The "free" valence electrons are assumed to move freely in a box which represents the solid. If an electric field is applied, the electric current is due to electrons drifting in response to the field and averaged over scattering processes due to imperfections. In the free-electron model, all substances would be conductors. To understand why some materials are conductors and others are insulators, we must consider the effect of the periodic lattice on the electron wave functions.

A wave function for an electron in an isolated atom is localized or bound to that atom. For example, see the illustrations for some states of an electron in the hydrogen atom in Fig. 41-6. In contrast, a wave function for an electron in a crystalline solid is not localized on an atomic site but extends throughout the crystal. This behavior is suggested by the form of the free-particle wave function in Eq. (42-1). This wave function extends throughout the box. In a more realistic model, a wave function extends over all of the ions. That is, an electron in a solid interacts with all of the ions of the lattice instead of being localized on a particular ion.

One approach to seeing the effect of an extended wave function in a solid is to imagine the ions to be well separated rather than close together in the crystal. As a definite example, consider a large number N of sodium (Na) atoms arranged so that each atom is essentially isolated. From the position of Na in the periodic table (see the discussion in Sec. 41-7), we expect the single valence electron in Na to be in a 3s subshell. For simplicity, we neglect the more tightly bound core electrons in each atom. The 3s energy levels for several Na atoms are shown schematically in Fig. 42-7a. As indicated there, these levels have the same energy because each atom is isolated. That is, the 3s states in different, isolated atoms are degenerate.

Now imagine bringing the atoms closer together so that an electron can interact with more than one atom. Because of this interaction, the wave functions are changed to extend over all the atoms, and the states have slightly different energies. Thus the energy levels for these 3s electrons become nondegenerate as the atoms are brought together. This behavior is shown schematically in Fig. 42-7b, where the energies of the states are slightly different. We can no longer associate an electron with a particular atom because the wave functions have become extended.

The diagrams in Fig. 42-7 show the effect for a few of the atoms and for only one type of state, a 3s state. If a large number of atoms are involved, the 3s states form a *band* of states in the solid. The energy levels in the band are very close together and cannot be resolved. The total number of states in the band is the

An electron wave function extends throughout the crystal.

Energy levels form bands in a crystal.

Figure 42-7. (a) The 3s states of five isolated Na atoms are degenerate. (b) If the atoms are close together, the states have slightly different energies.

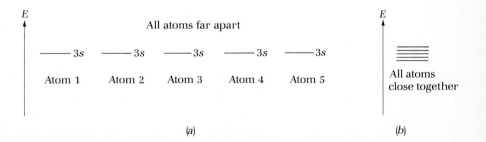

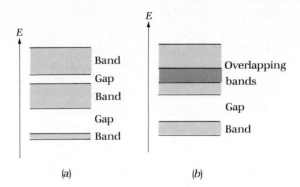

Figure 42-8. (a) Energy levels form bands that are separated by gaps. (b) Some of the energy levels form overlapping bands.

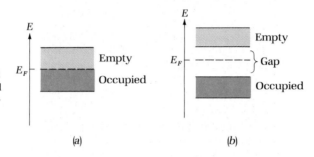

Figure 42-9. (a) In the band structure for a conductor, the Fermi energy lies within a partly occupied band. (b) For an insulator, the lower band is full and the upper band is empty. The two bands are separated by a large gap.

same as the number of $3s$ states of N isolated atoms. This number is $2N$ since there are two $3s$ states in each atom. In addition to the band of states formed from the $3s$ levels, there are bands formed from other levels of the isolated atoms. For example, there is a band formed from the $2p$ states, and there is a band formed from the $3p$ states.

Several bands are shown schematically on the energy-level diagram in Fig. 42-8a. Within each band there are states with a nearly continuous range of energies. Notice that there are also regions between bands, called *energy gaps* in which there are *no states.* Thus the electronic structure of a crystalline solid is characterized by energy bands separated by gaps. There can also be regions in which two or more bands overlap in energy, as shown in Fig. 42-8b. The electronic properties of a solid depend on the arrangement of the bands and the gaps and on how they are populated by the electrons. This approach to describing electrons in solids is called the *band theory of solids.*

We can use the band theory to understand why some materials are conductors and others are insulators. Consider a substance with the simple band structure shown in Fig. 42-9a. We imagine filling these states in bands in accordance with the Pauli principle, just as in the free-electron model. The Fermi energy is the level at which the occupation probability is $1/2$. For this substance, the Fermi energy is at a level within the band, as shown in the figure. Thus there are many electrons and many available states near the Fermi energy, and conduction occurs as in the free-electron case. That is, a substance that has the Fermi energy within a band is a conductor. Put yet another way, a conductor has a band with many occupied and many unoccupied states. The band is not full. Since the electrons in such a band are responsible for conduction, the band is often called the *conduction band.*

A typical band structure for an insulator is shown in Fig. 42-9b. The insulating property is a consequence of two features:

Bands are separated by energy gaps.

Band theory of solids

The conduction band is partially occupied in a conductor.

An insulator has a large gap between an occupied valence band and an empty conduction band.

1 The number of electrons occupying a band equals the number of states in that band. That is, the band is full (at $T = 0$). This band is often called the *valence band.*

2 A large energy gap separates the occupied valence band from the next band of higher energy, which is the empty conduction band. For example, the energy gap for the diamond form of carbon, an excellent insulator, is about 6 eV.

The Fermi energy for an insulator lies midway between the valence and conduction band, as indicated in Fig. 42-9*b*.

To see the effect of the first feature, imagine a substance at $T = 0$. We can picture a current in the material as due to an applied electric field inducing transitions between electron states of almost the same energy. In a conductor, with the Fermi energy within the band, there are many occupied states and many unoccupied states near the Fermi energy that can participate in these transitions. If the band is full, however, there are no unoccupied states to participate. The electrons in a full band do not contribute to a current. A substance that has only full bands separated by gaps from empty bands (at $T = 0$) cannot have a current: It is an insulator.

The second feature accounts for the fact that a substance that is insulating at low temperature remains insulating at high temperatures if the energy gap is large—large compared with kT. In a good insulator with energy gap $E_g \gg kT$, only a few electrons are excited from the otherwise full valence band to the nominally empty conduction band. Such a small concentration of charge carriers results in a miniscule current, and the material is still an effective insulator.

EXAMPLE 42-6. The Fermi energy for an insulator is midway in the gap between the full band and the empty band. (See Prob. 42-4.) For diamond ($E_g = 6$ eV) at 1000 K, determine the probability that a state of lowest energy in the conduction band is occupied.

SOLUTION. The occupation probability is given by the Fermi-Dirac distribution function in Eq. (42-8). Since the Fermi energy is midway in the gap, the state of lowest energy in the conduction band has energy E_c such that $E_c - E_F = \frac{1}{2}E_g = 3$ eV. At 1000 K, $kT = 1.38 \times 10^{-20}$ J = 0.09 eV. Thus

$$p(E_c) = \frac{1}{e^{(E_c - E_F)/kT} + 1} = \frac{1}{e^{(3\ \text{eV})/(0.09\ \text{eV})} + 1}$$

$$= 3 \times 10^{-15}$$

This very small occupation probability accounts for the high resistivity of diamond.

42-6 SEMICONDUCTORS

In the last section we saw that an insulator has a large energy gap between occupied and unoccupied bands. There are materials, such as silicon and gallium arsenide, that have a smaller energy gap separating the full valence band from the empty conduction band at $T = 0$. For example, the gap for Si is 1.1 eV. For such materials at low temperatures, very few electrons are excited into the conduction band (see Exercise 42-25), and the resistivity is large, as for an insulator. At higher temperatures, room temperature for example, a small but significant fraction of electrons are excited across the gap into the conduction band. Thus the material can carry an appreciable current and have a resistivity that is more like a conductor than an insulator. Materials with this behavior are appropriately called *semiconductors.*

A semiconductor has a smaller band gap than an insulator.

The general features of conduction in semiconductors were discussed in Sec. 24-5. As you review that discussion, you can translate some of the explanations into the language of band theory that we have developed. It is important to distinguish between the two cases of pure, or *intrinsic*, semiconductors and doped, or *extrinsic*, semiconductors.

Intrinsic semiconductors. In a pure semiconductor at $T = 0$, all states in the valence band are occupied, and there are no electrons in the conduction band. In the pure and perfect crystal, the electrons completely fill the valence band. At higher temperatures some electrons are excited into the conduction band. Since each electron excited into the conduction band leaves behind a hole in the valence band, there are equal numbers of electrons and holes in the pure material. These electrons and holes are the charge carriers, and the current is due to their motion. The concentrations of these carriers in a pure semiconductor at a given temperature depend only on the material. For this reason, the semiconductor and the conduction that takes place in it are called *intrinsic*.

The resistivity of an intrinsic semiconductor decreases with increasing temperature.

The Fermi-Dirac distribution function determines the probability of occupation of states by the electrons. For an intrinsic semiconductor, the Fermi energy is approximately midway in the gap between the valence and conduction bands. (See Prob. 42-4.) As a result of the temperature dependence of the occupation probability, the concentration of electrons and holes depends strongly on temperature. If we use Eq. (42-10) for the contribution of either the electrons or the holes to the resistivity, then the resistivity is inversely proportional to the carrier concentration, $\rho = m/(ne^2\tau)$, and the resistivity of an intrinsic semiconductor depends strongly on temperature. Since the carrier concentration n increases with increasing temperature, the resistivity decreases with increasing temperature. In contrast, the resistivity of a metallic conductor increases with increasing temperature.

Extrinsic semiconductors. The semiconducting devices in computers, radios, and other electronic appliances utilize extrinsic semiconductors. To achieve the desired operating characteristics, selected impurities are added to the pure material in a controlled manner. These semiconductors are said to be "doped" with impurities. As discussed in Sec. 24-5, donor impurities donate additional electrons, and since electrons are the majority carriers, the material is called *n-type*. Acceptor impurities accept electrons so that additional holes are formed. For such *p-type* materials, positively charged holes are the majority carriers.

Extrinsic semiconductors are doped with impurities.

We can see from the band structure how different kinds of impurities lead to *n*-type or *p*-type semiconductors. An energy-level diagram for an *n*-type semiconductor is shown in Fig. 42-10*a*. Just as with the intrinsic semiconductor, the conduction and valence bands are separated by a gap. There are also energy levels in the gap that are localized on the donor impurity ions. These levels are very close in energy to the conduction band, and most of the electrons have been excited from the donor levels to the conduction band. Thus donor impurities have levels close to the conduction band and donate electrons to that band.

Donor levels are close to the conduction band.

Figure 42-10*b* shows an energy-level diagram for a *p*-type semiconductor. In this case, the localized impurity levels are close in energy to the valence band. Since the acceptor levels are close to the valence band, most of these levels are occupied by electrons. Each electron excited from the valence band into an

Acceptor levels are close to the valence band.

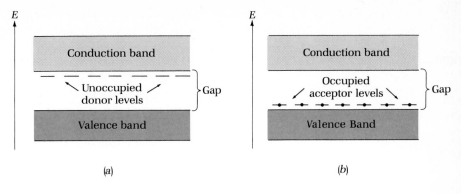

Figure 42-10. (a) Donor levels are close to the conduction band in an *n*-type semiconductor. (b) Acceptor levels are close to the valence band in a *p*-type semiconductor.

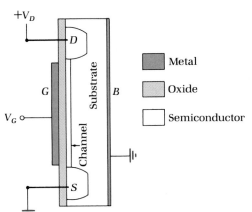

Figure 42-11. A positive gate voltage V_G causes an *n*-type channel in a MOSFET to be highly conducting.

acceptor level leaves behind a hole in the valence band. In this way, acceptor impurities increase the concentration of holes in the valence band.

The MOSFET. Modern electronic devices operate with integrated circuits that may contain millions of elements. A common element in such circuits is a *field-effect transistor.* We describe qualitatively the structure and operation of a *m*etal *o*xide *s*emiconductor *f*ield-*e*ffect *t*ransistor (a *MOSFET*). The structure of a single MOSFET hints at the technological complexity of the fabrication process that includes many such elements on a single chip. The operation of a MOSFET illustrates how the current in an element can be changed substantially by a relatively small change in applied voltage. Such changes are utilized in amplifying signals or for electronic switching in computers.

The structure of a type of MOSFET is shown schematically in Fig. 42-11. A thin, *p*-type semiconductor forms a substrate that is backed by a metal base *B*. Two *n*-type regions, called the *source S* and the *drain D,* are embedded in the substrate. Usually the base and the source are maintained at zero potential (ground), and the drain is at a positive potential, say $V_D = 5$ V. The gate *G* is formed from a metal electrode separated by an insulating SiO_2 layer from the semiconducting substrate (hence the Metal Oxide Semiconductor FET). If the gate electrode is also at zero potential, then conduction occurs mainly through the junction between the *n*-type drain and the *p*-type substrate. Under these conditions the device has a large resistance and carries a small current. (This junction is reverse-biased, as described in Sec. 24-5).

The current in the MOSFET changes significantly if the gate electrode potential is made positive. The change in the electric field just beneath the gate

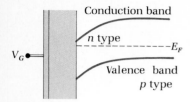

Figure 42-12. A positive gate voltage produces an *n*-type channel by bending the bands.

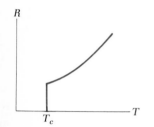

Figure 42-13. The resistance of a superconductor drops abruptly to zero at the transition temperature T_c.

Table 42-1. Some superconducting substances

Substance	Transition temperature, K
Al	1.2
In	3.4
Sn	3.7
Pb	7.2
Nb	9.3
Nb_3Sn	18
Nb_3Ge	23
$YBa_2Cu_3O_7$	90

Type I superconductor

electrode causes the material in a channel in the substrate to become more highly conducting. This field effect can be expressed as a "bending of bands," shown schematically in Fig. 42-12: Deep in the *p*-type substrate, the Fermi energy lies closer to the valence band. There, the hole concentration in the valence band is large compared with the electron concentration in the conduction band. Near the oxide layer, however, the field penetrates into the semiconductor and causes the energy levels to be lowered, as indicated by the bending of the bands in the figure. In this region, the Fermi energy can lie closer to the conduction band, and the material in this channel can become *n*-type. Thus the field draws electrons into the channel from the neighboring regions and the device can carry a large current. A small change in the gate voltage results in a large change in the MOSFET current, and this feature is utilized in amplifier applications.

42-7 SUPERCONDUCTIVITY

Of all the common gases, helium has the lowest liquefaction temperature (4.2 K at atmospheric pressure) and, as a consequence, is the most difficult to liquefy. In 1908 the Dutch physicist H. Kamerlingh Onnes (1853–1926) succeeded in liquefying helium. This achievement opened for experimentation the new area of low-temperature physics. The properties of substances at such low temperatures could be studied for the first time by using liquid helium as a coolant.

Kamerlingh Onnes made an astounding observation in 1911 as he was measuring the resistance of a sample of mercury at low temperature. The resistance dropped abruptly to zero at about 4 K! It is expected that the resistance of a nearly pure metal should decrease with temperature (as shown in Fig. 42-6 for Cu). But the sharp disappearance of the resistance, as shown in Fig. 42-13, was unexpected. Since the initial discovery of resistanceless currents, or *superconductivity*, a number of materials have been found to exhibit superconductivity.

Table 42-1 gives a list of a few superconducting substances along with their transition temperatures. The transition, or critical, temperature T_c is the temperature below which the substance becomes superconducting. A superconductor typically remains superconducting at temperatures below the transition temperature.

A superconductor is truly resistanceless; a current established in a superconducting ring persists for times of the order of years without any measurable diminution. One practical application of superconductivity is in the production of large magnetic fields by large currents in superconducting coils. Since the resistance of the coils is zero, there are no troublesome (and expensive) Joule heating losses (i^2R) in a large superconducting magnet. Large superconducting magnets are being used in research laboratories, in particle accelerators, and for medical imaging. (See Fig. 42-14.)

Superconductors behave very differently from normal conductors in the presence of a magnetic field, and not all superconductors behave in the same way. We describe here the behavior of a *type I superconductor*. Suppose that a cylindrical sample is in a uniform magnetic field directed along the cylinder axis. If the temperature is above the transition temperature so that the sample is a normal conductor, the magnetic field inside the sample is almost the same as outside. This situation is shown in Fig. 42-15a. When the temperature is low-

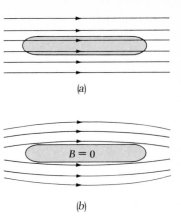

(a)

$B = 0$

(b)

Figure 42-15. (a) A magnetic field exists inside a normal conductor, $T > T_c$. (b) The magnetic field is expelled when the sample becomes superconducting, $T < T_c$.

Figure 42-14. A superconducting coil magnet is used for medical imaging. The coil has about a 1-m diameter and produces a uniform magnetic field of magnitude up to 2 T. *(Courtesy of GE Magnet Systems Engineering and Manufacturing, Florence, S.C.)*

The Meissner effect: no magnetic field inside a superconductor

Type II superconductor

High T_c superconductor

ered below T_c, the sample becomes superconducting and the magnetic field is expelled from the interior of the sample, as shown in Fig. 42-15b. *There is no magnetic field inside a type I superconductor.* This effect, called the *Meissner effect,* is due to the existence of superconducting screening currents at the surface of the superconductor. These screening currents produce a contribution to the magnetic field that cancels the applied magnetic field inside the superconductor. Thus $B = 0$ inside the superconducting sample. Superconductors exhibit the Meissner effect if the applied magnetic field is not too strong. Higher magnetic fields can cause a sample to become normal, losing its superconducting properties. Screening currents can also lead to dramatic levitation effects. One example is shown in Fig. 42-16.

Type II superconductors behave somewhat differently in magnetic fields. Such a superconductor will exclude a relatively low magnetic field from its interior. However, for larger magnetic fields, the magnetic field penetrates into regions of the sample, which are no longer superconducting. That is, the sample contains both superconducting and normal regions. In still-higher magnetic fields, the superconducting regions disappear, and the sample becomes normal.

Recently, superconductivity has been observed in ceramic materials, such as $YBa_2Cu_3O_7$, with transition temperatures above 77 K, the normal boiling point of liquid nitrogen. These "high T_c" superconductors are the subject of intensive research and development. They are potentially important for technological applications because of the relatively low cost of liquid nitrogen as a coolant.

Figure 42-16. A small magnet slowly rotates as it is suspended by the magnetic field produced by screening currents in a ceramic (high T_c) superconducting block. The screening currents exclude the magnetic field from the interior of the superconducting block, and this Meissner effect is a basic test of true superconductivity. *(Argonne National Laboratory photo.)*

The superconducting state. If a substance undergoes a phase transition, some of its properties change. For example, the specific heat of water changes as the vapor condenses into the liquid at the transition temperature (373.15 K at atmospheric pressure). The transition from the normal phase of a conductor to the superconducting phase or state is likewise a phase transition. The specific heat changes as a substance goes from the normal to the superconducting state. Another property that changes in this transition is the resistance. It changes from a nonzero value for the normal state to zero for the superconducting state.

The normal-to-superconducting transition is different from an ordinary structural phase change, such as the condensation of water from vapor to liquid. The crystal structure of the lattice, determined by the equilibrium positions of the ions, is essentially the same for the normal and superconducting states. It is the electronic structure that is radically different for these two states. In the normal state of a metal, the electronic structure can be described with the band picture of a conductor, as described in Sec. 42-5. Electrons occupy a band (or perhaps overlapping bands) that is not full. Electron states are available at the Fermi energy so that a small applied electric field can produce a current. Scattering of electrons by imperfections, such as vibrating ions, is responsible for the resistance. As in the free-electron model, we think of the electrons as moving essentially independently in the normal state, occupying the available states in accord with Fermi-Dirac statistics.

A fundamental understanding of the electronic structure of the superconducting state was achieved only long after the discovery of superconductivity by Onnes. A microscopic theory of superconductivity was given in 1957 by J. Bardeen, L. N. Cooper, and J. R. Schrieffer and is called the *BCS theory* (from the first letters of the scientists' last names). The BCS theory is a quantum-mechanical, many-body theory. Instead of treating the electrons independently, the many-body theory concentrates on a collective, or correlated, state of the whole assembly of electrons. In the superconducting state, there is a coherence among the wave functions of the electrons that extends over macroscopic dimensions. As we shall see, this coherence is manifested in some important superconducting phenomena that exhibit interference effects for macroscopic quantities.

A key concept in the BCS description of the superconducting state is the *Cooper pair*. An attractive interaction between electrons, even if weak, can lead to a bound state of an appropriate pair of electrons. That is, the energy of such a pair, a *Cooper pair*, is a discrete amount lower than their energy if the interaction did not exist. The formation of a Cooper pair depends on the presence of the other electrons. In a sense, the effect of the interaction is enhanced because of the nearly complete occupation of states below the Fermi energy. This limitation of available states results in the coupling of electrons with opposite spin and opposite momenta into a Cooper pair. The spins add to give a zero total spin angular momentum for the Cooper pair. Likewise, the total momentum of the pair is zero. The Cooper pair can then be described as a composite spinless particle with zero momentum. The superconducting state can be viewed approximately as a coherent condensate of these Cooper pairs.

In most superconductors, the interaction between electrons that leads to a Cooper pair is connected with the motion of the ion lattice. This interaction is suggested by the following scenario expressed in classical terms: (i) A negatively charged electron slightly draws neighboring positively charged ions

Electronic structure is different for superconducting and normal states.

BCS theory of superconductivity

Electrons in a Cooper pair have opposite spins and momenta.

toward it, distorting the lattice locally. (ii) Another electron is attracted by the slightly greater concentration of positive charge.

The interaction can also be expressed in quantum-mechanical terms. The vibrations of ions in a lattice can be described as waves, sound waves. In analogy with photons as the quantum of light, the *phonon* is the quantum of lattice vibrations. The interaction of an electron with the lattice is viewed as the absorption or the emission of a phonon by an electron. Thus one electron can emit a phonon that is subsequently absorbed by another electron. In this way, two electrons interact via the lattice. It is remarkable that the same basic process, represented by the emission or absorption of a phonon by an electron, can lead both to the resistance of the normal conductor and the resistanceless nature of the superconductor. In the normal conductor, the resistance is due to an electron being scattered by a phonon. In the superconductor, the exchange of phonons between electrons leads to a Cooper pair.

An important aspect of the bound state of a Cooper pair is that a nonzero amount of energy is required to break or separate the pair. This feature is responsible for the lack of resistance to the flow of charge. In a superconductor the Cooper pairs, with charge $-2e$, carry the current as they drift through the solid. The solid contains imperfections that would scatter electrons in the normal state. Recall that such scattering in the normal conductor, while essentially elastic, is dissipative and leads to resistance. This kind of scattering of individual electrons does lead to resistance in the normal conductor. But in a superconductor, the electrons are bound as Cooper pairs. Since the usual scattering processes cannot transfer enough energy to break a pair, no dissipative scattering occurs and there is no resistance.

Flux quantization. Some properties of a superconductor, such as the absence of resistance, can be understood using the Cooper-pair concept. The superconducting state is more than just a collection of Cooper pairs. There is a long-range coherence that exists among all the superconducting electrons. It can be expressed as a *coherence of phase*, similar to the phase of a wave. Just as for two waves with a coherent phase difference, there can be constructive and destructive interference for two sources of superconducting electrons.

One effect of phase coherence is the *quantization of magnetic flux*. A type I superconducting ring with a persistent current is shown schematically in Fig. 42-17. Although a superconductor excludes the magnetic field from its interior, a magnetic field can thread a hole in a superconductor such as the center of the superconducting ring. Consider the magnetic flux $\Phi_B = \int \mathbf{B} \cdot d\mathbf{S}$ for a surface bounded by the ring. The phase associated with the superconducting state varies with position around the ring. Since one circuit of the ring returns us to the starting point, the phase must also return to its value at the starting point of the circuit (similar to the way that θ and $\theta + 2\pi$ represent the same plane angle). It turns out that this requirement of single-valuedness of the coherent phase leads to the quantization of the magnetic flux. The magnetic flux Φ_B for the superconducting ring is restricted to an integer multiple n of the *flux quantum* Φ_0:

$$\Phi_B = n\Phi_0 \qquad (n = 0, 1, 2, \ldots) \qquad (42\text{-}11)$$

where $\Phi_0 = h/2e = 2.07 \times 10^{-15}$ Wb. The factor of $2e$ in the denominator reflects the charge of a Cooper pair, $-2e$.

The same phase coherence that leads to flux quantization is exhibited as an

A phonon is a quantized lattice vibration.

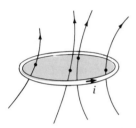

Figure 42-17. A magnetic field threads a superconducting ring.

Phase coherence for a superconductor

Magnetic-flux quantization and the flux quantum Φ_0

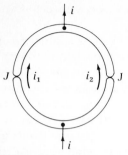

Figure 42-18. The total current i in a SQUID depends on the phase differences for the Josephson junctions J. The relative phase depends on the magnetic flux linking the ring.

interference phenomenon in a SQUID, a *superconducting quantum interference device*. A *SQUID*, shown schematically in Fig. 42-18, is similar to a superconducting ring, except for its much smaller size and for the presence of a *Josephson junction* in each arm of the ring. In a Josephson junction, a thin insulating layer separates two superconducting regions. The layer is so thin that Cooper pairs can tunnel (Sec. 40-10) through the insulating layers. The tunneling current in a Josephson junction depends on the phase difference across the junction.

The two Josephson junctions behave somewhat as slits in an optical double-slit system (Sec. 36-2). The total current in the device is the sum of the currents in the two arms and depends on the phase difference for pairs taking the two paths. This phase difference changes if the magnetic flux linking the SQUID changes. Changes of a fraction of a flux quantum are easily observed. Because the flux quantum is small, a SQUID is used in precision measurements of magnetic fields.

EXAMPLE 42-7. The ring in a simple SQUID has radius 0.1 mm. What change in magnitude of a magnetic field, perpendicular to the plane of the SQUID, corresponds to a flux change of Φ_0?

SOLUTION. The plane of the ring has area πr^2 so that the magnetic flux linking the SQUID is $B\pi r^2$. If B changes by ΔB,

then the flux changes by $\Delta B\pi r^2$. For a flux change of one unit of the flux quantum, $\Delta B\pi r^2 = \Phi_0$ and

$$\Delta B = \frac{\Phi_0}{\pi r^2} = \frac{2.07 \times 10^{-15} \text{ Wb}}{\pi(0.1 \text{ mm})^2}$$

$$= 70 \text{ nT}$$

COMMENTARY: HIGH TEMPERATURE SUPERCONDUCTIVITY

When Onnes discovered superconductivity, he found that mercury stopped being an ordinary metal and became superconducting when its temperature was lowered below 4.15 K. The usefulness of superconducting materials is obviously much enhanced if the superconducting transition temperature T_c is closer to room temperature (about 300 K). In subsequent years, the search for materials with higher T_c's made steady but slow progress, and by 1973 the superconductor with the highest known transition temperature was the alloy Nb_3Ge, for which $T_c = 23$ K. The primary goal was a material that became superconducting at room temperature, or at least above the boiling point of liquid nitrogen (77 K), a temperature that can be maintained at a cost that is about a factor of 10 less than temperatures in the neighborhood of 20 K.

The search was not aided appreciably by a theoretical understanding of superconductivity. No microscopic explanation of superconductivity was available between 1911 and 1956. Although in 1956 a theory — the "BCS theory" — was proposed, it did not lend itself to easy calculations of transition temperatures. Discoveries of new superconductors have been due as much to an intuitive use of the periodic table as to an understanding of the fundamental nature of superconductivity.

In 1986 there was a development that changed the scale of progress. K. Alex Müller and J. Georg Bednortz at the IBM research lab in Rushlikon, Switzerland, discovered a material, $La_{2-x}Ba_xCuO_{4-y}$, that had $T_c = 35$ K. Not only was this a large increase in T_c, but the material was of a new class. The record for highest T_c had been held for decades by metal alloys such as Nb_3Ge, all of which had the same crystalline structure. A few oxides were previously known to be superconducting, but none of them had been found to be superconducting above 10 K.

At a meeting of the Materials Research Society in late 1986, Koichi Kitazawa of the University of Tokyo and Ching-Wu (Paul) Chu of the University of Houston announced in a special session that they had confirmed the results of Bednortz and Müller. Paul Chu soon showed that the superconducting transition temperature of these oxides was greatly increased by pressure, and in January and February of 1987 Paul Chu in the U.S., Tanaka and Kitazawa in Japan, and workers at the Institute of Physics in Beijing, China, announced that oxides involving rare earths, such as $Y_1Ba_2Cu_3O_{7-x}$, had superconducting transition temperatures around 90 K. These discoveries essentially assured that superconductivity would become a common technological tool.

The excitement of the search for these materials (and the rewards to the finders) led to the "Woodstock" of physics at the American Physical Society meeting in New York, March 1987. Fifty-one speakers gave talks about the new materials in a session that lasted well past midnight, with the audience overflowing the largest room available and listening to loudspeakers set up in the halls. The session was transmitted via satellite to Japan. During the next year, a large fraction of the world's solid-state physicists devoted at least part of their time to these materials, trying to determine their properties and develop a theory that would explain their behavior. At the next similar meeting of the American Physical Society, over 500 speakers gave talks.

As this is being written, the highest T_c that has been reliably reported is about 125 K. There are several crystalline structures, composed of many elements, that have a T_c greater than 77 K — but all contain Cu and O atoms in a planar structure, and all are sensitive to the exact oxygen content. Many plausible, but incompatible, theories have been advanced, all of which are based on the fundamental quantum nature of the many electrons in solids.

The technological goals are to make magnets, motors, computers, and other useful devices out of these new superconducting materials. Presently, their usefulness is limited because most of them are brittle and fragile, and because they carry sizable electric currents only when the crystal alignments, oxygen content, and connections between crystallites are within close tolerances. Larger electric currents drive the samples into the normal, resistive state.

If it proves possible to surmount these difficulties, magnets can be built that dissipate no electric energy. Such magnets could be used to store energy, to support (levitate) trains, and to make more efficient motors. Further possible applications include the use of thin films of superconducting material in electronic circuitry. One of the limits of present day computing speeds is the distance between computing elements. It is difficult to make this distance shorter, because the elements must be able to dissipate the I^2R heating in the normally conducting materials that make up the computer. Such problems can be ameliorated with superconducting materials, since they have no I^2R losses.

Many other applications can be anticipated, such as lossless transmission lines and generators. Before these applications can occur, further development of engineering materials is necessary. But even that must wait until the materials themselves are better known and characterized.

SUMMARY WITH APPLICATIONS

Section 42-2. A free-electron model
A free particle in a three-dimensional box of edge L has wave functions and energy levels given by

$$\psi_{n_1 n_2 n_3} = \sqrt{\frac{8}{L^3}} \left(\sin \frac{n_1 \pi x}{L} \right) \left(\sin \frac{n_2 \pi y}{L} \right) \left(\sin \frac{n_3 \pi z}{L} \right) \text{(42-1)}$$

$$E_{n_1 n_2 n_3} = \frac{\hbar^2 \pi^2}{2mL^2} (n_1^2 + n_2^2 + n_3^2) \qquad \text{(42-2)}$$

Determine the energy levels and wave functions for electrons in a free-electron model.

Section 42-3. Fermi-Dirac statistics
The probability that a state of energy E is occupied is given by the Fermi-Dirac distribution function,

$$p(E) = \frac{1}{e^{(E - E_F)/kT} + 1} \qquad \text{(42-8)}$$

In the free-electron model, the Fermi energy is determined by the number density of electrons:

$$E_F = \frac{\hbar^2}{2m} (3\pi^2 n_e)^{2/3} \qquad \text{(42-9)}$$

Describe the occupation probability for fermions; determine the Fermi energy for a free-electron model.

Section 42-4. Conduction in the free-electron model
In the free-electron model, the resistivity of a conductor is given by

$$\rho = \frac{m}{n_e e^2 \tau} \qquad \text{(42-10)}$$

where the relaxation time τ characterizes the scattering of electrons by imperfections.

Explain how the Pauli exclusion principle limits the scattering to those states with energies near the Fermi energy.

Section 42-5. Electron energy bands
The energy levels for electrons in the periodic lattice of a crystal are arranged in bands, with gaps between some of the bands. A conductor has a partially occupied conduction band. An insulator has a full valence band separated by a large gap from an empty conduction band.

Use a band model to explain the conducting and insulating properties of solids.

Section 42-6. Semiconductors
A semiconductor has a smaller gap between the valence and conduction bands than an insulator. Conduction in intrinsic semiconductors is due to thermally excited electrons and holes. Extrinsic semiconductors are doped with impurities to modify the number density of electrons. In n-type material, conduction is mainly due to electrons in the conduction band. In p-type material, conduction is due mainly to holes in the valence band.

Explain properties of intrinsic and extrinsic semiconductors with a band model.

Section 42-7. Superconductivity
Below the transition temperature of a superconducting material, the resistance disappears. A type I superconductor exhibits the Meissner effect by expelling a magnetic field from its interior. Two interacting electrons with opposite spin and equal but opposite momenta can form a Cooper pair in the presence of other electrons. The superconducting state is approximately described as a condensate of Cooper pairs. Phase coherence for the electron wave functions in a superconductor leads to the quantization of magnetic flux.

Describe how Cooper pairs can be used to explain some properties of superconductors.

QUESTIONS

42-1   Each of the integers n_1, n_2, n_3 in Eq. (42-1) are chosen positive. Why can one or more of them not be zero? Can any of them be negative?

42-2   Consider the lattice that is partially shown in Fig. 42-1. A lattice point lies at each of the eight corners of a lattice cube. How many cubes have a given point at a corner? That is, how many cubes share a particular point? Explain why there is a correspondence of one lattice point to one cube.

42-3   The total number of states N with energy less than or equal to a specific value E is given by Eq. (42-6) for a particle in a box of cube edge L. How many states would be in a box (a) of cube edge $\frac{1}{2}L$, (b) of cube edge $2L$, (c) of twice the volume?

42-4   The "density" in the density of states $g(E)$ given in Eq. (42-7) refers to the number of states per unit energy range. Consider the (volume) density of the density of states, $g(E)/L^3$, which is the density of states per unit volume. How does this depend on the volume of the box?

42-5   The number density of electrons n_e is the number of conduction electrons per unit volume. Suppose conductor A has twice the electron number density of conductor B. Which conductor has the larger Fermi energy?

42-6   Give an explanation for the observation that the resistivity of Cu increases proportionally with the concentration of Fe impurities (for small concentrations).

42-7   In the free-electron model of conduction, is there anything that distinguishes one metal from another, say Cu from Ag? Explain.

42-8   Explain why the resistance of a typical metal wire increases when it carries a large current.

42-9   Bands and gaps are present in the electron-energy-level diagram for electrons in a solid. Would you expect to find bands in the energy-level diagram for electrons in a dilute monatomic gas? In a liquid? What about gaps? Explain.

42-10   In a conductor, the electrons partially fill a band, the conduction band. Where is the Fermi energy relative to this band on the energy-level diagram? Where is the Fermi energy for an insulator?

42-11   Can a current exist in an insulator at room temperature? Explain.

42-12   If the resistance of a metal increases with temperature, does the metal become an insulator at high temperature? Explain.

42-13   Does an intrinsic semiconductor become an insulator at low temperature? Explain.

42-14   The visible part of the spectrum has photons with energy in the range 1.8 to 3.1 eV. The gap between the valence and conduction bands in diamond is 6 eV. Explain why diamond is clear (transparent).

42-15   The band gap in Si is 1.1 eV. Refer to the previous question and explain why Si is transparent in the infrared but not in the visible spectrum.

42-16   Why do intrinsic semiconductors have equal numbers of electrons and holes? Why do extrinsic semiconductors have unequal numbers of electrons and holes?

42-17   What is the distinction between an insulator and an intrinsic semiconductor?

42-18   Germanium is a semiconductor with a band gap of 0.70 eV. Energy levels appear in the gap due to impurities. Measured relative to the top of the valence band, the impurity levels are at 0.01 eV for Al and 0.69 eV for P. Which impurity is a donor and which is

an acceptor? Explain.

42-19   A superconductor is connected in series with a normal conductor of resistance R. What is the resistance of the combination? What is the resistance of the combination if the two are connected in parallel?

42-20   A superconducting wire carries a current i. What is the potential difference between the two ends of the wire? What is the electric field inside the wire? What is the magnetic field inside the wire?

42-21   Why is the flux quantum $h/2e$ rather than h/e?

42-22   The temperature dependence of the resistivity is shown in Fig. 42-19 for four substances. Classify each as a conductor, a semiconductor, or a superconductor.

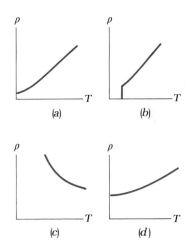

Figure 42-19. Ques. 42-22.

42-23   Complete the following table:

Symbol	Represents	Type	SI unit
$g(E)$		Scalar	
E_F			J
$p(E)$	Occupation probability		
n_e			
τ			
Φ_0			

EXERCISES

Section 42-2. A free-electron model

42-1   A particle is confined to a three-dimensional box. The faces of the box are at $x = 0, L; y = 0, L; z = 0, L$. Show that the wave function in Eq. (42-1) is zero at all of these faces if n_1, n_2, and n_3 are integers.

42-2   An electron is confined to a cube of edge 0.10 mm. Determine the energy of (a) the ground state and (b) the state of next-lowest energy. (c) The energy

levels in part (b) are degenerate. What are the quantum numbers n_1, n_2, n_3, m_s of each state with this energy?

42-3   Treat the free electrons in a Cu cube of edge 2.0 mm as particles in a box. (a) Consider a state with $n_1 = n_2 = n_3$ and determine these quantum numbers for a state with energy 1.0 eV. (b) Determine the energy difference between the state in part (a) and the state with the same n_1 and n_2 but with n_3 increased by 1.

42-4 (a) Show that the wave function in Eq. (42-1) is a solution of the Schrödinger equation [Eq. (40-10) with $U(x, y, z) = 0$] and that the energy is given by Eq. (42-2). (b) Show that this wave function is normalized; that is, $\int |\psi_{n_1 n_2 n_3}|^2 \, dx \, dy \, dz = 1$, where the integral extends over the volume L^3 of the cube.

42-5 One mole of He at atmospheric pressure and 273 K occupies a cubic container. Each He atom in the gas may be treated as a particle in a box. (a) Determine the lowest possible energy of a He atom in this gas. (b) What is the minimum speed of a He atom? (c) Compare the ground-state energy with kT. (d) Would you expect to see the effects of energy quantization for this gas? Explain.

42-6 Suppose that a He atom is confined to a small cube so that the ground-state energy is 1.0 eV. (a) Determine the edge L of the box. (b) Is it feasible to confine a He atom to such a region? Explain.

42-7 Determine the dimensions and the SI units for the density of states $g(E)$.

42-8 (a) Determine the density of states at 1.00 eV for the Cu sample in Exercise 42-3. How many states have energy in the 0.01-eV range from (b) 1.00 to 1.01 eV and (c) 4.00 to 4.01 eV?

42-9 (a) Determine the density of states per unit volume, $g(E)/L^3$, for free electrons of energy 2.5 eV. (b) Estimate the number of states in a penny with energy in a 0.10-eV range about 2.5 eV.

Section 42-3. Fermi-Dirac statistics

42-10 Show that the ratio $(E - E_F)/kT$, which appears as the argument of the exponential in the Fermi-Dirac distribution function, is dimensionless.

42-11 The Fermi energy for Ag is 6 eV. Determine the occupation probability for Ag at room temperature (300 K) for a state with energy (a) $E = E_F$; (b) $E = E_F - kT$; (c) $E = E_F + kT$; (d) $E = 5$ eV; (e) $E = 7$ eV.

42-12 Construct a graph of the Fermi-Dirac distribution function, $p(E)$ versus E, for Cu (take $E_F = 7.0$ eV) at (a) $T = 4.2$ K and (b) $T = 1000$ K. Choose an energy scale that will show clearly the behavior around E_F, even if you cannot fit $E = 0$ on your graph.

42-13 At what energy, measured relative to the Fermi energy, is the occupation probability of an electron state in a conductor at $T = 300$ K equal to (a) 0.999, (b) 0.90, (c) 0.10, (d) 0.001?

42-14 The Fermi-Dirac distribution function $p(E)$ gives the probability that a state is occupied by an electron. (a) What is the probability that a state is not occupied by an electron? (b) We can think of an unoccupied electron state as an occupied hole state. What is the probability that a hole state is occupied by a hole?

42-15 The Fermi energy for Ag is 5.5 eV. Estimate (a) the number density of free electrons and (b) the number of free electrons contributed by each Ag atom. (c) Do either of the answers depend appreciably on temperature? Explain.

42-16 Assume that each atom in metallic Na contributes one free electron. Estimate the Fermi energy for Na.

42-17 Three different metals have free-electron number densities in the ratio 1.62 : 1.31 : 1.00. What are the corresponding ratios of their Fermi energies?

Section 42-4. Conduction in the free-electron model

42-18 Estimate the resistivity of Cu at low temperature. Assume that the relaxation time for impurity scattering is $\tau_i = 10^{-15}$ s.

42-19 The Fermi speed v_F is the speed of a fermion with energy $E = E_F$. Estimate the Fermi speed of (a) an electron in Cu and (b) a neutron (a neutron is a fermion) in a neutron star. The number density of neutrons in a neutron star is about 10^{45} m^{-3}. (c) Can the nonrelativistic expression $E_F = \frac{1}{2}mv_F^2$ be used for both part (a) and part (b)?

42-20 The probability Δp that an electron is scattered in a small time interval Δt is expressed in terms of the relaxation time τ: $\Delta p = \Delta t/\tau$. (a) If electrons in a conductor are scattered by two independent processes, described by relaxation times τ_1 and τ_2, show that the effective relaxation time is given by $\tau = \tau_1\tau_2/(\tau_1 + \tau_2)$. (b) For low-impurity concentrations, impurity scattering and lattice scattering of electrons are independent. Show that the resistivity $\rho = \rho_i + \rho_v$, where ρ_i is due to impurities and ρ_v is due to lattice vibrations. The impurity contribution ρ_i is independent of temperature, and this result, $\rho = \rho_i + \rho_v$, is called *Matthiessen's rule*.

42-21 The resistivity of Ag at room temperature is 1.6×10^{-8} $\Omega \cdot$ m. (a) Estimate the relaxation time for electron scattering. (b) Estimate the mean free path for electrons with the Fermi energy. (c) The resistivity at 600 K is about twice the resistivity at room temperature. Is the room temperature resistivity due mostly to impurities or to lattice vibrations? Explain.

Section 42-5. Electron energy bands

42-22 When Na atoms are brought together to form the crystalline solid, the bands arising from the 3s and 3p levels overlap. (a) Is Na a conductor or an insulator? (b) Would your answer be different if the bands did not overlap? Explain.

42-23 The width of a band is the difference between the highest and lowest energy levels in the band. Estimate the width of the conduction band in Cu. Assume that the band is half-full, that the density of states for the entire band can be approximated by an average, $\langle g(E) \rangle = \frac{1}{2}g(E_F)$, and that $E_F = 7$ eV.

42-24 The Fermi energy for an insulator is about midway in the gap between the valence and conduction bands. (See Prob. 42-4.) Diamond has a band gap of 6 eV and

Ag I has a band gap of 3 eV. What is the ratio of the occupation probability for electrons in the conduction bands of diamond and Ag I at (a) 100 K and (b) 300 K?

Section 42-6. Semiconductors

42-25 Estimate the probability that an electron occupies a state at the bottom of the conduction band in pure Si at (a) 100 K and (b) 300 K. The band gap in Si is 1.1 eV and the Fermi energy is approximately midway in the gap.

42-26 Assume that the Fermi energy for a semiconductor is midway in the gap and that the gap energy is large compared with kT. Show that the occupation probability for a state of energy E is given approximately by (a) $p_e(E) = e^{-(E-E_F)/kT}$ for an electron in the conduction band and (b) $p_h(E) = 1 - p_e(E) = e^{(E-E_F)/kT}$ for a hole in the valence band.

Section 42-7. Superconductivity

42-27 At a temperature well below the transition temperature, a Cooper pair in a superconductor is bound with

an energy of about 0.1 meV below the energy of an unbound pair of electrons. That is, a gap exists between the bound state of a Cooper pair and the states of an unbound pair, which lie in a band. (a) Sketch an energy-level diagram showing these features for a Cooper pair and show on the diagram an energy interval of kT for $T = 1$ K. (b) Explain why a Cooper pair can be stable at $T = 1$ K.

42-28 A hollow pipe with superconducting walls has a 25-μm inner radius. A uniform magnetic field exists inside the hollow region parallel to the axis. Determine the magnitude of the magnetic field if there is one flux quantum in the hollow region.

42-29 A solenoid has 3000 turns per meter of superconducting wire and carries a 12-A current. The solenoid has a hollow core with a circular cross section of radius 7.5 mm. End effects may be neglected. (a) Determine the magnitude of the magnetic field inside the solenoid. (See Sec. 27-4.) (b) Determine the magnetic flux for a cross section of the hollow core. (c) Determine the number of flux quanta in the hollow core. (d) What change in B results in one additional flux quantum in the core?

PROBLEMS

42-1 Suppose that electron states in the conduction band of a metal are described by the free-electron model density of states $g(E)$. At or near $T = 0$, states with energy less than E_F are filled. The total number of electrons N_e in the band is given by

$$N_e = \int_0^{E_F} g(E)\, dE$$

Since $g(E)\, dE$ is the number of occupied states with energy E in the range dE (for $E \le E_F$), the average energy $\langle E \rangle$ of a conduction electron is

$$\langle E \rangle = \frac{1}{N_e} \int_0^{E_F} E\, g(E)\, dE$$

Show that $\langle E \rangle = \frac{3}{5} E_F$.

42-2 The Fermi energy for an insulator is midway in the gap between the valence and conduction bands. (See Prob. 42-4.) Suppose that the density of states for the conduction band is given by $g(E)$ in Eq. (42-7). (a) Show that the occupation probability of a state in the conduction band is given approximately by $p(E) = e^{-(E-E_F)/kT}$. (b) Evaluate $\int_0^\infty g(E)\, p(E)\, dE$ and determine the number density n_e of electrons in the conduction band of the insulator. (Hint: $\int_0^\infty x^{1/2} e^{-x}\, dx = \frac{1}{2}\sqrt{\pi}$.) (c) Determine n_e for an insulator with $E_g = 4.0$ eV ($E_F = -\frac{1}{2}E_g$) at $T = 300$ K and compare with n_e for a conductor such as Cu.

42-3 **Effective mass.** The density of states near the bottom of a band can be represented in many substances

by Eq. (42-7) if the electron mass m is replaced by an *effective mass* for that band. For example, the conduction band in a semiconductor has a density of states

$$g_C(E) = \frac{L^3 (2m_C)^{3/2}}{2\pi^2 \hbar^3} (E - E_C)^{1/2}$$

where m_C is the effective mass of electrons in the conduction band and E_C is the lowest energy level in the band so that $E \ge E_C$. (In the previous problem, we chose the zero of energy at the bottom of the conduction band so that $E_C = 0$.) Let m_H represent the effective mass of a hole in the valence band and E_H represent the highest energy in that band. Develop an analogous expression for the density of hole states $g_H(E)$ for the *top* of the valence band. Note that $E \le E_H$ for the energy of a state in the valence band so that $E_H - E$ is positive for states in the valence band. The graph in Fig. 42-20 shows g_C and g_H.

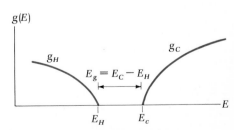

Figure 42-20. Prob. 42-3.

42-4   Use the approach in the previous two problems to determine the Fermi energy for a pure semiconductor or insulator. In these materials the Fermi energy is such that the number densities of electrons and holes are the same, $n_e = n_h$. (a) Show that this requirement gives $E_F = \frac{1}{2}(E_C + E_H) + (\frac{3}{2})kT \ln (m_H/m_C)$. (b) If the electron and hole effective masses are equal, show that the Fermi energy lies midway between the valence and conduction bands.

42-5   Although a bulk superconductor expels a magnetic field from its interior, the magnetic field is not discontinuous at the surface of the superconductor. The field penetrates into the superconductor to a depth comparable to the *penetration depth* λ. In the London theory of superconductivity (due to brothers Fritz and Heinz London in 1935), the penetration depth is given by $\lambda = \sqrt{m/\mu_0 n_s e^2}$, where n_s is the number density of superconducting electrons. Suppose that a superconductor occupies the region $x \geq 0$ and a uniform magnetic field $\mathbf{B} = B_0\mathbf{j}$ exists parallel to the surface for $x \leq 0$, as shown in Fig. 42-21. In the London theory, the magnetic field in the superconductor obeys the equation

$$\frac{d^2 B_y}{dx^2} = \lambda^2 B_y$$

with $B_y = B_0$ at $x = 0$ and $B_y \to 0$ as $x \to \infty$. (a) Solve this equation for $B_y(x)$. (b) Apply Ampere's law (Chap. 27) to the rectangular path shown in the figure to determine the (super) current density $J_z(x)$ near the surface of the superconductor. What do you conclude about the spatial distribution of currents in a bulk superconductor?

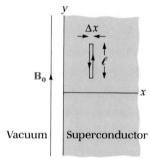

Figure 42-21. Prob. 42-5. A magnetic field is parallel to the surface of a superconductor that fills the space $x \geq 0$.

CHAPTER 43
THE ATOMIC
NUCLEUS

43-1 INTRODUCTION

In this chapter we encounter one of the frontiers of physics; a boundary between our knowledge of the physical world and our ignorance of it. Physics has other frontiers, but the unanswered questions at the nuclear frontier are especially profound. These questions are at the heart of our picture of the physical world. They involve the properties of matter at the smallest scale, and the nature of forces between the fundamental particles that compose matter.

You will notice that as we approach this frontier, our explanations seem more tenuous, our models more contrived, our assumptions more questionable, and, consequently, our conclusions more doubtful. That is the way it is at the frontier.

43-2 PROPERTIES OF THE NUCLEUS

The concept of the atomic nucleus was established by the experiments of Rutherford and his coworkers in 1911. By scattering α particles from a sheet of gold foil, Rutherford discovered that all the positive charge and nearly all the mass of an atom is contained in a very small region at the center of the atom (Sec. 39-7). This dense core of positively charged matter is the atomic nucleus.

Constituents of the nucleus. A nucleus consists of protons and neutrons, both of which are called *nucleons*. This proton-neutron picture of the nucleus was developed by Heisenberg shortly after the discovery of the neutron by James Chadwick (1891–1974) in 1932. As you know, a proton has an electric charge of $+e$, and a neutron is neutral; each has about the same mass, nearly

Sir Ernest Rutherford, Lord Rutherford of Nelson (1871–1937). Born in New Zealand and raised on a small family farm, Rutherford financed his education with scholarships. Known principally for his discovery of the nucleus, he also identified the α particle and the β^- particle, and was the first to artificially change one chemical element into another. He was an inspiring team leader as well as an outstanding scientist. Niels Bohr developed his atomic theory while visiting Rutherford at Cambridge. (*A.I.P., Niels Bohr Library*)

Table 43-1. Properties of the electron, proton, and neutron

	Electric charge	Mass, 10^{-30} kg	Spin
Electron	$-e$	0.911	1/2
Proton	$+e$	1674	1/2
Neutron	0	1675	1/2

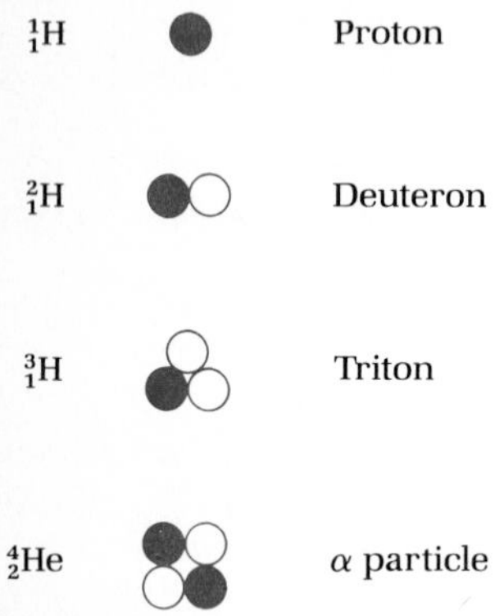

$^{1}_{1}$H ● Proton

$^{2}_{1}$H ●○ Deuteron

$^{3}_{1}$H ◐○ Triton

$^{4}_{2}$He ◐◐○○ α particle

Figure 43-1. Schematic representation of some of the lighter nuclides. A colored circle represents a proton and an open circle represents a neutron.

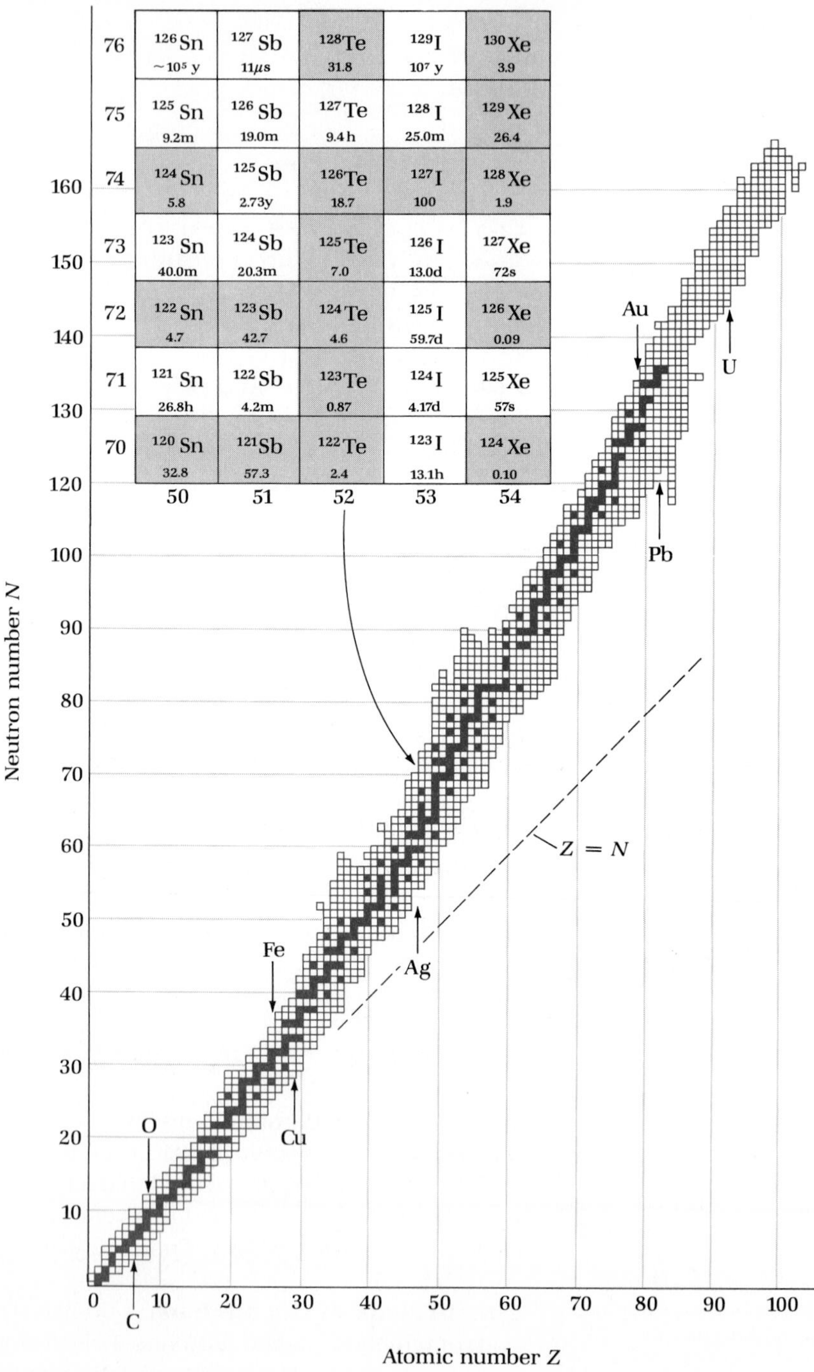

	50	51	52	53	54
76	^{126}Sn ~10^5 y	^{127}Sb 11μs	^{128}Te 31.8	^{129}I 10^7 y	^{130}Xe 3.9
75	^{125}Sn 9.2m	^{126}Sb 19.0m	^{127}Te 9.4h	^{128}I 25.0m	^{129}Xe 26.4
74	^{124}Sn 5.8	^{125}Sb 2.73y	^{126}Te 18.7	^{127}I 100	^{128}Xe 1.9
73	^{123}Sn 40.0m	^{124}Sb 20.3m	^{125}Te 7.0	^{126}I 13.0d	^{127}Xe 72s
72	^{122}Sn 4.7	^{123}Sb 42.7	^{124}Te 4.6	^{125}I 59.7d	^{126}Xe 0.09
71	^{121}Sn 26.8h	^{122}Sb 4.2m	^{123}Te 0.87	^{124}I 4.17d	^{125}Xe 57s
70	^{120}Sn 32.8	^{121}Sb 57.3	^{122}Te 2.4	^{123}I 13.1h	^{124}Xe 0.10

Neutron number N

Atomic number Z

$Z = N$

Au, U, Pb, Fe, Ag, O, Cu, C

Figure 43-2. Chart of nuclides. Colored squares correspond to stable nuclides and open squares correspond to unstable, or radioactive, nuclides.

2000 times that of an electron (Table 43-1). A phosphorus nucleus, as an example, has 15 protons and 16 neutrons. The 15 atomic electrons that are in bound quantum states about this nucleus are spread over a region with a radius which is about 50,000 times greater than that of the nucleons. Thus the volume of the atom is about 10^{14} (or $50{,}000^3$) times greater than that of the nucleus.

From the previous chapter we know that a type or species of atom is called an *element*, and an element is characterized by its atomic number Z. Similarly, a type or species of nucleus is called a *nuclide*. A nuclide is characterized by its atomic number Z and its *neutron number N*, which is the number of neutrons in the nucleus. The number of nucleons in a nucleus, which is nearly proportional to the nuclear mass, is called the *mass number A*:

Neutron number N

Mass number A

$$A = Z + N \qquad (43\text{-}1)$$

To completely specify a nuclide, we need only give two of the three numbers A, Z, and N because the third can be found from Eq. (43-1). We identify a nuclide with its chemical symbol, using its mass number as a superscript. For example, the symbol ^{31}P (stated orally as "phosphorus-31") represents a phosphorus nuclide. Since $Z = 15$ for phosphorus, $N = A - Z = 31 - 15 = 16$. For convenience, we often give the atomic number of a nuclide as a subscript. Our phosphorus nuclide is then designated by $^{31}_{15}P$. (See Fig. 43-1.)

Designation of a nuclide

The names "isotope," "isotone," or "isobar" are used to specify nuclides with the same Z, N, or A, respectively. As examples,

Isotopes, isotones, and isobars

1 $^{12}_{6}C$ and $^{14}_{6}C$ are isotopes because both have $Z = 6$.
2 $^{31}_{15}P$ and $^{32}_{16}S$ are isotones because both have $N = 16$.
3 $^{14}_{6}C$ and $^{14}_{7}N$ are isobars because both have $A = 14$.

A chart of nuclides, shown in Fig. 43-2, displays the nuclides in terms of N and Z. Each colored square represents a stable nuclide, and each uncolored square represents an unstable, or radioactive, nuclide that has been observed (Sec. 43-6). There are about 260 stable nuclides. Note that nuclides in the same vertical column are isotopes, nuclides in the same horizontal row are isotones, and isobars run along a diagonal. A conspicuous feature of the chart of nuclides is that small-mass nuclides tend to have about the same number of protons as neutrons, and large-mass nuclides tend to have more neutrons than protons. The surplus of neutrons over protons for large-mass nuclides becomes more and more pronounced with increasing mass. The reason for these characteristics is discussed in Secs. 43-4 and 43-5.

The chart of nuclides shown in Fig. 43-2 is compressed so that it fits on one page. A larger and more complete chart provides information about each nuclide, as indicated by the expanded patch in Fig. 43-2. For each stable nuclide, the relative abundance is given in percent. For example, 18.7 percent of the element tellurium found on earth is ^{126}Te. For each radioactive nuclide, the half-life (introduced in Sec. 43-6) is given in seconds (s), minutes (m), hours (h), days (d), or years (y); ^{127}Te has a half-life of 9.4 h.

Nuclear size. Experiments show that most nuclei are approximately spherical in shape. Several experimental methods have been used to determine the size of nuclei, and each method gives about the same result. (See Fig. 43-3.) An expression which gives the approximate radius R of a nucleus of mass number A is

Approximate nuclear radius

$$R \approx R_0 A^{1/3} \qquad (43\text{-}2)$$

where $R_0 = 1.1 \times 10^{-15}$ m $= 1.1$ fm. The approximate volume of a nucleus is

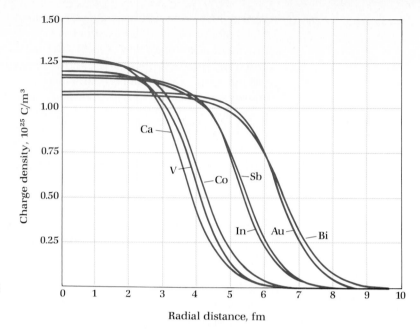

Figure 43-3. Charge density versus r for a number of nuclides. The nuclear radius R is taken to be the distance at which the charge density falls to half its value at the center. *(From R. Hofstadter, Annual Review of Nuclear Science, vol. 7, 1957, p. 231.)*

$V = 4\pi R^3/3 \approx 4\pi(R_0 A^{1/3})^3/3 = (4\pi R_0^3/3)A$. Therefore, the nuclear volume is proportional to the number of nucleons, which means that the mass densities of all nuclei are nearly the same, about 3×10^{17} kg/m^3, or about 10^{14} times the density of a typical rock. (See Exercise 43-4.) This remarkably large density is a reflection of the small size of nuclei.

The nuclear force. The existence of the nucleus implies the existence of a force of interaction that holds the nucleons together within this small region of space. What sort of force is this? It is not an electric force. Indeed, to overcome the repulsive electric forces that the protons exert on one another, this force must be very strongly attractive. It is not a gravitational force. Gravitational forces between nucleons in a nucleus are far too weak to be of significance. (See Exercise 43-6.) We have not encountered this force in our previous studies. We call this force the *nuclear force*.

The nuclear force is much more complicated than the gravitational force or the electromagnetic force. It cannot be represented by a simple expression similar to, say, Coulomb's law for the electric force. Despite our lack of an expression for the nuclear force, we can discuss some of its features:

1. The forces within the nucleus (besides electromagnetic forces) can be separated into two fundamental types: the *strong force* and the *weak force*. It is the strong force that accounts for the nuclear properties we discuss here, and, following custom, it is the strong force that we shall refer to as the nuclear force. [The weak force is responsible for beta decay (Sec. 43-6) and for the interaction between particles called leptons (Sec. 43-7). A comparison between the strong and weak forces is given in the Commentary in Chapter 7.]

2. Experiments indicate that the nuclear force is the same between a proton and a proton, a neutron and a neutron, and a proton and a neutron. That is, the nuclear force between two nucleons is independent of whether one or both or neither of the pair of nucleons has an electric charge.

3. The nuclear force has a very short range. It is effective in holding nucleons within the nucleus, in which case the nucleons are separated by distances

Properties of the nuclear force

less than 10^{-14} m, but beyond this range the nuclear force is negligible.

4. Within its range, the nuclear force is very strong. Inside the nucleus it overwhelms the repulsive electric force between a proton and the other $Z - 1$ protons so that the net force on the proton is attractive rather than repulsive.

EXAMPLE 43-1. (*a*) Estimate the electric potential energy U_e between the two protons in ^{4}He. (*b*) The energy required to separate a proton from ^{4}He is about 20 MeV. Use this to compare the electric force with the nuclear force that is exerted on one of the protons.

SOLUTION. (*a*) From Eq. (43-2), the approximate radius of ^{4}He is $R \approx (1.1 \text{ fm})(4)^{1/3} = 1.7$ fm. Assume that the two protons in ^{4}He behave as particles separated by this distance. Their electric potential energy of interaction is

$$U_e = \frac{e^2}{4\pi\epsilon_0 R}$$

$$U_e = e \frac{(9.0 \times 10^9 \text{ N} \cdot \text{m}^2/\text{C}^2)(1.6 \times 10^{-19} \text{ C})}{1.7 \times 10^{-15} \text{ m}}$$

$$= 8.2 \times 10^5 \text{ eV} \approx 1 \text{ MeV}$$

Since the electric force between protons is repulsive, this potential energy is positive. (*b*) The net force on one of the protons is the sum of the electric force on it due to the other proton and the nuclear force on it due to the other three nucleons. The electric force tends to expel the proton from the nucleus, and we found the potential energy associated with this force to be about 1 MeV. Since 20 MeV is required to separate a proton from ^{4}He, we must conclude that the nuclear force on the proton is attractive and its effect is significantly larger than that of the electric force.

43-3 NUCLEAR MASS AND BINDING ENERGY

In nuclear physics, a convenient unit of mass is the *unified atomic-mass unit*, abbreviated u. The atomic-mass unit is defined as 1/12 the mass of a ^{12}C atom (^{12}C nucleus plus six atomic electrons). Measurements give the relation between u and kg as

$$1 \text{ u} = 1.6605402 \times 10^{-27} \text{ kg}$$

Atomic-mass unit u

The masses of the electron, proton, neutron, and some representative nuclides are given in u in Table 43-2. As is customary, the mass listed for a nuclide

Table 43-2. Some representative masses in atomic-mass units

Mass	u	Mass	u
e	0.0005486	^{87}Rb	86.909186
p	1.0072766	^{87}Sr	86.908892
n	1.0086652	^{91}Mo	90.91175
^{1}H	1.0078252	^{92}Mo	91.906810
^{2}H	2.014102	^{93}Mo	92.906830
^{3}H	3.016049	^{103}Rh	102.90550
^{3}He	3.016029	^{119}In	118.9058
^{4}He	4.002603	^{120}Sn	119.902199
^{11}B	11.009305	^{121}Sb	120.903824
^{11}C	11.011433	^{123}Sb	122.904213
^{12}C	12.000000	^{123}Te	122.904277
^{13}C	13.003355	^{197}Au	196.96656
^{14}N	14.003074	^{202}Hg	201.97063
^{16}O	15.994915	^{205}Tl	204.97441
^{17}O	16.999133	^{222}Rn	222.017574
^{23}Na	22.989770	^{226}Ra	226.025406
^{27}Al	26.981541	^{228}Ra	228.031139
^{52}Cr	51.940510	^{232}Th	232.038054
^{56}Fe	55.934939	^{234}Th	234.043298
^{68}Zn	67.924857	^{235}U	235.043925
^{75}As	74.921596	^{238}U	238.050786

includes the mass of the electrons in the neutral atom. You can substantiate this by comparing the mass listed for ^{1}H with the sum of the electron and proton masses.

The energy associated with a nuclear process is usually large, of the order of MeV. Such a process involves measurable changes in rest-mass energy, $\Delta E = \Delta m c^2$. Consequently, it is useful to determine the energy equivalence of 1 u:

$$(1 \text{ u})c^2 = (1.6605402 \times 10^{-27} \text{ kg})(2.99792458 \times 10^8 \text{ m/s})^2 = 931.494 \text{ MeV}$$

Or,

$$1 \text{ u} = 931.5 \text{ MeV}/c^2$$

Sometimes for convenience, masses are given in units of MeV/c^2, or they are expressed as the value of mc^2 in units of MeV. Another useful procedure is to write c^2 in units of MeV/u. From above,

$$c^2 = 931.5 \text{ MeV/u}$$

Binding energy. The mass of a nucleus is less than the mass of its constituent nucleons when these nucleons are well separated. The energy equivalence of this mass difference is called the *binding energy B* of the nucleus. The binding energy of a nucleus is the energy required to disassemble the nucleus and to place each nucleon at a large enough separation distance (at rest) for their potential energy of interaction to be negligible. We can develop an expression for the binding energy by using conservation of mass-energy, as shown schematically in Fig. 43-4. The rest-mass energy of the bound system (the assembled nucleus) plus the binding energy is equal to the rest-mass energy of the separated nucleons:

$$m_{\text{nuc}}c^2 + B = Zm_p c^2 + Nm_n c^2$$

where m_{nuc} is the mass of a nucleus with Z protons and N neutrons, m_p is the proton mass, and m_n is the neutron mass. Solving for B, we have

$$B = (Zm_p + Nm_n - m_{\text{nuc}})c^2$$

Since atomic masses rather than nuclear masses are customarily tabulated, we substitute $M_a - Zm_e$ for m_{nuc}, where M_a is the atomic mass of the nuclide and m_e is the electron mass. Further, if we substitute $M_H - m_e$ for m_p, where M_H is the atomic mass of ^{1}H, then the mass of the Z electrons cancels. (This procedure neglects the binding energy of the atomic electrons, which is insignificant.) This gives

Binding energy of a nuclide

$$B = (ZM_H + Nm_n - M_a)c^2 \tag{43-3}$$

As an example, we can use the values listed in Table 43-2 to find B for $^{27}_{13}$Al:

Figure 43-4. The mass-energy of a nucleus plus the binding energy B (the energy required to disassemble the nucleus) is equal to the total mass-energy of the separated nucleons.

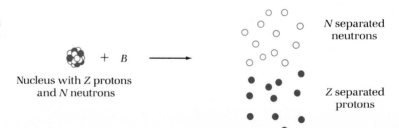

Nucleus with Z protons
and N neutrons

N separated
neutrons

Z separated
protons

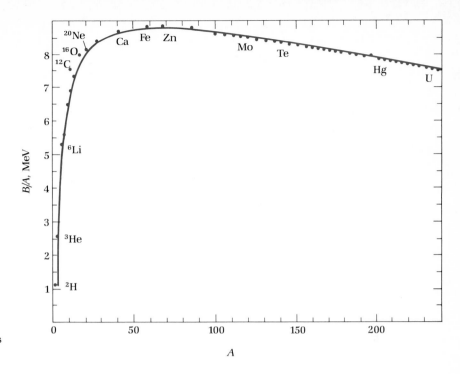

Figure 43-5. Graph of B/A versus A.

$$B = [13(1.007825 \text{ u}) + 14(1.008665 \text{ u}) - (26.981541 \text{ u})](931.5 \text{ MeV/u})$$

$$= 225.0 \text{ MeV}$$

Binding energy per nucleon. The binding energy per nucleon B/A is a useful criterion for comparing the binding energies of different nuclides. For ^{27}Al,

$$\frac{B}{A} = \frac{225.0 \text{ MeV}}{27 \text{ nucleons}} = 8.332 \text{ MeV/nucleon}$$

Figure 43-5 shows a graph of B/A versus A for many stable nuclides. An important feature of this graph is that for A greater than about 20, the points fall near a smooth curve and the value of B/A is roughly independent of A. Its value is about 8 MeV per nucleon. This means that the binding energy of a nuclide of mass number A is roughly proportional to A. Notice that B/A maximizes in the vicinity of iron (Fe). Small-mass and large-mass nuclides tend to be less tightly bound than medium-mass nuclides.

43-4 THE LIQUID-DROP MODEL

In some of its properties, a nucleus is similar to a drop of liquid. Using these similarities, Niels Bohr proposed a model known as the *liquid-drop model* in 1936. Based on this model, a semiempirical equation for the nuclear binding energy is

$$B = C_1 A - C_2 A^{2/3} - C_3 Z(Z - 1)A^{-1/3} \qquad (43\text{-}4)$$

Or

$$\frac{B}{A} = C_1 - C_2 A^{-1/3} - C_3 Z(Z - 1)A^{-4/3} \qquad (43\text{-}5)$$

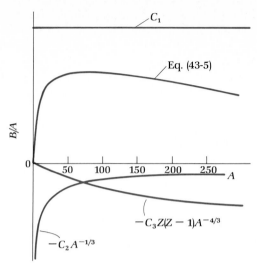

Figure 43-6. Showing the contribution to B/A from each of the terms in Eq. (43-5).

where C_1, C_2, and C_3 are constants. The values of these constants are determined by fitting Eq. (43-5) to the data of Fig. 43-5. Figure 43-6 shows how the three terms in Eq. (43-5) combine to produce a result that approximately fits the data of Fig. 43-5.

An examination of each of the three terms in Eq. (43-4) provides some insight into the nature of nuclear structure. As we examine these terms, keep in mind that the binding energy is the energy required to disassemble a nucleus and separate the nucleons. An attractive force produces a negative potential energy (relative to a zero of potential energy at infinite separation) and gives a positive contribution to the binding energy. A repulsive force produces a positive potential energy and gives a negative contribution to the binding energy.

Because it comes from the familiar Coulomb repulsion of the protons, we examine the third term first. Assume that the protons in a nucleus may be regarded as point charges. The contribution to the electric potential energy of a nucleus from the interaction of an average pair of protons is $(e^2/4\pi\epsilon_o)(\overline{1/r})$, where $\overline{1/r}$ is the average reciprocal spacing between protons. This contribution is called the *average-pair potential energy*. The electric potential energy U_e of a nucleus is the product of the number of pairs of protons in the nucleus and the average-pair potential energy. The number of proton pairs in a nucleus with Z protons is $\frac{1}{2}Z(Z-1)$. (See Exercise 43-16.) Therefore, the contribution to the binding energy from the electric repulsion of the protons is

$$B_e = -U_e = -\tfrac{1}{2}Z(Z-1)\left(\frac{e^2}{4\pi\epsilon_o}\right)\overline{(1/r)}$$

Next, we assume that $\overline{1/r}$ varies from one nuclide to another in the same way as $1/R$. That is, $\overline{1/r} \propto 1/R$. Since $1/R = 1/(R_0 A^{1/3})$, we have $\overline{1/r} \propto A^{-1/3}$. This gives $B_e \propto -Z(Z-1)A^{-1/3}$, or

$$B_e = -C_3 Z(Z-1)A^{-1/3}$$

This is the third term in Eq. (43-4).

Based on our experience in developing B_e, you might expect a term in Eq. (43-4) due to the nuclear interaction between each pair of nucleons, that is, a term proportional to $\frac{1}{2}A(A-1)$. Since the nuclear force is attractive, this term should be positive. Instead of being proportional to $\frac{1}{2}A(A-1)$, the positive term in Eq. (43-4), C_1A, is proportional to A. This is interpreted as a consequence of the short range of the nuclear force. This short range limits the interactions of a nucleon to its immediate neighbors only. It is often said that the nuclear interaction *saturates* so that there are a limited number of pair interactions, or *pair bonds*, for any nucleon. Since the number of immediate neighbors is the same for each nucleon (except those near the nuclear surface), the short-range nature of the nuclear force gives a term in the binding energy which is proportional to the number of nucleons A. In this sense, the nucleus is analogous to a liquid drop whose molecules interact only with immediate neighbors.

In finding that the short-range nature of the nuclear force is expected to give a term in Eq. (43-4) that is proportional to A, we neglected the effect of the surface. Nucleons near the surface will have fewer immediate neighbors than nucleons in the interior. That is, the number of pair bonds for a nucleon near the surface is less than for a nucleon well inside the nucleus. The second term in Eq. (43-4), $-C_2A^{2/3}$, accounts for this effect. The term is negative because it represents a reduction in the positive contribution to B due to the attractive nuclear force. The term is proportional to the surface area of the nucleus which is proportional to $A^{2/3}$. That is, $4\pi R^2 = 4\pi(R_0A^{1/3})^2 \propto A^{2/3}$.

Now we have a qualitative understanding of the graph of B/A versus A:

1. Due to the short-range nature of the nuclear force, B is roughly proportional to A and B/A is roughly constant [first term in Eq. (43-4)].

2. A nucleon near the surface of a nucleus has fewer immediate neighbors with which to interact. Because a small-mass nucleus has a larger fraction of its nucleons near the surface, it tends to be less stable than a nucleus with a larger mass [second term in Eq. (43-4)].

3. The electric repulsion between protons tends to make nuclei less stable, especially large-Z nuclei. For large-Z nuclei, $Z(Z-1) \approx Z^2$, so that the third term in Eq. (43-4) is approximately $-C_3Z^2A^{-1/3}$. Since nuclei tend to have roughly the same number of neutrons as protons, Z is roughly proportional to A, which makes the third term roughly proportional to $-A^{5/3}$. This means that beyond a certain value of A, nuclei become less stable with increasing A.

A more complete description of the liquid-drop model contains more terms in the expression for B than the three we have considered. These terms account for some of the fine details in the graph of B/A versus A.

EXAMPLE 43-2. Since Eqs. (43-4) and (43-5) contain three adjustable constants (C_1, C_2, and C_3), we can use three nuclide binding energies to estimate the values of these constants. Use the binding energies of ^{11}B, ^{68}Zn, and ^{197}Au to estimate the constants.

SOLUTION. Using the data in Table 43-2, we determine B/A for each nuclide, as we did earlier for ^{27}Al. The results in units of MeV per nucleon are 6.93, 8.76, and 7.92 for ^{11}B, ^{68}Zn, and ^{197}Au, respectively. Substitution of these values and the appropriate values of A and Z into Eq. (43-5) for each of these nuclides gives

$$6.93 \text{ MeV} = C_1 - 0.450C_2 - 0.818C_3$$

$$8.76 \text{ MeV} = C_1 - 0.245C_2 - 3.13C_3$$

$$7.92 \text{ MeV} = C_1 - 0.172C_2 - 5.38C_3$$

Solving these three equations for the three constants, we find $C_1 = 17.1$ MeV, $C_2 = 20.7$ MeV, and $C_3 = 1.05$ MeV.

These values for the constants are based on the binding energies of these three nuclides only. If we chose three other nuclides, then the values of the constants would be slightly different. A more appropriate procedure, but one that is beyond our scope, is to use a statistical method that includes the binding energies of all stable nuclides. The results of such procedures are given in books on nuclear physics.

43-5 THE SHELL MODEL

A prominent feature of the chart of nuclides (Fig. 43-2) is that $Z \approx N$ for small-mass nuclei, and large-mass nuclei tend to have a surplus of neutrons over protons. In addition, nuclei with particular numbers of protons and/or neutrons are especially stable. These so-called *magic numbers* are $Z = 2, 8, 20, 28, 50$, and 82; and $N = 2, 8, 20, 28, 50, 82$, and 126. The energy required to separate a nucleon from a magic-number nucleus is notably large. (See Exercises 43-19 and 43-20.) Also, there are an unusually large number of stable isotopes and isotones with magic numbers. From Fig. 43-2, there are ten stable isotopes with $Z = 50$ and seven stable isotones with $N = 82$. A successful model should explain these nuclear properties.

The nuclear magic numbers are reminiscent of the way electrons in atoms are arranged in shells and subshells (Sec. 41-6). There are two electrons in the first shell, eight in the second shell, eight in the third shell, eighteen in the fourth shell, and so on. The magic numbers for atoms are 2, 10 (or $2 + 8$), 18 (or $10 + 8$), 36 (or $18 + 18$), and so on. If an atom has a closed shell of electrons, then the atom is very stable; it has a large ionization energy and is chemically inert. These are the noble gas atoms: He, Ne, Ar, Kr, and Xe.

Since the shell structure of atoms emerges from the application of the Pauli exclusion principle to the quantum states of atomic electrons, we expect that a similar treatment of the nucleons in the nucleus will yield the shell structure of nuclei. But the nuclear problem is more difficult than the atomic problem. In the atomic problem, the massive nucleus acts as a fixed center for circulating electrons, and all the interactions are due to the familiar Coulomb force. In the nuclear problem, the nucleons are like a swarm of particles, each with nearly the same mass, and all interacting strongly through the more complicated nuclear force. If the classical analogy to the atom is the solar system, then the analogy to the nucleus is a planetary system with no central star, a system where planets with nearly equal mass move about in complex orbits while interacting through some unknown force law.

Despite these difficulties, the nuclear problem can be attacked by making some approximations. First, we treat each nucleon as an independent particle and assume that it moves in an average force field produced by the other nucleons. (Because of this approximation, the shell model is often called the *single-particle model*.) Next, guided by the knowledge that the nuclear force is short range and strongly attractive, we use neutron and proton potential-energy functions like those shown in Fig. 43-7. If the Schrödinger equation with such a potential-energy function is solved and the levels are filled in accordance with the exclusion principle (applied to protons and neutrons separately), we find that a shell structure does emerge. However, the magic numbers do not match the nuclear magic numbers. This difficulty was resolved independently by M. G. Mayer and J. H. Jensen in 1949. They showed that the shell model does produce the nuclear magic numbers if one assumes an additional strong spin-orbit coupling (Fig. 43-8).

The application of the Pauli exclusion principle to the filling of these nucleon energy levels shows why $Z \approx N$ for small-mass nuclei. Since the nuclear force dominates, the positions of the energy levels for protons and neutrons are nearly the same as long as Z is not too large. Therefore, the energy of the assembled nucleus is usually minimized by filling proton and neutron levels with the same number of nucleons when Z is small. As Z becomes larger, the

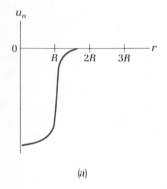

(a)

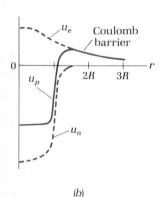

(b)

Figure 43-7. (a) Average-potential-energy function $u_n(r)$ for a neutron in a nucleus. Near the center of the nucleus, a neutron is surrounded by other nucleons so that the forces they exert tend to cancel and u_n is nearly constant. At the edge of the nucleus, the attractive forces tend to align; u_n has a large positive slope. Because the nuclear force is short-range, u_n quickly falls to zero when r becomes larger than R. The function u_n is called the *nuclear well*. (b) Average-potential-energy function $u_p(r)$ for a proton. Since protons are subject to both nuclear and electric forces, $u_p = u_n + u_e$, where u_e is the repulsive Coulomb potential energy due to the other protons. The positive part of u_p surrounds the nucleus and is called the *Coulomb barrier*.

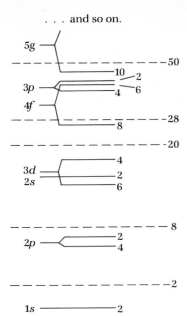

. . . and so on.

Figure 43-8. A few of the lower energy levels for neutrons. Subshells (1s, 2p, 2s, . . .) are identified on the left when spin-orbit splitting is neglected. Then the levels are shown with the splitting due to a large spin-orbit interaction. The number at the right of each level tells how many neutrons can occupy that level according to the Pauli exclusion principle, and the magic numbers are tallied at the far right. Notice the relatively large spacing between levels after a magic number is reached. Proton levels give similar results.

Decay constant λ

Time dependence of the population

Coulomb repulsion becomes more important. Then it becomes energetically favorable to place a surplus of nucleons in neutron levels.

43-6 RADIOACTIVE DECAY

The nuclei of some nuclides are inherently unstable, or *radioactive*. Such a nucleus may eject a particle spontaneously, without any external stimulus. When this happens, the nucleus changes form or decays. Historically, the nuclear age began with the observation of the radioactive decay of uranium by Henri Becquerel (1852–1908) in 1896. Early on, three types of radioactive emission were identified, and they were called *alpha* (α), *beta* (β), and *gamma* (γ) in the order of their penetration distance through matter; α rays are the least penetrating, β rays are intermediate, and γ rays are the most penetrating. We now know that an α ray (or α particle) is a ^{4}He nucleus, and a β ray (or β particle) is either an electron (β^-) or a positron (β^+). The positron is the antiparticle to the electron (see Sec. 43-8); it has the same mass as an electron, but is oppositely charged. A γ ray is a high-energy photon which is emitted from a nucleus that is in an excited state.

Kinetics of radioactive decay. When a nucleus decays, the emitted entity (α, β, or γ) can be detected with a radiation counter. To describe the time dependence of this measurement, let $\mathcal{N}$ represent the population of radioactive nuclei in some sample, such as a rock which contains nuclei that decay by α emission. The *activity* $\mathcal{R}$ of the rock is the rate at which α particles are emitted from radioactive nuclei in the rock. When a nucleus emits an α particle, it changes form and is no longer a member of the population represented by $\mathcal{N}$. Thus the population $\mathcal{N}$ decreases ($d\mathcal{N}/dt$ is negative) and $-d\mathcal{N}/dt$, which we call the *population decay rate*, is equal to the activity $\mathcal{R}$. That is,

$$\mathcal{R} = -\frac{d\mathcal{N}}{dt} \tag{43-6}$$

The decay of a particular nucleus is a random event. The probability the nucleus will decay in a time interval Δt is directly proportional to Δt. Consider two nuclei of the same radioactive nuclide. One of the nuclei was created in the explosion of a star 5 billion years ago and the other was created in a nuclear reactor 5 min ago. *The probability of decay during the next minute is the same for each nucleus, independent of when it was created.* Since the decay of a particular nucleus is random, the fractional reduction of the population, $-d\mathcal{N}/\mathcal{N}$, during an infinitesimal time interval dt is proportional to dt. Introducing a proportionality constant λ, called the *decay constant*, or *disintegration constant*, we write this

$$-\frac{d\mathcal{N}}{\mathcal{N}} = \lambda \, dt \tag{43-7}$$

You are already familiar with the procedures for solving Eq. (43-7) (see Secs. 25-5 and 29-3), so we leave it as a problem (Prob. 43-3). The solution is

$$\mathcal{N} = \mathcal{N}_0 e^{-\lambda t} \tag{43-8}$$

where $\mathcal{N}_0$ is the population of radioactive nuclei at the instant we choose for $t = 0$. Figure 43-9a shows a graph of the population $\mathcal{N}$ versus the time t. Notice

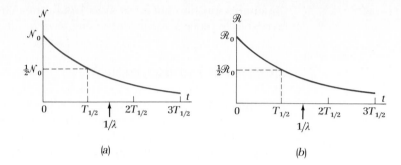

Figure 43-9. (a) Population $\mathcal{N}$ of radioactive nuclei versus time t. (b) Activity $\mathcal{R}$ versus t.

that the rate at which the population decreases is characterized by the decay constant λ.

The activity $\mathcal{R}$ can be found by rearranging Eq. (43-7):

$$-\frac{d\mathcal{N}}{dt} = \lambda\mathcal{N} \qquad \text{or} \qquad \mathcal{R} = \lambda\mathcal{N}$$

Substituting for $\mathcal{N}$ from Eq. (43-8), we have $\mathcal{R} = \lambda\mathcal{N}_0 e^{-\lambda t}$, or

Time dependence of the activity

$$\mathcal{R} = \mathcal{R}_0 e^{-\lambda t} \tag{43-9}$$

where $\mathcal{R}_0$ (which equals $\lambda\mathcal{N}_0$) is the activity at $t = 0$. Figure 43-9b shows a graph of the activity versus time. Since $\mathcal{R}$ is directly proportional to $\mathcal{N}$, $\mathcal{R}$ has the same time dependence as $\mathcal{N}$; each decreases exponentially and each has the same decay constant. The SI unit for activity $\mathcal{R}$ is the becquerel (Bq): 1 Bq = 1 emission/s.

Sometimes the *half-life* $T_{1/2}$ is used instead of λ. The half-life is the time required for $\mathcal{N}$ (or $\mathcal{R}$) to fall off by a factor of 1/2. Since $\mathcal{N} = \mathcal{N}_0$ at $t = 0$, we have that $\mathcal{N} = \frac{1}{2}\mathcal{N}_0$ at $t = T_{1/2}$. By substituting these values into Eq. (43-8) we can find the relation between λ and $T_{1/2}$:

$$\tfrac{1}{2}\mathcal{N}_0 = \mathcal{N}_0 e^{-\lambda T_{1/2}}$$

Solving for $T_{1/2}$, we find

Relation between $T_{1/2}$ and λ

$$T_{1/2} = \frac{\ln 2}{\lambda} = \frac{0.693}{\lambda} \tag{43-10}$$

Tables which list the properties of radioactive nuclides usually give the half-life rather than the decay constant (Fig. 43-2).

EXAMPLE 43-3. *Radioactive dating.* The activity of ^{14}C can be used to determine the age of some archeological discoveries. (See Prob. 43-4.) Suppose a sample of material which contains ^{14}C has an activity of 2.8×10^7 Bq. The half-life of ^{14}C is 5730 y. (a) Find the decay constant for ^{14}C in s^{-1}. (b) Determine the population of ^{14}C nuclei in this sample. (c) What will be the activity of this sample after 1000 y? (d) What will be the activity after 4 times the half-life?

SOLUTION. (a) The decay constant in s^{-1} is

$$\lambda = \frac{0.693}{T_{1/2}} = \frac{0.693}{(5730 \text{ y})(3.15 \times 10^7 \text{ s/y})} = 3.84 \times 10^{-12} \text{ s}^{-1}$$

(b) Since $\mathcal{R}_0 = \lambda\mathcal{N}_0$, the population of ^{14}C nuclei in the sample is

$$\mathcal{N}_0 = \frac{\mathcal{R}_0}{\lambda} = \frac{2.8 \times 10^7 \text{ Bq}}{3.84 \times 10^{-12} \text{ s}^{-1}} = 7.3 \times 10^{18} \text{ nuclei}$$

(c) Since $\mathcal{R}_0 = 2.8 \times 10^7$ Bq and 1000 y $= 3.15 \times 10^{10}$ s, the activity 1000 y from now will be

$$\mathcal{R} = \mathcal{R}_0 e^{-\lambda t} = (2.8 \times 10^7 \text{ Bq})e^{-(3.84 \times 10^{-12} \text{ s}^{-1})(3.15 \times 10^{10} \text{ s})}$$

$$= 2.5 \times 10^7 \text{ Bq}$$

(d) In each half-life, one-half of the remaining population decays. For a time interval of $4T_{1/2}$, $\mathcal{R} = \mathcal{R}_0(\frac{1}{2})^4 = \mathcal{R}_0/16 = 1.7 \times 10^6$ Bq.

Alpha decay. Many large-mass radioactive nuclei decay with the emission of an α particle. An example is the decay of ^{238}U to ^{234}Th:

$$^{238}_{92}\text{U} \rightarrow {}^{234}_{90}\text{Th} + {}^{4}_{2}\text{He}$$

The ^{238}U nuclide is called the *parent* and the ^{234}Th nuclide is called the *daughter*. Note that the sum of the superscripts is the same on each side of the reaction arrow, which means that the number of nucleons is conserved in this reaction. Also, the sum of the subscripts is the same on each side of the reaction arrow, which states that the number of protons is conserved, or that electric charge is conserved. Alpha decay can be expressed in general by

Alpha decay

$$^{A}_{Z}P \rightarrow {}^{A-4}_{Z-2}D + {}^{4}_{2}\text{He} \tag{43-11}$$

where P and D represent the chemical symbols of the parent and daughter nuclides, respectively.

When a parent nucleus decays, the α particle and the daughter nucleus fly apart, or are imparted with kinetic energy. Also, in some decays the daughter nucleus is created in an excited state. The *decay energy* Q_α (sometimes called the *disintegration energy*) is the sum of the kinetic energies and the excitation energy. The decay energy can be determined from conservation of mass-energy in the rest frame of the parent. In this reference frame, the initial energy of the system is just the rest-mass energy of the parent. Thus, if M_P, M_D, and M_{He} are the masses of the parent, daughter, and ^{4}He nuclides, respectively, then

$$M_P c^2 = (M_D + M_{\text{He}})c^2 + Q_\alpha$$

Or,

Decay energy for α emission

$$Q_\alpha = (M_P - M_D - M_{\text{He}})c^2 \tag{43-12}$$

As an example, the α decay of ^{238}U to ^{234}Th has a decay energy of about 4 MeV.

EXAMPLE 43-4. *Checking for stability.* Equation (43-12) provides a way to check whether a nuclide is unstable to α decay. Suppose we select some large-mass nuclide as the parent for a possible α decay. If substitution of the masses into Eq. (43-12) gives a positive value for Q_α, then this nuclide is unstable. Use this method to determine whether $^{226}_{88}$Ra is unstable to α decay.

SOLUTION. If $^{226}_{88}$Ra is unstable to α decay, then its daughter is $^{222}_{86}$Rn. Using the masses from Table 43-2, we have

$$Q_\alpha = (226.025406 \text{ u} - 222.017574 \text{ u}$$
$$- 4.002603 \text{ u})(931.5 \text{ MeV/u}) = 4.87 \text{ MeV}$$

Since $Q_\alpha > 0$, the nuclide ^{226}Ra is unstable to α decay. Incidentally, its half-life is 1620 y.

Beta decay. Before discussing beta-decay reactions, we introduce a fundamental particle which we have not considered previously. This particle is called the *neutrino* (represented by the symbol ν). The neutrino is emitted in beta-decay reactions, but is very difficult to detect. When beta-decay reactions were initially studied, it was assumed that the parent nucleus decayed to the daughter nucleus and an electron only (or a positron only) because no other particles were detected. However, the mass-energy of the system after decay (daughter plus emitted electron) was measured to be less than the mass-energy of the system before the decay (parent). Thus, beta decay apparently violated conservation of mass-energy. In addition, beta-decay reactions apparently violated conservation of angular momentum and conservation of linear momentum.

One of the leaders in nuclear physics during its early development. 'Enrico Fermi (1901–1954) was born in Rome and educated at Pisa. Fermi had a great talent for making the proper approximations to allow the solution to an otherwise hopelessly complex problem. Because of the political situation in Italy, he took the occasion of his being awarded the 1938 Nobel Prize to expatriate to the United States. During World War II, he supervised the construction of the first self-sustaining nuclear reactor, which was the precursor to modern nuclear power plants. *(A.I.P., Niels Bohr Library)*

In 1930, Pauli proposed the existence of a particle which would redeem these conservation principles during beta decay. To do this, the properties attributed to the particle were (i) zero electric charge, (ii) zero rest mass, and (iii) an intrinsic angular momentum or spin of 1/2. The famous Italian physicist Enrico Fermi dubbed this particle the "neutrino," which means little neutral one. After many years of searching, researchers were able to directly detect neutrinos in 1956.

Examples of the two types of beta decay are

$$^{14}_{6}C \rightarrow {}^{14}_{7}N + \beta^- + \bar{\nu} \qquad (\beta^- \text{ decay})$$

and

$$^{12}_{7}N \rightarrow {}^{12}_{6}C + \beta^+ + \nu \qquad (\beta^+ \text{ decay})$$

where $\bar{\nu}$ represents an antineutrino, the antiparticle of the neutrino. Thus, β^- decay produces a daughter with Z increased by 1 compared with the parent, and β^+ decay produces a daughter with Z decreased by 1 compared with the parent. The parent and the daughter are isobars. Note that electric charge and mass number are conserved in these reactions.

Beta decay can be represented in general by

$$^{A}_{Z}P \rightarrow {}_{Z+1}^{A}D + {}_{-1}^{0}e + \bar{\nu} \qquad (\beta^- \text{ decay})$$

and

$$^{A}_{Z}P \rightarrow {}_{Z-1}^{A}D + {}_{+1}^{0}e + \nu \qquad (\beta^+ \text{ decay})$$

where $_{-1}^{0}e$ represents an electron (β^-), and $_{+1}^{0}e$ represents a positron (β^+). This notation clearly shows conservation of charge and mass number in the subscripts and superscripts, respectively. In β^- emission, a neutron in the parent is converted into a proton, an electron, and an antineutrino. In β^+ emission, a proton in the parent is converted into a neutron, a positron, and a neutrino.

Similar to our development of the decay energy for α decay, the decay energy Q_β for each type of β decay can be found by using conservation of mass-energy in the rest frame of the parent (Exercise 43-35):

Decay energy for β emission

$$Q_{\beta-} = (M_P - M_D)c^2 \qquad (\beta^- \text{ decay}) \tag{43-13}$$

and

$$Q_{\beta+} = (M_P - M_D - 2m_e)c^2 \qquad (\beta^+ \text{ decay}) \tag{43-14}$$

where m_e is the electron (or positron) mass. This energy is shared between the electron (or positron), the antineutrino (or neutrino), and the daughter. Since $M_D \gg m_e$, the kinetic energy of the daughter is negligible, but the daughter may be created in an excited state. Measured half-lives for β decay are always longer than 10^{-2} s and can be greater than 10^{15} y.

Gamma decay. As we have mentioned, the daughter in an α decay or β decay is sometimes created in an excited state. The excited states of nuclei are analogous to the excited states of atoms, and a transition to a lower excited state or the ground state is accompanied by the emission of a photon. A photon emitted in a nuclear transition is called a γ *ray*. We represent a γ decay by

Gamma decay

$$^{A}_{Z}X^* \rightarrow {}^{A}_{Z}X + \gamma$$

where X is the chemical symbol for the nuclide and the asterisk indicates the excited state of a nuclide.

For example, the β^- decay of ^{12}B proceeds along one of two pathways, as

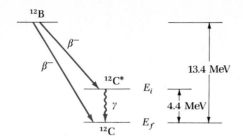

Figure 43-10. Two pathways for the β^- decay of ^{12}B. One pathway involves the formation of ^{12}C* and the emission of a 4.4-MeV γ ray.

shown in Fig. 43-10. The β^- decay can create either ^{12}C (ground state) or ^{12}C* (excited state). When ^{12}C* is created, it decays to ^{12}C by emitting a γ ray of energy $h\nu$, and

Energy of a γ-ray

$$h\nu = E_i - E_f$$

where E_i and E_f are the energies of the excited (or initial) state and the ground (or final) state, respectively.

Mechanism for α decay. The half-life for α decay can be very large. For example, the half-life of ^{238}U is 4.9×10^9 y. Why does it take so long for a ^{238}U nucleus to α-decay? As a model, let us treat the unstable ^{238}U nucleus as an α particle contained within a ^{234}Th nucleus. The potential-energy function $u_\alpha(r)$ for the α particle is shown schematically in Fig. 43-11. From scattering experiments, we know that the Coulomb barrier for an α particle *outside* a ^{234}Th nucleus is at least 8 MeV. Therefore, our question now becomes: How does the α particle, which is initially inside the nuclear well with an energy of about 4 MeV, *ever* get past this barrier and outside the nucleus? In other words, why is ^{238}U unstable to α decay?

α emission is an example of quantum-mechanical tunneling.

The answer comes from quantum mechanics. We must consider the wave properties of the α particle. When this is done we find that the α particle can tunnel through the barrier. (See Sec. 40-10.) The probability of tunneling depends strongly on the height and the width of the Coulomb barrier measured at the level of the α particle's energy. The α particle's energy is approximately the decay energy Q_α. This means that the half-life of the parent nuclide depends strongly on the decay energy. This prediction is well substantiated by α decays with half-lives that range from less than a microsecond to billions of years. This tunneling description of α decay was one of the early successes of the quantum theory.

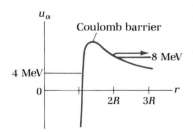

Figure 43-11. Potential-energy function $u_\alpha(r)$ for an α particle interacting with a ^{234}Th nucleus. Just outside the nuclear well, the repulsive Coulomb potential energy due to the nuclear protons dominates $u_\alpha(r)$. This part of $u_\alpha(r)$ is another manifestation of the *Coulomb barrier.*

43-7 NUCLEAR REACTIONS

A radioactive decay is a nuclear event which occurs spontaneously, without any stimulus from outside the parent atom. We now consider nuclear processes which are caused to occur by an external influence. When a particle such as an α particle encounters a nucleus, it may interact with the nucleus such that a *nuclear reaction* occurs. An example of such a reaction is the absorption of an α particle by nitrogen to produce an oxygen isotope and a proton:

$$^4_2\text{He} + ^{14}_7\text{N} \rightarrow ^{17}_8\text{O} + ^1_1\text{H}$$

This particular reaction, studied by Rutherford in 1919, provided the first

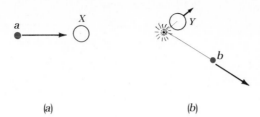

Figure 43-12. (a) Incident particle a is projected toward a target nucleus X. (b) After the reaction, residual nucleus Y recoils and emergent particle b is ejected.

Artificial transmutation

demonstration of the artificial transmutation of a chemical element. In this case, nitrogen was converted to oxygen.

In a typical nuclear reaction, an incident particle a is projected toward a target nucleus X, which is then converted to a residual nucleus Y and an emergent particle b (Fig. 43-12):

$$a + X \rightarrow Y + b$$

The reactants are a and X, and the products are Y and b. Alternatively, a reaction can be specified with an abbreviated notation: X(a, b)Y. For example, the reaction above can be written as $^{14}N(\alpha, p)^{17}O$.

The *reaction energy,* or *Q value,* of a reaction is defined as the difference between the kinetic energy of the products and the kinetic energy of the reactants. If these kinetic energies are measured in the rest frame of the target nucleus, then the kinetic energy of the target nucleus is zero. Letting K_Y, K_b, and K_a represent the kinetic energies of Y, b, and a, respectively, we have

Definition of reaction energy

$$Q = (K_Y + K_b) - K_a \qquad (43\text{-}15)$$

By analogy with chemical reactions, a nuclear reaction is called *exothermic* if $Q > 0$, and it is called *endothermic* if $Q < 0$. These names are appropriate because the kinetic energy of the system increases in an exothermic reaction and it decreases in an endothermic reaction.

We can express Q in terms of the rest masses of the reactants and products by using conservation of mass-energy. In the rest frame of the target nucleus, we have

$$(m_a c^2 + K_a) + M_X c^2 = (m_b c^2 + K_b) + (M_Y c^2 + K_Y) \qquad (43\text{-}16)$$

where m_a, M_X, m_b, and M_Y are the rest masses of a, X, b, and Y, respectively. Combining Eqs. (43-15) and (43-16), we obtain

Reaction energy in terms of rest masses

$$Q = [(m_a + M_X) - (m_b + M_Y)]c^2 \qquad (43\text{-}17)$$

The reaction energy is equal to the difference in rest-mass energy between the reactants and the products.

Artificial nuclides

Nuclear reactions are used to produce a number of nuclides, many of which are not among those occurring naturally on earth. These artificial nuclides are radioactive, and they are represented by most of the uncolored squares in Fig. 43-2. Only about 50 radioactive nuclides are found among the substances of the earth.

Nuclear fission. A particular type of nuclear reaction, quite unlike those described above, is one in which a large-mass nucleus absorbs a neutron and then splits into two medium-mass nuclei and several neutrons. Such a reaction is appropriately called *nuclear fission.* An example is the fission of ^{235}U:

$$^{1}_{0}n + ^{235}_{92}U \rightarrow ^{141}_{56}Ba + ^{92}_{36}Kr + 3^{1}_{0}n$$

The ^{235}U nucleus is called the *fissile nucleus* and the ^{141}Ba and ^{92}Kr nuclei are the *fission products*.

There are three technologically important fissile nuclides: ^{235}U, ^{233}U, and ^{239}Pu. The nuclide ^{235}U is naturally occurring (along with ^{238}U), and is obtained from ores that are mined as an energy resource. The nuclides ^{233}U and ^{239}Pu are artificial; they are produced from other nuclides in nuclear reactions similar to those discussed above.

The fission products resulting from the fission of a particular fissile nucleus are not unique. For example, another possible fission of ^{235}U is

$$\,^1_0n + \,^{235}_{92}U \rightarrow \,^{140}_{54}Xe + \,^{94}_{38}Sr + 2\,^1_0n$$

Indeed, as shown in Fig. 43-13, there is an entire distribution of possible fission products resulting from the fission of a particular fissile nucleus. From this figure, the likelihood that the two fission products will have nearly the same mass is very small. A more likely fission is one in which one of the fission products has a mass of around 90 to 100 u and the other a mass of around 133 to 143 u. From the two sample reactions above, note that the number of neutrons emerging from a fission can vary; this number averages around 2.5 neutrons.

The fission products are radioactive. Since the surplus of the number of neutrons over the number of protons in a nucleus increases with mass number, a fissile nucleus has a larger N/Z ratio than stable nuclei with about half the mass of the fissile nucleus. This means that the fission products are created with too many neutrons to be stable. Ordinarily the fission products are β^- emitters because a β^- decay converts a neutron into a proton. Typically, each fission product undergoes about four β^- decays on its way to stability.

There are two aspects of nuclear fission that make it important from a technological point of view.

1. The reaction is exothermic; about 200 MeV is released per fission event.

Figure 43-13. Percent yield of fission products from the fission of ^{235}U versus A. Note that the vertical axis is logarithmic.

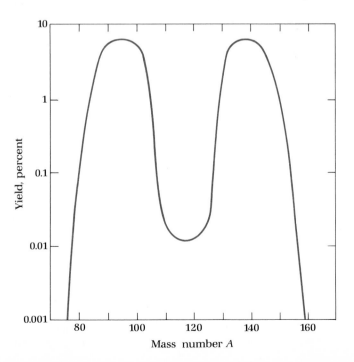

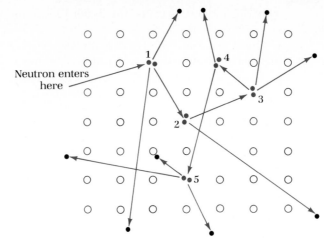

Figure 43-14. A chain reaction. Open circles represent fissile nuclei, colored circles represent fission products, and black dots represent neutrons. A neutron enters from the left and causes nucleus 1 to fission. Three neutrons emerge from this fission; two escape and the third causes nucleus 2 to fission. Two neutrons emerge from this fission; one escapes and the other causes nucleus 3 to fission; and so on.

This reaction energy is larger than typical chemical reaction energies by a factor of several million. Therefore, fissile material can be used to make a fuel with an exceedingly high energy density. (See Exercise 43-38.) A typical fuel rod in a nuclear electric power plant contains about 3 percent fissile material. Even with this dilution, the energy density is about 100,000 times greater than ordinary fossil fuels such as gasoline.

2. The incident particle which initiates fission, the neutron, is contained among the products of fission. If one of the several neutrons emerging from a fission event causes a subsequent fission event, and this self-sustaining process is continued time after time, then a *chain reaction* occurs (Fig. 43-14). To maintain a chain reaction, a minimum amount of fissile material is required so that too many neutrons do not escape from the fuel. This amount of material is called the *critical mass.* The value of the critical mass depends on the particular fissile nuclide and the environment of the fissile fuel. In a nuclear power plant, the environment of the fuel is controlled so that a steady reaction rate is maintained.

A dynamic version of the liquid-drop model provided an early theoretical description of nuclear fission, as shown schematically in Fig. 43-15. When the ^{235}U nucleus absorbs the neutron, the resulting ^{236}U nucleus can undergo oscillations and become deformed. If the oscillations result in a dumbell-like shape, then the long-range electrostatic repulsion between the two parts can overcome the short-range nuclear attraction and fission ensues.

Nuclear fusion. Nuclear fusion is a type of nuclear reaction in which two small-mass nuclei combine to produce a single larger-mass nucleus and some fragments (usually). The source of the sun's energy is a series of fusion reactions. One such series is called the *proton-proton cycle:*

$$\left\{ \begin{array}{l} ^1\text{H} + {}^1\text{H} \rightarrow {}^2\text{H} + \beta^+ + \nu \\ ^2\text{H} + {}^1\text{H} \rightarrow {}^3\text{He} + \gamma \end{array} \right\} \times 2$$

$$^3\text{He} + {}^3\text{He} \rightarrow {}^4\text{He} + {}^1\text{H} + {}^1\text{H}$$

Notice that a product of the first reaction is ^{2}H, which is one of the reactants of the second reaction. Further, a product of the second reaction is ^{3}He, which is one of the two ^{3}He nuclei needed for the third reaction. Thus, to produce the

Chain reaction

Critical mass

Proton-proton cycle

third reaction once, the first two reactions must each occur twice, as indicated. Each of these reactions is exothermic, and the reaction energy for the entire five-reaction sequence is about 25 MeV. The proton-proton cycle can be summarized with

$$6^1H \rightarrow {}^4He + 2^1H + 2\beta^+ + 2\nu + 2\gamma + 25 \text{ MeV}$$

The sun's "fuel" consists of protons, and the "ashes" left from the "burning" of this fuel are α particles.

Scientists around the world have been trying to utilize fusion reactions for the production of electric power. This goal is difficult to accomplish because the reactants of fusion are electrically charged, and repel one another by long-range electric forces. In the sun and other stars, the effects of these forces are overcome by the high temperatures and pressures that exist within the star. The quest for earth-based fusion reactors is an attempt by humans to utilize nuclear reactions similar to those which occur in the interior of stars such as our sun.

Artificial nuclear fusion

43-8 FUNDAMENTAL BUILDING BLOCKS OF MATTER

In the hope of developing a simple description of matter, scientists have nurtured the belief that all substances consist of a few fundamental, indivisible particles. In the fifth century B.C., the Greek philosopher Democritus introduced the concept that matter consists of indivisible particles called *atoms.* (The word "atom" comes from Greek and means indivisible.) The title "atom" was awarded to the chemical elements, and, by the beginning of the nineteenth century, the atomic theory of matter was well established, mostly because it explained the laws of chemistry.

By probing the structure of the atom, and by changing one chemical element into another, Rutherford showed that atoms can be taken apart, and that they are not immutable. Shortly afterward, the atoms of one chemical element were being changed into those of another. The search for fundamental particles was on again. By the early 1930s, scientists had identified three such particles: the electron, the proton, and the neutron.

To probe the structure of the atom and to establish the neutron-proton model of the nucleus required a giant leap in energy. Separating a molecule into its constituent atoms, or combining the atoms to make a molecule, involves energies of the order of an eV per reaction. A nuclear reaction, the rearranging of nucleons to form different nuclei, involves energies of the order of MeV per reaction. The "energy realm" for atoms is several eV; for nucleons it is several MeV.

Are the nucleons fundamental particles, or do they consist of still-smaller parts? One way to find out is to probe a nucleon. That is, perform a scattering experiment on a nucleon similar to the Rutherford experiment on the atom. Suppose we attempt to determine the structure of the proton by scattering electrons from protons. Consider the energy required for the bombarding electron. To resolve two objects that are separated a distance d, the wavelength λ of the probing particle must be less than the separation. Therefore, to detect separate parts inside a proton, the electron must have a wavelength less than 10^{-15} m. From the de Broglie relation, the momentum of the electron is $p = h/\lambda$. The kinetic energy is $K = E - mc^2$ and $E^2 = p^2c^2 + m^2c^4$. Thus

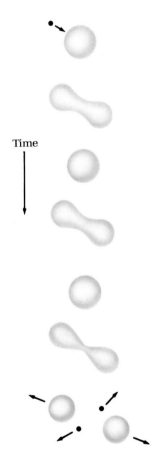

Time

Figure 43-15. Illustration of fission using the liquid-drop model. A ^{235}U nucleus absorbs a neutron and the resulting ^{236}U nucleus oscillates. If the ellipsoidal shape becomes too pronounced, the long-range electric repulsion overcomes the short-range nuclear attraction and the nucleus fissions.

$$K + mc^2 = \sqrt{p^2c^2 + m^2c^4}$$

If we anticipate that the electron's kinetic energy will turn out to be much larger than its rest-mass energy (0.5 MeV), then we can neglect the terms containing the rest mass and arrive at a simple expression for K:

$$K \approx pc = \frac{h}{\lambda}c = \frac{hc}{\lambda}$$

Table 43-3. Energy realms for different systems

System	Energy realm
Atom	eV
Nucleus	MeV
Nucleon	GeV

The kinetic energy of an electron whose wavelength is 10^{-15} m is

$$K \approx \frac{(4.14 \times 10^{-15} \text{ eV} \cdot \text{s})(3.0 \times 10^8 \text{ m/s})}{1 \times 10^{-15} \text{ m}} \approx 1 \times 10^9 \text{ eV} = 1 \text{ GeV}$$

Therefore, to probe a nucleon we must make another giant leap in energy, to an energy realm of around several GeV. (See Table 43-3.)

Such experiments were performed in the 1960s, and they indicated that the proton *does* have internal structure. The scattering of the electrons was compatible with a proton structure consisting of small particles which appear as point charges.

High-energy physics. High-energy physics, or particle physics, is the study of subnuclear matter. Experiments in this field of physics involve beams of particles, such as electrons or protons, colliding at high energies, from several GeV to hundreds of GeV and upward. These beams are produced by large accelerators which are located at several laboratories around the world (Fig. 43-16). The experiments performed at these laboratories, beginning in the early 1960s, have led to the discovery of hundreds of particles. (See Fig. 43-17.)

Table 43-4 lists a few of these particles. This list is organized as follows:

1. The *photon* is the single member of its group.

2. The *leptons* are a group of particles which include the electron, other electronlike particles (the muon and the tau), and neutrinos that are associated with each of these particles. (The word "lepton" comes from Greek and means small or slim.) The muon and the tau are unstable, and the final decay products

Table 43-4. Partial list of particles

Type	Name	Symbol	Mass, MeV/c^2
Photon			
	Photon	γ	0
Leptons			
	Electron	β^-	0.51
	Muon	μ^-	106
	Tau	τ^-	1784
	Neutrino (electron)	ν_e	≈ 0
	Neutrino (muon)	ν_μ	≈ 0
	Neutrino (tau)	ν_τ	≈ 0
Hadrons			
Mesons			
	Pion	π^+, π^0	140, 135
	Kaon	K^+, K^-	494
Baryons			
	Proton	p	938
	Neutron	n	940
	Lambda	Λ^0	1116
	Sigma	Σ^+, Σ^-	1189, 1197
	Xi	Ξ^0, Ξ^-	1315, 1321

Figure 43-16. The interior of the accelerating ring, which is over 2000 meters in diameter, at the Enrico Fermi Laboratory in Batavia, Illinois. The Fermilab accelerator is the largest in the world and can produce a beam of protons with an energy of 500 GeV. *(Fermilab)*

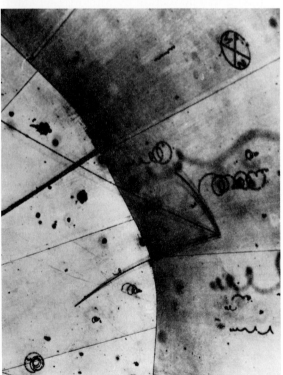

Figure 43-17. Bubble-chamber photograph. Elementary charged particles created by collisions leave tracks of bubbles in liquid hydrogen. Paths are curved because of a magnetic field. *(Argonne National Laboratory)*

Strong and weak nuclear forces

of each include an electron. Experiments to the present time indicate that the leptons are true particles in the sense that they have no measurable radius. The leptons interact through a force that is distinct from the strong nuclear force between nucleons. This force is called the *weak force* because it is weaker than the strong nuclear force. To clarify this distinction further, the strong nuclear force between nucleons is often called the *strong force*.

3. The *hadrons* are a group of particles that interact through the strong force. (The word "hadron" comes from Greek and means thick.) The hadrons are divided into two subgroups: (*a*) the *mesons* and (*b*) the *baryons*. (*a*) The first few mesons discovered had masses intermediate between an electron and a proton. (The word "meson" comes from Greek and means intermediate.) All the mesons are unstable with half-lives of 10^{-8} s and less. The decay products of a meson never include a baryon. (*b*) The proton and the neutron are included among the baryons. (The word "baryon" comes from Greek and means heavy.) Other than the proton, all baryons are unstable. (Some theories predict that the proton is also unstable with a half-life greater than the age of the universe.) A baryon is either a proton or another hadron that has a proton as one of its final decay products.

For brevity, we have not included the antiparticles of the particles in Table 43-4. As we have seen previously, the antiparticle of a particle is normally indicated with a bar over the symbol for the particle. For example, the antiproton is represented as $\bar{p}$. An antiparticle has the same mass as its corresponding particle, but opposite charge.

Quarks. As more and more particles were discovered during the 1960s, the subnuclear world seemed more complex. A simplifying theory was introduced independently by Murray Gell-Mann and George Zweig in 1963. As experimental evidence mounted, this theory gradually won general acceptance. According to this theory, hadrons are composed of particles called *quarks*. Originally, the theory used three types of quarks, called *up*, *down*, and *strange*; they are listed in Table 43-5. A curious property of quarks is that they possess fractional electronic charge in increments of 1/3 or 2/3.

A baryon consists of three quarks. For example, the proton is a combination of $u + u + d$, which gives a charge of $(+\frac{2}{3}e) + (+\frac{2}{3}e) + (-\frac{1}{3}e) = e$. The neutron is a combination of $d + d + u$, which gives a charge of $(-\frac{1}{3}e) + (-\frac{1}{3}e) + (+\frac{2}{3}e) = 0$. *A meson consists of a quark-antiquark pair.* For example, the π^+ is a combination of $u + \bar{d}$. An antiquark has the opposite charge of its corresponding quark. This gives the charge of the π^+ as $(+\frac{2}{3}e) + (+\frac{1}{3}e) = e$, in agreement with observation.

> A baryon is made of three quarks.

> A meson is made of a quark-anti-quark pair.

Besides electric charge, the quark model correctly provides a number of other characteristics of hadrons, but we do not have the space to discuss them here. We can only state that the correct description of the many complex properties of hadrons by the quark model makes this model very useful.

The quark model is highly successful, but it has a puzzling feature: *An isolated quark has never been observed.* Extensive searches have been made, and there have been a few claims of success. However, none of these claims is widely accepted. The absence of an isolated quark is especially puzzling because (i) a free quark should not be particularly difficult to detect and (ii) a quark is expected to be stable.

High-energy physicists have continued to discover more and more particles. As the list of particles increases, the number of quarks required to account for them has also increased. Despite this proliferation in the number of quarks, the quark model remains the simplest theory devised so far.

Table 43-5. Quarks

Name	Symbol	Charge
Up	*u*	$-\frac{2}{3}e$
Down	*d*	$-\frac{1}{3}e$
Strange	*s*	$-\frac{1}{3}e$

COMMENTARY: THE BIG BANG

Is there any limit to the size of the universe, or does it extend an infinite distance in all directions? It is difficult to imagine that the universe has an edge, because, if it does, what is beyond the edge? But there is a way to imagine a finite-sized universe that does not have an edge. Suppose that we lived in a two-dimensional universe and that our universe was shaped as a sphere — or as any smooth surface that encloses a volume in three dimensions. As two-dimensional creatures, we could not visualize the third dimension, but our universe would be finite and have no edge. If we were clever and had the proper resources, we might be able to prove to ourselves that our universe was finite, or "closed." For example, we might send out a light beam, wait for it to go all the way around the universe, and then watch it come back from the opposite direction. Could it be that our three-dimensional universe is similarly closed? If this view is correct and the universe is finite, then how big is it? What is its circumference?

Did the universe have a beginning or has it always existed? Will it always exist or will it come to an end? In other words, is our universe finite or infinite in time? If the universe is finite in time, then how old is it and how much longer will it last?

The expanding universe. *Before we broach such questions about time and space, we should ask whether they are proper scientific questions. Are there any conceivable measurements that we can make that will have any bearing on the answers to these questions? Yes. Perhaps the best example is a discovery in 1925 by Edwin P. Hubble, an astronomer at Mount Wilson Observatory in California. Using a standard astronomical distance-measuring technique, Hubble found that the great spiral nebula of Andromeda (called M31) is a conglomeration of stars that is about a hundred times farther away than any single star previously measured. Such a conglomeration of stars is called a galaxy, and we now know that, at the very least, billions of galaxies exist in space. Discovery of these galaxies was accompanied by the realization that the individual stars we see in the night sky, as well as the single star we see in the day sky, are all members of our home galaxy, which we call the Milky Way galaxy.*

From measurements of the Doppler shift of spectral lines in the light from a galaxy, astronomers can determine the velocity of a galaxy relative to our own. They find that there is a general motion of galaxies away from us and that the speed v of recession of a galaxy is proportional to its distance d from us:

$$v = Hd$$

where the proportionality constant H is called the Hubble constant. The presently accepted value of H is highly controversial, but for the sake of being specific, let us accept a value often given: $H = 1.6 \times 10^{-18}$ s^{-1}. That value could easily be in error by 50 percent or more; its accuracy depends mostly on the accuracy of distance measurements to galaxies.

Why are the other galaxies receding from us, and why is there such a simple relation between their speed and their distance from us? Consider a two-dimensional model of the universe: a large balloon with many small, randomly spaced dots painted on it. Suppose you are an observer positioned on one of the dots and the balloon is being slowly inflated. You will find that all the other dots are receding from you and that the speed of recession of a particular dot is directly proportional to its distance from you. An observer on any dot would find the same relation between the speed of recession of the other dots and the distance to the other dots: $v \propto d$. Thus the galaxies are receding not only from us, they are receding from one another. The entire universe is expanding, and the Hubble constant characterizes the rate of expansion.

The question of the age of the universe now has meaning. The universe was "born" when all the galaxies were compressed together, and since that time, the time of the "big bang," the matter in the universe has been flying apart. If we assume that the expansion rate has always been the same as it is now, then we can determine how long it has been since the big bang. With this assumption, the age of the universe is $\tau = d/v = 1/H = 1/(1.6 \times 10^{-18} \, s^{-1}) \approx 20$ billion years.

But our assumption that the expansion rate is constant cannot be strictly valid because galaxies attract one another gravitationally. As the galaxies fly apart, their mutual attraction must cause their recession speeds to decrease, similar to the way a stone tossed upward slows while it is on the rise. The expansion rate in earlier epochs must have been greater than it is now, which means that using the present value of the Hubble constant gives an upper limit to τ. Using the so-called standard model of the universe, cosmologists find that $\tau \approx 14$ billion years.

The analogy between the expanding universe and a stone on the rise after being tossed upward suggests another question: Will the galaxies eventually slow to a stop and then fall back on one another? That is, will the universe expand to a maximum size, then begin contracting, and finally collapse? There is another possibility: The expansion rate may be too great or the density of the universe too small to reverse the expansion. The analogy in this case is a stone tossed upward with such a great speed that it never returns to earth; its speed is greater than the escape speed. The presently accepted value for the density of the universe indicates that it will not contract, but will go on expanding forever. However, the value is very close to the critical value needed for contraction and could easily be in error on the low side. For one thing, the amount of dark matter in the universe is difficult to determine. For another, the universe contains a tremendous number of neutrinos, and it is possible that the neutrino has a very small mass, below the present limit of detection. The neutrinos in the universe could tip the scales toward contraction. Which of these two possibilities is more likely — eventual contraction or eternal expansion — is possibly the most exciting problem facing cosmologists today.

The primal glow. *What was the universe like during earlier epochs? From thermodynamics, we know that the temperature of an expanding system decreases. Therefore, if we imagine going backward in time, we will find the temperature of the universe increasing — the farther back in time, the greater the density and the higher the temperature. Near the very beginning, there must have been a time when the universe was so hot that molecules could not exist because the kinetic energy of the atoms was too large for them to hold together as molecules. Still earlier, the kinetic energies must have been so great that no atom could hold its electrons, and matter was in the form of a plasma of electrons and bare nuclei. Still earlier the nuclei were disassembled into protons and neutrons, and still earlier protons and neutrons into quarks, and still earlier who knows what?*

Theoretical investigation of the path leading backward to the instant of the big bang links cosmology to particle physics. An important example of this linking is a paper published in 1948 by R. Alpher, G. Gamow, and H. Bethe. (Bethe's name is pronounced "beta." Gamow later joked that Bethe's name was added to the paper only to complete the first three letters of the Greek alphabet.) Based on a scenario of conditions following the big bang, these workers predicted that a cosmic radiation should presently exist that is the electromagnetic remnant or echo of the big bang. This radiation, which is characteristic of thermal radiation at a temperature of 3 K, was detected in 1964 by A. Penzias and R. Wilson. This primal glow is a crucial piece of the cosmological puzzle.

For the most part, the fundamental questions we have posed in this commentary are unresolved, but cosmologists appear to be making some progress. At this point, we should send you to the experts. The following list provides a good start: Steven Weinberg, The First Three Minutes, Basic Books, New York, 1977; Victor F. Weisskopf, "The Origin of the Universe," American Scientist, September-October 1983, pp. 473–480; and Alan H. Guth and Paul J. Steinhardt, "The Inflationary Universe," Scientific American, May 1984, pp. 116–128.

SUMMARY WITH APPLICATIONS

Section 43-2. Properties of the nucleus

The atomic nucleus is the small, positively charged center of the atom. A nucleus is designated by its atomic number Z, neutron number N, and mass number A. These nucleons are held within the nuclear radius (about $R_0 A^{1/3}$) by a strongly attractive nuclear force.

Use the nuclear designation to specify a nuclide; describe some of the properties of the nuclear force.

Section 43-3. Nuclear mass and binding energy

The binding energy of a nuclide is determined from the values of rest masses:

$$B = (ZM_H + Nm_n - M_a)c^2 \qquad (43\text{-}3)$$

The basis for comparing binding energies is the binding energy per nucleon B/A.

Determine B or B/A for any nuclide.

Section 43-4. The liquid-drop model

The liquid-drop model is used to develop an expression for B:

$$B = C_1 A - C_2 A^{2/3} - C_3 Z(Z-1)A^{-1/3} \qquad (43\text{-}4)$$

The first two terms describe the effects of nuclear forces, and the third term describes that of electric forces.

Describe the origin of each of the terms in the liquid-drop model's expression for B; use this expression to find B.

Section 43-5. The shell model

The shell model treats nucleons as independent particles and uses quantum mechanics and the exclusion principle to explain why $Z \approx N$ and why the magic-number nuclei are uncommonly stable.

Describe the assumptions and procedures used in the shell model; explain how the magic numbers emerge from this model.

Section 43-6. Radioactive decay

Some nuclei are unstable or radioactive. Since radioactive emission is a random process, the activity falls off exponentially with time:

$$\mathcal{R} = \mathcal{R}_0 e^{-\lambda t} \qquad (43\text{-}9)$$

Three types of radioactive emission often encountered are α, β, and γ.

Calculate the activity of a radioactive sample; give the relation between λ and $T_{1/2}$; calculate the decay energies for α and β decay; describe the mechaninism for α decay.

Section 43-7. Nuclear reactions

A nuclear reaction can be induced by bombarding a target nucleus with a high-energy particle. Nuclear fission is a particularly distinctive reaction where a large-mass nucleus absorbs a neutron and then splits into two medium-mass nuclei and several neutrons. Nuclear fusion is a reaction that involves two small-mass nuclei combining to produce a larger nucleus.

Calculate the reaction energy for a reaction; describe fission and fusion.

Section 43-8. Fundamental building blocks of matter

From recent advances in high-energy physics, particles are classified into groups: Electrons and neutrinos are leptons; protons, neutrons, and other baryons are hadrons. A promising theory postulates the existence of fundamental particles that are called quarks.

Explain why high energies are required in particle physics; discuss some of the properties of leptons and hadrons; discuss the status of the quark model.

QUESTIONS

43-1 In the Rutherford experiment, where α particles were scattered from a gold foil, some of the particles were scattered directly backward in the direction from which they came. Explain how this shows that the α particles, each with a kinetic energy of about 4 MeV, were unable to surmount the Coulomb barrier of the gold nuclei. Explain why this is consistent with a model of the atom in which all the positive charge and nearly all the mass of the atom occupy a very small volume at the center of the atom. What is the name of this small knot of mass and positive charge?

43-2 Present any evidence you can think of which requires the existence of a nuclear force.

43-3 State which (if any) of the following pairs of nuclides are isotopes, isotones, or isobars: (a) $^{36}_{16}$S and $^{36}_{18}$A, (b) $^{35}_{17}$Cl and $^{37}_{17}$Cl, (c) $^{26}_{12}$Mg and $^{27}_{13}$Al.

43-4 In chemical reactions, the different isotopes of a particular element behave essentially the same. Do you expect isotopes to behave essentially the same in nuclear reactions? Explain. Could the isotopes of a chemical element be separated readily in a chemical reaction? Could they be separated readily in a nuclear reaction?

43-5 The atomic masses of nuclides, when expressed in u, are all very nearly whole numbers, but often the atomic masses of elements are not. Explain.

43-6 In principle, it is possible to determine the binding energy of atomic electrons from the rest masses of atoms, ions, and the electron, similar to the way we found the binding energies of nucleons in a nucleus. Why is this not done in practice?

43-7 Why is the unified atomic-mass unit a useful unit in nuclear physics? Why is the mass unit MeV/c^2 useful in nuclear physics?

43-8 What are some characteristics which distinguish the nuclear force between nucleons from the electric force between charged particles?

43-9 **_Mirror isobars._** If nuclide 1 is a mirror isobar of nuclide 2, then $Z_1 = N_2$ and $N_1 = Z_2$. (a) What nuclide is the mirror isobar of $^{19}_9$F? (b) Suppose we compare the binding energies of this mirror isobar pair. Which nuclide is expected to have the larger binding energy? Explain.

43-10 Is the liquid-drop model useful in explaining why $Z \approx N$ for small-mass nuclei? Is the shell model useful in this? Using the appropriate model, explain this effect.

43-11 Is the liquid-drop model useful in explaining why very large mass nuclei are unstable? Is the shell model useful in this? Are both models needed? Using the appropriate model(s), explain this effect.

43-12 Is the liquid-drop model useful in explaining the low B/A values for low-mass nuclei? Is the shell model useful in this? Using the appropriate model, explain this effect.

43-13 Is the liquid-drop model useful in explaining the extraordinary stability of a nucleus with Z and/or N equal to a magic number? Is the shell model useful in this? Using the appropriate model, explain this effect.

43-14 Explain why the shell model is also called the *single-*

particle model.

43-15 Which model, the liquid-drop or the shell, has the stronger theoretical foundation? Explain.

43-16 (a) Which of the following nuclides has a filled shell of protons: $^{72}_{33}$As, $^{120}_{50}$Sn, $^{208}_{82}$Pb? (b) Which of the following nuclides has a filled shell of neutrons: $^{15}_7$N, $^{52}_{24}$Cr, $^{56}_{26}$Fe, $^{208}_{82}$Pb?

43-17 A doubly magic nuclide is one where both Z and N are magic. Using the chart of nuclides (Fig. 43-2), make a list of all stable doubly magic nuclides.

43-18 Consider distinguishing the three emissions—α, β^-, and γ—from one another by using a magnetic field. In Fig. 43-18, **B** is out of the page. State which emission corresponds to each of the paths shown.

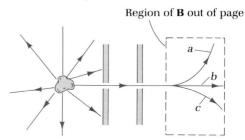

Figure 43-18. Ques. 43-18: Paths of an α particle, a β^- particle, and a γ ray in a magnetic field **B**.

43-19 Consider the relative positions on a chart of nuclides of the parent and the daughter in radioactive decay. Which type of decay, α, β^-, or β^+, corresponds to the following situations?

(a) Daughter is along a diagonal from the parent two spaces lower in Z and two spaces lower in N.

(b) Daughter is along a diagonal from the parent one space higher in Z and one space lower in N.

(c) Daughter is along a diagonal from parent one space lower in Z and one space higher in N.

43-20 What experimental information indicates that α decay must be a quantum-mechanical tunneling process? In α decay, why does a short half-life correspond to a large disintegration energy?

43-21 Why did physicists believe in the existence of neutrinos for a period of 26 years without having directly observed them? Explain.

43-22 What are some similarities between γ emission from a nucleus and photon emission from an atom? What are some differences?

43-23 The half-life of ^{238}U is 4.51×10^9 y. Explain how such a long half-life can be measured.

43-24 What fraction of the initial population of radioactive nuclei is remaining after a time interval of three half-lives?

43-25 Consider a nuclide that has a half-life of, say, 10 y. A particular nucleus of this nuclide was created in a nuclear reactor 10 y ago and another nucleus of this nuclide was created only 5 min ago. Which nucleus, the oldster or the youngster, is more likely to decay in the next 30 min? Explain.

43-26 To initiate an exothermic nuclear reaction, $a + X \rightarrow Y + b$, the kinetic energy K_a of the bombarding particle must be of the order of several MeV or more when particle a is a proton. If particle a is a neutron, then K_a can be essentially zero. Explain.

43-27 It has been stated that the energy released in fission is really not "nuclear" energy, rather it is "electric" energy. Use the liquid-drop model to support this contention.

43-28 Explain why fission products are radioactive and are predominantly β^- emitters.

43-29 Suppose we discover a fissile nuclide whose nuclei produce an average of only 0.8 neutrons per fission

reaction. Is a chain reaction possible for this fissile nuclide? Explain.

43-30 Complete the following table:

Symbol	Represents	Type	SI unit
Z			
N	Neutron number		
A			
R			m
$\mathcal{R}$			
λ		Scalar	
$T_{1/2}$			
B			
Q			

EXERCISES*

Section 43-2. Properties of the nucleus

43-1 Determine the number of protons, neutrons, and nucleons in nuclei of the following nuclides: (a) $^{18}_9$F, (b) $^{43}_{20}$Ca, (c) $^{202}_{80}$Hg.

43-2 Use the periodic table in App. P to find the symbol for X in the nuclear designation $^A_Z X$ for nuclides with (a) $Z = 7$ and $N = 8$, (b) $A = 23$ and $N = 12$, (c) $Z = 29$ and $A = 64$.

43-3 (a) Determine the approximate radii of the nuclei of ^{10}B and ^{197}Au. (b) Give the ratio of the approximate volumes of these nuclei as a ratio of whole numbers.

43-4 (a) Estimate the mass density of nuclear matter. (b) A typical rock has a mass density of 2.5×10^3 kg/m³. What is the ratio of the mass density of nuclear matter to that of a typical rock?

43-5 A neutron star (or pulsar) has the mass density of nuclear matter. Assuming the star is spherical, determine (a) the volume and (b) the radius of a neutron star whose mass is 4×10^{30} kg (twice the mass of the sun). (c) What is the ratio of the radius of this star to that of the earth ($R_e = 6.4 \times 10^6$ m)?

43-6 (a) Estimate the gravitational force between two nucleons inside a nucleus. Assume the nucleons behave as particles separated by about 1 fm. (b) Using the same assumption, estimate the electrostatic force between two protons inside a nucleus. (c) Determine the ratio of your answer for part (a) to that for part (b).

Section 43-3. Nuclear mass and binding energy

43-7 In units of MeV, determine the rest-mass energy of (a) the electron, (b) the proton, (c) the neutron.

43-8 The rest mass of the π^0 meson is 135 MeV/c^2. What is its rest mass (a) in atomic-mass units and (b) in kilograms?

43-9 Using Table 43-2, determine (a) the binding energy B and (b) the binding energy per nucleon B/A for ^{11}B, ^{68}Zn, and ^{197}Au. The answers to part (b) are given in Example 43-2.

43-10 In developing Eq. (43-3), we assumed that the effect of the binding energies of the atomic electrons was negligible. Show that if this approximation causes an error of less than 100 eV, then its effect is insignificant when using the data of Table 43-2.

43-11 Two nuclides with very large B/A values are ^{52}Cr and ^{56}Fe. (a) Determine these values. Two stable nuclides with very small B/A values are ^{2}H and ^{3}He. (b) Determine these values.

43-12 The proton-separation energy S_p for a nuclide is the minimum energy required to separate the least tightly bound proton from a nucleus of that nuclide. (a) Show that the proton-separation energy for a nuclide with atomic number Z and neutron number N is

$$S_p = (M_{Z-1,N} + M_H - M_{Z,N})c^2$$

The double subscripts on each atomic-mass symbol M indicate the number of protons and neutrons in a nucleus. (b) The approximate value of S_p for ^{4}He was used in Example 43-1. Determine this value.

43-13 The neutron-separation energy S_n for a nuclide is the minimum energy required to separate the least tightly bound neutron from a nucleus of that nuclide. (a) Show that the neutron-separation energy for a nuclide with atomic number Z and neutron number N is

$$S_n = (M_{Z,N-1} + m_n - M_{Z,N})c^2$$

* Use Table 43-2 for nuclide masses.

The double subscripts on each atomic-mass symbol M indicate the number of protons and neutrons in a nucleus. (b) Determine the neutron separation energy for ^{4}He.

Section 43-4. The liquid-drop model

43-14 (a) Use Eq. (43-3) and Table 43-2 to determine the binding energy of $^{103}_{45}$Rh. (b) Use Eq. (43-4) with the constants found in Example 43-2 to determine the binding energy of $^{103}_{45}$Rh. (c) What is the percentage error from using Eq. (43-4)?

43-15 (a) Use Eq. (43-5) with the constants found in Example 43-2 to find the B/A values for ^{202}Hg and ^{23}Na. (b) What is the ratio of the second term in Eq. (43-5) for ^{202}Hg to the second term for ^{23}Na? (c) What is the ratio of the third term in Eq. (43-5) for ^{202}Hg to the third term for ^{23}Na?

43-16 In Sec. 43-4, we gave the value $\frac{1}{2}Z(Z-1)$ for the number of electrostatic "pair bonds" among a group of Z charged particles. One way to corroborate this result is to let lines between dots represent pair bonds between particles, as shown in Fig. 43-19 for the cases in which $Z = 2$, 3, and 4. Count these lines in each case and verify that their number is given by $\frac{1}{2}Z(Z-1)$.

Figure 43-19. Exercise 43-16.

43-17 (a) Use data from Table 43-2 in Eq. (43-3) to find B/A values for ^{13}C, ^{75}As, and ^{205}Tl. (b) Use your answers from part (a) to find the three constants in Eq. (43-5). (c) Compare your answers with those found in Example 43-2 by finding the percent difference for each constant.

43-18 In Prob. 23-8, you were asked to show that the electric energy of a spherically symmetric uniform volume charge of radius r_0 and charge Q is $U_e = 3Q^2/20\pi\epsilon_o r_0$. (a) By treating the nucleus as such a charge distribution, show that

$$U_e = 0.8 \text{ MeV } \frac{Z^2}{A^{1/3}}$$

(b) With this expression, evaluate U_e for ^{75}As and compare your answer with $-B_e$ evaluated for this same nucleus. (Use the value of C_3 in Example 43-2.)

Section 43-5. The shell model

43-19 The proton-separation energy S_p is given in Exercise 43-12. According to the shell model, S_p should be relatively large for a nuclide in which Z is a magic number, and S_p should be relatively small for a nuclide in which Z is 1 greater than a magic number. Determine

S_p for (a) ^{120}Sn ($Z = 50$) and (b) ^{121}Sb ($Z = 51$). (c) By what percentage does S_p decrease in going from ^{120}Sn to ^{121}Sb?

43-20 The neutron-separation energy S_n is given in Exercise 43-13. According to the shell model, S_n should be relatively large for a nuclide in which N is a magic number, and S_n should be relatively small for a nuclide in which N is 1 greater than a magic number. Determine S_n for (a) ^{92}Mo ($N = 50$) and (b) ^{93}Mo ($N = 51$). (c) By what percentage does S_n decrease in going from ^{92}Mo to ^{93}Mo?

Section 43-6. Radioactive decay

43-21 Substitute the proper symbols in the following decay reactions:

(a) $$^3_1\text{H} \rightarrow {}^3_2\text{He} + \underline{\quad} + \bar{\nu}$$

(b) $$^{146}_{62}\text{Sm} \rightarrow \underline{\quad} + {}^4_2\text{He}$$

(c) $$^{12}_7\text{N} \rightarrow {}^{12}_6\text{C} + \beta^+ + \underline{\quad}$$

43-22 Radioactive ^{22}Na has a half-life of 2.60 y. (a) What is its disintegration constant in s^{-1}? (b) At the instant a sample contains 8.6×10^{16} ^{22}Na nuclei, what is its activity in becquerels? (c) What is its activity 1 y later? (d) What is its decay constant 1 y later? (e) When is its activity zero?

43-23 In addition to the becquerel, a unit of activity that is commonly used is the curie (Ci). The relation between the becquerel and the curie is

$$1 \text{ Ci} = 3.7 \times 10^{10} \text{ Bq}$$

The half-life of ^{226}Ra is 1620 y. Show that the activity of 1 g of ^{226}Ra is 1 Ci.

43-24 (a) Show that the time interval t required for the activity of a radioactive sample to reduce from an initial value of $\mathcal{R}_0$ to a final value $\mathcal{R}$ is

$$t = \frac{1}{\lambda} \ln \frac{\mathcal{R}_0}{\mathcal{R}}$$

(b) At a particular instant, the activity of a sample which contains radioactive ^{131}I ($T_{1/2} = 8.04$ d) is 59 MBq. What is the time required for this activity to fall to 5.9 MBq?

43-25 (a) Show that the half-life of the radioactive nuclide in a sample can be written

$$T_{1/2} = \frac{0.693t}{\ln (\mathcal{R}_0/\mathcal{R})}$$

where t is the time interval between the initial activity measurement $\mathcal{R}_0$ and the final activity measurement $\mathcal{R}$. (b) The activity of a radioactive sample is measured to be 3.8 MBq and 10.8 h later it is measured to be 3.1 MBq. What is the half-life of the radioactive nuclide?

43-26 (a) The base of a logarithm can be changed by using the relation $\log_b(x) = [\log_b(a)][\log_a(x)]$. Use this relation to show that the population of radioactive nuclei and the activity can be expressed

$$\mathcal{N} = \mathcal{N}_0 2^{-t/T_{1/2}} \quad \text{and} \quad \mathcal{R} = \mathcal{R}_0 2^{-t/T_{1/2}}$$

(*Hint:* Let $b = e$, $a = 2$, and $x = \mathcal{N}/\mathcal{N}_0$.) (*b*) Evaluate the expression for $\mathcal{N}$ at $t = 0$, $T_{1/2}$, $2T_{1/2}$, and $3T_{1/2}$. Plot these four points on a graph of $\mathcal{N}$ versus t and sketch the curve through the points.

43-27 The nuclide $^{232}_{90}$Th decays by α emission. Write the expression for this decay reaction. Use the periodic table in App. P to find the chemical symbol of the daughter.

43-28 Determine Q_α for the α decay of $^{238}_{92}$U.

43-29 The nuclide $^{87}_{37}$Rb decays by β^- emission. Write the expression for this decay reaction. Use the periodic table in App. P to find the chemical symbol of the daughter.

43-30 Determine $Q_{\beta-}$ for the β^- decay of $^{87}_{37}$Rb.

43-31 The nuclide $^{11}_{6}$C decays by β^+ emission. Write the expression for this decay reaction. Use the periodic table in App. P to find the chemical symbol of the daughter.

43-32 Determine $Q_{\beta+}$ for the β^+ decay of $^{11}_{6}$C.

43-33 When ^{232}Th α-decays, it begins a series of decays in which the daughter nuclei are radioactive. The series culminates with the stable nuclide ^{208}Pb. One pathway for this series involves the emission of particles in the following order: α, β^-, β^-, α, α, α, α, β^-, β^-, α. (*a*) Beginning with ^{232}Th and ending with ^{208}Pb, list the nuclei involved in this series. (*b*) Plot the results of part (*a*) on a graph of N versus Z. Let the N axis of your graph span from 125 to 142 and the Z axis span from 80 to 90. Place a dot at the position of each nuclide in the series and connect the dots with arrows that indicate the direction of the decay processes.

43-34 Repeat the previous exercise for the series which begins with ^{238}U and culminates with ^{206}Pb along the pathway α, β^-, β^-, α, α, α, α, β^-, α, β^-, α, β^-, β^-, α.

43-35 (*a*) Develop the expression for $Q_{\beta-}$ [Eq. (43-13)]. (*b*) Develop the expression for $Q_{\beta+}$ [Eq. (43-14)].

Section 43-7. Nuclear reactions

43-36 Substitute the missing symbol in the following reactions:

(*a*) $\qquad ^{59}_{27}$Co $+$ _____ $\rightarrow$ $^{60}_{27}$Co $+ \gamma$

(*b*) $\qquad ^{19}_{9}$F $+ ^{1}_{1}$H $\rightarrow$ _____ $+ ^{4}_{2}$He

(*c*) $\qquad ^{1}_{0}$n $+ ^{233}_{92}$U $\rightarrow ^{134}_{52}$Te $+$ _____ $+ 2^{1}_{0}$n

The first reaction above is used to produce ^{60}Co commercially. This nuclide is utilized in cancer therapy.

43-37 Determine the reaction energy for the reaction

$$^{4}\text{He} + {}^{14}\text{N} \rightarrow {}^{17}\text{O} + {}^{1}\text{H}$$

Is this reaction exothermic or endothermic?

43-38 The energy density of a fuel is the ratio of the energy released from the fuel to the mass of the fuel used in the release. (*a*) Determine the energy density of a fuel composed of pure ^{235}U in units of MeV/u. (*b*) The energy density of fossil fuels (such as gasoline) is about 0.3 eV/u. Determine the approximate ratio of the energy density of a fuel composed of a pure fissile material to that of a fossil fuel.

43-39 (*a*) Determine the reaction energies in each reaction of the proton-proton fusion cycle. (*b*) What is the energy released in the full process?

43-40 Consider the reaction $\bar{\nu} + p \rightarrow n + \beta^+$. With the proton as the target, what is the minimum energy that the incident antineutrino must have to produce this reaction?

43-41 Consider estimating the energy released in fission reactions by using the graph of B/A versus A (Fig. 43-5). (*a*) Carefully ascertain from this graph the value of B/A for two nuclides whose mass numbers are typical of the two fission products, say 100 and 135. (*b*) Determine the binding energies of each of these nuclides by multiplying each nuclide's B/A value by its mass number. (*c*) Similarly, determine the binding energy of a typical fissile nuclide, say $A \approx 235$. (*d*) Add the two binding energies found in part (*b*) and subtract the binding energy found in part (*c*). (*e*) Explain why this difference provides an estimate of the energy released in fission.

Section 43-8. Fundamental building blocks of matter

43-42 (*a*) The combination of quarks which compose the Λ^0 is $u + d + s$. What is the charge of the Λ^0? (*b*) The combination of quarks which compose the Σ^+ is $u + u + s$. What is the charge of the Σ^+? (*c*) The combination of quarks which compose the π^0 is $d + \bar{d}$. What is the charge of the π^0?

PROBLEMS

43-1 **A model of radioactive decay.** Suppose we have a box which contains 1000 dice. We shake the box and roll the dice on the floor. After casting aside the dice that come up with three dots on top, we collect all the other dice and return them to the box. We continue to roll the dice and discard the ones that come up with three dots on top. Estimate the number of dice in the box (*a*) after one throw, (*b*) after two throws, (*c*) after six throws. (*d*) Write an expression which gives the approximate number $\mathcal{N}$ of dice in the box after t

throws. (e) Cast the expression you found in part (d) in the form $\mathcal{N} = \mathcal{N}_0 e^{-\lambda t}$. (Hint: $a^t = e^{t \ln a}$.)

43-2 (a) Develop Eq. (43-8) from Eq. (43-7). (b) Equation (43-8) gives the population of radioactive parent nuclei in a sample. To distinguish the parent population from the population of daughter nuclei, let us designate the former as $\mathcal{N}_P$ and the latter as $\mathcal{N}_D$. Thus, Eq. (43-8) becomes $\mathcal{N}_P = \mathcal{N}_{P0} e^{-\lambda t}$. Assuming the daughter is stable and that the initial population of the daughter is zero, show that

$$\mathcal{N}_D = \mathcal{N}_{P0}(1 - e^{-\lambda t})$$

(c) Make a graph of $\mathcal{N}_D$ versus t that spans about three half-lives.

43-3 ***Production of a radioactive nuclide.*** Suppose the nuclei of a radioactive nuclide are being produced at a constant rate $\mathcal{R}_0$ in a nuclear reactor. (a) Explain why the population $\mathcal{N}$ of these nuclei is described by the differential equation

$$\frac{d\mathcal{N}}{dt} = \mathcal{R}_0 - \lambda \mathcal{N}$$

where λ is the nuclide's disintegration constant. (b) Show that if the population is zero at $t = 0$, then the population $\mathcal{N}$ at time t is

$$\mathcal{N} = \frac{\mathcal{R}_0}{\lambda}(1 - e^{-\lambda t})$$

(c) Make a graph of $\mathcal{N}$ versus t that spans about three half-lives.

43-4 ***Radioactive dating.*** A nuclear reaction in the earth's upper atmosphere due to cosmic rays produces the radioactive nuclide ^{14}C ($T_{1/2} = 5730$ y). Consequently, the CO_2 in the earth's atmosphere, and in living organisms, contains a small amount of ^{14}C along with the stable nuclides ^{12}C (99.63 percent) and ^{13}C (0.37 percent). The ratio of radioactive carbon to stable carbon in living organisms is about 1.3×10^{-12}. After the organism dies, it ceases to assimilate CO_2, so that this ratio decreases because of the decay of ^{14}C. Suppose we find a bone fragment in an ancient burial ground. When we separate 100 g of carbon from the bone, we find that this sample has a ^{14}C activity of 6.5 Bq. Estimate how long the former owner of this bone has been dead.

43-5 The energy most often measured in α decay is the kinetic energy K_α of the α particle. (a) Use conservation of momentum in the rest frame of the parent nucleus to show that the relation between K_α and the disintegration energy Q_α is

$$K_\alpha = \frac{A - 4}{A} Q_\alpha$$

Use the approximation that the mass of the daughter nucleus and the α particle in atomic-mass units can be

rounded to the nearest integer. (Hint: Nonrelativistic expressions can be used for the kinetic energies and momenta because Q_α is always less than about 10 MeV and the rest-mass energy of the α particle is about 4 GeV.) (b) For the α decay of ^{226}Ra, $Q_\alpha = 4.87$ MeV. Find K_α for this case.

43-6 ***Electron capture.*** Electron capture is a radioactive-decay mechanism that causes the same transmutation as β^+ decay. In this type of decay, the unstable parent nucleus absorbs one of the atomic electrons. The parent converts to a daughter nucleus that has an atomic number 1 lower than the parent and emits a neutrino. The reaction is written

$$-_{-1}^{0}e + {}_{Z}^{A}P \rightarrow {}_{Z-1}^{A}D + \nu$$

(a) The nuclide $^{123}_{52}Te$ decays by electron capture. Write the reaction for this particular decay. (b) Neglecting the energy associated with the electron orbits, show that the disintegration energy Q_{ec} for electron capture is

$$Q_{ec} = (M_P - M_D)c^2$$

(c) Determine the disintegration energy for the decay of part (a).

43-7 ***Discovery of the neutron.*** Chadwick discovered the neutron by investigating a reaction which had been mistakenly described as $^4He + {}^9Be \rightarrow {}^{13}C + \gamma$. He properly identified the reaction as $^4He + {}^9Be \rightarrow {}^{12}C + {}^1n$ by showing that the emergent particle, known to be uncharged, had a mass about the same as a proton. When these emergent particles bombarded paraffin (which consists largely of hydrogen), protons that were struck head on were ejected with a maximum energy of 5.7 MeV. Further, when these emergent particles collided head on with nitrogen atoms, the atoms were ejected with a maximum energy of 1.4 MeV. By using conservation of energy and of momentum, show that these results are consistent with the fact that the emergent particle was a neutron.

43-8 ***Reaction threshold.*** If an endothermic reaction $a + X \rightarrow Y + b$ is to occur, then the required energy must be supplied by the kinetic energy of the incident particle a. The *threshold energy* K_{th} is the minimum kinetic energy of the incident particle (measured in the rest frame of the target nucleus X) which can lead to a reaction. This rest frame is called the *laboratory frame*. The velocity $\mathbf{v}_{cm}$ of the center of mass is unaffected by the reaction. Thus K_{th} must equal the kinetic energy K_{cm} of the system relative to the laboratory frame plus the required reaction energy Q: $K_{th} = K_{cm} - Q$. (Recall that Q is negative for endothermic reactions.) Show that

$$K_{th} = -Q \frac{M_X + m_a}{M_X}$$

Assume that the kinetic energies are small enough so

that nonrelativistic expressions may be used.

43-9   Consider the reaction $^1_1\text{H} + ^1_0n \rightarrow ^2_1\text{H} + \gamma$, where the proton and the neutron each have a kinetic energy of 2.2 MeV before they collide head on. What are the energies of (a) the γ ray and (b) the deuteron? (*Hint:* In applying conservation of momentum, neglect the mass difference between the proton and the neutron.)

43-10 The reaction energy Q for a nuclear reaction $a + X \rightarrow Y + b$ can be determined by measuring the kinetic energy K_a of the incident particle a and the kinetic energy K_b of the emergent particle b. Show that if the emergent particle is ejected perpendicular to the path of the incident particle in the rest frame of the target, then

$$Q = K_b \left(1 + \frac{m_b}{M_Y} \right) - K_a \left(1 - \frac{m_a}{M_Y} \right)$$

Assume nonrelativistic expressions are valid.

43-11 **Mean life.** The mean life τ of a radioactive nuclide is defined as

$$\tau = \frac{\int_0^\infty t \, \mathcal{N} \, dt}{\int_0^\infty \mathcal{N} \, dt}$$

(a) Show that $\tau = 1/\lambda$. (b) What fraction of the initial population is remaining after one mean life?

APPENDIX C
CONVERSION
FACTORS

Length

	m	inch	ft	mi
1 meter	1	39.37	3.281	6.214×10^{-4}
1 inch	2.540×10^{-2}	1	8.333×10^{-2}	1.578×10^{-5}
1 foot	0.3048	12	1	1.894×10^{-4}

1 fermi = 10^{-15} m
1 Bohr radius = 5.292×10^{-11} m
1 angstrom = 10^{-10} m
1 light-year = 9.460×10^{15} m
1 parsec = 3.084×10^{16} m

1 mil = 10^{-3} inch
1 yard = 3 ft
1 fathom = 6 ft
1 nautical mile = 1852 m

Time

	s	min	h	d	yr
1 second	1	1.667×10^{-2}	2.778×10^{-4}	1.157×10^{-5}	3.169×10^{-8}
1 minute	60	1	1.667×10^{-2}	6.944×10^{-4}	1.901×10^{-6}
1 hour	3600	60	1	4.167×10^{-2}	1.141×10^{-4}
1 day	8.640×10^4	1440	24	1	2.738×10^{-3}
1 year	3.156×10^7	5.260×10^5	8.766×10^3	365.2	1

Mass   Quantities in the colored areas are weights, not masses, but are commonly equated to masses. For example, 1 kg has a weight of 2.205 lb in a region in which $g = 9.80665$ m/s².

	kg	u	slug	oz	lb	ton
1 kilogram	1	6.022×10^{26}	6.852×10^{-2}	35.27	2.205	1.102×10^{-3}
1 atomic mass unit	1.661×10^{-27}	1	1.138×10^{-28}	5.857×10^{-27}	3.661×10^{-27}	1.830×10^{-30}
1 slug	14.59	8.788×10^{27}	1	514.8	32.17	1.609×10^{-2}
1 ounce	2.835×10^{-2}	1.707×10^{25}	1.943×10^{-5}	1	6.250×10^{-2}	3.125×10^{-5}
1 pound	0.4536	2.732×10^{26}	3.108×10^{-2}	16	1	0.0005
1 ton	9.072×10^2	5.463×10^{29}	62.16	3.200×10^4	2000	1

1 metric tonne = 1000 kg

Area

	m²	in²	ft²
1 square meter	1	1550	10.76
1 square inch	6.452×10^{-4}	1	6.944×10^{-3}
1 square foot	9.290×10^{-2}	144	1

1 barn = 10^{-28} m²
1 hectare = 10^4 m² = 2.471 acres
1 acre = 4.356×10^4 ft²
1 square mile = 640 acres = 2.788×10^7 m²

Volume

	m³	cm³	ℓ	inch³	ft³
1 cubic meter	1	10^6	10^3	6.102×10^4	35.31
1 cubic centimeter	10^{-6}	1	10^{-3}	6.102×10^{-2}	3.531×10^{-5}
1 liter	10^{-3}	10^3	1	61.02	3.531×10^{-2}
1 cubic inch	1.639×10^{-5}	16.39	1.639×10^{-2}	1	5.787×10^{-4}
1 cubic foot	2.832×10^{-2}	2.831×10^4	28.32	1728	1

1 U.S. fluid gallon = 4 U.S. fluid qt = 8 U.S. pt = 128 U.S. fluid oz = 231 inches³
1 British Imperial gallon = 277.42 inches³
1 U.S. barrel = $31\frac{1}{2}$ gal (Other definitions of the barrel exist.)

Speed

	m/s	km/h	ft/s	mi/h
1 meter per second	1	3.600	3.281	2.237
1 kilometer per hour	0.2778	1	0.9113	0.6214
1 foot per second	0.3048	1.097	1	0.6818
1 mile per hour	0.4470	1.609	1.467	1

Force

	N	dyn	lb
1 newton	1	10^5	0.2248
1 dyne	10^{-5}	1	2.248×10^{-6}
1 pound	4.448	4.448×10^5	1

Power

	W	cal/s	hp	ft · lb/s	Btu/h
1 watt	1	0.2390	1.341×10^{-3}	0.7376	3.414
1 calorie* per second	4.184	1	5.611×10^{-3}	3.086	14.29
1 horsepower	745.7	178.2	1	550	2546
1 foot pound per second	1.356	0.3240	1.818×10^{-3}	1	4.629
1 British thermal unit per second	0.2929	7.000×10^{-2}	3.928×10^{-4}	0.2160	1

* The thermochemical calorie is defined to be 4.184 J. The Calorie used in human diets is 10^3 cal.

Density   The pound per cubic foot is weight density, the others mass density. See Mass table.

	kg/m³	g/cm³	lb/ft³
1 kilogram per cubic meter	1	10^{-3}	6.243×10^{-2}
1 gram per cubic centimeter	10^3	1	62.43
1 pound per cubic foot	16.02	1.602×10^{-2}	1

Pressure

	Pa	dyn/cm²	atm	mmHg (torr)	lb/inch²	inch of water
1 pascal (1 N/m²)	1	10	9.869×10^{-6}	7.501×10^{-3}	1.450×10^{-4}	4.015×10^{-3}
1 dyne per square centimeter	0.1	1	9.869×10^{-7}	7.501×10^{-4}	1.450×10^{-5}	4.015×10^{-4}
1 atmosphere	1.013×10^5	1.013×10^6	1	760	14.70	406.8
1 millimeter of mercury	133.3	1.333×10^3	1.316×10^{-3}	1	1.934×10^{-2}	0.5352
1 pound per square inch	6895	6.895×10^4	0.6805	51.71	1	27.68
1 inch of water	249.1	2491	2.458×10^{-3}	1.868	3.613×10^{-2}	1

Energy

	J	erg	eV	cal	kW · h	ft · lb	hp · h	Btu
1 joule	1	10^7	6.242×10^{18}	0.2390	2.778×10^{-7}	0.7376	3.725×10^{-7}	9.484×10^{-4}
1 erg	10^7	1	6.242×10^{11}	2.390×10^{-8}	2.778×10^{-14}	7.376×10^{-8}	3.725×10^{-14}	9.484×10^{-11}
1 electron volt	1.602×10^{-19}	1.602×10^{-12}	1	3.829×10^{-20}	4.450×10^{-26}	1.182×10^{-19}	5.968×10^{-26}	1.520×10^{-22}
1 calorie*	4.184	4.184×10^7	2.611×10^{19}	1	1.162×10^{-6}	3.086	1.559×10^{-6}	3.968×10^{-3}
1 kilowatt-hour	3.6×10^6	3.6×10^{13}	2.247×10^{25}	8.604×10^5	1	2.655×10^6	1.341	3414
1 foot pound	1.356	1.356×10^7	8.462×10^{18}	0.3240	3.766×10^{-7}	1	5.051×10^{-7}	1.286×10^{-3}
1 horsepower-hour	2.685×10^6	2.685×10^{13}	1.676×10^{25}	6.416×10^5	0.7457	1.980×10^6	1	2546
1 British thermal unit	1054	1.054×10^{10}	6.581×10^{21}	252	2.929×10^{-4}	7.777×10^2	3.928×10^{-4}	1

* The thermochemical calorie is defined to be 4.184 J. The Calorie used in human diets is 10^3 cal.

APPENDIX S
MATHEMATICAL SYMBOLS
AND THE GREEK
ALPHABET

Mathematical symbols

Symbol	Definition
$=$	is equal to
$\neq$	is not equal to
$\approx$	is approximately equal to
$\propto$	is proportional to
$>$	is greater than
$\gg$	is much greater than
$<$	is less than
$\ll$	is much less than
Δx	change in x
$n!$	$n(n-1)(n-2) \cdots 1$
Σ	sum
lim	limit
$\Delta t \to 0$	Δt approaches zero
$\int$	integral
$\dfrac{df}{dx}$	derivative of f with respect to x
$\dfrac{\partial f}{\partial x}$	partial derivative of f with respect to x

The Greek alphabet

Character	Upper case	Lower case	Character	Upper case	Lower case
Alpha	A	α	Nu	N	ν
Beta	B	β	Xi	Ξ	ξ
Gamma	Γ	γ	Omicron	O	o
Delta	Δ	δ	Pi	Π	π
Epsilon	E	ϵ	Rho	P	ρ
Zeta	Z	ζ	Sigma	Σ	σ
Eta	H	η	Tau	T	τ
Theta	Θ	θ	Upsilon	Y	υ
Iota	I	ι	Phi	Φ	ϕ, φ
Kappa	K	κ	Chi	X	χ
Lambda	Λ	λ	Psi	Ψ	ψ
Mu	M	μ	Omega	Ω	ω

APPENDIX M
MATHEMATICAL APPROXIMATIONS AND FORMULAS

Expansions

$$(1 + x)^n = 1 + nx + \frac{n(n-1)}{2!}x^2 + \cdots \qquad |x| < 1$$

$$\sin \theta = \theta - \frac{\theta^3}{3!} + \frac{\theta^5}{5!} - \cdots \qquad \theta \text{ in rad}$$

$$\cos \theta = 1 - \frac{\theta^2}{2!} + \frac{\theta^4}{4!} - \cdots \qquad \theta \text{ in rad}$$

$$\tan \theta = \theta + \frac{\theta^3}{3} + \frac{2}{15}\theta^5 + \cdots \qquad \theta \text{ in rad}$$

$$\sin^{-1} x = x + \tfrac{1}{6}x^3 + \tfrac{3}{40}x^5 + \cdots \qquad |x| < 1, \text{ angle in rad}$$

$$\cos^{-1} x = \frac{\pi}{2} - \sin^{-1} x$$

$$\tan^{-1} x = x - \frac{x^3}{3} + \frac{x^5}{5} - \cdots \qquad x^2 < 1$$

$$= \frac{\pi}{2} - \frac{1}{x} + \frac{1}{3x^3} - \frac{1}{5x^5} + \cdots \qquad x^2 > 1$$

$$e^x = 1 + x + \frac{x^2}{2!} + \frac{x^3}{3!} + \cdots$$

$$\ln(1 + x) = x - \tfrac{1}{2}x^2 + \tfrac{1}{3}x^3 - \cdots \qquad x < 1$$

Areas

Square of side a $\qquad\qquad a^2$

Rectangle with sides a and b $\qquad\qquad ab$

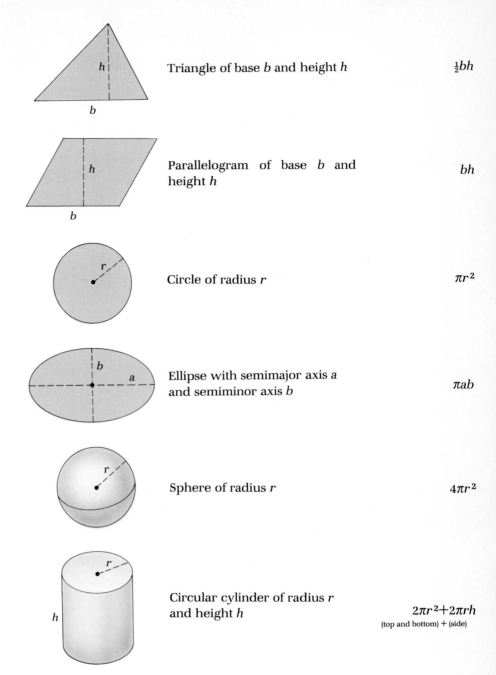

Triangle of base b and height h $\frac{1}{2}bh$

Parallelogram of base b and height h bh

Circle of radius r πr^2

Ellipse with semimajor axis a and semiminor axis b πab

Sphere of radius r $4\pi r^2$

Circular cylinder of radius r and height h $2\pi r^2 + 2\pi rh$
(top and bottom) + (side)

Volumes

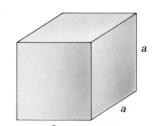

Cube of side a a^3

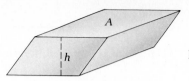

Parallelepiped with base area A and height h Ah

Sphere of radius r $\frac{4}{3}\pi r^3$

Cylinder of base area A and height h Ah

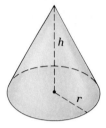

Cone of base area A and height h $\frac{1}{3}Ah$

Equations of curves

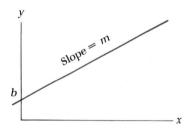

Straight line of slope m and intercept b $y = mx + b$

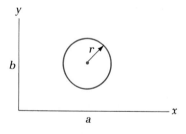

Circle of radius r centered at (a, b) $(x - a)^2 + (y - b)^2 = r^2$

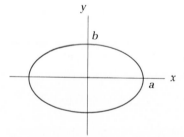

Ellipse with semiaxes a and b and center at $(0, 0)$ $\dfrac{x^2}{a^2} + \dfrac{y^2}{b^2} = 1$

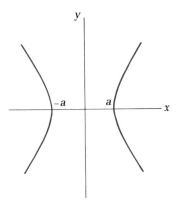

Parabola with vertex at origin branching upward $y = Ax^2$

Hyperbola with vertices at $(\pm a, 0)$ and eccentricity e given by $e^2 = (b^2/a^2) + 1$ $\dfrac{x^2}{a^2} - \dfrac{y^2}{b^2} = 1$

Quadratic equations   The solutions to the equation $ax^2 + bx + c = 0$ are given by

$$x = \frac{-b \pm \sqrt{b^2 - 4ac}}{2a}$$

Logarithms   If $x = a^y$, then $y = \log_a x$.

The base of the natural logarithms is $e = 2.718281828 \ldots ,$ so that $y = \log_e x = \ln x$.

$\log 1 = 0$

$\log_a a = 1$

$\log (uv) = \log u + \log v$

$\log (u/v) = \log u - \log v$

$\log u^n = n \log u$

$\ln e = 1$

$\ln e^n = n$

$\ln 10 = 2.303$

$\ln 2 = 0.693$

APPENDIX T
TRIGONOMETRY

The sine, cosine, and tangent of θ (see Fig. T-1) are given by

$$\sin \theta = \frac{y}{r} \qquad \cos \theta = \frac{x}{r} \qquad \tan \theta = \frac{y}{x} = \frac{\sin \theta}{\cos \theta}$$

The cosecant, secant, and cotangent of θ are given by

$$\csc \theta = \frac{r}{y} = \frac{1}{\sin \theta} \qquad \sec \theta = \frac{r}{x} = \frac{1}{\cos \theta} \qquad \cot \theta = \frac{x}{y} = \frac{1}{\tan \theta}$$

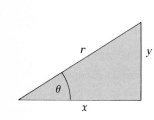

From Fig. T-1,

$$\sin\left(\theta \pm \frac{\pi}{2}\right) = \pm \cos \theta \qquad \cos\left(\theta \pm \frac{\pi}{2}\right) = \mp \sin \theta \qquad \tan\left(\theta - \frac{\pi}{2}\right) = \mp \cot \theta$$

From the pythagorean theorem, $x^2 + y^2 = r^2$, and

$$\sin^2 \theta + \cos^2 \theta = 1 \qquad \sec^2 \theta - \tan^2 \theta = 1 \qquad \csc^2 \theta - \cot^2 \theta = 1$$

The following related identities are derived in trigonometry:

$$\sin (\alpha \pm \beta) = \sin \alpha \cos \beta \pm \sin \beta \cos \alpha$$

$$\cos (\alpha \pm \beta) = \cos \alpha \cos \beta \mp \sin \alpha \sin \beta$$

$$\tan (\alpha \pm \beta) = \frac{\tan \alpha \pm \tan \beta}{1 \mp \tan \alpha \tan \beta}$$

$$\sin \alpha \pm \sin \beta = 2 \sin \tfrac{1}{2}(\alpha \pm \beta) \cos \tfrac{1}{2}(\alpha \mp \beta)$$

$$\cos \alpha + \cos \beta = 2 \cos \tfrac{1}{2}(\alpha + \beta) \cos \tfrac{1}{2}(\alpha - \beta)$$

$$\cos \alpha - \cos \beta = 2 \sin \tfrac{1}{2}(\alpha + \beta) \sin \tfrac{1}{2}(\beta - \alpha)$$

$$\tan \alpha \pm \tan \beta = \frac{\sin (\alpha \pm \beta)}{\cos \alpha \cos \beta}$$

$$\sin \alpha \sin \beta = \tfrac{1}{2}[\cos (\alpha - \beta) - \cos (\alpha + \beta)]$$

$$\cos \alpha \cos \beta = \tfrac{1}{2}[\cos (\alpha + \beta) + \cos (\alpha - \beta)]$$

$$\sin \alpha \cos \beta = \tfrac{1}{2}[\sin (\alpha + \beta) + \sin (\alpha - \beta)]$$

$$\sin^2 \alpha - \sin^2 \beta = \sin (\alpha + \beta) \sin (\alpha - \beta) = \cos^2 \beta - \cos^2 \alpha$$

$$\cos^2 \alpha - \sin^2 \beta = \cos (\alpha + \beta) \cos (\alpha - \beta) = \cos^2 \beta - \sin^2 \alpha$$

$$\sin 2\theta = 2 \sin \theta \cos \theta$$

$$\cos 2\theta = \cos^2 \theta - \sin^2 \theta = 2 \cos^2 \theta - 1 = 1 - 2 \cos \theta$$

$$\tan 2\theta = \frac{2 \tan \theta}{1 - \tan^2 \theta}$$

$$\sin^2 \frac{\theta}{2} = \frac{1}{2}(1 - \cos \theta) \qquad\qquad \cos^2 \frac{\theta}{2} = \frac{1}{2}(1 + \cos \theta)$$

$$\sin^3 \theta = \tfrac{1}{4}(-\sin 3\theta + 3 \sin \theta) \qquad \cos^3 \theta = \tfrac{1}{4}(\cos 3\theta + 3 \cos \theta)$$

$$\sin 3\theta = 3 \sin \theta - 4 \sin^3 \theta \qquad\qquad \cos 3\theta = 4 \cos \theta - 3 \cos \theta$$

$$\sin^4 \theta = \tfrac{1}{8}(\cos 4\theta - 4 \cos 2\theta + 3) \qquad \cos^4 \theta = \tfrac{1}{8}(\cos 4\theta + 4 \cos 2\theta + 3)$$

$$\sin 4\theta = \cos \theta \, (4 \sin \theta - 8 \sin^3 \theta) \qquad \cos 4\theta = 8 \cos^4 \theta - 8 \cos^2 \theta + 1$$

$$\sin(-\theta) = -\sin \theta \qquad \cos(-\theta) = \cos \theta \qquad \tan(-\theta) = -\tan \theta$$

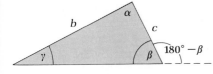

For any triangle (see Fig. T-2),

$$\alpha + \beta + \gamma = \pi \text{ rad} = 180°$$

Law of cosines:

$$a^2 = b^2 + c^2 - 2bc \cos \alpha$$
$$= a^2 + b^2 + 2bc \cos(180° - \alpha)$$

Law of sines:

$$\frac{a}{\sin \alpha} = \frac{b}{\sin \beta} = \frac{c}{\sin \gamma}$$

APPENDIX D
DIFFERENTIAL
CALCULUS

The derivative of $y = f(x)$ is defined to be the limit of the slope $\Delta y / \Delta x$ of the y-versus-x curve:

$$\frac{dy}{dx} = \lim_{\Delta x \to 0} \frac{\Delta y}{\Delta x} = \lim_{\Delta x \to 0} \frac{f(x + \Delta x) - f(x)}{\Delta x}$$

Some general relations about derivatives:

Sums of functions

$$\frac{d}{dx}[f(x) \pm g(x)] = \frac{df}{dx} \pm \frac{dg}{dx}$$

Products of functions

$$\frac{d}{dx}[f(x)g(x)] = f\frac{dg}{dx} + g\frac{df}{dx}$$

Quotient of two functions

$$\frac{d(f/g)}{dx} = \frac{g\,df/dx - f\,dg/dx}{g^2}$$

Chain rule   If $y = f(x)$ and $x = g(z)$, then

$$\frac{df(x)}{dz} = \frac{df(x)}{dx}\frac{dx}{dz}$$

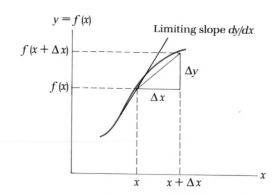

Derivatives of some particular functions (a and n are constants):

$$\frac{da}{dx} = 0$$

$$\frac{d(ax^n)}{dx} = nax^{n-1}$$

$$\frac{d}{dx} \sin ax = a \cos ax \qquad \frac{d}{dx} \sin^{-1} ax = \frac{a}{\sqrt{1 - a^2x^2}}$$

$$\frac{d}{dx} \cos ax = -a \sin ax \qquad \frac{d}{dx} \cos^{-1} ax = \frac{-a}{\sqrt{1 - a^2x^2}}$$

$$\frac{d}{dx} \tan ax = a \sec^2 ax \qquad \frac{d}{dx} \tan^{-1} ax = \frac{a}{1 + a^2x^2}$$

$$\frac{d}{dx} a^{nx} = na^x \ln a$$

$$\frac{d}{dx} e^{ax} = ae^{ax} \qquad \frac{d}{dx} \ln ax = \frac{1}{x}$$

APPENDIX I
INTEGRAL
CALCULUS

The *integral I* of the function $f(x)$ between the limits a and b is written

$$I = \int_a^b f(x)\, dx$$

and is equal to the area under the curve $f(x)$ between the lines $x = a$ and $x = b$, as shown in Fig. I-1. The fundamental theorem of calculus shows that if the upper limit is a variable w, then

$$I(w) = \int_a^w f(x)\, dx$$

$$\frac{d}{dw} I(w) = \frac{d}{dw} \int_a^w f(x)\, dx = f(w)$$

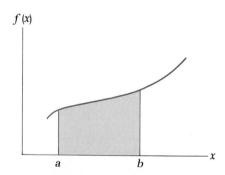

Thus we think of integration as the inverse of differentiation. The *indefinite integral I(x)* of $f(x)$ is the function whose differential is $f(x)$; for example, the indefinite integral of $ax^2 + bx + c$ is $\frac{1}{3}ax^3 + \frac{1}{2}bx^2 + cx + d$.

Some general rules about indefinite integrals (f, g, u, and v are functions; a, b and c are constants) can be expressed as

$$\int dx = x + c$$

$$\int \frac{d[\,f(x)]}{dx}\, dx = f(x) + c$$

$$\int af(x)\, dx = a \int f(x)\, dx$$

$$\int [af(x) + bg(x)]\, dx = a \int f(x)\, dx + b \int g(x)\, dx$$

$$\int u \, dv = uv - \int v \, du$$

Below are tables of some indefinite and definite integrals.

Indefinite integrals   An arbitrary constant should be added to each integral. a, b, and n represent constants.

$$\int x^n \, dx = \frac{x^{n+1}}{n+1}$$

$$\int (a + bx)^n \, dx = \frac{(a + bx)^{n+1}}{b(n+1)} \qquad \text{(provided } n \neq -1)$$

$$\int \frac{dx}{x} = \ln x$$

$$\int \frac{dx}{a + bx} = \frac{1}{b} \ln (a + bx)$$

$$\int \frac{dx}{a + bx^2} = \frac{1}{\sqrt{ab}} \tan^{-1} \left(\frac{\sqrt{b}}{a} x \right) \qquad \text{(provided } ab > 0)$$

$$\int \frac{dx}{a + bx^2} = \frac{1}{2\sqrt{|ab|}} \ln \left(\frac{a - x\sqrt{|ab|}}{a + x\sqrt{|ab|}} \right) \qquad \text{(provided } ab < 0)$$

$$\int \frac{x \, dx}{(a + bx^2)^n} = -\frac{1}{2b(n-1)(a + bx^2)^{n-1}} \qquad \text{(provided } n \neq 1)$$

$$\int \frac{x \, dx}{a + bx^2} = \frac{1}{2b} \ln (a + bx)$$

Let $u = \sqrt{a + cx^2}$, $I = \dfrac{1}{\sqrt{c}} \ln (x\sqrt{c} + u)$ if $c > 0$

$$= \frac{1}{\sqrt{-c}} \sin^{-1} \left(x \sqrt{\frac{-c}{a}} \right) \qquad \text{if } c < 0 \text{ and } a > 0$$

then $$\int u \, dx = \tfrac{1}{2}(xu + aI)$$

$$\int \frac{dx}{u} = I$$

$$\int xu \, dx = \frac{u^3}{3c}$$

$$\int \frac{x \, dx}{u} = \frac{u}{c}$$

$$\int e^{ax} \, dx = \frac{e^{ax}}{a}$$

$$\int xe^{ax} = \frac{e^{ax}}{a^2} (ax - 1)$$

$$\int x^2 e^{ax} \, dx = \frac{e^{ax}}{a^3} \left(a^2 x^2 - 2ax + 2 \right)$$

$$\int \frac{dx}{a + be^{nx}} = \frac{x}{a} - \frac{\ln \left(a + be^{ax} \right)}{an}$$

$$\int \ln ax \, dx = (x \ln ax) - x$$

$$\int \sin ax \, dx = -\frac{\cos ax}{a}$$

$$\int \cos ax \, dx = \frac{\sin ax}{a}$$

$$\int \tan ax \, dx = -\frac{\ln \left(\cos ax \right)}{a}$$

$$\int \sin^2 ax \, dx = \frac{x}{2} - \frac{\sin 2ax}{4a}$$

$$\int \cos^2 ax \, dx = \frac{x}{2} + \frac{\sin 2ax}{4a}$$

$$\int \tan^2 ax \, dx = \frac{\tan ax}{a} - x$$

$$\int \sin^{-1} \left(\frac{x}{a} \right) dx = x \sin^{-1} \left(\frac{x}{a} \right) + \sqrt{a^2 + x^2}$$

$$\int \cos^{-1} \left(\frac{x}{a} \right) dx = x \cos^{-1} \left(\frac{x}{a} \right) - \sqrt{a^2 - x^2}$$

$$\int \tan^{-1} \left(\frac{x}{a} \right) dx = x \tan^{-1} \left(\frac{x}{a} \right) - \left(\frac{a}{2} \right) \ln \left(a^2 + x^2 \right)$$

Definite integrals
$(a > 0)$

$$\int_0^\infty e^{-ax} \, dx = \frac{1}{a}$$

$$\int_0^\infty x^n e^{-ax} \, dx = n! a^{-n-1}$$

$$\int_0^\infty \frac{dx}{1 + e^{ax}} = \frac{\ln 2}{a}$$

$$\int_0^\infty e^{-a^2 x^2} \, dx = \frac{\sqrt{\pi}}{2a}$$

$$\int_0^\infty x e^{-ax^2} \, dx = \frac{1}{2a}$$

$$\int_0^\infty x^2 e^{-ax^2} \, dx = \frac{1}{4} \sqrt{\frac{\pi}{a^3}}$$

$$\int_0^\infty x^3 e^{-ax^2}\, dx = \frac{1}{2a^2}$$

$$\int_0^\infty x^4 e^{-ax^2}\, dx = \frac{3}{8} \sqrt{\frac{\pi}{a^5}}$$

$$\int_0^\infty \frac{\sin ax}{x} = \frac{\pi}{2}$$

APPENDIX F
FUNDAMENTAL CONSTANTS

Summary of the 1986 recommended values of the fundamental physical constants.

Quantity	Symbol	Value	Units	Relative uncertainty, ppm
Speed of light in vacuum	c	299 792 458	$m \cdot s^{-1}$	(Exact)
Triple-point temperature	T_t	273.16	K	(Exact)
Permeability of vacuum	μ_0	$4\pi \times 10^{-7}$	$N \cdot A^{-2}$	
		$= 12.566\ 370\ 614. . .$	$10^{-7}\ N \cdot A^{-2}$	(Exact)
Permittivity of vacuum, $1/\mu_0 c^2$	ϵ_0	$8.854\ 187\ 817. . .$	$10^{-12}\ F \cdot m^{-1}$	(Exact)
Newtonian constant of gravitation	G	6.672 59(85)	$10^{-11}\ m^3 \cdot kg^{-1} \cdot s^{-2}$	128
Planck constant	h	6.626 075 5(40)	$10^{-34}\ J \cdot s$	0.60
$h/2\pi$	$\hbar$	1.054 572 66(63)	$10^{-34}\ J \cdot s$	0.60
Elementary charge	e	1.602 177 33(49)	$10^{-19}\ C$	0.30
Magnetic flux quantum, $h/2e$	Φ_0	2.067 834 61(61)	$10^{-15}\ Wb$	0.30
Electron mass	m_e	9.109 389 7(54)	$10^{-31}\ kg$	0.59
Proton mass	m_p	1.672 623 1(10)	$10^{-27}\ kg$	0.59
Proton-electron mass ratio	m_p/m_e	1836.152 701(37)		0.020
Neutron mass	m_n	1.674 928 6(10)	$10^{-27}\ kg$	0.59
Compton wavelength, $h/m_e c$	λ_c	2.426 310 58(22)	$10^{-12}\ m$	0.089
Fine-structure constant, $\mu_0 c e^2/2h$	α	7.297 353 08(33)	10^{-3}	0.045
Inverse fine-structure constant	α^{-1}	137.035 989 5(61)		0.045
Rydberg constant, $m_e c \alpha^2/2h$	R_∞	10 973 731.534(13)	m^{-1}	0.0012
Avogadro constant	N_A, L	6.022 136 7(36)	$10^{23}\ mol^{-1}$	0.59
Faraday constant, $N_A e$	F	96 485.309(29)	$C \cdot mol^{-1}$	0.30
Molar gas constant	R	8.314 510(70)	$J \cdot mol^{-1} \cdot K^{-1}$	8.4
Boltzmann constant, R/N_A	k	1.380 658(12)	$10^{-23}\ J \cdot K^{-1}$	8.5
Stefan-Boltzmann constant, $(\pi^2/60)k^4/\hbar^3 c^2$	σ	5.670 51(19)	$10^{-8}\ Wm^{-2} \cdot K^{-4}$	34
Non-SI units used with SI				
Electron volt, $(e/C)J = \{e\}J$	eV	1.602 177 33(49)	$10^{-19}\ J$	0.30
Atomic mass unit (unified), $1\ u = m_u = \frac{1}{12}m(^{12}C)$	u	1.660 540 2(10)	$10^{-27}\ kg$	0.59

From E. Richard Cohen and B. N. Taylor, *Reviews of Modern Physics*, vol. 59, No. 4, October 1987, p 1139.

APPENDIX A
ASTRONOMICAL DATA

Body	Body orbited	Mean radius of orbit, m	Radius of body, m	Period of orbit, s	Mass of body, kg
Sun	Galaxy	5.6×10^{20}	6.96×10^{8}	8×10^{15}	1.99×10^{30}
Mercury	Sun	5.79×10^{10}	2.42×10^{6}	7.60×10^{6}	3.35×10^{23}
Venus	Sun	1.08×10^{11}	6.10×10^{6}	1.94×10^{7}	4.89×10^{24}
Earth	Sun	1.50×10^{11}	6.38×10^{6}	3.16×10^{7}	5.97×10^{24}
Mars	Sun	2.28×10^{11}	3.38×10^{6}	5.94×10^{7}	6.46×10^{23}
Jupiter	Sun	7.78×10^{11}	7.13×10^{7}	3.74×10^{8}	1.90×10^{27}
Saturn	Sun	1.43×10^{12}	6.04×10^{7}	9.35×10^{8}	5.69×10^{26}
Uranus	Sun	2.87×10^{12}	2.38×10^{7}	2.64×10^{9}	8.73×10^{25}
Neptune	Sun	4.50×10^{12}	2.22×10^{7}	5.22×10^{9}	1.03×10^{26}
Pluto	Sun	5.91×10^{12}	3×10^{6}	7.82×10^{9}	5.4×10^{24}
Moon	Earth	3.84×10^{8}	1.74×10^{6}	2.36×10^{6}	7.35×10^{22}
Phobos	Mars	9×10^{6}	6×10^{3}	3×10^{4}	1×10^{16}
Deimos	Mars	2.3×10^{7}	3×10^{3}	1.09×10^{5}	2×10^{15}
Io	Jupiter	4.22×10^{8}	1.67×10^{6}	1.53×10^{5}	7.3×10^{22}
Europa	Jupiter	6.71×10^{8}	1.46×10^{6}	3.07×10^{5}	4.75×10^{22}
Ganymede	Jupiter	1.07×10^{9}	2.55×10^{6}	6.18×10^{5}	1.54×10^{23}
Callisto	Jupiter	1.88×10^{9}	2.36×10^{6}	1.44×10^{6}	9.5×10^{22}
Mimas	Saturn	1.86×10^{8}	3×10^{5}	8.12×10^{4}	4×10^{19}
Enceladus	Saturn	2.38×10^{8}	3×10^{5}	1.18×10^{5}	7×10^{19}
Tethys	Saturn	2.95×10^{8}	5×10^{5}	1.63×10^{5}	6.5×10^{20}
Dione	Saturn	3.77×10^{8}	5×10^{5}	2.37×10^{5}	1.0×10^{21}
Rhea	Saturn	5.27×10^{8}	7×10^{5}	3.91×10^{5}	2.3×10^{21}
Titan	Saturn	1.22×10^{9}	2.44×10^{7}	1.38×10^{6}	1.37×10^{23}
Iapetus	Saturn	1.48×10^{9}	5×10^{5}	6.85×10^{6}	1×10^{21}
Ariel	Uranus	1.92×10^{8}	3×10^{5}	2.18×10^{5}	1.2×10^{21}
Umbriel	Uranus	2.67×10^{8}	2×10^{5}	3.58×10^{5}	5×10^{20}
Titania	Uranus	4.38×10^{8}	5×10^{5}	7.53×10^{5}	4×10^{21}
Oberon	Uranus	5.86×10^{9}	4×10^{5}	1.16×10^{6}	2.6×10^{21}
Triton	Neptune	3.53×10^{8}	2×10^{6}	4.82×10^{5}	1.40×10^{23}
Nereid	Neptune	5.6×10^{9}	1×10^{5}	3.11×10^{7}	3×10^{19}

APPENDIX P
PERIODIC TABLE OF THE ELEMENTS

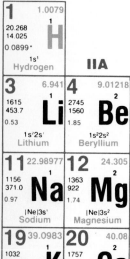

KEY

- ATOMIC NUMBER
- ATOMIC WEIGHT (2)
- BOILING POINT, K
- MELTING POINT, K
- OXIDATION STATES (Bold most stable)
- SYMBOL (1)
- DENSITY at 300 K (3) (g cm³)
- ELECTRON CONFIGURATION (4)
- NAME

30 65.38 — 2 — 1180 / 692.73 / 7.14 — **Zn** — |Ar|3d¹⁰4s² — Zinc

NOTES:
(1) Black — solid.
Light color — gas.
Full color — liquid.
Outline — synthetically prepared.
(2) Based upon carbon-12. ( ) indicates most stable or best known isotope.
(3) Entries marked with asterisks refer to the gaseous state at 273 K and 1 atm and are given in units of g/l.
(4) The principal quantum number is not included when its value would be repeated. For example, $1s^22s^22p^1$ is written $1s^22s^2p^1$.

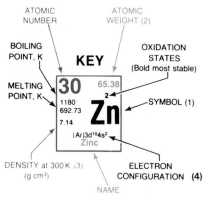

Group IA
| 1 | 1.0079 | 20.268 / 14.025 / 0.0899* | **H** | 1s¹ Hydrogen |

Group IIA
| 3 | 6.941 | 1615 / 453.7 / 0.53 | **Li** | 1s²2s¹ Lithium |
| 4 | 9.01218 | 2745 / 1560 / 1.85 | **Be** | 1s²2s² Beryllium |

| 11 | 22.98977 | 1156 / 371.0 / 0.97 | **Na** | |Ne|3s¹ Sodium |
| 12 | 24.305 | 1363 / 922 / 1.74 | **Mg** | |Ne|3s² Magnesium |

Main table

IIIA	IVA	VA	VIA	VIIA		VIIIA	
19 K 39.0983 · 1 · 1032/336.35/0.86 · [Ar]4s · Potassium	**20** Ca 40.08 · 2 · 1757/1112/1.55 · |Ar|4s² · Calcium	**21** Sc 44.9559 · 3 · 3104/1812/3.0 · [Ar]3d·4s · Scandium	**22** Ti 47.90 · 4,3 · 3562/1943/4.50 · |Ar|3d²4s² · Titanium	**23** V 50.9415 · 5,4,3,2 · 3682/2175/5.8 · |Ar|3d³4s² · Vanadium	**24** Cr 51.996 · 6,3,2 · 2945/2130/7.19 · |Ar|3d⁵4s · Chromium	**25** Mn 54.9380 · 7,6,4,2,3 · 2335/1809/7.43 · |Ar|3d⁵4s² · Manganese	
37 Rb 85.4678 · 1 · 961/312.64/1.53 · |Kr|5s¹ · Rubidium	**38** Sr 87.62 · 2 · 1650/1041/2.6 · |Kr|5s² · Strontium	**39** Y 88.9059 · 3 · 3611/1799/4.5 · |Kr|4d·5s² · Yttrium	**40** Zr 91.22 · 4 · 4682/2125/6.49 · [Kr]4d²5s² · Zirconium	**41** Nb 92.9064 · 5,3 · 5017/2740/8.55 · [Kr]4d⁴5s¹ · Niobium	**42** Mo 95.94 · 6,5,4,3,2 · 4912/2890/10.2 · [Kr]4d⁵5s¹ · Molybdenum	**43** Tc (98) · 7 · 4538/2473/11.5 · [Kr]4d⁵5s² · Technetium	
55 Cs 132.9054 · 1 · 944/301.55/1.87 · [Xe]6s¹ · Cesium	**56** Ba 137.33 · 2 · 2171/1002/3.5 · [Xe]6s² · Barium	**57** La ★ 138.9055 · 3 · 3730/1193/6.7 · [Xe]5d·6s² · Lanthanum	**72** Hf 178.49 · 4 · 4876/2500/13.1 · [Xe]4f¹⁴5d²6s² · Hafnium	**73** Ta 180.9479 · 5 · 5731/3287/16.6 · [Xe]4f¹⁴5d³6s² · Tantalum	**74** W 183.85 · 6,5,4,3,2 · 5828/3680/19.3 · [Xe]4f¹⁴5d⁴6s² · Tungsten	**75** Re 186.207 · 7,6,4,2,-1 · 5869/3453/21.0 · [Xe]4f¹⁴5d⁵6s² · Rhenium	
87 Fr (223) · 1 · 950/300/— · [Rn]7s¹ · Francium	**88** Ra 226.0254 · 2 · 1809/973/5 · |Rn|7s² · Radium	**89** Ac ★★ 227.0278 · 3 · 3473/1323/10.07 · [Rn]6d·7s² · Actinium	**104** Unq (261) · 5061/2028/11.7 · [Rn]5f¹⁴6d²7s² † · (Unnilquadium)	**105** Unp (262) · [Rn]5f¹⁴6d³7s² † · (Unnilpentium)	**106** Unh (263) · [Rn]5f¹⁴6d⁴7s² † · (Unnilhexium)		

VIIIA		
26 Fe 55.847 · 2,3 · 3135/1809/7.86 · |Ar|3d⁶4s² · Iron	**27** Co 58.9332 · 2,3 · 3201/1768/8.90 · |Ar|3d⁷4s² · Cobalt	**28** Ni 58.70 · 2,3 · 3187/1726/8.90 · |Ar|3d⁸4s² · Nickel
44 Ru 101.07 · 2,3,4,6,8 · 4423/2523/12.2 · [Kr] 4d⁷5s¹ · Ruthenium	**45** Rh 102.9055 · 2,3,4 · 3970/2236/12.4 · |Kr|4d⁸5s¹ · Rhodium	**46** Pd 106.4 · 2,4 · 3237/1825/12.0 · |Kr|4d¹⁰ · Palladium
76 Os 190.2 · 2,3,4,6,8 · 5285/3300/22.4 · [Xe]4f¹⁴5d⁶6s² · Osmium	**77** Ir 192.22 · 2,3,4,6 · 4701/2716/22.5 · [Xe]4f¹⁴5d⁷6s² · Iridium	**78** Pt 195.09 · 2,4 · 4100/2045/21.4 · [Xe]4f¹⁴5d⁹6s · Platinum

† The names and symbols of elements 104–106 are those recommended by IUPAC as systematic alternatives to those suggested by the purported discoverers. Berkeley (USA) researchers have proposed Rutherfordium, Rf, for element 104 and Hahnium, Ha, for element 105. Dubna (USSR) researchers, who also claim the discovery of these elements have proposed different names (and symbols).

Lanthanides (★)

| **58** Ce 140.12 · 3,4 · 3699/1071/6.78 · [Xe]4f¹5d¹6s² · Cerium | **59** Pr 140.9077 · 3,4 · 3785/1204/6.77 · |Xe|4f³6s² · Praseodymium | **60** Nd 144.24 · 3 · 3341/1204/7.00 · |Xe|4f⁴6s² · Neodymium | **61** Pm (145) · 3 · 3785/1204/7.54 · |Xe|4f⁵6s² · Promethium | **62** Sm 150.4 · 3,2 · 2064/1345/5.26 · |Xe|4f⁶6s² · Samarium | **63** Eu 151.96 · 3,2 · 1870/1090/7.89 · |Xe|4f⁷6s² · Europium | **64** Gd 157.25 · 3 · 3539/1585/ · [Xe]4f⁷5d¹6s² · Gadolinium |

Actinides (★★)

| **90** Th 232.0381 · 4 · 5061/2028/11.7 · [Rn]6d²7s² · Thorium | **91** Pa 231.0359 · 5,4 · 4407/1405/15.4 · |Rn|5f²6d¹7s² · Protactinium | **92** U 238.029 · 6,5,4,3 · 4407/1405/18.90 · |Rn|5f³6d¹7s² · Uranium | **93** Np 237.0482 · 6,5,4,3 · 910/20.4 · |Rn|5f⁴6d¹7s² · Neptunium | **94** Pu (244) · 6,5,4,3 · 3503/913/19.8 · |Rn|5f⁶7s² · Plutonium | **95** Am (243) · 6,5,4,3 · 2880/1268/13.6 · |Rn|5f⁷7s² · Americium | **96** Cm (247) · 3 · 1340/13.511 · |Rn|5f⁷6d¹7s² · Curium |

Modified from Sargent-Welch Scientific Company © Copyright 1979.

VIII

2	4.00260
4.215	
0.95	
0.1/87*	**He**
$1s^2$	
Helium	

IIIB   IVB   VB   VIB   VIIB

5	10.81
4275	
2300	**B** (3)
2.34	
$1s^22s^2p^1$	
Boron	

6	12.011
4470*	
4100*	**C** (±4,2)
2.62	
$1s^22s^2p^2$	
Carbon	

7	14.0067
77.35	
63.14	**N** (±3,5,4,2)
1.251*	
$1s^22s^2p^3$	
Nitrogen	

8	15.9994
90.18	
50.35	**O** (−2)
1.429*	
$1s^22s^2p^4$	
Oxygen	

9	18.998403
84.95	
53.48	**F** (−1)
1.696*	
$1s^22s^2p^5$	
Fluorine	

10	20.179
27.096	
24.553	**Ne**
0.901*	
$1s^22s^2p^6$	
Neon	

13	26.98154
2793	
933.25	**Al** (3)
2.70	
$|Ne|3s^2p^1$	
Aluminum	

14	28.0855
3540	
1685	**Si** (4)
2.33	
$|Ne|3s^2p^2$	
Silicon	

15	30.97376
550	
317.30	**P** (±3,5,4)
1.82	
$|Ne|3s^2p^3$	
Phosphorus	

16	32.06
717.75	
388.36	**S** (±2,4,6)
2.07	
$|Ne|3s^2p^4$	
Sulfur	

17	35.453
239.1	
172.16	**Cl** (±1,3,5,7)
3.17*	
$|Ne|3s^2p^5$	
Chlorine	

18	39.948
87.30	
83.81	**Ar**
1.784*	
$|Ne|3s^2p^6$	
Argon	

IB   IIB

29	63.546
2836	
1357.6	**Cu** (2,1)
8.96	
$|Ar|3d^{10}4s^1$	
Copper	

30	65.38
1180	
692.73	**Zn** (2)
7.14	
$|Ar|3d^{10}4s^2$	
Zinc	

31	69.72
2478	
302.90	**Ga** (3)
5.91	
$|Ar|3d^{10}4s^2p^1$	
Gallium	

32	72.59
3107	
1210.4	**Ge** (4)
5.32	
$|Ar|3d^{10}4s^2p^2$	
Germanium	

33	74.9216
876 (subl)	
1081 (28 atm)	**As** (±3,5)
5.72	
$|Ar|3d^{10}4s^2p^3$	
Arsenic	

34	78.96
958	
494	**Se** (−2,4,6)
4.80	
$|Ar|3d^{10}4s^2p^4$	
Selenium	

35	79.904
332.25	
265.90	**Br** (±1,5)
3.12	
$|Ar|3d^{10}4s^2p^5$	
Bromine	

36	83.80
119.80	
115.78	**Kr**
3.74*	
$|Ar|3d^{10}4s^2p^6$	
Krypton	

47	107.868
2436	
1234	**Ag** (1)
10.5	
$|Kr|4d^{10}5s^1$	
Silver	

48	112.41
1040	
594.18	**Cd** (2)
8.65	
$|Kr|4d^{10}5s^2$	
Cadmium	

49	114.82
2346	
429.76	**In** (3)
7.31	
$|Kr|4d^{10}5s^2p^1$	
Indium	

50	118.69
2876	
505.06	**Sn** (4,2)
7.30	
$|Kr|4d^{10}5s^2p^2$	
Tin	

51	121.75
1860	
904	**Sb** (±3,5)
6.68	
$|Kr|4d^{10}5s^2p^3$	
Antimony	

52	127.60
1261	
722.65	**Te** (−2,4,6)
6.24	
$|Kr|4d^{10}5s^2p^4$	
Tellurium	

53	126.9045
458.4	
386.7	**I** (±1,5,7)
4.92	
$|Kr|4d^{10}5s^2p^5$	
Iodine	

54	131.30
165.03	
161.36	**Xe**
5.89*	
$|Kr|4d^{10}5s^2p^6$	
Xenon	

79	196.9665
3130	
1337.58	**Au** (3,1)
19.3	
$4f^{14}5d^{10}6s^1$	
Gold	

80	200.59
630	
234.28	**Hg** (2,1)
13.53	
$|Xe|4f^{14}5d^{10}6s^2$	
Mercury	

81	204.37
1746	
577	**Tl** (3,1)
11.85	
$|Xe|4f^{14}5d^{10}6s^2p^1$	
Thallium	

82	207.2
2023	
600.6	**Pb** (4,2)
11.4	
$|Xe|4f^{14}5d^{10}6s^2p^2$	
Lead	

83	208.9804
1837	
544.52	**Bi** (3,5)
9.8	
$|Xe|4f^{14}5d^{10}6s^2p^3$	
Bismuth	

84	(209)
1235	
527	**Po** (4,2)
9.4	
$|Xe|4f^{14}5d^{10}6s^2p^4$	
Polonium	

85	(210)
610	
575	**At** (±1,3,5,7)
—	
$|Xe|4f^{14}5d^{10}6s^2p^5$	
Astatine	

86	(222)
211	
202	**Rn**
9.91*	
$|Xe|4f^{14}5d^{10}6s^2p^6$	
Radon	

The A & B subgroup designations, applicable to elements in rows 4, 5, 6, and 7, are those recommended by the International Union of Pure and Applied Chemistry. It should be noted that some authors and organizations use the opposite convention in distinguishing these subgroups.

* **Estimated Values**

65	158.9254
3496	
1630	**Tb** (3,4)
8.27	
$|Xe|4f^96s^2$	
Terbium	

66	162.50
2835	
1682	**Dy** (3)
8.54	
$|Xe|4f^{10}6s^2$	
Dysprosium	

67	164.9304
2968	
1743	**Ho** (3)
8.80	
$|Xe|4f^{11}6s^2$	
Holmium	

68	167.26
3136	
1795	**Er** (3)
9.05	
$|Xe|4f^{12}6s^2$	
Erbium	

69	168.9342
2220	
1818	**Tm** (3,2)
9.33	
$|Xe|4f^{13}6s^2$	
Thulium	

70	173.04
1467	
1097	**Yb** (3,2)
6.98	
$|Xe|4f^{14}6s^2$	
Ytterbium	

71	174.967
3668	
1936	**Lu** (3)
9.84	
$|Xe|4f^{14}5d^16s^2$	
Lutetium	

97	(247)
	Bk (4,3)
$|Rn|5f^97s^2$	
Berkelium	

98	(251)
900	**Cf**
$|Rn|5f^{10}7s^2$	
Californium	

99	(252)
	Es
$|Rn|5f^{11}7s^2$	
Einsteinium	

100	(257)
	Fm
$|Rn|5f^{12}7s^2$	
Fermium	

101	(258)
	Md
$|Rn|5f^{13}7s^2$	
Mendelevium	

102	(259)
	No
$|Rn|5f^{14}7s^2$	
Nobelium	

103	(260)
	Lr
$[Rn]5f^{14}6d^17s^2$	
Lawrencium	

APPENDIX Q
SOLUTIONS TO SELECTED ODD-NUMBERED EXERCISES AND PROBLEMS

CHAPTER 1

Exercises

1-1. Yes.

1-3. [mass][length]^2/[time]^2.

1-5. $b = 1, c = -1, d = 1$.

1-7. 0.2778 (m/s)/(km/h).

1-9. 4.5 m/s^2.

1-11. 62.4 pound-mass/ft^3.

1-13. 1007.7 s.

1-15. 7.69×10^{17}.

1-17. (a) 1.0100; (b) 1.0005; (c) near zero our rule holds, but near 90° the number of significant figures in sin x is greater than in x.

CHAPTER 2

Exercises

2-1. (a) 2.2 m; (b) 2.2 m; (c) 3.7 m.

2-7. (a) **d** and **e** opposite; (b) **d** and **e** parallel; (c) **d** and **e** opposite; (d) **d** and **e** perpendicular.

2-9. (b) 58 mm, 22°; (c) 54 mm, 22 mm.

2-11. (a) -260 m, 220 m; (b) 260 m, -220 m; (c) -260 m, 220 m, 35 m.

2-13. (a) $\sqrt{x^2 + y^2}$; (b) $(x/r)\mathbf{i} + (y/r)\mathbf{j}$.

2-15. (a) $\mathbf{i} - 2\mathbf{j} + 5\mathbf{k}$; (b) $5\mathbf{i} + 10\mathbf{j} - 5\mathbf{k}$; (c) $-5\mathbf{i} - 10\mathbf{j} + 5\mathbf{k}$; (d) $\mathbf{i} - 2\mathbf{j} + 5\mathbf{k}$.

2-19. (a) 1.9 km, 80° north of east.

2-21. (a) (25 mm, 0), (18 mm, 18 mm), (0, 25 mm), (-18 mm, 18 mm), (-25 mm, 0), (-18 mm, -18 mm), (0, -25 mm), (18 mm, -18 mm); (b) (**a**: 61 mm, 45°), (**b**: 66 mm, 112°), (**c**: 47 mm, 160°).

2-23. 170°.

2-25. (b) 180°; (c) 0.

Problems

2-1. (c) $F_x = F \cos \alpha, F_y = F \cos \beta, F_z = F \cos \gamma$.

2-3. (a) 90°; (b) 60°; (c) 180°; (d) 0°.

2-5. (b) $x/r, y/r, z/r; r = \sqrt{x^2 + y^2 + z^2}$.

CHAPTER 3

Exercises

3-1. (a) -16 m; (b) 37 m; (c) $(-16$ m$)\mathbf{i}$; (d) $(37$ m$)\mathbf{i}$; (e) $(53$ m$)\mathbf{i}$.

3-3.   (a) For example, $x(2.0 \text{ s}) = 40$ mm; (b) 153 mm; (c) $(-49 \text{ mm})\mathbf{i}$.
3-5.   (a) 0.3048 (m/s)/(ft/s); (b) 82 ft/s.
3-7.   (a) 500 s; (b) 9 light-minutes.
3-9.   200 m.
3-11. (a) 29 m/s; (b) 26 m/s.
3-13. (a) 0.87 m/s; (b) 1.3 m/s; (c) 1.7 m/s; (d) 2.0 m/s; (e) 2.5 m/s.
3-15. 4×10^4 m/s.
3-17. (a) $x(t) = 0.03 \text{ m} + (1.3 \text{ m/s})t$; (b) $x(t) = 0.95 \text{ m} - (1.3 \text{ m/s})t$.
3-19. (a) 0.9 m/s²; (b) -0.9 m/s².
3-21. (a) -0.17 m/s²; (b) 0.21 m/s²; (c) 0.25 m/s².
3-23. (a) $a_x(t) = 4.2 \text{ m/s}^2 - (9.6 \text{ m/s}^3)t$; (b) -35 m/s²; (c) 4.2 m/s².
3-25. 3.6 m/s.
3-27. (a) $x(t) = 15 \text{ m} + (2.2 \text{ m/s})t$; (b) 77 m; (c) 16 s.
3-29. (a) $v_x(t) = (3.6 \text{ m/s}^2)t$; (b) 86 m/s; (c) $x(t) = (1.8 \text{ m/s}^2)t^2$.
3-31. (a) 12 m/s; (b) 16 m/s.
3-33. 1.8 m/s².
3-35. (a) 1.65; (b) 2.3 s.
3-37. 4.2 s.
3-39. 2×10^5 m/s².
3-41. (a) 3.0 m; (b) 2.9 m/s; (c) 3.2 m/s²; (d) $x(t) = 3.0 \text{ m} + (2.9 \text{ m/s})t + (1.6 \text{ m/s}^2)t^2$.
3-43. 0.64 g.
3-45. 10 m/s².
3-47. (a) $h_m = 9.1 \text{ m}$, $t_m = 1.2 \text{ s}$; (b) 0.71 s and 1.7 s; (c) 7.8 m and 7.8 m.
3-49. 10 m/s.

Problems

3-1.   (a) 11.5 m/s; (b) 2.6 s; (c) 7.4 s; (d) 4.4 m/s².
3-3.   (a) 7.8 s; (b) 140 m; (c) 36 m/s.
3-5.   1.6 km.
3-11. Tails up.

CHAPTER 4

Exercises

4-1.   (a) $\mathbf{r} = (31.8 \text{ m})\mathbf{i} + (31.8 \text{ m})\mathbf{j}$; (b) $\Delta\mathbf{r} = -(45.0 \text{ m})\mathbf{i} + (45.0 \text{ m})\mathbf{j}$; (c) 70.7 m.
4-3.   (a) $\overline{\mathbf{v}} = -(1.34 \text{ m/s})\mathbf{i} + (1.34 \text{ m/s})\mathbf{j}$; (b) $\overline{\mathbf{v}} = -(1.45 \text{ m/s})\mathbf{i} + (1.45 \text{ m/s})\mathbf{j}$.
4-5.   (a) $\mathbf{v} = (11.5 \text{ m/s})\mathbf{j}$; (b) $\mathbf{a} = (0.88 \text{ m/s})\mathbf{j}$; (c) $\mathbf{v} = (16 \text{ m/s})\mathbf{i} + (16 \text{ m/s})\mathbf{j}$; (d) $\overline{\mathbf{a}} = (1.7 \text{ m/s}^2)\mathbf{i} - (1.7 \text{ m/s}^2)\mathbf{j}$.
4-7.   (a) $\mathbf{v} = (3.5 \text{ m/s})\mathbf{i} + (5.1 \text{ m/s})\mathbf{j}$.
4-9.   (a) $v_h = 14$ m/s; (b) $v_v = 7.8$ m/s.
4-11. (a) $a_x = 1.7 \text{ m/s}^2$, $a_y = -0.47 \text{ m/s}^2$, $v_x = (1.7 \text{ m/s}^2)t$, $v_y = -(0.47 \text{ m/s}^2)t$, $x = (0.87 \text{ m/s}^2)t^2$, $y = -(0.23 \text{ m/s}^2)t^2$; (b) $a_x = 1.81 \text{ m/s}^2$, $a_y = 0$, $v_x = (1.81 \text{ m/s}^2)t$, $v_y = 0$, $x = (0.905 \text{ m/s}^2)t^2$, $y = 0$.
4-13. $v_x = 17 \text{ m/s}$, $v_y = 32 \text{ m/s} - (9.8 \text{ m/s}^2)t$, $x = (17 \text{ m/s})t$, $y = (32 \text{ m/s})t - (4.9 \text{ m/s}^2)t^2$.
4-15. 16 m/s.
4-17. (a) 13°; (b) 77°.
4-19. (a) 5.1 s; (b) 130 m; (c) 140 m.
4-21. $v_0 = 28 \text{ m/s}$, $\theta_0 = 45°$.

4-23. (a) 1.6 m/s²; (b) 2.9 m/s².

4-25. (a) 23 m/s northeast; (b) 23 m/s southwest; (c) $\mathbf{a}_D = (2.6 \text{ m/s}^2)\mathbf{i} - (2.6 \text{ m/s}^2)\mathbf{j}$, $\mathbf{a}_H = -(1.3 \text{ m/s}^2)\mathbf{i} - (1.3 \text{ m/s}^2)\mathbf{j}$.

4-27. (a) 5.5 m/s; (b) 31 m/s.

4-29. (a) 3.37×10^{-2} m/s² $= 3.44 \times 10^{-3}$ g; (b) 5.9×10^{-3} m/s² $= 6.1 \times 10^{-4}$ g; (c) 2.2×10^{-10} m/s² $= 2.2 \times 10^{-11}$ g.

4-31. (b) 14 m/s².

4-33. (a) 6 m/s; (b) 6 m/s south; (c) 6 m/s; (d) 6 m/s north.

4-35. 4.3 m/s 11° north of east.

4-37. (a) $\mathbf{v}_{BW} = -(2.3 \text{ m/s})\mathbf{i} + (7.5 \text{ m/s})\mathbf{j}$; (b) 4.0 min; (c) $\mathbf{v}_{BW} = -(4.6 \text{ m/s})\mathbf{i} + (6.3 \text{ m/s})\mathbf{j}$, 4.8 min.

Problems

4-1. (e) $\mathbf{v} = -(1.49 \text{ m/s})\mathbf{i} + (1.49 \text{ m/s})\mathbf{j}$, $\mathbf{a} = -(6.95 \times 10^{-2} \text{ m/s}^2)\mathbf{i} - (6.95 \times 10^{-2} \text{ m/s}^2)\mathbf{j}$; (f) uniform circular motion.

4-3. (b) 38°; (c) 76°; (d) $h_m = R_m/4$.

4-5. 130 m.

4-9. (b) $(0.900)v^2/R$; (c) $(0.974)v^2/R$; (d) $(0.996)v^2/R$; (e) $(1.000)v^2/R$; (f) 1/2.

4-11. 3.8 m/s².

4-13. (a) 108 s; (b) 87 s; (c) parallel to the current took longer by 21 s.

4-15. 70 m/s.

4-17. (a) 8.4 m/s; (b) 13 m/s.

4-19. (b) $v_x = v - v \cos (vt/R)$, $v_y = v \sin (vt/R)$; (c) $a_x = (v^2/R) \sin (vt/R)$, $a_y = (v^2/R) \cos (vt/R)$.

CHAPTER 5

Exercises

5-1. 4.9 sl.

5-3. (a) 14 kN; (b) 630 tons.

5-5. (a) $F_1 = 6.6$ N, F_2 13.0 N; (b) $\theta_1 = 111°$, $\theta_2 = -49°$; (d) $|\Sigma F| = 7.1$ N, $\theta = 31°$.

5-7. 300 N, 19° east of north.

5-9. (b) $\mathbf{F}_{air} = 720$ N up, $\mathbf{F}_e = 720$ N down.

5-11. 1.8 kN.

5-13. (a) 10 N; (b) 10^{-21} s.

5-15. 50 N.

5-17. 2 kN.

5-19. (a) 7×10^{28} N; (b) 3.5×10^{22} N.

5-21. 1.24 kg.

5-23. (a) $\mathbf{F}_{12} = (4 \text{ N})\mathbf{i}$, $\mathbf{F}_{21} = -(4 \text{ N})\mathbf{i}$; (b) $\mathbf{F}_{12} = (8 \text{ N})\mathbf{i}$, $\mathbf{F}_{21} = -(8 \text{ N})\mathbf{i}$.

5-25. 13 m/s².

5-27. (a) 8.9×10^{-30} N.

5-29. (a) 970 N; (b) 520 N; (c) 750 N

5-31. 1.7 s.

5-33. (b) 270 N up; (c) 4.2 m/s²; (d) 3.5 m.

5-35. (a) 21 N; (b) 6.5 N.

5-37. (a) 2.5 mN; (b) 7.2 mN.

5-39. (b) 1.5 N; (c) 15 N.

Problems

5-1. 6.5×10^{-3} m/s^2.

5-3. (b) 16 kg.

5-5. 7.6 m/s^2.

5-7. $F_{T1} = 10$ N, $F_{T2} = 6$ N, $F_{T3} = 4$ N.

5-11. 9.5 m.

CHAPTER 6

Exercises

6-1. (a) 310 N; (b) 190 N; (c) zero.

6-3. (a) 180 N; (b) 160 N.

6-5. (a) 1.1; (b) 0.75.

6-7. Yes, $v = 30$ m/s.

6-9. 11 m.

6-11. (c) $F_N = 310$ N, $F_c = 370$ N.

6-13. 4.2 m/s^2.

6-15. (a) 77 N; (b) 71 N.

6-17. 83 N.

6-19. 0.25 m/s^2.

6-21. 0.061 m/s^2.

6-23. 12°.

6-25. 1.1 km.

6-27. (a) 3.7 m/s^2; (b) 3.3 kN; (c) 8.6 kN; (d) 9.2 kN; (e) 21°.

6-29. 0.11.

6-31. (a) $v_m = \sqrt{gR}$; (b) 3.1 m/s.

6-33. (a) 1.0 kN; (b) 6.7 m/s; (c) 6.6 s.

6-35. (a) 12.8 m/s^2; (b) 5.2 Mm.

6-37. (a) 1.5 N away from center; (b) 13°.

Problems

6-3. $F_{a,\mathrm{min}} = \dfrac{mg}{\mu_s}\left(1 + \dfrac{m}{M}\right).$

6-5. (c) 290 N; (d) 35°; (e) 350 N.

6-7. 33 m.

6-9. (a) 0.64 m/s^2; (b) 46 N.

CHAPTER 7

Exercises

7-3. (a) 2.72×10^{-3} m/s^2; (b) 4.01×10^{14} m^3/s^2; (c) 4.0×10^{14} m^3/s^2; (d) it is an inverse-square force.

7-5. 1.3×10^{-10} N.

7-7. 0.64 m.

7-9. 20 Mm.

7-11. (a) 1.80×10^{15} N; (b) 41.8×10^{15} N; (c) 8.69×10^{15} N.

7-13. See Table 7-1.

7-15. (a) 1.984×10^{-29} C/kg; (b) 39.5 C.

7-17. 259 Mm, 0.175 percent.

7-19. 432 Mm.

7-21. 3.18×10^{-5}.

7-23. $F = \sqrt{3}Gm^2/a^2$

7-25. 9.75 m/s².

7-27. 0.003.

7-29.   (a) 3.7 N/kg; (b) 260 N.

7-31. $\mathbf{g} = (2.2 \times 10^{-11}$ N/kg$)\mathbf{i} - (5.5 \times 10^{-11}$ N/kg$)\mathbf{j}$.

7-33.   (a) 7.44×10^3 m/s; (b) 6.07×10^3 s.

7-35.   (a) 1.37×10^3 m/s; (b) same as Table 7-2 except

```
110 Y=2.61E+7
120 VX=1.37E+3
130 DT=12
210 AX=-4.90E+12*X/(X*X+Y*Y)^1.5
220 AY=-4.90E+12*Y/(X*X+Y*Y)^1.5
```

7-37.   (a) 42.2 Mm; (b) 3.07×10^3 m/s; (c) 0.223 m/s².

7-39. $r^3/T^2 = 3.21 \times 10^{15}$ m³/s².

7-41.   See Table 7-1.

Problems

7-1.   (a) $G \approx 14 \times 10^{-11}$ N · m²/kg² (in error by more than a factor of 2); (b) 5.51×10^3 kg/m³.

7-3.   (a) 2.908×10^{25} kg; (b) 8.00×10^3 kg/m³; (c) 21.3 N/kg; (d) 17.8 N.

7-5.   (a) $x_n = x_c/(1 + \sqrt{m_c/m_b})$; (b) $x_n = 2$m.

7-7.
```
275 R=(X*X+Y*Y)^0.5
280 IF I=50*INT(I/50) THEN PRINT T,X,Y,R
```

7-9.
```
275 L=(X*VY+Y*VX)
280 IF I=50*INT(I/50) THEN PRINT T,X,Y,L
```

CHAPTER 8

Exercises

8-1.   (a) 40 N, up; (b) 80 J.

8-5.   (a) -15 J; (b) 0.030.

8-9.   (a) 3 J; (b) $87°$.

8-13.   (a) 21 J; (b) minimum $= 0$, maximum $= 290$ N.

8-17. $C(1/z_f - 1/z_i)$.

8-21.   (a) 22 J; (b) 0.

8-23.   (a) 86 kJ; (b) 170 kJ.

8-25. 11 m/s.

8-27.   (a) -2.9 J; (b) 0.050; (c) 4.6 N; (d) 0.

8-29.   (a) -5.8 J; (b) 12 m/s.

8-31. 4.8 m/s.

8-33. 210 J.

8-35. 410 N.

8-37.   (a) 2100 hp; (b) 690 kN; (c) 2.1 MN.

Problems

8-1.   (a) -160 J; (b) -100 J; (c) 0; (d) -60 J; (e) 1.4 m.

8-3. 0.

8-5.   (a) 14 kJ; (b) -14 kJ; (c) 1.0 kW; (d) 1.2 kW; (e) 0.5 kW.

8-7.   (a) 4.7 m/s; (b) 42 N.

CHAPTER 9

Exercises

9-1. (a) 54 J; (b) 54 J; (c) 10 m.
9-3. (a) 0.21 m; (b) 11 m/s; (c) 0.18 m.
9-5. 4.2 MN/m.
9-7. (a) 3.5 kJ; (b) no; (c) 9.6 m/s.
9-9. (a) 60 J; (b) 4.9 m/s; (c) 4.2 m/s.
9-11. (a) 2.0 m; (b) 200 J; (c) 1.0 m; (d) 100 N.
9-13. (a) 0.18×10^{-20} J; (b) -0.067 nm.
9-15. (a) -2 kJ; (b) 2 kJ; (c) 0.
9-17. (a) $-(3 \text{ N})(x_f - x_i) - (4 \text{ N})(y_f - y_i)$; (b) $-(3 \text{ N})x - (4 \text{ N})y$; (c) -48 J; (d) 0.
9-19. (a) 87 J; (b) 26 m/s; (c) 44 J.
9-21. (a) 1.1 m/s; (b) $mg(3 - 2 \cos 30°)$.
9-23. $\sqrt{3gr}$.
9-25. (a) 2.7 J if y is measured from the initial position on the countertop;
       (b) 8.6 kN/m; (c) 6.2 m.
9-27. (a) -4200 J.
9-29. (a) 6 kJ.
9-31. (a) $0.05 \, mg \approx 500$ N; (b) 10 kW.
9-33. (a) $\Delta K = -59$ J, $\Delta U = 45$ J, $\Delta E_{\text{int}} = 14$ J.
9-35. (a) -1.7×10^{11} J; (b) 8.5×10^{10} J; (c) -8.5×10^{10} J; (d) kinetic energy.
9-37. (a) -3.8×10^{32} J; (b) 2.3×10^{32} J.
9-39. (a) 7.0 km/s; (b) 7.5 km/s.

Problems

9-1. (a) 0.19 m; (b) 7.7 m/s.
9-3. (a) $U = mgy + \frac{1}{2}ky^2$; (b) $F_y = -mg - ky$.
9-7. (b) $\sqrt{2ghm_1/(m_1 + m_2)}$.

CHAPTER 10

Exercises

10-1. $x_{cm} = 1.1$ m. $y_{cm} = 0.79$ m.
10-3. $x_{cm} = 25$ mm, $y_{cm} = 25$ mm.
10-5. $x_{cm} = 0$, $y_{cm} = 0$, $z_{cm} = 3R/8$.
10-7. 0.50 m/s.
10-9. 1.2 m/s² in a direction down the plane.
10-11. (a) Gravity and tension on each mass; (b) 0.34 m above the 2.5-kg
        mass; (c) 0.98 m/s².
10-13. 1.78×10^{29} kg m/s; perpendicular to radior to sun.
10-15. 1.4×10^5 kg m/s, southeast.
10-17. (a) 4.02 m/s; (b) 29.3 J.
10-19. 0.23 m/s.
10-21. m_2/m_1.
10-23. 9.0×10^4 N.
10-25. 600 bullets/s.
10-27. 0.68 m/s, -1.4×10^4 J.
10-29. $(-0.17 \text{ m/s})\mathbf{i} + (-0.24 \text{ m/s})\mathbf{j}$; (0.29 m/s, 54.7°).
10-31. 9.1 s.
10-33. 5.0 m/s.
10-35. 1.2×10^5 m/s.

10-37.   420 m/s.

10-39. $v_A = 5.4$ m/s (west), $v_B = 3.1$ m/s (east).

10-43.   18 km/h, 79° south of east.

10-47.   (a) $\Delta P = 20$ kg m/s (if system is truck plus water remaining in truck); (b) 20 N.

10-49.   (a) 1.1 kN, 9.5° from incoming direction toward outgoing direction; (b) 9.5 kN.

10-51.   (a) 20 N; (b) 10^4 s; (c) 100 kg.

Problems

10-7.   (a) 2×10^{-5} mm; (b) gravity and the string tension. Large internal forces are present.

CHAPTER 11

Exercises

11-1.   (a) 7.8 N · m, clockwise; (b) 0; (c) 7.8 N · m, counterclockwise; (d) 0.

11-3.   (a) 200 N; (b) 200 N, assuming a l-m moment arm.

11-5.   (a) at 20.9 cm; (b) 14 N.

11-7.   400 N.

11-9.   (a) 0 vertical, 24 kN horizontal, 31 kN tension; (b) along the boom to the right.

11-11.   (a) 10 kN front, 40 kN rear; (b) 36 kN.

11-13.   280 N horizontal, 310 N tension, 350 N vertical.

11-15.   (a) $0.81\,F_e$; (b) $0.33\,F_e$ horizontal to the left, $0.19\,F_e$ vertically up; (c) toward the center of the disk.

11-17.   (a) $F_a/\sqrt{2}$ tension, $\frac{1}{2}F_a$ friction, $\frac{1}{2}F_a$ normal.

11-19. $x = 0.56$ m, $y = 3.44$ m relative to the pin.

11-21.   45°.

11-23. $(369$ N · m$)\mathbf{i} + (224$ N · m$)\mathbf{j} + (660$ N · m$)\mathbf{k}$.

11-25.   1 m³.

11-27.   (b) $\mathbf{i} + 7\mathbf{j} - 5\mathbf{k}$.

Problems

11-1.   6.0 m.

11-3. $\frac{1}{2}F_e$, $\mu_s \geqslant \frac{1}{2}$.

11-5.   (a) 150 N on the left, 130 N on the right; (b) 120 N; (c) 120 N at 15° with the horizontal.

11-7.   (a) 28-kN tension, $P_x = 28$ kN, $P_y = 18$ kN; (b) 12-kN tension, $P_x = 11$ kN, $P_y = 21$ kN.

11-11. 10^{-9} N · m.

CHAPTER 12

Exercises

12-1.   (a) 2.1 rad; (b) 120°; (c) 0.33 r.

12-3.   (a) 0.51 m; (b) 0.51 m.

12-5. 2.6×10^9 m.

12-7.   8.2 rad/s.

12-9.   (a) $-(4.2$ rad/s³$)t^2$; (b) -19 rad/s; (d) 19 rad/s; (c) -6.2 rad.

12-11. $\theta(t) = -(3.5$ rad/s$)t$.

12-13.   (a) $\alpha_z = -2.2$ rad/s²; (b) $\theta(t) = (5.8$ rad/s$)t - (1.1$ rad/s²$)t^2$; (c) $t_q =$

2.6 s; (d) north before t_q, south after t_q; (e) $\omega_z{}^2 = (5.8 \text{ rad/s})^2 - (4.4 \text{ rad/s}^2)\theta$.

12-15. (a) $\omega_z(t) = -(1.4 \text{ rad/s}^2)t$; (b) $\theta(t) = -(0.7 \text{ rad/s}^2)t^2$; (c) $\omega_z{}^2 = -(2.7 \text{ rad/s}^2)\theta$.

12-17. 9.7 mm/s.

12-19. (a) $|a_t| = 0.25 \text{ m/s}^2$, $|a_R| = 0.16 \text{ m/s}^2$; (b) $v = 0.48 \text{ m/s}$, $a = 0.30 \text{ m/s}^2$.

12-21. (a) $(ML^2)(T^{-2}) = ML^2T^{-2}$; (b) $(\text{kg} \cdot \text{m}^2)(\text{s}^{-2}) = \text{kg}(\text{m/s})^2 = \text{J}$.

12-23. $0.34 \text{ kg} \cdot \text{m}^2$.

12-25. (a) $20 \text{ kg} \cdot \text{m}^2$; (b) $9 \text{ kg} \cdot \text{m}^2$; (c) $29 \text{ kg} \cdot \text{m}^2$.

12-27. $34 \text{ kg} \cdot \text{m}^2$.

12-29. $Ma^2/6$.

12-31. $13Mr_0{}^2/20$.

12-33. (a) 4.1 rad/s; (b) 2.8 m/s.

12-35. (a) 3.9 m/s; (b) 41 rad/s.

12-37. 5 J, 1/2.

Problems

12-1. (a) $\alpha_z = 2.6 \text{ rad/s}^2$, $\omega_{z0} = -5.1 \text{ rad/s}$; (b) $\omega_z = -5.1 \text{ rad/s} + (2.6 \text{ rad/s}^2)t$, $\theta = -(5.1 \text{ rad/s})t + (1.3 \text{ rad/s}^2)t^2$.

12-3. $K_{\text{orbit}} = 2.7 \times 10^{33} \text{ J}$, $K_{\text{spin}} = 2.6 \times 10^{29} \text{ J}$.

12-5. (b) $v = \sqrt{2gh/(1 + K^2/R^2)}$.

12-7. $I = MR^2/4$.

12-9. $6.0 \times 10^{-5} \text{ kg} \cdot \text{m}^2$.

12-11. (a) $v = \sqrt{2gh/[1 + (M/2m)]}$; (b) $\omega = (1/R_0)\sqrt{2gh/[1 + (M/2m)]}$.

12-13. (a) $(2.5 \text{ rad/s})\mathbf{k}$; (b) $-(1.8 \text{ rad/s}^2)\mathbf{k}$; (c) $-(32 \text{ m/s}^2)\mathbf{i} - (9.8 \text{ m/s}^2)\mathbf{j}$.

CHAPTER 13

Exercises

13-1. (a) $6.10 \times 10^6 \text{ kg} \cdot \text{m}^2/\text{s}$, down; (b) $6.10 \times 10^6 \text{ kg} \cdot \text{m}^2/\text{s}$, down.

13-3. $(100 \text{ kg} \cdot \text{m}^2/\text{s})\mathbf{k}$.

13-5. $-(0.25 \text{ kg} \cdot \text{m}^2/\text{s})\mathbf{k}$.

13-7. $-(2.4 \text{ kg} \cdot \text{m}^2/\text{s})\mathbf{i} + (1.6 \text{ kg} \cdot \text{m}^2/\text{s})\mathbf{j} - (6.1 \text{ kg} \cdot \text{m}^2/\text{s})\mathbf{k}$.

13-11. $3.3 \times 10^{-3} \text{ kg} \cdot \text{m}^2/\text{s}$, down.

13-13. $\alpha_z = 120 \text{ rad/s}^2$, $\omega_z = (120 \text{ rad/s}^2)t$, $\theta = \theta_0 + (60 \text{ rad/s}^2)t^2$.

13-15. (a) $\alpha = 64 \text{ rad/s}^2$; (b) 30 rad/s².

13-17. $0.016 \text{ kg} \cdot \text{m}^2$.

13-19. (a) $m_c g/[m_c + m_b + (I_0/R_0{}^2)]$ (b) $m_b m_c g/[m_c + m_b + (I_0/R_0{}^2)]$ (c) $m_c g[m_b + (I_0/R_0{}^2)]/[m_c + m_b + (I_0/R_0{}^2)]$

13-21. 720 N.

13-25. 0.21 m/s.

13-27. (a) 42 rad/s; (b) $K_f - K_i = 350$ J.

13-29. (c) $\omega = mD(v_i + v_f)/(Mw^2/3)$; (d) 4.7 rad/s.

13-31. (b) 27 N.

13-33. (a) $2v/D$; (b) $\Delta K = 0$.

Problems

13-3. $h = 2r_0/5$.

13-7. $h = 27R_0/10$.

13-11. (b) $W = -\frac{1}{2}mv_i{}^2(1 - R_i{}^2/R_f{}^2)$.

13-15. (b) $Mg\sqrt{1 + [M^4g^2D^6/(I_s\omega_s)^4]}$; (c) $\tan^{-1}[M^2gD^3/(I_s\omega_s)^2]$.

CHAPTER 14

Exercises

14-1. 1.1 s, 0.92 Hz.

14-3. (a) $x(t) = (0.063$ m$)$ cos $[(4.1$ rad/s$)t]$,
$v_x(t) = -(0.26$ m/s$)$ sin $[(4.1$ rad/s$)t]$,
$a_x(t) = -(1.1$ m/s$^2)$ cos $[(4.1$ rad/s$)t]$,
(b) $x(1.7$ s$) = 0.049$ m, $v_x(1.7$ s$) = -0.16$ m/s, $a_x(1.7$ s$) = -0.82$ m/s^2.

14-5. (a) $\omega = 7.1$ rad/s, $A = 0.25$ m, $\nu = 1.1$ Hz, $T = 0.88$ s, $\phi = \pi$ rad;
(b) $x(t) = -(0.25$ m$)$ cos $[(7.1$ rad/s$)t]$, $a_x(t) = (13$ m/s$^2)$ cos $[(7.1$ rad/s$)t]$
(c) $x(0.25$ s$) = 0.051$ m, $v_x(0.25$ s$) = 1.8$ m/s, $a_x(0.25$ s$) = -2.6$ m/s^2.

14-7. (a) $x(t) = (0.29$ m$)$ cos $[(6.7$ rad/s$)t + \pi/2]$,
$v_x(t) = -(1.9$ m/s$)$ sin $[(6.7$ rad/s$)t + \pi/2]$,
$a_x(t) = -(13$ m/s$^2)$ cos $[(6.7$ rad/s$)t + \pi/2]$;
(b) $x(0.54$ s$) = 0.13$ m, $v_x(0.54$ s$) = 1.7$ m/s, $a_x(0.54$ s$) = -5.9$ m/s^2.

14-9. $A = 0.49$ m, $v_{max} = 1.3$ m/s, $a_{max} = 3.4$ m/s^2.

14-11. (a) 7.2 rad/s; (b) 1.1 Hz; (c) 0.88 s.

14-13. 32 N/m.

14-15. 0.34 kg.

14-17. 0.083 J.

14-19. (a) $U = (24$ mJ$)$cos$^2[(6.5$ rad/s$)t]$.
(b) $K = (24$ mJ$)$sin$^2[(6.5$ rad/s$)t]$.

14-21. (a) 0.047 m; (b) 0.33 m/s; (c) 0.32 m/s; (d) 0.030 m.

14-23. (a) 1.67 kg; (b) 19.3 N/m.

14-25. (a) 1.00 J; (b) 1.38 J; (c) at $y = 0$, 0.39 m/s; (d) 1.2 J.

14-27. (a) 3 s; (b) 0.3 Hz, 0.4 m/s.

14-29. (a) 1.6 s; (b) 1.5 s.

14-31. (a) 2.65×10^{-5} N $\cdot$ m; (b) 284 rad/s^2.

14-33. (a) 2.1 s; (b) 0.13 mJ.

14-35. $x = (150$ mm$)$ cos $[(3.5$ rad/s$)t]$, $v_x = -(0.52$ m/s$)$ sin $[(3.5$ rad/s$)t]$,
$a_x = -(1.8$ m/s$^2)$ cos $[(3.5$ rad/s$)t]$.

14-37. (b) L sin θ, $\sqrt{g/(L \sin \theta)}$.

14-39. (a) After an additional 2.4 min; (b) 4.8×10^{-3} s^{-1}.

14-41. (a) 1.2×10^{-3} s^{-1}; (b) 9:31.

14-47. (a) 9.3 mm; (b) $\tan^{-1}(-4.0) = -1.3$ rad $[+\pi] = 1.8$ rad; (c) 11 mm
for $\omega_E = \omega$.

Problems

14-1. $T/6$.

14-3. (a) 0.09 s; (b) 0.11 s; (c) 0.16 s.

14-7. 0.75 s.

14-9. (a) $P(t) = -\dfrac{F_0{}^2\omega_E}{m\sqrt{\omega_E{}^2 - \omega^2)^2 + 4\gamma^2\omega_E{}^2}}$ cos $\omega_E t$ sin $(\omega_E t - \phi_E)$

CHAPTER 15

Exercises

15-1. 1.33 MPa.

15-3. (a) 34 kPa; (b) 30 kPa.

15-5. (a) 1.21×10^5; (b) 154 nm.

15-7. (a) 8.4×10^{-7}; (b) 8.4×10^{-7} rad; (c) 0.43 μm.

15-9. 1.98×10^4 kg/m^3.

15-11. (a) 1.01×10^3 kg/m^3; (b) 11.3×10^3 kg/m^3.

15-13.   98 MPa.

15-15.   37.1 kPa.

15-17.   4.8 N.

15-19.   1050 m^3.

15-23.   1.00129.

15-25.   (a) 3.3×10^{-3} m^3/s, 6.7×10^{-3} m^3/s; (b) 3.4 m/s; (c) 71 kPa.

15-29. -2.5 kPa.

15-31.   (a) 7.7 m/s; (b) 0.19 m^3/s; (c) 1.8×10^4 Pa, 2.3×10^4 Pa.

15-33.   0.32 N.

15-35.   0.544 m^3.

Problems

15-1.   (a) 4.8 kg; (b) 6.8×10^3 kg/m^3; (c) 0.47 mm.

15-3. $(\rho_c - \rho_0)/(\rho - \rho_0)$.

15-5.   1.06 km, 2.6 km.

15-7. $80h_1$.

15-9.   42 min.

15-11.   (b) 12.3°, (c) $(mg)^2/(4YA \sin^2 \theta)$, $(mg)^2/(2YA \sin^2 \theta)$, if the weight were slowly lowered, other forces would do work.

CHAPTER 16

Exercises

16-1. 10^6 years

16-3.   (a) 0.282 m; (b) 8.03 kN.

16-5.   (a) 3650 Pa; (b) 77.1 K.

16-7.   (a) 17.9 mm$_{Hg}$; (b) 17.9 mm$_{Hg}$; (c) 20.4 mm$_{Hg}$.

16-9.   35°C.

16-11.   (a) $-40°$; (b) 575 K; (c) 0; (d) none.

16-13.   (a) 9.997 mm; (b) 0.03%; (c) 30 mm.

16-15.   (a) $-22°$C; (b) no.

16-17.   (a) -2.8×10^{-5} s; (b) 2.4 s gain.

16-19.   280 mm.

16-23.   600 W.

16-25.   (a) 1700°C/m; (b) 0.070 W $\cdot$ K^{-1} $\cdot$ m^{-1}; (c) insulator.

16-27.   (a) 3800 Btu/h; (b) 0.77; (c) 0.14 W $\cdot$ K^{-1} $\cdot$ m^{-1}.

16-31.   (a) 45 W; (b) 160 kJ.

16-33.   (a) 70 MW/m^2; (b) 500 W/m^2; (c) 100 W/m^2; (d) 5 μW/m^2.

Problems

16-5.   (a) 86 W; (b) $T = 140°C - (124°C) \ln (r/12 \text{ mm})$; (d) -6.2×10^3 C°/m.

16-9. $T = T_2 - \dfrac{T_2 - T_1}{L} x$

CHAPTER 17

Exercises

17-1.   (a) 2/3.

17-3.   (a) 3.3×10^{-3} mol; (b) 0.49 kPa.

17-5.   0.0823 atm $\cdot$ L $\cdot$ mol^{-1} $\cdot$ K^{-1}.

17-7. 2.7×10^{25} molecules/m^3.

17-9.   30 J.

17-11.   (a) 24°C; (b) 11 kJ.

17-13.   1.1 kg.

17-15.   (a) 58.1°C.

17-17.   (a) 8.08 kJ; (b) −8.08 kJ.

17-19.   (a) 60 kJ; (b) −55 kJ; (c) 5 kJ.

17-21.   (a) $\frac{1}{2}(p_i + p_f)(V_f - V_i)$.

17-23.   (a) 3.1 kJ; (b) 120 kPa; (c) 1100 K, 940 K.

17-25.   (a) 9 kJ; (b) 21 kJ; (c) 25 kJ.

17-27.   (a) 6.0 kJ; (b) 9.0 kJ; (c) 15.0 kJ.

17-29.   7.53 kJ.

Problems

17-1.   (a) 20.7 J · mol⁻¹ · K⁻¹ + (0.0123 J · mol⁻¹ · K⁻²)T; (c) 13 kJ.

17-3.   (a) $1/p$; (b) $\dfrac{1 - b/V}{p - a/V^2 + 2ab/V^3}$

CHAPTER 18

Exercises

18-1.   (a) 298 m/s; (b) 1.01 × 10⁵ m²/s²; (c) $\langle v \rangle^2 = 0.89 \times 10^5$ m²/s².

18-5.   500.

18-9.   (a) 520 m/s; (b) 480 m/s; (c) 410 m/s; (d) 6.2 × 10⁻²¹ J.

18-11.   (a) 1.2; (b) 0.8; (c) 2.3.

18-13.   (a) 0.01 eV; (b) 0.04 eV; (c) 0.8 eV.

18-15.   (a) $\langle v_x \rangle = 80$ km/h, $\langle v_y \rangle = \langle v_z \rangle = 0$; (b) $\langle v_x \rangle = \langle v_y \rangle = \langle v_z \rangle = 0$.

18-17.   (a) 6.0 kJ.

18-19.   (a) 6.0 kJ, 0; (b) 29.4 J · mol⁻¹ · K⁻¹; (c) 8.4 kJ, 2.4 kJ.

18-21.   (a) 23.1 J · mol⁻¹ · K⁻¹.

18-23.   1.7, 1.4, 1.3.

18-25.   (a) 0, approximately; (b) −1.1 kJ.

18-27.   (a) 160 kPa; (b) 330 K, 250 K.

18-29. $T_i/V_i = T_f/V_f$ for an isobaric process.

18-31.   (a) 1.3 kJ; (b) 1.3 kJ; (c) 1.3 kJ.

18-37.   (a) 260 m/s; (b) 280 m/s; (c) 250 m/s.

18-39.   0.80, 0.74.

Problems

18-3.   (a) 940 m/s; (b) 1 × 10⁻⁸⁷ ($v_{escape} = 1.1 \times 10^4$ m/s); (c) yes.

18-5.   (a) 5 × 10⁻⁴⁶ kg · m²; (b) 3 × 10¹² rad/s.

CHAPTER 19

Exercises

19-1.   (a) 120 J; (b) 320 J; (c) 0.

19-3.   (a) 0.28; (b) 1600 J; (c) 67 kW, 49 kW, 18 kW.

19-5.   (a) 272 K, 544 K, 1088 K, 544 K; (b) 14.7 kJ; (c) 2.3 kJ; (d) 12.4 kJ; (e) 15 percent.

19-7.   (a) 170 J; (b) 2.1.

19-9.   (a) 7.7 kW; (b) 4.2 kW; (c) $0.35.

19-13.   (a) $|Q_C|/|Q_H| = 0.732$; (b) 9.15 mJ; (c) no.

19-17. (a) $\Delta\eta = +0.05$; (b) 0.04; (c) 0.08, 0.07.

19-19. (a) 5 percent; (b) 40 MW; (c) 10 m³/s.

19-21. 1 kW.

19-23. (a) Q/T; (b) 0.1 J/K.

19-25. 6.1 kJ/K.

19-27. (a) 51°C; (b) $\Delta S_{250} = 490$ J/K, $\Delta S_{950} = -400$ K; (c) 90 J/K;
(d) irreversible.

19-31. (a) -0.1 J/K; (b) -0.1 J/K; (c) greater than 0.1 J/K.

Problems

19-1. Q_H/T_H, 0, $-|Q_C|/T_C$, 0.

19-7. (a) 0.40 J/K; (b) 140 J additional.

19-9. 23 J/K.

CHAPTER 20

Exercises

20-3.
r, m	0.10	0.20	0.30	0.40	0.50
F, μN	4.0	1.0	0.44	0.25	0.16

20-5. (a) 6.25×10^9; (b) 1.875×10^{10}.

20-7. (a) 9.63×10^4 C/faraday; (b) 4×10^3 C.

20-9. (a) $F_{ab} = 0.23$ mN, $F_{cb} = 0.19$ mN, $F_b = 0.04$ mN toward a; (b) $F_{ac} = 0.034$ mN, $F_{bc} = 0.19$ mN, $F_c = 0.016$ mN toward b.

20-11. $\sqrt{3}q^2/4\pi\epsilon_0 d^2$ directed away from the center of the triangle.

20-13. 420 nC.

20-15. (a) 220 N/C up; (b) 2.9 μN down.

20-17. (a) -0.065 C/kg; (b) 1.4×10^{-9}.

20-19. (a) $E_x = 2300$ N/C, $E_y = 0$, $E_z = 0$; $E_x = 820$ N/C, $E_y = 820$ N/C, $E_z = 0$; $E_x = 450$ N/C, $E_y = 450$ N/C, $E_z = 450$ N/C; $E_x = 470$ N/C, $E_y = 930$ N/C, $E_z = 0$; (b) $E = 2300$ N/C, $E = 1160$ N/C, $E = 770$ N/C, $E = 1040$ N/C.

20-21. (a) 1400 N/C to the right; (b) 7500 N/C to the left.

20-23. (a) $q/\pi\epsilon_0 d^2$ toward vacant corner (positive q); (b) $(\sqrt{2} + \frac{1}{2})q^2/4\pi\epsilon_0 d^2$ away from center (positive q).

20-25. $\mathbf{E} = 2\mathbf{p}/4\pi\epsilon_0 z^3$.

20-29. 71 N/C, -140 N/C.

20-31. 0.19×10^{-10} m.

20-35. $Q/2\pi^2\epsilon_0 a^2$.

20-39. (a) -1.76×10^{11} C/kg, 9.58×10^7 C/kg; (b) 1.76×10^{11} m/s², 9.58×10^7 m/s²; (c) 5.46×10^{-4}.

20-41. (a) 9.7×10^7; (b) proton.

20-43. 20°.

Problems

20-1. (a) $q = -Q/2\sqrt{2}$; (b) $3q^2/8\pi\epsilon_0 a^2$.

20-7. (a) $-(3100 \text{ N/C})\mathbf{i}$; (b) 0.

20-9. $\mathbf{E} = \dfrac{2\lambda\ell x}{\pi\epsilon_0(x^2 + \ell^2)\sqrt{x^2 + 2\ell^2}}\mathbf{i}$

20-11. (a) Oscillatory; (b) $T = 2\pi\sqrt{4\pi\epsilon_0 a^3 m/Q|q|}$.

20-13.   BASIC program for E in units of $\lambda/2\pi\epsilon_0\ell$ evaluated at $x = 0.2\ell$:

```
100     E=0
110     X=0.2
200         FOR I=1 TO 9 STEP 2
210         Y=I/20
220         R=(X*X+Y*Y)^0.5
230         DE=2*X*R*R/(1+R*R)^0.5
240         E=E+DE
250         NEXT I
300     PRINT E
310     END
```

20-15. $E_x = \dfrac{Qx}{4\pi\epsilon_0(x^2 + a^2)^{3/2}}$, $E_\perp = \dfrac{Qa}{2\pi^2\epsilon_0(x^2 + a^2)^{3/2}}$

CHAPTER 21

Exercises

21-1.   (a) 2100 N $\cdot$ m²/C; (b) 0; (c) 1800 N $\cdot$ m²/C.

21-3.   (a) 440 N $\cdot$ m²/C; (b) 200 N $\cdot$ m²/C.

21-5. $\Delta S_x = 9.0$ m², $\Delta S_y = 12.0$ m².

21-7.   67°.

21-9.   (a) 13 m²; (b) 9.0 N/C; (c) 110 N $\cdot$ m²/C; (d) 50 m², 2.2 N/C, 110 N $\cdot$ m²/C.

21-11. -2900 N $\cdot$ m²/C.

21-15. 4.4×10^{-12} C/m³.

21-17. $\Phi_E = -480$ N $\cdot$ m²/C for the entire cube; $\Phi_E = 0$ for each of the three sides in the xy, xz, and yz planes; $\Phi_E = -160$ N $\cdot$ m²/C for each of the other three sides.

21-21.   (a) -37 nC/m; (b) 26×10^3 N/C toward rod.

21-23.   (a) 66 nC/m²; (b) 3.7×10^3 N/C in each case.

21-25.   (a) -2.3 μC/m²; (b) 0, 0, 140 kN/C, 78 kN/C.

21-27.   (a) 130 μC/m³; (b) 120 kN/C, 240 kN/C, 60 kN/C.

21-29.   (a) None of the quantities can be determined; (b) $Q = 37$ nC, $r_0 = 26$ mm, $\rho = 50$ μC/m³.

21-31.   8.3 nC/m².

21-33.   5.5 nC/m².

Problems

21-3.   (a) $\sigma_{\text{inner}} = 160$ nC/m², $\sigma_{\text{outer}} = -110$ nC/m².

21-5.   (a) $E = 0$, $r < a$; $E = Q/4\pi\epsilon_0 r^2$, $a < r < b$; $E = 0$, $r > b$.

21-7.   (a) $\sigma_{\text{inner}} = -2.5$ μC/m², $\sigma_{\text{outer}} = 0.89$ μC/m²; (b) $E = q/4\pi\epsilon_0 r^2$, $r < 30$ mm; $E = 0$, 30 mm $< r <$ 50 mm; $E = q/4\pi\epsilon_0 r^2$, $r > 50$ mm.

CHAPTER 22

Exercises

22-1.   (a) $U_a = 87$ μJ, $U_b = 40$ μJ; (b) $U_b - U_a = -47$ μJ; (c) $W = 47$ μJ.

22-3.   (a) 54 μJ; (b) 0.022 m/s.

22-5.   (a) 65 μJ; (b) 130 μJ.

22-7.   (a) 33 kV; (b) 33 kV; (c) 33 kV.

22-9.   12 μJ.

22-15.   (a) 330 V; (b) 330 V; (c) -330 V; (d) 660 V; (e) 330 V.

22-17. (a) 1.3×10^6 V/m; (b) 430 V.

22-21. (a) 18 kV; (b) 10 kV.

22-23. 4×10^6 V.

22-25. $E = 0$.

22-27. $E = Qr/4\pi\epsilon_0 r_0^3$.

22-29. $E_x = \dfrac{\sigma}{2\epsilon_0}\left(\dfrac{x}{\sqrt{x^2}} - \dfrac{x}{\sqrt{x^2 + R^2}}\right)$.

22-33. 17 V.

22-39. (a) 4.5 nC; (b) 62 nC/m^2; (c) 7.0 kV/m.

Problems

22-3. (c) 0.053 nm; (d) 2.2×10^6 m/s.

22-5. 8×10^{-15} m.

22-13. (a) $V_a = \dfrac{Q_a + Q_b}{4\pi\epsilon_0 r_{bo}}$

(b) $V_a - V_b = \dfrac{Q_a}{4\pi\epsilon_0}\left(\dfrac{1}{r_a} - \dfrac{1}{r_{bi}}\right)$

(c) $V_a = \dfrac{Q_a}{4\pi\epsilon_0}\left(\dfrac{1}{r_a} - \dfrac{1}{r_{bi}}\right) + \dfrac{Q_a + Q_b}{4\pi\epsilon_0 r_{bo}}$

22-15. $V = \dfrac{Q}{4\pi\epsilon_0 r}$ $r > r_0$

$V = \dfrac{Q}{4\pi\epsilon_0}\left[\dfrac{1}{r} + \dfrac{\frac{1}{2}(r_0^2 - r^2) + r_0^3(r_0^{-1} - r^{-1})}{r_0^3 - r_i^3}\right]$ $r_0 > r > r_i$

$V = \dfrac{Q}{4\pi\epsilon_0}\left[\dfrac{1}{r_i} + \dfrac{\frac{1}{2}(r_0^2 - r_i^2) + r_0^3(r_0^{-1} - r_i^{-1})}{r_0^3 - r_i^3}\right]$ $r < r_i$

CHAPTER 23

Exercises

23-3. 0.58 μF.

23-5. 34 km.

23-9. (b) 46 mF.

23-11. (a) 5.5 μF; (b) 6.1 V; (c) 15 μC, 19 μC.

23-13. 5.8 μF, in series.

23-15. (a) 740 nC and 460 nC; (b) 12 V; (c) 179 nC and 109 nC; (d) 2.9 V.

23-17. (b) $C_{eq} = \dfrac{C_1 C_2 C_3 C_4}{C_2 C_3 C_4 + C_3 C_4 C_1 + C_4 C_1 C_2 + C_1 C_2 C_3}$

23-19. (a) 7.4 μF; (b) $V_3 = 65$ V, $V_1 = 39$ V, $V_2 = 26$ V; (c) $Q_3 = 320$ μC, $Q_1 = 160$ μC, $Q_2 = 160$ μC.

23-21. (a) 50 μJ; (b) 200 μJ.

23-23. (a) 40 nJ/m^3; (b) 2×10^{12} J.

23-25. 16 mJ.

23-31. 1 MeV.

23-33. (b) $W = -Q^2 d/\epsilon_0 A$; (c) $\Delta E = -W$.

23-35. 5.6 nF.

23-37. 5.6.

23-39. 3000 V.

23-41. 0.3 m^2.

23-43. (a) 0.6 μC/m^2; (b) 0.5 μC/m^2; (c) 10,000 V/m; (d) 60,000 V/m;

(e) 50,000 V/m.

23-45. 2×10^{-15} m.

Problems

23-3. C_1.

23-5.   (b) 1.1×10^{-12} F.

23-7.   (a) 2.5 kV; (c) 3.0×10^4 V/m.

23-9.   2 mm.

23-11.   (b) $F_x = \dfrac{Q^2 d(\kappa - 1)}{2\epsilon_0 w_2 [w_1 + (\kappa - 1)x]^2}$

CHAPTER 24

Exercises

24-1.   (a) 750 C; (b) 4.7×10^{21}.

24-3.   (a) $I(t) = (13.0 \text{ C/s}^2)t$; (b) $I(3.4 \text{ s}) = 44$ A.

24-5.   (a) $I_+ = 0.645$, $I_- = 0.215$ A; (b) $j_+ = 1400$ A/m^2, $j_- = 480$ A/m^2; (c) $v_{d+} = 0.16$ mm/s, $v_{d-} = 0.052$ mm/s.

24-9.   (a) 0.29 A; (b) 4.1 V/m.

24-11.   (a) 3.2 mΩ; (b) 5.0 mΩ.

24-13.   (a) 7.7×10^{-9} m; (b) 19 Ω. Resistance is independent of the ratio of length to width.

24-15.   57 mΩ.

24-17.   360 mΩ.

24-19. 1.1×10^{-7} $\Omega \cdot$ m.

24-21. $-19°$C, or 254 K.

24-23.   (a) 6.1 mV/m; (b) 2.8×10^4 A/m^2; (c) 4.6×10^6 $\Omega^{-1} \cdot$ m^{-1}; (d) 2.2×10^{-7} $\Omega \cdot$ m.

24-25. 2×10^{-12} s.

24-27.   (a) 2.7 mA; (b) -1.0 μA; (c) $R_f = 74$ Ω, $R_r = 200$ kΩ.

24-29.   (a) 7.4 Ω; (b) $I_{16} = 0.87$ A, $V_{16} = 14$ V; $I_{25} = 0.56$ A, $V_{25} = 14$ V; $I_{31} = 0.45$ A, $V_{31} = 14$ V.

24-33.   (a) 0; (b) 4.0 Ω; (c) $V_{ca} = V_{da} = 5.0$ V, $V_{bc} = V_{bd} = 3.0$ V; $I = 1.0$ A in all resistors except resistor 3; $I = 0$ in resistor 3.

Problems

24-3.   (b) $\alpha = -E_g/2kT_0^2 = -7.4 \times 10^{-2}$ K^{-1}; (c) $\rho_0 = \rho_1 e^{E_g/2kT_0}$.

24-9.   (b) 900 MΩ.

24-11.   (b) 160 kΩ.

CHAPTER 25

Exercises

25-1.   1.4 V.

25-3. $\mathscr{E} = 6.3$ V, $r = 3$ Ω.

25-5. $\mathscr{E} = 6.1$ V, $r = 0.2$ Ω.

25-7.   (a) 0.46 W; (b) 4.6×10^{-4} kW $\cdot$ h $= 1.7 \times 10^3$ J.

25-9.   (a) 240 Ω; (b) 0.50 A; (c) 50 W.

25-11.   (a) 16 mA; (b) 16 V.

25-13.   75 mA, 10 V.

25-15.   (a) 3.2×10^5 C; (b) 3.9×10^6 J.

25-17. (a) 88 W; (b) 88 W; (c) 0.59 W.

25-21. (a) 4 V; (b) 36 V.

25-23. $i_2 = -0.5$ A, $i_3 = 1$ A.

25-25. (a) 0.0 A; (b) 0.5 A; (c) 0.3 A; (d) 0.2 A.

25-27. 2.2 Ω.

25-29. $i_5 = 0.1$ A, $i_2 = i_4 = 0.6$ A, $i_3 = 0.9$ A, $i_7 = 0.5$ A; $V_5 = 1$ V, $V_2 = 1$ V, $V_4 = 2$ V, $V_3 = 3$ V, $V_7 = 3$ V.

25-31. (a) 0.063 s; (b) 6.4 μC; (c) 0.19 mA; (d) 84 μA; (e) 12 μC.

25-33. (a) 28 μC; (b) 0.14 mJ; (c) 0.58 mJ; (d) 0.44 mJ.

25-35. (a) 0.32 mA; (b) 11 mW; (c) 6.4 mW; (d) 5 mW.

25-39. 0.72 μF.

Problems

25-3.   92 percent.

25-9. $i_1 = 1.1$ A, $i_2 = 0.87$ A, $i_3 = 0.73$ A, $i_4 = 0.36$ A, $i_5 = 0.15$ A, $i_6 = 0.22$ A.

25-11. 2 ms.

CHAPTER 26

Exercises

26-1.   (b) 3.30×10^{-14} N; (c) 3.30×10^{-14} N.

26-3.   (a) $F_x = 6.1 \times 10^{-15}$ N, $F_y = 8.5 \times 10^{-15}$ N, $F_z = 8.5 \times 10^{-15}$ N.

26-5. $F_g/F_B = 5.6 \times 10^{-12}$.

26-7.   (a) $F_g = 0.02$ N, $F_E = 8 \times 10^{-10}$ N, $F_B = 2 \times 10^{-14}$ N.

26-9.   (a) 26 mA.

26-11. (a) Positive z direction if $A > 0$; (b) $AI \ln 3$.

26-13. (b) 0.

26-15. (a) 6.1×10^{-3} N · m; (b) 7.1×10^{-3} N · m; (c) 6.1×10^{-3} N · m.

26-17. 1.0×10^{-4} A.

26-19. (a) 0.026 A · m²; (b) 0.031 N · m; (c) $\pm 30°, \pm 150°$.

26-21. (a) 5 μJ; (b) 5 μN · m; (c) 0, 5 μJ.

26-23. (a) 0.004 A · m²; (b) 7×10^{-5} m²; (c) -1 mJ; (d) 3 mJ.

26-25. (a) 4.8×10^{-20} kg · m/s; (b) 7.1×10^6 m/s; (c) 1.1 MeV.

26-27. (a) 8.2×10^7 rad/s; (b) 13 mm; (c) 21 MeV; (d) 2.1×10^4.

26-29. (a) Outer part; (b) positive; (c) 6×10^{-22} to 45×10^{-22} kg · m/s.

26-31. (a) From upper to lower plate; (b) 80 μT into the plane of the figure; (c) 5×10^7 m/s, 10 MeV.

26-33. (a) 1×10^{13} rad/s; (b) 1×10^7 m/s; (c) 3×10^8 m/s, or $c(1 - 5 \times 10^{-10})$.

Problems

26-3.   (b) 0.41 T.

26-5.   (b) 11.01 u.

26-7.   (b) $mg/(2NLB)$; (c) 90°; (d) 30°; (e) stable.

CHAPTER 27

Exercises

27-3.   (a) 8.6×10^{-5} T.

27-5.   (a) $2\mu_0 I/(\pi a)$ to the right; (b) $\mu_0 I/(2\pi a)$ to the right; (c) 3.8×10^{-5} T at

P, 9.6×10^{-6} T at Q.

27-7. (a) $D/3$; (b) none.

27-11. (a) $\dfrac{\mu_0 I}{8ab}(b-a)$; (b) 142 μT.

27-13. (a) $\dfrac{\mu_0 IL}{4\pi R \sqrt{R^2 + L^2}}$; (b) $\mu_0 I/(4\pi R)$.

27-15. (a) 1.5×10^{-7} A $\cdot$ m^2; (b) 2.9×10^{-14} T; (c) 1.9×10^{-6} T.

27-17. $-\mu_0 \mathbf{m}/4\pi r^3$.

27-19. (a) 10.0 A; (b) $4\pi \times 10^{-6}$ T $\cdot$ m.

27-21. (a) 1.25 mm.

27-25. (a) $B = 0$, $R \leqslant b$; (b) $B = \dfrac{\mu_0 I_0 (R^2 - b^2)}{2\pi R(c^2 - b^2)}$, $b \leqslant R \leqslant c$; (c) $B = \mu_0 I_0/(2\pi R)$, $c \leqslant R$.

27-27. (a) 2.6 mT; (b) 170; (c) 1.2 mm.

27-29. (a) 290; (b) 16 m; (c) 1.3 Ω; (d) 0.95 V.

27-31. (a) $\dfrac{\mu_0 I x}{2\pi a^2} + \dfrac{\mu_0 I}{2\pi(D - x)}$; (b) $\dfrac{\mu_0 I}{2\pi}\left(\dfrac{1}{x} + \dfrac{1}{D - x}\right)$; (c) $\dfrac{\mu_0 I}{2\pi}\left(\dfrac{1}{x} + \dfrac{D - x}{a^2}\right)$, all directed toward the top of the page.

27-33. (a) 17 A; (b) 1/4.

27-35. 0.055 Wb.

27-37. (a) $(\mu_0 Ic/2\pi) \ln (b/a)$; (b) $(\mu_0 Ic/2\pi) \ln (b/a)$.

27-39. (a) ρI; (b) for $d(\rho I)/dt \neq 0$.

27-41. (a) 460 μC; (b) 2.2×10^{11} N $\cdot$ C^{-1} $\cdot$ s^{-1}.

Problems

27-3. $\mu_0 ni$.

27-5. $\dfrac{\mu_0 nIL}{\sqrt{L^2 + 4a^2}}$

27-7. $B = 0$ above the top sheet, $B = \mu_0 K$ between the sheets, $B = 0$ below the bottom sheet.

CHAPTER 28

Exercises

28-1. (a) 1.5 mWb, 2.3 mWb; (b) 6.4 mV.

28-3. (a) 23 μWb; (b) 7.8 mV; (c) 7.9 μWb, 2.7 mV.

28-5. (a) 0.030 Wb/s; (b) 0.47 T/s.

28-7. (a) 45 mV; (b) 1.5 s; (c) 3.0 μA.

28-9. (a) 0.17 V; (b) 0.22 mA; (c) 14 μN, opposite the velocity.

28-11. (a) 0; (b) 0; (c) $B\ell v \cos \theta$.

28-13. (a) $2B\ell v$; (b) counterclockwise.

28-15. (a) 71 ms; (b) 170 mV; (c) counterclockwise; (d) 4.2 μN, opposite the velocity; (e) no.

28-17. (a) $B\ell^2 \omega/2R$; (b) 900 μA; (c) counterclockwise; (d) 3 μN $\cdot$ m.

28-21. (a) 20 mWb; (b) 5 mA; (c) 4 ms, 12 ms, ...

28-23. (a) $\omega C_1 \sin \omega t + 3\omega C_3 \sin 3\omega t$; (b) 2.2 V; (c) 1.7 V.

28-25. (a) $300 \, \omega_1 C \sin \omega_1 t$; (b) 20 V; (c) 100 V.

28-27. (a) 0; (b) 0.7 mN/C; (c) 0.8 mN/C; (d) the same.

Problems

28-3. (a) $B\ell vt(1 + t/t_1)$; (b) $B\ell v(1 + 2t/t_1)$; (c) 0.62 V.

28-5.   (b) Clockwise; (c) to the left; (d) counterclockwise, to the right.

28-7.   (a) $\dfrac{\mu_0 i\ell}{2\pi}\ln\dfrac{w + R_0 + vt}{R_0 + vt}$; (b) $\dfrac{\mu_0 i\ell wv}{2\pi(R_0 + vt)(R_0 + w + vt)}$; (c) clockwise.

28-11.   (a) Opposite the sense of the current: into the page on the left, out of the page on the right.

CHAPTER 29

Exercises

29-3.   (a) 850 μV; (b) 850 μV; (c) 850 μV, with opposite sense from (a) and (b); (d) 0.

29-5.   (a) 15 A/s; (b) either.

29-9.   (b) $\dfrac{\mu_0 i\ell}{\pi}\ln\dfrac{D - a}{a}$.

29-11.   (a) 19 ms; (b) 0.35 A; (c) 0.48 A; (d) 0.48 A.

29-13.   Many possibilities consistent with $\mathscr{E}_0/R = 0.80$ A, $R \gg 2.3$ Ω; for example, $\mathscr{E}_0 = 24$ V, $R = 30$ Ω.

29-17.   (a) 0, 74 mA, 110 mA, 130 mA; (b) 0, 5.3 V, 8.1 V, 9.2 V; (c) 9.2 V, 3.9 V, 1.1 V, 0.

29-19.   (a) 94 ms; (b) 47 mH.

29-21.   (a) $\frac{1}{2}Li_0^2 e^{-2t/\tau_L}$.

29-23.   (a) $i_0^2 R e^{-2t/\tau_L}$; (b) energy dissipated $= U_0$.

29-25. $u_B \approx 0.6$ J/m³, $u_E \approx 0.04$ J/m³.

29-27.   (b) 60 μH.

29-29.   (a) To the left; (b) to the right; (c) to the left.

29-31.   (a) 0.011; (b) 1.1 A; (c) 24 kW.

29-33.   (a) 14 A; (b) 4 kW; (c) 0.2 percent; (d) 10 mm.

29-35.   (a) $N_s/N_p = 50$: if $N_p = 10$, then $N_s = 500$; (b) 0.09 A; (c) 70 kΩ.

Problems

29-1.   (a) $\dfrac{\mu_0 Nib}{2\pi}\ln\dfrac{c + a}{c}$; (b) $\dfrac{\mu_0 N^2 b}{2\pi}\ln\dfrac{c + a}{c}$

29-3.   (a) $\dfrac{\mu_0 i\ell}{2\pi}\ln b/a$; (b) $\dfrac{\mu_0}{2\pi}\ln b/a$; (c) the same.

29-7.   (a) 200 mm; (b) 16 m; (c) 0.34 Ω; (d) 0.12 mH.

29-9.   (b) $i_1 = \dfrac{\mathscr{E}_0}{R_1}(1 - e^{-R_1 t/L_1})$, $i_2 = \dfrac{M\mathscr{E}_0}{L_1 R_2}(e^{-R_2 t/L_2} - e^{-R_1 t/L_1})$ (d) 48 V across R_1 asymptotically, 30 V across R_2 at $t = 0.01$ s.

CHAPTER 30

Exercises

30-1. -9.31×10^{-24} A · m².

30-3. -5.3×10^{-35} kg · m²/s.

30-5.   (a) 5.05×10^{-27} A · m²; (b) $m_N/m_B = 5.46 \times 10^{-4}$.

30-7. 1×10^6 A · m², assuming 1×10^{29} atoms per cubic meter.

30-11.   (a) 1.7 A/m; (b) 210 K.

30-13.   (b) 1×10^{-23} J; (c) $m_0 B/kT \leqslant 0.1$ for $T > 7$ K.

30-15. 0.6×10^6 A/m, 1.6×10^6 A/m, 2.1×10^6 A/m, assuming 1×10^{29} atoms per cubic meter.

30-17.   33 A/m.

30-19.   (a) 3.19×10^{-3} T · m/A; (b) 8.75×10^5 A/m; (c) 0.04 percent.

30-21.   20 μT, horizontal; 56 μT vertical (down).

Problems

30-1. $H = nI$.
30-3.   (a) Parallel; (b) positive y direction, toward the stronger field region; (c) negative y direction.
30-7.   (a) 1×10^{14} A/m; (b) 6×10^{17} A/m.

CHAPTER 31

Exercises

31-3.   5.1 mH.
31-5. $q(t) = (2.2 \ \mu\text{C}) \cos [(11 \ \text{Mrad/s})t]$, $i(t) = (230 \ \text{mA}) \sin [(11 \ \text{Mrad/s})t]$, $U = 140 \ \mu\text{J}$, $U_E(t) = (140 \ \mu\text{J}) \cos^2 [(11 \ \text{Mrad/s})t]$, $U_B(t) = (140 \ \mu\text{J}) \sin^2 [(11 \ \text{Mrad/s})t]$.
31-7. $q(t) = (20 \ \mu\text{C}) \cos [(14 \ \text{krad/s})t - 1.2 \ \text{rad}]$, $i(t) = (280 \ \text{mA}) \sin [(14 \ \text{krad/s})t - 1.2 \ \text{rad}]$, $U = 1.3 \ \text{mJ}$, $U_E(t) = (1.3 \ \text{mJ}) \cos^2 [(14 \ \text{krad/s})t - 1.2 \ \text{rad}]$, $U_B(t) = (1.3 \ \text{mJ}) \sin^2 [(14 \ \text{krad/s})t - 1.2 \ \text{rad}]$.
31-9.   (a) $i(t) = -(3.8 \ \text{A}) \sin [(54 \ \text{krad/s})t - \pi/4]$; (b) 20 nF; (c) $U = 130 \ \text{mJ}$, $U_E(t) = (130 \ \text{mJ}) \cos^2 [(54 \ \text{krad/s})t - \pi/4]$, $U_B(t) = (130 \ \text{mJ}) \sin^2 [(54 \ \text{krad/s})t - \pi/4]$.
31-11.   (a) $q(t) = -(260 \ \text{nC}) \cos [(16 \ \text{krad/s})t]$; (b) $i(t) = (4.2 \ \text{mA}) \sin [(16 \ \text{krad/s})t]$; (c) $V_C = (4.8 \ \text{V}) \cos [(16 \ \text{krad/s})t]$; (d) $U = 630 \ \text{nJ}$; (e) $U_E = (630 \ \text{nJ}) \cos^2 [(16 \ \text{krad/s})t]$; (f) $U_B = (630 \ \text{nJ}) \sin^2 [(16 \ \text{krad/s})t]$.
31-13. $q(t) = (1.1 \ \mu\text{C}) \cos [(25 \ \text{krad/s})t - \pi/2]$; $i(t) = -(27 \ \text{mA}) \sin [(25 \ \text{krad/s})t - \pi/2]$.
31-15.   (a) $q = Q_m/2$; (b) $i = -\sqrt{3}I_m/2$.
31-17.   790 μH, 3.0 Mrad/s or 0.48 MHz.
31-19.   (a) Underdamped; (b) 6.3 krad/s; (c) 91 μs.
31-21.   (a) 2.7 Ω; (b) 120 nF.
31-23. $R = \sqrt{3L/C}$.
31-27.   (a) 17 ms; (b) 170 V; (c) 0; (d) 0.12 A; (e) 0.
31-29.   (a) 1.6 MΩ; (b) 1.6 kΩ; (c) 1.6 Ω.
31-31.   0.11 μF.
31-33.   66 μA.
31-35.   3.0 krad/s.
31-37.   (a) 0.63 Ω; (b) 630 Ω; (c) 630 kΩ.
31-39.   4.7 mH.
31-41.   4.9 A.
31-43.   820 rad/s.
31-45.   (a) $i(t) = (120 \ \text{mA}) \sin [(830 \ \text{rad/s})t - 0.54 \ \text{rad}]$.
31-55.   560 mW.
31-57.   9.5 mW.

Problems

31-9.   (a) 54 Ω; (b) 7.1 V.

CHAPTER 32

Exercises

32-1.   (a) 1.1 m/s; (b) 1 mm; (c) 0.7 mm.

32-3.   (b) $h = 10.0$ mm, $w = 2.00$ m.

32-7.   1 and 2.

32-9.   (a) 6.8 mm; (b) 1.47 rad/m; (c) 4.18 rad/s; (d) 2.84 m/s; (e) 4.27 m;
        (f) 0.665 Hz; (g) 1.50 s; (h) $+\mathbf{i}$; (i) -2.2 mm.

32-11. (a) $v_x = -(28$ mm/s$)$ cos $[(1.47$ rad/m$)x - (4.18$ rad/s$)t]$; (b) $a_x =$
        $-(120$ mm/s$^2)$ sin $[(1.47$ rad/m$)x - (4.18$ rad/s$)t]$; (c) 28 mm/s;
        (d) 120 mm/s^2; (e) 27 mm/s; (f) 38 mm/s^2; (g) bending upward.

32-13. (a) (0.010) cos $[(1.47$ rad/m$)x - (4.18$ rad/s$)t]$;
        (b) $-(0.015$ m$^{-1})$ sin $[(1.47$ rad/m$)x - (4.18$ rad/s$)t]$; (c) -9.4×10^{-3};
        (d) 4.8×10^{-3} m^{-1}; (e) upward.

32-15. 4×10^{14} to 7.5×10^{14} Hz.

32-17. 16.5 mm to 16.5 m.

32-19. (a) $y = (17$ mm$)$ sin $[(5.3$ rad/m$)x + (19$ rad/s$)t]$; (b) 3.6 m/s;
        (c) 0.32 m/s; (d) 6.1 m/s^2; (e) 0.090; (f) 0.48 m^{-1}.

32-21. (a) A: 4.0 m/s, B: 0, C: -4.0 m/s, D: -2.8 m/s, E: 0;
        (b) A: 0, B: 640 m/s^2, C: 0, D: -450 m/s^2, E: -640 m/s^2;
        (c) A: 0.087, B: 0, C: -0.087, D: -0.061, E: 0;
        (d) A: 0, B: 0.30 m^{-1}, C: 0, D: -0.21 m^{-1}, E: -0.30 m^{-1}.

32-23. 1200 m/s.

32-27. 100 N.

32-29. A: 21 W, B: 0, C: 21 W, D: 11 W, E: 0.

32-33. 600 W.

32-35. 0.49 W/m^2.

32-37. (a) 0.56 rad; (b) 27 mm.

32-39. 2.4 rad.

32-41. 25 Hz.

32-45. 110 N.

32-47. (a) 160 nm; (b) 3200.

Problems

32-11. (b) $4\mu v^3 y_0^2 / x_0^2$.

CHAPTER 33

Exercises

33-1.   (a) 1.3 kHz; (b) 8.0×10^3 rad/s; (c) 8.4 m^{-1}; (d) $(5.0$ μm$)$ cos
        $[(8.4$ rad/m$)x - (8.0 \times 10^3$ rad/s$)t]$.

33-3.   330 m/s.

33-5.   (a) 1.1×10^3 m/s; (b) 2.0×10^3 m/s.

33-7.   0.2 s.

33-9.   (a) 5.1×10^3 m/s; (b) 3.5×10^3 m/s; (c) 5.1×10^3 m/s.

33-11. (a) 3.9×10^3 m/s; (b) 1.5×10^3 m/s.

33-13. (a) 0.16 Pa; (b) 1.7×10^{-11} m; (c) 2.7×10^{-3} Pa, 1.0×10^{-9} m.

33-15. (a) 466 Hz; (b) 880 Hz.

33-17. 73 nW/m^2.

33-19. (a) 3; (b) 6; (c) 10; (d) 13; (e) 17; (f) 20; (g) 60.

33-23. 29 Hz, 88 Hz, 146 Hz, ...

33-25. (a) 0.66 m; (b) 0.70 m.

33-27. 8.7 kHz.

33-29. 8×10^{-3}.

33-33. 0.3 Hz.

33-35. 886 Hz.

33-37. 10 m/s.

33-39. 260 Hz following, 300 Hz approaching.

33-41. (a) 450 Hz; (b) 540 Hz.

33-45. (b) (210 Pa) cos [(3.73 rad/m)x − (5530 rad/s)t].

33-47. 1 mW/m².

Problems

33-3. (b) 15 percent.

33-5. (b) $\nu_b = \nu_s(2v_0/v) = v_0/(0.25 \text{ m})$.

33-7. (b) 0.057 W/m²; (c) 0.051 W/m²; (d) 7.0×10^{-4} W/m², 0.

CHAPTER 34

Exercises

34-3. (a) +**i**; (b) −**i**.

34-5. 2.29×10^8 m/s.

34-11. (a) 3 m; (b) 300 m.

34-13. 150 N/C.

34-15. (a) −**j**; (b) 3.5 m; (c) 86 MHz; (d) 100 nT;
(e) (100 nT) cos [(1.8 rad/m)y + (5.4×10^8 rad/s)t]**k**.

34-19. 3 µJ/m³.

34-25. (a) −**k**; (b) 0.52 m; (c) 570 MHz;
(d) **E** = (290 N/C) cos [(12 rad/m)z + (3.6 Grad/s)t]**i**,
B = −(960 nT) cos [(12 rad/m)z +(3.6 Grad/s)t]**j**. This answer is
not unique.

34-27. **E** = (26 N/C) cos [(1.1×10^7 rad/m)x − (3.2×10^{15} rad/s)t]**j**,
B = (85 nT) cos [(1.1×10^7 rad/m)x − (3.2×10^{15} rad/s)t]**k**,
S = (1.7 W/m²) cos² [(1.1×10^7 rad/m)x − (3.2×10^{15} rad/s)t]**i**.

34-29. (a) 1.1 kW/m²; (b) 1.2×10^{-11} J; (c) 920 N/C; (d) 3.1 µT; (e) up and
down; (f) 4.7×10^{14} Hz.

34-31. (a) 3.2 mN/m²; (b) 1.4×10^{-11} N.

34-33. (b) 5.8×10^5 N; (c) 1.6×10^{-17}.

34-35. (a) 0.4 W/m²; (b) 0.004 W/m².

34-37. (a) 1 W/m²; (b) 0.1 W/m².

34-39. 5.1×10^{14} Hz.

34-41. 499.0 s = 8.317 min.

Problems

34-7. (c) 0.56 µm.

34-9. (b) 6.7×10^{-7} N·m/rad.

CHAPTER 35

Exercises

35-1. 120°.

35-3. (a) AN and BC are traveled by the light in the same time;
(b) side AB is common, $AN = AC$ as in (a) and AC and BN are
bounded by the same parallel rays;

(c) they are equivalent angles in congruent triangles.

35-7. 1.734×10^8 m/s.

35-9.   (a) $60°$; (b) $55°$.

35-11. Soda lime.

35-13. $24.44°$.

35-15. $7.827°$.

35-17. (a) 0.765 m; (b) 1.59 m; (c) any distance.

35-19. (a) 111 mm; (b) erect; (c) 2 mm.

35-21. (a) 2 m; (b) 1 m behind mirror.

35-23. 315 mm beyond small mirror.

35-25. 1.48.

35-27.

Type	f	s	s'	Real?	Inverted?	m
Converging	96	144	288	Yes	Yes	-2.0
Diverging	-300	300	-150	No	No	1/2
Diverging	-120	120	-60	No	No	1/2
Positive	480	120	-160	No	No	4/3
Negative	-58	96	-36	No	No	15/4
Diverging	-360	-240	720	Yes	No	$+3$
Positive	180	$+\infty$	180	Yes	—	0
Positive	113	68	-170	No	No	2.5

35-29. 222 mm.

35-31. 162 mm.

35-33. 810 mm.

35-35. (a) 165 mm; (b) s' for second lens is 186 mm, real.

35-39. 3.05 mm.

35-41. 220 mm.

35-43. (a) 80 mm; (b) 7.

35-45. (a) 4.9 mm; (b) 33; (c) 980.

CHAPTER 36

Exercises

36-1.   (a) $\theta_1 = \pm 0.18°$, $\theta_2 = \pm 0.36°$; (b) $\theta_1 = \pm 0.27°$, $\theta_2 = \pm 0.45°$.

36-5.   2.5 m.

36-15. 5.0 mm and 3.5 mm.

36-17. (a) 2.09 μm; (b) 566 nm.

36-23. (a) $\pm 14.3°$ and $\pm 29.6°$; (b) 336 and 374 μrad.

36-27. (a) $\pm 15.1°$; (b) 4.91×10^5 m^{-1}.

36-31. 998 slits.

36-35. 0.13 nm.

36-37. 0.23 μm.

36-41. 36.84 μm.

36-43. 305.5 fringes.

Problems

36-1. $d \sin \theta_m = \pm (m + \frac{1}{2})\lambda$ and $d \sin \theta_{m'} = \pm m'\lambda$.

36-11. (a) $I_2 = (0.0200)I_1$; (b) $I_6 = (0.0200)(1 - 0.0200)^2 I_1 = (0.0193)I_1$.

CHAPTER 37

Exercises

37-1.   280 nm (ultraviolet).

37-3. 0.280 mm.

37-5. 1.3 μm.

37-7. 4.9 and 1.6 percent.

37-13. 4.6 and 1.6 percent.

37-17. 2.

37-19. 10

37-21. 8.1 μrad.

37-23. 0.10 m.

37-25. 60°.

37-27. (a) Vertical; (b) 82 percent.

37-29. 53.1°.

37-31. 1.23.

37-35. (a) 0.56 rad; (b) 1.0 rad.

Problems

37-5. (c) 2.97.

37-7. -0.057.

37-11. (b) 0.781; (c) 0.976; (d) 0.998.

CHAPTER 38

Exercises

38-5. (a) $\mathbf{u}' = \mathbf{u} - \mathbf{v}$; (b) $-\mathbf{v}$.

38-7. $v'' = v + v'$.

38-11. (a) 1×10^{-4}.

38-13. (a) -1.65×10^5 m, 0.55 s; (b) -1.66×10^7 m, 0.55 s; (c) -1.37×10^9 m, 3.9 s.

38-17. $x = \gamma(x' + vt')$, $y = y'$, $z = z'$, $t = \gamma(t + vx'/c^2)$ with $\gamma = 1/\sqrt{1 - v^2/c^2}$.

38-19. (a) $x' = \gamma(x - \beta ct)$, $y' = y$, $z' = z$, $t' = \gamma(t - \beta x/c)$ with $\gamma = 1/\sqrt{1 - \beta^2}$; (c) negligible; (d) 0.06 percent; (e) 2.6 percent.

38-21. (a) Eruption in Mexico; (b) 14×10^{11} m.

38-23. (a) $x_1' = 88$ ly, $t_1' = -83$ years; $x_2' = 134$ ly, $t_2' = -126$ years; (b) observer O; (c) observer O.

38-27. (a) 7×10^3 s; (b) 2×10^3 s; (c) 1×10^3 s; (d) 1×10^3 s.

38-31. $0.99999995c$.

38-33. (a) 3.1 MeV, 1.9×10^{-22} kg · m/s; (b) 79 keV, 1.6×10^{-22} kg · m/s; (c) 2.6 keV, 2.7×10^{-23} kg · m/s; (d) 0.26 eV, 2.7×10^{-25} kg · m/s.

38-35. (a) $0.12c$; (b) $0.36c$.

38-39. (a) $0.866c$; (b) $0.866c$.

38-41. (a) 1.0×10^{-4} u; (b) 7.6×10^{-15} J; (c) 1.0×10^{-20} kg · m/s; (d) 1.5×10^6 m/s.

Problems

38-3. (a) 110 years old.

CHAPTER 39

Exercises

39-1. (a) 360 W; (b) 5.8 kW; (c) 230 kW.

39-3. (a) 7.4 kJ; (b) 7.7×10^{-5} m².

39-5. (a) 7×10^{-21} J; (b) 2×10^{14} Hz, 2×10^{33} Hz.

39-7. (a) 7×10^{-121} J; (b) 2×10^{-31} J; (c) 4×10^{-21} J; (d) 1×10^{-20} J.

39-11. 1.7 to 3.1 eV, 2.7×10^{-19} to 5.0×10^{-19} J.

39-13. (a) 6.0×10^{14} Hz; (b) no.

39-17. (a) 1.87 eV; (b) 4.5×10^{14} Hz; (c) 2.14 eV; (d) none.

39-19. (a) 1.3 to 0.7 eV; (b) 3.1 to 3.7 eV; (c) 7.6×10^{14} to 8.9×10^{14} Hz; (d) no change.

39-23. (a) 76 pm; (b) 73 pm; (c) 71 pm.

39-25. $53°$.

39-27. (a) 0.48 MeV; (b) $p = 4.4 \times 10^{-21}$ kg $\cdot$ m/s at $3.3°$ from the initial direction, $93.3°$ from the scattered photon.

39-29. (b) $b = n^2/R_H = 4/R_H$; (c) $b = 3.646 \times 10^{-7}$.

39-33. (b) 5.29×10^{-11} m.

39-35. (a) Paschen series, second longest wavelength; (b) -0.54 eV, -1.51 eV; (c) 2.3×10^{14} Hz, 1.3 μm.

39-37. $r_n = \dfrac{\epsilon_0 h^2}{\pi m e^2} n^2$, $v = \dfrac{e^2}{2\epsilon_0 hn}$

39-39. (b) $R_H = 1.0974 \times 10^7$ m^{-1}.

39-41. (a) $1/\lambda = R_H(1 - 1/n_f^2)$; (c) Lyman.

CHAPTER 40

Exercises

40-3. 3.1×10^{-18} J, 1.7×10^{-21} J, 8.1×10^{-24} J.

40-5. (a) 1.5×10^{-10} m; (b) 8.9×10^{-11} m.

40-7. (a) 7×10^{-28} kg $\cdot$ m/s; (b) 2×10^{-46} J; (c) $3/2kT = 6 \times 10^{-21}$ J.

40-9. (a) 8.5×10^{-24} kg $\cdot$ m/s; (b) 7.8×10^{-11} m.

40-11. 59 to 150 pm.

40-13. (a) 12 pm; (b) 0.29 pm; (c) 0.10 pm.

40-15. 12 eV.

40-17. (a) About 0.1 nm or smaller; (b) 0.1 nm, 0.04 nm, 0.03 nm.

40-19. 0.12 nm.

40-23. 1×10^{-10} m.

40-25. (b) 4×10^{-6} eV.

40-29. (a) 3×10^{-22} s; (b) 2×10^{-25} s; (c) 1×10^{-53} s.

40-31. (a) 0.043; (b) 0.957.

40-39. (a) 0.3 meV; (b) 0.8 nm.

40-45. (a) 2 meV; (b) 4 meV; (c) $kT = 26$ meV.

Problems

40-3. (c) $15°$, $78°$.

40-5. (b) $\omega = \hbar k^2/2m$; (c) $\omega = c\sqrt{k^2 + m^2c^2/\hbar^2}$; (d) wave velocity: c, $\hbar k/2m$, $c\sqrt{1 + (m^2c^2/\hbar^2k^2)}$; group velocity: c, $\hbar k/m$, $c/\sqrt{1 + (m^2c^2/\hbar^2k^2)}$.

40-7. (b) $L^2(1/3 - 1/2n^2\pi^2)$.

40-11. (b) $\frac{1}{4}\hbar\omega$ for $n = 0$, $\frac{3}{4}\hbar\omega$ for $n = 1$; (c) $\frac{1}{4}\hbar\omega$ for $n = 0$, $\frac{3}{4}\hbar\omega$ for $n = 1$.

CHAPTER 41

Exercises

41-1. (a) -1.51 eV; (b) $\sqrt{6}\hbar$; (c) $+\hbar$.

41-3. (a) $12\hbar^2$; (b) $\hbar^2$; (c) $11\hbar^2$; (d) yes.

41-5. $\ell = 5.0 \times 10^{31}$, unobservable.

41-7. $(0.21)a_0{}^{-3/2}$.

41-9.   (a) $(0.51)a_0$ and $(26.5)a_0$; (b) ψ_{300} is positive between $r = 0$ and $r = (0.51)a_0$, and between $r = (26.5)a_0$ and $r = \infty$; (c) ψ_{300} is negative between $r = (0.51)a_0$ and $r = (26.5)a_0$.

41-13. (a) $\psi_{21y} = (32\pi a_0{}^5)^{-1/2}ye^{-r/2a_0}$; (b) $\psi_{21x} = (32\pi a_0{}^5)^{-1/2}xe^{-r/2a_0}$.

41-15. (a) 5; (b) 2.0×10^{-5} eV.

41-17. (b) As λ becomes larger, E becomes smaller; (c) 2×10^{-3} eV.

41-19. (a) 5.79×10^{-5} eV/T; (b) -5.79×10^{-5} eV/T.

41-21. (a) 1.4×10^{-20} N; (b) 7.8×10^4 m/s²; (c) 63 μm.

41-23. (a) 14; (b) -0.850 eV; (c) $\sqrt{12}\hbar = 3.7 \times 10^{-34}$ kg · m²/s.

41-25. 0, 1, 2.

41-29. 50.

41-31. (a) 54.4 eV; (b) 122.4 eV.

41-35. (a) $n = 3$, $\ell = 1$; (b) $n = 4$, $\ell = 1$.

41-37. Yes.

CHAPTER 42

Exercises

42-3.   (a) $n_1 = n_2 = n_3 = 1.9 \times 10^6$; (b) 4×10^{-7} eV.

42-5.   (a) 1.9×10^{-21} eV; (b) 3×10^{-7} m/s; (c) 0.024 eV; (d) no.

42-7.   [energy]$^{-1}$, J^{-1}.

42-9.   (a) 6.7×10^{46} J^{-1} · m^{-3} = 1.1×10^{28} eV^{-1} · m^{-3}; (b) estimate volume of penny as 3×10^{-7} m³: 3×10^{20} states.

42-11. (a) 0.50; (b) 0.73; (c) 0.27; (d) 1.0; (e) 2×10^{-17}.

42-13. (a) -0.18 eV; (b) -0.057 eV; (c) 0.057 eV; (d) 0.18 eV.

42-15. (a) 5.8×10^{28} electrons per cubic meter; (b) 1 electron per atom; (c) no.

42-17. 1.38 : 1.20 : 1.00.

42-19. (a) 1.6×10^6 m/s; (b) 2×10^8 m/s; (c) no.

42-21. (a) 4×10^{-14} s; (b) 60 nm; (c) vibrations.

42-23. $\Delta E = 8/3 E_F = 20$ eV.

42-25. (a) 2×10^{-28}; (b) 6×10^{-10}.

42-29. (a) 45 mT; (b) 8.0×10^{-6} Wb; (c) 3.9×10^9 quanta; (d) 1×10^{-11} T.

Problems

42-3. $\dfrac{L^3(2m_H)^{3/2}}{2\pi^2\hbar^3}(E_H - E)^{1/2}$

42-5. $J_z = -\dfrac{B_0\lambda}{\mu_0}e^{-\lambda x}$

CHAPTER 43

Exercises

43-1.   (a) 9, 9, 18; (b) 20, 23, 43; (c) 80, 122, 202.

43-3.   (a) 2.4 and 6.4 fm; (b) 10/197.

43-5.   (a) 1.3×10^{13} m³; (b) 15 km; (c) 0.0023.

43-7.   (a) 0.51 MeV; (b) 938.3 MeV; (c) 939.6 MeV.

43-11. (a) 8.54 and 8.48 MeV; (b) 0.86 and 2.23 MeV.

43-13. (b) 20.58 MeV.

43-15. (a) 7.97 and 8.06 MeV; (b) 0.485; (c) 3.17.

43-17.   (a) 7.23, 8.48, 7.68 MeV; (b) $C_1 = 16.75$ MeV, $C_2 = 19.94$ MeV, $C_3 = 1.06$ MeV; (c) 2.1, 3.7, and 0.9 percent.
43-19.   (a) 10.64 MeV; (b) 5.78 MeV.
43-21.   (a) β^-; (b) $^{142}_{60}$Nd; (c) ν.
43-25.   (b) 1.3×10^5 s.
43-27. $^{232}_{90}$Th $\rightarrow$ $^{228}_{88}$Ra $+ ^4_2$He.
43-29. $^{87}_{37}$Rb $\rightarrow$ $^{87}_{38}$Sr $+ \beta^- + \bar{\nu}$.
43-31. $^{11}_{6}$C $\rightarrow$ $^{11}_{5}$B $+ \beta^+ + \nu$.
43-37. -1.19 MeV, endothermic.

Problems

43-1.   (a) 833; (b) 694; (c) 335; (d) $\mathcal{N}(t) = 1000(5/6)^t$; (e) $\mathcal{N}(t) = \mathcal{N}_0 e^{-(0.182)t}$.
43-5.   (b) 4.78 MeV.
43-9.   (a) 6.6 MeV; (b) its kinetic energy is zero after the collision.

INDEX